TEXTBOOK OF HUMAN VIROLOGY

Textbook of Human Virology

ROBERT B. BELSHE, M.D.
Director, Division of Infectious Diseases
Professor of Medicine and Pediatrics
St. Louis University School of Medicine
St. Louis, Missouri

Mosby
Year Book

St. Louis   Baltimore   Boston   Chicago   London   Philadelphia   Sydney   Toronto

Mosby Year Book

Dedicated to Publishing Excellence

Sponsoring Editor: Stephanie Manning
Associate Managing Editor, Manuscript Services: Deborah Thorp
Production Project Coordinator: Karen Halm
Proofroom Supervisor: Barbara Kelly

Mosby-Year Book, Inc.
11830 Westline Industrial Drive
St. Louis, MO 63146

1 2 3 4 5 6 7 8 9 0 V R 95 94 93 92 91

Library of Congress Cataloging-in-Publication Data

Textbook of human virology / [edited by] Robert B. Belshe.—2nd ed.
   p. cm.
  Includes bibliographical references.
  Includes index.
  ISBN 0-8151-0667-X
  1. Medical virology. I. Belshe, Robert B.
  [DNLM: 1. Virus Diseases. 2. Viruses. WC 500 T355]
QR201.V55T49 1990
616'.0194—dc20   91-12505
DNLM/DLC   CIP
for Library of Congress

For my teachers and students

CONTRIBUTORS

EDWIN L. ANDERSON, M.D.
Professor of Medicine and Pediatrics
St. Louis University School of Medicine
St. Louis, Missouri

M. J. ANDERSON, M.D.
Faculty of Clinical Medicine
University College, London
London, England

DERRICK BAXBY, PH.D.
Senior Lecturer in Medical Microbiology
University of Liverpool
Liverpool, England

ROBERT B. BELSHE, M.D.
Director, Division of Infectious Diseases
Professor of Medicine and Pediatrics
St. Louis University School of Medicine
St. Louis, Missouri

DANIEL W. BRADLEY, M.D.
Hepatitis Branch
Division of Viral Diseases
Centers for Disease Control
Atlanta, Georgia

ROBERT B. CRAVEN, M.D.
Medical Epidemiologist
Division of Vector-Borne Viral Diseases
Centers for Disease Control
Fort Collins, Colorado

JOSEPH J. EIDEN, M.D., PH.D.
Eudowood Division of Infectious Diseases
The Johns Hopkins University School of Medicine
Baltimore, Maryland

ROSELYN J. EISENBERG, PH.D.
Professor of Microbiology
Department of Pathobiology
School of Veterinary Medicine
University of Pennsylvania
Philadelphia, Pennsylvania

VOLKER ERFLE, D.V.M.
Gosellschraft F. Strahlen
U. Umweltforschung M.B.H.
Munich, Federal Republic of Germany

STEPHEN M. FEINSTONE, M.D.
Laboratory of Hepatitis Branch
Centers for Biologics Evaluation and Research
Food and Drug Administration
Bethesda, Maryland

TERRY W. FENGER, PH.D.
Associate Professor of Microbiology
Department of Microbiology
Marshall University School of Medicine
Huntington, West Virginia

HOWARD A. FIELDS, PH.D.
Hepatitis Branch
Division of Viral Diseases
Centers for Disease Control
Atlanta, Georgia

GARY R. FLEISHER, M.D.
Associate Professor of Pediatrics
Harvard Medical School
Director, Division of Emergency Medicine
The Children's Hospital
Boston, Massachusetts

GERT FRÖSNER, M.D.
Professor of Virology
Max von Pettenkofer-Institute
University of Munich
Munich, Federal Republic of Germany

GEOFFREY J. GORSE, M.D.
Associate Professor of Medicine
St. Louis University School of Medicine
St. Louis, Missouri

STEPHEN C. HADLER, M.D.
Hepatitis Branch
Division of Viral Diseases
Centers for Disease Control
Atlanta, Georgia

ALAN J. HAY, PH.D.
Department of Virology
National Institute for Medical Research
London, England

RÜDIGER HEHLMANN, M.D.
III. Medizinische Klinik Mannheim
Universität Heidelberg
Mannheim, Federal Republic of Germany

THOMAS F. HOGAN, M.D.
Medical Oncologist
Marshfield Clinic
Marshfield, Wisconsin

A. BENNETT JENSON, M.D.
Professor of Pathology
Georgetown University School of Medicine and Dentistry
Washington, D.C.

EUGENE D. JOHNSON, PH.D., M.P.H.
Microbiologist, Department of Epidemiology
Disease Assessment Division
United States Army Medical Research Institute of
    Infectious Diseases
Fort Detrick
Frederick, Maryland

MARK A. KANE, M.D.
Hepatitis Branch
Division of Viral Diseases
Centers for Disease Control
Atlanta, Georgia

KRZYSZTOF KRAWCZYNSKI, M.D., PH.D.
Hepatitis Branch
Division of Viral Diseases
Centers for Disease Control
Atlanta, Georgia

PRUDENCE KRIEGER, M.D.
Assistant Professor of Pediatrics
University of Illinois School of Medicine
Director of Pediatric Infectious Diseases
Lutheran General Children's Medical Center
Park Ridge, Illinois

CATHERINE L. LAMPRECHT, M.D.
Director, Division of Infectious Diseases
Assistant Professor of Pediatrics
Loyola University Medical Center
Maywood, Illinois

WAYNE D. LANCASTER, M.D.
Professor
Department of Molecular Biology and Genetics, Obstetrics
    and Gynecology
Center for Molecular Biology
Wayne State University School of Medicine
Detroit, Michigan

JAMES W. LeDUC, PH.D.
Chief, Department of Epidemiology
Disease Assessment Division
United States Army Medical Research Institute of
    Infectious Diseases
Fort Detrick
Frederick, Maryland

ROLAND A. LEVANDOWSKI, M.D.
Centers for Biologics Evaluation and Research
Division of Virology
Food and Drug Administration
Bethesda, Maryland

CHIEN LIU, M.D.
Professor of Medicine and Pediatrics
Director, Division of Infectious Diseases
University of Kansas College of Health Sciences and Hospital
Kansas City, Kansas

LARRY I. LUTWICK, M.D.
Director, Division of Infectious Diseases
Maimonides Medical Center
Associate Professor of Medicine
State University of New York
Health Science Center at Brooklyn
Brooklyn, New York

NYVEN J. MARCHETTE, PH.D.
Professor of Tropical Medicine and Public Health
John A. Burns School of Medicine
University of Hawaii
Honolulu, Hawaii

COLIN L. MASTERS, M.D.
Department of Pathology
University of Melbourne
Melbourne, Victoria, Australia

H. REID MATTISON, M.D.
Assistant Professor of Medicine
Infectious Diseases Unit
University of Rochester School of Medicine and Dentistry
Rochester, New York

KELLY T. McKEE, M.D.
Adjunct Assistant Professor
Preventive Medicine/Biometrics
Uniformed Services University of the Health Sciences
Bethesda, Maryland

MARIAN E. MELISH, M.D.
Department of Pediatrics
University of Hawaii School of Medicine
Honolulu, Hawaii

JOSEPH L. MELNICK, PH.D.
Distinguished Service Professor
Virology and Epidemiology
Baylor College of Medicine
Houston, Texas

MARILYN A. MENEGUS, B.S., PH.D.
Associate Professor
Microbiology, Immunology, Pathology, and Pediatrics
University of Rochester Medical Center
Director, Clinical Microbiology Laboratories
Strong Memorial Hospital
Rochester, New York

JAMES R. MINOR, PHARM.D.
Pharmacy Department
The Clinical Center
National Institutes of Health
Bethesda, Maryland

JOHN MODLIN, M.D.
Associate Professor of Pediatrics
Department of Pediatrics
Division of Infectious Diseases
The Johns Hopkins University
Baltimore, Maryland

MELINDA MOORE, M.D.
Medical Epidemiologist
Office of the Director
Center for Prevention Services
Centers for Disease Control
Atlanta, Georgia

DAVID M. MORENS, M.D.
Professor and Head
Section of Epidemiology
Professor, Department of Tropical Medicine and Microbiology
University of Hawaii
Honolulu, Hawaii

MAURICE A. MUFSON, M.D.
Professor of Medicine
Professor of Microbiology
Chairman, Department of Medicine
Marshall University School of Medicine
Huntington, West Virginia

SIRUS NARAQI, M.D.
Professor and Head
Department of Clinical Sciences
Division of Medicine
The University of Papuan New Guinea
Boroko Papua, New Guinea

BILLIE L. PADGETT, PH.D.
Project Associate
Department of Medical Microbiology
University of Wisconsin
Madison, Wisconsin

MARK A. PALLANSCH, M.D.
Department of Tropical Medicine and Medical Microbiology
John A. Burns School of Medicine
Honolulu, Hawaii

C. J. PETERS, M.D.
Chief, Disease Assessment Division
United States Army Medical Research Institute of
    Infectious Diseases
Fort Detrick
Frederick, Maryland

GERALD V. QUINNAN, JR., M.D.
Acting Director
Center for Biologics Evaluation and Research
Food and Drug Administration
Bethesda, Maryland

RICHARD C. REICHMAN, M.D.
Associate Professor of Medicine, Microbiology and
    Immunology
University of Rochester School of Medicine and Dentistry
Rochester, New York

PATRICK A. ROBINSON, M.D.
Clinical Research
Pfizer Central Research
Groton, Connecticut

FREDERICK L. RUBEN, M.D.
Professor of Medicine
University of Pittsburgh School of Medicine
Associate Head, Infectious Diseases Unit
Montefiore Hospital
Pittsburgh, Pennsylvania

RICHARD J. SALO, M.D.
Nassau County Medical Center
Department of Pediatrics
East Meadow, New York

VICTORIA SCHAUF, M.D.
Professor of Pediatrics
State University of New York at Stoneybrook
Stoneybrook, New York

MARK D. TOLPIN, M.D.
Senior Associate Director,
TA IV–Infectious Diseases
Sandoz Research Institute
East Hanover, New Jersey

WILLIAM M. VALENTI, M.D.
Associate Professor of Medicine
University of Rochester School of Medicine and Dentistry
Medical Director
Community Health Network
Rochester, New York

DUARD L. WALKER, M.D.
Professor and Chairman
Department of Medical Microbiology
University of Wisconsin Medical School
Madison, Wisconsin

T. ULF WESTBLOM, M.D.
Assistant Professor of Medicine
St. Louis University School of Medicine
St. Louis, Missouri

ALEC E. WITTEK, M.D.
Centers for Biologics Evaluation and Research
Food and Drug Administration
Bethesda, Maryland

PETER F. WRIGHT, M.D.
Head, Division of Infectious Diseases
Professor of Pediatrics
Vanderbilt University School of Medicine
Nashville, Tennessee

ROBERT H. YOLKEN, M.D.
Professor of Pediatrics
Director, Pediatric Infectious Diseases
Eudowood Division of Infectious Diseases
The Johns Hopkins University School of Medicine
Baltimore, Maryland

FOREWORD

About three decades ago clinical virology emerged as a recognized discipline encompassing its own body of knowledge and providing the link between fundamental virology research and its practical application in the practice of medicine. The surge of discoveries in virology during the 1950s and 1960s opened the door to a myriad of clinical applications that compelled physicians to become involved in the prevention, diagnosis, and treatment of previously nonpreventable and/or nontreatable viral diseases. En passant, the practicing physician became a clinical virologist.

In the 1950s and 1960s, viruses isolated and identified for the first time included respiratory syncytial virus, the parainfluenza viruses, adenoviruses, rhinoviruses, coronaviruses, rubella virus, and Epstein-Barr virus. The innovation of modern tissue culture techniques represented the breakthrough that permitted the isolation and characterization of these viruses. These successes encouraged virologists to intensify the search for hepatitis viruses, the slow viruses infecting the human central nervous system, and human cancer viruses, several of which have been found. The discovery of a spectrum of new viruses and their clinical importance encouraged the development of new diagnostic procedures. However, the prospect of establishing specific diagnoses seemed impractical considering the paucity of effective modalities for prevention or treatment of virus diseases.

Eventually the development of effective vaccines for poliovirus, the viruses of communicable exanthematous diseases, and mumps virus not only provided the basis for control of these serious virus infections of childhood, but also signaled the beginning of an era of practical application of research in basic virology. Further investigation led to the first potent antiviral drugs for the treatment of serious herpesvirus infections and vaccines effective against hepatitis B virus.

The 1970s and 1980s added momentum to these events mainly because of the recognition of the acquired immunodeficiency syndrome (AIDS) and the seminal discovery of the retrovirus, human immunodeficiency virus (HIV), as the etiologic agent of AIDS. Clinical virologists and physicians around the world became deeply engrossed not only in exploring the unique nature of HIV, but also in developing the means for the diagnosis, treatment, and prevention of AIDS. The worldwide spread of AIDS placed the burden of urgent action on the medical profession, and especially virologists, to halt the spread of the epidemic, care for those persons affected, and manage the vast social and ethical impact of this disease. At no time in this century had the leaders and citizens of so many countries turned to the medical profession for help, and at no time in this century had so much money been allocated for research on one virus disease.

These events underscore the rapidity of technological and scientific advances in the field of clinical virology during the past few decades. The new information on virus nomenclature, the epidemiology of virus infections, host immune responses and their measurement, the delineation of clinical syndromes, and the development of rapid diagnostic tests form a basis for the rational approach to the diagnosis and treatment of virus diseases. New virus vaccines and antiviral drugs provide opportunities for preventive and therapeutic intervention previously only available in the treatment of bacterial infections. This edition of *Textbook of Human Virology* addresses these advances in a comprehensive manner for all scientists and physicians. As a compendium of current information, it provides a resource for virologists, physicians, medical students, and residents that can facilitate clinical care and stimulate further investigative inquiry.

MAURICE A. MUFSON, M.D.
Professor and Chairman
Department of Medicine
Marshall University School of Medicine
Huntington, West Virginia

PREFACE

Since the publication in 1984 of the first edition of the *Textbook of Human Virology*, the field of medical virology has continued to develop at a brisk pace. The acquired immunodeficiency syndrome (AIDS) pandemic has driven major research efforts to muster clinical and basic investigators to study retroviruses as well as opportunistic viral, bacterial, fungal, and protozoal infections that occur in patients infected with human immunodeficiency virus (HIV). The objective of this second edition is to assemble and synthesize information in a single volume that incorporates the new knowledge in virology that has been gained in the last six years.

The AIDS pandemic produced explosive growth in information on retroviruses and also in many other areas covered by this textbook. A new chapter on human retroviruses has been added to the text. The chapter on immunology of viral infections has been updated to include the immunology of HIV infections. The chapter on diagnosis of viral infections includes new information on the diagnosis of retrovirus infections, and the chapter on antiviral chemotherapy has been extensively rewritten to reflect the new information on chemotherapy of retroviruses as well as other agents. The immunosuppression resulting from AIDS allows many secondary opportunistic viral infections, including those caused by human polyomaviruses, human papillomaviruses, cytomegalovirus, the varicella-zoster and herpes simplex viruses, and the enteric adenoviruses and other gastroenteritis viruses. Co-infections with HIV frequently include hepatitis B or other hepatitis viruses. Many of the chapters have added sections on infections in immunocompromised patients.

All chapters have been updated to include contemporary information on the molecular biology of the viruses as well as the revised clinical descriptions of the diseases associated with various viral infections. The chapters on replication of viruses have been expanded to include new information on the different schemes of DNA and RNA virus replication. A new chapter has been added on hantaviruses as well as a chapter on filoviruses and the management of viral hemorrhagic fevers. Separate chapters cover not only hepatitis B but other hepatitis agents, including delta virus (hepatitis D), bloodborne non-A, non-B hepatitis (hepatitis C), and enterically transmitted non-A, non-B hepatitis (hepatitis E). Renewed interest in the poxviruses as vectors for carrying additional genetic material to immunize not only against smallpox but simultaneously against other viruses is discussed. The association of newly described viruses with two exanthemas of childhood, fifth disease and exanthem subitum, are discussed in new chapters on human parvovirus infections and roseola infantum.

The rapid growth in information on viruses and the diseases they cause is ample reason to revise the textbook. I have assembled an international group of authors who are active investigators in the fields encompassed by their respective chapters and they have presented fresh approaches to the description of various aspects of viruses and the diseases they cause. This textbook has been extensively referenced in order to encourage the reader to review the original articles for more detailed discussions of methodology and clinical observations. The textbook is organized with introductory chapters to include the nomenclature and classification of viruses, the replication of DNA and RNA viruses, the immunology of viruses, and the diagnosis of viral infections. Antiviral chemotherapy and nosocomial viral infections are covered in these initial chapters. The text then turns to a discussion of each individual virus group. The text concludes with discussions of syndromes, including Kawasaki syndrome and Reye syndrome.

This textbook serves to bridge the gap between virologist and practicing physician by encompassing those aspects of basic virology relevant to clinical medicine. I hope that both clinicians and basic investigators will find this work to be a useful springboard to further study. I am indebted to Mrs. Judy Hayes for coordinating the development of the manuscript. I gratefully acknowledge the assistance and encouragement of my colleagues and staff, the continued stimulation of students, and the challenges placed before me by my mentor, Maurice A. Mufson, M.D., and other teachers.

ROBERT B. BELSHE, M.D.

CONTENTS

Structure and Classification of Viruses

Joseph L. Melnick

VIRUSES WITH A DNA GENOME

PARVOVIRIDAE
PAPOVAVIRIDAE
ADENOVIRIDAE
HEPADNAVIRIDAE
HERPESVIRIDAE
IRIDOVIRIDAE
POXVIRIDAE

VIRUSES WITH AN RNA GENOME

PICORNAVIRIDAE
CALICIVIRIDAE
REOVIRIDAE
BIRNAVIRIDAE
TOGAVIRIDAE
FLAVIVIRIDAE
ORTHOMYXOVIRIDAE
PARAMYXOVIRIDAE
RHABDOVIRIDAE
FILOVIRIDAE
CORONAVIRIDAE
BUNYAVIRIDAE
RETROVIRIDAE
ARENAVIRIDAE

EMERGING PROBLEMS IN CLASSIFICATION

VIROIDS
PRIONS
VIRUS HYBRIDS
PSEUDOVIRIONS
RECOMBINANT DNA

APPENDIX

Until about 1950, little was known about viruses other than their pathogenic effect in causing diseases; therefore, any efforts at classification tended to focus on host responses rather than on properties of the virus particle. At present, the end of an important phase of discovery and characterization of animal viruses is approaching. The knowledge gained in recent years concerning the molecular biology of viruses and their biophysical and biochemical properties has made it possible to establish and broadly define groupings for these agents. It appears that most of the major groups of viruses of vertebrates—at least, most of those affecting man and the animals of direct importance to man—have been recognized and described. Many of these virus groupings, initially established on tentative and provisional bases, now appear to form "real" families and genera, in which the members are indeed related in fundamental ways. For example, the validity of the original grouping of the enteroviruses based on an enteric habitat and small size is being borne out by current studies that utilize sophisticated techniques of modern molecular virology to compare the genetic makeup of different members of the group and their mode of replication.

The shift from sketching broad outlines of the virus kingdom (based in large part on disease causation and ecological setting) to defining group relationships on the basis of properties of the viruses themselves is reflected in the name of the committee responsible for these matters. The original name, International Committee on Nomenclature of Viruses (ICNV), was changed in 1974 to International Committee on Taxonomy of Viruses (ICTV). The ICNV was established in 1966 at a historic meeting in Moscow, the very city where viruses were first discovered by Ivanovski three quarters of a century earlier. Four comprehensive reports of the ICNV/ICTV have been published.[1-4] Summaries of ICTV sessions and decisions also have been published.[5, 6] Work of specialized study groups of the ICTV has also proceeded, and these groups report regularly in *Intervirology*, the journal of the Virology Division of the International Union of Microbiological Societies. Figures 1–1 and 1–2 serve as useful reference points in the following discussion of classification based on properties of the virus particles. Comparison of these two figures also gives some indication of the rapid accumulation of knowledge about virus composition and structure. Figure 1–1 is taken from a text[7] first published over 20 years ago; it remains fundamentally applicable. However, Figure 1–2 not only includes additional information that has been gained about viruses but also illustrates the wide variety of size and structure that is found among the viruses of vertebrates.[4]

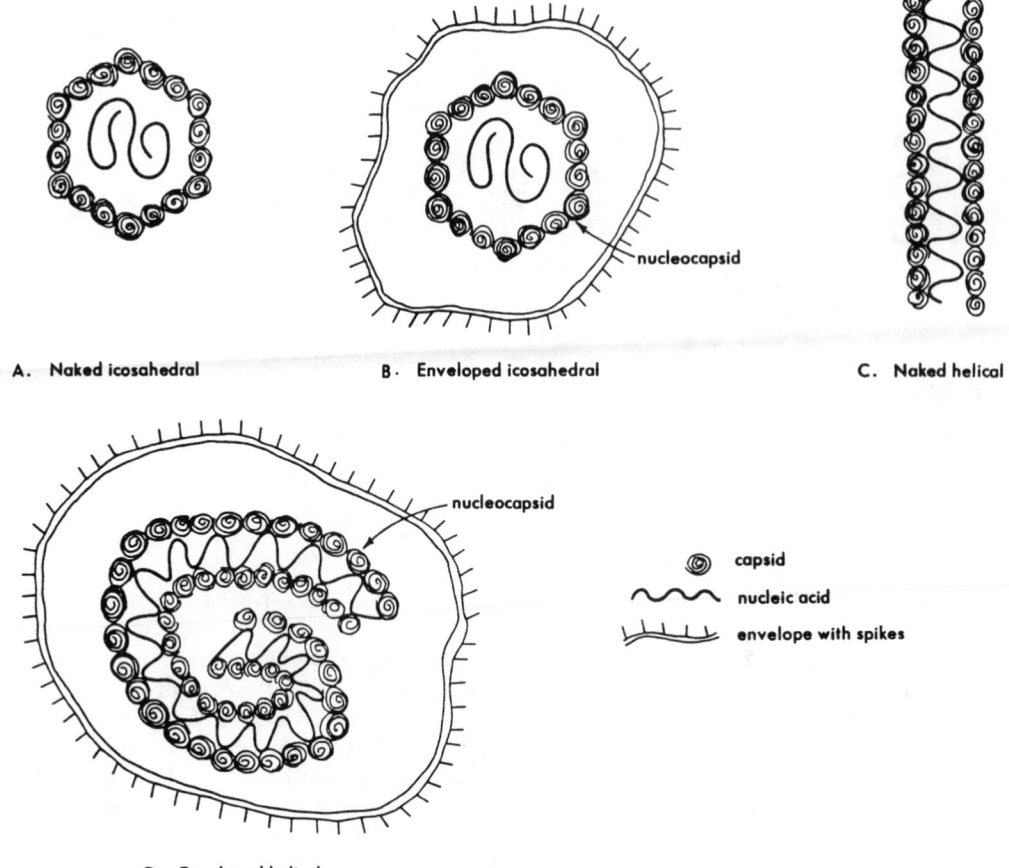

A. Naked icosahedral   B. Enveloped icosahedral   C. Naked helical

D. Enveloped helical

Figure 1–1. Schematic diagram of simple forms of virions and their components. The naked icosahedral virions resemble small crystals; the naked helical virions resemble rods with a fine regular helical pattern in their surface. The enveloped icosahedral virions are made up of icosahedral nucleocapsids surrounded by the envelope; the enveloped helical virions are helical nucleocapsids bent to form a coarse, often irregular, coil within the envelope. (From Davis BD, et al: *Microbiology.* New York, Hoeber, 1967. Used with permission.)

In addition to the ICTV and its study groups, the student is referred to the review in the *Manual of Clinical Microbiology,* fourth edition,[8] and to the annual reviews in *Progress in Medical Virology,* 1966 through 1982,[9] to follow the developments in taxonomy.

Tables 1–1, 1–2, 1–3, 1–4, and 1–6 show separation of viruses of vertebrates into 21 families. Table 1–1 includes viruses having a DNA genome, cubic symmetry, and a naked nucleocapsid, and Table 1–2 depicts DNA-containing viruses having envelopes or complex coats. RNA-containing viruses are presented in three tables: Table 1–3, those with cubic capsid symmetry; Table 1–4, those with capsids having helical symmetry; and Table 1–6, those with capsid architecture that is either asymmetric or unknown. Commentaries follow concerning these families, their properties, and their subgroups and individual members. Some important viruses not yet placed taxonomically are also discussed, along with some viruses and viruslike agents presenting taxonomic problems that need to be resolved. Finally, in the Appendix at the end of the chapter, there is a tabulation of some members of the families of vertebrate viruses. This is not meant to be an exhaustive list, but it should be useful to the reader wishing to survey the taxonomic placement of many viruses that infect vertebrates or to have an overview of the nature of some of the virus families as illustrated by their commonly known members.

VIRUSES WITH A DNA GENOME

Parvoviridae[4, 10, 11]

Originally named picodnaviruses to reflect their small size and DNA genome,[12] the family *Parvoviridae* now includes three genera, *Parvovirus, Densovirus,* and *Dependovirus.* A typical dependovirus is adeno-associated satellite virus, several serotypes of which are indigenous to man, although with no known association with human disease. As shown in Table 1–1, these are viruses with a DNA genome, cubic symmetry, and a naked (unenveloped) nucleocapsid. Infectivity is resistant to ether and other lipid solvents and to heat (56°C, 60 min). The capsid has 32 capsomers, and the diameter of the virus particle is 18 to 26 nm. (The capsomers that form the outer layers of the nucleocapsid are each 2 to 4 nm in diameter.) The molecular weight of the nucleic acid is between 1.5 and 2.0 × 10⁶.

The genus *Parvovirus* includes autonomously replicating agents that infect vertebrates: Kilham's rat virus (the type species) and other viruses of mammals and birds, and Aleutian mink disease virus.

The members of the *Densovirus* genus are the densonucleosis viruses of insects, but they are also capable of producing cytopathic effects in L cells (of vertebrates); they replicate autonomously. Adeno-associated satellite viruses (genus *Dependovirus*), however, are defective and cannot multiply in the absence of a replicating adenovirus that serves as a "helper virus." Herpesvirus can act as a partial helper; in cells coinfected with herpesvirus, infectious satellite DNA and capsid proteins are produced, but they are not assembled into satellite virions.

Members of the family ***Parvoviridae*** are the only DNA-containing viruses of vertebrates whose DNA genome is single-stranded within the virion; all the others have double-stranded DNA. In adeno-associated viruses and densoviruses, separate virions contain single strands of positive or negative DNA; these strands are complementary, and, when isolated from the virion shells, they come together to form a double strand. In some members of the genus *Parvovirus,* the DNA in the virion is a negative strand only. This was initially believed to be true of all members of this genus, but further study has indicated considerable variation. In other members of the genus, plus-strand DNA is also incorporated. The percentage of particles that also contain a strand of DNA of positive polarity may vary from 1% to 50%; the reasons for the variations have not yet been defined. Members of this genus show preference for actively dividing cells, have been shown to be transmissible transplacentally, and are receiving attention for their special disease potential in fetuses and neonates.

Disease in human beings is associated with several members of ***Parvoviridae***.[13] Within the genus *Parvovirus*, strain B19 has been shown to cause a transient shutdown of red blood cell production by killing the late erythroid progenitor cells. This shutdown presents special problems for individuals already suffering from hemolytic anemias, such as sickle cell anemia, causing aplastic

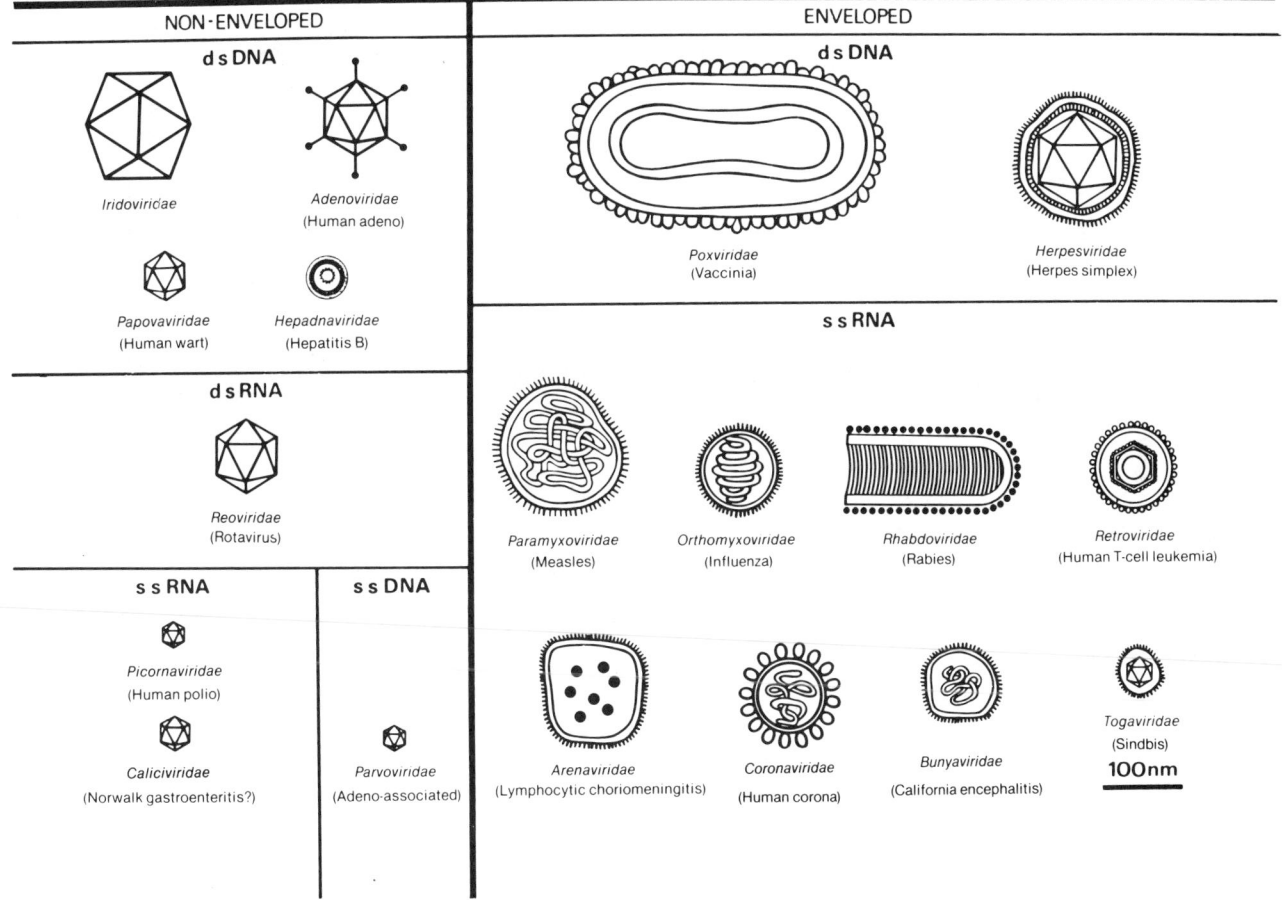

Figure 1–2. Diagram illustrating the shapes and relative sizes of animal viruses of the major families (bar = 100 nm; ds = double-stranded; ss = single-stranded). Representative members that infect humans are listed in parentheses. ***Iridoviridae*** are not known to infect humans. In addition, (1) the *Flavivirus* genus has been elevated to the status of a family, the ***Flaviviridae*** (represented by yellow fever virus); (2) the family ***Filoviridae*** has been established, to include Marburg and Ebola viruses (worm-shaped, filamentous viruses); and (3) the family ***Birnaviridae*** has been established, to include two icosahedral viruses. See text for details.

Table 1–1
DNA-Containing Viruses with Cubic Symmetry and Naked Nucleocapsid

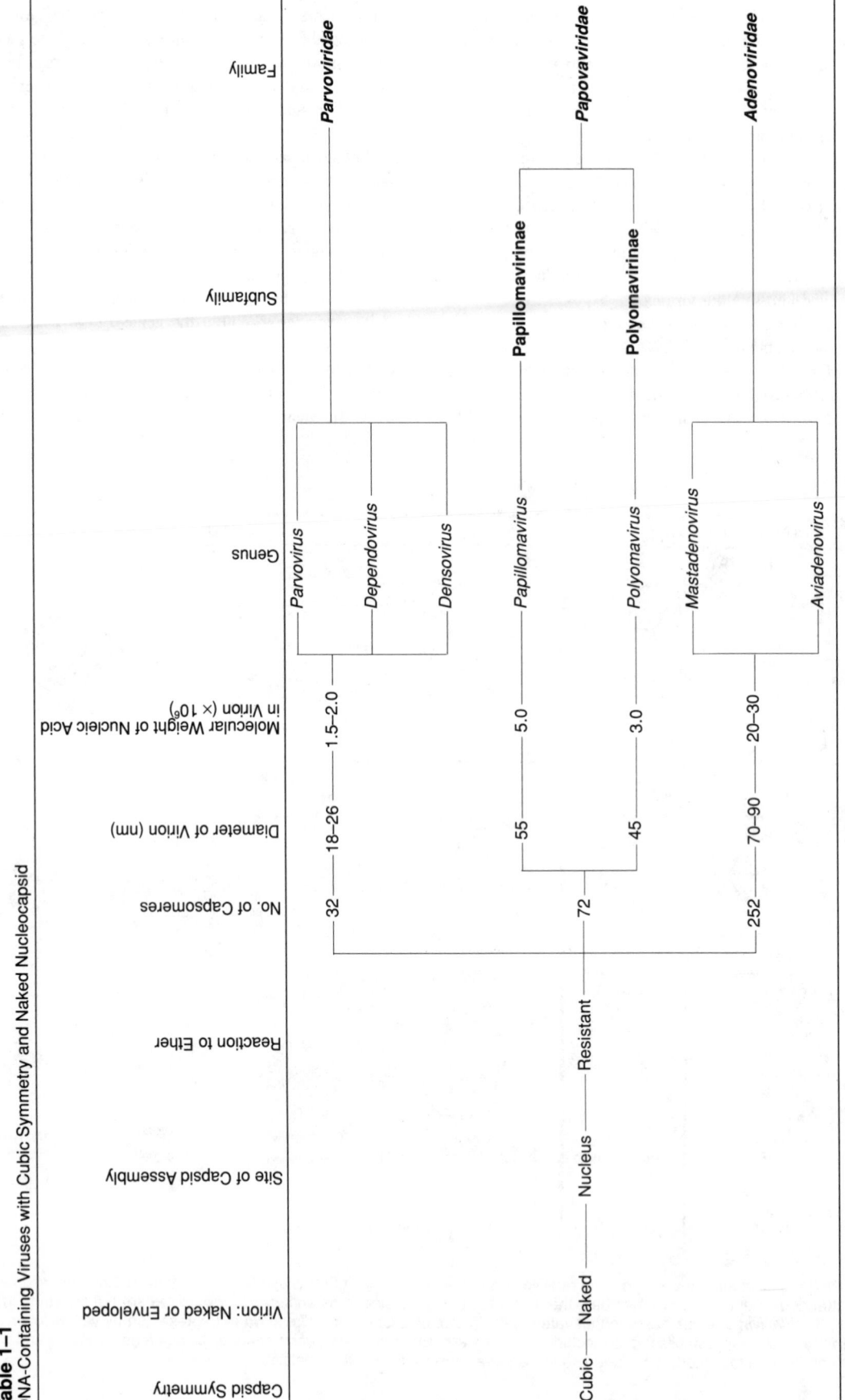

crises. Parvovirus B19 in normal persons may cause erythema infectiosum, or fifth disease of childhood. RA–1 virus, which is associated with rheumatoid arthritis, is another member of the genus that infects humans. Maternal infection with a parvovirus has been documented in temporal association with a generalized fetal infection and hydrops fetalis.

Papovaviridae[3, 4, 14]

These relatively small, ether-resistant viruses contain double-stranded DNA in circular form. Many are unusually heat-stable, surviving temperatures that inactivate most viruses. Representative members that infect human beings are the papilloma or wart virus and SV40-like viruses.

These viruses have relatively slow growth cycles characterized by replication within the nucleus. Papovaviruses produce latent and chronic infections in their natural hosts; all are tumorigenic in at least some animal species. The genome integrates into cellular chromosomes of transformed cells.

The two genera now have been assigned to separate subfamilies, **Papillomavirinae** and **Polyomavirinae**, each monogeneric. The genus *Papillomavirus* has as its type species the well-known rabbit (Shope) papillomavirus. Other members are known for man (nine types) and other vertebrate species. Each virus species contains a distinct surface antigen, but all members of the genus share a common antigen revealed by disrupting the virions. Papilloma-viruses have a capsid diameter of about 55 nm; the molecular weight of the DNA in the virion is 5×10^6. Thus far, papilloma-viruses have not been successfully cultivated in tissue culture. Some investigations have suggested that human genital infection by papillomaviruses may be at least a cofactor in the development of cancer of the uterine cervix.[15]

For the single genus, *Polyomavirus,* in the second subfamily, the type species is the polyomavirus of mice. This genus includes SV40 virus (vacuolating virus) of the rhesus monkey and JC and BK viruses of man. JC virus has been isolated from the brain tissue of patients having progressive multifocal leukoencephalopathy (PML), and BK virus from the urine of immunosuppressed recipients of renal transplants. In addition, several isolates that appear to be identical to simian virus 40 (SV40) of monkeys also have been isolated from patients with PML. In this genus there are several other viruses of monkeys, mice, rabbits, and hamsters. The ICTV has designated this genus, and now the subfamily, by names that incorporate "Polyoma-." It should be noted, however, that the members of this group that infect human beings do not fit the literal meaning of the name—"viruses producing many types of tumors in their natural hosts"—for there is no evidence that these viruses are associated with human neoplasms. Poly-omaviruses are smaller than the papillomaviruses, having a virion diameter of about 45 nm and a DNA molecular weight of about 3×10^6. For the members of this genus, as with the papilloma-viruses, there is no serologic cross-reactivity between most species, but a common genus antigen can be detected in disrupted virions of all species. The tumor antigens produced by primate papova-viruses cross-react.

When SV40 and adenoviruses replicate together within the same cell, they may interact to form various kinds of SV40-ad-enovirus "hybrid" virus particles, in which a portion of the SV40 genome is covalently linked to incomplete or complete adenovirus DNA and is carried within an adenovirus capsid (see section on Virus Hybrids).

Adenoviridae[4, 16, 17]

Among these medium-sized viruses, at least 42 serotypes infect man, and distinct serotypes exist for a number of other species. The virion is a nonenveloped isometric particle with 252 capso-mers, each 7 to 9 nm in diameter. Vertex capsomers are antigen-ically distinct from the others and carry one or two filamentous projections. The adenovirus genome is a single linear molecule of double-stranded DNA.

Adenoviruses have a predilection for mucous membranes and may persist for years in lymphoid tissue. Some of the adenoviruses cause acute respiratory diseases, febrile catarrhs, pharyngitis, and conjunctivitis. Human adenoviruses rarely cause disease in labo-ratory animals, but certain serotypes produce tumors in newborn hamsters. Common antigens are shared by all mammalian ade-noviruses, which are classified as members of the *Mastadenovirus* genus; these antigens are different from the corresponding antigens of the members of the genus *Aviadenovirus,* adenoviruses that infect birds.

Human adenovirus species are designated by the letter *h* fol-lowed by the present Arabic numeral series (eg, mastadenovirus h 1). Adenoviruses of domestic animals are designated by a three-letter code based on the genus of the respective host animal (eg, mastadenovirus bos 1). Species of aviadenoviruses are named in the same way. Thus, for the adenoviruses of man, the species are h 1–h 42; for those of cattle, bos 1–bos 9; for those of pig, sus 1–sus 4; for those of fowl, gal 1–gal 9; of turkeys, mel 1–mel 2; and so on.

Hepadnaviridae[18–20]

Although much is known about hepatitis B virus, it has not yet been successfully propagated in cell culture. However, it is now established as the prototype member of a new family. Hepatitis B virus of man and three similar viruses found in woodchucks, ground squirrels, and domestic ducks share many basic ultrastructural, molecular, and biologic features. The name *Hepadnaviridae* re-flects the DNA-containing genomes of its members and their rep-lication within hepatocytes (see Table 1–2).

Hepadnaviridae share the following properties[21]: (1) Charac-teristic ultrastructure of the virion (a double-shelled particle 40–50 nm in diameter with a core 27 nm in diameter) and incomplete forms (22-nm spheres and filaments); (2) circular viral DNA with length corresponding to DNA of 3200 base pairs and containing a single-stranded region; (3) virion DNA polymerase that repairs the single-stranded region in the viral DNA; (4) polypeptide co-valently attached to the 5′ end of the long DNA strand; (5) char-acteristic surface, core, and e antigens in the virion; (6) charac-teristic virion polypeptides; (7) sharing of some DNA and virion polypeptide homology; (8) protein kinase activity in the virion core; (9) liver tropism; (10) persistent infection with large amounts of incomplete viral forms continuously in the blood; and (11) infection associated with hepatitis, hepatocellular carcinoma, and immune complex-mediated extrahepatic injury.[22]

Table 1–2
DNA-Containing Viruses with Envelopes or Complex Coats

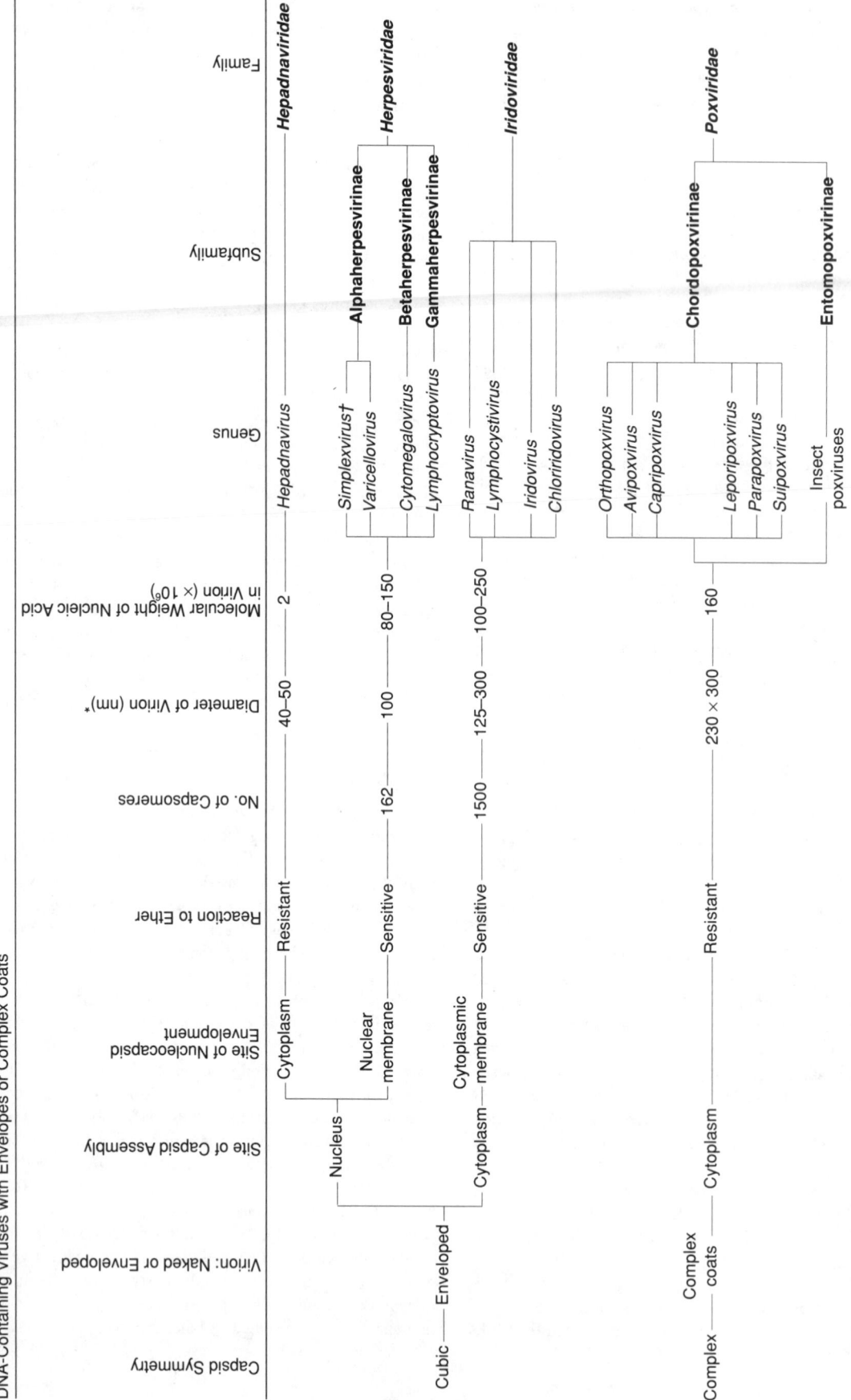

Capsid Symmetry	Virion: Naked or Enveloped	Site of Capsid Assembly	Site of Nucleocapsid Envelopment	Reaction to Ether	No. of Capsomeres	Diameter of Virion (nm)*	Molecular Weight of Nucleic Acid in Virion (× 10⁶)	Genus	Subfamily	Family
Cubic	Enveloped	Nucleus	Cytoplasm	Resistant		40–50	2	*Hepadnavirus*		***Hepadnaviridae***
			Nuclear membrane	Sensitive	162	100	80–150	*Simplexvirus†* *Varicellovirus*	**Alphaherpesvirinae**	***Herpesviridae***
								Cytomegalovirus *Lymphocryptovirus*	**Betaherpesvirinae** **Gammaherpesvirinae**	
		Cytoplasm	Cytoplasmic membrane	Sensitive	1500	125–300	100–250	*Ranavirus* *Lymphocystivirus* *Iridovirus* *Chloriridovirus*		***Iridoviridae***
Complex	Complex coats	Cytoplasm		Resistant		230 × 300	160	*Orthopoxvirus* *Avipoxvirus* *Capripoxvirus* *Leporipoxvirus* *Parapoxvirus* *Suipoxvirus* Insect poxviruses	**Chordopoxvirinae** **Entomopoxvirinae**	***Poxviridae***

*Diameter, or diameter times length.
†The only genera listed in this table for ***Herpesviridae*** are those that include herpesviruses of human beings. A number of other genera have been established or proposed.

In infections with the human hepatitis B virus (HBV), sera from patients reveal three distinct morphologic entities in varying proportions. The more numerous forms (by a factor of more than 1000) are the small pleomorphic spherical particles, of about 22-nm diameter, which occur in concentrations as high as 10^{12} particles per milliliter of serum. Tubular or filamentous forms of varying length, but with a diameter similar to that of the smaller particles, are also observed. HBV is a complex, double-shelled particle with a diameter of 45 nm. It contains a 28-nm core surrounded by a lipoprotein coat that is 7 nm thick. Within the core is a circular, double-stranded DNA molecule and a DNA-dependent DNA polymerase. The DNA is made up of one strand of fixed length and a shorter strand of variable length. By means of a reaction in which the DNA polymerase takes part, the single-stranded region is closed to yield a double-stranded circle of 3200 base pairs having a molecular weight of 2.1×10^6.

One antigenic specificity, designated *a*, is common to all HB surface antigen (HBsAg) preparations. In addition, there are two sets of mutually exclusive determinants, *d* or *y* and *w* or *r*. This results in four principal subtypes of HBsAg: *adw*, *ayw*, *adr*, and *ayr*. Treatment of HBV with a nonanionic detergent exposes the core antigen, HBcAg is produced in the nuclei of infected hepatocytes, whereas HBsAg is produced in the cytoplasm. A second specificity of HBV associated with the core particle is the "e" antigen, HBeAg. When present in blood as a slightly smaller nonparticulate antigen, it serves as a useful marker to indicate the infectiousness of the blood.

Herpesviridae[23, 24]

Herpesviruses constitute a diverse group of agents; the virion contains a core of double-stranded, linear DNA of molecular weight 80 to 150×10^6, with cytosine and guanine content ranging from 35% to 75%. The DNA is wrapped on a fibrillar spool, the ends of which are anchored to the underside of the capsid shell. The capsid, which is 100 to 110 nm in diameter, is icosahedral. There are five capsomers on each edge of the capsid; 150 of them are hexameric and 12 pentameric. The hexameric capsomers contain a hole running halfway through the long axis. Surrounding the nucleocapsid is a tegument of globular material, often distributed asymmetrically, with a bilayered membrane or envelope surrounding the tegument. The prototype, human herpes simplex virus, has a complex structural organization, including in the genome a terminally redundant section and internal inverted repetitions of sequences present at both ends of the DNA molecule, with a long and short unique sequence region. Other members of the herpesvirus family may have simpler structural organization of the genome. The DNA of herpesviruses is sufficiently large to code for 80 to 100 proteins, of which about 50 have been observed. As many as 30 of these may be structural proteins of the virus particle, whereas others may be the virus-induced enzymes, including thymidine kinase, DNA polymerase, and DNase. Neutralizing antibody reacts with major viral glycoproteins located in the viral envelope.

Herpesviruses are noteworthy for their ability to establish latent or persistent infections, or both. Latent infections may last for the lifetime of the host, even in the presence of circulating antibodies. Special interest has been generated by the association of Epstein-Barr herpesvirus (EBV) with human Burkitt's lymphoma and nasopharyngeal carcinoma and by the association of the genital herpesvirus, human herpesvirus 2, with cancer of the uterine cervix and the vulva. Several simian herpesviruses have been shown to be oncogenic in experimentally infected animals. Infections of heterologous species are often fatal; examples are the fatal meningoencephalitis of man caused by one of the simian herpesviruses, the so-called B virus, and the fatal encephalitis of cattle produced by swine pseudorabies virus. Human diseases caused by herpesviruses include oral and genital lesions, chickenpox and shingles due to varicella-zoster virus, cytomegalic inclusion disease, and infectious mononucleosis.

Host range, duration of reproductive cycle, cytopathology, and characteristics of latent infection form the chief bases for establishment of the subfamilies, **Alphaherpesvirinae, Betaherpesvirinae,** and **Gammaherpesvirinae.** The classification of herpesviruses into genera seems to reflect true phylogenetic relationships; the generic groupings are based on genome structure, serologic relationships, and nucleotide sequence homology.

Alphaherpesvirinae are rapidly growing, highly cytolytic viruses, characterized by a variable host range and a short reproductive cyle with rapid spread of infection in cell culture, resulting in mass destruction of susceptible cells. The establishment of carrier cultures of susceptible cells harboring nondefective genomes is difficult to accomplish. Latent infections are seen frequently, but not exclusively, in ganglia. Two genera have been approved for viruses in this subfamily. They are: *Simplexvirus,* to include herpes simplex viruses and similar agents; and *Varicellovirus,* including the varicella-zoster virus (species designation human herpesvirus 3 or human alphaherpesvirus 3) and the pseudorabies virus of swine (suid herpesvirus 1), as well as two viruses of horses and one of cattle. The second part of the species label illustrates an alternative designation for individual herpesviruses to show clearly their subfamily affiliation, for example, human alphaherpesvirus 1, murid betaherpesvirus 1, gallid gammaherpes virus 2.

Betaherpesvirinae (slow-growing, cytomegalic viruses) are characterized by a narrow host range in vivo, a relatively long reproductive cycle, and slowly progressing lytic foci in cell culture. Infected cells frequently become enlarged (cytomegaly) both in vitro and in vivo. Inclusions containing DNA frequently are present in both the nucleus and the cytoplasm. Carrier cultures are easily established. Latent infections may be established in secretory glands, lymphoreticular cells, kidneys, and other tissues. Genera within the **Betaherpesvirinae** include *Cytomegalovirus,* containing the human cytomegaloviruses (species designation, human herpesvirus 5); and *Muromegalovirus,* cytomegaloviruses of mice (species designation, murid herpesvirus 1). A recently discovered herpesvirus, isolated from leukocytes and capable of infecting both T cells and B cells in vitro, has been designated lymphotropic human herpesvirus or human herpesvirus 6 (HHV-6).[25] The genome of the virus exhibits marked cross-hybridization with human cytomegalovirus and is therefore provisionally classified as a member of the **Betaherpesvirinae.**

For the **Gammaherpesvirinae,** the host range in vivo usually is limited to the same family or order as the host that it naturally infects. In vitro, all members of **Gammaherpesvirinae** replicate in lymphoblastoid cells; some also cause lytic infections in some types of epithelioid and fibroblastoid cells. Viruses in this group are specific for either B or T lymphocytes. The genera proposed for this subfamily are: *Lymphocryptovirus,* which includes Epstein-Barr virus (human herpesvirus 4), as well as Epstein-Barr-like viruses of baboon and of chimpanzee (cercopithecine herpesvirus 12 and pongine herpesvirus 1, respectively); *Thetalymphocryptovirus,* Marek's disease herpesvirus (gallid herpesvirus 2) and related viruses; and *Rhadinovirus,* to include herpesvirus ateles, herpesvirus saimiri, and similar agents (ateline herpesviruses 2 and 3; saimirine herpesvirus 2).

Iridoviridae[4, 5]

The best-known members of this family are the small iridescent viruses of insects (eg, *Tipula* iridescent virus), now placed in the genus *Iridovirus,* and the large iridescent viruses of insects (genus *Chloriridovirus*). Other members of this family belong to the genus *Ranavirus* (which infects frogs) and the genus *Lymphocystivirus* (which includes a large number of viruses of fish). No iridovirus of humans is known. Vertebrate iridoviruses are enveloped; iridoviruses that infect insects contain a lipid fraction in the virion as an integral part of the icosahedral shell, but do not have an envelope as such. The genome is a single large molecule of linear double-stranded DNA, possibly two molecules in some viruses.

Poxviridae[2, 3, 6]

These large viruses are brick-shaped or ovoid, with a complex virion structure: an external coat contains lipid and tubular or globular protein structures; the coat encloses one or two lateral bodies and an internal body (core) that contains the genome. The virion contains more than 30 structural proteins and several viral enzymes, including a DNA-dependent RNA polymerase. The genome consists of a single molecule of double-stranded DNA. Genetic recombination occurs within genera; nongenetic reactivation occurs both within and between genera of the poxviruses that infect vertebrates. Most poxviruses of vertebrates share at least one antigen; members of each genus of vertebrate poxviruses have additional antigens in common. This is a major family of DNA-containing viruses whose members replicate entirely within the cytoplasm; a number of them produce intracytoplasmic inclusion bodies (type B, viral factory; and type A, cytoplasmic accumulation).

Two subfamilies have been designated: **Chordopoxvirinae**—the poxviruses of vertebrates; and **Entomopoxvirinae**—the poxviruses of insects. Within the subfamily **Chordopoxvirinae,** six genera have been named. The genus *Orthopoxvirus* includes the poxviruses of man and of several other species. The members of this genus produce a hemagglutinin, separate from the virion; the hemagglutinin is serologically specific and is a lipid-rich pleomorphic particle 50 to 65 nm in diameter. Some of the animal poxviruses (eg, monkeypox virus) can infect humans, and with the eradication of smallpox from the world, human infections by these agents are being detected more frequently.

VIRUSES WITH AN RNA GENOME

Picornaviridae[26, 27, 28]

In naming this group, an attempt was made to represent the subgroups constituting the family, together with important prop-

erties that led to the grouping, namely, the fact that the viruses were insensitive to ether and had an RNA genome (see Table 1–3). Thus, the name was derived as follows:[29]

picorna: an acronym from
  *p*oliovirus
  *i*nsensitivity to ether (one of its chief distinguishing properties)
  *c*oxsackievirus
  *o*rphan virus
  *r*hinovirus
  *r*ibo-
  *n*ucleic (genome character for the group)
  *a*cid

The two *rr*'s were contracted to one. The term *pico* also was being used by physicists to designate a very small unit of measurement (10^{-12}), and thus supported the etymology to designate very small RNA viruses.

Members of this family, which have the smallest virions among the animal viruses with RNA genomes, have been classed in four genera and several hundred species.

At least 70 members of the *Enterovirus* genus are known to infect man; these include polioviruses, coxsackieviruses of the A and the B groups, echoviruses, and new enterovirus serotypes that have been assigned sequential numbers (enterovirus 68–enterovirus 72 to date), rather than being placed in ill-defined subgroups.

Well over 100 viruses infecting human beings belong to the genus *Rhinovirus.* Large numbers of agents from both the *Enterovirus* and the *Rhinovirus* genera also exist for other host species. A third genus in the family is *Cardiovirus,* with encephalomyocarditis (EMC) virus of mice as the type species. A fourth genus is *Aphthovirus,* foot-and-mouth disease (FMD) virus, typified by FMD viruses O and A, now termed aphthoviruses O and A. A new genus has been recognized, *Heparnavirus* (see below). The aphthoviruses infect most cloven-hoofed animals.

The picornavirus genome is one piece of linear, single-stranded positive RNA of low molecular weight (about 2.5×10^6). The RNA is infectious and serves as its own messenger for protein translation. The enteroviruses are acid-stable and have a buoyant density in cesium chloride of about 1.34 g/cm³; the rhinoviruses in contrast, are acid-labile and have a higher buoyant density, about 1.4 g/cm³.

Diseases caused by picornaviruses range from severe paralysis (paralytic poliomyelitis) to aseptic meningitis, hepatitis, pleurodynia, myocarditis, skin rashes, and common colds; inapparent infection is common. Different viruses may produce the same syndrome; on the other hand, the same picornavirus may cause more than a single syndrome.

Among the polioviruses, strain differentiation is of direct concern in public health and medical virology. In the years since 1951 (when the existence of three serotypes was established), antigenic differences within serotypes have been demonstrated by various serodifferentiation tests, using highly strain-specific adsorbed sera, or monoclonal antibody produced by hybridoma techniques. Poliovirus isolates should now be identified by type, country (or city), strain number, and year of isolation. Thus, P1/England/119/65 designates a type 1 poliovirus strain, number 119, isolated in England in 1965.

Table 1–3
RNA-Containing Viruses with Cubic Capsid Symmetry*

Family	Genus	Molecular Weight of Nucleic Acid in Virion (× 10⁶)	Diameter of Virion (nm)	No. of Capsomeres	Reaction to Ether	Site of Nucleocapsid Envelopment	Site of Capsid Assembly	Virion: Naked or Enveloped	Capsid Symmetry*
Picornaviridae	Enterovirus†	2.5	24–30	32	Resistant (or relatively resistant)		Cytoplasm	Naked	Cubic*
	Rhinovirus	2.3–2.8							
	Heparnavirus	2.5							
	Cardiovirus	2.5							
	Aphthovirus	2.3–2.8							
Caliciviridae	Calicivirus	2.7	37	32					
Reoviridae‡	Orbivirus	12	60–80	32					
	Reovirus†	15	75	92					
	Rotavirus†	12	70	32					
Birnaviridae	Birnavirus	4.8	60	92					
Togaviridae	Alphavirus	4	60–70	32 or 42	Sensitive	Surface membrane	Cytoplasm	Enveloped	
	Rubivirus								
	Arterivirus								
	Pestivirus								
Flaviviridae*	Flavivirus	4	40–50	?	Sensitive	Intracytoplasmic membrane			

*For **Flaviviridae**, symmetry of the nucleocapsid is not known.
†Most of the RNA-containing viruses are sensitive to pH3 treatment; exceptions are the genera *Enterovirus*, *Reovirus*, and *Rotavirus*.
‡The only genera listed for **Reoviridae** are those that include reoviruses of vertebrates. A number of other genera have been established or are proposed.

After decades of investigation, hepatitis A virus has been classed as a picornavirus. This virus has been shown to have physico-chemical properties similar to members of the genus *Enterovirus*.[18, 30] These properties include a nonenveloped icosahedral virion about 28 nm in diameter with 32 capsomers, a buoyant density in CsCl of about 1.33 to 1.34 g/cm³, and four major polypeptides with molecular weights of about 33,000, 27,000, 23,000, and 6000. The genome consists of a single piece of single-stranded RNA of molecular weight about 2.5×10^6. Like the enteroviruses, hepatitis A virus is stable to acid pH and resistant to ether. Because of its unique nucleic acid and amino acid sequences, hepatitis A virus is recognized as the prototype of a new genus, *Heparnavirus*.

Caliciviridae[31]

This is a relatively new taxon, now clearly separate from the *Picornaviridae*. The virion is roughly spherical, 38 nm in diameter, with 32 cup-shaped surface depressions arranged in icosahedral symmetry. The genome is a single molecule of infectious, single-stranded, positive RNA with molecular weight (mol wt) 2.7×10^6. There is no lipid and no envelope, and there is a single major structural polypeptide (mol wt about 70×10^3), which is present in 180 copies.

The single genus, *Calicivirus*, includes a number of serotypes of each of the following: vesicular exanthema of swine virus (VESV); feline calicivirus (FCV)—formerly called feline picornavirus; and San Miguel sea lion virus (SMSV). Neutralization indicates distinct serotypes of VESV and SMSV, but there is considerable cross-reactivity among FCV strains.

There are at least five types of human caliciviruses that inhabit the intestinal tract. The Norwalk virus, a widespread human agent causing acute epidemic gastroenteritis, has a virion protein structure similar to that of the caliciviruses; it also resembles caliciviruses in several other properties. Because these agents have not yet been successfully adapted to tissue culture, it is difficult to study their properties.

Reoviridae[2, 4, 5, 32]

Members of this virus family share a property unique among the currently established families of RNA-containing viruses of vertebrates in that the genome is composed of double-stranded rather than single-stranded RNA, and consists of several segments. The capsid has a double shell. Spikes protrude from the outer capsid layer of reovirus and rotavirus particles. Icosahedral symmetry has been demonstrated in the inner capsid layers of all three recognized groups of reoviruses that infect vertebrates, that is, the genera *Reovirus*, *Orbivirus*, and *Rotavirus*.

Members of the genus *Reovirus* have been thought to have 92 capsomers (but the number is being restudied); each of the other two groups has 32 capsomers. The capsomers of orbiviruses are unusually large (10–15 nm wide) and appear ring-shaped.

Members of the genus *Reovirus* that infect human beings are found in the enteric tract, but their association with disease is not clear; members of this genus recovered from lower animals are similar to those of man. The *Orbivirus* genus includes a large number of viruses that infect both vertebrates and invertebrates; some have been considered to be arboviruses. Several have been recovered only from insects. The diseases caused by orbiviruses include Colorado tick fever of humans, bluetongue of sheep and other ruminants, African horse sickness, and epizootic hemorrhagic disease of deer.

Members of the *Rotavirus* genus that infect human beings are increasingly recognized as major pathogens of nonbacterial infantile diarrhea[33]; the gastroenteritis syndrome is clinically more severe and of longer duration than the illness caused by the 27-nm Norwalk agent, and occurs in sporadic outbreaks rather than epidemic form. Rotavirus infection is one of the most common childhood illnesses throughout the world and is a leading cause of death among children in developing countries. Much of the initial study of the rotaviruses was accomplished by use of electron microscopy; isolation of some members of this group that infect humans has been achieved in cell cultures, but these fastidious agents still require special culture conditions and procedures. For the rotaviruses that infect humans, two subgroups and six serotypes are recognized at present. The subgroup antigen, coded for by the sixth genomic segment, is located in the major inner capsid protein. Serotype antigens, coded for by the fourth and ninth genomic segments, are located in the major outer capsid protein. Antibodies directed against the serotype antigens neutralize the infectivity of the virion. Other members of this antigenically interrelated rotavirus group include calf diarrhea virus, the virus of epizootic diarrhea of infant mice, SA11 rotavirus of monkeys, and similar viruses from swine and other species.

In addition to the members of *Reoviridae* that infect vertebrates, other genera within the family are *Cypovirus* (cytoplasmic polyhedrosis group of insect viruses), and two genera of plant reoviruses, *Phytoreovirus* and *Fijivirus*.

Birnaviridae[6]

Members of this newly established family have bisegmented double-stranded linear RNA, with a total molecular weight of 4.8×10^6. The nonenveloped virions are 60 nm in diameter and have icosahedral symmetry. There are 92 capsomers. There are four major structural polypeptides, including a transcriptase. Replication and assembly take place in the cytoplasm, and release of mature virus occurs when the infected cell is destroyed. The family contains one genus, *Birnavirus*. Members include infectious pancreatic necrosis virus of fish and infectious bursal disease virus of chickens.

Togaviridae[6, 34, 35]

Members of this family include most arboviruses* of antigenic group A, now classed as the genus *Alphavirus*, as well as genera that include nonarthropod-borne togaviruses—rubella (*Rubivirus*),

---

*One important and well-known virus group name that is not discussed in this chapter is a category based on ecologic properties, the arbovirus group. The more than 350 arthropod-borne viruses survive through a complex cycle involving vertebrate hosts and arthropods that serve as vectors, transmitting the viruses by their bites. This grouping, based on transmission, remains a very useful one despite the wide diversity of its members with regard to properties of the virion. Most arboviruses now have been sufficiently well characterized to permit their taxonomic placement. Their classic serologic interrelationships previously delineated by arbovirologists have been found to be paralleled by morphologic similarities. Arboviruses now are included in a number of families, chiefly **Togaviridae, Flaviviridae, Bunyaviridae, Rhabdoviridae, Arenaviridae,** and **Reoviridae.**

the mucosal disease virus group (*Pestivirus*), and a newly designated genus, *Arterivirus* (equine arteritis virus)—for which the avenues of transmission are not known. The genus *Flavivirus* has now been removed from the *Togaviridae* and elevated to the status of a separate family, the *Flaviviridae*.

Virions of *Togaviridae* are spherical, 60 to 70 nm in diameter. A lipoprotein envelope with lipid and virus-specified glycopeptides (usually two) is tightly bound to a nucleocapsid 25 to 35 nm in diameter, with proven or presumed icosahedral symmetry. Surface projections protrude from the envelope. The genome is a single linear molecule of single-stranded positive-sense RNA of molecular weight 4×10^6, which is infectious. The 5' end is capped, and the 3' end is polyadenylated. Full-length and subgenomic messenger RNAs have been demonstrated, and posttranslational cleavage of polyproteins occurs during RNA replication. Togaviruses replicate within the cytoplasm, mature at the plasma membrane, and assemble by budding.

The alphaviruses include many of the major human arboviral pathogens: the viruses of Venezuelan, eastern and western equine encephalitis, and a number of other viruses. Rubella virus thus far is the only member of the genus *Rubivirus*. Members of the *Pestivirus* genus include bovine virus diarrhea (mucosal disease complex) virus, hog cholera (European swine fever) virus, and border disease virus. The only member of the genus *Arterivirus* is equine arteritis virus. Lactic dehydrogenase virus of mice is considered a possible member of the togavirus family.

Flaviviridae[5, 36]

Members of this newly established family include the members of the genus *Flavivirus,* which previously had been included in the ***Togaviridae.*** Its members differ from the *Alphavirus* genus of the ***Togaviridae*** in the molecular structure of the virion, the gene sequence and replication strategy, and their mode of morphogenesis.

Members of this family include a number of serious human pathogens. Among them are the mosquito-borne viruses of yellow fever, West Nile fever, Japanese encephalitis, St. Louis encephalitis, Murray Valley encephalitis, and dengue, as well as the tick-borne agents of Omsk hemorrhagic fever and Russian spring-summer encephalitis.

The flavivirus virion, 40 to 50 nm in diameter, is slightly smaller than that of togaviruses, and in contrast to the icosahedral symmetry of the alphavirus nucleocapsid, the symmetry of the flavivirus nucleocapsid has not been fully defined. Whereas the togavirus envelope usually contains two species of glycoprotein, that of the flaviviruses contains only one. As with the togaviruses, the flavivirus genome is a single linear molecule of single-stranded positive-sense RNA of molecular weight 4×10^6, which is infectious. The 5' end is capped, but—unlike togaviruses—the 3' end is not polyadenylated. As yet, no subgenomic messenger RNA nor polyprotein precursors have been detected for flaviviruses. In contrast to the alphaviruses, which mature at the plasma membrane, virions of the ***Flaviviridae*** mature within cisternae, and their morphogenesis is not yet clearly defined.

Orthomyxoviridae[2, 4, 37]

All orthomyxoviruses recognized to the present are influenza viruses (see Table 1–4). The virions may be spherical, elongated, or filamentous. They are 80 to 120 nm in diameter. For most members of the family, "spikes" project from the surface of the envelope; these are glycosylated protein peplomers 10 to 14 nm long and 4 nm in diameter, consisting of two types: the hemagglutinin and the neuraminidase. The ribonucleoprotein capsid is helically symmetric and 9 to 15 nm in diameter. The genome is linear, single-stranded, negative RNA (See Chapter 2) in eight segments. The total molecular weight of the RNA is about 5×10^6. An RNA-dependent RNA polymerase is associated with purified virions. The virions mature by budding at the cell surface membrane. Reassortment of genes between viruses of the same type readily occurs in mixed infections, producing new genetic combinations. This frequency of recombination, particularly among members of type A, is a factor in the occurrence of periodic epidemics and pandemics of influenza. The genus, *Influenzavirus,* includes viruses of type A and type B. Type C has been designated as a separate genus. Type A influenza viruses include agents of human, equine, and swine influenza and of fowl plague. For types B and C, only human strains are known.

Identification and clear description of influenza subtypes, particularly within type A, have long been recognized as essential for dealing with the antigenic variability of these viruses and the periodic emergence of new strains against which population immunity is low or absent. The recommended nomenclature includes a type and strain designation and a description of the antigenic specificity of the surface antigens, the hemagglutinin (H) and the neuraminidase (N).[38] For all three types, the strain designation includes information on the antigenic type of the virus (based on the antigenic specificity of the nucleoprotein) as A, B, C, the host of origin (for strains isolated for nonhuman species), geographic origin, strain number, and year of isolation. For viruses of type A, this strain designation is followed by a second part, in parentheses, indicating the antigenic subtype of the hemagglutinin and of the neuraminidase antigens. For influenza A viruses from all species, the H antigens are now grouped into 12 subtypes, H1 to H12; the N antigens are divided into nine subtypes, N1 to N9. Table 1–5 contains examples of reference strains from man, swine, and horses, using the new nomenclature. Although it is recognized that antigenic variation occurs among influenza B strains, division into subtypes is not recommended.

Paramyxoviridae[4, 39]

Members of this family have virions that are pleomorphic, but which are usually roughly spherical, 150 nm or more in diameter; filamentous forms may be several micrometers long. On the lipid bilayer envelope are surface projections. The genome consists of single-stranded, negative RNA and is in unsegmented, linear form. The helical nucleocapsid is 12 to 18 nm in diameter. Infectivity is sensitive to ether, acid, and heat, but paramyxoviruses (unlike orthomyxoviruses) are resistant to dactinomycin. The genera include *Paramyxovirus* (parainfluenza viruses of man and several animal species, mumps virus, Newcastle disease virus, and Yucaipa and other avian paramyxoviruses); *Morbillivirus* (the viruses of measles, canine distemper, rinderpest, and peste de petits ruminants); and *Pneumovirus* (respiratory syncytial viruses of man and of cattle and pneumonia virus of mice). Members of the genus *Paramyxovirus* have both hemagglutinin and neuraminidase in the

Table 1–4
RNA-Containing Viruses with Helical Symmetry

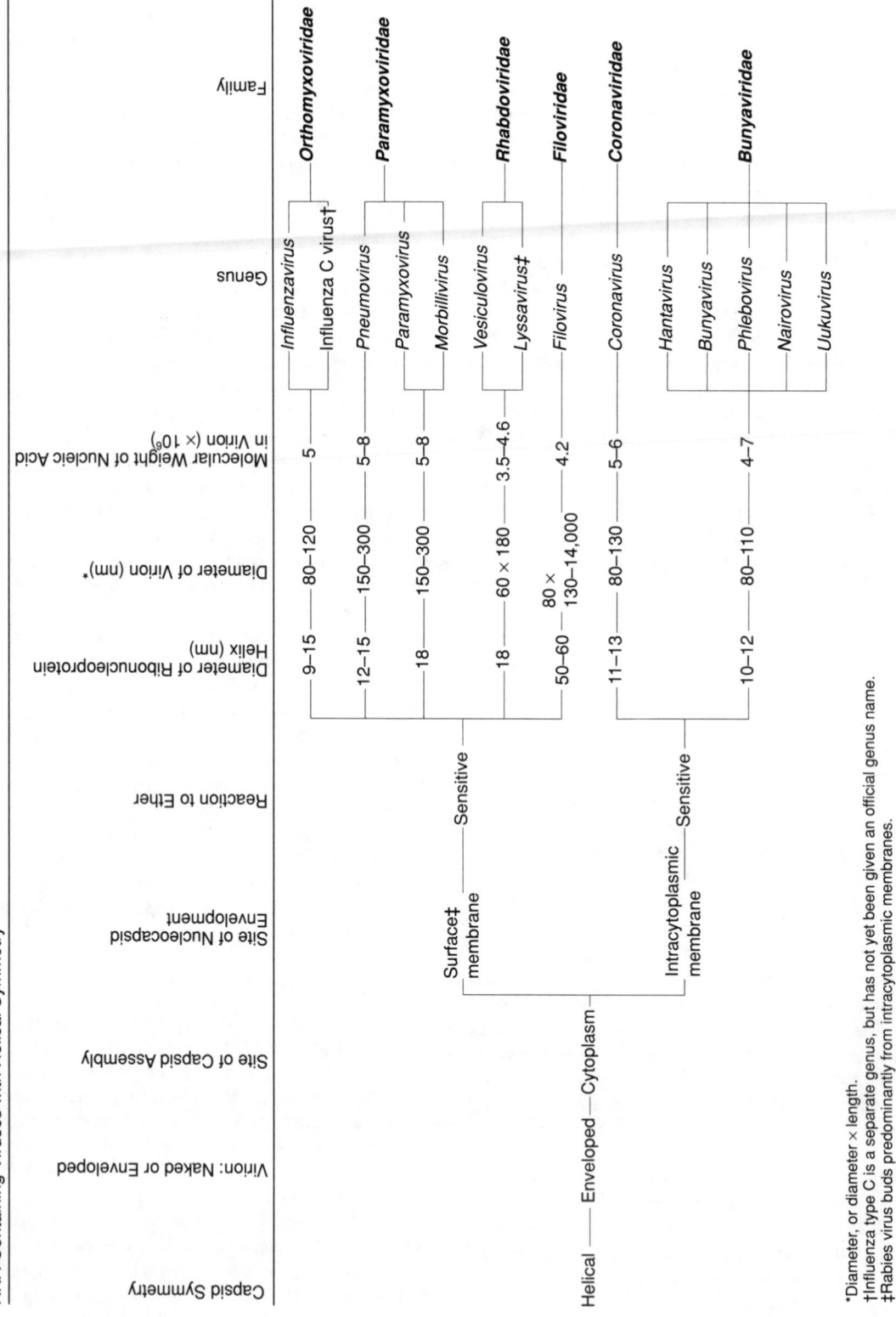

Capsid Symmetry	Virion: Naked or Enveloped	Site of Capsid Assembly	Site of Nucleocapsid Envelopment	Reaction to Ether	Diameter of Ribonucleoprotein Helix (nm)	Diameter of Virion (nm)*	Molecular Weight of Nucleic Acid in Virion ($\times 10^6$)	Genus	Family
Helical	Enveloped	Cytoplasm	Surface‡ membrane	Sensitive	9–15	80–120	5	Influenzavirus	*Orthomyxoviridae*
								Influenza C virus†	
					12–15	150–300	5–8	Pneumovirus	*Paramyxoviridae*
					18	150–300	5–8	Paramyxovirus	
								Morbillivirus	
					18	60 × 180	3.5–4.6	Vesiculovirus	*Rhabdoviridae*
								Lyssavirus‡	
					50–60	80 × 130–14,000	4.2	Filovirus	*Filoviridae*
			Intracytoplasmic membrane	Sensitive	11–13	80–130	5–6	Coronavirus	*Coronaviridae*
					10–12	80–110	4–7	Hantavirus	*Bunyaviridae*
								Bunyavirus	
								Phlebovirus	
								Nairovirus	
								Uukuvirus	

*Diameter, or diameter × length.
†Influenza type C is a separate genus, but has not yet been given an official genus name.
‡Rabies virus buds predominantly from intracytoplasmic membranes.

Table 1–5
Examples of Reference Strains for Newly Designated Subtypes of Hemagglutinin and Neuraminidase Antigens of Influenza A Viruses Isolated from Man, Swine, and Horses

H and N Subtypes	Reference Strains
H1N1	A/PR/8/34 (H1N1)
	A/New Jersey/8/76 (H1N1)
H2N2	A/Singapore/1/57 (H2N2)
H3N2	A/Texas/1/77 (H3N2)
H1N1	A/swine/Wisconsin/67 (H1N1)
H3N2	A/swine/Taiwan/1/70 (H3N2)
H7N7	A/equine/Prague/1/56 (H7N7)
H3N8	A/equine/Miami/1/63 (H3N8)

virion. *Morbillivirus* members have hemagglutinin in the viral envelope but not neuraminidase, whereas for members of the genus *Pneumovirus,* the virions contain neither hemagglutinin nor neuraminidase but may contain fusion glycoprotein. Members of *Paramyxoviridae* are genetically stable, and genetic recombination does not occur.

Rhabdoviridae[40]

Members of this family have enveloped virions that are rod-shaped, resembling a bullet (with one end rounded and the other flattened), or bacilliform. Enclosed within the lipoprotein envelope and membrane protein is the long tubular nucleocapsid (about 50 nm in diameter) with helical symmetry. The nucleocapsid contains a transcriptase and is infectious. The genome of single-stranded negative RNA is in unsegmented, linear form. Some rhabdoviruses multiply in arthropods as well as in vertebrates; others multiply in arthropods and plants. Infectivity is sensitive to ether, acid, and heat. The genera that include agents that infect vertebrates are *Lyssavirus* (members include rabies virus and several agents thus far isolated only from insects) and *Vesiculovirus* (vesicular stomatitis virus and a number of antigenically interrelated viruses). Among the vesiculoviruses are Chandipura virus (from man), and other viruses isolated from vertebrates and invertebrates.

Filoviridae[41, 42]

Marburg virus is a simian virus highly pathogenic for man, producing a severe hemorrhagic fever syndrome, and Ebola virus is a newly recognized agent of outbreaks of hemorrhagic fever in Africa. Both of these agents are considered dangerous pathogens which should be worked on in the laboratory only under maximum containment.

These viruses resemble rhabdoviruses in some respects and were at first considered for inclusion in that family. However, it has become clear that they are significantly different from any other known vertebrate viruses, and they have been established as a separate family.

By electron microscopy, the virus particles are pleomorphic, often appearing as exceedingly long filamentous forms (the basis for the name), sometimes branching extensively, sometimes appearing as U-shaped or circular forms or in the shape of the numeral 6. The diameter of the virions is 80 nm, but their length may range from 130 to 14,000 nm. In terms of infectivity, the infectious unit is 790 nm (Marburg) or 970 nm (Ebola). The virion has a lipid-containing envelope with surface projections. The nucleocapsid consists of a central axis 20 to 30 nm in diameter, surrounded by a helically wound capsid of 50 to 60 nm; the genome is a single molecule of negative single-stranded RNA of molecular weight 4.2×10^6. The virion contains at least five major polypeptides. In replication, viral proteins accumulate in cytoplasm and plasma membranes, the nucleocapsid is assembled in the cytoplasm, and the virus matures by budding.

Coronaviridae[43, 44]

This family is named for unique petal-shaped or club-shaped peplomers that project from the envelope. In negatively stained electron micrographs, these projections form a fringe resembling the solar corona. The internal ribonucleoprotein is seen as a helical structure with a diameter of 10 to 20 nm. The genome consists of one large molecule of single-stranded, positive RNA. Infectivity is sensitive to ether, acid, and heat. A single genus, *Coronavirus,* has been designated. Several serotypes of human coronaviruses have been isolated from patients with acute upper respiratory infections, through the use of human embryonic tracheal and nasal organ cultures. There are distinct coronaviruses that infect a number of animal species: avian infectious bronchitis virus (IBV), mouse hepatitis virus, porcine transmissible gastroenteritis virus, and porcine hemagglutinating encephalitis virus. Probable members include canine coronavirus, the coronavirus of turkey bluecomb disease, neonatal calf diarrhea coronavirus, and at least two viruses infecting rats.

Bunyaviridae[4, 45, 46]

This family is the largest and most recently recognized taxonomic grouping constituted for an antigenically interrelated set of arboviruses. Electron microscopic studies have indicated that all members of this family are structurally comparable to Bunyamwera virus. The family comprises more than 225 viruses (serotypes, subtypes and varieties) that infect vertebrates and invertebrates. The virions of member viruses are spherical, 80 to 110 nm in diameter, and have a unit membrane envelope from which protrude polypeptide spikes 5 to 10 nm long. The virion contains a helical nucleocapsid, with a segmented genome consisting of three molecules of single-stranded RNA, generally negative-sense, sometimes ambisense (positive- and negative-sense in different halves of one molecule); "sticky ends" allow circularization. There are at least three major virion polypeptides. The virions develop in the cytoplasm and mature by budding through intracytoplasmic membranes into smooth-surfaced vesicles in or near the Golgi region. Infectivity is sensitive to ether, acid, and heat. Virus particles hemagglutinate.

Subdivision of the family *Bunyaviridae* into genera reflects both the antigenic supergroup relationships that have been demonstrated and the molecular differences that have been observed among selected members of the four genera. The genus *Bunyavirus* includes at least 145 viruses, most of them belonging to 13 serologically cross-related groups. Several ungrouped arboviruses also are included; most of these agents are mosquito-transmitted. Among the members are the virus of California encephalitis, and also the

La Crosse virus which causes human encephalitis with occasional fatal outcome, as well as other viruses that cause febrile diseases in man. Other bunyaviruses cause disease in some ruminants. On the basis of serologic interrelationships, viruses of this genus are members of the Bunyamwera supergroup. The genus *Phlebovirus,* named from the prototype member, the virus of phlebotomus (sandfly) fever of man, also includes Rift Valley fever virus and at least 28 other serotypes, subtypes, and varieties. These viruses are predominantly sandfly-borne, but some have been recovered from mosquitoes; a wide variety of vertebrates, especially rodents, may be infected. Rift Valley fever is a serious pathogen of sheep, and infections of man are sometimes fatal. Sandfly fever infections of man involve a self-limiting febrile illness. The genus *Nairovirus* was named from the virus of Nairobi sheep disease, but its prototype virus species is the more intensively studied Crimean-Congo hemorrhagic fever virus. Nairobi sheep disease virus produces disease with high morbidity in these animals, and often involves catastrophically high mortality in certain ruminants. The nairoviruses are predominantly tick-transmitted. At least 19 serotypes belong to this genus.

Members of the genus *Uukuvirus* are tick-transmitted and have been isolated in nature from certain rodents and from ticks; they have no known pathogenicity for man.

Another important group of pathogens recently has been shown to belong to the family ***Bunyaviridae***. These viruses constitute a separate genus, *Hantavirus*.[47] Human illness caused by Hantaan virus has been recognized in the Far East as Korean hemorrhagic fever, and a variant is known in Scandinavian and eastern European countries as epidemic nephropathy. The illness has been collectively named "hemorrhagic fever with renal syndrome (HFRS)"[48] or "muroid virus nephropathy." However, hemorrhagic symptoms are not regularly present, and although mice are the common natural hosts and presumably the chief reservoir of virus in nature in Korea, voles are the most common reservoir hosts in Europe. Hence, it has been recommended[49] that *Hantavirus* be used as part of more accurate and descriptive terms for all cases of disease, for example, *Hantavirus* infection, *Hantavirus* disease, *Hantavirus* nephropathy, *Hantavirus* hemorrhagic fever. The virions have a labile membrane and a tripartite single-stranded RNA genome, with a unique nucleotide sequence at the 3′ end of each RNA segment. There have been several instances of infection of staff members handling laboratory rats infected with the virus, both in the Far East and more recently in Europe.

Retroviridae[4, 50, 51, 52]

The viruses in this family include not only the RNA tumor viruses ("oncornaviruses," "leukoviruses") that are now assigned to a subfamily, **Oncovirinae**, but also the slow viruses of the maedi/visna group (now the subfamily **Lentivirinae**) and the foamy virus group of agents that form syncytia in cell cultures (now assigned to the subfamily **Spumavirinae** (see Table 1–6). The human immunodeficiency viruses associated with acquired immunodeficiency syndrome (AIDS) are members of **Lentivirinae.**[53, 54]

Retroviruses characteristically have a reverse transcriptase (RNA-dependent DNA polymerase) within the virion. The spherical virions, 80 to 100 nm in diameter, have glycoprotein surface pro-

jections approximately 8 nm in diameter. Within the envelope is an inner shell or capsid, probably icosahedral, containing ribonucleoprotein that possibly is helical. The genome is an inverted dimer of linear, single-stranded, positive RNA that dissociates readily into two or three pieces. Infectivity is sensitive to ether, acid, and heat. Replication of the viral RNA involves a DNA provirus that is integrated into host cellular DNA.

Endogenous members of the **Oncovirinae** may be part of the germ line of vertebrate hosts, being inherited as mendelian genes. The oncovirus genes may not be expressed, but can be activated by physical and chemical agents, by superinfection with other oncoviruses, and even by herpesviruses. It was through studies of oncoviruses that the cellular "oncogenes" became recognized.

With some exceptions, oncoviruses fall into host-species-specific groups of agents, inducing either leukemias or sarcomas, that is, leukemia-sarcoma complexes of avian, murine, feline, and hamster oncoviruses. Other groups are murine mammary tumor virus and primate oncoviruses. Recent evidence indicates that all strains of mice studied to date contain oncoviruses that are xenotropic (ie, replicate in cells of other species but not in the homologous murine cells).

The subfamily **Oncovirinae** has been divided into types A, B, C, and a possible type D, according to morphologic, antigenic, and enzymatic differences. Two of these groups have been formally designated as genus-level, and a third genus-level group (type D) has been tentatively defined. The type C oncovirus group includes mammalian, avian, and reptilian subgenus groupings, as well as a number of ungrouped species. Two members of **Oncovirinae** type C that infect humans, human T-lymphotropic viruses I and II (HTLV-I, HTLV-II), have been recognized; they are associated with human T cell leukemias.[55] The type B oncovirus group includes the mouse mammary tumor virus and probably similar viruses from guinea pigs and perhaps other species. Type D includes viruses of monkeys. Special features observed in thin-section electron microscopy include outer envelope, inner membrane (shell), and central nucleoid. In type B oncoviruses, the central nucleoid is located asymmetrically, whereas in type C viruses it is located symmetrically.

The members of the subfamily **Spumavirinae**, "foamy viruses," do not induce tumors or cellular transformation but cause persistent asymptomatic infections in natural and experimental host animals. They perhaps have been best known because they induce syncytia in cell cultures being prepared for cultivation of other viruses. Foamy or syncytial viruses are known for a number of mammalian species, including man.

The slow viruses of the maedi/visna group that have been placed in the subfamily **Lentivirinae** are morphologically and chemically like other members of the *Retroviridae* family but do not induce tumors. Visna virus resembles type C oncoviruses in morphology, physical properties, and chemical composition. Synthesis of viral DNA continues throughout the infectious cycle under permissive conditions. Most of the DNA is extrachromosomal, but integrated DNA is present. It is not clear if the integration is required for replication. Natural infections are known only in sheep. Visna virus causes panleukoencephalitis and infects all the organs of the animal. Pathologic changes, however, are confined chiefly to the brain, lungs, and reticuloendothelial system. The incubation period is long, and virus can be recovered from the animal as long as 4 years after inoculation. Serologically related viruses (variously designated in different countries as maedi or progressive pneumonia viruses) cause interstitial pneumonitis.

The most widespread and severe human disease caused by members of the *Retroviridae* is AIDS.[54, 55, 56] This immunoregulatory disorder is often fatal, because it predisposes the infected individual to severe opportunistic infections and cancers. Susceptibility results from the depletion of helper T lymphocytes which are infected by a retrovirus that is now officially named human immunodeficiency virus (HIV). In initial studies the virus was called human T-lymphotropic virus type III (HTLV-III), or lymphadenopathy-associated virus (LAV), or AIDS-related virus (ARV).

HIV strains possess the physicochemical properties typical of the *Retroviridae*. Two types have been recognized; type 1 is more widespread and more virulent. Their unique morphologic characteristic is a cylindrical nucleoid in the mature virion. The diagnostic bar-shaped nucleoid is visible in electron micrographs in those extracellular particles that happen to be sectioned at the appropriate angle.

On the basis of a number of characteristics (nucleic acid homology, genome and protein sizes, virion morphology, and biologic characteristics of infections, including an incubation period ranging from 6 months to more than 7 years), HIV is a member of the retrovirus subfamily **Lentivirinae,** particularly bearing resemblance to visna virus, the slow virus of sheep.

HIV is T-lymphotropic, especially for a particular group of helper T cells—those identified by monoclonal antibody OKT4 (Leu-3). Cell infection produces a pronounced cytopathic effect, including the formation of multinucleated giant cells, and cell death follows. The depletion of this T4 subset of lymphocytes is a hallmark of AIDS. In contrast to the effect of other retrovirus pathogens of humans, HTLV-I and HTLV-II, the target cells are killed, not transformed. HIV can also infect other cell types, which carry the T4 antigen.

No animal model has been developed for AIDS. Although chimpanzees can be infected by HIV, developing antibodies and transient changes in T cell ratios, they do not develop clinical signs of AIDS.

HIV is a completely exogenous virus, in contrast to the transforming retroviruses in which the viral genome is part of the conserved cellular genes. Individuals become infected by the introduction of HIV from outside sources and not by activation of silent viral sequences contained in cellular DNA. After an individual is exposed to HIV, proviral DNA is integrated into the cellular DNA of infected cells.

The genome of HIV-1 is known to encode at least seven genes, including the three structural genes (*gag, pol,* and *env*) and two transactivating genes (*tat*). One acts similarly to the *tat* gene of HTLV-I and HTLV-II in regulating transcription from the long terminal repeat (LTR), while the other acts principally on translation of viral proteins. The functions of the other nonstructural genes are unknown at present.

The many different isolates of HIV exhibit considerable divergence, particularly in the gene that codes for viral envelope proteins. Visna virus, the prototype of the genus *Lentivirus* within the subfamily **Lentivirinae,** undergoes progressive antigenic variation in reaction to the host's immune response during persistent infection. This property of HIV may complicate efforts in vaccine development.

HIV is completely inactivated by treatment for ten minutes at room temperature with any of the following: 10% household bleach, 50% ethyl alcohol, 35% isopropyl alcohol, 1% NP40 detergent, 0.5% Lysol, 0.5% paraformaldehyde, or 0.3% hydrogen peroxide. The virus also is sensitive to extremes in pH (pH 1.0 or pH 13.0). In liquids, or in 10% serum, it also is inactivated by heating at 56°C for ten minutes. However, dried proteinaceous material is markedly protective; lyophilized blood products would need to be heated at 68°C for 72 hours to ensure inactivation of contaminating HIV.

Arenaviridae[4, 57, 58]

Members of this family have spherical or pleomorphic virions, ranging in diameter from 50 to 300 nm (mean, 110–130 nm). The envelope is a dense lipid bilayer membrane bearing club-shaped surface projections 10 nm long. Within the virion core are electron-dense RNA-containing granules about 20 to 25 nm in diameter that resemble ribosomes in size, shape, and density. The genome consists of two pieces of single-stranded RNA that is negative-sense or ambisense; sticky ends allow a circular configuration. There is an associated transcriptase. Most member viruses have a single restricted rodent host in which persistent infection occurs, accompanied by viremia, viruria, or both. Spread to other mammals, including humans, can occur, but is unusual.

A single genus has been established: *Arenavirus*. The type species is lymphocytic choriomeningitis virus, which can establish persistent infection causing immune complex disease in congenitally or neonatally infected mice, and occasionally can infect man, causing aseptic meningitis. This genus includes Junin virus (the agent of Argentinian hemorrhagic fever), Machupo virus (of Bolivian hemorrhagic fever), as well as other members of the Tacaribe complex of antigenically interrelated arboviruses. Pichinde virus, another member of the Tacaribe complex, has been studied most intensively as a laboratory model because it does not produce illness in humans. Lassa fever virus is a member of the genus *Arenavirus*. When this virus spreads to humans, it causes a severe febrile illness with a high mortality rate.

EMERGING PROBLEMS IN CLASSIFICATION

There are known viruses about which information is insufficient to permit their taxonomic classification. Such is the status of the non-A, non-B hepatitis viruses (hepatitis C and E) and of agents of some of the slow virus diseases. At this writing, the recently recognized hepatitis C virus seems to be the cause of the major proportion of transfusion-associated hepatitis. The virus appears to have the properties of a flavivirus. Another non-A, non-B hepatitis agent is being classified as hepatitis E. This agent, which is responsible for waterborne epidemics, particularly in developing countries, is tentatively classified as a calicivirus.

In addition to unclassified but known viral agents, some of the current and developing problems that viral taxonomists need to address are those presented by the recently discovered forms of life that have properties differing from those of any other known biologic entities, such as the forms termed viroids and prions. Another kind of problem is presented by viral hybrids (between unrelated viruses), pseudovirions, and recombinant DNA.

Viroids[59]

A class of infectious agents smaller than viruses, termed viroids, has been discovered. These agents cause diseases of plants (eg, potato spindle tuber disease) and may ultimately be found to cause disease in humans and animals. Viroids exhibit the characteristics of nucleic acids in crude extracts, that is, they are insensitive to heat and organic solvents but sensitive to nucleases, and they do not appear to possess a protein coat. Viroids known at present consist solely of a short, single-stranded, circular RNA molecule with a molecular weight of 70,000 to 120,000. Recently, the complete nucleotide sequence of a viroid has been determined, and it indicates that the secondary structure is a series of double-stranded helical structures with several short single-stranded loops. There is no indication of how disease is caused by these small nucleic acids. Recent studies suggest that a host RNA polymerase is used to replicate viroid RNA and that the genome does not function as a messenger RNA (mRNA). If this RNA codes for proteins, a complementary RNA message may be implicated.

Prions

Unusual kinds of infectious agents that may be similar to viroids have been implicated in degenerative brain diseases such as scrapie in sheep and Creutzfeldt-Jakob disease, a rare form of early senile dementia in humans. The scrapie agent has been considered to be an infectious DNA molecule with a molecular weight of 70,000 to 100,000, similar in size to plant RNA viroids. However, a new concept has recently been proposed as to the nature of the scrapie agent. The agent may be a small *proteinaceous infectious* particle, anagrammatically, the *prion*. The "prion protein," PrP 27–30, has a molecular weight of 27,000 to 30,000. PrP 27–30 copurifies with scrapie infectivity, aggregates, and behaves like amyloid. Preparations containing only PrP and no detectable nucleic acid have been found in many normal brains, but PrP has been reported to accumulate in infected brains.[60]

A number of lines of evidence are set forth for consideration, including the marked resistance of the scrapie agent to procedures that attack most nucleic acids, its inactivation by procedures directed against proteins, its heterogeneity of size, and other novel properties. The evidence assembled is not claimed to rule out the possibility that a very small nucleic acid may be present, buried within a tightly packed protein shell; neither does it rule out the possible presence of a highly unusual nucleic acid, whose coat or chemical structure protects it from most procedures that inactivate nucleic acids.

If prions eventually are shown to be devoid of nucleic acid, then they would indeed be unique among microorganisms, and many new questions would be raised, including that of the mode whereby an infectious protein could replicate.

Virus Hybrids

The fact that virus hybrids can exist in nature should be more widely recognized. If SV40 had not already been known as a virus before the discovery of SV40-adenovirus "hybrid" particles, these particles would have presented virus taxonomists with a confusing puzzle. In these hybrid particles, portions of SV40 genome material are covalently linked to adenovirus genetic material encased within an adenovirus coat. They would, therefore, have seemed to be virions of a new and strange virus that reacted antigenically as an adenovirus (of the serotype from which the coat had been derived) but which had many properties altogether unlike an adenovirus when grown in cultures.

Two types of adenovirus-SV40 hybrids have been detected. PARA-adenovirus populations consist of two types of particles: (1) a nonhybrid typical adenovirion, and (2) a defective adenovirus-SV40 genome encased in an adenovirus capsid (PARA). PARA can be transcapsidated from one adenovirus serotype to another. The second type of hybrid, the AD2 + ND viruses, consists of a series of nondefective adenovirus type 2 isolates carrying different amounts (5%–44%) of the SV40 genome.

A similar problem of identification and classification exists with respect to another type of particle found in some human adenovirus populations. That particle, termed MAC (monkey-adapting component), behaves somewhat like the adenovirus-SV40 hybrid particle, permitting the true human adenovirus to replicate in monkey cell cultures. The particle, with a MAC genome and an adenovirus coat, does not contain any SV40 nucleic acid fragments, and its origin remains unknown.

Pseudovirions

Another virus form that is difficult to classify is the pseudovirion. During virus replication, the capsid sometimes encloses host nucleic acid rather than viral nucleic acid. Such particles look like ordinary virus particles when observed by electron microscopy, but they do not replicate. Pseudovirions contain the "wrong" nucleic acid. For example, fragments of host-cell DNA (instead of viral DNA) may be incorporated into papovavirus capsids forming pseudovirion particles. This situation resembles the phenomenon of generalized transduction by bacteriophages (ie, transfer of random portions of nucleic acid from donor to recipient bacterial cells). Hybridization studies also indicate the occurrence of covalent linkage of cell DNA segments into the circular DNA of papovaviruses during replication in cells infected at high multiplicity. This phenomenon is analogous to specialized transduction by bacteriophages (ie, transfer by virus of a specific segment of donor bacterial cell DNA). Furthermore, a DNA segment containing functional genes of a λ bacteriophage has been incorporated into the circular DNA of papovavirus SV40. These findings open avenues for the study of possible transducing events in eukaryotic cells whereby functionally defined segments of genetic information might be transmitted from cell to cell. Pseudovirions present the taxonomist with problems based on natural events, but future laboratory manipulations will probably add to these problems of classification.

Recombinant DNA

Recently developed techniques allow DNA to be cleaved into specific pieces by use of restriction endonucleases from bacteria. The distinct fragments can be recombined and replicated. The

Table 1–6
RNA-Containing Viruses with Unusually Complex Architecture

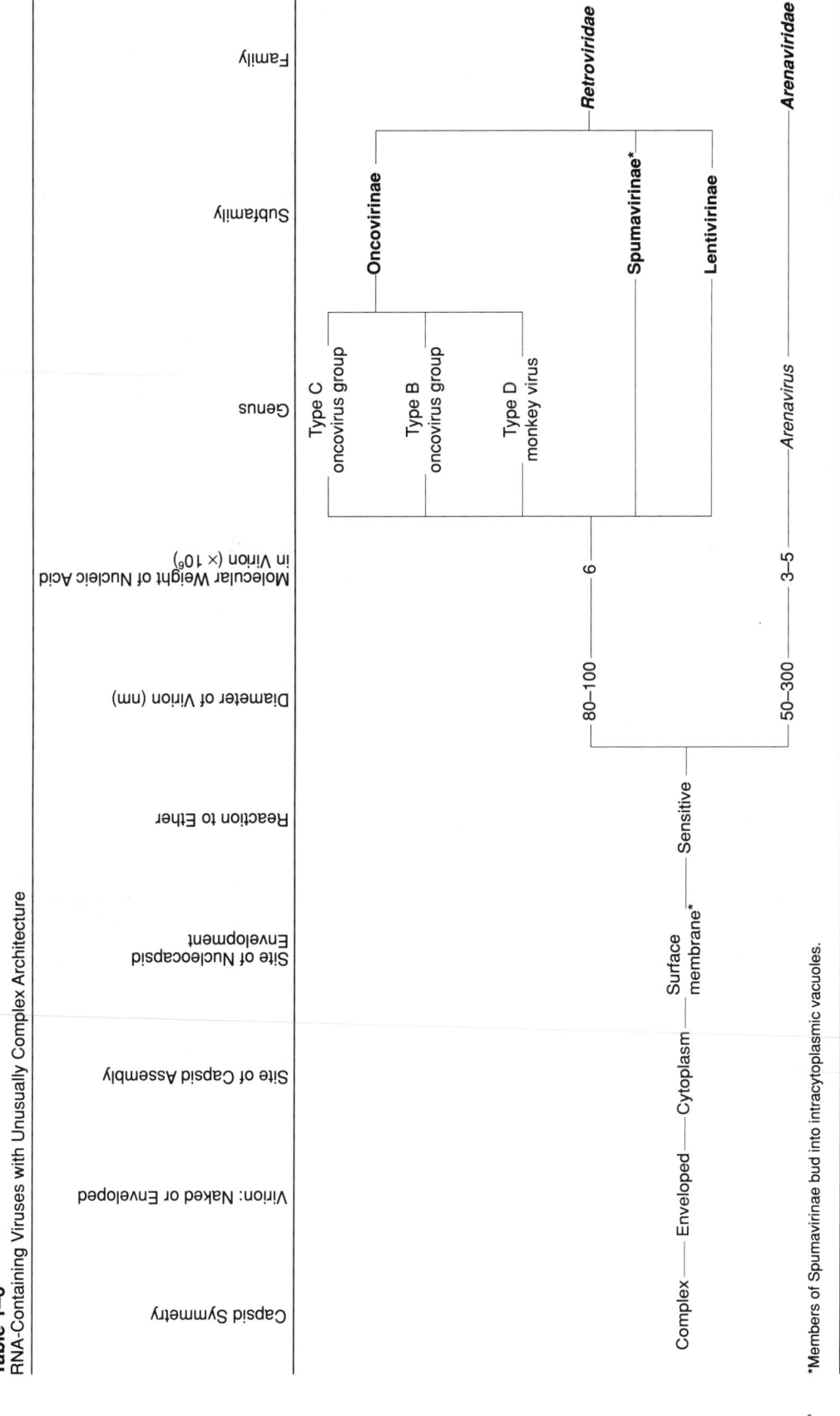

Capsid Symmetry	Virion: Naked or Enveloped	Site of Capsid Assembly	Site of Nucleocapsid Envelopment	Reaction to Ether	Diameter of Virion (nm)	Molecular Weight of Nucleic Acid in Virion ($\times 10^6$)	Genus	Subfamily	Family
Complex	Enveloped	Cytoplasm	Surface membrane*	Sensitive	80–100	6	Type C oncovirus group	Oncovirinae	*Retroviridae*
							Type B oncovirus group		
							Type D monkey virus		
								Spumavirinae*	
								Lentivirinae	
					50–300	3–5	Arenavirus		*Arenaviridae*

*Members of Spumavirinae bud into intracytoplasmic vacuoles.

genomic materials from two distinct viruses multiply together, and these new forms pose new problems for classification.

Already available are vaccinia viruses that contain genes of hepatitis B virus, influenza virus, herpes simplex virus, HIV, and measles virus. Such recombinants grow in all hosts in which native vaccinia virus can replicate.

Acknowledgment

The able assistance of Miss Verle Rennick in the preparation of this chapter is gratefully acknowledged.

REFERENCES

1. Wildy P: *Classification and Nomenclature of Viruses: First Report of the International Committee on Nomenclature of Viruses. Monographs in Virology*. Basel, Karger, 1971, vol 5.
2. Fenner F: Classification and nomenclature of viruses: Second report of the International Committee on Taxonomy of Viruses. *Intervirology* 1976;7:1–115.
3. Matthews REF: Classification and nomenclature of viruses: Third report of the International Committee on Taxonomy of Viruses. *Intervirology* 1979;12:129–296.
4. Matthews REF: Classification and nomenclature of viruses: Fourth report of the International Committee on Taxonomy of Viruses. *Intervirology* 1982;17:1–199.
5. Fenner F, Pereira HG, Porterfield JS, et al: Family and generic names for viruses approved by the International Committee on Taxonomy of Viruses, June 1974. *Intervirology* 1974;3:193–198.
6. Brown F: The classification and nomenclature of viruses: Summary of results of meetings of the International Committee on Taxonomy of Viruses in Sendai, September 1984. *Intervirology* 1986;25:141–143.
7. Davis BD, Dulbecco R, Eisen HN, et al: *Microbiology*. New York, Hoeber, 1967.
8. Melnick JL: Taxonomy of viruses, in Lennette EH (ed): *Manual of Clinical Microbiology,* ed 4. Washington, DC, American Society for Microbiology, 1985, pp 694–700.
9. Melnick JL: Summaries on viral taxonomy, published annually in *Progress in Medical Virology*. Basel, S Karger, 1966–1982.
10. Bachmann PA, Hoggan MD, Melnick JL, et al: Parvoviridae. *Intervirology* 1975;5:92–93.
11. Siegl G, Bates RC, Berns KI, et al: Characteristics and taxonomy of Parvoviridae. *Intervirology* 1985;23:61–73.
12. Mayor HD, Melnick JL: Small deoxyribonucleic acid-containing viruses (picodnavirus group). *Nature* 1966;210:331–332.
13. Anderson MJ: Parvoviruses as agents of human disease, in Melnick JL (ed): *Prog Med Virol*. Basel, Karger, 1987, vol. 34, pp 55–69.
14. Melnick JL, Allison AC, Butel JS, et al: Papovaviridae. *Intervirology* 1974;3:106–120.
15. zur Hausen H: Genital papillomavirus infections, in Melnick JL, Ochoa S, Orö J (eds): Viruses, oncogenes and cancer, in Melnick JL (ed): *Prog Med Virol*. Basel, Karger, 1985, vol 32, pp 15–21.
16. Norrby E, Bartha A, Boulanger P, et al: Adenoviridae. *Intervirology* 1976;7:117–125.
17. Wigand R, Bartha A, Dreizin RS, et al: Adenoviridae: second report. *Intervirology* 1982;18:169–176.
18. Melnick JL: Classification of hepatitis A virus as enterovirus type 72 and of hepatitis B virus as hepadnavirus type 1. *Intervirology* 1982;18:105–106.
19. Gust ID, Burrell CJ, Coulepis AG, et al: Taxonomic classification of human hepatitis B virus. *Intervirology* 1986;25:14–29.
20. Maupas P, Melnick JL (eds): Hepatitis B virus and primary hepatocellular carcinoma, in Melnick JL (ed): *Prog Med Virol*. Basel, Karger, 1981, Vol 27.
21. Marion PL: Use of animal models to study hepatitis B virus, in Melnick JL (ed): *Prog Med Virol*. Basel, Karger, 1988, vol 35, pp 43–75.
22. Melnick JL: Hepatocellular carcinoma caused by hepatitis B virus, in Evans AS (ed): *Viral Infections of Humans: Epidemiology and Control*, ed 3. New York, Plenum, 1989, pp 769–780.
23. Roizman B, Bartha A, Biggs PM, et al: Provisional labels for herpesviruses. *J Gen Virol* 1973;20:417–419.
24. Roizman B, Carmichael LE, Deinhardt F, et al: Herpesviridae: Definition, provisional nomenclature, and taxonomy. *Intervirology* 1981;16:201–217.
25. Efstathiou S, Gompels UA, Craxton MA, et al: DNA homology between a novel human herpesvirus (HHV-6) and human cytomegalovirus. *Lancet* 1988;1:63–64.
26. Melnick JL, Agol VI, Bachrach HL, et al: Picornaviridae. *Intervirology* 1974;4:303–316.
27. Cooper PD, Agol VI, Bachrach HL, et al: Picornaviridae. Second report. *Intervirology* 1978;10:165–180.
28. Melnick JL: Portraits of viruses: the picornaviruses. *Intervirology* 1983;20:61–100.
29. Melnick JL, Cockburn WC, Dalldorf G, et al: Picornavirus group. *Virology* 1963;19:114–116.
30. Gust ID, Coulepis AG, Feinstone SM, et al: Taxonomic classification of hepatitis A virus. *Intervirology* 1983;20:1–7.
31. Schaffer FL, Bachrach HL, Brown F, et al: Caliciviridae. *Intervirology* 1980;14:1–6.
32. Joklik WK (ed.): The Reoviridae, in Fraenkel-Conrat H, Wagner RR (series eds): *The Viruses*. New York, Plenum, 1983.
33. Estes MK, Palmer EL, Obijeski JF: Rotaviruses: a review. *Curr Top Microbiol Immunol* 1983;105:123–184.
34. Porterfield JS, Casals J, Chumakov MP, et al: Togaviridae. *Intervirology* 1978;9:129–148.
35. Westaway EG, Brinton MA, Gaidamovich SYa, et al: Togaviridae. *Intervirology* 1985;24:125–139.
36. Westaway EG, Brinton MA, Gaidamovich SYa, et al: Flaviviridae. *Intervirology* 1985;24:183–192.
37. Dowdle WR, Davenport FM, Fukumi H, et al: Orthomyxoviridae. *Intervirology* 1975;5:245–251.
38. World Health Organization Consultation. A revision of the system of nomenclature for influenza viruses: A WHO memorandum. *Bull WHO* 1980;58:585–591.
39. Kingsbury DW, Bratt MA, Choppin PW, et al: Paramyxoviridae. *Intervirology* 1978;10:137–152.
40. Brown F, Bishop DHL, Crick J, et al: Rhabdoviridae. *Intervirology* 1979;12:1–7.
41. Kiley MP, Bowen ETW, Eddy GA, et al: Filoviridae: a taxonomic home for Marburg and Ebola viruses? *Intervirology* 1982;18:24–32.
42. Murphy FA, Kiley MP, Fisher-Hoch SP: Filoviridae: Marburg and Ebola viruses, in Fields BN, Knipe DM, Chanock RM, et al (eds): *Virology*. New York, Raven Press, 1990, pp 933–942.
43. Tyrrell DAJ, Almeida JD, Cunningham CH, et al: Coronaviridae. *Intervirology* 1975;5:76–82.
44. Tyrrell DAJ, Alexander DJ, Almeida JD, et al: Coronaviridae: Second report. *Intervirology* 1978;10:321–328.
45. Porterfield JS, Casals J, Chumakov MP, et al: Bunyaviruses and Bunyaviridae. *Intervirology* 1973/1974;2:270–272.
46. Bishop DHL, Calisher CH, Casals J, et al: Bunyaviridae. *Intervirology* 1980;14:125–143.
47. Schmaljohn DS, Dalrymple JM: Analysis of Hantaan virus RNA. Evidence for a new genus of Bunyaviridae, *Virology* 1983;131:482–491.
48. Lee HW, van der Groen G: Hemorrhagic fever with renal syndrome, in Melnick JL (ed): *Prog Med Virol*. Basel, Karger, 1989, vol 36, pp 62–102.
49. Desmyter J, van Ypersele de Strihou C, van der Groen G: Hantavirus disease. *Lancet* 1984;2:158.
50. Dalton AG, Melnick JL, Bauer H, et al: The case for a family of reverse transcriptase viruses: Retraviridae. *Intervirology* 1974;4:201–206.
51. Vogt PK: The oncovirinae—A definition of the group, in Thein P (ed): *Report of WHO Centre for Collection and Evaluation of Data on Comparative Virology: Report No. 1,* Munich, 1976, pp 327–339.

52. Bishop JM: Exploring carcinogenesis with retroviral and cellular oncogenes, in Melnick JL (ed): *Prog Med Virol*. Basel, Karger, 1985, vol 32, pp 5–14.

53. Gonda MA, Wong-Staal F, Gallo RC, et al: Sequence homology and morphologic similarity of HTLV-III and visna virus, a pathogenic lentivirus. *Science* 1985;227:173–176.

54. Human Retrovirus Subcommittee, International Committee on Taxonomy of Viruses: Human immunodeficiency viruses. *Science* 1986;232:697.

55. Gallo RC: Human T-cell leukaemia-lymphoma virus and T-cell malignancies in adults. *Cancer Surveys* 1984;3:113–159.

56. Montagnier L, Alizon M: The human immune deficiency virus (HIV): An update. *Ann Inst Pasteur Virol* 1987;138:1–11.

57. Pfau CF, Bergold GH, Casals J, et al: Arenaviruses. *Intervirology* 1974;4:207–213.

58. Lehmann-Grube F: Portraits of viruses: arenaviruses. *Intervirology* 1984;22:121–145.

59. Diener TO: Portraits of viruses: the viroid. *Intervirology* 1984;22:1–16.

60. Prusiner SB: Prions: Novel infectious pathogens. *Adv Virus Res* 1984;29:1–56.

APPENDIX
Members of Vertebrate Virus Families, With Emphasis on Viruses That Infect Human Beings

Family and Subfamily*	Genus	Common Species†	No. of Members
Parvoviridae	*Parvovirus*	Rat virus (Kilham's) (parvovirus r-1) and other viruses of mammalian and avian species, including feline panleukopenia virus, a strain of which is causing widespread outbreaks among dogs; another member is Aleutian mink disease virus Parvoviruses B19 and RA-1 are associated with human diseases	Many
	Dependovirus	Adeno-associated virus (AAV) (adeno-satellite virus) types 1-3: man; type 4: monkeys; also bovine, canine, and avian AAVs; possibly equine AAVs	≥8
	Densovirus	Densonucleosis viruses of insects: densovirus of the lepidopteran, *Galleria mellonella,* and densoviruses of other insect species	≥6
Papovaviridae			
Papillomavirinae	*Papillomavirus*	Rabbit (Shope) papillomavirus	1
		Human papilloma (warts) viruses	9
		Papillomaviruses of other mammalian species	≥11
Polyomavirinae	*Polyomavirus*	Polyomavirus of mice	1
		BK and JC viruses of man	≥2
		Simian virus 40 (SV40) of rhesus monkey	1
		Lymphotropic virus (LPV) of green monkey, human (?)	1
		Viruses of mouse, rabbit, hamster, macaque, baboon	≥5
Adenoviridae	*Mastadenovirus*	Adenoviruses of man, types 1–36 (h 1–h 36)	≥36
		Viruses of numerous other mammalian species (eg, bos 1–bos 9; sus 1–sus 4)	≥45
	Aviadenovirus	Chicken embryo lethal orphan (CELO) virus of fowl	1
		Other viruses of fowl and of other avian species	≥12
Herpesviridae‡			
Alphaherpesvirinae*	*Simplexvirus*	Human herpes simplex viruses types 1 and 2 (human herpesvirus 1; human herpesvirus 2)‡	
		Bovine mammillitis virus (bovine herpesvirus 2)	
		Herpes B virus of monkeys (ceropithecine herpesvirus 1)	
		SA8 virus of monkeys (cercopithecine herpesvirus 2)	
	Varicellovirus	Varicella-zoster virus (human herpesvirus 3)	
		Pseudorabies virus and equine rhinopneumonitis virus (suid herpesvirus 1; equid herpesvirus 1); infectious bovine rhinotracheitis virus (bovid herpesvirus 1); equid herpesvirus 2	
Betaherpesvirinae	*Cytomegalovirus*	Human cytomegaloviruses (human herpesvirus 5)	
		Lymphotropic human herpesvirus (HHV-6)	
	Muromegalovirus	Murine cytomegaloviruses (murid herpesvirus 1)	
Gammaherpesvirinae	*Lymphocryptovirus*	Epstein-Barr virus (human herpesvirus 4)	
		Baboon herpesvirus (cercopithecine herpesvirus 12)	
		Chimpanzee herpesvirus (pongine herpesvirus)	
	Thetalymphocryptovirus	Marek's disease herpesvirus (gallid herpesvirus 2)	
		Turkey herpesvirus (meleagrid herpesvirus 1)	
	Rhadinovirus	Herpesvirus ateles, strains 810 and 73 (ateline herpesvirus 2; ateline herpesvirus 3)	
		Herpesvirus saimiri (saimirine herpesvirus 2)	
Iridoviridae (icosahedral cytoplasmic deoxyriboviruses)	*Ranavirus*	Frog virus 3	1
		Other viruses of *Rana pipiens,* other frogs, and newts	≥30
	Lymphocystivirus	Lymphocystis disease virus of fish	Many
	Iridovirus (small iridescent virus group)	*Tipula* iridescent virus and other small iridescent viruses (Possible member: *Octopus vulgaris* disease iridescent virus)	≥30
	Chloriridovirus (large iridescent virus group)	Mosquito iridescent virus and other large iridescent viruses of insects	≥10

Poxviridae			
Chordopoxvirinae	*Orthopoxvirus*	Vaccinia virus	1
(poxviruses of	(vaccinia subgroup)	Smallpox virus (variola)	1
vertebrates)		Cowpox, monkeypox, buffalopox, camelpox, ectromelia of mice, rabbitpox	6
	Parapoxvirus (Orf subgroup)	Orf virus and other viruses of ungulates; virus of milker's node	1
	Avipoxvirus (fowlpox subgroup)	Fowlpox virus and other viruses of birds	8
	Capripoxvirus (sheep pox subgroup)	Sheep-pox virus, goatpox virus, lumpy skin disease (Neethling) virus	3
	Leporipoxvirus (myxoma subgroup)	Myxoma virus of hares, fibroma viruses of rabbits and squirrels	4
	Suipoxvirus (swinepox subgroup)	Swinepox virus	1

(Other members of Poxviridae that have vertebrate hosts but have not been allocated to genera are the viruses of carnivorepox and elephantpox, molluscum contagiosum of man, raccoonpox, and tanapox and Yaba monkey tumor pox)

Entomopoxvirinae (poxviruses of insects)	Three probable genera, at present termed genus A, genus B, genus C		≥24

Hepadnaviridae	*Hepadnavirus*	Human hepatitis B virus (HBV) (hepadnavirus type 1)	1
		Woodchuck hepatitis virus (WHV)	1
		Ground squirrel hepatitis virus (GSHV)	1
		Duck hepatitis virus (DHV)	1

Picornaviridae	*Enterovirus*	Polioviruses	3
		Coxsackieviruses A	23
		Coxsackieviruses B	6
		Echoviruses	31
		Enteroviruses 68–71	4
		Enterovirus 72 (Heparnavirus)	1
		Viruses of other vertebrates	≥34
	Cardiovirus (EMC virus group)	Encephalomyocarditis (EMC) virus, Mengo virus, murine encephalomyelitis (ME) virus	3
	Rhinovirus (common cold viruses)	Virus types 1A–114	>115
		Viruses of cattle	2
	Aphthovirus (foot-and-mouth disease viruses)	Aphthoviruses of cattle and other cloven-hoofed animals	7
	Heparnavirus	Hepatitis A virus of humans	1
	(Other picornaviruses not yet assigned to genera)	Equine viruses	2
		Viruses of invertebrates (including several viruses of bees, and viruses infecting drosophila, gonometa, and other insects)	≥30

Caliciviridae	*Calicivirus*	Vesicular exanthema of swine virus (VESV)	13
		Viruses of cats, sea lions	Many
		(Possible members; human calicivirus, Norwalk gastroenteritis virus of man)	≥5

Reoviridae	*Reovirus*	Types 1–3 (from man, monkeys, dogs, cattle)	3
		Viruses of birds	≥5
	Orbivirus	Bluetongue subgroup: bluetongue virus of sheep	> 90
		Sixteen other subgroups, including Colorado tick fever and Kemerovo viruses of man, and African horse sickness viruses	
	Rotavirus	Human rotavirus	≥6
		Rotaviruses of many mammalian species, including SA-11 virus of monkeys and Nebraska calf diarrhea virus	Many

*Where subfamilies have been designated, these are listed in this column, indented below the family name.
†In most instances, the first species listed is the type species. Only selected members of the genera are listed, to serve as examples.
‡An alternative designation for the individual members, to keep clear their subfamily classification, would include the subfamily name, eg, human alphaherpesvirus 1, murid betaherpesvirus 1, etc.

(Continued)

APPENDIX *(Cont.)*

Family and Subfamily*	Genus	Common Species†	No. of Members
Members of Reoviridae infecting plants and invertebrates:			
	Phytoreovirus (plant reovirus subgroup 1)	Wound tumor virus, rice dwarf virus	2
	Fijivirus (plant reovirus subgroup 2)	Fiji disease virus and others	≥9
	Cypovirus	Cytoplasmic polyhedrosis virus (CPV) of *Bombyx mori*, and CPVs of other insects	≥12
Birnaviridae	*Birnavirus*	Infectious pancreatic necrosis virus of fish; infectious bursal disease virus of chickens	2
Togaviridae	*Alphavirus* (arbovirus group A)	Sindbis virus and many other mosquito-borne viruses, including the viruses of eastern equine, Venezuelan, and western equine encephalitis, and Semliki Forest virus	23
	Rubivirus	Rubella virus	1
	Pestivirus (mucosal disease virus group)	Mucosal disease virus (bovine virus diarrhea virus)	3
		Border disease virus	
		Hog cholera virus	
	Arterivirus	Equine arteritis virus	1
(Another possible member of Togaviridae: lactic dehydrogenase virus of mice)			
Flaviviridae	*Flavivirus* (arbovirus group B)	Yellow fever virus and other mosquito-borne viruses, including the viruses of dengue; of Japanese, Murray Valley, and St Louis encephalitis, and of West Nile fever	26
		Tick-borne viruses including the viruses of Kyasanur Forest disease; Omsk hemorrhagic fever; European and Far Eastern tick-borne encephalitis; louping-ill of sheep	11
		Viruses whose vectors are unknown	17
(Other possible members of Flaviviridae: simian hemorrhagic fever virus, and a cell-fusing agent of mosquitoes)			
Orthomyxoviridae	*Influenzavirus*	Influenzavirus type A	Many
		Influenzavirus type B	Several
	Type C *Influenzavirus*	Influenzavirus type C	1
Paramyxoviridae	*Paramyxovirus*	Newcastle disease virus of fowl	1
		Human parainfluenza viruses (including Sendai virus)	4
		Mumps virus	1
		Viruses of several other avian and mammalian species	≥6
	Morbillivirus	Measles virus	1
		Rinderpest virus of cattle	1
		Canine distemper virus	1
		Peste-des-petits-ruminants (PPR) virus of sheep and goats	1
	Pneumovirus	Respiratory syncytial (RS) virus of man	1
		Bovine respiratory syncytial virus	?
		Pneumonia virus of mice	?
Rhabdoviridae	*Vesiculovirus*	Vesicular stomatitis virus of horses, cattle, swine, with some human infections also	Several subtypes
		Chandipura and other viruses isolated from vertebrate and invertebrate species	Several
	Lyssavirus	Rabies virus	1
		Duvenhage virus, Lagos bat virus, Mokola virus; others	≥5
	(Numerous other viruses infecting vertebrates and invertebrates are probable members of the family, but genera have not been established to include them)		≥38
	(Members of Rhabdoviridae infecting plants: Plant rhabdoviruses, ungrouped)		≥8
Filoviridae	*Filovirus*	Marburg virus	1
		Ebola virus	2

Coronaviridae	*Coronavirus*	Avian infectious bronchitis virus (IBV)	1
		Human coronavirus	1
		Viruses of murine hepatitis, porcine hemagglutinating encephalitis, and porcine transmissible gastroenteritis	≥3
		(Numerous probable and possible members infecting several vertebrate species, including another coronavirus of man)	≥7
Bunyaviridae (Bunyamwera supergroup and related viruses)	*Bunyavirus*	Bunyamwera virus 15 other serologically cross-related groups and several ungrouped viruses; included are California encephalitis viruses, La Crosse virus, and some pathogens of ruminants	(Total in genus: ≥145)
	Phlebovirus	Sandfly fever viruses Other viruses of man and animals (considered to be one serogroup), including Rift Valley fever virus of sheep and other ruminants, which may cause human disease	(Total in genus: ≥30)
	Nairovirus	Crimean-Congo hemorrhagic fever viruses Viruses belonging to five other serogroups; included is the virus of Nairobi sheep disease	(Total in genus: ≥27)
	Uukuvirus	Uukuniemi virus Six other agents, all belonging to the same serogroup	(Total in genus: 7)
	Hantavirus	Korean hemorrhagic fever virus, Hantaan virus; other isolates from many parts of the world	Many
	Members or possible members of Bunyaviridae not assigned to genera	At least four serogroups and some ungrouped agents	21
Retroviridae **Oncovirinae*** (RNA tumor virus group)	Type C oncovirus group (three subgenera have been designated: mammalian, avian, and reptilian type C oncoviruses)	Sarcoma and leukemia viruses of mice, cats, cattle, birds, snakes, and primates. Human T cell leukemia-associated viruses (HTLV-I, HTLV-II)	Many (≥13)
	Type B oncovirus group	Mouse mammary tumor viruses	?
	Proposed genus: type D retrovirus group	Monkey (mammary tumor?) virus (Mason-Pfizer monkey virus)	?
Spumavirinae (foamy virus group)		Syncytial and foamy viruses of humans, monkeys, cattle, cats	≥4
Lentivirinae (maedi/ visna virus group)		Visna virus of sheep Maedi, progressive pneumonia viruses of sheep Human immunodeficiency virus (HIV)	? ≥2
Arenaviridae	*Arenavirus* (LCM virus group)	Lymphocytic choriomeningitis virus (LCM)	1
		Lassa fever virus	1
		Viruses of the Tacaribe complex, including Junin and Machupo viruses of South American hemorrhagic fevers	≥8

*Where subfamilies have been designated, these are listed in this column, indented below the family name.

†In most instances, the first species listed is the type species. Only selected members of the genera are listed, to serve as examples.

‡An alternative designation for the individual members, to keep clear their subfamily classification, would include the subfamily name, eg, human alphaherpesvirus 1, murid betaherpesvirus 1, etc.

Replication of DNA Viruses

Terry W. Fenger

Animal viruses have been classified into families based on their unique structures, sizes, nature and coding capacity of their genomes, and presence or absence of envelopes (see Chapter 1). They can also be distinguished based on their mechanisms of replication, which are presented in this chapter for several DNA viruses and in Chapter 3 for RNA viruses.

The replication cycles of DNA and RNA viruses have several events in common. Virus particles attach to specific receptors on the plasma membranes, penetrate into the cell, and then release their nucleic acids (genomes) at specific intracellular locations. The viral nucleic acids can then serve two purposes leading toward the formation of virus progeny: (1) act directly as messenger RNAs (mRNAs) or as templates for transcription of mRNAs, and (2) act as templates for the replication of the viral genome. Viral proteins translated from mRNAs assemble with replicated genomes to form progeny virus particles. The yield of virus particles, either infectious or noninfectious, produced within a given cell population varies with the type of virus and host cells.

The replication cycle of animal viruses utilizes host cell macromolecules, enzymes, and cellular structures for viral genome replication and transcriptional-translational events. The degree of dependence of virus replication on cellular components is related to the capacity of viral genomes to encode proteins essential for their replication. Poxviruses have the largest genomes of animal viruses with the capacity to encode several hundred proteins, some having enzymatic activity. Compared with members of other animal virus families, poxviruses are less dependent on cellular enzymes for DNA replication. Parvoviruses, on the other hand, have sufficient DNA to encode only a few proteins, and replication depends almost entirely on cellular enzymes. Between these two extremes are families of viruses that depend in varying degrees on cellular functions.

A relationship between genome size (coding capacity) and the site of nucleic acid replication is also seen for DNA viruses. Since poxviruses code for enzymes involved in nucleic acid synthesis, their DNA genomes can replicate within cytoplasmic sites devoid of many nuclear enzymes necessary for cellular DNA replication. However, DNA viruses with smaller genomes depend on the environment and enzymes of the nucleus for their synthetic events. Except for influenza virus, most RNA viruses replicate exclusively in the cytoplasm and must supply their own enzyme(s), including replicases and transcriptases for synthesis of genomic RNAs and mRNAs, respectively.

Replication cycles of animal viruses are being investigated from two general perspectives. First, molecular details of viral replication are sought to understand the intricacies of viral pathogenesis. By defining those synthetic processes unique to viral replication within infected cells, chemotherapeutic and immunologic agents can be developed. Secondly, viruses serve as models for understanding nucleic acid replication, transcription, translation, different levels of control operative during these synthetic events, and transport of macromolecules between various locations within the cell.

Sites for the initiation of viral DNA replication (orgins = ORI) have been analyzed for several DNA viruses and have aided in investigations of DNA replication in eukaryotic cells. Some ORI of DNA replication correspond to palindromic sequences, for example, the ORI of herpes simplex virus, which can potentially form secondary structures through intrastrand base pairing of complementary nucleotide sequences.[1, 2] The primary nucleotide sequence or secondary structure at the ORI sites, in conjunction with primers for DNA synthesis, are recognized by DNA polymerases and other proteins involved in the initiation of DNA synthesis.

Several different types of primer molecules are used for the initiation of viral DNA synthesis. A protein-nucleotide complex primes adenovirus DNA synthesis in conjunction with viral DNA polymerase and several DNA-binding proteins (DBPs) of both viral and cellular origins.[3, 4] Alternatively, poxviruses and parvoviruses employ DNA structures formed by intrastrand base pairing of a terminal sequence of DNA with a complementary sequence at a more internal site. Fold-back loops or hairpin structures of this kind provide a DNA primer which is extended by DNA polymerase.[5-7] The third type of primer, which probably serves this function most often in eukaryotic cell and viral systems, is a short sequence of RNA which binds to the template (sense) strand of DNA for initiation of DNA synthesis. DNA-binding proteins (DBPs) involved in initiation of DNA synthesis recognize and bind to either primary nucleotide sequences or structural features inherent in the ORIs or to both.[8, 9] However, binding of proteins to DNA in a sequence-independent manner has also been shown to influence DNA replication, as exemplified by ICP-8 of herpes simplex virus. ICP-8 is required for DNA replication and binds in vitro in a nonspecific manner to single-stranded DNA, but not significantly to double-stranded DNA.[10]

Viral transcription via RNA polymerase II and III also serves as a model for analogous processes occurring in uninfected eukaryotic cells. The rate and temporal control of transcription is regulated by multiple regions usually adjacent to the gene under its control. A single nucleotide, designated +1, represents the first nucleotide of a gene to be transcribed and corresponds to the 5′ end of the primary transcript. It also serves as a point of reference for numbering other nucleotides along the DNA molecule. Nucleotides within the region of a gene, which are transcribed into mRNA, are sequentially designated with positive numbers of increasing values starting from the +1 site, whereas nucleotides in the control (promoter-regulatory) region are designated with neg-

ative numbers again increasing in absolute value at greater distances from the +1 site. Relative to the +1 site, nucleotides designated by positive numbers are considered to be "downstream" of the +1 site and negatively numbered nucleotides are "upstream" from that same site.

Several regulatory elements (*cis*-elements) have been defined in the upstream, promoter-regulatory regions of viral and eukaryotic cell genes. (*Cis*-elements refer to specific deoxynucleotide sequences which control DNA replication, transcription, etc.) The cis-regulatory element most proximal to the +1 transcriptional start site at approximately −30 nucleotides is a TATA sequence (TATA box) or one of it homologues. This sequence helps define the precise location for initiation of transcription. The TATA box is present in the regulatory regions of most genes, yet several genes lack this element and are transcribed efficiently. Numerous other upstream cis-elements have been implicated in controlling rates of transcription. The fact that these elements (consensus sequences) are conserved in the regulatory regions of many diverse viral and eukaryotic genes supports their role in regulation. For example, the CAAT sequence and sequences rich in GC, which bind SP-1 DBP, are found upstream of the TATA box in promoter-regulatory regions and greatly influence the rate of transcription.[11] Mutations in any of these sequences can modify the efficiency of transcription. Transcriptional enhancer elements located hundreds or even thousands of nucleotides from the +1 site in either an upstream or downstream location can greatly influence the rate of transcription of a gene. In addition, enhancer elements can occur in two orientations, one flip-flopped 180 degrees relative to the other, and retain control over transcription.[12]

In some genes nucleotides downstream from the +1 site in the +1 to +100 region influence the rate of RNA polymerase II-mediated transcription. Downstream sequences have also been shown to regulate RNA polymerase III-directed transcription in a number of eukaryotic cell types, although the upstream control regions are also utilized.[13]

The level of transcriptional control imparted by elements of the promoter-regulatory region and enhancers is affected by proteins binding to these elements. DBPs, such as SP-1 and TFIID-binding proteins, "transactivates" transcription by binding to specific cis-regulatory sequences within the promoter-regulatory region. This also facilitates binding of RNA polymerase to DNA, thereby initiating transcription. It is also possible that protein binding to cis-sequences causes conformation changes within the DNA at or near the +1 transcriptional start site which facilitates RNA polymerase binding.[13a]

Transactivation may depend on binding of several DBPs to adjacent cis-elements within the promoter. Proteins in close proximity may interact with one another to form a multimeric complex that is required for RNA polymerase binding and maximum transcription.[14] In viral systems DBPs of both cellular and viral origin transactivate viral genes. Moreover, transacting viral DBPs may bind directly or indirectly to cis-recognition sequences within the promoter-regulatory region. The indirect mechanism requires initial binding of cellular DBPs to cis-elements which enables secondary binding of viral proteins to the bound cellular DBPs themselves.

The structure and amino acid composition of DBPs have been investigated. Although a universal mode of action or protein structure has not been defined for all DBPs, several characteristics have been noted. Some DBPs possess a "zinc finger" motif which in its simplest form corresponds to a peptide loop consisting of approximately 12 amino acids that projects from the surface of DBPs. The base of the loop contains Zn^{++} or other metals ions bound by cysteine and histidine residues. One or more zinc fingers interact directly with sites along the DNA molecule, one zinc finger interacting with about five nucleotides within the major groove of the double helix.[15]

Several proteins with the potential to bind to DNA may have another structural motif. These proteins possess α helices which have leucine residues repeated at regular intervals and displayed along a face of the helix. Two of these helical structures can dimerize through direct interactions of their leucine residues (leucine zipper). Protein dimers of this type may interact with specific DNA conformations to regulate transcription.[16]

Transcription usually initiates from a single start site under the control of a promoter-regulatory region. However, secondary or minor initiation sites also exist for certain genes in close proximity to the major site. Another aspect of transcriptional control relates to variations seen between different promoters in their ability to regulate transcription. Transactivation of some promoters (strong promoter) leads to extensive transcriptional activity, whereas other promoters are normally less active following activation.

Some overlap has been observed between those sequences involved in initiation of DNA synthesis (ORI sequences) and those which regulate transcription. Sequences which flank some core sequences of origins of DNA replication may not only be important for maximum DNA synthesis, but contain enhancer and promoter elements for transcriptional control. Thus, transcriptional control and regulation of DNA synthesis may be coordinated under certain conditions.[17]

Some of the more complex DNA viruses (eg, poxviruses and herpesviruses) exhibit intricate mechanisms of transcriptional control. Transcriptional units have been shown to overlap in several ways, which allows a given length of DNA to maximally encode viral proteins. For example, one strand in a given region of DNA can serve as a template for multiple transcription events; transcripts regulated by one promoter extend into promoter-regulatory regions or encoding regions of adjacent genes to give rise to overlapping primary transcripts. Alternatively, complementary strands of DNA may be transcribed in divergent or convergent directions to produce mRNAs of opposite polarity.[18]

After transcription initiates from a +1 start site, RNA polymerase II synthesizes RNA in a 5'-to-3' direction and extends the primary transcript until a termination signal is reached. These signals have been recently defined for a few viral and eukaryotic cell transcripts and are T-rich sequences, ATTTTTAT being a conserved sequence found in several instances.[19] The T-rich sequence also may be involved in termination of RNA polymerase III transcription in the context of flanking GC-rich sequences.[20] Termination is not precise in that heterogeneous lengths of RNA are formed from a single transcriptional unit. A second and perhaps separate process is site-specific cleavage and subsequent polyadenylation at the 3' ends of primary transcripts. Consensus sequence, AAUAAA, located within the 3' terminal sequence of primary transcript, helps determine cleavage at a downstream (3') site. AAUAAA sites may be repeated several times, but only one

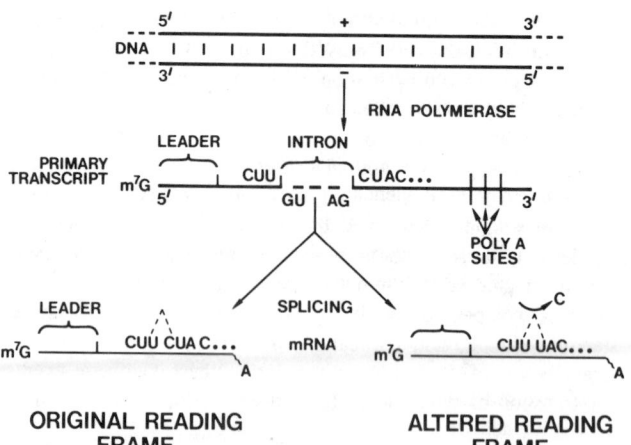

Figure 2–1. General scheme for processing a primary transcript into mRNA. Double-stranded DNA is transcribed by RNA polymerase II into a primary transcript which is then capped (m^7G) at its 5' end and polyadenylated at one of several possible sites at its 3' end. Through splicing, an intron is removed from the primary transcript and exons are rejoined to form mRNA. The reading frame of mRNA is the same as that of the primary transcript if the number of nucleotides in the intron is a multiple of three, and the triplets, CUU and CUA, which flanked the intron in the primary transcript, remain as codons in mRNA *(left side of diagram)*. On the other hand, an altered reading frame is obtained if the intron consists of one or two nucleotides in excess of multiple triplets. Therefore, triplet CUU is ligated with the new triplet UAC after the intron plus C is removed *(right side of diagram)*.

sequence is preferentially employed during the cleavage process.[21]

Investigations of viral and eukaryotic cell transcription have shown that a complex series of processing steps occur in which primary transcripts are trimmed in size and modified at their 5' and 3' ends to yield functional RNAs (Figure 2–1).

The primary transcript is modified at its 5' end by the addition of a "cap" structure, which has the form $m^7G(5')PPP(5')XY$.[22] Unique features of this structure are a terminal guanosine residue methylated in the 7 position, a 5'-5' triphosphate linkage between terminal guanosine and the penultimate nucleotide (X), and methylated riboses of nucleotides X and Y. In addition, adenosines located along the RNA strand are often methylated at the 6 position (m^6A). The length of the primary transcript is shortened by a splicing process which involves the removal of one or more internal RNA segments (introns) and the rejoining of conserved RNA segments (exons) in a precise manner (see Figure 2–1). If the original reading frame seen in the primary transcript is to be maintained in the full length of the corresponding mRNA, rejoining of exons must be precise so that the codon order is retained and does not deviate even by one nucleotide. In certain instances an intron may be excised from primary transcripts which consist of one or two nucleotides in addition to the original length of the intron. Rejoining of exons yields a shifted reading frame and on translation, this change is reflected by the synthesis of proteins having a different amino acid sequence translated from the region of the mRNA 3' to the splice site.

A rather unusual splicing event, transplicing, has been described for transcripts of poxviruses, trypanosomes, and nematodes. In these examples certain mRNAs are generated by splicing together RNA fragments transcribed from different portions of the genome and not contained within single primary transcripts. The 5' RNA sequence is usually not translated into protein (leader RNA), whereas the 3' RNA sequence encodes protein. The two RNAs (5' leader and 3' coding) are joined by a poly(A) sequence of approximately 30 adenosine residues or larger.[23]

Several mechanisms of splicing may be operative in different cell types. In *Tetrahymena,* for example, the splicing event is possibly catalyzed by the intron RNA itself as suggested by data obtained from splicing of ribosomal RNA.[24] More frequently, however, splicing is mediated by small nuclear ribonucleoproteins (sn RNPs) which form multimeric complexes that allow the intron(s) to be excised from primary transcripts by nucleases, while the exons are held in the proper orientation to be rejoined to form mRNAs.

Approximately 200 adenosine residues [poly(A)] are added to the 3' end of most eukaryotic cellular and viral mRNAs by poly (A) polymerase. However, several sites for this addition (see above) may exist at the 3' end, one of which is preferentially utilized.[21]

After processing, viral or cellular mRNAs are transported from the nucleus to the cytoplasm to be translated into proteins. Likewise, once proteins are synthesized in association with the endoplasmic reticulum (ER) (glycoproteins) or in free polysomes (unglycosylated proteins), they must be transported to specific sites within the cell or released extracellularly as soluble proteins. Transport of both mRNAs from the nucleus to the cytoplasm and proteins to different locations within the cell seems to be determined by transport signals within the macromolecules themselves. For example, certain amino acid sequences are commonly found in proteins destined to be transported to specific sites or structures within the cell. Consensus sequences have been noted in membrane-associated proteins which possess a hydrophobic stretch of amino acids at their N-terminal ends. The hydrophobic sequence allows the initial interaction and translocation of nascent proteins through lipid membranes of the ER.[25] Other amino acid sequences may be important for nuclear protein to be transported from the cytoplasm to the nucleus.[26] By analyzing amino acid sequences of large numbers of proteins with similar functions, consensus sequences influencing these and other transport events may be ascertained.

ADENOVIRUSES

Viruses belonging to the *Adenoviridae* are classified into *Mastadenovirus* and *Aviadenovirus* genera. Human adenoviruses, of which there are 42 serotypes, belong to the former genus along with adenoviruses of several animal species (see Chapter 1). The scheme of DNA replication, transcription, RNA processing, and transport of macromolecules has been well characterized in the replication cycles of several adenovirus serotypes.

Virus Structure

Virus particles consist of cores containing double-stranded DNA enclosed by an icosahedral shell or capsid which is about 80 nm in diameter.[27] Capsids are composed of 252 capsomers, which can be visualized by electron microscopy as distinct subunits.[28, 29] Each

capsomer in turn is formed from viral structural proteins. Capsomers located at each of the 12 vertices of the icosahedral capsid are designated as pentons, while hexon capsomers are located in positions other than the vertices. Pentons consist of several components: a base, fiber, and knob.[29, 30] Both antigenic and functional characteristics have been associated with hexons and penton capsomers. The penton fibers are a major type-specific antigen,[31] while the hexons contain both family cross-reactive (group) and type-specific antigenic determinants.[32, 33] Isolated penton bases are toxic to cells in culture, causing them to round up and detach from culture flasks.[34] Ten proteins constitute the outer capsid and core structure,[35] as listed in Table 2–1 and shown in Figure 2–2.

Core proteins V, μ, and VII, which bind to viral DNA, are rich in arginine and may neutralize negative charges on DNA, as do histone proteins on cell DNA.[36–39] In addition, a 55,000-dalton (55 kilodaltons or 55 kd) protein is covalently linked to the 5' termini of both DNA strands through phosphodiester bonds.[40, 41] In virus particles, this protein links the termini of DNA to yield a circular form.[42] Upon breakage of this linker protein, adenovirus DNA forms a linear, double-stranded molecule of approximately 22×10^6 daltons (35 kilobases, or 35 kb).[43] The first 102 to 103 terminal nucleotides at each end of the DNA are inverted repetitions. Upon denaturation of double-stranded DNA, complementary termini of each single strand will base-pair to form single-stranded circular structures. Complementary sequences also have been demonstrated between terminal nucleotides of single strands and sequences located inward about 180 nucleotides from each end.[44–46]

Full-length, double-stranded DNA has been divided into 100 map units (mu) which serve to designate sites of transcription and orient regions of the DNA relative to the termini. As shown in Figure 2–3, map unit 0 corresponds to the left end, while the right one represents map unit 100. In this orientation the uppermost strand of DNA is transcribed in a rightward direction and is designated "r" strand, while the lower strand, "l", is transcribed in the leftward direction.

Table 2–1
Proteins of Adenovirus

Protein	Location	Characteristics
II	Hexon	Type-specific, family cross-reactive antigens
IIIA	Hexon-associated	
VI	Hexon-associated	
VIII	Hexon-associated	
IX	Hexon-associated	Early protein
III	Penton base	Toxic to cells, family cross-reactive antigen
IV	Penton fiber	Type-specific antigen, virus attachment to receptors
V	Core	Bound to DNA, arginine-rich
VII	Core	Bound to DNA, arginine-rich
μ	Core	Bound to DNA
55,000	Linked to 5' end of each DNA strand	Derived from 80,000 mol wt precursor, necessary for DNA synthesis

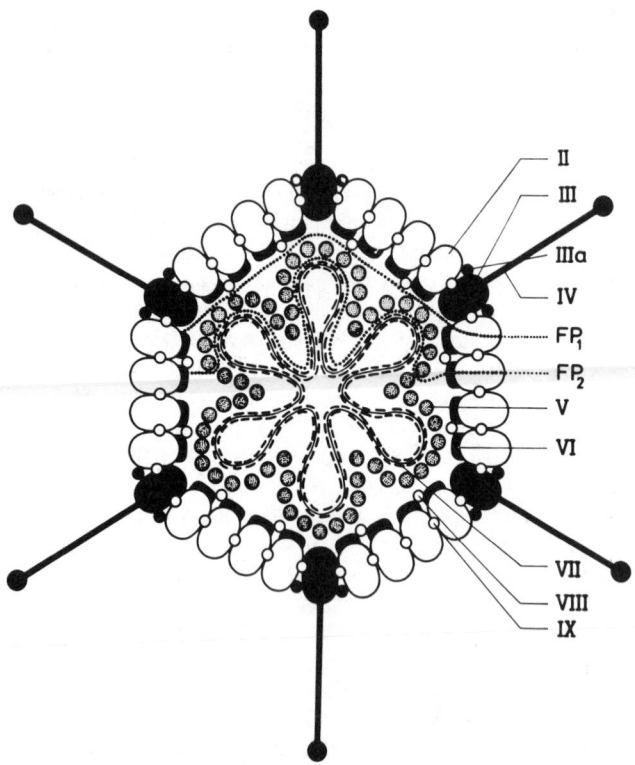

Figure 2–2. Model of adenovirus showing the structural proteins (Roman numerals) constituting morphologic subunits. FP$_1$ and FP$_2$ represent fracture planes produced by freeze-cleaving virus particles aggregated within infected cell nuclei. (Reproduced with permission from Brown DT, et al. Structure and composition of the adenovirus type 2 core. *J Virol* 1975; 16:366–367.)

Virus Cell Interactions

Although productive infections and transformation caused by adenoviruses will be considered in detail, it should be noted that adenoviruses can also initiate abortive or persistent infections.[42, 47–51] Factors that influence types of infection include viral serotype, cell type, and presence or absence of a helper virus. For example, human adenoviruses fail to productively infect cells of monkey origin, possibly due to a block in viral translation[52]; however, coinfection with SV40 (papovavirus) provides a necessary factor to allow complete adenovirus replication.[52a] Under certain conditions, human adenovirus types 2 and 7 can persistently infect African green monkey cells.[51] These cells produce low levels of virus, but the morphologic and growth characteristics of the cells appear normal. Certain adenoviruses can also transform cells in culture at a frequency of one transformation event per 10^4 to 10^6 infectious virus particles. Again, cell factors, multiplicity of infection, and length of time cells have been maintained in culture influence the efficiency of transformation.[53, 54] Transformed cells display alterations in growth, metabolic, antigenic, and morphologic characteristics when compared with normal cell populations, as discussed in the latter part of this section.

Attachment, Penetration, Uncoating

The productive replication cycle for adenovirus begins with attachment of penton fibers present on viral particles to glycoprotein receptors distributed on plasma membranes.[55–57] Additional receptors move laterally through the plasma membrane to the point of attachment to form a receptor site that allows stronger binding between receptors and other penton fibers.[58, 59] Penetration occurs by either phagocytosis (Ad 7 and Ad 12) or by pinocytosis (Ad 2 and Ad 5).[60, 61] Penton capsomers are lost in varying amounts during this process. In the case of the nonphagocytosed serotypes, transport from the site of entry to the nucleus occurs in association with the cytoskeletal system.[62] Virus particles bound to B-tubulin of microtubules or vimentin of intermediate filaments assume an altered structure, which may facilitate uncoating. A cell protease, perhaps activated by virus particles themselves, causes degradation of intermediate filaments (constructed of vimentin); greater multiplicities of infection lead to more extensive cleavage. Dissociation of intermediate filaments is also seen in the final stages of cell death in adenovirus-infected cells. Uncoating is completed at the cell nuclear membrane with the release of viral DNA into the nucleus.[63]

Early Transcription

DNA Strands are next transcribed by cellular DNA-dependent RNA polymerase II.[64] Transcription occurring before viral DNA synthesis is termed "early" and begins approximately one to four hours after infection. Those proteins synthesized from early mRNAs are therefore designated early proteins. DNA synthesis begins at six to 12 hours after infection, at which time late transcription from progeny DNA also ensues.[53, 65]

Early (E) transcription is a controlled process whereby six separate regions of the viral genome serve as templates for RNA synthesis (see Figure 2–3).[66–69] For the most part, each DNA region has its own promoter for initiation of transcription of the corresponding mRNAs designated E1A, E1B, E2A, E2B, E3, and E4.[70–72] E1A, E1B, and E3 mRNAs are transcribed from the r strand in a rightward direction (5'→3'), while E2A,B and E4 regions are transcribed in the leftward direction (3'←5') from the l strand (see Figure 2–3).

Most adenovirus mRNAs are formed by splicing primary transcripts.[67, 71–74] Exons, sequences retained in the messenger, are rejoined in a specific manner in order to maintain the original reading frame for translation. Splicing of several RNAs with a shift in the reading frame (E1B of Ad 12) has also been documented (see Figure 2–1).[75] Additional modifications to mRNAs include the formation of methylated caps at 5' termini,[76–78] polyadenylation of 3' termini,[79–81] and methylation of internal adenosines at the N6 position, the sequences containing the latter modification being conserved during the splicing process.[82, 83]

Transcription from early regions is controlled in a temporal fashion. Transcription of E1A (1.3–11.2 mu) is prerequisite for that of other early genes (see Figure 2–3).[84, 85] In addition, products of E1A seemed to be directly involved in cell transformation.[86–88] Transcription of E1A yields a primary transcript that is larger in size than the corresponding mRNAs. Three mRNAs, 13S, 12S, and 9S, are formed from E1A primary transcripts by removal of introns 115, 253, and 590 base pairs, respectively (Figure 2–4, E1A).[73, 89] The nucleotide sequence 3' to the splice site is common to all three transcripts, whereas variability exists in the length of 5' exons. The 13S mRNA possesses a 46-base-pair region 5' to its splice site which is not present in the 12 or 9S mRNAs.[90] The 13S and 12S mRNAs are formed throughout infection, whereas the 9S mRNA is primarily found late.[91] The gene products translated from the 13S and 12S mRNA are 289-amino acid (AA) (45-kd) and 243-AA (42-kd) polypeptides, respectively. These molecular weight values represent modified, highly phosphorylated forms of the 289- and 243-AA E1A gene products.[92, 93] Based on calculations using the primary nucleotide sequence, the molecular

weights of the unmodified polypeptides are 32 and 26 kd for 289- and 243-AA polypeptides, respectively. These gene products are translated in the same reading frame and transported rapidly from the cytoplasm to the nucleus, where they associate in varying amounts with the nuclear matrix.[94]

Several functional and corresponding structural domains have been defined in the 289-AA gene product, a subset of these also being associated with the 243-AA polypeptide. Based on amino acid sequence analysis of the 289-AA polypeptide, three domains are conserved among various adenovirus serotypes.[95]

Domains 1 and 2 are common to the 289- and 243-AA gene products, whereas domain 3, which corresponds to the extra 46-base-pair region of 13S RNA, is only present in the 289-AA

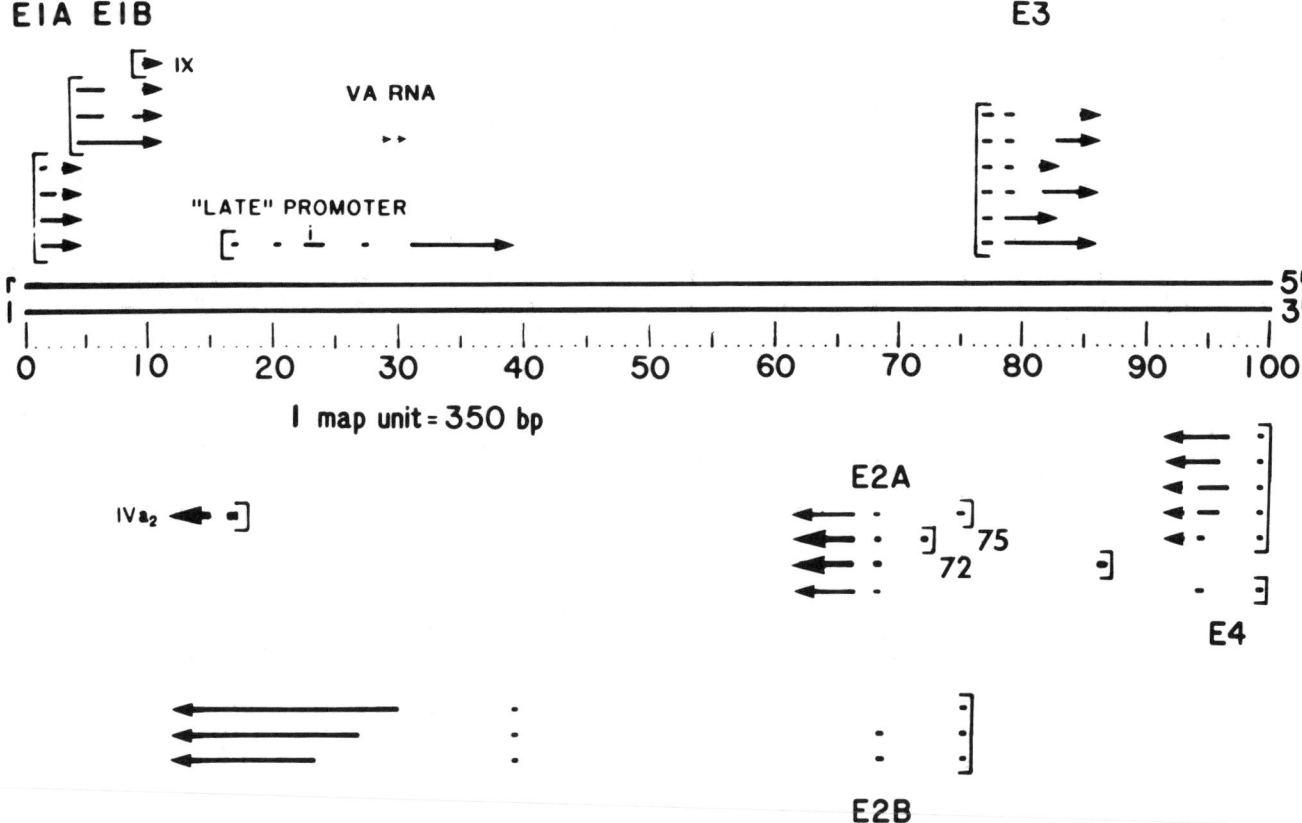

Figure 2–3. Map of Ad 2 genome. Linear double-stranded DNA is divided into 100 map units (mu), each corresponding to 350 base pairs (bp). The r strand of the DNA duplex is transcribed in a rightward direction whereas the 1 strand is transcribed in a leftward direction. Early primary transcripts corresponding to DNA regions E1A, E1B, E2A, E2B, E3, and E4 are transcribed from individual promoters *(brackets)* from both DNA strands. E2A gene has promoters at 72 and 75 mu which are used at late and early times postinfection, respectively. Introns *(spaces)* are removed from primary transcripts and exons *(bold horizontal lines)* are rejoined to form mRNAs. Arrows designate directions of transcription and 3' termini of mRNAs. Messenger RNAs for structural proteins IVa₂ and IX are transcribed early and at intermediate times, respectively. The transcript for protein IVa₂, unlike mRNAs of other structural proteins, is transcribed from the l strand of DNA. The transcript for protein IX, which is unspliced, is synthesized beginning at a promoter located in the E1B region; however, the promoter differs from that of the E1B mRNAs. VA RNAs are transcribed during both the early and late periods of the infectious cycle from a region of the r strand which is also transcribed as part of the late primary transcripts. Most late mRNAs are spliced from primary transcripts which are transcribed from a promoter located at map unit 16 on the r strand. The primary transcript is then spliced to form five families of mRNAs. Each mRNA has in common a tripartite leader sequence which consists of RNA from map units 16, 19, and 27. An i DNA segment is also present within some of the leader regions of late mRNAs. The exons of each mRNA family are derived from specific regions of the primary transcript mapping at one of five locations between 30 and 92 units. (Modified from Richardson WD, Westphal H: A cascade of adenovirus early functions is required for expression of adeno-associated virus. *Cell* 1981; 27:133–141.)

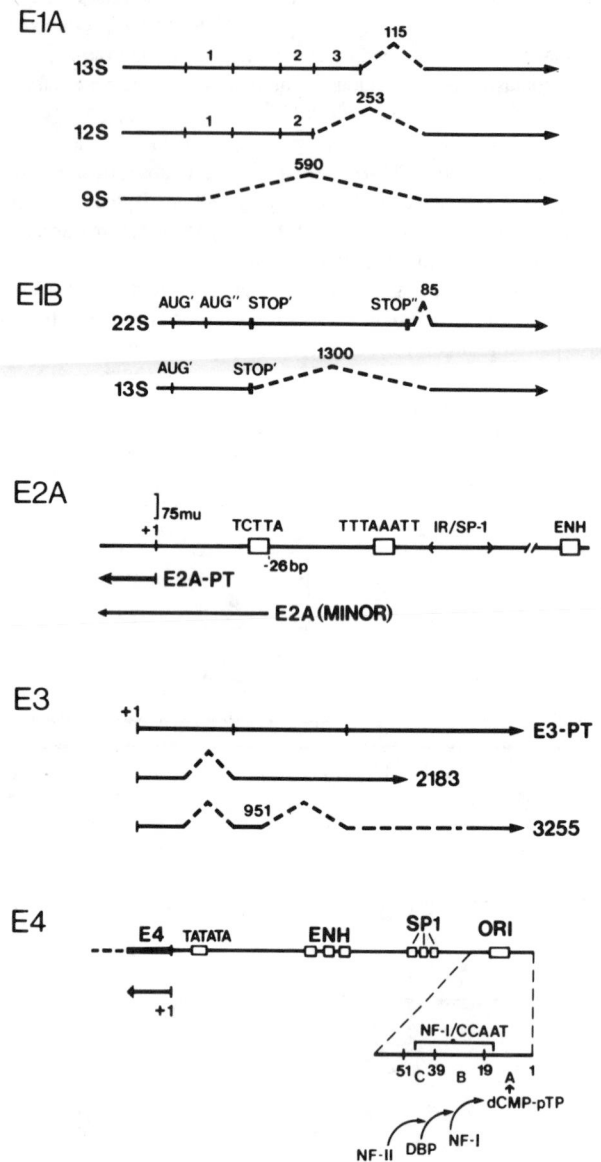

Figure 2–4. Transcription of early (E) genes of adenovirus.

E1A: Formation of 13S, 12S, and 9S mRNAs through the removal of introns 115, 253, and 590 nucleotides in length, respectively. Domains 1, 2, and 3 are located in 13S mRNA, whereas 1 and 2 are found in 12S mRNA. Arrowheads represent 3′ ends of mRNAs; dashed lines represent introns.[96]

E1B: Splicing of E1B primary transcripts to form 22S and 13S mRNAs. Removal of an 85-nucleotide intron to form 22S mRNA conserves two open reading frames (ORFs) for translation; AUG′-STOP′ and AUG″-STOP″. Excision of a 1300-nucleotide intron during splicing of 13S mRNA eliminates AUG″-STOP″ ORF and retains AUG′-STOP′ ORF. Arrowheads represent 3′ ends of mRNAs; dashed lines represent introns.[75, 106, 107]

E2A: Promoter-regulatory region of E2A gene. Top horizontal line represents adenovirus DNA with a +1 transcriptional start site at 75 map units (mu), a primary and secondary TATA box (TCTTA and TTTAAATT), inverted repeats possessing SP-1 binding sites <IR/SP-1>, and an enhancer (ENH). E2A primary transcripts (E2A-PT) are transcribed starting at the +1 site (75 mu) under the control of TCTTA sequence at −26bp (base pairs) and upstream cis-elements, SP-1 and ENH. Alternatively, a minor transcript [E2A-(MINOR)] initiates at TCTTA (−26bp) and is regulated by the upstream TATA box homologue, TTTAAATT, and upstream elements SP-1 and ENH.[96, 120]

E3: Formation of mRNAs from the primary transcript of E3 gene (E3-PT).[134] Two 3′ coterminal families of mRNAs are derived from E3-PT. In one family of mRNAs the +1 and 2183 nucleotide correspond to the 5′ and 3′ ends. Either a single intron (left intron) or two introns (left and right) can be spliced from the primary transcript. A second family of E3 mRNAs are 3′ coterminal at nucleotide 3255; individual mRNAs vary in the introns removed from E3-PT. The left intron alone may be excised or the left plus one of a series of right introns can be removed which vary in length from the 5′ splice site at 951 nucleotide. Dashed peaks represent the left intron and the minimal size of the right intron having its 5′ splice site at 951 nucleotide. The dashed horizontal line represents extensions of the right intron toward the 3′ end of E3-PT.

E4 gene and origin of adenovirus DNA replication: Upper line represents right terminus of adenovirus DNA showing elements which control E4 gene transcription which initiates in a leftward direction from the +1 site. The arrowhead points toward the direction of the E4 transcription. Cis-element of the E4 promoter-regulatory region, which includes a TATATA box, enhancer (ENH), and binding sites for SP-1 proteins, overlaps the origin of DNA replication (ORI). ORI is composed of three domains, A, B, and C, which fall between nucleotides 1 to 19, 19 to 39, and 39 to 51, respectively. Domain A binds the primer for DNA synthesis, dCMP bound to the precursor terminal protein (pTP). A binding site for DNA-binding protein (DBP) NF-1/CCAAT is contained within domains B and C.[159–165] Binding of 72-kd DPB and NF-II facilitates elongation of the nascent DNA strand.

polypeptide (see Figure 2–4, E1A). Specific functions, which control viral and/or cellular processes in both productively infected or transformed cells, correspond to these three domains.[96] Domains 1 and 2 are involved in the induction of cellular DNA synthesis and mitosis in infected cells and are also involved in repression of transcription and initiation transformation.[97] Both E1A proteins (289- and 243-AA) specifically repress those promoters that are governed by enhancers, which suggests that domain 3, which is missing from the 243-AA polypeptide, is not involved in repression.[98] Domain 3 of the 289-AA polypeptide, on the other hand, controls transactivation of other early and late viral genes in infected cells.[97] Located at the C-terminus of both the 289-AA and 243-AA polypeptides is a sequence of primarily basic amino acids which directs the transport of these polypeptides from the cyto-

plasm to the nucleus.[99] Once in the nucleus the 289-AA polypeptide preferentially associates with the nuclear matrix.[100]

Transactivation by the 289-AA polypeptide may depend on its ability to bind either directly or indirectly to promoter-regulatory regions of genes under its control. Domain 3 has certain characteristics of a DBP, basic amino acids and the zinc finger motif, which might enable it to bind directly to DNA.[97] Alternatively, analysis of promoters from genes known to be regulated by E1A gene products failed to detect common sequence(s) corresponding to E1A binding sites. A number of investigations suggest that 289-AA polypeptides recognize and associate with cellular DBPs, the latter binding directly to specific nucleotide sequences of the DNA.[101, 102] Furthermore, adenoviruses mutated in the E1A gene at sites corresponding to the transactivating region (domain 3) of the 289-AA polypeptide are able to replicate in certain cell types, albeit over an extended period of time. These cells apparently synthesize a protein which partially compensates for lost transactivating functions of E1A polypeptides. This is best exemplified by undifferentiated F9 embryonal carcinoma cells which produce an E1A polypeptide substitute. However, differentiated F9 cells lose the E1A counterpart and no longer support replication of E1A mutant virus.[103] Certain cellular genes are also induced by E1A gene products, including at least three genes for heat shock proteins[104, 105] and B-tubulin,[106] thymidylate synthetase,[96] cyclin, and rat preproinsulin I genes.[101] E1A can also transactivate genes of other viruses; herpes simplex virus (HSV)-thymidine kinase gene as well as human T-lymphotropic virus (HTLV)-I and II promoters.[101] Moreover, E1A can transactivate not only genes transcribed via RNA polymerase II, but also the adenovirus virus-associated (VA) genes transcribed by RNA polymerase III.[101]

The E1B gene is transcribed into two major spliced mRNAs, 13S and 22S, as well as two minor ones (see Figure 2–3). The 22S mRNA encodes two polypeptides, 496 AA and 176 AA, which vary in molecular weights for different serotypes of adenovirus, for example, Ad 12, 58 kd and 19 kd and Ad 5, 55 kd and 21 kd, respectively. Translation of 22S mRNA initiates from two codons, AUG′ and AUG″, (see Figure 2–4, E1B) located within the 5′ exon and terminates at two separate stop codons, STOP′ and STOP″, respectively. Translation from AUG′ and AUG″ proceeds in different reading frames to synthesize the two polypeptides, 176 AA (19 kd) and 496 AA (58 kd), respectively.[75] Whereas the 22S mRNA is synthesized and translated primarily at early times during infection, the 13S mRNA is predominantly formed by splicing at late times and is translated only into the 19-kd polypeptide.[106, 107] The 13S mRNA is also more stable at late times than the 22S mRNA.

Several functions have been associated with gene products of E1B. The 55- and 58-kd (496-AA) polypeptide has been implicated in shutoff of host cell protein synthesis,[108] transport and processing of late viral mRNAs, and transformation of rat cells.[109, 110] At least in the case of the 58-kd polypeptide of Ad 12, it may also be required for viral DNA replication in KB and HeLa cells.[111] In productively infected cells the 496-AA polypeptide is found in a soluble form in the cytoplasm as well as the nucleoplasm. The 19- and 21-kd (176-AA) polypeptide of E1B also has several functions in both productively infected and transformed cells. It has a propensity to associate with cell membranes and at early times during infection the 19-kd polypeptide localizes to cytoplasmic membranes, but later it associates with nuclear membranes.[112] The 19-kd polypeptide is not glycosylated as would be expected for most membrane proteins, yet acylation has been demonstrated. Both radiolabeled palmitate and myristate bind covalently via amide linkages to the 19-kd polypeptide.[113] One function of the 19-kd polypeptide is to prevent degradation of host chromosomal and viral DNA.[114, 115] Mutations in the gene for the 19-kd polypeptide often yield variant viruses which cause rapid lytic infections. This polypeptide also helps maintain transformed rodent cells in the transformed state.[116]

As indicated above, the 289-AA polypeptide of the E1A gene transactivates other early genes. Conflicting data concerning the exact order of early gene expression have been obtained. Although the order E1A → E4 → E2 is supported experimentally, E1A →

E2 → E4 has also been proposed (see section on parvovirus replication).[117–119]

E2 is divided into two regions, E2A and E2B, both of which are transcribed from the l strand of DNA (see Figure 2–3). Transcription of the E2A gene initiates from two promoters located at 75 (+1 site) and 72 mu, which are preferentially employed at early and late times, respectively (see Figure 2–4, E2A, and Figure 2–3).[101] Furthermore, at early times the 75-mu promoter possesses major (+1 site) and minor (−26 base pairs) transcriptional start sites which are separated by 26 base pairs (see Figure 2–4, E2A). The minor site accounts for 20% of the early transcripts, whereas the remaining early transcripts originate from the +1 site.[120] Due to the differential splicing of the primary transcripts and the alternative transcriptional start sites at +1 and −26 base pairs, at least three mRNAs are formed early (see Figure 2–4, E2A).[121]

The early promoter region directing transcription at 75 mu (+1 site) consists of a sequence resembling a TATA box (AGAAT), an upstream element composed of an imperfect inverted repeat (IR) with binding sites for SP-1 DBP and possibly an enhancerlike sequence (ENH), which is E1A-polypeptide 289 AA-responsive (see Figure 2–4, E2A). E1A gene products (289-AA and 243-AA polypeptides) seem to stimulate synthesis of cell factors (DBPs) which bind to specific recognition sites (AGAAT, SP-1) on the E2A promoter, thereby stimulating transcription.[122] Transcription from the late promoter at 72 mu is not induced by the 289-AA E1A polypeptide and is actually repressed by the 243-AA polypeptide.[101]

E2A mRNAs are translated to form the major DBP originally designated 72-kd DBP, but in actuality having a molecular weight of 59 kd. This phosphoprotein possesses two domains which have defined functions.[123] The N-terminal one third of the protein (24 kd) determines the host range of particular adenovirus serotypes in cultured cells and late viral functions.[124] The remaining two thirds, which is highly conserved among serotypes, is involved in binding to single-stranded DNA in a tight, cooperative manner.[125] Apparently this latter function causes viral DNA to assume an extended conformation, thereby facilitating strand elongation during DNA replication (see below). The host-range function of DBP is exemplified by the inability of wild-type adenovirus to productively infect monkey cells.[126] An apparent block in late transcription and alterations in splicing of mRNAs for fiber polypeptide partially account for the failure to replicate.[127] Mutation(s) in the DBP gene corresponding to the N-terminus of the polypeptide can alter the host range of the virus, thereby enabling the virus to replicate in monkey cells. Proteolytic cleavage of DBP at sites between the two functional domains generates cleavage products which retain their corresponding functions found in intact protein.[128] The role of DBP as a regulatory factor in both early and late transcription has been controversial. DBP may stimulate transcription from E1B and E4 genes as well as autoregulate its own gene.[129] In addition, DBP represses transcription of early gene(s), for example, E4 at intermediate and late times during infection.[130] As stated above, DBP controls expression of certain late proteins in a host-range-determined manner. Mutated DBP gene produces a protein that allows gene expression in normally nonpermissive cells, possibly by bypassing the formation of attenuated late RNAs.[130a] Finally, DBP controls the level of translation of E1 mRNAs by reducing the stability of these messengers at late times.

E2B gene encodes two proteins involved in DNA synthesis, DNA polymerase and a primer protein for initiation of DNA synthesis, pTP (see Figure 2–3).[131, 132] The E2B gene is transcribed from the leftward strand of DNA, transcription initiating at 75 mu (see Figure 2–3). Splicing of the primary transcript yields several mRNAs consisting of multiple leader sequences joined to a single exon which possesses the coding sequences for translation.[131] The DNA polymerase is a 140-kd protein which complexes with the precursor terminal protein (pTP). The latter protein serves as an 80-kd primer for initiation of DNA synthesis. A cleavage product of pTP, 55-kd polypeptide, is also found in association with the 5′ ends of DNA isolated from infectious virus particles.

E3 gene is located between 76 and 86 mu and is transcribed from the r strand of DNA (see Figure 2–3). Following splicing of the primary transcripts, approximately ten mRNAs are formed which are classified into two 3′-coterminal families, terminating either at 2183 or 3255 base pairs from the initiation site for transcription (+1) (see Figure 2–4, E3).[133] The splicing pattern observed varies with the time after infection; a splicing site at nucleotide 951 and multiple sites further downstream from the 5′ splice site are preferentially used late during infection to yield one family of mRNAs.[134] Although most of the E3 gene products have not been well characterized, they appear to be nonessential for viral replication in cultured cells. One E3 polypeptide, a glycoprotein of 19,000 daltons (gP 19 kd), apparently has a role in vivo in facilitating the escape of infected cells from major histocompatibility complex (MHC)-restricted immune recognition.[135] Glycoprotein 19 kd is synthesized at early times in the rough-surfaced endoplasmic reticulum (RER), as are glycoproteins destined for transport to other membrane locations.[73] A specific sequence in the C-terminal, cytoplasmic tail of gP 19 kd, however, causes its retention in the ER membrane.[136, 137] In this location, gP 19 kd has the ability to bind class 1 MHC proteins, preventing their transport from ER membranes to the plasma membrane. By this mechanism adenovirus-infected cells possibly escape immune recognition and destruction by cytotoxic T lymphocytes. The MHC protein-binding site apparently resides in the 15-AA cytoplasmic region of gP 19 kd and possesses sequence homology with proteins of the immunoglobulin superfamily which may explain their interactions with MHC proteins.[138] Ad 12 exhibits an alternative mechanism for decreased expression of MHC proteins in that Ad 12-transformed cells have reduced transcriptional levels of class I MHC mRNAs.[136, 138]

Early gene 4 (E4) maps at the right-hand terminus of viral DNA, transcription occurring from the l strand of DNA (see Figure 2–3) to yield at least seven mRNAs.[139] This region also corresponds to an origin of DNA replication and there appears to be coordinated control of E4 transcription and initiation of DNA synthesis (see below). E4 gene transcription is controlled in either a positive or negative manner by other early gene products. It is stimulated early by E1A products and repressed by 72-kd DBP at intermediate and late times.[130] It seems likely that the same cellular factors that bind to the origin of DNA replication also inhibit E4 transcription (see Figure 2–4, E4). E4 gene products, although not characterized in depth, perform several diverse functions. At intermediate times they are involved in viral DNA synthesis and the induction of cellular dihydrofolate reductase (DHFR), an enzyme involved in DNA synthesis.[140] In addition, certain E4 prod-

ucts govern the transition from early to late stages of infection. Deletion mutations in the E4 genes showed that the many functions of E4 gene products are not absolutely required for replication.[141] DNA synthesis and DHFR production were delayed, but they eventually reached wild-type levels in mutant virus-infected cells. Complete removal of the E4 region produced a mutant which failed to replicate.[142]

Although transcription from the majority of the r strand of DNA does not occur significantly until intermediate and late times postinfection, low levels of transcription from a restricted portion of this region are seen early. The primary transcript at early time initiates at a 16.4-mu promoter-regulatory region and extends to about 63 mu (Figure 2–5). This primary transcript is a shorter version than the one seen at late times, 16.4 to 98 mu (see Figure 2–3). The early primary transcript corresponds to the total length of the L1, L2, and L3 families of mRNAs, which is a subset of the total length of the late primary transcript, 5′-L1-L2-L3-L4-L5-3′ (see Figure 2–5).[143] At early times an RNA, the full length of the L1 region, is preferentially cleaved from the L1-L2-L3 primary transcript. The exact location of cleavage is determined in part by an AAUAAA consensus sequence upstream from the cleavage site and a U-rich or GU-rich region downstream from the cleavage site.[144] The L1 RNA product is then preferentially spliced to yield a single mRNA L1c, which is only one of four L1 mRNAs produced at late times. L1c formation occurs very early during infection before or at the time of E1A transcription.[145] Transcription of early L1 is not dependent on the synthesis of E1A polypeptide

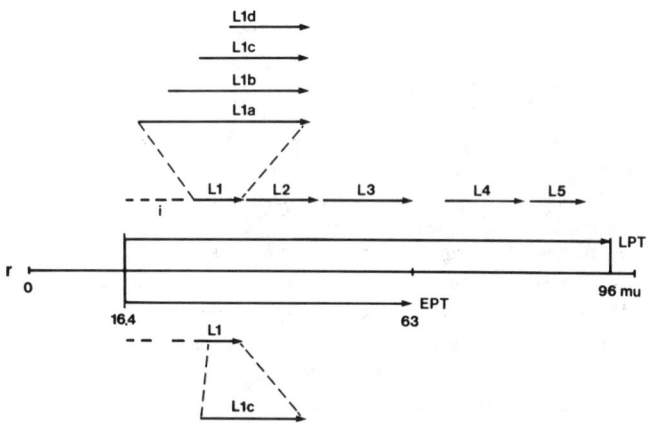

Figure 2–5. Transcription from the major late promoter of the adenovirus genome at early and late times postinfection. Transcription of both the early primary transcript (EPT) and the late primary transcript (LPT) begins from 16.4 map units (mu) in a rightward direction. (The rightward [r] strand of DNA is shown with 0 mu at the left and 100 mu at the right end.) The EPT extends from 16.4 at its 5′ end to 63 mu at its 3′ end, whereas the LPT is located between 16.4 and 96 mu. LPT is cleaved into five RNAs, L1 to L5, each of which serves a precursor for a family of mRNAs. Messenger RNAs derived from LPT are capped and polyadenylated and have a common tripartite leader sequence at their 5′ ends. EPT corresponds to the combined length of L1, L2, and L3 RNA. L1 RNA is preferentially derived from EPT and is spliced into only one (L1c) of the four L1 mRNAs seen at late times. Arrowheads represent the 3′ termini of primary transcripts and the shorter RNAs derived from them.

289 AA, as are other viral genes. A polypeptide of approximately 52 kd is translated from L1c. The role of this gene product has not been determined.[146]

Two genes encoding structural proteins IVa$_2$ and IX have been classified as intermediate genes. Their transcription begins after early transcription at approximately the same time as the initiation of viral DNA synthesis and reaches peak synthesis later during infection.[147, 148] Although most virion structural proteins are synthesized late during infection, structural polypeptide IVa$_2$ and hexon-associated protein IX are synthesized earlier before viral assembly ensues.

In addition to the RNAs described above, which serve as messengers, at least two nonmessenger species of early RNAs, VA RNAs, are also transcribed. Virus-associated (VA) RNAs are relatively small, approximately 160 nucleotides in length,[149] with sedimentation rates of 5.5S and 5.2S. Whereas both are found early during infection, only 5.5S RNA is synthesized in increased quantities during the late period.[150] As previously stated, RNA polymerase II is responsible for transcription of viral mRNAs; however, VA RNAs are transcribed by cellular RNA polymerase III off of the r strand of DNA from two individual promoters.[151, 152]

Virus-associated RNAs may serve several functions in infected cells, including splicing of late viral mRNAs.[153] Possibly, these small RNAs connect adjacent exons, while introns are removed. Base homology between VA RNAs and nucleotides near the splice junctions of late primary transcripts support this contention. This process resembles splicing of eukaryotic cell RNAs which involves small nuclear RNA-protein complexes. The secondary structure present in VA RNA is seemingly required for this and its other possible functions.[154] A second role for VA RNAs is the facilitation of late translation of viral mRNAs. An antiviral defense mechanism present in many eukaryotic cells is the induction of interferon which indirectly causes the phosphorylation of eukaryotic initiation factor 2 (eIF-2) which is necessary for translation. In this way the eIF-2 is rendered inactive for initiation of translation, and late viral protein synthesis in particular is inhibited. Virus-associated RNAs are capable of inactivating the protein kinase which phosphorylates eIF-2.[155, 156] The factor is then capable of participating in the initiation of viral protein synthesis. In a manner yet to be fully elucidated, RNA or cleavage products thereof generated as a result of SV40 infection can compensate for nonfunctional VA mRNA in adenovirus-infected cells. Virus-associated RNAs have also been detected in the cytoplasm of infected cells complexed with a 45-kd cellular phosphoprotein, La antigen.[157, 158] The same antigen is complexed with small nuclear U1 RNA in uninfected cells. The significance of this association has not been determined.

DNA Replication

Adenovirus DNA synthesis occurs within nuclei of cells starting at six to ten hours postinfection and requires both cellular and viral proteins. Origins for DNA synthesis reside within the inverted repeats at both termini of the DNA molecule.[159, 160] These regions vary in size, 103 base pairs for Ad 2 and 165 base pairs for Ad 18, and contain several domains necessary for proper initiation and elongation of DNA (see Figure 2–4, E4).[4, 161] The most terminal domain, domain A, consists of nucleotide sequence 9–18, as measured from the most terminal nucleotide 1. This sequence

is essential for binding of viral DNA polymerase complexed with pTP and deoxycytidine monophosphate (dCMP).[159] Domains B and C, located between the 19–39 and 40–51 nucleotides, respectively, are also essential for DNA synthesis and bind DBPs which augment the domain A-binding proteins (see Figure 2–4, E4).[4, 161] For Ad 2 an essential cellular DBP, nuclear factor I (NF-I),[162] binds to a recognition sequence TGG(A/C)N$_5$GCCAA between 17–48 nucleotides, which overlaps domains B and C.[163] In the Ad 2 system NF-I has recently been shown to not only act as an initiation factor for DNA synthesis, but also as a regulatory protein for transcription, being identical to the CCAAT-binding protein.[164] Viral DBP (72 kd) is also important for elongation and efficient initiation of DNA synthesis and binds at a site in close proximity to NF-I. NF-II, a type-I DNA topoisomerase, is also required for elongation of nascent DNA and most likely unwinds parental DNA in order for synthesis to proceed.[165]

Additional requirements for DNA synthesis include 55-kd protein, attached to the 5′ ends of parental DNA strands and 80-kd pTP, the precursor of 55-kd protein, bound to the 3′ terminus of parental DNA strands at nucleotide sequence 9–18 in domain A (see Figure 2–4, E4). Nascent DNA synthesis starts with the addition of dCMP to pTP through an ester linkage.[41] The pTp-dCMP primer associates with viral DNA polymerase to form a replication complex and DNA synthesis is initiated. As mentioned above, NF-I and -II, as well as (72-kd) DBP, facilitate elongation. The DBPs that associate with domains A, B, and C not only bind to the origin of DNA replication but apparently interact with one another.[165a] This contention is supported by altering the space between domains through the removal of one or more nucleotides, which in turn changes protein-protein interactions and greatly reduces the efficiency of DNA initiation and elongation.[161]

DNA synthesis begins with equal efficiency from both termini and proceeds in a 5′ → 3 direction until each parental strand is copied into a full-length progeny strand through a semiconservative mechanism (Figure 2–6). The final products consist of two double-stranded DNA molecules, each with one progeny strand having an 80-kd protein at its 5′ terminus and a parental strand with a 55-kd product at its 5′ end. The 80-kd protein is proteolytically cleaved to the 55-kd product during late stages of viral maturation.

As previously mentioned, the E4 gene overlaps the right origin for DNA replication, and transcription of the E4 gene and initiation of DNA replication may be mutually exclusive events (see Figure 2–4, E4). DBP (72 kd) binding mediates this selection process by repressing E4 gene transcription at intermediate and late times postinfection, which facilitates elongation of DNA strands during DNA replication.[166]

Although some of the viral DNA may be integrated into cell DNA during lytic infection, the purpose or function of this process has not been elucidated. Terminal regions in viral DNA enable DNA to associate with the nuclear matrix, which may be required for DNA replication.[166a]

Late Transcription

Transcription of late mRNAs occurs shortly after the onset of viral DNA replication. Synthesis of a primary transcript begins at mu 16.4 on the r strand and continues to mu 98. Concomitant with late transcription, the primary transcript is cleaved internally at

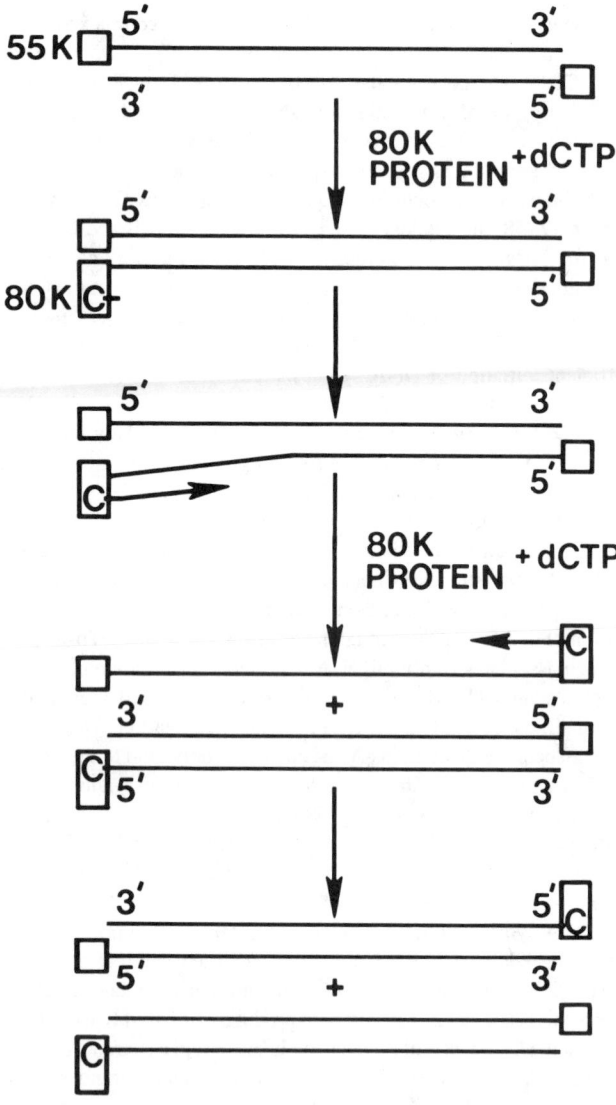

Figure 2–6. Model of adenovirus DNA replication. An 80-kd (kilo-dalton) protein or pTP complexed with deoxycytidine (dCMP) binds to the 3′ end of the template strand and serves as a primer for DNA synthesis. Nascent DNA synthesis displaces the template strand from its complementary parental strand and continues until the full-length progeny strand is formed. The other parental strand is likewise replicated. The 80-kd proteins are later cleaved to 55-kd proteins during viral maturation.

one of five sites, thereby generating five RNA species (L1–L5), each of which serves as a precursor to a group of spliced mRNAs (see Figure 2–5).

The spliced mRNAs within each of the five groups share 5′ noncoding tripartite leader sequences originating from three small, noncontiguous regions at map units 16.4, 19, and 27. Certain late mRNAs have an additional leader segment, "i", originating from between 21.75 and 22.96 mu, which is spliced between the second and third RNAs of the tripartite leader. Sequence analysis of the i segment showed that an open reading frame (ORF) is present with the coding potential for a 16-kd polypeptide. The polypeptide

has been isolated from infected cells at intermediate times, but its role in replication has not been characterized fully, although it seems to destabilize L1 RNAs.[167, 167a] The coding regions within each group of mRNAs are 3′ coterminal yet differ in the length at their 5′ ends.

Each of the five groups of late mRNAs (L1–L5) consist of at least two and as many as six mRNAs, all of which are capped at their 5′ ends and polyadenylated at their 3′ termini. Although the addition of poly(A) to the 3′ end of mRNA is believed to occur before splicing, it is not absolutely required for splicing. Late mRNAs are transported to the cytoplasm where they are translated into primarily structural proteins or their precursors. Several early mRNAs and their corresponding proteins continue to be produced late during infection. For example, mRNAs of E2A (DBP) are transcribed at late times using a different promoter at 72 mu and possess a different leader sequence relative to that of early transcripts.

The major late promoter-regulatory region (MLP) for late transcription is adjacent to and partially overlaps the control region for IVa$_2$ gene (see Figure 2–3).[168, 169] Whereas the r DNA strand is used as a template for MLP-directed transcription late during infection, IVa$_2$ transcription occurs from the l strand at intermediate times. These overlapping regulatory regions therefore serve as a good model for investigating the interactions between control mechanisms governing two transcriptional units. The regulatory region for the major late region consists of several defined regulatory elements (Figure 2–7).[101] With the transcription start site at +1, the upstream elements include (1) a TAATTA box at −30 flanked on both sides by G-rich sequences, (2) the upstream promoter sequence (UPS) between −50 and −66 which contains an imperfect palindrome, and (3) an enhancer further upstream from UPS which is E1A 289-AA polypeptide-responsive. Transcription from MLP is induced by binding transactivating factors TFIID to the TATA sequence and the major late transcription factor (MLTF), also designated upstream stimulatory factor (USF), to UPS. TFIID and USF apparently interact with RNA polymerase II for initiation of late transcription.

Transcription of the IVa$_2$ gene is controlled by: (1) a GC-rich region between −38 and −49 nucleotides upstream from the +1 transcriptional start site on the l strand, and (2) UPS, the same sequence involved in MLP-directed regulation.[170] Notably, the IVa$_2$ gene lacks a TATA consensus sequence at −30.[168, 171] The utilization of UPS as a common regulatory element for IVa$_2$ and MLP has been demonstrated. Under conditions where TFIID and USF are present in infected cells, TAATTA and UPS are induced to promote late transcription.[172] On the other hand, when TFIID is only present at low levels, USF binds to UPS to induce IVa$_2$ gene transcription.[173, 174]

This one example of differential regulation of two adjacent genes with overlapping promoter-regulatory regions is indicative of the complex regulatory mechanisms employed during adenovirus infection. In addition, numerous examples are evident where one strand of DNA is employed early during infection and the opposite DNA strand from the same region is used at intermediate or late times. Also, late transcription occurs from both the major late region at 16.4 → 98 mu of the r strand of DNA and from EIIA gene at 72 → 61 mu of the l strand (see Figure 2–3). This suggests that DBPs bound to the promoter-regulatory region of

E2A at 72 mu do not hinder transcription from the complementary DNA strand, and that RNA polymerase II can move through this region. Thus spatial considerations between various DBPs must be met to allow maximal utilization of a given segment of the genome for several transcriptional events.

Virus Assembly

With the synthesis of late structural proteins, maturation of virus particles occurs in nuclei of infected cells.[175] Therefore, as with other nuclear replicating viruses, mRNAs produced in the nucleus must be transported to the cytoplasm to be translated. Early and late viral proteins, the latter being produced in great excess, are then transported back to the nucleus.[176] Structural protein II in the form of trimers are assembled into hexons in the cytoplasm with the aid of a 100-kd nonstructural protein and rapidly transported to the nucleus. Within the nucleus capsomers assemble to form empty shells which lack core proteins and viral DNA.[177] The penton base (III) and fiber (IV) proteins assemble independently and are added to the virus structure at an early stage during maturation. The fiber protein is modified by the addition of glucosamine at some stage during its formation. Precursor proteins VI, VIII, and IIIa are also found in empty capsids. It appears that one vertex of the empty capsids remains open to allow DNA to enter capsids in a unidirectional manner; the left terminus containing a packaging signal for its insertion enters first.[178, 179] Topoisomerase is also required for packaging DNA into immature particles.[179a] Arginine-rich core proteins, V, u, and pVII, then enter the capsid and associate with the DNA. Protein IX, which has a stabilizing effect on the immature capsid, is next added.[180] The final stage of maturation requires proteolytic cleavage of four precursor proteins into structural proteins, as well as the 80-kd pTP bound to the 5′ end of one DNA strand into its 55-kd product. The viral endoprotease(s) responsible for these cleavages resides within the virus particle.[181, 182] One protease is specific for -glycine-alanine- peptide bonds and is encoded by the L3 gene.[183] Recent evidence suggests that much of the assembly process occurs in association with the nuclear matrix.[184]

Maturation is inefficient, with only 10% of viral DNA being encapsidated.[185, 186] Therefore, excess viral DNA and protein accumulate within the nucleus and stain as basophilic inclusion bodies. Eosinophilic intranuclear inclusions also are seen and correspond to accumulations of core proteins of the virus.[187–189]

Effects of Host Cells

Viral replication effects macromolecular synthesis of infected host cells. At times, immediately after virus infection, certain serotypes of adenoviruses can temporarily stimulate cellular DNA synthesis in undividing cells; this event depends on the expression of E1A and E2.[190, 191] In suspension cell cultures and dividing cells in monolayer, cell DNA synthesis declines at approximately eight hours after infection, whereas synthesis of cell protein and ribosomal RNA is greatly decreased by approximately 12 hours.[192, 193] Although cell division is also inhibited, cells are not lysed, but maintain low levels of metabolic activity, such as glucose utilization. Hence, progeny virus particles remain associated with infected cells and only small quantities are found outside the cells.

Associated with both transformation and productive infection are changes in cell morphology, which correspond to alterations in the cytoskeleton. More extensive changes in this structure are seen during productive infection than during transformation. Cytoskeletal dissolution occurs in stages beginning with microtubular rearrangement at about 12 hours postinfection. Changes in microfilaments initiate at about 14 hours, whereas intermediate filaments, vimentin and cytokeratin types, dissociate at 16 to 20 hours.[194] In the cytoskeletal system of transformed cells, less extensive changes are seen; bundles of microfilaments dissociate and the total number of microfilaments decreases. At least in the latter situation, products of E1A are important mediators for the process.[195]

Transformation

Although the primary consideration of this chapter is to describe the productive replication cycles for several virus groups, an al-

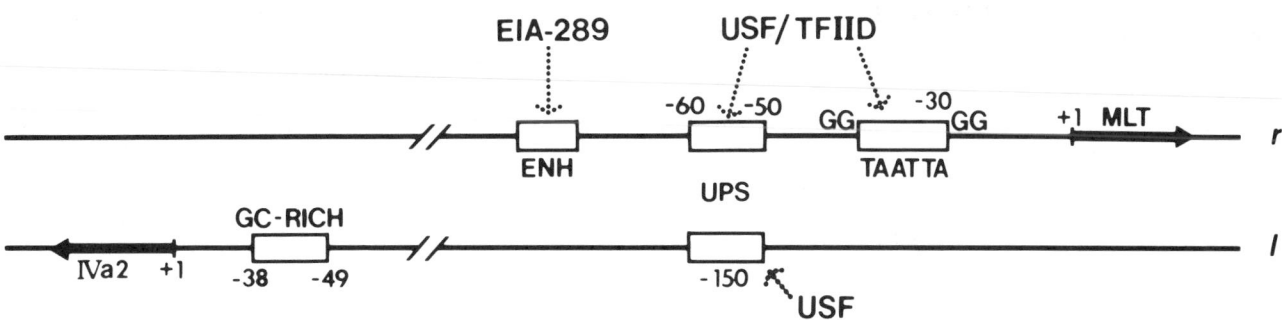

Figure 2–7. Overlapping regulatory regions that control transcription from the major late transcriptional unit (MLT) and the IVa2 gene. The MLT is transcribed from the rightward (r) strand beginning at the +1 site and the IVa2 gene from the +1 site of the leftward (l) strand. MLT is regulated by a proximal TAATTA box which is flanked by G-rich sequences, an upstream sequence (UPS), and an enhancer (ENH) element, which are transactivated by factors TFIID, upstream stimulating factor (USF), and E1A-289 amino acid polypeptides, respectively. The IVa2 gene is regulated for transcription by a proximal GC-rich sequence and the (UPS) sequence which also controls MLT. In the presence of USF alone, the IVa2 gene is preferentially transcribed. USF in combination with TFIID initiates transcription of MLT.

Table 2–2
Properties of Normal and Transformed Cells

Normal Cells*	Transformed Cells
1. Cessation of growth when cells reach confluency, monolayer formation (density-dependent inhibition)	1. Continued cell growth beyond the formation of a monolayer (decreased density-dependent inhibition)
2. Requirement for attachment of cells to plastic or glass for growth (anchorage dependence)	2. Growth of cells in suspension
3. Alignment of cultured cells in an orderly array	3. Random orientation of cells
4. Requirement of serum growth hormones for cell multiplication	4. Reduced requirement for growth hormones
5. Fail to grow suspended in soft agar	5. Form cell clones within soft agar
6. Maintenance of the integrity of the cytoskeleton; microfilaments and microtubules are present	6. Dissociation and/or decreased formation of microfilaments
7. Presence of fibronectin on cell membranes	7. Decreased fibronectin
8. Glycosylation of membrane glycoproteins and glycolipids in a manner characteristic of a particular cell type	8. Altered glycosylation of glycoproteins and glycolipids
9. Expression of antigens characteristic of differentiated cells	9. Reexpression of fetal antigens, loss of antigens signifying differentiation
10. No expression of viral and/or tumor antigens	10. Production of viral and/or tumor antigens
11. Lectin binding to membrane glycoproteins and glycolipids; restricted lateral movement of glycoproteins; limited lectin-mediated cell aggregation	11. Increased lateral movement of membrane glycoproteins; condensation of glycoprotein due to cross-links formed by lectins, extensive cell aggregation mediated by lectins
12. Production of protease	12. Increased protease production
13. Glycolysis, normal levels of glucose transport and binding	13. Increased glycolysis, increased transport and binding of glucose
14. Do not produce tumors in laboratory animals	14. Often produce tumors in laboratory animals
15. Limited cell viability in culture	15. Cells are "immortal"
16. Euploid karyotype	16. Heteroploid karyotype, chromosomal aberrations

Primary cells passaged once or twice in culture. Passage of primary cells in cultures often yields cell lines that no longer have characteristics of their progenitors, but instead have at least some of the properties of transformed cells.

ternate virus-cell relationship also will be described for the adenoviruses. It has been shown that under appropriate conditions certain viruses, such as adenovirus, can infect cells in culture and change their growth properties and other characteristics without resulting in cell lysis or death. This process, called transformation, produces alterations of a number of properties observed in primary (untransformed) cells in culture (Table 2–2). Cells transformed by tumor viruses vary in the expression of these characteristics, however.

In general, the outcome of tumor virus infections, establishment of a lytic infection or transformation, depends on a number of factors, including animal species and tissue origin of cultured cells, time of cell maintenance in culture, cell growth conditions, transforming capabilities of specific virus strains, and the number of virus particles used to infect each cell (multiplicity of infection [MOI]). Cultured cells capable of supporting productive infections are designated "permissive," while those cells lacking factors necessary for viral replication are "nonpermissive" and can be transformed by tumor viruses. Although transformation appears to be in vitro the correlate of tumor formation within animal hosts, transformed cells vary in their ability to induce tumors in vivo.

Adenoviruses have been investigated extensively at the molecular level to elucidate viral functions involved in transformation and those factors required for transformed cells and virus to induce tumors.[196] Highly oncogenic adenoviruses, including types 12, 18, and 31, can produce tumors in the majority of newborn hamsters within 2 months after virus inoculation. Weakly oncogenic adenoviruses, types 3, 7, 11, 14, 16, and 21, require a longer period

of time for tumor formation, which occurs in a smaller proportion of the inoculated animals. Nononcogenic serotypes, exemplified by types 2 and 5, do not cause tumors in newborn hamsters and rats, but, like the oncogenic types, they transform cells in culture. Cells transformed by highly oncogenic viruses readily induce tumors in newborn hamsters, as do, to a lesser extent, cells transformed by weakly oncogenic viruses. Even certain cell lines transformed by nononcogenic viruses can induce tumors in immunosuppressed newborn rats or nude mice.[53]

In addition to sharing relatively equivalent oncogenic potentials, members of each group are related by base-sequence homology and the percent guanosine plus cytosine (% G + C) present in their DNA. Highly oncogenic viruses have the lowest % G + C (48%–49%), while weakly and nononcogenic adenoviruses have a % G + C of 49% to 52% and 57% to 59%, respectively.[196]

Extensive research has been conducted with cells transformed by both highly oncogenic adenovirus (Ad 12) and nononcogenic viruses (Ad 2 and Ad 5) in order to determine the expression or lack of expression of early and late DNA regions and to characterize the gene products required to initiate and maintain the transformed state.

Unlike productively infected cells, adenovirus-transformed cells do not yield virus progeny. Attempts have failed to induce the formation of virus particles from transformed cells through cocultivation of transformed and permissive cells, a procedure used to stimulate other DNA tumor viruses to replicate. Seemingly, not all components necessary for virus production are present in adenovirus-transformed cells.[197]

Adenovirus-transformed cells have been analyzed to establish the form and location of viral DNA within the cell nucleus. Varying numbers of fragments or portions of the viral genome are present in transformed cells, and this may be correlated with the oncogenic potential of the adenovirus serotype. In Ad 12-transformed cells, DNA fragments corresponding to almost the entire viral genome are integrated into host cell DNA. This DNA-DNA association represents a covalent linkage between both DNA species, and therefore viral DNA is replicated along the cellular DNA.[198] On the other hand, cells transformed by nononcogenic viruses, Ad 2 and Ad 5, often have only the leftmost portion of the viral genome integrated into cell DNA.[199-201] This DNA corresponds to a segment mapping between 0 to 11 mu (see Figure 2–3) and is the least amount of DNA required for the initiation and maintenance of transformation.[202] Several Ad 2- or Ad 5-transformed cells contain integrated DNA consisting of both the right and left ends of the viral DNA, possibly linked together.[203]

Analyses of cell DNA from Ad 2-transformed cells indicate that only a few viral DNA segments are integrated into the DNA of each cell and that the exact number may depend on the MOI. In the case of Ad 2-transformed cells, higher MOIs yield a larger number of viral segments integrated into host cell DNA. Ad 12-transformed cells may contain between one and as many as 22 copies of viral DNA per cell, depending on the particular cell line.[204] The larger number of copies, however, may not be a true representation of the amount of viral DNA integrated into cellular DNA during establishment of the transformed state. Several investigations support the hypothesis that only a few viral DNA fragments are initially integrated, but these DNAs, especially fragments near the terminal regions, may be amplified in number during passage of the cells in culture.[205]

Not only is there variance in the amount of viral DNA found within transformed cells, but several investigations have failed to define specific sites within cell DNA for integration to occur.[203,206,207] However, in a recent analysis of fowl adenovirus-transformed cells, 50 or more copies of viral DNA were found integrated as a cluster into specific chromosomes. The chromosome in which integration occurred varied with each adenovirus-transformed cell line. In several transformed cell lines the chromosomal DNA flanking the integrated cluster of viral DNA was rearranged, possibly playing a role in the transformation process.[208] The location(s) of integrated DNA, once established, remains stable during subcultivation of transformed cells.

In contrast to transformed cells, permissive cells productively infected with Ad 2 virus exhibit selective and limited integration of viral DNA fragments into cellular DNA containing redundant sequences. Possibly one requirement for viral DNA integration is the replication of cell DNA, whereas viral DNA replication is not essential. Perhaps related to this fact is an activity of Ad 5 and other adenoviruses that stimulates cell DNA synthesis in quiescent rodent cells.[209]

Since most adenovirus-transformed cells do not contain full-length viral DNA, it is apparent that these cells lack some of the genetic information necessary to produce progeny virus.[210] As stated previously, transformed cells contain at least the leftmost 11% of the genome, which corresponds to DNA regions E1A and E1B. Some transformed cells contain additional early regions of viral DNA, namely E2A and E2B, which influence the frequency at which transformation is initiated. This is exemplified by mutations in the E2A gene which alter the carboxyl terminus of 72-kd DBP. Mutant virus is capable of transforming cells at greatly increased efficiencies compared with wild-type virus. Mutations at other sites in the 72-kd DBP gene effect transformation to varying degrees.[211] The viral DNA polymerase encoded by E2B gene also effects transformation.[212] Temperature-sensitive mutants in E2B fail to initiate transformation at the nonpermissive temperature, but are able to maintain transformation at that temperature.

Extensive research has been conducted to sort out the transforming functions associated with E1A and E1B gene products. E1A polypeptides, primarily 289- and 243-AA polypeptides, can partially transform (immortalize) primary rodent cells in culture.[213] The cells acquire the capacity to grow as a continuous cell line, but fail to induce tumors in newborn hamsters. Other functions associated with E1A polypeptides which are seemingly involved with transformation include the ability to stimulate progression of the cell cycle, induction of cell DNA synthesis, and induction of the synthesis of specific cellular proteins.[96]

As stated previously, three conserved domains, 1, 2, 3 for 289-AA polypeptide, and domains 1 and 2 for 243-AA polypeptide, have been delineated. Functions necessary for transformation include stimulation of cell DNA synthesis, which is associated with domain 1, and induction of mitosis, progression through the cell cycle, and stimulation of replication of primary cells, which are associated with domain 2. The repressive effect of E1A for certain viral and cellular genes, which possess enhancers in their regulatory regions, may preferentially favor transformation over lytic infection of cells. In an attempt to determine defined sequences of the E1A gene crucial for transformation, deletion mutants were constructed which eliminated a 69-base pair region in the gene encoding the 289-AA polypeptide. This abolished its transforming, but not its transactivating activity, and indicated that transformation and transactivation are separate functional entities. Furthermore, amino acids located in the region of 1 to 85 and 120 to 127 (1 AA = N-terminal AA) are critical for the development of complete transformation of cells. It has not been established whether these regions act in concert or independently.[214]

Since E1A-mediated transformation is incomplete, other gene products are necessary to fully transform cells and cause tumors in rodents. Gene products of E1B,[215] as well as the large T antigens of polyomavirus, p53 cell protein, myc oncogene products, and T24-ras, can augment the activity of E1A to completely transform cells.[96,216,217] The process of tumorigenesis is apparently a sequential, multistage process which requires several gene products to progress to the fully transformed state. The specific functions of the 496- and 176-AA polypeptides encoded by the E1B gene in transforming cells have been investigated. Polypeptide 496 AA (58 kd) is required for efficient transformation and helps initiate the process. In the case of Ad 5, E1B polypeptide 496 AA associates with cell protein p53 in transformed cells to form an active complex found both in the nucleus and cytoplasm.[218] The viral protein acts to stabilize p53 and increase its steady-state levels in cells.[219,220] The 176-AA (19-kd) polypeptide is important in maintaining transformation and, as pointed out earlier, it prevents degradation of cell DNA. It may be noteworthy that 176 AA is acylated by palmitate and myristate in a manner analogous to oncogenes p21 ras and pp 60 src.[221,222] Polypeptide 176 AA is also associated with the cytoplasmic and nuclear membranes in transformed cells, as are other oncogene products.[223]

Numerous questions need to be resolved concerning the differences between early gene products expressed in cells transformed or productively infected with specific adenovirus serotypes. In addition, differences between the gene products of highly oncogenic and weakly or nononcogenic serotypes need to be resolved.

Comparisons of early mRNAs present in productively infected cells and transformed cells showed only minor differences in their synthesis; both types of cells had 12S and 13S E1A mRNAs and 13S and 22S mRNAs encoded by E1B.[53] However, a difference has been noted in transcription of region E3 during productive infection and in a transformed cell line containing integrated E3 DNA fragments.[224] In vitro translation of mRNAs from productively infected cells resulted in the synthesis of three more early polypeptides than from transformed cells. Differences between E1B mRNA species transcribed in cells transformed by highly oncogenic Ad 12 and nononcogenic Ad 5 were also detected. E1B of Ad 12 encoded three mRNAs, two of which are formed by removal of one large and one small intron. On the other hand, the primary transcript of Ad 5-E1B is spliced to form two mRNAs by removal of only one intron. The difference in the number of the mRNAs and their splicing patterns may affect the production of different gene products that determine oncogenicity. As stated previously, some transformed cells, particularly those transformed by Ad 12, also contain DNA fragments that are normally transcribed late during productive infections. In transformed cells, however, these late DNA sequences do not encode late proteins, and early mRNAs and proteins are specifically synthesized.[53]

The gene products of early DNA regions present in transformed cells have been analyzed in an effort to find unique or altered proteins directly responsible for induction and maintenance of transformation. Specifically, proteins encoded by the E1A and E1B region, and collectively designated as tumor or T antigens, have received much attention.

The characterization of T antigens requires not only a comparison among proteins found early in productively infected and transformed cells, but also among cells transformed by highly oncogenic and nononcogenic adenoviruses. Possibly unique T antigens or E1A or E1B polypeptides, which are present in increased quantities or with altered functions, are responsible for changing a normal cell into a transformed or tumor cell.

The number and the molecular size of T antigens vary with the transformed cells under investigation, the viral serotype used to transformed cells, and the methodologies employed to detect the antigens.[53] In one investigation fragments of genome DNA corresponding to the entire E1 region and the E1A region alone were used to transform cells.[225] The T antigens obtained by immunoprecipitation from these cells showed that 41-kd and 19-kd polypeptides were encoded by E1A regions, while cells transformed by the entire E1 region produced 60-kd, 41-kd, and 19-kd polypeptides. Since cells transformed by the E1A DNA fragment lacked the genetic information to encode 60-kd polypeptide and were nononcogenic, it appears that 60-kd polypeptide is essential for oncogenicity. In other investigations the molecular weights for many of the T antigens obtained from adenovirus-transformed cells were comparable to those stated above.

The functions of early proteins identified only in certain transformed cells have not been elucidated. A 15-kd polypeptide apparently related to the 19-kd (176-AA) polypeptide is encoded by E1B. It is seemingly an integral protein found in transformed cell membranes and does not appear to be glycosylated. It may serve as a tumor-specific transplantation antigen (TSTA) on these cells.[53] Possibly the expression of all or some TSTAs on transformed cells determined the type of immunologic response directed toward tumor cells transplanted into rodents and thereby helps to determine their oncogenicity.[53]

As stated previously, adenovirus-infected cells possibly escape immune recognition by failure to display MHC class I proteins on their surface. In the case of six members of virus subgenera B to E, the MHC polypeptide is retained in the RER complexed with E3/gp 19-kd polypeptide, thereby diminishing its expression on the surface of infected cells.[136] However, in Ad 12 (subgenus A) transformed cells MHC expression is inhibited because of the failure to process MHC transcripts into functional mRNAs.[138] It is possible that tumor formation is facilitated by the lack of MHC expression on cells and an associated reduction of cell lysis by cytotoxic T cells. Evidence has been presented, however, which contradicts this hypothesis and lack of immune recognition may not correlate with tumorigenicity. Ad 12-transformed cells also resist cytolysis by natural killer cells.

A possible correlation between the ability of adenovirus-transformed cells to induce tumors, and their interactions with proteins found in the extracellular matrix, has been noted. Cells transformed by Ad 12 attach to type IV collagen substrates, whereas Ad 2-transformed cells bind to type 1 collagen.[226] This difference is controlled by the E1A gene of the particular serotype. E1B gene, on the other hand, controls the levels of laminin on the cell surface.[227] An earlier investigation showed that fibronectin, which is present on normal cells, is found in decreased amounts on some adenovirus-transformed cells. Correlated with the absence of fibronectin on certain transformed cells is a higher potential for the induction of tumors, while cells transformed by nononcogenic serotype possess more fibronectin and are less tumorigenic.[53]

PARVOVIRUSES

Virus Structure

Members of *Parvoviridae* have a genome of single-stranded DNA with a molecular weight of 1.2 to 2.2×10^6, corresponding to about 5000 nucleotides. The genome length has been divided into 100 mu in order to provide points of reference for numbering transcribed regions and sites for splicing transcripts. The DNA genome is housed in a nonenveloped, icosahedral capsid 18 to 26 nm in diameter. The capsid formed from 32 capsomers is composed of three structural proteins, VP1, VP2, and VP3, which are related to one another in amino acid sequence.

Two genera of *Parvoviridae*, *Parvovirus* (autonomously replicating viruses) and *Dependovirus* (defective, helper-requiring viruses), are distinguished by several criteria including their requirements for viral DNA synthesis and certain structural characteristics of the viral genome.

Members of the *Dependovirus* genus such as adeno-associated virus (AAV) contain DNA strands of either plus or minus polarity, a given population of virus having equivalent numbers of each. Autonomously replicating viruses, on the other hand, have variable proportions of positive- and negative-polarity DNA strands within a given virus population. Whereas minute virus of mice (MVM) possesses negative-stranded DNA almost exclusively, 50% of a population of B19 virus has positive-polarity DNA. In the case of certain autonomously replicating viruses, host cells influence the extent of encapsidation of positve- and negativity-polarity DNA strands.[228]

Replication of Autonomous Parvoviruses

The autonomously replicating viruses include viruses isolated from rodents, for example, Kilham rat virus (KRV) and MVM, as well as from other animals and humans (H1 virus). These viruses have a limited host range both in animals and in tissue culture. Parvoviruses replicate optimally in the nuclei of host cells in late S phase or early G2 phase of the cell cycle, which enables cells to supply factors (cell DNA polymerase) necessary for viral replication.[228–232] Although viral DNA is predominantly single-stranded, the 5' and 3' termini each contain a double-stranded region (hairpin or fold-back structures), which results from complementary sequences found in the terminal 160 and 115 nucleotides, respectively (Figure 2–8).[233–235] Within the 3' terminal sequence, nucleotides 1 through 43 are found inverted in sequence 73 through 115, and therefore base pairing is achieved by the DNA strand folding back upon itself. Between nucleotides 44 and 72, there are two regions rich in guanine and cytosine that allow internal base pairing and result in the formation of additional secondary structures. This may impart a Y configuration to the 3' termini, as was demonstrated for several rodent parvoviruses.[234] Fold-back structures are also found at the 5' end of the DNA, but the sequence and size differ from that at the 3' end.[233]

Attachment, Penetration, Uncoating

The replication cycle begins with parvovirus attachment to specific receptors located both on filopodial surfaces and undifferentiated areas of cell membranes. Virus particles penetrate the cell by endocytosis and are found in the nucleus, the site of viral replication, within two hours after infection.[227]

Early Transcription

In order for viral DNA replication to occur, several host cell and viral proteins are required. These include an early viral polypeptide NS-1, host cell DNA polymeras α and possibly γ, a terminal DBP, most probably of cellular origin, and other as yet unidentified cellular proteins. Thus replication of viral DNA requires prior transcription and synthesis of nonstructural virus protein(s). The monomeric single-stranded DNA from infectious virus particles and, at later times postinfection the negative-polarity strand of DNA within replicative forms (RFs), serve as templates for transcription of viral mRNAs. Cellular RNA polymerase II recognizes two promoter regions in parvovirus DNA at 4 and 38 mu (P4 and P38) which are sites for the initiation of transcription (Figure 2–9A).[228]

During early times of viral replication before or at the time of DNA replication, P4 is preferentially employed to yield a primary

transcript extending from 4 to 96 mu. Splicing of this primary transcript results in two mRNAs, both of which are capped and polyadenylated.[236] The longer of the two mRNAs is 4.8 kb in length (designated R1 mRNA) and is formed by the removal of an intron at 46 to 48 mu. A 3.2-kb mRNA (R2 mRNA) is alternatively formed by the removal of two introns between 10 to 40 mu and 46 to 48 mu.[237, 238] Interestingly, the exons at 1 to 10 mu and 41 to 46 mu are spliced together in a manner which offsets the 41- to 46-mu exon to a different reading frame (ORF″) when compared with that of the corresponding region of R1 mRNA (ORF′).

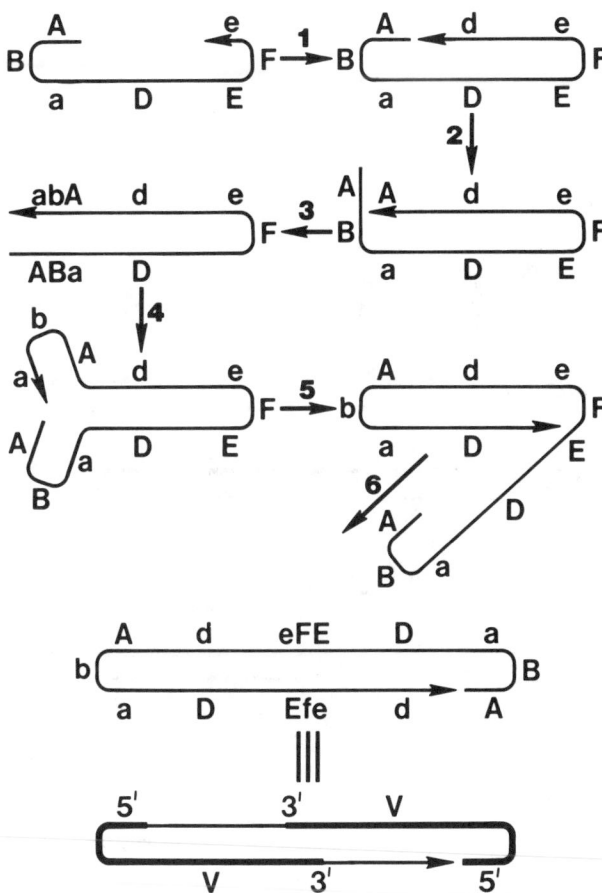

Figure 2–8. DNA replication of autonomous parvovirus. DNA synthesis initiates at the 3' hairpin structures of parental DNA and proceeds to the 5' hairpin (1) causing it to unfold (2) as it is used as a template (3). The open-end duplex is further replicated after hairpin structures form (4). The 3' hairpin serves as a primer for additional DNA synthesis (5). The DNA structure that is formed consists of viral DNA (minus polarity) interspersed with complementary strands (6). Tetrameric and higher multimeric forms arise following repeated unfolding of the duplex and concurrent DNA synthesis. Arrows indicate 5' → 3' DNA synthesis; A BDEF sequence is complementary to a bdef sequence; V represents viral DNA. (Reproduced with permission from Tattersall P, Ward DC: Rolling hairpin model for replication of parvovirus and linear chromosomal DNA. *Nature* 1976; 263:106–109.)

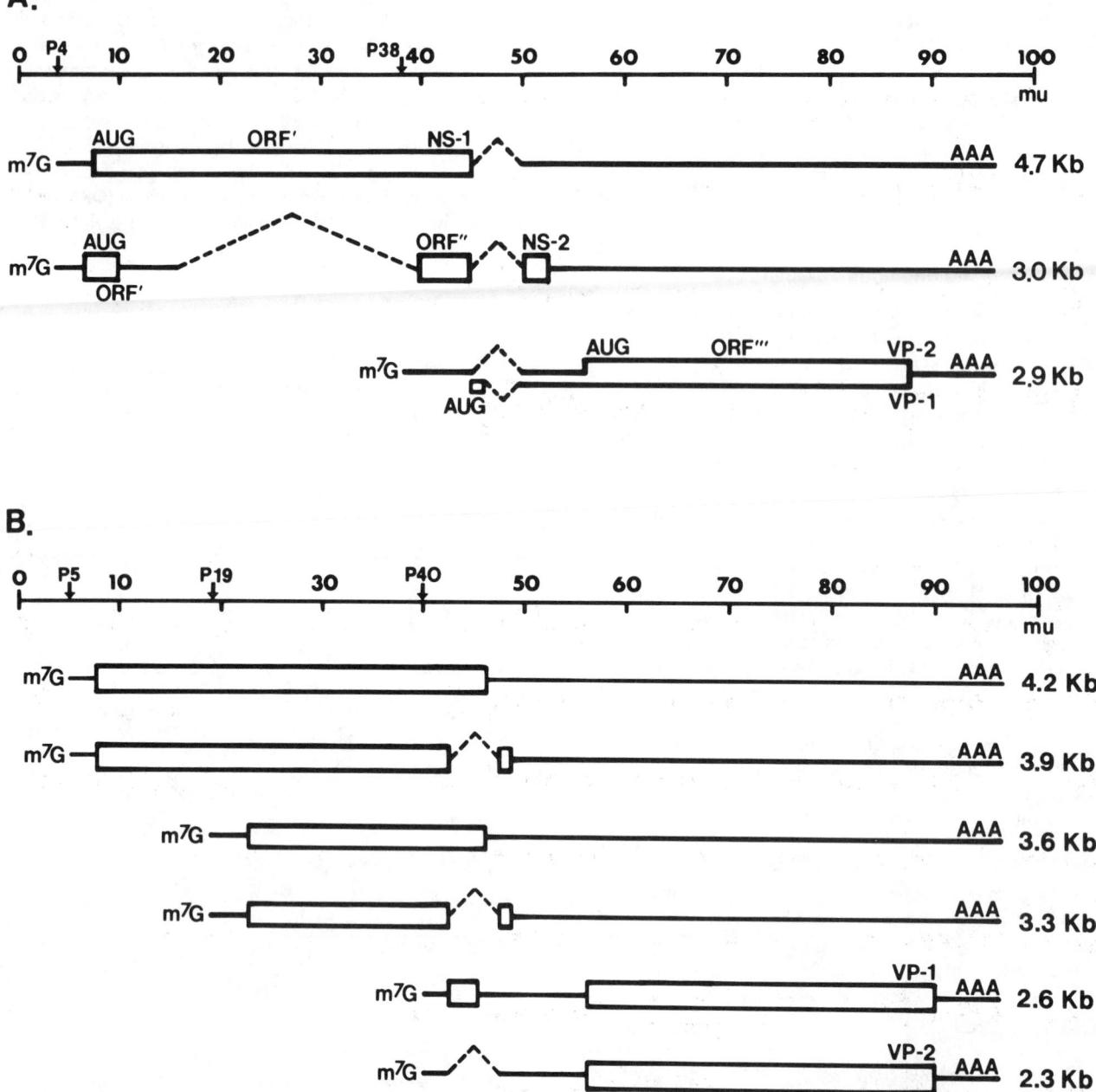

Figure 2–9. Transcription-translation from the genomes of autonomously replicating parvoviruses (A) and the dependoviruses (B). Both genomes are represented by horizontal lines divided into 100 map units (mu). Transcriptional start sites are indicated at 4 and 38 mu. (P4 and P38) for the parvoviruses genome (A) and at 5, 19, and 40 mu (P5, P19, and P40) for dependoviruses (B). Parvovirus transcripts originating from P4 are spliced to 4.7- and 3.0-kb mRNAs through the removal of a single intron or two introns (dashed lines), respectively (A). Splicing of the 3.0-kb mRNA causes a shift in the ORF (open rectangles) (ie, ORF' to ORF") at the site 3' of the left intron. The ORF' of 4.7-kb mRNA and the ORF' plus ORF" of 3.0-kb mRNA are translated into NS-1 and NS-2 polypeptides which have regulatory activities and possibly transactivate transcription from P38. Transcripts originating from P38 (A) are spliced by the removal of introns of two different lengths; the intron of VP₂ mRNAs is larger than the intron excised to form VP₁ mRNAs. An initiation codon for translation (AUG) is retained in the intron region of VP₁ whereas it is removed by splicing during VP₂ mRNA formation. Another initiation codon (AUG) situated further downstream is used for translation of VP₂. VP₁ and VP₂ mRNAs are translated in the same reading frame (ORF'''). Dependovirus primary transcripts originating from P5, P19, and P40 are each spliced into smaller mRNAs through the removal of single introns between 41 and 46 mu (dashed lines). The four mRNAs, 4.2, 3.9, 3.6, and 3.3 kb, are translated from their ORFs (open rectangles) into proteins possibly involved in regulation. The 2.6- and 2.3-kb mRNAs are translated into structural proteins VP₁, VP₂, and VP₃, VP₂ and VP₃ being translated from the 2.3-kb mRNA. m⁷G = capped 5' ends; AAA = poly(A) sequences at 3' ends; open rectangles = open reading frames; solid horizontal lines = noncoding portions of mRNAs.

Portions of R1 and R2 mRNAs to the left of 46 mu are translated into nonstructural polypeptides (NS) 1 and 2, respectively (see Figure 2–9A). NS-1 and NS-2 polypeptides of MVM have molecular weights of 83 kd and 24 kd, respectively,[239] but some minor variability in these values is seen among other autonomous parvoviruses, which may reflect their degree of phosphorylation.[240] Although NS-1 has not been extensively characterized it does contain a sequence of approximately 60 amino acids in length, which may serve as a binding site for purine nucleotide triphosphate.[241] NS-1 is primarily localized in the nucleus, where it controls viral transcription[242, 242a] and in combination with cellular factors is required for viral DNA replication.[243]

DNA Replication

With the formation of NS-1 and appropriate cell proteins, DNA replication begins from the 3′ hairpin structure, which acts as a primer for cellular DNA polymerase, and strand elongation proceeds toward the 5′ hairpin using nucleotide sequences internal to the 3′ hairpin as a template strand (see Figure 2–8, 1).[235, 244, 245] The 5′ hairpin structure unfolds and is copied as well (see Figure 2–8, 2). The duplex so formed can serve as a template for additional DNA synthesis. The 3′ and 5′ terminal sequences at the open end of the DNA duplex disassociate to form two fold-back structures (see Figure 2–8,4) and the 3′ terminus can again serve as an initiation site for DNA synthesis (see Figure 2–8,5). As the nascent DNA strand is synthesized, it displaces the strand opposite the template strand to form an even larger extended template strand that corresponds to the entire length of the unfolded duplex. The replicative intermediate formed in this manner thus contains two copies of the viral DNA strands (minus polarity) interspersed with two complementary (plus) strands. Replicative intermediates then serve as templates for further synthesis of viral DNA, which is rapidly incorporated into virus particles, as shown in Figure 2–10.[246] DNA replication occurs in association with nuclear matrix of the cell, which is mediated by a terminal sequence in viral DNA.[166a]

At least several forms of parvovirus DNA believed to be formed during viral DNA synthesis have a protein covalently bound to their 5′ ends of one or both strands of DNA. For H1 and MVM the protein has an approximate molecular weight of 60 kd,[247] and possibly has endonucleolytic activity similar to that associated with cellular topoisomerase I. A cleavage event requiring this activity may be important during DNA replication in order to maintain the orientation of 3′ terminal DNA sequences in progeny DNA. KRV DNA, however, has similar-size polypeptides noncovalently bound to its viral DNA, and polypeptides of unknown origin, having molecular weights of 90 and 40 kd, are covalently bound to its 5′ end.[248] It has also been reported that MVM DNA exists in association with protein to form a replication complex. These structures resemble nucleosomes seen in eukaryotic cell nuclei, which correspond to repeating units of condensed DNA in association with histones or histonelike proteins.[249, 250]

Parvovirus DNA replication can produce defective DNA molecules at high frequencies. Deleted DNA sequences vary in size from 2.0 to 4.5 kb and can be distributed over 90% of the length of DNA molecules. Selective regions within the terminal palindromes are spared from deletions: sequences involved in viral DNA

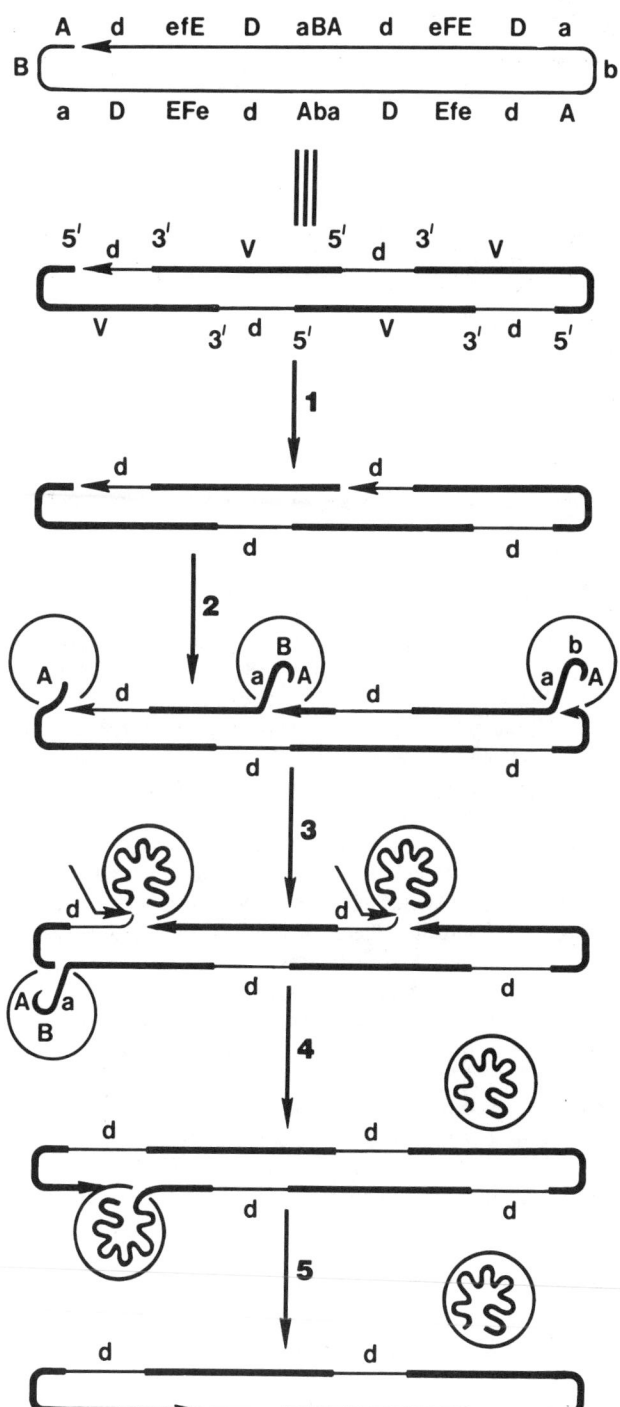

Figure 2–10. Parvovirus DNA synthesis from a replicative intermediate (RI) and DNA encapsidation. A tetrameric replicative intermediate formed as shown in Figure 2–8 serves as a template for DNA synthesis. (1) Nascent DNA synthesis displaces viral DNA from the RI (2,3); the latter is immediately encapsidated (4). Heavy lines = viral DNA; light lines = complementary DNA; circles = viral capsids. (Reproduced with permission from Tattersall P, Ward DC: Rolling hairpin model for replication of parvovirus and linear chromosomal DNA. *Nature* 1976; 263:106–109.)

replication, and encapidation.[251] Thus populations of progeny virus may contain high proportions of defective particles, which are incapable of replication except in the presence of fully infectious parvovirus.[251] Deletion of a specific 64-nucleotide sequence from the region adjacent to the 3' hairpin of prototype MVM (MVMp) results in a variant virus (MVMi) with an altered host range.[252, 253] In general, deletions occur at specific sites within the genome which are flanked by 4- to 10-base pair direct repeats. The flanking repeats participate in nonhomologous recombination with one another during the deletion process, which results in the loss of the DNA segment. One copy of the repeat sequence, however, remains at the recombination site.[225] A recognition sequence similar to that cleaved by cellular topoisomerase I is found at these recombination junctions and may be the site of action of the 60-kd polypeptide of H1 virus and MVM which is covalently linked to the 5' terminal DNA sequences and has topoisomerase-like activity. This polypeptide may therefore be involved not only in DNA replication, as stated previously, but also in recombination processes leading to deletions.[254, 255]

Late Transcription

At later times during infection, transcription initiates from P38 and primary transcripts extend from 38 to 96 mu (see Figure 2–9A). NS-1 is required for efficient transcription from P38 and may act as a transactivating factor which binds to an enhancer-like region (tar) upstream from the CAAT and TATA control regions of the p38 promoter.[243] A site downstream of p38 promoter has also been shown to be NS-1 responsive and regulate transcription.[243a] Splicing of the primary transcript involves removal of introns between 46 and 48 mu which vary in actual size to yield at least two mRNAs (R3 mRNAs), both about 2.9 kb in size. At late times postinfection the 2.9-kb mRNAs are in great excess relative to 3.0- and 4.7-kb early transcripts, and like early mRNAs, 2.9-kb mRNAs are capped and polyadenylated.[256]

For MVMp, four polyadenylation sites (AATAAA) for R3 mRNAs exist between the translation termination codon of the right ORF (ORF'''; see Figure 2–9A) and the downstream palindromic sequence at the right end of MVM DNA. Therefore, this region corresponds to the noncoding region at the 3' end of 2.9-kb mRNAs.[252, 253] Two of these polyadenylation sequences are contained within one of duplicate A + T-rich, 64-nucleotide sequences (see above). A host-range variant of MVMp, designated MVMi, has an altered tissue tropism and unlike the prototype which replicates in differentiated fibroblastic cells, MVMi replicates in mouse T lymphocytes.[257, 258] One of the primary differences between the prototype and variant at the DNA level is the presence of only two polyadenylation sequences within one 64-nucleotide sequence in the 3' noncoding region of MVMi-DNA. Thus sequences within single or duplicate 64-nucleotide sequences of MVMi or MVMp, respectively, may impart tissue specificity for viral replication. Evidence in support of this concept is the detection of enhancerlike sequences within the 64-nucleotide regions. In other viral systems, enhancers control the rates of transcription and impart tissue specificity to particular viruses, and may do likewise for parvoviruses.[253] In addition, although there are multiple polyadenylation sites within this region, polyadenylation preferentially occurs at a single site to form the 2.9-kb mRNA of MVMp.[259]

For a subset of the R3 transcripts, the intron is small, and upon splicing an initiation codon for translation located at 47 mu, remains as part of the resulting mRNA. This mRNA is translated using the conserved initiation codon into 80-kd to 85-kd capsid polypeptide, VP₁. An alternative splicing pattern results in the removal of a larger intron between 46 to 48 mu, which includes the initiation codon. A second codon to the right (3') of the splice junction initiates VP_2 (64–67 kd) synthesis (see Figure 2–9A).[238, 260] The two splicing events yield mRNAs which have the same reading frames for translation, and therefore the amino acid sequence of VP_2 is a subset of VP_1. Proteolytic cleavage of an N-terminal amino acid sequence from VP_2 yields of 60- to 64-kd capsid protein (VP_3). The relative amounts of VP_2 and VP_3 found in mature virus particles vary with the conditions of viral replication and the time at which the virus particles are isolated from infected cells.[261] Overall, VP_3 is much more abundant in virus particles than VP_1 or VP_2, the latter two polypeptides constituting approximately 20% of the total capsid polypeptide composition.

The control of parvovirus transcription may depend on multiple factors. As stated above, NS-1 and possibly NS-2 are required for late transcription of R3 mRNAs. In addition, the availability of cell proteins such as RNA polymerase II affects viral transcription. Differential splicing coupled with utilization of P4 or P38 determines the type of mRNAs available at certain times during the replication cycle. Furthermore, an attenuation model for coordinated control of P4- and P38-directed transcription has been proposed.[262]

Replication of Dependoviruses

Dependoviruses, such as adeno-associated virus (AAV), are defective in their replication and require coinfection of cells by a helper virus in order to efficiently replicate and form progeny AAV particles.[263, 264] AAV has a capsid similar in size and in number of proteins to the nondefective parvoviruses, but differs in certain aspects of the DNA structure.

DNA Structure

Adeno-associated virus DNA contains hairpin structures at both ends of the genome and, like autonomously replicating virus, these are formed by base pairing of palindromic sequences.[265, 266] Whereas autonomously replicating viruses have different nucleotide sequences constituting hairpin structures at their 5' and 3' termini, defective parvoviruses have an inverted, repeated sequence of 145 nucleotides at each end of the DNA molecule.

The nucleotide sequence corresponding to the 3' inverted repeat is shown in Figure 2–11. Nucleotides 1 to 41 are complemented exactly by sequence 125 through 85, while nucleotide sequence 42 to 84 contains two internal palindromic sequences that are found in different orientations in DNA molecules.[267] Single-stranded DNA isolated from viral particles has either negative or positive polarity, equal numbers being found in virus preparations.[268–270] Therefore, during replication of DNA, both plus and minus strands serve as templates for the synthesis of complementary strands. Positive or minus strands of DNA are equally infectious in cell cultures.

DNA Replication

Figure 2–12 shows a model for AAV DNA replication. The 3' hairpin on plus and minus strands are, for the most part, identical

```
      1-41  AACCGGTGAGGGAGAGACGCGCGAGCGAGCGAGTGACTCCG

                  50    54          62 64        72   76          84
  a   42-84  {GCCCGCTGG}TTT(CCAGCGGGC)T<GCGGGCCCG>AAA/CGGGCCCGC/


     85-125  CGGAGTCACTCGCTCGCTCGCGCGTCTCTCCCTCACCGGTT


    125-145  GAGGTAGTGATCCCCAAGGA




      1-41  AACCGGTGAGGGAGAGACGCGCGAGCGAGCGAGTGACTCCG

                  50    54          62 64        72   76          84
  b   42-84  <GCGGGCCCG>TTT/CGGGCCCGC/A{GCCCGCTGG}AAA(CCAGCGGGC)


     85-125  CGGAGTCACTCGCTCGCTCGCGCGTCTCTCCCTCACCGGTT


    125-145  GAGGTAGTGATCCCCAAGGA
```

Figure 2-11. Nucleotide sequence of the 3' terminus of adeno-associated virus (type 2) DNA. Nucleotides 1 through 145 represent an inverted terminal repetition in which nucleotide sequences 1–41 and 125–85 are complementary and help form the hairpin structure. Nucleotides 42 through 84 are present within the terminal hairpin in one of two orientations: a or b. Within orientation a, nucleotides 42–50 are complemented by nucleotides 62–54 and nucleotides 64–72 complement 84–76. Likewise, in orientation b, the sequences located at the equivalent positions are complementary. In "a" 42–50 { }, 54–62 ( ), 64–72 ⟨ ⟩ and 76–84 / / are identical, respectively, to nucleotides 64–72 { }, 76–84 ( ), 42–50 ⟨ ⟩, and 54–62 / / seen in "b". (Reproduced with permission from Lusby E, et al: Nucleotide sequence of the inverted terminal repetition in adeno-associated virus DNA. *J Virol* 1980; 34:402–409.)

in nucleotide sequence and serve as primers for DNA synthesis.[271] Cell DNA polymerase γ copies the single-stranded region beginning at the primer and continues the full length of the template strand.[272] Endonucleolytic cleavage occurs at or near nucleotide 145 within the 3' terminal sequence of the parental strand, and the hairpin structure unfolds to become the 5' terminal sequence of the progeny strand, which is present in an inverted orientation relative to its original orientation on the parental DNA (see Figure 2–12). The 3' terminal sequence of the parental strand is then regenerated using the complementary 5' region of the progeny strand. Strands dissociate and single (plus and minus) strands are immediately incorporated into viral capsids. As a result of transferring terminal sequences between parental and progeny DNA, the two internal palindromes present in the regenerated 3' terminus of the parental strand are inverted and complementary relative to the internal palindromes present at the 3' terminus of the parental DNA molecule before replication occurred. Although the model of DNA replication depicts the production of unit-length progeny DNA, multiple-length intermediates have also been isolated. This suggests that a mechanism similar to DNA replication of autonomously replicating parvoviruses may also occur.[273, 274]

Transcription

Transcription of AAV mRNAs initiates from three promoters (p5, p19, and p 40) in viral DNA at 5, 19, and 40 mu to produce primary transcripts 4.2, 3.6, and 2.6 kb in size, respectively (see Figure 2–9B). Each of these primary transcripts is spliced by the removal of a single intron between 41 and 46 mu to yield mRNAs of 3.9, 3.3, and 2.3 kb. The primary transcripts and their corresponding spliced forms each possess ORFs and are translated into polypeptides. The 4.2-, 3.9-, 3.6-, and 3.3-kb transcripts have ORFs correspondong to the left-hand (3') portion of the genome, whereas the 2.6- and 2.3-kb transcripts have ORFs corresponding to the right half (5') of the genome. Both primary transcripts and their spliced forms are capped and polyadenylated.[228, 275]

Transcription from the three promoters is controlled by cis-elements (TATA box), approximately 30 nucleotides upstream (− 30) from the transcriptional start sites.[276, 277] Termination of transcription is signaled by an AAUAAA polyadenylation cleavage site, which produces 3' coterminal transcripts at 96 mu.[278] Viral transacting factors have been implicated in regulation of transcription. Gene products expressed from p5 and p19 transcripts positively regulate transcription from p40.[279] In addition, gene products from p5 may also autoregulate transcription of the p5 gene itself and possibly that originating from p19.[280] Strict transcriptional regulation can be seen in AAV-infected cells coinfected with helper virus, where the 2.3-kd mRNA constitutes approximately 90% of the AAV transcripts. Other transacting factors contributed by the infected cell and/or helper virus control transcription of AAV DNA. It appears that helper virus infection induces expression of cellular transactivating factors which stimulate AAV transcription, the latter being greatly reduced in cells not infected by helper virus.

Several gene products of AAV have been detected in lytically infected cells that correspond to the right (3′) and left (5′) ORFs. Four polypeptides are encoded by the left ORFs: 78- and 68-kb polypeptides from 4.2- and 3.9-kd transcripts and 52- and 40-kd polypeptides from the p19 transcripts, 3.6 and 3.3 kb, respectively. The right ORFs encode three capsid polypeptides, VP_1 (90kd), VP_2 (72 kd), and VP_3 (60 kd), the former being translated by the 2.6-kb messenger RNA and the latter two by the 2.3-kb messenger.[281]

VP_1, VP_2, and VP_3 are translated in the same reading frame from independent initiation codons, unlike the situation for autonomously replicating parvoviruses, where VP_3 is formed by the proteolytic cleavage of VP_2. The AUG initiation codons for VP_1

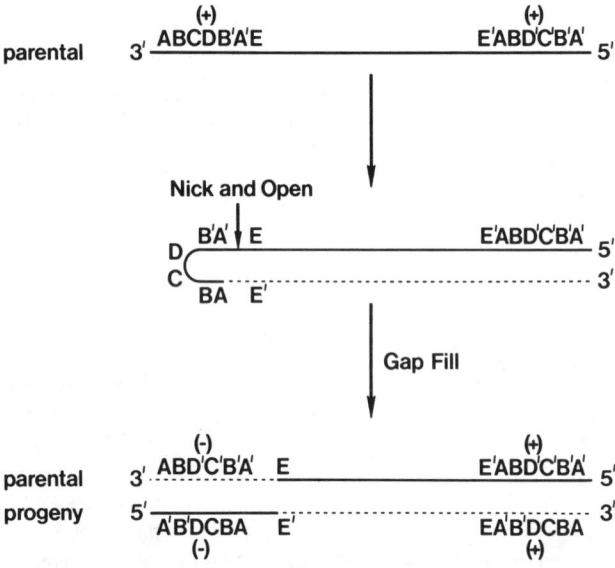

Figure 2–12. Adeno-associated virus DNA replication. The parental strand *(solid line)* has inverted terminal repetitions, ABCDB′A′E(+) or E′ABD′C′B′A′(+), corresponding to 145 nucleotides present in each terminus, with CD and D′C′ representing the two orientations of internal palindromes (nucleotides 42–84). DNA synthesis begins at the 3′ hairpin and copies the parental strand into a progeny strand *(dashed line)*. The hairpin unfolds following endonucleolytic cleavage and the missing terminus of the parental strand is resynthesized. Following DNA replication the 3′ terminus of parental DNA has the form ABD′C′B′A′E in which sequences D′C′ are complementary and in the opposite orientation than corresponding sequences (CD) in the 3′ terminus of the original parental strand. (Reproduced with permission from Lusby E, et al: Nucleotide sequence of the inverted terminal repetition in adeno-associated virus DNA. *J Virol* 1980; 34:402–409.)

and VP_2 were located in RNAs by examining the nucleotide sequence of the AAV genome. The initiation codon for VP_2 was not apparent and it is possible that ACG on the 2.3-kb mRNA serves this function (see Figure 2–9B).[281] VP_1, VP_2, and VP_3 were found within AAV-infected cells, as well as mature virus particles, at a ratio of 1:1:10, respectively. This suggests that translation from their corresponding mRNAs is regulated perhaps by a nonstructural protein encoded by the left ORFs. Notably, 55- and 40-kb nonstructural polypeptides translated from the 3.6 and 3.3 mRNAs, respectively, accumulate in the cytoplasm as well as in the nucleus of AAV-infected cells. Possibly these polypeptides regulate rates of translation of late transcripts or influence their stability or transport from the nucleus to the cytoplasm.[282]

Helper Requirements

As stated previously, AAV replication requires help from coinfecting viruses, namely adenovirus, herpes simplex virus, or vaccinia virus.[283] In addition, SV40-transformed hamster and human cells are conducive for AAV DNA replication and protein synthesis when treated with chemical carcinogens.[283, 284] This and other treatments of uninfected cells produce a limited number of progeny cells capable of supporting AAV replication, which suggests that induction of cellular genes is necessary for cells to support AAV replication. Although chemical or drug treatment of cells accomplishes this process in a limited manner, helper virus coinfection greatly facilitates activation of cells to a state permissive for AAV replication.

Adenovirus has been extensively investigated for helper functions which influence AAV replication at the levels of transcription, DNA replication, and protein synthesis. Expression of several adenovirus early genes including E1A, E1B, E2A, and E4 provide helper function(s) (see Adenoviruses above for details).[285, 286] Gene products of E1A and E1B together provide high levels of helper functions for AAV replication, but either one alone can enhance AAV transcription. The 72-kd DBP of adenovirus encoded by E2A may serve multiple roles including positive regulation of AAV translation and DNA replication.[287] E4 gene products also influences AAV DNA replication.[288] VAI genes of adenovirus, which is expressed at intermediate times during infection, also regulate AAV translation.[287, 289] Whether these various adenovirus gene products regulate AAV functions directly or indirectly is not as yet known. HSV types 1 and 2 also supply factors necessary for AAV replication, but the mechanism or specific gene products have not been well characterized.[290-294] HSV was shown to provide complete help in one system for AAV replication and AAV yields were of the same order obtained when adenovirus served as a helper virus. The fact that diverse viruses as well as chemical treatment of cells provide help for AAV replication supports indirect mechanisms.

Latent Infections

In the absence of helper virus, AAV can only replicate to a limited extent in a few variant cells within a population. Alternative types of virus-cell interactions, latent infections, are most often established.[295] This process involves viral penetration into cells followed by uncoating of AAV particles at the nuclear membrane with release of AAV DNA into the nucleus. Integration of AAV DNA into chromosomal DNA ensues, requiring a recombination event between terminal palindromic sequences of AAV DNA and host nucleotide sequences. Recombination is most likely mediated by cellular enzymes and apparently does not depend on recognition of specific nucleotide sequences within cell DNA, since it can occur at more than one site. AAV DNA is often integrated as a tandem repeat consisting of three to five copies of the viral genome covalently linked to flanking cell DNA.[296, 297]

Superinfection of AAV latently infected cells with helper virus such as adenovirus causes integrated AAV genome to be excised or to replicate to form extrachromosomal DNA. Excision is dependent on the presence of at least one and possibly both of the terminal palindromic sequences within the integrated AAV DNA molecules.[298] In its unintegrated form AAV DNA is transcribed and replicated to yield progeny virus particles. As stated previously, numerous gene products of adenovirus facilitate AAV replication either in an indirect or direct manner. Presumably one or more of these same polypeptides induces integrated AAV genomes to replicate. The 55-kd polypeptide of E1B, possibly in direct association with an E4 polypeptide, has been shown in part to rescue AAV DNA from latently infected cells.[299] The rescue process of integrated DNA by helper viruses is also more efficient in rapidly growing cells, which indicates that cell factors are involved in activation of AAV DNA.[297]

Virus Assembly

Assembly and maturation of AAV begins following concurrent viral protein and DNA synthesis. Newly synthesized DNA rapidly associates with capsid proteins to form virus particles (heavy full, or HF) with a density of 1.47 g/cm³ as determined by CsCl gradient centrifugation.[300] These virus particles are found first in the nucleus and then in the cytoplasm at early times during infection. At later times, 1.47-g/cm³ particles are converted to 1.43-g/cm³ particles, designated light-full (LF) virus. At times corresponding to conversion from HF to LF particles, proteolysis of the 68,000-mol-wt capsid protein yields a 65,000-mol-wt cleavage product as seen in autonomously replicating virus.[301, 302] However, other rearrangements of viral proteins during proteolysis seem to be unrelated to HF-to-LF conversion.[303]

Various AAV synthetic events are associated with specific nuclear structures within infected cell nuclei. Viral DNA synthesis occurs in close proximity to nuclear and nucleolar euchromatin, while at early times viral proteins are found with heterochromatin near the nuclear membrane. As viral antigens accumulate, they become associated with nuclear and nucleolar heterochromatin which, in turn, condenses at the nuclear membranes. Although capsid proteins are found with heterochromatin, mature capsids are seen near euchromatin, presumably at locations of AAV DNA synthesis.[304]

HERPESVIRUSES

The family ***Herpetoviridae*** has several members which are widely disseminated human pathogens. These include herpes simplex virus (HSV), Epstein-Barr virus, cytomegalovirus, and varicella-zoster virus. HSV, types 1 and 2, have been investigated in great detail at the molecular level, because of their rapid replication cycle and high yields in tissue culture. Mechanisms of replication of the other three viruses have been more difficult to analyze

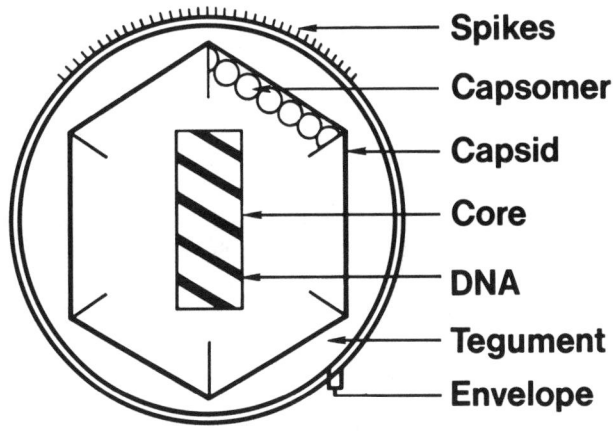

Figure 2–13. Model of herpes simplex virus showing the morphologic substructures; envelope, capsid, and core.

because of their protracted replication cycles and poor yields of progeny virus. However, with the advent of molecular cloning techniques great strides have been made over the last several years in understanding the replication cycles of the other herpes viruses.

Virus Structure

As shown in Figure 2–13, HSV particles consist of a linear, double-stranded DNA molecule wound around a centrally located spool-shaped core. The core DNA complex, in turn, is enclosed by an icosahedral capsid composed of 162 capsomers.[305] An envelope having small protein spikes projecting outward from its surface forms the outermost structure of mature virus particles. At least seven viral glycoproteins, gB, gC, gD, gE, gG, gH, and gI, as well as several nonglycosylated polypeptides, are associated with the envelope of HSV-1, some proteins constituting spikes.[306–308] A layer of amorphous material, tegument, is found in variable amounts between the envelope and capsid, contributing to the range of particle diameters of mature virus particles: 150 to 200 nm.[305] Several structural proteins of the virus particle have also been shown to have regulatory properties during infection. These include Vmw 65 protein, which is found in tegument, and a virion-associated protein (vhs) responsible for shutoff of host protein synthesis as well as control of specific viral proteins.[309, 310]

The HSV genome has a molecular weight of 96×10^6, which corresponds to a true genetic complexity of approximately 86×10^6, when noncoding regions are considered.[311–313] The genome of HSV-1 has been sequenced, and HSV-2 DNA sequencing is nearly complete.[313] Based on genetic mapping and sequencing of HSV genomes, 70 genes either known to encode viral proteins or having ORFs with the potential to encode proteins have been identified (see Figure 2–15 and reference 313 for a complete map of HSV-1). About 50 of these proteins have actually been identified in infected cells and may function in numerous capacities: as regulatory factors in viral and cellular events, and as enzymes and structural proteins of the virus.[314, 315]

HSV DNA has several distinctive features, including the presence of random breaks in phosphodiester linkages,[316, 317] short stretches of RNA,[318] inverted repeat sequences, and several different arrangements of unique sequences.[319, 320] Genomic DNA has two regions of unique nucleotide sequences, unique large (U_L) and unique small (U_S), which are each bracketed by inverted repeats.[321–324] As shown in Figure 2-14, "ab" and "b'a'" sequences, each about 9 kb in length, flank U_L, and "a'c'" and "ca" sequences, each about 6.5 kb in length, flank U_S. Therefore sequence "a" is terminally redundant. Although only one "a" sequence is shown in Figure 2–14 within the inverted repetitions flanking U_L, variable numbers of "a" sequences ranging from one to ten have been detected at these locations,[324] while only one copy of an "a" sequence is found at the U_S terminus. The actual length of individual "a" sequences varies from approximately 250 base pairs to 500 base pairs.[325] The size variation of "a" sequences corresponds to variable numbers of direct repeat sequences (DR) located within the "a" sequence itself. The "a" sequence has the organizational format DRI-U-(DR2)$_{19-23}$-(DR4)$_{2-3}$-U-DR1.[326] The variability in length of an "a" sequence corresponds to the number of times DR2 and DR4 are repeated, 19 to 23 times and 2 to 3 times, respectively. The two unique (U) sequences are fixed in length; each is present only once per "a" sequence. In the situation where two "a" sequences adjoin, there is one shared DR1 at their junction.[327]

HSV DNA isolated from infected cells or from a population of purified virus particles consists of four arrangements of DNA (see Figure 2–14). In three of these arrangements one or the other or both unique regions are inverted relative to that of the prototype

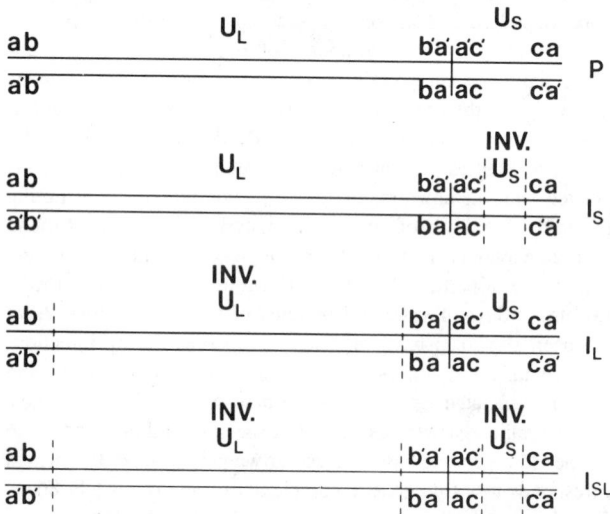

Figure 2–14. Four isomers of herpes simplex virus DNA. Two regions of unique DNA sequences, unique large (U_L) and unique small (U_S), are present in each isomer. Flanking each unique region are inverted repeats;

```
         a b    b'a'                    a'c'    c a
flank U_S, | |  and | |   flank U_L, and  | |  and | |
         a'b'   b a                     a c    c a'
```

respectively. The top isomer represents a prototype (P) with respect to the orientation of U_L and U_S. The other three isomers, I_S, I_L, and I_{SL}, have inverted U_S (INV U_S), inverted U_L (INV U_L), and inverted U_L and U_S, respectively. Dashed vertical lines represent boundaries of the inverted unique sequences.

configuration.[320] Given the arrangement of U_L plus U_S as a prototype DNA molecule, the other three orientations are: (1) U_L plus inverted region U_S, (2) inverted region U_L plus U_S, or (3) inverted region U_L plus inverted region U_S (see Figure 2–14). Virus particles isolated from a single plaque yield equimolar amounts of all four DNA configurations, which shows that the four forms are generated during successive infectious cycles and perhaps within a single cell. Virus particles containing any one of the four configurations of viral DNA are infectious.

Attachment, Penetration, Uncoating

HSV productively infects cells both in culture or in vivo, as well as causing latent infections in neurons of animals and man. The productive infection of cultured cells not only results in the formation of virus progeny but also in the lysis of infected cells. Lytic infection begins with the attachment of virus particles to specific receptor molecules (possibly heparan sulfate) on the cell surface.[327a] This interaction seems to be mediated by at least glycoprotein D or gH,[327b] which can interact with receptors on a wide variety of cultured cells. It has been demonstrated that high concentrations of neutralizing antibody specific for gD block attachment.[328, 329]

Penetration of the virus particles into cells occurs primarily through a fusion event between the viral envelope and the plasma membrane.[330] Early studies had suggested that HSV particles gain entry into cells through endocytosis, whereby the virus particles are incorporated into vesicles at the cell surface. At low pH the viral envelope then fuses with the vesicular membrane to release viral capsids into the cytoplasm. This latter mechanism now seems to be of secondary importance. Penetration via fusion at the plasma membrane is the primary mode of penetration and involves four viral glycoproteins. Glycoprotein B is a major factor in the fusion process as evidenced by temperature-sensitive mutants in gB, which attach but fail to penetrate at a nonpermissive temperature.[331–333] Furthermore, antibodies specific for gD, gE, or gH prevent penetration by inhibiting fusion.[307, 308, 334] Possibly these four glycoproteins as well as other minor viral proteins form a multimeric complex which mediates penetration. Alternatively, these glycoproteins may be redundant, any one being capable of mediating the fusion procsss. Viral capsids released in the cytoplasm proceed to the nuclear membrane, where viral DNA is released into the nucleus at the nuclear pores.

Early Transcription

Viral DNA then acts as a template for regulated and ordered transcription. Based on the relative abundance of mRNAs during infection and the temporal order in which they appear, three stages of transcription have been delineated: immediate-early (α), early (β), and late (γ).[335] The last stage can be further subdivided into γ_1, and γ_2 based on the requirements for viral DNA synthesis.[336] Furthermore, the appearance of mRNAs in polysomes during these periods may be controlled by several different mechanisms including selective transcription,[337–339] preferential RNA transport from the nucleus to the cytoplasm, differential processing of RNAs,[339–341] and inherent stabilities of the mRNAs.[342] Although the bulk of evidence has supported selective transcription, the other mechanisms are also supported experimentally.

Initiation of immediate early (IE) transcription is enhanced by a virion-associated protein, Vmw 65, also designated transinducing factor (TIF), which is located in the tegument of virus particles.[309] This protein along with viral DNA enters infected cell nuclei following viral uncoating.

The Vmw 65 associates with sequences within the promoter-regulatory region of all five α (IE) genes which encode infected cell proteins (ICP): ICP-0, ICP-4, ICP-22, ICP-27, and ICP-47.[343] A consensus sequence, TAATGARATTC,[344] where R represents a purine, is found in one to three copies in promoter-regulatory regions and binds Vmw 65 in an indirect manner.[345] Apparently, a cellular DBP designated variously TRF, NFIII, or H1 by different investigators binds directly to these sequences and mediates the secondary binding of Vmw 65.[346] The ability of Vmw 65 to transactivate α genes is seemingly modulated by two other gene products which map near the Vmw 65 genes.[346a, 347] In addition to Vmw 65 binding indirectly to promoter-regulatory-specific sequences, other sequences within the promoter-regulatory regions of α genes have been recognized to play a role in regulation. These include a TATA box, GC-rich regions which bind SP-1 cell protein; and in several IE genes, an ATCGTC hexanucleotide, which is a core domain for a larger sequence that binds ICP-4 either directly or indirectly.[348–350]

IE mRNAs are transcribed by cellular DNA-dependent RNA polymerase II without the requirement for previous viral protein synthesis.[351–353] IE mRNAs are primarily transcribed from sequences within or adjacent to the inverted repeats (Figure 2–15) which bracket the unique sequences.[338, 354] Unlike most HSV mRNAs, which are not spliced, primary transcripts for ICP-0, ICP-22, and ICP-47 are spliced to form functional mRNAs.[313, 355] Following transport of IE mRNAs from the nucleus to the cytoplasm, translation ensues, reaching a peak at two to four hours after infection.

The immediate-early (α) proteins as a whole regulate transcription of early (β) and late (γ$_1$, γ$_2$) genes, as well as autoregulate α genes.[335] The regulatory mechanisms involving α proteins have been elucidated using transient expression systems and HSV mutants; temperature-sensitive, deletion, and nonsense.

In general, viral genes have been designated as being either essential or nonessential for viral replication in cells grown in culture. The fact that "nonessential" genes are retained as part of the HSV genome suggests that their gene products have functions required for infection of animals or man. Of the five gene products encoded by the α genes, ICP-4 and ICP-27 are essential for viral replication,[356, 357] whereas ICP-0 is seemingly nonessential for virus growth, although ICP-0 mutants replicate over a protracted period of time.[358] ICP-22 and ICP-47 are also nonessential in infected cells in culture. The best characterized α proteins are ICP-0 and ICP-4, which are encoded within the inverted repeats flanking U$_L$ and U$_S$, respectively, making both genes diploid (see Figure 2–15).

ICP-4 is a central control element for the induction of transcription of β and γ genes[359] and can negatively effect transcription of its own gene as well as other α genes.[360] ICP-4 protein (175 kd mol wt) is present in infected cells in at least three forms differing in their extent of phosphorylation and possibly adenosine diphosphate (ADP) ribosylation.[361, 362] ICP-4 exists as a homodimer in extracts of infected cells, which possibly represents its

functional form.[363, 363a] Early during infection, newly synthesized ICP-4 quickly localizes to the nucleus and is distributed in a diffuse pattern. Nuclear localization is possibly directed by a conserved amino acid sequence of ICP-4, rich in lysine and arginine residues.[364] Concomitant with viral DNA synthesis at later times during infection, ICP-4 is redistributed to "replication compartments" in the nucleus, thereby assuming a more condensed, globular distribution.[365]

The role of ICP-4 in regulation of transcription has been ascribed to its ability to interact with the promoter-regulatory regions of α, β, and γ genes. Indirect and direct binding of ICP-4 to viral DNA interactions has been demonstrated. ICP-4 associates with the consensus sequence ATCGTCnnnnYCGRC (n = any nucleotide, Y = pyrimidine, R = purine) in the promoter-regulatory regions of α genes, ICP-0 and ICP-4,[366] β gene gD,[367] and γ genes, α-TIF,[368] gC, and γ$_2$42.[367, 368] Data have accumulated which support the indirect binding of ICP-4 to this consensus sequence. The fact that many promoter-regulatory regions of α, β, and γ genes bind ICP-4 but lack ATCGTCnnnnYCGRC consensus sequences suggests that other DNA sequences are involved in ICP-4 binding. Perhaps cellular proteins, which are found both in infected as well as in uninfected cells, initially bind to promoter-regulatory regions. ICP-4 then binds to the prebound cellular proteins to form a multimeric complex.[367]

Investigations by other researchers have led to the conclusion that ICP-4 binds directly to sequences on the viral genome.[343, 349] Furthermore, the three different phosphorylated forms of ICP-4 may recognize alternative nucleotide sequences in promoter-regulatory regions which are not homologues of the ATCGTC nnnnYCGRC consensus sequence.[368] The interaction of ICP-4 with the promoter-regulatory region for the most part induces transcription of various classes of genes. Alternatively, ICP-4 can downregulate expression of several IE genes, including the ICP-4 gene itself. Its action as a negative effector may require that ICP-4 bind either directly or indirectly to nucleotide sequences at or near the initiation site for transcription (+1 site) which are different from sequences involved in ICP-4-mediated induction of transcription.[367]

Although ICP-4 is essential for viral infections and is a major regulatory protein, ICP-0 also functions in a regulatory capacity.[369, 370] ICP-0, a phosphoprotein of 110 kd, is not essential for productive infection in cell culture, but its altered expression may be an integral aspect in the establishment of latency in vivo (see below).[371] ICP-0 can induce β gene expression in transient systems independent of ICP-4, but it cannot substitute for nonfunctional ICP-4 in HSV-infected cultures.[369, 372, 373] ICP-0 also has the capacity to augment stimulatory activities of ICP-4 for β and γ genes in HSV-infected cells. The inducing activity of ICP-0 and ICP-4 for other IE genes depends on the ratio of the combined amounts of ICP-0 plus ICP-4 to the relative concentration of the α genes (or promoter-regulatory regions thereof). At low ratios of ICP-0 plus ICP-4 to α gene targets, their promoter-regulatory regions are activated, whereas at high ratios the expression is repressed.[374] Structural analysis of ICP-0 polypeptide indicated that it contains an amino acid sequence characteristic of the Zn^{++} binding finger motif of certain DBPs.[375] Perhaps ICP-0 has the capacity to directly bind to nucleotide sequences within the promoter-regulatory regions of various genes.

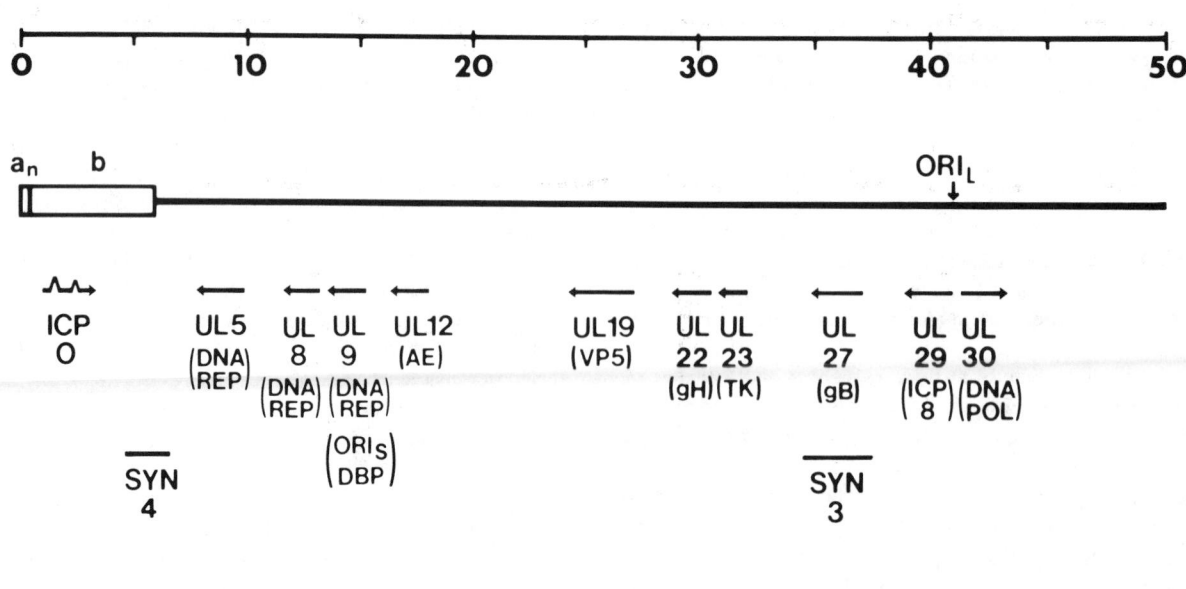

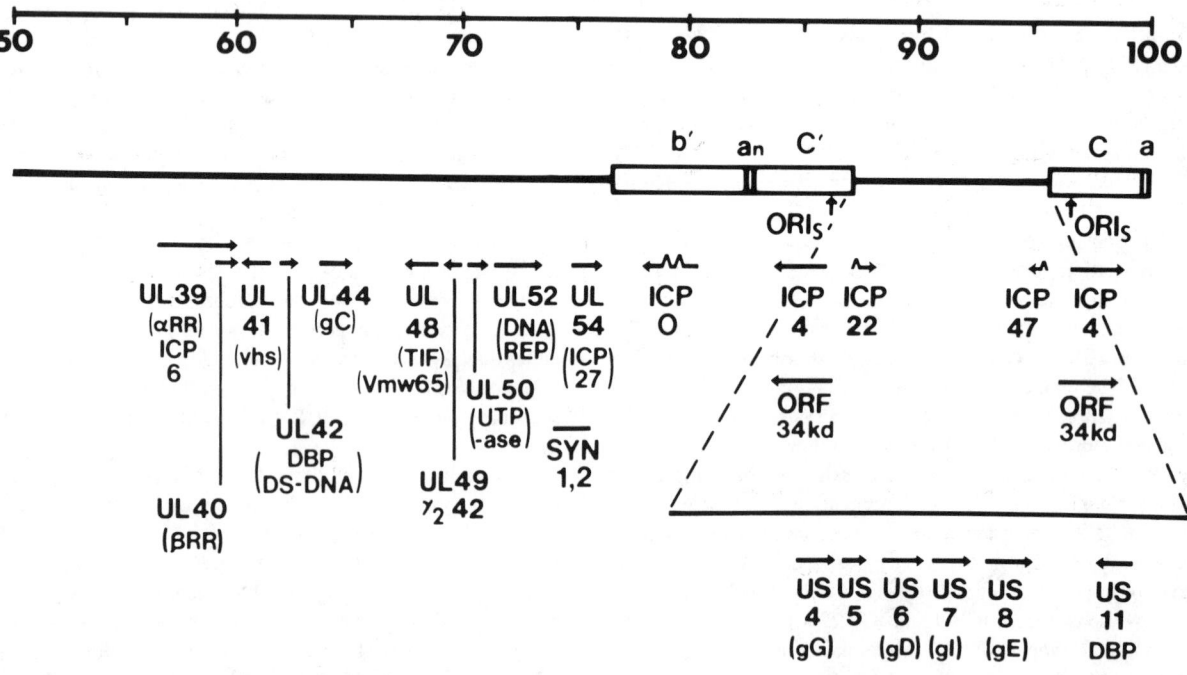

Figure 2–15. Map locations of origins of replication (ORI$_S$) and select genes within the unique large (U$_L$), unique small (U$_S$), and inverted repeat regions. The length of the herpes simplex virus (HSV) genome is divided into 100 map units (mu) and the relative locations of a subset of the total number of mapped genes is indicated. Arrowheads represent the 3′ end of mRNAs and the relative size of the primary transcript is shown by the length of the arrow. Immediate early genes map within inverted repeats, ICP-0 and ICP-4, or at locations adjacent to inverted repeats, ICP-27, ICP-22, and ICP-47. ICP-0, ICP-22, and ICP-47 are spliced *(arrows with spiked lines)*, whereas the remaining transcripts are not spliced. Map locations of genes involved in syncytia (SYN) formation are indicated without reference to corresponding gene products. ORI$_L$ is located within the U$_L$ region surrounded by genes encoding the DNA polymerase and DNA-binding protein (DBP), ICP-8. Identical ORI$_S$ are located in the inverted repeats flanking U$_S$ and overlap open reading frames (ORF) possibly encoding a 34-kd polypeptide. Locations of genes encoding alkaline exonuclease (AE), virion protein 5 (VP5), thymidine kinase (TK), the α and β subunits of ribonucleotide reductase (RR), virion-host shutoff protein (vhs), transinducing factor (TIF) with a molecular weight of 65 kd, deoxyuridine triphosphate nucleotidohydrolase (UTPase), and several glycoproteins (g) are indicated. Several genes referred to in the text which map in the U$_L$ and U$_S$ regions and have only tentative functions assigned to their gene products are also indicated (see ref 313 for complete HSV-1 map).

ICP-27, 63 kd mol wt, is also essential for HSV gene expression in virus-infected cells, serving several functions.[357] ICP-27 can negatively regulate the expression of other α genes. In addition, ICP-27 is required for expression of certain late proteins; mutants in the ICP-27 gene have altered abundance and temporal expression of late gene products. ICP-27 seemingly interacts with ICP-0 or ICP-4 or both to augment their ability in inducing late gene (γ gene) expression.[357, 376]

ICP-22, 67 kd mol wt, is essential for the expression of certain late genes in specific cell types but not in others.[377] In those cells in which ICP-22 is not essential, a host cell protein may compensate for the deficit of ICP-22. ICP-47, 12 kd, is apparently not essential for virus growth in cell culture.[377, 378] Two characteristics of ICP-47 suggest that it lacks the regulatory properties of other IE proteins—its relatively small size and its cytoplasmic rather than nuclear location within HSV-infected cells.

Concomitant with the induction of α events in HSV-infected cells, host cell protein synthesis is terminated or reduced. This occurs in spite of continued transcription of cellular mRNAs. A component of the virus particle causes dissociation of host cell polysomes and destabilizes cellular mRNA, especially in Vero cells.[379] Various factors determine the extent of inhibition of cell protein synthesis. The inherent characteristics of cell mRNAs affects their rate of degradation. Also, the type of HSV influences the decline of cell mRNAs; HSV-2 causes a more rapid degradation than HSV-1. The cell line infected by HSV has a bearing on inhibition of host cell proteins. In Vero cells the virion component primarily inhibits protein synthesis, whereas in other cell lines HSV gene expression is required for inhibition.[380] Despite numerous mechanisms for termination of cell protein synthesis, it is not a prerequisite for viral replication.

HSV mutants, vhs mutants, have been isolated which lack a functional virion-associated component and are incapable of immediate-early shutoff of cell protein synthesis. These mutant viruses retain the ability to reduce host cell macromolecular synthesis at later times, but this event depends on the expression of viral genes. Vhs mutants also exhibit an increase in α protein synthesis, which suggests that α mRNAs are more stable in vhs mutant-infected cells.[381, 382] Therefore, vhs protein of wt HSV apparently not only shuts off host cell protein synthesis, but also limits the stability of α, β, and γ mRNAs. This in turn limits the time frame for translation of the three classes of mRNAs. In vhs mutants not only do mRNAs have a prolonged half-life, but β and mRNAs likewise are more stable.[382]

Following the IE stage of gene expression a second class of genes (β) is expressed. As indicated above, β gene expression requires the prior synthesis of at least ICP-4 and ICP-27 with ICP-0 and ICP-22 facilitating β expression. Approximately 15 β proteins are synthesized early, reaching their peak synthesis between five and seven hours after infection.[335] Several functions have been associated with β proteins, including shutoff of host cell DNA and protein synthesis, termination of mRNA synthesis, initiation and continuation of viral DNA synthesis, and initiation of transcription of mRNAs. A number of enzymes that participate in viral DNA synthesis are β proteins, including a DNA polymerase having 3′ to 5′ exonuclease activity,[383, 384] a major DBP (ICP-8),[385] alkaline exonuclease,[386] ribonucleotide reductase,[387] thymidine kinase,[388] deoxyuridine triphosphate nucleotidohydrolase (dUTPase),[389] a 54-kd polymerase-associated protein,[390] a 94-kd protein essential for DNA replication,[391] and possibly a DNA primase[392] and helicase.[393] Other proteins, perhaps of viral origin, that function in viral DNA synthesis include a protein which binds to origins of DNA synthesis (ORIs),[394] uracil DNA glycosylase,[395] dCMP deaminase,[396] and topoisomerase.[397]

Although β genes are in general scattered throughout the length of the HSV genome, at least three minor clusters of genes encoding β proteins involved in viral DNA synthesis have been delineated.[313] Genes for DNA polymerase and DBP ICP-8 flank the origin of DNA replication located in the U_L region (ORI$_L$) (see Figure 2–15). A second gene cluster is located within the left portion of the HSV genome in close proximity to the alkaline exonuclease gene. It includes genes for a 94-kd protein (U_L 9 gene) essential for DNA replication and two other genes (U_L 5 and U_L 8) whose gene products have not been well characterized but may also participate in DNA synthesis. Two other genes, U_L 42 and U_L 52, which map in the right third of the U_L region, also encode proteins essential for DNA replication.[393]

The physical and biologic properties of several of the β proteins involved in DNA synthesis have been elucidated. The DNA polymerase of HSV differs in immunologic and biochemical properties from DNA polymerases of mammalian cells. The viral polymerase protein itself is 140 kd in size and possesses some sequence homology with the DNA polymerases of Epstein-Barr virus, adenovirus type 2, and vaccinia virus. The C-terminus of the polymerase of HSV contains at least in part the catalytic site(s) of the protein.[398]

ICP-8 (mol wt = 128, 341), a β protein that preferentially binds to single-stranded viral DNA with high avidity without recognizing specific nucleotide sequences has also been shown to be essential for HSV DNA replication.[385, 398] Temperature-sensitive mutants in the ICP-8 gene fail to replicate at nonpermissive temperatures. ICP-8 associates with viral DNA polymerase in vitro and in infected cells. In addition, alkaline exonuclease may also be incorporated into this multimeric structure to form a replication complex.[399] ICP-8 plays a role in controlling or modulating the expression of α, β, and γ genes, by negatively regulating transcription of these mRNAs at specific times during infection.[400] The protein itself has been analyzed to delineate the possible domain(s) involved in binding to DNA as well as those necessary for negative control of transcription. ICP-8 exhibits cooperative binding to single-stranded DNA (ss-DNA), which can be inhibited through modifications of sulfhydryl groups of cysteine residues found throughout the protein. Two clusters of cysteines exist: one in the middle of the protein and the other near the carboxy terminus.[401] The central cysteine cluster corresponds in part to the putative DNA-binding region and contains the Zn^{++} finger motif, which potentially complexes with divalent metal cations. The role of ICP-8 in controlling transcription has not been determined, but its mechanism of action may involve an interaction with ICP-4. These two viral proteins have been shown to co-localize to specific regions of infected cell nuclei at late times, suggesting an indirect or direct association.[365]

Another DBP shown to be essential for DNA synthesis is the 65-kd protein probably encoded by the U_L 42 gene (see Figure 2–15). Like ICP-8 this protein associates with the DNA polymerase-alkaline exonuclease complex and may function as an accessory protein for DNA synthesis.[402, 402a]

A viral enzyme, ribonucleotide reductase (RR), consisting of 140-kd and 38-kd polypeptides, reduces ribonucleotides to deoxyribonucleotides to produce precursors for viral DNA synthesis. Sequence homology was demonstrated between the HSV-encoded enzyme and RR encoded by *Escherichia coli* and mammalian cells.[403] Temperature-sensitive mutants in HSV-1 RR have the capacity to replicate in tissue culture at nonpermissive temperatures but at much reduced levels, which suggests that cell RR can compensate for the absence of its viral counterpart.[404] The synthesis of the 140-kd polypeptide (ICP-6) component of RR does not seem to be regulated in a manner analogous to the 38-kd component of RR, a β protein. Expression of ICP-6 occurs very early in lytic infection and limited synthesis occurs in the presence of the protein synthesis inhibitor cycloheximide.[405, 406] Furthermore, ICP-4 is not essential for 140-kd polypeptide synthesis, whereas ICP-0 possibly regulates 140-kd polypeptide expression in a positive manner.[373]

Thymidine kinase (TK), another β protein that is nonessential for HSV replication in tissue culture cells, has been well characterized for its enzymatic activity and control of its expression. The enzyme has broader substrate specificity compared to its cellular TK counterpart. It can phosphorylate both pyrimidines and purines as well as various nucleoside analogues. This latter activity enables viral TK to phosphorylate the antiviral drug acycloguanosine, which initiates activation of the drug. The HSV-TK polypeptide is synthesized in infected cells in two and possibly three sizes which are related in amino acid sequence; 43-kd, 39-kd, and 38-kd polypeptides.[407] Functionally active TK exists as a dimer composed of two polypeptides.[408] It is possible that several forms of the dimer exist in infected cells and are composed of the 43-kd polypeptide in combination with an identical-size polypeptide, or one of the smaller polypeptides, to yield varied activities. The different-size TK polypeptides are direct translation products from three different AUG initiation codons in the TK mRNA and are apparently not derived by cleavage of a precursor polypeptide.

The regulation of the HSV-TK gene has been extensively investigated and serves as a model for control of β genes in general. The promoter-regulatory region consists of at least three domains which bind cellular DBP.[409, 410] These include a proximal sequence (TATA box), two distal sequences both possessing SP-1 protein-binding sites, and a distal CAAT site. Thus the proteins which bind to the viral TK promoter region are apparently not unique to infected cells. Perhaps control of TK is achieved in infected cells by differential quantities of cellular DBPs (SP-1, TATA-binding protein, and NF-1/CAAT-binding protein), being available at various times during infection.

In addition, ICP-4, possibly in combination with at least ICP-0 and ICP-27, and ICP-8 control TK and other β gene transcription.[359, 373, 358, 400] These viral regulatory proteins may bind to cellular DBPs, thereby affecting promoter-regulated transcription indirectly. Furthermore, preliminary evidence suggests that sequences downstream from the transcriptional start site may influence the level of transcription.[410]

DNA Replication

HSV DNA replication begins within the cell nucleus at three hours postinfection and continues to approximately 15 hours postinfection. A model of HSV DNA synthesis that accounts for the formation of DNA intermediates with different configurations as well as the four isomers of the replicated DNA has been proposed (Figure 2–16). Basically the linear, double-stranded genomic DNA is converted to a circular form through the action of a processive, single-stranded exonuclease, which exposes complementary sequences a and a' at the termini. Circular DNA is then formed by the base pairing of single-stranded ends and subsequently serves as a template for DNA replication through a rolling circle mechanism.

Three origins of replication have been determined for the HSV genome, one each in the c and c' sequences which flank U_S (ORI$_S$) and one near the middle of the U_L (ORI$_L$) (see Figure 2–15).[411, 412] Through deletions of the origins from genomic DNA it has been shown that all three origins are not required for DNA replication. As a minimal requirement, one ORI$_S$ will suffice for in vitro replication and the absence of ORI$_L$ does not prevent viral replication in vitro or the establishment of latency in animals.[413] The ORI$_L$ corresponds to a 144-base pair perfect palindrome, each arm consisting of 72 base pairs around the axis of symmetry.[398, 414] ORI$_S$ is composed of a smaller palindrome of 45 base pairs in length located within a 90-base pair origin-related sequence.[415] The middle regions of the three origins are homologous in nucleotide sequence and resemble origins of DNA replication found in papovaviruses and adenoviruses.

The relative importance of any one of these origins in DNA replication has not been delineated. A requirement for at least one ORI$_S$ per genome may depend on an essential gene product encoded by an ORF which encompasses ORI$_S$.[416] The mRNA from this ORF overlaps the transcriptional initiation sites of ICP-4 and ICP-22 of the ac' on one side of U_s, or of ICP-4 and ICP-47 at the other side, and is 3' coterminal with ICP-4 mRNAs. Potentially, this mRNA encodes a protein that is 330 amino acids in length (34 kd), which may be required for initiation of DNA synthesis from ORI$_s$. Transcription from the ORI$_s$-associated ORF is not regulated in its expression in a manner analogous to the overlapping α genes and is most likely expressed as a β or $γ_1$ gene.

As stated above, a multimeric complex consisting of at least viral DNA polymerase, alkaline exonuclease, ICP-8, and a 65-kd DBP is necessary for DNA replication. Possible roles of other proteins have also been noted. The concatemeric DNA, which results from a rolling circle mechanism of DNA synthesis, is cleaved into near unit-length DNA. The predominant junction between genome-length DNA within the concatemer is U_S-cab-U_L, only one "a" sequence being present.[417] When -cab- is cleaved within the DR1 region of the single "a" sequence (see previous discussion on the sequences constituting the a sequences) U_S-ca and b-U_L result; the latter sequence being the precursor to the U_L terminus, lacks the terminal "a" sequence. The common "a" sequence in the -cab- junction itself appears to govern cleavage. Although cleavage occurs within the shared DR1 sequence of "a," another site within an internal portion of "a" determines the exact site for cleavage at a fixed distance from the internal site. The terminal "a" sequence(s) missing on some of the cleavage products (b-U_L, see above) must be regenerated to yield full-length DNA. A proposed mechanism for the synthesis of new terminal "a" sequences necessitates that the incomplete terminus fold back upon complementary sequences located near the L-S junction, for example, terminal "b" sequence base-pairs with internal "b'''". The missing

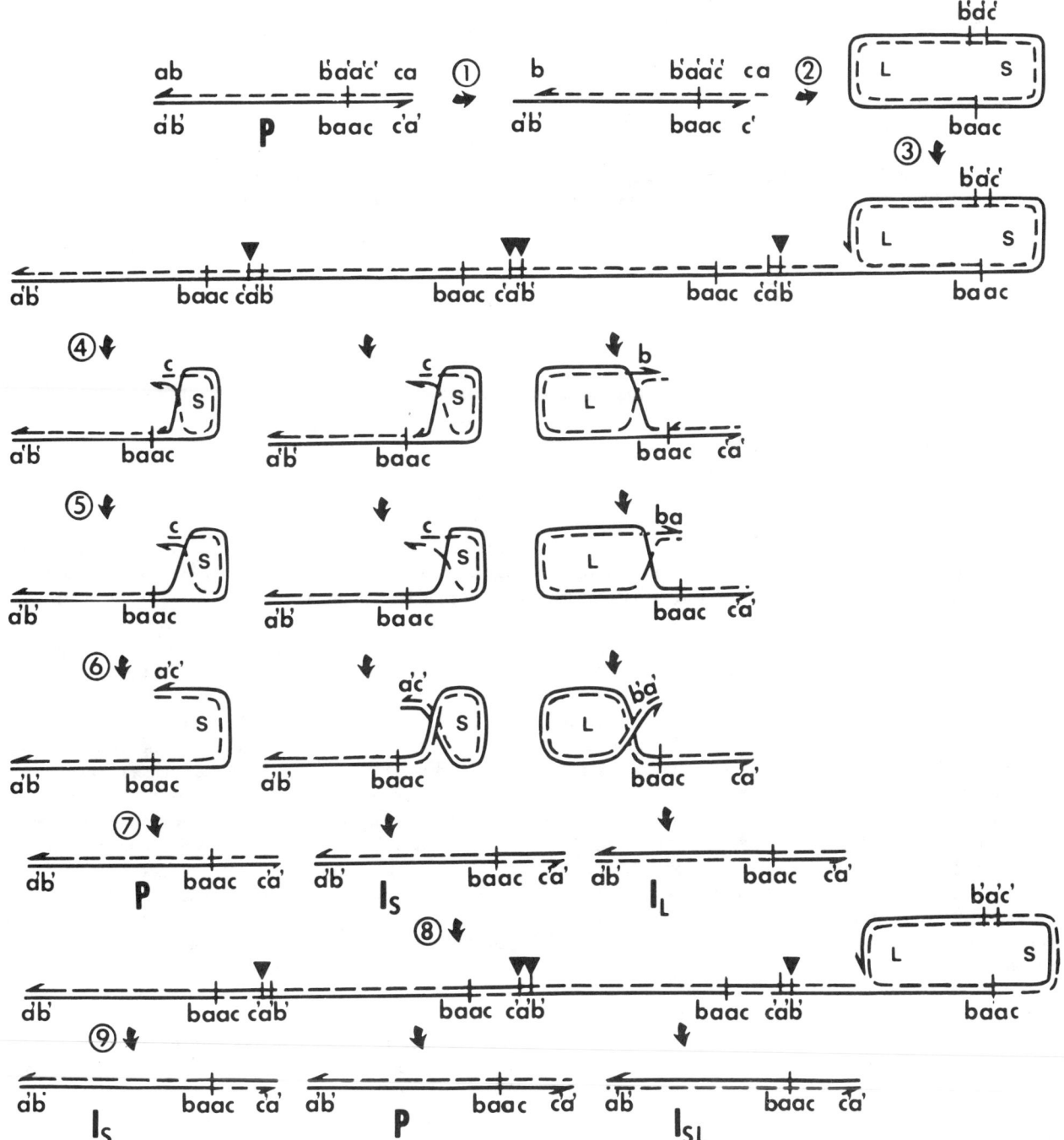

Figure 2–16. Replication and isomer formation of herpes simplex virus DNA. Prototype DNA(P) is digested at its termini by processive exonuclease (1) to expose sequences a and a′ at opposite termini. DNA circularizes via cohesive ends (2) and serves as a template for DNA synthesis of concatemers by the rolling circle mechanism (3). Concatemer DNA is cleaved *(black triangles)* between c′a′ or a′b′. Individual double-stranded DNAs formed by cleavage lack terminal a and a′ sequences. Incomplete termini are regenerated by each of the DNA strands folding back upon the U_L-U_S junction. For example, full-length P-DNA (left pathway) is formed by the terminal c sequence of one strand of DNA *(dashed line)* base-pairing with internal c′ of b′a′a′c′ *(dashed line)*. Similarly, terminal c′ *(solid line)* base-pairs with internal c of baac *(solid line)* (4). Sequence a′ is synthesized using sequence a as template (5), and sequence a is likewise synthesized using sequence a′ as template (6). Intrastrand base pairs within P dissociate and the U_S region unfolds without being inverted (6 and 7). It is at this stage, however, that inversions can occur as in the case of I_S formation (middle pathway, 6 and 7). Replication of I_S by steps 1–7 generates I_{SL} in addition to P and I_S (8, 9). (Reproduced with permission from Roizman B: The structure and isomerization of herpes simplex virus genomes. *Cell* 1979; 16:481–494.)

terminal a sequence can then be synthesized from the "a'" sequence of the template strand of DNA near the L-S junction (see Figure 2–16). Formation of as many as ten copies of "a" sequence at the terminus of the b-U_L region of progeny DNA requires an amplification process which has not been elucidated.[418]

As a result of the fold-back process used to regenerate terminal "a" sequences, the U_L or U_S regions can invert relative to the prototype isomer to yield three additional isomers (see section on HSV DNA structure). All isomeric forms of HSV DNA are equally infectious. The cis-site, which partially governs the inversion process, is located primarily in the a sequence itself. Deletion of the "a" sequence(s) at the L-S junction, however, does not totally eliminate inversion of U_L, which suggests that the "b" sequence of the inverted repeat also contains cis-acting elements which effect inversion.[419]

Of note is the fact that the BAM H1-L cleavage product, which represents a DNA fragment derived from a region in U_L immediately adjacent to the internal inverted repeat, can be artificially inserted into the HSV genome in a inverted orientation relative to the homologous sequence in its natural location. The DNA flanked by these BAM H1-L sequences can invert during DNA replication indicating the presence of additional cis-acting regions involved in inversion.[420]

Data have also been presented to support recombination mediated by inverted repeats which is independent of concatemer formation during DNA replication. Thus inversion of U_L and U_S may occur by an alternate mechanism.[421]

In addition, it has been demonstrated that cleavage of concatemeric DNA is closely linked to packaging of DNA into newly formed virus particles during maturation. The cleavage of concatemers, inversion of unique sequences U_L and U_S, amplification of "a" sequences, and packaging of DNA seem closely linked.[422] The exact order and control of these events need further study.

The packaging of unit-length DNA requires a signal located within the a sequence which is possibly analogous to or associated with the cis-site for cleavage. This has been demonstrated by investigating defective HSV genomes which are packaged as multiples of tandemly linked smaller DNA segments to equal the length of full-size genomic DNA. The presence of one or more "a" sequences is required for this process.[418]

Several DBPs have been shown to associate with viral DNA during packaging, specifically the "a" sequence based on in vitro studies.[423, 423a] ICP-32, a major nucleocapsid protein, binds to viral DNA and seems to play an important role in maturation. Several polypeptides expressed later during infection and encoded by the U_S 11 gene seem to bind to the "a" sequence directly and may influence its cleavage-packaging capabilities.

Late Transcription

Concomitant with the initiation of viral DNA synthesis, late (γ) transcription begins.[424] Transcripts correspond to genes distributed along the entire length of the genome and far exceed the number of mRNAs transcribed at immediate-early and early times postinfection. γ Transcription can be differentiated into two classes (γ$_1$ and γ$_2$) based on the requirements for transcription. γ$_1$ Transcription does not absolutely require prerequisite DNA synthesis, although γ$_1$ transcripts are found at their highest levels following

DNA replication. On the other hand, γ$_2$ transcription in infected cells requires viral DNA synthesis. Although the differential regulation of γ$_1$ and γ$_2$ transcription has not been fully explained, investigations involving the γ$_1$ gene encoding the major capsid protein, VP$_5$, and the γ$_2$ gene encoding gC have provided information about their regulation.

ICP-4 is an essential trans-acting factor for transcription of γ$_1$-VP$_5$ gene. ICP-0 may augment ICP-4 in its induction of γ genes, whereas ICP-27 may only transactivate certain γ genes. In addition, ICP-22 seems to affect expression of late genes only in certain cell types in culture. Since ICP-4 is present at early times during infection, additional factor(s) must delay ICP-4 transactivation of γ genes until late stages of infection.

The regulatory-promoter region of the γ$_1$-VP$_5$ and other γ$_1$ genes have core promoter and regulatory regions, which can be activated by cellular trans-acting factors and possess sequences similar or identical to those found in corresponding regions for cellular genes.[425, 426] However, a regulatory region located upstream from the promoter negatively regulates the VP$_5$ coding region. Only in the late period is the negative effect of the VP$_5$ regulatory region suppressed. Since ICP-4 is necessary for induction of the VP$_5$ gene, and in general ICP-8 negatively regulates γ genes, the mode of induction of VP$_5$ involves suppression of both the negative control of its regulatory region and the negative effect(s) of ICP-8. Because VP$_5$ is not expressed maximally until DNA synthesis occurs, possibly the altered conformation of newly synthesized DNA also facilitates expression of the VP$_5$ gene.

The gC gene serves as a model for the control of γ$_2$ genes. As is the case for γ$_1$ mRNAs, the transcription of γ$_2$ genes is induced and maintained by ICP-4 in collaboration with other α proteins. ICP-8 also negatively regulates gC expression. A feature which distinguishes γ$_1$ and γ$_2$ expression is the stringent requirement for DNA synthesis needed for γ$_2$ transcription.[427] γ$_1$ Genes, on the other hand, are transcribed only minimally before DNA replication, beginning at approximately two hours postinfection, but transcription greatly increases after DNA synthesis. With the onset of γ$_1$ and/or γ$_2$ expression, β protein synthesis is reduced or terminated. The control of gC, one of the best-studied γ$_2$ genes, apparently does not depend on any unusual cis-elements in its promoter-regulatory region. Sequences in gC promoter seem to be analogous to those controlling cellular genes. The γ$_2$ 42 gene, on the other hand, has a site for the direct binding of ICP-4, which is not a homologue for a site previously demonstrated to bind ICP-4, ATCGTCnnnnYCGRC.[368] Potentially, gC may also have an ICP-4 binding site not related to the known sequence detailed above. Deletions made in both the promoter-regulatory and the coding regions of gC indicated that a sequence between −34 and +124 imparted the ability of the gC gene to be regulated as a γ$_2$ protein. Perhaps the distinguishing feature of γ$_2$ transcriptional control resides in DNA conformations or cis-acting elements within newly replicated viral DNA which are not found in parental DNA.[428]

Virus Assembly

The proteins encoded by the γ genes are primarily structural in nature and include primary translation products, which require modification through glycosylation, phosphorylation, and cleavage. In addition to structural functions, at least two proteins incorporated into virus particles possess regulatory activity; Vmw 65 (TIF), which transactivates α genes, and a virion protein which destabilizes host and viral mRNAs during subsequent infections.

The γ proteins are synthesized maximally between 12 and 15 hours. Formation of progeny virus requires transport of proteins from cytoplasmic sites of translation to the nucleus, the site of viral assembly. As shown by electron microscopy the sequence of maturation includes the formation of empty capsids, insertion of DNA into capsids, and condensation of DNA around core proteins, ICP-32 (a major nucleocapsid protein) being involved in the process.[429] Fully formed capsids are then enveloped by budding through the inner lamellae of the nuclear membrane at sites modified by insertion of viral glycoproteins.

The viral glycoproteins associated with the budding site are synthesized in the ER in a manner analogous to the majority of cell glycoproteins.[430, 431] Hydrophobic signal sequences at the N-terminus allow the membrane polypeptides to translocate across the ER membrane. Following entry into the ER lumen, the signal sequences are removed by cleavage. The polypeptides become stabilized in the membrane as a result of one or more hydrophobic domains, each about 20 amino acids in length, becoming embedded within ER membranes. The C-terminal end remains on the cytoplasmic side and varies in length depending on the specific glycoprotein. Concomitant with transport into the ER lumen, the polypeptide is modified by addition of mannose-rich polysaccharide chains to asparagine residues. These high-mannose glycopolypeptides move laterally through contiguous membranes from the ER to the inner lamellae of the nuclear membrane. Thus, the precursors for gB, gG, gD, gE, and gH localize to specific membrane areas which lack cellular glycoproteins and correspond to HSV budding sites. Viral capsids containing unit-length or near unit-length DNA acquire an envelope, whereas empty capsids fail to bud and remain within the nucleus.

Immature enveloped virus particles migrate to the Golgi apparatus and polysaccharide chains are processed by the removal of several mannose residues. The addition of N-acetylglucosamine-galactose-sialic acid side chains to N-linked mannose chains modifies the glycoprotein to produce a complex type. O-linked carbohydrate chains, usually N-acetylgalactosamine-galactose-sialic acid, and fatty acids may also be added to certain viral glycoproteins in Golgi membranes.[432] Depending on the strain of HSV, viral particles can either migrate from the Golgi apparatus to defined cytoplasmic areas where they accumulate, or egress into the extracellular environment.

Viral glycoproteins are also transported in a multistage process to the cell surface, beginning with their synthesis and partial glycosylation in the ER, their transport to the Golgi apparatus where further modification takes place, and finally their insertion into the plasma membrane. Seven glycoproteins, gB, gC, gD, gE, gG, gH, and gI, have been detected on HSV-1 infected cells. Several ORFs located in the U_s region of viral DNA adjacent to the genes for gD (U_s 6) and gE (U_s 8) have been analyzed. Based on sequence analysis, U_s 4 (probably gG), U_s 5, and U_s 7 (probably gI) encode glycoproteins, but their gene products have not been fully characterized as to structure and function.[313, 433]

Effects on Host Cells

HSV infection alters cell organization at two levels. Changes in intracellular structures as well as in cell interactions have been noted. As already mentioned, cell protein and DNA synthesis are inhibited by viral protein(s). Chromosomes fragment during infection and remnants relocate to the inner surface of the nuclear membrane, thereby clearing the center of the nucleus for viral replication. At a different level, interactions between cells are altered as a result of HSV infections in a manner influenced by viral strain or cell type or both. This is shown by varying degrees of aggregation of rounded cells and cell fusions. Cultured cells infected with variants of HSV often exhibit altered cell-cell associations, with increased clumping or syncytia formation (SYN mutants) relative to wild-type virus-infected cells.[430, 434, 435]

The type of interaction between HSV-infected cells and other infected or uninfected cells is determined in part by the viral glycoproteins expressed on the cell surface. Several gene products may participate in cell fusion: gB, gD, gE, and gH.[307, 430] In addition, gene products encoded by four regions of the genome, SYN 1, 2, 3, and 4, influence syncytia formation (see Figure 2–15). Although SYN 3 and the gene for gB overlap, they are distinct entities.[436] Antibodies specific to gD, gH, and gE block fusion of infected cells, but gB-directed antibodies do not. On the other hand, temperature-sensitive mutants in gB show it to be essential in cell fusion, as well as viral penetration.[437] gB seems to have a crucial role in cell fusion since gC, gE, gG, and gI are not essential for either viral infectivity or cell-to-cell fusion.[438]

gB has also been intensively investigated for its antigenic characteristics and the immune responses it elicits in vivo. Analysis of the protein (amino acid sequence) and the type and extent of glycosylation has indicated that a change in either can effect the nature and function of the molecule. Mutations in the gB gene, which primarily change the amino acid sequence and secondarily affect its overall configuration, affect the rate of viral entry or penetration during initial stages of infection, the susceptibility or resistance to neutralizing monoclonal antibodies,[333] and the formation of syncytia.[437] Deletion of the C-terminal end of gB, which corresponds to its transmembrane and long cytoplasmic domains, prevents gB association with membranes and eliminates its cell fusion activity. Truncated forms such as these, however, maintain their ability to form dimers as seen for native gB.[439, 440] The carbohydrate chains of gB influence the conformation of the final product as well as the processing and transport of gB from the ER to cell surfaces. Inhibition of N-linked glycosylation of gB by tunicamycin treatment of infected cells prevents its transport from the ER to the Golgi apparatus and interferes with formation of infectious, enveloped virus particles.[430] Virus particles with immature glycoproteins remain cell-associated.[441]

gC, a γ_2 protein, is not essential for replication of HSV in cultured cells, but clinical isolates of HSV-1 synthesize the protein, which suggests a role for gC in vivo. In HSV-1-infected cells, gC serves as a receptor for the third component of complement, C3b.[442] Following translation in the RER, gC is glycosylated in the lumen of the ER and in the Golgi apparatus. During the latter stage of glycosylation, sialic acid is added as a terminal moiety to carbohydrate chains. Treatment of HSV-1-infected cells or virus particles with neuramindase removes sialic acid, concomitantly increasing complement receptor activity.[443] In addition, monoclonal antibodies directed against gC inhibit C3b receptor activity.[444] Factors also affecting C3b receptor activity include the strain of HSV-1 as well as the host cells used to propagate virus. The latter characteristic resides with the specific glycosylation enzymes present in different cell lines, which produce variable N-linked glycosylation patterns.[443] O-linked glycosylation has also been demonstrated for gC.[445] It should be noted that HSV-2, although possessing a protein similar to gC-1, does not bind C3b.

HSV-infected cells, as well as virus particles, display receptors for the Fc portion of IgG on their surface.[446] Some specificity for human IgG subclasses has been demonstrated, IgG4 binds strongly and IgG3 does not bind at all.[447] The protein responsible for IgG binding is gE, a viral glycoprotein nonessential for HSV replication in cultured cells. gE is encoded by gene U_s 8 and is found in several molecular weight forms differing in the extent of glycosylation. In the case of HSV-1, gE apparently does not act alone in binding IgG and requires a second glycoprotein, g70 or gI, to form an active complex.[448, 449] Mutations in either the gE or gI (U_s 7) gene prevent IgG binding.

Although gC and gE-gI seem nonessential for viral replication they may act in vivo to diminish immune recognition or immune cytolysis of infected cells. Binding of C3b to the cell surface possibly prevents complement-mediated cell lysis, whereas binding of IgG through the Fc segment to the cell surface may block HSV-specific antibodies from binding to and killing infected cells.

Glycoprotein D is also found on infected cell surfaces and virus particles. As stated previously, gD is necessary for attachment of virus particles to cell receptors and participates in virus-cell fusion, which can be blocked by neutralizing monoclonal antibodies. gD appears to be highly immunogenic in mice; gD protein alone induces antibodies, which protect mice from virus challenge.[450] Passive administration of monoclonal antibodies (MAB) directed against gD is also protective.[451]

Of the major viral glycoproteins, gB, gD, and gE are considered γ_1 proteins, whereas gC is a γ_2. Their time and order of synthesis, however, does not necessarily reflect their appearance on cell surfaces. For example, gC and gD appear on plasma membranes of certain murine and human cell lines at approximately the same time. On the other hand, gC appears on cell surfaces later then gD in simian cells. An explanation for these cell-specific variations may be that glycoproteins are processed at different rates in cells from different species.[452] Although HSV glycoproteins are expressed on cell surfaces with variable kinetics, they all are transported preferentially to the basolateral membranes of infected, polarized epithelial cells.[453]

Latent Infections

Although cells productively infected by HSV have been investigated in detail, latent infections of animals and humans have not been as well characterized.[454] Neurons in both the peripheral (PNS) and central nervous systems (CNS) can be latently infected with HSV. In addition, small numbers of nonneuronal cells, glial cells in the CNS and satellite cells in the PNS, are possibly latently infected.[455] Once latent infections have been established in neurons of the CNS and PNS, productive replication can be reactivated consistently from the PNS, but rarely or not at all from the CNS. During latent infections HSV DNA can be detected at low levels— 0.15 ot 0.015 genome equivalents per cell.[456] Thus, only a small portion of the total number of neurons are apparently latently infected. The viral DNA exists in single-circular or concatemeric episomes within cell nuclei; linear molecules are seldom detected in neurons.[456] The distinguishing characteristic of latent infections is that most viral genes are not transcribed. Initial investigations indicated that ICP-4 genes were transcribed at low levels, but this finding was not routinely confirmed.[457] Recently, latency-associated transcripts (LATs) which map to the ICP-0 gene were found in the CNS of mice.[458, 459] They are not extensively polyadenylated and apparently are not translated into proteins. Whereas LATs are found at relatively high levels in latently infected cells, they are found only at low levels during productive infection. LATs are apparently transcribed from the DNA strand complementary to that used for transcription of ICP-0 mRNAs. One possible mode of action of LATs is that they bind directly to ICP-0 mRNAs to form a double-stranded RNA complex which inhibits ICP-0 translation. The formation of LATs may not be the only mechanism for establishment of latency, since mutations in the LAT regulatory-promoter region do not prevent latency.[460]

POXVIRUSES

Virus Structure

Poxviridae consists of large viruses with dimensions of 250 to 390 nm × 200 to 250 nm. Vaccinia virus is the prototype virus, having been investigated in most detail at the molecular level.[461, 462] Vaccinia virus, as well as other poxviruses, has a complex capsid composed of several substructures: a core, lateral bodies, and a lipid envelope[463] (see Figure 2–17). The centrally located, biconcave core contains the genome and from 13 to over 21 proteins, as determined by SDS-PAGE or two-dimensional electrophoresis[464, 465] A number of core proteins function enzymatically during infection. Within the indentations of the virus core are located oval structures called lateral bodies which have not been well characterized for protein composition or function. Virus particles present within infected cells have an envelope that completely surrounds internal structures and consists of lipids and at least two and as many as 14 viral glycoproteins,[464, 467] the latter proteins being closely related in their electrophoretic mobility. Morphologically, the virus particles have parallel arrays of globular structures (surface tubular elements, STE) on their outermost surface. The 1% to 10% of virus progeny that leave infected cells and are found as extracellular particles have an additional membrane enclosing the entire particle.[470] As a result, extracellular viruses contain several surface proteins not seen on their intracellular counterparts; these include at least nine glycoproteins,[471, 472] one of which is a virus-coded hemagglutinin.[473, 474] These glycoproteins may account for antigenic differences between extra- and intracellular particles.[475, 476]

The nucleic acid housed in the viral core is a large linear double-stranded DNA molecule ($120 × 10^6$ daltons, approximately 185 kb),[477, 478] which is covalently linked at its termini.[479, 480] A DNA genome of this size has a theoretical coding capacity of approximately 200 to 300[481] proteins, although between 84 and 111 viral polypeptides have been resolved by gel electrophoresis from mature viruses and approximately 280 from vaccinia virus-infected cells.[482]

Each DNA terminus consists of a terminal inverted repeat (TIR) of over 10,000 base pairs in length.[483, 484] This region has been sequenced for the genomes of several poxviruses, including VV

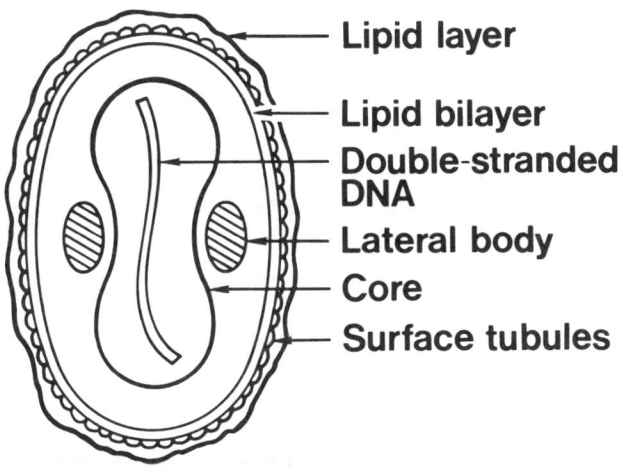

Figure 2–17. Diagram of extracellular vaccinia virus. Shown are the outer layer derived from cell membranes and found in extracellular but not intracellular virus, and three viral substructures: lipid bilayer (envelope), lateral bodies, and core. Linear double-stranded DNA is shown within the core.

and Shopes fibroma virus (SFV).[485] There are several features of TIRs that are conserved and may therefore play a crucial role in initiation of DNA synthesis, formation of virosomes (cytoplasmic structures involved in DNA replication), or packaging of DNA into newly formed virus particles.[486] Specific regions of the TIRs are also readily deleted or transposed, which may effect the host range, virulence, or cytopathogenicity of poxviruses.[487–489] The gene products responsible for these properties have not been characterized. In the case of VV a portion of the TIR contains at least four genes, whereas 12 ORFs have been detected in the TIR of SFV.

The terminal region of the TIR of VV is divided into different domains based on overall sequence composition (Figure 2–18). The most terminal base-paired sequence is an AT-rich, imperfect palindrome (in the form of a hairpin loop structure) having its axis of symmetry at the covalent cross-link between the two strands of DNA. Within this region several bases are unpaired to allow for proper alignment and base pairing between complementary DNA strands.[490] This same region can exist in two orientations; one is inverted relative to the other. Several domains have been defined within the region adjacent to the AT-rich, imperfect palindrome, which are designated domains I, II, III, and IIIa in order of increasing distances from the terminus (see Figure 2–18).[491] They are 11, 13, 17, and 15 base pairs in length, respectively, and consist of sequences conserved among various isolates. A 10-base pair perfect palindrome is found primarily in domain III with partial overlap into the IIIa domain.

An 87-nucleotide sequence which includes domain I through domain IIIa separates the AT-rich region from two sets of tandemly repeated sequences; the first set consists of a 70-nucleotide sequence which is repeated approximately 13 times and the second set consists of a 70-nucleotide sequence repeated approximately 18 times. The two sets of tandemly repeated sequences are separated by a 325-base pair segment.[490] Approximately 600 base pairs exist between the ends of the most internal tandem repeat

and a transcriptionally active region of the TIR. Vaccinia virus isolates vary in the exact number of tandem repeats in the TIR which contributes to the variability of the overall lengths of TIRs.[492] The TIRs located at the right and left termini of a DNA molecule have the same sequence composition. The remaining region of VV DNA (90%) is sandwiched between TIRs and is composed of unique sequences. Genes encoding known proteins and ORFs with coding potential are distributed within the unique region and within TIRs.[493–496] A particular DNA region can be utilized for maximal transcription by employing both DNA strands as templates or by tight clustering of genes in overlapping arrangements.

Data suggest that viral DNA in association with basic proteins and polyamines form condensed units of DNA interspersed with relaxed regions, similar to nucleosomes found in eukaryotic DNA.[497] Possibly, the basic proteins neutralize the negative charges on the DNA, thereby allowing these globular structures to form.

Attachment, Penetration, Uncoating

Poxvirus infection begins with the attachment of virus particles to cell membranes through a viral protein-cell receptor linkage. Viral hemagglutinin present on extracellular virus particles seems to facilitate attachment and/or penetration, since extracellular particles more readily enter cells than do viral particles without the out membrane.[498]

In addition to the hemagglutinin protein, several other viral envelope proteins have been implicated in mediating viral entry into host cells. Attachment of VV to specific receptors and viral penetration can be distinguished by using specific neutralizing antibodies to viral proteins. Vaccinia virus primarily binds to receptors for epidermal growth factor, but other receptor molecules also exist.[499] Attachment and penetration are mediated by a 54-kd viral protein, which forms surface tubules of virus particles.[500] A 37-kd viral envelope protein has also been implicated in penetration by mediating viral envelope-plasma membrane fusion.[501] Although the latter protein does not appear to be a glycoprotein, it has several characteristics of a membrane protein, including hydrophobic sequences, acylation by palmitic acid, and associations with Golgi membranes.[502] Substantial data also support the role of a 14-kd protein, which forms a trimer on cell surfaces, in mediating VV-cell fusion as well as fusion of infected cells.[503, 504] Other biologic properties associated with the 14-kd protein include antigenic determinants for neutralizing antibodies and functions effecting plaque

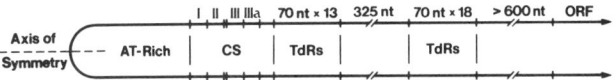

Figure 2–18. Hairpin loop formed during vaccinia virus (VV) replication (see Fig 2–19,b, step 3) and sequence composition of the terminal inverted repeats (TIR) of VV-DNA. The terminal AT-rich palindrome possesses an axis of symmetry at its covalently linked end. Conserved sequences (CS) are designed by domains I, II, III, and IIIa. Two sets of tandem repeats (TdRs) are separated by 325 nucleotides. Approximately 600 nucleotides are located between the last of the TdRs and the first open reading frame (ORF) within the TIR.[490, 491]

size. In combination with products from "virulence" gene(s) located at the left end of the VV genome, 14-kd protein also determines viral cytopathogenicity.[487, 488, 505] Specific neutralizing monoclonal antibodies directed against epitopes on the 14-kd protein do not block attachment of the virus to receptors,[506, 507] but are capable of blocking fusion during penetration, which suggests that attachment and penetration result from different proteins (see below).

Five additional viral envelope proteins having molecular weights of 54 kd, 34 kd, 32 kd, 29 kd, and 17 to 25 kd have been isolated and seem to be involved in adsorption and/or penetration.[506] Specific monoclonal antibodies reactive with each of these proteins neutralized viral infectivity. In addition, VVs treated with proteolytic enzymes display enhanced infectivity through more efficient penetration, which correlated with configurational changes in envelope proteins, VP 54 kd and VP 17 to 25 kd. This treatment also facilitated interactions between neutralizing antibody and specific epitopes.

Penetration at the plasma membrane may occur by either viropexis or fusion.[508, 509, 510] In the former process virus particles are engulfed in vacuoles which then associate with lysosomes. Lysosomal enzymes strip away envelopes and lateral bodies to yield cores which lose their indentations and become distended. During penetration by fusion, the outer envelopes of virus particles coalesce with the plasma membrane, thereby releasing distended cores minus lateral bodies into the cytoplasm.

Early Transcription

The site of viral replication of poxviruses is in the cell cytoplasm, a characteristic that distinguishes them from most other DNA viruses.[511] In order for replication to occur without the aid of nuclear enzymes, poxviruses have an array of enzymes within viral cores. In addition, the large amount of viral DNA is sufficient to code for enzymes required at different phases of replication. After the first stage of uncoating, the enzymes of distended cores are activated and mediate controlled transcription from parental DNA.[512, 513] Messenger RNAs produced within viral cores share many characteristics with those from eukaryotic cells, and therefore transcription requires certain enzymatic activities with functions similar to their eukaryotic counterparts. A DNA-dependent RNA polymerase,[514, 515] enzymes necessary for CAP addition to 5′ termini of messengers (including guanylyltransferase, 2-guanine-7-methyltransferase, and a ribose-2-methyltransferase),[516, 517] poly(A) polymerase for adenosine addition to 3′ termini,[518, 519, 520] and other enzymes listed in Table 2–3 are located in viral cores.

RNAs initially transcribed within cores serve as precursors to messengers and are shortened by removal of a 3′ RNA segment by an adenosine triphosphate (ATP)-requiring endoribonuclease.[521–523] The 5′ terminus is capped, poly(A) is added at the 3′ end, and fully modified messenger, which has been designated immediate-early mRNA, is extruded from cores into the cytoplasm.

Eight immediate-early mRNAs are transcribed from a specific region adjacent to the inverted terminal repetitions[524, 525] but are apparently nonessential for virus replication.[526] Poxvirus variants lacking these sequences replicate as well as the wild type in tissue culture. Several proteins having known functions are translated

Table 2–3
Core Enzymes of Vaccinia Virus

DNA-dependent RNA polymerase
Guanylytransferase
mRNA transmethylases
Poly (A) polymerase
Topoisomerase
Two single-stranded specific DNases
Protein kinase
Two nucleic acid–dependent phosphohydrolases

from this class of messengers. One protein further uncoats viral DNA, releasing it into the cytoplasm. Thymidine kinase, another immediate-early protein,[527] is not essential for viral replication, since TK-mutant virus replicates by utilizing the corresponding cellular enzyme.[528] Early during infections, normal cell metabolic activities rapidly decline, apparently without expression of the viral genome. One report suggests that the protein constituting surface tubules on virus particles alone can inhibit cell protein synthesis,[529] which in turn inhibits other synthetic events. Also, newly synthesized host cell DNA may be degraded by viral nucleases. In this context cell macromolecules and their synthetic processes are redirected for viral replication.

During the next stage of infection, uncoated DNA is transcribed into delayed-early mRNAs. Several proteins translated from these messengers are essential for DNA replication, while others are core structural proteins[532, 533] or have unknown functions. DNA-dependent DNA polymerase, a subunit of ribonucleotide reductase,[534–536] polynucleotide ligase,[537] and two DNAses with different pH optima for their activities[538, 539] have been detected at this stage in infected cells and fulfill roles in DNA synthesis.

An early gene of VV which maps within the TIR encodes a 19-kd vaccinia growth factor (VGF) that is seemingly nonessential for viral growth in tissue culture, but which determines virulence in animals.[540–543] VGF is partially homologous in amino acid sequence to epidermal growth factor (EGF) and transforming growth factor (TGF), as well as to proteins involved in blood coagulation.[544] Vaccinia growth factor is capable of binding to cell surface receptors for EGF, thereby mitogenically stimulating cells and inducing phosphorylation of EGF receptors.[545] VGF is synthesized as a precursor polypeptide 140 amino acids in length. Hydrophobic amino acid sequences at the N-terminus and near the C-terminal end suggest that the precursor of VGF has characteristics of membrane proteins, signal and transmembrane regions. The precursor to VGF also acquires N-linked carbohydrate chains in a manner analogous to other glycoproteins. The high-mannose chains are added to the primary gene product of 19 K, which converts it to a 22-kd glycoprotein. Further modification by complex carbohydrate chain formation produces a 25-kd glycoprotein, which is proteolytically cleaved to yield a 22-kd product. This last polypeptide lacks the original signal and transmembrane sequences and is found in a soluble form in the extracellular environment.[542, 546]

One possible role of VGF and similar growth factors encoded by other poxviruses is mitogenic stimulation of quiescent cells. VGF-induced cell proliferation may make cells more susceptibile to viral infection, possibly facilitating cell-cell spread of virus particles.[543]

The regulation of early transcription is controlled in part by promoters that are relatively short, about 20 to 30 base pairs, which differ from promoters that control transcription in other DNA viruses and eukaryotic cells.[547] Overall, these regions are AT-rich, but lack TATA and CAAT consensus sequences. Instead, a consensus sequence, TAAATG, is found immediately upstream of many late genes, as well as at the transcriptional start sites of a few early genes.[548, 549] Approximately 30 nucleotides upstream from the TAAATG site are required for efficient transcription.[550–552] In addition, the ATG sequence within TAAATG is the initiation site (AUG) for translation from these mRNAs.[548]

Early and late viral mRNAs are not generated from primary transcripts by splicing, and possess cap structures at their 5′ ends and poly(A) tails at their 3′ termini.[553] The 5′ regions of most early mRNAs are untranslated leader sequences. Early mRNAs average approximately 1500 nucleotides in length and each RNA species has a defined length as a result of precise transcriptional termination following a TTTTTNT consensus sequence (N = any nucleotide).[554–556]

DNA Replication

DNA synthesis begins at approximately 1.5 hours after infection and peaks between 2.0 and 2.5 hours. Viral DNA, in association with phosphorylated viral proteins, forms defined structures (virosomes)[557–559] that are located in areas of the cytoplasm devoid of normal cell organelles.[560] Viral DNA polymerase as well as a 90 kd and possibly a 30 kd protein must be continually synthesized for DNA synthesis to occur.[560a, 560b]

The mechanism of poxvirus DNA synthesis has not been fully characterized, but two models have been proposed based on experimental observations of structural features of viral DNA and the types of replicative intermediates found in infected cells.[561, 562]

In one model described by Esteban et al[561] (Figure 2–19a), DNA synthesis is initiated at one terminus from RNA primers, the latter possibly being formed by a viral DNA-dependent RNA polymerase. Discontinuous DNA synthesis gives rise to several segments of DNA that are ligated following removal of the primers. DNA synthesis proceeds until both parental strands are replicated. Terminal nicking of the replicative intermediate yields two double-stranded DNA molecules cross-linked to form completed progeny genomes. Since one terminal sequence of both strands in incomplete, each must be resynthesized using the complete terminus on the opposite strand as a primer and template (see Figure 2–19a). Ligation at the terminus results in full-length DNA cross-linked at both ends.

In a second model detailed by Moyer and Graves[562] (Figure 2–19b), site-specific endonucleolytic cleavage of a single DNA strand occurs within the terminal-inverted repetition with subsequent unfolding of the strands at that location.[563] The longer terminal sequence (L) serves as a template for elongation of the terminal sequence of the opposite strand (L′). DNA synthesis continues when the sequence BA at the terminus of L′ folds back and base-pairs with internal sequence A′B′. This hairpin structure serves as a primer for nascent synthesis of DNA and, as a synthesis proceeds, the two strands of parental DNA are displaced (LR and L′R′). After both LR and L′R′ strands are copied, further fold-back synthesis can occur using de novo strands as templates (Figure 2–19b,4). Concatemers formed by this process are cleaved into

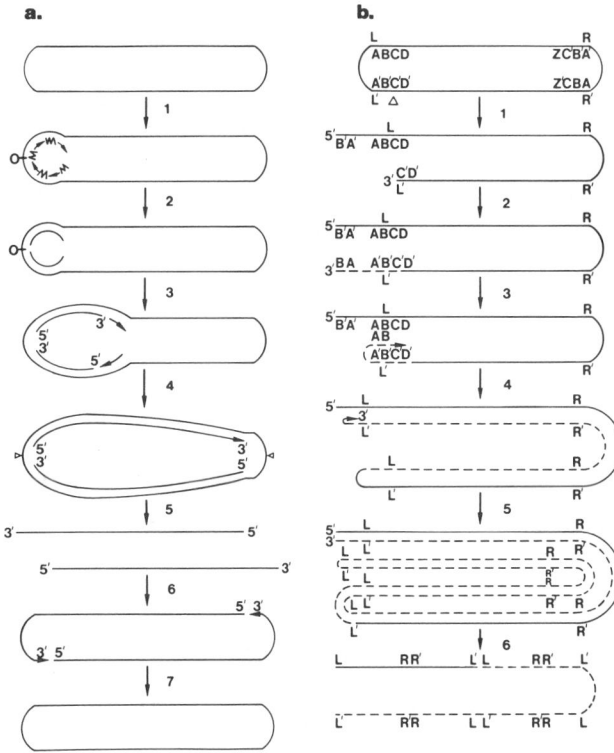

Figure 2–19. Two models for replication of poxvirus DNA.

a, parental DNA, cross-linked at its termini, acts as a template for RNA (〜)-primed DNA synthesis (- - -), which begins at one terminus (1). Primer RNA is removed and the DNA segments are ligated (2). Parental DNA strands continue to unwind and DNA synthesis progresses (3) until the opposite end is reached (4). A single-strand nick (open triangle) at both ends of parental DNA yield two linear duplexes, one of which is shown at step 5. Termini are cross-linked by the formation of fold-back structures (6) which serve as a primer for gap-fill DNA synthesis (7). (Adapted with permission from Esteban M, et al: Model for vaccinia virus DNA replication. *Virology* 1977; 83:467–473.)

b, DNA replication may also occur through the formation of concatemers. Initially, one end of the DNA duplex is nicked between the terminal repeated sequences (B′C′) which allows unfolding of the left terminus (1). Using region B′A′AB as a template and sequence C′ as a primer, DNA synthesis (dashed lines) begins (2) and continues after sequences BA fold back upon sequences A′B′ (3). Both strands of parental DNA, L′R′ and RL, are copied (4) to form progeny DNA LR and R′L′, respectively. Again, DNA synthesis continues as the nascent strand folds back upon the completed progeny DNA, L′R′ (4), and uses it as a template. This process continues (5) and a large concatemer forms which consists of two unit-length regions corresponding to parental DNA (solid line) plus five unit lengths of progeny DNA (6). A concatemer is then cleaved into DNA duplexes. (Adapted with permission from Moyer RW, Graves RL: The mechanism of cytoplasmic orthopoxvirus DNA replication. *Cell* 1981; 27:391–401.)

unit-length, double-stranded DNAs which are then incorporated into virus particles.

DNA of poxviruses recombines at high frequencies within the cytoplasm of infected cells.[564] The uninfected-cell cytoplasm is most likely devoid of cellular enzymes which facilitate recombination events like those occurring in the nucleus. Thus it is feasible that poxviruses encode enzymes necessary for recombination. Plasmids introduced into poxvirus-infected cells readily undergo both intra- and intermolecular recombination forming concatameric products as a result, which supports the concept of poxvirus-mediated recombination. Recombination frequencies among different poxviruses vary; VV exhibits 5 times lower levels than SFV. Although recombination and viral DNA replication occur at about the same time during viral replication, the two are separate events.[565]

Late Transcription

Following initiation of DNA synthesis, late mRNAs are transcribed from newly synthesized DNA and subsequently translated into late proteins, the majority of which are structural.[566] Several core enzymes and proteins that regulate translation of early messengers are also synthesized at this time.

Transcription of most late mRNAs is promoted by a short region of DNA approximately 36 base pairs in length which contains the transcriptional start site, TAAATG.[548] Late transcription can occur from opposite strands of DNA as evidenced by annealing between mRNAs to form double-stranded structures.[567] Unlike early mRNAs which have defined sizes, the length of a given species of late mRNA is heterogeneous.[568, 569] This results from the lack of definitive termination signals which enables transcription to proceed into overlapping early genes at adjacent downstream locations. This fact may account for the presence of early transcripts during late times of infection.[569] The RNA polymerase apparently fails to recognize early termination signals at late times, which results in the formation of late mRNAs about twice the size of early ones.[570]

In addition, transcription of genes located in TIRs that encode 7.5-kd proteins employs alternative initiation sites at early and late times during infection. These sites are separated by 55 nucleotides; the one proximal to the coding region is employed early, whereas a distal sequence initiates transcription late. The 5′ end of this late mRNA is formed by transcription from DNA sequences immediately downstream of the actual promoter.[550]

In the case of a late gene encoding an 11-kd polypeptide, the 5′ noncoding leader sequence of its mRNA is composed of an RNA sequence noncontiguous with the coding portions of the transcript. The 5′ leader region is transcribed from genomic DNA at a site separate from the actual 11-kd gene itself and is coupled together though an internal poly(A) linker to form a chimeric mRNA.[571, 572, 572a] Similar transplicing events have been reported for other systems.[573]

As stated previously, cis-sequences comparable to those found in promoter-regulatory regions of eukaryotic genes are not found in most regulatory regions of VV genes. However, in the case of a particular cluster of late genes, which are tightly packed in a tandem orientation in the highly conserved Hind III D fragment of VV DNA, sequences further upstream than the TAAATG sequence play a role in regulation (see below). Cis-elements of several VV genes are similar to eukaryotic regulatory signals.[574] Each gene of this cluster is independently regulated via its own promoter, which suggests a complex system of transcriptional controls.[575]

It should be noted that transcription of the three classes of mRNAs, immediate-early, delayed-early, and late, is strictly regulated during infection and only 50% to 80% of the genome is transcribed at early times, while 100% is transcribed late.[576-578] When the relative amounts of specific messengers are quantitated, however, differences in abundance are recognized. For example, certain genes transcribed repeatedly at early times are transcribed in decreased amounts at late times.[579]

Therefore transcriptional controls determine the levels of gene expression at different times during infection. Vaccinia virus DNA-dependent RNA polymerase, which exists as part of a complex with nucleoside triphosphate phosphohydrolase I (DNA-dependent adenosine triphosphatase [ATPase]) and capping enzymes,[580] may control transcription. The VV RNA polymerase differs from its eukaryotic cell counterpart in chromatographic and electrophoretic properties as well as in its sensitivity to the drug amanitin.[581, 582] Possibly, VV RNA polymerase exists in two forms, one at early and the other at late times, since it recognizes transcription termination signals early during infection yet transcribes through them at late times. This concept is supported by investigations of a VV gene encoding a 33-kd polypeptide which is expressed at both early and late times. Early, the RNA polymerase ceases transcription at a termination signal, whereas at late times it fails to recognize it.[583]

Over 100 early and late genes have been mapped on the genome and are distributed throughout the length of the DNA. However, gene clusters have been mapped to conserved regions of the genome. Gene clusters transcribed at late times do not seem to be coordinately controlled, suggesting that individual genes have their own promoters that are responsive to specific regulatory signals for transcription.[583, 583a] The control of both early and late gene transcription has recently been investigated using the Hind III D fragment from VV DNA. This 16-kb fragment is capable of encoding 13 gene products, six of which are expressed early, one at early and late times and six only at late times. The cis-elements governing the expression of genes within this cluster were investigated relative to their organization and their ability to control transcriptional initiation and termination.[569]

Genes within the cluster are so tightly packed that the transcriptional regulatory regions of one gene overlap into coding regions of adjacent genes. Furthermore, termination sites of genes are located in adjacent genes. Thus regulatory mechanisms must have evolved to allow a termination signal for an early gene to reside in the coding region of an adjacent late gene without interfering with the late expression. Some overlapping genes are transcribed from complementary strands in either convergent or divergent manners. In the case of complementary RNAs transcribed in a convergent orientation at the same time during infection, it would be expected that they would associate to form double-stranded RNA molecules, thereby reducing their ability to be translated. Since this does not appear to be the case, a mechanism must exist which allows each mRNA to be translated before this RNA-RNA association can occur.[569, 575]

Translational control also has been demonstrated for some early mRNAs that have long half-lives and remain within infected cells during the late period. These early mRNAs obtained from cells at late times can be translated in vitro, yet their translation is inhibited within infected cells, probably as a result of either delayed-early[584] or late proteins.[527, 585-587]

Virus Assembly

Morphogenesis proceeds as an ordered sequence of events. Beginning at approximately three hours after infection, envelopes are formed de novo by the combination of lipids with viral proteins and appear by electron microscopy as arcs coated with projections or spicules.[588] Spicules essentially act as a framework and help determine the dimensions of virus particles. Lipids present in poxvirus envelopes may represent either cell lipids modified by virus infection or those derived from membranous structures other than the plasma membrane. This differs from other enveloped viruses that have lipid compositions similar to that of the plasma membrane. For example, a major phospholipid in poxvirus envelopes is found predominantly in membranes of lysosomes, but not significantly in plasma membranes.[589] Replicated DNA and a number of viral proteins are then incorporated into immature particles before envelopment is completed.

Conformational rearrangements of DNA and proteins yield an internal core structure, plus lateral bodies. A critical process during this stage is proteolytic cleavage of several precursor proteins to form core structural proteins. Short-lived viral proteases that are apparently incorporated into viral particles are responsible for this cleavage.[590, 591]

The outer surface of the viral envelope also changes with the replacement of spicules by surface tubular elements. The latter are arranged in parallel ridges over the smooth surface of the lipid bilayer and consist of a single polypeptide (mol wt 58,000).[592, 593] Antibodies directed against STE polypeptide neutralize virus infectivity and inhibit cell fusion.[500]

A small percentage of intracellular virus particles gain an additional outer membrane by budding through membranes of Golgi bodies en route to the extracellular environment.[594]

These doubly membranate particles migrate to the cell surface where fusion occurs between the cell-derived membrane of virus particles and plasma membranes. Enveloped extracellular virus (EEV) particles formed by this process have two envelopes: (1) the inner layer of the Golgi membrane bilayer (the outer layer is removed by fusion), and (2) the viral membrane that immediately surrounds the lateral bodies and core.

As mentioned previously, viral hemagglutinin is present on EEV particles. Variants have been isolated that are incapable of synthesizing the intact hemagglutinin but do code for a related, smaller glycoprotein containing less carbohydrate.[595] Cells infected with hemagglutination-negative (HA⁻) variants express the smaller glycoprotein on their cell surfaces and gain the property of enhanced cell fusion, which may aid the intercellular spread of virus particles.[473, 475, 595]

During vaccinia virus infection, alterations in cell morphology occur, resulting partially from the termination of normal cell metabolism. Late in the infectious cycle, microvilli are formed at the cell surfaces with microfilaments located in their center. Formation of microvilli requires late viral event(s) associated with maturation of virus particles.[596] Another morphologically distinct change associated with poxvirus replication is the production of cytoplasmic inclusion bodies that correspond to accumulation of maturing virus particles and sites of viral DNA synthesis.[597]

Acknowledgments

I greatly appreciate the excellent secretarial assistance provided by Ms Pamela McClung and the literature searches conducted by Mrs Constance Berk. The understanding and encouragement of Sandy and Cindy Fenger during the preparation of these manuscripts greatly helped me maintain my outlook on life.

REFERENCES

1. Gray CP, Kaerner HC: Sequence of the putative origin of replication in the UL region of herpes simplex virus type 1 ANG DNA. *J Gen Virol* 1984; 65:2109–2119.
2. Stow N, McMonagle EC: Characterization of the TRs/IRs origin of DNA replication of herpes simplex virus type. *Virology* 1983; 130:427–438.
3. Rekosh DMK, Russell WC, Bellett AJD, et al: Identification of a protein linked to the ends of adenovirus DNA. *Cell* 1977; 11:283–295.
4. Wides RJ, Challberg MD, Rawlins DR, et al: Adenovirus origin of DNA replication: Sequence requirements for replication in vitro. *Mol Cell Biol* 1987; 7:864–874.
5. Tattersall P, Ward DC: Rolling hairpin model for replication of parvovirus and linear chromosomal DNA. *Nature* 1976; 263:106–109.
6. Geshelin P, Berns KI: Characterization and localization of the naturally occurring crosslinks in vaccinia virus DNA. *J Mol Biol* 1974; 88:785–796.
7. Blackburn EH: Telomers: Do the ends justify the means? *Cell* 1984; 37:7–8.
8. Li JJ, Kelly TJ: Simian virus 40 DNA replication in vitro. *Proc Natl Acad Sci USA* 1984; 81:6973–6977.
9. Elias P, Lehman IR: Interaction of origin binding protein with an origin of replication of herpes simplex virus 1. *Proc Natl Acad Sci USA* 1988; 85:2959–2963.
10. Gao M, Bouchey J, Curtin K, et al: Genetic identification of a portion of the herpes simplex virus ICP8 protein required for DNA-binding. *Virology* 1988; 163:319–329.
11. Shenk T: Transcriptional control regions: Nucleotide sequence requirements for initiation by RNA polymerase II and III. *Curr Top Microbiol Immunol* 1981; 93:25–46.
12. Khoury G, Gruss P: Enhancer elements. *Cell* 1983; 33:313–314.
13. Sollner-Webb B: Surprises in polymerase III transcription. *Cell* 1988; 52:153–154.
13a. Saltzman AG, Weinmann R: Promoter specificity and modulation of RNA polymerase II transcription. *FASEB J* 1989; 3:1723–1733.
14. Mitchell P, Tijan R: Transcriptional regulation in mammalian cells by sequence-specific DNA binding proteins. *Science* 1989; 245:371–378.
15. Johnson PF, McKnight SL: Eukaryotic transcriptional regulatory proteins. *Annu Rev Biochem* 1989; 58:799–839.
16. Landschulz WH, Johnson PF, McKnight SL: The leucine zipper: A hypothetical structure common to a new class of DNA binding proteins. *Science* 1988; 240:1759–1764.
17. De Pamphilis ML: Transcriptional elements as components of eukaryotic origins of DNA replication. *Cell* 1988; 52:635–638.
18. Lee-Chen G-J, Niles EG: Transcription and translation mapping of the 13 genes in the vaccinia virus Hind III D fragment. *Virology* 1988; 163:52–63.
19. Rohrmann G, Yuen L, Moss B: Transcription of vaccinia virus early genes by enzymes isolated from vaccinia virions terminates downstream of a regulatory sequence. *Cell* 1986; 46:1029–1035.
20. Cozzarelli NR, Gerrard SP, Schlissel M, et al: Purified RNA polymerase III accurately and efficiently terminates transcription of 5S RNA genes. *Cell* 1983; 34:829–835.

21. Leff SE, Rosenfeld MG, Evans RM: Complex transcriptional units: Diversity in gene expression by alternative RNA processing. *Ann Rev Biochem* 1986; 55:1091–1117.

22. Salditt-Georgieff M, Harpold M, Chen-Kiang S, et al: The addition of 5′ cap structures occurs early in hnRNA synthesis and prematurely terminated molecules are capped. *Cell* 1980; 19:69–78.

23. Schwer B, Visca P, Vos JC, et al: Discontinuous transcription or RNA processing of vaccinia virus late messengers results in a 5′ poly (A) leader. *Cell* 1987; 50:163–169.

24. Kruger K, Grabowski PJ, Zaug AJ, et al: Self splicing RNA: Autoexcision and autocyclization of ribosomal RNA intervening sequence of *Tetrahymena. Cell* 1982; 31:147–157.

25. Schatz G: A common mechanism for different membrane systems? *Nature* 1986; 321:108–109.

26. Dingwall C, Laskey RA: Protein import into the cell nucleus. *Ann Rev Cell Biol* 1986; 2:367–390.

27. Nermut V: The architecture of adenoviruses, in Ginsberg HS (ed.): *The Adenoviruses.* New York, Plenum, 1984, pp 6–34.

28. Norrby E: The relationship between the soluble antigens and the virion of adenovirus type 3: I. Morphological characteristics. *Virology* 1966; 28:236–248.

29. Valentine RC, Pereira HG: Antigens and structure of the adenovirus. *J Mol Biol* 1965; 13:13–20.

30. Pettersson U, Philipson L, Hoglund S: Structural proteins of adenoviruses: I. Purification and characterization of the adenovirus type 2 hexon antigen. *Virology* 1967; 33:575–590.

31. Norrby E, Marusyk H, Hammarskjold ML: The relationship between the soluble antigens and the virion of adenovirus type 3. V. Identification of antigen specificities available at the surface of virions. *Virology* 1969; 38:477–482.

32. Pettersson U: Structural proteins of adenoviruses: VI. On the antigenic determinants of the hexon. *Virology* 1971; 43:123–136.

33. Norrby E: The relationship between soluble antigens and the virion of adenovirus type 3. IV. Immunological characteristics. *Virology* 1969; 37:565–576.

34. Pettersson U, Hoglund S: Structural proteins of adenoviruses. III. Purification and characterization of the adenovirus type 2 penton antigen. *Virology* 1969; 39:90–106.

35. Pettersson U: Structural and nonstructural adenovirus protein, in Ginsberg HS (ed) *The Adenoviruses.* New York, Plenum, 1984, pp 205–270.

36. Brown DT, Westphal M, Burlingham BT, et al: Structure and composition of the adenovirus type 2 core. *J Virol* 1975; 16:366–387.

37. Prage L, Pettersson U: Structural proteins of adenoviruses. VII. Purification and properties of an arginine-rich core protein from adenovirus type 2 and type 3. *Virology* 1971; 45:364–373.

38. Laver WG: Isolation of an arginine-rich protein from particles of adenovirus type 2. *Virology* 1970; 41:488–500.

39. Everitt E, Lutter L, Philipson L: Structural proteins of adenoviruses. XII. Location and neighbor relationships among proteins of adenovirion type 2 as revealed by enzymatic iodination, immunoprecipitation and chemical cross-linking. *Virology* 1975;67:197–208.

40. Rekosh DMK, Russell WC, Bellett AJD, et al: Identification of a protein linked to the ends of adenovirus DNA. *Cell* 1977; 11:283–295.

41. Desiderio SV, Kelly TJ: The structure of the linkage between adenovirus DNA and the 55,000 dalton terminal protein. *J Mol Biol* 1981; 145:319–337.

42. Robinson AF, Bellett AJD: A circular DNA-protein complex from adenovirus and its possible role in DNA replication. *Cold Spring Harbor Symp Quant Biol* 1975; 39:523–531.

43. Green M, Piña M, Kimes R, et al: Adenovirus DNA. I. Molecular weight and conformation. *Proc Natl Acad Sci USA* 1967; 57:1302–1309.

44. Roberts RJ, Arrand JR, Keller W: The length of the terminal repetition in adenovirus-2 DNA. *Proc Natl Acad Sci USA* 1974; 71:3829–3833.

45. Steenbergh PH, Maat J, van Ormondt H, et al: The nucleotide sequence at the terminus of adenovirus type 5 DNA. *Nucleic Acids Res* 1977; 4:4371–4389.

46. Padmanabhan R, Green M: Evidence for palindromic sequences near the termini of adenovirus 2 DNA. *Biochem Biophys Res Commun* 1976; 69:860–867.

47. McAllister RM, Nicholson MO, Lewis AM, et al: Transformation of rat embryo cells by adenovirus type 1. *J Gen Virol* 1969; 4:29–36.

48. Freeman AE, Black PH, Wolford R, et al: Adenovirus type 12–rat embryo transformation system. *J Virol* 1967; 1:362–367.

49. Strohl WA: Alterations in hamster cell regulatory mechanisms resulting from abortive infection with an oncogenic adenovirus. *Prog Exp Tumor Res* 1973; 18:199–239.

50. Vardimon L, Doerfler W: Persistent infection of *Muntiacus muntjak* cells with adenovirus type 2 and abortive infection with adenovirus type 12. *Virology* 1980; 101:72–80.

51. Baum SG: Persistent adenovirus infection of nonpermissive monkey cells. *J Virol* 1977; 23:412–420.

52. Silverman L, Klessig DF: Characterization of the translational defect to fiber synthesis in monkey cells abortively infected with human adenovirus: Role of ancillary leaders. *J Virol* 1989; 63:4376–4385

52a. Rabson AS, O'Connor GT, Berezesky IK, et al: Enhancement of adenovirus growth in African green monkey kidney cell cultures by SV40. *Proc Soc Exp Biol Med* 1964; 116:187–190.

53. Tooze J: *DNA Tumor Viruses: Molecular Biology of Tumor Viruses*, part 2, ed 2. New York, Cold Spring Harbor Laboratory, 1980, pp 443–546.

54. Philipson L, Pettersson U, Linberg U: Molecular biology of adenoviruses, in Gard S, Hallaver C (eds): *Virology Monographs* New York, Springer-Verlag, 1975, vol 14, pp 53–57.

55. Svensson U, Person R, Everite E: Virus receptor interaction in the adenovirus system. I. Identification of virion attachment proteins of the HeLa cell plasma membrane. *J Virol* 1981; 38:70–81.

56. Morgan C, Rosenkranz HS, Mednis B: Structure and development of viruses as observed in the electron microscope. V. Entry and uncoating of adenoviruses. *J Virol* 1969; 4:777–796.

57. Chardonnet Y, Dales S: Early events in the interaction of adenovirus with HeLa cells. I. Penetration of type 5 and intracellular release of the DNA genome. *Virology* 1970; 40:462–477.

58. Dales S: Penetration of animal viruses into cells. *Prog Med Virol* 1965; 7:1–43.

59. Lonberg-Holm K, Philipson L: Early event of virus-cell interaction in an adenovirus system. *J Virol* 1969; 4:323–338.

60. Belin MT, Boulanger PA: Cytoskeletal proteins associated with intracytoplasmic human adenoviruses at an early stage of infection. *Exp Cell Res* 1985; 160:356–370.

61. Miles BD, Luftig RB, Weatherbee JA, et al: Quantitation of the interaction between adenovirus types 2 and 5 and microtubules inside infected cells. *Virology* 1980; 105:265–269.

62. Belin MT, Boulanger P: Processing vimentin occurs during the early stages of adenovirus infection. *J Virol* 1987; 61:2559–2566.

63. Dales S, Chardonnet Y: Early events in the interaction of adenoviruses with HeLa cells. IV. Association with microtubules and the nuclear pore complex during vectorial movement of the inoculum. *Virology* 1973; 56:465–483.

64. Price R, Penman SJ: Transcription of the adenovirus genome by an α amanitine-sensitive ribonucleic acid polymerase in HeLa cells. *J Virol* 1972; 9:621–626.

65. Ziff EB: Transcription and RNA processing by the DNA tumor viruses. *Nature* 1980; 287:491–499.

66. Berk AJ, Sharp PA: Sizing and mapping of early adenovirus mRNAs by gel electrophoresis of S1 endonuclease digested hybrids. *Cell* 1977; 12:721–732.

67. Berk AJ, Sharp PA: Structure of the adenovirus 2 early mRNAs *Cell* 1978; 14:695–711.

68. Westphal R, Lai SP: Quantitative electron microscopy of early adenovirus RNA *J Mol Biol* 1977; 116:525–548.

69. Pettersson U, Tibbetts C, Philipson L: Hybridization maps of early and late messenger RNA sequences on the adenovirus type 2 genome. *J Mol Biol* 1976; 101:479–501.

70. Evans RM, Fraser N, Ziff E, et al: The initiation sites for RNA transcription in Ad 2 DNA. *Cell* 1977; 12:733–739.

71. Kitchingman GR, Lai SP, Westphal H: Loop structures in hybrids of early RNA and the separated strands of adenovirus DNA. *Proc Natl Acad Sci USA* 1977; 74:4392–4395.

72. Berk AJ, Sharp PA: Ultraviolet mapping of the adenovirus 2 early promotors. *Cell* 1977; 12:45–55.

73. Chow L, Broker T, Lewis J: Complex splicing patterns of RNA from the early regions of Ad 2. *J Mol Biol* 1979; 134:265–303.

74. Chow LT, Lewis JB, Broker TR: RNA transcription and splicing at early and intermediate times after adenovirus 2 infection. *Cold Spring Harbor Symp Quant Biol* 1979; 44:401–414.

75. Bos JL, Polder LJ, Bernards R, et al: The 2.2 Kb Elb mRNA of human Ad 12 and Ad 5 codes for two tumor antigens starting at different AUG triplets. *Cell* 1981; 27:121–131.

76. Weil PA, Luse DS, Segall J, et al: Selective and accurate initiation of transcription at the Ad 2 major late promoter in a soluble system dependent on purified RNA polymerase II and DNA. *Cell* 1979; 18:469–484.

77. Babich A, Nevins JR, Darnell JE Jr: Early capping of transcripts from the adenovirus major transcription unit. *Nature* 1980; 287:246–248.

78. Salditt-Georgieff M, Harpold M, Chen-Kiang S, et al: The addition of 5' cap structures occurs early in hnRNA synthesis and prematurely terminated molecules are capped. *Cell* 1980; 19:69–78.

79. Fraser NW, Nevins JR, Ziff E, et al: The major late adenovirus type 2 transcription unit: termination is downstream from the last poly(A) site. *J Mol Biol* 1979; 129:643–659.

80. Nevins JR, Darnell JE Jr: Steps in the processing of Ad 2 mRNA: poly (A)⁺ nuclear sequences are conserved and poly (A) addition precedes splicing. *Cell* 1978; 15:1477–1493.

81. Salditt-Georgieff M, Harpold M, Sawicki S, et al: The addition of poly (A) to nuclear RNA occurs soon after RNA synthesis. *J Cell Biol* 1980; 86:844–848.

82. Shatkin AJ: Capping of eucaryotic mRNAs. *Cell* 1976; 9:645–653.

83. Chen-Kiang S, Nevins JR, Darnell JE Jr: N-6 methyl-adenosine in adenovirus type 2 nuclear RNA is conserved in the formation of messenger RNA. *J Mol Biol* 1979; 135:733–752.

84. Jones N, Shenk T: An adenovirus type 5 early gene function regulates expression of other early viral genes. *Proc Natl Acad Sci USA* 1979; 76:3665–3669.

85. Berk AJ, Lee F, Harrison T, et al: Pre-early adenovirus 5 gene product regulates synthesis of early viral messenger RNAs. *Cell* 1979; 17:935–944.

86. Gallimore PH, Sharp PA, Sambrook J: A study of sequences of adenovirus-2 DNA in 9 lines of transformed rat cells using specific fragments of the viral genome. *J Mol Biol* 1974; 89:49–72.

87. Sharp PA, Gallimore PH, Flint SJ: Mapping of adenovirus 2 RNA sequences in lytically infected cells and transformed cell lines. *Cold Spring Harbor Symp Quant Biol* 1974; 39:457–474.

88. Carlock LR, Jones NC: Transformation-defective mutant of adenovirus type 5 containing a single altered EIA and mRNA species. *J Virol* 1981; 40:657–664.

89. Perricaudet M, Akusjarvi G, Virtanen A, et al: Structure of two spliced mRNAs from the transforming region of human subgroup c adenoviruses. *Nature* 1979; 281:694–696.

90. Green MR: Pre-mRNA splicing. *Ann Rev Genet* 1986; 20:671–706.

91. Virtanen A, Pettersson U: The molecular structure of the 9S mRNA from early region 1A of adenovirus serotype 2. *J Mol Biol* 1983; 165:496–499.

92. Harlow EB, Franza B, Schley C: Monoclonal antibodies specific for adenovirus early region 1A proteins: extensive heterogeneity in early region 1A products. *J Virol* 1985; 55:533–546.

93. Richter JD, Slavicek JM, Schneider JF, et al: Heterogeneity of adenovirus type 5 E1A proteins: Multiple serine phosphorylation induces slow-migrating electrophoretic variants but do not affect E1A-induced transcriptional activation or transformation. *J Virol* 1988; 62:1948–1955.

94. Feldman LT, Nevins JR: Localization of the adenovirus E1A protein, a positive-acting transcriptional factor, in infected cell. *Mol Cell Biol* 1983; 3:829–839.

95. van Ormondt H, Maat J, Dijkema R: Comparison of nucleotide sequences of the early E1A regions for subgroups A, B, and C of human adenoviruses. *Gene* 1980; 12:63–76.

96. Moran E, Mathews MB: Multiple functional domains in the adenovirus E1A gene. *Cell* 1987; 48:177–178.

97. Lillie JW, Loewenstein PM, Green MR, et al: Functional domains of adenovirus type 5 E1A proteins. *Cell* 1987; 50:1091–1100.

98. Borrelli E, Hen R, Chambon P: Adenovirus-2 E1A products repress enhancer-induced stimulation of transcription. *Nature* 1984; 312:608–612.

99. Richardson WD, Roberts BL, Smith AE: Nuclear location signals in polyoma virus large-T. *Cell* 1986; 44:77–85.

100. Schmitt RC, Fahnestock ML, Lewis JB: Differential nuclear localization of the major adenovirus type 2 E1A proteins. *J Virol* 1987; 61:247–255.

101. Berk AJ: Adenovirus promoters and E1A transactivation. *Ann Rev Genet* 1986; 20:45–79.

102. Ko J-L, Dalie BL, Goldman E, et al: Adenovirus 2 early region 1A protein synthesized in *Escherichia coli* extracts indirectly associates with DNA. *EMBO J* 1986; 5:1645–1651.

103. Imperiale MJ, Kao H-T, Feldman LT: Common control of the heat shock gene and early adenovirus genes: Evidence for a cellular E1A-like activity. *Mol Cell Biol* 1984; 4:867–874.

104. Simon MC, Kitchener K, Kao H-T, et al: Selective induction of human heat shock gene transcription by the adenovirus E1A gene products, including the 12S E1A product. *Mol Cell Biol* 1987; 7:2884–2890.

105. Stein R, Ziff E: HeLa cell B-tubulin gene transcription is stimulated by adenovirus 5 in parallel with viral early gene by an E1A-dependent mechanism. *Mol Cell Biol* 1984; 4:2792–2801.

106. Spector DJ, McGrogan M, Raskas HJ: Regulation of the appearance of cytoplasmic RNA from region 1 of adenovirus 2 genome. *J Mol Biol* 1978; 126:395–414.

107. Montell C, Fisher EF, Caruthers MH, et al: Control of adenovirus E1B mRNA synthesis by a shift in the activities of RNA splice sites. *Mol Cell Biol* 1984; 4:966–972.

108. Babiss LE, Ginsberg HS: Adenovirus type 5 early region 1 b gene product is required for efficient shut off of host protein synthesis. *J Virol* 1984; 50:202–212.

109. Babiss LE, Ginsberg HS, Fisher PB: Cold sensitive expression of transformation by a host-range mutant of type 5 adenovirus. *Proc Natl Acad Sci USA* 1983; 80:1352–1356.

110. Pilder S, Moore M, Logan J, et al: The adenovirus E1B 55 K transforming polypeptide modulates transport or cytoplasmic stabilization of viral and host cell mRNAs. *Mol Cell Biol* 1986; 6:470–476.

111. Shiroki K, Ohshima K, Fukui Y, et al: The adenovirus type 12 early-region 1B 58,000-Mr gene product is required for viral DNA synthesis and for initiation of cell transformation. *J Virol* 1986; 57:792–806.

112. Persson H, Katze MG, Philipson L: Purification of a native membrane-associated adenovirus tumor antigen. *J Virol* 1982; 42:905–917.

113. McGlade CJ, Tremblay ML, Yee S-P, et al: Acylation of the 176R (19-kilodalton) early region 1-B protein of human adenovirus type 5. *J Virol* 1987; 61:3227–3234.

114. Subramanian T, Kuppuswamy M, Gysbers J, et al: 19K-Da tumor antigen coded by early region E1B of adenovirus 2 is required for efficient synthesis and for protection of viral DNA. *J*

Biol Chem 1984; 259:11777–11783.

115. White E, Grodzicker T, Stillman BW: Mutations in the gene encoding the adenovirus early region 1B 19,000-molecular-weight tumor antigen cause the degradation of chromosomal DNA. *J Virol* 1984; 52:410–419.

116. Branton PE, Bayley ST, Graham FL: Transformation by human adenoviruses. *Biochim Biophys Acta* 1985; 780:67–94.

117. Richardson WD, Westphal H: A cascade of adenovirus early functions is required for expression of adeno-associated virus. *Cell* 1981; 27:133–141.

118. Nevins JR, Ginsberg HS, Blanchard JM, et al: Regulation of the primary expression of the early adenovirus transcription units. *J Virol* 1979; 32:727–733.

119. Nevins JR, Winkler JJ: Regulation of early adenovirus transcription: A protein product of early region 2 specifically represses region 4 transcription. *Proc Natl Acad Sci USA* 1980; 77:1893–1897.

120. Elkaim R, Goding C, Kedinger C: The adenovirus-2 EIIa early gene promoter: sequences required for efficient in vitro and in vivo transcription, *Nucleic Acids Res* 1983; 11:7105–7117.

121. Rosenthal R, Raskas H: Nuclei of adenovirus 2-infected cells contain an RNA species that corresponds to an intron excised intact from mRNA precursors. *Mol Cell Biol* 1985; 5:1084–1092.

122. Kovesdi I, Reichel R, Nevins JR: Role of an adenovirus E2 promoter binding factor in E1A-mediated coordinate gene control. *Proc Natl Acad Sci USA* 1987; 84:2180–2184.

123. Guilfoyle RA, Osheroff WP, Rossini M: Two functions encoded by adenovirus early region 1A are responsible for the activation and repression of the DNA-binding protein gene. *EMBO J* 1985; 4:707–713.

124. Rice SA, Klessig DF: The function(s) provided by the adenovirus-specified, DNA-binding protein required for viral late gene expression is independent of the role of the protein in viral DNA replication. *J Virol* 1984; 49:35–49.

125. Kruijer W, Nicolas JC, van Schaik FMA, et al: Structure and function of DNA binding proteins from revertants of adenovirus type 5 mutants with a temperature-sensitive DNA replication. *Virology* 1983; 124:425–433.

126. Brough DE, Rice SA, Sell S, et al: Restricted changes in the adenovirus DNA-binding protein that lead to extended host range or temperature-sensitive phenotypes. *J Virol* 1985; 55:206–212.

127. Anderson KP, Klessig DF: Altered splicing in monkey cells abortively infected with human adenovirus may be responsible for inefficient synthesis of the virion fiber polypeptide. *Proc Natl Acad Sci USA* 1984; 81:4023–4027.

128. Klein H, Maltzman W, Levine AJ: Structure-function relationships of the adenovirus DNA binding protein. *J Biol Chem* 1979; 254:11051–11060.

129. Richardson WD, Westphal H: A cascade of adenovirus early functions is required for expression of adenovirus associated virus. *Cell* 1981; 27:133–141.

130. Handa H, Kingston RE, Sharp PA: Inhibition of adenovirus early region IV transcription in vitro by a purified viral DNA binding protein. *Nature* 1983; 302:545–547.

130a. Seiberg M, Aloni Y, Levine AJ: The adenovirus type 2 DNA-binding protein interacts with the major late promoter attenuated RNA. *J Virol* 1989; 63:1134–1141.

131. Gingeras TR, Sciaky D, Gelinas RE, et al: Nucleotide sequences from the adenovirus 2 genome. *J Biol Chem* 1982; 257:13475–13491.

132. Smart JE, Stillman BE: Adenovirus terminal protein precursor. Partial amino acid sequence and the site of covalent linkage to virus DNA. *J Biol Chem* 1982; 257:13499–13506.

133. Cladaras C, Wold WSM: DNA sequences of the E3 transcription unit of adenovirus 5. *Virology* 1985; 140:28–43.

134. Bhat BM, Brady HA, Wold W: Virus deletion mutants that affect a 3′ splice site in the E3 transcription unit of adenovirus 2. *Mol Cell Biol* 1985; 5:2405–2413.

135. Burgert H-G, Maryanski JL, Kvist S: E3/19K protein of adenovirus type 2 inhibits lysis of cytolytic T lymphocytes by blocking cell-surface expression of histocompatibility class I antigens. *Proc Natl Acad Sci USA* 1987; 84:1356–1360.

136. Päabo S, Bhat BM, Wold WSM, et al: A short sequence in the COOH-terminus makes an adenovirus membrane glycoprotein a resident of the endoplastic reticulum. *Cell* 1987; 50:311–317.

137. Andersson M, Päabo S, Nilsson T, et al: Impaired intracellular transport of class I MHC antigens as a possible means for adenovirus to evade immunosurveillance. *Cell* 1985; 43:215–222.

138. Päabo S, Nilsson T, Peterson PA: Adenoviruses of subgenera B, C, D, and E modulate cell-surface expression of major histocompatibility complex class I antigens. *Proc Natl Acad Sci USA* 1986; 83:9665–9669.

139. Virtanen A, Gilardi P, Naslund A, et al: mRNAs from human adenovirus 2 early region 4. *J Virol* 1984; 51:822–831.

140. Yoder S, Berget S: Role of adenovirus type 2 early region 4 in the early-to-late switch during productive infection. *J Virol* 1986; 60:779–781.

141. Weinberg DH, Ketner G: A cell line that supports the growth of a defective early region 4 deletion mutant of human adenovirus type 2. *Proc Natl Acad Sci USA* 1983; 80:5383–5386.

142. Halbert DN, Cutt JR, Shenk T: Adenovirus early region 4 encodes functions required for efficient DNA replication, late gene expression, and host cell shutoff. *J Virol* 1985; 56:250–257.

143. Iwamoto S, Eggerding F, Falck-Pedersen E, et al: Transcription unit mapping in adenovirus: regions of termination. *J Virol* 1986; 59:112–119.

144. Hales K, Birk JM, Imperiale MJ: Analysis of adenovirus type 2 L1 RNA 3′ end formation in vivo and in vitro. *J Virol* 1988; 62:1464–1468.

145. Akusjärvi G: Anatomy of region L1 from adenovirus type 2. *J Virol* 1985; 56:879–886.

146. Akusjärvi G, Persson H: Controls of RNA splicing and termination in the major late adenovirus transcription unit. *Nature* 1981; 292:420–426.

147. Crossland LD, Raskas HJJ: Identification of adenovirus genes that require template replication for expression. *Virology* 1983; 46:737–748.

148. Matsui T, Murayama M, Mita T: Adenovirus 2 peptide IX gene is expressed on replicated DNA molecules. *Mol Cell Biol* 1986; 6:4149–4154.

149. Akusjärvi G, Mathews MB, Anderson P, et al: Structure of genes for virus-associated RNA I and RNA II of adenovirus type 2. *Proc Natl Acad Sci USA* 1980; 77:2424–2428.

150. Soderlund H, Pettersson U, Vennstrom B, et al: A new species of virus-coded low molecular weight RNA from cells infected with adenovirus type 2. *Cell* 1976; 7:585–593.

151. Mathews MB, Pettersson U: The low molecular weight of RNAs of adenovirus 2 infected cells. *J Mol Biol* 1978; 119:293–328.

152. Celma ML, Pan J, Weissman SM: Studies of low molecular weight RNA from cells infected with adenovirus 2. I. The sequences of the 3′ end of VA-RNA. *J Biol Chem* 1977; 252:9032–9042.

153. Svensson C, Akusjärvi G: Defective RNA splicing in the absence of adenovirus-associated RNA I. *Proc Natl Acad Sci USA* 1986; 83:4690–4694.

154. Larsson S, Swensson C, Akusjärvi G: Characterization of a low-molecular-weight virus-associated (VA) RNA encoded by simian adenovirus type 7 which functionally can substitute for adenovirus type 5 VA RNA I. *J Virol* 1986; 60:635–644.

155. Siekierka J, Marino TM, Reichel PA, et al: Translational control by adenovirus: Lack of virus-associated RNA I during adenovirus infection results in phosphorylation of initiation factor eIF-2 and inhibition of protein synthesis. *Proc Natl Acad Sci USA* 1985; 82:1959–1963.

156. Schneider RJ, Safer B, Munemitsu SM: Adenovirus VA I RNA prevents phosphorylation of the eukaryotic initiation factor 2 subunit subsequent to infection. *Proc Natl Acad Sci USA* 1985; 82:4321–4325.

157. Francoeur AM, Mathews MB: Interactions between VA RNA and lupus antigen La: formation of a ribonucleoprotein particle in vitro. *Pro Natl Acad Sci USA* 1982; 79:6772–6776.

158. Lerner MR, Boyle JA, Hardin JA: Two novel classes of small ribonucleoproteins detected by antibodies with lupus erythematosus. *Science* 1981; 211:400–402.

159. Challberg MD, Rawlins DR: Template requirement for the initiation of adenovirus DNA replication. *Proc Natl Acad Sci USA* 1984; 81:100–104.

160. Guggenheimer RA, Stillman BW, Nagata K, et al: DNA sequences required for the in vitro replication of adenovirus DNA. *Proc Natl Acad Sci USA* 1984; 81:3069–3073.

161. Rawlins DR, Rosenfeld PJ, Wides RJ, et al: Structure and function of the adenovirus origin of replication. *Cell* 1984; 37:309–319.

162. Nagata K, Guggenheimer RA, Enomoto T, et al: Adenovirus DNA replication in vitro: identification of a host factor that stimulates synthesis of the preterminal protein-dCMP complex. *Proc Natl Acad Sci USA* 1982; 79:6438–6442.

163. Rosenfeld PJ, O'Neill EA, Wides RJ: Sequence-specific interactions between cellular DNA-binding proteins and the adenovirus origin of DNA replication. *Mol Cell Biol* 1987; 7:875–886.

164. Jones KA, Kadonaga JT, Rosenfeld PJ, et al: A cellular DNA-binding protein that activates eukaryotic transcription and DNA replication. *Cell* 1987; 48:79–89.

165. Schaack J, Schedl P, Shenk T: Topoisomerase I and II cleavage of adenovirus DNA in vivo: Both topoisomerase activities appear to be required for adenovirus DNA replication. *J Virol* 1990; 64:78–85.

165a. Stuiver MH, van der Vliet PC: Adenovirus DNA-binding protein forms a multimeric protein complex with double-stranded DNA and enhances binding of nuclear factor I. *J Virol* 1990; 65:379–386.

166. Nevins JR, Winkler JJ: Regulation of early adenovirus transcription: a protein product of early region 2 specifically represses region 4 transcription. *Proc Natl Acad Sci USA* 1980; 77:1893–1897.

166a. Bodnar JW, Hanson PI, Polvino-Bodnar M, et al: The terminal regions of adenovirus and minute virus of mice DNAs are preferentially associated with the nuclear matrix in infected cells. *J Virol* 1989; 63:4344–4353.

167. Symington JS, Lucher LA, Brackman KH: Biosynthesis of adenovirus type 2 i-leader protein. *J Virol* 1986; 57:846–856.

167a. Soloway PD, Shenk T: The adenovirus type 5-i-leader open reading frame in cis to reduce the half-life of L1 mRNAs. *J Virol* 1990; 64:551–558.

168. Baker CC, Ziff EB: Promoters and heterogeneous 5′ termini of the messenger RNAs of adenovirus serotype 2. *J Mol Biol* 1981; 149:189–221.

169. Burnet LJ, Babiss LE, Young CSH, et al: Mutations in the adenovirus major late promoter: effects on viability and transcription during infection. *Mol Cell Biol* 1987; 7:1091–1100.

170. Natarajan V, Madden MJ, Salzman NP: Positive and negative control sequences within the distal domain of the adenovirus IV_{a2} promoter overlaps with the major late promoter. *J Virol* 1985; 55:10–15.

171. Binger MH, Flint SJ: Accumulation of early and intermediate mRNA species during subgroup C adenovirus productive infections. *Virology* 1984; 136:387–403.

172. Sawadogo M, Roeder RG: Interactions of a gene-specific transcription factor with the adenovirus major late promoter upstream of the TATA box region. *Cell* 1985; 43:165–175.

173. Natarajan V, Madden MJ, Salzman NP: Identification of a transcription factor which interacts with the distal domain of the adenovirus IVa2 promoter. *J Virol* 1987; 61:646–652.

174. Workman JL, Roeder RG: Binding of transcription factor TFIID to the major late promoter during in vitro nucleosome assembly potentiates subsequent initiation by RNA polymerase. *Cell* 1987; 51:613–622.

175. Philipson L: Structure and assembly of adenoviruses. *Curr Top Microbiol Immunol* 1983; 109:1–52.

176. Horwitz MS, Scharff MD, Maizel JV: Synthesis and assembly of adenovirus 2. I. Polypeptide synthesis, assembly of capsomers, and the morphogenesis of the virion. *Virology* 1969; 39:682–684.

177. D'Halluin JC, Milleville M, Boulanger PA: Temperature-sensitive mutant of adenovirus type 2 blocked in virion assembly: accumulation of light intermediate particles. *J Virol* 1978; 26:344–356.

178. Hammarskjold ML, Winberg G: Encapsidation of adenovirus 16 DNA is directed by a small DNA sequence at the left end of the genome. *Cell* 1980; 20:787–795.

179. Hearing P, Samulski RJ, Wishart WL, et al: Identification of a repeated sequence element required for efficient encapsidation of the adenovirus type 5 chromosome. *J Virol* 1987; 61:2555–2558.

179a. Wong M-L, Hsu M-T: Involvement of topoisomerases in replication, transcription, and packaging of the linear adenovirus genome. *J Virol* 1990; 64:691–699.

180. Colby WW, Shenk T: Adenovirus type 5 virions can be assembled in vivo in the absence of detectable polypeptide IX. *J Virol* 1981; 39:977–980.

181. Trembley ML, Dery CV, Talbot BG, et al: In vitro cleavage specificity of the adenovirus type 2 proteinase. *Biochem Biophys Acta* 1983; 743:239–245.

182. Chatterjee PK, Flint SJ: Adenovirus type 2 endopeptidase: an unusual phosphoprotein enzyme matured by autocatalysis. *Proc Natl Acad Sci USA* 1987; 84:714–718.

183. Yeh-Kai L, Adusjärvi P, Alestrom U, et al: Genetic identification of an endoproteinase encoded by the adenovirus genome. *J Mol Biol* 1983; 167:217–222.

184. Zhonghe Z, Nickerson JA, Krochmalnic G, et al: Alterations in nuclear matrix structure after adenovirus infection. *J Virol* 1987; 61:1007–1018.

185. Green M: Biochemical studies on adenovirus multiplication. III. Requirement for DNA synthesis. *Virology* 1962; 18:601–613.

186. White DO, Scharff MD, Maizel JV Jr: The polypeptides of adenoviruses. III. Synthesis in infected cells. *Virology* 1969; 38:395–406.

187. Boulanger PA, Torrier G, Biserte G: Investigations on intranuclear paracrystalline inclusions induced by adenovirus 5 in KB-cells. *J Gen Virol* 1970; 6:329–332.

188. Marusyk R, Norrby E, and Marusyk H: The relationship of adenovirus-induced paracrystalline structures to the virus core protein(s). *J Gen Virol* 1972; 14:261–270.

189. Schrom M, Bablanian R: Altered cellular morphology resulting from cytocidal virus infections. *Arch Virol* 1981; 70:173–187.

190. Braithwaite AW, Murry JB, Bellet AJD: Alterations to controls of cellular DNA synthesis by adenovirus infection. *J Virol* 1981; 39:331–340.

191. Rossini M, Jonak GJ, Baserga R: Identification of adenovirus 2 early genes required for induction of cellular DNA synthesis in resting hamster cells. *J Virol* 1981; 38:982–986.

192. Ginsberg HS, Bello LJ, Levine AJ: Control of biosynthesis of host macromolecules in cells infected with adenovirus, in Colter JS, Paranchych W (eds): *The Molecular Biology of Viruses.* New York, Academic Press, 1967, p 547.

193. Raskas HJ, Thomas DC, Green M: Biochemical studies on adenovirus multiplication. XVII. Ribosome synthesis in uninfected and infected KB cells. *Virology* 1970; 40:893–902.

194. Staufenbiel M, Epple P, Deppert W: Progressive reorganization of the host cell cytoskeleton during adenovirus infection. *J Virol* 1986; 60:1186–1191.

195. Jackson P, Bellet AJD: Reduced microfilament organization in adenovirus type 5-infected rat embryo cells: a function of early region 1a. *J Virol* 1985; 55:644–650.

196. Tooze J: *The Molecular Biology of Tumor Viruses,* ed 1. New York, Cold Spring Harbor Laboratory, 1973, pp 420–469.

197. Dunn AR, Gallimore PH, Jones KW, et al: In situ hybridization of adenovirus RNA and DNA. II. Detection of adenovirus-specific DNA in transformed and tumor cells. *Int J Cancer* 1973; 11:628–636.

198. Green MR, Green M, Mackey JM: Evidence for post transcriptional selection of viral mRNA in cells transformed by human adenovirus 12. *Nature* 1976; 261:340–342.

199. Sambrook J, Williams, J, Sharp P, et al: Physical mapping of temperature-sensitive mutations of adenoviruses. *J Mol Biol* 1975; 97:369–390.

200. Gallimore PH, Sharp PA, Sambrook J: Viral DNA in transformed cells. *J Mol Biol* 1974; 89:49–72.

201. van der Eb AJ, Mulder C, Graham FL, et al: Transformation with specific fragments of adenovirus DNAs. I. Isolation of specific fragments with transformation activity of adenovirus 2 and 5 DNA. *Gene* 1977; 2:115–132.

202. Graham FL, Harrison T, Williams J: Defective transforming capacity of adenovirus type 5 host-range mutants. *Virology* 1978; 86:10–21.

203. Visser L, Wassenaar A-T DC, van Maarschalkerweerd MW, et al: Arrangement of integrated viral DNA sequences in cells transformed by adenovirus types 2 and 5. *J Virol* 1981; 39:684–693.

204. Schirm S, Doerfler W: Expression of viral DNA in adenovirus type 12 transformed cells, in tumor cells, and in revertants. *J Virol* 1981; 39:694–702.

205. Stabel S, Doerfler W, Frus RR: Integration sites of adenovirus type 12 DNA in transformed hamster cells and hamster tumor cells. *J Virol* 1980; 36:22–40.

206. Dorsch-Hasler K, Fisher PB, Weinstein IB, et al: Patterns of viral DNA integration in cells transformed by wild type or DNA-binding protein mutants of adenovirus type 5 and effects of chemical carcinogens on integration. *J Virol* 1980; 34:305–314.

207. Sutter D, Westphal M, Doerfler W: Patterns of integration of viral DNA sequences in the genomes of adenovirus type 12-transformed hamster cells. *Cell* 1978; 14:569–585.

208. Ishibashi M, Yosida TH, Yasue H: Preferential clustering of viral DNA sequences at or near the site of chromosomal rearrangement in fowl adenovirus type 1 DNA-transformed cell lines. *J Virol* 1987; 61:151–158.

209. Spindler KR, Eng CY, Berk AJ: An adenovirus early region 1A protein is required for maximal viral DNA replication in growth-arrested human cells. *J Virol* 1985; 53:742–750.

210. Graham FL: Transformation by and oncogenicity of human adenovirus, in Ginsberg, HS (ed): *The Adenovirus*. New York, Plenum, 1984, pp 339–398.

211. Rice SA, Klessig DF, Williams, J: Multiple effects of the 72-KDa adenovirus-specified DNA binding protein on the efficiency of cellular transformation. *Virology* 1987; 156:366–376.

212. Miller BW, Williams J: Cellular transformation by adenovirus type 5 is influenced by the viral DNA polymerase. *J Virol* 1987; 61:3630–3634.

213. Haley KP, Overhauser G, Babiss LE, et al: Transformation properties of type 5 adenovirus mutants that differentially express the E1A gene products. *Proc Natl Acad Sci USA* 1984; 81:5734–5738.

214. Byrd PJ, Grand RJA, Breiding D, et al: Host range mutants of adenovirus type 12 E1 defective for lytic infection, transformation and oncogenicity. *Virology* 1988; 163:155–165.

215. Solnick D, Anderson MH: Transformation-deficient adenovirus mutant defective in expression of region 1A but not region 1B. *J Virol* 1982; 42:106–113.

216. Jochemsen AG, Bernards R, van Kranen HJ, et al: Different activities of the adenovirus types 5 and 12 E1A regions in transformation with the E J Ha-ras oncogene. *J Virol* 1986; 59:684–691.

217. Velcick A, Ziff E: Adenovirus E1a ras cooperation activity is separate from its positive and negative transcription regulatory functions. *Mol Cell Biol* 1988; 8:2177–2183.

218. Sarnow P, Ho YS, Williams J, et al: Adenovirus E1b-58Kd tumor antigen and SV40 large tumor antigen are physically associated with the same 54Kd cellular protein in transformed cells. *Cell* 1982; 28:387–394.

219. Thomas R, Kaplan L, Reich N, et al: Characterization of human p53 antigens employing primate specific monoclonal antibodies. *Virology* 1983; 131:502–517.

220. Zantema A, Schrier PI, Davis-Oliver A, et al: Adenovirus serotype determines association and localization of the large E1B tumor antigen with cellular tumor antigen p 53 in transformed cells. *Mol Cell Biol* 1985; 5:3084–3091.

221. Chen Z-Q, Ulsh LS, Du Bois G, et al: Posttranslational processing of p 21 ras proteins involves palmitylation of the C-terminal tetrapeptide containing cysteine-186. *J Virol* 1985; 56:607–612.

222. Cross FR, Garber EA, Pellman D, et al: A short sequence in p 60 src N terminal is required for p 60 src myristylation and membrane association and for cell transformation. *Mol Cell Biol* 1984; 5:1834–1842.

223. White E, Blose SH, Stillman BW: Nuclear envelope localization of an adenovirus tumor antigen maintains the integrity of cellular DNA. *Mol Cell Biol* 1984; 4:2865–2875.

224. Ortin J, Scheidtmann KH, Greenberg R, et al: Transcription of the genome of adenovirus type 12. III. Maps of stable RNA from productively infected human cells and abortively infected and transformed hamster cells. *J Virol* 1976; 20:355–372.

225. Jochemsen H, Daniels GSG, Hertoghs JJL: Identification of adenovirus-type 12 gene products involved in transformation and oncogenesis. *Virology* 1982; 122:15–28.

226. Levine EL, Birk DE, Raska K: Attachment to and degradation of collagen substrata by adenovirus-transformed cells of varying tumorigenicity. *Coll Relat Res* 1984; 4:49–61.

227. Bober FJ, Birk DE, Shenk T, et al: Tumorigenicity of adenovirus-transformed cells: collagen interaction and cell surface laminin are controlled by the serotype origin of the E1A and E1B genes. *J Virol* 1988; 62:580–585.

228. Berns KI, Labow MA: Parvovirus gene regulation. *J Gen Virol* 1987; 68:601–614.

229. Parris DS, Bates RC: Effect of bovine parvovirus replication on DNA, RNA, and protein synthesis in S phase cells. *Virology* 1976; 73:72–78.

230. Rhode SL III: Replication process of the parvovirus H-1 kinetics in a parasynchronous cell system. *J Virol* 1973; 11:856–861.

231. Tattersall P: Replication of the parvovirus MVM. I. Dependence of virus multiplication and plaque formation on cell growth. *J Virol* 1972; 10:586–590.

232. Tennant RW, Hand RE Jr: Requirement of cellular DNA synthesis for Kilham rat virus replication. *Virology* 1970; 42:1054–1063.

233. Pritchard C, Stout ER, Bates RC: Replication of parvoviral DNA. I. Characterization of a nuclear lysate system. *J Virol* 1981; 37:352–362.

234. Bourguignon GJ, Tattersall PJ, Ward DC: DNA of minute virus of mice: Self-forming, nonpermuted, single-stranded genome with a 5'-terminal hairpin duplex. *J Virol* 1976; 20:290–306.

235. Astel CR, Smith M, Chow MB, et al: Structure of the 3'-hairpin termini of four rodent parvovirus genomes: Nucleotide sequences homology at origins of DNA replication. *Cell* 1979; 17:691–703.

236. Cotmore S, Tattersall P: Organization of nonstructural genes of the autonomous parvovirus minute virus of mice. *J Virol* 1986; 58:724–732.

237. Jongeneel CV, Sahli R, McMaster GK, et al: A precise map of the splice junctions in the RNAs of the minute virus of mice, an autonomous parvovirus. *J Virol* 1986; 59:564–573.

238. Lebovitz RM, Roeder RG: Parvovirus H-1 expression: mapping of the abundant cytoplasmic transcripts and identification of promoter sites and overlapping transcription units. *J Virol* 1986; 58:271–280.

239. Cotmore SF, Sturzenbecker LJ, Tattersall P: The autonomous parvovirus MVM encodes two nonstructural proteins in addition to its capsid proteins. *Virology* 1983; 129:333–343.

240. Paradiso PR: Identification of multiple forms of the noncapsid

parvovirus protein NCVP1 in H-1 parvovirus-infected cells. *J Virol* 1984; 52:82–87.

241. Chen KC, Shull BC, Moses EA, et al: Complete nucleotide sequence and genome organization of bovine parvovirus. *J Virol* 1986; 60:1085–1097.

242. Cotmore SF, Tattersall P: The NS-1 polypeptide of the autonomous parvovirus MVM is a nuclear phosphoprotein. *Virus Res* 1986; 4:243–250.

242a. Doerig C, Hirt B, Antoinette J-P, et al: Nonstructural protein of parvovirus B19 and minute virus of mice controls transcription. *J Virol* 1990; 64:387–396.

243. Rhode SL III, Richard SM: Characterization of the transactivation-responsive element of the paravovirus H-1 P38 promoter. *J Virol* 1987; 61:2807–2815.

243a. Krauskopf A, Resnekov O, Aloni Y: A cis downstream element participates in regulation of in vitro transcription initiation from the p38 promoter of minute virus of mice. *J Virol* 1990; 64:354–360.

244. Salzman LA, Fabisch P: Nucleotide sequence of the self-priming 3′ terminus of the single stranded DNA extracted from the parvovirus Kilham rat virus. *J Virol* 1979; 30:946–950.

245. Rhode SL III: Replication process of the parvovirus H-1. VI. Characterization of a replication terminus of H-1 replicative-form DNA. *J Virol* 1977; 21:694–712.

246. Tattersall P, Ward DC: Rolling hairpin model for replication of parvovirus and linear chromosomal DNA. *Nature* 1976; 263:106–109.

247. Chow M, Bodnar JW, Polvino-Bodnar M, et al: Identification and characterization of a protein covalently bound to DNA of minute virus of mice. *J Virol* 1986; 57:1094–1104.

248. Wobbe CR, Mitra S: Proteins tightly associated with the termini of replicative form DNA of Kilham rat virus, an autonomous parvovirus. *Proc Natl Acad Sci USA* 1985; 82:8335–8339.

249. Ben-Asher E, Bratosin S, Aloni Y: Intracellular DNA of the parvovirus minute virus of mice is organized in a minichromosome structure. *J Virol* 1982; 41:1044–1054.

250. Doerig C, McMaster G, Sogo J, et al: Nucleoprotein complexes of minute virus of mice have a distinct structure different from that of chromatin. *J Virol* 1986; 58:817–824.

251. Faust EA, Ward DC: Incomplete genomes of the parvovirus minute virus of mice: Selective conservation of genome termini, including the origin for DNA replication. *J Virol* 1979; 32:276–292.

252. Sahli R, McMaster GK, Hirt B: DNA sequence comparison between two tissue-specific variants of the autonomous parvovirus, minute virus of mice. *Nucleic Acids Res* 1985; 13:3617–3633.

253. Astell CR, Gardiner EM, Tattersall P: DNA sequence of the lymphotrophic variant of minute virus of mice, MVM (i) and comparison with the DNA sequence of the fibrotropic prototype strain. *J Virol* 1986; 57:656–669.

254. Hogan A, Faust EA: Nonhomologous recombination in the parvovirus chromosome: Role for a CTA/TTTC/T motif. *Mol Cell Biol* 1986; 6:3005–3009.

255. Hogan A, Faust EA: Short direct repeats mediate spontaneous high-frequency deletions in DNA of minute virus of mice. *Mol Cell Biol* 1984; 4:2239–2242.

256. Pintel D, Dadachanji D, Astell CR, et al: The genome of minute virus of mice, an autonomous parvovirus, encodes two overlapping transcription units. *Nucleic Acids Res* 1983; 11:1019–1038.

257. McMaster GK, Beard P, Engers HD, et al: Characterization of an immunosuppressive parvovirus related to the minute virus of mice. *J Virol* 1981; 38:317–326.

258. Tattersall P, Bratton J: Reciprocal productive and restrictive virus-cell interactions of immunosuppressive and prototype strains of minute virus of mice. *J Virol* 1983; 46:944–955.

259. Clemens KE, Pintel D: Minute virus of mice (MVM) mRNAs predominantly polyadenylate at a single site. *Virology* 1987; 160:511–514.

260. Morgan WR, Ward DC: Three splicing patterns are used to excise the small intron common to all minute virus of mice RNAs. *J Virol* 1986; 60:1170–1174.

261. Tattersall P, Shatkin AJ, Ward DC: Sequence homology between the structural polypeptides of minute virus of mice. *J Mol Biol* 1977; 111:375–394.

262. Ben-Asher E, Aloni Y: Transcription of minute virus of mice, an autonomous parvovirus, may be regulated by attenuation. *J Virol* 1984; 52:266–276.

263. Adenovirus-associated defective virus particles. *Science* 1965; 194:754–756.

264. Hoggan MD, Blacklow NR, Rowe WP: Studies of small DNA viruses found in various adenovirus preparations: Physical, biological, and immunological characteristics. *Proc Natl Acad Sci USA* 1966; 55:1464–1471.

265. Berns KI, Hauswirth WW, Fife KH, et al: Adeno-associated virus DNA replication. *Cold Spring Harbor Symp Quant Biol* 1979; 43:781–787.

266. Lusby E, Fife KH, Berns KI: Nucleotide sequence of the inverted terminal repetition in adeno-associated virus DNA. *J Virol* 1980; 34:402–409.

267. Spear IS, Fife KH, Hauswirth WW, et al: Evidence for two nucleotide sequence orientations within the terminal repetition of adeno-associated virus DNA. *Virology* 1977; 24:627–634.

268. Berns KI, Adler S: Separation of two types of adeno-associated virus particles containing complementary polynucleotide chains. *Virology* 1972; 9:394–396.

269. Berns KI, Rose JA: Evidence for a single-stranded adenovirus associated virus genome: Isolation and separation of complementary single strands. *Virology* 1970; 5:693–699.

270. Mayor HD, Torikai K, Melnick JL, et al: Plus and minus single-stranded DNA separately encapsidated in adeno-associated satellite virions. *Science* 1969; 166:1280–1282.

271. Lusby E, Bohenzky R, Berns KI: Inverted terminal repetition in adeno-associated virus DNA: Independence of the orientation at either end of the genome. *J Virol* 1981; 37:1083–1086.

272. Handa H, Carter BJ: Adeno-associated virus DNA replication complexes in herpes simplex virus or adenovirus infected cells. *J Biol Chem* 1979; 254:6603–6610.

273. Hauswirth WW, Berns KI: Adeno-associated virus DNA replication: Non unit-length molecules. *Virology* 1979; 93:57–68.

274. Straus SE, Sebring ED, Rose JA: Concatemers of altering plus and minus strands are intermediates in adenovirus-associated virus DNA synthesis. *Proc Natl Acad Sci USA* 1976; 73:742–746.

275. Green MR, Straus SE, Roeder RG: Transcripts of the adenovirus-associated virus genome: Multiple polyadenylated RNAs including a potential primary transcript. *J Virol* 1980; 35:560–565.

276. Green MR, Roeder RG: Definition of a novel promoter for the major adenovirus-associated virus mRNA. *Cell* 1980; 22:231–242.

277. Lusby EW, Berns KI: Mapping of the 5′ termini of two adeno-associated virus 2 RNAs in the left half of the genome. *J Virol* 1982; 41:518–526.

278. Srivastava A, Lusby EW, Berns KI: Nucleotide sequence and organization of the adeno-associated virus 2 genome. *J Virol* 1983; 45:555–564.

279. Tratschin J-D, Tal J, Carter BJ: Negative and positive regulation in trans of gene expression from adeno-associated virus vectors in mammalian cells by a viral Rep gene product. *Mol Cell Biol* 1986; 6:2884–2894.

280. Labow MA, Hermonat PL, Berns KI: Positive and negative autoregulation of the adeno-associated virus type 2 genome. *J Virol* 1986; 60:251–258.

281. Becerra SP, Rose JA, Hardy M, et al: Direct mapping of adeno-associated virus capsid proteins B and C: A possible ACG initiation codon. *Proc Natl Acad Sci USA* 1985; 82:7919–7923.

282. Mendelson E, Trempe JP, Carter BJ: Identification of the trans-acting Rep proteins of adeno-associated virus by antibodies to a

synthetic oligopeptide. *J Virol* 1986; 60:823–832.

283. Schlehofer JR, Ehrbar M, zur Hausen H: Vaccinia virus, herpes simplex virus, and carcinogens induce DNA amplification in a human cell line and support replication of a helper virus dependent parvovirus. *Virology* 1986; 152:110–117.

284. Heibronn R, Schlehofer JR, Yalkinoglu AO, et al: Selective DNA-amplification induced by carcinogens (initiators): Evidence for a role of proteases and DNA polymerase alpha. *Int J Cancer* 1985; 36:85–91.

285. Ostrove JM, Duckworth DH, Berns KI: Inhibition of adenovirus-transformed cell oncogenicity by adeno-associated virus. *Virology* 1981; 113:521–533.

286. Richardson WD, Westphal H: Requirement for either early region 1a or early region 1b adenovirus gene products in the helper effect for adeno-associated virus. *J Virol* 1984; 51:404–410.

287. Quinn CO, Kitchingman GR: Functional analysis of the adenovirus type 5 DNA-binding protein: site-directed mutants which are defective for adeno-associated virus helper activity. *J Virol* 1986; 60:653–661.

288. Carter BT, Marcus-Sekura CJ, Laughlin CA, et al: Properties of an adenovirus type 2 mutant, Ad 2 d1807, having a deletion near the right-hand genome terminus: Failure to help AAV replication. *Virology* 1983; 125:505–516.

289. Janik JE, Huston MM, Rose JA: Location of adenovirus genes required for the replication of adenovirus associated virus. *Proc Natl Acad Sci USA* 1981; 78:1925–1929.

290. Buller RML, Janik JE, Sebring ED, et al: Herpes simplex virus types 1 and 2 completely help adenovirus-associated replication. *J Virol* 1981; 40:241–247.

291. Atchison RW: The role of herpes viruses in adenovirus-associated virus replication in vitro. *Virology* 1970; 42:155–162.

292. Blacklow NR, Dolin R, Hoggan MD: Studies of the enhancement of an adenovirus-associated virus by herpes simplex virus. *J Gen Virol* 1971; 10:29–36.

293. Blacklow NR, Hoggan MD, McClanahan MS: Adenovirus-associated viruses: Enhancement by human herpesviruses. *Proc Soc Exp Biol Med* 1970; 134:952–954.

294. Rose JA, Koczot F: Adenovirus-associated virus multiplication. VII. Helper requirement for viral deoxyribonucleic acid and ribonucleic acid synthesis. *J Virol* 1972; 10:1–8.

295. Berns KI, Cheung AK-M, Ostrove JM, et al, in Mahy BWJ, Mirson AC, Ddarby GK (eds): *Virus Persistence.* New York, Cambridge University Press, 1982, pp 249–265.

296. Cheung AKM, Hoggan MD, Hauswirth WW, et al: Integration of the adeno-associated virus genome into cellular DNA in latently infected human Detroit 6 cells. *J Virol* 1980; 33:739–748.

297. Laughlin CA, Cardellichio CB, Coon HC: Latent infection of KB cells with adeno-associated virus type 2. *J Virol* 1986; 60:515–524.

298. Samulski RJ, Srivastava A, Berns KI, et al: Rescue of adeno-associated virus from recombinant plasmids: Gene correction within the terminal repeats of AAV. *Cell* 1983; 33:135–143.

299. Ostrove JM, Berns KI: Adenovirus early region 1b gene function required for rescue of latent adeno-associated virus. *Virology* 1980; 104:502–505.

300. Kongsvik JR, Hopkins MS, Ellem KAO: Two populations of infectious virus produced during H-1 infection of synchronized transformed cells, in Ward DC, Tattersall P (eds): *Replication of Mammalian Parvoviruses.* New York, Cold Spring Harbor Laboratory, 1978.

301. Clinton G, Hayashi M: The parvovirus MVM: Particles with altered structural proteins. *Virology* 1975; 66:261–267.

302. Tattersall P, Cawte PJ, Shatkin AJ, et al: Three structural polypeptides coded for by minute virus of mice, a parvovirus. *J Virol* 1976; 20:273–289.

303. Paradiso P: Infectious process of the parvovirus H-1: Correlation of protein content, particle density, and viral infectivity. *J Virol* 1981; 39:800–807.

304. Singer II, Rhode SL III: Electron microscopy and cytochemistry of H-1 parvovirus intracellular morphogenesis, in Ward DC, Tattersall P (eds): *Replication of Mammalian Parvovirus.* New York, Cold Spring Harbor Laboratory, 1978, pp 479–504.

305. Wildy P, Watson PH: Electron microscopic studies on the architecture of animal viruses. *Cold Spring Harbor Symp Quant Biol* 1963; 27:25–47.

306. Spear PG: Glycoproteins specified by herpes simplex viruses, in Roizman B (ed): *The Herpesviruses.* New York, Plenum, 1985, vol 3, pp 315–356.

307. Gompels U, Minson A: The properties and sequence of glycoprotein H of herpes simplex virus type 1. *Virology* 1986; 153:230–247.

308. Langeland N, Oyan A, Marsden H, et al: Localization on the HSV-1 genome of a region encoding proteins involved in adsorption of the cellular receptor. *J Virol* 1990; 64:1271–1277.

309. Campbell MEM, Palfreyman JW, Preston CM: Identification of herpes simplex virus sequences which encode a transacting polypeptide responsible for stimulation of immediate early transcription. *J Mol Biol* 1984; 180:1–19.

310. Fenwick M: The effects of herpesviruses on cellular macromolecular synthesis, in Fraenkel-Conrat H, Wagner RR (ed): *Comprehensive Virology.* New York, Plenum, 1984, vol 19, pp 359–390.

311. Frenkel N, Roizman B: Herpes simplex virus: Genome size and redundancy studies by renaturation kinetics. *J Virol* 1971; 8:591–593.

312. Wadsworth S, Jacob RJ, Roizman B: Anatomy of herpes virus DNA. II. Size, composition and arrangement of inverted terminal repetitions. *J Virol* 1975; 15:1487–1497.

313. McGeoch DJ, Dabrymple MA, Davison AJ, et al: The complete DNA sequence of the long unique region in the genome of herpes simplex virus type 1. *J Gen Virol* 1988; 69:1531–1574.

314. Honess RW, Roizman B: Proteins specified by herpes simplex virus. XI. Identification and relative molar rates of synthesis of structural and nonstructural herpes virus polypeptides in the infected cell. *J Virol* 1973; 12:1347–1365.

315. Powell KL, Courtney RJ: Polypeptides synthesized in herpes simplex virus type 2-infected HEp-2 cells. *Virology* 1975; 66:217–228.

316. Frenkel N, Roizman B: Separation of the herpes-virus deoxyribonucleic acid duplex into unique fragment and intact strand on sedimentation in alkaline gradients. *J Virol* 1972; 10:565–572.

317. Wilke NM: The synthesis and substructure of herpesvirus DNA: the distribution of alkali-labile single strand interruptions in HSV-1 DNA. *J Gen Virol* 1973; 21:453–467.

318. Hirsch I, Vonka V: Ribonucleotides linked to DNA of herpes simplex virus type I. *J Virol* 1974; 13:1162–1168.

319. Roizman B: The structure and isomerization of herpes simplex virus genomes. *Cell* 1979; 16:481–494.

320. Sheldrick P, Berthelot N: Inverted repetitions in the chromosome of herpes simplex virus. *Cold Spring Harbor Symp Quant Biol* 1975; 39:667–678.

321. Wadsworth S, Hayward GS, Roizman B: Anatomy of herpes simplex virus DNA. V. Terminal repetitive sequences. *J Virol* 1976; 17:503–512.

322. Wagner MJ, Summers WC: Structure of the joint region and the termini of the DNA of herpes simplex virus type 1. *J Virol* 1978; 27:374–387.

323. Hyman RW, Burke S, Kudler L: A nearby inverted repeat of the terminal sequence of herpes simplex virus DNA. *Virology* 1976; 76:286–294.

324. Locker H, Frenkel N: Bam 1, Kpn 1, and Sal 1 restriction enzyme maps of the DNAs of herpes simplex virus strains Justin and F: Occurrence of heterogeneities in defined regions of the viral DNA. *J Virol* 1979; 32:429–441.

325. Davison AJ, Wilkie NM: Nucleotide sequence of the joint between the L and S segments of herpes simplex virus types 1 and 2. *J Gen Virol* 1981; 55:315–331.

326. Mocarski ES, Roizman B: Site-specific inversion sequence of

the herpes simplex virus genome: domain and structural features. *Proc Natl Acad Sci USA* 1981; 78:7047–7051.

327. Mocarski ES, Roizman B: Structure and role of the herpes simplex virus DNA termini in inversion, circularization and generation of virion DNA. *Cell* 1982; 31:89–97.

327a. WuDunn D, Spear PG: Initial interactions of herpes simplex virus with cells is binding to heparan sulfate. *J Virol* 1989; 63:52–58.

327b. Desai PJ, Schaeffer PA, Minson AC: Excretion of non-infectious virus particles lacking glycoprotein H by a ts mutant of herpes simplex virus type I: Evidence that gH is essential for virion infectivity. *J Gen Virol* 1988; 69:1147–1156.

328. Spear PG: Herpesviruses, in Blough HA, Tiffany JM (eds): *Cell Membranes and Viral Envelopes.* New York, Academic Press, 1989, vol 2, pp 709–750.

329. Fuller AO, Spear PG: Specificities of monoclonal and polyclonal antibodies that inhibit absorption of herpes simplex virus to cells and lack of inhibition by potent neutralizing antibodies. *J Virol* 1985; 55:475–482.

330. Spear PG: Virus-induced cell fusion, in Sowers AE (ed): *Cell Fusion.* New York, Plenum, 1987, pp 3–32.

331. Little SP, Jofre JT, Courtney RJ, et al: A virion-associated glycoprotein essential for infectivity of herpes simplex virus type 1. *Virology* 1981; 115:149–160.

332. Sarmiento M, Haffey M, Spear PG: Membrane proteins specified by herpes simplex virus. III. Role of glycoprotein VP7(B$_2$) in virion infectivity. *J Virol* 1979; 29:1149–1158.

333. Marlin SD, Highlander SL, Holland TC, et al: Antigenic variation (mar mutations) in herpes simplex virus glycoprotein B can induce temperature-dependent alteration in gB processing and virus production. *J Virol* 1986; 59:142–153.

334. Highlander SL, Sutherland SL, Gage PJ, et al: Neutralizing monoclonal antibodies specific for herpes simplex virus glycoprotein D inhibit virus penetration. *J Virol* 1987; 61:3356–3364.

335. Honess RW, Roisman B: Regulation of herpesvirus macromolecular synthesis. I. Cascade regulation of the synthesis of three groups of viral proteins. *J Virol* 1979; 14:8–19.

336. Conley AF, Knipe DM, Jones PC, et al: Molecular genetics of herpes simplex virus. VII. Characterization of a temperature-sensitive mutant produced by in vitro mutagenesis and defective in DNA synthesis and accumulation of γ polypeptides. *J Virol* 1981; 37:191–206.

337. Wagner E, Swanstrom R, Stafford M: Transcription of the herpes simplex virus genome in human cells. *J Virol* 1972; 10:675–682.

338. Clements JB, Watson RJ, Wilkie NM: Temporal regulation of herpes simplex virus type 1 transcription: Location of transcripts on the viral genome. *Cell* 1977; 12:275–285.

339. Jones PC, Roizman B: Regulation of herpes macromolecular synthesis: VIII. The transcription program consists of three phases during which both extent of transcription and accumulation of RNA in the cytoplasm are regulated. *J Virol* 1979; 31:299–314.

340. Kozak M, Roizman B: Regulation of herpesvirus macromolecular synthesis: Nucleus retention of nontranslated viral RNA sequences. *Proc Natl Acad Sci USA* 1974; 71:4322–4326.

341. Jacquemont B, Garcia A, Huppert J: Nuclear processing of viral high molecular weight RNA in cells infected with HSV type I. *J Virol* 1980; 35:382–389.

342. Feldman LT, Demarchi JM, Ben-Porat T, et al: Control of abundance of immediate-early mRNA in herpesvirus (pseudorabies)-infected cells. *Virology* 1982; 116:250–263.

343. Kristie TM, Roizman B: Differentiation and DNA contact points of host proteins binding at the cis site for virion-mediated induction of α genes of herpes simplex virus 1. *J Virol* 1988; 62:1145–1157.

344. Murchie MJ, McGeoch DJ: DNA sequence analysis of an immediate-early gene region of the herpes simplex virus type 1 genome (map coordinates 0.950 to 0.978). *J Gen Virol* 1982; 62:1–15.

345. O'Hare P, Goding CR: Herpes simplex virus regulatory elements and the immunoglobulin octamer domain bind a common factor and are both targets for virion transactivation. *Cell* 1988; 52:435–445.

346. Kristie TM, Roizman B: Host cell proteins bind to the cis-acting site required for virion mediated induction of herpes simplex virus 1α genes. *Proc Natl Acad Sci USA* 1987; 84:71–75.

346a. Werstuck G, Bilan P, Capone JP: Enhanced infectivity of herpes simplex virus type I viral DNA in a cell line expressing the trans-inducing factor Vmw65. *J Virol* 1990; 64:984–991.

347. McKnight JLC, Pellett PE, Jenkins FJ, et al: Characterization and nucleotide sequence of two herpes simplex virus 1 genes whose products modulate α-trans-inducing factor dependent activation of α genes. *J Virol* 1987; 61:992–1001.

348. Bzik DJ, Preston CM: Analysis of DNA sequences which regulate the transcription of herpes simplex virus immediate early gene 3: DNA sequences required for enhancer-like activity and response to trans-activation by a virion polypeptide. *Nucleic Acids Res* 1986; 14:929–943.

349. Kristie TM, Roisman B: Separation of sequences defining basal expression from those conferring α gene recognition within the regulatory domains of herpes simplex virus 1 genes. *Proc Natl Acad Sci USA* 1984; 80:4065–4069.

350. Faber SW, Wilcox KW: Association of the herpes simplex virus regulatory protein ICP4 with specific nucleotide sequences in DNA. *Nucleic Acids Res* 1986; 14:6067–6083.

351. Silver M, Dales S: Evidence against involvement of host transcription in the replication of vaccinia and herpes simplex viruses. *Virology* 1982; 118:214–218.

352. Costanzo F, Campadelli-Fiume G, Foa-Tomas L, et al: Evidence that herpes simplex virus DNA is transcribed by cellular RNA polymerase II. *J Virol* 1977; 21:996–1001.

353. Mackem S, Roizman B: Regulation of herpesvirus macromolecular synthesis: Temporal order of transcription of α genes is not dependent on the stringency of inhibition of protein synthesis. *J Virol* 1981; 40:319–322.

354. Jones PC, Hayward GS, Roizman B: Anatomy of herpes simplex virus DNA. VII. α RNA is homologous to noncontiguous sites in both the L and S components of viral DNA. *J Virol* 1977; 21:268–276.

355. Watson R, Sullivan M, Vande Woude GF: Structures of two spliced herpes simplex virus type 1 immediate-early mRNAs which map at the junctions of the unique and reiterated regions of the virus DNA component. *J Virol* 1981; 37:431–444.

356. Dixon RAF, Schaffer PA: Fine-structure mapping and functional analysis of temperature-sensitive mutants in the gene encoding the herpes simplex virus type 1 immediate early protein, VP175. *J Virol* 1980; 36:189–203.

357. Sacks WR, Greene CC, Aschman DP, et al: Herpes simplex virus type 1 ICP 27 is an essential regulatory protein. *J Virol* 1985; 55:796–805.

358. Sacks WR, Schaffer PA: Deletion mutants in the gene encoding the herpes simplex virus type 1 immediate-early protein ICP0 exhibit impaired growth in cell culture. *J Virol* 1987; 61:829–839.

359. DeLuca NA, Schaffer PA: Activation of immediate-early, early and late promoters by temperature-sensitive and wild-type forms of herpes simplex virus type 1 protein ICP4. *Mol Cell Biol* 1985; 5:1997–2008.

360. O'Hare P, Hayward GS: Three trans-acting regulatory proteins of herpes simplex virus modulate immediate-early gene expression in a pathway involving positive and negative feedback regulation. *J Virol* 1985; 56:723–733.

361. Wilcox KW, Kohn A, Sklyanskaya E, et al: Herpes simplex virus phosphoproteins. I. Phosphate cycles on and off some viral polypeptides and can alter their affinity for DNA. *J Virol* 1980; 33:167–182.

362. Preston CM, Notarianni EL: Poly ADP-ribosylation of a herpes simplex virus immediate early polypeptide. *Virology* 1983; 131:492–501.

363. Metzler DW, Wilcox K: Isolation of herpes simplex virus regu-

latory protein ICP 4 as a homodimeric complex. *J Virol* 1985; 55:329–337.

363a. Shepard AA, DeLuca NA: Intragenic complementation among partial peptides of herpes simplex virus regulatory protein ICP 4. *J Virol* 1989; 63:1203–1211.

364. DeLuca NA, Schaffer PA: Activities of herpes simplex virus type 1 (HSV-1) ICP4 genes specifying nonsense peptides. *Nucleic Acids Res* 1987; 15:4491–4511.

365. Knipe DM, Senechek D, Rice SA, et al: Stages in the nuclear association of the herpes simplex virus transcriptional activator protein ICP4. *J Virol* 1987; 61:276–284.

366. Mackem S, Roizman B: Structural features of the herpes simplex virus α gene 4, 0 and 27 promoter-regulatory sequences which confer α regulation on chimeric thymidine kinase genes. *J Virol* 1982; 44:939–949.

367. Faber SW, Wilcox KW: Association of herpes simplex virus regulatory protein ICP-4 with sequences spanning the ICP4 gene transcription start site. *Nucleic Acids Res* 1988; 16:555–570.

368. Micheal N, Spector D, Mavromara-Nazos, et al: The DNA binding properties of the major regulatory protein α 4 of herpessimplex viruses. *Science* 1988; 239:1531–1533.

369. Everett RD: Transactivation of transcription by herpes virus product: requirement for two HSV-1 immediate-early polypeptides for maximum activity. *EMBO J* 1984; 3:3135–3141.

370. Quinlan MP, Knipe DM: Stimulation of expression of a herpes simplex virus DNA binding protein by two viral functions. *Mol Cell Biol* 1985; 5:957–963.

371. Stevens JS, Wagner EK, Devi-Rao GB, et al: RNA complementary to herpes virus alpha mRNA is prominent in latently infected neurons. *Science* 1987; 235:1056–1059.

372. O'Hare P, Hayward GS: Evidence for a direct role of both the 175,000 and 10,000 molecular-weight immediate-early proteins of herpes simplex virus in the transactivation of delayed-early promoters. *J Virol* 1985; 53:751–760.

373. DeLuca NA, McCarthy A, Schaffer PA: Isolation and characterization of deletion mutants of herpes simplex virus type 1 in the gene encoding immediate-early regulatory protein ICP4. *J Virol* 1985; 56:558–570.

374. Gelman IH, Silverstein S: Herpes simplex virus immediate-early promoters are responsive to virus and cell trans-acting factors. *J Virol* 1987; 67:2286–2296.

375. Perry LJ, Rixon FJ, Everett RD, et al: Characterization of the IE 110 gene of herpes simplex virus type 1. *J Gen Virol* 1986; 67:2365–2380.

376. Everett RD: The products of herpes simplex virus type 1 (HSV-1) immediate-early genes 1, 2, and 3 can activate HSV-1 gene expression in trans. *J Gen Virol* 1986; 67:2507–2513.

377. Sears AE, Halliburton IW, Meignier B, et al: Herpes simplex virus 1 mutant deleted in α 22 gene: growth and gene expression in permissive and restrictive cells and establishment of latency in mice. *J Virol* 1985; 55:338–341.

378. Longnecker R, Roizman B: Generation of an inverting herpes simplex virus 1 mutant lacking the L-S junction a sequences, an origin of DNA syntheses, and several genes including those specifying glycoprotein E and the α 47 gene. *J Virol* 58:583–591.

379. Strom T, Frenkel N: Effects of herpes simplex virus on mRNA stability. *J Virol* 1987; 61:2198–2207.

380. Fenwick ML, McMenamin MM: Early virion associated suppression of cellular protein synthesis by herpes simplex virus is accomplished by inactivation of mRNA. *J Gen Virol* 1984; 65:1225–1228.

381. Oroskar AA, Read GS: A mutant of herpes simplex virus type 1 exhibits increased stability of immediate-early (alpha) mRNAs. *J Virol* 1987; 61:604–606.

382. Kwong AD, Kruper JA, Frenkel N: Herpes simplex virus virion host shutoff function. *J Virol* 1988; 62:912–921.

383. Keir HM, Gold E: Deoxyribonucleic acid nucleotidyl transferase and deoxyribonuclease from cultured cells infected with herpes simplex virus. *Biochim Biophys Acta* 1963; 72:263–276.

384. Knoph K: Properties of herpes simplex virus DNA polymerase and characterization of its associated exonuclease activity. *Eur J Biochem* 1979; 98:231–234.

385. Weller S, Lee KJ, Sabourin DJ, et al: Genetic analysis of temperature-sensitive mutants which define the gene for the major herpes simplex virus 1 DNA-binding protein. *J Virol* 1983; 45:354–366.

386. Preston CM, Cordingly MG: mRNA- and DNA-directed synthesis of herpes simplex virus-coded exonuclease in *Xenopus laevis* oocytes. *J Virol* 1982; 43:386–394.

387. Swain MA, Galloway DA: Herpes simplex virus specifies two subunits of ribonucleotide reductase encoded by 3′ coterminal transcripts. *J Virol* 1986; 57:802–808.

388. Dubbs DR, Kit S: Mutant strains of herpes simplex deficient in thymidine kinase-inducing activity. *Virology* 1964; 22:493–502.

389. Preston VG, Palfreyman JW, Dutia BM: Identification of a herpes simplex type 1 polypeptide which is a component of the virus-induced ribonucleotide reductase. *J Gen Virol* 1984; 65:1457–1466.

390. Vaughn PJ, Purifoy DJM, Powell KL: DNA-binding protein associated with herpes simplex virus DNA polymerase. *J Virol* 1985; 53:501–508.

391. Carmichael EP, Kosovsky MJ, Weller SK: Isolation and characterization of herpes simplex virus type 1 host range mutants defective in viral DNA synthesis. *J Virol* 1988; 62:91–99.

392. Holmes AM, Wietstock SM, Ruyechan WT: Identification and characterization of a DNA primase activity present in herpes simplex virus type 1 infected HeLa cells. *J Virol* 1988; 62:1038–1045.

393. McGeoch DJ, Dalrymple MA, Dolin A, et al: Structures of herpes simplex virus type 1 genes required for replication of virus DNA. *J Virol* 1988; 62:444–453.

394. Elias P, O'Donnell ME, Mocarski E, et al: A DNA binding protein specific for an origin of replication of herpes simplex virus type 1. *Proc Natl Acad Sci USA* 1986; 83:6322–6326.

395. Caradonna S, Worrad D, Lirette R: Isolation of a herpes simplex virus cDNA encoding the DNA repair enzyme uracil-DNA glycosylase. *J Virol* 1987; 61:3040–3047.

396. Chan I: Induction of deoxycytidine deaminase activity in mammamian cell lines by infections with herpes simplex virus type 1. *Proc Natl Acad Sci USA* 1977; 74:1734–1738.

397. Leary K, Francke B: The interaction of a topoisomerase-like enzyme from herpes-simplex virus type 1-infected cells with non-viral circular DNA. *J Gen Virol* 1984; 65:1341–1350.

398. Quinn JP, McGeoch DJ: DNA sequence of the region in the genome of herpes simplex virus type 1 containing the genes for DNA polymerase and the major DNA binding protein. *Nucleic Acids Res* 1985; 13:8143–8163.

399. Vaughn PJ, Banks LM, Purifoy DJM, et al: Interactions between herpes simplex virus DNA-binding proteins. *J Gen Virol* 1984; 65:2033–2041.

400. Godowski PJ, Knipe DM: Transcriptional control of herpesvirus gene expression: Gene functions required for positive and negative regulation. *Proc Natl Acad Sci USA* 1986; 83:256–260.

401. Ruyechan WT: N-ethylmaleimide inhibition of the DNA-binding activity of the herpes simplex virus type 1 major DNA-binding protein. *J Virol* 1988; 62:810–817.

402. Parris DS, Cross A, Haarr L, et al: Identification of the gene encoding the 65-kilodalton DNA-binding protein of herpes simplex virus type 1. *J Virol* 1988; 62:818–825.

402a. Gallo ML, Dorsky DI, Crumpacker CS, et al: The essential 65-kilodalton DNA-binding protein of herpes simplex virus stimulates the virus-encoded DNA polymerase. *J Virol* 1989; 63:5023–5029.

403. Caras IW, Levinson BB, Fabry M, et al: Cloned mouse ribonucleotide reductase subunit M1 DNA reveals amino acid sequence homology with *Escherichia coli* and herpes virus ribonucleotide reductase. *J Biol Chem* 1985; 260:7015–7022.

404. Goldstein DJ, Weller SK: Herpes simplex virus type 1-induced ribonucleotide reductase activity is dispensable for virus growth

and DNA synthesis: Isolation and characterization of an ICP6 lac Z insertion mutant. *J Virol* 1988; 62:196–205.

405. Easton AJ, Clements JB: Temporal regulation of herpes simplex virus type 2 transcription and characterization of virus immediate early mRNAs. *Nucleic Acids Res* 1980; 8:2627–2645.

406. Smith CA, Schaffer PA: Mutants defective in herpes simplex virus type 2 ICP 4: Isolation and preliminary characterization. *J Virol* 1987; 61:1092–1097.

407. Marsden HS, Haarr L, Preston CM: Processing of herpes simplex virus proteins and evidence that translation of thymidine kinase mRNA is initiated at three separate AUG codons. *J Virol* 1983; 46:434–445.

408. Ogino T, Shiman R, Rapp F: Deoxythymidine kinase from rabbit kidney cells infected with herpes simplex virus types 1 and 2. *Intervirology* 1973; 1:80–95.

409. Jones KA, Yamamoto KR, Tjian R: Two distinct transcription factors bind to the HSV thymidine kinase promoter in vitro. *Cell* 1985; 42:559–572.

410. Coen DM, Weinheimer SP, McKnight SL: A genetic approach to promoter recognition during trans induction of viral gene expression. *Science* 1986; 234:53–59.

411. Stow ND: Localization of an origin of DNA replication within the TRs/IRs repeated region of the herpes simplex virus type 1 genome. *EMBO J* 1982; 1:863–867.

412. Vlazny DA, Frenkel N: Replication of herpes simplex virus DNA: localization of replication signals within defective virus genomes. *Proc Natl Acad Sci USA* 1981; 78:742–746.

413. Polvino-Bodnar M, Orberg PK, Schaffer PA: Herpes simplex virus type 1 ORI$_L$ is not required for virus replication or for the establishment and reactivation of latent infection in mice. *J Virol* 1987; 61:3528–3535.

414. Gray CP, Kaerner HC: Sequence of the putative origin of replication in the U$_L$ region of herpes simplex virus type 1 ANG DNA. *J Gen Virol* 1984; 65:2109–2119.

415. Stow N, McMonagle EC: Characterization of the TRs/IRs origin of DNA replication of herpes simplex virus type 1. *Virology* 1983; 130:427–438.

416. Hubenthal-Voss J, Starr L, Roizman B: The herpes simplex virus origins of DNA synthesis in the S component are each contained in a transcribed open reading frame. *J Virol* 1987; 61:3349–3355.

417. Davison AJ, Wilkie NM: Nucleotide sequence of the joint between the L and S segments of herpes simplex virus type 1 and 2. *J Gen Virol* 1981; 55:315–331.

418. Deiss LP, Frenkel N: The herpes simplex amplicon: cleavage of concatermeric DNA is linked to packaging and involves the amplification of the terminally reiterated a sequence. *J Virol* 1986; 57:933–941.

419. Longnecker R, Roizman B: Generation of an inverting herpes simplex virus 1 mutant lacking the L-S junction a sequence, an origin of DNA synthesis and several genes including those specifying glycoprotein E and the α 47 gene. *J Virol* 1986; 58:583–591.

420. Pogue-Geile KL, Lee GTY, Spear PG: Novel rearrangements of herpes simplex virus DNA sequences resulting from duplication of a sequence within the unique region of the L component. *J Virol* 1985; 53:456–461.

421. Umene K: Transition from a heterozygous to a homozygous state of a pair of loci in the inverted repeat sequences of the L component of the herpes simplex virus type 1 genome. *J Virol* 1987; 61:1187–1192.

422. Preston VG, Coates JA, Rixon F: Identification and characterization of a herpes simplex virus gene product required for encapsidation of viral DNA. *J Virol* 1983; 45:1056–1064.

423. Dalziel RG, Marsden HS: Identification of two herpes simplex virus type 1-induced proteins (21K and 22K) which interact specifically with the a sequence of herpes simplex virus DNA. *J Gen Virol* 1984; 65:1467–1475.

423a. Chow J, Roizman B: Characterization of DNA sequence-common and sequence-specific proteins binding to cis-acting sites

424. Wagner EK: Individual HSV transcripts: Characterization of specific genes, in Roizman B (ed): *The Herpesviruses*. New York, Plenum, 1985, vol 3, pp 65–104.

425. Chisholm GE, Summers WC: The promoter for the late gene encoding VP5 of herpes simplex virus type 1 is recognized by cell extracts derived from uninfected cells. *J Virol* 1986; 60:620–625.

426. Blair ED, Wagner EK: A single regulatory region modulates both cis activation and trans activation of the herpes simplex virus VP5 promoter in transient expression assays in vivo. *J Virol* 1986; 60:460–469.

427. Conley AJ, Knipe DM, Jones PC, et al: Molecular genetics of herpes simplex virus VII. Characterization of a temperature sensitive mutant produced by in vitro mutagenesis and defective in DNA synthesis and accumulation of γ polypeptides. *J Virol* 1981; 37:191–206.

428. Arsenakis M, Campadelli-Fiume G, Roizman B: Regulation of glycoprotein D synthesis: Does α 4, the major regulatory protein of herpes simplex virus 1, regulate late genes both positively and negatively? *J Virol* 1988; 62:148–158.

429. Braun DK, Batterson W, Roizman B: Identification and genetic mapping of a herpes simplex virus capsid protein which binds DNA. *J Virol* 1984; 50:645–648.

430. Spear PG: Glycoproteins specified by herpes simplex viruses, in Roizman B (ed): *The Herpesviruses*. New York, Plenum, 1985, vol 3, pp 315–356.

431. Campadelli-Fiume G, Serafini-Cessi F: Processing of the oligosaccharide chains of herpes simplex virus type 1 glycoproteins, in Roizman B (ed): *The Herpesviruses*. New York, Plenum, 1985, vol 3, pp 357–382.

432. Johnson DC, Spear PG: Monensin inhibits the processing of herpes simplex virus glycoproteins, their transport to the cell surface and the egress of virion from infected cells. *J Virol* 1982; 43:1102–1112.

433. McGeoch DJ, Dolan A, Donald S, et al: Sequence determination and genetic content of the short unique region in the genome of herpes simplex virus 1. *J Mol Biol* 1985; 181:1–13.

434. Manservigi R, Spear PG, Buchan A: Cell fusion induced by herpes simplex virus is prompted and suppressed by different viral glycoproteins. *Proc Natl Acad Sci USA* 1977; 74:3913–3917.

435. Ruyechan WT, Morses LS, Knipe DM, et al: Molecular genetics of herpes simplex virus. II. Mapping of the major viral glycoproteins and of the genetic loci specifying the social behavior of infected cells. *J Virol* 1979; 29:677–697.

436. Kousoulas KG, Pellet PE, Pereira L, et al: Mutations affecting conformation or sequence of neutralizing epitopes identified by reactivity of viable plaques segregated from syn and ts domains of HSV-1 (F) gB gene. *Virology* 1984; 135:379–394.

437. Little SP, Jofre JT, Courtney RJ, et al: A virion-associated glycoprotein essential for infectivity of herpes simplex virus type 1. *Virology* 1981; 115:149–160.

438. Bzik CJ, Fox BA, DeLuca NA, et al: Nucleotide sequences of a region of the herpes simplex virus type 1 gB glycoprotein gene: mutations affecting rate of entry and cell fusion. *Virology* 1984; 137:185–190.

439. Claesson-Welsh L, Spear PG: Oligomerization of herpes simplex virus glycoprotein B. *J Virol* 1986; 60:803–806.

440. Pachl C, Burke RL, Stuve LL, et al: Expression of cell-associated and secreted forms of herpes simplex virus type 1 glycoprotein gB in mammalian cells. *J Virol* 1987; 61:315–325.

441. Cai W, Person S, Warner SC, et al: Linker-insertion nonsense and restriction-site deletion mutation of the gB glycoprotein gene of herpes simplex virus type 1. *J Virol* 1987; 61:714–721.

442. Friedman HM, Cohen GH, Eisenberg RJ, et al: Glycoprotein C of herpes simplex virus 1 acts as a receptor for the C3b complement component on infected cells. *Nature* 1984; 309:633–635.

443. Smiley ML, Friedman HM: Binding of complement component

C3b to glycoprotein C is modulated by sialic acid on herpes simplex virus type 1 infected cells. *J Virol* 1985; 55:857–861.

444. Friedman HM, Glorioso JC, Cohen GH, et al: Binding of complement component C3b to glycoprotein gC of herpes simplex virus type 1: Mapping of gC-binding sites and demonstration of conserved C3b binding in low-passage clinical isolates. *J Virol* 1986; 60:470–475.

445. Dall'Olio F, Malagolini W, Speziali V, et al: Sialylated oligosaccharides O-glycosidically linked to glycoprotein C from herpes simplex virus type 1. *J Virol* 1985; 56:127–134.

446. Para MF, Baucke RB, Spear PG: Immunoglobulin G (Fc)–binding receptors on virions of herpes simplex virus type 1 and transfer of these receptors to the cell surface by infection. *J Virol* 1980; 34:512–520.

447. Johansson PJH, Myhre EB, Blomberg J: Specificity of Fc receptors induced by herpes simplex virus type 1: comparison of immunoglobulin G from different animal species. *J Virol* 1985; 56:489–494.

448. Sullivan V, Smith GL: The herpes simplex virus type 1 US7 gene product is a 66K glycoprotein and is a target for complement-dependent virus neutralization. *J Gen Virol* 1988; 69:859–867.

449. Johnson DC, Frame MC, Ligas MW, et al: Herpes simplex virus immunoglobulin G Fc receptor activity depends on a complex of two viral glycoproteins, gE and gI. *J Virol* 1988; 62:1347–1354.

450. Chan W: Protective immunization of mice with specific HSV-1 glycoproteins. *Immunology* 1983; 49:343–352.

451. Balachandran N, Bacchetti S, Rawls WE: Protection against lethal challenge of BALB/c mice by passive transfer of monoclonal antibodies to five glycoproteins of herpes simplex virus type 2. *Infect Immun* 1982; 37:1132–1137.

452. Jennings SR, Lippe PA, Pauza KJ, et al: Kinetics of expression of herpes simplex virus type 1-specific glycoprotein species on the surfaces of infected murine, simian and human cells: Flow cytometric analysis. *J Virol* 1987; 61:104–112.

453. Srinivas RV, Balachandran N, Alonso-Caplen FV, et al: Expression of herpes simplex virus glycoproteins in polarized epithelial cells. *J Virol* 1986; 58:689–693.

454. Baichiwal VR, Sugden B: Latency comes of age for herpesviruses. *Cell* 1988; 52:787–789.

455. Deatly AM, Spivack JG, Lavi E, et al: Latent herpes simplex virus type 1 transcripts in peripheral and central nervous system tissues of mice map to similar regions of the viral genome. *J Virol* 1988; 62:749–756.

456. Rock DL, Fraser NW: Detection of HSV-1 genome in central nervous system of latency infected mice. *Nature* 1983; 302:523–525.

457. Green MT, Courtney RJ, Dunkel EC: Detection of an immediate early herpes simplex virus type 1 polypeptide in trigeminal ganglia from latently infected animals. *Infect Immun* 1981; 34:987–992.

458. Puga A, Notkins AL: Continued expression of a poly (A)⁺ transcript of herpes simplex virus type 1 in trigeminal ganglia of latently infected mice. *J Virol* 1987; 61:1700–1703.

459. Wagner EK, Devi-Rao G, Feldman LT, et al: Physical characterization of the herpes simplex virus latency-associated transcript in neurons. *J Virol* 1988; 62:1194–1202.

460. Javier RT, Stevens JG, Dissette VB, et al: A herpes simplex virus transcript abundant in latently infected neurons is dispensable for establishment of the latent state. *Virology* 1988; 166:254–257.

461. Moss B: Reproduction of poxviruses, in Fraenkel-Conrat H, Wagner RR (eds): *Comprehensive Virology: DNA Animal Viruses.* New York, Plenum Press, 1974, vol 3, pp 405–474.

462. Moss B: Poxviruses, in Nayak DP (ed): *The Molecular Biology of Animal Viruses.* New York, Dekker, 1979, vol 2, pp 849–890.

463. Westwood JCN, Harris WJ, Zwartouw HT, et al: Studies on the structure of vaccinia virus. *J Gen Microbiol* 1964; 34:67–78.

464. Sarov I, Joklik WK: Studies of the nature of the capsid polypeptides of vaccinia virions. *Virology* 1972; 50:579–592.

465. Oie M, Ichihashi Y: Characterization of vaccinia polypeptides. *Virology* 1981; 113:263–276.

466. Holowczak JA: Glycopeptides of vaccinia virus. I. Preliminary characterization and hexosamine content. *Virology* 1970; 42:87–99.

467. Garon CF, Moss B: Glycoprotein synthesis in cells infected with vaccinia virus. II. A glycoprotein component of the virion. *Virology* 1971; 46:232–246.

468. Medzon E, Bauer H: Structural features of vaccinia virus revealed by negative staining, sectioning and freeze etching. *Virology* 1970; 40:860–867.

469. Mitchiner MB: The envelope of vaccinia and orf viruses: An electron cytochemical investigation. *J Gen Virol* 1969; 5:211–220.

470. Boulter E, Appleyard G: Differences between extracellular and intracellular forms of poxviruses and their implications. *Prog Med Virol* 1973; 16:86–108.

471. Payne L: Polypeptide composition of extracellular enveloped vaccinia virus. *J Virol* 1978; 27:28–37.

472. Payne L: Identification of the vaccinia hemagglutinin polypeptide from a cell system yielding large amounts of extracellular enveloped virus. *J Virol* 1979; 31:147–155.

473. Payne LG: Significance of extracellular enveloped virus in the in vitro and in vivo dissemination of vaccinia. *J Gen Virol* 1980; 50:89–100.

474. Payne LG, Norrby E: Presence of hemagglutinin in the envelope of extracellular vaccinia virus particles. *J Gen Virol* 1976; 32:63–72.

475. Appleyard G, Haspel A, Boulter EA: An antigenic difference between intracellular and extracellular rabbit poxvirus. *J Gen Virol* 1971; 13:9–17.

476. Balachandran N, Seth P, Mohapatra LN: Use of the ⁵¹chromium release test to demonstrate antigenic differences between extracellular and intracellular forms of vaccinia virus. *J Gen Virol* 1979; 45:65–72.

477. McCarron RJ, Cabrera CV, Estaban M, et al: Structure of vaccinia DNA: Analysis of the viral genome by restriction endonucleases. *Virology* 1978; 86:88–101.

478. Grady LJ, Paoletti E: Molecular complexity of vaccinia DNA and the presence of reiterated sequences in the genome. *Virology* 1977; 70:337–341.

479. Geshelin P, Berns KI: Characterization and localization of the naturally occurring crosslinks in vaccinia virus DNA. *J Mol Biol* 1974; 88:785–796.

480. Holowczak JA: Poxvirus DNA. I. Studies on the structure of the vaccinia genome. *Virology* 1976; 72:121–133.

481. Essani K, Dales S: Biogenesis of vaccinia: Evidence for more than 100 polypeptides in the virion. *Virology* 1979; 95:385–394.

482. Carrasco L, Bravo R: Specific proteins synthesized during the viral lytic cycle in vaccinia-virus infected HeLa cells: Analysis by high-resolution two-dimensional gel electrophoresis. *J Virol* 1986; 58:569–577.

483. Garon CF, Barbosa E, Moss B: Visualization of an inverted terminal repetition in vaccinia virus DNA. *Proc Natl Acad Sci USA* 1978; 75:4863–4867.

484. Wittek R, Menna A, Muller HK, et al: Inverted terminal repeats in rabbit poxvirus and vaccinia virus DNA. *J Virol* 1978; 28:171–181.

485. Upton C, DeLange AM, McFadden G: Tumorigenic poxviruses: Genomic organization and DNA sequence of the telomeric region of the Shope fibroma virus genome. *Virology* 1987; 160:20–30.

486. Moss B, Winters E, Jones EV: Replication of vaccinia virus, in Cozarelli NR (ed): *Mechanism of DNA Replication and Recombination.* New York, Alan R Liss, 1983, pp 449–461.

487. Dallo S, Esteban M: Isolation and characterization of attenuated mutants of vaccinia virus. *Virology* 1987; 159:408–422.

488. Paez E, Esteban M: Stability of vaccinia virus DNA during persistent infections: Accumulation of left-end deletions and tandem repeats at both ends of the viral genome and prevention by interferon. *Virology* 1988; 163:145–154.

489. Gillard S, Spehner D, Drillien R, et al: Localization and sequence of a vaccinia virus gene required for multiplication in human cells. *Proc Natl Acad Sci USA* 1986; 83:5573–5577.

490. Baroudy BM, Venkatesan S, Moss B: Incompletely base-paired flip-flop terminal loops link the two DNA strands of the vaccinia virus genome into one uninterrupted polynucleotide chain. *Cell* 1982; 28:315–324.

491. DeLange AM, Reddy M, Scraba D: Replication and resolution of cloned poxvirus telomers in vivo generates linear minichromosomes with intact viral hairpin termini. *J Virol* 1986; 59:249–259.

492. Moss B, Winter E, Cooper N: Instability and reiteration of DNA sequences within the vaccinia virus genome. *Proc Natl Acad Sci USA* 1981; 78:614–618.

493. Whittek R, Barbosa E, Cooper JA, et al: Inverted terminal repetition in vaccinia virus DNA encodes early mRNAs. *Nature* 1980; 285:21–25.

494. Cooper JA, Wittek R, Moss B: Hybridization selection and cell-free translation of mRNAs encoded within the inverted terminal repetition of the vaccinia virus genome. *J Virol* 1981; 37:284–294.

495. Wittek R, Cooper JA, Barbosa E, et al: Expression of the vaccinia virus genome: Analysis and mapping of mRNA encoded within the inverted terminal repetition. *Cell* 1980; 21:487–493.

496. Wittek R, Moss B: Tandem repeats within the inverted terminal repetition of vaccinia virus DNA. *Cell* 1980; 21:277–284.

497. Soloski MJ, Holowczak JA: Characterization of supercoiled nucleoprotein complexes released from detergent treated vaccinia virus. *J Virol* 1981; 37:770–783.

498. Payne LG, Norrby E: Adsorption and penetration of enveloped and naked vaccinia virus particles. *J Virol* 1978; 27:19–27.

499. Epstein D, Marsh YV, Schreiber AB, et al: Epidermal growth factor receptor occupancy inhibits vaccinia virus infection. *Nature* 1985; 318:663–665.

500. Stern W, Dales S: Biogenesis of vaccinia. Isolation and characterization of a surface component that elicits antibody suppressing infectivity and cell-cell fusion. *Virology* 1976; 75:232–241.

501. Ichihaski Y, Oie M: Adsorption and penetration of the trypsinized vaccinia virion. *Virology* 1980; 101:50–60.

502. Hirt P, Hiller G, Wittek R: Localization and fine structure of a vaccinia virus gene encoding an envelope antigen. *J Virol* 1986; 58:757–764.

503. Janeczko RA, Rodriguez JF, Esteban M: Studies on the mechanism of entry of vaccinia virus in animal cells. *Arch Virol* 1987; 92:135–150.

504. Rodriguez JF, Paez E, Esteban M: A 14,000-Mr envelope protein of vaccinia is involved in cell fusion and forms covalently linked trimers. *J Virol* 1987; 61:395–404.

505. Paez E, Dallo S, Esteban M: Generation of a dominant 8-Mda deletion at the left terminus of vaccinia virus DNA. *Proc Natl Acad Sci USA* 1985; 82:3365–3369.

506. Oie M, Ichihashi Y: Modification of vaccinia virus penetration proteins analyzed by monoclonal antibodies. *Virology* 1987; 157:449–459.

507. Ichihashi Y, Oie M: Epitope mosaic on the surface proteins of orthopoxviruses. *Virology* 1988; 163:133–144.

508. Dales S, Kajioka R: The cycle of multiplication of vaccinia virus in Earle's strain L cells. I. Uptake and penetration. *Virology* 1964; 24:278–294.

509. Armstrong JA, Metz DH, Young R: The mode of entry of vaccinia virus into L cells. *J Gen Virol* 1973; 21:533–537.

510. Chang A, Metz DH: Further investigations on the mode of entry of vaccinia virus into cells. *J Gen Virol* 1976; 32:275–282.

511. Prescott DM, Kates J, Kirkpatrick JB: Replication of vaccinia virus DNA in enucleated L-cells. *J Mol Biol* 1971; 59:505–508.

512. Pelham HRB, Sykes JMM, Hunt T: Characteristics of a coupled cell-free transcription and translation system directed by vaccinia cores. *Eur J Biochem* 1978; 82:199–209.

513. Venkatesan S, Moss B: In vitro transcription of the inverted terminal repetition of the vaccinia virus genome: Correspondence of initiation and cap sites. *J Virol* 1981; 37:738–747.

514. Kates JR, McAuslan BR: Poxvirus DNA-dependent RNA polymerase. *Proc Natl Acad Sci USA* 1967; 58:134–141.

515. Munyon W, Paoletti E, Grace JT Jr: RNA polymerase activity in purified infectious vaccinia virus. *Proc Natl Acad Sci USA* 1967; 58:2280–2287.

516. Ensinger MJ, Martin S, Paoletti E, et al: Modification of the 5' terminus of mRNA by soluble guanyl and methyl transferases from vaccinia virus. *Proc Natl Acad Sci USA* 1975; 72:3385–3389.

517. Wei CM, Moss B: Methylated nucleotides block 5' terminus of vaccinia virus messenger RNA. *Proc Natl Acad Sci USA* 1975; 72:318–322.

518. Kates J, Beeson J: Ribonucleic acid synthesis in vaccinia virus. II. Synthesis of polyriboadenylic acid. *J Mol Biol* 1970; 50:19–33.

519. Moss B, Rosenblum EN, Paoletti E: Polyadenylate polymerase from vaccinia virus. *Nature* 1973; 254:59–63.

520. Nevins JR, Joklik WK: Poly (A) sequences of vaccinia virus messenger RNA: Nature, mode of addition and function during translation in vitro and in vivo. *Virology* 1975; 63:1–14.

521. Paoletti E: In vitro synthesis of a high molecular weight virion-associated RNA by vaccinia. *J Biol Chem* 1977; 252:866–871.

522. Paoletti E: High molecular weight virion-associated RNA of vaccinia. A possible precursor to 8 to 12 S mRNA. *J Biol Chem* 1977; 252:872–877.

523. Paoletti E, Lipinskas BR: Soluble endoribonuclease activity from vaccinia virus: Specific cleavage of virion associated high molecular weight RNA. *J Virol* 1978; 26:822–824.

524. Bauer WR, Ressner EC, Kates J, et al: A DNA nick-closing enzyme encapsidated in vaccinia virus, partial purification and properties. *Proc Natl Acad Sci USA* 1977; 74:1841–1845.

525. Cooper JA, Wittek R, Moss B: Extension of the transcriptional and translational map of the left end of the vaccinia virus genome to 21 kilobase pairs. *J Virol* 1981; 39:733–745.

526. Moss B, Winters E, Cooper JA: Deletion of a 9000 base-pair segment of the vaccinia virus genome that encodes nonessential polypeptides. *J Virol* 1981; 40:387–395.

527. McAuslan BR: Control of induced thymidine kinase activity in the poxvirus infected cell. *Virology* 1963; 20:162–168.

528. Dubbs DR, Kit S: Isolation and properties of vaccinia mutants deficient in thymidine kinase-inducing activity. *Virology* 1964; 22:214–225.

529. Mbuy GN, Morris RE, Bubel HC: Inhibition of cellular protein synthesis by vaccinia virus surface tubules. *Virology* 1982; 116:137–147.

530. Des Gouttes-Olgiati D, Pogo BGT, Dales S: Biogenesis of vaccinia. Specific inhibition of rapidly labeled host DNA in vaccinia inoculated cells. *Virology* 1976; 71:325–335.

531. Pogo BGT, Dales S: Biogenesis of poxviruses: Further evidence for inhibition of host and virus DNA synthesis by a component of the invading inoculum particle. *Virology* 1974; 58:377–386.

532. Moss B, Rosenblum EN, Garon CF: Glycoprotein synthesis in cells infected with vaccinia virus. III. Purification and biosynthesis of the virion glycoprotein. *Virology* 1973; 55:143–156.

533. Holowczak JA, Joklik WK: Studies of the structural proteins of vaccinia virus. II. Kinetics of the synthesis of individual groups of structural proteins. *Virology* 1967; 33:726–739.

534. Challberg MD, England PT: Purification and properties of the deoxyribonucleic acid polymerase induced by vaccinia virus. *J Biol Chem* 1979; 254:7812–7819.

535. Jungwirth C, Joklik WK: Studies on early enzymes in HeLa cells infected with vaccinia virus. *Virology* 1965; 27:80–93.

536. Magee WE, Miller OV: Immunological evidence for the appearance of a new DNA-polymerase in cells infected with vaccinia virus. *Virology* 1967; 31:64–69.

537. Sambrook J, Shatkin AJ: Polynucleotide ligase activity in cells infected with simian virus 40, polyoma virus, or vaccinia virus. *J Virol* 1969; 4:719–726.

538. McAuslan BR, Kates JR: Regulation of virus-induced deoxyribonucleases. *Proc Natl Acad Sci USA* 1966; 55:1581–1587.

539. Rosemond-Hornbeak H, Moss B: Single-stranded deoxyribonucleic acid–specific nuclease from vaccinia virus. Endonucleolytic and exonucleolytic activities. *J Clin Invest* 1974; 53:3292–3296.

540. Blomquist MC, Hunt LT, Barker WC: Vaccinia virus 19-kilodalton protein: Relationship to several mammalian proteins, including two growth factors. *Proc Natl Acad Sci USA* 1984; 81:7363–7367.

541. Brown JP, Twardzik DR, Marquardt H, et al: Vaccinia virus encodes a polypeptide homologous to epidermal growth factor and transforming growth factor. *Nature* 1985; 313:491–492.

542. Stroobant P, Rice AP, Gullick WJ, et al: Purification and characterization of vaccinia virus growth factor. *Cell* 1985; 42:383–393.

543. Buller RML, Chakrabarti S, Cooper JA, et al: Deletion of the vaccinia virus growth factor gene reduces virus virulence. *J Virol* 1988; 62:866–874.

544. Reisner AH: Similarity between the vaccinia virus 19K early protein and epidermal growth factor. *Nature* 1985; 313:801–803.

545. King CS, Cooper JA, Moss B, et al: Vaccinia virus growth factor stimulates tyrosine protein kinase activity of A431 cell epidermal growth factor receptors. *Mol Cell Biol* 1986; 6:332–336.

546. Chang W, Lim JG, Hellstrom I, et al: Characterization of vaccinia virus growth factor biosynthetic pathway with an antipeptide antiserum. *J Virol* 1988; 62:1080–1083.

547. Venkatesan S, Gershowitz A, Moss B: Complete nucleotide sequence of two adjacent early vaccinia virus genes located within the inverted terminal repetition. *J Virol* 1982; 44:637–646.

548. Rosel JL, Earl PL, Weir JP, et al: Conserved TAAATG sequence at the transcriptional and translational initiation sites of vaccinia virus late genes deduced by structural and functional analysis of the Hind III H genome fragment. *J Virol* 1986; 60:436–449.

549. Lee-Chen G-J, Bourgeois N, Davidson K, et al: Structure of the transcription initiation and termination sequences of seven early genes in the vaccinia virus Hind III D fragment. *Virology* 1988; 163:64–79.

550. Cochran MA, Puckett C, Moss B: In vitro mutagenesis of the promoter region for a vaccinia virus gene: Evidence for tandem early and late regulatory signals. *J Virol* 1985; 54:30–37.

551. Bertholet C, Stocco P, Van Meir E, et al: Functional analysis of the 5' flanking sequence of a vaccinia virus late gene. *EMBO J* 1986; 5:1951–1957.

552. Weir JP, Moss B: Determination of the promoter region of an early vaccinia virus gene encoding thymidine kinase. *Virology* 1987; 158:206–210.

553. Wittek R, Cooper J, Barbosa E, et al: Expression of the vaccinia virus genome. Analysis and mapping of mRNAs and polypeptides encoded within the inverted terminal repetition. *Cell* 1980; 21:487–493.

554. Oda K, Joklik WK: Hybridization and sedimentation studies on "early" and "late" vaccinia messenger RNA. *J Mol Biol* 1967; 27:395–419.

555. Mahr A, Roberts B: Arrangement of late mRNAs transcribed from a 7.1 kilobase EcoRI vaccinia virus DNA fragment. *J Virol* 1984; 49:510–520.

556. Yuen L, Moss B: Oligonucleotide sequence signaling transcriptional termination of vaccinia virus early genes. *Proc Natl Acad Sci USA* 1987; 84:6417–6421.

557. Dahl R, Kates JR: Intracellular structure containing vaccinia DNA: Isolation and characterization. *Virology* 1970; 42:453–462.

558. Polisky B, Kates J: Vaccinia virus intracellular DNA-protein complex: Biochemical characteristics of associated protein. *Virology* 1972; 49:168–179.

559. Sarov I, Joklik W: Characterization of intermediates in the uncoating of vaccinia virus DNA. *Virology* 1972; 50:593–602.

560. Cains J: The initiation of vaccinia infection. *Virology* 1960; 11:603–623.

560a. Roseman NA, Hruby DE: Nucleotide sequence and transcript organization of a region of the vaccinia virus genome which encodes a constitutively expressed gene required for DNA replication. *J Virol* 1987; 61:1398–1406.

560b. Rempel RE, Anderson MK, Evans E, et al: Temperature-sensitive vaccinia virus mutants identify a gene with an essential role in viral replication. *J Virol* 1990; 64:574–583.

561. Esteban M, Flores L, Holowczak JA: Model for vaccinia virus DNA replication. *Virology* 1977; 83:467–473.

562. Moyer RW, Graves RL: The mechanism of cytoplasmic orthopoxvirus DNA replication. *Cell* 1981; 27:391–401.

563. Pogo BGT: Elimination of naturally occurring crosslinks in vaccinia virus DNA after viral penetration into cells. *Proc Natl Acad Sci USA* 1977; 74:1739–1742.

564. Ball LA: High frequency recombination in vaccinia virus DNA. *J Virol* 1987; 61:1788–1795.

565. Evans DH, Stuart D, McFadden G: High levels of genetic recombination among cotransfected plasmid DNAs in poxvirus-infected mammalian cells. *J Virol* 1988; 62:367–375.

566. Salzman NP, Sebring ED: Sequential formation of vaccinia virus proteins and viral deoxyribonucleic acid. *J Virol* 1967; 1:16–23.

567. Pluienniczak A, Schroeder E, Zettlmeissl G, et al: Nucleotide sequence of a cluster of early and late genes in a conserved segment of the vaccinia virus genome. *Nucleic Acids Res* 1985; 13:985–998.

568. Mahr A, Roberts B: Organization of six early transcripts synthesized from a vaccinia virus EcoRI DNA fragment. *J Virol* 1984; 49:497–509.

569. Lee-Chen G-J, Niles EG: Transcription and translation mapping of the 13 genes in the vaccinia virus Hind III D fragment. *Virology* 1988; 163:52–63.

570. Golini F, Kates JR: A soluble transcription system derived from purified vaccinia virions. *J Virol* 1985; 53:205–213.

571. Bertholet C, Van Meir E, ten Heggeler-Bordier B, et al: Vaccinia virus produces late mRNAs by discontinuous synthesis. *Cell* 1987; 50:153–162.

572. Schwer B, Visca P, Vos JC, et al: Discontinuous transcription or RNA processing of vaccinia virus late messengers results in a 5' poly (A) leader. *Cell* 1987; 50:163–169.

572a. Ahn B-Y, Moss B: Capped poly(A) leaders of variable lengths at the 5' ends of vaccinia virus late in mRNAs. *J Virol* 1989; 63:226–232.

573. Sharp PA: Trans splicing: Variation on a familiar theme? *Cell* 1987; 50:147–148.

574. Miner JN, Weinrick SL, Hruby DE: Molecular dissection of cis-acting regulatory elements from 5'-proximal regions of a vaccinia virus late gene cluster. *J Virol* 1988; 62:297–304.

575. Lee-Chen G-J, Niles EG: Map positions of the 5' ends of eight mRNAs synthesized from the late genes in the vaccinia virus Hind III D fragment. *Virology* 1988; 163:80–92.

576. Kaverin NV, Varich NL, Surgay VV, et al: A quantitative estimation of poxvirus genome fraction transcribed as "early" and "late" mRNA. *Virology* 1975; 65:112–119.

577. Boone RF, Moss B: Sequence complexity and relative abundance of vaccinia virus mRNAs synthesized in vivo and in vitro. *J Virol* 1978; 26:554–569.

578. Paoletti E, Grady LJ: Transcriptional complexity of vaccinia virus in vivo and in vitro. *J Virol* 1977; 23:608–615.

579. Cabrera CV, Esteban M, McCarron R, et al: Vaccinia virus transcription: Hybridization of mRNA to restriction fragments of vaccinia DNA. *Virology* 1978; 86:102–114.

580. Broyles SS, Moss B: Sedimentation of an RNA polymerase complex from vaccinia virus that specifically initiates and terminates transcription. *Mol Cell Biol* 1987; 7:7–14.

581. Baroudy BM, Moss B: Purification and characterization of a DNA-dependent RNA polymerase from vaccinia virions. *J Biol*

Chem 1980; 255:4372–4380.

582. Spencer E, Schuman S, Hurwitz J: Purification and properties of vaccinia virus DNA-dependent RNA polymerase. *J Biol Chem* 1980; 255:5388–5395.

583. Weinrich SL, Hruby DE: Noncoordinate regulation of a vaccinia virus late gene cluster. *J Virol* 1987; 61:639–645.

583a. Wright CF, Moss B: Identification of factors specific for transcription of the late class of vaccinia virus genes. *J Virol* 1989; 63:4224–4233.

584. Hruby DE, Ball LA: Control of expression of the vaccinia virus thymidine kinase gene. *J Virol* 1981; 40:456–464.

585. Vassef A, Ben-Hamida F, Dru A, et al: Translational control of early protein synthesis at the late stage of vaccinia virus infection. *Virology* 1982; 118:45–53.

586. McAuslan BR: The induction and repression of thymidine kinase in the poxvirus-infected HeLa cell. *Virology* 1963; 21:383–389.

587. McAuslan BR, Kates JR: Regulation of virus-induced deoxyribonucleases. *Proc Natl Acad Sci USA* 1966; 55:1581–1587.

588. Dales S, Mosbach EH: Vaccinia as a model for membrane biogenesis. *Virology* 1968; 35:564–583.

589. Hiller G, Hansjörg E, Weber K: Acyl bis (monoacylglycero) phosphate, assumed to be a marker for lysosomes is a major phospholipid of vaccinia virions. *Virology* 1981; 113:761–764.

590. Silver M, Dales S: Biogenesis of vaccinia: Interrelationship between post-translational cleavage, virus assembly and maturation. *Virology* 1982; 117:341–356.

591. Katz E, Moss B: Formation of a vaccinia virus structural polypeptide from a higher molecular weight precursor: Inhibition by rifampicin. *Proc Natl Acad Sci USA* 1970; 677–684.

592. Medzon E, Bauer H: Structural features of vaccinia virus released by negative staining, sectioning and freeze etching. *Virology* 1970; 40:860–867.

593. Mitchiner MB: The envelope of vaccinia and orf viruses: An electron cytochemical investigation. *J Gen Virol* 1969; 5:211–220.

594. Payne LG, Kristensson K: Effect of glycosylation inhibitors on the release of enveloped vaccinia virus. *J Virol* 1982; 41:367–375.

595. Shida H, Dales S: Biogenesis of vaccinia: Molecular basis for the hemagglutination-negative phenotype of the 1HD-W strain. *Virology* 1982; 117:219–237.

596. Krempien V, Schneider L, Hiller G, et al: Conditions for poxvirus-specific microvilli formation studies during synchronized virus assembly. *Virology* 1981; 113:556–564.

597. Morgan C, Ellison SA, Rose HM, et al: Structure and development of viruses observed in the electron microscope. II. Vaccinia and fowlpox viruses. *J Exp Med* 1954; 100:301–310.

Replication of RNA Viruses

Terry W. Fenger

The mechanisms of RNA virus replication described in this chapter are diverse, each replication scheme showing unique features. As a matter of convention, the nucleotide sequences constituting viral messenger RNAs (mRNAs) during replication are designated as having positive polarities. This provides a means for the classification of RNA virus as (1) negative-stranded (− polarity) viruses, if they have genomes with nucleotide sequences comlementary to those present in mRNAs, or (2) positive-stranded (+ polarity) viruses, if they have genomes with sequences identical to those found in mRNAs. In addition, some viruses contain double-stranded RNA; complementary RNA strands (+ and − polarity) base-pair to form genomic RNAs.

Members of the *Orthomyxoviridae, Rhabdoviridae,* and *Paramyxoviridae* are negative-stranded RNA viruses that will be considered in this chapter. *Picornaviridae, Togaviridae, Flaviviridae,* and *Coronaviridae* are virus families consisting of positive-stranded RNA viruses, while members of the *Reoviridae* have double-stranded RNA genomes. In addition to the polarity differences among viral genomes, these viruses can be distinguished based on the segmentation of viral RNAs.

Viruses with segmented genomes include orthomyxoviruses and reoviruses, while picornaviruses, togaviruses, flaviviruses, coronaviruses, rhabdoviruses, and paramyxoviruses all have unsegmented genomes.

The polarity of the viral RNAs determines the mechanisms by which viruses replicate and synthesize proteins. Genomes of RNA viruses having single-stranded RNAs of plus polarity can be directly translated in infected cells without the requirement of viral mRNA synthesis.

Replication of negative- and double-stranded RNA viruses, however, requires that transcription from genomic RNA occur prior to translation. Since normal cells lack an enzyme that transcribes RNA templates into complementary RNA strands, the latter viruses must encode the appropriate enzyme(s) during their replication cycles. Furthermore, the enzyme must be incorporated into progeny virus particles in order to initiate transcription and replication during subsequent infections.

PICORNAVIRUSES

Virus Structure

Picornaviruses are small, nonenveloped viruses (27 nm) having icosahedral capsids composed of four structural proteins: VP_1 (1D), VP_2 (1B), VP_3 (1C), and VP_4 (1A) (Figure 3–1).[1–3] (Several systems of nomenclature for designating poliovirus proteins have been developed over the years. More traditional designations are used here for capsid proteins VP_1, VP_2, VP_3, VP_4, and VP_g followed by a newer L434 system written within parentheses. The L434 designation refers to the number of final cleavage products including leader protein [L] and nine other proteins, which are derived from the three primary cleavage products of the viral polyprotein [see below]. The latter system is employed solely for designating the noncapsid viral proteins.)[4] Genomic RNA (7.4 kb) is single-stranded and has a viral protein, VP_g, covalently linked to uridylic acid at the 5′ terminus of RNA;[5–7] poly (A) is present in heterogenous lengths at the 3′ end.[8] The genome polarity is the same as that of mRNA (+), and therefore isolated RNA can transfect cells and act directly as mRNA.

Attachment, Penetration, Uncoating

The replication cycle of poliovirus, the most extensively investigated member of the family *Picornaviridae,* begins with attachment of virus particles to specific receptors (ICAM-1) on cell surfaces. It has been proposed that the receptor complexes, possessing five-fold symmetry, project from the cell surface. The receptor complexes possibly associate with the vertices of the capsid; each possesses five pores or canyons peripherally oriented around the vertex.[9] Thus the five symmetric units of the receptor match the five pores at the vertex. Although one such association yields a low-avidity, reversible interaction, numerous receptor interactions with vertices produce tightly bound particles. The receptor interactions alone result in the relocation of VP_4 capsid protein from an internal position to a more external site on the virus particle. Virus particles enter cells within endosomes where

at low pH the virus particle is either partially or fully uncoated. Concomitantly, a virion-associated protein kinase, which is stimulated by divalent cations, phosphorylates capsid proteins.[10] This process may facilitate uncoating of the virus particles and depends on the presence of cellular adenosine triphosphate (ATP).[11] Furthermore, if partially uncoated virus particles are released from endosomes they bind to the endoplasmic reticulum (ER) to be fully uncoated and release RNA into the cytoplasm. Poliovirus strains have different binding affinities for cells from different host species; this suggests that more than one receptor for poliovirus may exist.[12–14]

Primary Translation

Within the cytoplasm genomic RNA acts as messenger which necessitates removal of VP_g by an enzyme detected in both infected or uninfected cells.[15–19] Poliovirus mRNA has a relatively long, noncoding leader sequence (L) of about 745 nucleotides at its 5′ end which precedes the primary initiation site for translation.[20, 21] Although several AUG initiation codons reside within this region, most are immediately followed by a termination codon, and only the one AUG apparently acts in initiation of translation.[22] Within the L sequence there are subsequences exhibiting partial homology with ribosomal RNA which may help bind the 40S ribosomal subunit to a specific site.[23, 24] Multiple functions map within the 5′-noncoding region which are involved not only in translation but also in RNA replication, stabilization of RNA, RNA encapsidation, and in determining neurovirulence.[25, 26] Translation efficiency of poliovirus mRNA is determined by cis-acting sites in the noncoding region, which reduce translation in certain cell types and in vitro translation systems. Deletion of nucleotide sequences in the 5′ half of the noncoding region can overcome translation inhibition.[27] In addition, sequences in the other half of the noncoding region allow translation in a manner which does not require a CAP structure at its 5′ terminus (as in the case of most eukaryotic mRNAs).

Messenger RNAs in membrane-associated polysomes are then translated into one continuous protein or polyprotein of 247 kd molecular weight (mol wt). Translation terminates about 71 nucleotides short of the 3′ end of mRNA.[28] The full-length polyprotein is subsequently cleaved into 11 polypeptide products through a sequential series of cleavage steps (Figure 3–1,a).[29] Primary cleavage of polyprotein P123 yields smaller polyproteins, P1, P2, and P3, having molecular weights of 97 kd, 65 kd, and 84 kd, respectively.[30, 31] During translation the nascent polyprotein is cleaved at the junction between P1 and P2. This cleavage occurs between tyrosine-glycine (YG) and is mediated by viral protease 2A (located adjacent to the cleavage site) through an autocatalytic process.[32] Tyrosine-glycine alone may be insufficient to signal specific cleavage at this site and adjacent amino acids apparently help in cleavage site recognition.[33]

Following translation of poliovirus mRNA and primary cleavage, P1, P2, and P3 are cleaved sequentially to yield both structural proteins of virus particles and nonstructural polypeptides, some with enzymatic functions necessary for viral replication. The viral proteinase, 3C, is derived from P3 and cleaves between glutamine-glycine within P1, P2, and P3 to yield ten products.[34] P1 is cleaved to VP_0 (1AB), VP_3 (1C), and VP_1 (1D), P2 forms 2A (a proteinase),

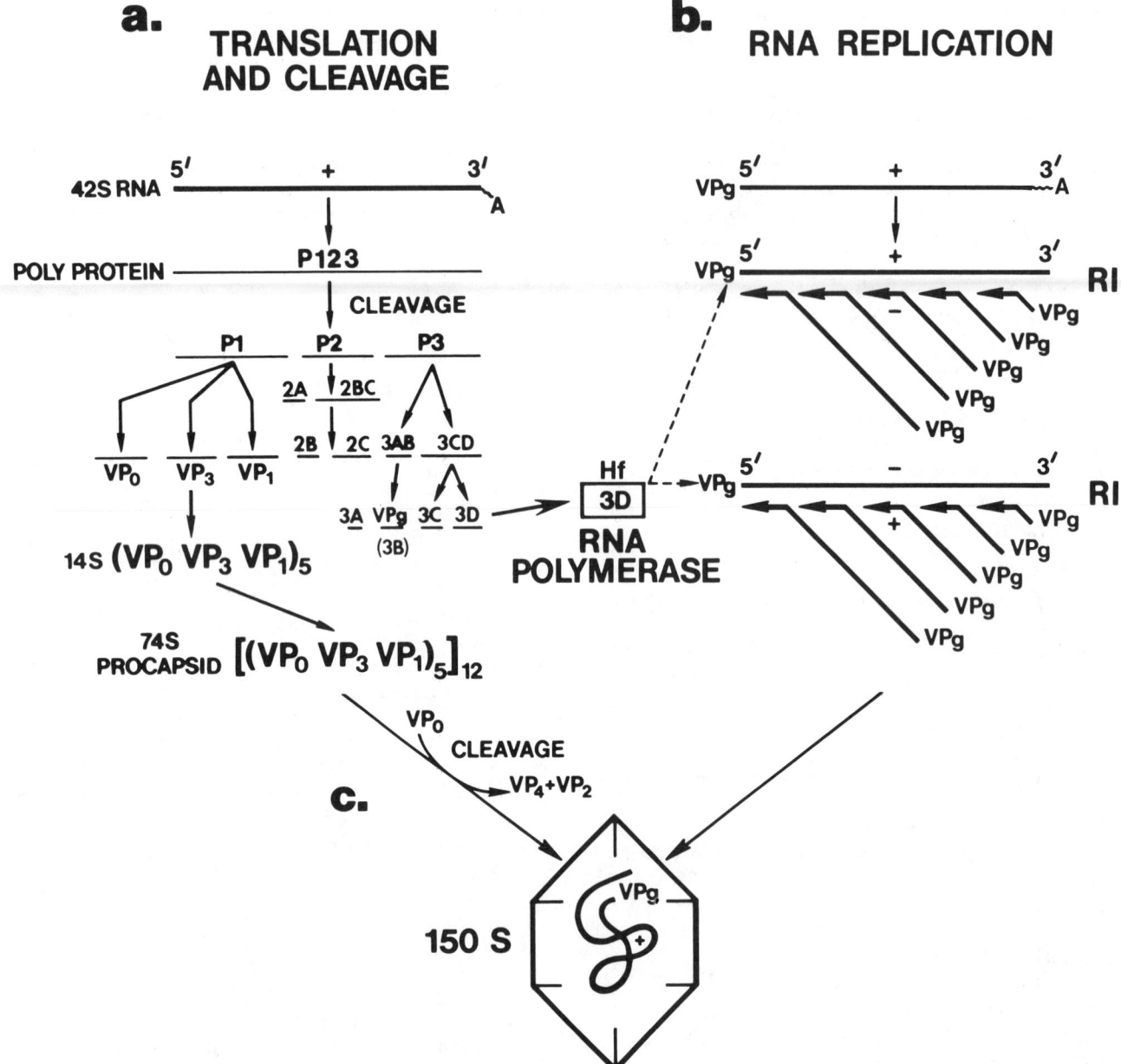

Figure 3–1. Replication of poliovirus. Parental RNA acts as messenger following the removal of VP_g. **a,** primary translation of viral RNA yields a polyprotein (P123) which is cleaved into smaller polyproteins P1, P2, and P3. P1 is cleaved into structural proteins VP_0, VP_3, VP_1; VP_0 is further cleaved to VP_4 and VP_2 during viral assembly (c). P3 is cleaved into polymerase protein 3D and 3C proteinase, as well as VP_g (3B). Protein 2A derived from P2 may be a protease. **b,** RNA replication occurs through replicative intermediates (RI) to yield progeny RNA and is mediated by a complex consisting of 3D polymerase plus host factor (Hf). **c,** viral maturation includes aggregation and cleavage of P1 to form a 14S pentamer (VP_0, VP_3, VP_1)$_5$. Twelve pentamers constitute the procapsid to which viral RNA is added. VP_0 is then cleaved and mature poliovirus is formed.

2B, and 2C, and P3 forms 3A, 3B (VP$_g$), 3C (a proteinase), and 3D (RNA polymerase) (see Figure 3–1,a).[35] It has also been determined that 3C proteinase can autocatalytically cleave QG sites at its flanking sequences.[36] VP$_0$ (1AB) is further cleaved to yield structural proteins VP$_4$ (1A) and VP$_2$ (1B) within virus particles during the later stages of maturation.[37] This latter cleavage event apparently does not involve either 2A or 3C proteinases nor cellular enzymes. VP$_0$ (1AB) cleavage occurs at a time when the newly formed virus particles are impervious to exogenous proteases and therefore the cleavage must occur within particles (see below).[38]

RNA Replication

Following primary translation, RNA replication ensues (Figure 3–1,b). Polyprotein cleavage products VP$_g$ (3B) and 3D (polymerase or POL) are necessary for the replication process. VP$_g$ is bound to the 5' end of plus-polarity genomic RNA, whereas 3D POL serves as an RNA-dependent RNA polymerase (replicase).[39–41] Poliovirus RNA replication occurs within a replication complex associated with membrane vesicles located in the cytoplasm of infected cells.[42, 43] Protein 2BC is involved in the formation of these vesicles from membranes of the rough endoplasmic reticulum (RER). Cleavage of 2BC produces 2C which binds the replication complex to these membranous structures.[44]

Negative-strand RNA replication initiates from the 3' end [poly (A) region] of genomic RNA using a primer molecule. The nature of the primer is a matter of controversy and is based on data from in vitro systems. In one model (model 1), the poly (A) tail of the 3' end of genomic RNA may serve as a primer and may be extended by a host factor (HF),[45] which has a molecular weight of approximately 68 kd and has terminal uridylyltransferase activity.[46, 47] Thus a poly (U) extension formed by HF is capable of bending back to base-pair with the 3' poly (A) tail to form a hairpin structure, which would serve as a primer.[48] Initiation of RNA synthesis by HF may also require a phosphorylation step. HF is capable of autophosphorylation and hydrolysis of ATP is necessary for RNA replication to initiate.[49] Alternatively, evidence that VP$_g$ (3B) serves as a primer (model 2) for negative-strand synthesis comes from the isolation of VP$_g$-pUU or more extended products, which may base-pair with poly (A) to form a primer structure.[50, 51] Critics of this concept suggest that VP$_g$-UUU is only an aberrant form derived from the positive polarity template itself.

Following hairpin formation (model 1) the 5' end of the negative-strand RNA can be generated by nuclease cleavage within the poly (U) segment with the addition of VP$_g$ to the 5' terminus. The HF requirement can be bypassed by the addition of oligo (U) primer which binds directly to 3' poly (A) of the template RNA in in vitro systems.[52] Using either oligo (U) primer or VP$_g$ the template strand is copied to form a full-length negative-polarity strand by 3D POL. A resulting structure found in poliovirus-infected cells consisting of template RNA and attached nascent RNA strands at successive stages of synthesis is designated as a replicative intermediate (RI) (see Figure 3–1,b).[53, 54] Synthesis of new genomic RNAs from negative-polarity RNA templates again requires a primer and viral RNA polymerase. In this case VP$_g$ may serve as a primer since oligo (U) does not seem to fulfill this role and VP$_g$ is bound to the 5' end of progeny genomic RNA through a covalent linkage between a tyrosine residue of VP$_g$ and uridylic

acid.[55–58] Positive-stranded RNA synthesized in this manner can be either translated or incorporated into progeny virus particles as genomic RNA, which again depends on whether VP$_g$ remains attached to the 5' end or dissociates from it.

In mixed infections involving different serotypes of poliovirus or avirulent and virulent strains of poliovirus type 1, recombination between genomic RNAs has been demonstrated.[59] Recombination occurs primarily in the middle region of the viral genomes, although recombination events outside of this region have been detected. The mechanism by which recombination occurs (possibly breakage and reunion or copy choice) also introduces point mutations within the recombinant RNA.[60]

Virus Assembly

Following RNA replication and viral protein synthesis, virus particles form and mature in the cytoplasm of infected cells. It has shown that encapsidation of progeny genomes occurs in association with smooth membranes,[61] which may depend on initial alteration of capsid polyprotein precursor P1. Capsid protein VP$_4$ and its precursors VP$_0$ and P1 are modified by the addition of myristic acid to their N-termini, which possibly facilitates virion assembly by allowing an association between capsid protein(s) and membrane vesicles. Myristylation of P1 may enable it to associate with membranes during the initial steps of protein cleavage, yet allow dissociation of mature virion or procapsids from membranes during the final stages. These membrane structures are probably analogous to those involved in RNA replication.[62]

With the accumulation of genome RNA and viral proteins, morphogenesis proceeds through several stages (Figure 3–1,c). During the first stage, polyprotein P1 aggregates to form a pentameric structure with a sedimentation rate of 14S and the polyprotein is then cleaved into VP$_0$, VP$_1$, and VP$_3$.[63–65] Aggregates of 12 pentameric units constitute the 74S procapsid which encapsidates RNA to form a provirion of 150S.[66, 67] Concomitant with RNA encapsidation, VP$_0$ is cleaved within the interior of provirions. The mechanism of cleavage does not involve either 2A or 3C proteases, which are active at other cleavage sites along the polyprotein. VP$_0$ is cleaved by autocatalytic process whereby amino groups on RNA bases abstract protons from serine located 10 amino acids (AA) from the C-terminus of VP$_0$. This in turn allows a nucleophilic attack of an asparigine located at the VP$_4$-VP$_2$ junction within VP$_0$, which cleaves the precursor into VP$_4$ plus VP$_2$.[38, 68, 69]

Effects on Host Cells

Shortly after initiation of poliovirus infection, many cellular processes terminate. In particular, the polysomes containing cellular mRNAs dissociate, leaving the ribosomes free to form new polysomes with viral mRNA.[70, 71] Although numerous explanations have been advanced to account for the rapid inhibition of host protein synthesis, the selective inhibition of the translation of 5'-capped mRNAs will be described. In uninfected eukaryotic cells the association of capped mRNAs with ribosomes is mediated by a cap-binding protein complex (eIF-4F).[72] This complex consists of at least three cellular proteins: cap-binding protein (CBP, 24 kd),[73] eIF-4A (50 kd),[74] and protein 220 (p220, 220 kd).[75] CBP binds directly to 5' cap structures which in turn facilitates binding of eIF-4A and p220. This specific recognition of cap structures along with the binding of the 40S ribosomal subunit to cellular mRNAs, which is mediated by the eIF-2-GTP-Met-tRNA complex, is prerequisite for the initiation of cellular translation. Poliovirus infection, however, causes the cleavage of p220 so that it is not able to bind properly within the eIF-4F complex.[75] Viral proteinase 2A is believed to induce cellular protease(s) which is responsible for cleavage of p220.[76] As stated previously, poliovirus mRNA lacks a cap structure and is therefore not affected by p220 cleavage. The ability of ribosomes to bind to a recognition site at an internal location within the noncoding region of viral mRNA may eliminate the requirement for a capped 5' terminus.

It has been determined that 50% to 75% of host protein synthesis is inhibited either by the above mechanism or other early-acting process. Total shutoff of host protein synthesis requires an additional process that occurs after viral RNA replication.

Not only is cell protein synthesis inhibited, but cell RNA synthesis rapidly terminates after poliovirus infection.[77, 78] RNA synthesis directed by cellular DNA-dependent RNA polymerases I, II, and III are each inhibited, but not necessarily at the same rate.[79, 80] Inhibition does not occur because of degradation of RNA or inactivation of RNA polymerase, but may depend on the absence or inactivation of factor(s) associated with the polymerases and necessary for their transcriptional functions.[81]

Intracellular structural changes also accompany poliovirus infection of cells in culture.[82–84] Within infected cell nuclei, chromatin condenses and marginates at the nuclear membrane followed by the appearance of eosinophilic inclusion bodies. Nuclei also become smaller and irregular in shape. Smooth membrane vacuoles first form in the cytoplasm at about three hours after infection in areas surrounding the nucleus which corresponds to sites of viral RNA replication.[85] Although these changes are seen in unsynchronized poliovirus-infected cells, little or no cytopathic effect (CPE) was seen in synchronized mitotic cells even though the latter cells produced comparable amounts of infectious virus. Thus, CPE is not a necessary characteristic in viral replication and may require specific physiologic or metabolic states of cells to be manifested.[86]

TOGAVIRUSES

The *Togaviridae* consists of a large number of human pathogens which are classified in the *Alphavirus* and *Rubivirus* genera. In this discussion Sindbis (SIN) and Semliki Forest viruses (SFV) serve as representative viruses for other members of this family.

Virus Structure

Togavirus particles vary in diameter from 45 to 76 nm for alphaviruses and approximately 60 nm for rubella virus (rubivirus).[87] All togaviruses have an icosahedral capsid composed of one capsid protein (C) which is organized into 32 capsomers (Figure 3–2,d).[88, 89] Envelopes surrounding the viral capsids of SIN[90] and SFV[91, 92] have embedded in their lipid bilayers two (E1 and E2) or three (E1, E2 and E3) membrane proteins, respectively (see Figure 3–2,d). E1 serves as a hemagglutinin, whereas E2 elicits neutralizing antibodies. E1 and E2 interact to form heterodimers which appear as spikes by electron microscopy. Located within the nucleocapsid of SIN and SFV are genomic RNAs with S values of 49 and 42, respectively, which correspond to approximately 11.7 kilobases (kb). Genomic RNA is infectious, having the same polarity (+) as mRNA. It also has the hallmarks of most eukaryotic cell mRNAs, a cap structure at its 5' terminus and poly (A) at its 3' end.[93, 94]

Attachment, Penetration, Uncoating

Virus particles can agglutinate erythrocytes over a narrow pH range through interactions of envelope glycoproteins (E1) with cell receptors. The receptors on erythrocytes appear to be phospholipids rather than glycoproteins, although histocompatibility antigens (H-2K and H-2d) may be part of receptors on cultured cells.[13, 14, 95]

Togaviruses can attach to a wide range of cultured cells including those from invertebrates and vertebrates.[96] Virus particles gain entry into the cell cytoplasm primarily by endocytosis. The viral envelope fuses with the membrane of the endocytic vesicle, the process being facilitated by its low pH which causes a conformational alteration of E2 glycoprotein. The role of E2 in the penetration process was demonstrated by isolating mutants with a single base substitution in the E2 gene. Avirulent isolates were shown to possess an arginine in place of serine at position 114 in E2 glycoprotein. Coupled with an avirulent phenotype, the viral isolate was capable of rapid penetration. Conversely, virulent virus penetrated more slowly.[97] The mechanism of release of RNA from nucleocapsids has been reviewed.[98]

Primary Translation

Within the cytoplasm of infected cells, genomic RNA (SIN) is then translated into two polyproteins,[99] NS1-NS2-NS3 and NS1-NS2-NS3-NS4, which both serve as precursors for nonstructural (NS) proteins.[100] NS1-NS2-NS3-NS4 (70 kd-86 kd-60 kd-72 kd) corresponds in length to approximately two thirds of the genome extending from the 5' terminus (see Figure 3–2,a).[101, 102] Although translation of NS1-NS2-NS3 terminates at a stop codon, this can be bypassed possibly by suppression to yield the longer translation product.[103] The restricted synthesis of the NS4-containing polyprotein is reflected by its lower levels within infected cells. Proteolytic cleavage between NS proteins may be mediated by NS2, which has characteristics of a serine protease. NS1-NS2-NS3-NS4 polyprotein for SFV seems to be the primary translation product, since a termination codon between NS3 and NS4 is absent.[104] Although NS4 is synthesized in larger amounts in the latter replication cycle, it may have a shorter half-life than other NS proteins.[105]

RNA Replication

Following primary translation, viral 42S or 49S (SFV or SIN) RNA is replicated. Positive-polarity RNA serves as a template for synthesis of full-length negative-polarity RNA. Analysis of SIN-defective RNAs synthesized in rat cells detected rat tRNA for aspartic acid covalently linked to 5' termini of the defective RNAs.[106] These and other investigations suggest that cellular tRNA may act as a primer for viral RNA synthesis, perhaps explaining the relationship seen between the status of the cell nucleus and the extent of viral replication. Based on sequence comparisons of NS proteins with those of known RNA polymerases, NS4 has a gly-asp-asp consensus sequence, which suggests that it has polymerase activity.[107] Thus NS4 (72 kd) alone or in combination with other viral NS1, NS2 (70 kd, 86 kd), and/or host factors proteins (see Figure 3–2,a) is probably involved in RNA replication. Negative-polarity RNAs then serve as templates for synthesis of plus-strand RNAs of two different sizes: 42S and 26S RNAs.

During SFV RNA replication, the viral RNA polymerase is involved in two events: the (+) 42S RNA → (−) 42S RNA synthesis and the (−) 42S RNA → (+) 42S RNA and (+) 26S RNA synthesis (see Figure 3–2,b).[100] At about three hours after infection, (−) 42S RNA synthesis terminates, while (+) 42S and (+) 26S RNA synthesis continue at constant rates. Differential synthesis of the latter two RNAs is also seen. The 26S RNA is synthesized at least in a threefold excess over 42S RNA. Selective synthesis of plus RNA over minus RNA after the early periods of infection indicates that possibly two forms of the polymerase (RNA polymerase* and RNA polymerase**) may be involved in RNA replication, the polymerase involved in negative-polarity RNA synthesis possibly having a shorter half-life.[108–110] Full-length (+) 42S RNAs are complete copies of their negative-stranded RNA templates and are either destined to be incorporated as genomes into progeny virus, employed in secondary translation, or as templates in a second round of RNA replication.[111, 112]

Transcription-Translation

The 26S RNA corresponds to a 3.7-kb sequence at the 3′ end of SFV genome RNA (see Figure 3–2,c).[113] Transcription of 26S RNA requires the binding of RNA polymerase to a highly con-

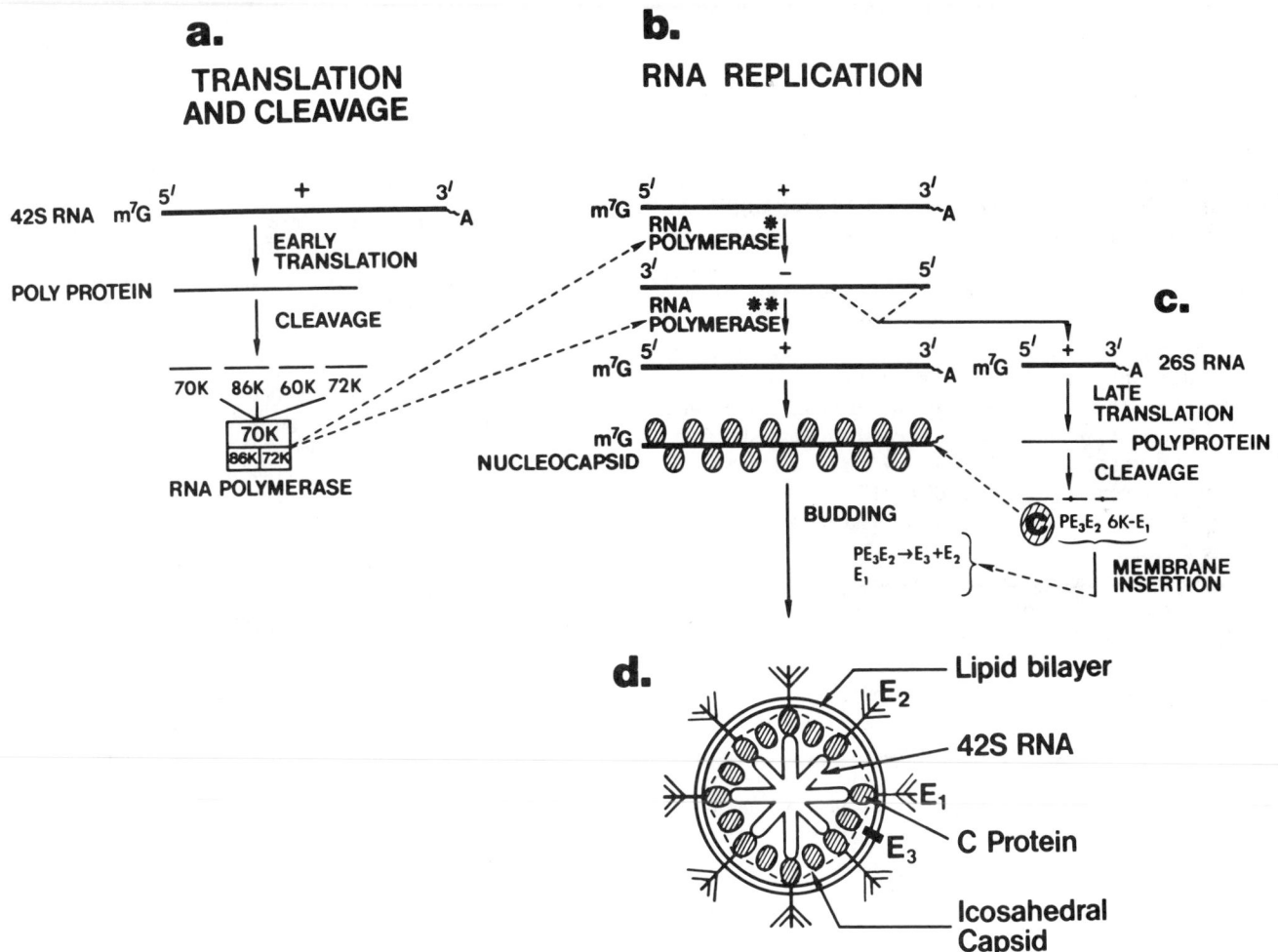

Figure 3–2. Replication of togavirus (Semliki Forest virus). Viral RNA is translated into a polyprotein which is cleaved into proteins NS1, NS2, NS3, and NS4, having molecular weights of approximately 70, 86, 60, and 72 kd, respectively. Protein NS4 (72 kd) in combination with other viral proteins, perhaps 86- (NS2) and 70(NS1)-kd proteins, forms the RNA polymerase **(a)**. Two polymerase activities (*) and (**) are involved in RNA replication which entails the formation of replicative intermediates **(b;** see Figure 3–1). Negative-polarity viral RNA serves as a template for synthesis of full-length viral RNA and a 26S mRNA **(b)**. The latter is translated into a polyprotein from which two precursor envelope proteins (PE_3E_2 and $6K$-E_1) and capsid (C) protein, are derived **(c)**. Viral maturation occurs by budding of nucleocapsids through modified cell membranes with E1 and PE_3E_2 inserted into the lipid bilayer; the latter protein is cleaved to E2 plus E3 during the budding process **(d)**.

served internal site of approximately 21 nucleotides, located on the negative-polarity RNA.[114] Subgenomic 26S RNA serves in part as the mRNA for a 130-kd polyprotein.[115–117] Fifty-one nucleotides at the 5′ terminus of 26S RNA are not translated[118] and a single initiation codon is employed for translation. This codon, however, is not utilized for translation as part of the 42S (+) RNA, possibly due to secondary structure within the region, which masks recognition sequences. Following RNA replication selective translation of 26S RNA in preference to 42S RNA–directed translation depends on the synthesis and accumulation of C protein, which inhibits translation of the latter RNA.[100]

After their formation, the SFV polyproteins are cleaved proteolytically through successive steps into four structural proteins: C, E1, E2, and E3 (see Figure 3–2,c).[115–117] Proteolysis of togavirus polyproteins occurs during nascent polyprotein translation. The N-terminal end of the polyprotein, corresponding to C protein, is synthesized free of a direct association with ER membranes.[119] Based on amino acid sequence analysis, the C protein possesses a sequence characteristic of serine proteases within its C-terminal region.[120] C protein can autocatalytically cleave itself from the nascent polyprotein, thereby exposing a hydrophobic signal sequence at the N-terminus of the adjacent region.[121, 122] Ribosomes in association with ER membranes then translate the precursor protein of E3 and E2 glycoproteins (pE3E2 = 62 kd).[123] The hydrophobic signal sequence of pE3E2 allows translocation of nascent chains across the ER membrane; the process terminates with the association of a C-terminal anchor sequence with the lipid bilayer.[124] A second signal sequence located at the N-terminus of a 6-kd linker protein, which separates E2 and E1 in the polyprotein, is responsible for translocation of 6-kd + E1 protein across the membrane.[125] E1 is anchored into the ER membrane and the 6-kd protein is removed from its N-terminus by cell protease, signalase. Following their synthesis pE3E2 and E1 often remain together in the form of a complex. Cleavage of pE3E2 to form E3 and E2 glycoproteins occurs later in Golgi membranes, probably by a cellular protease.[126]

The three membrane proteins, E1, E2, and E3, are glycosylated in the ER through the addition of three asparagine-linked, high-mannose chains to pE3E2 and either two chains to E1 of SIN or a single chain to E1 of SFV.[127–129] pE3E2 is further modified through the acetylation of its N-terminal amino acid, as well as at several sites near its C-terminus.[130, 131] E1 glycoprotein is also modified by addition of fatty acid chains.[132,133] Immature glycoproteins are transported to the Golgi apparatus for conversion of high-mannose chains into complex forms which may terminate with sialic acids. pE3E2 is also cleaved at this point. Mature glycoproteins are then transported to the plasma membrane to form sites for viral budding.[134, 135]

Virus Assembly

Nucleocapsid formation occurs rapidly following the synthesis of C protein and (+) 42S RNA. Nucleocapsid assembly is a multistage process which requires the formation of an initial complex between newly synthesized C protein and the 60S ribosomal subunit derived from ribosomes involved in C protein translation. Core proteins then associate with viral RNA through their N-termini to form subcomplexes. These structures further aggregate

to form the larger viral core. The necessity for this stepwise assembly process is emphasized by the failure of C proteins to self-assemble to form empty capsids. Apparently the initial C protein–RNA interactions are an essential step for initiating assembly of nucleocapsids.[98] Newly formed capsids migrate to the plasma membrane budding sites, where C proteins interact with the C-termini of E2 glycoproteins which project from the cytoplasmic side of the plasma membrane.[136] Budding then ensues to form extracellular virus particles. SFV retains all three glycoproteins as part of its envelope (see Figure 3–2,d), where SIN envelopes lack E3 and retain E1 and E2.[137, 138]

Effects on Host Cells

The production of SIN particles is rapid, with 10^4 particles per cell being synthesized per hour. Extensive CPE is seen in infected vertebrate cells with granular cytoplasmic inclusions and, in some infections, proliferation of cytoplasmic membranes. Fusion of cells to form syncytia often occurs as a result of infections by one of several alphaviruses. This occurs at mildly acidic pH with the expenditure of ATP.[139] In addition, most host cell macromolecular synthesis is terminated within two to three hours after infection.[140] Shutoff of host protein synthesis seems to be controlled by the availability of C protein, which inhibits initiation of translation.[141]

SIN virus infection of certain invertebrate cells results in cell survival rather than cell destruction. During the first 15 hours of infection, SIN replicates in mosquito cells, with virus production being equivalent to that detected in infected vertebrate cells.[142, 143] After that time period, however, the cells fail to lyse and exhibit little CPE. Cells subsequently become persistently infected and have the same growth rate and morphology as uninfected cells. Persistently infected cells produce greatly decreased quantities of virus, and only about 1% of the cells produce virus at any given time.[144] An apparent alteration of virus morphogenesis was observed in persistently infected cells, as budding at the plasma membrane was greatly inhibited. SIN virus is instead replicated and assembled in cytoplasmic vesicles and is thereby isolated from the cell cytoplasm. Sequestration of virus particles may therefore inhibit some detrimental effects of virus infection on the host cell.[145]

Defective-Interfering Particles

Defective-interfering (DI) particles of togaviruses help establish persistent infections in culture, especially invertebrate cells.[146] As with other viruses, RNAs of DI particles (DI RNAs) effectively compete for essential factors (RNA polymerase) necessary for viral replication. Replication of standard viral genomes is greatly reduced, thereby neutralizing the viral shutoff of cellular pathways and allowing cells to survive. As is true for many other viruses, DI particles of togaviruses can be generated in viral populations by passaging virus at high multiplicities of infection (MOIs). The resulting DI particles possess RNAs which are smaller (18–20S) than nondefective viral RNAs. By comparing a series of defective RNAs only certain RNA sequences are conserved, which supports their essential role in RNA replication and packaging of RNA into viral capsids. The 162-nucleotide sequence at the 5′ end and the 19 nucleotides at the 3′ end of alphavirus RNAs lack deletions, whereas deletions can be found in other areas of genomic

a. PRIMARY TRANSLATION

b. RNA REPLICATION

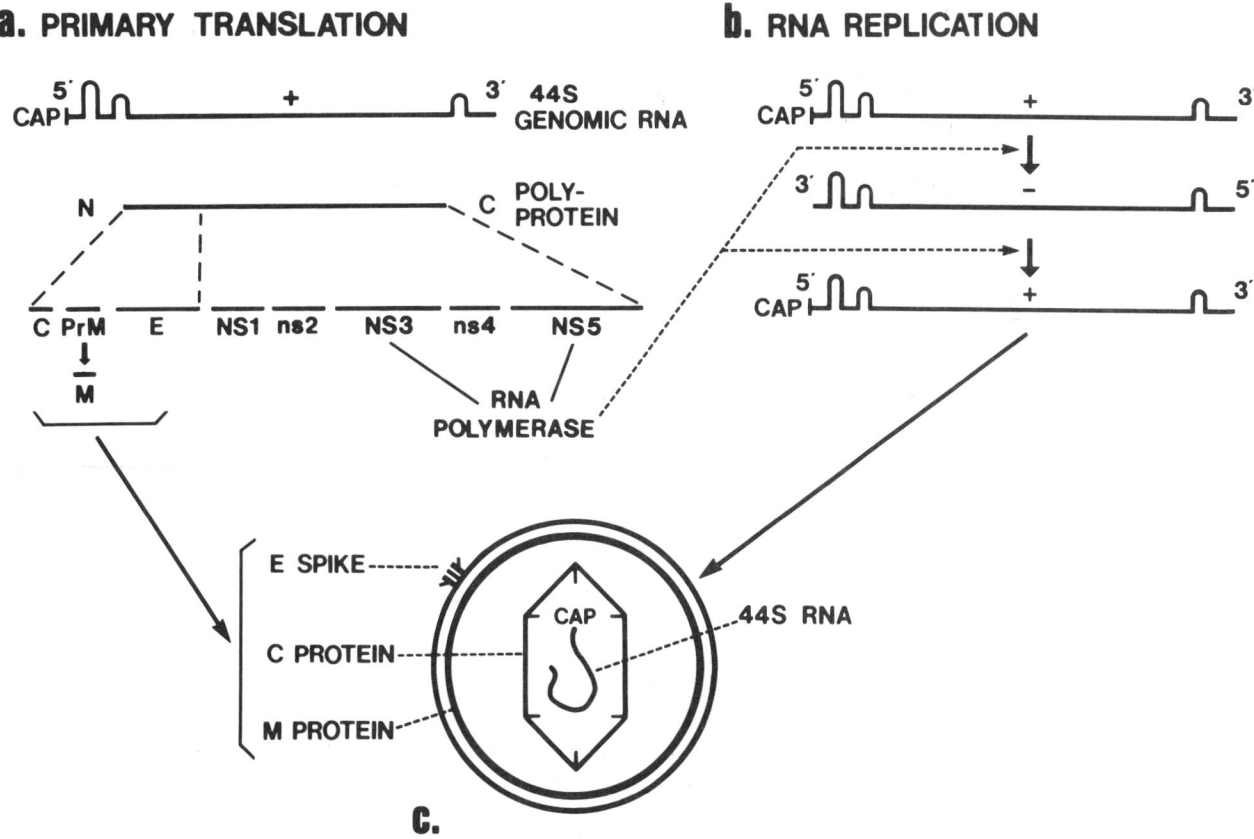

Figure 3–3. Replication of flavivirus. Genomic RNA (44S) is translated into a polyprotein **(a).** Following or concomitant with proteolytic cleavage of the polyprotein (see text), three polypeptides, precursor M (PrM), E, and NS1, associate with membranes, whereas capsid (C) protein accumulates in the cytoplasm. Genomic RNA is replicated into complementary negative-stranded RNA by RNA polymerase consisting of NS3 and NS5 **(b).** Likewise, negative-stranded RNA is replicated into progeny genomes. Secondary structures (Ω) at the 5' and 3' ends of genomic RNA and negative-stranded RNA may serve as recognition sites for RNA polymerase necessary for replication and possibly for macromolecules involved in translation. Progeny RNA is encapsidated within a nucleocapsid composed of C protein, which in turn buds to acquire an envelope. E protein-trimer constitutes spikes on the external surface of envelopes, and M protein, a nonglycosylated cleavage product of PrM, is located on the internal surface **(c).**

RNAs.[147, 148] In addition to deletions, sequence rearrangements including formation of repeated sequences (duplications) have been detected in DI RNAs.[149] Early during infection DI RNAs within infected cells are only minimally replicated and transcribed into mRNAs and translated. At later times translation of DI mRNAs is greatly decreased, perhaps due to accumulations of C protein, a known inhibitor of translation.

FLAVIVIRUSES

Members of the *Flaviviridae* were formally classified in the flavivirus genus of the *Togaviridae*. Size and structural differences between virus particles of togaviruses and flaviviruses, as well as variations in their replication cycles, mechanisms of protein processing, and virus maturation, warranted the reclassification of flavivirus into a separate family.[150]

Virus Structure

Flaviviruses are smaller than togaviruses with a diameter of about 45 to 50 nm. They possess single-stranded nonsegmented

RNAs of positive polarity which have cap structures at the 5' ends, but lack poly (A) at the 3' ends.[151] Secondary folding of RNA in the 3' region has been detected, however.[152] Genome RNAs of virus particles are surrounded by icosahedral capsids composed of a single capsid protein (C, 14 kd). The outermost structure, the viral envelope, is a lipid bilayer in which viral glycoprotein (E, 60 kd) is embedded in the form of spikes. E glycopolypeptides apparently form multimeric (probably trimeric) spikes which appear to be ring-shaped by electron microscopy.[153, 154] E spikes act as hemagglutinins and induce neutralizing and hemagglutination-inhibiting antibodies.[155] Underlying the viral envelope is the third viral protein, M, which is nonglycosylated and is derived from a glycosylated precursor protein (pr M, 21 kd) by proteolytic cleavage (Figure 3–3,c).[156]

Attachment, Penetration, Uncoating

Virus infection begins with the attachment of flaviviruses to specific receptors on a variety of vertebrate and invertebrate cells subsequent to release of capsids into the cytoplasm. E glycoprotein mediates attachment in a manner not strictly dependent on its state of glycosylation. Removal of its carbohydrate chains only minimally decreases infection or hemagglutination.[157] Viral particles penetrate cells by endocytosis and viral RNAs are subsequently released from nucleocapsids either directly into endosomal vesicles or from capsids released into the cytoplasm, the site of viral replication.[158, 159]

Primary Translation

Viral 44S RNA (approximately 10.8 kb) is translated by host cell macromolecules into one long polyprotein. Translation begins at an initiation codon (AUG) located at variable lengths from the 5' cap site. For West Nile virus (WNV) and yellow fever virus (YFV) RNAs, AUG codons are 96 and 118 residues, respectively, from their 5' ends.[151, 160] In WNV RNA a second AUG is located 97 residues downstream from the first AUG, both codons being in the same reading frame. The 5' proximal AUG, however, is primarily used for initiation of translation.

Analysis of the 5' noncoding regions of several flavivirus RNAs suggested that two secondary structures with similar sizes and shapes are present in these regions (see Figure 3–3,a). One loop structure includes the initiation codon for translation and may facilitate interactions between viral RNA and ribosomes.[161] Translation of polyproteins from YFV RNA terminates at one of several in-phase stop codons, the first being located 511 residues from the 3' end of RNA.[151] The polyprotein with a predicted molecular weight of 380,763 is proteolytically cleaved through a series of steps into both structural and nonstructural polypeptides (NS or ns) (see Figure 3–3,a).[151] The structural proteins are derived from approximately the N-terminal fourth of the polyprotein in the order N-terminus←C-prM-E→C-terminus, where prM is a precursor of M protein. Nonstructural proteins are derived from the remaining 75% of the genome in the order N-terminus←NS1-ns2a,b-NS3-ns4a,b-NS5→C-terminus, where NS proteins are the more abundant, higher-molecular-weight species and ns proteins are smaller, less characterized proteins.[157]

Cleavage of polyproteins into intermediate and end products requires proteases of both cellular and viral origin.[162] Polyproteins are initially cleaved during translation while associated with ER membranes. A mechanism for polyprotein cleavage may require initial cleavage of C protein from the N-terminus of nascent polyprotein. A hydrophobic signal sequence thereby exposed at the N-terminus of prM aids in polyprotein transport through the ER membranes. A hydrophobic sequence near the C-terminus serves to anchor prM in the lipid bilayer. In a similar manner the E and NS1 proteins are embedded in the ER membrane with their N-terminal portions located in the ER lumen. prM, E, and NS1 (45 kd) are glycosylated beginning with the addition of high-mannose chains in the ER, and following transport to Golgi membranes carbohydrate chains are converted to complex types (see section on morphogenesis). The remainder of the polyprotein is cleaved to form NS3 (70 kd) and NS5 (95 kd) as well as the ns proteins.[162]

Three primary types of cleavage mechanisms are possibly employed in processing the viral polyprotein. Cleavage of prM, E, and NS1 from nascent polyproteins is mediated by a cellular "signalase" which removes signal sequences from N-termini to separate these polypeptides.[163] Glycosylated prM is further cleaved before its cleavage product M becomes incorporated into progeny virus particles. For several flaviviruses sequence data of prM indicate that a cysteine-tryptophan dipeptide, characteristic of thiol proteases, is located within its primary sequence.[164] This suggests that cleavage of prM (21 kd) to yield nonglycosylated M (8.5 kd) and a 12.5-kd polypeptide may be autocatalytic.[29] A third type of cleavage at sites flanked by two basic amino acids, for example, arginine-arginine at one side and a polar amino acid on the other, is employed during the formation of several viral polypeptides. Most or all of these cleavage events occur in association with the ER or possibly Golgi membranes.[163, 163a]

RNA Replication

Following formation of viral polypeptides, genome RNA is replicated via the formation of full-length negative-polarity RNA intermediates which serve as templates for the formation of new genomic RNAs (see Figure 3–3,b). RNA polymerase and capping enzymes involved in replication most likely correspond to complexes composed of nonstructural proteins, NS3 and NS5 being two strong possibilities.[151, 165, 166] Enzyme complexes are associated with perinuclear membranes of the ER.[167] The binding of the RNA polymerase to membranes may be mediated by the small ns protein(s) which is hydrophobic in nature.

Initiation of (+ or −) RNA replication possibly requires specific recognition of the secondary structures (stem loop) at the 3' ends of positive and minus-strand RNAs by the RNA polymerase complex.[168] As noted previously, a single conserved secondary structure is located at the 3' end of genomic RNA, whereas two such structures are possible at the 5' end. When genomic RNAs are replicated, negative-strand RNAs possess secondary structures at their 5' and 3' ends, which are complementary to those in corresponding regions of template (+) strands. The 3' complementary structure on the minus-strand RNA may in turn serve as a recognition signal for initiation of progeny genomic RNA synthesis. Secondary structures at the 3' ends of RNAs (both + and −) may not only initiate RNA synthesis, but may regulate the rate of RNA synthesis. In dengue virus–infected cells differential rates of synthesis of positive- and negative-polarity RNAs are seen. Negative strands are formed at one-tenth the rate of positive-stranded RNA, which may reflect structural differences at the 3' ends of template RNAs.[169]

RNA replication as well as translation occurs in association with cytoplasmic membranes, which characteristically proliferate as a result of flavivirus infection. RNA used for translation is restricted to perinuclear membranes, whereas RNA replication is not localized to membranes in any one area.[170] Inclusion bodies containing viral proteins also accumulate in infected cells.

Virus Assembly

Progeny genomic RNAs are either translated, replicated, or incorporated into maturing virus particles, the latter event occurring in association with ER or vacuolar membranes.[159] Numerous investigations into the pathways of morphogenesis have suggested that characteristics of the host cell and that of the particular flavivirus determine the sites of viral maturation, including the cell membranes used for envelopment of nucleocapsids.[171]

Investigations of YFV morphogenesis suggest that formation

of nucleocapsids and their envelopment occur primarily at ER or vacuolar membranes. Virus particles egress from cells within vesicles, which transport preformed virus to the plasma membrane. Vesicle–plasma membrane fusion then ensues to release virus particles into the extracellular environment.[171] A problem of using this pathway as a general model for flavivirus maturation is the lack of involvement of the Golgi apparatus in the assembly process. It has been demonstrated that several flaviviruses possess E proteins glycosylated with complex carbohydrate chains. Formation of complex carbohydrates would necessitate that E proteins, either incorporated into vesicles or in direct association with immature virus particles, pass through the Golgi apparatus to acquire final modification of carbohydrate chains. As exemplified by YFV, Golgi membranes were not significantly linked with viral maturation.[159] Ultrastructure studies of dengue virus in certain cell systems showed that virus particles were observed budding directly from the plasma membrane as well as ER and vacuolar membranes.[171] Other investigations with the same virus failed to demonstrate budding at the plasma membrane. Japanese encephalitis virus in Vero cells initiates assembly at ER membranes to form immature virus particles, which in turn migrate to the Golgi apparatus for final stages of maturation.[172] In summary, several pathways for viral assembly may exist for flavivirus, which are dependent on cell and virus types.

CORONAVIRUSES

Members of the *Coronaviridae* are classified together as a family based on unique structural features of virus particles, RNA type, and mode of RNA synthesis. Mouse hepatitis virus (MHV) is one of the more extensively researched coronaviruses and will serve as a basis for most of this discussion.

Virus Structure

The overall dimensions of coronaviruses range from approximately 60 to 200 nm in diameter, variations in virus size reflecting the size range of the viral envelopes. The coronavirus genome is single-stranded RNA of positive polarity which possesses a cap structure at its 5' terminus and poly (A) at its 3' end. For MHV the genome is approximately 6×10^6 daltons.[173, 174]

MHV and most of the other well-characterized coronaviruses consist of three proteins, two glycoproteins (E2 and E1) and a phosphorylated nucleocapsid protein (N). Bovine enteric coronavirus has an additional protein which serves as its hemagglutinin.[175] The N protein of MHV is found in direct association with genomic RNA in the form of a helical nucleocapsid possessing varying degrees of both tight and relaxed coils.[176, 177] A lipid envelope forms the outer structure of virus particles and has clublike structures (peplomers) on its external surface.[174] Peplomers are formed from monomeric E2 glycoprotein (180 kd) which may be cleaved into two disulfide-linked, nonidentical subunits of 90 kd.[178] The majority of the length of the E2 glycoprotein is located external to the envelope, whereas a short tail is located internally.[179, 180] Mature E2 glycoproteins possess asparagine-linked carbohydrate chains of the complex type.[181] Various functions have been associated with E2, including virus binding to cell receptors, stimulation of neutralizing antibodies, and mediating cell-cell or viral

envelope–cell membrane fusion.[178, 182] E1 protein (26 kd) is also an envelope-associated integral protein.[183] It has a short N-terminal end that is external to the envelope surface, a transmembrane region that possibly crosses the membrane 3 times, and a C-terminal sequence that interacts with the nucleocapsid. The extent of glycosylation varies with infected host cells, but E1 of MHV possesses carbohydrate chains O-linked to serine or threonine residues.[184] E1 is able to induce the production of neutralizing antibodies which require complement for their activity.[182]

Attachment, Penetration, Uncoating

The lytic replication cycle begins with attachment of virus particles to cell receptors which are probably glycoproteins.[13] Virus particles with proteolytically cleaved E2 enter the cell by either fusing directly with the cell plasma membranes or penetrating within endocytic vesicles and then fusing with endosomal membranes to release nucleocapsids into the cytoplasm.[173, 178]

Primary Translation

Genome RNA is translated by cellular mechanisms to yield a 250-kd precursor protein corresponding to a 5' open reading frame (ORF) of the RNA (Figure 3–4,a). Based on in vitro studies, the primary translation product is cleaved to 220-kd and 28-kd polypeptides, the latter corresponding to an N-terminal sequence.[185, 186]

RNA Replication

During viral RNA replication, polypeptide 220 kd, possessing RNA-dependent RNA polymerase activity, replicates positive-stranded RNA into a full-length negative-stranded copy (see Figure 3–4,b). Polypeptide 28 kd may remain associated with polypeptide 220 kd in the form of a polymerase complex. Negative-stranded RNA has a poly (U) sequence at its 5' end which is copied from poly (A) at the 3' end of the genome RNA template. Negative-stranded RNA then serves as a template for the synthesis of both full-length genome RNA (also a species of mRNA) (see Figure 3–4,c) and six subgenomic mRNAs, each mRNA encoding a unique protein (see Figure 3–4,d).[187–190] RNA polymerase involved in negative-strand synthesis may differ in activity from the enzyme involved in genome or subgenomic mRNA synthesis.[191]

Transcription-Translation

The mechanism of mRNA synthesis requires transcription of a noncoding leader sequence of approximately 70 nucleotides in length from the 3' terminal region of the negative-polarity RNA (see Figure 3–4,d). The capped leader RNAs dissociate from the template and translocate to one of six regions along negative-stranded templates.[192, 193] Sequences complementary to those of the leader RNA located at multiple, specific sites within the internal regions of negative templates allow for base pairing between the two RNAs.[194] Consequently, each leader RNA at these secondary sites serves as a primer for synthesis of individual mRNAs, all initiating at unique 5' sites but terminating at a common 3' end (see Figure 3–4,d).[195] The relative abundance of subgenomic RNAs differs greatly, possibly due to preferential association of some leader RNAs with certain sites along the negative strand. This in turn may depend on the extent of homology between sequences of the two RNAs.[194]

Continuous N protein synthesis may also be necessary for the synthesis of genome RNAs and possibly subgenomic RNAs, since antibody to N prevents positive RNA synthesis.[196] Also, treatment of MHV-infected cells with cycloheximide has been shown to inhibit both negative and positive RNA synthesis.[197]

The seven mRNAs (one full length and six subgenomic) are translated into seven proteins: four nonstructural and three structural proteins, N, E2, and E1.[187, 191, 198] The relationships between specific mRNAs and their gene products have been determined. Each mRNA contains an ORF which is located at a 5′ region, downstream of the common noncoding, leader RNA (see Figure 3–4,d). Thus the total length of mRNAs is not translated and each species of mRNA has a unique ORF which does not overlap the ORFs of the other messengers.[186, 199, 200] The largest mRNA (1) most likely is translated into RNA polymerase, while the other nonstructural polypeptides translated from mRNAs 2, 4, and 5, are 35, 14, and 10 kd, respectively.[186, 200] The functions of these last three proteins are unknown. Structural polypeptides E2, E1, and N are translated from ORFs of mRNAs 3, 6, and 7, respectively.[186, 201] Translation of the seven mRNAs differs in efficiencies within infected cells. For example, RNA 1 is translated into RNA polymerase at low levels, whereas N polypeptide is much more abundant.[186] It has been shown that removal of the noncoding leader sequence from RNA 1 actually increases its efficiency of translation, suggesting that a sequence or secondary structure within leader RNA may in certain situations interfere with translation.[202, 203]

As stated previously glycoproteins E1 and E2 are incorporated into envelopes of progeny virus. Their formation within infected cells occurs by two biosynthetic pathways. E2 glycoprotein is synthesized in a manner characteristic of glycoproteins possessing complex carbohydrate chains. High-mannose chains N-linked to asparagine are added to E2 polypeptide in the lumen of the RER. Following transport to the Golgi apparatus, carbohydrate chains of E2 are reduced in size and further modified by formation of complex carbohydrate chains.[181] E2 is also acylated within the Golgi apparatus.[178] Some of E2 glycoproteins are transported from the Golgi apparatus to the cell surface, but only small quantities are released into the extracellular environment, this latter process occurring on a host cell–dependent basis.[178, 204] Inhibition of glycosylation in MHV-infected cells by tunicamycin treatment caused degradation of E2 proteins, yet virus particles continued to form with only E1 glycoprotein being present.[181, 205, 206]

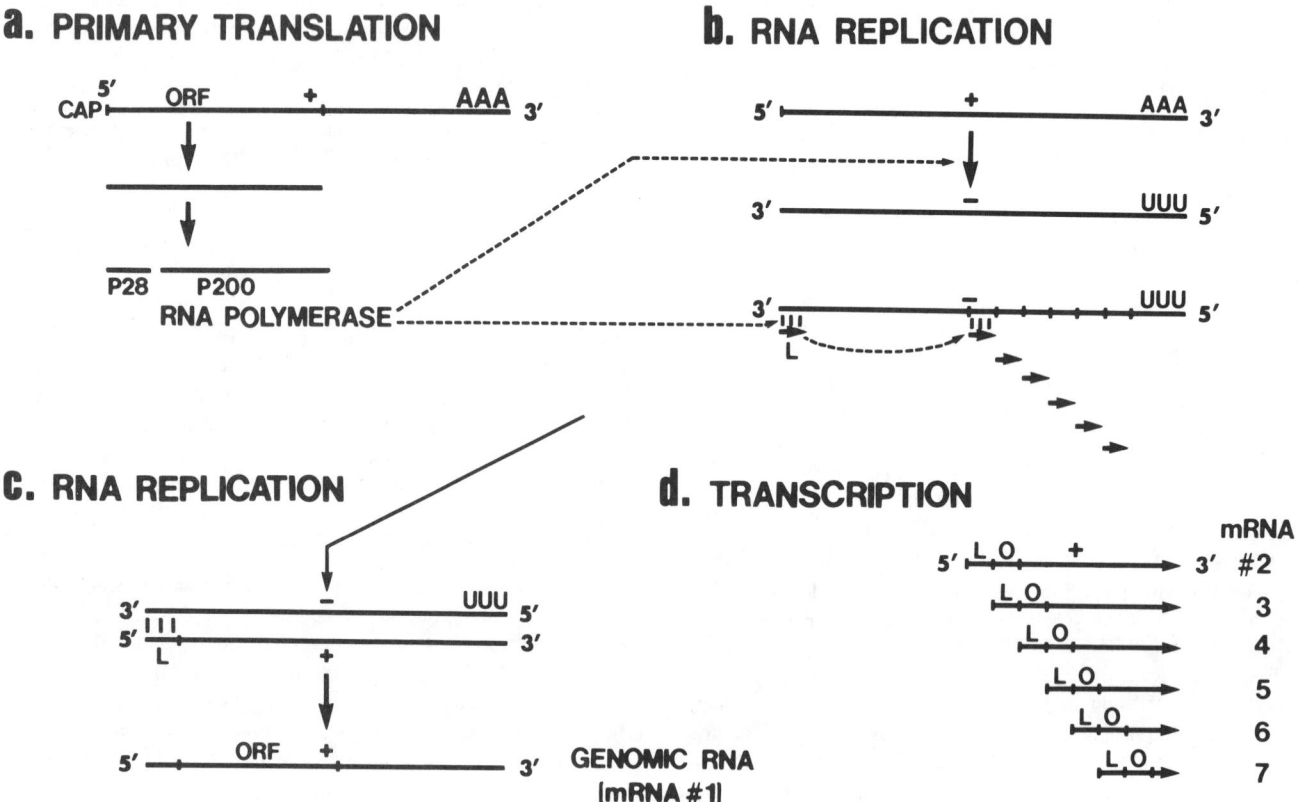

Figure 3–4. Replication of coronavirus. Genoma RNA is translated into a polyprotein which is proteolytically cleaved into 220- and 28-kd polypeptides, P220 and P28 **(a).** RNA polymerase, p220, replicates genomic RNA into a complementary negative strand **(b).** The negative strand serves as a template for a series of synthetic events in which seven positive-stranded mRNAs are generated. Leader RNA (L), which is synthesized from the 3′ end of the negative-stranded template, can translocate and base-pair with six sites along the template strands (staggered series of arrows, **b**). Transcription can initiate from the L at these secondary sites to form sequentially shorter RNAs coterminal at their 3′ ends **(d).** Only nonoverlapping open reading frames (ORF = 0) of these mRNAs are translated into polypeptides **(d).** RNA replication from the negative-stranded template initiates from L, which does not translocate and is extended the full length of the template **(c).**

Virus Assembly

E1 glycoprotein of MHV is synthesized in the RER and transported to the Golgi apparatus, where it is modified at the N-terminus by the addition of carbohydrate chain(s) through an O-linkage to serine or threonine.[205] E1 glycoprotein remains in membranes at this location and is not transported to the cell surface membrane as is E2.[207] This viral protein, again unlike E2, is essential for envelopment of virus particles. Because of this latter fact it would appear that envelopment of progeny nucleocapsids occurs in association with membranes of the ER and Golgi apparatus. Nucleocapsids bud from the cytoplasmic sides of these membranes into the lumina of the organelles.[207, 208]

Once enveloped virus particles are formed, the E2 glycoprotein is cleaved by host cell proteases either in the Golgi apparatus or at the cell surface. The specificity of proteases in specific cells determines the extent of cleavage of E2 molecules and thus the fusion capabilities of virus particles or infected cells expressing E2 on their surfaces. Viral egress from infected cells occurs primarily through the formation of virus-containing vesicles from Golgi membranes. Vesicles transport virus to the plasma membrane where vesicular fusion to surface membranes releases virus particles from cells.[177, 209, 210]

Recombinants and Defective-Interfering Particles

Progeny coronavirus particles produced during productive infection may deviate genetically from parental virus due to point mutations which may occur at high frequencies within genomic RNA.[211] Also, in cells coinfected by two strains of MHV, recombination has been demonstrated between viral genomes. A possible mechanism of recombination between genomic RNAs of two closely related viral strains requires the initial synthesis of leader RNA plus a length of adjoining RNA from negative-stranded template RNA of one viral strain. Instead of continued elongation, RNA synthesis terminates prematurely and the RNA product dissociates from template RNA. It can then base-pair with homologous sequences of a template (−) RNA from a second viral strain. Resumption of RNA synthesis results in recombinant (chimeric) RNA of full genome length which can be incorporated in progeny virions.[212–214]

A similar mechanism can result in the formation of defective genomes resulting in the production of DI particles. Cultured cells serially infected with MHV at high MOIs generate defective RNAs (DI RNAs) which vary in size and number of deletions.[215] A predominant DI RNA which is incorporated into progeny virus particles corresponds to almost full–genome length RNA. Apparently this type of DI RNA is generated following one or more small deletions in sequences outside the N and RNA polymerase coding regions.[196] One portion of the RNA that is seemingly spared from deletions is the RNA polymerase gene. Other DI RNAs sustain more substantial multiple deletions which results in much shorter-length RNAs. These latter RNAs are not significantly packaged into virus particles and probably most DI RNAs of this type have lost the packaging signal from their RNAs. Unlike the DI RNAs with minor deletions, DI RNAs with extensive multiple deletions require helper virus for their replication. In a given coronavirus population DI RNAs have been shown to replicate more efficiently than standard virus. It is possible that RNA polymerase

recognizes or associates with DI RNA much more readily, thereby reducing that available for replication of standard-length RNA.[216]

DI RNAs can possibly be generated during RNA replication in infected cells by dissociation of replication complexes from template (−) RNAs. The complex consisting of RNA polymerase and leader RNA then reassociate with the template RNA at a point further downstream. Multiple dissociation-reassociation events during RNA replication would result in shorter RNAs with multiple deletions.[217]

An alternative to the lytic interactions between host cells and virus described above is the establishment of persistent infections both in cultured cells and host organisms. It seems likely that DI particles as well as avirulent variants help to establish persistence.[174, 218, 219]

ORTHOMYXOVIRUSES

Three families of RNA viruses, **Bunyaviridae, Arenaviridae,** and **Orthomyxoviridae,** have single-stranded, segmented genomes of negative polarity, that is, they possess base sequences complementary to that of mRNA (+ polarity).[220–222] Although each family has different numbers of genome segments and unique aspects in their replication cycles, only influenza virus, an orthomyxovirus, will be considered as it has been investigated in more detail. Influenza viruses are divided into three serotypes, A, B, and C, as determined by the antigenicity of two internal structural proteins of the virus: nucleocapsid and matrix.

Virus Structure

The structure of influenza viruses, approximately 120 nm in diameter, includes an internal helical nucleocapsid enclosed by a tightly bound membranous outer structure or envelope. The genome consists of eight individual RNA segments for both influenza viruses types A and B and seven segments for influenza C virus.[223–226]

For influenza A virus, segments 1 through 7 encode structural proteins of the virus and segment 8 encodes nonstructural (NS) proteins found in infected cells. Four proteins are associated with RNA to form nucleocapsids: nucleoprotein (NP), constituting 90% of the total protein associated with genome RNA; and polymerase proteins, PB1, PB2, and PA (Figure 3–5,c).[227, 228] NP is structural in nature and imparts the helical conformation to nucleocapsids by interacting directly with the RNA, approximately 20 ribonucleotides being associated with each NP molecule.[228, 229] This association does not impart RNAse resistance to genomic RNA, however, as is the case for helical nucleocapsids of paramyxoviruses.[230] Intact nucleocapsids exhibit a higher level of order beyond their helical conformation in that supercoiling of the structure has also been observed and the ends have been shown to be in close proximity to one another.[231, 232]

Viral envelopes consist of a lipid bilayer, which is derived from host cell membranes, and three major viral proteins: matrix, hemagglutinin, and neuraminidase (see Figure 3–5,c).[233–236] Matrix protein (M1), which is the most abundant structural protein of influenza A virus, is located for the most part in association with the inner surface of the envelope. Possibly, at least a portion of

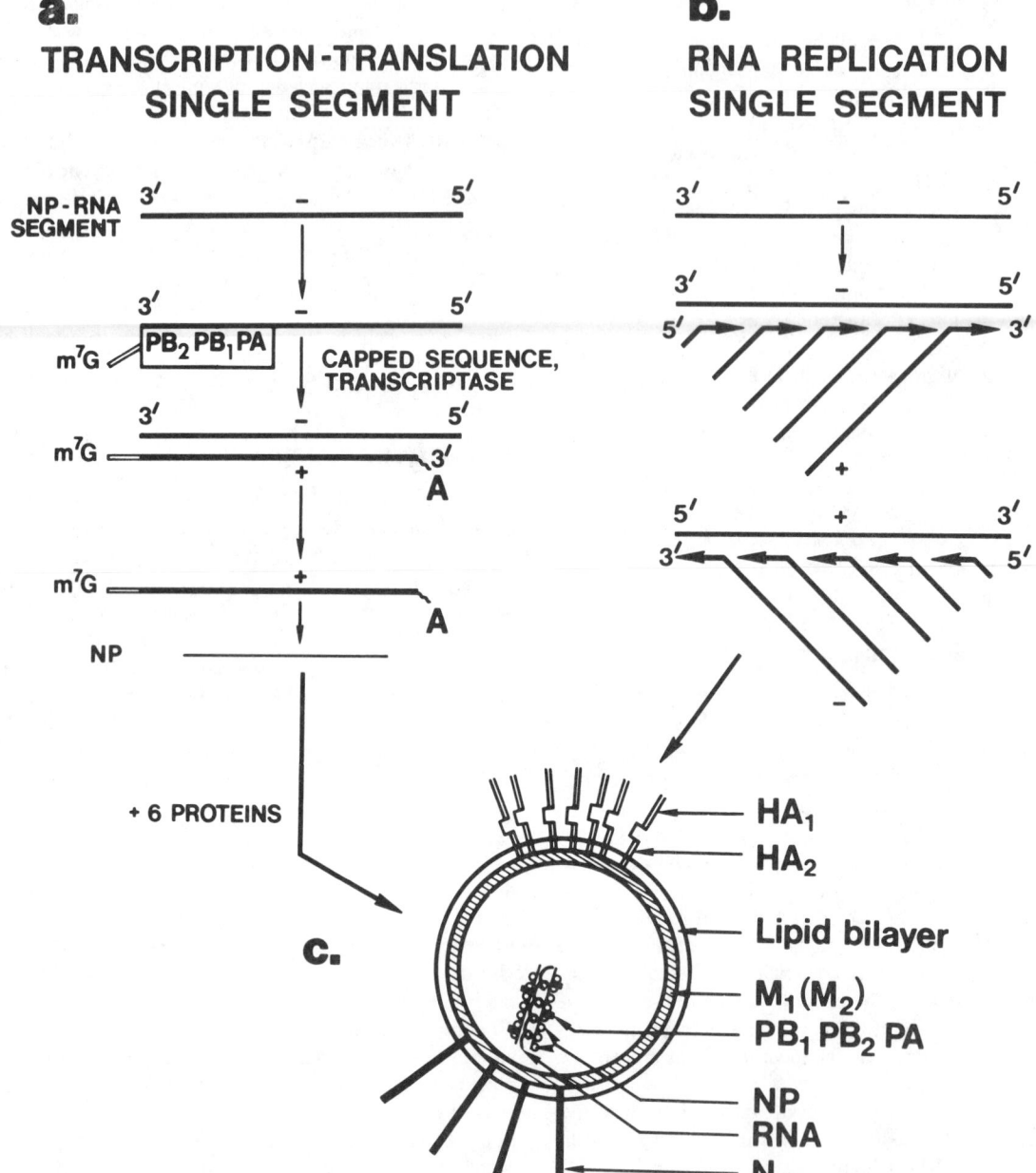

a.

TRANSCRIPTION-TRANSLATION SINGLE SEGMENT

b.

RNA REPLICATION SINGLE SEGMENT

c.

Figure 3–5. Replication of influenza virus. Transcription and translation of the RNA segment for nucleocapsid protein (NP) serves as an example for the other seven segments **(a).** A capped RNA primer (open rectangle) donated by cell RNA associates with RNA polymerase, PB_2, PB_1, PA. This complex initiates mRNA synthesis using the genomic segment of RNA as a template to produce NP mRNA which is shorter than the full-length template RNA. Translation occurs from all but the 5′ and 3′ terminal regions of viral mRNA to yield NP. As shown in **(b),** two replicative intermediates are involved in replication of each RNA segment; one with minus (−)-strand RNA serving as a template and the other with a plus (+)-strand RNA template. Viral nucleocapsids are formed by the association of the PB_2, PB_1, PA complex and NP with the eight segments of RNA. Nucleocapsids consisting of all eight RNA segments bud through areas of the cell membrane which have HA and N proteins on their external surfaces and M located at their cytoplasmic sides to form viral particles **(c,** only one nucleocapsid segment shown). HA is illustrated in its cleaved form; HA_2 and HA_1 linked by a disulfide bond. HA and N are actually interspersed on the virus particle and HA spikes are more abundant.

M1 spans the envelope and is exposed on the outermost surface of virus particles.[237] The M2 protein present in membranes of influenza A virus–infected cells also is present, but at low levels in virus envelopes.[238–240] It plays an ill-defined role in the assembly and uncoating of virus particles and is the target of the specific anti-influenza A drugs, amantadine and rimantadine (see Chapter 6). The two other envelope proteins, hemagglutinin (HA) and neuraminidase (NA), are integral proteins and span the lipid bilayer, projecting outward from its surface in the form of spikes. HA and NA spikes are not only found on virus particles, but also on the surface of influenza A virus–infected cells. HA spikes are composed of three closely associated glycopolypeptide (84-kd) subunits, whereas NA spikes are tetrameric.[241] Between 700 and 1000 HA and about 100 NA spikes are present on virus particles.[242]

The majority of the length (approximately 500 amino acids depending on the virus strain) of the HA glycopolypeptide is located external to the envelope, while a hydrophobic region of approximately 26 amino acids spans the lipid bilayer and a short 11-amino acid sequence extends internally.[243, 244] In its precursor form the HA polypeptide is uncleaved, but in the presence of specific cellular proteases or exogenous proteases added to virus preparations, precursor HA polypeptide is cleaved into two subunits, distal HA1 (58 kd) and proximal HA2 (26 kd) (see below).[245–248] HA1 is the most heavily glycosylated subunit with six complex carbohydrate chains, whereas the HA2 subunit most often has only one such chain.

The site of proteolytic cleavage between HA1 and HA2 is usually a single arginine residue; however, in certain avian strains that exhibit virulence in infected hosts, a series of basic amino acids is found at this site. It is possible that this array of basic amino acids allows cleavage in a greater variety of cell types and increases HA protein susceptibility to proteolytic enzymes with different specificities.[249] This is not the only factor that modulates cleavage and virulence, because viral strains with multiple basic amino acids at the HA1-HA2 junction can still possess an avirulent phenotype. For these latter strains, a carbohydrate chain adjacent to the cleavage site appears to deny access to the protease(s).[250, 250a] Once the initial endoprotease cleavage occurs, an influenza virion-associated carboxypeptidase widens the gap by removing the single arginine or a larger amino acid sequence.[251] The N-terminal sequence of HA2 generated in this manner has a hydrophobic sequence of about nine amino acids which is important in mediating envelope–cell membrane fusion during the early stages of infection.[252]

As stated above, three HA polypeptides form a complex which can be seen by electron microscopy as spikes on the surface of virus particles. The three-dimensional structure of HA spikes is composed of a distal globular head formed by three globular subunits, one contributed by each of the three HA monomers.[241] This structure is joined to the lipid envelope through a stalklike structure formed by another section of the HA monomers. Whereas a portion of HA1 polypeptide constitutes the distal globular structures and also part of the stalk, HA2 is found only in the stalk portion of the HA complex. Thus the cleavage site between HA1 and HA2 subunits is present in the stalk region. Located in the distal, globular domains of each HA monomer are four or five major antigenic determinants and a site which binds to cellular receptors.[253]

The overall tertiary structure of HA spikes depends on several types of bonds including intrachain disulfide bonds within or between HA1 or HA2 subunits, and possibly interchain disulfide bonds between cysteine residues located within the C-terminal amino acid sequence of HA2 polypeptides.[254] Hydrophobic bonds also determine the conformation of the HA trimer, especially within the stalk structure, where the inner faces of the three HA2 polypeptides interact.[254] Additional hydrophobic interactions between HA polypeptides may occur within the transmembrane regions. Hydrogen bonding and salt bridges also are important in maintaining the three-dimensional conformation of HA.

The NA spike is composed of four identical glycopolypeptides, approximately 469 amino acids in length. The tetrameric structure consists of two substructures, a boxlike, distal head region composed of four globular domains, one from each of the four NA polypeptides, and secondly, a slender stalk which connects the distal structure to the virus envelope.[242, 255] Each of the four domains in the distal region possesses a catalytic site capable of removing terminal sialic acids from complex carbohydrate chains. Four major antigenic determinants are associated with each head region, two on the outermost distal surfaces and two on its innermost surfaces.[256, 257] NA polypeptides are associated with viral envelopes or cell plasma membranes in the opposite orientation to that seen with HA polypeptides. Whereas HA polypeptides traverse the lipid bilayer near their C-terminus, the transmembrane region of NA polypeptides (30 residues) corresponds to sequences near the N-terminus. The six conserved N-terminal residues form the amino acid sequence extending from the inner surface of viral envelopes or cell membranes while the remaining 430 or so residues are external to the membrane.[258] NA polypeptides, unlike HA polypeptides, are not proteolytically cleaved.

A second, rather ill-defined activity of NA of certain virus strains, besides cleavage of sialic acids, is its ability to hemagglutinate. Although the HA polypeptides are presumably responsible for this process, specific monoclonal antibodies to NA may inhibit hemagglutination in an as yet undetermined manner.[257]

In mature influenza A virus particles, the amino acid sequences of HA and NA polypeptides on the internal side of the lipid envelope apparently interact with M1 proteins in a way that stabilizes virus particles. Furthermore, the C-terminal end of M1 interacts with NP of nucleocapsids, thereby linking the envelope proteins with the nucleocapsid.[238]

Attachment, Penetration, Uncoating

Influenza virus infection begins with the attachment of hemagglutinin spikes on virus particles to cell glycoprotein receptors. Terminal sialic acids of complex carbohydrate chains on receptors play a crucial role in the binding process. Their removal from receptors by either exogenous neuraminidase or enzyme located on the virus particle itself prevents HA1-receptor interactions. The specificity of HA for receptors depends on several factors, including the type of sialic acid and the nature of its linkage to penultimate galactose in carbohydrate chains of the receptor.[259] For example, some strains of influenza A virus recognize 2,6 linkages, while others are specific for 2,3 linkages.[253] Point mutations, which alter amino acid residues in the receptor binding site of HA, may affect specificity for 2,3 or 2,6 carbohydrate linkages. Specific carbohydrates of the hemagglutinin may not be essential for attachment. Removal of between 25% and 50% of the carbohydrate moieties from HA does not significantly reduce hemagglutination or infectivity.[260] Since most of the oligosaccharides are located on the stalk they may not be required for HA-receptor interactions. However, more subtle effects of oligosaccharide chains have been noted relative to the cell tropism of certain strains of influenza virus.

Since the exact carbohydrate composition of the oligosaccharide chains linked to viral glycoproteins is determined by the enzymes of host cells, virus grown in certain cells may possess more complex or extensively glycosylated chains than virus from other cells. It has been suggested, for example, that some wild-type strains of influenza A virus are incapable of binding to receptors because of large HA-associated carbohydrate chains, one or more of which block or overlap the receptor binding sites on the head of the HA spike. However, when these same wild-type strains are grown in other cells which yield simpler glycosylation patterns, comparable blocking of receptor sites is not seen. Furthermore, a mutation in the HA gene, which eliminates asparagine required for N-linked glycosylation at a location next to the receptor binding site, enhances the tropism of the variant virus.[261, 262]

Following attachment, virus penetrates into cells either directly by fusion of the viral envelope with the plasma membrane or by endocytosis which is followed by fusion of the envelopes of virus particles with membranes of endocytic vesicles.[263–265] As stated previously, HA polypeptides must be proteolytically cleaved into HA1 and HA2 subunits in order for penetration to occur. A hydrophobic amino acid sequence exposed at the N-terminus of HA2 interacts with the cell membrane. This process is facilitated by an irreversible conformational change in the HA trimer.[254, 266] The globular domains in the head region of HA spikes separate to expose the HA2-HA1 junctions, which interact with cell membranes.[267] The conformational rearrangement occurs optimally within the pH range 5 to 6.2 found in endocytic vesicles, whereas fusion at the plasma membrane is inefficient due to suboptimal pH at this location. Variants of influenza A virus have been isolated that are capable of membrane fusion at higher pH values 0.2 to 0.7 units above wild-type virus.[268]

In vitro fusions between either intact influenza virus or isolated viral envelopes possessing viral glycoproteins with liposomes without proteins have been conducted to ascertain the requirements for fusion. Influenza A virus is capable of fusing with liposomes composed of either negatively charged or neutral phospholipids and lacking receptor glycoproteins. In liposomes formed by neutral lipids such as phosphotidylcholine, cholesterol is a necessary requirement for fusion with influenza virus or isolated viral envelopes.[269] Although HA, and specifically HA2, have been shown to primarily control the fusion process, some investigations have implicated HA1 and NA polypeptides as having ancillary roles in membrane fusion.[270]

Transcription-Translation

Following membrane fusion, nucleocapsids are released into the cell cytoplasm and transported to the nucleus, which is the site of RNA transcription and genome replication.[271, 273] Initially, genomic RNAs serve as templates for synthesis of complementary mRNAs of positive polarity.[273] In order for transcription of the eight genomic RNAs of influenza A virus to occur, minimal re-

quirements include a RNA primer and a RNA-dependent RNA polymerase (transcriptase).[274, 275] Primer RNA, approximately ten to 15 nucleotides in length, is cleaved from the 5' end of newly synthesized host cell mRNAs by a viral endonuclease.[276–278] A methylated cap structure (m⁷GpppXm, where m is a methyl group and X is any nucleotide) is located at the 5' end of primer RNA and is specifically recognized in its methylated form by the PB2 component of viral RNA polymerase.[228] For initiation of transcription, adenosine residues at the 3' ends of primer RNAs hydrogen-bonds to uridine at the 3' end of genome RNAs; no other sequence homology is apparent between the two RNAs.[279] Transcription initiates from the primer in a 5'-to-3' direction using genome RNA as a template. PB2 is responsible for initiation of RNA synthesis, while PB1 is involved in chain elongation. The function of PA, another component of the polymerase complex, is not known.[228] Transcription terminates 20 to 30 nucleotides short of copying the full-length RNA template.[280] Messenger RNAs are then modified at their 3' ends by the addition of poly (A) sequences of variable lengths (see Figure 3–5,a).[281–283]

In addition to primary transcripts synthesized from all eight genome RNAs functioning as mRNAs, primary transcripts from genome segments 7 (M) and 8 (NS) are also spliced by host cell enzymes to form two mRNAs, M2 and NS2.[284–286] Both spliced mRNAs lose single, large introns from either the 5' half of the primary transcript (NS2) or from the 5' two thirds of the primary transcripts (M2). Thus NS2- and M2-spliced mRNAs retain a short 5' exon joined to a larger 3' exon. The splicing process causes a shift in the reading frame in the 3' exons relative to their full-length primary transcripts. Therefore, only the 5' exons possess codons identical to the corresponding sequence of unspliced transcripts.

Once formed, mRNAs are transported from the nucleus to the cytoplasm for translation. As exemplified by mRNAs for nucleocapsid proteins, a number of these mRNAs have untranslated sequences at both the 5' and 3' ends (see Figure 3–5,a).[287–289] Messenger RNAs from genome segments 1 through 7 are translated into the eight structural proteins of influenza A virus: PB1, PB2, PA, HA, NP, NA, M1, and M2. RNA segment 8, on the other hand, encodes nonstructural polypeptides NS1 and NS2. Investigations into the temporal control of mRNA synthesis and corresponding protein synthesis have indicated that the level of mRNA synthesis largely determines the abundance of viral proteins within infected cells.[290] Therefore, mRNAs transcribed in large amounts result in high levels of corresponding proteins. To a certain extent translational controls seem to determine the levels of M1, and possibly other viral proteins, within infected cells. As detailed below, M1 protein may inhibit transcription late in the replication cycle. Therefore, a translational delay in M1 polypeptide synthesis from previously transcribed M1 mRNAs would prevent premature termination of overall viral transcription.

RNA Replication

Replication of genome RNA segments (see Figure 3–5,b) is also a nuclear event and like transcription involves a similar polymerase complex of PA, PB1, and PB2, perhaps with altered specificities or in different arrangements from that involved in transcription. Beginning at approximately one to two hours after infection, parental genome RNAs are independently copied to form eight full-size, positive-stranded RNAs, which lack both poly (A) sequences at their 3' termini and cap structures at their 5' ends.[291] Positive RNA synthesis does not depend on primer RNA for its initiation and involves bypassing stop signals recognized during transcription that give rise to the corresponding shorter mRNAs. Unlike positive-stranded mRNAs, which are synthesized free of nucleocapsid proteins, the positive-stranded RNAs synthesized during replication are associated with NP as well as polymerase complexes. NPs bound to positive-polarity RNAs may act as antiterminators and allow RNA synthesis to proceed through transcriptional termination sites.[292] Positive-stranded RNAs are then used as templates for synthesis of progeny viral RNAs (V RNAs), again in association with polymerase and nucleocapsid proteins.

Various investigations have focused on the regulation of synthesis of full-length positive-stranded RNAs, mRNAs, and V RNAs during the replication cycle. Some data suggest coordinated regulation of mRNAs and corresponding full-length RNAs synthesized from a specific genome RNA segment. For example, NS1 mRNAs and full-length NS1 positive-stranded RNAs were both synthesized at high levels throughout the infectious cycle, whereas both species of RNAs (mRNAs and full-length) were synthesized from other RNA segments in lesser amounts.

More recent evidence distinguished early and late stages of synthesis for mRNAs, and full-length positive- and negative-polarity RNAs. During the early stage, coupled RNA synthesis of all three types was observed, as exemplified for NS1-RNAs (see above). However, at later times during infection, RNA synthesis was no longer coupled. Late synthesis of mRNAs and positive full-template-length RNA were greatly decreased, whereas progeny genomic (negative-stranded V RNA) RNA was synthesized at maximal rates. Within the early stage further distinctions could be made between viral and mRNA synthesis of NS1 and NP on the one hand, both of which occurred early, and on the other hand, synthesis of M1 RNAs, which was delayed until later times during infection. Delayed transcription of M1 mRNA, plus its delayed translation (see above), may allow transcription of the other genome segments to proceed without interruption within the early phase. Once formed, M1 protein associates with nucleocapsids and overall transcription is greatly decreased.[293] Accumulation of NP has also been implicated in the switch from early to late phase. As NP reaches high levels, RNA replication is favored over transcription of mRNAs.[292]

Defective-Interfering Particles

During RNA replication defective RNAs are formed due to aberrant synthetic events. Replication from positive-stranded RNA templates to yield progeny viral RNAs can result in dissociation of the polymerase + nascent-strand RNA complex from template RNA. In cells coinfected by two strains of influenza A virus the nascent complex can reassociate with the same genome segment of the coinfecting strain. If the nascent strand reassociates to a position analogous to its point of termination on the original strand, then RNA synthesis can proceed to yield a full-length, chimeric RNA segment with no apparent deletion of RNA. On the other hand, reassociation at a point downstream of the original termination point results in a deleted genome segment.

Virus particles harboring one or more of these deleted RNA segments are not capable of independent replication and require coinfection of cells with an infectious influenza A virus. Helper virus supplies the missing protein(s) to support replication of the defective virus. Deletion mutants of this type compete for limited quantities of viral proteins necessary for replication, for example, polymerase, and thus interfere with the replication of the infectious helper virus. Defective-interfering particles can increase proportionally to infectious particles during repeated passages in culture at high MOIs.[294] In the absence of coinfecting helper virus, DI RNAs within host cells will fail to replicate but can remain stable for at least several weeks and can be rescued by helper virus after prolonged periods of time.[295] DI particles of influenza A virus have also been demonstrated in natural infections.

Virus Assembly

In addition to replication of genomic RNA, progeny virus formation requires the production of structural proteins which must be synthesized, modified, and transported to specific sites for virus assembly.

Envelope glycoproteins HA, NA, and M2 are translated in association with the RER. A hydrophobic signal sequence at the N-terminus of nascent HA polypeptides promotes their translocation through the ER membrane and once within the lumen the signal sequence is removed by proteolytic cleavage. Translation of HA continues until a hydrophobic region near the C-terminus anchors the polypeptide in the lipid membrane. As stated previously, the NA polypeptide assumes an opposite orientation with its N-terminus possessing a hydrophobic sequence (approximately 30 residues) which apparently serves both as a signal and a membrane anchor sequence.[296, 297] The N-terminus of NA inserts into the ER membrane where it remains lodged, while in an undetermined manner nascent polypeptide is fed through the membrane and into the ER lumen, resulting in the C-terminus of NA on the lumen side.[298]

At the present time both the rate of transport of HA from the ER to the Golgi apparatus and the structural conformation of HA polypeptide(s) within the ER are matters of controversy. Several investigations support the concepts that trimerization of HA polypeptides occurs within the ER and a seven- to ten-minute period of time elapses before HA trimers are transported to Golgi membranes.[299, 300] Alternatively, other investigations indicate that monomeric HA polypeptides are transported rapidly from the ER at one to two minutes after synthesis and only after reaching the Golgi apparatus is trimerization achieved.[301] Apparently glycosylation is not prerequisite for trimer formation, since the latter occurs in the presence of tunicamycin, an inhibitor of N-linked glycosylation. Transport and assembly of NA spikes is not well characterized although certain amino acids (residues 11, 17, and 26) in the hydrophobic region at the N-terminus may serve as trafficking signals between organelles.[297] Mannose-rich carbohydrate chains are linked to asparagine residues of the HA and NA polypeptides prior to their transport within lipid vesicles to the Golgi apparatus. In the Golgi apparatus HA and NA polypeptides are further modified by trimming of the high-mannose chains and addition of other carbohydrates to form complex oligosaccharides. Addition of palmitic acid to HA and M2 also occurs at this location.

HA and NA polypeptides, in association with lipid vesicles, are transported to the plasma membrane where they are inserted as spikes.[302] Envelope proteins are associated with areas of plasma membranes that are devoid of host cell glycoproteins and serve as budding sites for virus particle formation. An ill-defined mechanism targets these glycoproteins preferentially to the apical surface of the polarized epithelial cells, which is also the site for virus envelopment.[303-305] At the time of HA insertion into plasma membranes or shortly thereafter, precursor HA is cleaved into HA1 and HA2 subunits by host cell protease(s).[306-308] M1 protein, which has self-polymerization properties, is deposited under these sites and possibly links the internal portion of the envelope proteins to nucleocapsids. Nucleocapsids are enveloped during the budding process to produce progeny virus (see Figure 3–5,c).[309] Depending on host cell and virus strain, virus production begins approximately four hours after infection and reaches maximal levels as early as seven to eight hours.

Investigations into the assembly process have been conducted using mutants temperature-sensitive in HA synthesis. At nonpermissive temperatures HA polypeptides were not synthesized, yet noninfectious enveloped virus particles lacking HA spikes were formed. Thus in this system HA was not required for viral assembly, although NA may have substituted for HA in directing M1 polypeptide to the budding site.[310]

Recombination

In cells coinfected with two strains of influenza A virus, genome segments originating from each strain may be incorporated into progeny nucleocapsids to yield a full complement of eight genomic RNA segments. Reassortment of genome segments is reflected in major antigenic shifts in the progeny virions which cause changes in pathogenicity.[311-314] The genome of influenza A viruses also undergoes rather high levels of point mutations relative to mutation rates for several other RNA viruses. Analyses of NS genes in influenza A variants, which arose from a common progenitor virus, indicated mutation rates on the order of 1.5×10^{-5} per nucleotide per infectious cycle, whereas a 2.1×10^{-6} mutation rate was calculated for poliovirus. Similar rates of point mutations are expected for the other genome segments, thereby contributing to the antigenic drift of the virus (see Chapter 10 for a more detailed discussion).[315]

Effects on Host Cells

Influenza A virus infection inhibits host cell macromolecular synthesis in several ways. Cellular mRNAs that are synthesized following infection fail to be transported out of the nucleus and are readily degraded at this site.[316] Cytoplasmic cell mRNA species remain stable, but are selectively not translated in infected cells.

Viral mRNAs are translated at high levels in the same environment, which suggests that structural features of influenza virus mRNAs aid in preferential initiation of translation. Numerous hypotheses have been proposed to explain this specificity. It is possible, for example, that cell-derived primer at the 5′ end of viral mRNAs facilitates their translation through interactions with ribosomes.[317]

UNSEGMENTED NEGATIVE-STRANDED RNA VIRUSES

Members of the ***Rhabdoviridae*** and ***Paramyxoviridae*** are RNA viruses with nonsegmented, negative-stranded genomes. Human pathogens belonging to these families include measles, mumps, and parainfluenza viruses (paramyxoviruses) and rabies virus (rhabdovirus). Vesicular stomatitis virus (VSV), a rhabdovirus, is not primarily a human pathogen, but it has been studied extensively and exemplifies certain aspects of the replication schemes for viruses in both families.

Virus Structure

VSV is bullet-shaped, about 180 nm in length and 70 nm in width. Like influenza virus, VSV has a helical nucleocapsid, but has a single continuous strand of RNA instead of a segmented genome. Three viral proteins are associated with RNA to form the nucleocapsid: large nucleocapsid (L), nucleocapsid (N), and smaller nucleocapsid (NS, also designated P) proteins (Figure 3–6,c). The lipid envelope consists of two viral proteins: the matrix (M) protein and a glycoprotein (G).[318] M protein is found along the internal surface of the envelope, while G protein forms spikes extending outward from the surface of the virus particle (see Figure 3–6,c).[319-321] G proteins involved in viral attachment to nucleated cells or erythrocytes seemingly exist as multimers, possibly composed of as many as 15G polypeptides.[322] M protein binds to both the nucleocapsid and viral envelope, thereby linking the two structures within viral particles (see Figure 3–6,c).[323-325] M protein is phosphorylated to varying degrees, which may influence its binding activity.

Several enzyme activities are associated with NS and L proteins which form a complex in the nucleocapsid; they include RNA-dependent RNA polymerase, guanylyltransferase, guanine-7-methyltransferase, nucleoside-2′-O-methyltransferase, and a poly (A) polymerase, all necessary for mRNA production.[325-331] The degree of phosphorylation of NS may help determine the activity of the enzyme complex, with the most phosphorylated form having maximum transcriptase activity.[332-335]

Attachment, Penetration, Assembly

The infectious cycle of VSV begins with binding of G proteins on virus particles to glycolipid and phospholipid receptors on cell surfaces. Gangliosides inserted into L-α-phosphotidylserine–containing liposomes were also shown to inhibit VSV attachment to cells, which suggests that this combination may compete with cell receptor complexes for VSV attachment. A large variety of cells originating from numerous animal species support VSV infection, which indicates that receptors for VSV are common constituents of cell membranes and that viral-receptor interaction may be rather nonspecific.[336, 337]

Numerous pathways for VSV penetration into the cell have been described. These include viropexis, direct fusion of virus particles with the plasma membrane, and endocytosis, which results in viral envelope fusion with membranes of endocytic vesicles.[338] The latter mechanism is currently thought to be the primary mode of penetration for VSV.[339] G protein also has the ability to fuse membranes and to hemolyze erythrocytes. The hemolytic function has been localized to a specific sequence of six amino acids located at its N-terminus.[340] The fusion activity, however, apparently resides in another part of the molecule. Fusion mediated by G glycoprotein most likely depends on a conformational change

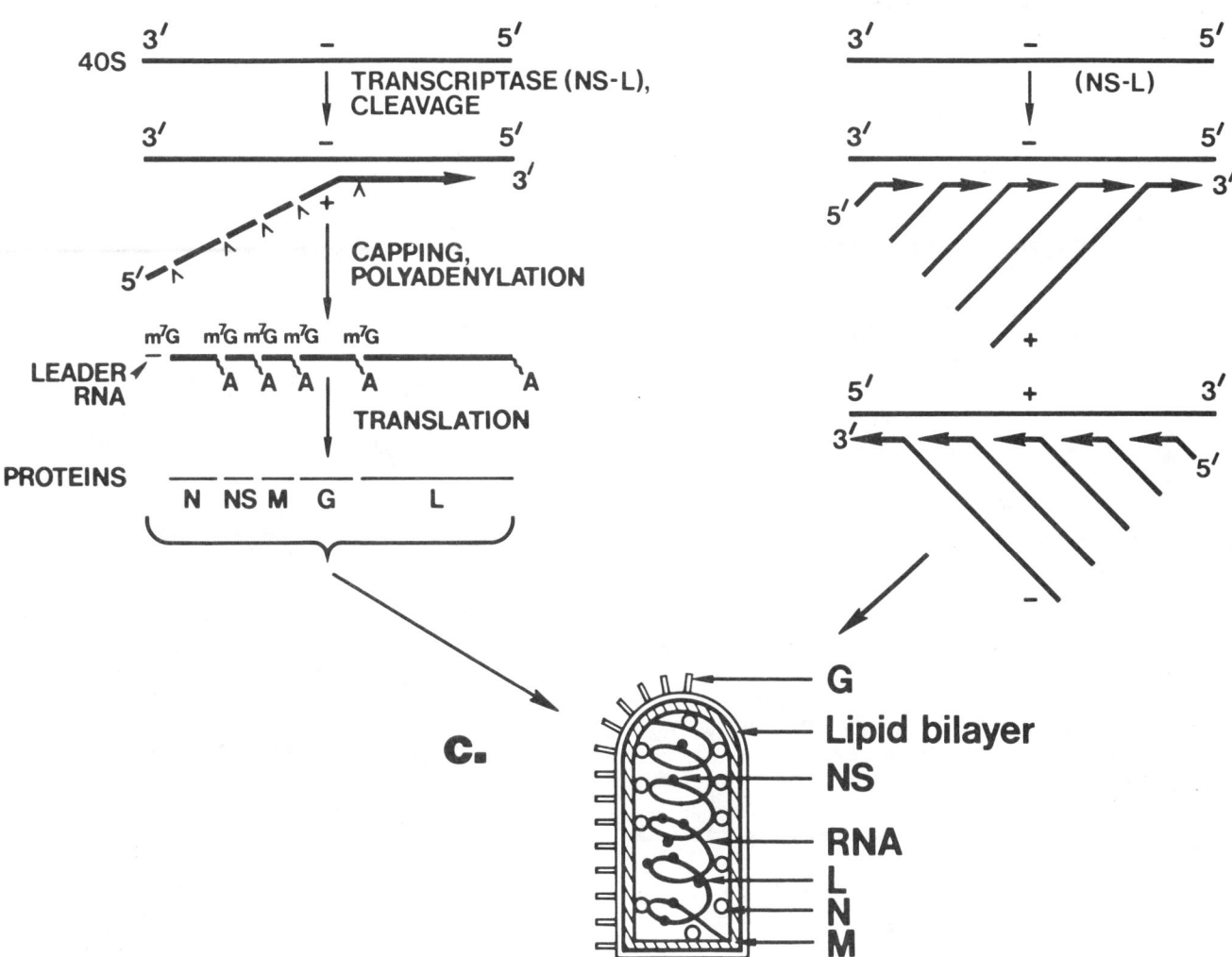

Figure 3–6. Replication of rhabdovirus (vesicular stomatitis virus). Genomic RNA is transcribed by RNA polymerase (NS–L) into a leader RNA plus five mRNAs by one of two possible mechanisms. A single positive-stranded RNA with a length equivalent to template RNA is endonucleolytically cleaved at specific sites (∧) to produce individual mRNAs. Alternatively, transcription terminates at the 3′ end of leader RNA and reinitiates to synthesize N mRNA. Successive termination-reinitiation events at specific sites (∧) lead to formation of mRNAs for N, NS, M, G, and L proteins. Messenger RNAs are capped (m7G) at their 5′ ends and polyadenylated (∿A) at their 3′ ends **(a)**. RNA replication requires the formation of replicative intermediates for both plus (+)- and minus (−)-strand RNA synthesis, which is mediated by the NS–L complex acting as the replicase **(b)**. Progeny RNAs plus NS, L, and N proteins form nucleocapsids which bud through cell membranes containing G and M proteins to form bullet-shaped virus particles **(c)**.

in G at acidic pH, since above pH 6 fusion activity is reduced.[341, 342] Endocytic vesicles provide the low pH environment necessary for optimal fusion.

Primary Transcription

Nucleocapsids released into the cytoplasm from endocytic vesicles act as templates for two synthetic processes, transcription and genome RNA replication (Figure 3–6).[343–345] The NS-L protein complexes associated with nucleocapsids released from virus particles or synthesized de novo during infection are pivotal for both transcription and RNA replication. NS-L activity, however, may be dependent on other viral proteins, for example, N and M proteins, and host cell proteins. Primary transcription is the first event to occur and requires neither viral nor host protein synthesis.[346, 347] Negative-stranded genome RNA is transcribed into five mRNAs, which are capped at their 5′ ends and polyadenylated at their 3′ termini. L-NS for primary transcription is present on nucleocapsids and possesses enzymatic activities necessary for transcription (RNA-dependent RNA polymerase), capping, and polyadenylation.[348, 349] L protein, the largest structural protein of VSV (241 kd), is present in catalytic amounts on nucleocapsids[350] and possesses most if not all of these enzymatic activities.[351] In addition, L may act as a protein kinase and nucleoside diphosphate kinase.[335, 352] Sequence analysis of L genes from several strains of VSV delineated six highly conserved sequences which may be essential for its enzymatic functions.[353]

NS protein (30 kd) is tightly bound to L protein on nucleocapsids, the interaction of the two proteins being required for enzyme activities of L. NS protein is a highly phosphorylated polypeptide with 48 potential phosphorylation sites at serines and threonines; eight are conserved among NS polypeptides of several strains.[354] NS polypeptide has been analyzed for functional domains based on its interaction with both L and N polypeptides, three such domains having been detected.[355] Domain I, which corresponds to the N-terminal half of NS polypeptide, is highly negatively charged due to its acidic amino acid composition and the number of phosphorylated amino acids.[354, 356] However, several of these phosphorylated amino acids assume an internal location within the three-dimensional structure of NS, making them phosphatase-resistant.[357] Domain I seems to control, at least in part, NS-N binding.[349] Domain II, corresponding to a sequence between amino acids 213 and 247, is required for transcription and contains two conserved phosphorylation sites at serine 236 and serine 242.[355] NS binding to L protein as well as the N-RNA template is governed by this domain and specifically depends on the phosphorylation at the two serines. Base substitutions at one or both of the serines greatly reduces or eliminates L binding and transcription.[358] The protein kinase activity associated with L protein determines the phosphorylation level of the two serine residues in domain II and perhaps those in other parts of NS.[335] The 21-amino acid C-terminal sequence, domain III, can be eliminated without effecting transcription. It has been implicated in strengthening binding between NS and N-RNA template, perhaps due to its overall basic amino acid composition, which is conserved among several strains of VSV.[349]

Despite the noted conservation of several amino acid sequences in NS among VSV serotypes, overall amino acid homology within NS molecules is relatively low (approximately 32%).[359] This rather high rate of diversity suggests that NS can accommodate changes at certain locations in its primary structure without losing in binding affinities.

Primary transcription initiates at the 3′ terminus of the template strand (see Figure 3–6,a).[360, 361] It has been shown that L protein alone can initiate limited synthesis of short oligonucleotides in vitro, which suggests a similar initiation function in vivo.[362] On the other hand, NS protein tightly bound to L protein is required for elongation of the transcript. Transcripts synthesized from template RNA include a 5′ leader RNA followed by N, NS, M, G, and L mRNAs in a 5′-to-3′ order. The 5′ and 3′ termini of each messenger are capped and polyadenylated, respectively, while leader RNA is neither capped nor polyadenylated.[345] Primary transcripts vary in abundance within infected cells, their relative abundance decreasing from the most abundant 5′ transcript (N) to the least abundant 3′ transcript (L). Several models have been advanced to explain transcription and account for decreased concentrations of mRNAs relative to the 5′-to-3′ progression of transcript formation.[345, 349]

Two models in particular will be detailed.[345] The first is based on the formation of a single primary transcript originating from a single promoter (3′ end of the template strand).[360, 361] The primary transcript is subsequently cleaved at sites corresponding to dinucleotides CU or GU into a 47-ribonucleotide leader RNA and five monocistronic mRNAs.[363, 364] Dinucleotides are removed during the process and are not found at the termini of mRNAs. Sequences flanking the cleavage sites are identical (see below) and perhaps specify the precise location of these breaks.[365] For this model to account for the range of concentrations of the five mRNAs, selective cleavage at the mRNA junctions must occur.[366] However, experimental data to support this contention are minimal.

In a second model, transcription initiates at multiple locations corresponding to the 5′ end of the leader RNA and again at the 5′ ends of each of the five monocistronic mRNAs. This process could occur by at least two mechanisms. Transcription could initiate at only one site (3′ end of template RNA) and RNA polymerase would proceed to the 3′ end of leader RNA where transcription would temporarily terminate. This same RNA polymerase would reinitiate transcription of N gene and proceed to a second termination site. Thus a continued initiation-termination process would produce the various mRNA species. Alternatively, multiple RNA polymerases could concurrently associate with all transcription initiation sites and synthesize RNA in an independent fashion. Again, selective initiation of the most abundant RNAs must occur.[345, 349]

The nucleotide sequences on genomic (template) RNAs of most strains of VSV that correspond to junctions between genes and sequences that flank junctions have been determined.[365] GA dinucleotides are found at the junctions between most genes for VSV (Indiana), but the CA dinucleotide is located at the NS-M junction. Junction dinucleotides are either not transcribed during the formation of mRNAs (model 2) or are cleaved from precursor mRNAs (model 1) during nucleolytic processing.

The consensus sequence, including sequences flanking dinucleotides, found at junctions within genomic RNA is 5′ GANNN-CUGUU *AG/AC* U7CAU3′, where the junction dinucleotide is italicized and N represents any nucleotide.[367] Thus a sequence complementary to GANNNCUGUU and U7CAU forms the 5′ capped and 3′ polyadenylated termini of individual mRNAs, respectively. It had been suggested that the seven U residues of U7CAU are used to generate poly (A) tails (approximately 200 A residues) by a recycling process, whereby poly (A) polymerase continuously reuses the U sequence as a template.[368] Another sequence located on the genomic RNA 3′ to the junction sites is an AU-rich region which possibly acts as promoter for transcription if model 2 is assumed.[369] Serotype variations in genomic RNA sequences have been noted at the G/L junction of the NJ serotype relative to that determined for VSV Indiana. An extra 19-nucleotide sequence at this location may contain a second site for initiation of transcription.[367]

Translation

Once transcribed, capped and polyadenylated viral mRNAs are translated into five structural proteins; leader RNA is untranslated (see Figure 3–6,a). Unlike influenza virus infection, nonstructural proteins are not synthesized during VSV replication. However, evidence for a second ORF corresponding to the 3′ one third of the NS gene has been presented. Ribosome binding to an internally located recognition sequence within the NS gene allows translation of a 7-kd protein. Its exact function is yet to be determined.[370]

RNA Replication

Viral protein synthesis is required for replication of genomic RNAs[371, 372]; viral proteins accumulate in cytoplasmic pools until appropriate quantities of NS, and particularly N, proteins are present in stoichiometric levels. L protein is only required in catalytic amounts.[345, 373, 374] Both in vivo and in vitro analyses of these proteins indicate that N protein synthesized de novo is necessary for initiating the process of RNA replication in preference to primary transcription. L-NS complex serves as the RNA polymerase for replication, perhaps with altered activities relative to the transcriptional polymerase. The transition from transcription to RNA replication can be explained employing transcription model 2 (see above). Instead of RNA synthesis terminating at the end of leader RNA as in the case of primary transcription, RNA elongation proceeds through the leader-N junction and all of the remaining intergenic sequences to produce full-length, positive-polarity copy of genome RNA. For this to occur N protein must be present at high-enough levels to associate immediately with nascent RNA, beginning with the leader sequence, so that nucleocapsids are formed from the nascent RNA in preference to mRNAs.[373, 375]

Results from several investigations also support the concept that newly synthesized N and NS proteins form complexes immediately after synthesis. Approximately six different-size NS-N complexes, which vary in the ratio of these two components, have been isolated from an in vitro system.[376] This N-NS association helps maintain N protein in a form capable of binding to RNA and prevents self-aggregation of N proteins. As in the case of transcription the activity of NS in these complexes may depend on phosphorylation at specific sites. Furthermore, although N alone can bind to RNA in a nonspecific manner, N-NS complexes seemingly help N bind to RNA in a more specific way.[376] Of the different N-NS complexes those consisting of N and NS at a 1:1 or 2:1 ratio are capable of optimally supporting RNA replication.[377, 378]

Nucleocapsids possessing positive-stranded RNA then act as templates for L-NS–mediated synthesis of progeny genomic RNAs, which again are encapsidated with NS, N, and L as they are synthesized. The latter nucleocapsids can serve as templates for further transcription (secondary) to yield additional mRNAs or are incorporated into virus particles.[345]

Both VSV RNA replication and transcription are influenced by factors within host cells. As is the case of several other viruses, for example, adenoviruses, VSV may replicate its RNA and form nucleocapsids in association with the cytoskeletal system, particularly microtubules.[379, 380] Microtubule-associated proteins (MAPS) and tubulin stimulate VSV transcription in vitro.[381] This may be related in part to the ability of tubulin to substitute for domain I of NS protein and thereby facilitate transcription and replication. Additional evidence showed that L associates directly with the cytoskeletal system of VSV-infected cells for extended periods after its synthesis.[382] Perhaps tubulin or MAPS regulate various enzymatic activities associated with L protein.

Structural Proteins and Virus Assembly

The next step in VSV replication is the envelopment of progeny nucleocapsids to form mature virus particles (see Figure 3–6,c).[383, 384] Selection of those nucleocapsids containing only negative-polarity RNA for envelopment must require a specific sorting system which has not been well characterized.

Viral assembly is a multistep process requiring (1) synthesis, glycosylation, and membrane insertion of G glycoproteins; (2) formation of progeny nucleocapsids, their transport to budding sites on plasma membranes, and conversion of nucleocapsids from loosely coiled to tightly coiled structures; (3) synthesis of M proteins and their direct interactions with plasma membranes and nucleocapsids; and (4) budding of nucleocapsids through membrane sites possessing G glycoproteins on their outer surface and M protein underlying their inner surface.

G protein synthesis, glycosylation, and transport to the plasma membrane have been extensively investigated and have provided information about membrane glycoproteins in general. Several factors have enabled G protein synthesis to be readily analyzed in infected cells, including inhibition of cell protein synthesis, the isolation of G mutants, and the fact that G is the only viral glycoprotein present on VSV.[385] G protein synthesis begins in the RER with the passage of the first 16 N-terminal hydrophobic amino acids (signal sequence) of the nascent G protein through the ER membrane.[386–389] Once the signal sequence enters the lumen of the ER, it is removed from nascent G polypeptide by proteolytic cleavage (signalase). As translation continues, G proteins pass through the membrane until only 30 C-terminal amino acids of the fully synthesized protein remain on the cytoplasmic side.

Ultimately, the main portion of G polypeptide extends into the ER lumen, a hydrophobic transmembrane region remains embedded in the membrane, and the C-terminal end extends into the cytoplasm. The first step of glycosylation then occurs with the addition of mannose-rich oligosaccharides to two asparagine residues in the N-terminal portion. G polypeptides are then transported to the Golgi apparatus enclosed in vesicles formed from ER membranes.[390] The partially glycosylated, N-terminal portion of G polypeptide is oriented inside the vesicle, while the C-terminal end remains on the cytoplasmic side.[391] Fusion of the vesicles with Golgi membranes maintains the internal orientation of the N-terminal portion of G polypeptide. At this site, further modification and glycosylation of G polypeptides occur, including the initial shortening of the mannose chains followed by additions of terminal carbohydrates.[392–395] Vesicles reform and transport glycoproteins to plasma membranes where the two membrane structures fuse, thereby placing viral glycoproteins in the cell membrane. The glycosylated N-terminal end is positioned on the outer surface and appears as spikes by electron microscopy.[396] During late stages of G protein synthesis, fatty acids are added near the junction of G protein and the surface of the vesicular or Golgi membranes, perhaps stabilizing the membrane-protein association.[397, 398]

The extent of final glycosylation of G proteins may depend on the cell lines used for infection.[399–402] In addition to the two primary carbohydrate chains, several other chains have been demonstrated on G proteins of different strains of VSV, but the significance of the latter has not been fully determined.[403, 404] The functions of the two primary carbohydrate chains are also a matter of controversy, but they may stabilize the protein, aid in its intracellular transport between RER and plasma membranes,[404a] and determine biologic activities, such as viral attachment to cell receptors. That the state of glycosolation required for viral morphogenesis differs has been demonstrated for various strains of VSV. For example, total inhibition of G protein glycosylation prevents morphogenesis of San Juan strain of VSV by 95%,[405] yet maturation of Orsay strain was inhibited by only 30% to 50%.[406–408]

In addition to membrane-bound G glycoprotein, a fully glycosylated, truncated form of G protein (Gs) is released from infected cells in a soluble form and can be isolated from tissue culture media.[409–411] Several hypotheses have been proposed to account for the synthesis of Gs. Possibly Gs is a proteolytic cleavage product originating from the external domain of G protein. Alternatively, evidence that Gs is synthesized intracellularly either from truncated G mRNAs or more probably from mRNAs possessing frame shifts has been presented.[412] In the latter situation, translation is terminated at sites short of the normal location.[413]

M protein of VSV is important for initiating the budding process and acting as a link between nucleocapsids and sites on the cell membrane containing G protein.[414–419] At late stages of infection, M protein is abundant, constituting almost a third of the total viral proteins within infected cells. The temporal order in which M protein interacts directly with budding sites on plasma membranes or nucleocapsids in the cytoplasm has not been absolutely determined. Probably M initially forms an association with the inner surface of plasma membranes in areas of G protein clusters[420] by directly binding to C-terminal sequences of G which extend into the cytoplasm. The requirement of G protein for M protein–membrane interaction is controversial. On the one hand, spikeless (G negative) virus particles have been assembled which indicate that M protein alone determines envelopment.[421, 422] Recent data suggest, however, that fully intact G may not be required, but the presence of the transmembrane C-terminal sequence of G protein is necessary.[423] In support of this concept, G protein is transported specifically to the basolateral plasma membrane in certain polarized cells, such as differentiated epithelial cells, where envelopment of nucleocapsids also occurs. This suggests that the location of G proteins determines the sites of viral assembly.[424] M protein

may also induce a redistribution of membrane acidic phospholipids (phosphotidylserine) causing them to preferentially concentrate at budding sites, which is reflected in the composition of the viral envelope.[425]

Alternatively, instead of first interacting with plasma membranes, M proteins may initially interact with progeny nucleocapsids causing a change in their conformations from relaxed, extended structures to tightly coiled, condensed nucleocapsids.[426] Concomitantly, secondary transcription from condensed nucleocapsids is inhibited.[427–432]

Structural analysis of M protein indicates that N- and C-terminal sequences lack a complex conformation, while the majority of the middle segment assumes a globular structure. The N-terminal sequence inclusive of residues 18 to 43 of M protein interacts electrostatically with nucleocapsids and inhibits viral transcription,[433] whereas the C-terminus in part mediates membrane binding.[434] With binding sites at opposite poles of the protein, M protein may be in the correct spatial orientation to act as a bridge between membranes at the budding sites and nucleocapsids.

The final stages of viral assembly require an association of only nucleocapsids possessing genomic (negative-stranded) RNA with membrane sites having clusters of G proteins and little or no cellular proteins on their surfaces. In an energy-requiring process the nucleocapsid protrudes into the membrane, becoming completely surrounded to form the viral envelope.

Defective-Interfering (DI) Particles

In addition to VSV representing the replication schemes of unsegmented, negative-stranded RNA viruses, it also serves as a good model for studying DI particles generated during replication.[435–438] DI particles have been detected in stocks of both DNA and RNA viruses, although those of the RNA viruses, especially VSV, have been investigated in most detail. VSV is particularly amenable for study due to the ease of separating smaller DI particles from standard virus by centrifugation in sucrose gradients.[439]

DI particles are so named because they are deletion mutants derived from standard, nondefective VSV and have less RNA than that required for viral replication. In particular, deletions most often include at least a portion of the L gene.[440] DI particles also "interfere" with replication of nondefective VSV, from which they were originally derived, as well as other types of VSV DI particles.[441] On the other hand, the nondefective virus provide factors necessary for the replication of DI particles in the confines of cells coinfected with both nondefective and defective viruses.[437, 438]

DI particles possibly arise in a given virus population by several different mechanisms and are amplified in number after successive infections of cells at high multiplicities.[442] DI particles having different RNA sizes may be found in a given virus population, indicating that RNA segments of various sizes can be deleted from either the 5′ or 3′ portions of full-sized (42S) genome. The majority of DI particles, however, retain their 5′ terminal sequences, while the 3′ terminal sequences may be altered.[440, 443] Usually, only one or a few types of DI particles predominate at a given time in cells, but new dominant species may evolve during successive infections.[444, 445] The 20 terminal nucleotides at the 5′ end of DI-particle RNA are identical to the twenty 5′ terminal nucleotides present in nondefective virus from which they were derived. In addition, sequence complementarity has been demonstrated between nucleotides at the 3′ and 5′ ends in most DI-particles RNAs. Three general classes of RNAs can be distinguished in DI particles based on the size of the complementary sequences present at their termini.[441]

In one group, approximately 18 to 20 terminal nucleotides are complementary at the 3′ and 5′ ends; this is also the number found in nondefective VSV.[446] A second group has approximately 45 nucleotides which are complementary. A third group consists of DI particles with about 60 complementary terminal nucleotides, but as many as 200 nucleotides have been detected in one population of DI particles.[447] DI RNAs with the longer complementary terminal sequences may have an advantage in binding the polymerase proteins NS and L, and possibly N protein, and these sequences may potentiate DI-particles replication over nondefective VSV and other DI particles.[441] Based on binding studies of NS and L proteins to the 3′ terminal sequences of both nondefective and defective RNAs, two separate binding sites have been detected. The NS protein associates with an internal adenosine plus uridine–rich region, 17 to 37 nucleotides inward from the 3′ end, which may indirectly influence the binding of L protein to the exact 3′ end.[448] The affinities of NS protein for its binding site may be greater for DI-particle RNAs compared to binding of NS to a similar site on nondefective VSV RNA. Binding affinities in turn may depend on differences in both nucleotide composition and the actual sequence present in analogous NS binding sites.

DI-particle RNAs freed from nucleocapsids and having terminal complementarity can circularize by self-annealing with the formation of double-stranded ends.[449] Similarly panhandle-shaped RNAs formed during the infection cycle also may be advantageous for polymerase binding.

Although the exact mechanism(s) for generation of DI particles has not been elucidated, several models have been proposed.[440] It is believed that most DI RNAs are formed during the step of RNA replication in which full-length positive RNA serves as a template for genome RNA synthesis. Accordingly, the RNA polymerase initiates replication at the 3′ end of the positive strand and synthesizes a partial nascent (−) strand until a point is reached on the genome where the polymerase and its attached nascent strand dissociate from the template (Figure 3–7). Synthesis is reinitiated at one of several locations: (1) at a different position on the same template (see Figure 3–7,b); (2) at a position within the 5′ terminal sequence on the same nascent strand (see Figure 3–7,c); (3) on a second nascent strand of RNA that precedes the displaced strand in its movement along the template (copy-back) (see Figure 3–7,d); and (4) at the 3′ terminus of an already existing DI RNA (see Figure 3–7,e).[440] A crucial aspect of these models is the relocation of the polymerase-nascent strand complex as one unit. The molecular details and control mechanisms governing the dissociation and reinitiation of the polymerase-nascent strand complex have not been ascertained.

Additional factors may be involved in DI particle formation, some being related to particular cell types, levels of cell differentiation, or genetic traits of animal hosts.[450–453] Certain strains of mice and cell cultures derived from them are either resistant to lytic virus infection as a result of DI particle formation or susceptible to infection due to the failure to produce DI particles. Also, inhibiton of host cell functions prior to VSV infection greatly decreased DI particle production.[454] Additional evidence for the importance of host cell functions in the generation of DI particles was obtained from VSV infection of mouse-human cell hybrids.[455] Functions associated with mouse chromosomes seem to induce DI particles in hybrids, while certain dominant human cell functions suppress their formation. However, mechanisms involving host cell factors are only speculative at this time.

Persistent Infection

VSV is considered to be cytolytic for most vertebrate cell cultures with cell death resulting from infection. An alternative type of VSV infection, persistent infection, is seen in most insect cells, including those from *Drosophila melanogaster* where little or no CPE is seen.[456] The infected cells remain viable and although some virus replication may occur, progeny virus is usually produced at lower levels compared to those found in lytic infections.[457] In human B lymphoid cells latently infected by a herpesvirus (Epstein-Barr virus), a nonpermissive state also prevents VSV lytic infection.[458]

In a drosophila cell line VSV proteins are synthesized at relatively normal levels during the first seven hours postinfection, but steadily decline to low levels thereafter.[457] Reduced synthesis and aberrant modification of G and M proteins by altered glycosylation and hyperphosphorylation, respectively, have been observed.[457, 459] Viral RNA synthesis is also greatly reduced. Leader RNA, for example, is present in the cytoplasm of persistently infected drosophila cells at approximately 70 copies per cell, whereas 2000 copies per cell are detected in productively infected cells. Leader RNA (see below) is primarily responsible for shutoff of host cell DNA and RNA synthesis during lytic infections, the process requiring the transport of leader RNA from the cytoplasm to the nucleus. In most VSV-infected insect cells the leader RNA remains within the cytoplasm and is not transported to the nucleus, which may be the primary reason for continued cell transcription and DNA synthesis during persistent infections.[460]

In addition to nonpermissiveness for VSV replication seen in insect cells, lytic infections can be curtailed in vertebrate cells in favor of persistent infections by various means. Coinfection of vertebrate cells with VSV and DI particles of VSV at high concentrations can result in persistent infections.[461] Treatment of cells with interferon prior to VSV infection also leads to the development of persistent infections as opposed to lytic infections.[462, 463] In both situations the replication of VSV is initially inhibited, while cellular processes continue. Not only does VSV fail to inhibit cellular processes, but the virus genome itself is altered during continued propagation of persistently infected cells in cultures. VSV isolated from persistently infected cells usually has acquired temperature sensitivity, which is often coupled with an RNA-negative phenotype.[464, 465] Alterations in the viral genome may greatly reduce the lytic nature of the virus and further aid in the establishment of long-term persistent infections. Nonsegmented, negative-stranded RNA virus has a rather high rate of mutation

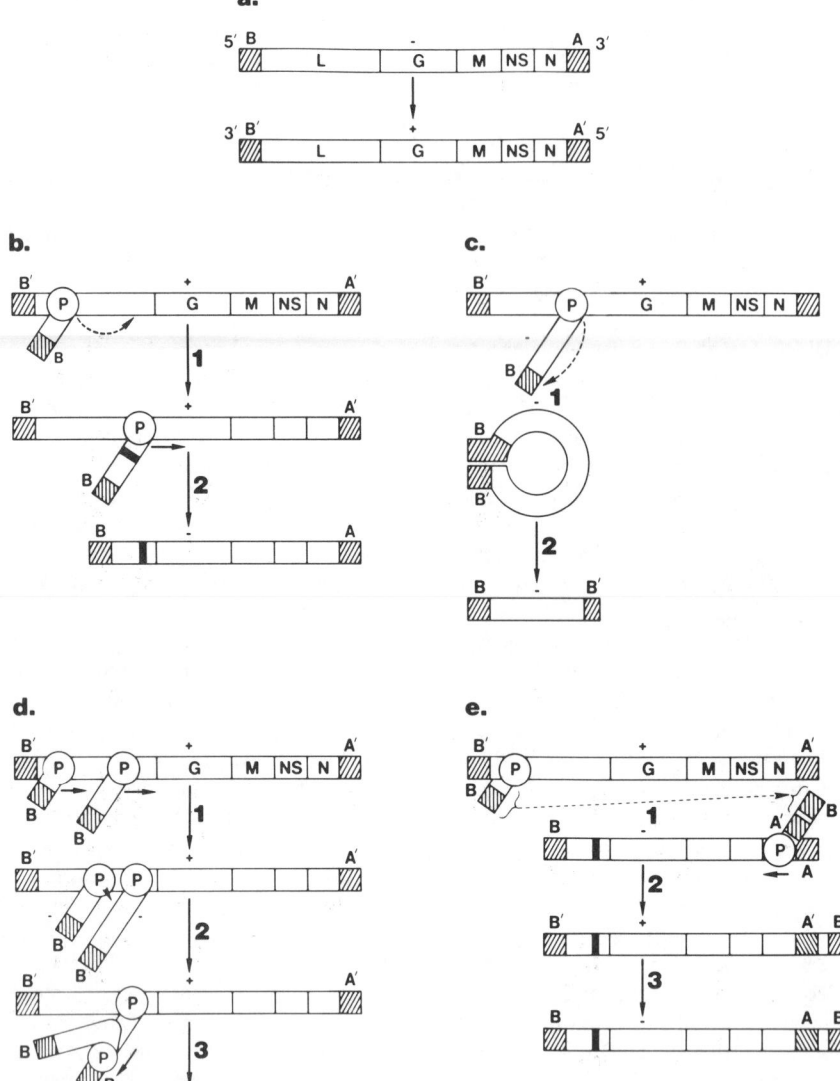

Figure 3–7. Models for the synthesis of defective viral RNAs present in defective-interfering (DI) particles. In the first stage of RNA replication viral RNA (minus [−]-polarity RNA) serves as a template for plus (+) RNA synthesis (a). The latter RNA then serves as a template for synthesis of progeny RNA, some of which may be defective (b–e). The formation of simple deletions (b) results from the termination of RNA synthesis at a point within the L gene. The RNA polymerase (P) with its attached nascent RNA relocates to a position at the other end of L gene and reinitiates RNA synthesis (b1). The completed progeny RNA therefore has a portion of its L gene deleted (b2). A second type of deletion (c) occurs through the termination of polymerase movement along an RNA template and the relocation of P and attached RNA to the terminus of the nascent strand (c1). RNA synthesis continues (c2) using part of the terminal sequence B as a template to form shortened B′. A third model requires that two polymerases move along the template strand, each involved in the synthesis of viral RNA (d1). The leading polymerase is overtaken by the trailing polymerase-RNA complex which allows the latter to relocate from the plus (+)-strand template to the leading nascent RNA (d2). The translocated polymerase continues to synthesize RNA from this second template (d3), the final product having both plus (+)- and minus (−)-polarity RNA. The model illustrated in (e) represents a mechanism for the formation of compound DI-particle RNA. Nascent RNA and its attached polymerase is translocated from a plus (+) RNA template to the terminus of viral RNA containing a simple deletion (− polarity) as shown in (e1), and P uses the latter as a template. The completed strand has plus (+) polarity with an additional terminal sequence B adjacent to A′. Viral RNA copied from plus (+) RNA (e3) likewise has two terminal sequences at one terminus; sequence B′ is complementary to B at the other terminus. (Reproduced with permission from Lazzarini RA, et al: The origins of defective interfering particles of the negative-strand RNA viruses. *Cell* 1981; 26:145–154.)

(approximately 10^{-3}) most probably due to the error-prone nature of RNA-dependent RNA polymerase, plus the lack of an appropriate repair system.[466]

Effects on Host Cells

Several investigations have shown that at high multiplicities of infection with VSV or certain VSV deletion mutants, cellular RNA and protein syntheses decline, although cells remain viable.[467-469] This type of inhibition of macromolecular synthesis does not require expression of the VSV genome and depends on G structural protein of the virus particle. In addition, high concentrations of purified G glycoprotein will also inhibit both cellular RNA and DNA synthesis.[470]

A second type of inhibition of cell synthetic events requires primary transcription of a select portion of the VSV genome. Unlike high multiplicity inhibition, this latter type leads to cell death.[471-473] Several mechanisms for inhibition of both cellular proteins and nucleic acid synthesis have been proposed. Inhibition of protein synthesis occurs at the level of translation and may result from a competitive advantage of large numbers of viral mRNAs over fewer cell mRNAs for limited amounts of ribosomes.[474] Alternatively, infected cells contain decreased amounts of translation factor(s) (eIF-2), which limits the initiation of translation and perhaps establishes a competition between viral and cellular mRNAs for these factors.[475, 476] A third possibility is that inhibition results from a viral protein (N or NS) which interferes with cell mRNA-directed translation.[477] These and other mechanisms involved in inhibition of protein synthesis may be virus strain–dependent.

Inhibition of cell RNA and DNA synthesis may proceed by an entirely different mechanism from protein inhibition, as was suggested by different kinetics at a given MOI. Thus, one viral gene product may be responsible for inhibition of both cell DNA and RNA synthesis, while another inhibits translation. Both cell DNA and RNA synthesis seem to be blocked at initiation steps.[478, 479] Inhibition of cell RNA synthesis in vertebrate cells begins at approximately two hours postinfection and requires transcription of select regions of the viral genome.[480, 480a]

Leader RNA is central to the inhibitory process, but N gene transcription facilitates inhibition.[481-483] Leader RNA formed during viral transcription is transported to the nucleus, the process being dependent on both viral and cellular proteins.[484] N protein synthesized de novo interacts with leader RNA, possibly to stabilize it,[485] while a cell protein, La, is necessary for its transport to the cell nucleus.[486] Alternatively, a 65-kd cell protein can reduce the inhibitory activity of leader RNA in in vitro systems.[487]

Approximately 2000 leader RNAs can accumulate in each VSV-infected cell nucleus, leading to inhibition of cellular RNA polymerase II and III–mediated transcription.[488] Critical to the inhibitory activity of leader RNAs is a centrally located AU-rich region, which along with its flanking sequences is necessary for inhibition.[489]

Using an adenovirus DNA model, VSV-leader RNA was also inhibitory for initiation of DNA synthesis.[490] Specifically, adenovirus DNA polymerase and possibly cell DNA polymerase-primase bind to leader RNA, thereby lowering their intranuclear levels and reducing their availability to support DNA synthesis. This concept is supported by sequence homology between leader RNA and terminal DNA sequences involved in initiation of adenovirus DNA synthesis. In sum, leader RNA most likely inhibits both cell DNA and RNA synthesis in a process dependent on its transport to the nucleus.

PARAMYXOVIRUSES

Glycoproteins

Members of the *Paramyxoviridae* possess mechanisms of replication similar to that of VSV. A discussion of the envelope protein(s) of paramyxoviruses is presented in order to compare them with envelope glycoproteins of VSV (G protein) and influenza A virus (HA and NA proteins).[491, 492]

Viruses classified within the genus *Paramyxovirus* (see Chapter 1), include mumps, Sendai, and Newcastle disease viruses, which have two types of glycoprotein spikes inserted into their envelopes: hemagglutinin-neuraminidase (HN) and fusion (F) spikes. *Morbilliviruses,* such as measles and canine distemper virus, likewise have two types of spikes: hemagglutinin (H) and fusion (F). Respiratory syncytial virus, a *Pneumovirus,* does not possess hemagglutinin activity, but at least one of its two glycoproteins can initiate fusion and the other attachment (G).[493-496]

Envelope proteins of rhabdovirus, orthomyxovirus, and paramyxovirus which bind to cell receptors to initiate infection are the G glycoprotein (VSV), HA glycoprotein (influenza A virus), and HN (Sendai virus), respectively. Both G and HA glycoproteins are necessary for viral penetration into cells, whereas HN proteins of paramyxoviruses lack fusion ability. For the last-named virus group a separate protein spike, F, determines fusion. Influenza A virus HA and Sendai virus F proteins, which have partial amino acid homology, must be proteolytically cleaved at an internal site to form HA1 + HA2 and F2 + F1, respectively.[497-500a] The subunits remain linked through a disulfide bond. Cleavage exposes a sequence of hydrophobic amino acids which interacts with lipid bilayers to facilitate fusion at the N-terminal ends of HA2 or F1.[501, 502] The cleavage sites in HA and F0 of the more virulent strains of influenza A virus and Sendai virus, respectively, possess a sequence of basic amino acids rather than a single basic residue as found in some avirulent strains. This imparts a wider range of susceptibility for proteolysis.[500, 503]

A second spike found in envelopes of influenza A virus possesses neuraminidase (NA) activity and is important for the release of progeny virus from infected cells during the budding process. A similar enzymatic activity is found associated with the hemagglutinin (HN) spike of paramyxovirus, whereas the G protein of VSV lacks this activity.[498, 499] Results obtained using monoclonal antibodies showed that the neuraminidase activity of Sendai virus is associated with a site nearby but distinct from the site responsible for hemagglutination.[504, 505]

As discussed previously (see influenza virus section) both the HA and NA spikes of influenza virus exist in their mature forms as a trimer or tetramer, respectively.[506] Preliminary results suggest that G proteins of VSV and HN of Sendai virus assume multimeric forms on the surface of viral envelopes.[322] HN of a number of paramyxoviruses has ten conserved cysteine residues located within their amino acid sequences which suggests a role in stabilization of its secondary structure. Cysteines may also facilitate the formation of HN multimers.[507] In support of this concept the HN of Newcastle disease virus (a paramyxovirus) exists as a disulfide-linked dimer.

Interestingly the orientation of G, HA, NA, and HN proteins differs relative to their membrane insertions. G and HA are inserted into the membrane at C-terminal anchor regions which orients the glycosylated N-terminal portion of the proteins to the external side of the envelope. HN and NA, on the other hand, are embedded in membranes in the opposite orientation, the C-termini are external, and the transmembrane region is near the N-terminus.[508, 509] Furthermore, sequence comparisons of HN and NA glycoproteins suggest that sites responsible for neuraminidase activity on both proteins are related, which suggests an evolutionary tie between the corresponding viral genes.[509]

REOVIRUSES

Virus Structure

In the family *Reoviridae* the structure and replication cycles of members of the *Reovirus* genus have been investigated in most detail as compared to human rotaviruses and Colorado tick fever virus, which are the primary human pathogens. Reovirus particles (Figure 3–8,d) consist of two concentric capsids 75 and 50 nm in diameter, each being icosahedral.[510, 511] The outer capsid is formed from morphologically distinct capsomers that are composed of three viral proteins (Table 3–1). The inner capsid or core is composed of six proteins, which are also arranged into capsomers, but these are less distinct morphologically than those constituting the outer capsid.[512–514] Extending outward from the 12 vertices of the core are hollow tubelike projections which partially protrude through the vertices of the outer capsid.[510] Within the core structure are ten individual segments of double-stranded (DS) RNA, each segment consisting of complementary positive and negative strands.[515–517] The 5' termini of the positive strands (same nucleotide sequence as mRNAs) are capped and methylated, but the 3' ends do not terminate with poly (A) (see Figure 3–8,a).[518–520] The negative strand is not capped and also lacks poly (A). Genome RNA segments fall into three size groups: large (L), medium (M), and small (S).[517, 521] The mRNAs transcribed from the negative strand of DS RNA segments reflect the size variation of their templates and, unlike mRNAs of most other animal viruses, lack poly (A) at their 3' termini. The three large double-stranded RNAs, L1, L2, and L3, encode three core proteins (see Table 3–1) that are designated λ_3, λ_2, and λ_1, respectively.[522] Protein λ_2 comprises the hollow tubes extending outward from the core, while λ_1 is a major structural protein of the core.[523, 524]

Three medium-sized genomic RNAs, M1, M2, and M3, encode core proteins μ_2 and μ_1, and a nonstructural protein, μNS, respectively.[522] A major outer capsid protein, μ1c, is derived from μ_1 by proteolytic cleavage.[514]

Of the four small proteins encoded by S1, S2, S3, and S4, σ_1 and σ_3 are found in the outer capsid, while σ_2 is core-associated; σ_3 may act to seal the tubelike projections at the vertices and, along with λ_2 and σ_1, stimulates the production of neutralizing antibodies.[525–527] S1 RNA also possesses a second ORF which is translated into a 14-kd polypeptide, σ_{1s}, which is found in infected cells.[528] σ_{NS}, like μ_{NS}, is found within infected cells but is not part of mature virus particles. At least five enzymatic activities inside the core are activated by partial uncoating of virus particles during infection or by chymotrypsin or trypsin treatment of intact virus particles.[529–532] These include RNA-dependent RNA polymerase,[529] a nucleoside triphosphate phosphohydrolase,[530, 533] guanylyltransferase, and two methylases,[519] all of which are necessary for the transcription of genome RNAs into messengers with cap structures at their 5' ends. It is believed that several of the core structural proteins harbor these activities, with λ_3 possibly in conjunction with σ_2, λ_1, and σ_{NS} possessing transcriptase activity, and λ_2 having capping functions (see below).[534]

Attachment, Penetration, Uncoating

The multiplication cycle of reovirus occurs within the cytoplasm of infected cells. Initial stages of infection include attachment of virus particles to cell surfaces through specific binding between outer capsid protein σ_1 and cell receptor molecules.[13, 535] Receptors for reovirus on various cell types have been characterized as glycoproteins or possibly glycolipids, the carbohydrates, especially neuraminic acid, being essential for receptor activity.[536, 537] A polypeptide isolated from lymphoid and neuronal cells having sequence homology with beta-adrenergic receptors also has receptor activity for reoviruses.[538, 539] It is possible that more than one receptor exists or that different forms, monomeric versus dimeric, are present on various cell types. Reovirus receptors on human erythrocytes have been characterized as the sialoglycoprotein glycophorin, which also possesses the M-N blood group determinants.[540]

The viral protein σ_1 interacts directly with cell receptors and is located at the vertices of the icosahedral capsid of intact viral particles.[535] This protein exists as a complex composed of four σ_1 polypeptides.[541] In its native configuration the N-terminal sequences of monomeric σ_1 associate to form a fiberlike structure, while the C-termini form a globular structure.[542, 543] The fiber portion of the σ_1 complex is most likely housed within the tubular structure composed of λ_2, whereas the globular portion may project outward into the external environment. This latter structural organization seemingly changes to facilitate receptor binding. The fiber portion of the σ_1 complex has been observed by electron microscopy in an extended conformation, whereby most of the length of the fiber with its globular end protrudes out away from the virus particle instead of being buried within the confines of the λ_2 tubular structure. It is possible that extension involves reorganization of the σ_1 tetramer through its interactions with receptors.[544] The σ_1 polypeptide has been analyzed for functional domains involved in hemagglutination, binding to nucleated cell receptors, and neutralization. Different domains of σ_1 located within the C-terminus bind to erythrocytes and nucleated cell receptors. In addition, several epitopes located at the C-terminus, as defined by monoclonal antibodies, are sites for viral neutralization.[545–547]

Following attachment, reoviruses enter cells by endocytosis. Virus-containing vesicles fuse with lysosomes, and provide a low pH environment which results in limited degradation of the outer capsid.[548, 549] Removal of σ_3 unseals the hollow tubes to allow transport of macromolecules to and from the viral core and initiates sequential activation of core enzymes. Proteolytic cleavage of μ1c to form a 60-kd δ protein and its eventual removal along with σ_1

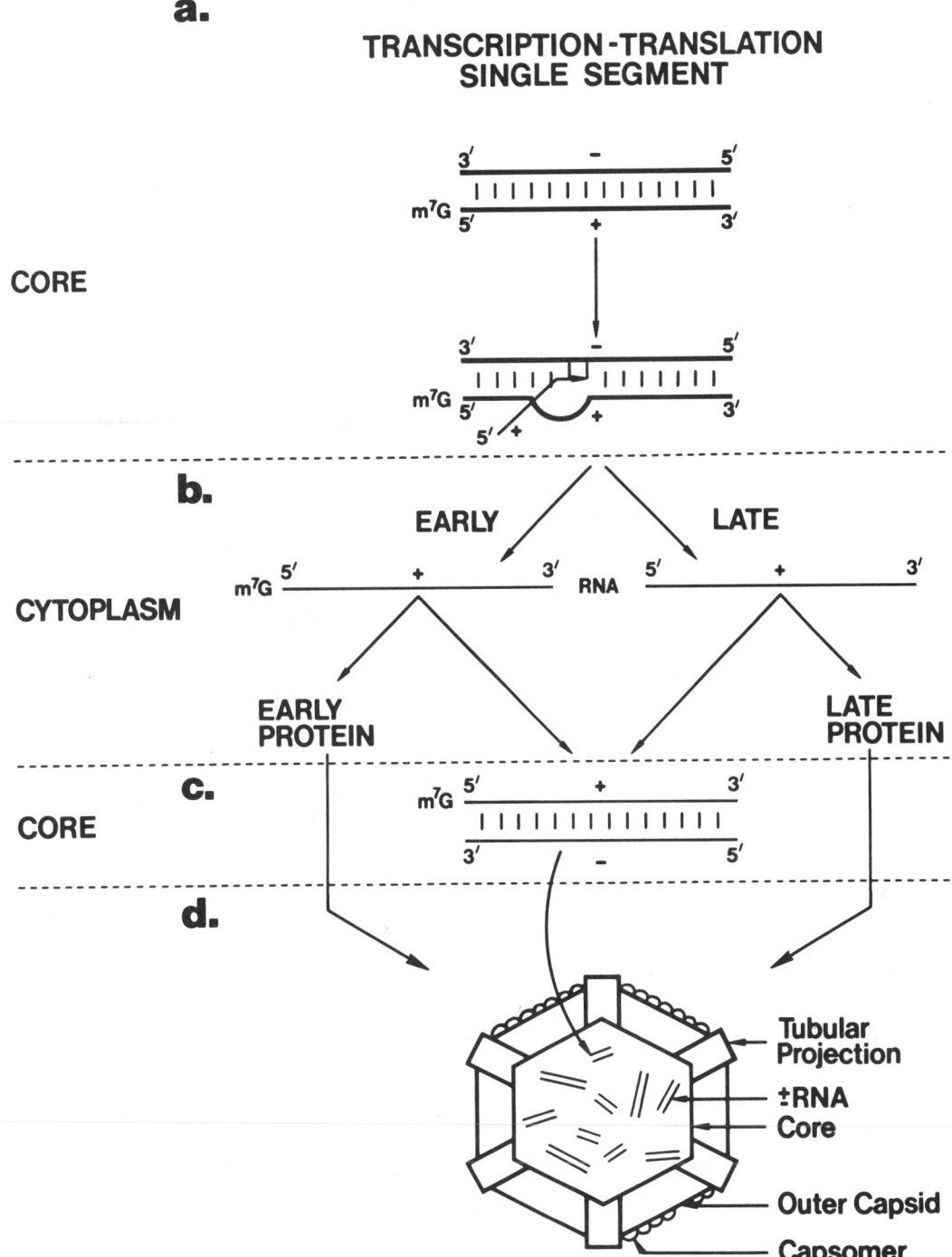

a.

**TRANSCRIPTION-TRANSLATION
SINGLE SEGMENT**

CORE

CYTOPLASM

b.

EARLY   LATE

EARLY
PROTEIN

LATE
PROTEIN

c.

CORE

d.

Tubular
Projection

±RNA
Core

Outer Capsid

Capsomer

Figure 3-8. Replication of reovirus. RNA transcription from each of the ten RNA segments occurs within viral cores; transcription from a single segment is shown (a). Single-stranded plus (+) RNAs leave viral cores and are translated within the cytoplasm into early viral proteins (b). Single-stranded plus (+) RNAs are also partially encapsidated to form cores in which complementary strands are synthesized (c). Progeny cores can either be fully encapsidated into virus particles (d) or serve as sites for late mRNA synthesis (a). Late mRNA, unlike early mRNA, is not capped (b).

Table 3–1
RNA Segments and Proteins of Reovirus

Double-Stranded RNA Segment	Viral Protein	Viral Location	Function
L1	λ_3	Core	Minor protein,* transcriptase
L2	λ_2	Core, vertices (tubular projections)	Major protein* capping enzymes; stimulates nt abs†
L3	λ_1	Core	Transcriptase-associated, possibly regulatory, major protein
M1	μ_2	Core	Minor protein
M2	$\mu1\rightarrow\mu1c\rightarrow\delta$	Core, outer capsid	$\mu1$ Minor protein; $\mu1$ cleaved to $\mu1c$ (major outer capsid); $\mu1c$ cleaved to δ; δ facilitates penetration; $\mu1c$ influences pathogenesis; $\mu1c$ complexed to σ_3 inhibits viral transcripts
M3	μ_{NS}	—	Infected cells only, association with microtubules, viral assembly
S1	σ_1, σ_{1S}	Outer capsid (tetrameric)	Hemagglutinin; interacts with receptors on cells; inhibits cell DNA synthesis; stimulates nt abs†; σ_{1S}: infected cell protein; progeny virus formation in association with microtubules; mutation in S1→establishment of persistent infections
S2	σ_2	Core	Transcriptase-associated, major protein
S3	σ_{NS}		Infected cell protein, transcriptase-associated, SS-RNA–binding protein
S4	σ_3	Outer capsid	Nucleic acid–binding protein and/or protease; facilitates late viral translation; shutoff of host protein synthesis; mutation in S4 establishment of persistent infections; seals tubular projection, stimulates nt abs†

*Relative abundance of protein within virus particles.
†nt abs = neutralizing antibody.

produces subviral particles (SVP) capable of transcription.[550–554] Formation of δ proteins also greatly facilitates penetration of reovirus into cells.[549]

Transcription

Reoviruses are unusual in that the genome can be transcribed within partially uncoated virus particles. Transcription occurs from the negative strand of each of the ten double-stranded segments to produce mRNAs (+ polarity) of lengths equal to that of the corresponding genome segment (see Figure 3–8a). In addition to the λ_3 protein complex serving as the transcriptase, several viral proteins are possibly involved in control and regulation of transcription. Sequence analysis of genome segments to predict RNA-binding properties of their corresponding gene products, as well as detection of viral proteins directly bound to reovirus DS RNA, indicate that σ_3, σ_2, and λ_1 are candidate-regulatory proteins.[555] Although σ_3 protein is found in the outer capsid of mature reovirus particles, it possesses a consensus sequence with the potential to bind zinc ions and assumes a "zinc finger" configuration. These characteristics are indicative of nucleic acid–binding proteins, some of which have regulatory function. Alternatively, σ_3 may possess protease activity which is modulated through zinc binding.[556] Core proteins σ_2 and λ_1 seemingly constitute part of the transcriptase complex and are capable of binding to double-stranded RNA; they bind zinc and possibly have a role in transcriptional regulation.[556] Also, σ_{NS}, which is a nonstructural viral protein, is capable of binding to single-stranded RNA and can protect a 20- to 40-nucleotide sequence on reovirus RNAs from nuclease digestion.[555, 557, 558] Its location within progeny SVP suggests that it may be involved in RNA synthesis, that is, synthesis of minus-strand RNAs from the positive-strand templates.

Early during infection, mRNAs from L1, M3, S3, and S4 are synthesized at greater frequencies than other messengers.[559] The frequency of transcription changes later during infection so that S segments are all transcribed at higher rates than M RNAs, which in turn are transcribed more frequently than L RNAs.[560] In addition, those mRNAs transcribed early during viral multiplication are both capped and methylated, while those synthesized at later times are uncapped.[561]

Translation

Translation of early as well as late mRNAs into the viral proteins is a regulated series of events. Since early viral and host cellular mRNAs are capped at their 5′ ends and late viral mRNAs lack cap structures, differential recognition of these mRNA types by macromolecules involved in translation must occur.[562, 563] Furthermore, at specific times during reovirus infection, viral mRNAs are translated at different frequencies despite the fact that equivalent quantities of the mRNAs are present in the cell. Several, although not necessarily mutually exclusive, mechanisms have been proposed to explain the varying degrees of translation efficiencies. At late times, preferential translation of uncapped viral mRNAs over early viral and host cellular mRNA may depend on the inactivation of cap-binding protein, a necessary component in translation of capped mRNAs.[564, 565] Alternatively, viral protein σ_3 has been shown to facilitate late translation, possibly by binding to the uncapped 5' termini of late mRNAs, specifically.[566]

Differential translation of S_1 and S_4 mRNAs, which have similar size characteristics, stabilities, and abundance within infected cells have been observed. S_4 mRNA is translated approximately sevenfold more efficiently than S_1 mRNA.[567–569] Sequence analysis indicates that specific nucleotides relative to the initiation codon AUG at position -3 (three ribonucleotides 5' to AUG) and at $+4$ (3' to AUG) determine the efficiency of translation. Thus a purine in position -3 and G in position $+4$ optimize translation, this combination being observed in S_4 mRNA but not in S_1 mRNA.[528, 570] The seemingly clear explanation for the differential translation of S_1 and S_4 mRNAs has been complicated by experiments involving site-specific mutagenesis within the -3 to $+5$ sequence, which includes AUG. Alteration in the ribonucleotide sequence did not greatly effect the levels of translation that would have been expected based on previous data.[571] Following translation certain viral proteins (μ_1, μ_{NS}, λ_1, and λ_2) are cleaved proteolytically to yield products that may also function during viral replication.[565]

RNA Replication

After early transcription and translation, the ten ($+$ polarity) segments of RNA condense with specific viral proteins to form SVPs. A mechanism by which only one RNA segment of each size is incorporated per SVP operates in the early stages of assembly. Possibly the single-stranded RNA-binding protein σ_{NS} mediates this process.[555, 557, 572] Protein μ_{NS} participates in early assembly and binds immature particles to the cytoskeletal system.[573] Next, the addition of core proteins λ_2 and λ_1 occurs in sequential stages.[565] The first immature SVP also consists of two nonstructural polypeptides, μ_{NS} and σ_{NS}, plus μlc-σ_3 complexes.

Inside newly synthesized SVPs the plus strands are copied into their complementary minus strands to form ten double-stranded RNAs (Figure 3–8,c).[574–576] Progeny viral cores can serve as sites for further synthesis of plus-stranded mRNAs which are extruded into the cytoplasm and translated into viral proteins.[577] During the infection cycle, the main surge of mRNA synthesis originates from progeny SVPs; these mRNAs are also translated into the greatest abundance of viral proteins. Alternatively, newly formed SVPs can serve as precursors for mature virus. Several steps in the formation of virus particles are known. Capsomers of the outer capsid are formed through the association of one μlc protein (a dimer consisting of two μlc polypeptides) and two σ_3 proteins. Cleavage of one μ protein concurrent with its association with σ_3 proteins produces polypeptide μlc.[565]

Addition of σ_3 to SVPs also inhibits the transcriptase activity

and seals off tubular structures at vertices to block macromolecular and ion transport.[578, 579] The remaining outer capsid proteins are added in an ill-defined manner to yield mature virus particles (see Figure 3–8,d). Infectious virus appears at six to seven hours after infection.[565, 573]

In cultured cells infected with more than one serotype of reovirus, random reassortment of all genome segments has been demonstrated in progeny virus.[580] Thus no linkage between parental genome segments was observed. On the other hand, analysis of reassortant viruses produced in mice coinfected by virus types 1 and 3 indicated that the nonrandom reassortment occurred in vivo and infections in different tissues yielded different reassortant viruses.[581] It should be noted that the last example could possibly be explained as a random event if only a subset of the total reassortant population was capable of replication and the remaining progeny reassortants were selected against.[581]

Under conditions of serial infections of cultured cells at high MOIs by a single serotype of reovirus, progeny viruses are produced which may lack any one of the ten genome segments. Certain segments, L1, L3, and M1, seem to be preferentially lost in this process.[582] In addition, at high MOIs, progeny RNA molecules also accumulate point mutations and the resulting mutant virus can interfere with replication of wild-type virus.[583]

Effects on Host Cells

At late times, sites of viral replication as well as resulting immature and mature reovirus particles are often located to varying degrees with microtubules within infected cells. Reovirus type 1, for example, is replicated in close proximity to microtubules, whereas replication of reovirus type 3 is not as closely associated; σ_1 has been shown to govern these type-specific associations.[584] Another viral protein, μ_{NS}, is involved in the association of SVPs with microtubules and may serve to directly anchor immature particles undergoing RNA synthesis.[573] In addition, μ_{NS} may control viral assembly in association with microtubules, since temperature-sensitive mutations in the M3 genome segment block assembly at nonpermissive temperatures. Intermediate filaments also disaggregate as a result of infection, but reorganize at sites used for progeny virus formation.[585]

Reovirus infection also alters cell morphology as observed by light microscopy of stained cells or by electron microscopy. Large eosinophilic inclusion bodies, often in perinuclear locations, which correspond to accumulated viral antigens and double-stranded RNA, are readily observed within the cytoplasm. In addition, cytoplasmic inclusions stain bright-green with acridine orange as observed by fluorescent microscopy, which is characteristic of double-stranded nucleic acids. Electron microscopy of inclusion bodies reveals crystalline arrays of both mature and immature viral particles.[586–588]

Host macromolecular synthesis is also effected at several levels. Inhibition of cell DNA synthesis begins at approximately six hours postinfection and precedes the decrease of both host cell protein synthesis and mitosis. Cell DNA synthesis is inhibited in a virus type–specific manner as shown by its termination in L cells infected by type 3 reovirus, but not in type 1–infected cells. Protein σ_1 of type 3 is responsible for this latter inhibition.[589] Host protein synthesis is also inhibited in L cells, reovirus type 2 being more efficient than types 1 and 3.[585] As stated previously, at late times during infection, uncapped viral mRNAs are preferentially translated over capped mRNAs, possibly due to inactivation of cellular cap binding protein (CBP). Several investigators have implicated σ_3 in shutoff of host protein synthesis. However, in at least one system, σ_3 protein was actually shown to stimulate late viral translation and not inhibit that of the host cell.[566, 590] Protein σ_3 may, on the other hand, directly inhibit host RNA synthesis.[591]

Persistent Infections

An alternative to the lytic virus–host cell interactions discussed above is the establishment of persistent infections (PIs) in cultured cells. Both viral and host cell factors are involved in the establishment and maintenance of persistence. Within a given population of PI cells, approximately 20% to 40% of the cells actually produce virus, while the remaining cells are seemingly nonpermissive for viral replication. Under certain circumstances, infectious virus can be produced at high titers within PI cells, reaching 10^6 plaque-forming units (PFU) per milliliter.[592] Analysis of the reovirus genomic segments within PI cells indicated that S1 and S4 gene products, σ_1 and σ_3, respectively, are crucial for establishment of the persistent state. These proteins from wild-type virus are known to inhibit cell DNA, RNA, and protein synthesis (see above) and to facilitate establishment of lytic infection. Mutations in S1 and S4 segments seen in virus from PI cells most likely decrease the inhibitory activity of σ_1 and σ_3, allowing the cells to survive, replicate, and support limited viral replication.[589, 593, 594] In addition to S1 and S4 segments, other genes are involved in the persistence process, including L2 and M3 segments.[595]

Acknowledgments

I wish to thank Dr Alan Hay for his critical reading of the influenza virus section. I also greatly appreciate the excellent secretarial assistance provided by Ms Pamela McClung and the literature searches conducted by Mrs Constance Berk. The understanding and encouragement of Sandy and Cindy Fenger during the preparation of these manuscripts greatly helped me to maintain my outlook on life.

REFERENCES

1. Maizel JV, Phillips BA, Summers DF: Composition of artificially produced and naturally occurring empty capsid of poliovirus type 1. *Virology* 1967; 32:692–699.
2. Grubman MJ, Baxt B, Latorre JF, et al: Identification of a protein kinase activity in purified foot–and–mouth disease virus. *J Virol* 1981; 39:455–462.
3. Butterworth BE: Comparison of the virus-specific polypeptides of encephalomyocarditis virus, human rhinovirus 1A and poliovirus. *Virology* 1973; 56:439–453.
4. Rueckert RR, Wimmer E: Systematic nomenclature of picornavirus proteins. *J Virol* 1984; 50:957–959.
5. Lee YF, Nomoto A, Detjen BM, et al: The genome-linked protein of picornaviruses. 1. A protein convalently linked to poliovirus genome RNA. *Proc Natl Acad Sci USA* 1977; 74:59–63.
6. Nomoto A, Detjen B, Pozzatti R, et al: The location of the polio genome protein in viral RNAs and its implication for RNA synthesis. *Nature* 1977; 268:208–213.
7. Pettersson RF, Ambros V, Baltimore D: Identification of a protein linked to nascent poliovirus RNA and to the polyuridylic acid of negative-stranded RNA. *J Virol* 1978; 27:357–365.

8. Yogo Y, Wimmer E: Polyadenylic acid at the 3; pr-terminus of poliovirus RNA. *Proc Natl Acad Sci USA* 1972; 69:1877–1882.
9. Tomassini JE, Colonno RJ: Isolation of a receptor protein involved in attachment of human rhinoviruses. *J Virol* 1986; 58:290–295.
9a. Mendelsohn CL, Wimmer E, Racaniello VR: Cellular receptor for poliovirus: Molecular cloning, nucleotide sequence and expression of a new member of the immunoglobulin superfamily. *Cell* 1989; 56:855–865.
10. Scharli CE, Koch G: Protein kinase activity in purified poliovirus particles and empty capsid preparations. *J Gen Virol* 1984; 65:129–139.
11. Lackmann M, Ueckermann C, Engelman K, et al: Properties of poliovirus associated protein kinase. *Arch Virol* 1987; 95:1–6.
12. Lonberg–Holm K, Philipson L: Molecular aspects of virus receptors and cell surfaces, in Blough HA, Tiffany JM (eds): *Cell Membranes and Viral Envelopes,* New York, Academic Press, 1980, Vol 2, pp 789–848.
13. Crowell RL: Cellular receptors in virus infections. *ASM News* 1987; 53:422–425.
14. Crowell RL, Hsu K-HL, Schultz M, et al: Cellular receptors in coxsackievirus infections, in Brinton MA, Rueckert RR (eds): *Positive Strand RNA Viruses.* New York, Alan R Liss, 1987, pp 453–466.
15. Lee YF, Nomoto A, Wimmer E: The genome of poliovirus is an exceptional eukaryotic mRNA. *Prog Nucleic Acid Res Mol Biol* 1976; 19:89–96.
16. Nomoto A, Kilamura N, Golini F, et al: Poliovirion RNA and polio-mRNA are identical molecules with the exception of the 5' terminal genome linked protein VPg. *Proc Natl Acad Sci USA* 1977; 74:5344–5349.
17. Pettersson RF, Flanegan JB, Rose JK, et al: 5' terminal nucleotide sequence of poliovirus polyribosomal RNA and virion RNA are identical. *Nature* 1977; 268:270–272.
18. Ambros V, Baltimore D: Purification and properties of a HeLa cell enzyme able to remove the 5' terminal protein from poliovirus RNA. *J Biol Chem* 1980; 255:6739–6744.
19. Ambros V, Pettersson RF, Baltimore D: An enzymatic activity in uninfected cells that cleaves the linkage between poliovirion RNA and the 5' terminal protein. *Cell* 1978; 15:1439–1446.
20. Kitamura N, Semler BL, Rothberg PG, et al: Primary structure, gene organization and polypeptide expression of poliovirus RNA. *Nature* 1981; 291:547–553.
21. Toyoda H, Kohara M, Kataoka Y, et al: Complete nucleotide sequences of all three poliovirus serotype genomes: Implications for genetic relationship, gene function and antigenic determinants. *J Mol Biol* 1984; 174:562–585.
22. Dorner AJ, Dorner LF, Larsen GR, et al: Identification of the initiation site of poliovirus polyprotein synthesis. *J Virol* 1982; 42:1017–1028.
23. Pelletier J, Kaplan G, Racaniello VR, et al: Cap-independent translation of poliovirus mRNA is conferred by sequence elements within the 5' noncoding region. *Mol Cell Biol* 1988; 8:1103–1112.
24. Trono D, Pelletier J, Sonenberg N, et al: Translation in mammalian cells of a gene linked to the poliovirus 5' noncoding region. *Science* 1988; 241:445–448.
25. Iizuka N, Kohara M, Hagino-Yamagishi K, et al: Construction of less neurovirulent polioviruses by introducing deletions into the 5' noncoding sequence of the genome. *J Virol* 1989; 63:5354.
26. Trono D, Andino R, Baltimore D: An RNA sequence of hundreds of nucleotides at the 5' end of poliovirus RNA is involved in allowing viral protein synthesis. *J Virol* 1988; 62:2291–2299.
27. Pelletier J, Kaplan G, Racaniello VR, et al: Translational efficiency of poliovirus mRNA: Mapping inhibitory cis-acting elements within the 5' noncoding region. *J Virol* 1988; 62:2219–2227.
28. Racaniello VR, Baltimore D: Molecular cloning of poliovirus cDNA and determination of the complete nucleotide sequence

of the viral genome. *Proc Natl Acad Sci USA* 1981; 78:4887–4891.

29. Wellink J, van Kammen A: Proteases involved in the processing of viral polypeptides. *Arch Virol* 1988; 98:1–26.

30. Summers DF, Maizel JV Jr: Determination of the gene sequence of poliovirus and pactamycin. *Proc Natl Acad Sci USA* 1971; 68:2852–2856.

31. Taber R, Rekosh D, Baltimore D: Effect of pactamycin on synthesis of poliovirus proteins: A method for genetic mapping. *J Virol* 1971; 8:395–401.

32. Toyoda H, Nicklin MJH, Murray MG, et al: A second virus-encoded proteinase involved in proteolytic processing of poliovirus polyprotein. *Cell* 1986; 45:761–770.

33. Ypma-Wong MF, Semler BL: Processing determinants required for in vitro cleavage of the poliovirus P1 precursor to capsid proteins. *J Virol* 1987; 61:3181–3189.

34. Hanecak R, Semler BL, Anderson CW, et al: Proteolytic processing of poliovirus polypeptides: Antibodies to polypeptide P3-7C inhibit cleavage at glutamine-glycine pairs. *Proc Natl Acad Sci USA* 1982; 79:3973–3977.

35. Jacobson MF, Baltimore D: Morphogenesis of poliovirus. I. Association of viral RNA with coat protein. *J Mol Biol* 1968; 33:369–378.

36. Hanecak R, Semler BL, Ariga H, et al: Expression of a cloned gene segment of poliovirus in *E. coli:* Evidence for autocatalytic production of viral proteinase. *Cell* 1984; 37:1063–1073.

37. Kitamur N, Adler CJ, Rothberg PG, et al: The genome–linked protein of picornaviruses. VII. Genetic mapping of poliovirus VPg by protein and RNA sequence studies. *Cell* 1980; 21:295–302.

38. Arnold E, Luo M, Vriend G, et al: Implications of the picornavirus capsid structure for polyprotein processing. *Proc Natl Acad Sci USA* 1987; 84:21–25.

39. Semler BL, Anderson CW, Hanecak R, et al: A membrane–associated precursor to poliovirus VPg identified by immunoprecipitation with antibodies directed against a synthetic heptapeptide. *Cell* 1982; 28:405–412.

40. Plotch SJ, Palant O, Gluzman Y: Purification and properties of poliovirus RNA polymerase expressed in *Escherichia coli. J Virol* 1989; 63:216–225.

41. Flanegan JB, Baltimore D: Poliovirus polyuridylic acid polymerase and RNA replicase have the same viral polypeptide. *J Virol* 1979; 29:352–360.

42. Caliguiri LA, Tamm I: The role of cytoplasmic membranes in poliovirus biosynthesis. *Virology* 1970; 42:100–111.

43. Bienz K, Egger D, Rasser Y, et al: Intracellular distribution of poliovirus proteins and the induction of virus-specific cytoplasmic structures. *Virology* 1983; 131:39–48.

44. Bienz K, Egger D, Troxler M, et al: Structural organization of poliovirus RNA replication is mediated by viral proteins of the P2 genomic region. *J Virol* 1990; 64:1156–1163.

45. Dasgupta A, Zabel P, Baltimore D: Dependence of the activity of the poliovirus replicase on a host cell protein. *Cell* 1980; 19:423–429.

46. Baron M, Baltimore D: In vitro copying of viral positive strand RNA by poliovirus replicase. *J Bio Chem* 1982; 257:12359–12366.

47. Andrews NC, Baltimore D: Purification of a terminal uridylyltransferase that acts as host factor in the in vitro poliovirus replicase reaction. *Proc Natl Acad Sci USA* 1986, 83:221–225.

48. Young DC, Tuschall DM, Flanegan JB: Poliovirus RNA-dependent RNA polymerase and host cell protein synthesize product RNA twice the size of poliovirion RNA in vitro. *J Virol* 1985; 54:256–264.

49. Morrow CD, Gibbons GF, Dasgupta A: The host protein required for in vitro replication of poliovirus is a protein kinase that phosphorylates eukaryotic initiation factor-2. *Cell* 1985; 40:913–921.

50. Takeda N, Kuhn RJ, Yang C-F, et al: Initiation of poliovirus plus-strand RNA synthesis in a membrane complex of infected HeLa cell. *J Virol* 1986; 60:43–53.

51. Toyoda H, Young C-F, Takeda N, et al: Analysis of RNA synthesis of type 1 poliovirus by using an in vitro molecular genetic approach. *J Virol* 1987; 61:2816–2822.

52. Van Dyke T, Rickles R, Flanegan JB: Genome-length copies of poliovirion RNA are synthesized in vitro by the poliovirus RNA-dependent RNA polymerase. *J Biol Chem* 1982; 257:4610–4617.

53. Baltimore D, Girard M: An intermediate in the synthesis of poliovirus RNA. *Proc Natl Acad Sci USA* 1966; 56:741–748.

54. Girard M, Baltimore D, Darnell JE: The poliovirus replication complex: Site from synthesis of poliovirus RNA. *J Mol Biol* 1967; 24:59–74.

55. Ambros V, Baltimore D: Protein is linked to the 5′ end of poliovirus RNA by a phosphodiester linkage to tyrosine. *J Biol Chem* 1978; 253:5263–5266.

56. Wu M, Davidson N, Wimmer E: An electron microscope study of the proteins attached to poliovirus RNA and its replicative form (RF). *Nucleic Acids Res* 1978; 5:4711–4723.

57. Hewlett MJ, Rose JK, Baltimore D: 5′-terminal structure of poliovirus polyribosomal RNA is pUp. *Proc Natl Acad Sci USA* 1976; 73:327–330.

58. Nomoto A, Lee YF, Wimmer E: The 5′ end of poliovirus mRNA is not capped with m^7G (5′)-PPP-(5′) Np. *Proc Natl Acad Sci USA* 1976; 73:375–380.

59. Agal VI, Drozdov SG, Grachev VP, et al: Recombinants between attenuated and virulent strains of poliovirus type 1: Derivation and characterization of recombinants with centrally located cross-over points. *Virology* 1985; 143:467–477.

60. Agut H, Kean KM, Bellocq C, et al: Intratypic recombination of poliovirus: Evidence for multiple crossing-over sites on the viral genome. *J Virol* 1987; 61:1722–1725.

61. Madshus IH, Olsnes S, Sandvig K: Mechanism of entry into the cytosol of poliovirus type 1: Requirements for low pH. *J Cell Biol* 1984; 98:1194–1200.

62. Chow M, Newman JFE, Filman D, et al: Myristylation of picornavirus capsid protein VP4 and its structural significance. *Nature* 1987; 327:482–486.

63. McGregor S, Hall L, Rueckert RR: Evidence for the existence of protomers in the assembly of encephalomyocarditis virus. *J Virol* 1975; 15:1107–1120.

64. Holland J, Kiehn ED: Specific cleavage of viral proteins as steps in the synthesis and maturation of enteroviruses. *Proc Natl Acad Sci USA* 1968; 60:1015–1022.

65. Summers DF, Maizel JV Jr: Evidence for large precursor proteins in poliovirus synthesis. *Proc Natl Acad Sci USA* 1968; 59:966–971.

66. Fernandez-Tomas CB, Baltimore D: Morphogenesis of poliovirus. II. Demonstration of a new intermediate, the provirion. *J Virol* 1973; 12:1122–1130.

67. Guttman N, Baltimore D: Morphogenesis of poliovirus. IV. Existence of particles sedimenting at 150S and having the properties of provirion. *J Virol* 1977; 23:363–367.

68. Jacobson MF, Baltimore D: Morphogenesis of poliovirus. Association of the viral RNA with coat protein. *J Mol Biol* 1968; 33:369–378.

69. Yafal AG, Palma EL: Morphogenesis of foot-and-mouth disease virus. I. Role of procapsids as virion precursors. *J Virol* 1979; 30:643–649.

70. Rose JK, Trachsel H, Leong K, et al: Inhibition of translation by poliovirus: Inactivation of a specific initiation factor. *Proc Natl Acad Sci USA* 1978; 75:2732–2736.

71. Helentjari T, Ehrenfeld E, Brown-Luedi ML, et al: Alteration in initiation factor activity from poliovirus-infected HeLa cells. *J Biol Chem* 1979; 254:10973–10978.

72. Sonenberg N: Regulation of translation by poliovirus. *Adv Virus Res* 1987; 33:175–204.

73. Rychlik W, Gardner PR, Vanaman TC, et al: Structural analysis of the messenger RNA cap-binding protein. *J Biol Chem* 1986; 261:71–75.

74. Edery I, Humbelin M, Darveau A, et al: Involvement of eIF-4A in the cap recognition process. *J Biol Chem* 1983; 258:11398–11403.

75. Etchison D, Miburn SC, Edery I, et al: Inhibition of the HeLa cell protein synthesis following poliovirus infection correlates with the proteolysis of a 220,000 dalton polypeptide associated with eukaryotic initiation factor 3 and a cap binding protein complex. *J Biol Chem* 1982; 257:14806–14810.

76. Lloyd RE, Toyoda H, Etchison D, et al: Cleavage of the cap binding protein complex polypeptide p 220 is not effected by the second poliovirus protease 2A. *Virology* 1986; 150:299–303.

77. Zimmerman EF, Hector M, Darnell JE: RNA synthesis in poliovirus-infected cells. *Virology* 1963; 19:400–408.

78. Holland JJ, Peterson JA: Nucleic acid and protein synthesis during poliovirus infection of human cells. *J Mol Biol* 1964; 8:556–573.

79. Contreras G, Summers DF, Maizel JV, et al: HeLa cell nucleolar RNA synthesis after poliovirus infection. *Virology* 1973; 53:120–129.

80. Darnell JE, Girard M, Baltimore D, et al: The synthesis and translation of poliovirus RNA, in Colter J, Paranchych W (eds): *The Molecular Biology of Viruses,* New York, Academic Press, 1967, pp 375–401.

81. Crawford N, Fire A, Samuels M, et al: Inhibition of transcription factor by poliovirus. *Cell* 1981; 27:555–561.

82. Bienz K, Egger D, Wolff DA: Virus replication cytopathology and lysosomal enzyme response of mitotic and interphase HEp-2 cells infected with poliovirus. *J Virol* 1973; 11:565–574.

83. Dales S, Eggers HJ, Tamm I, et al: Electron microscopic study of the formation of poliovirus. *Virology* 1965; 26:379–389.

84. Mattern CFT, Daniel WA: Replication of poliovirus in HeLa cells: Electron microscopic observation. *Virology* 1965; 26:646–663.

85. Bienz K, Egger D, Rasser Y, et al: Kinetics and location of poliovirus macromolecular synthesis in correlation to virus-induced cytopathology. *Virology* 1980; 100:390–399.

86. Guskey LE, Wolff DA: Effects of actinomycin D on the cytopathology induced by poliovirus in HEp-2 cells. *J Virol* 1974; 14:1229–1234.

87. Pfefferkorn ER, Shapiro D: Reproduction of togaviruses, in Fraenkel-Conrat H, Wagner RR (eds): *Comprehensive Virology, Reproduction: Small and Intermediate RNA Viruses.* New York, Plenum Press, 1974, pp 171–230.

88. Strauss JH Jr, Burge BW, Pfefferkorn ER, et al: Identification of the membrane protein and "core" protein of Sindbis virus. *Proc Natl Acad Sci USA* 1968; 59:533–537.

89. Kennedy SIT, Burke DC: Studies on the structural proteins of Semliki Forest virus. *J Gen Virol* 1972; 14:87–98.

90. Schlesinger MJ, Schlesinger S, Burge BW: Identification of a second glycoprotein in Sindbis virus. *Virology* 1972; 47:539–541.

91. Garoff H, Simons K, Renkonen O: Isolation and characterization of the membrane proteins of Semliki Forest virus. *Virology* 1974; 61:493–504.

92. Ziemiecki A, Garoff H: Subunit composition of the membrane glycoprotein complex of Semliki Forest virus. *J Mol Biol* 1978; 122:259–269.

93. Pettersson RF, Söderlung H, Kääriäinen L: The nucleotide sequence of the 5'-terminal T₁ oligonucleotides of Semliki Forest virus 42S and 26S RNAs are different. *Eur J Biochem* 1980; 105:435–443.

94. Johnston RE, Bose HR: Correlation of messenger RNA function with adenylate-rich segments in the genomes of single-stranded RNA viruses. *Proc Natl Acad Sci USA* 1972; 69:1514–1516.

95. Howe C, Coward JE, Fenger TW: Viral invasion: Morphological, biochemical and biophysical aspects, in Fraenkel-Conrat H, Wagner RR (eds): *Comprehensive Virology, Virus-Host Interactions: Viral Invasion Persistence and Disease.* New York, Plenum Press, 1980, pp 1–63.

96. Hielian M, Helenius A: Entry of alphaviruses, in Schlesinger S Schlesinger MJ (eds): *The Togaviridae and Flaviviridae.* New York, Plenum, 1986, pp 91–119.

97. Davis NL, Fuller FJ, Dougherty WG, et al: A single nucleotide change in the E2 glycoprotein gene of Sindbis virus affects penetration rate in cell culture and virulence in neonatal mice. *Proc Natl Acad Sci USA* 1986; 83:6771–6775.

98. Wengler G: The mode of assembly of alphavirus cores implies a mechanism for the disassembly of the cores in the early stages of infection. *Arch Virol* 1987; 94:1–14.

99. Wengler G: Comparative studies on polyribosomal, nonpolyribosomal–associated and viral 42S RNA from BHK21 cells infected with Semliki Forest virus. *Virology* 1975; 65:601–605.

100. Strauss EG, Strauss JH: Structure and replication of the alphavirus genome, in Schlesinger S, Schlesinger MJ (eds): *The Togaviridae and Flaviviridae.* New York, Plenum, 1986, pp 35–90.

101. Clegg JCS, Brzeski H, Kennedy SIT: RNA polymerase components in Semliki Forest virus-infected cells: Synthesis from large precursors. *J Gen Virol* 1976; 32:413–430.

102. Lachmi B-L, Kääriäinen L: Sequential translation of nonstructural proteins in cells infected with a Semliki Forest virus mutant. *Proc Natl Acad Sci USA* 1976; 73:1936–1940.

103. Li G, Rice CM: Mutagenesis of the in frame opal termination codon preceding ns P₄ of Sindbis virus: Studies of translational readthrough and its effect on virus replication. *J Virol* 1989; 63:1326–1337.

104. Takkinen K: Complete nucleotide sequence of the nonstructural protein genes of Semliki Forest virus. *Nucleic Acids Res* 1986; 14:5667–5682.

105. Keränen S, Ruohonen L: Nonstructural proteins of Semliki Forest virus: Synthesis, processing and stability in infected cells. *J Virol* 1983; 47:505–515.

106. Monroe SS, Schlesinger S: RNAs from two independently isolated defective interfering particles of Sindbis virus contain a cellular tRNA sequence at their 5' ends. *Proc Natl Acad Sci USA* 1983; 80:3279–3283.

107. Ishihama A, Nagata K: Viral RNA polymerases. *CRC Crit Rev Biochem* 1988; 23:27–76.

108. Sawicki DL, Sawicki SG: Short-lived minus-strand polymerase for Semliki Forest virus. *J Virol* 1980; 34:108–118.

109. Waite MRF: Protein synthesis directed by an RNA-temperature sensitive mutant of Sindbis virus. *J Virol* 1973; 11:198–206.

110. Sawicki DL, Sawicki SG, Keränen S, et al: Specific Sindbis virus-coded function for minus-strand RNA synthesis. *J Virol* 1981; 39:348–358.

111. Bruton CJ, Kennedy SIT: Semliki Forest virus intracellular RNA: Properties of the multi-stranded RNA species and kinetics of positive and negative strand synthesis. *J Gen Virol* 1975; 28:111–127.

112. Strauss JH, Strauss EG: Togaviruses, in Nayak DP (ed): *The Molecular Biology of Animal Viruses.* New York, Marcel Dekker, 1977, pp 111–166.

113. Kennedy SIT: Sequence relationships between the genome and the intracellular RNA species of standard and defective interfering Semliki Forest virus. *J Mol Biol* 1976; 108:491–511.

114. Ou J-H, Rice CM, Dalgarno L, et al: Sequence studies of several alphavirus genomic RNAs in the region containing the start of the subgenomic RNA. *Proc Natl Acad Sci USA* 1982; 79:5235–5239.

115. Cancedda R, Swanson R, Schlesinger MJ: Effects of different RNAs and components of the cell-free system on in vitro synthesis of Sindbis virus proteins. *J Virol* 1974; 14:652–663.

116. Simmons DT, Strauss JH: Translation of Sindbis virus 26S RNA and 49S RNA in lysates of rabbit reticulocytes. *J Mol Biol* 1974; 86:397–409.

117. Schlesinger MJ, Schlesinger S: Large molecular weight precursors of Sindbis virus proteins. *J Virol* 1973; 11:1013–1016.

118. Garoff H, Frischauf A-M, Simons K, et al: Nucleotide sequence of cDNA coding for Semliki Forest virus membrane glycoproteins. *Nature* 1980; 288:236–241.

119. Martire G, Bonatti S, Aliperti G, et al: Free and membrane-bound polyribosomes in BHK cells infected with Sindbis virus. *J Virol* 1977; 21:610–618.

120. Boege U, Wengler G, et al: Primary structure of the core proteins of the alphavirus Semliki Forest virus and Sindbis virus. *Virology* 1981; 113:292–303.

121. Aliperti G, Schlesinger MJ: Evidence for an autoprotease activity of Sindbis virus capsid protein. *Virology* 1978; 90:366–369.

122. Hahn CS, Strauss EG, Strauss JH: Sequence analysis of three Sindbis virus mutants temperature–sensitive in the capsid protein autoprotease. *Proc Natl Acad Sci USA* 1985; 82:4648–4652.

123. Garoff H, Simons K, Dobberstein B: Assembly of the Semliki Forest virus membrane glycoproteins in the membrane of the endoplasmic reticulum in vitro. *J Mol Biol* 1978; 124:587–600.

124. Culter DF, Melancon P, Garoff H: Mutants of the membrane-binding region of Semliki Forest virus E2 protein. II. Topology and membrane binding. *J Cell Biol* 1986; 102:902–910.

125. Melancon P, Garoff H: Reinitiation of translocation in the Semliki Forest virus structural polyprotein: Identification of the signal for the E1 glycoprotein. *EMBO J* 1986; 7:1543–1550.

126. Mayne JT, Rice CM, Strauss EG, et al: Biochemical studies of the maturation of the small Sindbis virus glycoprotein E3. *Virology* 1984; 134:338–357.

127. Sefton BM: Immediate glycosylation of Sindbis virus membrane proteins. *Cell* 1977; 10:659–668.

128. Burke D, Keegstra K: Carbohydrate structure of Sindbis virus glycoprotein E_2 from virus grown in hamster and chicken cells. *J Virol* 1979; 29:546–554.

129. Keegstra K, Sefton B, Burke D: Sindbis virus glycoprotein effect of the host cell on the oligosaccharides. *J Virol* 1975; 16:613–620.

130. Schmidt MFG, Schlesinger MJ: Fatty acid binding to vesicular stomatitis virus glycoproteins: A new type of post–translational modification of the viral glycoprotein. *Cell* 1979; 17:813–819.

131. Schmidt MFG, Schlesinger MJ: Relation of fatty acid attachment to the translation and maturation of vesicular stomatitis and Sindbis virus membrane glycoproteins. *J Biol Chem* 1980; 155:3334–3339.

132. Bell JR, Strauss JH: In vitro N-terminal acetylation of Sindbis virus proteins. *J Biol Chem* 1981; 256:8006–8011.

133. Schmidt MFG, Schlesinger MJ: Relation of fatty acid attachment to the translation and maturation of vesicular stomatitis and Sindbis virus membrane glycoproteins. *J Biol Chem* 1980; 255:3334–3339.

134. Bonatti S, Cancedda R, Blobel G: Membrane biogenesis: In vitro cleavage, core glycosylation and integration into microsomal membranes of Sindbis virus glycoproteins. *J Cell Biol* 1979; 80:219–224.

135. Garoff H, Kondor-Koch C, Riedel H: Structure and assembly of alphaviruses. *Curr Top Microbiol Immunol* 1982; 99:1–50.

136. Hahn CS, Rice CM, Strauss EG, et al: Sindbis virus ts 103 has a mutation in glycoprotein E2 that leads to defective assembly of virions. *J Virol* 1989; 63:3459–3465.

137. Brache M, Schlesinger MJ: Defects in RNA temperature sensitive mutants of Sindbis virus and evidence for a complex of PE_2-E_1 viral glycoproteins. *Virology* 1976; 74:441–449.

138. Smith JF, Brown DT: Envelopment of Sindbis virus: Synthesis and organization of proteins in cells infected with wild-type and maturation-defective mutants. *J Virol* 1977; 22:662–678.

139. Kempf C, Michel MR, Kohler U, et al: A novel method for the detection of early events in cell–cell fusion of Semliki Forest virus infected cells growing in monolayer cultures. *Arch Virol* 1987; 95:283–289.

140. Wengler G: Effects of alphavirus on host cell macro-molecular synthesis, in Schlesinger RW (ed): *The Togaviruses.* New York, Academic Press, 1980, pp 459–471.

141. Van Steeg H, Kasperaitis M, Voorma HO, et al: Infection of neuroblastoma cells by Semliki Forest virus. The interference of viral capsid protein with the binding of host messenger RNAs

142. Riedel B, Brown DT: The role of extracellular virus in the maintenance of the persistent infection induced in *Aedes albopictus* (mosquito) cells by Sindbis virus. *J Virol* 1977; 23:554–561.

143. Peleg J: Inapparent persistent virus infection in continuously grown *Aedes aegypti* mosquito cells. *J Gen Virol* 1969; 5:463–468.

144. Igarashi A, Koo R, Stollar V: Evolution and properties of *Aedes albopictus* cell cultures persistently infected with Sindbis virus. *Virology* 1977; 82:69–83.

145. Gliedman JB, Smith JF, Brown DT: Morphogenesis of Sindbis virus in cultured *Aedes albopictus* cells. *J Virol* 1975; 16:913–926.

146. Stollar V: Defective interfering alphaviruses, in Schlesinger RW (ed): *The Togaviruses: Biology, Structure, Replication.* New York, Academic Press, 1980, pp 427–457.

147. Levis R, Weiss BG, Tsiang M, et al: Deletion mapping of Sindbis virus DI RNAs derived from cDNA defines the sequences essential for replication and packaging. *Cell* 1986; 44:137–145.

148. Ou J-H, Strauss EG, Strauss JH: Comparative studies of the 3' terminal sequences of several alphavirus RNAs. *Virology* 1981; 109:281–289.

149. Lehtovaara P, Söderlund H, Keränen S, et al: 18S defective interfering RNA of Semliki Forest virus contain a triplicated linear repeat. *Proc Natl Acad Sci USA* 1981; 78:5353–5357.

150. Westaway EG, Brinton MA, Gaidamovich SY, et al: Flaviviridae. *Intervirology* 1985; 24:183–192.

151. Rice CM, Lenches EM, Eddy SR, et al: Nucleotide sequence of yellow fever virus: Implications for flavivirus gene expression and evolution. *Science* 1985; 229:726–735.

152. Brinton MA, Fernandez AV, Dispoto JH: The 3' nucleotides of flavivirus genome RNA form a conserved secondary structure. *Virology* 1986; 153:113–121.

153. Nowak T, Wengler G: Analysis of disulfides present in the membrane proteins of the West Nile flavivirus. *Virology* 1987; 156:127–137.

154. Wengler G, Wengler G, Nowak T, et al: Analysis of the influence of proteolytic cleavage on the structural organization of the surface of the West Nile flavivirus leads to the isolation of a protease-resistant E protein oligomer from the viral surface. *Virology* 1987; 160:210–219.

155. Heinz FX, Tuma W, Kunz C: Antigenic and immunogenic properties of defined physical forms of tick-borne encephalitis virus structural proteins. *Infect Immun* 1981; 33:250–257.

156. Castle E, Nowak T, Leidner U, et al: Sequence analysis of the viral core protein and the membrane-associated proteins V1 and NV2 of the flavivirus West Nile virus and of the genome sequences for these proteins. *Virology* 1985; 147:227–236.

157. Winkler G, Heinz FX, Kunz C: Studies on the glycosylation of flavivirus E proteins and the role of carbohydrate in antigenic structure. *Virology* 1987; 159:237–243.

158. Gollins SW, Porterfield JS: Flavivirus infection enhancement in macrophages: An electron microscopic study of viral cellular entry. *J Gen Virol* 1985; 66:1969–1982.

159. Ishak R, Tovey DG, Howard CR: Morphogenesis of yellow fever virus 17D in infected cell cultures. *J Gen Virol* 1988; 69:325–335.

160. Castle E, Wengler G: Nucleotide sequence of the 5' terminal untranslated part of the genome of the flavivirus West Nile Virus. *Arch Virol* 1987; 92:309–313.

161. Brinton MA, Dispoto JH: Sequence and secondary structure analysis of the 5' terminal region of flavivirus genome RNA. *Virology* 1988; 162:290–299.

162. Strauss JH, Strauss EG, Hahn CS, et al: Replication of alphaviruses and flaviviruses: Proteolytic processing of polyproteins, in Briton MA, Rueckert RR (eds): *Positive Strand RNA Viruses.* New York, Alan R Liss, 1987, pp 209–226.

163. Rice CM, Aebersold R, Teplow DB, et al: Partial N-termini amino acid sequences of three nonstructural proteins of two flaviviruses. *Virology* 1986; 151:1–9.

163a. Ruiz-Linares A, Cahour A, Desprès P, et al: Processing of yellow fever virus polyprotein: Role of cellular proteases in maturation of structural proteins. *J Virol* 1989; 63:4199–4209.

164. Trent DW, Kinney RM, Johnson BJB, et al: Partial nucleotide sequence of St. Louis encephalitis virus RNA: Structural proteins, NS1, ns2a, and ns2b. *Virology* 1987; 156:293–304.

165. Grun JB, Brinton MA: Characterization of West Nile virus RNA-dependent RNA polymerase and cellular terminal adenylyl and uridylyl transferases in cell-free extracts. *J Virol* 1986; 60:1113–1124.

166. Mackow E, Makino Y, Zhao B, et al: The nucleotide sequence of dengue type 4 virus: Analysis of genes coding for nonstructural proteins. *Virology* 1987; 159:217–228.

167. Chu PWG, Westaway EG: Characterization of Kunjin virus RNA-dependent RNA polymerase: Reinitiation of synthesis in vitro. *Virology* 1987; 157:330–337.

168. Brinton MA, Fernandez AV, Dispoto JH: The 3′ nucleotides of flavivirus genome RNA form a conserved secondary structure. *Virology* 1986; 153:113–121.

169. Cleaves GR, Ryan TE, Schlesinger RW: Identification and characterization of type 2 dengue virus replicative intermediate and replicative form RNAs. *Virology* 1981; 111:73–83.

170. Ng ML, Pedersen JS, Toh BH, et al: Immunofluorescent sites in Vero cells infected with the flavivirus Kunjin. *Arch Virol* 1983; 78:177–190.

171. Hase T, Summers PL, Eckels KH, et al: An electron and immunoelectron microscopic study of dengue-2 virus infection of cultured mosquito cells: Maturation events. *Arch Virol* 1987; 92:273–291.

172. Leary K, Blair CD: Sequential events in the morphogenesis of Japanese encephalitis virus. *J Ultrastruct Res* 1980; 72:123–129.

173. Sturman LS, Holmes KV: The molecular biology of coronaviruses. *Adv Virus Res* 1983; 28:35–112.

174. Siddell S, Wege H, ter Meulen V: The biology of coronaviruses. *J Gen Virol* 1983; 64:761–776.

175. King B, Potts BJ, Brian DA: Bovine coronavirus hemagglutinin protein. *Virus Res* 1985; 2:53–59.

176. Macnaughton MR, Davies HA, Nermut MV: Ribonucleoprotein-like structures from coronavirus particles. *J Virol* 1978; 39:545–549.

177. Massalski A, Coulter-Mackie M, Knobler RL, et al: In vivo and in vitro models of demyelinating diseases. *Intervirology* 1982; 18:135–146.

178. Sturman LS, Ricard CS, Holmes KV: Proteolytic cleavage of the E2 glycoprotein of murine coronavirus: Activation of cell-fusing activity of virions by trypsin and separation of two different 90K cleavage fragments. *J Virol* 1985; 56:904–911.

179. Sturman LS: The structure and behavior of coronavirus A59 glycoproteins. *Adv Exp Med Biol* 1981; 142:1–8.

180. Cavanagh D: Coronavirus IBV: Structural characterization of the spike glycoprotein. *J Gen Virol* 1983; 64:2577–2583.

181. Holmes KV, Doller EW, Sturman LS: Tunicamycin resistant glycosylation of a coronavirus glycoprotein: Demonstration of a novel type of viral glycoprotein. *Virology* 1981; 115:334–344.

182. Collins AR, Knobler RL, Powell H, et al: Monoclonal antibodies to murine hepatitis virus-4 (strain JHM) define the viral glycoproteins responsible for attachment and cell-cell fusion. *Virology* 1982; 119:358–371.

183. Rottier PJM, Vranderburg P, Armstrong J, et al: In vitro assembly of the murine coronavirus membrane protein E1. *Adv Exp Med Biol* 1984; 173:53–64.

184. Armstrong J, Niemann H, Smeekens S, et al: Sequence and topology of a model intracellular membrane protein, E1 glycoprotein, from a coronavirus. *Nature* 1984; 308:751–752.

185. Denison MR, Perlman S, et al: Translation and processing of mouse hepatitis virus virion RNA in a cell-free system. *J Virol* 1986; 60:12–18.

186. Leibowitz JL, Weiss SR, Paavola E, et al: Cell-free translation of murine coronavirus RNA. *J Virol* 1982; 43:905–913.

187. Lai MMC, Brayton PR, Armen RC, et al: Mouse hepatitis virus A 59; mRNA structure and genetic localization of the sequence divergence from hepatotopic strain MHV-3. *J Virol* 1981; 39:823–834.

188. Pachuk C, Bredenbeck PJ, Zoltick PW, et al: Molecular cloning of the gene encoding the putative polymerase of mouse hepatitis coronavirus, strain A59. *Virology* 1989; 171:141–148.

189. Brayton PR, Stohlman SA, Lai MMC: Further characterization of mouse hepatitis virus RNA-dependent RNA polymerase. *Virology* 1984; 133:197–201.

190. Spaan W, Cavanagh D, Horzinek M: Coronaviruses: Structure and genome expression. *J Gen Virol* 1988; 69:2939–2952.

191. Brayton PR, Lai MMC, Patton CD, et al: Characterization of two RNA polymerase activities induced by mouse hepatitis virus. *J Virol* 1982; 42:847–853.

192. Baric RS, Stohlman SA, Razavi MK, et al: Characterization of leader-related small RNAs in coronavirus-infected cells: Further evidence for leader-primed mechanism of transcription. *Virus Res* 1985; 3:19–33.

193. Makino S, Stohlman SA, Lai MMC: Leader sequences of murine coronavirus mRNAs can be freely reassorted: Evidence for the role of free leader RNA in transcription. *Proc Natl Acad Sci USA* 1986; 83:4204–4208.

194. Budzilowicz CJ, Wilczynski SP, Weiss SR: Three intergenic regions of coronavirus mouse hepatitis virus strain A59 genome RNA contain a common nucleotide sequence that is homologous to the 3′ end of the viral mRNA leader sequence. *J Virol* 1985; 53:834–840.

195. Sawicki SG, Sawicki DL: Coronavirus transcription: Subgenomic mouse hepatitis virus replicative intermediates function in RNA synthesis. *J Virol* 1990; 64:1050–1056.

196. Compton SR, Rogers DB, Holmes KV, et al: In vitro replication of mouse hepatitis virus strain A 59. *J Virol* 1987; 61:1814–1820.

197. Sawicki SG, Sawicki DL: Coronavirus minus-strand RNA synthesis and effect of cycloheximide on coronavirus RNA synthesis. *J Virol* 1986; 57:328–334.

198. Lai MMC, Patton CD, Stohlman SA: Replication of mouse hepatitis virus: Negative-stranded RNA and replicative form RNA are of genome length. *J Virol* 1982; 44:487–492.

199. Rottier PJM, Spaan WJM, Horzinek MC, et al: Translation of three mouse hepatitis virus strain A 59 subgenomic RNAs in *Xenopus laevis* oocytes. *J Virol* 1981; 38:20–26.

200. Siddell S: Coronavirus JHM: Coding assignments of subgenomic mRNAs. *J Gen Virol* 1983; 64:113–125.

201. Cheley S, Anderson R, Cupples MJ, et al: Intracellular murine hepatitis virus-specific RNAs contain common sequences. *Virology* 1981; 112:596–604.

202. Brown JDK, Boursnell MEG, Binns MM, et al: Cloning and sequencing of 5′ terminal sequences from avian infectious bronchitis virus genomic RNA. *J Gen Virol* 1986; 67:221–228.

203. Soe LH, Shieh C-K, Baker SC, et al: Sequence and translation of the murine coronavirus 5′-end genomic RNA reveals the N-terminal structure of the putative RNA polymerase. *J Virol* 1987; 61:3968–3976.

204. Frana MF, Behnke JN, Sturman LS, et al: Proteolytic cleavage of the E2 glycoprotein of murine coronavirus: Host-dependent differences in proteolytic cleavage and cell fusion. *J Virol* 1985; 56:912–920.

205. Holmes KV, Doller EW, Behnke JW: Analysis of the functions of coronavirus glycoproteins by differential inhibition of synthesis with tunicamycin. *Adv Exp Med Biol* 1981; 142:133–142.

206. Niemann H, Klenk H-D: Coronavirus glycoprotein E1: A new type of viral glycoprotein. *J Med Biol* 1981; 153:993–1010.

207. Dubois-Dalcq ME, Dollar EW, Haspel MW, et al: Cell tropism and expression of mouse hepatitis virus (MHV) in mouse spinal cord cultures. *Virology* 1982; 119:317–331.

208. Niemann H, Boschek B, Evans D, et al: Post-translational glycosylation of coronavirus glycoprotein E 1: Inhibition by monensin. *EMBO J* 1982; 1:1499–1504.

209. Massalski A, Coulter-Mackie M, Dales S: Assembly of mouse hepatitis virus strain J H M. *Adv Exp Med Biol* 1981; 142:111–118.

210. Yennema H, Heijnen L, Zijderveld, et al: Intracellular transport of recombinant coronavirus spike proteins: Implications for virus assembly. *J Virol* 1990; 64:339–346.

211. Holland J, Spindler K, Horodyski F, et al: Rapid evolution of RNA genomes. *Science* 1982; 215:1577–1585.

212. Lai MMC, Baric RS, Makino S, et al: Recombination between nonsegmented RNA genomes of murine coronaviruses. *J Virol* 1985; 56:449–456.

213. Makino S, Keck JG, Stohlman SA, et al: High-frequency RNA recombination of murine coronaviruses. *J Virol* 1986; 57:729–737.

214. Keck JG, Matsushima GK, Makino S, et al: In vivo RNA-RNA recombination of coronavirus in mouse brain. *J Virol* 1988; 62:1810–1813.

215. Makino S, Taguchi F, Fujiwara K: Defective interfering particles of mouse hepatitis virus. *Virology* 1984; 133:9–17.

216. Makino S, Fujioka N, Fujiwara K: Structure of the intracellular defective interfering viral RNAs of defective interfering particles of mouse hepatitis virus. *J Virol* 1985; 54:329–336.

217. Makino S, Sheih C-K, Keck JG, et al: Defective-interfering particles of murine coronavirus: Mechanism of synthesis of defective viral RNAs. *Virology* 1988; 163:104–111.

218. Holmes KV, Behnke JN: Evolution of a coronavirus during persistent infection in vitro. *Adv Exp Med Biol* 1981; 142:287–299.

219. Chaloner-Larsson G, Johnson-Lussenburg CM: Characteristics of a long-term in vitro persistent infection with human coronavirus 229E. *Adv Exp Med Biol* 1982; 142:309–322.

220. Etkind PR, Krug RM: Purification of influenza viral complementary RNA: Its genetic content and activity in wheat germ cell-free extracts. *J Virol* 1975; 16:1464–1475.

221. Glass SE, McGeoch D, Barry RD: Characterization of the mRNA of influenza virus. *J Virol* 1975; 16:1435–1443.

222. Content J: Cell-free translation of influenza virus mRNA. *J Virol* 1976; 18:604–618.

223. Pons MW: A reexamination of influenza single and double stranded RNAs by gel electrophoresis. *Virology* 1976; 69:789–792.

224. Ritchey MB, Palese P, Kilbourne ED: RNAs of influenza A, B, and C viruses. *J Virol* 1976; 18:738–744.

225. Cox NJ, Kendal AP: Presence of a segmented single stranded RNA genome in influenza C virus. *Virology* 1976; 74:239–241.

226. Palese P, Schulman JL: Mapping of the influenza virus genome: Identification of the hemagglutinin and the neuraminidase gene. *Proc Natl Acad Sci USA* 1976; 73:2142–2146.

227. Chow NL, Simpson RW: RNA-dependent RNA polymerase activity associated with virions and subviral particles of myxoviruses. *Proc Natl Acad Sci USA* 1971; 68:752–756.

228. Braam J, Ulmanen I, Krug RM: Molecular model of a eukaryotic transcription complex: Functions and movements of influenza P during capped RNA-primed transcription. *Cell* 1983; 34:609–618.

229. Winter G, Fields S: The structure of the gene encoding the nucleoprotein of human influenza virus. A/PR/8/34. *Virology* 1981; 114:423–428.

230. Kingsbury DW, Webster RG: some properties of influenza virus nucleocapsids. *J Virol* 1969; 4:219–225.

231. Jennings PA, Finch JT, Winter G, et al: Does the higher order structure of the influenza virus ribonucleoprotein guide sequence rearrangements in influenza viral RNA? *Cell* 1983; 34:619–627.

232. Hsu M-T, Parvin JD, Gupta S, et al: Genomic RNAs of influenza viruses are held in a circular conformation in virions and in infected cells by a terminal panhandle. *Proc Natl Acad Sci USA* 1987; 84:8140–8144.

233. Compans RW, Klenk H-D, Caliguiri LA, et al: Influenza virus proteins I. Analysis of polypeptides of the virion and identification of spike glycoproteins. *Virology* 1970; 42:880–889.

234. Lamb RA, Choppin PW: Identification of a second protein (M_2) encoded by RNA segment 7 of influenza virus. *Virology* 1981; 112:737–745.

235. Schulze IT: The structure of influenza virus, I. The polypeptides of the virion. *Virology* 1970; 42:890–904.

236. Bucher D, Palese P: The biologically active proteins of influenza virus: neuraminidase, in Kilbourne E (ed): *The Influenza Virus and Influenza*. New York, Academic Press, 1975, pp 83–123.

237. Joassin L, Vincenzotto C, Cloes JM, et al: Monoclonal antibodies detect M-protein epitopes on the surface of influenza virions. *Arch Virol* 1987; 95:183–195.

238. Zebedee SL, Richardson CD, Lamb RA: Characterization of the influenza virus M2 integral membrane protein and expression at the infected cell surface from cloned cDNA. *J Virol* 1985; 56:502–511.

239. Hay AJ, Wolstenholme AJ, Skehel JJ, et al: The molecular basis of the specific anti-influenza action of amantadine. *EMBO J* 1985; 4:3021–3024.

240. Zebedee SL, Lamb RA: Influenza A virus M2 protein: Monoclonal antibody restriction of virus growth and detection of M2 in virions. *J Virol* 1988; 62:2762–2772.

241. Wilson IA, Skehel JJ, Wiley DC: Structure of the haemagglutinin membrane glycoprotein of influenza virus at 3A resolution. *Nature* 1981; 289:366–373.

242. Wrigley NG: Electron microscopy of the influenza haemagglutinin-monoclonal antibody complexes. *Virology* 1983; 131:308–314.

243. Ward CW: Structure of the influenza virus hemagglutinin. *Curr Top Microbiol Immunol* 1981; 94:2–74.

244. Lamb RA, Choppin PW: Gene structure and replication of influenza virus. *Ann Rev Biochem* 1983; 52:467–506.

245. Garten W, Bosch FX, Linder D, et al: Proteolytic activation of the influenza virus hemagglutinin: The structure of the cleavage site and the enzymes involved in cleavage. *Virology* 1981; 115:361–374.

246. Klenk H-D, Rott R, Orlich M, et al: Activation of influenza A viruses by trypsin treatment. *Virology* 1975; 68:429–439.

247. Lazarowitz SG, Choppin PW: Enhancement of the infectivity of influenza A and B viruses by proteolytic cleavage of the hemagglutinin polypeptide. *Virology* 1975; 68:440–455.

248. Bosch FX, Garten W, Klenk H-D, et al: Proteolytic cleavage of influenza virus hemagglutinin. Primary structure of the connecting peptide between HA1 and HA2 determines proteolytic cleavability and pathogenicity of avian influenza viruses. *Virology* 1981; 113:725–735.

249. Kuroda K, Hauser C, Rott R, et al: Expression of the influenza virus hemagglutinin in insect cells by a baculovirus vector. *EMBO J* 1986; 5:1359–1365.

250. Kawaoka Y, Naeve CW, Webster RG: Is virulence of H5N2 influenza viruses in chickens associated with loss of carbohydrate from the hemagglutinin? *Virology* 1984; 139:303–316.

250a. Kawaoka Y, Webster RG: Interplay between carbohydrate in the stalk and the length of connecting peptide determines the cleavability of influenza virus hemagglutinin. *J Virol* 1989; 63:3296–3300.

251. Garten W, Klenk HD: Characterization of the carboxypeptidase involved in the proteolytic cleavage of the influenza haemagglutinin. *J Gen Virol* 1983; 64:2127–2137.

252. Skehel JJ, Waterfield MD: Studies on the primary structure of the influenza virus hemagglutinin. *Proc Natl Acad Sci USA* 1975; 72:93–97.

253. Rogers GN, Paulson JC, Daniels RS, et al: Single amino acid substitutions in influenza haemagglutinin change receptor binding specificity. *Nature* 1983; 304:76–78.

254. Doms RW, Helenius A: Quarternary structure of influenza virus hemagglutinin after acid treatment. *J Virol* 1986; 60:833–839.

255. Varghese JN, Laver WG, Colman PM: Structure of the influenza virus glycoprotein antigen neuraminidase at 2.9 Å resolution. *Nature* 1983; 303:35–40.

256. Colman PM, Laver WG, Varghese JN, et al: Three-dimensional structure of a complex of antibody with influenza virus neuraminidase. *Nature* 1987; 326:358–363.

257. Webster RG, Air GM, Metzger DW, et al: Antigenic structure and variation in an influenza virus N9 neuraminidase. *J Virol* 1987; 61:2910–2916.

258. Blok J, Air GM: Variation in the membrane-insertion and "stalk" sequences in eight subtypes of influenza type A virus neuraminidase. *Biochemistry* 1982; 21:4001–4007.

259. Higa HH, Rogers RN, Paulson JC: Influenza virus haemagglutinins differentiate between receptor determinants bearing N-acetyl, N-glycolyl and N, O-diacetyl-neuraminic acids. *Virology* 1985; 144:279–282.

260. Collins J, Knight CA: Removal of carbohydrate from influenza A virus and its hemagglutinin and the effect on biological activities. *J Virol* 1978; 27:164–171.

261. Deom CM, Caton AJ, Schluze IT: Host cell–mediated selection of a mutant influenza A virus that has lost a complex oligosaccharide from the tip of the hemagglutinin. *Proc Natl Acad Sci USA* 1986; 83:3771–3775.

262. Katz JM, Naeve CW, Webster RG: Host cell–mediated variation in H3N2 influenza virus. *Virology* 1987; 156:386–395.

263. Yoshimura A, Kuroda K, Kawasaki K, et al: Infectious cell entry mechanism of influenza virus. *J Virol* 1982; 43:284–293.

264. Maeda T, Kawasaki K, Ohnishi S: Interactions of influenza virus hemagglutinin with target membrane lipids is a key step in virus–induced hemolysis and fusion at pH 5.2. *Proc Natl Acad Sci USA* 1981; 78:4133–4237.

265. Maeda T, Ohnishi S: Activation of influenza virus by acidic media causes hemolysis and fusion of erythrocytes. *FEBS Lett* 1980; 122:283–287.

266. Nestorowicz A, Laver G, Jackson DC: Antigenic determinants of influenza virus haemagglutinin. X. A comparison of the physical and antigenic properties of monomeric and trimeric forms. *J Gen Virol* 1985; 66:1687–1695.

267. Gething MJ, White JM, Waterfield MD: Purification of the fusion protein of Sendai virus: Analysis of the HN2-terminal sequence generated during precursor activation. *Proc Natl Acad Sci USA* 1978; 75:2737–2740.

268. Doms RW, Gething M-J, Henneberry J, et al: Variant influenza virus hemagglutinin that induces fusion at elevated pH. *J Virol* 1986; 57:603–613.

269. Nussbaum O, Lapidot M, Loyter A: Reconstitution of functional influenza virus envelopes and fusion with membranes and liposomes lacking virus receptors. *J Virol* 1987; 61:2245–2252.

270. Huang RTC, Rott R, Wahn K, et al: The function of neuraminidase in membrane fusion induced by myxoviruses. *Virology* 1980; 107:313–319.

271. Herz C, Stavnezer E, Krug RM: Influenza virus, an RNA virus, synthesizes its messenger RNA in the nucleus of infected cells. *Cell* 1981; 26; 391–400.

272. Mark GE, Taylor JM, Broni B, et al: Nuclear accumulation of influenza viral RNA transcripts and the effects of cycloheximide, actinomycin D and α-amanitin. *J Virol* 1979; 29:744–752.

273. Ritchey MB, Palese P, Schulman JL: Mapping of the influenza virus genome. III. Identification of genes coding for nucleoprotein, membrane protein and nonstructural protein. *J Virol* 1976; 20:307–313.

274. Plotch SJ, Bouloy M, Ulmanen I, et al: A unique cap (m^{7}GpppXm)–dependent influenza virion endonuclease cleaves capped RNAs to generate the primers that initiate viral RNA transcription. *Cell* 1981; 23:847–858.

275. Krug RM: The role of RNA priming in viral and trypanosomal mRNA synthesis. *Cell* 1985; 41:651–652.

276. Plotch SJ, Bouloy M, Drug RM: Transfer of 5' terminal cap of globin mRNA to influenza viral complementary RNA during transcription in vitro. *Proc Natl Acad Sci USA* 1979; 76:1618–1622.

277. Bouloy M, Morgan MA, Shatkin AJ, et al: Cap and internal nucleotides of reovirus mRNA primers are incorporated into influenza viral complementary RNA during transcription in vitro. *J Virol* 1979; 32:895–904.

278. Krug RM, Broni BA, Bouloy M: Are the 5' ends of influenza viral mRNAs synthesized in vivo donated by host mRNAs? *Cell* 1979; 18:329–334.

279. Blaas D, Patzelt E, Kuechler E: Cap-recognizing protein of influenza virus. *Virology* 1982; 116:339–348.

280. Hay AJ, Abraham G, Skehel JJ, et al: Influenza virus messenger RNAs are incomplete transcripts of the genome RNAs. *Nucleic Acids Res* 1977; 4:4197–4209.

281. Skehel JJ, Hay AJ: Influenza virus transcription. *J Gen Virol* 1978; 39:1–8.

282. Etkind PR, Krug RM: Influenza viral messenger RNA. *Virology* 1974; 62:38–45.

283. Glass SE, McGeoch D, Barry RD: Characterization of the mRNA of influenza virus. *J Virol* 1975; 16:1435–1443.

284. Lamb RA, Lai C-J: Sequence of interrupted and uninterrupted mRNAs and cloned DNA coding for the two overlapping nonstructural proteins of influenza virus. *Cell* 1980; 21:475–485.

285. Lamb RA, Choppin PW, Chanock RM, et al: Mapping of the two overlapping genes for polypeptides NS$_1$ and NS$_2$ on RNA segment 8 of influenza virus genome. *Proc Natl Acad Sci USA* 1980; 77:1857–1861.

286. Lamb RA, Lai C-J, Choppin PW: Sequences of mRNAs derived from genome RNA segment 7 of influenza virus: Colinear and interrupted mRNAs code for overlapping proteins. *Proc Natl Acad Sci USA* 1981; 78:4170–4174.

287. Fields S, Winter G, Brownlee GG: Structure of the neuraminidase gene in human influenza virus A/PR/8/34. *Nature* 1981; 290:213–217.

288. Winter G, Fields S: Cloning of influenza cDNA into M13: The sequence of the RNA segment encoding the A/PR/8/34 matrix protein. *Nucleic Acids Res* 1980; 8:1965–1974.

289. Winter G, Fields S, Brownlee GG: The nucleotide sequence of the haemagglutinin gene of a human influenza virus H1 subtype. *Nature* 1981; 292:72–75.

290. Inglis SC, Mahy BWJ: Polypeptides specified by the influenza virus genome. III. Control of synthesis in infected cells. *Virology* 1979; 95:154–164.

291. Hay AJ, Lomniczi B, Bellamy AR, et al: Transcription of the influenza virus genome. *Virology* 1977; 83:337–355.

292. Beaton AR, Krug RM: Transcription antitermination during influenza viral template RNA synthesis requires the nucleocapsid protein and the absence of a 5' capped end. *Proc Natl Acad Sci USA* 1986; 83:6282–6286.

293. Shapiro GI, Gurney T Jr, Krug RM: Influenza virus gene expression: Control mechanisms at early and late times of infection and nuclear cytoplasmic transport of virus-specific RNAs. *J Virol* 1987; 61:764–773.

294. Nayak DP, Chambers TM, Akkina RK: Defective-interfering (DI) RNAs of influenza viruses: Origin, structure, expression, and interference. *Curr Top Microbiol Immunol* 1985; 114:103–151.

295. Cane C, Mc Lain L, Dimmock NJ: Intracellular stability of the interfering activity of a defective interfering influenza virus in the absence of virus multiplication. *Virology* 1987; 159:259–264.

296. Bos TJ, Davis AR, Nayak DP: NH2-terminal hydrophobic region of influenza virus neuraminidase provides the signal function in translocation. *Proc Natl Acad Sci USA* 1984; 81:2327–2331.

297. Sivasubramanian N, Nayak DP: Mutational analysis of the signal-anchor domain of influenza virus neuraminidase. *Proc Natl Acad Sci USA* 1987; 84:1–5.

298. Jones LV, Compans RW, Davis AR, et al: Surface expression of influenza virus neuraminidase, and amino-terminally anchored viral membrane glycoprotein in polarized epithelial cells. *Mol Cell Biol* 1985; 5:2181–2189.

299. Gething M-J, McCammon K, Sambrook J: Expression of wild-type and mutant forms of influenza hemagglutinin: The role of folding in intracellular transport. *Cell* 1986; 46:939–950.

300. Copeland CS, Doms RW, Bolzau EM, et al: Assembly of influenza hemagglutinin trimers and its role in intracellular transport. *J Cell Biol* 1986; 103:1179–1192.

301. Yewdell JW, Yellen A, Bächi T: Monoclonal antibodies localize events in the folding, assembly, and intracellular transport of the influenza virus hemagglutinin glycoprotein. *Cell* 1988; 52:843–852.

302. Ueda M, Kilbourne ED: Temperature-sensitive mutants of influenza virus: A mutation in the hemagglutinin gene. *Virology* 1976; 70:425–431.

303. Roth MG, Srinivas RV, Compans RW: Basolateral maturation of retroviruses in polarized epithelial cells. *J Virol* 1983; 45:1065–1073.

304. Misek DE, Bard E, Rodriguez-Boulan E: Biogenesis of epithelial cell polarity: Intracellular sorting and vectorial exocytosis of an apical plasma membrane glycoprotein. *Cell* 1984; 39:537–546.

305. Fuller S, von-Bonsdorff CJ, Simons K: Vesicular stomatitis virus infects and matures only through the basolateral surface of the polarized epithelial cell line, MDCK. *Cell* 1984; 38:65–77.

306. Garten W, Bosch FX, Linder D, et al: Proteolytic activation of the influenza virus hemagglutinin: The structure of the cleavage site and the enzymes involved in cleavage. *Virology* 1981; 115:361–374.

307. Laver WG: Separation of two polypeptide chains from the hemagglutinin subunit of influenza virus. *Virology* 1971; 45:275–288.

308. Lazarowitz SG, Goldberg AR, Choppin PW: Proteolytic cleavage by plasmin of the HA polypeptide of influenza virus. *Virology* 1973; 56:172–180.

309. Ye Z, Baylor NW, Wagner RR: Transcription-inhibition and RNA-binding domains of influenza A virus matrix protein mapped with anti-idiotypic antibodies and synthetic peptides. *J Virol* 1989; 63:3586–3594.

310. Pattnaik AK, Brown DJ, Nayak DP: Formation of influenza virus particles lacking hemagglutinin on the viral envelope. *J Virol* 1986; 60:994–1001.

311. Palese P, Young JF: Variation of influenza A, B, and C viruses. *Science* 1982; 215:1468–1473.

312. Webster RG, Laver WG, Air GM, et al: Molecular mechanisms of variation of influenza viruses. *Nature* 1982; 296:115–121.

313. Rott R, Orlich M, Scholtissek C: Attenuation of pathogenicity of fowl plague virus by recombination with other influenza A viruses nonpathogenic for fowl: Nonexclusive dependence of pathogenicity on hemagglutinin and neuraminidase of the virus. *J Virol* 1976; 19:54–60.

314. Scholtissek C, Vallbracht A, Flehmig B, et al: Correlation of pathogenicity and gene constellation of influenza A viruses. II. Highly neurovirulent recombinants derived from nonneurovirulent or weakly neurovirulent parent virus strains. *Virology* 1979; 95:492–500.

315. Parvin JD, Moscona A, Pan WT, et al: Measurement of the mutation rates of animal viruses: Influenza A virus and poliovirus type 1. *J Virol* 1986; 59:377–383.

316. Katze MG, Krug RM: Metabolism and expression of RNA polymerase II transcripts in influenza virus infected cell. *Mol Cell Biol* 1984; 4:2198–2206.

317. Katze MG, DeCorato D, Krug RM: Cellular mRNA translation is blocked at both initiation and elongation after infection by influenza virus or adenovirus. *J Virol* 1986; 60:1027–1039.

318. Wagner RR: Reproduction of rhabdovirus, in Fraenkel–Conrat H, Wagner RR (eds): *Comprehensive Virology, Reproduction: Large RNA Viruses.* New York, Plenum Press, 1975, pp 1–93.

319. Rose JK, Welch WJ, Sefton BM, et al: Vesicular stomatitis glycoprotein is anchored in the viral membrane by a hydrophobic domain near the COOH–terminus. *Proc Natl Acad Sci USA* 1980; 77:3884–3888.

320. Zakowski JJ, Wagner RR: Localization of membrane-associated proteins in vesicular stomatitis virus by the use of hydrophobic membrane probes and cross-linking reagents. *J Virol* 1980; 36:93–102.

321. Capone J, Leblanc P, Gerber GE, et al: Localization of membrane proteins by the use of a photoreactive fatty acid incorporated in vivo into vesicular stomatitis virus. *J Biol Chem* 1983; 258:1395–1398.

322. Bundo-Morita K, Gibson S, Lenard J: Radiation inactivation analysis of fusion and hemolysis by vesicular stomatitis virus. *Virology* 1988; 163:622–624.

323. Newcomb WW, Brown JC: Role of the vesicular stomatitis virus matrix protein in maintaining the viral nucleocapsid in the condensed form found in native virions. *J Virol* 1981; 39:295–299.

324. Newcomb WW, Tobin GJ, McGowan JJ, et al: In vitro reassembly of vesicular stomatitis virus skeletons. *J Virol* 1982; 41:1055–1062.

325. Banerjee AK: 5'-terminal cap structure in eucaryotic messenger ribonucleic acids. *Microbiol Rev* 1980; 44:175–205.

326. Abraham G, Rhodes DP, Banerjee AK: The 5' terminal structure of the methylated mRNA synthesized in vitro by vesicular stomatitis virus. *Cell* 1975; 5:51–58.

327. Herman RC, Schubert M, Keene JD, et al: Polycistronic vesicular stomatitis virus RNA transcripts. *Proc Natl Acad Sci USA* 1980; 77:4662–4665.

328. Emerson SU, Yu Y-H: Both NS and L proteins are required for in vitro RNA synthesis by vesicular stomatitis virus. *J Virol* 1975; 15:1348–1356.

329. Banerjee AK, Abraham G, Colonno RJ: Vesicular stomatitis virus: Mode of transcription. *J Gen Virol* 1977; 34:1–8.

330. Baltimore D, Huang AS, Stampfer M: Ribonucleic acid synthesis of vesicular stomatitis virus, II. An RNA polymerase in the virion. *Proc Natl Acad Sci USA* 1970; 66:572–576.

331. Moyer SA, Graubman MJ, Ehrenfeld E, et al: Studies on the in vivo and in vitro messenger RNA species of vesicular stomatitis virus. *Virology* 1975; 67:463–473.

332. Sokol F, Clark HF: Phosphoproteins, structural components of rhabdoviruses. *Virology* 1973; 52:246–263.

333. Kingsford L, Emerson SU: Transcriptional activities of different phosphorylated species of NS protein purified from vesicular stomatitis virions and cytoplasm of infected cells. *J Virol* 1980; 33:1097–1105.

334. Hsu C-H, Morgan EM, Kingsbury DW: Site-specific phosphorylation regulates the transcriptive activity of vesicular stomatitis virus NS protein. *J Virol* 1982; 43:104–112.

335. Sanchez A, De BP, Banerjee AK: In vitro phosphorylation of the NS protein by the L protein of vesicular stomatitis virus. *J Gen Virol* 1985; 66:1025–1036.

336. Viti D, Sinibaldi L, Superti F, et al: VSV binding to lipids from different cell lines. *Arch Virol* 1987; 93:279–285.

337. Thimmig L, Hughes JU, Kinders RJ, et al: Isolation of the glycoprotein of vesicular stomatitis virus and its binding to cell surface. *J Virol* 1980; 50:279–291.

338. Heine JW, Schnaitman CH: Fusion of vesicular stomatitis virus with the cytoplasmic membrane of L cells. *J Virol* 1969; 3:619–622.

339. Matlin K, Reggio A, Simons K, et al: Pathway of vesicular stomatitis virus entry leading to infection. *J Mol Biol* 1982; 156:609–631.

340. Schlegal R, Wade M: Biologically active peptides of vesicular stomatitis virus glycoprotein. *J Virol* 1985; 53:319–323.

341. White J, Matlin K, Helenius A: Cell fusion by Semliki Forest virus, influenza, and vesicular stomatitis virus. *J Cell Biol* 1981; 89:674–679.

342. Woodgett C, Rose JK: Amino-terminal mutation of the vesicu-

lar stomatitis virus glycoprotein does not affect its fusion activity. *J Virol* 1986; 59:486–489.

343. Emerson SU, Wagner RR: Dissociation and reconstitution of the transcriptase and template activities of vesicular stomatitis B and T virions. *J Virol* 1972; 10:297–309.

344. Hill VM, Marnell L, Summers DF: In vitro replication and assembly of vesicular stomatitis virus nucleocapsids. *Virology* 1981; 113:109–118.

345. Banerjee AK: Transcription and replication of rhabdoviruses. *Microbiol Rev* 1987; 51:66–87.

346. Huang AS, Manders EK: RNA synthesis of versicular stomatitis virus. IV. Transcription by standard virus in the presence of defective interfering particles. *J Virol* 1972; 9:901–916.

347. Wertz GW, Levine M: RNA synthesis by vesicular stomatitis virus and a small–plaque mutant: Effects of cycloheximide. *J Virol* 1973; 12:253–264.

348. Emerson SU: Transcription of vesicular stomatitis virus, in Wagner RR (ed): *The Rhabdoviruses.* New York, Plenum, 1987, pp 245–269.

349. Banerjee AK: The transcriptional complex of vesicular stomatitis virus. *Cell* 1987; 48:363–364.

350. Harmon SA, Robinson EN Jr, Summers DF: Ultrastructural localization of L and NS enzyme subunits on vesicular stomatitis virus RNPs using gold sphere–staphylococcal protein A-mono-specific IgG conjugates. *Virology* 1985; 142:406–410.

351. Pringle CR: Rhabdovirus genetics, in Wagner RR (ed): *The Rhabdoviruses.* New York, Plenum, 1987, pp 167–243.

352. Testa D, Banerjee AK: Nucleoside diphosphate kinase activity in purified cores of vesicular stomatitis virus. *J Biol Chem* 1979; 254:9075–9079.

353. Feldhaus AL, Lesnaw JA: Nucleotide sequence of the L gene of vesicular stomatitis virus (New Jersey): Identification of conserved domains in the New Jersey and Indiana L proteins. *Virology* 1988; 163:359–368.

354. Hsu C-H, Kingsbury DW: Constitutively phosphorylated residues in the NS protein of vesicular stomatitis virus. *J Biol Chem* 1985; 260:8990–8995.

355. Gill DS, Chattopadhyay D, Banerjee AK: Identification of a domain within the phosphoprotein of vesicular stomatitis virus that is essential for transcription in vitro. *Proc Natl Acad Sci USA* 1986; 83:8873–8877.

356. Bell JC, Prevec L: Phosphorylation site on phosphoprotein NS of vesicular stomatitis virus. *J Virol* 1985; 54:697–702.

357. Masters PS, Banerjee AK: Phosphoprotein NS of vesicular stomatitis virus: Phosphorylated states and transcriptional activities of intracellular and virion forms. *Virology* 1986; 154:259–270.

358. Chattopadhyay D, Banerjee AK: Phosphorylation within a specific domain of the phosphoprotein of vesicular stomatitis virus regulates transcription in vitro. *Cell* 1987; 49:407–414.

359. Gill DS, Banerjee AK: Vesicular stomatitis virus NS proteins: Structural similarity without extensive homology. *J Virol* 1985; 55:60–66.

360. Ball LA: Transcriptional mapping of vesicular stomatitis virus in vivo. *J Virol* 1977; 21:411–414.

361. Ball LA, White CN: Order of transcription of genes of vesicular stomatitis virus. *Proc Natl Acad Sci USA* 1976; 73:442–446.

362. De BP, Banerjee AK: Requirements and functions of vesicular stomatitis virus L and NS proteins in the transcription process in vitro. *Biochem Biophys Res Commun* 1985; 126:40–49.

363. Colonno RJ, Banerjee AK: Complete nucleotide sequence of the leader RNA synthesized in vitro by vesicular stomatitis virus, *Cell* 1978; 15:93–101.

364. Colonno RJ, Banerjee AK: A unique RNA species involved in initiation of vesicular stomatitis virus RNA transcription in vitro. *Cell* 1976; 8:197–204.

365. Rose JK: Complete intergenic and flanking gene sequences from the genome of vesicular stomatitis virus. *Cell* 1980; 19:415–421.

366. Abraham G, Banerjee AK: Sequential transcription of the genes of vesicular stomatitis virus. *Proc Natl Acad Sci USA* 1976; 73:1504–1508.

367. Luk D, Masters PS, Gill DS, et al: Intergenic sequences of the vesicular stomatitis virus genome (New Jersey serotype): Evidence for two transcription initiation sites within the L gene. *Virology* 1987; 160:88–94.

368. Schubert M, Keene JD, Herman RC, et al: Site on the vesicular stomatitis genome specifying polyadenylation and the end of the L gene mRNA. *J Virol* 1980; 34:550–559.

369. Iverson LE, Rose JK: Localized attenuation and discontinuous synthesis during vesicular stomatitis virus transcription. *Cell* 1981; 23:477–484.

370. Herman RC: Internal initiation of translation on the vesicular stomatitis virus phosphoprotein mRNA yields a second protein. *J Virol* 1986; 58:797–804.

371. Wertz GW, Levine M: RNA synthesis by vesicular stomatitis virus and a small plaque mutant: Effects of cycloheximide. *J Virol* 1973; 12:253–264.

372. Davis NL, Wertz GW: Synthesis of vesicular stomatitis virus negative–strand RNA in vitro: Dependence on viral protein synthesis. *J Virol* 1982; 41:821–832.

373. Blumberg BM, Leppert M, Kolakofsky D: Interaction of VSV leader RNA and nucleocapsid protein may control VSV genome replication. *Cell* 1981; 23:837–845.

374. Leppert M, Rittenhouse L, Perrault J, et al: Plus and minus strand leader RNAs in negative–strand virus–infected cells. *Cell* 1979; 18:735–747.

375. Blumberg BM, Colomba G, Kolakofsky D: N protein of vesicular stomatitis virus selectively encapsidates leader RNA in vitro. *Cell* 1983; 32:559–567.

376. Masters PS, Banerjee AK: Resolution of multiple complexes of phosphoprotein NS with nucleocapsid protein N of vesicular stomatitis virus. *J Virol* 1988; 62:2651–2657.

377. Masters PS, Banerjee AK: Complex formation with vesicular stomatitis virus phosphoprotein NS prevents binding of nucleocapsid protein N to nonspecific RNA. *J Virol* 1988; 62:2658–2664.

378. LaFerla FM, Peluso RW: The 1:1 N-NS protein complex of vesicular stomatitis virus is essential for efficient genome replication. *J Virol* 1989; 63:3852–3857.

379. Chatterjee PK, Cervera MM, Penman S: Formation of vesicular stomatitis virus nucleocapsid from cytoskeletal framework-bound N protein: Possible model for structure assembly. *Mol Cell Biol* 1984; 4:2231–2234.

380. Dillon PJ, Gupta KC: Early steps in the assembly of vesicular stomatitis virus nucleocapsids in infected cells. *J Virol* 1988; 62:1582–1589.

381. Hill VM, Harmon SA, Summers DF: Stimulation of vesicular stomatitis virus in vitro RNA synthesis by microtubule-associated proteins. *Proc Natl Acad Sci USA* 1986; 83:5410–5413.

382. Rubio C, Kolakofsky C, Hill VM, et al: Replication and assembly of VSV nucleocapsids: Protein association with RNPs and the effects of cycloheximide on replication. *Virology* 1980; 105:123–135.

383. Emerson SU: Vesicular stomatitis virus: Structure and function of virion components. *Curr Top Microbiol Immunol* 1976; 73:1–34.

384. McSharry JJ, Compans RW, Choppin PW: Proteins of vesicular stomatitis virus and of phenotypically mixed vesicular stomatitis virus–simian virus 5 virions. *J Virol* 1971; 8:722–729.

385. Lodish HF, Weiss RA: Selective isolation of mutants of vesicular stomatitis virus defective in production of the viral glycoprotein. *J Virol* 1979; 30:177–189.

386. Morrison T, Lodish HF: Site of synthesis of membrane and nonmembrane proteins of vesicular stomatitis virus. *J Biol Chem* 1975; 250:6955–6962.

387. Atkinson PH: Glycoprotein and protein precursors to plasma membranes in vesicular stomatitis virus infected HeLa cells. *J Supramol Struct Cell Biochem* 1978; 8:89–109.

388. Toneguzzo F, Ghosh HP: In vitro synthesis of vesicular stomatitis virus membrane glycoprotein and insertion into membranes. *Proc Natl Acad Sci USA* 1978; 75:715–719.

389. Lingappa V, Katz FN, Lodish HF, et al: A signal sequence for

the insertion of a transmembrane glycoprotein. Similarities to the signals of secretory proteins in primary structure and function. *J Biol Chem* 1978; 253:8667–8670.

390. Rothman JE, Fine RE: Coated vesicles transport newly synthesized membrane glycoproteins from endoplasmic reticulum to plasma membrane in two successive stages. *Proc Natl Acad Sci USA* 1980; 77:780–784.

391. Chatis PA, Morrison TG: Vesicular stomatitis virus glycoprotein is anchored to intracellular membranes near its carboxyl end and is proteolytically cleaved at its amino terminus. *J Virol* 1979; 29:957–963.

392. Bergeron JJ, Borts H, Palade GE: Distribution of terminal glycosyltransferases in hepatic Golgi fractions. *J Cell Biol* 1980; 84:87–101.

393. Tabas I, Kornfeld S: Purification and characterization of a rat liver Golgi ; ga-mannosidase capable of processing asparagine-linked oligosaccharides. *J Biol Chem* 1979; 254:11655–11663.

394. Reading CL, Penhoet EF, Ballow CE: Carbohydrate structure of vesicular stomatitis virus glycoprotein. *J Biol Chem* 1978; 253:5600–5612.

395. Hunt LA, Etchinson JR, Summers DF: Oligosaccharide chains are trimmed during synthesis of the envelope glycoprotein of vesicular stomatitis virus. *Proc Natl Acad Sci USA* 1978; 75:754–758.

396. Lenard J, Compans RW: The membrane structure of lipid-containing viruses. *Biochim Biophys Acta* 1974; 344:51–94.

397. Schmidt MFG, Schlesinger MJ: Fatty acid binding to vesicular stomatitis virus glycoprotein: A new type of post-translational modification of the viral glycoprotein. *Cell* 1979; 17:813–819.

398. Schmidt MFG, Bracha M, Schlesinger MJ: Evidence for covalent attachment of fatty acids to Sindbis virus glycoproteins. *Proc Natl Acad Sci USA* 1979; 76:1687–1691.

399. Burge BW, Huang AS: Comparison of membrane protein glycopeptides of Sindbis virus and vesicular stomatitis virus. *J Virol* 1970; 6:176–182.

400. Etchinson JR, Holland JJ: Carbohydrate composition of the membrane glycoprotein of vesicular stomatitis virus. *Virology* 1974; 60:217–229.

401. Moyers SA, Summers DF: Vesicular stomatitis envelope glycoprotein alterations induced by host cell transformation. *Cell* 1974; 2:71–78.

402. Moyers SA, Tsang JM, Atkinson PH, et al: Oligosaccharide moieties of the glycoprotein of vesicular stomatitis virus. *J Virol* 1976; 18:167–175.

403. Kingsford L, Emerson SU, Kelley JM: Separation of cyanogen bromide–cleaved peptides of the vesicular stomatitis virus glycoprotein and analysis of their carbohydrate content. *J Virol* 1980; 36:309–316.

404. Robertson JS, Etchinson JR, Summers DF: Glycosylation sites of vesicular stomatitis virus glycoprotein. *J Virol* 1976; 19:871–878.

404a. Pitta AM, Rose JK, Machamer CE: A single-amino acid substitution eliminates the stringent carbohydrate requirement for intracellular transport of a viral glycoprotein. *J Virol* 1989; 63:3801–3809.

405. Leavitt R, Schlesinger S, Kornfeld S: Tunicamycin inhibits glycosylation and multiplication of Sindbis and vesicular stomatitis viruses. *J Virol* 1977; 21:375–385.

406. Gibson R, Leavitt R, Kornfeld S, et al: Synthesis and infectivity of vesicular stomatitis virus containing nonglycosylated G protein. *Cell* 1978; 13:671–679.

407. Gibson R, Schlesinger S, Kornfeld S: The nonglycosylated glycoprotein of vesicular stomatitis virus is temperature sensitive and undergoes intracellular aggregation at elevated temperatures. *J Biol Chem* 1979; 254:3600–3607.

408. Chatis PA, Morrison TG: Mutational changes in the vesicular stomatitis virus glycoprotein affect the requirement of carbohydrate in morphogenesis. *J Virol* 1981; 37:307–316.

409. Little SP, Huang AS: Shedding of the glycoprotein from vesicular stomatitis virus–infected cells. *J Virol* 1978; 27:330–339.

410. Irving RA, Ghosh HP: Shedding of vesicular stomatitis virus soluble glycoprotein by removal of carboxyterminal peptide. *J Virol* 1982; 42:322–325.

411. Chatis PA, Morrison TG: Characterization of the soluble glycoprotein released from vesicular stomatitis virus–infected cells. *J Virol* 1983; 45:80–90.

412. Garreis-Wabnitz C, Kruppa J: Intracellular appearance of a glycoprotein in VSV-infected BHK cells lacking the membrane-anchoring oligopeptide of the viral G-protein. *EMBO J* 1984; 3:1469–1476.

413. Graeve L, Garreis-Wabnitz C, Zauke M, et al: The soluble glycoprotein of vesicular stomatitis virus is formed during or shortly after the translation process. *J Virol* 1986; 57:968–975.

414. Patzer EJ, Wagner RR, Dubovi EJ: Viral membranes: Model systems for studying biological membranes. *Crit Rev Biochem* 1979; 6:165–217.

415. Schloemer RH, Wagner RR: Association of vesicular stomatitis virus glycoprotein with virion membrane: Characterization of the lipophilic tail fragment. *J Virol* 1975; 16:237–249.

416. Zakowaski JJ, Wagner RR: Localization of membrane-associated proteins in vesicular stomatitis virus by use of hydrophobic membrane probes and cross-linking reagents. *J Virol* 1980; 36:93–102.

417. Knipe D, Baltimore D, Lodish H: Separate pathways of maturation of the major structural proteins of vesicular stomatitis virus. *J Virol* 1977; 21:1128–1139.

418. Mancarella DA, Lenard J: Interactions of wild-type and mutant M protein of vesicular stomatitis virus with viral nucleocapsid and envelope in intact virions. Evidence from (^{125}I) iodonapthyl azide labeling and specific cross-linking. *Biochemistry* 1981; 20:6872–6877.

419. Newcomb WW, Tobin GJ, Mc Gowan JJ, et al: In vitro reassembly of vesicular stomatitis virus skeletons. *J Virol* 1982; 56:386–394.

420. Odenwald WF, Arnheiter H, Dubois-Dalcq M, et al: Stereo images of vesicular stomatitis virus assembly. *J Virol* 1986; 57:922–932.

421. Jacobs BL, Penhoet EE: Assembly of vesicular stomatitis virus: Distribution of the glycoprotein on the surface of infected cells. *J Virol* 1982; 44:1047–1055.

422. Dubois-Dalcq M, Holmes KV, Rentier B: Assembly of Rhabdoviridae, in Kingsbury DW: *Assembly of Enveloped RNA Viruses.* New York, Springer-Verlag, 1984, pp 21–43.

423. Metsikkö K, Simons K: The budding mechanism of spikeless vesicular stomatitis virus particles. *EMBO J* 1986; 5:1913–1920.

423a. Whitt MA, Chong L, Rose JK: Glycoprotein cytoplasmic domain sequences required for rescue of a vesicular stomatitis virus glycoprotein mutant. *J Virol* 1989; 63:3569–3578.

424. Rodriguez-Boulan E, Pendergast M: Polarized distribution of viral envelope proteins in the plasma membrane of infected epithelial cells. *Cell* 1980; 20:45–54.

425. Wiener JR, Pal R, Barenholz Y, et al: Effect of the vesicular stomatitis matrix protein on lateral organization of lipid bilayers containing phosphatidylglycerol: Use of fluorescent phospholipid analogs. *Biochemistry* 1985; 24:7651–7658.

426. Ono K, Dubois-Dalcq ME, Schubert M, et al: A mutated membrane protein of vesicular stomatitis virus has an abnormal distribution within the infected cell and causes defective budding. *J Virol* 1987; 61:1332–1341.

427. Pinney DF, Emerson SU: In vitro synthesis of triphosphate-initiated N-Gene mRNA oligonucleotides is regulated by the matrix protein of vesicular stomatitis virus. *J Virol* 1982; 42:897–904.

428. Carroll AR, Wagner RR: Role of the membrane protein in endogenous inhibition of in vitro transcription by vesicular stomatitis virus. *J Virol* 1979; 29:134–142.

429. Clinton GM, Little SP, Hagen FS, et al: The matrix (M) protein of vesicular stomatitis virus regulates transcription. *Cell* 1978; 15:1455–1462.

430. Perrault J, Kingsbury DT: Inhibitor of vesicular stomatitis virus

transcriptase in purified virions. *Nature* 1974; 248:45–47.

431. Wilson T, Lenard J: Interaction of wild-type and mutant M protein of vesicular stomatitis virus with nucleocapsids in vitro. *Biochemistry* 1981; 20:1349–1354.

432. De BP, Thornton GB, Luk D, et al: Purified matrix protein of vesicular stomatitis virus blocks viral transcription in vitro. *Proc Natl Acad Sci USA* 1982; 79:7137–7141.

433. Rose JK, Gallione CJ: Nucleotide sequences of the mRNAs encoding the vesicular stomatitis virus G and M proteins determined from cDNA clones containing the complete coding regions. *J Virol* 1981; 39:519–528.

434. Ogden JR, Pal R, Wagner RR: Mapping regions of the matrix protein of vesicular stomatitis virus which bind to ribonucleocapsid, lipsome, and monoclonal antibodies. *J Virol* 1986; 58:860–868.

435. Reichmann ME, Schnitzlein WM: Defective inferfering particles of rhabdoviruses. *Curr Top Microbiol Immunol* 1979; 86:123–168.

436. Holland JJ, Kennedy SIT, Semler BL, et al: Defective interfering RNA viruses and the host–cell response, in Fraenkel–Conrat H, Wagner RR (eds): *Comprehensive Virology*. New York, Plenum, Vol 16, 1980, pp 137–192.

437. Blumberg BM, Kolakofsky D: An analytical review of defective infections of vesicular stomatitis virus. *J Gen Virol* 1983; 64:1839–1847.

438. Holland JJ: Defective interfering rhabdoviruses, in Wagner RR (ed): *The Rhabdoviruses*. New York, Plenum, 1987, pp 297–360.

439. Huang AS, Greenawalt JW, Wagner RR: Defective T particles of vesicular stomatitis virus. I. Preparation, morphology, and some biologic properties. *Virology* 1966; 30:161–172.

440. Lazzarini RA, Keene JD, Schubert M: The origins of defective interfering particles of the negative–strand RNA viruses. *Cell* 1981; 26:145–154.

441. Rao DD, Huang AS: Interference among defective interfering particles of vesicular stomatitis virus. *J Virol* 1982; 41:210–221.

442. Holland JJ, Villarreal LP, Breindl M: Factors involved in the generation and replication of rhabdovirus defective T particles. *J Virol* 1976; 17:805–815.

443. Colonno RJ, Lazzarini RA, Keene JD, et al: In vitro synthesis of messenger RNA by a defective interfering particle of vesicular stomatitis virus. *Proc Natl Acad Sci USA* 1977; 74:1884–1888.

444. Spindler KR, Horodyski FM, Holland JJ: High multiplicities of infection favor rapid and random evolution of vesicular stomatitis virus. *Virology* 1982; 119:96–108.

445. Kang CY, Glimp T, Clewley JP, et al: Studies on the generation of vesicular stomatitis virus (Indiana serotype) defective interfering particles. *Virology* 1978; 84:142–152.

446. Keene JD, Schubert M, Lazzarini RA: Terminal sequences of vesicular stomatitis virus RNA are both complementary and conserved. *J Virol* 1979; 32:167–174.

447. Kolakofsky D: Isolation of vesicular stomatitis virus defective interfering genomes with different amounts of 5′-terminal complementarity. *J Virol* 1982; 41:566–574.

448. Isaac CL, Keene JD: RNA polymerase-associated interactions near template promoter sequences of defective interfering particles of vesicular stomatitis virus. *J Virol* 1982; 43:241–249.

449. Perrault J, Leavitt RW: Inverted complementary terminal sequences in single-stranded RNAs and snap-back RNAs from vesicular stomatitis defective interfering particles. *J Gen Virol* 1977; 38:35–50.

450. Choppin PW, Pons MW: The RNAs of infective and incomplete influenza virions grown in MDBK and HeLa cells. *Virology* 1970; 42:603–610.

451. Darnell MB, Koprowski H: Genetically determined resistance to infection with group B arboviruses: II. Increased production of interfering particles in cell cultures from resistant mice. *J Infect Dis* 1974; 129:248–256.

452. Roman JM, Simon EH: Defective interfering particles in monolayer-propagated Newcastle disease virus. *Virology* 1976; 69:298–303.

453. Goodman GT, Koprowski H: Study of the mechanism of innate resistance to virus infection. *J Cell Comp Physiol* 1962; 59:333–373.

454. Kang CY, Allen R: Host function-dependent induction of defective interfering particles of vesicular stomatitis virus. *J Virol* 1978; 25:202–206.

455. Kang CY, Weide LG, Tischfield JA: Suppression of vesicular stomatitis virus defective interfering particle generation by a function(s) associated with human chromosome 16. *J Virol* 1981; 40:946–952.

456. Artsob H, Spence L: Persistent infection of mosquito cell lines with vesicular stomatitis virus. *Acta Virol* 1974; 18:331–340.

457. Wyers F, Richard-Molard C, Blondel D, et al: Vesicular stomatitis virus growth in *Drosophila melanogaster* cells: G protein deficiency. *J Virol* 1980; 33:411–422.

458. Piwnica-Worms H, Keene JD: Replication of the vesicular stomatitis virus genome in permissive and non-permissive host cells. *J Biol Chem* 1985; 260:10503–10511.

459. Blondel D, Dezélée S, Wyers F: Vesicular stomatitis virus growth in *Drosophila melanogaster* cells. II. Modification of viral protein phosphorylation. *J Gen Virol* 1983; 64:1793–1799.

460. Dezélée S, Blondel D, Wyer F, et al: Vesicular stomatitis virus in *Drosophila melanogaster* cells: Lack of leader RNA transport into the nuclei and frequent abortion of the replication step. *J Virol* 1987; 61:1391–1397.

461. Grabau EA, Holland JJ: Analysis of viral and defective interfering nucleocapsids in acute and persistent infections by rhabdoviruses. *J Gen Virol* 1982; 60:87–97.

462. Youngner JS, Preble OT, Jones EV: Persistent infections of L cells with vesicular stomatitis virus: Evaluation of virus populations. *J Virol* 1978; 28:6–13.

463. Belkowski LS, Sen GC: Inhibition of vesicular stomatitis viral mRNA synthesis by interferons. *J Virol* 1987; 61:653–660.

464. Frey TK, Youngner JS: Further studies on the RNA synthesis phenotype selected during persistent infection with vesicular stomatitis virus. *Virology* 1984; 136:211–220.

465. Jordan JA, Youngner JS: Dominance of temperature-sensitive phenotypes. II. Vesicular stomatitis virus mutants from a persistent infection interfere with shut-off of host protein synthesis by wild-type virus. *Virology* 1987; 158:407–413.

466. Pringle CR: Rhabdovirus genetics, in Wagner RR (ed): *The Rhabdoviruses*. New York, Plenum, 1987, pp 186–191.

467. Baxt B, Bablanian R: Mechanism of vesicular stomatitis virus-induced cytopathic effects. I. Early morphological changes induced by infectious and DI particles. *Virology* 1976; 72:370–382.

468. Wertz GW, Youngner JS: Inhibition of protein synthesis in L cells infected with vesicular stomatitis virus. *J Virol* 1972; 9:85–87.

469. Huang AS, Wagner RR: Inhibition of cellular RNA synthesis by nonreplicating vesicular stomatitis virus. *Proc Natl Acad Sci USA* 1965; 54:1579–1584.

470. McSharry JJ, Choppin PW: Biological properties of the VSV glycoprotein. I. Effects of the isolated glycoprotein on host macromolecular synthesis. *Virology* 1978; 84:172–182.

471. Marcus PI, Sekellick MJ: Cell killing by viruses. II. Cell killing by vesicular stomatitis virus: A requirement for virion derived transcription. *Virology* 1975; 63:176–190.

472. McGowan JJ, Wagner RR: Inhibition of cellular DNA synthesis by vesicular stomatitis virus. *J Virol* 1981; 38:356–367.

473. Marvaldi JL, Lucas-Lenard J, Sekellick MJ, et al: Cell killing by viruses. IV. Cell killing and protein synthesis inhibition by vesicular stomatitis virus require the same gene functions. *Virology* 1977; 79:267–280.

474. Lodish HF, Porter M: Translational control of protein synthesis after infection by vesicular stomatitis virus. *J Virol* 1980; 36:719–733.

475. Centrella M, Lucas-Lenard J: Regulation of protein synthesis in vesicular stomatitis virus–infected mouse L-929 cells by decreased protein synthesis initiation factor 2 activity. *J Virol* 1982; 41:781–791.

476. Nuss DL, Opperman H, Kock G: Selective blockage of initiation of host protein synthesis in RNA-virus infected cells. *Proc Natl Acad Sci USA* 1975; 72:1258–1262.

477. Stanners CP, Francoeur AM, Lam T: Analysis of VSV mutant with attenuated cytopathogenicity; mutation in viral function, P, for inhibition of protein synthesis. *Cell* 1977; 11:273–281.

478. Weck PK, Wagner RR: Transcription of vesicular stomatitis virus is required to shut off cellular RNA synthesis. *J Virol* 1979; 30:410–413.

479. Weck PK, Carroll AR, Shattuck DM, et al: Use of UV irradiation to identify the genetic information of vesicular stomatitis virus responsible for shutting off cellular RNA synthesis. *J Virol* 1979; 30:746–753.

480. Kurilla MG, Piwnica-Worms H, Keene JD: Rapid and transient localization of the leader RNA of vesicular stomatitis virus in the nuclei of infected cells. *Proc Natl Acad Sci USA* 1982; 79:5240–5244.

480a. Crone DE, Keene JD: Viral transcription is necessary and sufficient for vesicular stomatitis virus to inhibit maturation of small nuclear ribonucleoproteins. *J Virol* 1989; 63:4172–4180.

481. Grinnell BW, Wagner RR: Comparative inhibition of cellular transcription by vesicular stomatitis serotypes New Jersey and Indiana: Role of each viral leader RNA. *J Virol* 1983; 48:88–101.

482. Wagner RR, Thomas JR, McGowan JJ: Rhabdovirus cytopathology: Effect on cellular macromolecular synthesis, in Frankel-Conrat H, Wagner RR (eds): *Comprehensive Virology*. New York, Plenum, 1984, vol 19, pp 223–295.

483. Dunigan DD, Baird S, Lucas-Lenard J: Lack of correlation between the accumulation of plus-strand leader RNA and the inhibition of protein and RNA synthesis in vesicular stomatitis virus infected mouse L cells. *Virology* 1986; 150:231–246.

484. Wilusz J, Youngner JS, Keene JD: Base mutations in the terminal noncoding regions of the genome of vesicular stomatitis virus isolated from persistent infections of L cells. *Virology* 1985; 140:249–256.

485. Blumberg BM, Giorgi C, Kolakofsky D: N protein of vesicular stomatitis virus selectively encapsidates leader RNA in vitro. *Cell* 1983; 32:559–567.

486. Kurilla MG, Keene JD: The leader RNA of vesicular stomatitis virus is bound by a cellular protein reactive with anti-La lupus antibodies. *Cell* 1983; 34:837–845.

487. Grinnell BW, Wagner RR: Inhibition of DNA-dependent transcription by the leader RNA of vesicular stomatitis virus: Role of specific nucleotide sequences and cell protein binding. *Mol Cell Biol* 1985; 5:2502–2513.

488. McGowan JJ, Emerson SU, Wagner RR: The plus-strand leader RNA of VSV inhibits DNA dependent transcription of adenovirus and SV40 genes in a soluble whole cell extract. *Cell* 1982; 28:325–333.

489. Grinnell BW, Wagner RR: Nucleotide sequence and secondary structure of VSV leader RNA and homologous DNA involved in inhibition of DNA dependent transcription. *Cell* 1984; 36:533–543.

490. Remenick J, Kenny MK, McGowan JJ: Inhibition of adenovirus DNA replication by vesicular stomatitis virus leader RNA. *J Virol* 1988; 62:1286–1292.

491. Choppin PW, Scheid A: The role of viral glycoproteins in adsorption, penetration, and pathogenicity of viruses. *Rev Infect Dis* 1980; 2:40–61.

492. Morrison TG: Structure, function, and intracellular processing of paramyxovirus membrane proteins. *Virus Res* 1988; 10:113–136.

493. Levine S: Polypeptides of respiratory syncytial virus. *J Virol* 1977; 21:427–431.

494. Ueba O: Purification and polypeptides of respiratory syncytial virus. *Microbiol Immunol* 1980; 24:361–364.

495. Dubovi EJ: Analysis of proteins synthesized in respiratory syncytial virus–infected cells. *J Virol* 1982; 42:372–378.

496. Fernie BF, Gerin JL: Immunochemical identification of viral and nonviral proteins of the respiratory syncytial virus virion. *Infect Immun* 1982; 37:243–249.

497. Homma M, Ohuchi M: Trypsin action on the growth of Sendai virus in tissue culture cells. III. Structural difference of Sendai viruses grown in eggs and in tissue culture cells. *J Virol* 1973; 12:1457–1465.

498. Scheid A, Choppin PW: Protease activation mutants of Sendai virus: Activation of biological properties by specific proteases. *Virology* 1976; 69:265–277.

499. van Wyke Coelingh K, Tierney EL: Identification of amino acids recognized by syncytium-inhibiting and neutralizing monoclonal antibodies to the human parainfluenza type 3 virus fusion protein. *J Virol* 1989; 63:3755–3760.

500. Blumberg BM, Giorgi C, Rose K, et al: Sequence determination of the Sendai virus fusion protein gene. *J Gen Virol* 1985; 66:317–331.

500a. Paterson RG, Shaughnessy MA, Lamb RA: Analysis of the relationship between cleavability of a paramyxovirus fusion protein and length of the connecting peptides. *J Virol* 1989; 63:1293–1301.

501. Hsu M, Scheid A, Choppin PW: Activation of the Sendai virus fusion protein (F) involves a conformational change with exposure of a new hydrophobic region. *J Biol Chem* 1981; 256:3557–3563.

502. Kohama T, Garten W, Klenk HD: Changes in conformation and charge paralleling proteolytic activation of Newcastle disease virus glycoproteins. *Virology* 1981; 111:364–376.

503. Paterson RG, Harris TJR, Lamb RA: Fusion protein of the paramyxovirus simian virus 5: Nucleotide sequence of mRNA predicts a highly hydrophobic glycoprotein. *Proc Natl Acad Sci USA* 1984; 81:6706–6710.

504. Thompson SD, Portner A: localization of functional sites on the hemagglutinin-neuraminidase glycoprotein of Sendai virus by sequence analysis of antigenic and temperature-sensitive mutants. *Virology* 1987; 160:1–8.

505. Portner A, Scroggs RA, Metzger DW: Distinct functions of antigenic sites of the HN glycoprotein of Sendai virus. *Virology* 1987; 158:61–68.

506. Colman PM, Ward CW: Structure and diversity of the influenza virus neuraminidase. *Curr Top Microbiol Immunol* 1985; 114:177–255.

507. Jorgensen ED, Collins PL, Lomedico PT: Cloning and nucleotide sequence of Newcastle disease virus hemagglutinin-neuraminidase mRNA: Identification of a putative sialic acid binding site. *Virology* 1987; 156:12–24.

508. Blumberg B, Giorgi C, Roux L, et al: Sequence determination of the Sendai virus HN gene and its comparison to the influenza virus glycoproteins. *Cell* 1985; 41:269–278.

509. Hiebert SW, Paterson RG, Lamb RA: Hemagglutinin-neuraminidase protein of simian virus 5: Nucleotide sequence of the mRNA predicts an N-terminal membrane anchor. *J Virol* 1985; 54:1–6.

510. Liftig RB, Kilham SS, Hay AJ, et al: An ultra–structure study of virions and cores of reovirus type 3. *Virology* 1972; 48:170–181.

511. Palmer EL, Martin ML: The fine structure of the capsid of reovirus type 3. *Virology* 1977; 76:109–113.

512. Joklik WK: Structure and function of the reovirus genome. *Microbiol Rev* 1981; 45:483–501.

513. Loh PC, Shatkin AJ: Structural proteins of reovirus. *J Virol* 1968; 2:1353–1359.

514. Smith RE, Zweerink JH, Joklik WK: Polypeptide components of virions, top components and cores of reovirus type 3. *Virology* 1969; 39:791–810.

515. Bellamy AR, Shapiro L, August JT, et al: Studies on reovirus RNA. I. Characterization of reovirus genome RNA. *J Mol Biol* 1967; 29:1–18.

516. Iglewski WJ, Franklin RM: Purification and properties of reovirus ribonucleic acid. *J Virol* 1967; 1:302–307.

517. Shatkin AJ, Sipe JD, Loh PC: Separation of ten reovirus genome segments by polyacrylamide gel electrophoresis. *J Virol* 1968; 2:986–991.

518. Furvichi Y, Morgan M, Muthukrishnan S, et al: Reovirus messenger RNA contains a methylated, blocked 5'-terminal structure: m⁷G (5') ppp (5') GmpCp-. *Proc Natl Acad Sci USA* 1975; 72:363–366.

519. Shatkin AJ: Methylated messenger RNA synthesis in vitro by purified reovirus. *Proc Natl Acad Sci USA* 1974; 71:3204–3207.

520. Li JK-K, Keene JD, Scheible PP, et al: Nature of the 3'-terminal sequences of the plus and minus strands of the S_1 gene of reovirus serotypes 1, 2, and 3. *Virology* 1980; 150:41–51.

521. Watanabe Y, Graham AF: Structural units of reovirus ribonucleic acid and their possible functional significance. *J Virol* 1976; 1:665–677.

522. McCrae MA, Joklik WK: The nature of the polypeptide encoded by each of the double-stranded RNA segments of reovirus type 3. *Virology* 1978; 89:578–593.

523. Hayes EC, Lee PWK, Miller SE, et al: The interaction of a series of hybridoma IgGs with reovirus particles: Demonstration that the core protein λ_2 is exposed on the particle surface. *Virology* 1981; 108:147–155.

524. White CK, Zweerink HJ: Studies on the structure of reovirus cores: Selective removal of polypeptide 2. *Virology* 1976; 70:171–180.

525. Weiner HL, Ramig RF, Mustoe TA, et al: Identification of the gene coding for the hemagglutinin of reovirus. *Virology* 1978; 86:581–584.

526. Weiner HL, Fields BN: Neutralization of reovirus: The gene responsible for the neutralization antigen. *J Exp Med* 1977; 146:1305–1310.

527. Hayes EC, Lee PWK, Miller SE, et al: The interaction of a series of hybridoma IgGs with reovirus particles: Demonstration that the core protein λ_2 is exposed on the particle surface. *Virology* 1981; 108:147–155.

528. Cashdollar LW, Chmelo RA, Wiener JR, et al: Sequences of the S1 genes of the three serotypes of reovirus. *Proc Natl Acad Sci USA* 1985; 82:24–28.

529. Shatkin AJ, Sipe JD: RNA polymerase activity in purified reoviruses. *Proc Natl Acad Sci USA* 1968; 61:1462–1469.

530. Kapuler AM, Mendelsohn N, Klett H, et al: Four base-specific 5'-triphosphatases in the subviral core of reovirus. *Nature* 1970; 225:1209–1211.

531. Joklik WK: Studies on the effect of chymotrypsin on reovirions. *Virology* 1972; 49:700–715.

532. Spendlove RS, McClain ME, Lennette EH: Enhancement of reovirus infectivity by extracellular removal or alteration of the viral capsid by proteolytic enzymes. *J Gen Virol* 1970; 8:83–93.

533. Borsa J, Grover J, Chapman JD: Presence of nucleoside triphosphate phosphohydrolase activity in purified virions of reovirus. *J Virol* 1970; 6:295–300.

534. Morgan EM, Kingsbury DW: Reovirus enzymes that modify mRNA are inhibited by perturbation of lambda proteins. *Virology* 1981; 113:565–572.

535. Lee PWK, Hayes EC, Joklik WK: Protein σ 1 is the reovirus cell attachment protein. *Virology* 1981; 108:156–163.

536. Armstrong GD, Paul RW, Lee PWK: Studies on reovirus receptors of L cells: Virus binding characteristics and comparison with reovirus receptors of erythrocytes. *Virology* 1984; 138:37–48.

537. Gentsch JR, Pacitti AF: Effect of neuraminidase treatment of cells and effect of soluble glycoproteins on type 3 reovirus attachment to murine L cells. *J Virol* 1985; 56:356–364.

538. Donta ST, Shanley JD: Reovirus type 3 binds to antagonist domains of the β-adrenergic receptor. *J Virol* 1990; 639–641.

539. Co MS, Gaulton GN, Tominaga A, et al: Structural similarities between the mammalian β-adrenergic and reovirus type 3 receptors. *Proc Natl Acad Sci USA* 1985; 82:5315–5318.

540. Paul RW, Lee PWK: Glycophorin is the reovirus receptor on human erythrocytes. *Virology* 1987; 159:94–101.

541. Bassel-Duby R, Nibert ML, Homcy CJ, et al: Evidence that the sigma 1 protein of reovirus serotype 3 is a multimer. *J Virol* 1987; 61:1834–1841.

542. Bassel-Duby R, Jayasuriya A, Chatterjee D, et al: Sequence of reovirus haemagglutinin predicts a coiled-coil structure. *Nature* 1985; 315:421–423.

543. Nagata L, Masri SA, Mah DCW, et al: Molecular cloning and sequencing of the reovirus (serotype 3) S1 gene which encodes the viral cell attachment protein σ1. *Nucleic Acids Res* 1984; 12:8699–8710.

544. Furlong DB, Nibert ML, Fields BN: Sigma 1 protein of mammalian reoviruses extends from the surfaces of viral particles. *J Virol* 1988; 62:246–256.

545. Kaye KM, Spriggs DR, Bassel-Duby R, et al: Genetic basis for altered pathogenesis of an immune-selected antigenic variant of reovirus type 3 (Dearing). *J Virol* 1986; 59:90–97.

546. Bassel-Duby R, Spriggs DR, Tyler KL, et al: Identification of attenuating mutations on the reovirus type 3 S1 double-stranded RNA segment with a rapid sequencing technique. *J Virol* 1986; 60:64–67.

547. Nagata L, Masri SA, Pon RT, et al: Analysis of functional domains on reovirus cell attachment protein 1 using cloned S1 gene deletion mutations. *Virology* 1987; 160:162–168.

548. Silverstein SC, Dales S: The penetration of reovirus RNA and initiation of its genetic function in L-strain fibroblasts. *J Cell Biol* 1968; 35:197–230.

549. Sturzenbecker LJ, Nibert M, Furlong D, et al: Intracellular digestion of reovirus particles requires a low pH and is an essential step in the viral infectious cycle. *J Virol* 1987; 61:2351–2361.

550. Chang C, Zweerink JH: Fate of parental reovirus in infected cells. *Virology* 1971; 46:544–555.

551. Silverstein SC, Astell C, Levin DH, et al: Mechanism of reovirus uncoating and gene activation in vivo. *Virology* 1972; 47:797–806.

552. Borsa J, Sargent MD, Lievaart PA, et al: Reovirus: Evidence for a second step in the intracellular uncoating and transcriptase activation process. *Virology* 1981; 111:191–200.

553. Drayna D, Fields BN: Activation and characterization of the reovirus transcriptase: Genetic analysis. *J Virol* 1982; 41:110–118.

554. Jayasuriya AK, Nibert ML, Fields BN: Complete nucleotide sequence of the M2 gene segment of reovirus type 3 Dearing and analysis of its protein product μ_1. *Virology* 1988; 163:591–602.

555. Huismans H, Joklik WK: Reovirus-coded polypeptides in infected cells: Isolation of two native monomeric polypeptides with affinity for single-stranded and double-stranded RNA, respectively. *Virology* 1976; 70:411–424.

556. Schiff LA, Nibert ML, Co MS, et al: Distinct binding sites for zinc and double-stranded RNA in the reovirus outer capsid protein 3. *Mol Cell Biol* 1988; 8:273–283.

557. Gomatos PJ, Prakash O, Stamatos NM: Small reovirus particles composed solely of sigma NS, with specificity for binding different nucleic acids. *J Virol* 1981; 39:115–124.

558. Stamatos NM, Gomatos PJ: Binding to selected regions of reovirus mRNAs by a nonstructural reovirus protein. *Proc Natl Acad Sci USA* 1982; 79:3457–3461.

559. Watanabe Y, Millward S, Graham AF: Regulation of transcriptase of reovirus genome. *J Mol Biol* 1968; 36:107–123.

560. Skehel JJ, Joklik WK: Studies on the in vitro transcription of reovirus RNA catalyzed by reovirus cores. *Virology* 1969; 39:822–831.

561. Skup D, Millward S: mRNA capping enzymes are masked in reovirus progeny subviral particles. *J Virol* 1980; 34:490–496.

562. Zarbl H, Skup D, Millward S: Reovirus progeny subviral particles synthesized uncapped mRNA. *J Virol* 1980; 34:497–505.

563. Skup D, Zarbl H, Millward S: Regulation of translation in L-cells infected with reovirus. *J Mol Biol* 1981; 151:35–55.

564. Sonenberg N, Skup D, Trachsel H, et al: In vitro translation in reovirus and poliovirus-infected cell extracts: Effects of anti-cap binding protein monoclonal antibody. *J Biol Chem* 1981; 256:4138–4141.

565. Joklik WK: Recent progress in reovirus research. *Annu Rev Genet* 1985; 19:537–575.

566. Lemieux R, Lemay G, Millward S: The viral protein sigma 3 participates in translation of late viral mRNA in reovirus-infected L cells. *J Virol* 1987; 61:2472–2479.

567. Levin KH, Samuel CE: Biosynthesis of reovirus-specified polypeptides. Purification and characterization of the small-sized class mRNAs of reovirus type 3: Coding assignment and translational efficiencies. *Virology* 1980; 106:1–13.

568. Gaillard RK, Joklik WK: The relative translational efficiencies of reovirus messenger RNAs. *Virology* 1985; 147:336–348.

569. Atwater JA, Munemitsu SM, Samuel CE: Biosynthesis of reovirus-specified polypeptides. Efficiency of expression of cDNAs of the reovirus S1 and S4 genes in transfected animal cells differs at the level of translation. *Virology* 1987; 159:350–357.

570. Munemitsu SM, Atwater JA, Sanuel CE: Biosynthesis of reovirus-specified polypeptides. Molecular cDNA cloning and nucleotide sequence of the reovirus serotype 1 Lang strain bicistronic S1 mRNA which encodes the minor capsid polypeptide sigma 1a and the nonstructural polypeptide sigma 1bNS. *Biochem Biophys Res Commun* 1986; 140:508–514.

571. Munemitsu SM, Samuel CE: Biosynthesis of reovirus-specified polypeptides: Effect of point mutation of the sequences flanking the 5' proximal AUG initiator codons of the reovirus S1 and S4 genes on the efficiency of mRNA translation. *Virology* 1988; 163:643–646.

572. Acs G, Klett H, Schonberg M, et al: Mechanism of reovirus double–stranded ribonucleic acid synthesis in vivo and in vitro. *J Virol* 1971; 8:684–689.

573. Mora M, Partin K, Bhatia M, et al: Association of reovirus proteins with the structural matrix of infected cells. *Virology* 1987; 159:265–277.

574. Sakuma S, Watanabe Y: Incorporation of in vitro synthesized reovirus double-stranded ribonucleic acid into virus core-like particles. *J Virol* 1972; 10:943–950.

575. Sakuma S, Watanabe Y: Reovirus replicase-directed synthesis of double-stranded ribonucleic acid. *J Virol* 1972; 10:628–638.

576. Zweerink HJ, Ito Y, Matsuhisa T: Synthesis of reovirus double-stranded RNA within virion-like particles. *Virology* 1972; 50:349–358.

577. Morgan EM, Zweerink HJ: Characterization of transcriptase and replicase particles isolated from reovirus-infected cells. *Virology* 1975; 68:455–466.

578. Zweerink JH, Morgan EM, Skyler JS: Reovirus morphogenesis: Characterization of subviral particles in infected cells. *Virology* 1976; 73:442–453.

579. Astell C, Silverstein SC, Levin DH: Regulation of the reovirus RNA transcriptase by a viral capsomere protein. *Virology* 1972; 48:648–654.

580. Sharpe AH, Ramig RF, Mustoe TA, et al: A genetic map of reovirus. I. Correlation of genome RNAs between serotypes 1, 2, and 3. *Virology* 1978; 84:63–74.

581. Wenske EA, Chanock SJ, Krata L, et al: Genetic reassortment of mammalian reoviruses in mice. *J Virol* 1985; 56:613–616.

582. Ahmed R, Fields BN: Reassortment of genome segments between reovirus defective interfering particles and infectious virus: Construction of temperature-sensitive and attenuated viruses by rescue of mutations from DI particles. *Virology* 1981; 111:351–363.

583. Ahmed R, Chakraborty PR, Fields BN: Genetic variations during lytic virus infection: High–passage stocks of wild-type reovirus contain temperature-sensitive mutants. *J Virol* 1980; 34:285–287.

584. Babiss LE, Luftig RB, Weatherbee JA, et al: Reovirus serotypes 1 and 3 differ in their in vitro association with microtubules. *J Virol* 1979; 30:863–874.

585. Sharpe AH, Chen LB, Fields BN: The interaction of mammalian reoviruses with the cytoskeleton of monkey kidney CV-1 cells. *Virology* 1982; 120:399–411.

586. Gomatos PJ, Tamm I, Dales S, et al: Reovirus type 3: Physical characteristics and interactions with L cells. *Virology* 1962; 17:441–454.

587. Spendlove RS, Lennette EH, Knight CO, et al: Development of viral antigen and infectious virus on HeLa cells infected with reovirus. *J Immunol* 1963; 90:548–553.

588. Fields BN, Raine CS, Baum SG: Temperature-sensitive mutants of reovirus type 3: Defects in viral maturation as studied by immunofluorescence and electron microscopy. *Virology* 1971; 43:569–578.

589. Sharpe AH, Fields BN: Reovirus inhibition of cellular DNA synthesis: Role of the S1 gene. *J Virol* 1981; 38:389–392.

590. Lemieux R, Zarbl H, Millward S: mRNA discrimination in extracts from uninfected and reovirus-infected L cells. *J Virol* 1984; 51:215–222.

591. Sharpe AH, Fields BN: Reovirus inhibition of cellular RNA and protein synthesis: Role of the S4 gene. *Virology* 1982; 122:381–391.

592. Canning WM, Fields BN: Ammonium chloride prevents lytic growth of reovirus and helps to establish persistent infection in mouse L cells. *Science* 1983; 219:987–988.

593. Ahmed R, Fields BN: Role of the S4 gene in establishment of persistent reovirus infections in L cells. *Cell* 1982; 28:605–612.

594. Kauffman RS, Ahmed R, Fields BN: Selection of a mutant S1 gene during reovirus persistent infection of L cells: Role in maintenance of the persistent state. *Virology* 1983; 131:79–87.

595. Brown EG, Nibert ML, Fields BN: The L2 gene of reovirus serotype 3 controls the capacity to interfere, accumulate deletions and establish persistent infection, in Compans RW, Bishop DHL (eds): *International Symposium on Double–Stranded RNA Viruses*. New York, Elsevier, 1983, pp 275–288.

Immunology of Viral Infections

Alec E. Wittek
Gerald V. Quinnan, Jr.

Principles of immunology underlie much of clinical diagnosis and management of patients with viral infections. Laboratory diagnosis of viral infection is often based on demonstration of specific immune responses that occur during or following acute infection. Patient management is often limited to modifying treatments that inhibit immune responsiveness. In recent years advances in viral immunology have occurred at a rapid rate. New methods for antibody determinations have been developed that offer advantages of increased sensitivity and rapidity of diagnosis. Hybridoma technology is fast producing a large group of diagnostic (and possibly therapeutic) reagents. Developments in cellular immunology are

approaching the point where the clinician will soon be able to design treatment regimens with the intent of modifying one specific response or another. At least some of the immune functions that determine the outcome of infection have been defined and a comprehensive understanding is soon to come. Although the distinction between humoral and cellular immunity is somewhat artificial, since these functions are interdependent, it is still a useful concept. The following is intended as an overview of basic principles of humoral and cellular immunity and emerging concepts most relevant to understanding of viral diseases.

HUMORAL IMMUNITY

Within the context of humoral immunity are generally included the functions of B lymphocytes and their immunoglobulin products. The biologic functions of immunoglobulins are reflected in some of the assays used to test for their presence. The sensitivity and specificity of a serologic assay is dependent on the nature of the assay itself, the properties of the individual virus, and the methods used for standardization.

Standardization of Virus Antigen-Antibody Interactions

The principle that a finite number of immunoglobulin molecules will bind to a specific number of virus particles or virus antigenic determinants underlies the design and interpretation of all serologic assays. This concept is commonly reflected in the practice of expressing antibody concentration as a titration end point. The extent to which antigen-antibody binding can be detected in any given assay depends on having present the appropriate relative amounts of each. The optimum total amount of antigen is not necessarily a maximum amount but is related to the method used to detect the reaction. Serologic assays generally can be divided into two categories, depending on how the optimum amount of antigen used in the assay is determined:

Density of Sedimented Erythrocytes

		Serum Dilution								Control Complement Titration			
		Positive						Negative					
		1:8	1:16	1:32	1:64	1:128	1:256	1:8		2.0 Units	1.5 Units	1.0 Units	0.5 Units
Antigen Dilution		1	2	3	4	5	6	7	8	9	10	11	12
1:2	A	4	4	4	2	0	0	0		0	0	±	4
1:4	B	4	4	4	4	2	0	0		0	0	±	4
1:8	C	4	4	4	3	1	0	0		0	0	0	4
1:16	D	4	4	1	0	0	0	0		0	0	±	4
1:32	E	1	0	0	0	0	0	0		0	0	0	4
1:64	F	0	0	0	0	0	0	0		0	0	0	4
0 (Serum Control)	G												
	H	0	0	0	0	0	0	0					

Figure 4–1. Complement fixation test: design and interpretation exemplified by checkerboard titration of antigen and antiserum. To perform the antigen titration, diluent (0.025 mL) is placed in each of the indicated wells of a microplate. Equal volumes of a 1:4 dilution of a known positive and a known negative serum are added to rows A to F of columns 1 and 7, respectively. Diluters are used to make serial twofold dilutions, from columns 1 to 6. Antigen at the indicated dilution is added to wells of each row. The plate is refrigerated (4–8°C) overnight. Complement is added to each well, 0.025 mL of 1.5 units, or the units indicated in columns 9 to 12 (complement potency is determined previously). After 30 minutes at 37°C, hemolysin (2 units anti-sheep red cell antibody) sensitized erythrocytes are added, and the plate is returned to 37°C until hemolysis is complete in the 1.5-unit complement control and red cells have sedimented to form a small, round pellet in the 0.5-unit wells. If complement is fixed by antigen-antibody complexes, hemolysis of the sensitized erythrocytes is inhibited. To interpret the test, hemolysis inhibition is graded as none (0), the least amount detectable (±), more than ± but less than 50% (1), 50% to <75% (2), ≥75% but less than complete (3), and complete (4). Complement fixation (inhibition) graded 3 or 4 is considered a strong reaction. One "unit" of antigen is the highest dilution that produces a strong reaction with the highest serum dilution producing a strong reaction. In the test result shown, a 1:8 antigen dilution is 1 unit. For routine testing 2 units (in this case a 1:4 dilution) of antigen are used to assure that more than the minimum necessary amount is present. The antigen titration also confirmed that 4 units of antigen did not inhibit complement fixation as was the case with 2 units. Hemolysis is standardized by prior titration of serial dilutions of hemolysin to sensitize erythrocytes to lysis by 1.0 units of complement. Complement is titrated in a similar manner. The actual concentration of complement used in the test is usually just slightly more than the minimum amount necessary to produce complete hemolysis in the absence of specific antibody (1.5 units). Using this concentration assures that hemolysis will be complete unless there is at least a low concentration of complement-fixing antibodies in the test serum.

1. Those assays that measure the amount of antibody bound to antigen, in which cases the presence of excess antigen will assure maximum binding. An example of the methods used to define appropriate concentrations of antigen for this type of assay is shown in Figure 4–1. Many serologic tests fall into this category, including complement fixation (CF) and indirect immunoassays.

2. Those assays that measure the capacity of antibodies to inhibit biologic activities of viruses. In these assays the smallest amount of virus that has easily detectable activity should be used to maximize the extent to which small amounts of antibody can produce detectable inhibition. Competitive inhibition assays are of this type,[1] as well as conventional assays such as neutralization and hemagglutination inhibition (HI).

Design and Interpretation of Specific Assays
Virus Infectivity Neutralization

The mechanism by which specific antibodies render virus particles noninfectious most likely involves binding of immunoglobulin molecules to or near virion surface structures involved in attachment of the virus to host cell membranes. Due to the symmetry of virus particles, it is likely that each particle contains more than one attachment site and that multiple, although a limited number of immunoglobulin molecules are required for neutralization.[2] Neutralizing-antibody determinations generally are found to be moderately, but not highly, sensitive assays.

A variety of methods are used to measure neutralizing antibodies, the most common of which is the plaque reduction technique.[3, 4] This method takes advantage of the capacity of viruses to spread from cell to neighboring cell in tissue culture–producing plaques, consisting of focal cytopathic effect (CPE), when spread to distant cells through extracellular fluid is inhibited by the presence of a semisolid overlay. A 50% reduction in the number of plaques that develop generally is considered significant neutralization. Each plaque represents a single focus of infection. However, virus infection of cells in culture is not completely efficient, and the number of infectious virus particles in the inoculum may be some multiple of the number of plaques that develop. Moreover, virus suspensions often contain a number of noninfectious particles. The smaller the number of viruses, the fewer the number of immunoglobulin molecules required for neutralization. The sensitivity of neutralization assays is dependent on the total number of virus particles inoculated.

Neutralization tests can also be performed under a liquid overlay by testing the capacity of serum-treated virus suspensions to produce diffuse CPE in cell cultures. Virus neutralization by antibodies usually is a reversible process. Therefore, a virus inoculum is used that produces extensive destruction of the cell monolayer within a limited period of time, usually a few days. A larger number of infectious virus particles usually are used in tissue culture infectivity neutralization than in plaque reduction neutralization assays, with the result that the latter technique is frequently more sensitive.

Modifications of both plaque reduction and infectivity neutralization assays are used in specific circumstances in which examination for cytopathic effect is not useful. For example, a test commonly used to detect antibodies that neutralize influenza viruses measures the inhibition of hemadsorption in cell culture monolayers infected with serum-treated virus.[5] To measure neutralization of rabies virus, the rapid fluorescent focus inhibition test (RFFIT) utilizes immunofluorescence to detect virus replication in the indicator monolayer.[6] The metabolic inhibition test, sometimes used for measuring antibodies to measles, polio, and rubella viruses, is based on inhibition of metabolism of cells infected by these viruses.[7] Acidic metabolites of uninfected cells induce a change in color of pH indicator included in the medium.

A number of novel strategies have been devised for the measurement of neutralizing antibodies to human immunodeficiency viruses (HIV). Syncytium inhibition assays take advantage of the fact that HIV causes syncytium formation in cultures of susceptible CD-4–bearing T lymphocytes or T cell lines. Preincubation of HIV with neutralizing sera results in a reduction of giant cell formation which can be measured by light microscopic examination. The assay can be performed in microplate wells, and allows rapid evaluation of large numbers of sera.[8, 9] Other HIV neutralization assays are based on measurement of the inhibition of production of viral proteins, such as reverse transcriptase activity or HIV core antigen in cell cultures.[10–12] Cell survival or proliferation as measured by uptake of ^{3}H-thymidine has also been used to evaluate neutralization of HIV.[13, 14] A plaque reduction assay for neutralizing antibodies to HIV has been described. This assay involves the adhesion of a continuous T cell line to poly-L-lysine-treated plasticware.[15] The vesicular stomatitis virus (VSV) pseudotype assay is a rapid and convenient test. VSV pseudotypes are prepared by superinfecting, with VSV, cell lines chronically infected with HIV. As the virus buds off the cell, HIV envelope antigen–bearing cytoplasmic membranes are incorporated into the virus envelope. Wild-type VSV is inactivated by the addition of high-titer neutralizing antisera to VSV-specific envelope determinants, so that only virions retaining the HIV envelope antigens remain viable. These pseudotypes are then used in syncytium inhibition assays.[16] Collaborative studies involving laboratories performing assays for HIV-neutralizing antibodies have shown generally equivalent sensitivities for these diverse assay methodologies.

The sensitivity of plaque neutralization assays can be enhanced in some cases by the addition of complement or antispecies immunoglobulin to the virus-serum mixture prior to adsorption of the mixture to the target cell monolayer. The mechanism by which the addition of either of these substances might enhance neutralization is unknown; possible mechanisms include stabilization of the virus-antibody complex and steric inhibition of the attachment site. The immunoglobulin-enhanced neutralization assay has markedly enhanced sensitivity for determinations of antibodies to some, but not all, viruses tested.[17–19] It has proved useful for measuring antibodies in cerebral spinal fluid[18] and maternal antibody persistence in young children.[19] The phenomenon of complement enhancement of neutralization is of interest for its potential significance in vivo in herpesvirus infections.[20–22]

The biologic relevance of virus neutralization with regard to protective immunity is probably more important for some viruses than others. For example, individuals with serum neutralizing antibodies are protected against paralytic poliomyelitis,[23] rabies,[24] measles,[25] and influenza;[26] in the case of influenza, a certain minimal level of serum antibodies is needed.[26] With regard to some other viruses, neutralizing antibodies appear to be less important, for example, as with rubella, in which administration of immune globulin appears to be of no value,[27] and herpesviruses, in which virus reactivation and dissemination can occur despite the presence of neutralizing antibodies.[28, 29]

Assays Involving Complement Binding and Activation

Complement Fixation (CF) Test.—The CF test is a long-time favorite of virologists due to ease and rapidity of performance and low cost. However, newer and more sensitive serologic tests such as radioimmunoassays (RIA), and to a greater extent, enzyme-linked immunosorbent assays (ELISA), have largely supplanted CF tests in the diagnostic virology laboratory. The performance of the assay is described in Figure 4–1. Not all virus antigens bind antibodies that fix complement. For example, anticytomegalovirus (CMV) antibodies that bind nuclear antigens in infected cells fix complement more efficiently than antibodies to cytoplasmic antigens.[30] The CF test is moderately sensitive and specific, although the level of specificity is somewhat broad. The test distinguishes antibodies against types A and B influenza viruses from each other, but not those against different subtypes of influenza A.[31] The sensitivity and specificity of the CF test are greatly influenced by the methods used to prepare the test antigen. For example, an antigen prepared simply as a partially clarified suspension of disrupted, infected cells is useful for some viruses,[32] whereas an antigen that has been solubilized by extraction with a solution of buffered glycine is sometimes far superior.[33] Certain types of immunoglobulin react more strongly in CF assays than others. By virtue of its pentavalent structure, IgM fixes complement more efficiently than IgG. Moreover, some subclasses of IgG have higher affinity for complement than do others. These differences in relative affinity have little impact on the use of the CF test in clinical practice but are relevant to the design and interpretation of some other tests that depend on complement activation.

Immune Adherence Hemagglutination (IAHA).—Immune adherence is a property attributed to the antigen-antibody-C3b complex, and refers to the propensity of this complex to adhere to the membranes of cells with which it comes in contact. Conveniently, erythrocytes are one cell type to which these complexes adhere well. Immunoglobulin in serum being tested is allowed to adhere to virus antigens in infected cell monolayers; then complement is added and allowed to adhere. Adherence of added erythrocytes indicates the presence of complexes. The IAHA assay is useful for measuring antibodies to CMV[34, 35] and varicella-zoster virus,[36] and theoretically could be used to measure antibodies to many viruses. It appears to be more sensitive than the CF test. Because the test involves use of tissue culture, it is not widely used for clinical serology.

Antibody-Dependent Complement-Mediated Cytotoxicity.—Virus antigens usually are present on the surface of infected cells. Antibodies bound to these antigens can fix and activate complement with resultant cell lysis. This technique can be used to demonstrate the presence of antigens on infected cells if a known positive serum is used. Conversely, complement-mediated lysis can be used to measure antibodies in unknown sera. This type of assay has been used to measure antibodies to influenza viruses.[37] The technique used was a chromium-release assay, similar to the cell-mediated cytotoxicity assays described in detail below. Antibody-dependent complement-mediated cytotoxicity may be an important immune defense mechanism in vivo. Destruction of infected cells before infectious virions have been formed can prevent viruses from multiplying and supplement the extracellular activity of neutralizing antibodies.

Hemolytic Plaque Assay.—The hemolytic plaque assay is similar to the complement-mediated lysis assay in that antibody detection requires the formation of the hemolytic complex and lysis of erythrocytes with virus antigens on their surface. It differs in the following respects: (1) The target cells used are erythrocytes with virus antigens attached to their surface. If the antigen of concern is hemagglutinin, its affinity for erythrocytes allows it to coat untreated red blood cells. For other antigens, pretreatment of erythrocytes may be necessary. (2) The assay is performed by suspending antigen-coated erythrocytes and lymphocytes to be tested in semisolid medium. Complement is later added on top of the suspension and allowed to diffuse through to the erythrocytes. Where antibody-producing B cells are present in the suspension, there is radial diffusion of immunoglobulin to nearby erythrocytes. Hemolysis thus occurs only where erythrocytes have been sensitized in a zone surrounding individual antibody-producing B cells, giving a plaquelike appearance. By quantitating the number of plaques produced in relation to the total number of lymphocytes added, the frequency of B cells producing the specific immunoglobulin of interest can be quantitated. (3) Unless anti-IgG immunoglobulin is overlaid on the medium prior to the addition of complement, hemolysis usually occurs only in the vicinity of IgM-producing B cells. When an anti-IgG overlay is used, the assay is called an "indirect," and in the absence of the overlay, a "direct" hemolytic plaque assay.[38]

The hemolytic plaque assay has been a useful tool for studying the immunoregulatory factors that modulate specific antibody-producing B cells.[39] It also has been used successfully to demonstrate the production of antibodies by B cells present locally in infected tissues well in advance of the time after onset of infection when specific antibodies can be detected in serum.[38]

Single Radial Hemolysis.—The single radial hemolysis (SRH) test is very similar to the hemolytic plaque assay. Antigen-coated erythrocytes are suspended in semisolid medium, such as agarose. Wells are then cut in the agarose in which test sera are placed and allowed to diffuse radially. Addition of a complement-containing overlay results in hemolysis around wells containing antibodies. The test is convenient for measuring antibodies to influenza viruses and is preferred by some to the hemagglutinin inhibition test.[40]

Inhibition of Biologically Active Virus Proteins
Hemagglutination Inhibition (HI) Assay.—Numerous viruses possess glycoprotein surface antigens which agglutinate red blood cells, including the ortho- and paramyxoviruses,[41, 42] rubella,[43] rubeola,[44] and others. Antibodies to each of these viruses typically block the hemagglutinating capacity of these proteins. Hemagglutination inhibition (HI) tests for antibodies to these viruses

are commonly used because of their ease of performance. The tests generally are highly specific even to the point of differentiating closely related strains of influenza viruses.[41] The sensitivity of these assays is usually moderate, approximately as good as that of CF tests.

Neuraminidase Inhibition Test.—The neuraminidase enzymatic activity of the orthomyxoviruses is also a property of a surface glycoprotein. Similar to hemagglutinin, its activity is inhibited by antibodies.[45] The assay is used relatively infrequently, but may be used to detect antibodies to influenza. As discussed in the chapter on influenza viruses, inhibition of both neuraminidase and hemagglutinating activity of viral glycoproteins by antibodies contributes to protection against disease.

Indirect Antibody Assays

Three general types of indirect immunoglobulin assays are in common use, including the indirect immunofluorescence assay (IFA), enzyme immunoassays, and the RIA (Figure 4–2). A fourth technique, immunoelectrophoretic immunoblotting, more commonly referred to as western blotting, while principally a research tool, has gained importance as a test for the presence of antibodies to HIV. It is considered more specific in this case than ELISA, because antibodies to specific proteins can be recognized.[46] These assays are termed indirect because the binding of specific antibodies to virus antigens is detected by the addition of a second antibody from a different species immunized against immunoglobulins of the species from which the test sera are obtained. The anti-immunoglobulin is conjugated to a chemical that fluoresces in ultraviolet light (eg, fluorescein isothiocyanate), an enzyme, or a radionuclide (usually ^{125}I). The effect is a two-step amplification of the original antigen-antibody reaction. In the first place multiple anti-immunoglobulin molecules can bind to a single antiviral antibody. Secondly, the methods used to detect the conjugated chemicals involve additional physical or chemical amplifications. In general, all three types of assays are widely applicable, highly sensitive, and specific.

Immunofluorescence.—In IFA the chemicals conjugated to the IgG are either fluorescein isothiocyanate (FITC) or rhodamine. Each of these will fluoresce when irradiated with UV light, emitting light in a specific limited range of wavelengths. Light of other wavelengths can be filtered so that only specific emissions are visualized microscopically. Antigen used in IFA typically consists of virus-infected cells. The assay can be performed using cells grown and infected in monolayers or in suspension. The cells may be fixed with a solvent such as alcohol, acetone, or methanol, or a detergent, in order to make them permeable to immunoglobulin and permit detection of cytoplasmic or nuclear antigens. Alternatively, unfixed viable cells may be used to permit selective detection of cell surface (membrane) antigens. Mild fixation with glutaraldehyde has been used in the latter case to inactivate varicella virus without destroying cell membrane integrity.[47] Whatever fixative is used, the extent of fixation is critical, since excessive denaturation of proteins by the fixation may destroy antigen integrity.

IFA is exceptional in its flexibility. It may be used to detect either specific IgG, IgM, or both, depending on the antihuman

A. Antigen Binding to Solid Phase

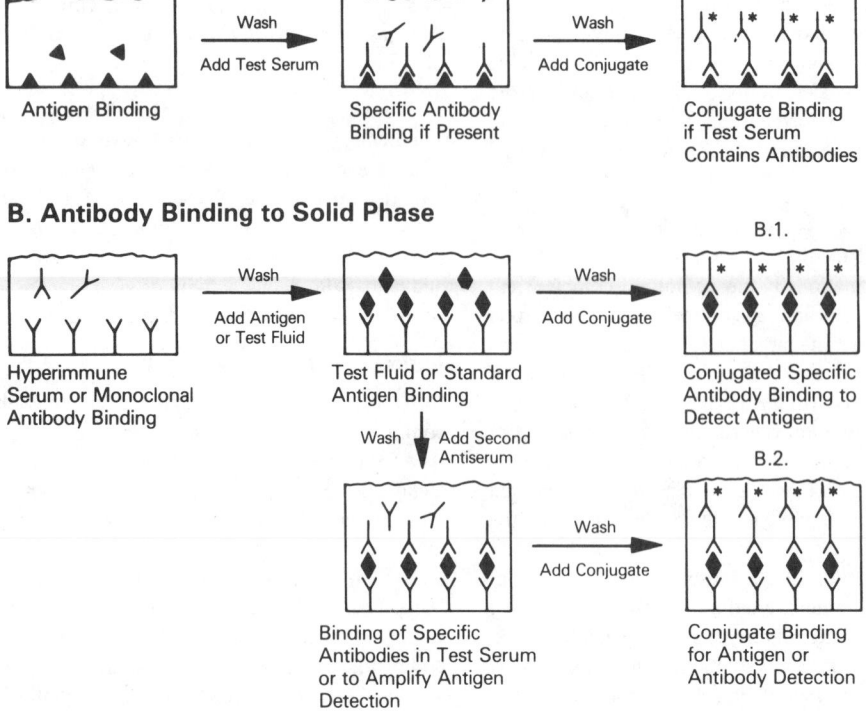

B. Antibody Binding to Solid Phase

C. Homogenous Enzyme Immunoassay

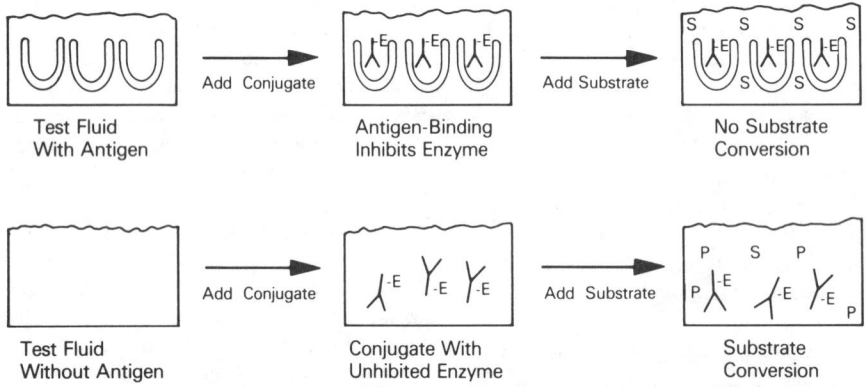

Figure 4–2. Immunoassays using conjugated antibodies. **A.** Common procedure for enzyme-linked immunosorbent assay (ELISA), immunofluorescence (IFA), and radioimmunoassay (RIA) is the standard indirect antibody assay. The antigen is either infected cells grown in monolayers or viral antigen from disrupted infected cells. Excess conjugate is removed by washing. Fluorescence is determined by microscopy or fluorimetry. For the ELISA, enzyme substrate is added and color development is read visually or with a microplate spectrophotometer. For the RIA each well of the microplate is counted separately on a gamma counter. **B.** For antigen detection or quantitation, the specificity and avidity of antigen binding is enhanced by first binding specific antibodies to the solid phase. After antigen is added, an enzyme- or radionuclide-conjugated antiserum specific for the antigen may be added (B.1.). Alternatively, a second antibody from a different species than the first (B.2.) may be added followed by addition of a conjugate directed against the second antibody. **C.** Large antigens can produce steric inhibition of enzyme activity after binding to the conjugate. Conversion of the substrate (S) to the colored product (P) is inhibited if antigen is present. Since binding to a solid phase and washing are not necessary, application to bedside diagnosis is possible.

globulin–FITC conjugate used. Moreover, the infected cells used may be specifically prepared to permit detection of antibodies to certain antigens and not to others. For example, herpesvirus early antigens, antigens synthesized prior to the synthesis of viral DNA, can be detected using cells infected in the presence of inhibitors of viral DNA synthesis.[48]

An approach called the anticomplement immunofluorescence (ACIF) test has been used to detect antibody to Epstein-Barr virus nuclear antigen (EBNA) and CMV nuclear antigen.[49, 50] Antibodies bound to nuclear, but not to cytoplasmic, antigens in cells infected with these viruses fix complement. The ACIF test is performed in three steps: (1) antigen-antibody binding; (2) complement fixation; and (3) binding of an FITC-conjugated anticomplement immunoglobulin.

The assay for Epstein-Barr virus membrane antigen (MA) antibodies is another unique variation of IFA. This antigen can be detected in a standard indirect IFA using viable target cells. However, the procedure generally used to measure these antibodies is a direct IFA.[1] Serum from a child with African Burkitt's lymphoma with a very high anti-MA titer is conjugated to FITC and reacted with the indicator cells directly. Unknown sera to be tested for anti-MA antibodies are assayed by their ability to compete with the binding of the FITC-conjugated antibodies. It is, thus, a direct immunofluorescence competitive inhibition assay. This approach helps assure uniform specificity of the assay.

The fluorescent antibody-to-membrane antigen (FAMA) test is a sensitive means for the detection of antibodies to varicella-zoster virus (VZV).[51] In this variant of the indirect IFA, VZV-infected cells are gently fixed in glutaraldehyde so that noninfectious, intact, antigen-expressing cells are obtained. The cells are incubated in sequence with antibody, then with FITC-conjugated anti-immunoglobulin. The performance of the test in microtiter plates permits rapid screening of large numbers of sera, and the production of large and standardized lots of targets at one time contributes to assay consistency. FAMA is used extensively in the evaluation of susceptibility to VZV infection and for detection of seroconversions in wide-scale clinical trials of an attenuated VZV vaccine.[52]

Additional examples of the flexibility of immunofluorescence testing are seen in tests that detect antibodies to antigens that have unique distributions within cells. Among such antigens are the T antigens of SV40[53] and adenovirus,[54] and the diffuse and restricted components of Epstein-Barr virus early antigen.[55]

In general, IFA is highly sensitive and specific. The sensitivity of the test is attributable, in part, to the "amplification" inherent in the assay. Even if only one of several hundred cells in a slide displays a specific pattern of fluorescence, the reaction can be interpreted as truly positive. It is often possible for the experienced observer to interpret patterns as being specific that could not be distinguished from nonspecific background reactions in most other assays. Numerous other factors obviously relate to the sensitivity of the test, including the amount of antigen present in the infected indicator cells, the amount of FITC conjugated per Ig molecule, the intensity of UV light, the nature of the filter system, and the resolution of the optics of the fluorescence microscopy system used. The specificity of the assay depends on the appropriateness of negative controls used to assure that only virus antigens are

detected. Factors relating to the occurrence of false-positives include lack of experience of the observer and cross-reactivity of the conjugated antiglobulin (this problem can often be eliminated by adsorption of the conjugated antiglobulin to uninfected cells, guinea pig liver powder, or activated charcoal). Another factor which is relevant to members of the herpesvirus group is the production of receptors for the Fc portion of IgG in infected cells that bind FITC-conjugated immunoglobulin nonspecifically.[56, 57]

The principal limitations of IFA, other than the special considerations relating to sensitivity and specificity mentioned above, are the need for reading by an experienced observer, the amount of time spent in reading a test, and the subjective nature of the results.

Enzyme-Linked Immunoassay.—In enzyme immunoassays the antigen-antibody reaction is amplified by the capacity of the immunoglobulin-enzyme conjugate to react with multiple molecules of enzyme substrate. Typically, the substrate is converted to a colored product that can be measured spectrophotometrically. The methodology most commonly used for enzyme immunoassays involves attachment of the reactants to a solid phase, or immunosorbent; hence, the name *enzyme-linked immunosorbent assay* (ELISA). The immunosorbent may be the surface of a plastic tube or well of a tissue culture tray, filter paper, nitrocellulose membrane, or other appropriate material. The use of a solid phase makes it possible to remove unbound reactants by washing at each step, so that the extent of substrate conversion at the end is proportional to the amount of specific antibody bound from the test serum. The first step in the assay may be to bind either antigen or a high-titered antiserum to the solid phase. If antigen is bound directly, it must retain its antigenic configuration.[58] The use of an antiserum as the first reactant may increase efficiency of binding of the antigen and is the most common approach used when testing for antigen, rather than antibodies, in clinical specimens. Monoclonal antibodies can be used instead of polyvalent antisera to increase specificity of the assay. Subsequent to attachment of antigen to the solid phase, the test serum is added; unbound serum components are removed by washing, the conjugate is added and washed, and substrate is added and allowed to react. An additional amplification step may be inserted using a nonconjugated antibody to the test serum and then a conjugate specific for the second immunoglobulin.

Numerous enzymes can be conjugated to immunoglobulins without affecting the antigen specificity of the antibody or the activity of the enzyme. The enzymes most commonly used are alkaline phosphatase and horseradish peroxidase. Biotin-avidin ELISAs are gaining favor because they provide a marked amplification of a positive signal. Large numbers of biotin molecules can easily be linked to immunoglobulin without significantly altering antibody activity. Enzyme-labeled avidin, with high-affinity biotin receptors, binds to the heavily biotinylated immunoglobulin in large quantity, achieving a ratio of enzyme molecules to immunoglobulin not achieved by other assay configurations.[59] Peroxidase conjugates are also used for indirect antibody staining of infected cells in culture or tissue biopsies.[60] Other enzymes are used for selected purposes. The "homogeneous" enzyme immunoassays are used principally for antigen detection. In these tests enzyme-conjugated, virus-specific antisera are allowed to bind antigen in the test specimen.[61, 62] If antigen is present, steric inhibition of enzyme-substrate interaction occurs. The special requirement for an enzyme used in this type of assay is that its substrate must not react with enzymes present in body fluids. Certain bacterial enzymes such as β-lactamase, can be used for this purpose.[62] Such assays are, for the most part, used for the detection of macromolecular substances such as drugs and biologically active proteins. They are rarely used in diagnostic virology.[63]

Competitive immunoassays have been developed with both ELISA and RIA formats, for both antibody and antigen detection. The prototypic antigen capture competitive immunoassay is the confirmatory test for hepatitis B surface antigen (HBsAg). In this assay, the solid phase is coated with anti-HBsAg antibodies, and the serum specimen added. Following serum incubation, labeled HBsAg is added. If the serum contains HBsAg, binding of the labeled antigen to the solid phase is inhibited.

In the competitive ELISA for antibody detection, the solid phase is coated with antigen and incubated with test serum, followed by the addition of enzyme-labeled antibody to the antigen of interest. If the serum contains specific antibody to the coating antigen, binding of the labeled antibody to the solid phase is inhibited. Thus, the intensity of substrate development varies inversely to the amount of antibody in the serum sample. Competitive ELISA assays have been described for the detection of antibodies to a number of viruses including rubella virus,[64] and HIV,[65] and for detection of HIV antigens in serum and body fluids.[66]

The conventional ELISA test can be read visually or with a spectrophotometer. Tests done in suitable microplates can be read on a spectrophotometer designed to transmit light through the wells, eliminating the need to transfer each specimen to a cuvette.[67] Tests are sometimes used that have reaction products which are fluorescent[68] or radioactive,[69] or in which the enzyme-substrate reaction produces chemiluminescence.[70] Assays of these types are designed to provide increased sensitivity. The results of each specimen are determined individually by appropriate instrumentation. By comparison to the IFA test, ELISA results can be determined more rapidly and quantitatively with less subjectivity.

The ELISA is a highly sensitive and specific test for measurement of antibodies to many viruses.[71–73] ELISA has gained acceptance as the standard screening assay for antibodies to HIV.[46] Like other indirect immunoassays, it can be used to measure specific types of immunoglobulin, such as IgM in acute sera, or IgA in secretions.[74] Great specificity can be achieved by use of purified viral protein antigens, such as influenza hemagglutinin,[75] and the F and G surface glycoproteins of respiratory syncytial virus,[76] recombinant viral proteins, or peptide antigens, such as envelope or core proteins of HIV.[65, 77, 78] Other factors accounting for its popularity are its suitability for rapid screening of hybridoma cultures and application to rapid viral diagnosis.

In the electrophoretic immunoblot, or western blot, viral particles or virus-infected cells are disrupted and the viral antigens solubilized and subjected to polyacrylamide gel electrophoresis. Following electrophoretic separation, the viral proteins are transferred to a nitrocellulose membrane by diffusion or electrophoretic transfer. This nitrocellulose membrane is cut into strips and serves as the solid phase for an ELISA-like immunoassay. Using this method, specific antibody response to a number of viral and virus-induced cellular antigens can be determined. Western blots have been used to characterize the immunogenic components and the fine specificity of immune responses to a wide range of viruses.[51, 79–86] While generally qualitative, antibody reactivity on western blots can be quantitated by scanning blots with a reflectance densitometer.[81, 83] Western blots are often more sensitive and specific than ELISA assays once standardized criteria for interpretation have been established. Because of cost and the complex and time-intensive nature of immunoblot preparation, the technique finds its widest application in the research rather than the diagnostic virology laboratory. The exception to this is the use of commercially prepared western blot assays for HIV antibodies.[46]

Radioimmunoassay (RIA).—Like the ELISA, the RIA for measurement of serum immunoglobulins is typically an indirect, solid-phase immunoassay. The specific antigen-antibody reaction is detected using a radionuclide-conjugated antiglobulin. The most commonly used nuclide is ^{125}I, which can be easily linked to immunoglobulins without altering their specificity.[87] Radioimmunoassays to detect antigens can be performed either as solid-phase procedures or in solution. In the latter case antigen-antibody complexes are precipitated by the addition of ammonium sulfate[88] or of staphylococcal protein A linked to sepharose.[89]

The RIA generally is a very sensitive and specific test for antiviral antibodies. It is easily and rapidly performed and produces quantitative results. It is a useful test for measuring antibodies to CMV,[90] varicella,[91, 92] and other viruses.[93] It is the standard "third-generation" test for screening banked blood for hepatitis B virus.[94] ELISA assays have also been developed for this purpose.[95] The RIA would probably be used more widely if alternative tests of equivalent sensitivity that do not use radionuclides were not available.

Latex Agglutination Assays

Microscopic latex beads can be coated with a wide variety of viral antigens, and used in simple and very rapid assays for specific antibody. These assays are generally performed on small cardboard slides and can be read by visual examination within minutes of addition of the test sample. Addition of a positive serum sample to the latex bead suspension results in the agglutination of the latex particles and the formation of clumps on the slide. The advantages of this assay configuration are its potentially low cost, speed, and lack of requirement for sophisticated laboratory instrumentation. Latex agglutination assays have been described for the detection of antibodies to CMV,[96] rubella virus,[97] and HIV.[98] These assays can be reasonably sensitive and specific. However, like IFA techniques subjective interpretation and level of training of the observer can adversely affect assay reliability.

Immunoprecipitation Assays

A variety of immunoprecipitation methods are used to detect virus antigen-antibody interaction. In all cases the assays are dependent upon antigen and antibody interacting in a zone of slight antibody excess so that immunoprecipitation occurs. Typically, concentration gradients of one or both reactants are established in gels of semisolid material such as agarose. In the Ouchterlony assay, the concentration gradients that generate the zone of precipitation are produced simply by allowing antigen and antibodies to diffuse toward each other from wells cut in the agar.[99] The single radial diffusion test is similar to the Ouchterlony, except that the antibodies are mixed uniformly with the gel before it solidifies. Antigen diffuses radially from the well and a circular precipitin line is formed. The diameter of the precipitin line is proportional to the concentration of antigen in the well.[100] In other cases, such as the Laurell assay, or "rocket immunoelectrophoresis," and counterimmunoelectrophoresis, the concentration gradient is developed electrophoretically.[101, 102] In the Laurell assay, antigen is placed in a well at one end of a gel. Throughout the gel, antibodies are suspended in an appropriate concentration. Antigen diffuses radially from the well and at the same time is electrophoresed in the direction of the long axis of the gel. The result is development of a long, narrow, rocketlike area demarcated by the precipitin line.

The radioimmunoprecipitation assay (RIPA) is a very sensitive but cumbersome tool for antibody determination. In this assay, virus-infected cells are exposed to a radioisotope such as ^{35}S-methionine which is incorporated into viral and cellular proteins. The infected cells are then lysed and the cell lysate, containing radiolabeled viral proteins, is collected by ultracentrifugation. Serum samples absorbed to protein A–coupled Sepharose beads are mixed with the cell lysate, the beads are sedimented, and the immunoprecipitates recovered. These precipitates are then separated by SDS-PAGE electrophoresis, and the banding patterns determined by autoradiography. The result is a banding pattern analogous to that seen on western blot, enabling the determination of antibody responses to specific viral proteins. RIPA assays were important in early experiments defining immune responses to HIV infection,[82, 103, 104] and have also been applied to a number of other viral infections in man.[105, 106] RIPA assays are not widely performed because they are costly, time-consuming, and labor-intensive, and they require the maintenance of infected cells and the utilization of radioisotopes.

With the exception of RIPA, immunoprecipitation techniques are not highly sensitive. These assays are useful for a variety of specialized needs, however. For example, a modification of the Ouchterlony technique can be used for measurement of poliovirus antigen in vaccines,[107] and the single radial diffusion and Laurell techniques have been used for quantitative determinations of influenza virus antigen in vaccines.[100, 101]

Measurement of Specific Classes of Immunoglobulin

IgA.—Mucosal antibody secretion is of interest as a first line of defense against viral infections. The importance of this defense mechanism is reflected in the difference in effects of live and inactivated poliovirus vaccines. The inactivated vaccines induce less effective gastrointestinal (GI) mucosal immunity. Even though they protect an individual from subsequent disease, they do not prevent asymptomatic infection and virus shedding in stool.[108, 109] Secretory IgA is actively secreted at mucosal surfaces but is still present in secretions in low concentrations. Thus, it is most easily measured using sensitive, indirect immunoassays, such as the ELISA used to assay influenza antibodies in nasal wash specimens.[74]

IgM.—The principal use of specific IgM determinations is for rapid diagnosis of acute infection, based on the premise that antigen-specific IgM is present in serum only for a finite period of time after primary exposure to the virus in question. For example, CMV-specific IgM in cord blood is a reliable indicator of congenital infection.[110] Assays for IgM determination are usually indirect, using anti-IgM or anti-μ immunoglobulin conjugates.[111] The presence of rheumatoid factor in a test serum may produce false-positive results.[112]

Some assays will detect IgM without specifically differentiating it from IgG. For example, both IgG and IgM may be capable of virus neutralization. Assays which depend on complement fixation or activation will generally detect IgM. The direct hemolytic plaque assay detects IgM exclusively, under most circumstances, because of greater complement binding activity of IgM than IgG.

Role of Immunoglobulins in Viral Infections

Humoral immune responses are important both as diagnostic indicators of the occurrence of infection and in protection against viral infections.[112a] Passive immunization with specific immunoglobulins is known to be of prophylactic value against measles,[113] hepatitis A[114] and B,[115] vaccinia,[116] varicella-zoster,[117] and rabies[118] viruses. Transplacentally acquired antibodies are well-known to be inhibitory for live virus vaccines, and their presence often prevents effective immunization.[119, 120] The severity of certain infections, such as with measles virus,[25] is apparently attenuated when occurring in the first few months of life due to the presence of maternal antibodies. Loss of transplacentally acquired maternal antibodies through phlebotomy and blood replacement has been implicated as a mechanism for severe CMV infection in premature infants.[121]

Another type of evidence that antibodies are important in viral infections is that in certain infections the presence of adequate levels of antibodies, and not simply evidence of prior exposure to the virus, correlates with protective immunity. Individuals with HI antibodies to influenza virus in titers of 1:40 or greater are usually protected whereas those with lower titers may not be.[26] Levels of maternal antibodies to herpes simplex virus in amniotic fluid appear to be inversely related to the risk of neonatal infection.[122]

The mechanisms by which antibodies mediate their protective effects are multiple. In cases where infection is acquired by exposure at a mucosal surface, secretory antibodies may constitute a first line of defense. Neutralization of viral infectivity may take place at this level or by soluble antibodies in blood or extracellular fluid subsequent to virus having traversed mucosal barriers. With respect to protective immunity, that is, immunity which persists after resolution of infection and prevents subsequent infection, the presence of neutralizing antibodies must result in an increase in the numbers of virus particles required to establish infection. Antibodies that inhibit the actions of virus proteins such as hemagglutinin or neuraminidase may be important in neutralization or in preventing the virus from entering a cell once it has attached. Once a virus has entered a host cell, virus proteins may be expressed on the cell surface before virus replication and assembly is complete. Antibodies to these membrane antigens can participate in complement- or (as will be discussed below) cell-mediated immune cytolysis, preventing the formation of infectious virions. These multiple functions of humoral immunity may not be sufficient to

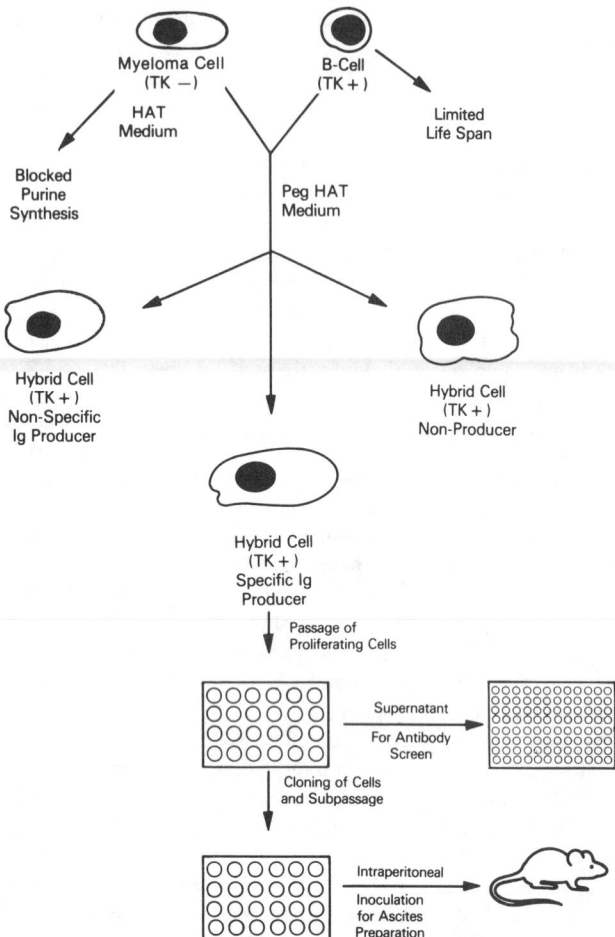

Figure 4–3. Schematic diagram of hybridoma methodology. Thymidine kinase–negative (TK⁻) continuously growing myeloma cells are fused by polyethylene glycol with TK positive (Tk⁺) B cells. Unfused B cells have a limited life span in culture, and unfused myeloma cells (TK⁻) cannot synthesize DNA in the presence of aminopterin. Hybrid cells are continuously growing, TK⁺, and use hypoxanthine and tryptophyan in the pathway for purine synthesis. Fusions are usually done in microplates at limit dilutions so that emerging hybrids are likely to be clonally derived. Unfused B cells may secrete immunoglobulin into the culture medium prior to senescence, but specific antibody present in supernatants of the first passage of hybrids indicate that fusion has occurred. Since a small fraction of the total spleen cell population are B cells–specific for a given antigen, even in hyperimmunized animals, typical fusion experiment will involve seeding of 0.5 cell per microplate well into each of 100 to 1000 wells. Supernatants from successful fusions are sampled from the original well or from the first passage culture. Antibody screening procedures must be rapid and extremely sensitive since the antibodies are secreted initially in low concentration and, due to their monoclonal nature, only a single immunoglobulin molecule binds to each protein molecule. Hybrid cultures producing no antibodies are quickly discarded to permit intensive care of the few specific clones which result. Genetic stability of a clone is uncertain until it has been repeatedly subcloned and serially passaged. Clones may be maintained by passage in tissue culture or serial passage of ascitic fluid from mouse to mouse. Higher concentrations of monoclonal antibodies are usually obtained in ascitic fluid. HAT = hypoxanthine–aminopterin–tryptophan.

prevent all harmful effects of virus infection, but certainly supplement the antiviral effects of cellular immunity.

Monoclonal Antibodies and Hybridoma Technology

The fusion of immune B lymphocyte with myeloma cells to form an antibody-producing, continuous hybrid cell line was first described by Kohler and Milstein.[123] The procedure (Figure 4–3) involved cocultivation of mouse spleen cells and myeloma cells in the presence of polyethylene glycol, a membrane fusion inducer. Myeloma cells are used that have a deficiency in thymidine kinase activity. In the presence of aminopterin, purine synthesis is dependent on this enzymatic pathway. With the addition of hypoxanthine and tryptophan, myeloma cells that have acquired thymidine kinase activity by fusion with B cells continue to grow, while unfused cells of either type die. Individual hybrid cell lines are cloned to select fusion products of individual B cells which produce the monoclonal immunoglobulins originally specified by those B cells. If the spleens used have a high density of cells producing antibodies to the antigen of concern, then there is a good possibility that some of the hybrid clones produced will elaborate antibodies to that antigen.

Application of this procedure has evolved rapidly. A number of myeloma cell lines have been found that are suitable for use, including lines that grow rapidly and do not, of themselves, produce an immunoglobulin.[124, 125] Both mouse-human[124] and human-human[126] hybridomas have also been produced, although the former tend to be unstable due to extrusion of genetic material, and the latter can so far be produced only with low efficiency. Even mouse-mouse hybrids are often unstable and must be cloned repeatedly to avoid overgrowth of the desired clones by clones producing no or irrelevant antibodies. The initial fusions are typically performed at limiting dilutions of spleen cells to help avoid this problem but, as a result, only a small percentage of the hybrids formed produce antibodies to the desired antigens. Rapid, sensitive screening procedures are needed to reduce the numbers of cultures being carried from hundreds to a few. The ELISA and RIA techniques are often most suitable for this purpose. Once a hybrid cell line has been repeatedly cloned, stabilized, and characterized, it can be propagated indefinitely either by in vitro or in vivo cultivation. The latter is usually performed by intraperitoneal inoculation of mice and repeated abdominal paracentesis to collect antibody-containing ascites or cells for subsequent passage. The procedure is always laborious, and the likelihood of success is highly dependent on the regimen used initially for immunization of the mice.

Hybridoma technology has been or might be exploited for many purposes. The most obvious application is to produce monospecific antibodies of uniform consistency. Murine monoclonal antibodies have been used since the early 1980s for experimental therapy of leukemias, lymphomas, and solid tumors with varying success.[127, 128] The monoclonal antibody OKT3 is used for prophylaxis and treatment of graft rejection following renal transplantation. The development of antimouse IgG responses in treated patients may limit the clinical value of this form of therapy.[129, 130]

There is the potential to use monoclonal antibodies for passive

Table 4–1
Characteristics of Human Peripheral Blood Mononuclear Cells Commonly Used in Identification and Purification

Cell Type	Cell Surface Receptors	Membrane Antigens*	Morphology	Other Characteristics
T Cell	E rosette	CD2+, CD3+	Small lymphocytes	
T helper cell	E rosette	CD4+	<10% large lymphocytes	Nonadherent
Helper subset	E rosette	CD45R−, (4B4+)	<10% large lymphocytes	Nonadherent
Inflammatory subset	E rosette	CD45R+, (4B4−)	<10% large lymphocytes	Nonadherent
T supressor cell	E rosette	CD8+, CD11b+	<10% large lymphocytes	Nylon wool–adherent and nonadherent
T cytotoxic cell	E rosette	CD8+, CD11b−	<10% large lymphocytes	Nonadherent
B cell	Complement (EAC rosette, Epstein-Barr virus)	CD19+, CD21+, CD20+, CD22+	Small lymphocytes	Nylon wool–adherent
Natural killer and antibody-dependent killer lymphocytes	Immunoglubulin Fc (EA rosette, fixed antigen-antibody complexes)	CD2+, CD16+, (Leu19+)	Large granular lymphocytes	Nonadherent
Monocytes	Immunoglobulin Fc	CD11b+, CD16+, CD14+, CD15+	Large mononuclear cell	Plastic-, glass-, and nylon wool–adherent; phagocytic; carageenan-sensitive; esterase-positive

Where a CD designation has not been assigned, monoclonal antibodies reactive with membrane antigens are listed in parentheses.

immunization against viral diseases, although such an application has not yet been demonstrated.[131]

Anti-idiotype monoclonal antibodies have been developed as potential immunogens for the prevention of CMV and HIV infections, although neither has been used in the clinical setting.[132, 133] Anti-idiotypes bearing the image of the CD4 receptor are being tested in humans for possible treatment of HIV infections.[134]

In addition to these current and possible future clinical applications of hybridoma technology, monoclonal antibodies serve useful purposes in vitro. They have been used to define antigenic determinants on a number of viral proteins such as the influenza virus hemagglutinin and the envelope glycoprotein of HIV,[135, 136] and for defining antigens related to strain variability, as exemplified by monoclonal antibodies specific for types 1 and 2 of herpes simplex virus, and those reactive with type-specific surface glycoproteins of respiratory syncytial virus.[23, 76] Monoclonal antibodies are used for affinity purification of specific proteins, such as recombinant DNA–derived viral proteins,[137] and as standard reagents in immunoassays. The potential applications of hybridoma technology seem almost limitless.

CELL-MEDIATED IMMUNITY

Cell-mediated immunity is a collective term which refers to the effects of numerous distinct immune functions. The different cell types involved have been defined on the basis of their morphology, physical characteristics, cell surface markers, and function. These functions include antigen presentation and recognition, immunoregulation, elaboration of soluble mediators, and cytotoxic activities of effector cells. The morphology and surface characteristics of immune cells are important as identifying characteristics, as

they relate to methods used to purify different cell types and to their mechanisms of action.

Characteristics of Different Lymphocyte Classes

Definition of the antigenic diversity of human lymphocyte populations has been greatly enhanced by the use of monoclonal antibodies. Although it was long anticipated that human T cells possessed a specific antigen analogous to the theta antigen of murine T cells,[138, 139] it was only through the use of hybridoma technology that such an antigen was clearly identified. A large number of lymphocyte class-specific monoclonal antibodies now exist, some of which are indicated in Table 4–1. Reagents are available which are specific for thymic differentiation antigens, T cells, helper T cells, cytotoxic and suppressor T cells, bone marrow–derived cells, natural killer (NK) cells, and other distinct lymphocyte classes.

The development of large numbers of monoclonal antibodies which recognize molecules on the surface of lymphoid cells has led to some confusion. Like cytokines, different researchers assigned differing designations to monoclonal antibodies recognizing the same or very similar cell surface determinants. Under the auspices of the World Health Organization, a standard nomenclature has been devised, the "cluster of differentiation," or CD antigen system.[140, 141] At present, there are more than 50 CD antigens recognized. The reader is referred to recent reviews for a more complete description of these antigenic determinants.[140, 141]

The combined use of monoclonal antibodies and the fluorescence-activated cell sorter (FACS) has greatly expanded the capacity of immunologists to enumerate and purify different classes of lymphocytes. The FACS uses a laser light source to determine the size and fluorescence of cells in suspension. As a cell passes through the laser beam, light is scattered in proportion to cell size and diverted away from the light detector. The instrumentation can be adjusted to be activated by cells in a specific size range which are deflected electromagnetically as they pass through the cytometer and diverted into a separate collection apparatus. A separate detector senses fluorescence emission from fluorochrome-labeled cells and activates deflection of the cell path independently. The light sensed by the detector is processed to give a graphic image of the numbers of fluorescent cells of different sizes.[142] The procedure has been applied to the study of changes in lymphocyte populations during viral infections,[143] for purification of lymphocytes for further study, and for identifying viral antigens on infected cells.[144]

The identifying characteristics of different types of immune cells are summarized in Table 4–1. Lymphocytes can be classified physically according to their size, density, and a morphology.[145–147] Unless induced into blastogenesis, B cells and most T cells are typical small lymphocytes (about 10 μm in diameter) with scant cytoplasm and deeply basophilic, round nuclei. Approximately 10% of human peripheral blood lymphocytes are notably larger (about 12–14 μm). Because these cells have a higher cytoplasmic-to-nuclear ratio, they are less dense and can be separated from small T and B cells by density gradient centrifugation.[148] The cells obtained by this method are mainly non-T ("null" cell) lymphocytes, many with indented nuclei and eosinophilic cytoplasmic granules. These large granular lymphocytes (LGL) are normally present in peripheral blood and are morphologically distinct from the atypical lymphocytes which develop during infectious mononucleosis. The LGL fraction of lymphocytes contains the NK cell activity, whereas the atypical lymphocytes of infectious mononucleosis appear to be predominantly T cells. Atypical lymphocytes can be seen to a lesser extent in other viral infections, such as with hepatitis B virus,[149, 150] and are a manifestation of immunologic reactivity, rather than a continuously present cell type.

Adherence to inert surfaces is a property of some mononuclear cells. At 37°C in the presence of calcium and magnesium, monocytes will attach to plastic and glass surfaces.[151] B lymphocytes and some suppressor T cells, as well as monocytes, will adhere to nylon wool with high efficiency under appropriate conditions.[152] The morphology and adherence characteristics of lymphocytes may change in culture so that their microscopic appearance resembles that of monocytes. Differentiation of lymphocytes and monocytes under these conditions is usually accomplished either by staining cells for monocyte nonspecific esterase[153] or by examining the cells for toxicity from silica,[154] or carageenan,[154] or for phagocytosis of particles such as latex beads,[155] or iron particles.[156]

Cell surface receptors on mononuclear cells correlate with their functions and methods used for their purification. The classic method for identification of T lymphocytes is by rosetting with sheep erythrocytes. Approximately 60% to 80% of human peripheral blood lymphocytes have receptors for sheep red blood cells.[157] This number varies slightly depending on how the red cells are prepared and on whether rosetting is performed at 29 to 37°C or 4°C. The receptor is present on all thymus-derived lymphocytes and is acquired during processing in the thymus.[158] It correlates with a thymic differentiation antigen identified by monoclonal antibodies.[159] B cells are classically identified by the presence of surface membrane immunoglobulin[160] which can itself be considered an antigen receptor. They also possess receptors for complement which can be identified by rosetting with erythrocyte-antibody-complement complexes (EAC rosetting).[161] This receptor appears closely related to the binding site for Epstein-Barr virus.[162]

Natural killer cells and antibody-dependent killer cells are nonspecific cytotoxic cells that are similar to identical lymphocyte types formerly classified as null cells, indicating a lack of the receptors typical of B and T lymphocytes. In actuality, these cells do have identifying surface markers, and most express the characteristic phenotype CD2 +, CD3 −, Leu 19 +, CD16 + (IgG Fc receptor).[163] Binding of immunoglobulin to these receptors is the mechanism that arms antibody-dependent killer cells to become antigen-specific and apparently exerts a negative influence on cytotoxicity of NK cells.[164] It has been hypothesized that CD2 plays a role in the induction of NK activity, as part of the NK cell receptor complex.[165] NK cell–mediated cytotoxicity and antibody-dependent cellular cytotoxicity (ADCC) may involve a common lytic mechanism, although initiation and regulation of the pathways leading to cytolysis differ.[166] The conventional method for identifying cells with Fc receptors is by rosetting with antibody-coated erythrocytes (EA rosetting).[167] Alternatively, antibody-erythrocyte[168] or antibody-antigen complexes[169] attached to a plastic surface form a suitable solid phase for binding of cells with Fc receptors. Monocytes[170] and, to a certain extent, granulocytes[171] also have Fc receptors. Both cell types can mediate antibody-dependent cells killing the latter in the presence of complement.[172]

The recognition of an increasing number of cell surface lymphocyte markers has led to some controversy with respect to the actual lineage of the NK cell, so that a functional definition of the NK cell may be preferable to one based on morphology or reactivity with currently available monoclonal antibodies. In general, NK cells can be defined as "cells capable of mediating spontaneous in vitro cytotoxicity against a variety of target cells without prior sensitization."[173]

While NK cells are clearly different from T cells, a number of observations suggest that some relationship exists between NK and T cells. These possible relationships were recently summarized by Grossman and Herberman.[174] Among similarities between NK and T cells are expression by NK cells of some T cell surface markers such as CD2, the sheep red blood cell receptor, and CD8; the responsiveness of both cell types to interleukin-2 (IL-2) and their capacities to express IL-2 receptors; and the use of identical or similar cytolytic mechanisms. Occasionally, T cells may develop an LGL morphology, as seen during lymphocytic choriomeningitis virus infections in mice.[175] Certain lymphokines that are produced by T cells can also be made by LGL, such as gamma interferon and IL-2, and T cell surface markers are induced on purified LGL populations by IL-2.[174]

Components of Cellular Response to Viral Infections
Delayed-Type Hypersensitivity

The classic manifestation of cell-mediated immunity is the delayed-type hypersensitivity (DTH) response. This response is readily visualized as the delayed cutaneous reaction to injected viral antigens. Histologically this response consists of a mixed mononuclear cell infiltrate that resembles the inflammatory response seen in virus-infected tissues.[176] Cutaneous hypersensitivity reactions to mumps antigen have been used clinically as a measure of integrity of cellular immune function. An expert panel recently reviewed this application of mumps skin test antigen and found the data regarding its use for this purpose to be unconvincing.[177] The major concern of the panel was that an adequate definition of criteria for a specific positive response was lacking. Varicella skin test antigen has been used to define immune responsiveness to this virus in clinical studies of an experimental vaccine[178] and of transfer factor.[179] Not all cutaneous reactions to virus antigens reflect the same type of inflammatory process. For example, inactivated influenza vaccines induce local inflammatory responses that are most apparent in the first 24 to 48 hours and occur with equal frequency in previously immune and nonimmune individuals.[180] An experimental live CMV vaccine induces a local inflammatory response about ten days after inoculation into seronegative but not seropositive individuals.[181] This reaction might actually be a DTH response that is dependent on replication of the virus in seronegatives to produce an adequate antigenic stimulus. Prior recipients of killed measles vaccine can develop very severe local reactions to live vaccine that may be the result of an Arthus-type reaction.[182]

Cutaneous DTH testing is an attractive method for determining specific cellular immunity. Testing is inexpensive and easily performed. In general, a positive response reflects both integrity of cellular immunity and prior experience with relevant virus antigens.

Lymphocyte Transformation

Immune resting lymphocytes can be induced to proliferate in vitro in response to specific antigens. Similar effects on resting lymphocytes can be caused nonspecifically by a variety of lymphocyte mitogens, most of which are plant lectins. Assays that measure the ability of lymphocytes to multiply specifically or nonspecifically in response to antigens or mitogens are referred to as proliferation, transformation, or blastogenesis assays. The tests are usually performed by incubating the lymphocytes at 37°C in nutrient medium containing appropriate concentrations of the virus antigens or lymphocyte mitogen for a number of days. During this time lymphocyte activation and recruitment takes place, resulting in cellular proliferation. After sufficient time has elapsed, lymphocyte proliferation is measured by determining the amount of ^{3}H-methyl thymidine incorporated into cellular DNA within a specific period of time. Occasionally, radiolabeled amino acid incorporation into newly synthesized proteins is the method used for quantitation.

Lymphocyte mitogens may be selective stimulants of B cells, such as bacterial lipopolysaccharides[183] or influenza A (H3N2) antigens.[184] Pokeweed mitogen stimulates both B cells and T cells, but both effects depend on T cell activation.[185] Concanavalin A (Con A) and phytohemagglutinin M (PHA-M) are principally T cell mitogens.[186, 187] Antigen-induced lymphocyte proliferation in vitro is usually an indication of T cell responsiveness. Immune B lymphocytes can be induced to proliferate by antigens in vitro, although special conditions are usually required to enhance production of specific immunoglobulin. Proliferation responses to T cell mitogens and virus antigens have some similar characteristics. Both are measures of the integrity of the lymphocyte recruitment process, and gamma interferon[188] and IL-2[189] are induced in both cases. There are differences between responses to virus antigens and lectins mitogenic for T cells. Mitogen-induced responses tend

to be of greater magnitude and consistency than responses to antigens. Lymphocytes stimulated by Con A elaborate a soluble suppressor substance,[190] and develop suppressor cell[191] and nonspecific cytotoxic cell activity.[192] In contrast, lymphocytes stimulated by virus antigens respond only if they are from a previously immune individual and can develop, under appropriate conditions, into virus antigen-specific cytotoxic T cells.

Normal human lymphocytes proliferate dramatically in response to Con A or PHA. Changes in responsiveness to these lectins sometimes occur during viral infections. After influenza vaccination, depression of responses to Con A occurs followed by an enhancement of the response.[193] Measles virus appears to have a direct suppressive effect on mitogenic responses to lectins.[194] During CMV infection, suppresson of this response is also seen.[195] In this case the suppression might be due to a direct depressive effect of the virus.[196] Alternatively, interferon (IFN) activity induced by infection could be involved since IFN treatment of lymphocytes suppresses the response in vitro.[197] In general, changes in responses to mitogens do not appear to relate to the outcome of viral infections, but individuals whose responsiveness is suppressed for other reasons might be at risk for serious complications should they become infected. Suppression of responsiveness during infection may relate to the increased susceptibility of individuals with measles virus or CMV infections to other types of infection.[198, 199]

The lymphocyte proliferation response to virus antigens typically develops after recovery from infection. It is an in vitro measure of preexisting immunity. Lymphocytes from most individuals will proliferate in response to virus antigens to which they are immune. One notable exception is measles virus which apparently stimulates proliferation of lymphocytes from prior recipients of killed measles vaccine, but not lymphocytes from individuals who had previously received live vaccines or had been naturally infected.[200] Lymphocyte proliferation assays tend to be moderately specific. For example, they are cross-reactive between herpes simplex viruses types 1 and 2 but not between these viruses and another herpesvirus, CMV.[201] The responses also tend to be cross-reactive among different subtypes of influenza A virus.[202] In this case, studies of cloned lymphocytes have indicated that the response is directed against both internal and surface proteins of the influenza virus; clones directed against the internal proteins are cross-reactive, whereas a clone directed against hemagglutinin was subtype-specific.[203] The sensitivity of lymphocyte proliferation assays for diagnosis of preexisting immunity is related to the virus in question and must be established individually in each laboratory performing the assay.

Macrophage Monocyte Function

Macrophages perform a wide variety of functions in cell-mediated immunity. Phagocytosis is undoubtedly important for removal of cellular debris resulting from virus cytopathic effect. Phagocytosis of cell-free virus particles does not appear to be as significant as in the case of bacterial infections. The relative ineffectiveness of this process in viral infections may, in part, be related to the fact that some viruses can actually replicate in macrophages.[204] Macrophages can be activated by lymphokines, such as gamma interferon[205] and granulocyte-monocyte colony stimulating factor (GM-CSF),[206] which are elaborated by antigen-specific T lymphocytes, or nonspecifically by bacterial lipopolysaccharide, thioglycolate, endotoxin, the adjuvant muramyl dipeptide,[207] and bacille Calmette-Guérin.[208] Activated macrophages elaborate a large variety of pharmacologically active substances, including proteolytic enzymes, bioactive lipids, and reactive oxygen intermediates.[209] Commonly used assays for macrophage activation depend on measurement of plasmin-mediated fibrinolysis or reactive oxygen moieties. Activated macrophages elaborate lymphokines including interleukin-1 (IL-1), tumor necrosis factor, and interferons.[209–212] Activation leads to an increase in the density of IgG Fc receptor expression on the macrophage surface.[213] During CMV mononucleosis,[214] there are increased numbers of adherent suppressor cells, presumably activated macrophages, in peripheral blood. This suppressor effect may serve to predispose to opportunistic infections with other agents.[215] Armed macrophages can mediate antibody-dependent cytotoxicity,[170, 216] but unarmed macrophages are also cytotoxic. The extent to which they can kill Kunjin virus–infected cells is increased by activation.[217] Macrophages are thus involved in initiation of the inflammatory response, recruitment of other cell types to the site of infection, and direct and indirect virus-inhibitory effects.

Activated macrophages have the potential for serving several immune functions of importance in viral infections. Since activation can take place rapidly, they may constitute an early, nonspecific defense mechanism.[217] Macrophage activation has been associated with resistance to influenza, herpes simplex, and other viruses.[218–221] Viruses may be readily phagocytosed by macrophages, particularly after opsonization, or may enter the cell by membrane fusion.[222–225] This process may result in destruction of the virus particle, activation of the macrophage,[224] facilitation of antigen processing, or depression of immunoregulatory functions of the phagocytic cell.[225]

Macrophages play important roles in the development of specific immune responses. Macrophages ingest antigens, process them internally, and present them on the cell surface. Presumably, antigen processing involves proteolytic cleavage of antigen, and transport of the resulting peptides to the cell membrane. Antigen-specific lymphocyte stimulation requires presentation of antigen in conjunction with major histocompatibility complex (MHC) class II antigens, which are expressed at greater density on activated as compared to resting macrophages. The synthesis of IL-1 by activated macrophages is also instrumental to the generation of antigen-specific responses, augmenting B cell proliferation and antibody production, and T cell production of IL-2 and other lymphokines.[226] For many antigens, additional processing by T cells or cooperation between B cells and T cells is necessary before B cell responses can develop, accounting for their designation as T cell–dependent antigens.[227] In general, IgM responses and responses to polysaccharide antigens are T cell–independent. Since viruses lack polysaccharides, such as those forming bacterial cell walls, IgG responses to viruses are typically T cell–dependent.

Cell-Mediated Cytotoxicity

Among the numerous functions collectively referred to as cell-mediated immunity, cytotoxic lymphocyte responses are the main mechanisms whereby mononuclear cells have a direct effect on virus replication within host cells. Cytotoxic cells possess the ability to attach to and destroy virus-infected cells early in the replicative cycle of a virus before infectious virions have formed within the cell.[170] Destruction of one infected cell may abort a cycle that would otherwise have resulted in production of hundreds of infectious virions. Several cell types have the capacity to kill virus-infected cells, including: (1) cytotoxic T cells, cells that recognize virus antigens specifically and have classic T cell markers[195]; (2) NK cells, large granular lymphocytes that kill many types of target cells and are not virus antigen-specific[228]; (3) antibody-dependent killer lymphocytes, cells that possess the same characteristics as NK cells, and may be the same cell type, but recognize cell-surface virus antigens specifically by virtue of an armed receptor for the Fc portion of IgG[229]; (4) macrophages, which can apparently kill nonspecifically when activated but also have very avid receptors for IgG Fc[217]; and (5) armed neutrophils in the presence of a complement.[172] Each of these functions probably has a unique role in viral infections based on its time of appearance during infection and its mechanism for target cell recognition.

Cytotoxic T Cells.—The classic method for generation of cytotoxic T cell responses is the mixed lymphocyte reaction (MLR). The components of the reaction are the stimulating and responding cell populations. Very potent alloantigen-specific responses are obtained when responding cells and irradiated stimulator cells differ in their major histocompatibility antigens. Such MLR responses can be quantitated either in terms of lymphocyte proliferation or in an assay for cytotoxic lymphocyte activity.

A major advance in the measurement of virus-specific cytotoxic T cell responses was made by Zinkernagel and Doherty, who demonstrated that murine cytotoxic T cells specific for lymphocytic choriomeningitis virus killed only target cells with which they shared an antigen in the H2 histocompatibility complex.[230] Further studies demonstrated that this restriction related to antigens coded for by the K and D regions of the H2 complex.[231] This phenomenon has been termed H2 restriction and has been found to be a common property of cytotoxic T cells from many mouse species directed against numerous viruses. The K and D regions of the H2 complex are analogous to the A and B regions of the human leukocyte antigen (HLA) histocompatibility complex. Human cytotoxic T cells develop in vivo during infection[195, 232] and can be generated in vitro in MLR where the stimulator cells are from the same donor as the responder cells[233–236] but are modified to express viral antigens on their surface. Human cytotoxic T cells are HLA-restricted.

Cytotoxic T cell activity was believed to be resident only in the CD8 + subset of T lymphocytes, and believed to be restricted solely by MHC class I antigens. Recently, a subset of CD4 + T cells were shown to mediate MHC-II–restricted cytotoxicity against a number of infectious agents including members of the herpesvirus group,[237–242] measles virus,[243–245] and influenza virus.[246–248] The population of CD4 + cells with the capacity for mediating MHC-II–restricted cytotoxicity can be recognized by the expression of the CD45R cell surface antigen at high density, and constitutes part of the inflammatory CD4 + subclass of CD4 + cells.[249] An exception to this generalization was reported by Seely et al,[250] who found that cytotoxic T cells from individuals with infectious mononucleosis killed both HLA-matched and -mismatched Epstein-Barr virus (EBV)–transformed cell lines. However, the antigenic spec-ificities of these cytotoxic cells is not clearly known. They might actually have been directed against nonviral antigens or have been a nonspecific form of cytotoxic cell. EBV-specific cytotoxic T cells generated in vitro are HLA-restricted in their activity.[251]

T cell binding of antigen requires the recognition of both antigen and self-class I or II MHC molecules on the surface of an antigen-presenting cell. While the biochemistry of the T cell receptor has been widely studied, the exact mechanism of MHC restriction of immune responses remains elusive. It is widely held that one receptor recognized both antigen and the restricting MHC element, and it is believed that MHC restriction occurs because antigen is presented in a specific conformational interaction with MHC that is achieved through a noncovalent binding.[252] This exogenous path-way for antigen presentation appears to be important in recognition by most MHC class II–restricted cytotoxic cells.

In contrast, classic CD8+ cytotoxic lymphocytes appear to rely principally on endogenous pathways for antigen recognition. Infected cells synthesize viral proteins which are associated with MHC-I molecules in the cytoplasm, and are subsequently ex-pressed on the cell surface. A preference for endogenous pro-cessing of antigen could explain the difficulties encountered when inducing CD8+ cytotoxic cell lines in vivo following exposure to nonreplicating viruses.[252]

There may also be other pathways for antigen presentation to cytotoxic lymphocyte precursors. For example, antigen presen-tation to measles virus–specific, MHC-II–restricted CD4+ cy-totoxic cells by HLA-Dr transfected, measles-infected human fibroblasts can occur in the presence of inhibitors of viral antigen processing.[253] Conversely, cells treated with synthetic peptides from the nucleoprotein of influenza A virus can act as targets for MHC-I–restricted cytotoxic cells, demonstrating that endogenous processing is not always essential for the induction of CD8+ cytotoxic effectors.[254]

Cytotoxic T cell responses (Figure 4–4) develop during acute viral infections[195, 232, 255, 256] and following vaccination with live or inactivated vaccines.[257] The responses wane as infection sub-sides,[232] and these cells are not found circulating in blood of nor-mal, previously immune individuals.[258] They can develop in vivo during either primary or repeated infection but are not readily generated in vitro unless the lymphocyte donor was previously immune.[233–236] Substantial evidence indicates that this cell type plays a major role in mediating recovery from viral infections. Adoptive transfer to cytotoxic T cells specific for influenza[259] or CMV[260] protects mice from lethal infection with these viruses. More recent experiments involving transfer of cloned murine influenza-specific cytotoxic T cells also demonstrated protection from lethal challenge. These experiments also documented the antigenic specificity of the in vivo cytotoxic T cell response.[261]

Moreover, the protective effects are H2-restricted and are not seen if the cells are given to mice of different H2 types. In humans the capacity of bone marrow and renal transplant recipients infected with CMV to develop a virus-specific cytotoxic response correlates with their ability to survive infection.[232, 262] In influenza A antibody–negative human volunteers challenged with influenza virus, early development of cytotoxic T cell responses correlated with lower viral titers in nasopharyngeal secretions.[263] These find-ings probably account for the long-standing impression of clini-

cians that cell-mediated immunity is responsible for recovery from viral infections.

The process of differentiation of T cells into antigen-specific cytotoxic cells is only partially understood. The current model of cytotoxic T cell development involves three stages: activation, proliferation, and differentiation. In the first stage, circulating, functionally immature cytotoxic lymphocyte precursors recognize their target antigen when presented in association with the appro-priate MHC molecule. Antigenic recognition leads to the induction of receptors for IL-2 and other cytokines on the cell surface. In the second phase, IL-2 and other cytokines bind to the appropriate receptors on the activated cytotoxic precursor, resulting in clonal

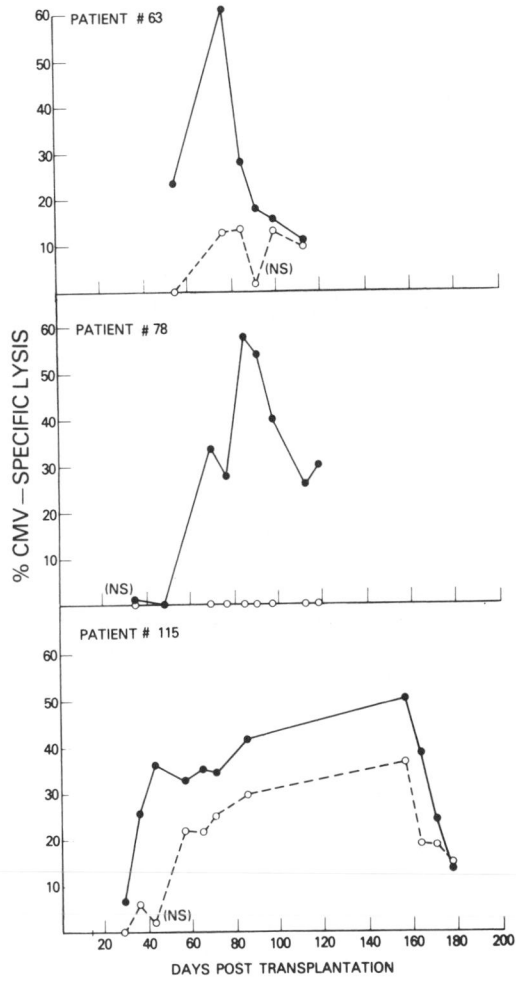

Figure 4–4. Cytotoxic lymphocyte responses of bone marrow trans-plant recipients to cytomegalovirus (CMV) infection. At onset of in-fection an increase in virus–specific T cell cytotoxicity occurs which is greater against human lymphocyte antigen (HLA)–matched (black circles) than mismatched (white circles) target cells (HLA–restricted). Variable amounts of non–restricted, non–T–cell mediated killing of mismatched target cells may also develop. With resolution of infec-tion, HLA–restricted activity disappears, but non–T cell activity per-sists. (Reprinted courtesy of Quinnan GV, Kirmani N, Rook AH, et al: Cytotoxic T cells in cytomegalovirus infection. HLA–restricted T–lymphocyte and non–T–lymphocyte cytotoxic responses cor-relate with recovery from cytomegalovirus infection in bone-marrow-transplant recipients. *N Engl J Med* 1982; 302:7–13.)

expansion.[252] In the final stage, at least two cytokines in addition to IL-2 are required for the differentiation into mature, functional cytotoxic effector cells. Interleukin-4,[264] and an as yet incompletely characterized lymphokine present in conditioned medium from Con A–stimulated peripheral blood mononuclear cell cultures,[265, 266] and tentatively identified as IL-6,[266] are involved in the differentiation stage, and probably contribute to proliferation of the activated cytotoxic precursors as well. Gamma interferon can augment cytotoxic activity but its requirement for the proliferation and differentiation of cytotoxic precursors is controversial.[267]

New evidence from animal models suggests that the regulation of cytotoxic lymphocyte responses may be more complex, and that maturation of cytotoxic lymphocytes can be inhibited by suppressor factors released by other T cell subsets in response to specific antigenic stimulation.[173]

Proliferation of immune lymphocytes in response to a specific virus antigen can occur under conditions that do not result in development of cytotoxic T cells. Crude antigen prepared by physical disruption of virus-infected cells will stimulate a lymphocyte proliferation response in vitro, but it appears that virus antigens must be presented to the responding cells in association with self-HLA to generate a cytotoxic response. Cytotoxic T cell responses that develop during in vitro stimulation are typically short-lived, with maximum activity developing after five to seven days in culture, and a subsequent rapid dissipation. The addition of new antigen alone at this point does not result in restimulation, possibly as a result of development of a suppressor cell response.[268] However, if IL-2 and antigen are fed to the cultures repeatedly at appropriate intervals, the cytotoxic response can be maintained, and individual cells can be cloned for studies of their antigenic specificity.[269] As understanding of this process unfolds in future research, clinical management of patients with viral infections should be benefited through treatments that enhance immune responsiveness and by avoidance of immunosuppressive therapy that blocks conversion of precursors into mature cytotoxic T cells.

Natural Killer (NK) Cells

The importance of NK cells in viral infection is partially understood. In mice, an increase in NK cell activity in spleens and peripheral blood occurs within two to three days of initiation of experimental infection.[270, 271] This increase in activity corresponds to a rise in serum interferon.[272] The time of increase in NK cell activity highlights this response as one of the earliest immune responses to viral infections. Suppression of the NK cell responses by hydrocortisone treatment is accompanied by an increase in susceptibility of mice to CMV infection.[272] Moreover, differences in genetically determined susceptibility to herpesvirus infections in mice correlate with the magnitude of the NK cell response which they develop.[273, 274] NK cells also constitute a significant part of the early inflammatory cell response to CMV interstitial pneumonitis in mice.[272] These observations suggest that they may mediate a virus-inhibition effect, but it is also clear that they are not completely specific for virus-infected cells. The cells most susceptible to killing by NK cells are continuous tumor cell lines. In some cases NK cells can kill virus-infected cells to a greater extent than uninfected cells. One possible mechanism whereby they may mediate a relatively specific antiviral effect could involve activation of cells in the vicinity of virus-infected cells either by interferon or viral antigens with subsequent nonspecific cell killing of cells in the area of infection.

One implication of activation of NK cells in this fashion is that they may kill both infected and uninfected cells. In the case of infection with a virus which is itself lytic to host cells, killing of infected cells that would die anyway would not be deleterious. However, nonspecific killing of uninfected cells could have a significant detrimental effect. In addition, immunologic destruction of virus-infected cells that otherwise survive might also be undesirable. It thus seems likely that these cells might produce an effect which would be pathologic in some circumstances and beneficial in others. NK cells themselves produce interferon in vitro when stimulated with viral antigens, a potential mechanism for autoregulation and for indirect viral inhibitory effects.[275] A possible example of the beneficial effect of NK cells is seen in CMV infection of bone marrow transplant recipients, where patients with low activity have an increased risk of dying from infection.[232]

Antibody-Dependent Cell-Mediated Cytotoxicity (ADCC)

The effector cells that participate in ADCC may be either adherent cells (monocytes or macrophages) or nonadherent lymphocytes with properties of NK cells. Cells of each of these types possess receptors for the Fc portion of IgG by which they bind antibodies that allow for specific attachment to antigens on the surface of virus-infected cells. As a result, their cytotoxic effect is virus-specific. The cells that mediate this killing are pleuripotent, with their specificity depending on the antibody with which they are armed.

ADCC has been demonstrated against a number of viruses including herpes simplex virus,[170, 276] influenza,[277] varicella-zoster virus,[278] CMV,[258, 279] and HIV.[280, 281] ADCC assays can be designed to be methods for measuring antibodies. A known source of killer cells is used with virus-infected target cells; the variable in the assay is the serum specimen being tested for its capacity to arm the killer cells. Assays of this type tend to be highly sensitive, particularly in the case of herpes simplex virus, indicating that only small amounts of antibodies are needed to arm the cytotoxic cells. ADCC is an efficient immune function both with respect to the pleuripotential function of the effector cell and the requirement for only low concentrations of antibodies in infected tissue. ADCC may serve an important function in primary infection, once antibodies have developed, in preventing reactivation of latent infection due to herpesviruses, and in reducing the severity of or protecting against secondary infection.

Methods for Cell-Mediated Cytotoxicity Assays

The two main components of a cytotoxicity assay are the lymphocyte effector cells and the target cells. Most methods used to measure target cell killing by effector cells are chromium release assays. Cell killing is expressed as a percent lysis which reflects the amount of ^{51}Cr released from labeled target cells in the presence of effector cells compared to the total releasable chromium. The relative cytotoxic activity of different lymphocyte preparations can be ascertained by direct comparison of counts per minute of ^{51}Cr released or percent lysis at a given concentration of effector cells and target cells. Alternatively, the ratio of effector cells to target cells (E/T) can be varied, and the percent lysis obtained at different

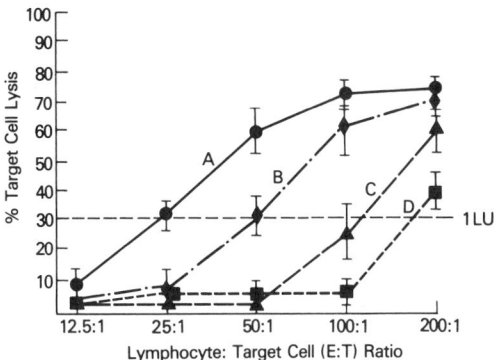

Figure 4–5. Quantitative estimation of cytotoxic lymphocyte activity. Lymphocytes from patients A, B, and C produce approximately equal lysis at 200:1 effector-to-target (E:T) ratio, each about twofold greater than lysis by lymphocytes from patient D. At lower E/T ratios, differences among patients A, B, and C are also evident. Mean percent lysis values at a specific E/T ratio can be compared directly by Student's *t* test. By this type of comparison the following results were obtained: At E/T = 100:1, A = B > C > D; at E/T = 50:1, A > B > C = D; at E/T = 25:1, A > B = C = D. The alternative method of comparison involves determining lytic units (LU) of activity, where 1 LU equals the E/T ratio which produces a certain percent lysis of the target cells (eg, 30%). In the example shown at a 200:1 E/T ratio, patient A lymphocytes had 8 LU, patient B had 4 LU, patient C had 1.8 LU, and patient D had 1.2 LU. Thus, a range of percent lysis values from 38% to 75% at E/T = 200:1 represented a difference in activity of nearly eightfold. Comparing cytotoxic lymphocyte suspensions at multiple E/T ratios, when possible, provides a much better indication of their relative activities than comparing single E/T ratios.

E/T ratios can be compared. This type of comparison is exemplified in Figure 4–5. The relationship between target cell killing and E/T ratio is linear over a limited range. At higher E/T ratios a further increase in effector cell numbers is not accompanied by a proportionate increase in target cell lysis. Within the range where the relationship is linear, it is still evident that a doubling in effector cell numbers results in less than a twofold increase in lysis. A consequence of these relationships is that comparisons of different effector cell suspensions at multiple E/T ratios gives a better indication of differences in activity than comparison of percent lysis values at a single ratio. Results obtained at multiple E/T ratios can be conveniently expressed in lytic units, where one lytic unit equals the E/T ratio that produces lysis of a specific percent of target cells.

Cytotoxicity tests other than chromium release assays are also used. One method recently developed involves microscopical visualization of target cells treated with vital stain. Effector cells and target cells are first suspended together in medium, centrifuged to increase cell–cell contact, and resuspended in semisolid medium. Effector cell–target cell conjugates are formed during centrifugation. The semisolid medium retards dissociation of the conjugates. After an appropriate incubation period, an overlay containing trypan blue is placed on the semisolid suspension and the dye is allowed to diffuse to the target cells. The numbers of conjugated target cells which are stained can be enumerated microscopically. A photograph of this type of preparation is shown in Figure 4–6. Through such assays it has been shown that lymphocyte-mediated killing of target cells is extracellular and involves direct contact between the two cell types, that only a fraction

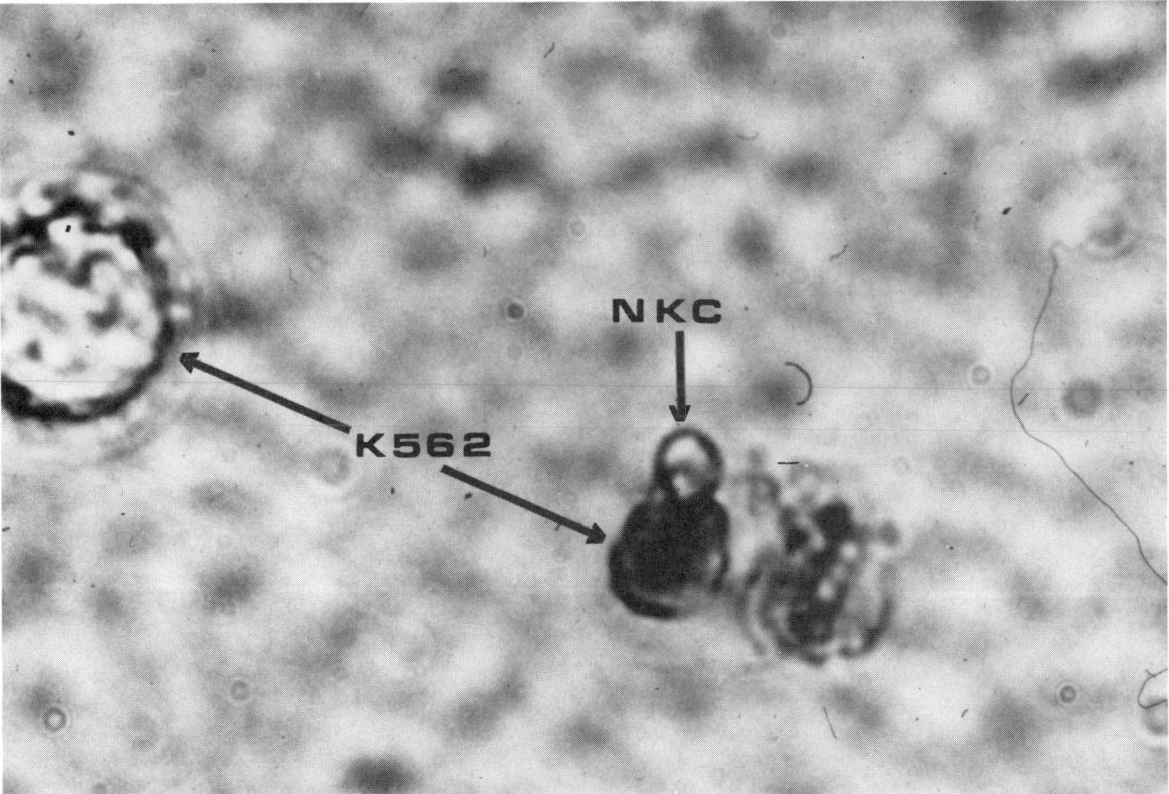

Figure 4–6. Cell-mediated killing of K562 cell by natural killer cell (NKC) in semisolid medium. The K562 cell conjugated to the NKC is no longer viable and appears darkened due to uptake of trypan blue dye. The unconjugated K562 cell remains intact. Lymphocytes and target cells are differentiated by their size. Target cell killing involves direct contact with the lymphocyte.

of the conjugated lymphocytes are cytotoxic, and that several hours may be required between the time the conjugate is first formed and the time when target cell death is demonstrable by dye uptake.[282]

Regardless of the type of cytotoxicity assay employed, the test may be adapted to measure any or all of the different types of cytotoxic cells of concern. The factors that determine which cell types are measured are the type of target cell used and the manner in which the effector cell suspension is prepared. Tumor cells tend to be more sensitive targets for measuring NK cell activity than nontumor lines, and certain cell lines, such as K562 and Daudi, are extremely sensitive.[283, 284] Conversely, if the assay does not contain antibodies to these cells and the lymphocyte donor has not been immunized, then the only cytotoxic cell type that would be measured using K562 cells for targets would be NK cells. To measure nonspecific antibody-dependent killer cell activity, a target cell can be sensitized with a serum known to contain antibodies to the target cell and the killing of the sensitized and unsensitized target cells by the lymphocytes being tested can be compared. A slightly different approach can be used to detect antibodies in sera. A lymphocyte suspension known to contain antibody-dependent killer cells is added to the target cells in the presence and absence of the serum being tested.

Target cells for measuring HLA-restricted cytotoxic T cells must be both virus-infected and matched to the effector cell for HLA type, usually at an HLA-A or -B locus antigen. However, killing of such a target cell does not necessarily reflect cytotoxic T cell activity. NK cells can kill either infected or uninfected target cells, and antibody-dependent killer cells already armed with specific antibodies may be present in lymphocyte suspensions from immune individuals. Criteria that establish virus-specific target cell killing as being T cell–mediated are either that HLA-matched targets are consistently lysed to a greater degree than mismatched targets or that cytotoxicity is present in T cell–enriched, but not T cell–depleted, fractions of lymphocytes.

Immunoregulatory Cells

The major cell types involved in immunoregulation are helper and suppressor cells. These cells are T lymphocytes, form rosettes with sheep erythrocytes, and possess T cell antigens defined by monoclonal antibodies. In addition, cell surface antigens have been defined using monoclonal antibodies that are specific for helper T cells (CD4+) and suppressor and cytotoxic T cells (CD8+). The helper T cell (CD4+) population recognizes both nonself MHC-II molecules and antigens in association with class II MHC molecules.[285] The CD4+ population of lymphocytes can be further subdivided into two types based on differences in function and membrane antigen expression. These two types of CD4+ cells are the helper population and the inflammatory population.[286] Inflammatory CD4+ cells express the high-density CD45R differentiation antigens on their cell surface, and are capable of mediating MHC-II–restricted cytotoxic activity, DTH, and suppression of immunoglobulin secretion. Inflammatory CD4+ cells also release IL-2 and gamma interferon, and modulate cellular immune function through this mechanism. In contrast, helper activity for specific antibody production is resident in the helper CD4+ subpopulation. In keeping with this function, helper cells release IL-4, a stimulatory lymphokine for B cells, rather than IL-2 and

gamma interferon. A function common to both cell types is stimulation of B cell proliferation and subsequent polyclonal IgG secretion. Both cell types release IL-3 and granulocyte-monocyte colony–stimulating factor. Thus, generation of both functional humoral immunity and cell-mediated responses are dependent upon CD4+ cell activity. The most extreme example of the critical role of CD4+ cells in immune responses is acquired immunodeficiency syndrome (AIDS) where many immunopathologic abnormalities can be directly or indirectly related to the depletion of the CD4-bearing T lymphocyte subset. The immunologic derangements observed in AIDS are summarized later in the chapter.

Like the T lymphocyte population that recognized antigens in association with MHC class II molecules, the CD8+ MHC class I–restricted lymphocyte is dichotomous for function and cell surface markers. The CD8+ CD11b− cytotoxic T cells have been discussed in detail. The other major subclass, the CD8+, CD11b+ suppressor cells, serve an immunoregulatory function.

In vitro, suppressor cells inhibit antigen and mitogen-induced T cell proliferation and immunoglobulin synthesis. In vivo, it is probable that suppressor cells function to limit the extent and duration of desirable immune responses, and to prevent deleterious responses against self-antigens.[287]

To date, the regulatory mechanisms involved in suppressor cell activity have not been fully elaborated. However, some cellular interactions and soluble mediators involved in suppression have been defined using in vitro models. The proliferation of suppressor cells is dependent upon antigen receptor stimulation and two lymphokines, an 8-kd protein designated T suppressor cell growth factor (TsGF), and IL-2, derived from the inflammatory subset of CD4+ cells. TsGF functions to increase the expression of IL-2 receptors on the surface of resting suppressor cells, thus serving as a cofactor for IL-2–driven suppressor cell proliferation.[288] Differentiation of the expanded suppressor precursors is dependent upon monocyte-derived substances including an indomethacin-sensitive product which is probably a prostaglandin, followed by secondary stimulation with gamma interferon.[289, 290]

The potential significance of these cell types interacting with other components of the immune response is self-evident. The normal ratio of helper cells to suppressor cells in circulating lymphocyte populations is about 1.7:1, and the sum of these two is approximately equal to the total T cell population.[291] In CMV[292] and EBV[293] infections inversion of the helper-to-suppressor cell ratios occurs. This inversion could underlie the reduced capacity of some infected patients to develop adequate immune responses to other types of opportunistic infections. Drug-induced abnormalities in immunoregulatory cell function may have significance in viral infections. For example, the drug cyclosporin A is presently in wide use experimentally for prevention of graft rejection and graft-versus-host disease in transplant recipients.[294] The mechanism of action of this drug apparently involves direct or indirect enhancement of suppressor cell activity which permits the development of immunologic tolerance to alloantigens in the graft. While tolerance to alloantigens is desirable, a complete suppression of responses to viruses could have profound adverse effects. But to the contrary, administration of cyclosporin A reduces the requirement for other immunosuppressive therapies, such as OKT3 monoclonal antibodies and high-dose steroids, which significantly depress immune mechanisms important in viral infections. The net result is a reduction in life-threatening CMV infections, and increased survival following bone marrow and renal transplantation (A.E. Wittek et al, unpublished data, May 1988). Absence of helper cell function has been associated with susceptibility to serious infections in the common variable immunodeficiency syndrome.[295] In mice immunoregulation is under the influence of immune response genes, most of which are in the I region of the H2 complex.[296] The relevance of such genes for human immune responses to viral infections is unknown. The possibility that such genes exist is suggested by the association of certain immunopathologic conditions with specific HLA types.[297] A similar finding has been reported for recurrent herpes simplex virus infections.[298] The availability of specific monoclonal antibodies will simplify definition of abnormalities of immunoregulatory cell function in viral infections.

SOLUBLE MEDIATORS OF IMMUNE RESPONSE

Numerous soluble immunologically active proteins or protein-containing substances of molecular weight less than 100,000 daltons are elaborated by lymphocytes during immune responses. These factors, collectively called lymphokines, include the various interleukins, helper and suppressor factors, and interferons. The reader is referred to recent reviews for more extensive discussion of each of these substances.[226, 299–303, 303a, 303b, 303c]

Interleukins

Interleukins are a diverse group of low-molecular-weight proteins that serve as intercellular hormones of importance in immune and inflammatory processes To date, eight interleukins have been described. These mediators are predominantly, but not exclusively, produced by mononuclear cells. They are involved in various stages of maturation and differentiation of lymphocytes and other hematopoietic cells, and in the recruitment of inflammatory cells. Some functions currently attributed to this class of cytokines are summarized in Table 4–2.

IL-2 is the most extensively studied of the eight. Its role in the development of cytotoxic T cell responses was discussed above. IL-2 is produced by lymphocytes stimulated with T cell mitogens, such as phorbol myristic acetate and phytohemagglutinin M (PHA).[304] There are also cell lines that constitutively produce IL-2.[305] Most current research and clinical applications utilize recombinant IL-2 which is produced in *Escherichia coli*. Activity of IL-

Table 4–2
Classification of Interleukins

Interleukin	Functions	Synonyms
1	With antigen, activates T and B cells	Lymphocyte activation factor
	Inducer of colony-stimulating factors	Endogenous pyrogen
	Enhances NK and T cell cytocidal activity	Osteoclast activation factor
	Inducer of B cell growth and differentiation factors	
	Stimulates endothelial cell and fibroblast proliferation	
	Inducer of protaglandin E_2 synthesis	
	Endogenous pyrogen	
	Stimulates bone resorption	
2	T cell proliferation	T cell growth factor
	Augments LAK and NK cells	
3	Stimulates growth of hematopoietic cell lines	Multi-CSF
	Induces basophil proliferation	
4	Cofactor for proliferation of resting B cells	T replacing factor
	Induction of MHC-II antigens on B cells	B cell growth factor
	Enhancement of IgG_1 and IgE production	B cell stimulating factor I
	Augments CTL development	
	Inhibits IL-2–dependent LAK cells in humans	
5	Enhancement of IL-2–mediated killer cell induction	B cell growth factor II
	Induces proliferation of B cells	
	Enhancement of IgA and IgM production	
	Enhancement of IL-4–induced IgE production	
6	Promotes IgG synthesis by EBV-transformed B cells	B cell stimulating factor II
	Promotes growth of hybridomas and plasmacytomas	Interferon-β_2
	? Weak antiviral activity	26K protein
	Stimulates hepatocytes to produce acute-phase proteins	Hybridoma-plasmacytoma growth factor
	Differentiation of activated B cells to IgG secreting cells	B cell differentiation factor
7	Induces IL-2 receptor expression on CD4 and CD8 positive T cells	Pre B cell growth factor
	Stimulates T cell proliferation in the absence of IL-2	
	Supports growth of B cell progenitors	
8	Promotes neutrophil chemotaxis	Neutrophil chemotactic factor I

NK cells = natural killer cells; LAK cells = lymphokine-activated killer cells; MHC = major histocompatibility complex; CTL = cytotoxic T lymphocytes; IL = interleukin; EBV = Epstein-Barr virus; CSF = colony-stimulating factor.

2 is usually standardized by testing the ability of the preparation to support the growth of an IL-2–dependent continuous cell line.[304] The utilization of IL-2 for the stimulation of T lymphocytes from patients with adult T cell leukemia led to the discovery of the first human retrovirus, human T-lymphotropic virus, type I (HTLV-I),[306, 307] and was an instrumental tool in the discovery of HIV, the etiologic agent of AIDS.[103, 308]

Treatment of resting lymphocytes with IL-2 gives rise to a population of cells which can destroy malignant cells including melanomas, sarcomas, and carcinomas, but not normal cells, in short-term assays. These lymphokine-activated killer (LAK) cells are distinct from mature T cells and bear Fc receptors and the complement receptor C3bi.[309] LAK cells can be expanded both in vitro and in vivo with IL-2, and have been administered experimentally in conjunction with IL-2 as immunotherapy of cancer in man. IL-2 causes changes in endothelial cell function, leading to increased capillary permeability, and resulting pulmonary edema, fluid retention, and organ dysfunction.[309]

IL-2 stimulates and activates T4 helper cells, NK cells, and cytotoxic T cells. Impaired IL-2 production, circulating suppressors of IL-2 production, T helper cell depletion, and deficiencies in lymphocyte effector functions, which are in part reversible in vitro with the addition of exogenous IL-2, are characteristics of AIDS which potentially could be reversed by addition of IL-2.[310]

Efforts to influence the course of AIDS by administration of IL-2 have not been promising. Lane et al treated 12 patients with AIDS with up to 250,000 units per day of intravenous (IV) recombinant IL-2 without observing any significant clinical responses.[311] In three patients with AIDS and Kaposi's sarcoma receiving 1×10^6 U IL-2/m²/day subcutaneously for 1 to 2 weeks, no changes in immune status were seen, although some clinical improvement in Kaposi's sarcoma lesions were observed.[312]

Interferons

Interferon (IFN) was first described in 1957 by Isaacs and Lindenmann who found that virus-infected cells produce a soluble factor that made uninfected cells resistant to virus challenge.[313] There are three major types of IFN: alpha, beta, and gamma. There are numerous species of alpha and beta IFN.

Alpha IFN is produced by leukocytes in response to virus challenge, and is the predominant type produced by lymphoblastoid cells.[314] Beta IFN is produced by fibroblasts induced by synthetic polynucleotides or viruses; it is also a minor component of IFN produced by lymphoblastoid cells. Gamma IFN is produced by lymphocytes stimulated with an antigen to which they are immune. In comparison to alpha and beta IFN, gamma IFN has relatively weak direct antiviral properties. However, it is a far more potent immunomodulator than other IFNs. Gamma IFN has now been recognized as the cytokine responsible for most activities ascribed to a number of poorly defined monocyte-macrophage–activating compounds including migration inhibitory factor (MIF),[305] macrophage chemotactic factor (MCF), and macrophage activation factor (MAF),[302] although it is probable that other cytokines possess similar activities.

All of the IFNs are proteins with molecular weights varying in the range of 15,000 to 27,000. Beta and gamma IFN are glycosylated, whereas most species of alpha IFN are nonglycosylated.

All three IFN classes have been produced by recombinant DNA technology in prokaryotic and eukaryotic cell lines. Alpha and beta IFN have been produced in *E coli*. Gamma IFN has been successfully purified from *E. coli* and mammalian cell lines.[301, 315] These recombinant molecules are equivalent to native IFNs in terms of specific activity and function, even when nonglycosylated. Using cDNA recombinant plasmids as probes to identify IFN genes, 14 separate loci coding for functional alpha IFN have been identified. These have substantial homology and constitute six linkage groups.[316] In contrast, only one gene codes for beta IFN, and one for gamma IFN.[315] It is possible that some alpha IFN genes may represent allelic variants of the same gene. Allelic variation of these genes could have important consequences in clinical studies since an individual could develop antibodies to an allelic variant recognized as foreign. Clinical studies tend to support this hypothesis, as antibodies to alpha IFN have been detected in some patients receiving IFN therapy.[317]

The availability of monoclonal antibodies to IFN has led to the development of sensitive ELISAs and RIAs for the various IFN classes. However, potency of most IFN preparations is still standardized in terms of the ability of the material to inhibit virus growth in tissue culture in comparison to a reference standard.[318] Most often the viruses used are vesicular stomatitis virus or encephalomyocarditis virus because they are highly sensitive to IFN effects. The choice of cell line used for measuring IFN is somewhat critical, particularly with reference to recombinant DNA–derived IFNs. Potency of IFN preparations is expressed in international units (IU) per milliliter. Specific activity is expressed as international units per milligram (IU/mg) of protein. One international unit is defined as the dilution of an IFN preparation that contains equivalent IFN activity to one dilution unit of an independent reference standard. IFNs purified to homogeneity have specific activities ranging from 1 to 4×10^8 IU/mg. Many of the early clinical studies were performed using leukocyte-derived IFN with specific activity of approximately 1×10^6 IU/mg. Most current clinical studies utilize highly purified IFN produced by recombinant DNA technology.

The mechanisms of action of IFNs are still under study. A number of biologic effects are known in addition to the viral inhibitory effect. At the molecular level, IFNs appear to affect enzymes involved in polysome formation and protein synthesis.[319] These changes may account for the virus inhibitory effect. A major effect of IFNs is their modulation of MHC antigens. All IFNs can induce increased expression of class I MHC antigens, including β_2-microglobulin.[320] Class II antigens are induced by gamma IFN.[321] Alteration in the expression of these cell surface antigens may be an important mechanism by which IFN modulates cellular interactions. Interferons can also modulate cellular growth and differentiation.[322] They can inhibit lymphocyte proliferative responses to antigens or mitogens[323] and growth of tumor cells.[324]

A number of adverse effects of IFN have been noted in clinical studies. Fever and myalgia are common after IFN administration, but some tolerance to these effects develops, and they are usually not effects that limit its use. Malaise is a common side effect and does not remit with continued treatment. It is a common reason for patients withdrawing from long-term treatment programs. Bone marrow suppression is a predictable side effect which is generally only dose-limiting in patients whose marrows are suppressed for other reasons. Hypotension has been seen rarely. Minor reversible alopecia has also been described. Reported effects on hepatic functions include mild elevation of serum transaminase, inhibition of the cytochrome P450 enzyme system,[325] and impaired metabolism of the antiviral drug, adenine arabinoside.[326]

As discussed above, IFNs can simulate NK cells and macrophages and may also affect cytotoxic T cell responses.[327] Therapeutic effects of IFN in viral infections could be related to either viral inhibitory effects or immune enhancing effects. Many viral infections have been treated experimentaly with IFN. Promising results were obtained by Greenberg and coworkers in treatment of chronic hepatitis B virus infections.[328] Using repeated cycles of IFN alternating with cycles of adenine arabinoside treatment, they were able to induce sustained remission of evidence of infection. These results were obtained in an open study and need to be confirmed. The same group of investigators, using leukocyte IFN for treatment of herpes zoster in immunosuppressed patients, shortened the time to healing of lesions and reduced the frequency of dissemination from the primary dermatome.[329] Very encouraging results have been obtained in treatment of recurrent laryngeal papilloma, a disease of childhood which is probably caused by a polyomavirus.[330] Treatment of this disease is normally surgical and often involves repeated hospitalization, general anesthesia, and tracheostomy. Hagland et al noted marked regression of lesions during IFN treatment, although recurrence was noted when treatment was discontinued.[330] It is not yet known whether long-term remission or cure can be obtained. Prophylactic use of IFN to prevent recurrence of herpesvirus infections after trigeminal nerve surgery[331] or renal transplantation[332] has been partially effective. Topical treatment of herpes keratitis is probably effective when coupled with limited debridement.[333] In one study, leukocyte IFN was shown to shorten the duration of viral shedding and accelerate lesion healing in primary genital herpes simplex virus (HSV) infections in women, although clinical benefit was no greater than that seen with acyclovir therapy, and treatment did not influence the frequency of recurrences.[334] In other studies, efficacy has not been demonstrated in recurrent genital HSV infections. Fulminant CMV infection in bone marrow transplant recipients did not respond to IFN therapy.[335] Intranasal inoculation of IFN reduced the severity of experimental influenza infection, but only when repeated, frequent administrations were applied.[336] A single case of herpes simplex encephalitis and three cases of rabies encephalitis have failed to respond to intrathecal IFN administration.[337, 338] All of these studies were performed using leukocyte IFN prepared by the Cantell method.[339]

The efficacy of recombinant alpha IFN for the prevention of respiratory infections has been assessed in a number of clinical trials. Intranasal IFN was shown to offer protection against experimentally induced influenza A virus infection. While the incidence and severity of respiratory illness were diminished, IFN treatment had no influence on the frequency of viral shedding.[340] When administered at lower doses, intranasal IFN showed no efficacy in the prevention of natural influenza virus infections, but was shown to reduce the incidence of rhinovirus colds and reduce the severity of parainfluenza virus infections.[341] Prophylaxis with IFN has also been shown to reduce the incidence of rhinovirus colds in a household setting.[342] Local symptoms such as nasal

congestion, blood-tinged mucous secretions, and nasal mucosal ulcerations are complications of this type of treatment.

Intralesional IFN is effective in the treatment of condyloma acuminata, including cases that are refractory to standard treatments.[343, 344]

Clinical improvement has been seen in several trials of recombinant alpha-2b interferon following short-course prednisone for the treatment of chronic hepatitis B infection. Markers of viral replication such as hepatitis B antigen and surface antigen were significantly reduced in some treated patients.[345, 346] The variable responses seen with treatment may reflect duration of infection or age at acquisition of infection, because efficacy of interferon therapy is much lower in patients who presumably acquired infection during infancy.[347] Interferon has also been shown to reduce liver enzyme levels in patients with chronic non-A, non-B hepatitis.[348]

Recombinant alpha IFN has also been tried in patients with AIDS, both for its possible effect on AIDS-associated Kaposi's sarcoma, and for evaluation of possible direct antiviral effect. Both alpha and beta IFN are suppressive to HIV in vitro.[349, 350] Krown and associates reported that IFN doses of 36 to 54 million units led to complete or partial tumor regression in some patients with Kaposi's sarcoma, and improvement in T4/T8 ratios, NK cell activity, and lymphocyte proliferative responses.[351] Likewise, Groopman et al found that alpha IFN treatment of Kaposi's sarcoma in AIDS resulted in some degree of tumor regression in 42% of patients.[352] Similar results were obtained by Lane and colleagues, who also observed decreases in HIV p24 antigen levels and reversion of HIV cultures to negative during therapy.[353] Response to IFN therapy in AIDS may be influenced by the clinical status of the patient. High response rates for Kaposi's sarcoma may be associated with higher CD4 counts at the start of therapy.[353] The effects of IFN therapy on asymptomatic HIV seropositive subjects is now being evaluated. Clinical trials of combination therapy of HIV infection with alpha IFN and zidovudine are also in progress.

IMMUNOPATHOLOGY OF VIRAL INFECTIONS

Viral replication is always intracellular, and neutralization of cell-free virus by immunoglobulin is a reversible process. Even when neutralization does occur, it may not be completely effective, and neutralizing antibodies do not develop until several days after onset of primary infection. Effective prevention of virus replication necessarily involves some attack by the immune system on infected cells in most or all cases. In this sense effective immunity against viruses can be considered a form of autoimmunity. In T cell–deficient mice, inoculation with lymphocytic choriomeningitis virus can lead to a chronic infection with relatively minor pathologic changes. Partial immunologic reconstitution of the animals by infusion of cytotoxic T cells from lymphocytic choriomeningitis virus–primed, MHC compatible donors led to severe hepatitis[354] or fatal encephalitis.[355] These observations not only support a role for cytotoxic T lymphocytes (CTLs) in viral-specific responses in vivo, but also serve to demonstrate that some virus-induced pathologic disorders may actually be the result of specific immune responses. When the immune response is rapid, highly specific, and efficient in destroying infected cells before virus replication has occurred, minimal damage to host cells occurs. If the immune response is relatively nonspecific, greater amounts of immune destruction of uninfected host cells may result. Possible examples of this type of immunopathologic disorder are seen in the effect of interferon treatment to exacerbate lymphocytic choriomeningitis virus infection in mice and the apparent association of CMV infection and graft rejection in renal transplant recipients.[356] A possible mechanism for this association is the induction of MHC antigen expression in the allograft in response to gamma interferon released as a consequence of CMV-specific immune responses.[357]

Immune complex disease is occasionally encountered during viral infections. Richardson and coworkers found that renal dysfunction following renal transplantation may be related to CMV antigen-antibody complex deposition.[358] Circulating immune complexes and vasculitis are seen in hepatitis B, rubella, and CMV infections.[359] Several manifestations of HIV infection, such as some glomerular diseases, appear to be due to immune complex deposition,[360, 360a] and other autoimmune phenomena such as idiopathic thrombocytopenic purpura are also observed in some infected individuals.[361] It has been proposed that severe respiratory syncytial virus[362] infection and atypical measles[363] during infection after killed-virus vaccination may result from systemic Arthus reactions. Other types of antibody-mediated immunopathologic changes are seen in the mononucleosis syndrome, including cold agglutinin hemolytic anemia and the development of a variety of different types of abnormal antibodies.[364]

Guillain-Barré syndrome has been associated with many viral infections,[365–367] although the cause-effect nature of these relationships and the pathogenesis of neurologic dysfunction is uncertain. The disease was also seen rarely in individuals who had received influenza vaccines containing A/New Jersey/76 (HSW1N1) antigens.[368] It has not been associated with more recent influenza vaccines.[369] Reye syndrome has been associated with influenza A and B, varicella, and a number of other viruses.[370] The pathogenesis of this disease is also unknown. Salicylates used for symtomatic treatment of the antecedent infection have been implicated as a cofactor in the causation of Reye syndrome.[371, 372] The observation that Reye and Guillain-Barré syndromes develop after resolution of the antecedent illness suggests that development of some late immune response may underlie their pathogenesis.

Some pathological processes seen in viral infections are related to the presence of specific immune-responsiveness alleles in the infected host. For example, a diffuse infiltrative lymphocytosis consisting primarily of CD8+ lymphocytes and clinically resembling Sjögren syndrome is seen in HLA-DR5 positive patients with HIV infection.[372a] Diabetes mellitus occurring after a viral syndrome also appears to be associated with the presence of specific MHC class II alleles in the host.

Suppressive effects of viral infections on the immune system are a form of immunopathologic abnormality. Mechanisms of viral suppression of immune function have been the subjects of two recent reviews.[373, 374] Cytomegalovirus and measles virus infections suppress lymphocyte responses to mitogens[194, 195] and predispose to infections with other agents.[198, 199] Reactivation of EBV infection during CMV infection has been noted.[375] Coinfection with both of these agents is common in AIDS.[376, 377] The lymphoid malignancies associated with chronic EBV infection[378] and the X-linked lymphoproliferative syndrome[379] may also be manifestations of virus-induced immunosuppression.

A number of chronic inflammatory diseases of unknown cause are characterized by polyclonal or oligoclonal gammopathy, such as multiple sclerosis and systemic lupus erythematosus. Patients with subacute sclerosing panencephalitis (SSPE) have increased spinal fluid immunoglobulins, often oligoclonal.[380] The relative concentrations of antimeasles virus antibodies in spinal fluid of patients with SSPE, compared to serum concentration, is much greater than could be accounted for by diffusion across the blood-brain barrier, indicating that the antibodies are produced locally in the central nervous system.[381] Recently, expression of measles virus genes coding for measles matrix protein was shown in the brain of a patient with SSPE using molecular probes.[382] There have been numerous conflicting reports concerning the presence or absence of antibodies specific for a number of pathogenic viruses in the serum and cerebrospinal fluid of patients with multiple sclerosis (MS).[383] Most recently, a role for HTLV-I in the pathogenesis of MS was proposed on the basis of a high frequency of serum antibodies to the virus in patients with MS.[384] Numerous subsequent studies have failed to confirm the observation.[385, 386]

Antigenic stimulation of B cells ordinarily results in an antigen-specific antibody response. When stimulation is excessive, however, a polyclonal, nonspecific response results.[387] B cell activation by EBV commonly induces nonspecific antibody production.[388] The occurrence of a similar polyclonal gammopathy in collagen vascular diseases raises questions regarding the nature of the antigenic stimulus (or stimuli) which induces the nonspecific response, as well as the possibility that the response includes production of autoantibodies. The etiologic significance of the sporadic reports of visualization of viruslike particles in tissues from patients with systemic lupus erythematosus is unknown.[389] It is possible that a viral agent acting as a polyclonal antibody inducer could be responsible for this disease.

ACQUIRED IMMUNODEFICIENCY SYNDROME

The acquired immunodeficiency syndrome (AIDS) was first recognized in 1981, following a clustering of cases of opportunistic infections and Kaposi's sarcoma among homosexual men.[390, 391] The etiologic agent of AIDS, the human immunodeficiency virus (HIV), was isolated in 1984.[103, 308] In the past 7 years, AIDS has evolved into a major pandemic, with cases being reported from every continent.

Most of the varied clinical manifestations of AIDS, particularly opportunistic infections and neoplasms, are sequelae of the failure of the immune system of the HIV-infected host. While our understanding of diverse aspects of HIV infections has rapidly increased, our comprehension of factors which influence the clinical manifestations of HIV infection, and the rate of progression to AIDS, is incomplete. The clinical course of HIV infection is most likely influenced by a complex interplay of viral effects and host immune responses.

Immunopathology of AIDS

Rouse and Horohov recently summarized four recognized

Table 4–3
Immunologic Abnormalities in Acquired Immunodeficiency
Syndrome (AIDS)

Abnormalities of T Lymphocytes

Depletion of CD4 + cells
Decreased delayed-type hypersensitivity responses
Decreased proliferative responses to mitogens and soluble
    antigens
Decreased proliferative response to alloantigens
Decreased cytotoxic T cell activity
Increased spontaneous proliferation
Increased expression of T cell activation markers (HLA DR, Tac)
Decreased B cell helper function

Abnormalities of B lymphocytes

Polyclonal B cell activation
Hypergammaglobulinemia
Increased number of circulating spontaneous plaque-forming cells
Decreased humoral response to immunization
Production of autoantibodies
Circulating immune complexes

Abnormalities of monocytes/macrophages

Defective chemotaxis
Decreased granulomatous response
Increased expression of IL-2 and Fc receptors
Defective Fc receptor binding and phagocytosis
Defective C3 receptor function
Decreased intracellular killing of microorganisms
Altered MHC Class II expression
Decreased accessory cell function?

Other immunologic abnormalities

Decreased natural killer cell activity
Decreased lymphokine production
Serum suppressor substances

mechanisms of virus-induced immunosuppression: (1) lysis or functional impairment of immunocompetent cells by complete or abortive viral replication; (2) release of host or virus-induced suppressor substances from infected cells; (3) viral lysis of or virus-induced damage to cells involved in nonspecific immune responses, phagocytosis, and antigen presentation; and (4) viral triggering of a regulatory imbalance leading to excessive suppressor activity.[374] Evidence points to the involvement of at least the first three of these mechanisms in the progressive immunodeficiency characteristics of AIDS. The recognition that HIV-specific humoral and cellular responses occur following infection raises the question of whether HIV stimulates the host to target its own immune system for destruction.

While the primary cellular target for HIV infection is the CD4 + T helper cell, and depletion of the CD4 population is a hallmark of AIDS, abnormalities in almost all aspects of immune function can occur in individuals infected with HIV (Table 4–3). Some immunologic abnormalities are direct effects of infection with HIV, while others may be secondary phenomena.

Abnormalities of T Lymphocytes

One of the immunologic abnormalities of AIDS recognized earliest was inversion in the ratio of helper to suppressor T lymphocytes. This abnormality is due predominantly to a progressive depletion of helper cells, whereas the CD8 + supressor/cytotoxic cell population is generally normal or only slightly increased or decreased. This selective depletion of CD4 + cells provided an

important clue to the cellular tropism of HIV, and guided investigators to a successful approach to viral isolation. The pathogenic mechanism or mechanisms leading to the loss of CD4 + cells is still not fully understood, and several mechanisms have been proposed.

HIV has a direct cytopathic effect on CD4 + cells. In vitro, HIV replicates in peripheral blood mononuclear cells (PBL) and CD4 + cell lines only if they are proliferating. Activation of latently infected CD4 + cells in vivo by antigen-specific or nonspecific mechanisms could lead to viral replication, cell death, and failure of clonal expansion of the stimulated T cells.[392, 393] Enhancement of viral replication with antigenic stimulation has been demonstrated in vitro.[394]

The CD4 molecule serves as a recognition site for MHC class II antigens. Two highly conserved sequences of the β_1 domain of human lymphocyte antigen (HLA) class II molecules show some homology with sequences of the gp41 portion of the HIV envelope glycoprotein.[395] Thus it is possible that HIV may mimic MHC class II molecules leading to nonspecific stimulation of CD4 + cells.[395, 396]

HIV itself has been reported to have direct stimulatory effects on T cell activation. Incubation of PBLs from noninfected individuals with disrupted HIV was shown to lead to increased expression of Tac antigen, the IL-2 receptor, and a marker of T cell activation.[397] It is unclear whether HIV causes lymphocyte activation in vivo. Reports of lymphocyte proliferation responses to HIV antigen in 50% to 70% of infected individuals[398] conflict with reports that HIV antigen–induced lymphoproliferation occurs in less than 5% of HIV-infected individuals without AIDS in another study.[399] Direct activation of CD4 + cells by HIV would provide an efficient circuit for enhanced viral replication, cytolysis, and elimination of specific immune responses against the virus.

Experiments in which the HIV-1 gp160 gene was cloned into human CD4 + and CD4 − cell lines have provided strong evidence for a direct cytotoxic effect of the HIV envelope protein in association with the CD4 molecule.[400a] While both CD4 + and CD4 − cells could be made to express gp160, cytopathic effect, syncitium formation, and cell death was only observed in cells bearing CD4.

Cells expressing HIV antigens may be targets of cytotoxic effector cells including cytotoxic T lymphocytes, NK cells, and cells that function in ADCC. Activity of any or all of these effector mechanisms in vivo could lead to destruction of those cells expressing HIV antigens, and depletion of the CD4 + cell population.[400] The depletion of T helper cells is a central feature of the immunodeficiency of AIDS, but other mechanisms have been found for specific functional impairment in T lymphocyte activities.

Lymphocytes from patients with HIV infection show decreased responsiveness to mitogens and antigens.[400] Lane and Fauci attributed mitogen unresponsiveness to helper cell depletion.[400] It has also been shown that whole virus or purified gp120 can suppress phytohemagglutinin (PHA)-stimulated blastogenesis,[401] and disrupted whole virus can suppress proliferative responses to PHA, Con A, and pokeweed mitogen (PWM).[397] Binding of gp120 to CD4 + cells can block adhesion of CD4 molecules to MHC class II antigens, disrupting the normal interactions between the helper T cells and antigen-presenting cells.[401a] Synthetic peptides with homology to regions of the gp41 transmembrane glycoprotein can suppress lymphocyte proliferative responses to Con A, PHA, and

PWM as well, although this effect is seen only following several days of preincubation of the responder cells with peptides conjugated to a protein carrier.[402]

Cytotoxic T cell responses are also impaired in HIV infection. While both CMV and EBV infections are frequently encountered in patients with HIV infection, CTL responses to these viruses are deficient.[403–405] Given that MHC-restricted cytotoxicity resides for the most part in the CD8+ subset of T cells, and that this population is spared in HIV infection, this phenomenon is likely due to lack of inducer signals ordinarily provided by CD4+ cells and macrophages, and which are required for the differentiation and expansion of CTL precursors into effector CTL. In the case of EBV, CTL activity correlates with CD4+ cell numbers and IL-2 production in vitro. Indeed, the addition of exogenous IL-2 permits restoration of CTL responses to both CMV and EBV in vitro.[403, 405] Alloantigen-specific CTL responses are also deficient in HIV infection.[406] Like viral specific responses, CTL activity can be restored to variable degrees by the introduction of exogenous IL-2. In contrast, deficient activity in autologous mixed lymphocyte cultures is not reversible by addition of increasing numbers of CD4+ cells.

Interleukin-2 and AIDS

Numerous immunologic abnormalities observed in patients with AIDS are at least partially reversible in vitro with exogenous IL-2. For the most part, these abnormalities appear to be secondary to the depletion of the CD4+ cell population. However, other mechanisms may also play a role in the deficiency in IL-2–mediated responses seen in AIDS.

Siegel and colleagues demonstrated the presence of a factor in sera from patients with AIDS which suppresses IL-2 production by PHA-stimulated PBL.[407] A similar activity was also found in the serum of one individual with active CMV infection secondary to a live viral challenge. The in vitro generation of factors which suppress IL-2 production in cultured mononuclear cells from patients with AIDS have also been reported.[408, 409] Another immunoglobulinlike serum factor has been described which suppresses IL-2 responsiveness in cell lines by decreasing the level of IL-2 receptor expression on the IL-2–dependent target cell.[410] Thus, mechanisms other than depletion of the major cellular source of IL-2 may play a role in the deficiencies in IL-2–dependent immune processes in AIDS.

Natural Killer Cells

NK cell populations appear to be resistant to HIV, and thus are not depleted until late in the course of HIV infection. Likewise, their binding to target cells is essentially intact.[411] In advanced stages of AIDS there can be a profound deficiency in NK activity.[403, 412] Deficient NK activity is reversible in vitro with IL-2.[403, 412]

Abnormalities of B Lymphocytes

B cell abnormalities are a prominent feature of HIV infection. Polyclonal activation of B cells with hypergammaglobulinemia is a frequent observation. Immunoglobulin-secreting B cells are present in the circulation in unusually large numbers. Circulating immune complexes, and autoantibodies to normal and viral-associated cell constituents, may contribute to the pathologic changes of HIV infection. While small numbers of B cells express CD4 antigen,

and EBV-transformed B cells can be infected with HIV in vitro, direct infection of B cells is not considered a major pathogenic mechanism.

Despite this hyperactivity of the humoral immune system, challenge with new or recall antigens such as keyhole limpet hemocyanin (KLH) and influenza virus vaccine result in no or weak antibody responses[413] (KS Chen et al, unpublished data, October 1988). Clinical manifestation of this loss of specific antibody production is most prominent in children, where recurrent bacterial infections are common, although it is now recognized that pyogenic infections occur with increased frequency in adult patients with AIDS.

There may be multiple mechanisms for the B cell abnormalities observed in AIDS. Both EBV and CMV can cause polyclonal B cell activation, and infections with these viruses are common in HIV-infected patients. The high frequency of spontaneously proliferating B cells in these patients is consistent with a role of EBV in some of the B cell abnormalities observed.[414] In addition, HIV itself is a potent stimulator of polyclonal IgG production by a T cell–dependent mechanism.[414, 415] Very high levels of IL-6, which induces the differentiation of activated B cells into IgG-secreting cells, are measurable in the serum of individuals infected with HIV, and IL-6 production in cultured lymphocytes from infected subjects is also markedly elevated.[415a] The disruption of normal regulatory T cell activity may permit this unrestricted activation of B cells to continue.[400] Paradoxically, HIV antigens can be potent inhibitors of B cell proliferation induced by PWM or EBV by both direct effects on the B cell and indirectly through T cells.[397, 415]

Recently, a discrepancy between in vitro antibody responses to T cell–dependent and T cell–independent antigens was shown. Following immunization with tetanus toxoid or inactivated poliovirus vaccine, PBLs from HIV-seropositive individuals failed to proliferate or produce specific antibodies when stimulated with the respective T cell–dependent antigen. Stimulation of the PBL with tetanus toxoid coupled to agarose beads, which functions as a T cell–independent antigen, resulted in the generation of IgG anti-tetanus toxoid antibody–forming cells.[416] While other accessory cells may have been responsible for the failure to produce antibodies, this observation suggests that at least in part, weak or absent specific antibody responses following infection or immunization may be due to the depletion of or functional defects in the T helper cell population.

The role of circulating immune complexes in AIDS is unclear. Both thrombocytopenic purpura[361] and a glomerulopathy[360] have been observed in some HIV-infected individuals and may be associated with circulating immune complex. Immune complexes containing predominantly IgM,[417] IgG,[418] and IgA[419, 420] have been described. The presence of IgA immune complexes is of note, since serum IgA has no known function, and its presence may prevent recognition and binding of functional antibodies of the IgM and IgG classes. If this effect occurs, elevated levels of IgA and IgA immune complexes may be detrimental.[419]

Monocytes and Macrophages

There is a growing body of evidence to suggest that monocytes and macrophages play a major role in the pathogenesis and propagation of HIV infection. Monocytes can be infected with HIV in vitro, and HIV has been isolated from macrophages in the brain,[421] follicular dendritic cells in lymph nodes,[422, 423] and peripheral blood monocytes.[394, 424–426] Susceptibility of monocytes to infection with HIV correlates with the expression of CD4 on the monocyte cell surface.[394, 426] Unlike CD4 + cells, monocytes are refractory to the lytic effects of HIV, and the persistently infected cells may serve, chronically or intermittently, as major sources of infectious virus in vivo.

Production of infectious virus by monocytes may be influenced by cytokines, including colony-stimulating factors.[427] Latently infected monocytes may not display viral antigens on their cell surface, enabling them to evade detection and destruction by specific cytotoxic immune mechanisms.[428] Such cells could disseminate HIV to the brain, lungs, and other organs. Pauza has developed a compelling argument for the integral role of monocytes in the subversion of normal immune responses through virus dissemination and helper cell depletion.[428]

The question of whether or not infection of monocytes leads to functional impairment is rather controversial. Some investigators have reported that accessory cell functions, such as MHC class II antigen expression,[429] IL-1 production, and participation in T cell proliferative responses,[430] are generally intact in HIV-infected individuals, including patients with AIDS. Others report defects in accessory cell functions in monocytic cell lines infected with HIV and in monocytes from infected subjects.[431, 432] Monocyte chemotactic responses to a variety of stimuli can also be impaired[433, 434] and defective chemotaxis in vivo may also occur because of the absence of chemotactic factors derived from CD4 + lymphocytes. There is controversy as well regarding whether intracellular killing of microorganisms by monocytes from patients with HIV infection is also impaired.[434, 435]

Immune Responses to HIV Infection

Following infection with HIV, most individuals develop humoral and cellular immune responses. The interval from the onset of clinically recognized infection to the production of anti-HIV antibodies is highly variable, ranging from several weeks to several months.[436] There are anecdotal reports of individuals who have failed to seroconvert for over three years following primary infection with HIV.[436a] While specific patterns of antibody reactivity vary among individuals, antibodies reactive with products of the major structural gene of HIV, gag, tend to precede development of antibodies to envelope glycoproteins when analyzed by western blot.[437, 438] This selectivity may be artifactual, as RIPA on sera from early seroconverters can demonstrate antienvelope reactivity concomitant with or prior to an anti-p24 response,[439] and RIPA appears, in general, to be a more efficient means than western blot for detecting antibodies to the large envelope glycoproteins gp120 and gp160.[82]

Humoral immune responses to HIV include reactivity to the gag proteins p55, p24, and p17; the polymerase (pol) gene products endonuclease (p31) and reverse transcriptase (p66); and the envelope glycoproteins gp160, gp120, and gp41. The intensity of responses to specific viral antigens can be highly variable. Efforts have been made to correlate patterns of antibody response to disease status or progression. A loss of anti-p24 reactivity late in the course of infection is associated with disease progression and development of p24 antigenemia.[440–442]

As described previously, a number of assays have been developed for the measurement of functions of antibody responses to HIV. Neutralizing antibodies are detected in the sera of many patients with HIV infection.[8, 10–14, 16] In studies of patients with varying degrees of severity of infection, results have not been consistent with respect to correlation between clinical status and the presence of neutralizing antibodies. However, a recent study suggests that antibodies directed against a peptide sequence that represents part of the major neutralizing epitope of the virus[442a] may be associated with an uninfected status of children born to women infected with HIV-1.[442b] The reported prevalence of neutralizing antibodies ranges from 71% to 88% in asymptomatic patients, from 73% to 96% for patients with AIDS-related complex (ARC) and lymphadenopathy, and from 67% to 100% in patients with AIDS.[8, 11, 12] When highly sensitive tests are used it is rare to find patients with AIDS who lack antibodies, while negative results are obtained consistently in a proportion of asymptomatic patients. In a study where limited numbers of individual patients were followed longitudinally, rising neutralizing antibody titers appeared associated with a stable clinical course, and it was suggested that increasing neutralizing antibody titers may prevent disease progression.[13, 14] Another possible explanation for this observed association is that patients with rising titers were early in the clinical course of infection and had yet to achieve a peak neutralizing antibody response. In a prospective study of early seroconverters, neutralizing antibody appeared to develop approximately 16 to 18 months after a decline in CD4 + cells was noted, and may have been associated with a decrease in the rate of decline in the CD4 cell count.[442c]

When neutralizing antibody titers are compared with reactivity against HIV by ELISA, very poor correlations are found.[11, 14, 442a] When compared to antigen-specific reactivity on western blots, neutralizing antibody titers correlate with reactivity to gp120. The envelope glycoprotein is the site of neutralizing epitopes on HIV.[12, 13, 442a] Animals immunized with recombinant envelope glycoproteins or synthetic peptides representing neutralizing epitopes develop neutralizing antibodies.[343, 443, 444]

Some investigators have also reported a paradoxical increase in the in vitro infectivity of HIV-1 in the presence of HIV-antibody positive serum induced by infection or vaccination.[444a, 444b] One proposed mechanism for this antibody-mediated enhancement is that enhanced viral entry into monocytes can be effected by binding of virions complexed to specific antibody via the Fc receptor. The significance of this phenomenon in terms of pathogenesis is unclear, but constitutes a major concern in terms of development of vaccines for AIDS. It has also been shown that cells other than lymphocytes and monocyte/macrophages can be rendered sensitive to infection with HIV-1 by the induction of Fc receptors on their surface by infection with CMV.[444c] This may be one explanation for the apparent correlation between active CMV infection and severity of AIDS.

Antibodies which mediate anti-HIV ADCC have been identified following natural infection.[280, 281, 445–448] Like neutralizing antibodies, antibodies capable of participating in ADCC are prevalent in infected patients. In one study, ADCC was measured in sera from 53% of asymptomatic seropositives, 78% of patients with ARC, and 83% of patients with AIDS.[280] Whether levels of ADCC activity correlate with disease stage is still unclear. In conflicting studies, Ljunggren and associates[447] found that ADCC titers were lower in patients with AIDS than in asymptomatic carriers, whereas Shepp and coworkers[280] found that ADCC activity at a titer of 1:1000 was more common among those with symptomatic disease than among a small group of healthy seropositive volunteers. The development of ADCC responses early in the course of HIV infection may be associated with slower rates of decline in CD4 cell counts, and a lower incidence of lymphadenopathy in the first two years following infection.[442c] ADCC-mediating antibodies can be directed toward determinants on the HIV envelope glycoprotein gp120.[280, 281, 445] In addition, Rook et al reported that ADCC activity correlated closely with the level of antibody to the HIV core antigen p24.[448] Antibodies that mediate ADCC appear to be more broadly reactive against a variety of HIV strains than neutralizing antibodies.

Lymphoproliferative responses to solubilized, inactivated HIV antigens have been reported in 50% of asymptomatically infected intravenous drug abusers. Among drug abusers with lymphadenopathy and AIDS, lymphoproliferative responses were seen in 70% and 54%, respectively.[398]

Cytotoxic T lymphocytes, as previously described, are an important effector mechanism in numerous viral infections including influenza and CMV infections.[201, 255, 262] Several reports describing CTL responses to HIV infection have appeared.[449–455] CTL activity has been demonstrated against a number of viral antigens including gp120, p24, and p55. CTL activity appears to be a fairly common response to HIV infection. In one study, 20 of 20 asymptomatic seropositive volunteers had circulating CTLs specific for HIV envelope–expressing targets, and in another, eight of ten patients had CTL activity directed against HIV p55.[451, 455] The frequency and magnitude of CTL responsiveness falls as HIV infection progresses.[452, 453] Circulating CTLs against gag-expressing targets appear to be somewhat less common, but can be induced by secondary in vitro stimulation with p24 antigen.[455] CTLs have been recovered from bronchoalveolar lavage fluid of patients with lymphocytic interstitial pneumonitis. These cells lyse autologous infected alveolar macrophages, and may be involved in the pathogenesis of this common complication of AIDS.[450] Envelope antigen–specific CTLs have not been found to be virus strain–specific.[452, 453] Thus, it has been hypothesized that the target of anti-gp120 CTL is a conserved region of the glycoprotein.

The ultimate objectives of defining the immunopathogenesis of HIV infection are the development of methods of infection prevention and treatment. For example, because of the high affinity of HIV-1 envelope for the CD4 molecule on the surface of helper T cells, therapy with CD4 has been proposed as a potential treatment for HIV infection. Preliminary data from phase I clinical trials of recombinant soluble CD4 show that the therapy is well tolerated, but an antiviral effect has not clearly been demonstrated.[455a, 455b] Clinical trials of candidate AIDS vaccines have begun in the form of very small pilot studies. In the absence of animal models of AIDS vaccine efficacy, it is difficult to conceive of eventual directions of AIDS vaccine development. However, the definition of specific immune responses to HIV and of mechanisms of suppression of immune function may clarify the nature of immune responses necessary to protect against AIDS. Such studies have already led to experimental approaches to AIDS therapy. Interleukin-2 treatment modifies some immune activities in vivo, but does not correct immunodeficiency. Alpha interferon has activity against Kaposi's sarcoma in AIDS and inhibits HIV replication in vitro and possibly in vivo. A possible role of bone marrow transplantation has also been studied.[445c] The realization of benefits by patients and those at risk of HIV infection from understanding of the immunopathogenesis of AIDS awaits further development.

RAPID DIAGNOSIS OF VIRAL INFECTIONS

Rapid diagnosis of viral infections is useful for patient management and for guiding public health infection control measures. Effectiveness of anti-infective treatment of viral diseases is dependent on early initiation of treatment, at least in the case of herpesvirus infections and influenza.[456–459] The need for rapid containment of infected mosquito populations during outbreaks of flavivirus encephalitis exemplifies the importance of rapid diagnosis in public health measures. Standard approaches to laboratory diagnosis of viral infections are often painfully slow. Diagnosis by virus isolation from infected fluids or tissues is costly and, in some cases (eg, CMV), requires several weeks. Diagnosis by demonstration of seroconversion requires 2 or more weeks to collect acute and convalescent sera. Conventional approaches to more rapid diagnosis rely on demonstration of virus-specific IgM in acute sera and the histologic appearance of infected tissues typical of a specific agent. In addition, there are a few situations in which acute sera contain unique diagnostic antibodies such as heterophile antibodies in infectious mononucleosis.[364]

Indirect immunofluorescence and immunoenzymatic staining with peroxidase-conjugated antibodies can both be used to stain viral antigens in frozen sections of tissue biopsies, and immunoenzymatic staining has been used to examine sections of fixed tissues.[60] Direct immunofluorescent assays on cells scraped from the base of vesicular skin lesions can rapidly establish the diagnosis of herpes simplex virus or varicella-zoster virus infection,[460] and direct immunofluorescent staining of cells in nasal washes or nasopharyngeal swabs can verify infection with a number of respiratory pathogens.[461] These techniques have suffered in the past from nonspecificity. However, newer monoclonal antibody reagents have increased the specificity of direct immunofluorescent techniques. Immunofluorescent and immunoenzymatic techniques have also been utilized in conjunction with virus isolation techniques to accelerate viral diagnosis. CMV-induced early antigens can be detected by staining of tissue culture monolayers in advance of the appearance of any cytopathic effect visible by routine light microscopy.[462, 463]

Numerous RIA and ELISA assays have been developed for the rapid detection of viral antigens in clinical samples. The oldest and most widely utilized antigen detection test is that for hepatitis B surface antigen. Rapid antigen capture ELISA assays have also been developed for the detection of enteroviruses,[464] rotaviruses,[75] influenza virus,[74] respiratory syncytial virus,[465] and adenoviruses.[466] With the advent of effective antiviral therapies for some herpesvirus infections, the availability of rapid diagnostic tests has assumed clinical importance. ELISA assays have been developed for the detection of herpes simplex and varicella-zoster virus antigens.[467–469] Attempts to develop ELISA assays for CMV antigens have met with less success.[470, 471] HIV p24 core antigenemia may occur early in HIV infection.[436] The role of HIV antigen detection assays in applications such as diagnosis and patient monitoring awaits further definition.

Cell-mediated immunity studies are not currently used for routine clinical diagnosis. One type of assay has the potential for use in making early diagnosis, at least in a research setting. Specifically, cytotoxic T cells are apparently present only during acute infection, and documentation that this response has occurred should establish the presence of infection with the virus being tested.

IMMUNIZATION AGAINST VIRAL INFECTIONS

Viral vaccines have had an astounding impact on public health. To appreciate their significance, one need only consider the current world situation with regard to measles epidemiology. In some countries the mortality rate associated with measles infection is as high as 5% to 10%, and nearly 100% of nonvaccinated individuals become infected in childhood: one of every 20 children born dies from this preventable childhood illness. The impact of vaccines against paralytic poliomyelitis, rabies, and congenital rubella syndrome in the United States has been similarly impressive. The complete eradication of smallpox must be regarded as one of the outstanding accomplishments of modern public health efforts. Measles and polioviruses have characteristics similar to smallpox that may eventually permit their eradication, as well. These characteristics include: (1) the only natural hosts for the viruses are humans; (2) infection confers lifelong immunity to all related strains of the specific virus; (3) prolonged asymptomatic virus shedding or reactivation of latent virus in a previously infected host does not occur; (4) infection is associated with a clearly recognizable disease syndrome, so that rapid identification of cases and outbreaks is possible; and (5) vaccines are available that may be effective in one or a few doses. These diseases are included in those targeted by WHO's Expanded Program on Immunization.

Traditionally, viral vaccines were of two general types: live and killed. Live virus vaccines induce immunity by producing modified infection in the vaccinee. In general, the amount of virus antigen inoculated in these vaccines is not sufficient to induce a protective immune response unless virus replication takes place. In most cases live vaccines are attenuated viruses; the vaccine virus has been modified in some way, such as serial passage in tissue culture so that it is less able to produce disease in humans. One live virus vaccine that is not attenuated is an adenovirus vaccine that is administered orally in an enteric-coated capsule.[472] By this route the respiratory system is not infected but the virus replicates in the intestines and induces immunity. To be suitable for a live vaccine, a virus strain must rarely produce significant illness yet induce immunity in almost all vaccinated individuals. No live vaccine is absolutely perfect in both respects. Vaccine virus replication may occasionally fail to occur because of interfering antibodies passively acquired transplacentally or from blood products. Conversely, symptomatic infection is occasionally encountered, particularly in an individual with suppressed immunity.

Immune responses to killed virus vaccines are quantitatively related to the amount of antigen inoculated.[100] Attenuation of the virus is not necessary and the vaccines can be safely administered to individuals with suppressed immunity. Adverse effects are uncommon and are relatively minor except for rare serious allergic reactions and unexpected reactions such as Guillian-Barré syndrome associated with swine influenza vaccines.[368] Immunity induced by inactivated vaccines may be less persistent than after live vaccines, as is the case with measles and mumps. Killed measles[473] and respiratory syncytial virus[474] vaccines induced atypical immunity which resulted in more serious or atypical infection upon exposure to live virus, rather than protection. This type of response does not occur after administration of rabies, influenza, and inactivated poliovirus vaccines. Since killed virus vaccines require more viral antigen, they are more costly than live vaccines. Conversely, responses to them are not usually inhibited by passively acquired antibodies. Each of the two types of vaccine has advantages and disadvantages that determine which type of vaccine is most appropriate for protection against any given virus.

Passive immunization is useful for prophylaxis against several viruses, including hepatitis A and B,[114, 115] rabies,[118] and varicella-zoster viruses.[117] Some recent studies of IV immunoglobulin preparations in immunosuppressed patients have shown benefit in the prevention of primary CMV disease.[475] Immunoglobulin was previously administered concurrently with live measles vaccine but is not necessary with the more attenuated strain.[113] It may be helpful for immunosuppressed individuals exposed to measles.

General recommendations for vaccination are made periodically by the US Public Health Service's Immunization Practices Advisory Committee and the American Academy of Pediatrics Committee on Infectious Diseases. Specific recommendations are also discussed in the respective chapters of this text.

A number of experimental vaccines are now being tested. A live, attenuated varicella virus[178] developed in Japan protected normal and immunosuppressed children and susceptible adults. The vaccine is commercially available in Japan and Europe, but is still under investigation in the United States.[52] A candidate live CMV vaccine[181] has been tested in patients awaiting renal transplantation, but its efficacy remains unclear. A herpes simplex virus glycoprotein subunit vaccine has also been used in early clinical trials.[476] The eventual applications of herpesvirus vaccines may be quite different from most current viral vaccines. They might not prevent subsequent infection, but they may reduce severity of disease or the development of latency. The immunologic functions responsible for protective immunity and control of latency in these infections need to be better defined.

Initial results obtained on testing of an experimental dengue virus type 2 vaccine suggest that individuals with prior immunity to yellow fever virus were more likely to develop immune responses. Infection with wild dengue virus is more severe in the presence of cross-reactive antibodies.[477] Cross-reactive immunity may result in a greater degree of internalization of the virus into macrophages, with resultant enhancement of both virus replication and antigen processing.[204]

Advances in molecular biology and recombinant DNA technology have permitted the synthesis of highly purified viral antigens for use as vaccines. Recombinant HBsAg vaccines are now commercially available.[478, 479]

The AIDS epidemic has spurred a vigorous effort at vaccine development. Recombinant proteins and glycoproteins of HIV expressed in bacteria, yeast, mammalian, and insect cells are in various stages of development as possible vaccines.[480–485] The solid-phase synthesis of peptides homologous to structural components of HIV is another approach under study.[486] The large size of the vaccinia virus genome has also been exploited for the purpose of developing live recombinant viral vaccines. Deletion of nonessential genes of vaccinia permits the insertion of foreign genes, such as the HIV envelope gene, into the vaccinia genome.[487, 488] Viral replication leads to the expression of the inserted gene, stimulating immune responses. Other virsues such as adenovirus and herpes simplex virus can be used as vectors similarly. Anti-idiotype monclonal antibodies, which mimic viral antigens conformationally, have also been developed.[132, 133] The development of improved adjuvants is an important aspect of vaccine development, and substances such as muramyl tripeptide[489, 490] and immune-stimulating complexes, or ISCOMs,[491] are likely to be evaluated as components of newer viral vaccines. Advances in viral immunology should facilitate new vaccine development as well as progress in antivirals, immune response modulators, and patient management and health.

IMMUNITY AND VIRUS LATENCY

Latent viral infection, specifically with herpesviruses, involves active immunologic processes that prevent reactivation. Drug-induced immunosuppression results in prompt reactivation of CMV infection in a murine model.[492] A similar effect is probably reflected in the high frequency of reactivation of herpesvirus infections after allograft transplantation. This close relationship of immunosuppression to reactivation suggests that latent virus is frequently in a state of activation, but that overt reactivation is prevented by specific immunity.

In addition to immunosuppression, host cell proliferation may result in reactivation of latent virus. For example, long-term culture of B cells latently infected with EBV[493] and cultivation of spleen[494] or ganglion[495] explants harboring CMV or herpes simplex virus all result in expression of viral protein or virus replication. Immune stimulation of lymphocytes by cocultivation with allogeneic cells induces lymphocyte proliferation and has been reported to activate latent murine CMV[496] and type C virus infections.[497] Measles virus can persist in lymphocytes in vivo and be activated by cocultivation.[498] The allogeneic stimulus provided by blood transfusion or transplantation may account for infection occurring in this setting. The extremely high rates of reactivation of herpesvirus infections in transplant recipients may result from the combined effects of immunosuppression and allogeneic stimulation.

It is probably an important manifestation of the mechanism of latent and persistent infections that they tend to occur in immunologically privileged sites. By establishing nonlytic infection within immune cells, EBV escapes immunologic elimination. Herpes simplex and varicella-zoster viruses apparently reside in relatively privileged sites within the nervous system. A similar phenomenon characterizes slow viral diseases, such as kuru and subacute sclerosing panencephalitis, which are central nervous system infections.

The specific immune functions that prevent reactivation of latent infection are unknown. Cheeseman et al.[332] found that prophylactic interferon treatment could delay reactivation of CMV and EBV infections after renal transplantation. Interferon could inhibit virus replication directly or could stimulate other functions, such as NK cells or antibody-dependent killer cells. Decline of

serum antibody levels has been associated with herpes simplex virus reactivation and antibody production is often depressed after transplantation. The immunosuppressive drug treatments that are associated with reactivation have varied and often multiple effects on the immune system, so it is difficult to speculate, on the basis of drug effects alone, on which suppressed functions may be critical to preventing reactivation. However, the occurrence of reactivation in some patients with high serum antibody levels suggests that cell-mediated immunity is involved. Cellular functions that persist during latent infections and may contribute to control of latency include DTH[499] and ADCC.[500] Observations during herpes simplex virus latency suggest that virus reactivation may be subclinical in some instances. Virus particles can be found in nerve axons or in dermal tissue in the absence of overt evidence of infection or inflammation.[501] Hence, soluble factors (ie, antibodies, interferon, etc) may be sufficient to control reactivation in some circumstances, whereas cellular mechanisms appear to be essential once these mechanisms are overcome.

CONCLUSION

Study of the immunology of viral infections is important for facilitating the diagnosis, treatment, and prevention of viral diseases. Discoveries and technological developments made over the last two decades have markedly enhanced the value and potential value of this discipline. The significance of monoclonal antibodies, recombinant and synthetic antigens, and solid-phase assay techniques for diagnosis of viral infections is obvious. The potential for rational immunotherapy of viral infections can now be envisioned. Some critical conceptual advances provide the basis for potential development of therapeutics. The definition of specific functions which were once referred to collectively as cell-mediated immunity and the ongoing definition of the role of these functions in disease states is at the heart of this progress. The application of monoclonal antibodies and cell-sorting technologies have resulted in progressive refinement in the understanding of the numbers and functions of different classes of lymphocytes. The application of recombinant DNA technologies has resulted in the discovery and functional characterization of many lymphokines. As a result of these developments, it is evident that immunologic effector functions will be understood, in a progressively improving way, as a biochemical process which follows the proliferation and differentiation of these effectors through a regulated series of events. Once the effects of lymphokines on various cell types are well enough understood, it should be possible to define immunodeficiencies at the biochemical level and modulate them by selective therapy.

With regard to prevention, the capacity to produce candidate vaccines by numerous techniques is now an almost trivial reality. A new era in adjuvant research may lead to significant new ways of presenting antigens to the immune system. Perhaps more important than the capacity to make vaccines is the value of new technologies in facilitating studies of disease pathogenesis, which forms the basis for determining how vaccines should be made. The extraordinary advances in viral immunology in the past decade contrast sharply with the emergence of AIDS as a problem in diagnosis, treatment, and prevention. Consideration of the decade ahead evokes great apprehension and anticipation.

REFERENCES

1. Gunven P, Klein G: Blocking of direct membrane immunofluorescence in titration of membrane-reactive antibodies associated with Epstein-Barr virus. *J Natl Cancer Inst* 1962; 9:1–125.
2. Fazekas de St Groth S: The neutralization of viruses. *Adv Virus Res* 1962; 9:1–125.
3. Royston I, Aurelian L: The association of genital herpesvirus with cervical atypia and carcinoma in situ. *Am J Epidemiol* 1970; 91:531–538.
4. Webb PA, Johnson KM, MacKenzie RB: The measurement of specific antibodies in Bolivian hemorrhagic fever by neutralization of virus plaques. *Proc Soc Exp Biol Med* 1969; 130:1013–1019.
5. Dowdle WR, Laver WG, Galphin JC, et al: Antigenic relationships among influenza virus A neuraminidase (N2) antigens by immunodiffusion and postinfection neutralization tests. *J Clin Microbiol* 1976; 3:233–238.
6. Smith JS, Yager PA, Baer GM: A rapid reproducible test for determining rabies neutralizing antibody. *Bull WHO* 1973; 48:535–541.
7. Schmidt NJ, Lennette EH, Hanahoe MF: Microneutralization test for the reoviruses. Application to detection and assay of antibodies in sera of laboratory animals. *Proc Soc Exp Biol Med* 1966; 121:1268–1275.
8. Vujcic LK, Shepp DH, Klutch M, et al: Use of a sensitive neutralization assay to measure the prevalence of antibodies to the human immunodeficiency virus. *J Infect Dis* 1988; 157:1047–1050.
9. Faulkner-Valle GP, DeRossi A, Dalla Gassa O, et al: Human retrovirus infection and immunodeficiencies. Detection and significance of virus-neutralizing antibodies. *Antibiot Chemother* 1987; 38:159–166.
10. Robert-Guroff M, Brown M, Gallo RC: HTLV-III–neutralizing antibodies in patients with AIDS or AIDS-related complex. *Nature* 1985; 316:72–76.
11. Prince AM, Pascual D, Bardina-Kosolopov L, et al: Neutralizing antibody to the AIDS virus. Prevalence, clinical significance and virus strain specificity. *Antibiot Chemother* 1987; 38:151–158.
12. Groopman JE, Benz PM, Ferriani R, et al: Characterization of serum neutralization response to the human immunodeficiency virus (HIV). *AIDS Res Hum Retroviruses* 1987; 3:71–85.
13. Ranki A, Weiss SH, Valle SL, et al: Neutralizing antibodies in HIV (HTLV-III) infection: Correlation with clinical outcome and antibody response against different viral proteins. *Clin Exp Immunol* 1987; 69:231–239.
14. Wendler I, Bienzle U, Hunsmann G: Neutralizing antibodies and the course of HIV. *AIDS Res Hum Retroviruses* 1987; 2:157–163.
15. Harada S, Koyangi Y, Yamamoto N: Infection of HTLV-III/LAV in HTLV-I carrying cells MT-2 and MT-4 and application in a plaque assay. *Science* 1985; 229:563–566.
16. Weiss RA, Clapham PR, Chiengsong-Popov R, et al: Neutralisation of human T lymphotropic virus type III by sera of AIDS and AIDS-risk patients. *Nature* 1985; 316:69–72.
17. Albrecht P, Hermann K, Burns GR: Role of virus strain in conventional and enhanced measles plaque neutralization test. *J Virol Methods* 1981; 3:251–260.
18. Albrecht P, Torrey EF, Boone E, et al: Raised cytomegalovirus antibody level in cerebrospinal fluid of schizophrenic patients. *Lancet* 1980; 2:769–772.
19. Sato H, Albrecht P, Hicks JT, et al: Sensitive neutralization test for virus antibody. 1. Mumps antibody. *Arch Virol* 1978; 58:301–311.
20. Schmidt NJ, Foghani B, Lennette EH: Type specificity of complement-requiring and immunoglobulin M neutralizing antibody in initial herpes simplex virus infections of humans. *Infect Immun* 1975; 12:728–732.
21. Graham BJ, Minamishima Y, Dreesman GR, et al: Complement-requiring neutralizing antibodies in hyperimmune sera to human cytomegalovirus. *J Immunol* 1971; 107:1618–1630.
22. Schmidt NJ, Lennette EH: Neutralizing antibody responses to varicella-zoster virus. *Infect Immun* 1975; 12:606–613.
23. Plotkin SA, Koprowski H, Stokes J Jr: Clinical trials in infants of orally administered attenuated poliomyelitis viruses. *Pediatrics* 1959; 23:1041–1062.
24. Loofbourow JC, Cabasso VJ, Roby RE, et al: Rabies immune globulin (human) clinical trials and dose determination. *JAMA* 1971; 217:1825–1831.
25. Wilkins J, Wehrle PF: Additional evidence against measels vaccine administration to infants less than 12 months of age: Altered immune response following active/passive immunization. *J Pediatr* 1979; 94:865–869.
26. Hobson D, Curry RL, Beare AS, et al: The role of serum hemagglutination-inhibiting antibody in protection against challenge with influenza A_2 and B viruses. *J Hygiene* 1972; 70:767–777.
27. Schiff GM, Sever JL, Huebner RJ: Rubella virus: Neutralizing antibody in commercial gamma globulin. *Science* 1963; 142:58–60.
28. Dowling JN, Saslow AR, Armstrong JK, et al: Cytomegalovirus infection in patients receiving immunosuppressive therapy for rheumatologic disorders. *Infect Dis* 1976; 133:399–408.
29. Chang TW, Fiumara NJ, Weinstein L: Genital herpes: Some clinical and laboratory observations. *JAMA* 1974; 229:544–545.
30. Rao N, Waruszewski DT, Armstrong JA, et al: Evaluations of anti-complement immunofluorescence test in cytomegalovirus infection. *J Clin Microbiol* 1977; 6:633–638.
31. Lief FS, Henle W: Methods and procedures for use of complement-fixation technique in type and strain-specific diagnosis of influenza. *Bull WHO* 1959; 20:411–420.
32. Dresman GR, Benyesh-Melnick M: Spectrum of human cytomegalovirus complement-fixing antigens. *J Immunol* 1967; 99:1106–1114.
33. Kettering JD, Schmidt NJ, Lennette EH: Improved glycine-extracted complement-fixing antigen for human cytomegalovirus. *J Clin Microbiol* 1977; 6:647–649.
34. Dienstag JL, Cline WL, Purcell RH: Detection of cytomegalovirus antibody by immune adherence hemagglutination (39588). *Proc Soc Exp Biol Med* 1976; 153:543–548.
35. Yeager AS: Improved indirect hemagglutination test for cytomegalovirus using human O erythrocytes in lysine. *J Clin Microbiol* 1979; 10:64–68.
36. Gershon AA, Kalter ZG, Steinberg S: Detection of antibody to varicella-zoster virus by immune adherence hemagglutination (39302). *Proc Soc Exp Biol Med* 1976; 151:762–765.
37. Quinnan GV, Ennis FA, Tuazon CU, et al: Cytotoxic lymphocytes and antibody-dependent complement-mediated cytotoxicity induced by administration of influenza vaccine. *Infect Immun* 1980; 30:362–369.
38. McLaren C: Regional B cell responses to inactivated influenza virus vaccine in ferrets. *J Infect Dis* 1979; 140:249–250.
39. McLaren C, Pope BJ: Macrophage dependency of in vitro B cell response to influenza virus antigens. *J Immunol* 1980; 125:2679–2684.
40. Farrohi KH, Farrohi FK, Noble GR, et al: Evaluation of the single radial hemolysis test for measuring hemagglutinin- and neuraminidase-specific antibodies to H3N2 influenza strains and antibodies to influenza B. *J Clin Microbiol* 1977; 5:353–360.
41. Noble GR, Kaye HS, Yarbrough WB, et al: Measurement of hemagglutinin-inhibiting antibody to influenza virus in the 1976 influenza vaccine program: Methods and test reproducibility. *J Infect Dis* 1977; 136(suppl):S429–S434.
42. Dick EC, Mogabgab WJ: Characteristics of parainfluenza 1(HA-27) virus hemagglutination, hemagglutination-inhibition and neutralization. *Am J Hygiene* 1961; 73:273–287.
43. Stewart GL, Parkman PD, Hopps HE, et al: Rubella-virus hemagglutination-inhibition test. *N Engl J Med* 1967; 276:554–557.

44. Norby E: The effect of a carbobenzoxy tripeptide on the biological activities of measles virus. *Virology* 1971; 44:599–608.

45. Aymard-Henry M, Coleman MT, Dowdle WR, et al: Influenza virus neuraminidase and neuraminidase-inhibition test procedures. *Bull WHO* 1973; 48:199–202.

46. Jackson JB, Balfour HH Jr: Practical diagnostic tests for human immunodeficiency virus. *Clin Microbiol Rev* 1988; 1:124–138.

47. Williams V, Gershon A, Brunell PA: Serologic response to varicella-zoster membrane antigens measured by indirect immunofluorescence. *J Infect Dis* 1974; 130:669–672.

48. Henle W, Henle G, Gunven P, et al: Patterns of antibody to Epstein-Barr virus–induced early antigens in Burkitt's-lymphoma. Comparison of dying patient with long-term survivors. *J Natl Cancer Inst* 1973; 50:1163–1173.

49. Pope JH, Horne MK, Wetters EJ: Significance of a complement-fixing antigen associated with herpes-like virus and detected in the Raji cell line. *Nature* 1969; 222:186–187.

50. Reedman BM, Klein G: Cellular localization of an Epstein-Barr virus (EBV)–associated complement-fixing antigen in producer and non-producer lymphoblastoid cell lines. *Int J Cancer* 1973; 11:935–941.

51. Zaia JA, Oxman MN: Antibody to varicella-zoster virus–induced membrane antigen: Immunofluorescent assay using monodisperse glutaraldehyde-fixed target cells. *J Infect Dis* 1974; 136:519–530.

52. Gershon AA: Live attenuated varicella vaccine. *Annu Rev Med* 1987; 38:41–50.

53. Kit S: Viral-induced enzymes and the problem of viral oncogenesis. *Adv Cancer Res* 1968; 11:73–221.

54. Huebner RJ, Casey MJ, Chanock RM, et al: Tumors induced in hamsters by a strain of adenovirus type 3: Sharing of tumor antigens and "neantigens" with those produced by adenovirus type 7 tumors. *Proc Natl Acad Sci USA* 1965; 54:381–388.

55. Henle G, Henle W, Klein G: Demonstration of two distinct components in the early antigen complex of Epstein-Barr virus–infected cells. *Int J Cancer* 1971; 8:272–282.

56. Rahman AA, Teschner M, Sethi KK, et al: Appearance of IgG(Fc) receptor(s) on cultured human fibroblasts infected with human cytomegalovirus. *J Immunol* 1976; 117:253–258.

57. Watkins JF: Adsorption of sensitized sheep erythrocytes to HeLa cells infected with herpes simplex virus. *Nature* 1964; 202:1364–1365.

58. Singer C, Knauert F, Lundquist RE, et al: Indirect enzyme-linked immunosorbent assay for the detection of type 1 poliovirus D antigen and antibodies. Presented at 21st Interscience Conference on Antimicrobial Agents and Chemotherapy, Chicago, abstract, 1981.

59. Bayer EA, Ben-Hur H, Wilchek M: Enzyme based detection of glycoproteins on blot transfers using avidin–biotin technology. *Anal Biochem* 1987; 161:123–131.

60. Burns J: Immunoperoxidase localization of hepatitis B antigen in formalin–paraffin processed liner tissue. *Histochemistry* 1975; 44:113–135.

61. Rubenstein KE, Schneider RS, Ullman EF: "Homogenous" enzyme immunoassay. *Biochem Biophys Res Commun* 1972; 47:846–850.

62. Wong RC, Burd JF, Carrico RJ, et al: Substrate-labelled fluorescent immunoassay for phenytoin in human serum. *Clin Chem* 1979; 25:686–691.

63. Ishikawa E: Development and clinical application of sensitive enzyme immunoassay for macromolecular antigens—a review. *Clin Biochem* 1987; 20:375–388.

64. Varela Y, Ortega E, Gomez B: Quantitation of rubella virus by competitive enzyme immunosorbent assay. *J Virol Methods* 1988; 19:79–87.

65. Dawson GJ, Heller JS, Wood CA, et al: Reliable detection of individuals seropositive for the human immunodeficiency virus (HIV) by competitive immunoassay using *Escherichia coli*–expressed HIV structural proteins. *J Infect Dis* 1988; 157:149–155.

66. Homsy J, Thomson-Honnebier GA, Cheng-Mayer C, et al: Detection of human immunodeficiency virus (HIV) in serum and body fluids by sequential competition ELISA. *J Virol Methods* 1988; 19:43–56.

67. Clem TR, Yolken RH: Practical colorimeter for direct measurement of microplates in enzyme immunoassay systems. *J Clin Microbiol* 1978; 7:55–58.

68. Soini E, Hemmila I: Fluoroimmunoassay: Present status and key problems. *Clin Chem* 1979; 25:353–361.

69. Harris CC, Yolken RH, Krokan H, et al: Ultrasensitive enzymatic radioimmunoassay: Application to detection of cholera toxin and rotavirus. *Proc Natl Acad Sci USA* 1979; 76:5336–5339.

70. Konshi E, Inasa S, Kondo K, et al: Chemiluminescence-linked immunoassay for detection of mumps virus antibodies. *J Clin Microbiol* 1980; 12:140–143.

71. Kurstak E, Tijssen P, Kurstak C, et al: Enzyme immunoassays and related procedures in diagnostic medical virology. *Bull WHO* 1986; 64:465–479.

72. Drew WL: Controversies in viral diagnosis. *Rev Infect Dis* 1986; 8:814–824.

73. Bryan JA: The serologic diagnosis of viral infection. An update. *Arch Pathol Lab Med* 1987; 111:1015–1023.

74. Berg RA, Yolken RH, Rennard SI, et al: New enzyme immunoassays for measurement of influenza A/Victoria/3/75 virus in nasal washes. *Lancet* 1980; 1:851–853.

75. Yolken RH, Stopa PJ, Harris CC: Enzyme immunoassay for the detection of rotavirus antigen and antibody, in Rose N, Friedman H (eds): *Manual of Clinical Immunology*, ed 2. Washington DC, American Society for Microbiology, 1980, pp 692–699.

76. Hendry RM, Burns JC, Walsh EW, et al: Strain-specific serum antibody response in infants undergoing primary infection with respiratory syncytial virus. *J Infect Dis* 1988; 157:640–647.

77. Gnann JW Jr, Schwimmbeck PL, Nelson JA, et al: Diagnosis of AIDS by using a 12-amino acid peptide representing an immunodominant epitope of the human immunodeficiency virus. *J Infect Dis* 1987; 156:261–267.

78. Wang JJG, Steel S, Wisniewolski R, et al: Detection of antibodies to human T-lymphotropic virus type III by using a synthetic peptide of 21 amino acid residues corresponding to a highly antigenic segment of gp41 envelope protein. *Proc Natl Acad Sci USA* 1986; 83:6159–6163.

79. Blomberg J, Klasse PJ: Specificities and sensitivies of three systems for determination of antibodies to human immunodeficiency virus by electrophoretic immunoblot. *J Clin Microbiol* 1988; 26:106–110.

80. Dubey L, Steinberg SP, Larussa P, et al: Western blot analysis of antibody to varicella-zoster virus. *J Infect Dis* 1988; 157:882–888.

81. Schmidt G, Amiraian K, Frey H, et al: Densitometric analysis of western blot (immunoblot) assays for human immunodeficiency virus antibodies and correlation with clinical status. *J Clin Microbiol* 1987; 25:1993–1998.

82. Chiodi F, Bredberg-Raden U, Biberfeld G, et al: Radioimmunoprecipitation and western blotting of sera of human immunodeficiency virus infected patients: A comparative study. *AIDS Res Hum Retroviruses* 1987; 3:165–175.

83. Blomberg J, Klasse PJ: Quantification of immunoglobulin on electrophoretic immunoblot strips as a tool for human immunodeficiency virus serodiagnosis. *J Clin Microbiol* 1988; 26:111–115.

84. Palumbo PE, Arvin AM, Koropchak CM, et al: Investigation of varicella-zoster infected cell proteins which elicit an immune response during primary varicella infections. *J Gen Virol* 1984; 65:2141–2147.

85. Arvin AM, Kinney-Thomas E, Shriver K, et al: Immunity to varicella-zoster viral glycoproteins, gp I (gp90/58) and gp III (gp118) and to a nonglycosylated protein, p170. *J Immunol* 1986; 137:1346–1351.

86. Mertz GJ, Coombs RW, Ashley R, et al: Transmission of genital herpes in couples with one symptomatic and one asymptomatic partner. A prospective study. *J Infect Dis* 1988; 157:1169–1177.

87. Hughes WL: The chemistry of iodination. *Ann NY Acad Sci* 1957; 70:3–18.

88. Brownstone A, Mitchison NA, Pitt-Rivers R: Chemical and serological studies with an iodine-containing synthetic immunological determinant 4-hydroxy-3-IODO-nitrophenylacetic acid (NIP) and related compounds. *Immunology* 1966; 10:465–479.

89. Mallinson H, Roberts C, Bruce-White GB: Staphylococcal protein A: Its preparation and an application to rubella serology. *J Clin Pathol* 1976; 29:999–1002.

90. Forghani B, Schmidt N, Lennette EH: Antisera to human cytomegalovirus produced in hamsters: Reactivity in radioimmunoassay and other antibody systems. *Infect Immun* 1976; 14:1184–1190.

91. Arvin A, Koropchak CM: Immunoglobulins M and G to varicella-zoster virus measured by solid-phase radioimmunoassay antibody responses to varicella herpes zoster infections. *J Clin Microbiol* 1980; 12:367–374.

92. Wittek AE, Arvin AM, Koropchak CM: Serum immunoglobulin A antibody to varicella-zoster virus in subjects with primary varicella and herpes zoster, and in immune subjects. *J Clin Microbiol* 1983; 18:1146–1149.

93. Greenberg HB, Wyatt RG, Valdesuso J, et al: Solid-phase microtiter radioimmunoassay for the detection of the Norwalk strain of acute nonbacterial epidemic gastroenteritis virus and its antibodies. *J Med Virol* 1978; 2:97–108.

94. Hollinger FB, Vorndam V, Dressman GR: Assay of Australia antigen and antibody employing double antibody and solid-phase radioimmunoassay techniques and comparison with the passive hemagglutination methods. *J Immunol* 1971; 107:1099–1111.

95. Voller A, Bidwell DE: A simple method for detecting antibodies to rubella. *Br J Exp Pathol* 1975; 56:338–340.

96. Beckwith DG, Halstead DC, Alpaugh K, et al: Comparison of a latex agglutination test with five other methods for determining the presence of antibody against cytomegalovirus. *J Clin Microbiol* 1985; 21:328–331.

97. Meegan JM, Evans BK, Horstmann DM: Use of enzyme immunoassays and the latex agglutination test to measure the temporal appearance of immunoglobulin G and M antibodies after natural infection or immunization with rubella virus. *J Clin Microbiol* 1983; 18:745–748.

98. Riggin CH, Beltz GA, Hung CH, et al: Detection of antibodies to human immunodeficiency virus by latex agglutination with recombinant antigen. *J Clin Microbiol* 1987; 25:1772–1773.

99. Kabat EA, Mayee MM: Precipitin reactions, in Kabat EA, Mayer MM (eds): *Experimental Immunochemistry*. Springfield, Ill, Thomas, 1961, pp 22–96.

100. Schild GC, Wood JM, Newman RW: Single-radial-immuno-diffusion technique for the assay of influenza hemagglutinin antigen. *Bull WHO* 1975; 52:223–231.

101. Mayner RE, Blackburn RJ, Barry DW: Quantitation of influenza vaccine hemagglutinin by immunoelectrophoresis. International symposium on influenza immunization (II). *Dev Biol Stan* 1977; 39:169–178.

102. Niebojewski RA, Aguilan-Torres FG, Rytel MW: Application of counterimmune ectrophoresis in rapid detection of cytomegalovirus antibodies. *Am J Clin Pathol* 1977; 68:343–346.

103. Barre-Sinoussi F, Chermann J-C, Rey F, et al: Isolation of a T-lymphotropic retrovirus from a patient at risk of acquired immunodeficiency syndrome (AIDS). *Science* 1983; 220:868–871.

104. Allan JS, Colgan JE, Barin F, et al: Major glycoprotein antigens that induce antibodies in AIDS patients are encoded by HTLV-III. *Science* 1985; 228:1091–1094.

105. Berstein JM, Hruska JR: Respiratory syncitial virus proteins: Identification by immunoprecipitation. *J Virol* 1981; 38:278–285.

106. Stinski MF: The proteins of human cytomegalovirus. *Birth Defects* 1984; 20:49–62.

107. Van Ramshorst JD, Polak MF: The in vitro determination of the D antigens of poliomyelitis viruses. *Immunology* 1966; 11:297–311.

108. Drugman RD, Hardy GE, Sellers C, et al: Antibody persistence after primary immunization with trivalent oral poliovirus vaccine. *Pediatrics* 1977; 60:80–82.

109. Roden AT: Surveillance of Salk vaccination in England and Wales F156–61. *Proc R Soc Med* 1964; 57:464–466.

110. Reynolds DW, Stagno S, Stubbs KG, et al: Inapparent congenital cytomegalovirus infection with elevated cord IgM levels. *N Engl J Med* 1974; 290:291–296.

111. Vesikaris T, Vaheri A, Pettray O, et al: Congenital rubella. Immune responses of the neonate and diagnosis by demonstration of specific IgM antibodies. *J Pediatr* 1969; 75:658–664.

112. Edelman GM, Kunkel HG, Franklin EC: Interaction of the rheumatoid factor with antigen-antibody complexes and aggregated gammaglobulin. *J Exp Med* 1963; 108:105–120.

112a. Berkman SA, Lee ML, Gale RP: Clinical uses of intravenous immunoglobulins. *Ann Intern Med* 1990; 112:278–292.

113. Krugman S, Giles JP, Jacobs AM, et al: Studies with further attenuated live measles-virus vaccine. *Pediatrics* 1963; 31:919–928.

114. Kluge T: Gammaglobulin in the prevention of viral hepatitis. A study on the effect of medium-size doses. *Acta Med Scand* 1963; 174:469–477.

115. Krugman S, Giles JP, Hammond J: Viral hepatitis type B (MS-2 strain) prevention with specific hepatitis B immune serum globulin. *JAMA* 1971; 218:1665–1670.

116. Kempe CH: Studies on smallpox and complications of smallpox vaccines. *Pediatrics* 1960; 26:176–189.

117. Ross AH: Modification of chicken pox in family contacts by administration of gammaglobulin. *N Engl J Med* 1962; 267:369–376.

118. Sabeti A, Bahmanyar M, Ghodssi M: Traitement des mordus par loups enragés en Iran. *Ann Inst Pasteur* 1964; 106:303–306.

119. Sato H, Albrecht P, Stagno S, et al: Transfer of measles, mumps and rubella antibodies from mother to infant. *Am J Dis Child* 1979; 133:1240–1243.

120. Krugman S: Present status of measles and rubella immunization in the United States: A medical progress report. *J Pediatr* 1977; 90:1–12.

121. Yeager AS, Grumet FC, Hafleigh EB, et al: Prevention of transfusion-acquired cytomegalovirus infections in newborn infants. *J Pediatr* 1981; 78:281–287.

122. Yeager AS, Arvin AM, Urbani LJ, et al: Relationship of antibody to outcome in neonatal herpes simplex virus infections. *Infect Immun* 1980; 29:532–538.

123. Kohler G, Milstein C: Continuous cultures of fused cells secreting antibody of predefined specificity. *Nature* 1975; 256:495–497.

124. Fazekas de St Groth S, Scheidegger D: Production of monoclonal antibodies: Strategy and tactics. *J Immuno Methods* 1980; 35:1–21.

125. Gerhard W, Croce CM, Lopes D, et al: Repertoire of antiviral antibodies expressed by somatic cell hybrids. *Proc Natl Acad Sci USA* 1978; 75:1510–1514.

126. Zurawski V, Black P, Haber E: Monoclonal antibodies and cell surface differentiation, in Kennett RH, McKearns T, Bechtal K (eds): *Monoclonal Antibodies*. New York, Plenum, 1980.

127. Miller R, Oseroff A, Stratte P, et al: Monoclonal antibody therapeutic trial in seven patients with T-cell lymphoma. *Blood* 1983; 62:988–995.

128. Oldham R, Thurman G, Talmadge J, et al: Lymphokines, monoclonal antibodies, and other biological response modifiers in the treatment of cancer. *Cancer* 1984; 54:2795–2806.

129. Ortho Multicenter Transplant Study Group: A randomized clinical trial of OKT3 monoclonal antibody for acute rejection of cadaveric renal transplants. *N Engl J Med* 1985; 313:337–342.

130. Herve P, Flesch M, Cahn J, et al: Removal of marrow T cells with OKT3-OKT11 monoclonal antibodies and complement to prevent acute graft-versus-host disease. *Transplantation* 1985; 39:138–143.

131. Larrick JW, Bourla JM: Prospects for the therapeutic use of human monoclonal antibodies. *J Biol Respir Modif* 1986; 5:379–393.

132. Keay S, Rasmussen L, Merigan TC: Syngeneic monoclonal anti-idiotype antibodies that bear the internal image of a human cytomegalovirus epitope. *J Immunol* 1988; 140:944–948.

133. Zhou E-M, Chanh TC, Dreesman GR, et al: Immune response to human immunodeficiency virus. In vivo administration of anti-idiotype induces an anti-gp160 response specific for a synthetic peptide. *J Immunol* 1987; 139:2950–2956.

134. Dalgleish AG, Thompson BJ, Chanh TC, et al: Neutralisation of HIV isolates by anti-idiotypic antibodies which mimic the T4 (CD4) epitope: A potential AIDS vaccine. *Lancet* 1987; 2:1047–1050.

135. Laver WG, Gerhard W, Webster RE, et al: Influenza virus: Peptide mapping and antigenic analysis of A/PR/8/34/(HON1) variants selected with monoclonal antibodies. *Proc Natl Acad Sci USA* 1979; 76:1425–1429.

136. Webster RG, Laver WG: Determination of the number of non-overlapping antigenic areas on Hong Kong (H3N3) influenza virus hemagglutinin with monoclonal antibodies and the selection of variants with potential epidemiological significance. *Virology* 1980; 104:139–148.

137. Pereira L, Hoffman M, Gallo D, et al: Monoclonals for purification of viral proteins. *Infect Immun* 1982; 36:924–932.

138. Van Ewijk W, Van Soest PL, von den Engh GJ: Fluorescence analysis and anatomic distribution of mouse T lymphocyte subsets defined by monoclonal antibodies to the antigens THY-1, LYT-1, LYT-2, and T-200[1]. *J Immunol* 1981; 127:2594–2604.

139. Golub ES: Brain-associated antigen Reactivity of rabbit anti-mouse brain with mouse lymphoid cells. *Cell Immunol* 1971; 2:353–361.

140. Blann AD: T lymphocyte surface molecules: Structure and function. *Med Lab Sci* 1987; 44:220–236.

141. Shaw S: Characterization of human leukocyte differentiation antigens. *Immuno Today* 1987; 8:1–3.

142. Herzenberg LA, Herzenberg LA: Analysis and separation using the fluorescence activated cell sorter (FACS), in Weir DA (ed): *Handbook of Experimental Immunology*. Oxford, Blackwell, 1978, pp 22.1–22.21.

143. Quinnan GV, Burns WH, Kirmani N, et al: HLA-restricted cytotoxic T lymphocytes are an early immune response and important defense mechanism in cytomegalovirus infection. *Rev Infect Dis* 1984; 6:156–163.

144. Cram LS, Brunsting A: Fluorescence and light-scattering measurements on hog cholera–infected PK-15 cells. *Exp Cell Res* 1973; 78:209–213.

145. Timonen T, Ortaldo JR, Herberman RB: Characteristics of human large granular lymphocytes and relationship to natural killer and K cells. *J Exp Med* 1981; 153:569–582.

146. Timonen T, Saksela E: Isolation of human NK cells by density gradient centrifugation. *J Immunol Methods* 1980; 36:285–291.

147. Sheldon PJ, Hemsted EH, Papamichail M, et al: Thymic origin of atypical lymphoid cells in infectious mononucleosis. *Lancet* 1973; 1:1153–1155.

148. Denman AM, Pelton BK: Control mechanisms in infectious mononucleosis. *Clin Exp Immunol* 1974; 18:13–25.

149. Litwins J, Leibowitz S: Abnormal lymphocytes (virocytes) in virus diseases other than infectious mononucleosis. *Acta Haematol* 1951; 5:223–231.

150. Kaplan ME, Clark C: An improved rosetting assay for detection of human T lymphocytes. *J Immunol Methods* 1974; 5:131–135.

151. Koller CA, King GW, Hurtubise PE, et al: Characterization of glass adherent human mononuclear cells. *J Immunol* 1973; 111:1610–1612.

152. Julius M, Simpson E, Herzenber LA: A rapid method for the isolation of functional thymus-derived murine lymphocytes. *Eur J Immunol* 1973; 3:645–649.

153. Yam LT, Li CY, Crosby WH: Cytochemical identification of monocytes and granulocytes. *Am J Clin* 1971; 55:283–290.

154. Allison AC, Harrington JS, Birbeck M: An examination of the cytotoxic effects of silica on macrophages. *J Exp Med* 1966; 124:141–153.

155. Thomas DW, Forni G, Shevoch EM, et al: The role of the macrophage as the stimulator cell in contact sensitivity. *J Immunol* 1977; 118:1677–1681.

156. Sjoberg O, Anderson J, Moller G: Requirement for adherent cells in the primary and secondary immune responses in vitro. *Eur J Immunol* 1972; 2:123–126.

157. Touraine JL, Hadden JW, Gord RA: Sequential stages of human T lymphocyte differentiation. *Proc Natl Acad Sci USA* 1977; 74:3414–3418.

158. Scheffel JW, Swartz SJ: Inhibition of autologous rosette formation by monoclonal antibody to the sheep erythrocyte receptor. *J Immunol* 1982; 128:1930–1932.

159. Seligman M, Preud'homme JL, Brouet JC: B and T cell markers in human proliferative blood diseases and primary immunodeficiencies, with special reference to membrane bound immunoglobulins. *Transplant Rev* 1973; 16:85–113.

160. Urboniak SJ, White AG, Barclay GRE, et al: Tests of immune function, in Wier DM (ed): *Handbook of Experimental Immunology*. Oxford, Blackwell, 1978, pp 47.1–47.32.

161. Yefonof E, Klein G: Membrane receptor stripping confirms the association between EBV receptors and complement receptors on the surface of human B lymphoma lines. *Int J Cancer* 1977; 20:347–352.

162. Herberman RB, Bartram S, Haskill SJ, et al: Fc receptors on mouse effector cells mediating natural cytotoxicity against tumor cells. *J Immunol* 1977; 119:322–326.

163. Ortaldo JR: Comparison of natural killer and natural cytotoxic cells: Characteristics, regulation, and mechanisms of action. *Pathol Immunopathol Res* 1986; 5:203–218.

164. Sulica A, Gherman M, Galatuic C, et al: Inhibition of human natural killer cell activity by cytophilic immunoglobulin G. *J Immunol* 1982; 128:1031–1036.

165. Jondal M: The human NK cell—a short over-view and an hypothesis on NK recognition. *Clin Exp Immunol* 1987; 70:255–262.

166. Abrams SI, Brahmi Z: Target cell directed NK inactivation. Concomitant loss of NK and antibody-dependent-cellular cytotoxicity activities. *J Immunol* 1988; 140:2090–2095.

167. Samarut C, Brochier J, Revillard JP: Distribution of cells binding erythrocyte-antibody (EA) complexes in human lymphoid populations. *Scand J Immunol* 1976; 5:221–231.

168. Van Oers MHJ, Zieilemaker WP, Schellekens P: Separation and properties of EA rosette-forming lymphocytes in humans. *Eur J Immunol* 1977; 7:143–150.

169. Henkart P, Alexander E: The adherence of human receptor bearing lymphocytes to immobilized antigen-antibody complexes. *J Immunol Methods* 1978; 20:155–172.

170. Ragsdale CG, Arend WP: Loss of Fc receptor activity after culture of human monocytes on surface-bound immune complexes. *J Exp Med* 1980; 151:32–44.

171. Kerbel RS, Davies AJS: Significance of Fc receptors on mammalian lymphocytes and tumor cells. *Cell* 1974; 3:105–112.

172. Hellstrom I, Garrigues U, Lavie E, et al: Antibody-mediated killing of human tumor cells by attached effector cells. *Cancer Res* 1988; 48:624–627.

173. Ritz J, Schmidt RE, Michon J, et al: Characterization of functional surface structures on human natural killer cells. *Adv Immunol* 1988; 42:181–211.

174. Grossman Z, Herberman RB: Natural killer cells and their relationship to T-cells: Hypothesis on the role of T-cell receptor gene rearrangement on the course of adaptive differentiation. *Cancer Res* 1986; 46:2651–2658.

175. Biron CA, Natuk RJ, Welsh RM: Generation of large granular T lymphocytes in vivo during viral infection. *J Immunol* 1986; 136:2280–2286.

176. Turk JL: *Delayed Hypersensitivity.* Amsterdam, North Holland Publishing Co, 1967.

177. Skin test antigens. *Federal Register* 1977; 42:52689–52693.

178. Baba K, Yabuuchi H, Okuni H, et al: Studies with live varicella vaccine and inactivated skin test antigen: Protective effect of the vaccine and clinical application of the skin test. *Pediatrics* 1978; 61:550–555.

179. Steele RW, Meyers MG, Vincent MM: Transfer factor for the prevention of varicella-zoster infection in childhood leukemia. *N Engl J Med* 1980; 303:355–359.

180. Parkman PD, Hopps HE, Rastogi SC, et al: Summary of clinical trials of influenza virus vaccines in adults. *J Infect Dis* 1977; 136(suppl):S722–S730.

181. Glazer JP, Friedman HM, Grossman RA, et al: Live cytomegalovirus vaccination of renal transplant candidates. *Ann Intern Med* 1979; 91:676–683.

182. Fulginiti VA, Arthur J, Perlman DS, et al: Serious local reactions following live measles virus immunization in previous killed-vaccine recipients. *Pediatrics* 1966; 69:891–892.

183. Andersson J, Sjoberg O, Moller G: Mitogens as probes for immunocyte activation and cellular cooperation. *Transplant Rev* 1972; 11:131–177.

184. Ennis F, Phelan M, Armstrong R, et al: Influenza virus hemagglutinin is a lymphocyte mitogen. *Curr Chemother Infect Dis* 1980; 1:1353–1359.

185. Jones, G: Lymphocyte activation I. *Clin Exp Immunol* 1972; 12:391–402.

186. Schimpl A, Wecker E: Con A and PHA–T cell mitogens. *Nature* 1972; 237:15–17.

187. Peavy DL, Adler WH, Shands JW, et al: Selective effects of mitogens on subpopulations of mouse lymphoid cells. *Cell Immunol* 1974; 11:86–98.

188. Kelsey DK, Overall JC, Glasgow LA: Production of alpha and gamma interferons by spleen cells from cytomegalovirus-infected mice. *Infect Immun* 1982; 36:651–656.

189. Mier JW, Gallo RC: Purification and some characteristics of human T cell growth factor from phytohemagglutinin-stimulated lymphocyte-conditioned media. *Proc Natl Acad Sci USA* 1980; 77:6134–6138.

190. Reinertsen JL, Steinberg AD: In vivo immune response suppression by the supernatant from concanavalin A–activated spleen cells. *J Immunol* 1977; 119:217–222.

191. Palacios R, Moller G: T cell growth factor abrogates concanavalin A–induced suppressor cell function. *J Exp Med* 1981; 153:1360–1365.

192. Analerio A, Waterfield JD, Moller G: Induction of lymphocyte-mediated cytotoxicity against allogeneic tumor cells by concanavalin A in vivo. *J Immunol* 1974; 113:870–875.

193. Dolin R, Murphy BR, Caplan EA: Lymphocyte blastogenic responses to influenza virus antigens after influenza infection and vaccination in humans. *Infect Immun* 1978; 19:867–874.

194. Sullivan JL, Barry DW, Albrecht P, et al: Inhibition of lymphocyte stimulation by measles virus. *J Immunol* 1975; 114:1458–1461.

195. Quinnan GV, Kirmani N, Burns WH, et al: HLA-restricted cytotoxic T lymphocyte and nonthymic cytotoxic lymphocyte responses to cytomegalovirus infection of bone marrow transplant recipients. *J Immunol* 1981; 136:2036–2041.

196. Booss J, Wheelock EF: Role of viremia in the suppression of T-cell function during murine cytomegalovirus infection. *Infect Immun* 1977; 17:378–381.

197. Cooper HL, Fagnani R, London J, et al: Effect of interferons on protein synthesis in human lymphocytes: Enhanced synthesis of eight specific peptides in T cells and activation-dependent inhibition of overall protein synthesis. *J Immunol* 1982; 128:828–833.

198. Bech V: Measles epidemics in Greenland. *Am J Dis Child* 1962; 103:252–253.

199. Rand KH, Pollard RB, Merigan TC: Increased pulmonary superinfections in cardiac-transplant patients undergoing primary cytomegalovirus infection. *N Engl J Med* 1978; 298:951–953.

200. Krause PJ, Cherry JD, Carney JM, et al: Measles-specific lymphocyte reactivity and serum antibody in subjects with different measles histories. *Am J Dis Child* 1980; 134:567–571.

201. Corey L, Reeve WC, Holmes KV: Cellular immune response in genital herpes simplex virus infection. *N Engl J Med* 1978; 299:986–991.

202. Jennings RR, Nicholson K, Potter CW: Immunity to influenza virus infection induced by heterologous inactivated vaccines. *Med Microbiol Immunol* 1978; 166:99–108.

203. Lamb JR, Eckels DD, Phelan M, et al: Antigen-specific human T lymphocyte clones: Viral antigen specificity of influenza virus–immune clones. *J Immunol* 1982; 128:1428–1432.

204. Brandt WE, McCown JM, Gentry MK, et al: Infection enhancement of dengue type-2 virus in the U-937 human monocyte cell line by antibodies to flavivirus cross-reactive determinants. *Infect Immun* 1982; 36:1036–1041.

205. Nathan CF, Prendergast TJ, Wiebe ME, et al: Activation of human macrophages: Comparison of other cytokines with interferon-γ. *J Exp Med* 1984; 160:600–605.

206. Wieser WY, van Niel A, Clark SC, et al: Recombinant human granulocyte/monocyte colony–stimulating factor activates intracellular killing of *Leishmania donovani* by human monocyte–derived macrophages. *J Exp Med* 1987; 166:1436–1446.

207. Cummings NP, Pabst MJ, Johnston RB Jr: Activation of macrophages or enhanced release of superoxide anion and greater killing of *Candida albicans* by injection of muramyl dipeptide. *J Exp Med* 1980; 152:1659–1669.

208. Morahan PS, Edelson PJ, Gass K: Changes in macrophage ectoenzymes associated with antitumor activity. *J Immunol* 1980; 125:1312–1317.

209. Nathan CR: Secretory products of macrophages. *J Clin Invest* 1987; 79:319–326.

210. Kurland JI, Kinkaid PW, Moore MAS: Regulation of B-lymphocyte clonal proliferation by stimulatory and inhibitory macrophage-derived factors. *J Exp Med* 1977; 146:1420–1435.

211. Morse SS, Morahan PS: Activated macrophages mediate interferon-independent inhibition of herpes simplex virus. *Cell Immunol* 1981; 58:72–84.

212. Unanue ER: The regulatory role of macrophages in antigenic stimulation. *Adv Immunol* 1972; 15:95–165.

213. Perussia B, Dayton ET, Lazarus R, et al: Immune interferon induces the receptor for monomeric IgGl on human monocytic and myeloid cells. *J Exp Med* 1983; 158:1092–1113.

214. Rinaldo CR, Carney WP, Richter BS, et al: Mechanisms of immunosuppression in cytomegalovirus mononucleosis. *J Infect Dis* 1980; 141:488–495.

215. Osborn JE, Medearis DN: Suppression of interferon and antibody and multiplication of Newcastle disease virus in cytomegalovirus infected mice. *Proc Soc Exp Biol Med* 1967; 124:347–353.

216. Kohl S, Starr SE, Oleske JM, et al: Human monocyte-macrophage mediated antibody-dependent cytotoxicity to herpes simplex virus infected cells. *J Immunol* 1977; 118:729–735.

217. Rodda SJ, White DO: Cytotoxic macrophages: A rapid nonspecific response to viral infection. *J Immunol* 1976; 117:2067–2072.

218. Mims CA, Gould J: The role of macrophages in mice infected with murine cytomegalovirus. *J Gen Virol* 1978; 41:143–153.

219. Selgrade MK, Osborne JE: Role of macrophages in resistance to murine cytomegalovirus. *Infect Immun* 1974; 10:1383–1390.

220. Blanden RV, Mims CA: Macrophage activation in mice infected with ectromelia or lymphocytic choriomeningitis viruses. *J Exp Med Sci* 1973; 51:393–398.

221. Hirsch MS, Zisman B, Allison AC: Macrophages and age-

dependent resistance to herpes simplex virus in mice. *J Immunol* 1974; 104:1160–1165.

222. Silverstein SC, Dales S: The penetration of reovirus RNA and initiation of its genetic function in L-strain fibroblasts. *J Cell Biol* 1968; 36:197–230.

223. Dales S, Choppin PW: Attachment and penetration of influenza virus. *Virology* 1962; 18:489–493.

224. Simpson RW, Hausen RE, Dales S: Viropexis of vesicular stomatitis virus by L cells. *Virology* 1969; 37:285–290.

225. Bang FB: Genetics of resistance of animals to viruses: Introduction and studies in mice. *Adv Virus Res* 1978; 23:270–349.

226. Dinarello CA: Biology of interleukin 1. *FASEB J* 1988; 1:108–115.

227. Chused TM, Kassan SS, Mosier DE: Macrophage requirement for the in vitro response to TNP Ficoll: A thymic independent antigen. *J Immunol* 1976; 116:1579–1581.

228. Welsh RM, Zinkernagel RM, Hallenbeck LA: Cytotoxic cells induced during lymphocytic choriomeningitis virus infection of mice. *J Immunol* 1979; 122:475–481.

229. Manischewitz JF, Quinnan GV: Antivirus antibody-dependent cell-mediated cytotoxicity during murine cytomegalovirus infection. *Infect Immun* 1980; 29:1050–1054.

230. Zinkernagel RM, Doherty PC: Restriction of in vitro T cell-mediated cytotoxicity in lymphocytic choriomeningitis within a syngeneic or semiallogeneic system. *Nature* 1974; 248:701–702.

231. Zinkernagel RM, Doherty PC: MHC-restricted cytotoxic T cells: Studies on the biological role of polymorphic major transplantation antigens determining T-cell restriction, specificity function and responsiveness. *Adv Immunol* 1979; 27:51–180.

232. Quinnan GV, Kirmani N, Rook AH, et al: Cytotoxic T cells in cytomegalovirus infection. HLA-restricted T-lymphocyte and non-T-lymphocyte cytotoxic responses correlate with recovery from cytomegalovirus infection in bone-marrow-transplant recipients. *N Engl J Med* 1982; 307:7–13.

233. Biddison WE, Shearer GM, Shaw S: Influenza virus–specific cytotoxic T cells are restricted by multiple HLA-A3-related self antigens: Evidence for recognition of distinct self structures in conjunction with different foreign antigens. *J Immunol* 1981; 127:2231–2236.

234. McMichael AJ, Ting A, Zweerink HJ: HLA restriction of cell-mediated lysis of influenza virus-infected human cells. *Nature* 1977; 270:524–526.

235. Biddison WE, Shaw S, Nelson DL: Virus specificity of human influenza virus–immune cytotoxic T cells. *J Immunol* 1979; 122:660–664.

236. Chiba Y, Tsutsumi H, Nakao T, et al: Human leukocyte antigen–linked genetic controls for T cell–mediated cytotoxic response to mumps virus in humans. *Infect Immun* 1982; 35:600–604.

237. Spits H, Ijssel H, Terhorst C, et al: Establishment of human T lymphocytic clones highly cytotoxic for an EBV transformed B cell line in serum-free medium: Isolation of clones that differ in phenotype and specificity. *J Immunol* 1982; 128:95–683.

238. Yasukawa M, Aarling JM: Human cytotoxic T cell clones directed against herpes simplex virus infected cells. I. Lysis restricted by HLA class II MB and DR antigens. *J Immunol* 1984; 133:422–427.

239. Yasukawa M, Inatsuki A, Kobayashi Y: Helper activity in antigen-specific antibody production mediated by human CD4 + human cytotoxic T cell clones directed against herpes simplex virus. *J Immunol* 1988; 140:3419–3425.

240. Misko IS, Pope JH, Hutter R, et al: HLA-DR antigen–associated restriction of EBV-specific cytotoxic T cell colonies. *Int J Cancer* 1984; 33:239–243.

241. Lindsley MD, Torpey DJ III, Rinaldo CR Jr: HLA-DR–restricted cytotoxicity of cytomegalovirus-infected monocytes mediated by Leu-3-positive T cells. *J Immunol* 1986; 136:3045–3051.

342. Hayward AR, Pontessili O, Herberger M, et al: Specific lysis of varicella zoster virus–infected B lymphoblasts by human T cells. *J Virol* 1986; 58:179–184.

243. Norcross MA, Bentley DM, Margulies DH, et al: Membrane Ia expression and antigen-presenting accessory cell function of L cells transfected with class II major histocompatibility complex genes. *J Exp Med* 1984; 160:1316–1337.

244. Richert JR, McFarland HF, McFarlin DE, et al: Cloned measles virus–specific T lymphocytes from a twin with multiple sclerosis. *Proc Natl Acad Sci USA* 1983; 80:555–558.

245. Jacobson S, Richert JR, Biddison WE, et al: Measles virus specific T4 + human cytotoxic T cell clones are restricted by class II HLA antigens. *J Immunol* 1984; 133:754–757.

246. Morrison LA, Lukacher AE, Braaciale LV, et al: Differences in antigen presentation to MHC class-I and class-II restricted influenza virus–specific cytolytic T lymphocyte clones. *J Exp Med* 1986; 163:901–923.

247. Kaplan DR, Griffith R, Braciale VR, et al: Influenza virus–specific human cytotoxic T cell clones: Heterogeneity in antigenic specificity and restriction by class II MHC products. *Cell Immunol* 1984; 88:193–206.

248. Gomard E, Henin Y, Sterkers G, et al: An influenza A virus–specific and HLA-DRw8–restricted T cell clone cross-reacting with a transcomplementation product of the HLA-DR2 and DR4 haplotypes. *J Immunol* 1986; 136:3961–3967.

249. Bottomly K: A functional dichotomy in CD4 + T lymphocytes. *Immunol Today* 1988; 9:268–273.

250. Seely J, Svednyr E, Weiland O, et al: Epstein-Barr virus selective T cells in infectious mononucleosis are not restricted to HLA-A and B antigens. *J Immunol* 1981; 127:293–300.

251. Misko IS, Moss DJ, Pope JH: HLA antigen-related restriction of T lymphocyte cytotoxicity to Epstein-Barr virus. *Proc Natl Acad Sci USA* 1980; 77:4247–4250.

252. Rouse BT, Norley S, Martin S: Antiviral cytotoxic T lymphocyte induction and vaccination. *Rev Infect Dis* 1986; 10:16–33.

253. Sekaly RP, Jacobson S, Richert JR, et al: Antigen presentation to HLA class II–restricted measles virus–specific T-cell clones can occur in the absence of the invariant chain. *Proc Natl Acad Sci USA* 1988; 85:1209–1212.

254. Townsend ARM, Rotahbard J, Gotch FM, et al: The epitopes of influenza nucleoprotein recognized by cytotoxic T lymphocytes can be defined with short synthetic peptides. *Cell* 1986; 44:959–968.

255. Daisy JA, Tolpin MD, Quinnan GV, et al: Cytotoxic cellular immune responses during influenza A infection in human volunteers, in Bishop DHL, Compans RW (eds): *The Replication of Negative Strand Viruses*. New York, North Holland, Elsevier, 1981, pp 443–448.

256. Kreth HW, ter Meulen V, Eckert G: Demonstration of HLA-restricted killer cells in patients with acute measles. *Med Microbiol Immunol* 1979; 165:207–214.

257. Ennis FA, Rook AH, Yi-Hua Q, et al: HLA-restricted virus-specific cytotoxic T-lymphocyte responses to live and inactivated influenza vaccines. *Lancet* 1981; 2:887–891.

258. Kirmani N, Ginn RK, Mittal KK, et al: Cytomegalovirus-specific cytotoxicity mediated by non-T lymphocytes from peripheral blood of normal volunteers. *Infect Immun* 1981; 32:441–447.

259. Wells MA, Ennis FA, Albrecht P: Recovery from a viral respiratory infection I. Influenza pneumonia in normal and T-deficient mice. *J Immunol* 1981; 126:1042–1046.

260. Ho M: Role of specific cytotoxic lymphocytes in cellular immunity against murine cytomegalovirus. *Infect Immun* 1980; 27:767–776.

261. Lukacher AE, Braciale VL, Braciale TJ: In vivo effector function of influenza virus–specific cytotoxic T lymphocyte clones is highly specific. *J Exp Med* 1984; 160:814–826.

262. Rook AH, Quinnan GV, Frederick WF, et al: Importance of cytotoxic lymphocytes during cytomegalovirus infection of renal

transplant recipients. *Am J Med* 1984; 76:385–392.

263. McMichael AJ, Gotch FM, Noble GR, et al: Cytotoxic T-cell immunity to influenza. *N Engl J Med* 1983; 309:13–17.

264. Widmer MB, Grabstein KH: Regulation of cytotoxic T-lymphocyte generation by B-cell stimulatory factor. *Nature* 1987; 326:795–797.

265. Cernetti C, Steinman RM, Granelli-Piperno A: Identification of a 24-kDa cytokine that is required for development of cytolytic T lymphocytes. *Proc Natl Acad Sci USA* 1988; 85:1605–1609.

266. Takai YT, Wong GW, Clark SC, et al: B cell stimulatory factor-2 is involved in the differentiation of cytotoxic lymphocytes. *J Immunol* 1988; 140:508–512.

267. Siegel JP: Effects of interferon-γ on the activation of human T lymphocytes. *Cell Immunol* 1988; 111:461–472.

268. Liew FY, Russell SM: Delayed-type hypersensitivity to influenza virus. *J Exp Med* 1980; 151:799–814.

269. Lin Y, Askonas BA: Biological properties of an influenza A virus–specific killer T cell clone. *J Exp Med* 1981; 154:225–234.

270. Quinnan GV, Manischewitz JF: The role of natural killer cells and antibody-dependent cell-mediated cytotoxicity during murine cytomegalovirus infection. *J Exp Med* 1979; 150:1549–1554.

271. Welsh RM, Zinkernagel RM, Hallenbeck LA: Cytotoxic cells induced during lymphocyte choriomeningitis virus infection of mice. *J Immunol* 1979; 122:475–481.

272. Quinnan GV, Manischewitz JF, Kirmani N: Involvement of natural killer cells in the pathogenesis of murine cytomegalovirus interstitial pneumonitis and the immune response to infection. *J Gen Virol* 1982; 58:173–180.

273. Bancroft GJ, Shellam GR, Chalmer JE: Genetic influence on the augmentation of natural killer (NK) cells during murine cytomegalovirus infection: Correlation with patterns of resistance. *J Immunol* 1981; 126:988–994.

274. Riviere Y, Gresser I, Guillon JC, et al: Choriomeningitis virus disease in different strains of suckling mice correlates with increasing amounts of endogens interferon. *J Exp Med* 1980; 152:663–640.

275. Djeu JV, Stocks N, Zoon K, et al: Positive self-regulation of cytotoxicity in human natural killer cells by production of interferon upon exposure to influenza and herpes viruses. *J Exp Med* 1982; 156:1222–1234.

276. Kohl S, McCoig EL, Pickering LK, et al: Comparison of cytotoxicity mediated by human monocyte-macrophages and lymphocytes after prolonged in vitro incubation. *J Immunol Methods* 1978; 24:345–353.

277. Greenberg SB, Criswell BS, Six HR, et al: Lymphocyte cytotoxicity to influenza virus–infected cells. *J Immunol* 1977; 119:2100–2106.

278. Gershon AA, Steinberg SP: Inactivation of varicella zoster virus in vitro: Effect of leukocytes and specific antibody. *Infect Immun* 1981; 32:507–511.

279. Manischewitz JF, Quinnan GV: Antivirus antibody-dependent cell-mediated cytotoxicity during murine cytomegalovirus infection. *Infect Immun* 1980; 29:1050–1054.

280. Shepp DH, Chakrabarti S, Moss B, et al: Antibody-dependent cellular cytotoxicity specific for the envelope antigen of human immunodeficiency virus. *J Infect Dis* 1988; 157:1260–1264.

281. Blumberg RS, Paradis T, Hartshorn KL, et al: Antibody-dependent cell-mediated cytotoxicity against cells infected with human immunodeficiency virus. *J Infect Dis* 1987; 156:878–884.

282. Grimm EA, Thoma JA, Bonavida B: Mechanism of cell-mediated cytotoxicity at the single cell level. *J Immunol* 1979; 123:2870–2877.

283. Ortaldo JR, Bonnard GD, Kind PD, et al: Cytotoxicity by cultured human lymphocytes: Characteristics of effector cells and specificity of cytotoxicity. *J Immunol* 1979; 122:1489–1494.

284. Santoli D, Koprowski H: Mechanisms of activation of human natural killer cells against tumor and virus-infected cells. *Immunol Rev* 1979; 44:125–163.

285. Janeway CA Jr, Carding S, Jones B, et al: CD4 + T cells: Specificity and function. *Immunol Rev* 1988; 101:39–80.

286. Powrie F, Mason D: Phenotypic and functional heterogeneity of CD4 + T cells. *Immunol Today* 1988; 9:274–277.

287. Rich RR, ElMasry MN, Fox EJ: Human suppressor T cells: Induction, differentiation, and regulatory functions. *Hum Immunol* 1986; 17:369–387.

288. Fox EJ, Cook RG, Lewis DE, et al: Proliferative signals for suppressor T cells. Helper cells stimulated with pokeweed mitogen in vitro produce a suppressor cell growth factor. *J Clin Invest* 1986; 78:214–220.

289. ElMasry MN, Fox EJ, Rich RR: Sequential effects of prostaglandins and interferon-gamma on differentiation of CD8 + suppressor cells. *J Immunol* 1987; 139:688–694.

290. ElMasry MN, Fox EJ, Rich RR: Opposing immunoregulatory functions of T8 + lymphocytes: A requirement for monocytes in suppressor cell induction. *J Immunol* 1986; 137:2468–2477.

291. Reinherz EL, King PC, Goldstein G, et al: Separation of functional subsets of human T cells by a monoclonal antibody. *Proc Natl Acad Sci USA* 1979; 76:4061–4065.

292. Carney WP, Rubin RH, Hoffman RA, et al: Analysis of T lymphocyte subsets in cytomegalovirus mononucleosis. *J Immunol* 1981; 126:2214–2116.

293. Reinherz EL, O'Brien C, Rosenthal P, et al: The cellular basis for viral-induced immunodeficiency: Analysis by monoclonal antibodies. *J Immunol* 1980; 125:1269–1274.

294. Tsato G, Pike S, Koski IR, et al: Selective inhibition of immunoregulatory cell functions by cyclosporin A. *J Immunol* 1982; 128:1986–1991.

295. Cupps TR, Strauss SE, Waldman TA: Successful treatment with acyclovir of an immunodeficient patient infected simultaneously with multiple herpesviruses. *Am J Med* 1981; 70:882–886.

296. Katz D: Cell interactions between histoincompatible T and B lymphocytes. IV. Involvement of the immune response (I.R.) gene in the control of lymphocyte interactions in responses controlled by the gene. *J Exp Med* 1973; 138:734–739.

297. Svejgaard A, Platz P, Ryder LP, et al: HL-A and disease associations—A survey. *Transplant Rev* 1975; 22:3–43.

298. Blockwelder WC, Dolin R, Mittal KM, et al: A population study of herpesvirus infections and MLA antigens. *Am J Epidemiol* 1982; 115:569–576.

299. Miyajama S, Miyatake S, Schruers J, et al: Coordinate regulation of immune and inflammatory responses by T cell–derived lymphokines. *FASEB J* 1988; 2:2462–2473.

300. Smith KA: Interleukin-2: Inception, impact, and implications. *Science* 1988; 240:1169–1176.

301. Pestka S, Langer JA, Zoon KC, et al: Interferons and their actions. *Annu Rev Biochem* 1987; 56:727–777.

302. Billiau A: Redefining interferon: The interferon-like antiviral effects of certain cytokines (interleukin-1, interferon-β₂, interferon-γ) may be indirect or side effects. *Antiviral Res* 1987; 8:55–70.

303. Horohov DW, Siegel JP: Lymphokines. Progress and promise. *Drugs* 1987; 33:289–295.

303a. Goodwin RG, Lupton S, Schmierer A, et al: Human interleukin-7: Molecular cloning and growth factor activity on human and murine B-lineage cells. *Proc Natl Acad Sci USA* 1989; 84:302–308.

303b. Armitage RJ, Namen AE, Sassenfeld HM, et al: Regulation of human T cell proliferation by IL-7. *J Immunol* 1990; 144:938–941.

303c. Thornton AJ, Streiter RM, Lindley I, et al: Cytokine-induced gene expression of a neutrophil chemotactic factor/IL-8 in human hepatocytes. *J Immunol* 1990; 144:2609–2613.

304. Watson J, Mochizuk D: Interleukin-2: A class of T cell growth factors. *Immunol Rev* 1980; 51:257–278.

305. Mooney JJ, Waksman BH: Activation of normal rabbit macrophage monolayers by supernatants of antigen-stimulated lymphocytes. *J Immunol* 1970; 105:1138–1145.

306. Reitz MS, Poiesz BJ, Ruscetti PW, et al: Characterization and distribution of nucleic acid sequences of a novel type C retrovi-

rus isolated from neoplastic human T lymphocytes. *Proc Natl Acad Sci USA* 1981; 78:1887–1891.

307. Rho HM, Poiesz BJ, Ruscetti FW, et al: Characterization of the reverse transcriptase from a new retrovirus (HTLV) produced by a human cutaneous T cell lymphoma cell line. *Virology* 1981; 112:355–360.

308. Gallo RC, Salahuddin SZ, Popovic M, et al: Frequent detection and isolation of cytopathic retroviruses (HTLV-III) from patients with AIDS or at risk of AIDS. *Science* 1984; 224:500–502.

309. Rosenberg SA, Lotze MT, Mule JJ: New approaches to the immunotherapy of cancer using interleukin-2. *Ann Intern Med* 1988; 108:853–864.

310. Lane HC, Fauci AS: Immunological abnormalities in the acquired immune deficiency syndrome. *Annu Rev Immunol* 1985; 3:477–500.

311. Lane HC, Siegel JP, Rook AH, et al: Use of interleukin-2 in patients with acquired immunodeficiency syndrome. *J Biol Respir Modif* 1984; 3:512–516.

312. Toy PK, Dietrich M: Preliminary clinical observations with recombinant interleukin-2 in patients with AIDS or LAS. *Blut* 1985; 50:1–6.

313. Isaacs A, Lindenmann J: Virus interference. I. The interferon. *Proc R Soc (B)* 1957; 147:258–267.

314. Allen G, Fantes KH: A family of structural genes for human lymphoblastoid (leukocyte–type) interferon. *Nature* 1980; 287:408–411.

315. Gray PW, Leung DW, Pennica D, et al: Expression of human immune interferon cDNA in *E. coli* and monkey cells. *Nature* 1982; 295:503.

316. Henco K, Brosius J, Fujisawa A, et al: Structural relationship of human interferon alpha genes and pseudogenes. *J Mol Biol* 1985; 185:227–260.

317. Steis RG, Smith JW II, Urba WJ, et al: Resistance to recombinant interferon alfa-2a in hairy-cell leukemia associated with neutralizing anti-interferon antibodies. *N Engl J Med* 1988; 318:1409–1413.

318. Armstrong JA: Semi-Micro, Dye-binding assay for rabbit interferon. *Appl Microbiol* 1971; 21:723–726.

319. Kimchi A, Shulman L, Schmidt A, et al: Kinetics of the induction of three translation-regulatory enzymes by interferon. *Proc Natl Acad Sci USA* 1979; 76:3208–3212.

320. Heron I, Hokland M, Berg K: Enhanced expression of β_2-microglobulin and HLA antigen on human lymphoid cells by interferon. *Proc Natl Acad Sci USA* 1978; 75:6216–6219.

321. Yoshie O, Aso H, Sakakibara A, et al: Differential effects of recombinant human interferon αA/D on expression of three types of Fc receptors on murine macrophages in vivo and in vitro. *J Interferon Res* 1985; 5:531–540.

322. Fisher PB, Prignoli DR, Hermo H, et al: Effects of combined treatment with interferon and mezerein on melanogenesis and growth in human melanoma cells. *J Interferon Res* 1985; 5:11–22.

323. Hilfenhaus J, Damm H, Karges HE, et al: Growth inhibition of human lymphoblastoid Daudi cells in vitro by interferon preparations. *Arch Virol* 1976; 51:87–97.

324. Borden EC: Interferons: Rationale for clinical trials in neoplastic disease. *Ann Intern Med* 1979; 91:472–479.

325. Renton KW, Mannering GJ: Depression of hepatic cytochrome P-450-dependent monooxygenase systems with administered interferon inducing agents. *Biochem Biophys Res Commun* 1976; 73:343–348.

326. Pollard RB, Smith JL, Neal EA, et al: Effect of vidarabine on chronic hepatitis B virus infection. *JAMA* 1978; 239:1648–1650.

327. Heron I, Berg K, Cantell K: Regulatory effect of interferon on T cells in vitro. *J Immunol* 1976; 117:1370–1373.

328. Greenberg HD, Pollard RB, Lutwick LI, et al: Virus infection in patients with chronic active hepatitis. *N Engl J Med* 1976; 295:517–522.

329. Merigan TC, Rand KH, Pollard RB, et al: Human leukocyte interferon for the treatment of herpes zoster in patients with cancer. *N Engl J Med* 1978; 298:981–987.

330. Hagland S, Lundquist P, Cantell K, et al: Interferon therapy in juvenile laryngeal papillomatosis. *Arch Otolaryngeol* 1981; 107:327–332.

331. Pazin GJ, Armstrong JA, Lam MT, et al: Prevention of reactivated herpes simplex infection by human leukocyte interferon after operation on the trigeminal root. *N Engl J Med* 1979; 301:225–236.

332. Cheeseman SH, Rubin RH, Stewart JA, et al: Controlled clinical trial of prophylactic human-leukocyte interferon in renal transplantation. *N Engl J Med* 1979; 300:1345–1349.

333. McGill JI, Cantell K, Collins P, et al: Optimal usage of exogenous human interferon for prevention of therapy of herpetic keratitis. *Trans Ophthal Soc UK* 1977; 97:324–326.

334. Pazin GJ, Harger JH, Armstrong JA, et al: Leukocyte interferon for treating first episodes of genital herpes in women. *J Infect Dis* 1987; 156:891–897.

335. Meyers JD, McGuffin RW, Neiman PE, et al: Toxicity and efficacy of human leukocyte interferon for treatment of cytomegalovirus pneumonia after marrow transplantation. *J Infect Dis* 1980; 141:555–562.

336. Merigan TC, Reed SE, Hall TS, et al: Inhibition of respiratory virus infection by locally applied interferon. *Lancet* 1973; 1:563–567.

337. DeClerg E, Edy VG, DeVlieger H, et al: Intrathecal administration of interferon in neonatal herpes. *J Pediatr* 1975; 86:736–739.

338. Weinmann E, Majer M, Hilfenhaus J: Intramuscular and/or intralumbar posterposure treatment of rabies virus–infected cynomolgous monkeys with human interferon. *Infect Immun* 1979; 24:24–31.

339. Cantell K, Hervonen S, Morgensen KE, et al: Human leukocyte interferon: Production, purification, stability, and animal experiments, in Waymouth C (ed): *The Production and Use of Interferon for the Treatment and Prevention of Human Virus Infections.* Baltimore, The Tissue Culture Association, 1975, pp 35–38.

340. Treanor JJ, Betts RF, Erb SM, et al: Intranasally administered interferon as prophylaxis against experimentally induced influenza A virus infection in humans. *J Infect Dis* 1987; 156:379–383.

341. Monto AS, Albrecht JK, Schwartz SA: Demonstration of dose-response relationship in seasonal prophylaxis of respiratory infections with alpha-2b interferons. *Antimicrob Agents Chemother* 1988; 32:47–50.

342. Ho DD, Kaplan JC, Rackauskas IE, et al: Second conserved domain of gp120 is important for HIV infectivity and antibody neutralization. *Science* 1988; 239:1021–1023.

343. Vance JC, Bart BJ, Hansen RC, et al: Intralesional recombinant alpha-2 interferon for the treatment of patients with condyloma acuminata or verruca plantaris. *Arch Dermatol* 1986; 122:272–277.

344. Eron LJ, Judson F, Tucker S, et al: Interferon therapy for condyloma acuminata. *N Engl J Med* 1986; 315:1059–1064.

345. Omata M, Uchimi K: Combination of prednisolone withdrawal and antiviral agents (adenine arabinoside, interferon) in chronic hepatitis B: A long-term follow-up study. *Hepatology* 1986; 3(suppl 2):S65–S69.

346. Perrillo RP, Regenstein FG, Peters MG, et al: Prednisone withdrawal followed by recombinant alpha interferon in the treatment of chronic type B hepatitis. A randomized, controlled trial. *Ann Intern Med* 1988; 109:95–100.

347. Lok ASF, Wu P-C, Lai C-L, et al: Long-term follow-up in a randomised controlled trial of recombinant α_2-interferon in Chinese patients with chronic hepatitis B infection. *Lancet* 1988; 2:298–302.

348. Hoofnagle JH, Mullen KD, Jones DB, et al: Treatment of chronic non-A, non-B hepatitis with recombinant human alpha

interferon. *N Engl J Med* 1986; 315:1575–1578.

349. Ho DD, Rota TR, Kaplan JC, et al: Recombinant human interferon alpha-A suppresses HTLV-III replication in vivo. *Lancet* 1985; 1:602–604.

350. Yamamoto JK, Barre-Sinoussi F, Bolton V, et al: Human alpha- and beta-interferon—but not gamma—suppress the in vitro replication of LAV, HTLV-III and ARV-2. *J Interferon Res* 1986; 6:143–152.

351. Krown SE, Real FX, Cunningham-Rundles S, et al: Preliminary observations on the effect of recombinant leukocyte A interferon in homosexual men with Kaposi's sarcoma. *N Engl J Med* 1983; 308:1071–1076.

352. Groopman JE, Gottlieb MS, Goodman J, et al: Recombinant alpha-2 interferon therapy for Kaposi's sarcoma associated with the acquired immunodeficiency syndrome. *Ann Intern Med* 1984; 100:671–676.

353. Lane HC, Kovacs JA, Feinberg J, et al: Anti–retroviral effects of interferon–α in AIDS–associated Kaposi's sarcoma. *Lancet* 1988; 2:1218–1222.

354. Zinkernagel RM, Haenseler E, Leist T, et al: T cell–mediated hepatitis in mice infected with lymphocytic choriomeningitis virus. Liver cell destruction by H-2 class I–restricted virus-specific cytotoxic T cells as a physiologic correlate of the ^{51}Cr-release assay? *J Exp Med* 1986:164:1075–1092.

355. Baenziger J, Hengartner H, Zinkernagel RM, et al: Induction or prevention of immunopathological disease by cloned cytotoxic T cell lines specific for lymphocytic choriomeningitis virus. *Eur J Immunol* 1986; 16:387–393.

356. Naraqi S, Jonasson O, Jackson GG, et al: Clinical manifestations of infections with herpesviruses after kidney transplantation. *Ann Surg* 1978; 188:234–239.

357. Von Willebrand E, Pettersson E, Ahonen J, et al: CMV infection, class II antigen expression, and human kidney allograft rejection. *Transplantation* 1986; 42:364–367.

358. Richardson WP, Calvin RB, Cheeseman SH, et al: Glomerulopathy associated with cytomegalovirus viremia in renal allografts. *N Engl J Med* 1981; 305:57–62.

359. Oldstone MBA, Dixon FJ: Interferon as a mediator of cellular immunity in viral infections, in Notkins AL (ed): *Viral Immunology and Immunopathology.* New York, Academic Press, 1975, pp 341–356.

360. Pardo V, Aldana M, Colton RM, et al: Glomerular lesions in the acquired immunodeficiency syndrome. *Ann Intern Med* 1984; 101:429–434.

360a. Glassock RJ, Cohen AH, Danovitch G, et al: Human immunodeficiency virus (HIV) infection and the kidney. *Ann Intern Med* 1990; 112:34–59.

361. Karpatkin S, Nardi MA: Immunologic thrombocytopenic purpura in human immunodeficiency virus–seropositive patients with hemophilia. Comparison with patients with classic autoimmune thrombocytopenic purpura, homosexuals with thrombocytopenia, and narcotic addicts with thrombocytopenia. *J Clin Lab Med* 1988; 111:441–448.

362. Chanock RM, Kapikian AZ, Millis J: Influence of immunological factors in respiratory syncytial virus disease of the lower respiratory tract. *Arch Environ Health* 1970; 21:347–355.

363. Bellanti JA, Sanga RL, Klutinis B, et al: Antibody responses in serum and nasal secretions of inactivated and attenuated measles-virus vaccine. *N Engl J Med* 1969; 280:628–638.

364. Kantor GL, Goldberg LS, Johnson BL, et al: Immunologic abnormalities induced by postperfusion cytomegalovirus infection. *Ann Intern Med* 1970; 73:553–558.

365. Leneman F: The Guillain-Barré-syndrome. *Arch Intern Med* 1966; 118:139–144.

366. Rab DM, Choudhury GM: Landry-Guillain-Barré syndrome after chicken pox. *N Engl J Med* 1963; 268:200–201.

367. Miller HG, Stanton JB, Gibbons JL: Para-infectious encephalomyelitis and related syndromes. *Q J Med* 1956; 25:427–505.

368. Schonberger LB, Bregman DJ, Sullivan-Bolyai JZ, et al: Guillian-Barré syndrome following vaccination in the national influenza, immunization program US, 1976–1977. *Am J Epidemiol* 1979; 110:105–123.

369. Hurwitz ES, Schonberger LB, Nelson DB, et al: Guillian-Barré syndrome and the 1978–1979 influenza vaccine. *N Engl J Med* 1981; 304:1557–1561.

370. Hattwich MAW, Sayetta RB: Time trends of Reye's syndrome based on national statistics, Crocker JFS (ed): *Reye Syndrome II.* New York, Grune & Stratton, 1979, pp 13–32.

371. Starko KM, Ray G, Dominquez LB, et al: Reye's syndrome and salicylate use. *Pediatrics* 1980; 66:859–864.

372. Hurwitz ES, Barrett MJ, Bregman D, et al: Public Health Service study of Reye's syndrome and medications. Report of the main study. *JAMA* 1987; 257:1905–1911.

372a. Itescu S, Brancato LJ, Buxbaum J, et al: A diffuse infiltrative CD8 lymphocytosis syndrome in human immunodeficiency virus (HIV) infection: A host immune response associated with HLA-DR5. *Ann Intern Med* 1990; 112:3–10.

373. McChesney MB, Oldstone MBA: Viruses perturb lymphocyte functions: Selected principles characterizing virus-induced immunosuppression. *Ann Rev Immunol* 1987; 5:279–304.

374. Rouse BT, Horohov DW: Immunosuppression in viral infections. *Rev Infect Dis* 1986; 8:850–873.

375. Lemon DM, Hut LM, Huang H, et al: Simultaneous infection with multiple herpesviruses. *Am J Med* 1979; 66:270–276.

376. Goedert JJ, Wallen WC, Mann DL, et al: Amyl nitrite may alter T lymphocytes in homosexual men. *Lancet* 1982; 1:412–415.

377. Durack DT: Opportunistic infections and Kaposi's sarcoma in homosexual men. *N Engl J Med* 1981; 305:1465–1467.

378. Hanto DW, Fizzera G, Gajl-Peczalska KJ, et al: Epstein-Barr virus–induced B-cell lymphoma after renal transplantation. *N Engl J Med* 1982; 306:913–918.

379. Seeley J, Sakamoto K, Ip SH, et al: Abnormal lymphocyte subjects in X-linked lymphoproliferative syndrome. *J Immunol* 1981; 127:2618–2620.

380. Salmi AA, Norrby E, Panelius M: Identification of different measles virus–specific antibodies in the serum and cerebrospinal fluid from patients with subacute sclerosing panencephalitis and multiple sclerosis. *Infect Immun* 1972; 6:248–254.

381. Connolly JH, Allen IV, Hurwitz LJ, et al: Measles-virus antibody and antigen in subacute sclerosing panencephalitis. *Lancet* 1967; 1:542–544.

382. Brown HR, Goller NL, Thormar H, et al: Measles virus matrix protein gene expression in a subacute sclerosing panencephalitis patient brain and virus isolate demonstrated by cDNA hybridization and immunocytochemistry. *Acta Neuropathol* 1987; 75:123–130.

383. Cook SD, Dowling PC: Multiple sclerosis and viruses: An overview. *Neurology* 1980; 30:80–91.

384. Koprowski H, DeFreitas EC, Harper ME, et al: Multiple sclerosis and human T-cell lymphotropic viruses. *Nature* 1985; 318:154–160.

385. Rice GPA, Armstrong HA, Bulman DE, et al: Absence of antibody to HTLV I and III in sera of Canadian patients with multiple sclerosis and chronic myelopathy. *Ann Neurol* 1986; 20:533–534.

386. Epstein L, Blumberg B, Crowley J, et al: Serum and antibodies to HTLV-I in human demyelinating diseases. *Acta Neurol Scand* 1987; 75:231–233.

387. Chen W, Munoz J, Fundenberg H, et al: Polyclonal activation of human peripheral blood B lymphocytes by formaldehyde-fixed salmonella paratype B. *J Exp Med* 1981; 153:365–374.

388. Nillson K, Ponten J: Classification and biological nature of established human hematopoietic cell lines. *Int J Cancer* 1975; 15:321–341.

389. Schwartz RS: Viruses and systemic lupus erythematosus. *N Engl J Med* 1975; 293:132–136.

390. Gottlieb MS, Schroff R, Schanker HM, et al: *Pneumocystics carinii* pneumonia and mucosal candidiasis in previously healthy

homosexual men. Evidence of a new acquired cellular immunodeficiency. *N Engl J Med* 1981; 305:1425–1431.

391. Masur H, Michelis MA, Greene JB, et al: An outbreak of community-acquired *Pneumocystis carinii* pneumonia: Initial manifestation of cellular immune dysfunction. *N Engl J Med* 1981; 305:1431–1438.

392. Leonard R, Zagury D, Desportes I, et al: Cytopathic effect of human immunodeficiency virus in T4 cells is linked to the last stage of virus infection. *Proc Natl Acad Sci USA* 1988; 85:3570–3574.

393. Lewis DE, Yoffe B, Bosworth CG, et al: Human immunodeficiency virus–induced pathology favored by cellular transmission and activation. *FASEB J* 1988; 2:251–255.

394. Nicholson JK, Cross GD, Callaway CS, et al: In vitro infection of human monocytes with human T lymphotropic virus type III/lymphadenopathy–associated virus (HTLV-III/LAV). *J Immunol* 1986; 137:323–329.

395. Golding H, Robey FA, Gates FT, et al: Identification of homologous regions in human immunodeficiency virus 1 gp41 and human MHC class II β 1 domain. *J Exp Med* 1988; 1167:914–923.

396. Weissman I: Approaches to an understanding of pathogenetic mechanisms in AIDS. *Rev Infect Dis* 1988; 10:385–398.

397. Pahwa S, Pahwa R, Saxinger C, et al: Influence of the human T-lymphotropic virus/lymphadenopathy associated virus on functions of human lymphocytes: Evidence for immunosuppressive effects and polyclonal B-cell activation by banded viral preparations. *Proc Natl Acad Sci USA* 1985; 82:8198–8202.

398. Reddy MM, England A, Brown D, et al: Lymphoproliferative responses to human immunodeficiency virus antigen in asymptomatic intravenous drug abusers and in patients with lymphadenopathy or AIDS. *J Infect Dis* 1987; 156:374–376.

399. Wahren B, Morfeldt-Mansson L, Biberfeld G, et al: Impaired specific cellular immune response to HTLV-III before other immune defects in patients with HTLV-III infections. *N Engl J Med* 1986; 315:393–394.

400. Lane HC, Fauci AS: Immunologic abnormalities in the acquired immunodeficiency syndrome. *Annu Rev Immunol* 1985; 3:477–500.

400a. Koga Y, Sasaki M, Yoshida H, et al: Cytopathic effect determined by the amount of CD4 molecules in human cell lines expressing envelope glycoprotein of HIV. *J Immunol* 1990; 144:94–102.

401. Mann DL, Lasane F, Popovic M, et al: HTLV-III large envelope protein (p120) suppresses PHA-induced lymphocyte blastogenesis. *J Immunol* 1987; 138:2640–2644.

401a. Rosenstein Y, Burakoff SJ, Herrmann SH: HIV-gp120 can block CD4-class II MHC-mediated adhesion. *J Immunol* 1990; 144:526–531.

402. Chanh TC, Kennedy RC, Kanda P: Synthetic peptides homologous to HIV transmembrane glycoprotein suppress normal human lymphocyte blastogenic response. *Cell Immunol* 1988; 111:77–86.

403. Rook AH, Masur H, Lane HC, et al: Interleukin-2 enhances the depressed natural killer and cytomegalovirus-specific cytotoxic activities of lymphocytes from patients with the acquired immune deficiency syndrome. *J Clin Invest* 1983; 72:398–403.

404. Quinnan GV, Rook AH, Frederick WR, et al: Prevalence, clinical manifestations and immunology of herpesvirus infections in the acquired immunodeficiency syndrome. *Ann NY Acad Sci* 1984; 437:200–206.

405. Blumberg RS, Paradis T, Byington R, et al: Effects of human immunodeficiency virus on the cellular immune response to Epstein-Barr virus in homosexual men: Characterization of the cytotoxic response and lymphokine production. *J Infect Dis* 1987; 155:877–890.

406. Sharma B, Gupta S: Antigen-specific primary cytotoxic T lymphocyte (CTL) responses in acquired immune deficiency syndrome (AIDS) and AIDS-related complexes (ARC). *Clin Exp Immunol* 1985; 62:296–303.

407. Siegel JP, Djeu JY, Stocks NI, et al: Sera from patients with the acquired immunodeficiency syndrome inhibit production of interleukin-2 by normal lymphocytes. *J Clin Invest* 1985; 75:1957–1964.

408. Lawrence J, Gottlieb AB, Kunkel HG, et al: Soluble suppressor factors in patients with acquired immune deficiency syndrome and its prodrome: Elaboration in vitro by T lymphocyte–adherent cell interactions. *J Clin Invest* 1983; 72:2072–2081.

409. Kirkpatrick CH, Davis KC, Horsburgh CR Jr, et al: Interleukin-2 production by persons with the generalized lymphadenopathy syndrome or the acquired immunodeficiency syndrome. *J Clin Immunol* 1985; 5:31–37.

410. Donnelly RP, La Via MF, Tsang KY: Humoral-mediated suppression of interleukin-2 dependent target cell proliferation in acquired immune deficiency syndrome (AIDS): Interference with normal IL-2 receptor expression. *Clin Exp Immunol* 1987; 68:488–499.

411. Fauci AS: The human immunodeficiency virus: Infectivity and mechanisms of pathogenesis. *Science* 1988; 239:617–622.

412. Rook AH, Manischewitz JF, Frederick WR, et al: Deficient HLA-restricted cytomegalovirus-specific cytotoxic T cells and natural killer cells in patients with acquired immunodeficiency syndrome. *J Infect Dis* 1985; 152:627–630.

413. Lane HC, Masur H, Edgar LC, et al: Abnormalities of B cell activation and immunoregulation in patients with the acquired immunodeficiency syndrome. *N Engl J Med* 1983; 309:453–458.

414. Yarchoan R, Redfield RR, Broder S: Mechanism of B cell activation in patients with acquired immunodeficiency syndrome and related disorders. *J Clin Invest* 1986; 78:439–447.

415. Pahwa S, Pahwa R, Good RA, et al: Stimulatory and inhibitory influences of human immunodeficiency virus on normal B lymphocytes. *Proc Natl Acad Sci USA* 1986; 83:9124–9128.

415a. Breen EC, Rezai AR, Nakajima K, et al: Infection with HIV is associated with elevated IL-6 levels and production. *J Immunol* 1990; 144:480–484.

416. Lane HC, Depper JM, Greene WC, et al: Qualitative analysis of immune function in patients with the acquired immunodeficiency syndrome. Evidence for a selective defect in soluble antigen recognition. *N Engl J Med* 1985; 313:79–84.

417. Euler HH, Kern P, Loffler H, et al: Precipitable immune complexes in healthy homosexual men, acquired immune deficiency syndrome, and the related lymphadenopathy syndrome. *Clin Exp Immunol* 1985; 59:267–275.

418. Morrow WJW, Wharton M, Strickler RB, et al: Circulating immune complexes in patients with acquired immune deficiency syndrome contain the AIDS-associated retrovirus. *Clin Immunol Immunopathol* 1986; 40:515–524.

419. Jackson S, Dawson LM, Kotler DP: IgA1 is the major immunoglobulin component of the immune complexed in the acquired immunodeficiency syndrome. *J Clin Immunol* 1988; 8:64–68.

420. Lightfoote MM, Folks TM, Redfield R, et al: Circulating IgA immune complexes in AIDS. *Immunol Invest* 1985; 14:341–345.

421. Koenig S, Gendelman HE, Orenstein JM, et al: Detection of AIDS virus in macrophages in brain tissue from AIDS patients with encephalopathy. *Science* 1986; 233:1089–1093.

422. Armstrong JA, Horne R: Follicular dendritic cells and virus-like-particles in AIDS related lymphadenopathy. *Lancet* 1984; 2:370–372.

423. Piris MA, Rivas C, Morente M, et al: Persistent and generalized lymphadenopathy: A lesion of follicular dendritic cells? An immunohistologic and ultrastructural study. *Am J Clin Pathol* 1987; 87:716–724.

424. Ho DD, Rota TR, Hirsch MS: Infection of monocyte/macrophages by human T lymphotropic virus type III. *J Clin Invest* 1986; 77:1712–1715.

425. Gartner S, Markovits P, Markovitz DM, et al: The role of mononuclear phagocytes in HTLV-III/LAV infection. *Science* 1986; 233:215–219.

426. Salahuddin SZ, Rose RM, Groopman JE, et al: Human T lymphotropic virus type III infection of human alveolar macrophages. *Blood* 1986; 68:281–284.

427. Folks TM, Justement J, Kinter A, et al: Cytokine-induced expression of HIV-1 in a chronically infected promonocyte cell line. *Science* 1987; 238:800–802.

428. Pauza CD: HIV persistence in monocytes leads to pathogenesis and AIDS. *Cell Immunol* 1988;112:414–424.

429. Sei Y, Petrella RJ, Tsang P, et al: Monocytes in AIDS. *N Engl J Med* 1986; 315:1611–1612.

430. Murray HW, Jacobs JL, Bovbjerg DH: Accessory cell function in AIDS monocytes. *J Infect Dis* 1987; 156:696.

431. Chantal Petit AJ, Tersmette M, Terpstra FG, et al: Decreased accessory cell function by human monocytic cells after infection with HIV. *J Immunol* 1988; 140:1485–1489.

432. Prince HE, Moody DJ, Shubin BI, et al: Defective monocyte function in acquired immunodeficiency syndrome (AIDS): Evidence from a monocyte-dependent T-cell proliferative system. *J Clin Immunol* 1985; 5:21–25.

433. Smith PD, Otturk A, Masur H, et al: Monocyte function in AIDS. Defective chemotaxis. *J Clin Invest* 1984; 74:2121–2128.

434. Poli G, Bottazzi B, Acero R, et al: Monocyte function in intravenous drug abusers with lymphadenopathy syndrome and in patients with acquired immunodeficiency syndrome: Selective impairment of chemotaxis. *Clin Exp Immunol* 1985; 62:136–142.

435. Eales L-J, Moshatel D, Pinching AJ: Microbicidal activity of monocyte derived macrophages in AIDS and related disorders. *Clin Exp Immunol* 1987; 67:227–235.

436. Kessler HA, Blaauw B, Spear J, et al: Diagnosis of human immunodeficiency virus infection in seronegative homosexual men presenting with an acute viral syndrome. *JAMA* 1987; 258:1196–1199.

436a. Wolinsky SM, Rinaldo CR, Kwok S, et al: Human immunodeficiency virus type 1 (HIV-1) infection a median of 18 months before a diagnostic western blot: Evidence from a cohort of homosexual men. *Ann Intern Med* 1989; 111:961–972.

437. Jason J, McDougal JS, Holman RC, et al: Human T lymphotropic virus type III/lymphadenopathy-associated virus antibody. Association with hemophiliacs' immune status and blood component usage. *JAMA* 1985; 253:3409–3415.

438. Lange JMA, Couthino RA, Krone WJA, et al: Distinct IgG recognition patterns during progression of subclinical and clinical infections with lymphadenopathy associated virus/human T lymphotropic virus. *Br Med J (Clin Res)* 1986; 292:228–230.

439. Chou M-J, Lee T-H, Hatzakis A, et al: Antibody responses in early human immunodeficiency syndrome type 1 infections in hemophiliacs. *J Infect Dis* 1988; 157:805–811.

440. Wittek AE, Phelan MA, Wells MA, et al: Detection of human immunodeficiency virus core protein in plasma by enzyme immunoassay. Association of antigenemia with symptomatic disease and T-helper cell depletion. *Ann Intern Med* 1987; 107:286–292.

441. Franching G, Robert-Guroff M, Aldovini A, et al: Spectrum of natural antibodies against five HTLV-III antigens in infected individuals: Correlation of antibody prevalence with clinical status. *Blood* 1987; 69:437–441.

442. Lange JMA, Paul DA, Huisman HG, et al: Persistent HIV antigenemia and decline of HIV core antibodies associated with progression to AIDS. *Br Med J (Clin Res)* 1986; 293:1459–1462.

442a. Skinner MA, Ting R, Langlois AJ, et al: Characteristics of a neutralizing monoclonal antibody to the HIV envelope glycoprotein. *AIDS Res Hum Retroviruses* 1988; 4:187–197.

442b. Rossi P, Broliden PA, Fundaro C, et al: Presence of maternal antibodies to human immunodeficiency virus 1 envelope glycoprotein gp120 epitopes correlates with the uninfected status of children born to seropositive mothers. *Proc Natl Acad Sci USA* 1989; 86:8055–8058.

442c. Sawyer LA, Katzenstein DA, Hendry RM, et al: Possible beneficial effects of neutralizing antibodies and antibody-dependent, cell-mediated cytotoxicity in human immunodeficiency virus infection. *AIDS Res Hum Retroviruses* 1990; 6:341–356.

443. Rusche JR, Javaherian K, McDanal C, et al: Antibodies that inhibit fusion of human immunodeficiency virus-infected cells bind a 24-amino acid sequence of the viral envelope, gp120. *Proc Natl Acat Sci USA* 1988; 85:3198–3202.

444. Palker TJ, Clark ME, Langlois AJ, et al: Type-specific neutralization of the human immunodeficiency virus with antibodies to env-encoded synthetic peptides. *Proc Natl Acad Sci USA* 1988; 85:1932–1936.

444a. Takeda A, Tuazon CU, Ennis FA: Antibody-enhanced infection by HIV-1 via Fc receptor-mediated entry. *Science* 1989; 242:580–583.

444b. Robinson WE Jr, Montefiori DC, Mitchell WM, et al: Antibody-dependent enhancement of human immunodeficiency virus type 1 (HIV-1) infection in vitro by serum from HIV-1-infected and passively immunized chimpanzees. *Proc Natl Acad Sci USA* 1989; 86:4710–4714.

444c. McKeating JA, Griffiths PD, Weiss RA: HIV susceptibility conferred to human fibroblasts by cytomegalovirus-induced Fc receptor. *Nature* 1990; 343:651–661.

445. Lyerly HK, Reed DL, Matthews TJ, et al: Anti-gp 120 antibodies from HIV seropositive individuals mediate broadly reactive anti-HIV ADCC. *AIDS Res Hum Retroviruses* 1978; 3:409–422.

446. Ojo-Amazie EA, Nishanian P, Keith DE Jr, et al: Antibodies to human immunodeficiency virus in human sera induce cell-mediated lysis of human immunodeficiency virus–infected cells. *J Immunol* 1987; 139:2458–2463.

447. Ljunggren K, Bottiger B, Biberfeld G, et al: Antibody-dependent cellular cytotoxicity-inducing antibodies against human immunodeficiency virus. Presence at different clinical stages. *J Immunol* 1987; 139:2263–2267.

448. Rook AH, Lane HC, Folks T, et al: Sera from HTLV-III/LAV antibody positive individuals mediate antibody-dependent cellular cytotoxicity against HTLV-III/LAV infected T-cells. *J Infect Dis* 1987; 138:1064–1067.

449. Walker BD, Chakrabarti S, Moss B, et al: HIV-specific cytotoxic T lymphocytes in seropositive individuals. *Nature* 1987; 328:345–348.

450. Plata F, Autran B, Martins LP, et al: AIDS virus specific cytotoxic T lymphocytes in lung disorders. *Nature* 1987; 328:348–351.

451. Walker BD, Flexner C, Paradis TJ, et al: HIV-1 reverse transcriptase is a target for cytotoxic T lymphocytes in infected individuals. *Science* 1988; 240:64–66.

452. Koenig S, Earl P, Powell D, et al: Cell mediated cytotoxicity against target cells expressing HIV-1 proteins. Program and abstracts of the Fourth International Conference on AIDS, Stockholm, Sweden, June 4–9, 1988, abstract 2209.

453. Plata F, Hoffenbach A, Langlade-Demoyen P, et al: Qualitative analysis of HIV-specific target cells expressing HIV-1 proteins. Program and abstracts of the Fourth International Conference on AIDS, Stockholm, Sweden, June 4–9, 1988, abstract 2188.

454. Shepp DH, Daguillard F, Mann D, et al: Human class I MHC-restricted cytotoxic T-lymphocytes specific for human immunodeficiency virus envelope antigens. *AIDS* 1988; 2:113–117.

455. Walker BD, Paradis TJ, Flexner C, et al: Characteristics of the HIV-1 specific T cell mediated immune response. Program and abstracts of the Fourth International Conference on AIDS, Stockholm, Sweden, June 4–9, 1988, abstract 2184.

455a. Kahn JO, Allan JD, Hodges TL, et al: The safety and pharmacokinetics of recombinant soluble CD4 (rCD4) in subjects with the acquired immunodeficiency syndrome (AIDS) and AIDS-related complex: A phase 1 study. *Ann Intern Med* 1990; 112:254–261.

455b. Schooley RT, Merigan TC, Gaut P, et al: Recombinant soluble CD4 therapy in patients with the acquired immunodeficiency syndrome (AIDS) and AIDS-related complex: A phase I-II escalating dosage trial. *Ann Intern Med* 1990; 112:247–253.

455c. Holland HK, Saral R, Rossi JJ, et al: Allogeneic bone marrow transplantation, zidovudine, and human immunodeficiency virus type 1 (HIV-1) infection: Studies in a patient with non-Hodgkin's lymphoma. *Ann Intern Med* 1989; 111:973–981.

456. Whitley RJ, Soon SJ, Dolin R, et al: Adenine arabinoside therapy of biopsy-proved herpes simplex encephalitis. *N Engl J Med* 1977; 297:289–294.

457. Whitley RJ, Chien LT, Dolin R: Adenine arabinoside therapy of herpes zoster in the immunosuppressed NIAID. *N Engl J Med* 1976; 294:1193–1199.

458. Saral R, Burns WH, Lookin OL, et al: Acyclovir prophylaxis of herpes-simplex-virus infections. *N Engl J Med* 1981; 305:63–67.

459. Togo Y, Hornick RB, Felitti VJ, et al: Evaluation of therapeutic efficacy of amantadine in patients with naturally occurring A2 influenza. *JAMA* 1970; 211:1149–1156.

460. Schmidt NJ, Gallo D, Devlin V, et al: Direct immunofluorescence staining for detection of herpes simplex and varicella-zoster virus antigens in vesicular lesions and certain tissue specimens. *J Clin Microbiol* 1980; 12:651–655.

461. Ray GC, Minnich LL: Efficiency of immunofluorescence for rapid detection of common respiratory viruses. *J Clin Microbiol* 1987; 25:355–357.

462. Griffiths PD, Panjwani DD, Stirk PR, et al: Rapid diagnosis of cytomegalovirus infection in immunocompromised patients by detection of early antigen fluorescent foci. *Lancet* 1984; 2:1242–1245.

463. Gleaves CA, Smith TF, Shuster EA, et al: Rapid detection of cytomegalovirus in MRC-5 cells inoculated with urine specimens by using low speed centrifugation and monoclonal antibody to an early antigen. *J Clin Microbiol* 1984; 19:917–919.

464. Yolken RH, Torsch VM: Enzyme–linked immunosorbent assay for detection and identification of coxsackieviruses. *Infect Immun* 1981; 31:742–750.

465. McIntosh K, Hendry RM, Fahnestock ML, et al: Enzyme-linked immunosorbent assay for detection of respiratory syncytial virus infection: application to clinical samples. *J Clin Microbiol* 1982; 16:329–333.

466. Johansson ME, Uhnoo I, Kidd AH, et al: Direct identification of enteric adenovirus, a candidate new serotype, associated with infantile gastroenteritis. *J Clin Microbiol* 1980; 12:95–100.

467. Shekarchi IC, Fucillo DA, Strouse R, et al: Capillary enzyme immunoassay for rapid detection of herpes simplex virus in clinical specimens. *J Clin Microbiol* 1987; 25:320–322.

468. Cleveland PH, Richman DD: Enzyme immunofiltration staining assay for immediate diagnosis of herpes simplex virus and varicella-zoster virus directly from clinical specimens. *J Clin Microbiol* 1985; 25:416–420.

469. Nerukar LS, Namba M, Brashears G, et al: Rapid detection of herpes simplex virus in clinical specimens using a capture biotin-streptavidin enzyme linked immunosorbent assay. *J Clin Microbiol* 1984; 20:109–114.

470. McKeeting JA, Grundy JE, Varghese Z, et al: Detection of cytomegalovirus by ELISA in urine samples is inhibited by β_2 microglobulin. *J Med Virol* 1986; 18:341–348.

471. El-Mekki A, Al-Nakib W, Bibi R: Factors affecting the detection of cytomegalovirus in urine by sandwich enzyme immunoassays. *J Virol Methods* 1987; 15:75–83.

472. Dudding BA, Top FH, Winter PE, et al: Acute respiratory disease in military trainees. The adenovirus surveillance program 1966–1971. *Am J Epidemiol* 1973; 97:187–198.

473. Kim HW, Canchola JG, Brandt CD, et al: Respiratory syncytial virus disease in infants despite prior administration of antigenic inactivated vaccine. *Am J Epidemiol* 1969; 89:422–434.

474. Norrby E, Lagereranty R: The occurrence of antibodies against virus envelope components after immunization with inactivated vaccine effects of revaccination with live measles vaccine. *Acta Pediatr Scand* 1976; 65:171–176.

475. Snydman DR, Werner BG, Heinze-Lacey B, et al: Use of cytomegalovirus immune globulin to prevent cytomegalovirus disease in renal transplant recipients. *N Engl J Med* 1987; 317:1049–1054.

476. Epstein JS, Quinnan GV: Prevention of herpes simplex virus diseases in man, in Chang T (ed): *Clinics in Dermatology.* Philadelphia, Lippincott, 1984, vol 2, pp 133–149.

477. Halstead SB, Shortwell H, Casals J: Studies on the pathogenesis of dengue infection in monkeys. II. Clinical laboratory responses to heterologous infections. *Infec Dis* 1973; 128:15–22.

478. Zajac BA, West DJ, McAleer WJ, et al: Overview of clinical studies with hepatitis B vaccine made by recombinant DNA. *J Infect Dis* 1986; 13(suppl A):39–45.

479. Centers for Disease Control: Update on hepatitis B prevention. Recommendations from the Immunization Practices Advisory Committee. *Ann Intern Med* 1987; 107:353–357.

480. Barr PJ, Steimer KS, Sabin EA, et al: Antigenicity and immunogenicity of domains of the human immunodeficiency virus (HIV) envelope polypeptide expressed in the yeast *Saccharomyces cerevisiae. Vaccine* 1987; 5:90–101.

481. Crowl R, Ganguly K, Gordon M, et al: HTLV-III env gene products synthesized in *E. coli* are recognized by antibodies present in the sera of AIDS patients. *Cell* 1985; 41:979–986.

482. Putney SD, Matthews TJ, Robey WG, et al: HTLV-III/LAV neutralizing antibodies to an *E. coli* produced fragment of virus envelope. *Science* 1986; 234:1392–1395.

483. Krohn K, Robey WG, Putney SD, et al: Specific cellular immune response and neutralizing antibodies in goats immunized with native or recombinant envelope proteins derived from human T-lymphotropic virus type III$_B$ and in human immunodeficiency virus-infected men. *Proc Natl Acad Sci USA* 1987; 84:4994–4998.

484. Cochran MA, Ericson BL, Knell BD, et al: Use of baculovirus recombinants as a general method for the production of subunit vaccines, in Lerner RA, Channock RM, Brown F (eds): *Vaccines 87.* Cold Spring Harbor, NY, Cold Spring Harbor Laboratory, 1987, pp 384–388.

485. Rusche JR, Lynn DL, Robert-Guroff M, et al: Humoral immune response to the entire human immunodeficiency virus envelope glycoprotein made in insect cells. *Proc Natl Acad Sci USA* 1987; 84:6924–6928.

486. Naylor PH, Naylor CW, Badamchian M, et al: Human immunodeficiency virus contains an epitope immunoreactive with thymosin alpha$_1$ and the 30-amino acid synthetic p17 group-specific antigen peptide HGP-30. *Proc Natl Acad Sci USA* 1987; 84:2951–2955.

487. Chakrabarti S, Robert-Guroff M, Wong-Staal F, et al: Expression of the HTLV-III envelope gene by a recombinant vaccinia virus. *Nature* 1986; 320:535–537.

488. Hu S-L, Kowalski SG, Dalrymple JM: Expression of AIDS virus envelope gene in recombinant vaccinia viruses. *Nature* 1986; 320:537–540.

489. Audibert F, Chedid L, Lefrancier P, et al: Distinctive adjuvanticity of synthetic analogs of mycobacterial water soluble components. *Cell Immunol* 1976; 21:243–249.

490. Chedid L, Parent MA, Audibert FM, et al: Biological activity of a new synthetic muramyl peptide adjuvant devoid of pyrogenicity. *Infect Immun* 1982; 35:417–424.

491. Morein B, Sundquist B, Hoglund S, et al: Iscom, a novel structure for antigenic presentation of membrane proteins from enveloped viruses. *Nature* 1984; 308:457–462.

492. Cardner MB, Officer JE, Parker J, et al: Induction of disseminated virulent cytomegalovirus infection by immunosuppresion of naturally chronically infected wild mice. *Infect Immun* 1974; 10:966–969.

493. Miller C: Human lymphoblastoid cell lines and Epstein-Barr virus: A review of their interrelationships and their relevance to the etiology of leukoproliferative states in man. *Yale J Biol Med* 1971; 43:358–384.

494. Wise TG, Manischewitz JE, Quinnan GV, et al: Latent cytomegalovirus in Balb C mouse spleens detected by an explant culture technique. *J Gen Virol* 1979; 44:551–556.

495. Stevens JG, Cook ML: Latent herpes simplex virus in spinal ganglia of mice. *Science* 1971; 173:843–845.

496. Olding LB, Kingsbury DT, Oldstone MBA: Pathogenesis of cytomegalovirus infection. Distribution of viral products, immune complexes and autoimmunity during latent murine infection. *J Gen Virol* 1976; 33:267–280.

497. Hirsch MS, Phillips SM, Solnik C, et al: Activation of leukemia viruses by graft-versus-host and mixed lymphocyte reactions in vitro. *Proc Natl Acad Sci USA* 1972; 69:1069–1072.

498. Horta-Barbosa L, Hamilton R, Wittig B, et al: Subacute sclerosing panencephalitis: Isolation of suppressed measles virus from lymph node biopsies. *Science* 1971; 173:840–841.

499. Nash AA, Gell PGH: The delayed hypersensitivity T cell and its interaction with other cells. *Immunol Today* 1981; 2:162–165.

500. Shore SL, Cromeans TL, Romano TJ: Immune destruction of virus-infected cells early in the infectious cycle. *Nature* 1976; 262:695–696.

501. Hill TJ, Harbour DA, Blyth WA: Isolation of herpes simplex virus from the skin of clinically normal mice during latent infection. *J Gen Virol* 1980; 47:205–207.

Diagnostic Virology

Marilyn A. Menegus

The information that the viral diagnostic laboratory can provide to the practicing physician is largely dictated by the nature of the laboratory. Laboratories often differ in their emphasis on diagnostic methods—some stress cultivation, some stress serologic testing, and others provide both services.[1] Rapid methods that directly demonstrate viral antigen(s) in the clinical specimen are available through most diagnostic laboratories. Although all of these approaches are useful for determining the viral etiology of a disease, they differ considerably in their efficiency, speed, sensitivity, and specificity. It is important for the clinician in search of a specific viral etiology of the patient's illness to understand the methods employed and their varying potential for answering the diagnostic question posed.

VIRUS CULTIVATION

Specimen Collection and Transport

The first questions that must be asked in establishing the specific viral etiology of a disease are: (1) Does the patient have an illness that can be diagnosed by available methods? and (2) What specimens should be collected and how should they be transported to the laboratory? Unless the clinician is familiar with the laboratory, consultation regarding available services is advisable.

It is important to collect specimens as early in the course of the disease as possible since the quantity of virus shed is greatest at this time. Shedding of virus and the likelihood of obtaining a positive result decrease as the illness progresses.

Disease categories and the recommended types of specimens that should be collected for each are listed in Table 5–1. Choosing the type of specimen(s) for collection is dictated by the characteristics of the illness being studied. For example, for common respiratory illnesses such as croup and bronchiolitis, collecting a single specimen from the respiratory tract is usually sufficient. However, for more complex cases, such as pneumonia in an immunocompromised host, collecting specimens from multiple sites may be important.

Vials or tubes containing 2 to 3 mL of viral transport medium (VTM) are generally provided by the laboratory for specimen collection. Although VTM formulations differ from laboratory to laboratory, the basic elements remain similar: a fluid phase (either an isotonic salt solution or veal infusion broth) with a protein stabilizer and a pH indicator. VTM may also contain broad-spectrum antibiotics to help control fungal and bacterial contamination; therefore, specimens placed in it are unsuitable for cultivation of other microbial agents. VTM should be stored at refrigerator or freezer temperatures (4°C to −20°C) to maintain antibiotic potency.

Swab specimens should be broken off into vials of VTM and

Table 5–1
Clinical Specimen(s) to Be Obtained for Viral Diagnosis

Disease Category	Specimens That Should Be Taken Routinely	Comment
Respiratory tract	Nasal wash or throat wash or nasal/throat swab or sputum	Urine if CMV is suspected
Central nervous system	CSF throat swab, rectal swab or stool	Urine if mumps is suspected. Serologic methods are most useful in cases of suspected togaviruses and bunyaviruses and HIV-associated CNS disease; brain biopsy for suspected herpes simplex encephalitis
Genital tract Lesions, cervicitis, vaginitis	Lesion swab or scraping, cervico-vaginal swab	
Ocular	Conjunctival swab or corneal scraping	
Gastrointestinal	Stool	Viral antigen detection techniques and electron microscopy rather than culture used for most viruses associated with GI disease
Hepatitis	Serum	Urine if CMV is suspected; antigen detection and serologic techniques most useful for diagnosis
Exanthemas	Throat swab, rectal swab or stool, vesicular fluid or lesion swab	Serologic methods are generally more useful for the diagnosis of measles, rubella, varicella-zoster, togavirus, and bunyavirus exanthemas
Congenital and neonatal	Nasal/throat swab, urine, stool or rectal swab, CSF	In most instances virus isolation techniques are preferred to serodiagnostic methods
Nonspecific febrile illness	Throat swab, rectal swab or stool and urine	HIV serology if indicated by history or clinical picture
Miscellaneous Arthritis, carditis, parotitis, orchitis	Throat swab, rectal swab or stool, urine	HIV serology if indicated by history or clinical picture

CMV = cytomegalovirus; HIV = human immunodeficiency virus; GI = gastrointestinal.

special care taken to seal caps tightly since leaking specimens present problems with respect to adequacy of specimen and infection control. Other specimen types such as stool, urine, and tissues may be placed in VTM or sent to the laboratory in conventional containers. Most laboratories prefer to receive CSF undiluted in sterile tubes.

Although some viruses are quite stable and can survive adverse storage and transport conditions, others are very labile and viability may be lost after only a few hours under suboptimal conditions. Since the identity of the virus sought is often unknown, it is best to handle all specimens as if they contain the most labile viruses. Optimally, specimens for virus cultivation should be taken into the laboratory immediately. If short delays (1–48 h) are unavoidable, the specimen should be placed on wet ice or in a refrigerator (4°C). Freezing at −70°C is recommended if a longer delay is anticipated. However, it should be remembered that freezing reduces the viability of most viruses and should be avoided if at all possible. Among the commonly isolated viruses, only adenoviruses and enteroviruses will survive repeated freezing and thawing at conventional freezer temperatures (−20°C).

Specimens

In general, the methods for collecting specimens for virus isolation and the types of specimen collected are similar to those used for bacteriologic examination.

Respiratory Tract

A variety of specimens, including throat swabs and washings, nasopharyngeal (NP) swabs, nasal washings, sputum, bronchial brushings and washes, and tracheal aspirates are suitable for virus culture. Although some viruses replicate preferentially in the nasopharynx, the oropharynx is the preferred site for others. For example, rhinoviruses and respiratory syncytial virus are best isolated from nasopharyngeal secretions, whereas oropharyngeal secretions are best for the isolation of cytomegalovirus (CMV) and adenoviruses.[2] Specimens obtained from both sites can be combined in a single vial of VTM, thus maximizing virus yield and reducing the cost to the patient.

In general, washings and aspirates contain larger quantities of secretions than swabs[3] and are therefore superior for the isolation of many viruses. Washings should be done with sterile saline and then mixed with equal volumes of VTM. Neither VTM nor cell culture medium should ever be used in performing the wash since both contain several potential allergens.

The viral agents most frequently associated with respiratory disease in children and adults are listed in Table 5–2.

Tissue

Most tissue can be tested for the presence of viruses. Large specimens can be transported intact in a sterile Petri dish or wide-mouth vial. However, if only a small amount of tissue can be obtained, care must be taken to keep it from drying out. This can be done by placing the specimen in a vial of VTM or on a gauze wetted with sterile saline. If tissues from several organs are collected, each should be obtained with a clean set of instruments in order to avoid cross-contamination. Whenever possible, at least 1 g of tissue should be submitted for culture.

The standard method for processing tissue consists of homogenizing a 10% suspension in VTM, sedimenting larger debris by centrifugation, and then inoculating the supernatant fluid into the appropriate culture systems.

Cerebrospinal Fluid (CSF)

Because of its diagnostic value, CSF should always be sent for virus culture in suspected cases of central nervous system infection. Although virus can often be isolated from peripheral sites in patients with acute neurologic disease, a definitive diagnosis depends on virus recovery from the CSF or brain. Some viruses, such as echovirus and group B coxsackieviruses, are readily isolated and positive culture results may be available early enough (within 2–3 d) to influence patient management.[4] On the other hand, herpes simplex virus, poliovirus, and many of the togaviruses are infrequently grown from CSF, and cultures from peripheral sites, together with serologic tests, are more important in diagnosis.[5]

CSF is generally inoculated into cell cultures unprocessed since it is usually bacteriologically sterile. Most laboratories require approximately 1 mL for testing.

Feces

Virus isolation from fecal specimens is useful in very few situations other than for diagnosing enteroviral disease. Even enterovirus recovery during the course of an illness is of limited diagnostic value because these viruses are frequently shed asymptomatically and for prolonged periods (2–4 wk).[6] Although the common causes of gastroenteritis (rotavirus and the Norwalk-like viruses) can be demonstrated in fecal specimens by other methods such as enzyme-linked immunoassay or electron microscopy, they usually cannot be recovered by classic culture techniques.[7–9]

Either a rectal swab or stool specimen can be sent for culture. Stool specimens are superior for virus recovery; however, they are sometimes more difficult to obtain. If swabs are used, it is important to obtain sufficient fecal material.

Vesicular Fluid and Skin Scrapings

Vesicular fluid and cellular material from vesicle bases should be collected from the most recently erupted vesicles. Older lesions, particularly those which are already crusted, rarely yield virus.

Aspiration of vesicular fluid can be accomplished with a 26-gauge needle attached to a tuberculin syringe or with a fine-bore capillary pipette. The fluid should be introduced into a small volume of VTM or, if possible, inoculated directly onto cell culture. Direct inoculation is preferable for the isolation of varicella-zoster virus or the enteroviruses which cause vesicular exanthemas. Swabs may also be used for collection of vesicular fluid and cellular material but should be used only for those lesions thought to be caused by herpes simplex virus. Other viruses are less likely to be isolated from swab specimens.

Eye

Eye specimens may be collected by rubbing the palpebral conjunctiva with a sterile swab or by scraping the conjunctiva or cornea with a spatula. Corneal scraping should be obtained by an ophthalmologist. The volume of VTM used for eye swabs and scrapings should be kept to a minimum (1–2 mL) and, if possible, it is best to directly inoculate the scrapings onto cell culture.

Urine

Urine specimens are particularly important for the detection of CMV and are also useful for the isolation of mumps virus late in the course of the disease. In addition, adenovirus type 11 can be isolated from the urine of children or renal transplant recipients with acute hemorrhagic cystitis.[10, 11] Clean-voided urine should be collected in conventional containers and sent to the laboratory as is or diluted with an equal volume of VTM.

Blood

Although several viruses (eg, CMV and enteroviruses) can be isolated from leukocytes and serum, blood cultures are not routinely done by most virus laboratories.[12, 13] This may be because the yield of virus from blood is generally lower than from other sites. However, at least in the case of enteroviruses, blood cultures can improve diagnostic accuracy.

Table 5–2
Agents Most Frequently Associated with Viral Respiratory Disease

Disease	Causative Agents
Infants and Children	
URI and pharyngitis	Influenza, parainfluenza, respiratory syncytial virus, adenovirus, rhinovirus, enterovirus
Croup and bronchitis	Parainfluenza, influenza, respiratory synctial virus
Bronchiolitis	Respiratory synctial virus, parainfluenza
Pneumonia	Respiratory syncytial virus, parainfluenza, adenovirus, CMV*
Adults	
URI and pharyngitis	Influenza, parainfluenza, respiratory syncytial virus, adenovirus, rhinovirus, enterovirus, EBV
Pneumonia	Influenza, adenovirus, CMV*

*In infants and immunocompromised hosts. URI = upper respiratory tract infections; CMV = cytomegalovirus; EBV = Epstein-Barr virus.

Table 5–3
Optimal Cell Culture Systems for Primary Isolation of Human Viral Pathogens

Virus Family	Virus Type	Primary Monkey Kidney	Primary Human Embryonic Kidney	Semicontinuous Human Diploid	Continuous Human Heteroploid
Picornaviridae	Rhinovirus	+	±	+ +	0 to + +
	Polioviruses 1–3	+ +	+ +	+ +	+ +
	Coxsackievirus A1–24	0 to + +*	0 to + +*	0 to + +*	0 to + +*
	Coxsackievirus B1–6	+ +	+ +	±	+ +
	Echovirus 1–33	+ +	+	+ +	±
Orthomyxoviridae	Influenza A, B, C	0 to + +	±	±	±
Paramyxoviridae	Parainfluenza 1–4	+ +	+	+	±
	Respiratory syncytial virus	+	+	+ +	+ +
	Measles	+	+ +	0	±
	Mumps	+ +	+ +	+	±
Adenoviridae	Adenovirus types 1–34	± to +	+ +	+	+ +
Herpesviridae	Herpes simplex	0 to + +	+ +	+ +	0 to + +
	Varicella-zoster	0	+	+ +	0
	Cytomegalovirus	0	0	+ +	0
Togaviridae	Rubella virus	+	+	0	0

0 = not suitable for isolation; ± = some strains may be recovered; + = many strains may be recovered; + + = most strains will be recovered.
*Only coxsackievirus A-7, A-9, and A-16 strains grow well in cell culture.

Culture Methods

Living cells are necessary for virus replication. Cell culture, laboratory animals, embryonated hen's eggs, and organ culture are the traditional means by which the diagnostic laboratory has provided a living cell substrate for virus isolation. Cell culture is now, by far, the most widely used technique.

Cell Culture

Methods of Preparation.—Cell cultures can be derived from a wide variety of human and animal tissues. They are initiated by dissociating small pieces of the tissue into single cells by treatment with a proteolytic enzyme and a chelating agent (generally trypsin and EDTA). The dispersed cells are then suspended in cell culture medium which is composed of a balanced salt solution containing glucose, vitamins, amino acids, a buffer system, a pH indicator, serum, and antibiotics. The suspended cells may be placed in flasks, tubes, or Petri dishes, depending on the needs of the laboratory. The cells attach to the surface of the vessel and begin replicating. Replication ceases when a single layer (monolayer) of cells occupies all the available surface area of the vessel.

Cell cultures derived directly from tissue are called primary cultures and are usually composed of a mixed population of epithelial cells and fibroblasts. Cell strains are derived by splitting (dispersing and dividing) primary cultures. After several splits or subpassages, a dominant cell population, usually fibroblasts, emerges. Cell strains are usually diploid and, after a finite number of subpassages, either die or—more rarely—mutate, giving rise to a continuous cell line. Continuous cell lines are more easily derived from malignant tissue than from normal tissue, are aneuploid, and have an infinite life span (ie, there is no limit to the number of times they can be subpassaged).

Specimen Inoculation.—A wide variety of cell culture strains is available, and the range of viruses that can be isolated in them

varies considerably. Diagnostic laboratories, therefore, generally employ several cell systems for virus isolation. The sensitivity spectrum of the more commonly used cell culture types for frequently encountered viruses is shown in Table 5–3. The laboratory selects the appropriate combination of cell cultures for each specimen based on the viruses most likely to be responsible for the patient's illness and the culture site. The physician can aid in making this decision by providing a brief clinical history or list of the suspected etiologic agents. Once the selected cell systems are inoculated, any virus contained in the specimen is free to attach, penetrate, and begin replicating in the cultured cells. Depending on the viruses sought, cells are incubated from five to 21 days at temperatures ranging from 33°C to 36°C. Cultures are examined using a conventional light microscope, at a total magnification of 40 to 100×.

Viral Effects.—Virus replication in cell cultures is routinely detected in a number of ways: (1) by observing the cytopathic effect (CPE), (2) by hemadsorption, (3) by interference, and (4) by the application of immunoassays.

1. Cytopathic effect is an observable change which takes place in host cells as a result of virus replication. An example of viral CPE is presented in Figure 5–1. Since live, unstained cells are examined, if a suspicious area is observed the culture can be reincubated and examined the next day for progression of CPE. The speed with which CPE progresses, its nature (eg, diffuse, focal, giant cell formation, rounding, etc), and the range of cells infected all aid the virologist in identifying the virus isolated. Because some viruses exhibit very characteristic patterns, specific identification can be based on the aforementioned characteristics alone. For example, herpes simplex virus can be reliably identified on this basis.[14] However, for others (eg, picornaviruses) the pattern is not as clear-cut, and only the virus family can be identified with

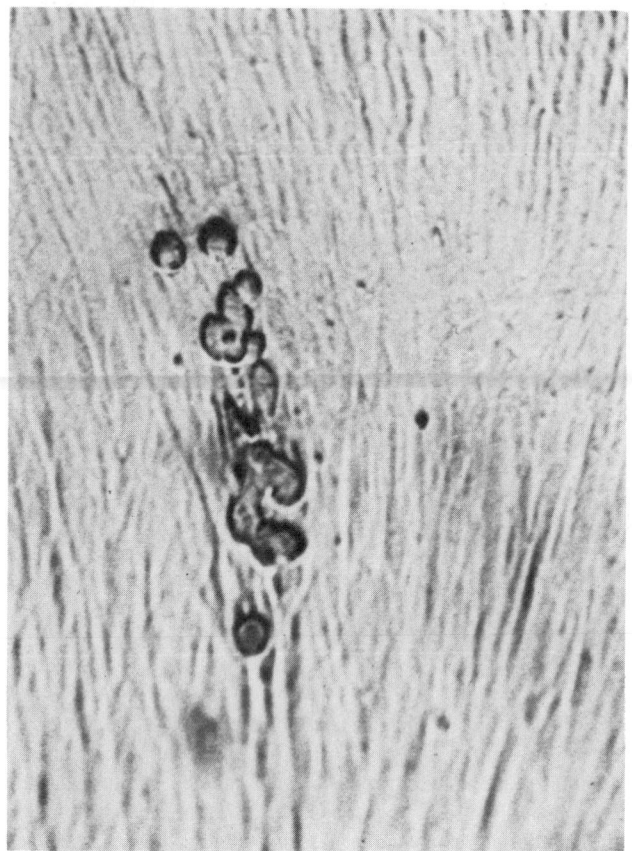

Figure 5–1. Human embryonic lung cells infected with cytomegalovirus. The focal rounding seen is the typical cytopathic effect of this virus.

certainty. Serologic methods must then be applied for specific identification. Most laboratories will issue a preliminary report when viral CPE is observed, followed by a final report when definitive identification of the isolate is completed.

2. During their replicative cycle some viruses produce and insert glycoproteins, which bind red blood cells, into the host cell membrane. Red blood cells added to cultures containing such viruses will adhere firmly to infected cells. This phenomenon, called hemadsorption, is commonly used for detecting influenza, parainfluenza, and mumps viruses. Hemadsorption tests are done at regular intervals following specimen inoculation since several of the viruses which cause hemadsorption cause little or no CPE. Hemadsorbing viruses can be specifically identified by serologic methods.

3. Although the replication of some viruses in cell culture does not result in visible CPE, cells infected with them are rendered refractory to superinfection with cytopathic viruses. This phenomenon, known as interference, is used by the clinical laboratory primarily for detecting rubella virus. The specimen suspected of containing rubella virus is first inoculated into susceptible cell cultures. After several days of incubation, a standard dose of cytopathic challenge virus (generally an enterovirus) is introduced. Then after further incubation, the cultures are examined for challenge virus CPE; its presence suggests that no interfering virus

was present in the inoculum and, conversely, its absence suggests the presence of an interfering virus. Serologic tests must be employed to identify specifically the interfering virus once it has been isolated.

4. A variety of immunoassays are now being used to detect virus replication in cell culture prior to the development of CPE. Specimens are first inoculated into susceptible cells and then after a brief period of incubation to allow for virus amplification, an immunodetection test is applied to the inoculated cells. For some viruses, CMV in particular, centrifugation of the specimen into the cell monolayer prior to incubation appears to increase sensitivity and shorten the time to detection.[15] The general approach can be applied to virtually any virus which replicates in cell culture. Immunodetection assays have now replaced the more cumbersome reverse transcriptase assays first used to detect human immunodeficiency virus (HIV) replication in cell culture and have been adopted by many laboratories for the early detection of CMV.[15, 16] Early intervention with immunoassays shortens the time required to detect virus and also results in a specific rather than a presumptive identification of the virus recovered. However, to successfully apply immunodetection methods the identity of the virus(es) sought must be known in advance.

Embryonated Eggs

Embryonated hen's eggs have been employed for over 50 years for virus isolation. Three main routes of inoculation are used: (1) into the amniotic cavity; (2) into the allantoic cavity; and (3) onto the chorioallantoic membrane. Virus is detected by demonstrating hemagglutinating activity in the allantoic and amniotic fluid, by observing pocks on the chorioallantoic membrane, and by death of the embryo. Although eggs are still preferred by some virologists for isolation of influenza virus, they have been largely supplanted by cell culture techniques in most clinical laboratories.

Laboratory Animals

Before the advent of cell culture, laboratory animals, particularly suckling mice, were widely used for virus isolation. Although a broader range of viruses can generally be isolated in cell culture, there are still a number of viruses that are best isolated in suckling mice, eg, most the group A coxsackieviruses, several of the togaviruses, and bunyaviruses. Inoculated animals are observed for specific signs of disease or death as an indicator of viral replication. However, few laboratories provide the service since maintaining a mouse program is very costly.

Practical Application of Viral Diagnosis Using Cell Culture

The ability of a viral diagnostic laboratory to produce clinically useful results is best appreciated by examining current experience. The virus spectrum isolated over a 1-year period in a present-day hospital diagnostic facility is illustrated in Table 5–4. The data presented here are those of the Strong Memorial Hospital and Monroe County Department of Health Viral Diagnostic Laboratory in Rochester, New York. This laboratory is the only diagnostic facility serving a community of 750,000 people. In the laboratory, primary cynomolgus monkey kidney, human embryonic kidney, and human embryonic fibroblast cell cultures are used routinely. HEp-2 cells are added in the winter months, primarily for the isolation of respiratory syncytial virus.

The speed with which viruses can be isolated is illustrated in Table 5–5. As can be seen, speed of isolation is extremely virus dependent. Other factors that influence the speed with which positive results are reported include the frequency with which cultures are examined, the amount of virus in the specimen, and the laboratory's reporting practices.

Techniques and practices in diagnostic virology are not well standardized. Therefore, it is always advisable to consult the particular laboratory being used when questions regarding the likelihood and speed of isolation arise.

DIRECT DETECTION OF VIRUS AND PRODUCTS OF VIRAL REPLICATION

A number of techniques, including electron microscopy, fluorescent antibody, solid-phase immunoassay (enzyme-linked immunoassay [ELISA] and radioimmunoassay [RIA]), and nucleic acid hybridization have recently been applied for the direct detection of virus and of the products of viral replication in clinical specimens. Some diagnostic laboratories now employ one or more of these rapid techniques on a routine basis.

Electron Microscopy (EM)

Direct examination of negatively stained specimen preparations by EM is a relatively simple means of demonstrating virus in clinical specimens. Many different virus types have been visualized by EM in preparations of CSF, urine, respiratory secretions, feces, and tissue.[17–19] However, the technique is most widely used for detecting the viral agents associated with gastroenteritis, eg, rotavirus, Norwalk and Norwalk-like viruses, astrovirus, and adenovirus.[9] EM is also frequently used to demonstrate herpes simplex and varicella-zoster virus in vesicular fluids, and CMV in the urine of congenitally and perinatally infected infants.[17, 20, 21]

EM is somewhat limited in its application by its relative insensitivity. To be detected directly, 10^6 to 10^7 virus particles must be present per milliliter of specimen. However, sensitivity can be increased (100- to 1000-fold) by using an ultracentrifuge to sediment virus onto EM grids, by aggregating virus with specific antiserum (immune electron microscopy), or by pseudoreplication.[21–23] If virus is detected without resorting to enhancement techniques, results can be available within an hour or two of specimen receipt.

Viruses are identified based on characteristic morphology, but since many viruses, eg, herpes simplex, varicella-zoster, and CMV, are morphologically similar, immune electron microscopy or other diagnostic methods must be used for specific identification.

Several excellent reviews describing the application of EM techniques for the diagnosis of viral infections have been published.[17–19]

Immunofluorescent Antibody (IF)

Two standard immunofluorescence methods, the direct and indirect tests (described in Chapter 4), can be used to demonstrate viral antigen in clinical specimens. For successful diagnosis by IF, an adequate number of well-preserved cells must be obtained from the infected site. The cells are fixed, stained with labeled antibody, and examined using a fluorescence microscope. Satisfactory results depend heavily on the use of quality reagents and interpretation by skilled technologists.

Specificity is conferred by the conjugate and by requiring that the appropriate pattern of fluorescence for the virus in question is observed (eg, cytoplasmic staining for respiratory syncytial virus, nuclear and cytoplasmic staining for herpes simplex virus). The latter assures that the nonspecific adsorption of labeled antibody to leukocytes, bacteria, and mucus, which frequently occurs, will not be misinterpreted as a positive result. The sensitivity of the test is highly dependent on the virus being sought. When compared to cell culture, IF was more sensitive for detecting varicella-zoster virus, about equally sensitive for demonstrating respiratory syn-

Table 5–4

Types of Virus Isolated from Clinical Specimens over a 1-Year Period (1980) by Strong Memorial Hospital–Monroe County Health Department Virus Laboratory

Type of Specimen Submitted	No. Submitted	Percentage Yielding Virus	No. and Type of Viruses Isolated
Genital culture	1149	27.8	304 Herpes simplex 15 Cytomegalovirus
Eye culture	76	9.2	5 Herpes simplex 2 Adenovirus
Urine and saliva	365	9.0	26 Cytomegalovirus 4 Enterovirus 2 Herpes simplex 1 Adenovirus
Fecal	630	12.9	55 Enterovirus 19 Adenovirus 4 Herpes simplex 2 Reovirus 1 Cytomegalovirus (22 Poliovirus)*
CSF	362	7.2	25 Enterovirus 1 Herpes simplex
Lesion culture and vesicular fluid (extragenital)	338	42.3	126 Herpes simplex 15 Varicella-zoster 2 Enterovirus
Respiratory tract culture	1324	24.3	71 Influenza B 61 Enterovirus 44 Herpes simplex 39 Rhinovirus 28 Parainfluenza virus 27 Respiratory syncytial virus 24 Adenovirus 17 Cytomegalovirus 11 Influenza A (6 Poliovirus)*
Tissues and effusions	172	6.4	8 Herpes simplex 2 Cytomegalovirus 1 Enterovirus

* Presumed to be vaccine strain—not included in calculating percentage of specimens yielding virus.

Table 5–5
Development of Culture Positivity* for Viruses Isolated over a 1-Year Period (1980)
by Strong Memorial Hospital–Monroe County Health Department Virus Laboratory

Virus	No. Positive	Day of Culture (Cumulative % Positive)										% Positive >10
		1	2	3	4	5	6	7	8	9	10	
Herpes simplex	484	49.6	81.2	95.7	98.6	99.2	99.6	100	—	—	—	
Enterovirus	148	10.8	39.2	61.5	73.7	81.1	86.0	91.9	96.6	98.0	98.7	1.4
Influenza	82	—	19.5	68.3	87.8	90.2	91.4	96.3	—	97.5	98.7	1.2
Cytomegalovirus	67	1.5	7.5	10.4	14.9	29.9	55.2	62.7	68.7	76.1	82.1	17.9
Varicella-zoster	15	—	—	—	26.7	60.0	73.3	80.0	86.6	93.3	—	6.7
Respiratory syncytial virus	27	—	—	—	7.4	18.5	29.6	44.4	51.8	55.5	77.7	22.3
Adenovirus	46	10.9	15.2	32.6	43.5	60.9	76.1	84.8	—	87.0	91.3	8.7
Rhinovirus	39	10.3	25.6	41.0	48.7	61.5	76.9	82.1	—	—	92.3	7.7
Parainfluenza	28	—	—	10.7	39.3	42.9	46.4	82.1	—	—	—	17.9
Total	936	28.4	52.2	69.5	77.3	82.4	87.8	92.2	93.7	94.9	96.0	4.0

Determined by cytopathic effect or hemadsorption.

cytial virus, and less sensitive for establishing the diagnosis of herpes simplex infection.[24, 25]

Enzyme (horseradish peroxidase)-linked antibody has been used as an alternative to fluorescein-conjugated antibody but nonspecific reactions are common where the former reagent is used on clinical specimens.

In experienced hands, IF is a rapid and efficient tool for the diagnosis of a number of viral infections.

Solid-Phase Immunoassays

Two methodologically similar solid-phase immunoassay (SPIA) systems, the radioimmunoassay (RIA) and enzyme-linked immunosorbent assay (ELISA), have been used for detecting many different viral antigens in a wide variety of clinical specimens.[26–29] Although different indicators are employed in each test (a radionuclide for RIA and the action of an enzyme label on a substrate for ELISA), if the same immunoreagents and methodology are used, the sensitivity and specificity of the two tests are similar.[26] However, virologists favor the ELISA technique because it is less expensive to perform and the reagents are more stable. Several of the methodologic variations that can be employed for both antibody and antigen detection are described in Chapter 4.

Significant advances in the development of ELISAs have been made in recent years. The more frequent use of monoclonal antibodies has led to greater reproducibility and standardization and the development of solid-phase membranes has resulted in tests which can be performed by nontechnical users and completed in less than 15 minutes.[30, 31] ELISAs are now widely used for the detection of rotavirus, hepatitis B virus, HIV, and respiratory syncytial virus in clinical specimens.[31–35]

SPIAs are, in general, more sensitive than EM and other immunologic methods for detecting antigen, but less sensitive than culture for demonstrating virus in clinical specimens.

Nucleic Acid Hybridization (NAH)

Great advances have been made in recent years in the field of molecular biology. As a result a powerful new technology for the detection of viruses in clinical specimens has emerged. NAH, simply the combination of labeled, single-stranded DNA or RNA molecules (probes) with single-stranded target nucleic acid in the specimen, has already been applied to the detection of a wide variety of viruses.[36] A number of hybridization methods, including filter hybridization, southern blot, northern blot and in situ hybridization, are in common use and each exploits the technology in a slightly different way.

Early studies of NAH for the detection of virus in clinical specimens suggested a high degree of specificity but a sensitivity no greater than most antigen detection assays.[36] However, substantial increases in sensitivity have recently been achieved by the application of a method which results in amplification of viral RNA or target DNA in the specimen.[37, 37a] The method, known as the polymerase chain reaction (PCR), has already proved useful for the detection of HIV in peripheral blood mononuclear cells.[38] Additional technical improvements, including the development of sensitive, nonradiometric methods for labeling probes, the use of PCR for the production of probes, and the evolution of simplified, rapid hybridization protocols as well as the commercialization of the technology, should lead to the widespread use of the NAH as a diagnostic tool in the not-too-distant future.

SEROLOGIC DETECTION OF VIRAL INFECTIONS

For many years serologic methods were the most widely used means for making a viral diagnosis, but in recent years the emphasis has shifted to cultivation and rapid direct detection. Nonetheless, there are still clinical situations in which serologic procedures can be helpful.

General Considerations

A variety of tests are now available for detecting antibody to viruses. The specifics of those most commonly used can be found in Chapter 4. When one is selecting a test method, it is important to remember that the sensitivity and specificity of tests vary considerably and that the efficiency of a given test may vary depending on the viral antigen being detected. For these reasons, the type of test performed should always be considered in interpreting results.

Clotted blood is acceptable for any serologic test. The blood can be refrigerated as is for two or three days; however, if a greater delay in transport is expected, the blood should be centrifuged and the serum kept frozen at $-20°C$. Avoiding anticoagulants is advisable since they interfere with or augment many serologic reactions.

CSF specimens can also be tested for virus-specific antibody, but, with the exception of measles, there is very little basis for interpreting results.[5] Any attempt to interpret CSF antibody titers should take into account the integrity of the blood-brain barrier. Positive CSF titers may be misinterpreted as indicating CNS involvement in diseases that are associated with a disrupted blood-brain barrier.[5, 39]

Serologic testing is most helpful when attempts to demonstrate virus by other means are negative, impractical, or impossible. Rubella, Epstein Barr virus (EBV), measles, and togavirus infections are examples of instances where serologic testing is preferred to virus isolation.

Serology may also aid in assessing the significance of a virus isolate. This is most important for viruses that are shed for long periods after the acute disease has resolved and for viruses that are commonly found in asymptomatic individuals (eg, enteroviruses).[6] For such viruses, a significant rise in antibody titer strengthens the diagnosis considerably. Serology on paired sera can also be used to exclude infection, but this should be limited only to those viruses for which seroconversion occurs in virtually all cases (eg, rubella and polio).

The two clinical applications of viral serology are diagnosing acute infection and determining immune status.

Diagnosis of Acute Infection Using Paired Sera
Definition of Negative and Positive Results

When comparing acute and convalescent serum pairs, a conversion from seronegative to seropositive or a significant rise in antibody titer is considered indicative of acute infection. Serial twofold dilutions of serum are employed in traditional serologic tests (eg, complement fixation), and the serum titer is expressed as the reciprocal of the highest dilution which produces a positive reaction. For such tests, a fourfold rise in titer is considered significant. Several of the newer serologic methods (eg, ELISA and RIA) measure antibody concentration using a linear scale. Criteria for defining a significant antibody titer rise are not yet completely standardized; most laboratories will provide an interpretation with the test results.

For many reasons, test-to-test variation is not uncommon in serology. Therefore, paired sera should always be tested in parallel. It is unreliable to compare results from different test runs, even if controls are consistent. Results obtained by different laboratories or by using different test methods should not be compared under any circumstances.

Specimen Collection

The acute serum should be drawn as early as possible in the course of the patient's illness, and the convalescent serum should be obtained 2/3 weeks later. More closely spaced sera (ie, 1 wk apart) can be tested if an early diagnosis is important, but an additional serum must be obtained if results are negative. For a few viruses (eg, rubella and several other togaviruses), the antibody response antedates or is coincident with the onset of illness, and sera drawn 1 week apart often reveal a titer rise. If sera are taken too far apart, an intervening infection may occur and result in a misdiagnosis.

Use of Single Acute-Phase Serum—IgM Detection

In some cases a single acute-phase serum can be used for the diagnosis of viral infections. During a primary infection virus-specific IgM develops early, persists for several weeks, and then becomes undetectable. Thus, demonstrating IgM often correlates with active or recent infection. A number of virus infections (eg, CMV, EBV, and measles) can be diagnosed using IgM assays; commercial kits are already available for detecting hepatitis A and rubella virus–specific IgM. Density gradient centrifugation, gel filtration, staphylococcal protein absorption, indirect immunofluorescence, and conventional and "reverse" solid-phase immunoassays have been applied for demonstrating IgM in serum specimens.[40–42] The sensitivity, specificity, and convenience of these techniques varies considerably.

Although detecting IgM appears ideally suited for diagnosis of acute infection, a number of problems limit reliable interpretation of results. False-positive reactions can occur due to impure reagents, failure to effect complete separation of IgM, and interference by IgM class rheumatoid factor.[43, 44] IgM may also be detected during recrudescent as well as primary infections caused by herpes group viruses.[41] False-negative results may be caused by competition between IgM and other immunoglobulin classes, collection of the specimen too late during the course of the illness, and failure of the individual to develop detectable IgM levels.[41, 43, 45] The latter is of particular concern in congenitally infected infants and severely immunocompromised patients. Because of these limitations IgM detection is not widely used for diagnosing acute viral infections.

Use of Single Convalescent-Phase Serum

Frequently patients are seen late in the course of their illness and only a convalescent serum can be obtained. Caution should be exercised in interpreting serologic results on such sera because a "high" antibody titer is not a reliable indicator of recent infection. However, experience with the seroresponse to and seroepidemiology of the agent(s) in question may permit a presumptive diagnosis to be made on the basis of a convalescent titer. For example, a high CF antibody titer to influenza virus (ie, 64) suggests recent infection since high antibody levels persist for only a few weeks or months after infection.[2] On the other hand, high neutralizing antibody titers to the echo- and coxsackieviruses may persist for many years and recent infection cannot be presumed based on such titers.[6] A causal relationship can also be presumed if antibody prevalence to a particular virus in the community is extremely low and a positive titer is coupled with a compatible clinical picture. In addition, testing for virus-specific IgM can be useful for convalescent-phase sera, if they are not obtained too late (21 d) after the onset of the illness.

Immune Status Testing

Knowing the immune status of an individual for a particular virus is important for good patient care in a number of situations. Rubella vaccine is recommended as a preventive for congenital infection for all antibody-negative women of childbearing age unless, of course, they are pregnant.[46] Knowing the pre-conception antibody status can also be helpful if the patient is exposed to or develops a rubellalike rash during pregnancy. In transplant patients and transfused premature infants, the CMV antibody status of the donor and the recipient are important for determining the risk of infection and the prognosis if infection does occur.[47, 48] Varicella-zoster virus immune status can be used to establish if exposed immunocompromised patients require passive immunization and as a guide for instituting infection control measures.[49, 50] Sensitive tests for rubella and CMV immunity are now widely available but, unfortunately, this is not yet the case for varicella-zoster.

The ideal antibody status test should be highly sensitive and highly specific; however, selecting for sensitivity sometimes compromises specificity and vice versa. Selecting the appropriate balance between the two should be based on which is more undesirable from a clinical standpoint—a false-negative or a false-positive result. It must also be kept in mind that antibody to some cross-reactive, internal, and nonstructual antigens may be completely unrelated to immunity. In general, unless selected antigens are used, the antibody detected by solid-phase immunoassays, indirect immunofluorescence, and complement fixation does not correlate as well with immunity as does antibody detected by neutralization and hemagglutination inhibition tests. In other words, the former tests are less specific than the latter. Specificity is of less concern for viruses that are antigenically unique, such as rubella and CMV.

HIV Immune Status

The presence of antibody to HIV in an individual predicts the eventual development of AIDS in up to 50% of infected persons within 10 years. The enormous consequences associated with a positive test for antibody have led to the development of a sophisticated and extremely accurate protocol for determining the immune status of individuals to HIV.

ELISA is the standard serologic method for screening serum for antibody to HIV. Many commercial tests are now in use, and most have sensitivities and specificities of 99% or more.[51] Unfortunately, even though the specificity of such tests is high, in very-low-prevalence populations a significant proportion of positive results are false-positives (ie, the positive predictive value of the tests is low). False-positives are thought to occur because the antigen preparation now used is contaminated with host cell proteins which react with antibodies in the patient's serum. Presently, attempts are being made to improve the performance characteristics of first-generation tests by replacing crude cell lysate antigen preparations with recombinant proteins and synthetic peptides. In most laboratories positive ELISA tests are repeated and repeat positives are confirmed by a western blot (WB) assay before any report is issued.

The WB is a qualitative means for detecting antibody to HIV. Virus is disrupted and the resulting fragments are separated by gel electrophoresis into discrete protein bands. The proteins are then transferred to a nitrocellulose membrane. When the patient's serum is applied to the nitrocellulose strip, antibodies react with the separated viral proteins. The detector antibody to human immunoglobulin is then added and the band pattern is developed. The WB is relatively difficult to perform and in some cases atypical band patterns develop. A strong positive and three examples of atypical band reactions are illustrated in Figure 5–2. Although criteria for interpreting the test are not yet standardized, most investigators agree that a reactive blot must contain at least two of the three major bands of diagnostic significance, gp160 or 120, gp41, and p24.[52] Nonreactive blots have no specific bands and indeterminate blots have at least one specific band but do not meet the criteria for a reactive blot. Indeterminant blots are common (15%) in uninfected healthy persons. Band patterns can vary depending on the stage of the infection. Sera from recently infected individuals and those with advanced disease may produce indeterminate WB patterns.[53, 54] Depending on the clinical circumstances, follow-up on indeterminant WBs, by a repeat WB on a second specimen, may be warranted.

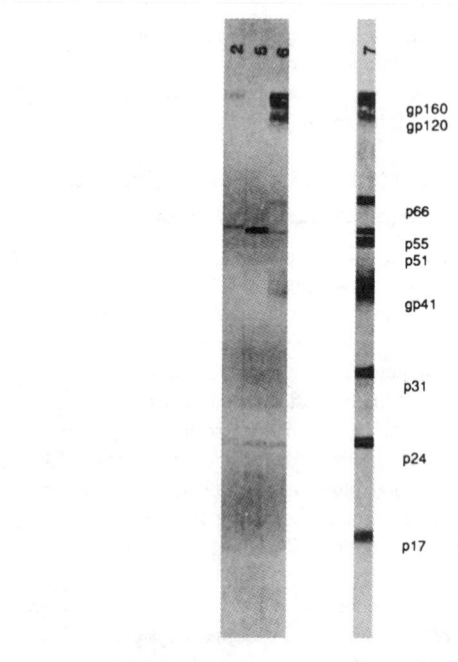

Strip	Interpretation	Bands Present
2	INDETERMINATE	p24, p55, gp160
5	INDETERMINATE	p24, p55
6	INDETERMINATE	p24, gp41, p55, p66, gp120, gp160
7	POSITIVE	p17, p24, p31, gp41, p51, p55, p66, gp120, gp160

Figure 5–2. Human immunodeficiency virus Western blot patterns of 4 sera. Lanes 2, 5, and 6 illustrate indeterminate reactions and lane 7 illustrates strong positive reaction.

REFERENCES

1. Lennette DA, Lennette ET: *A Users Guide to the Diagnostic Virology Laboratory.* Baltimore, University Park Press, 1981, pp 1–103.
2. Jackson GG, Muldoon RL: *Viruses Causing Common Respiratory Infections in Man.* Chicago, University of Chicago Press, 1973.
3. Hall CB, Douglas RG Jr: Clinically useful method for the isolation of respiratory syncytial virus. *J Infect Dis* 1975; 131:1–4.
4. Chonmaitree T, Menegus MA, Powell KR: The clinical relevance of CSF viral culture. *JAMA* 1982; 247:1843–1847.
5. Johnson RT: *Virus Infections of the Nervous System.* New York, Raven Press, 1982.
6. Melnick JL: Enteroviruses, in Evans AS (ed): *Viral Infections of Humans.* New York, Plenum, 1982, pp 187–251.
7. Dolin R: Norwalk and related agents of gastroenteritis, in Mandell GL, Douglas RG Jr, Bennett JE (eds): *Principles and Practice of Infectious Disease,* ed 2. New York, Wiley, 1982, pp 995–1000.
8. Kapikian AZ, Yolken RH: Rotavirus, in Mandell GL, Douglas RG Jr, Bennett JE (eds): *Principles and Practice of Infectious Disease,* ed 2. New York, Wiley, 1982, pp 933–944.
9. Kapikian AZ, Yolken RH, Greenberg HB, et al: Gastroenteritis viruses, in Lennette EH, Schmidt NJ (eds): *Diagnostic Procedures for Viral, Rickettsial and Chlamydial Infections.* Washington, DC, American Public Health Association, 1979, pp 927–995.
10. Belshe RB, Mufson MA: Identification by immunofluorescence of adenoviral antigen in exfoliated bladder epithelial cells from patients with acute hemorrhagic cystitis. *Proc Soc Exp Biol Med* 1974; 146:754–758.
11. Lecatsas G, Prozesky OW, Van Wyck J: Adenovirus type 11 associated with haemorrhagic cystitis after renal transplantation. *S Afr Med J* 1974; 48:1932.
12. Yoshiska I, Horstmann DM: Viremia in infection due to ECHO virus type 9. *N Engl J Med* 1960; 262:224–228.
13. Howell CL, Miller MJ, Martin WJ: Comparison of rates of virus isolation from leukocyte populations separated from blood by conventional and Ficoll-Paque/Macrodex method. *J Clin Microbiol* 1979; 10:533–537.
14. Herrmann EC: Experiences in laboratory diagnosis of herpes simplex, varicella-zoster and vaccinia virus infections in routine medical practice. *Mayo Clin Proc* 1967; 42:744–753.
15. Gleaves CA, Smith TF, Shuster EA, et al: Rapid detection of cytomegalovirus in MRC-5 cells inoculated with urine specimens by low-speed centrifugation and monoclonal antibody to an early antigen. *J Clin Microbiol* 1984; 19:917–919.
16. Feorino P, Forrester B, Schable D, et al: Comparison of antigen assay and reverse transcriptase assay for detecting human immunodeficiency virus in cell culture. *J Clin Microbiol* 1987; 25:2344–2346.
17. Hsiung GD, Fong CKY, August MJ: The use of electron microscopy for diagnosis of virus infections: An overview. *Prog Med Virol* 1979; 25:133–159.
18. Chernesky MA: The role of electron microscopy in diagnostic virology, in Lennette D, Specter S, Thompson KD (eds): *Diagnosis of Viral Infections: The Role of the Clinical Laboratory.* Baltimore, University Park Press, 1978, pp 125–142.
19. Almedia JD: Practical aspects of diagnostic electron microscopy. *Yale J Biol Med* 1980; 53:5–18.
20. Smith KO, Melnick JL: Recognition and quantitation of herpes virus particles in human vesicular lesions. *Science* 1962; 137:543–544.
21. Lee FK, Nahmias AJ, Stagno S: Rapid diagnosis of cytomegalovirus infection in infants by electron microscopy. *N Engl J Med* 1978; 299:1266–1270.
22. Hammond GW, Hazelton PR, Chuang I, et al: Improved detection of viruses by electron microscopy after direct ultracentrifuge preparation of specimens. *J Clin Microbiol* 1981; 14:210–221.
23. Doane FW, Anderson N: Electron microscopic and immune electron microscopic procedures for diagnosis of viral infections, in Kurstak E, Kurstak C (eds): *Comparative Diagnosis of Viral Diseases.* II. New York, Academic Press, 1977, pp 505–539.
24. Gardner PS, McQuillin J: *Rapid Virus Diagnosis Application of Immunofluorescence.* London, Butterworths, 1980, pp 110–123.
25. Schmidt NJ, Gallo D, Devlin V, et al: Direct immunofluorescence staining for detection of herpes simplex and varicella-zoster antigens in vesicular lesions and certain tissue specimens. *J Clin Microbiol* 1980; 12:651–655.
26. Halonen P, Meurman O: Radioimmunoassay in diagnostic virology, in Howard CR (ed): *New Developments in Practical Virology.* New York, Alan R Liss, 1982, pp 83–119.
27. Voller A, Bidwell DE, Bartlett A: ELISA techniques in virology, in Howard CR (ed): *New Developments in Practical Virology.* New York, Alan R Liss, 1982, pp 59–79.
28. Sarkkinen HK, Halonen PE, Salmi A: Detection of influenza virus by radioimmunoassay and enzyme-immunoassay from nasopharyngeal specimens. *J Med Virol* 1981; 7:213–220.
29. Sarkkinen HK, Halonen PE, Salmi A: Type-specific detection of parainfluenza viruses by enzyme immunoassay and radioimmunoassay in nasopharyngeal specimens of patients with acute respiratory disease. *J Gen Virol* 1981; 56:49–57.
30. Valkirs GE: Membranes and monoclonal antibodies in rapid immunodiagnostics. *Lab Med* 1988; 564–567.
31. Chernesky M, Castriciano S, Mahony J, et al: Ability of TEST-PAC ROTAVIRUS immunoassay to diagnose rotavirus gastroenteritis. *J Clin Microbiol* 1988; 27:2459–2461.
32. Dennehy PH, Gauntlett DR, Tente WE: Comparison of nine commercial immunoassays for the detection of rotavirus in fecal specimens. *J Clin Microbiol* 1988; 26:1630–1634.
33. Feinstone SM, Barker LF, Purcell RH: Hepatitis A and B, in Lennette EH, Schmidt NJ (eds): *Diagnostic Procedures for Viral, Rickettsial and Chlamydial Infections.* Washington, DC, American Public Health Association, 1979, pp 875–925.
34. Diggs JL: Testing for HIV antigen. *Infect Control Hosp Epidemiol* 1988; 9:353–354.
35. Ahlwalia GS, Hammond GW: Comparison of cell culture and three enzyme-linked immunosorbent assays for the rapid diagnosis of respiratory syncytial virus from nasopharyngeal aspirate and tracheal secretion specimens. *Diagn Microbiol Infect Dis* 1988; 9:187–192.
36. Zwadyk P Jr, Cooksey RC: Nucleic acid probes in clinical microbiology. *CRC Crit Rev Clin Lab Sci* 1987; 25:71–103.
37. Saiki RK, Gelfand DH, Stoffel S, et al: Primer-directed enzymatic amplification of DNA with a thermostable DNA polymerase. *Science* 1988; 239:487–491.
37a. Eisenstein BI: The polymerase chain reaction. *N Engl Med J* 1990; 322:178–183.
38. Loche M, Mach B: Identification of HIV-infected seronegative individuals by a direct diagnostic test based on hybridisation to amplified viral DNA. *Lancet* 1988; 2:418–421.
39. Eickoff K, Heipiertz R: Discrimination of elevated immunoglobulin concentrations in CSF due to inflammatory reaction of the central nervous system and blood-brain-barrier dysfunction. *Acta Neurol Scand* 1977; 56:475–482.
40. Zeigler DW: Determination of IgM antibodies in diagnostic virology, in Lennette D, Specter S, Thompson KD (eds): *Diagnosis of Viral Infections: The Role of the Clinical Laboratory.* Baltimore, University Park Press, 1979, pp 63–71.
41. Schmidt NJ: Application of class-specific antibody assays to viral serodiagnosis. *Clin Immunol Newslett* 1980; 1:1–4.
42. Handsher R, Fogel A: Modified staphylococcal absorption method used for detecting rubella-specific immunoglobulin M antibodies during a rubella epidemic. *J Clin Microbiol* 1977; 5:588–592.
43. Hermann KL: Problems associated with immunoglobulin M detection in the diagnosis of acute viral infections, in Schlessinger D (ed): *Microbiology 1981.* Washington, DC, American Society for Microbiology, 1981, pp 280–289.

44. Salonen EM, Vaheri A, Suni J, et al: Rheumatoid factor in acute viral infections—Interference with determination of IgM, IgG and IgA antibodies in an enzyme immunoassay. *J Infect Dis* 1980; 142:250–255.

45. Stagno S, Pass RF, Reynolds DW, et al: Comparative study of diagnostic procedures for congenital cytomegalovirus infection. *Pediatrics* 1980; 65:251–257.

46. Gershon AA: Rubella virus, in Mandell GL, Douglas RG Jr, Bennett RE (eds): *Principles and Practice of Infectious Diseases,* ed 2. New York, Wiley, 1982, pp 926–930.

47. Yeager AS, Grumet FC, Hafleigh EB, et al: Prevention of transfusion acquired cytomegalovirus infection in newborn infants. *J Pediatr* 1981; 98:281–287.

48. Ho M: Cytomegalovirus, in Mandell GL, Douglas RG Jr, Bennett JE (eds): *Principles and Practice of Infectious Diseases,* ed 2. New York, Wiley, 1982, pp 960–970.

49. Brunell PA, Gershon AA: Passive immunization against varicella-zoster infections and other modes of therapy. *J Infect Dis* 1973; 127:415–423.

50. Grandien M, Appelgren P, Espmark A, et al: Determination of varicella immunity by the indirect immunofluorescence test in urgent clinical situations. *Scand J Infect Dis* 1976; 8:65–69.

51. Ozanne G, Fauvel M: Performance and reliability of five commercial enzyme-linked immunoassay kits in screening for anti-human immunodeficiency virus antibody in high risk subjects. *J Clin Microbiol* 1988; 26:1496–1500.

52. Hausler WJ Jr: Report of the Third Consensus Conference on HIV Testing sponsored by the Association of State and Territorial Public Health Laboratory Directors. *Infect Control Hosp Epidemiol* 1988; 9:345–349.

53. Pan LZ, Cheng-Mayer C, Levy JA: Patterns of antibody response in individuals infected with the human immunodeficiency virus. *J Infect Dis* 1987; 155:626–632.

54. Saah AJ, Farzadegan H, Fox R, et al: Detection of early antibodies in human immunodeficiency virus infection by enzyme-linked immunosorbent assay, Western blot, and radioimmunoprecipitation. *J Clin Microbiol* 1987; 25:1605–1610.

6

Antiviral Drug Therapy

James R. Minor
Alan J. Hay
Robert B. Belshe

The twentieth century has seen major advances in the medical management of infectious diseases, with the discovery, development, and clinical application of a host of antibacterial drugs or antibiotics. With Alexander Fleming's announcement of the antibacterial properties of penicillin in the late 1920s, it became clear that the major clinical importance of these new drugs would lie in their ability to kill pathogenic bacteria without harming host cells. With the advent of effective drug regimens for many bacterial diseases, investigators are now focusing much research effort on the development of agents to treat viral infections.

Viruses are thought to be responsible for approximately 60% of illnesses occurring in the industrialized world today, including many diseases for which no effective drugs or vaccines exist. Selected viral infections, notably influenza viral infection of the upper respiratory tract, affect a large part of our population annually, with significant morbidity resulting in lost productivity and major expenditures for health care costs. Viral respiratory infections have been estimated to account for over 61 million office visits to physicians annually.[1] Pediatric viral infections, such as adenoviruses, rhinoviruses, rotaviruses, respiratory syncytial virus, and influenza and parainfluenza viruses result in up to five hospitalizations per 100 children during the first 4 years of life.[2]

Relative to bacteria, with their comparatively large molecular size and characteristic cell wall membranes and other structures, viruses are simple structures. Consisting only of a nucleic acid genome (DNA or RNA) surrounded by associated viral proteins and at times a glycoprotein envelope, viruses bind to specific host cell membrane receptor sites. After introduction into the host cell, the viral genome uses the host cell's biosynthetic machinery for the production of its own viral proteins. It is this latter step in a virus's infective life cycle that makes it so difficult to develop drugs that selectively block viral replication without interrupting the normal processes in uninfected host cells. Furthermore, those viruses capable of persisting in a stage of latent infection, in which they are either expressing only part of their normal functions or not actively replicating, may escape the antiviral activity of some drugs.

Antiviral drugs, like antibiotics, must be highly specific in fighting viral infections, effectively controlling the pathogenic viral agent without causing significant impairment in the health or physiologic function of the host. Because of the intimate life cycle relationship between viruses and their host cells, this targeted selectivity is difficult to achieve.

Some antiviral compounds, such as amantadine and rimantadine, were discovered by simple screening for activity against influenza or other viruses. The current approach in the development of antiviral compounds focuses on designing drugs to attack or inhibit the replication of a virus at a specific step in its life cycle. Many antiviral agents in clinical use today or undergoing active evaluation are in essence synthetic chemical analogues of nucleosides. Because of their close chemical similarity to naturally occurring analogues or substrates, they may be falsely incorporated into the viral biosynthetic process, thereby disrupting or terminating viral replication.

Pioneering work in the study of nucleic acid analogues and cancer chemotherapy in the 1940s and 1950s led to the development of the first antiviral agent, methisazone (Marboran). Methisazone and its parent compound, isatin-β-thiosemicarbazone, inhibit the replication of poxviruses in vitro through interference with translation of viral messenger RNA (mRNA), protein synthesis, and subsequent viral particle assembly.[3] Methisazone, initially marketed in 1963, was developed for the treatment and prevention of smallpox.[4–6] Currently not approved for use in the United States, the eradication of smallpox has made this drug obsolete. The thiosemicarbazones are under study for efficacy against other viral infections, such as herpes simplex. In addition, the growing use of vaccinia virus vectors in the development of various vaccines may generate a resurgence of interest in this agent.

Trifluorothymidine or trifluridine (Viroptic) was developed in the 1970s as an ophthalmic formulation to treat herpes simplex keratitis and keratoconjunctivitis. Continuing to focus on the major issue of antiviral selectivity, the first selective antiviral agent, acyclovir, was discovered in 1974. Formulations of acyclovir (Zovirax), first introduced in 1982 and 1985, are now in worldwide use for the treatment and suppression of a variety of infections caused by the herpes group of viruses.

Ironically, many advances in the science and practice of medicine have contributed directly to the modern threat of viral infections. Recent advances in immunosuppressive regimens for organ transplantation and cancer chemotherapy, the increasing average age and longevity of the American population, and the increasing number of individuals infected with human immunodeficiency virus (HIV) all combine to create a new population of immunocompromised individuals at significant risk of major mortality and morbidity from viral diseases not usually considered to be life-threatening.

Cases of viral diseases transmitted sexually, such as genital herpes and acquired immunodeficiency syndrome (AIDS), have increased exponentially in the United States in the last decade. Reaching epidemic proportions in the 1970s, genital herpes continues to occur at a rate of 300,000 to 500,000 new cases per year.[7–9] Similarly, the AIDS epidemic continues to increase from the first few cases reported in 1980, to over 130,000 cases by mid-1990, with an estimated projected total of over 365,000 cases in the United States by the year 1992. Of major clinical and epidemiologic significance is the fact that the latency of these viral infections allows asymptomatically infected individuals to continue functioning normally, thereby escaping or delaying early and accurate diagnosis, while remaining potentially infectious and capable of spreading infection to others.

With the advent of AIDS in late 1970s and early 1980s, an entirely different class of pathogenic viruses—the human retroviruses—emerged as a formidable new challenge to investigators involved in research, development, and clinical application of antiviral drug compounds. In early 1987, zidovudine (Retrovir), formerly know as azidothymidine or AZT, was approved for the treatment of selected patients having infection with the HIV and other serious manifestations of HIV infection.

GENERAL PRINCIPLES IN THE USE OF ANTIVIRAL AGENTS

During development and clinical application of antiviral drugs, several key features must be considered. Clinically effective levels of the drug must be achievable in patients by an appropriate route of administration. The compounds must possess an acceptable therapeutic ratio, displaying efficacy against the viral infection being treated without causing excessive or intolerable toxicity. Widespread distribution and penetration of the antiviral drug into biologic tissues and fluids is an important pharmacokinetic component of the drug's efficacy in controlling viral infection. This is of major importance in the treatment of those viral infections affecting the brain and the central nervous system, such as herpes encephalitis or infection of the brain by HIV. In these infections, effective antiviral drugs must be able to cross the barrier between the peripheral circulation and the central nervous system.

Two additional features of an "ideal" antiviral agent would be the availability of an oral dosage form with adequate bioavailability to produce effective in vivo drug levels in those patients not requiring more aggressive parenteral therapy, and the ability to manufacture and market the agent at an acceptable cost. These latter two features are likely to be of major importance in the ultimate

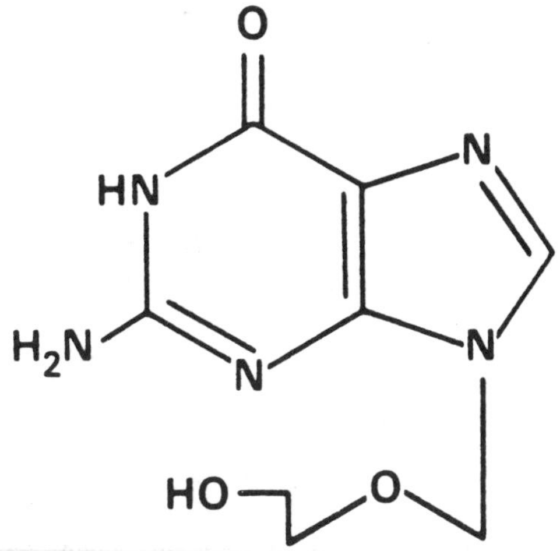

Figure 6-1. Structure of acyclovir.

development and usage of antiretroviral agents for the treatment of AIDS, especially as the increasing number of cases will mandate delivery of therapy in ambulatory, outpatient settings.

Regarding mechanisms of action, the challenge in antiviral drug research has been in identifying those agents capable of inhibiting virus-specific processes such as attachment to and subsequent entry into host cells, uncoating of viral genomic components, or assembly and release of progeny viral particles. Many dozens of compounds exist that exhibit antiviral activity in vitro. Most of these compounds, however, adversely affect some biologic function of host cells and are associated with low therapeutic ratios or unacceptable toxicity profiles in human subjects.

Those antiviral agents currently in use selectively inhibit specific steps in viral replication. Because of this selectivity, the majority of these agents have a rather restricted spectrum of antiviral activity. In addition, since these agents only inhibit actively replicating virus, they are not effective in eradicating latent or nonreplicating viruses.

The development of viral resistance to the inhibitory action of a drug may further limit the drug's efficacy. In fact, the development of drug-resistant viral strains supports the specificity of an antiviral agent's mechanism of action.[10] Drug resistance can easily be documented in the laboratory for many antiviral agents. In vivo drug resistance has developed during the use of acyclovir in treating mucocutaneous herpes simplex virus (HSV) infection,[11-15] in idoxuridine therapy of HSV keratitis,[16, 17] and in use of the adamantane compounds, amantadine or rimantadine (see below).

Since antiviral drugs are generally inhibitory or virustatic in their activity, infection may recur when therapy is discontinued. An essential component for adequate recovery from a viral infection is the competency of the host's immune response. This is a major aspect in several of the currently investigational treatment strategies in AIDS, combining an antiviral agent with biologic response modifiers intended to restore or ''reconstitute'' the immune response so severely crippled by HIV infection. Antivirals that impair normal host immune response to infection may actually prolong the course of infection.[18] Other host-related factors also play an important role in healing of certain viral infections, especially mucocutaneous HSV infections, where antiviral effects may be demonstrated without clinical benefit.[19]

Biologic response modifiers or immunomodulatory agents have been used for their antiviral activity, such as interferon derivatives in herpes zoster infection in immunocompromised hosts,[20] and in hepatitis B infection.[21-23] Protective cell-mediated immune responses to varicella have been transferred to susceptible leukemic children by the administration of transfer factor from persons recovering from chickenpox.[24] Other chemical agents such as levamisole or inosiplex (isoprinosine) have been used with varying degrees of success in augmenting cell-mediated immune responses in various viral infections.[25-33]

Combinations of antiviral agents with different mechanisms of action have been employed as a means of increasing antiviral activity without increasing toxicity. Selected combinations may exert synergistic antiviral activity, while others may result in antagonistic activity. Combination therapy has been used successfully in selected experimental infections due to various herpesviruses[34-36] and influenza.[37, 38] Although combined treatment with human leukocyte interferon and vidarabine has been clinically useful in chronic hepatitis B virus infection,[39, 40] the combination has also resulted in augmented vidarabine toxicity.[41, 42] Combinations of different antiviral compounds, or of antiviral drugs with immunomodulatory agents, are likely to play an increasingly important role in the management of viral infections in the future. Both the efficacy and the safety of such combination regimens will require careful evaluation.

Several reviews and monographs are available on the subject of antiviral durgs.[43-56]

ACYCLOVIR

Chemistry and Stability

Acyclovir (9-[2-hydroxyethoxymethyl]guanine, acycloguanosine, Zovirax) is the first antiviral agent to show true potent antiviral selectivity and good activity against members of the herpesvirus family, especially herpes simplex virus. Acyclovir is a synthetic, acyclic nucleoside analogue in which the deoxyribose component of the natural nucleoside deoxyguanosine has been replaced by a hydroxyethoxymethyl substituent in the purine ring (Figure 6-1).

The sodium salt of acyclovir (for parenteral use) contains 4.2 mEq of sodium per gram of acyclovir. Following reconstitution with sterile water for injection or bacteriostatic water for injection containing benzyl alcohol, acyclovir sodium solutions are clear and colorless, contain 50 mg of acyclovir per/milliliter, have a pH of 10.5 to 11.6, and are stable for 12 hours at 15 to 30°C. When further diluted in 50 to 100 mL of standard, commercially available 0.9% sodium chloride or 5% dextrose solutions, the manufacturer states that acyclovir sodium is chemically and physically compatible and stable for 24 hours at 25°C. Bacteriostatic water for injection preserved with parabens should not be used to reconstitute sterile acyclovir sodium lyophilized powder, as this diluent may cause precipitation of the drug. Likewise, refrigeration of the reconstituted solution, or of diluted solutions for intravenous (IV) infusion, may result in formation of a precipitate. This precipitate will redissolve at room temperature, and the precipitation and subsequent redissolution does not appear to affect the potency of the drug.

Mechanism of Action

Acyclovir exerts its antiviral effects on herpes simplex viruses by inhibiting viral replication via interfering with viral DNA synthesis. Against other susceptible viral isolates, its mechanism of action has not been clearly elucidated.

The selectivity of the drug against herpesviruses, particularly herpes simplex viruses types 1 and 2 and varicella-zoster virus, is due to the initial metabolic activation of acyclovir by phosphorylation by a herpesvirus-specific thymidine kinase (TK) in virus-infected cells.[57, 58]

The enzymatic conversion of acyclovir to its phosphorylated forms is depicted in Figure 6–2. The virus-coded TK initially converts acyclovir to acyclovir monophosphate (ACV-MP). The monophosphate is then phosphorylated to the diphosphate (ACV-DP) form via the cellular enzyme guanylate kinase, and lastly to the triphosphate form via other cellular enzymes, such as phosphoenol-pyruvate carboxykinase, phosphoglycerate kinase, and pyruvate kinase.[59, 60] The initial formation of acyclovir monophosphate appears to be the rate-limiting step in the formation of acyclovir triphosphate. In uninfected cells (in vitro), acyclovir undergoes minimal or no phosphorylation by host cellular enzymes. The binding affinity of acyclovir for viral TK is reported to be 200 times greater than its binding affinity for host cellular TK, and viral TK phosphorylates the acyclovir much more rapidly than does host cellular TK.[61, 62]

The extent of formation of the mono-, di- and triphosphorylated forms of acyclovir (in vitro) by both uninfected and virus-infected cells is directly related to the concentration of acyclovir in the culture medium.

Acyclovir triphosphate (ACV-TP) is thought to be the pharmacologically active form of the drug, acting both as a substrate for and preferential inhibitor of viral DNA polymerase. Non-phosphorylated parent drug, acyclovir monophosphate, and acyclovir diphosphate are thought to have no antiviral activity. By competing with the natural substrate (deoxyguanosine triphosphate) for viral DNA polymerase and subsequent incorporation into viral DNA, ACV-TP can be incorporated into growing chains of viral DNA, thereby inhibiting viral DNA synthesis by acting as a "chain terminator." Viral DNA polymerase exhibits a much higher affinity in vitro for ACV-TP than does host cellular alpha-DNA polymerase.

Acyclovir has minimal pharmacologic effects in vitro in uninfected (host) cells since drug uptake into these cells is poor, little phosphorylation takes place, and intracellular alpha-DNA polymerase exerts a significantly lower affinity for ACV-TP than does viral DNA polymerase.

The antiviral activity of acyclovir against other viruses such as Epstein-Barr virus (EBV) and cytomegalovirus (CMV), although not fully understood, appears to differ from that against herpes simplex virus. Although these other viruses do not encode for virus-specific TK, other unidentified cellular phosphorylating enzymes in cells infected with EBV or CMV appear to produce low concentrations of ACV-TP in vitro. In addition, the viral DNA polymerase of EBV is thought to be more sensitive to inhibition by low concentrations of ACV-TP (formed by cellular phosphorylating enzymes). Acyclovir's limited antiviral activity against human CMV infection may result from inhibition of virus-specific polypeptide synthesis, although such inhibition generally requires high in vitro concentrations of ACV-TP.

Further studies are required to evaluate the antiviral activity of acyclovir, and other potentially effective analogues of the drug, against EBV and CMV. In the management of these clinical infections, the efficacy of acyclovir appears to be minimal at best.[63, 64]

Spectrum of Activity

Various testing methods, each with different results and interpretations, have been used to test in vitro susceptibility of viruses to acyclovir: inhibition of cytopathic effect, plaque inhibition, dye uptake, disk-agar diffusion, and others. Although effective doses (ED) and inhibitory doses (ID) of acyclovir have been reported for various viruses, a standardized method for determination of these values does not currently exist. Furthermore, clear dose-response relationships between in vitro susceptibility tests and clinical response have not been determined. For in vitro viral susceptibility testing purposes, an acyclovir concentration of 1.0 µg/mL is approximately equivalent to 4.4 µmol/L.[45]

The drug's antiviral activity is limited to herpesviruses, including HSV types 1 and 2, varicella-zoster virus, and EBV.[65-68] Depending on the type of cell culture, acyclovir concentrations resulting in 50% inhibition of plaque formation (ID_{50}) average 0.02 to 0.2 µg/mL for HSV type 1, 0.02 to 0.4 µg/mL for HSV type 2, and 0.3 to 1.4 µg/mL for susceptible strains of varicella-zoster virus. Concentrations of approximately 1.4 to 1.6 µg/mL inhibit the replication of EBV in actively infected cells,[67] but even higher concentrations do not inhibit persistent or latent infection.[69] Much higher concentrations, ranging from 7.5 to 36 µg/mL, are required for inhibition of plaque formation in susceptible strains of CMV.[66, 70]

Pharmacokinetics

Acyclovir absorption from the gastrointestinal tract is variable and incomplete, with an estimated 15% to 30% of an oral dose

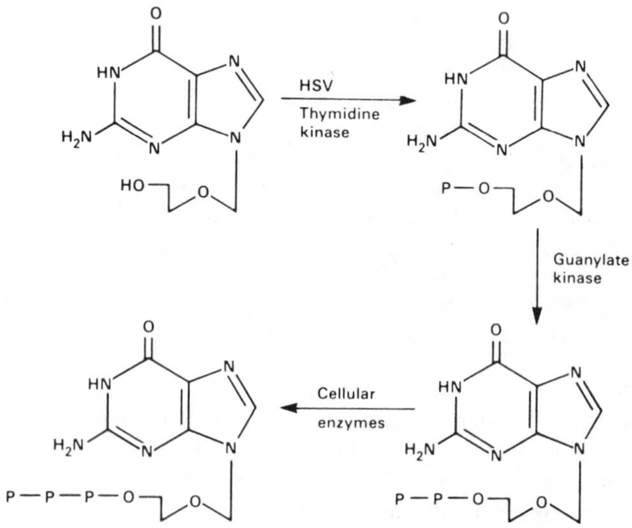

Figure 6–2. Enzymatic conversion of acyclovir to its phosphorylated forms.

being absorbed.[71] Peak plasma concentrations of 0.3 to 0.9 μg/mL occur between 1.5 and 4.0 hours after oral doses of 200 mg taken every four hours,[72] and steady-state peak concentrations averaging 1.4 μg/mL (range: 0.9–1.8 μg/mL) are reported in adults being treated for genital herpes with 200 mg orally 5 times per day.[73] Food does not appear to affect GI absorption of acyclovir.

The elimination half-life of systemic acyclovir averages two to three hours (range: 1.5–6.3 h) in adults with normal renal function, but is slightly longer, averaging 3 to 4 hours, in neonates and increases to 19 to 20 hours in anuric patients.[74–80]

Following one-hour IV infusions (5 mg/kg q8h), peak and trough plasma levels average 9.8 μg/mL and 0.7 μg/mL, respectively; after infusions of 10 mg/kg every eight hours, peak and trough levels average 20.7 and 2.3 μg/mL, respectively.[74] Following multiple IV doses, administered every eight hours, little, if any, drug accumulation is reported.[76]

Acyclovir is widely distributed into body tissues and fluids including the brain, kidney, lung, liver, muscle, spleen, saliva, uterus, vaginal mucosa and secretions, CSF, and vesicular fluid of herpetic lesions. Cerebrospinal fluid levels are approximately 50% of plasma values,[74] salivary concentrations average 13% of simultaneous plasma levels, and vaginal secretion concentrations range from 15% to 170% of plasma values.[72]

Percutaneous absorption of acyclovir after topical administration appears to be low, with plasma concentrations ranging from less than 0.01 to 0.3 μg/mL detectable in patients treated topically for herpes zoster. In patients with genital herpes treated with topical acyclovir ointment, drug concentrations in genital lesions at four to 12 hours after application range widely (0.002–38 μg/mL), and no detectable acyclovir is present in cervicovaginal secretions.[81]

In vitro, acyclovir is approximately 9% to 33% protein-bound at plasma concentrations of 0.41 to 5.2 μg/mL.[45] Acyclovir crosses the placenta, and limited data indicate that the drug distributes into breast milk, generally in concentrations greater than concurrent maternal plasma levels.[45, 81a] Consequently, caution should be exercised when administering acyclovir to a woman who is nursing.

Acyclovir is metabolized partially to 9-carboxymethoxymethylguanine (CMMG) and minimally to 8-hydroxy-9-(2-hydroxyethoxymethyl)guanine. In vitro, acyclovir is also metabolized to its mono-, di-, and triphosphate forms in cells infected with herpesviruses, principally by intracellular phosphorylation of the drug by virus-specific TK and selected cellular enzymes.

Acyclovir is excreted principally by tubular secretion and glomerular filtration. Sixty to ninety-one percent of an administered dose is excreted by these routes, while less than 15% is excreted as CMMG or other minor metabolites.[74, 82, 83] Following single IV doses, the majority is excreted in the urine as unchanged drug within 24 hours. Because of the importance of renal function on the excretion of acyclovir, dosage modifications are necessary in renal insufficiency (see below under Dosage and Administration).

Acyclovir is removed by hemodialysis, the amount removed during the procedure depending on the dialysis rate flow, type of coil used, and other factors. A six-hour period of hemodialysis in one study removed approximately 60% of a single dose of 2.5 mg/kg acyclovir, which had been infused over 60 minutes, 48 hours prior to dialysis.[76, 84]

Indications and Clinical Studies

Parenteral acyclovir, approved in 1982, has proved effective in the management of initial and recurrent episodes of mucocutaneous herpes simplex (types 1 and 2) infection in immunocompromised adults and children and for the treatment of severe first episodes of genital herpes infections in non-immunocompromised patients. In selected patients, the drug is used orally in the management of initial and recurrent episodes of genital herpes.

In initial and recurrent mucocutaneous herpes simplex infection (orofacial, nasal, esophageal, genital, labial) in immunocompromised individuals, parenteral acyclovir decreases the duration of itching and pain, the duration of viral shedding, the time required for crusting-over and healing of lesions, and the duration of positive cultures. In one placebo-controlled trial in patients with established mucocutaneous herpes simplex viral infection, parenteral acyclovir at 250 mg/m² every eight hours for seven days shortened the median healing time (9.3 d vs 13.5 d), the duration of pain (8.9 d vs 13.1 d), and duration of viral shedding (2.8 d vs 16.8 d), although no effect on recurrences after discontinuation of therapy was noted.[85] Other trials evaluating the efficacy of acyclovir in herpes simplex infections in immunocompromised hosts have shown similar results.[86–93] Mucocutaneous HSV lesions in immunocompromised patients also generally respond very well to therapy with topical acyclovir ointment.[94, 95] In addition to effectively treating active herpes simplex mucocutaneous infections in immunocompromised patients, acyclovir has also proved effective in preventing infection in these patients.[96–102]

In the management of first-episode mucocutaneous HSV infections, acyclovir is generally more effective when therapy is started as soon as possible after symptoms appear. In those patients plagued by recurrent infections, fewer than six recurrences per year may be managed with 200 mg of oral acyclovir 5 times daily for five days, beginning as soon as symptoms appear. More than six recurrences per year, as often as every month in some patients, may require continuous suppressive oral therapy.[103] Patients receiving chronic suppressive therapy must be observed closely for the potential emergence of acyclovir-resistant viral strains.[104, 105]

Initially marketed in the United States in 1982 for the topical treatment of primary genital and mucocutaneous herpes infections, topical acyclovir has been shown to reduce the duration of virus shedding in recurrent labial herpes simplex infections in normal hosts, although significant clinical benefit from topical therapy is considered minimal in these patients.[106, 107] However, in immunocompromised patients, topical therapy not only reduces the duration of virus shedding, but also significantly shortens the period of pain and healing of lesions.[94, 95, 106]

Topical therapy results in significant reduction in duration of virus shedding and time of healing in primary genital herpes,[108, 111] although in normal hosts, topical therapy has minimal efficacy in reducing new vesicle formation, or in treating recurrent genital herpes simplex infections.[110–116] Thus topical acyclovir ointment has found its most effective clinical application in the management of primary genital herpes infection and mucocutaneous HSV infections in immunocompromised individuals.

Following the introduction of the parenteral formulation of

acyclovir in 1982, IV therapy of severe initial, primary episodes of genital herpes was shown to dramatically reduce the median healing time, decrease formation of new lesions, and improve duration of pain when compared with placebo.[117, 118] It is now recognized that therapy for primary genital herpes infection has little or no impact on subsequent recurrence rates. Except for chronic oral suppressive therapy, no regimen has proved effective in reducing the frequency of recurrences of infection.[73, 119–121] In the therapy of primary genital herpes, outpatient oral acyclovir (200 mg 5 times daily) is the therapy of choice, with parenteral therapy being reserved for those few patients with infections severe enough to justify admission to the hospital.

A number of trials have shown that oral acyclovir, at doses of 200 mg 2 or 3 times daily, can effectively suppress recurrent genital herpes infection in 60% to 90% of patients on therapy for up to 6 months.[122–126] Treatment of recurrent genital lesions appears to be most effective when patients initiate their own oral therapy (200 mg orally 5 times daily) during the prodromal phase or when lesions are first noted. Results from a large number of studies now support the use of oral acyclovir, ranging from 600 to 1000 mg daily in divided doses, to suppress recurrent genital herpes infection.[99, 127–135]

Chronic suppressive regimens of this type appear to be well tolerated, with headache, nausea, and vomiting reported in a minimal number of patients. Selected patients do experience breakthrough recurrent infections, but prolonged episodes are generally of less severity and shorter duration in those patients receiving acyclovir. In one study of oral suppressive therapy, analysis of viral isolates obtained during breakthrough recurrences yielded three isolates resistant to acyclovir.[136] Subsequent isolates obtained immediately after the breakthrough episode had the same sensitivity patterns as the initial isolates, leading the authors to conclude that breakthrough episodes occurring on therapy may be due to acyclovir-resistant viral isolates. Although subsequent reports evaluating the emergence of resistant herpes isolates during suppressive acyclovir therapy in otherwise normal individuals have shown conflicting results, it is generally felt that the appearance of resistant virus during oral suppressive therapy will be of little clinical consequence.[137–139] However, more isolates from breakthrough episodes require further study to more clearly determine the exact mechanism of recurrent infection in patients receiving acyclovir. Emerging data on the management of HSV infections in AIDS patients may indicate that emergence of resistant isolates may become more clinically significant in the future. Likewise, data on the long-term safety and efficacy of acyclovir administered for periods of 1 year or longer is still accruing from ongoing trials.

Several clinical trials have demonstrated the efficacy of acyclovir against herpes zoster infections in immunocompromised patients,[91, 140–143] and many clinicians now consider acyclovir the drug of choice for this infection.[144–146] In one trial of acyclovir treatment of varicella-zoster infections in 40 bone marrow transplant patients,[143] the median times to cessation of virus positivity, new lesion formation, and total pustulation were shorter than those reported for vidarabine. In a randomized, prospective trial comparing IV therapy with acyclovir or vidarabine in 22 severely immunocompromised patients presenting within 72 hours of onset of varicella-zoster virus (VZV) infection, none of ten evaluable

patients treated with acyclovir developed cutaneous dissemination of infection, whereas five of ten evaluable patients receiving vidarabine developed localized dermatomal disease.[147] Acyclovir was also superior to vidarabine in reducing the period of virus shedding, new lesion formation, the pustulation and crusting of all lesions, and in accelerating complete healing of lesions.

Other studies have demonstrated the efficacy of acyclovir in immunocompetent patients with herpes zoster infection,[148–151] usually given in doses of 5 to 10 mg/kg IV every eight hours.

In an uncontrolled trial, dissemination of varicella-zoster infection in immunocompromised children was prevented by oral acyclovir doses of 400 mg 5 times daily for ten days.[152] In a double-blind, randomized trial in elderly patients with acute zoster infections, oral acyclovir at 400 mg 5 times daily for five days was reported to be as effective as IV acyclovir in shortening the duration of pain and accelerating the healing rate.[149] However, in a double-blind, placebo-controlled trial in immunocompetent patients over 50 years of age with herpes zoster, a decrease in the number of days of new lesion formation within the affected dermatome was the only statistically significant difference demonstrated by a similar regimen of oral acyclovir.[153] Other studies have confirmed the increased benefit of high-dose oral acyclovir therapy of herpes zoster infection.[154–159] Further studies are required to more precisely define the usefulness of oral acyclovir in the treatment of herpes zoster infections.

Immunocompromised patients with localized herpes zoster may benefit from topical acyclovir. In one double-blind trial in 43 immunocompromised patients, application of 5% acyclovir ointment 4 times daily for ten days significantly reduced mean times of pustulation, crusting, and healing.[160] Although IV or oral administration may be required to prevent dissemination of herpes zoster, concomitant application of topical acyclovir may further hasten healing time and shorten the duration of treatment.

Trials comparing acyclovir with vidarabine in severe disseminated VZV infections in immunocompromised patients have indicated that both drugs are effective, but that acyclovir may be preferred when the risk of cardiorespiratory failure is high, because of the large amount of diluent required for vidarabine administration.[161]

Acyclovir in parenteral doses of 15 to 30 mg/kg/d is also reported to be effective in the management of herpes zoster infections in patients with AIDS.[162, 163]

Encephalitis due to herpes simplex (hemorrhagic necrotizing encephalitis) is the most common cause of fatal sporadic encephalitis in the Western World, reported to affect approximately 1.5 million people per year.[164] Mortality without antiviral treatment exceeds 70%, and many survivors have serious residual disabilities, including altered levels of consciousness and mentation, fever, headache, and personality changes. These may progress in some patients to hemiparesis and seizures. Herpes simplex encephalitis is currently diagnosed by brain biopsy followed by identification of the virus in brain tissue, and much research is being focused on the development of noninvasive, specific, and sensitive diagnostic tests that are positive early in the disease.[165–169] Delivery of effective antiviral therapy early in the course of infection is critical to optimize recovery and return to normal function. Factors directly influencing the outcome of antiviral therapy are the age of the patient (patients less than 30 years of age show higher recovery rates), the level of consciousness, and the duration of disease.[170]

Intravenous vidarabine was shown in 1977 to decrease the mortality rate in biopsy-proven herpes simplex encephalitis, measuring 40% 6 months after treatment, compared with 70% mortality in placebo-treated patients.[171] Larger, subsequent trials have supported this finding.[172, 173]

Several more recent studies have shown very beneficial effects of acyclovir (10 mg/kg IV g8h for at least 10 d) in biopsy-proven infection.[174, 175] This latter study[175] found acyclovir to be more effective than vidarabine, with 28% mortality in acyclovir recipients versus 54% mortality in vidarabine-treated patients. In addition, 28% of acyclovir patients regained normal functioning 6 months after the acute illness, compared with 14% of vidarabine recipients. Given this significant reduction in mortality in herpes simplex encephalitis with acyclovir, the 6-month mortality in acyclovir-treated patients unfortunately is still 19%, and one third of the treated population does not regain normal baseline function.[175]

Evaluation of acyclovir and vidarabine in neonatal herpes simplex brain infection is ongoing, and one large study in neonates reported equivalent results.[176]

Other studies report significant reduction in mortality and morbidity from herpes simplex encephalitis in both children and adults.[177-180]

Despite better outcome with currently available antiviral agents in the treatment of biopsy-proven herpes simplex encephalitis, further improvement in diagnostic, therapeutic, and prophylactic strategies is required.[181]

Although acyclovir and other previously available antiviral agents have historically not provided effective treatment or prophylaxis of either CMV or EBV infection, emerging data indicate that acyclovir may play a role in the management of these infections.[188a, 189]

Trials of IV acyclovir in CMV infections have shown little or no consistent clinical benefit, although reductions in viral titers in urine and viremia have been noted.[182-184] Both CMV and EBV are less susceptible in vitro to acyclovir, when compared to HSV or VZV. The in vitro 50% inhibitory concentrations of acyclovir (IC_{50}) against CMV have been reported to range from 2.3 to 23 μg/mL or higher.[185, 186] Several studies using a cytohybridization assay have reported IC_{50} levels of acyclovir for susceptible strains of EBV ranging from 1.4 to 1.6 μg/mL.[45]

The relative resistance of EBV and CMV, compared with HSV, is thought to result from the inability of EBV and CMV to encode for virus-specific TK, the critical enzyme necessary for the initial phosphorylation of acyclovir in infected cells.[187] However, cytomegaloviral DNA polymerase is sensitive to inhibition by ACV-TP,[188] and minimal inhibition of CMV replication occurs in vitro due to low levels of phosphorylation thought to be mediated by other cellular kinases.

In an uncontrolled study of high-dose acyclovir (400–1200 mg/m² IV g8h) in bone marrow transplant recipients with CMV pneumonia, therapy was associated with possible bone marrow and neurologic toxicity, but with no clinical benefit in controlling infection.[182] In another study of acyclovir in bone marrow transplant recipients with CMV infection, doses of 500 mg/m² were given IV every eight hours from five days before to 30 days after trans-

plantation.[189] Patients receiving acyclovir, compared to controls, had improved survival, a longer interval to, and a lower overall probability of, CMV infection within the first 100 days after transplantation. This study[189] represents the first successful attempt to alter the occurrence and severity of CMV infection among seropositive patients undergoing allogeneic bone marrow transplantation.

Although acyclovir appears to have very limited efficacy against clinical infection caused by CMV, other antiviral agents, notably ganciclovir and foscarnet (discussed below), are in various stages of development and will hopefully have significant impact in the management of this serious viral infection.[190, 191]

Early studies of acyclovir therapy likewise failed to yield significant objective evidence for clinical improvement or antiviral effect in EBV infections, although transient remissions and suppression of viral shedding have been noted in selected cases.[192, 193] In three subsequent randomized, blinded trials of acyclovir in infectious mononucleosis, both IV therapy with 10 mg/kg every eight hours, and oral therapy with 800 mg 5 times daily for 1 week resulted in complete but transient inhibition of oropharyngeal EBV replication.[194-196]

Another small, open study in 11 patients with fulminant infectious mononucleosis requiring hospitalization evaluated IV acyclovir at a dose of 10 mg/kg every eight hours for three to seven days, followed by oral therapy with 800 mg 5 times daily for the remainder of a ten-day treatment period.[197] In addition, all patients in this study received oral prednisolone, starting at 0.7 mg/kg/d for four days, and tapering by 50% every other day over the remaining six days. This combination significantly reduced fever and oropharyngeal EBV shedding, though only transiently. Virus excretion returned to pretreatment levels within 1 week after drug withdrawal. Further evaluation of acyclovir in infectious mononucleosis, alone or in combination with immunomodulatory agents, and of newer antiviral agents is ongoing.

Drug Interactions

Renal function should be observed closely in patients receiving acyclovir, especially when in combination with amphotericin B, aminoglycosides, or other potentially nephrotoxic agents.

In vitro synergism and antagonism between acyclovir and other antiviral agents have been reported.[198, 199] Synergistic effects of acyclovir and foscarnet have been shown against CMV. Acyclovir also appears to be synergistic in both antiviral activity and toxicity with various interferon derivatives.[200, 201] An inhibitor of HSV ribonucleotide reductase, compound A723U (a 2-acetylpyridine thiosemicarbazone derivative), has been shown to greatly enhance the antiviral activity of acyclovir.[202] The combination of this compound with acyclovir significantly lowered the intracellular concentration of deoxyguanosine triphosphate and decreased the ability of deoxyguanosine triphosphate to compete with ACV-TP for incorporation into viral DNA. After further evaluation, the distinct synergy between acyclovir and this ribonucleotide reductase inhibitor may be useful in clinical trials.

Acyclovir has been shown to exert synergistic in vitro activity with zidovudine against HIV.[203, 203a] In addition, excessive lethargy and fatigue have been reported following coadministration of acyclovir and zidovudine.[204] The mechanism of this latter interaction is at present unknown.

Probenecid may decrease the renal clearance of acyclovir, potentially increasing both therapeutic and toxic effects of acyclovir.[205] The exact clinical significance of probenecid-induced changes in acyclovir kinetics remains to be established.

Adverse Effects

Adverse reactions following oral or parenteral administration of acyclovir are generally minimal. It is important to note, however, that potentially serious reactions, such as renal tubular damage, can occur with parenteral acyclovir.

Transient increases in serum creatinine or in BUN and decreases in creatinine clearance occur occasionally in patients receiving parenteral acyclovir, especially when the drug is administered too rapidly (over less than 10 minutes). The risk of adverse renal effects depends on the hydration status of the patient, preexisting renal disease, the dose and rate of acyclovir administration, urine output, and concomitant drug therapy. Adverse renal effects are thought to result from precipitation of the drug in the renal tubules; such precipitation may potentially result in acute renal failure.

Reversible renal dysfunction has been observed in approximately 5% to 10% of patients receiving a dose of 5 mg/kg every eight hours.[206] It is especially important to maintain adequate hydration and urine output during the first two hours after IV infusion of acyclovir, since the maximal urinary and renal concentrations of the drug occur during this period. It is generally recommended that a minmum 24-hour urine output be maintained at 500 mL per gram of acyclovir administered.

The most frequent adverse effects of parenteral acyclovir are local reactions at the injection site—erythema, pain, and phlebitis. These local effects occur more frequently after inadvertent extravasation of solutions containing more than 8 mg/mL (pH 9–11).

Headache is one of the most common adverse effects of oral acyclovir, reported in about 13% of patients receiving the drug as chronic suppressive therapy for herpes infections; headache occurs less frequently during short-term therapy. Vertigo, fatigue, insomnia, irritability, and depression have occurred rarely in patients receiving oral acyclovir.

Approximately 1% of patients receiving parenteral acyclovir have developed encephalopathic changes characterized by lethargy, tremors, obtundation, confusion, hallucinations, seizures, or coma.[182, 206] Concurrent interferon or intrathecal methotrexate administration may be additive risk factors for these neurologic symptoms.[207] Improvement of symptoms occurred within 1 to 2 weeks following discontinuation of acyclovir, but symptoms recurred in two patients after reinstitution of therapy.[207]

Uncommonly reported side effects include rash, urticaria, diaphoresis, hematuria, arthralgia, lymphadenopathy, acne, and hair loss. Nausea or vomiting have occurred in about 8% of patients receiving chronic suppressive therapy. Very few patients discontinue therapy because of adverse effects.

Topical therapy may cause transient burning when applied to genital lesions, especially in female patients treated for first episodes of genital herpes.[81] The polyethylene glycol base of the topical ointment may itself cause vaginal irritation, and is not approved for intravaginal use.

Acyclovir at high concentrations has shown mutagenic activity in some in vitro assays. No significant immunosuppressive activity or terogenicity has been noted in animal studies.[208] Although safety in the pregnant human has not been firmly established, emerging data indicate that acyclovir may be used with favorable results in treating viral infections in pregnant women.

Dosage and Administration

Acyclovir is administered orally and acyclovir sodium is administered by slow IV infusion. The drug should not be given by rapid IV infusion or injection (less than 10 minutes). Because of the risk of adverse local reaction (phlebitis), concentrations of infusion solutions administered by peripheral vein should not exceed 7 mg/mL. To avoid increased risk of adverse renal effects, diluted solutions of acyclovir for IV administration should not be infused over a period of less than one hour.

The usual IV dose of acyclovir for adults and children 12 years of age and older with normal renal function is 5 mg/kg every eight hours (15 mg/kg/d). For children less than 12 years of age, the usual IV dose is 250 mg/m^2 every eight hours (750 mg/m^2/d). For neonates, the manufacturer suggests doses of 5 to 15 mg/kg or 250 mg/m^2 every eight hours, with appropriate modifications based on maturity of renal function. The usual duration of parenteral therapy is 1 week in immunocompromised patients with mucocutaneous herpes simplex infections, and five days in non-immunocompromised patients with severe initial episodes of genital herpes.

The recommended adult oral dosage of acyclovir for treatment of initial episodes of genital herpes is 200 mg every four hours while awake (5 times daily) for ten days, initiated within 1 week of the onset of lesions. For prophylaxis of recurrent episodes, the recommended dosage for adults is 200 mg 3 times daily for up to 6 months. Selected patients may require 200 mg 5 times daily for up to 6 months. Chronic prophylaxis of longer than 6 months duration should be considered only for appropriate patients; ongoing studies will hopefully provide more data on the relative risks and benefits of prolonged therapy. For the treatment of intermittent, recurrent episodes of genital herpes, therapy should be initiated within two days of the onset of lesions with 200 mg every four hours while awake 5 times daily for five days.

In patients with renal impairment, doses and dosing intervals of acyclovir must be modified based on the degree of renal impairment. The manufacturer recommends that patients with creatinine clearances of 10 ml/min/1.73 m^2 or less receive oral doses not exceeding 200 mg every 12 hours.[45] Patients with higher creatinine clearances may receive the usual oral dosages. Recommended dosage modifications for adults and children over 12 years of age, based on creatinine clearance values, are outlined in Table 6–1.[45, 74, 76]

In the management of genital herpes and non–life-threatening mucocutaneous herpes simplex infections with topical acyclovir 5% ointment, therapy should be initiated as soon as possible following the onset of infection. The ointment should be applied with a finger cot or rubber glove, in sufficient quantity to adequately cover all lesions, every three hours 6 times daily for 1 week. The topical ointment should not be applied to the eye, or to the vagina, cervix, or other mucous membranes. Although not currently in-

Table 6–1
Recommended Acyclovir Dosage Modifications for Patients with Renal Impairment

Creatinine Clearance (ml/min/1.73m²)	Standard Dose (%)	Standard Dose (mg/kg)	Dosing Interval (h)
>50	100	5.0	8
25–50	100	5.0	12
10–25	100	5.0	24
0–10	50	2.5	24

cluded in the indications approved by the Food and Drug Administration, a 3% ophthalmic ointment of acyclovir (not currently available) has been used in the topical treatment of HSV ophthalmic infections.[45]

Patient Information

The importance of adequate hydration and fluid intake should be stressed to patients receiving acyclovir. Patients should be advised that oral acyclovir does not eliminate latent HSV infection, and should not be considered a cure. Patients should be instructed not to exceed recommended dosage or duration of therapy, and to notify their physician if frequency and severity of recurrences do not improve.

Because genital herpes is a sexually transmitted disease, advise patients to avoid sexual contact while visible lesions are present since there is a risk of infecting their sexual partners. Horizontal transmission of infection between sexual partners has been documented in association with asymptomatic virus shedding.[209] Patients being treated with topical acyclovir should be advised to apply the ointment with a disposable surgical glove or finger cot to prevent autoinoculation of other body sites and possible transmission of infection to other persons.

Female patients receiving the drug should also be instructed to consult their health care provider if they become pregnant or intend to become pregnant, or if they intend to breast-feed.

Availability

Commercially available dosage forms of acyclovir include the sodium salt (lyophilized crystalline powder, 500 or 1,000 mg per vial) for parenteral use, acyclovir base for oral use (200-mg capsules), and a topical ointment containing 5% acyclovir suspended in a polyethylene glycol vehicle. All of the above formulations are marketed as Zovirax by the Burroughs Wellcome Co.

Dosage forms not currently available in the United States include a 3% ophthalmic ointment, 200-, 400-, and 800- mg tablets, and an oral pediatric suspension containing 40 mg/mL.

Several promising chemical analogues of acyclovir are currently under evaluation as potentially valuable antiviral agents. Two such derivatives, deoxyacyclovir and buciclovir, are briefly discussed.

Because of the poor GI absorption and bioavailability of acyclovir (15%–30%) when administered orally, a prodrug of acyclovir has been developed which is well-absorbed from the GI tract and subsequently converted to acyclovir in vivo, presumably by xanthine oxidase.[210–214] This compound, 6-deoxyacyclovir (desciclovir, BW A515U, DCV) produces plasma levels after oral

administration similar to those achieved with IV acyclovir at doses of 5 mg/kg every eight hours. The chemical structure of deoxyacyclovir is depicted in Figure 6–3.

In one study of healthy human volunteers given 250 mg of desciclovir orally 3 times daily for ten days, the absorption of DCV was at least 75%, and over 60% of the administered oral dose was recovered in the urine as acyclovir.[211] Peak plasma acyclovir levels of 5 mg/mL were reached within one hour, and the plasma levels of acyclovir achieved were of the same magnitude as those reported in subjects given 2.5 mg/kg of IV acyclovir, and approximately tenfold higher than levels achieved after administration of 200 mg of acyclovir orally every four hours, as measured in previous studies. The half-life of DCV, measured at about 50 minutes, indicated rapid in vivo conversion of DCV to acyclovir. Also of note, no serious adverse effects were reported, and the serum creatinine level did not increase significantly, remaining within normal levels in all the subjects.

Because this drug undergoes in vivo conversion to acyclovir by xanthine oxidase, patients receiving concurrent therapy with xanthine oxidase inhibitors such as allopurinol should be observed carefully for signs or symptoms of toxicity related to potential adverse drug interactions. Likewise, the same potential drug interactions as listed above for acyclovir may also occur with desciclovir. Hampering the development of this compound however is data indicating increased incidence of tumors in laboratory animals receiving the drug.

Patients receiving this compound should receive the same general instructions as with acyclovir, emphasizing adequate hydration and fluid intake.

This compound, with increased oral bioavailability, may permit reductions in the frequency of administration and expansion of the range of herpesvirus infections amenable to oral therapy.

Currently available as 250-mg oral capsules for investigational use only, desciclovir is undergoing evaluation for oral treatment of selected herpesvirus infections, notably VZV and CMV infections.[215, 216]

Buciclovir, (R)-(3,4-dihydroxybutyl)guanine, is another promising acyclic guanosine analogue. This compound, and related analogues, are under investigational evaluation for treatment of herpes simplex and other viral infections.[217, 218] Buciclovir is activated by viral TK, phosphorylated by other cellular enzymes,

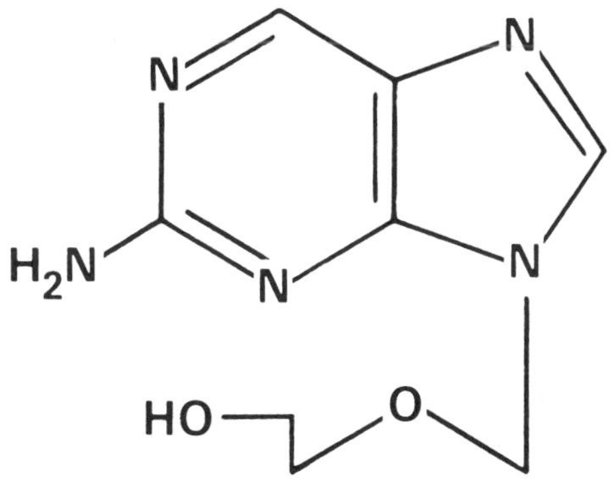

Figure 6–3. Structure of deoxyacyclovir (Desciclovir).

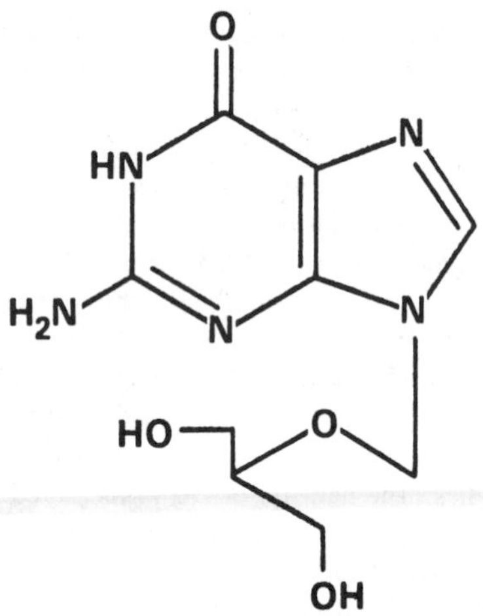

Figure 6–4. Structure of ganciclovir (DHPG).

and subsequently inhibits viral DNA synthesis in infected cells.[219] Topical buciclovir treatment, initiated early after intravaginal infection with HSV type 2 in mice and guinea pigs, appears efficacious in contrast to topical treatment delayed 24 hours or longer.[217] Systemic treatment of infected mice could not prevent spread of infection to the brain and subsequent mortality. The results of these studies suggest that buciclovir has only limited efficacy against herpesvirus infections once the virus is present in the nervous system of infected animals.[217]

GANCICLOVIR

The antiviral specificity of acyclovir against many herpesviruses has stimulated research and development of other acyclic nucleoside analogues with clinical activity against those viruses that are less sensitive to the antiviral activity of acyclovir, largely due to lack of virus-specific TK. Such a virus targeted for more effective antiviral drug development is CMV, a major cause of morbidity and mortality in patients undergoing organ transplantation, in neonates, and in patients with HIV infection.[220–236]

Ganciclovir (9-[1,3-dihydroxy-2-propoxymethyl] guanine, also known as DHPG, dihydroxypropoxymethylguanine, BW B759U, BIOLF-62, 2'-NDG, and Cytovene), is a new acyclic nucleoside analogue of 2'-deoxyguanosine, closely related chemically to acyclovir (Figure 6–4).

Chemistry and Stability

Ganciclovir is currently available as a sterile parenteral solution in 10-mL ampules containing 50 mg/mL. The pH of this solution is approximately 11. Solutions in original unopened ampules, stored at room temperature (15–30°C), are stable for at least 6 months. Stock solutions of undiluted drug should not be refrigerated, as crystallization of the drug may occur.

Once an ampule is opened, the drug should be diluted immediately, since undiluted solution will rapidly absorb carbon dioxide from the atmosphere, resulting in a decrease in pH and crystallization. Solutions for IV infusion are prepared by aseptically diluting the stock solution (50 mg/mL) in an appropriate diluent to yield a final concentration of 3 to 5 mg/mL in 100 to 150 mL of final volume. Suitable diluents include 5% dextrose in water, 0.9% sodium chloride injection, Ringer's injection, or lactated Ringer's injection. After dilution in this manner, the solution can be stored under refrigeration for up to 48 hours. Solutions at concentrations of 3 mg/mL in 5% dextrose injection or 0.9% sodium chloride injection have been shown to be stable when stored either at room temperature or under refrigeration for up to five days.[237] Diluted solutions may be stored in glass or plastic infusion containers, and are compatible with silicon-type IV tubing.

Data are lacking on the compatibility of ganciclovir solutions with other drugs in solutions. Consequently, it is recommended that ganciclovir not be mixed with any other drugs in solution. Also, acidic drugs or solutions which would lower the pH of ganciclovir solution would be expected to cause precipitation of the drug.

Mechanism of Action

The antiviral activity of ganciclovir results from the incorporation of the triphosphorylated form of the drug into replicating viral DNA, and subsequent termination of viral DNA replication.[238, 239] In HSV type 1 (HSV-1)– and HSV-2–infected cells, ganciclovir is phosphorylated to its monophosphate by virus-specific TK. The monophosphate is then further metabolized to the triphosphate by other cellular enzymes. Viral DNA polymerase then inserts ganciclovir triphosphate into the replicating viral DNA chain, and subsequent viral DNA synthesis is inhibited.

However, since CMV does not specify TK, the antiviral mechanism of ganciclovir in CMV-infected cells is less well understood. The initial phosphorylation of ganciclovir in CMV-infected cells is thought to be mediated by other cellular enzymes, probably deoxyguanosine kinase. It is then further phosphorylated to its triphosphate analogue. Subsequent inhibition of CMV nucleic acid synthesis is similar to that in HSV-infected cells, with the triphosphate analogue competitively inhibiting binding of deoxyguanosine triphosphate to DNA polymerase.

Ganciclovir triphosphate appears to be catabolized more slowly in virus-infected cells than acyclovir triphosphate, with 60% to 70% of the original level of ganciclovir triphosphate detectable up to 18 hours after the drug has been removed.[240] This slow degradation rate may allow accumulation of sufficient ganciclovir triphosphate to interfere with the production of viral DNA, and may also explain ganciclovir's superior in vivo potency compared to acyclovir, which is more quickly catabolized and excreted.[240]

Spectrum of Activity

Ganciclovir has potent in vitro activity against all of the pathogenic herpesviruses, including CMV. It also has some activity against other DNA viruses such as vaccinia and adenovirus. The drug is not active against RNA viruses.

Using plaque reduction assays, strains of HSV-1 and HSV-2 are inhibited by 0.12 to 2.0 μmol of ganciclovir;[241–245] CMV by 10 μmol;[243, 244, 246–249] EBV by 1.0 μmol;[242, 250] and VZV by 28 to 40 μmol. This agent may prove useful in the management of HSV infections caused by acyclovir-resistant isolates.

Ganciclovir is more active against CMV than is acyclovir. The

IC_{50} for ganciclovir against CMV is 5 to 7 μmol, compared with 40 to 95 μmol for acyclovir.[249, 251]

Studies in experimental animals have shown ganciclovir to be more effective than acyclovir in both treating and preventing CMV infection.[249, 252]

Pharmacokinetics

The pharmacokinetics of ganciclovir appear to be very similar to acyclovir. At doses of 2.5 to 5.0 mg/kg IV every eight to 12 hours, ganciclovir's elimination half-life ranges from 2.1 to 6.8 hours, and its steady-state volume of distribution is approximately 33 L/1.73 m² body surface area. Total renal clearance of ganciclovir is 2.4 times greater than creatinine clearance, suggesting that the drug undergoes extensive renal tubular secretion.[253]

The pharmacokinetics of oral ganciclovir have also been studied, although only a small amount of the drug is absorbed when the IV preparation is given orally. Oral doses of 10 to 20 mg/kg every six hours yield serum peak and trough concentrations of 2.5 to 3.0 μmol and 1.3 to 1.4 μmol, respectively.[254] Ninety-five percent or more of ganciclovir is excreted entirely unchanged in the urine; oral absorption is less than 5% of the dose. Because levels achieved in serum following oral ganciclovir administration approximate those required to inhibit CMV in vitro, and because most patients with severe CMV infection (especially patients with AIDS) may require lifelong suppressive therapy to control disease progression, administration of this drug in an appropriate oral dosage form may be of future interest for the use of ganciclovir in maintenance regimens.

Following IV doses of 2.5 mg/kg, peak serum concentrations ranging from 5 to 18 μmol have been reported in patients being treated for CMV infections.[253, 253a] Doses of 5 mg/kg produce peak serum levels of approximately 40 μmol. The drug penetrates the CNS, with CSF levels measured at 24% to 67% of concomitant serum concentrations.[253] Ganciclovir also appears to concentrate in lung and liver tissue, with levels averaging 99% and 92%, respectively, of levels obtained from heart blood at autopsy.[255]

Indications and Clinical Studies

Although ganciclovir has potent in vitro activity against all pathogenic herpesviruses, its primary clinical experience to date has been in the treatment of severe CMV infection (pulmonary, retinal, GI, or disseminated) in immunocompromised patients, notably organ transplant recipients and patients with AIDS.[256–262]

Erice and colleagues[258] evaluated 31 immunosuppressed patients receiving ganciclovir for treatment of CMV infection. CMV pneumonitis was found in 19 patients, retinitis in seven, GI infection in six, and hepatitis in three. Seventeen (55%) of these 31 patients (all non-AIDS patients) improved with ganciclovir therapy. The most frequent adverse reaction, neutropenia, occurred in 11 patients (35%), nine of whom were bone marrow transplant recipients.

Masur and colleagues[259] studied eight immunosuppressed homosexual men with CMV viremia (seven with bilateral retinitis, one with colitis and retinitis, and one with pneumonitis only) treated with 2.5 to 5.0 mg/kg of IV ganciclovir every eight to 12 hours, over ten to 35 days. All patients had clinical and virologic improvement, although significant granulocytopenia (< 500 neutro-

phils per microliter) required withdrawal of therapy in three patients. Both clinical and virologic relapses occurred within 30 days after cessation of treatment. This is not an uncommon finding in AIDS patients treated with ganciclovir for acute CMV infection.

In a multicenter, collaborative study of ganciclovir in 26 patients with AIDS or other immunodeficiency, clinical status improved or stabilized in 17 of the 22 patients (77%) with confirmed infection.[260] Patients with CMV pneumonia responded poorly, with four of seven patients (57%) expiring before completing 2 weeks of therapy. The poor clinical response in bone marrow transplant recipients with CMV pneumonia may be related to the contributing factors of pulmonary infiltration caused by radiation and/or chemotherapy, and the immunosuppressive effects of graft-versus-host disease and the medications used to treat it. In contrast, 11 of 13 patients (85%) with CMV retinitis, and five of eight (63%) with GI infection improved or stabilized.

Relapse occurred in 11 of 14 patients (79%) when the drug was discontinued. Reversible neutropenia was the most frequent adverse reaction, occurring in seven patients.

Laskin and colleagues treated serious CMV infection in 97 AIDS patients with IV ganciclovir at doses ranging from 3.0 to 15.0 mg/kg/d.[261, 262] CMV viremia cleared in 85 (88%) patients, and 87% of the evaluable patients with CMV retinitis displayed improvement or stabilization of their disease. As in the previous studies, however, progression or relapse of infection occurred in all patients following discontinuation of therapy. Of note was the significant prevention of recurrence of infection in patients receiving long-term suppressive therapy with 5.0 mg/kg, given IV five to seven days per week. Toxicities observed in these 97 patients included neutropenia in 53 (55%), leukopenia in 31 (32%), nausea in five (5%), thrombocytopenia in four (4%), and mental status changes in three (3%) patients.

Adverse Reactions

Reversible neutropenia is the most frequent adverse reaction associated with ganciclovir. A decrease in absolute neutrophils by 50% from baseline or to less than 1000/μL occurs in 25% to 68% of patients receiving either therapy for acute infection or maintenance regimens.[257, 259, 261] This neutropenia appears to be more frequent with longer courses of therapy, and at doses of 5.0 mg/kg given every eight hours, compared to 2.5-mg/kg doses. At least one death has been reported associated with neutropenia and sepsis in an AIDS patient treated with ganciclovir.[260]

Other reported adverse reactions to ganciclovir include thrombocytopenia, nausea, anorexia, hepatitis, skin rash, disorientation, psychosis, eosinophilia, and phlebitis at the infusion site.

Ganciclovir has been shown to cause azoospermia in experimental animals at doses roughly equivalent to those used in humans. Although data on testicular toxicity in humans are limited, the drug is presumed to cause reduced sperm production in humans as well, and those patients wishing to preserve their reproductive ability should receive this drug only for sight- or life-threatening indications, and then only after appropriate informed consent.

Dosage and Administration

Ganciclovir therapy for CMV disease is generally administered as an initial "induction" phase consisting of 2.5 to 5.0 mg/kg IV every 8 to 12 hours over a 10- to 30-day period. This is usually followed with a "maintenance" regimen, administered as single daily IV infusions of 5.0 to 7.5 mg/kg, given five to seven days per week.

Each infusion dose should be given over one hour, and the drug should be well diluted in either 100 to 150 mL of either dextrose 5% in water or 0.9% sodium chloride injection. Rapid or bolus IV administration may result in increased toxicity as a result of excessive plasma levels. IM injection may result in severe tissue irritation due to high pH.

Because the drug is primarily renally excreted, dosage modifications are necessary in patients with impaired renal function. Although a precise dose modification scheme has not yet been established, suggested dosage guidelines are offered in Table 6–2.[263, 263a]

Because of very limited clinical experience in treating pediatric patients younger than 12 years, and the potential for carcinogenicity and reproductive toxicity, administration in children should be undertaken only if potential benefits of treatment outweigh the risks.[263a]

Intravitreal administration of ganciclovir has been described in the treatment of CMV retinitis.[264, 265] Intravitreal ganciclovir appears to be reasonably well tolerated, and no systemic absorption of the drug from the eye is reported. Intravitreal ganciclovir concentrations remained above the ED_{50} for CMV for more than 60 hours following intravitreal injection.[264] One study of intravitreal ganciclovir infusions in rabbits found that concentrations up to 30 μg/mL produced no evidence of retinal toxicity.[266] Further trials evaluating this route of administration are ongoing.

Aerosol administration of ganciclovir in experimental animals has also been shown to inhibit CMV replication in the lung.[267] No data on the efficacy or safety of this route of administration in humans are available at present. In the future, this means of administering ganciclovir (or other antiviral agents) may play a role in treating CMV pneumonitis.

Drug Interactions

Clinically significant drug interactions reported with acyclovir may also occur in patients receiving ganciclovir, due to the close chemical and metabolic similarity between these two agents.

In patients receiving zidovudine, ganciclovir may contribute to additive hematologic toxocity, especially granulocytopenia. Patients receiving these two medications in combination should be observed closely for signs or symptoms attributable to this toxicity.

Combinations of ganciclovir with other antiviral agents may be exploited in the future to increase antiviral efficacy and reduce drug toxicity. Combination of the polyamine synthesis inhibitor difluoromethylornithine (DFMO) and ganciclovir has been reported to synergistically inhibit replication of CMV in vitro.[268]

Availability

Prior to commercial availability, the US Food and Drug Administration made ganciclovir available on a Treatment IND basis for therapy of immediately sight-threatening CMV retinitis in patients with AIDS.[269] Treatment of CMV retinitis in immunocompromised patients, including patients with AIDS, is the drug's current indication.

At present, IV ganciclovir is the only dosage form available for clinical use (Cytovene, Syntex Laboratories). Development of oral dosage forms and potential prodrug derivatives is under evaluation.

Overall experience to date with ganciclovir indicates that this drug is effective in the treatment of serious CMV infection in immunocompromised hosts. The drug is reasonably well tolerated, although significant toxicities have been reported.

Treatment of serious CMV infections in AIDS patients should be undertaken with the knowledge that relapse of infection following discontinuation of the drug is very common. In these patients, maintenance suppressive therapy is likely to be required for extended periods of time, and close monitoring of these individuals is required.

ADENINE ARABINOSIDE (ARA-A, VIDARABINE)

Structure

Ara-A, 1-β-D-arabinofuranosyladenine, is a nucleoside that contains the pentose sugar D-arabinose in place of ribose or deoxyribose (Figure 6–5). It was synthesized originally as an agent for chemotherapy of tumors.[270] It is prepared by fermentation with the NRRL strain of *Streptomyces antibioticus*.[271]

Mechanism of Action

It has been established that the main effect of ara-A in herpesvirus-infected cells is the preferential inhibition of viral relative to cellular DNA synthesis.[272–274] Available data indicate that it acts just before or at the time of viral DNA synthesis between two and four hours postinfection.[275]

It appears that there are several mechanisms by which this effect occurs. Ara-A is readily converted in cells to the corresponding 5' monotriphosphate (ara-ATP), which appears to competitively inhibit DNA-dependent DNA polymerases of DNA viruses 40 times more than those of the host cells.[276] Ara-A also is incorporated into herpes simplex virus DNA in terminal positions, preventing completion of the DNA chains.[277] In addition, it has a minimal cytostatic effect upon noninfected host cells.

Table 6–2
Suggested Ganciclovir Dosage Guidelines for Induction Therapy* in Patients with Impaired Renal Function[263, 263a]

Renal Function	Serum Creatinine (mg/100 μL)	Creatinine Clearance (mL/1.73M²/min)	Dose (mg/kg)	Interval (h)
Normal	≤1.3	≥80	5.0	12
Mild impairment	1.4–2.5	50–79	2.5	12
Moderate impairment	2.6–4.5	25–49	2.5	24
Severe impairment	>4.5	<25	1.0	24

*Recommended doses should be halved for maintenance therapy.

Human Pharmacology and Toxicity

Ara-A can be administered by the topical, intravenous (IV), or intramuscular (IM) routes, although it is irritating when administered IM. The main metabolic pathway for ara-A in humans is the conversion to ara-Hx (arabinofuranosylhypoxanthine), probably by erythrocytes.[278-280] After IV administration of the drug to humans in a dose of 1 mg/kg, ara-A plasma levels of 1 to 2 μg/mL are achieved, with an elimination half-life of 1.5 to 3 hours. Intramuscular administration of 1 mg/kg results in peak plasma ara-A levels of 0.2 to 0.3 μg/mL with a half-life of 10 to 16 hours, probably due to prolonged absorption at the injection site.[281] After 12 hours of constant infusion of 10 mg/kg, plasma levels reach 3 to 6 μg/mL, but these are mostly measurable ara-Hx. Unchanged ara-A is detectable at levels of 0.2 to 0.4 μg/mL after 12 hours of infusion.[280] Following IV or IM administration, approximately 50% of the dose is recovered in the urine, mainly as ara-Hx. The more rapid the IV infusion, the more of the administered dose is recovered in the urine.[278] There is some accumulation of the drug in erythrocytes over five to seven days.[280]

Information regarding tissue penetration of ara-A is sparse. In humans, ara-A has been found most highly concentrated in kidney, liver, and spleen; lower levels are present in brain and skeletal muscle. Ara-A and its metabolites can be found in CSF in concentrations of 50% to 60% of simultaneous plasma levels.[279, 280]

In patients with renal insufficiency, plasma levels of ara-Hx accumulate when a constant infusion of ara-A is administered.[279, 282] Plasma levels of ara-Hx can rise to as high as 75 μg/mL after an infusion of 20 mg/kg, but ara-A levels persist at low or undetectable levels.[279] In severe renal insufficiency, plasma half-life can be as long as four to seven hours. The dose of ara-A, therefore, should be reduced somewhat in these patients.[282] Ara-Hx is cleared by hemodialysis in a linear fashion (as much as 50% may be removed during a six-hour hemodialysis), making a post-dialysis dose a necessity.[282]

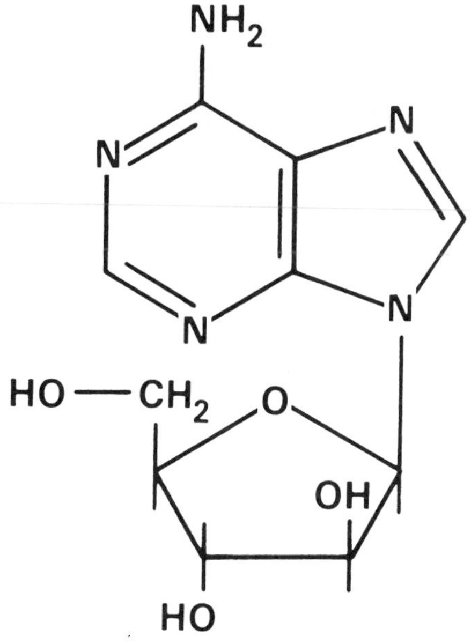

Figure 6-5. Structure of adenine arabinoside (Vidarabine, Ara-A).

Table 6-3
Sensitivity of DNA Viruses to Adenine Arabinoside

Virus	Concentrations of ARA-A (μg/mL) Required to Inhibit the Virus Effectively (≥ 50%)
Herpes simplex type 1	1–12
Herpes simplex type 2	1–24
Varicella-zoster	12–25
Cytomegalovirus	6–200
Vaccinia	10–100

Intraocular penetration of ara-A has been studied.[283] After topical administration of 3% ointment, no detectable ara-A and extremely low levels of ara-Hx (0.01 μg/mL to 0.28 μg/mL) can be found in aqueous humor.[283] The human cornea probably deaminates ara-A to ara-Hx. Therefore, topical ara-A therapy of deep herpetic ocular infections is not practical.[280]

A major problem with the administration of ara-A is its relative insolubility. One liter of IV fluid is required to solubilize 450 mg of drug. For an average dose (15 mg/kg/day), this means that 2 to 2.5 L of IV fluid per day may be necessary. In a patient with preexisting brain edema, this extra fluid load may prove detrimental. Warming IV fluid to 35° to 40°C may facilitate solution of the drug. Whitley et al recommend a final in-line membrane filter.[280] The use of a 0.45 μm or smaller in-line filter is required.[280a]

Parenteral ara-A is relatively nontoxic if it is used in appropriate doses. The major side effects that have been noted in clinical studies are gastrointestinal, mainly nausea and/or vomiting.[284-291] However, serious central nervous system (CNS) side effects such as tremor, myoclonus, dizziness, confusion, jitteriness, hallucinations, and ataxia have been reported, especially when doses of over 15 to 20 mg/kg/day are used or when renal insufficiency is present.[280, 284, 285, 292, 293] A case of fatal CNS toxicity due to ara-A in a patient with normal renal function has been reported.[294] Freidman and Grasela have noted a possible relationship of neurological symptoms to simultaneous use of allopurinol and ara-A in patients with neoplastic lymphoreticular diseases.[295] In individual patients, however, the clinician must be alert to the possibility that the primary disease process rather than the ara-A is the cause of neurological symptoms. Other side effects that have been related to ara-A therapy include myalgias, weakness, or fatigue; inappropriate ADH secretion;[296] suppression of granulocyte and platelet counts; and abnormal liver function studies. At doses of 10 and 15 mg/kg/day, laboratory abnormalities related to ara-A therapy have been clinically insignificant.[286-290] Newborn infants seem to tolerate higher doses (20 mg/kg/day) of ara-A well.[297, 298]

Ara-A does not appear to affect cellular immune mechanisms in patients receiving the drug. In vitro studies demonstrate no effect on blastogenic responses to phytohemagglutinin, pokeweed mitogen, or concanavalin A at ara-A concentrations of 3 μg/mL.[299] Also, humoral immune responses to viral infections are not affected.[300, 301]

The toxicity of topical ophthalmic ara-A is minimal. Local side effects such as burning, irritation, tearing, and photophobia have occurred, but often these symptoms occur with the primary disease as well.[280, 302] Ara-A appears to be somewhat less toxic than topical idoxuridine, especially when used for prolonged periods of time.[303]

In Vitro Antiviral Activity

The in vitro spectrum of ara-A is limited to DNA viruses, such as herpes simplex virus types 1 and 2, varicella-zoster, and cytomegalovirus, which are inhibited by variable concentrations (Table 6–3).[304] However, ara-Hx is less active against these viruses than the parent drug, making the process of deamination an important pharmacokinetic step in vitro and in vivo.[304, 305]

Cytomegalovirus is the least sensitive virus of this group, having a minimum inhibitory concentration (MIC) of about 87 µg/mL, whereas the MICs of HSV-1, HSV-2, and VZV are between 10 and 20 µg/mL.[306] Ara-A may be more effective in vitro against herpesviruses than idoxuridine, but less so than ara-C,[306, 307] and other studies have shown that ara-A is the least active of the three in vitro.[308] The sensitivity of herpesviruses to ara-A depends somewhat upon the cell line used in the assay.[308] Other DNA viruses that have variable sensitivities to ara-A are vaccinia virus and adenovirus. Most RNA viruses are not inhibited by ara-A at any concentration.[304] Ara-A does not have an effect upon in vitro production of hepatitis B surface antigen.[309]

In Vivo Antiviral Activity

Extensive preclinical studies examining the antiviral activity of ara-A in animals correlate well with the in vitro sensitivity data. Sloan has reviewed many of these studies.[310] Herpes simplex type 1 ocular infections are effectively treated in various animal models by the topical, subcutaneous, and subconjunctival routes of administration.[310] Vaccinial keratitis in rabbits also can be treated effectively with ara-A.[311] Cutaneous herpesvirus infections in animals have been treated with topical ara-A, but the compound does not appear to significantly affect the occurrence of latent infection in spinal root ganglia.[312] Intracerebral murine infections caused by HSV-1 and HSV-2 respond to ara-A administered via the intraperitoneal, oral, subcutaneous, percutaneous, intracerebral, and IV routes.[310] Ara-A is ineffective in the treatment of simian varicella infection.[313]

A large number of studies utilizing ara-A have been performed in human viral infections (Table 6–4). Early open and uncontrolled

therapeutic trials demonstrated promising results in mucocutaneous HSV-1 infection of the immunosuppressed,[314, 315] varicella-zoster infection,[316, 317] neonatal herpes simplex infection,[318, 319] and ocular herpes simplex infection.[320–322] Ara-A did not appear to be effective in the therapy of cytomegalovirus infections,[323–325] although some suppression of virus excretion was noted. Neither did it show promise in therapy of genital herpes simplex virus infections.[326, 327]

Well-controlled double-blind studies also have been performed in a variety of clinically important human viral diseases. Topical ara-A has been compared to idoxuridine and trifluorothymidine for therapy of ophthalmic herpes simplex infections. Ara-A is as effective as idoxuridine in this setting and may result in better corneal healing[302, 321, 328, 329] as well as less ocular irritation with prolonged use.[303] In addition, ara-A and trifluorothymidine are equally efficacious in treating herpes simplex virus keratitis, except in the case of ameboid ulcers when the latter is preferred.[330] Intravenous ara-A is more effective than placebo for therapy of deep herpetic infections of the eye.[320]

Because of the relative sensitivity of varicella-zoster virus to ara-A and the somewhat promising results of phase II clinical trials, several well-controlled trials of ara-A therapy of herpes zoster infection in immunosuppressed patients were performed.[288, 289] The first was a randomized crossover study in which patients received either ara-A, 10 mg/kg/day, or placebo for five days and then the alternate therapy for the second five days.[288] Patients who received ara-A during the first five days of their course did significantly better than the patients treated initially with placebo, as measured by improvement in local pain, lesion healing, viral clearance from vesicles, cessation of new vesicle formation, and time to total vesicle pustulation. Important factors in favorable response to ara-A were the initiation of therapy within six days of onset of zoster, age less than 38 years, and the presence of reticuloendothelial cancer. The incidence of postherpetic neuralgia did not appear to be affected by ara-A therapy, and patients with cutaneous dissemination responded to ara-A as well as those with localized zoster. The second study compared ara-A (10 md/kg/day for five days) to placebo in the treatment of localized herpes zoster of 72 hours duration or less in immunosuppressed patients and confirmed many observations of the first study.[289] Ara-A significantly accelerated cutaneous healing and decreased the rates of cutaneous dissemination and zoster-related visceral complications. Although the incidence of postherpetic neuralgia was not changed by ara-A therapy, its duration was significantly shortened. Age less than 38 years

Table 6–4
Efficacy of Adenine Arabinoside in Human Viral Diseases

Virus Causing Infection	Location of Infection	Type of Host	Dose (mg/kg/day) of Ara-A	Comments
Herpes simplex	Encephalitis	Normal	15	Reduction in mortality from 70% to 28%
	CNS, disseminated	Neonate	10–20	Significant reduction in mortality
	Keratitis	Normal	Topical	As effective as trifluorothymidine and IUDR
Varicella-zoster	Localized	Immuno-compromised	10	Accelerates healing and reduces cutaneous and visceral dissemination
	Disseminated	Immuno-compromised	10	Reduces new vesicles, fever, and varicella-related complications

did not correlate with better response, an unexplainable difference from the first study, but patients with lymphoproliferative malignancies derived the greatest benefit from therapy. It appears, then, that immunocompromised patients, especially those with lymphoproliferative cancers, would benefit from early therapy of zoster with ara-A.

Ara-A also is effective in therapy of varicella in immunosuppressed patients.[331, 332] Treatment with 10 mg/kg/day intravenously for five days resulted in less vesicle formation, less fever, and less varicella-related complications, compared to placebo therapy.[331]

Herpes simplex encephalitis can be treated effectively with ara-A, as shown by Whitley et al.[287] These investigators' double-blind study, published in 1977, demonstrated that ara-A administered in a dose of 15 mg/kg/day for ten days was able to reduce mortality in biopsy-proven encephalitis from 70% to 28%. Furthermore, in the group of survivors treated with ara-A, over 50% had no or only moderately debilitating neurologic sequelae, so that they were able to lead reasonably normal lives after recovery. It was important to institute therapy before the patient's level of consciousness deteriorated to coma; otherwise, morbidity was increased. In biopsy-negative patients, ara-A did not affect mortality. A subsequent publication detailed the results of a continued study conducted by the NIAID Collaborative Study Group in which all patients were treated with ara-A.[290] The results of this trial confirmed those found in the first study, reporting a mortality rate of 39% in 75 biopsy-confirmed cases of herpes simplex encephalitis. In addition, this study documented the necessity for obtaining a brain biopsy in suspected cases of herpes simplex encephalitis, because many treatable disorders such as pyogenic abscess, vascular disease, cryptococcal infection, *Toxoplasma gondii* infection, tuberculosis, and others mimicked herpes simplex encephalitis.[290] In spite of some investigators' opinions that clinical findings are sufficient to make the diagnosis of herpes simplex encephalitis,[333] this does not appear to be the case.[334] Therefore, the most prudent procedure in a patient with suspected herpes simplex encephalitis is a diagnostic brain biopsy[335] (see Chapter 29), after which ara-A, 15 mg/kg over 12 hours, should be administered each day. If the brain biopsy does not confirm the diagnostic impression of herpes simplex encephalitis within five days, discontinuance of the ara-A should be considered, unless a false-negative biopsy result is suspected. In these cases, and if it is clinically indicated, a full ten-day course would be advisable.[336]

Ara-A has been used in neonatal herpes simplex infection.[297, 337] In doses ranging from 10 to 30 mg/kg/day, it has appeared to have promise, especially when started early in the disease process. The most recent work[297] has shown that ara-A, 15 mg/kg/day, significantly reduces the high mortality rate of localized CNS as well as disseminated infection from 74%, in infants who received placebo, to 38%. In neonates with localized CNS disease, mortality was reduced from 50% to 10%, and in disseminated disease, from 85% to 57%.[297] Morbidity was most affected by ara-A in the infants with localized disease. Significant toxicity of ara-A was not observed in the neonates in this study. Of note is that neonatal herpes virus infection that was localized only to the skin progressed to more serious disease 70% of the time, suggesting that even localized disease should be treated expectantly with ara-A.[297, 338] Bryson et al have suggested that a dose of 20 mg/kg/day or more might be the optimal dose,[339] as newborns apparently tolerate higher doses of drug.[298]

Ara-A does not appear to be effective as therapy for several other herpesvirus infections. The course of cytomegalovirus infection in renal transplant recipients is not altered by ara-A therapy, and toxicity may be greater in these patients.[341] In addition, prophylactic regimens of ara-A in bone marrow transplant recipients have not been successful in reducing the incidence of CMV pneumonia.[340] However, progressive CMV retinitis in immunosuppressed (heart or renal transplant) hosts may be favorably affected by daily doses of 20 mg/kg of ara-A but not without significant side effects,[291] as shown by Marker et al.[341] In chronic carriers of HBsAg who are DNA polymerase positive, ara-A therapy reduces DNA polymerase activity, usually temporarily, but does not clear HBsAg from the serum.[292, 342] Ara-A at a dose of 20 mg/kg/day is not effective in human smallpox infection.[343]

AIDS AND TREATMENT STRATEGIES IN HIV INFECTION

Since the initial reports of Kaposi's sarcoma and *Pneumocystis carinii* pneumonia in homosexual men surfaced in 1981, AIDS has become recognized as an immunodeficiency state resulting from infection with a human retrovirus, the human immunodeficiency virus or HIV-1. As of April 1990, a cumulative total of over 128,000 cases of AIDS had been reported in the United States. Of these, over 78,000 (61%) have resulted in death.[344] Following these initial reports of this syndrome in 1981, it soon became clear that all its victims suffered from a depletion of a specific subset of lymphocytes, T4 cells. As a direct result of this T4 cell depletion, these individuals are at high risk for infection with pathogens which would generally be easily controlled in immunocompetent individuals.[345]

The causative agent of this syndrome (HTLV-III, LAV, HIV) was subsequently isolated and identified in 1983 by Luc Montagnier and his colleagues at the Pasteur Institute in Paris and by Robert Gallo and colleagues at the National Cancer Institute (NCI).[346–349] It has now become apparent that the virus infects and replicates not only in T4 cells, but also in monocytes, macrophages, and other cells called dendritic cells, located in the skin, mucous membranes, lymph nodes, spleen, liver, and brain.[345, 350] The profound depression of immune function, directly related to HIV infection of the T4 helper/inducer subset of human lymphocytes and other key cells, is discussed elsewhere.[351–355]

The replicative life cycle of HIV, as depicted in Figure 6–6,[356–358] begins with the attachment of viral particles to specific surface receptors on host cells, followed by entry into the host cell's cytoplasm by the process of endocytosis. After penetration into the host cell, HIV is uncoated and viral-specific reverse transcriptase then transcribes single-stranded RNA into double-stranded DNA. This stage is followed by generation of circular double-stranded "proviral" DNA, some of which integrates into the host cell's genome. This proviral DNA may then exist in a latent form, or it may undergo transcription to generate a new viral RNA, which is, in turn, translated into viral proteins. The final stages of viral replication are assembly and release of fully formed progeny viral particles by budding through the host cell membrane.

The highly complex genetic blueprint directing the life cycle and cellular structure of HIV is about 100,000 times smaller than the genetic units of a human cell.[359, 360] A complex set of regulatory genes controlling the production of viral proteins enables HIV to either lie in a state of latency within the target cells for an indefinite period of time, or to actively replicate at various rates.[359, 360] Expanding knowledge about these key regulatory genetic components of HIV may ultimately lead to development of an effective means of controlling this infection.

Now that the life cycle of HIV has been elucidated, specific points of attack are being explored as potential ways to halt or reduce the rate of viral replication.[203] The strategy of inhibiting the synthesis of viral DNA by the enzyme reverse transcriptase has to date received more attention than any other step in the life cycle of HIV. This strategy is attractive because it is targeted to attack a step unique to retroviruses. The first agent evaluated for its ability to inhibit HIV replication (by inhibition of reverse transcriptase) was suramin (see below).

Clinical trials of several dideoxynucleoside analogues belonging to a family of reverse transcriptase inhibitors have been undertaken, with zidovudine (azidothymidine, AZT, Retrovir) becoming the first such agent to be shown effective in inhibiting HIV replication at clinically achievable levels in large trials of AIDS patients. Dideoxynucleoside derivatives are analogues closely resembling the nucleotides that serve as building blocks in nucleic acid synthesis: the purines (adenosine and guanosine) and the pyrimidines (thymidine, cytidine, and uridine). A number of 2′,3′-dideoxynucleoside derivatives, based on their ability to selectively inhibit retroviral reverse transcriptase, have been reported to possess a broad spectrum of antiretroviral activity.[361–363]

The life cycle of HIV, the exploitation of potential targets for antiretroviral drugs, and overviews of the current epidemic in the United States, have been the subjects of numerous reviews.[203, 364–373] Before the epidemic of HIV infection is eventually conquered, many millions of individuals in the United States and worldwide will be directly affected.[374–377] The costs of medical care required by these individuals is likely to be a significant economic burden to our society.[378]

SURAMIN

Suramin, a large-molecular-weight urea derivative of the hexasodium salt of aminonaphthalene-trisulfonic acid, was the first drug reported to block the in vitro infectivity of the AIDS virus.[379] Suramin (Bayer 205, Antrypol, Germanin) was first synthesized by German chemists at Bayer in 1920. The drug was introduced shortly thereafter as an effective trypanocidal agent, based on its ability to bind to and inhibit the function of a variety of proteins.[380] It is currently used in the treatment of African trypanosomiasis and onchocerciasis.[380, 381]

Suramin was first shown to inhibit reverse transcriptase activity in selected murine and avian retrovirus models by de Clerq in 1979.[382] Because of this finding, and decades of clinical experience with this drug in humans, suramin was one of the first agents chosen for evaluation against the AIDS virus.[383]

In initial in vitro testing, suramin was shown to block the expression of viral proteins in H9 cells exposed to HIV. The drug was also shown to inhibit the cytopathic effect of HIV on a clone of helper/inducer T cells[379] at concentrations of 25 to 50 μg/mL. In addition, concentrations of 100 μg/mL or higher inhibited lymphocyte proliferation.[379] Further testing showed that suramin could

partially inhibit splenomegaly induced by Rauscher murine leukemia virus in mice,[384] and also inhibit the infection of other cell lines with HIV.[385]

Although suramin was originally chosen for evaluation in AIDS because of its reported activity against retroviral reverse transcriptase, it is possible that the drug may exert totally different mechanisms of antiretroviral activity.

In an initial pilot study of the safety and efficacy of suramin in ten patients with AIDS or AIDS-related complex (ARC), patients were dosed with a 20-minute IV test dose of 200 mg, followed by six 1-g doses given at weekly intervals, also as 20-minute IV infusions.[386] The design of this regimen was based on those employed clinically in the treatment of onchocerciasis and trypanosomiasis.

Pharmacokinetic profiling of suramin in four of these patients receiving 6.2 g IV over a 5-week period revealed a suramin plasma half-life of 44 to 54 days, reportedly among the longest half-lives for any therapeutic compound administered to humans.[387] Plasma levels of suramin exceeding 100 μg/mL persisted for several weeks, and in vitro activity of suramin was found at concentrations as low as 50 μg/mL.[387] The drug is approximately 99.7% bound to plasma proteins, and persistence of the drug in the circulation may be due to this avid protein binding. Urinary excretion is the principle route of elimination for most of the drug, and no metabolites were detected in the plasma.[387] In experimental animals, suramin appears to concentrate in kidney tissues more than in other organs, possibly contributing to the frequent occurrence of albuminuria following administration of the drug in man.[388]

Toxic reactions experienced by patients in this study[386] included fevers up to 40°C, macular skin rashes, hyperesthesias of the palms of the hands and soles of the feet, pyuria, proteinuria, and elevations of liver function tests. Many of these reactions occurred

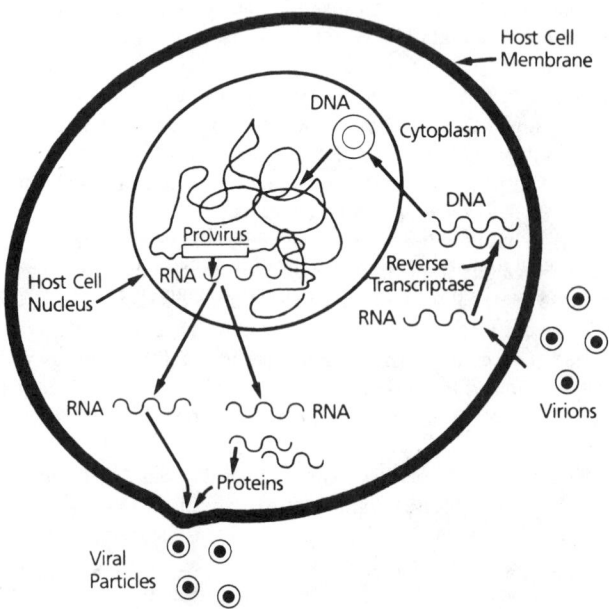

Figure 6–6. General schematic diagram of replication of retroviruses.

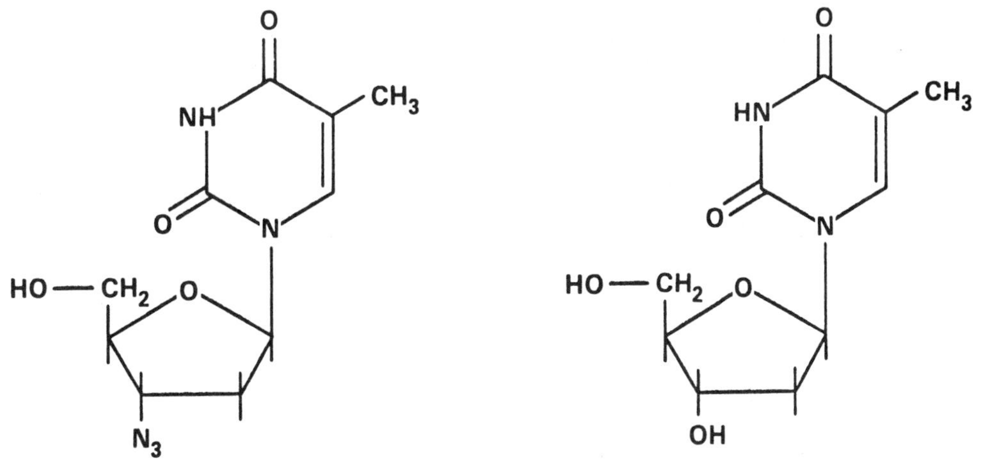

Figure 6–7. Structure of zidovudine (AZT) *(left)* and its natural deoxynucleoside counterpart, thymidine *(right).*

early in the course of therapy and subsequently abated, even on continued administration of the drug; all adverse reactions were reversible following discontinuation of therapy. Adrenal failure was reported in one patient after receiving a second 9-g course of suramin.[389] This particular toxicity, also reported by other investigators,[390–392] may be the primary dose-limiting toxicity in larger trials with this drug.

Primary cultures of HIV from four of the patients in this study,[386] positive at the time of study entry, were either undetectable or markedly diminished when plasma suramin concentrations were over 100 μg/mL; however, following discontinuation of the drug, HIV was again detectable in all four cases. Despite this apparent virustatic effect, no evidence of clinical improvement or of immunologic reconstitution was noted in any patient. This latter observation may be related to the lymphotoxicity of suramin, inhibiting immunologic reconstitution.

Other investigators evaluating suramin in patients infected with HIV have similarly reported persistence of HIV antigenemia, significant toxicities, and lack of effect on immune function.[390–392] Further limiting the potential usefulness of suramin as an antiretroviral agent is the drug's lack of penetration into the CNS.

Results of trials of suramin in AIDS conducted to date, combining knowledge gained about its ability to suppress HIV viremia at clinically achievable levels, its pharmacokinetic profile, and its significant toxicity, indicate that the drug as currently administered cannot be recommended as safe, effective single-agent therapy for HIV infection. In the design of future therapeutic trials, suramin may yet have some role when combined with other antiviral or immunoregulatory agents.

Shortly following trials of suramin in patients with AIDS and HIV infection, other studies were begun evaluating the safety and efficacy of the dideoxynucleoside analogue azidothymidine, in patients with AIDS or related diseases caused by HIV.

ZIDOVUDINE

Chemistry and Stability

Zidovudine (3'-azido-3'-deoxythymidine, azidothymidine, BW

A509U, N₃TdR, AZT, Retrovir) is a synthetic analogue of thymidine, in which the 3'-hydroxyl group of thymidine has been replaced with a 3'-azido ($-N_3$) group (Figure 6–7). Substitution of the azido group in the 3' position of the nucleoside blocks the ability of zidovudine to form phosphodiester linkages at this position, thus terminating the synthesis of nucleic acids by susceptible human and animal retroviruses. Based on this mechanism, this drug and other similar nucleoside antiviral agents are often referred to as "chain terminators."

Zidovudine occurs as a white, odorless, crystalline solid.

Mechanism of Action

Zidovudine exerts virustatic effects against selected human and animal retroviruses, including HIV, by inhibiting viral RNA-directed DNA polymerase (reverse transcriptase).

Similar to acyclovir, zidovudine's antiviral activity appears to be dependent on intracellular conversion of the drug to phosphorylated forms. Cellular TK initially converts zidovudine to zidovudine monophosphate. The monophosphate is then phosphorylated to zidovudine diphosphate via cellular thymidylate kinase, and to zidovudine triphosphate via other cellular enzymes.

Zidovudine triphosphate is the active antiretroviral form in vitro. Neither the parent compound nor its mono- or diphosphate forms have in vitro activity against retroviruses.[45] Because phosphorylation of the drug depends on host cell rather than viral enzymes, metabolic conversion of the drug to the active triphosphate form occurs in both virus-infected and uninfected cells.

Thymidine triphosphate is the normal substrate for viral DNA polymerase in the synthesis of viral nucleic acids. Zidovudine triphosphate, the structural analogue of thymidine triphosphate, appears to compete with thymidine triphosphate for viral RNA-directed DNA polymerase and incorporation into viral DNA. Viral DNA polymerase is reported to be 100 times more susceptible to inhibition by zidovudine triphosphate than is host cellular DNA polymerase.[395] Once incorporated into the viral DNA chain, the 3'-azido group of zidovudine prevents formation of 3'- to 5'-phosphodiester linkages, thus prematurely terminating viral DNA synthesis.

In vitro studies indicate that the major in vitro metabolite of zidovudine is 3'-azido-3'-deoxy-5'-O-beta-D-glucopyranuronosyl-thymidine (GAZT). This metabolite appears to be devoid of antiviral activity.

In addition to its antiviral activity, zidovudine is also bactericidal against selected gram-negative bacteria, especially many Enterobacteriaceae. Its antibacterial activity appears to result from incorporation of phosphorylated zidovudine into bacterial DNA chains, leading to premature termination of bacterial DNA synthesis. In contrast to its antiviral activity, the mono-, di-, and triphosphate forms of zidovudine all exhibit antibacterial activity in vitro, with the triphosphate being most active and the monophosphate being least active.

Organisms lacking TK, the enzyme required for phosphorylation of zidovudine (eg, *Pseudomonas aeruginosa* or *Mycobacterium avium*), are resistant to zidovudine. Organisms rich in TK are reported to be highly susceptible to the drug. Other factors, such as cell wall permeability of the organism, may also affect the antibacterial activity of zidovudine.

In vitro cell growth assays indicate that zidovudine displays cytotoxic effects against various cell lines. One human T cell line has been reported to be susceptible to the cytotoxic effect of zidovudine,[396] with a concentration of 5 μg/mL producing 50% inhibition of cell growth (ID_{50}). In a colony-forming unit assay designed to assess human bone marrow toxicity, zidovudine exhibited direct, dose-dependent in vitro inhibition of myeloid and erythroid cell function, and with an ID_{50} estimated to be less than 1.25 μg/mL.[396, 397]

Zidovudine appears to alter host cell nucleoside metabolism, resulting in decreased levels of thymidine phosphate, 2'-deoxycytidine triphosphate, and several other deoxynucleoside triphosphates. This drug-induced depletion of normal host cell pools of thymidine and pyrimidine is thought to contribute to the bone marrow toxicity frequently reported in patients receiving zidovudine.

Spectrum of Activity

Although limited in its antiviral spectrum of activity, zidovudine is active in vitro against many human retroviruses, including human T-lymphotropic virus type I (HTLV-I) and HIV. The drug is also active in vitro against many animal retroviruses, including feline leukemia virus, murine sarcoma virus, Friend leukemia virus, and simian T-lymphotropic virus. The drug is also reported to have some in vitro activity against EBV, with an ID_{50} ranging from 1.4 to 2.7 μg/mL.[396]

Various assay methods are used to test in vitro susceptibility of retroviruses to zidovudine. These include assays for cytopathic effect inhibition, plaque inhibition, reverse transcriptase (RT) activity, or assays for the presence of specific retroviral antigens such as the p24 core antigen. Results and interpretation of these tests tend to vary significantly depending on the laboratory performing the tests, specific methods and cell types used for cultures, and time between in vitro infection of susceptible cells and the addition of zidovudine.

Methods under evaluation to assess in vivo antiviral response to zidovudine in clincial trials include assays that measure serum concentrations of HIV p24 core antigen, reverse transcriptase activity, syncytia formation, or quantitative changes in cytopathic effects of the drug on specific target cell populations such as T4 lymphocytes. These methods, or others yet to be developed, may provide a more accurate means of determining the in vivo response to antiviral drug therapy.

In in vitro studies measuring reverse transcriptase activity in H9 cell lines or in peripheral blood lymphocytes, a zidovudine concentration of 0.13 μg/mL inhibited 90% of detectable HIV replication (ID_{90}) when the drug was added soon after the cells were infected with HIV.[396, 398] A 50% reduction in reverse transcriptase activity (ID_{50}) in H9 cells or peripheral blood lymphocytes was reported to occur at a drug concentration of 0.013 μg/mL.[396, 398] At concentrations of zidovudine that block the in vitro infectivity and cytopathic effect of HIV, the in vitro immune function of normal T cells remains essentially intact.[398]

In another in vitro study, zidovudine inhibited replication of HTLV-III in infected MT-4 cells when added to the cell cultures before HIV infection or up to 20 hours after infection.[399] However, the drug did not display inhibitory effects when added 30 to 50 hours after infection. In chronically infected cells, zidovudine appears to have little or no inhibitory effect on HIV replication; drug concentrations of 8.8 to 13.3 μg/mL are reported to only partially inhibit HIV replication in chronically infected cells.[396] These and other studies in experimental animals support the belief that optimal antiretroviral efficacy of zidovudine is achieved when therapy is initiated without delay following infection.

Recent reports have documented the emergence of HIV isolates resistant to zidovudine during prolonged administration of the drug[399a] The considerable genetic variability among HIV isolates, and mutation of viral reverse transcriptase, are potential mechanisms of resistance to the drug. Further investigation is required to identify regimens that are less likely to induce resistance.

Pharmacokinetics

Zidovudine is rapidly absorbed following oral administration, with peak serum concentrations generally occurring within 0.5 to 1.5 hours.[203, 395, 396] Interpatient variation in the oral absorption of zidovudine is reported, ranging from 63% to 95%, and the drug undergoes first-pass hepatic metabolism.[203, 395, 396] Approximately 65% of an oral dose reaches the systemic circulation as unchanged drug. Food or milk do not appear to significantly alter the GI absorption of zidovudine. One μg/mL of zidovudine is approximately equivalent to 3.74 μmol/L.

In HIV-infected patients receiving oral zidovudine at 250 mg every four hours, steady-state serum concentrations averaging 0.62 μg/mL (range: 0.05–1.46 μg/mL) were reached 1.5 hours after dosing.[396] Steady-state trough levels averaged 0.16 μg/mL (range: 0–0.84 μg/mL).[396] Following a one-hour IV infusion of a single 2.5- or 5.0-mg/kg dose of zidovudine in HIV-infected patients, peak plasma concentrations immediately following the completion of the infusion ranged from 1.07 to 1.6 μg/mL for the 2.5-mg/kg dose, and from 1.6 to 2.7 μg/mL for the 5.0-mg/kg dose.

Zidovudine distributes widely into body fluids and tissues, including the CSF. CSF concentrations approach 50% to 60% of plasma concentrations four hours after dosing. In one patient receiving oral zidovudine at 2.0 mg/kg every eight hours, CSF drug concentration of 0.04 μg/mL was measured 1.8 hours after a dose, and the CSF-plasma ratio of drug concentrations was 0.15.[396, 400]

After IV doses of 2.5 or 5.0 mg/kg every four hours, CSF drug levels two to four hours after dosing were about 0.1 to 0.13 or 0.23 to 0.37 μg/mL, respectively, and the CSF-plasma ratio was 0.2 to 0.5 or 0.64 to 0.73, respectively.[396, 400, 401]

Zidovudine is 34% to 38% bound to plasma proteins. The drug crosses the placenta and is distributed into breast milk in rodents; however, at present it is not known whether this occurs in humans.[45] Because of potential adverse effects in nursing infants, nursing mothers should be advised to stop breast feeding when starting treatment with zidovudine.

The plasma half-life of zidovudine averages one hour (range: 0.8–1.9 hours) after oral administration, and 1.1 hours (range: 0.5–2.9) hours after IV administration.

Zidovudine and its glucuronidated metabolite (GAZT) are both renally excreted via both glomerular filtration and tubular secretion. After oral dosing in HIV-infected patients, 63% to 95% of the dose is excreted within six hours in the urine, 14% to 18% as unchanged parent compound, and 72% to 74% as GAZT. Following IV administration, approximately 18% to 22% is excreted unchanged in the urine, and 57% to 60% is excreted as GAZT within six hours.

Indications and Clinical Studies

Zidovudine is currently indicated for the management of patients with HIV infection who have evidence of impaired immunity before therapy is begun (peripheral blood T4 cell count of 500/mm^3 or less). Although zidovudine may slow or arrest the progression of HIV infection, it is not at this time considered to be a cure for symptomatic HIV infection. The long-term efficacy of the drug remains to be established.

Zidovudine has been clearly shown to prolong the life of individuals infected with HIV. The speed with which this agent was developed and passed through phases I, II, and III clinical trials and on to FDA approval in 1987 and marketing for use in patients with AIDS and severe ARC has been unprecedented in the history of the drug development process for antiviral agents (or any other therapeutic agent) in the United States. Within 3 years of the first trials demonstrating the drug's in vitro activity against HIV-1, it had been administered to over 20,000 individuals worldwide.

Zidovudine was first synthesized in 1964 by Horowitz et al,[402] and its antiretroviral activity against Friend murine leukemia virus was reported in 1974.[403] Since 1974, numerous other animal retrovirus models have been shown to be inhibited by zidovudine, both in vitro and in vivo.

Phase I trials of zidovudine in patients with AIDS or ARC were first reported in 1986 by collaborating investigators at the National Cancer Institute and Duke University.[395] This 6-week clinical trial, evaluating four dosage regimens in 19 patients, indicated that the drug is well-absorbed orally, attains serum levels that inhibit HIV replication, and readily crosses the blood-brain barrier. Treatment was generally well tolerated, with headaches and leukopenia being the most common side effects reported.

This study also showed that zidovudine partially restored immune function in AIDS patients within 6 weeks after initiation of therapy with 15 to 30 mg/kg/d given orally, as manifested by increases in T4 cell counts and restoration of positive cutaneous delayed-type hypersensitivity reactions in six of 16 individuals.[395]

Patients also experienced increases in body weight and energy levels. Because of the encouraging results from this trial, a large randomized, double-blind, placebo-controlled trial was instituted.

Between February 1986 and June 1986, a total of 282 patients with AIDS or advanced ARC were enrolled in a multicenter clinical trial in the United States.[404] Patients in this controlled trial were either AIDS patients who had recovered from their first episode of *Pneumocystis carinii* pneumonia (PCP) within the previous 4 months, or ARC patients with multiple signs and symptoms of HIV infection, including mucocutaneous candidiasis or unexplained weight loss exceeding 10% of prior body weight. One hundred forty-five patients received active zidovudine at a dose of 250 mg orally every four hours around the clock, and 137 patients received placebo.

By September 1986, an apparent difference in survival had emerged, and the study was terminated before all patients had completed the planned 24 weeks of treatment. Data evaluation at that time by an independent data safety monitoring board revealed a significant reduction in mortality, with 19 deaths in the placebo group compared with only one death in the zidovudine group ($P < .001$). All deaths were apparently due to opportunistic infections or to other complications of HIV infection. In addition, a significant difference ($P < .001$) in the occurrence of opportunistic infections (OIs) was noted in patients receiving zidovudine (24 OIs) compared with the placebo group (45 OIs) after 6 weeks of treatment. Patients receiving zidovudine also generally did better than the placebo group in terms of weight gain, Karnofsky scores of functional capability, and modest increases in T4 cell counts. The decreased mortality rates observed in this study in patients treated with zidovudine are also reported during extended follow-up study of the originally enrolled patient population.

Following 36 weeks of observation, 9 (6.2%) of the original 145 patients randomized to receive zidovudine had died, compared with 29 (39.3%) of the original 137 patients who received placebo.

Results of this controlled study and other uncontrolled studies indicate that zidovudine at least temporarily decreases mortality and morbidity in some patients with AIDS or ARC. Zidovudine therapy also appears to partially restore immune function in some patients, reduce both the frequency and severity of opportunistic infections, and result in subjective and objective parameters of clinical improvement. Importantly, evidence now exists that zidovudine therapy may, at least transiently, partially reverse HIV-induced neurologic dysfunction in some patients.[395, 404–407] This has been a very significant finding, given the propensity of HIV to infect and damage cells and tissues of the CNS.[408–412]

Adverse Reactions

The most common adverse effects of zidovudine include hematologic toxicity (anemia, granulocytopenia), nausea, and headache. Because of the complex nature of the underlying disease, and the fact that many adverse effects that occurred in zidovudine-treated patients also occurred in patients receiving placebo, distinguishing adverse effects related to these factors from those directly attributable to the drug may be difficult in many cases.

During the placebo-controlled study, macrocytic anemia occurred frequently in the zidovudine group, requiring transfusion support in 40 patients (compared with 11 patients in the placebo group).[413] Neutropenia also occurred, requiring dosage reduction in about 16% of patients receiving zidovudine.[413] Together, these adverse hematologic toxicities have been significant enough to require blood transfusions and dosage modification or discontinuation of therapy in up to 34% of patients receiving the drug.

Hematologic toxicity appears to be directly related to both dosage and duration of therapy, and has been reported most frequently in patients with low baseline neutrophil counts, T4 cell counts, and hemoglobin levels. Also, patients with low vitamin B_{12} or serum folate concentrations may be at increased risk for development of hematologic toxicity during zidovudine therapy.

Anemia (defined as a hemoglobin level < 7.5 g/dL) has occurred in approximately 30% of patients, and granulocytopenia (defined as a granulocyte count <750/μL) in 47% of patients with pretreatment T4 cell counts of 200 per microliter or less. These same hematologic effects, however, have occurred in only 3% and 10%, respectively, of patients whose pretreatment T4 cell counts exceeded 200 per microliter.[45, 396] Hemoglobin levels decreased more than 25% from baseline in 45% of patients with pretreatment T4 cell counts of less than 200 per microliter, and in only 10% of those with pretreatment T4 cell counts greater than 200 per microliter. Likewise, granulocyte counts decreased more than 50% from baseline in 55% of patients with pretreatment T4 cell counts of 200 per microliter or less, and in 40% of those with pretreatment counts of over 200 per microliter.

Anemia, manifested by falling hemoglobin levels, occurs most commonly after 4 to 6 weeks of therapy, although this effect may occur as early as 2 to 4 weeks after beginning therapy. Granulocytopenia occurs most commonly after 6 to 8 weeks of therapy.[45, 396] Zidovudine-induced anemia appears to result from impaired erythrocyte maturation, and increases in mean corpuscular volume (MCV), which reflect megaloblastic changes, are often an early indication of zidovudine-induced anemia.

Frequent monitoring of complete blood and differential counts is essential in all patients receiving zidovudine. Changes in MCV, although not necessarily predictive of subsequent toxicity, may occur before other drug-induced alterations. Tests of liver and renal function should be closely monitored as well. Measurements of HIV p24 antigenemia, absolute or percentage counts of T4 lymphocyte subsets, reverse transcriptase activity, and syncytia formation may reflect drug efficacy, but are not necessary for monitoring a patient's overall clinical status. Other tests measuring the drug's antiviral activity, such as polymerase chain reaction (PCR) activity, are at present in investigational development stages.

Precise management guidelines for zidovudine toxicity are still being established. For moderate granulocytopenia (750–1300/μL), dose reduction is recommended. For more severe granulocytopenia, temporary suspension of therapy should be considered.

For red cell or hemoglobin toxicity, many clinicians transfuse patients with packed red blood cells every 2 to 3 weeks for severe hemoglobin reductions (6.5–8.0 g/dL). Dosage reduction or discontinuation of therapy is indicated if transfusion requirements exceed 4 units every 3 weeks. In the future, combinations of zidovudine with hematologic growth stimulatory factor(s) such as erythropoietin[414–416] or granulocyte-macrophage colony-stimulating factor (GM-CSF)[417–420] may prove useful in ameliorating the anemia and the neutropenia commonly seen in patients receiving zidovudine.

GM-CSF is one of a family of hematologic growth factors which regulate proliferation and differentiation of hematopoietic stem cells and function of mature cells.[417] This factor has been shown to reduce reverse transcriptase activity in vitro,[418] and to enhance in vitro cytotoxic function of neutrophils from AIDS patients.[419] In trials of recombinant GM-CSF in leukopenic patients with AIDS, the drug was well tolerated and biologically active, with a dose-dependent increase in circulating leukocytes following bolus and continuous IV infusion.[420] Dosing in human phase I trials has ranged from 0.3 to 60 μg/kg/d, administered by subcutaneous or IV routes, over treatment periods extending from ten days to over 1 month.

Pancytopenia with bone marrow hypocellularity, and rare cases of bone marrow failure have also been reported in association with zidovudine therapy.[421]

Headache, the most common adverse symptom observed, has been reported in up to 50% of patients receiving zidovudine. Somnolence, malaise, paresthesias, dizziness, and insomnia have been reported in up to 8% of patients. Nausea and skin rash also occur often. Most patients endure these symptoms because of the potential benefit of the drug, and these effects often subside with time. Severe reactions may diminish when the dose is reduced. Anxiety, confusion, nervousness, depression, and vertigo have been reported in less than 5% of patients receiving zidovudine.

More severe neurologic toxicity, such as seizures, has been reported in patients receiving zidovudine, and can be very problematic, since seizures can occur in patients with AIDS even in the absence of definitive neuroradiologic abnormalities. Although none of the original 282 study patients receiving zidovudine were reported to have seizures (127 of which received the drug for over 1 year), several case reports of seizures temporally related to the administration of zidovudine have since been reported.[422, 423] Reinstitution of zidovudine in a patient following a seizure requires careful risk-benefit analysis by both the physician and the patient.

Myalgia has been reported in 8% of patients receiving zidovudine,[413] as well as a severe polymyositis-like syndrome[424] and necrotizing myopathy.[425]

Pigmentation of finger and toenails has been reported in several patients receiving zidovudine.[426] A dark, bluish discoloration at the base of the fingernails was evident in several black patients 2 to 6 weeks after initiation of therapy.

The clinical symptoms of acute zidovudine overdose in humans are unknown. One case of zidovudine overdosage has been reported in a 26-year-old AIDS patient who intentionally ingested 10 to 20 g of zidovudine, equivalent to 110 to 220 mg/kg body weight, along with unknown amounts of phenobarbital and triazolam.[427] The serum level of zidovudine in this patient, measured by high-performance liquid chromatography (HPLC) eight hours after ingestion, was 23.8 μg/mL. The only clinical abnormalities observed were ataxia and nystagmus, both of which resolved within 48 hours. Six weeks after discharge, the patient had no symptoms and his physical examination was entirely normal. In depressed and debilitated AIDS patients, zidovudine may be a potential means for attempted suicide.[427]

Safety and efficacy data during prolonged administration of zidovudine or during its use in patients with less-advanced HIV infections are limited. Consequently, except for use in carefully controlled trials, it is recommended at present that zidovudine administration be limited to those individuals for whom it has been licensed. Controlled trials are currently under way to accumulate valuable safety and efficacy data in other populations, such as in asymptomatic HIV carriers; patients with early ARC; disease limited to Kaposi's sarcoma, renal, or hepatic insufficiency; newborn and pediatric patients; pregnant women testing positive for HIV; patients with AIDS-related dementia (HIV encephalopathy); and health care professionals exposed to HIV via needle stick injuries or mucosal membrane contact with HIV-contaminated biologic fluids. Until results from such trials become available in the future, it is not possible to predict accurately whether the potential long-range benefits of zidovudine therapy in these other patient populations will outweigh the drug's considerable risks and toxicities. Evaluations of alternative zidovudine regimens utilizing lower dosages, longer dosing intervals, or combinations with other antiviral or immunodulatory agents are also ongoing.

Newer and potentially less toxic alternatives to zidovudine are also in early stages of evaluation. Agents such as other dideoxynucleoside analogues, foscarnet, HPA-23, interferon derivatives, ampligen, and selected other compounds are discussed below.

Drug Interactions

Because of the complexity of medication regimens in many patients with AIDS, the potential for adverse drug interactions is significant. Although limited at present, knowledge concerning specific interactions of zidovudine with other drugs is accumulating.

Because zidovudine undergoes extensive hepatic glucuronidation, concomitant administration of other medications which may competitively inhibit or interfere with this glucuronidation may potentiate hematologic toxicity in patients receiving zidovudine. Drugs which may competitively inhibit glucuronidation and decrease the clearance of zidovudine include acetaminophen, aspirin, benzodiazepines, cimetidine, indomethacin, sulfonamides, or morphine sulfate. These agents, although very commonly administered concomitantly with zidovudine in AIDS patients, should be used with caution and with appropriate close monitoring for potentially increased toxicity. Studies evaluating the clinical significance of these and other drug interactions are ongoing.

Acyclovir has been used concomitantly in some patients receiving zidovudine infected with both HIV and herpesviruses without evidence of increased toxicity. However, profound neurotoxicity, manifested as excessive lethargy and drowsiness, has been reported in at least one patient with AIDS during concomitant therapy with these two drugs.[428] This neurotoxicity became evident within 30 to 60 days after initiation of IV acyclovir therapy, persisted with slight improvement when acyclovir was administered orally, and resolved after discontinuation of acyclovir in this patient. This neurotoxicity recurred, however, on rechallenge with acyclovir. Since concurrent therapy of herpetic infections with acyclovir may be required in patients receiving zidovudine, these patients should be monitored closely during combined therapy. Studies evaluating the safety and pharmacokinetics of concurrent administration of zidovudine and acyclovir in patients with AIDS or HIV-related disease are ongoing. Preliminary data from pilot studies indicate that acyclovir may potentiate the antiretroviral activity of zidovudine in vitro.[429]

Limited information suggests that concurrent use of probenecid with zidovudine may cause competitive inhibition of zidovudine hepatic glucuronidation, and may also decrease renal excretion of zidovudine, resulting in increased serum zidovudine concentrations, prolonged elimination half-life, and increased risk of toxicity.[45]

Drugs that could potentially interfere with hepatic blood flow or renal excretion pathways may decrease zidovudine clearance and increase the risk of toxicity. Likewise, agents that are nephrotoxic, cytotoxic, or myelosuppressive should be used with caution in patients receiving zidovudine, as concurrent use of these agents may also potentially increase the risk of zidovudine toxicity. Drugs in these latter categories include aminoglycosides, amphotericin B, flucytosine, dapsone, pentamidine, vincristine or vinblastine, doxorubicin, cyclophosphamide, and interferons. Likewise, concurrent use of radiation therapy in patients receiving zidovudine may increase the risk of bone marrow suppression. The full clinical significance and potential for adverse drug interactions in patients receiving these or other medications concurrently with zidovudine has not yet been fully evaluated.

Patients with underlying impairment of hepatic or renal function may have reduced metabolism and elimination of zidovudine resulting in increased toxicity. Also, patients with folic acid or vitamin B_{12} deficiencies, or individuals receiving medications which may cause depletion of folic acid or vitamin B_{12} stores (such as anticonvulsants, oral contraceptives, pyrimethamine, or trimethoprim-sulfonamide combinations), may be more susceptible to zidovudine-related hematologic toxicity.

Concomitant use of zidovudine with other nucleoside analogues may result in either synergistic or antagonistic in vitro antiretroviral activity. Phase I pilot studies of concurrent administration of zidovudine with dideoxycytidine in an alternating regimen have been shown to have synergistic antiretroviral activity in vitro and to be well tolerated in a small number of patients evaluated to date.[430]

The antiviral activity of zidovudine with either lymphoblastoid or recombinant alpha interferon derivatives is synergistic in vitro at serum concentrations easily achievable in humans. Clinical studies employing this combination, primarily in AIDS patients with Kaposi's sarcoma, are ongoing.[431, 432, 432a] In addition to the in vitro synergistic antiretroviral activity of this combination, patients receiving concurrent therapy with these two agents must be observed closely for potential additive hematologic toxicities.

In vitro synergistic virustatic effects have also been reported during combined use of zidovudine with ampligen, a mismatched double-stranded RNA polymer.[433]

In vitro trials evaluating the combination of zidovudine with the immunomodulatory polysaccharide lentinan have reported enhanced effect of the combination in the suppression of HIV replication in various human cell lines.[434]

Ribavirin, another nucleoside antiviral agent, may antagonize the in vitro activity of zidovudine against HIV.[435] This antagonism appears to be related to inhibition of zidovudine phosphorylation by ribavirin. Although the full clinical significance of this in vitro antagonism has not been determined, combined use of these two agents should be undertaken cautiously, if at all. Although ribavirin antagonizes the in vitro activity of pyrimidine dideoxynucleoside analogues such as zidovudine, it appears to enhance the in vitro antiretroviral activity of purine dideoxynucleoside analogues such as dideoxyadenosine (ddA).[436]

Dosage and Administration

For adults with symptomatic HIV infection or AIDS, the recommended oral starting dose is 200 mg every four hours (1,200 mg total daily dose) for one month. After one month the dose may be reduced to 100 mg every four hours (600 mg/day). For asymptomatic HIV infection, the recommended dose is 100 mg every four hours while awake (500 mg/day).[396a] Until further studies more precisely establish an optimal dose and frequency of administration, or until an extended-release oral dosage form is developed, patients receiving zidovudine should be advised to take the medication exactly as prescribed.

Hematologic toxicities appear to be related to pretreatment immune status and to dose and duration of therapy. Blood cell counts and indices of anemia (hemoglobin, MCV) should be monitored at 2-week intervals to detect serious granulocytopenia or anemia during therapy. Dose adjustments of zidovudine are necessary in patients who develop significant granulocytopenia or anemia during therapy. Significant anemia (defined as hemoglobin < 7.5 g/dL or > 25% reduction from baseline) or granulocytopenia (defined as a granulocyte count < 750 cells/μL or > 50% reduction from baseline) will generally require interruption of therapy until some evidence of marrow recovery is documented.[396]

If bone marrow recovery occurs following interruption of therapy or reduction of zidovudine dosage, gradual increases in dosage may be undertaken, with appropriate careful monitoring of the hematologic indices and patient tolerance.[396]

Data on the safe and effective dosage and frequency of administration in pediatric patients, geriatric patients, individuals with significant hepatic or renal impairment, during pregnancy, and in other selected populations are being collected in ongoing clinical studies.

Patient Information

Patients receiving zidovudine should be advised not to take more than the prescribed amount of drug, not to discontinue the medication without his or her physician's consultation, and not to share the medication with others. Patients should be informed of the importance of regular clinic or office visits, and having their WBC and RBC indices monitored closely and frequently during therapy, recommended at least every 2 weeks. Likewise, any signs of symptoms consistent with serious anemia or granulocytopenia should be reported promptly to the health care provider.

Regarding potential adverse drug interactions, patients should be counseled not to take any other medications concurrently (prescribed or otherwise) without consulting with the health care provider.

Women receiving zidovudine who become pregnant must be informed of the unknown but potential adverse effects to the fetus. In these cases, the potential risks of continuing therapy must be carefully weighed against the possible beneficial effects of the drug. Likewise, nursing mothers in whom zidovudine is administered should be advised to stop breast feeding while on therapy.

Availability

At present, zidovudine is available in the United States as oral capsules of 100 mg each, as a strawberry-flavored syrup containing 50 mg per teaspoonful, and as a sterile parenteral solution of 10 mg/mL. An extended-release oral solid dosage form is currently under development.

Other Dideoxynucleoside Analogues

Other investigational drugs belonging to the class of 2',3'-dideoxynucleoside analogues have shown potent in vitro ability to inhibit HIV replication, and some of these agents are currently being evaluated in clinical trials in humans. As noted above for zidovudine, these dideoxynucleosides must be phosphorylated to an active 5'-triphosphate moiety by intracellular kinases. Also like zidovudine, these other analogues act by inhibiting HIV reverse transcriptase.

2',3'-Dideoxycytidine (ddC, DDC, ddCyt), a pyrimidine analogue developed at the NCI, is more potent than zidovudine on a molar basis. Structural formulas of ddC and its normal 2'-deoxynucleoside counterpart (2'-deoxycytidine) are depicted in Figure 6–8.

At a concentration of 0.5 to 5.0 μmol, ddC essentially completely inhibits in vitro HIV replication, even under conditions of substantial viral excess. Furthermore, this inhibitory effect remains for prolonged periods.[437, 438, 438a]

Substantial antiretroviral activity can be seen at low viral doses, even at concentrations of 10 nM. Additional tests have shown that ddC has other properties desirable in an agent useful for controlling HIV infection: good oral absorption, straightforward renal clearance pathways of elimination, and relative resistance to degradation by cytidine deaminase, a major catabolic enzyme for cytidine analogues.[439, 440] The drug also produces comparatively few toxic effects in laboratory animals.[441] Phase I and II studies of ddC in humans are currently being conducted.

Preliminary clinical trials in patients with AIDS and ARC have shown improvement in both clinical and immunologic parameters. Although little or no myelosuppression has been observed with this drug to date (in sharp contrast to zidovudine), a severe dose-related peripheral neurotoxicity, manifested primarily as painful burning sensations in the feet, has been observed. This particular dose-related toxicity is reportedly reduced when ddC is given in combined, alternating regimens with zidovudine.[430] Phase I and II trials evaluating the toxicity and efficacy of this combination are ongoing. Other adverse effects reported in phase I tests include rash, fever, mouth sores, and reversible neutropenia and thrombocytopenia.

Dideoxycytidine (currently investigational) is available as a parenteral formulation in vials containing 100 mg of lyophilized powder, as 2-mg oral tablets, and as an oral solution containing 50 or 200 mg/mL. In phase I trials at the NCI, adult patients receiving doses ranging from 0.03 to 0.25 mg/kg every eight hours attained peak plasma levels of 0.1 to 1.2 μmol after IV dosing. The drug appears to penetrate the CNS, with CSF levels ranging from 9% to 37% of concurrent plasma levels. The half-life of the drug is approximately 1.2 hours. Oral bioavailability is 70% to 80%. In order to enhance CNS penetration, more lipophilic analogues of ddC have been synthesized and are currently undergoing in vitro evaluation.[442]

Dideoxyadenosine (ddA), another purine nucleoside analogue, appears to have a more favorable therapeutic index as compared to ddC.[443, 444] Dideoxyadenosine inhibits HIV in vitro at a concentration of 10 μmol. The ddA concentration required for maximal anti-HIV activity is reported to be 20-fold higher than the ddC concentration required; however, ddA becomes cytotoxic to ATH8 cells only at levels 40-fold higher than cytotoxic levels of ddC. Dideoxyadenosine is likewise less toxic to bone marrow progenitor cells than either zidovudine or ddC. Preliminary data from phase I testing of ddA at the NCI in patients receiving 0.38 mg/kg IV twice daily for 2 weeks, then once daily for 4 to 8 weeks, indicate a slight increase in T4 cell counts in some patients. Minor side effects of headache and lightheadedness have been noted at these doses.

Pharmacokinetic evaluation has revealed a relatively short half-life of 30 to 40 minutes, oral bioavailability of 40% to 55%, and penetration into the CSF. Other studies have determined that the active, intracellular triphosphorylated form of ddA (ddA-5'-triphosphate or ddATP) has a much longer intracellular half-life of 12 to 24 hours in human T cell lines. This extended intracellular half-life may permit less frequent dosing of this compound to maintain adequate antiretroviral activity. Of note, only a metabolite of ddA, dideoxyinosine (ddI), and not ddA, has been detectable in serum and CSF of patients receiving ddA. The drug appears to be rapidly and completely metabolized by adenosine deaminase in vivo to this other analogue, ddI.

In experimental animals, oral administration of ddA has resulted in renal toxicity, possibly related to accumulation of adenine when ddA is catabolized in the gastric medium of the stomach. Based on results from animal studies, oral administration of ddA in humans may likewise lead to acute nephritis or acute renal failure. It is suggested that oral administration of ddI might not produce the renal toxicity associated with oral administration of ddA, since ddI is metabolized to hypoxanthine in the GI tract.

Dideoxyadenosine is currently available as vials containing 250 mg of ddA as sterile, lyophilized powder, for investigational use only. Because of the rapid in vivo conversion of ddA to ddI, as well as the potential for accumulation of nephrotoxic metabolites, interest in ddA has somewhat waned at the present and shifted to ddI.

Dideoxyinosine (ddI, ddIno) acts as a precursor to dideoxyadenosine triphosphate (ddATP), and is believed to exert antiretroviral activity in this phosphorylated form. Dideoxyinosine inhibits HIV in vitro at concentrations of 10 μmol.[445, 446]

At noted above, dideoxyadenosine (ddA) serves as a prodrug of ddI, and is rapidly deaminated in mammalian cell cultures and in vivo by serum adenosine deaminase to ddI.[443] Although ddI is about 10 times less potent than zidovudine, it is also significantly less toxic in vitro than either zidovudine or ddC. Preliminary observations suggest that ddI may have a short serum half-life of 30 to 90 minutes, but an extended intracellular half-life approaching 24 hours.

The drug is rapidly absorbed orally, with bioavailability calculated at 35% to 45%. Like ddA, ddI is acid-labile and rapidly broken down in the stomach to adenine, a potentially nephrotoxic metabolite. Consequently, in ongoing phase I and II studies, ddI is given on an empty stomach, two to five minutes after a dose of an oral antacid. In limited phase I trials, a CSF-blood ratio of 0.34 has been observed.

At doses of 0.2 to 0.8 mg/kg IV or 0.4 to 1.6 mg/kg orally given every eight to 12 hours, no bone marrow toxicity has been observed. Increased heart rate and abnormal liver function tests have been reported in animal toxicology studies.

Dideoxyinosine is currently available as vials containing 250 mg of sterile, lyophilized powder, for investigational use only. Because of poor stability in acidic media, ddI parenteral solution, when given orally, should be mixed in a nonacidic vehicle such as apple juice. The developer of this agent (Bristol-Myers Co) is developing a phosphate-buffered formulation, as well as an enteric-coated oral solid dosage form.

It is anticipated that a host of other dideoxynucleoside analogues will be developed for potential activity against HIV. Several such analogues currently in early stages of protocol development include AzdU, D4C, and D4T.

CS-87 (3'-azido-2',3'-dideoxyuridine; AzdU) is a synthetic analogue of zidovudine. In vitro studies of CS-87 have demonstrated

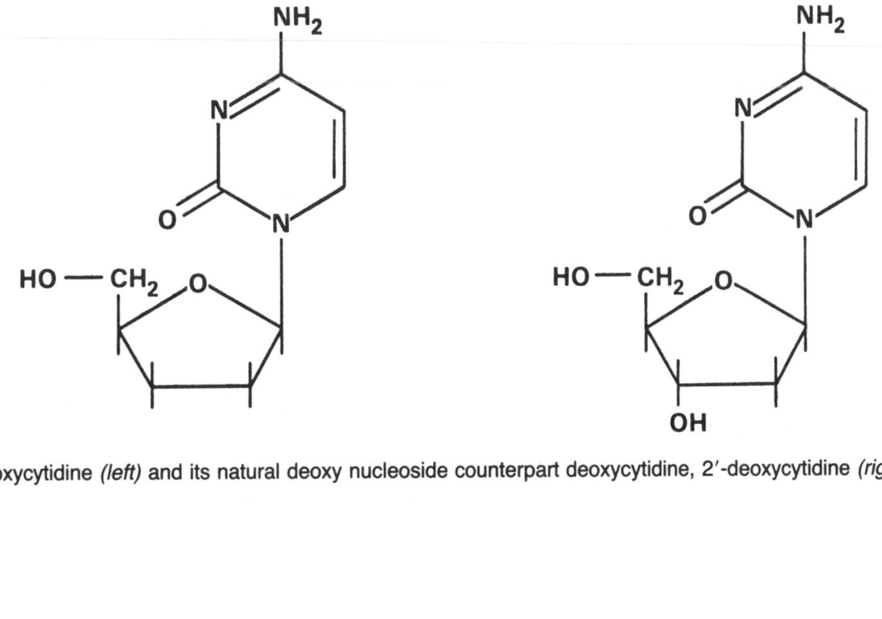

Figure 6–8. Dideoxycytidine *(left)* and its natural deoxy nucleoside counterpart deoxycytidine, 2'-deoxycytidine *(right)*.

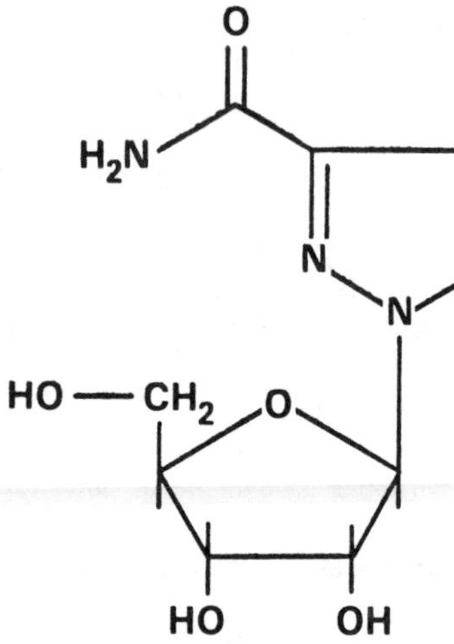

Figure 6–9. Structure of ribavirin.

significant anti-HIV activity, and less bone marrow toxicity than either zidovudine or its 5-ethyl analogue CS-85.[447, 448] D4C (2',3'-dideoxycytidin-2'-ene) is the 2',3'-unsaturated derivative of dideoxycytidine (ddC). This compound has been demonstrated to inhibit antigen expression and cytopathogenicity of HIV in vitro.[449–451] D4T (2',3'-dihydro-2',3'-dideoxythymidine) is the unsaturated analogue of zidovudine, and like other nucleoside derivatives inhibits HIV replication by inducing premature viral DNA chain termination. This drug was shown to be a potent and selective in vitro inhibitor of HIV, as measured by reverse transcriptase levels, at a concentration of 0.1 μmol.[452] In vitro tests in normal human hematopoietic progenitor cells have shown D4T to be less toxic than zidovudine or ddC, with 100-μmol concentrations of D4T required for 50% cell growth inhibition, as compared to 1.0 μmol for zidovudine and 10 μmol for dideoxycytidine.[453]

RIBAVIRIN

Ribavirin (1-β-D-ribofuranosyl-1,2,4-trizole-3-carboxamide, Virazole) is a synthetic triazole nucleoside. Its structure, indicated in Figure 6–9, is similar to that of guanosine and inosine.[454] The compound was synthesized in 1972 and shown to have promise as an antiviral agent against a large variety of DNA and RNA viruses.

The metabolism of the compound has been studied in tissue culture and in erythrocytes. Ribavirin is converted to its 5' phosphate derivatives by host cell enzymes; the major metabolite is ribavirin-5'-triphosphate.[455, 456] Erythrocytes concentrate ribavirin-5'-triphosphate because these cells are not able to dephosphorylate the ribavirin. The accumualtion of ribavirin trisphosphate in RBCs is believed to play a role in the anemia that is observed following high-dose therapy with ribavirin.[457] In vitro sensitivity of various viruses is largely dependent on the cell line that is used to assay for antiviral activity. Some tissue culture cell types appear to be relatively refractory, requiring ten- to 100-fold greater concentrations of ribavirin for antiviral activity than more sensitive cell lines. The basis for cell-dependent sensitivity has not been determined since the uptake for ribavirin by both sensitive and insensitive cells is equivalent.

Mechanisms of Action

Ribavirin is phosphorylated in cells and then rapidly converted to the 5'-triphosphate. Lesser amounts of the diphosphate and monophosphate are formed (20% and 5%, respectively, relative to the triphosphate form). Red blood cells, particularly human blood cells, have little phosphatase activity, and the relatively long time required for complete elimination of ribavirin from the body during pharmacokinetic studies is believed to be related to the retention of the drug in tissues (particularly RBCs) in the phosphorylated form.[455–457]

Inosine monophosphate dehydrogenase, an enzyme near the terminal steps in the pathway of synthesis of guanosine monophosphate (GMP), is regulated in vivo by the level of GMP; this enzyme is inhibited by ribavirin 5'-monophosphate and the ribavirin monophosphate has been found to be about a thousandfold more potent than GMP in regulating this enzyme in vitro. Other nucleotide levels are altered by the presence of ribavirin in tissue culture growth media. Deoxythmidine triphosphate (dTTP) increases by as much as 250% to 700% in tissue culture cells treated with ribavirin and deoxyguanosine triphosphate (dGTP) decreases by as much as 70%. Alterations in concentrations of these nucleotides is believed to have profound effects on intracellular metabolism, particularly in regard to synthesis of RNA and DNA. Neither ribavirin monophosphate nor ribavirin triphosphate are inhibitors of TK. However, TK is controlled by dTTP levels and increases several fold in the presence of ribavirin.

Ribavirin is not believed to be incorporated into the primary structure of DNA or RNA during cellular synthesis of nucleic acids. Ribavirin triphosphate inhibits the GTP-dependent capping of the 5' end of viral mRNA. Using influenza A virus-infected (MDCK) tissue culture cells, Wray et al have shown that ribavirin reduced viral RNA synthesis by 50%, although cellular RNA synthesis was not significantly altered.[458] Virtually all eukaryotic cells and many viruses process their mRNA after synthesis by elaborating a guanosine methylated on position 7 and attached to mRNA through its 5' hydroxyl group (see Chapter 2). These reactions involve the transfer of GMP from GTP to the 5' end of existing mRNA allowing methylation of the 7 position of the terminal guanosine utilizing 7-adenosylmethionine; this is followed by methylation of the penultimate nucleotide. This cap imparts stability to the mRNA to prevent degradation by RNAases. Without this cap mRNA cannot be translated into proteins. Ribavirin has a powerful inhibitory effect via ribavirin triphosphate on the guanylation reactions and results in inhibiting viral mRNA in its ability to synthesize viral proteins.[459, 460] Thus the most important mechanism of action may be inhibition of the viral-specific processes of mRNA translation.

Ribavirin triphosphate has been shown to inhibit influenza viral RNA polymerase complex. Viral mRNA primers are generated by cleavage of the capped mRNA at a purine residue 10 to 13 nucleotides from the cap. The viral endonuclease, PB2, requires the presence of the 5' terminal methylated cap structure.[458] Formation of this methylated cap structure is inhibited by ribavirin triphosphate as described above.

It has been postulated that ribavirin triphosphate inhibits several steps in viral replication and this phenomenon may explain the failure to detect viral isolates that are resistant to ribavirin. Many of the enzyme systems that utilize ribavirin as they do guanosine have been shown to be reversed by the addition of excess guanosine. However, this is not its only mechanism of action since ribavirin retains some antiviral activity even in the presence of added guanosine. Alterations to either the ribose or to the base portion of the ribavirin molecule results in loss of antiviral activity. Additions to the hydroxyl groups (eg, acetylation or phosphorylation) result in retained antiviral activity. The triacetate form has been shown to be effective in the treatment of dengue or Colorado tick fever in experimental animals. It is possible that the hydrophobic nature of triacetate alters the pharmacokinetics of ribavirin or allows it to cross the blood-brain barrier.[455, 456]

Pharmacokinetics

The pharmacology of oral ribavirin has been studied in small numbers of human subjects.[461] After ingestion of a single dose of 2.8 to 3.1 mg/kg of drug, peak levels of 1.0 to 2.0 μg/mL are reached in 1.0 to 1.5 hours. Plasma half-life appears to be in the range of 24 hours, with a later decay phase of several days. The drug and/or its metabolites concentrate in human RBCs, reaching a plateau at about four days, then decaying slowly. In monkeys, ribavirin has been found in high concentrations in skeletal muscle, RBCs, and liver, and in moderate concentrations in kidney, CNS tissue, and lung.[462]

Recently, newer techniques to quantitate ribavirin in serum has led to renewed interest in pharmacokinetic studies. Studies in rats do not correlate with human studies since the metabolism of this compound in rats is different than in humans or nonhuman primates. Luskin et al administered ribavirin orally or IV to 17 asymptomatic HIV-infected persons.[463] After IV administration drug elimination followed a three-compartment model; after oral administration the initial distribution phase was masked by the absorption process and elimination after oral administration followed a two-compartment model. The mean plasma half-life for the early phase of the drug elimination was 1.0 or 1.8 hours (oral vs IV dosing, respectively) and 27 or 36 hours (oral vs IV dosing, respectively), for the late phase. The volume of distribution was large, 650 L. Mean plasma concentrations, which occurred 1.5 hours after oral drug administration, were 5.2 and 12.6 μmol, respectively, following doses of 600 or 2400 mg.[463]

The drug and its metabolites are eliminated in the urine, but only 40% of the drug is eliminated within the first 72 hours after administration. Ribavirin may be partially eliminated in the stool, but the data regarding this are conflicting.[461]

Ribavirin has been administered by the small-particle aerosol route to human subjects, but data concerning measured plasma or tissue levels following this mode of administration have not been published.[464–467] In the study of Knight et al, an indirect measure (influenza A virus neutralization) of ribavirin levels in nasal secretions after aerosol administration could not demonstrate greater than 50 μg/mL of the drug in these secretions.[464] McClung et al and Hall et al were unable to demonstrate significant ribavirin activity in nasal wash specimens after ribavirin aerosol.[465, 467] Hruska et al have estimated that ribavirin does reach the upper respiratory passages and lungs in a cotton rat model, but exact concentrations were not determined.[468]

Ribavirin is not thought to be particularly toxic in human subjects with the exception of anemia. A number of studies have demonstrated that transient rises in serum bilirubin occur in 10% to 28% of treatment courses,[469–472] and occasional rises in serum transaminase levels also have been noted.[470, 472] Oral ribavirin otherwise is well tolerated. The principal toxicity of ribavirin in animals is on the hematopoietic system, manifested by mild reductions in erythrocyte counts after prolonged therapy.[473] Intravenous administration of high concentrations of the drug result in anemia, which is reversible by withdrawing the drug. This is believed to be due to the concentrations of the drug occurring within RBCs as described above.

Animal data suggest that ribavirin may be teratogenic, and its use in pregnant women is contraindicated. Health care workers and visitors to infants undergoing therapy with aerosolized ribavirin are exposed to the drug via inspired air depending on the mode of therapy of the patient (oxygen tent, mean concentration 161 μg/m³; ventilator, <6 μg/m³; figures refer to personal exposure levels of caregiver). In spite of exposure, detectable levels of ribavirin were only rarely found in the RBCs of exposed persons and never in the serum or urine.[474] It has been recommended that pregnant hospital workers and visitors be informed regarding exposure to aerosol ribavirin and pregnant employees offered alternative work assignments.[474, 475]

In Vitro Antiviral Activity

In vitro data support the claims regarding the broad spectrum of activity of ribavirin, as it has been shown to possess activity against both DNA and RNA viruses in infected cells. It has been found to have activity against various adenoviruses, human and animal herpesviruses, human CMV, vaccinia virus, influenza A and B viruses, parainfluenza viruses 1, 2, and 3, measles, mumps, respiratory syncytial virus, rhinovirus, and many others.[476, 477]

Inhibitory concentrations of ribavirin for adenoviruses have varied from 10 to 200 μg/mL, normally in the range of 10 to 32 μg/mL.[476] Activity against human herpesviruses appears to depend a great deal on the cell lines used for testing and the time at which ribavirin is added to the assay system. The greatest activity is from two hours preinfection to eight hours postinfection. Minimum inhibitory concentrations during this time period range from 1 to 10 μg/mL.[478, 479] The activity against herpesviruses is reversed by addition of guanosine or xanthosine.[480] Vaccinia virus has been shown to be inhibited by ribavirin.[481]

Ribavirin is capable of in vitro inhibition of many RNA viruses. Influenza A virus can be inhibited by concentrations of ribavirin as low as 0.05 μg/mL, depending on the cell system used.[476, 482] Combining ribavirin with amantadine or rimantadine results in enhanced antiviral activity agains influenza A virus, compared to the single drug.[483–485] Influenza B viruses, which are insensitive to amantadine or rimantadine, are reliably inhibited by ribavirin.[486, 487]

The paramyxoviruses are susceptible in vitro to ribavirin. Measles virus can be inhibited by low concentrations of ribavirin.[476, 488, 489] Parainfluenza viruses, types 1, 2, and 3, are inhibited by this agent in tissue culture also.[490]

Human reoviruses, 1, 2, and 3, and simian, porcine, and bovine rotaviruses are inhibited by ribavirin.[488, 489] Coronaviruses may be susceptible to ribavirin, but few data are available to confirm this. Sindbis, Chinkungunya, Semliki Forest, and St Louis encephalitis viruses are reported to be inhibited by concentrations of 1.2 to 32 μg/mL.[476] The enteroviruses and rhinoviruses are not easily inhibited by ribavirin in vitro.

Little is known about development of ribavirin resistance among viruses isolated from patients treated with ribavirin. However, it appears that resistance to ribavirin occurs less frequently than with idoxuridine (IUDR). Limited experiments have demonstrated that herpes simplex virus type 1, parainfluenza virus type 3, influenza viruses, and respiratory syncytial virus (RSV) do not develop resistance in vitro to ribavirin.[487–495] Hall et al found that RSV did not develop resistance in patients treated with aerosolized ribavirin.[466, 467]

Clinical Use

Ribavirin has made a major contribution to the therapy of children infected with RSV.[467, 496–502] The compound is effective in the treatment of RSV lower respiratory tract infection when admnistered as an aerosol. It can be given to infants in an enclosed environment such as a croup tent or to infants who are undergoing mechanical ventilation.[503, 504] Caution should be used when administering the drug to children being mechanically ventilated because of precipitation of the compound in the endotracheal tube.[505] Procedures for caring for children on respirators and who are receiving ribavirin aerosol have been published.[504]

Ribavirin has been studied in clinical trials in a number of viral infections, either naturally acquired or artificially induced in volunteers. The most extensive study has been in influenza virus infections. The oral preparation was tested in a 200-mg 3-times-daily dose as prophylaxis against experimentally induced infection with two different strains of influenza A (H3N2) viruses and was found to have no prophylactic efficacy.[472] A similar study, but with experimentally induced influenza B/Georgia/26/74 infection, showed some reduction in severity of illness in ribavirin-treated compared to placebo-treated volunteers, but no difference in the frequency of infection. Magnussen et al evaluated the therapeutic efficacy of oral ribavirin, 250 mg 4 times a day, begun six hours after the administration of influenza A virus (A/Victoria/3/75 H3N2) and found that moderate to severe symptoms and fever were ameliorated.[471] No effect was seen in mild illness. In addition, early administration of ribavirin resulted in a significant reduction in influenza A virus shedding.

Therapeutic efficacy also has been evaluated in natural infection with influenza A virus. Salido-Rengell et al showed in a double-blind, placebo-controlled study that ribavirin, 100 mg 3 times a day for five days, significantly ameliorated clinical illness at 24 hours after beginning therapy and reduced the frequency of A/England/42/72 (H3N2) virus isolation.[506] However, another study showed that 100 mg/daily did not affect clinical illness or influenza A/Brazil/11/78 (H1N1) virus shedding.[507] One study examining the efficacy of oral ribavirin in therapy of influenza B virus infection has been published.[487]

Aerosolized ribavirin has been tested for therapeutic efficacy in a number of respiratory virus infections. Knight et al showed that aerosolized ribavirin had minimal effect on the febrile course of naturally acquired influenza A (A/England/333/80 H1N1) infection, but a definite effect on other systemic symptoms and virus shedding.[464] The aerosol mode of therapy might be a promising

one for patients who are hospitalized with serious influenza A infection or primary influenza pneumonia. A double-blind study in naturally acquired influenza B virus infection showed that aerosolized ribavirin had a definite beneficial effect, resulting in more rapid resolution of the clinical illness and of virus shedding than placebo.[465]

Well-controlled studies have shown that ribavirin is moderately efficacious in the therapy of acute measles in children.[508, 509] In patients with Lassa fever, ribavirin reduced mortality following ten days of IV therapy, from 76% to 32%.[510] Oral ribavirin is also believed to be effective in viremic patients with Lassa fever if initiated within six days of onset of fever. Ribavirin had no effect on chronic hepatitis B surface antigenemia in chimpanzees.[511]

Combination with Other Agents

The course of antiviral research has led to the study of ribavirin in combination with other antiviral agents to try and improve efficacy for the therapy of a variety of infections. Poly (ICLC) and ribavirin was shown to be effective in the treatment of mice given Rift Valley fever virus. Poly (ICLC) is a potent interferon inducer, and in combination ribavirin shows promise for efficacy against a wide variety of hemorrhagic fever viruses.[512] Ribavirin is effective in treating RSV in small animals when combined with topically administered neutralizing antibody or with immunoglobulin that is administered parenterally.[513, 514] Clinical studies are planned to evaluate combination IV γ-globulin with aerosolized ribavirin in infants infected with RSV.

Ribavirin is unproven as an agent for treatment of HIV infection. Ribavirin may inhibit phosphorylation of zidovudine, possibly accounting for the antagonism observed when cultured lymphocytes infected with HIV are treated with zidovudine and ribavirin together.[435]

Results of trials of ribavirin in HIV-infected individuals, at oral doses ranging from 600 to 800 mg per day, have been equivocal, generally reporting little or no improvement in clinical or immunologic parameters. In one small phase I study of oral ribavirin in patients with AIDS and ARC, Crumpacker and colleagues demonstrated transient clinical improvement associated with enhanced lymphocyte proliferation and suppression of HIV replication.[515] Patients in this study received loading doses of 1200 mg twice daily for three days, followed by 300 mg twice daily for 8 weeks.

If ribavirin inhibits HIV by a mechanism other than reverse transcriptase inhibition, it may be potentially useful when combined with other drugs, even if not efficacious when used alone. Results of well-controlled studies (currently under way) will be required to determine the full usefulness of ribavirin in the management of HIV infection.

AMANTADINE AND RIMANTADINE

Amantadine hydrochloride (1-aminoadamantane hydrochloride) and rimantadine hydrochloride (α-methyl-1-adamantanemethylamine hydrochloride) (Figures 6–10, 6–11) are derived from the tricyclic cage molecule, adamantane (Greek, "diamond"). They were first synthesized and developed by EI Du Pont in the early 1960s.[516–518] Their action is highly selective. Effective against influenza A infections of animals and birds as well as humans, they confer no pro-

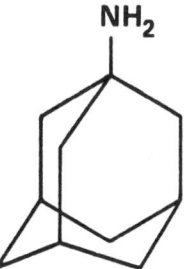

Figure 6–10. Structure of amantadine.

tection against influenza B infections. Inhibitory activity against other viruses in vitro generally occurs only at much higher concentrations of the drugs which appear to act in a nonvirus-specific manner, and there is no evidence of corresponding in vivo efficacy.[519] Amantadine, marketed as Symmetrel, was initially licensed in the United States in 1966 for use against H2N2 influenza viruses. Subsequently it has been approved for use against the current epidemic influenza A strains, H1N1 and H3N2, but has not been widely used.[520] The development of rimantadine was initially overshadowed by that of amantadine and it has not yet been marketed extensively other than in the USSR, where it has been available for prophylactic and therapeutic use for a number of years.[521] The activities of a wide variety of derivatives of adamantane and compounds with analogous ring structures have been investigated.[522–525] Most exhibit much lower anti-influenza A activity. Those with specific activities similar to amantadine and rimantadine, for example, ICI130685[526] and 1-methyl spiro (adamantane2'-3'-pyrolidine) maleate[524, 527, 528] have not been fully developed, principally in view of the cross-resistance exhibited by drug-resistant viruses.[529] This cross-resistance stresses the similarities in the actions of the different compounds. The two structural features of principal importance are the large hydrocarbon ring and the amino group. Addition of large side chains generally substantially reduces activity.[522, 524]

The mechanism of antiviral action of amantadine and rimantadine has been extensively studied. Early work indicated that the drugs are not virucidal and do not interfere with binding of virus to the cell receptor or penetration into the cell.[530] The principle action is directed against uncoating of the virus particle, prior to genome transcription.[530–538] The virus enters via the endocytic pathway of the cell and is uncoated by a process triggered by the acidity of the endosome, which involves fusion between the virus and endosomal membranes and release of the ribonucleoprotein core.[539, 540] It has been suggested that it is not the membrane fusion activity of the hemagglutinin which is inhibited but rather the subsequent destabilization of the inner matrix structure.[533–535] An alternative but more selective action against certain permissive infections in cell culture blocks virus maturation by causing a structural alteration in the virus hemagglutinin during its transport to the plasma membrane of the infected cell.[537, 538] Whether this action is of significance in vivo remains to be determined.

The molecular basis of drug action has been investigated by analyzing the genetic determinants of resistance to both amantadine and rimantadine. Phenotypic and genetic comparisons of reassortant viruses formed between a drug-sensitive and drug-resistant virus showed the M gene to be the principle determinant of drug

susceptibility.[538, 541, 542] Nucleotide sequence analyses of this RNA of drug-resistant mutants located the single amino acid changes responsible for conferring the drug-resistant phenotype. To date all such amino acid substitutions in mutants selected both in vivo and in vitro from a variety of human, avian, and equine virus strains, by growth in the presence of either amantadine or rimantadine, occur in one of four amino acids.[538, 543–546] These are all located within a sequence of eight amino acids within the transmembrane domain of the M2 protein, identifying this as the target of drug action. The precise function of this minor virus membrane protein[547] has yet to be elucidated. It has recently been suggested[548] that it forms a transmembrane ion channel which, on the one hand, may be involved in the transfer of protons across the virus membrane, resulting in a destabilization of the virus structure. On the other hand, by modifying the acidity of vesicles of the transport pathway within the infected cell, it may have a role in maintaining the structural integrity of the native hemagglutinin. The proposed channel-blocking action of amantadine is analogous to its anticholinergic action whereby it blocks neuromuscular transmission by interacting with the ion channel of the nicotinic acetylcholine receptor.[549]

Human Pharmacology and Toxicity

Recent comparisons in human volunteers have shown that despite their structural similarities, amantadine and rimantadine differ significantly in their pharmacokinetic parameters.[550, 551] Both compounds exhibit high bioavailability and are rapidly absorbed, within eight hours of oral administration.[550–552] In particular, the lower peak plasma drug concentrations attained from equivalent orally administered doses of rimantadine may account for the generally observed lower toxicity of this compound.[550, 553, 554] There appears to be little difference in the side reactions associated with equivalent plasma concentration of the two drugs.[550] Similar salivary and nasal mucus concentrations are attained, although relative to plasma concentrations these are some two- to threefold higher with rimantadine.[555] This may in part account for the apparent higher therapeutic index of rimantadine. Amantadine has a shorter plasma half-life and is excreted largely unchanged,[552] whereas a high proportion of rimantadine is metabolized.

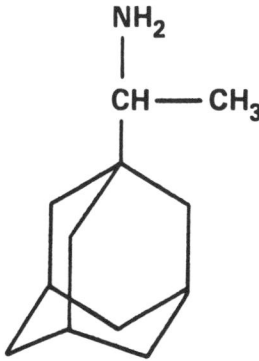

Figure 6–11. Structure of rimantadine.

Amantadine

In view of its anti-Parkinson[556, 557] as well as antiviral activity, the pharmacology of amantadine has been extensively studied. It is available either as 100-mg tablets or as a syrup (10 mg/mL). After oral administration amantadine is almost completely absorbed and peak plasma concentrations are attained within two to four hours.[552] Doses of 100, 200, or 300 mg per day produce peak levels within the ranges of 0.2 to 0.4 μg/mL, 0.5 to 0.7 μg/mL, or 0.7 to 1.0 μg/mL, respectively.[550, 555, 558–562] Steady-state plasma levels are achieved within three days with an average steady-state trough concentration of approximately 0.3 μg/mL in healthy adults given the recommended dose of 200 mg daily.[558, 562] It also appears in saliva, nasal secretions, breast milk, and other body tissues, including the lungs.[563] Concentrations in saliva and nasal mucus are similar to those in blood.[552, 555, 564] A concentration in the lungs some 14-fold that in serum has been reported for an infant with immunodeficiency.[565] In mice, concentrations in lungs were also found to be 15- to 60-fold greater than in blood.[552] Amantadine crosses the blood-brain barrier and attains a CSF concentration about 60% of that found in plasma.[566]

Approximately 90% of an orally administered dose is excreted unchanged in the urine with half-lives of elimination ranging from nine to 37 hours and an average value of 15 to 20 hours in healthy young adults.[552, 553, 558, 560] In patients with abnormal renal function, plasma levels of amantadine remain elevated for prolonged periods of time, and elimination half-lives are prolonged directly in proportion to the degree of renal insufficiency.[560, 567–569] In elderly subjects, peak concentrations are some 50% higher than in young adults and the elimination half-life is doubled.[570] To achieve the desired drug concentration, a lower dose of 1.4 mg/kg/d has been recommended for healthy elderly men.[570] An inverse correlation exists between creatinine clearance and plasma elimination. In patients with creatinine clearances of 10 mL per minute or less, elimination half-lives range from 72 to 812 hours. Hemodialysis removes only small amounts of amantadine from the plasma, while peritoneal dialysis removes substantially larger amounts.[569] Amantadine should be given to hemodialysis patients with caution, and, ideally, plasma levels should be monitored closely.[568] Patients receiving 3-times-weekly dialysis should receive a loading dose of 200 mg and then 200 mg alternating with 100 mg every seven days in order to avoid toxicity.[560, 569] Suggested doses for other patients with various degrees of renal insufficiency have been published.[560]

Amantadine has been administered via the aerosol route in small-particle form in concentrations of 1.0, 1.5, or 2.5 g/100 mL.[571–573] After aerosol treatment, amantadine is excreted in the urine in amounts directly proportional to the inspired concentration, indicating systemic absorption via this route, although significant plasma accumulation of amantadine does not appear to occur.[571] Amantadine levels in nasal wash specimens range from 20 to 280 μg/mL immediately after amantadine aerosol and from 1.7 to 108 μg/mL after 60 minutes.[572, 573] Allowing for dilution factors, amantadine levels in nasal secretions range from 20 to 91 μg/mL of nasal secretions and exceed those in plasma by greater than 4000-fold.[572]

The toxicity of amantadine has been well described. Side effects occur in 2% to 33% of recipients of amantadine during pharmacologic, prophylactic, or therapeutic studies. The most frequently described side effects are GI and include anorexia and nausea. In addition, minor CNS side effects can occur with routine dosing in patients with normal renal function.[574] Adult volunteers given 200 mg per day for 2 to 4 weeks noted significantly more dizziness, nervousness, or insomnia than did volunteers given placebo, and a number of volunteers discontinued amantadine because of marked side effects.[575] However, partial resolution of side effects can occur if the drug is continued.[575] Other studies also have shown that minor CNS side effects occur more frequently with amantadine than with placebo,[553, 554, 576, 577] although some studies have not demonstrated any significant difference.[578] Nevertheless, side effects, especially those of the CNS, tend to be dose-related and proportional to the plasma level.[550, 560] A dose of 300 mg per day or greater, or a plasma level of over 0.6 μg/mL, is associated with an increased incidence of side effects.[550] By way of comparison, side effects due to amantadine occur less frequently than do those related to aspirin therapy.[579] Also, administration of amantadine to patients with Parkinson's disease for periods in excess of 4 years has not been associated with serious effects due to the drug.[556, 557]

In patients with abnormal renal function amantadine can easily reach toxic levels as previously discussed. Symptoms noted in these patients include hallucinations, confusion, depression, dizziness, instability, and obtundation associated with plasma levels of greater than 1.0 to 2.0 μg/mL.[569, 580, 581] Physostigmine has been used successfully to reverse toxic manifestations of amantadine therapy.[582]

Toxicity of aerosolized amantadine appears to be minimal. However, with concentrations of 1.0, 1.5, and 2.5 g/mL, self-limited nasal irritation, rhinorrhea, and dysgeusia were noted.[571, 572] Small decreases in maximal expiratory flow rates and minor variations in small airway reactivity were also associated with aerosolized amantadine.[571, 573] Subjects who had sneezing, coughing, or wheezing after aerosolized amantadine usually suffered from preexisting abnormal pulmonary function or pre-amantadine small airway reactivity.[571] Aerosolized amantadine must be used with caution in patients with preexisting airway hyperreactivity.

Rimantadine

No differences in pharmacokinetic parameters were observed between oral administration of rimantadine in tablet form or as a syrup. Rimantadine is well absorbed and within three to six hours attains peak plasma concentrations of approximately 0.1 μg/mL or 0.25 μg/mL following single doses of 100 mg or 200 mg, approximately half that achieved with equivalent doses of amantadine.[550, 555, 583–585] Higher oral doses of 400 mg yield peak levels of approximately 0.6 μg/mL. No differences were noted between young and elderly healthy adults.[555] A single dose of 6.6 mg/kg given to children produced peak levels ranging from 0.4 to 1.0 μg/mL.[586] Steady-state levels of approximately 0.3 g/mL result from twice-daily administration of 100 mg to healthy adults.[585] Much higher levels of between 0.6 and 2.6 μg/mL (mean 1.2 μg/mL) have been noted, however, in nursing home residents.[587] Maximum mucus concentrations, similar to those for equivalent doses of amantadine, are twice the plasma level, suggesting the drug may be concentrated in nasal secretion.[555]

The plasma half-life is similar in healthy children and adults, and ranges from 27 to 36 hours, twice that of amantadine.[555] Less than 10% of rimantadine is excreted unchanged in urine, the majority being converted to hydroxylated or glucuronidated forms prior to excretion. The toxicity and antiviral activity of these metabolites have yet to be determined. Hemodialysis increases the half-life to around 44 hours.

A large number of studies have examined the toxicity of rimantadine, specifically or in concert with prophylactic or therapeutic activity. The CNS[583, 584, 588] and GI[553, 581] adverse reactions are qualitatively similar to those experienced with amantadine. At doses of 200 mg per day, these are generally no more frequent or only slightly enhanced relative to placebo.[553, 576, 578, 589, 590] No significant effects on performance of psychomotor functions were reported.[578] Experience in the USSR with large numbers of patients supports the relatively low toxicity of rimantadine.[521] The reduced toxicity relative to amantadine appears largely due to the lower plasma concentration of rimantadine resulting from equivalent doses of the two compounds.[550] The elevated plasma levels in elderly nursing home residents was associated with the development of nausea and anxiety in selected patients and may warrant the use of lower drug doses.[587] Aerosolized administration of rimantadine also did not cause measurable toxicity and was associated only with an unpleasant taste and smell and nasal irritation.[591]

In Vitro Antiviral Activity

The actions of amantadine and rimantadine are very similar. The activities of a variety of derivatives and compounds with analogous ring structures, for example, cycloctylamine and ICI130685, have indicated that the key structural features are the large hydrophobic ring and amine group.[522, 537, 543] The greater antiviral activity of rimantadine versus amantadine[545, 592–594] correlates with its greater lipid solubility as indicated by the tenfold higher octanol-water partition coefficient[545] and reflects the membrane-associated target (see above). The antiviral spectrum is highly specific to influenza A viruses and the majority of subtypes and recent human isolates have been shown to be sensitive.[519, 543, 545, 592–597] The 50% inhibitory concentrations in cell or organ culture range from 0.01 to 1.0 μg/mL for amantadine and 0.001 to 0.2 μg/mL for rimantadine, depending on virus strain and assay system used, and are within the range of clinically achievable drug levels. The inhibition of other enveloped viruses,[598–602] including, for example, influenza B, rhabdoviruses, alphaviruses, and arenaviruses at concentrations greater than 10 μg/mL is most likely due to a nonspecific action similar to that exhibited by other acidotropic amines, for example, methylamine and ammonium chloride.[603–605]

In the case of influenza viruses, the presence of the drug at these high concentrations causes an elevation in the pH of endosomes and indirectly blocks the activation of the virus hemagglutinin responsible for fusing the virus and endosomal membranes and initiating virus infection.[539, 540, 605] The pH of activation lies between 5 and 6, depending on the virus strain, and is higher in mutants resistant to this action of amantadine.[606] In contrast, mutants resistant to the specific anti-influenza A action of much lower concentrations of amantadine show no alteration in this regard. Furthermore, these two sets of mutants do not exhibit cross-resistance. The genetic bases for the two actions have also been shown to be different, showing clearly that the two inhibitory activities are quite distinct.[543, 606]

Two stages in influenza A virus replication are susceptible to specific inhibition by amantadine at less than 1 μg/mL: early during infection per se, involving an as yet undefined aspect of virus uncoating;[530, 538] and late in the cycle, preventing virus maturation,[537, 538] as discussed earlier. In tissue culture most influenza A viruses are susceptible to the early action whereas only certain H7 and H5 avian strains, which undergo permissive infections, succumb to the late action. The latter is the result of a structural conversion of the hemagglutinin from its native to the low pH form during its transport to the cell surface, which consequently prevents release of virus particles.[538] Several features of the virus-host cell interaction are important in determining susceptibility to this action. Analyses of genetic reassortants identified the HA gene as well as the M gene as important in determining drug sensitivity,[537, 538, 607] and it appears likely that the inhibitory action occurs only in cells effecting the intracellular proteolytic cleavage of the hemagglutinin. The importance of cellular factors is shown by the differential sensitivity of certain H7 viruses in MDCK cells and chick embryo fibroblasts.[548] Susceptibility to this particular action has yet to be tested in nasal or tracheal epithelial cultures.

Clinical Activity

Amantadine and rimantadine have been shown to be effective in the protection of several species, including mice, monkeys, horses, and domestic birds as well as humans, against infection by influenza A viruses.[608–612] Consistent with the in vitro data, the prophylactic efficacy is highly selective and does not provide any protection against influenza B infections.[618, 619]

Since being approved for clinical use in 1966, the efficacy of amantadine in the prevention and treatment of influenza A infections in human populations has been extensively studied. Double-blind, placebo-controlled trials have included both natural and experimental infections with all three human influenza A subtypes, H1N1, H2N2, and H3N2.[576, 577, 620–629] Renewed interest in rimantadine, which is expected soon to be licensed for oral use in the United States, has made it the subject of more recent investigations.[576, 588, 630–633] Comparative studies have indicated similar prophylactic and therapeutic efficacies for the same orally administered doses of the two drugs.[554, 576, 593, 631] On balance, however, rimantadine treatment is associated with a lower incidence of adverse reactions and is currently perceived as the preferred treatment.[520, 576, 632]

Table 6–5 lists the results of a number of studies of prophylaxis in adults and children using either amantadine or rimantadine in a variety of clinical settings. Reduction in illness by a daily dose of 200 mg of either drug was generally observed to be greater than 70%, comparable to that obtained with inactivated influenza vaccine. The somewhat lower efficacy rates based simply on laboratory-documented infection presumably reflects subclinical infections which could confer immunity against reinfection. In the placebo-controlled prophylactic study conducted by Dolin et al[576] during an outbreak of influenza A/Bangkok/79 (H3N2) and A/Brazil/78 (H1N1), 450, 18- to 45-year-old volunteers were given either placebo, amantadine, or rimantadine, 100 mg twice daily for 6 weeks. There were no significant differences in the rates of illness or virus infection in the two drug-treated groups, and the protective efficacy of amantadine (74%–91%) was similar to that

Table 6–5
Prophylaxis of Influenza A Virus Infections with Amantadine or Rimantadine

Reference	Study Group	Virus (yr)	Drug (mg/day)	Duration (wk)	Attack R (%)		Protection R (%)	
					Placebo	Drug	Illness	Virus Infection
Open populations								
Petterson et al[577]	Conscripts	H1N1(78)	Am(200)	3	83	60	—	39
Oker-Blom et al[622]	Students	H3N2(69)	Am(200)	5	29	14	68	52
Smorodintsev et al[624]	Adults (18–30 yr)	H3N2(69)	Am(100)	4	8	4	49	54
Monto et al[621]	Students	H1N1(78)	Am(200)	7	37	17	71	39
	Adults (18–45 yr)	H1N1(81)	Am(200)	6	24	6	91	74
Dolin et al[576]		H3N2(81)	Rim(200)	6	24	8	85	66
Clover et al[630]	Children	H1N1(84)	Rim(5 mg/kg)	5	32	3	100	91
Sears & Clements[626]	Adults (18–40 yr)	H1N1(85)	Am(100)	2	41	9	78	—
Institutions								
Nafia et al[623]	Hospital	H3N2(69)	Am(200)	3	19	2	94	100
Payler & Purdham[635]	School	H1N1(83)	Am(100)	2	11	1	90	—
	Hospital		Am(200)				100	80
O'Donoghue et al[627]	Nursing home (85 yr)		Rim(200		27	10	63	55
Bull WHO[638]								
Galbraith et al[629]	Family	H2N2(68)	Am(200)	10 d	14	4	100	63

Am = amantadine; Rim = rimantadine.

reported in most other field trials. The principle difference noted was that significantly fewer side effects were seen in the rimantadine recipients compared to those receiving amantadine. Other comparative studies have been less conclusive due to trials being initiated too late in the influenza outbreak.[590, 631] Reports of extensive studies in the USSR have claimed that rimantadine is more effective,[521] but the significance of some of the uncontrolled experiments is in question.

Amantadine prophylaxis has been shown to be effective in a variety of situations in preventing nosocomial infections in hospitals and institutions,[627, 628, 634] in boarding schools,[635, 636] and among family contacts.[637–639] Of particular interest was the effectiveness of amantadine in protecting against the first wave of the new Hong Kong/68 H3N2 virus pandemic.[622–624] In one family study, however, amantadine prophylaxis provided no protection[637] and it was suggested that this reflected the seronegative status of the individuals. The additive protective effect of influenza vaccine and amantadine has been noted in several reports.[521, 638–640] In view of the side effects associated with administration of 200-mg doses, lower doses have been tested. Claims of comparable efficacy of doses of 100 and 200 mg have been made and recent trials in boys' boarding schools[627] and in adults challenged with H1N1 virus[626] support the efficacy, 90% and 78% respectively, of the lower dose with no significant side effects.

Recent recommendations from the Immunization Practices Advisory Committee of the Centers for Disease Control indicate that the daily doses of amantadine for persons 65 years or older should be reduced from 200 mg to 100 mg to minimize adverse reactions.[641–643] Support for such a regimen was provided by an uncontrolled study in a nursing home indicating prevention of spread of influenza H3N2, with low incidence of toxicity.[639–641] Rimantadine has similarly been shown in a double-blind randomized trial to have an efficacy rate of 63% in preventing influenza among nursing home residents with a mean age of 83 years.[633, 638, 644] Most studies have used doses of rimantadine of 200 mg per day. Ex-

perience in the USSR has suggested that as little as 50 mg per day is effective in prophylaxis.[521] A recent study among children receiving rimantadine (5 mg/kg/d) indicated complete protection against illness caused by H1N1 virus in the absence of significant side effects as compared to placebo.[630]

The therapeutic efficacy of these compounds has been more controversial. Double-blind, placebo-controlled studies have repeatedly shown a definite but limited beneficial effect against infections with the various strains of influenza A viruses, provided therapy is started within 24 to 48 hours after the onset of symptoms. These studies have been[554, 589, 593, 645–655] conducted almost exclusively in mild self-limited disease in previously healthy young adults and children. Treatment is usually for a period of five to ten days with oral daily doses within the range of 100 to 200 mg. Two comparative studies have indicated similar efficacies for amantadine and rimantadine.[554, 593] During an outbreak of A/Virginia/68 infection, 150 mg administered twice daily resulted in a more rapid clinical improvement and defervescence compared to placebo.[593] No difference in the therapeutic efficacies of amantadine and rimanatadine was observed. A similar trial during an outbreak of influenza A/USSR/77 (H1N1) among college students indicated a corresponding improvement in symptoms and frequency of virus shedding with recipients of 100 mg twice daily for five days.[554] In this case the amantadine-treated patients showed a more rapid improvement than the rimanatadine-treated patients over the first 24 hours. In both groups students receiving drug returned to classes sooner than those receiving placebo. A lower frequency of virus shedding 72 hours after therapy was also noted. These data also support the findings of studies in the USSR that contacts of recipients of rimantadine are less exposed to virus infection.[521] Extensive studies in the USSR, many placebo-controlled, support the therapeutic efficacy of daily doses of 150 mg rimantadine for three to five days in alleviating clinical symptoms, shortening the duration of illness, and reducing the frequency of postinfluenza complications.

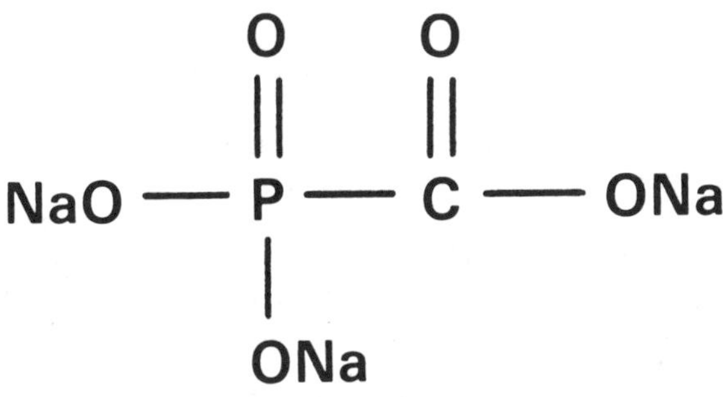

$$NaO - \overset{\overset{O}{\|}}{\underset{\underset{ONa}{|}}{P}} - \overset{\overset{O}{\|}}{C} - ONa$$

Figure 6–12. Structure of foscarnet.

In view of the long half-life and low initial plasma concentrations of rimantadine, one study tested the use of a higher initial dose of 400 to 500 mg within the first 24 hours of treating adults. The study showed rapid antiviral effects and clinical improvement.[653] A comparison of 100- and 200-mg daily doses of amantadine for five days showed that the lower dose was equally efficacious in improving symptoms following a naturally acquired H1N1 influenza infection. The effect was more marked than in a group receiving aspirin, 650 mg every four hours, although the aspirin therapy resulted in more rapid defervescence.[579] In addition, aspirin was less well tolerated than amantadine. Two recently reported studies[654, 655] compared rimantadine treatment with that of acetaminophen in children over a four- to seven-day period. Rimantadine exhibited a significantly greater reduction in severity of illness over the first three days of an infection with H3N2 influenza,[654] whereas in a milder H1N1 infection, rimantadine offered no significant therapeutic benefit over acetaminophen.[655] Rimantadine significantly diminished the frequency of virus shedding during the first two days of both studies; however, the subsequent increased virus shedding in one rimantadine-treated group by days 6 and 7 was associated with the recovery of drug-resistant virus.[654]

Aerosolized amantadine and rimantadine have also been shown to be effective in the treatment of natural and experimental influenza infections. A double-blind study showed that a small-particle aerosol of amantadine (1 g/100 mL) administered for 20 minutes 3 times a day to college students with acute influenza A (H1N1 or H3N2) infections caused significantly more rapid resolutions of clinical symptoms compared to the placebo-treated individuals.[572] In another study of three individuals, much higher doses of amantadine, 1.5 g/100 mL, administered as an aerosol for two- or four-hour courses ten to 11 hours daily for three days, promoted ''rapid'' recovery from influenza-like illness.[573] A comparison of aerosolized and oral rimantadine treatment of an experimentally induced influenza A H1N1 infection[591] indicated similar significant therapeutic activities in reducing illness sores and fever, but again showed no significant effect on virus shedding. A role for this type of therapy may exist in the treatment of hospitalized patients with severe influenza A illness.

Drug Resistance

Although exhibiting differences in degree of susceptibility in vitro, most virus strains tested, including recent human isolates, are sensitive to the actions of amantadine and rimantadine. Drug-resistant variants occur in tissue culture–grown virus preparations

with a frequency of 10^{-3} to 10^{-4}[541, 656] and have been isolated from animals and domestic birds[617] treated with drug. Although there are reports[592, 657] of drug-resistant human isolates, there is no clear evidence linking their selection with the use of amantadine or rimantadine. Recent clinical studies[654] have shown, however, that rimantadine-resistant viruses are readily selected in children receiving rimantadine therapy. Twenty-seven percent of children treated with rimantadine shed rimantadine-resistant virus. Analysis of the phenotypes of genetic reassortants and characterization of the mutations has shown that the basis of drug resistance is the same in viruses isolated in vitro or in vivo from chickens and humans as discussed earlier.[543, 546] The ability of drug-resistant viruses to infect their host and cause disease does not appear to be compromised in either instance.[545, 546] Thus, in a recent family study, the rimantadine-resistant virus generated during therapy of the index case appears to be responsible for the spread of virus to two other family members.[545] The extent to which the development of drug resistance will limit the usefulness of amantadine and rimantadine and whether the continual selection of antigenic variants will mitigate the occurrence of drug-resistant epidemic strains has yet to be evaluated.

OTHER ANTIVIRAL AGENTS

Foscarnet

Foscarnet sodium (trisodium phosphonoformate, PFA, Foscavir) is a nonnucleoside pyrophosphate derivative (Figure 6–12) which reversibly and competitively inhibits viral DNA polymerase of CMV and HSV. The drug is active in vitro against all human herpesviruses including CMV at concentrations of 100 to 300 µmol (approximately equivalent to 30–100 µg/mL). It is less potent in vitro than acyclovir against HSV. Unlike acyclovir and its analogues, foscarnet does not require cellular TK for activation.[662, 663]

Foscarnet also inhibits HIV and other RNA viruses by noncompetitive inhibition of reverse transcriptase,[664–668] with inhibition of viral replication occurring at foscarnet concentrations of less than 12.3 µg/mL. The drug appears to be virustatic, with viral replication recurring after discontinuation of the drug.[669]

Used topically in animal models, foscarnet has been shown to be more effective than topical acyclovir in the treatment of experimental mucocutaneous herpesvirus infection.[670, 671] However, in a double-blind, placebo-controlled study of foscarnet in recurrent genital herpes simplex infection, foscarnet topical cream failed to show beneficial effects.[672]

Preliminary clinical experience with foscarnet in treating CMV infections in immunosuppressed hosts (especially bone marrow and renal transplant recipients) is encouraging.[673–676] In Ringden's study in 13 bone marrow and 33 renal transplant recipients, foscarnet was used to treat 56 episodes of CMV infection.[675] The drug was administered as a 9-mg/kg IV bolus infusion, followed by a continuous infusion of 0.078 mg/kg/min. The duration of therapy ranged from four to 46 days. Of 25 evaluable patients, 12 died, CMV was eradicated in eight, and symptomatic improvement was noted in half of the patients. One patient with renal dysfunction experienced tremor and hallucinations, probably secondary to drug accumulation. After doses of 50 to 128 mg/kg of IV foscarnet, average steady-state serum concentrations ranged from 82 to 127 µg/mL. Maximum concentrations ranged from 44 to 447 µg/mL.[675]

Preliminary results with foscarnet in the treatment of CMV infections in patients with AIDS or ARC appear promising as well, although further trials of this drug administered over a longer period in AIDS and ARC patients are necessary to determine its ultimate efficacy in controlling CMV infection in these patients.[677-681]

To date, data on the adverse effects of foscarnet are limited. Toxicology studies in animals receiving chronic dosing over 1 to 6 months have shown histologic changes in bone, dental, and renal tissues. In ten AIDS patients receiving the drug for CMV retinitis, both increases and decreases in absolute neutrophil counts, mild increases in serum creatinine, mild proteinuria, and decreases in hemoglobin were observed.[682] Fluctuations in serum magnesium and calcium may also be observed. Asymptomatic hyperphosphatemia, premature ventricular contractions, and foscarnet-associated bacteremia also occurred.[682] Given the chemical nature of this compound, acute renal failure should be considered a potential side effect. Renal function and hydration status must be observed closely, and any other potentially nephrotoxic drugs, if given concurrently, must be given with caution. The drug has no myelosuppressive effects, and may be given safely concurrently with zidovudine.

Thrombophlebitis has been reported when the 24-mg/mL stock solution is infused via peripheral veins. Tiredness, instability, headache, tremors, and seizures have also been reported in patients receiving foscarnet. The drug is contraindicated in pregnant women, as safety data in this population are not available.

Foscarnet therapy is generally given in two phases: an induction phase of 14 to 21 days of either a continuous IV infusion or infusions of 60 mg/kg every eight hours followed by a maintenance phase of single daily IV infusions.[683] The maintenance regimen, usually given to prevent relapse or progression of infection, is administered as single one- to three-hour infusions of 60 to 90 mg/kg, five to seven days per week. Since the drug is excreted renally, dosage modification is required in patients with renal impairment.

Foscarnet sodium is supplied in 500-mL bottles containing 24 mg/mL in sterile isotonic solution. Drug at this concentration requires administration through a central venous line only, and long-term maintenance regimens generally require placement of indwelling catheters.

Interferons

Interferons are host cell–derived polypeptide molecules produced by cells in response to viral infection and other stimuli. These molecules exhibit potent antiviral, antiproliferative, and immunomodulatory effects.[684-686] Naturally derived interferons, or those produced by recombinant technology, show promise in the treatment of a host of viral and neoplastic diseases.[686-689]

In 1986, the FDA approved two genetically engineered human recombinant interferon products for the treatment of hairy cell leukemia: interferon alfa-2a (Roferon-A, Roche Laboratories), and interferon alfa-2b (Intron-A, Schering-Plough Corp). In late 1988, these same products received marketing approval for the management of AIDS-related Kaposi's sarcoma. In that same year, it was conclusively shown that interferon is effective in the prevention of natural ''colds'' and rhinovirus infections in a family contact setting.[690] The efficacy of interferons in the management of infections caused by rhino-, papilloma-, cytomegalo-, varicella-zoster, herpes simplex, and vaccinia viruses is well documented.

Clinical trials to determine the optimal dosage, frequency, and duration of administration in various clinical settings are ongoing. Likewise, studies combining interferon derivatives with antiviral agents are under way to assess the safety and efficacy of such combinations in AIDS and HIV infection.[432a] This approach, combining an immunomodulatory agent such as interferon with an effective antiretroviral agent, is considered by many to be the most rational treatment for HIV infection.

Interferons act by reversibly binding to a specific cell surface receptor, after which cytoplasmic enzymes (endonuclease, protein kinase, and $2',5'$-oligoadenylate synthetase) are activated. These enzymes, in turn, inhibit viral transcription, translation, assembly, and release from the infected cell.[691] Cells that do not possess interferon receptors on their cell surface are resistant to the drug. Interferons also have immunomodulating functions, enhancing T cell–mediated cytotoxicity, natural killer (NK) cell activity, macrophage functions, and antibody production.[692, 693]

Interferons are not virucidal. They prevent viral replication by interfering with protein and/or nucleic acid synthesis. These agents are not virus-specific, and can be used effectively before the infecting virus is identified by serology or culture.

Interferons have been reported effective in treatment and prophylaxis against CMV infections in immunosuppressed patients,[694] and in treating disseminated varicella-zoster disease in leukemic children and cancer patients.[695]

The antiviral use of interferons has been explored in the treatment of rhinovirus, urogenital warts, HSV, CMV, varicella-zoster, hepatitis B, papilloma, and HIV infections.[691, 696]

Alpha interferon given subcutaneously can suppress recurrent genital HSV infections, decreasing the number and shortening the duration of recurrences.[697] The drug must be given continually, however, as it has no effect on the clinical course of recurrent herpes once the prodrome has begun.[697]

Excellent results have been observed using alpha interferon in the treatment of chronic papillomavirus infections such as respiratory papillomatosis, condylomata acuminata, and common warts. Before the availability of interferon for the treatment of juvenile laryngeal papillomatosis, no effective therapy had been available. Interferon therapy can now lead to complete response and cure rates of 30% to 75%, alleviating the risks of laser surgery in many children, and reducing the length of hospitalizations as well.[698]

Chronic hepatitis B virus infection, a common cause of liver cirrhosis, and a possible causative agent of hepatocellular carcinoma, is responsive to treatment with interferon.[699-701]

Alpha interferon has been studied as a therapeutic agent for patients with AIDS and HIV infection since early in the epidemic.[702] Alpha interferon is capable of reducing in vitro HIV replication by at least 90% at levels clinically achievable in serum following parenteral administration.[703, 704] Mechanistically, class I interferons (alpha and beta) appear to act at the stage of viral assembly, as shown in the murine leukemia virus model.[705] During trials with interferon in AIDS-related Kaposi's sarcoma, objective responses have been reported in from 20% to 70% of patients.[702, 706-708] To date, controlled studies of alpha interferon in AIDS appear to indicate that patients with higher immune reserve, that is, patients in the earliest stages of HIV infection with only limited degrees of immune dysfunction, may benefit most from therapeutic regimens that include alpha interferon.

Investigational studies combining alpha interferon with antiretroviral agents such as zidovudine, to assess the safety and efficacy in patients with various stages of HIV infection, are ongoing.[432a]

Interferons can be administered IV, intramuscularly (IM), subcutaneously, and intranasally. Patients receiving IM or subcutaneous interferon can be taught self-administration techniques to receive their interferon doses on an outpatient basis, greatly simplifying patient management. Single maximal tolerated doses delivered IV for recombinant alpha, beta, and gamma interferons have been reported as 200, 150, and 20 million U/m^2 body surface area, respectively.[709-711]

Pharmacokinetic studies show that interferon is rapidly cleared from the circulation, and that high serum levels are difficult to maintain.[711, 712] Half-lives of two to three hours after IV administration, three to eight hours after IM administration, and 20 minutes after intranasal administration are reported. Short-lasting peak serum levels after IV infusions of 15 million units range from 500 to 600 U/mL. Subcutaneous and IM administration generally result in more sustained levels of approximately 200 U/mL, persisting for eight to 12 hours.

Interferon poorly penetrates the CNS. The metabolic pathways of interferon are unknown; catabolism appears to take place in the kidneys and liver, although little is excreted in the urine. The drug is catabolized in tubular cell lysosomes, following reabsorption from the glomerular filtrate.[713]

Interferon may be immunogenic in humans. Neutralizing antibodies have been detected following extended therapy; their presence has not been shown to cause adverse effects, but concomitant decreases in interferon serum levels appear to suggest a potential for interference with the biologic effects of interferon.[714]

Side effects of interferon occur with variable frequency and are related to the type of interferon, and the route, dose, and frequency of administration.[711, 714-716] Between 20% and 70% of patients experience fever, chills, anorexia, malaise, fatigue, leukopenia, and transient increases in liver enzyme tests. Extreme fatigue, leukopenia, and elevations in transaminases have been reported as dose-limiting toxicities. In addition, interferon-related congestive heart failure and cardiomyopathy have also been reported.[717] Most side effects abate rapidly on interruption or cessation of therapy. Side effects are generally better tolerated when doses and administration schedules are adjusted to each individual patient's tolerance. Most patients receiving alpha or beta interferon on a daily basis develop tachyphylaxis, manifested by a decrease in intensity of acute toxic side effects, generally occurring within seven to ten days.[714]

For long-term treatment of various malignant or viral diseases, doses of up to 15 million units of recombinant alpha, or natural alpha or beta interferon, given IM or subcutaneously 3 times weekly, is generally well tolerated. As mentioned above, such treatments may be given on an outpatient basis or self-administered by the patient at home.

The clinical applications for interferon in the future will no doubt continue to expand, given the current high degree of interest in this and other biologic response modifiers, and the availability, ease, and safety of administration of these agents.

Acknowledgement

Dr. Minor gratefully acknowledges the competent and unselfish support of Mrs. Della Copp in the preparation of this manuscript, and of Stephen E. Straus, M.D., Chief of the Medical Virology Section, NIAID, for his critical review.

References

1. Davis DJ: Measurements of the prevalence of viral infections. *J Infect Dis* 1976; 133:A3–A5.
2. Belshe RB, Van Voris LP, Mufson MA: Impact of viral respiratory diseases on infants and young children in a rural and urban area of southern West Virgina. *Am J Epidemiol* 1980; 117:467–474.
3. Woodson B, Joklik WK: The inhibition of vaccinia virus multiplication by isatin-β-thiosemicarbazone. *Proc Natl Acad Sci USA* 1965; 54:946–953.
4. Kucers A, Bennett NM: Methisazone, in Kucers A, Bennett NM (eds): *The Use of Antibiotics*. London, Heinemann, 1979, p 965.
5. Bauer DJ, St. Vincent L, Kempe CH, et al: Prophylactic treatment of smallpox contacts with N-methylisatin-β-thiosemicarbazone (compound 33T57, marboran). *Lancet* 1963; 2:494–496.
6. Heiner GG, Fatima N, Russell PK, et al: Field trials of methisazone as a prophylactic agent against smallpox. *Am J Epidemiol* 1971; 94:435–449.
7. Becker TM, Blount JH, Guinan ME: Genital herpes infections in private practice in the United States, 1966 to 1981. *JAMA* 1985; 253:1601–1603.
8. Centers for Disease Control: Genital herpes infection—United States, 1966–1984. *MMWR* 1986; 35:402–404.
9. Wheeler CE: The herpes simplex problem. *J Am Acad Dermatol* 1988; 18:163–168.
10. Herrmann EC Jr, Herrmann JA: A working hypothesis—virus resistance development as an indicator of specific antiviral activity. *Ann NY Acad Sci* 1977; 284:632–637.
11. Crumpacker CS, Schnipper LE, Marlowe SI, et al: Resistance to antiviral drugs of herpes simplex virus isolated from a patient treated with acyclovir. *N Engl J Med* 1982; 306:343–344.
12. Burns WH, Saral R, Santos GW, et al: Isolation and characterization of resistant herpes simplex after acyclovir therapy. *Lancet* 1982; 1:421–423.
13. Sibrack CD, Gutman LT, Wilfert CM, et al: Pathogenicity of acyclovir-resistant herpes simplex virus type 1 from an immunodeficient child. *J Infect Dis* 1982; 146:673–682.
14. Wade JC, McLaren C, Myers JD: Frequency and significance of acyclovir-resistant herpes simplex virus isolated from marrow transplant patients receiving multiple courses of treatment with acyclovir. *J Infect Dis* 1983; 148:1077–1082.
15. Parris DS, Harrington JE: Herpes simplex virus variants resistant to high concentrations of acyclovir exist in clinical isolates. *Antimicrob Agents Chemother* 1982; 22:71–77.
16. Coleman VR, Tsu E, Jawetz E: "Treatment resistance" to idoxuridine in herpetic keratitis. *Proc Soc Exp Biol Med* 1968; 129:761–765.
17. Hirano A, Yumura K, Kurimura T, et al: Analysis of herpes simplex virus isolated from patients with recurrent herpes keratitis exhibiting "treatment-resistance" to 5-iodo-2'-deoxyuridine. *Acta Virol* 1979; 23:226–230.
18. Stevens DA, Jordan GW, Waddell TF, et al: Adverse effect of cytosine arabinoside on disseminated zoster in a controlled trial. *N Engl J Med* 1973; 289:873–878.
19. Spruance SL, Schnipper LE, Overall JC Jr, et al: Treatment of herpes simplex labialis with topical acyclovir in polyethylene glycol. *J Infect Dis* 1982; 146:85–90.
20. Merigan TC, Rand KH, Pollard RB, et al: Human leukocyte interferon for the treatment of herpes zoster in patients with cancer. *N Engl J Med* 1978; 298:981–987.

21. Shindo M, Okuno T, Matsumoto M, et al: Serum 2′,5′-oligoadenylate synthetase activity during interferon treatment of chronic hepatitis B. *Hepatology* 1988; 8:366–370.

22. Billiau A: The mode of action of interferons in viral infections and their possible role in the control of hepatitis B. *J Hepatol* 1986; 3(suppl 2):S171–S179.

23. Davis GL, Hoofnagle JH: Interferon in viral hepatitis: role in pathogenesis and treatment. *Hepatology* 1986; 6:1038–1041.

24. Steele RW, Myers MG, Vincent MM, et al: Transfer factor for the prevention of varicella-zoster infection in childhood leukemia. *N Engl J Med* 1980; 303:355–359.

25. Munoz A, Garcia RA, Perez-Aranda A: Potentiation by levamisole, methisoprinol, and adenine of adenosine of the inhibitory activity of human interferon against encephalomyocarditis virus. *Antimicrob Agents Chemother* 1986; 30:192–195.

26. Fattovich G, Brollo L, Pontisso P, et al: Levamisole therapy in chronic type B hepatitis. Results of a double-blind randomized trial. *Gastroenterology* 1986; 91:692–696.

27. Werner GH: Immunopotentiating substances with antiviral activity. *Pharmacol Ther* 1979; 6:235–273.

28. Muller WEG: Mechanisms of action and pharmacology: Chemical agents, in Galasso GJ, Merigan TC, Buchanan RA (eds): *Antiviral Agents and Viral Diseases of Man.* New York, Raven Press, 1979, pp 77–149.

29. Gordon P, Ronsen B, Brown ER: Anti-herpes action of isoprinosine. *Antimicrob Agents Chemother* 1974; 5:153–160.

30. Ginsburg T, Glasky AJ: Inosiplex: An immunomodulation model for the treatment of viral disease. *Ann NY Acad Sci* 1977; 284:128–138.

31. Waldman RH, Ganguly R: Therapeutic efficacy of inosiplex (isoprinosine) in rhinovirus infection. *Ann NY Acad Sci* 1977; 384:153–160.

32. Corey L, Chiang WT, Reeves WE, et al: Effect of isoprinosine on the cellular immune response in initial genital herpes virus infection. *Clin Res* 1979; 27:41A.

33. Bradshaw LJ, Sumner HL: In vitro studies on cell-mediated immunity in patients treated with inosiplex for herpes virus infection. *Ann NY Acad Sci* 1977; 284:190–196.

34. Lerner AM, Bailey EJ: Synergy of 9-β-D-arabinofuranosyladenine and human interferon against herpes simplex virus, type 1. *J Infect Dia* 1974; 130:549–552.

35. Stanwick TL, Schinazi RF, Campbell DE, et al: Combined antiviral effect of interferon and acyclovir on herpes simplex virus types 1 and 2. *Antimicrob Agents Chemother* 1981; 19:672–674.

36. Schinazi RF, Peters J, Williams, CC, et al: Effect of combinations of acyclovir with vidarabine or its 5′-monophosphate on herpes simplex viruses in cell culture and in mice. *Antimicrob Agents Chemother* 1982; 22:499–507.

37. Wilson SZ, Knight V, Wyde PR, et al: Amantadine and ribavirin aerosol treatment of influenza A and B infection in mice. *Antimicrob Agents Chemother* 1980; 17:642–648.

38. Hayden FG, Douglas RG Jr, Simons R: Enhancement of activity against influenza viruses by combinations of antiviral agents. *Antimicrob Agents Chemother* 1980; 18:536–541.

39. Scullard GH, Pollard RB, Smith JL, et al: Antiviral treatment of chronic hepatitis B virus infection. I. Changes in viral markers with interferon combined with adenine arabinoside. *J Infect Dis* 1981; 143:772–783.

40. Scullard GH, Andres LL, Greenberg HB, et al: Antiviral treatment of chronic hepatitis B virus infection: Improvement in liver disease with interferon and adenine arabinoside. *Hepatology* 1981; 1:228–232.

41. Smith CI, Kitchen LW, Scullard GH, et al: Vidarabine monophosphate and human leukocyte interferon in chronic hepatitis B infection, *JAMA* 1982; 247:2261–2265.

42. Sacks SL, Scullard GH, Pollard RB, et al: Antiviral treatment of chronic hepatitis B virus infection: Pharmacokinetics and side effects of interferon and adenine arabinoside alone and in combination. *Antimicrob Agents Chemother* 1982; 21:93–100.

43. American Medical Association: Antiviral Agents, in *Drug Evaluations,* ed 6. Philadelphia, Saunders, 1986, pp 1615–1631.

44. Burroughs Wellcome Co: *The Antiviral Age.* New York, World Health Communications, 1987.

45. American Society of Hospital Pharmacists: *Drug Information 90.* Bethesda, Md, American Society of Hospital Pharmacists, 1990.

46. Bean B: Antiviral therapy: New drugs and their uses. *Postgrad Med* 1986; 80:109–120.

47. Bryson YJ: Antiviral agents. *Clin Chest Med* 1986; 7:453–467.

48. Bryson YJ: Promising new antiviral drugs. *J Am Acad Dermatol* 1988; 18:212–218.

49. Dolin R: Antiviral chemotherapy and chemoprophylaxis. *Science* 1985; 227:1296–1303.

50. Galasso GJ, Merigan TC, Buchanan RA (eds): *Antiviral Agents and Viral Disease of Man.* New York, Raven Press, 1984.

51. Hirsch MS, Kaplan JC: Antiviral therapy. *Sci Am* 1987; 256:76–85.

52. Hermans PE, Cockerill FR: Antiviral agents. *Mayo Clin Proc* 1987; 62:1108–1115.

53. Mandel GL, Douglas RG Jr, Bennett JE (eds): *Principles and Practice of Infectious Diseases,* ed 3. New York, Churchill Livingstone, 1990.

54. Prusoff WH, Lin TS, Zucker M: Potential targets for antiviral chemotherapy. *Antiviral Res* 1986; 6:311–328.

55. Wood MJ, Geddes AM: Antiviral therapy. *Lancet* 1987; 2:1189–1192.

56. Zuckerman AJ, Banatvala JE, Pattison JR (eds): *Principles and Practice of Clinical Virology.* New York, Wiley, 1987.

57. Elion GB: Mechanism of action and selectivity of acyclovir. *Am J Med* 1982; 73(1A):7–13.

58. Elion GB: The biochemistry and mechanism of action of acyclovir. *J Antimicrob Chemother* 1983; 12(suppl B):9–17.

59. Miller WH, Miller RL: Phosphorylation of acyclovir (acycloguanosine) monophosphate by GMP kinase. *J Biol Chem* 1980; 255:7204–7207.

60. Miller WH, Miller RL: Phosphorylation of acyclovir diphosphate by cellular enzymes. *Biochem Pharmacol* 1982; 31:3879–3884.

61. Fyfe JA, Keller PM, Furman PA, et al: Thymidine kinase from herpes simplex virus phosphorylates the new antiviral compound, 9-(2-hydroxyethoxymethyl) guanine. *J Biol Chem* 1978; 253:8721–8727.

62. Keller PM, Fyfe JA, Beauchamp L, et al: Enzymatic phosphorylation of acyclic nucleoside analogs and correlations with antiherpetic activities. *Biochem Pharmacol* 1981; 30:3071–3077.

63. Pagano JS, Sixbey JW, Lin JC: Acyclovir and Epstein-Barr virus infection. *J Antimicrob Chemother* 1983; 12(suppl B):113–121.

64. Meyers JD, Wade JC, McGuffin RW, et al: The use of acyclovir for cytomegalovirus infections in the immunocompromised host. *J Antimicrob Chemother* 1983; 12(suppl B):181–193.

65. Schaeffer HJ, Beauchamp L, de Miranda R, et al: 9-(2-Hydroxyethoxymethyl) guanine activity against viruses of the herpes group. *Nature* 1978; 272:583–585.

66. Crumpacker CS, Schnipper LE, Zaia JA, et al: Growth inhibition by acycloguanosine of herpesviruses isolated from human infections. *Antimicrob Agents Chemother* 1979; 15:642–645.

67. Colby BM, Shaw JE, Elion GB, et al: Effect of acyclovir [9-(2-hydroxyethoxymethyl)guanine] on Epstein-Barr virus DNA replication. *J Virol* 1980; 34:560–568.

68. Biron KK, Elion GB: In vitro susceptibility of varicella-zoster virus to acyclovir. *Antimicrob Agents Chemother* 1980; 18:443–447.

69. Lin JC, Smith MC, Cheng YC, et al: Epstein-Barr virus: Inhibition of replication by three new drugs. *Science* 1983; 221:578–579.

70. Lang DJ, Cheung KS: Effectiveness of acycloguanosine and trifluorothymidine as inhibitors of cytomegalovirus infection in vitro. *Am J Med* 1982; 73(1A):49–53.

71. Laskin OL: Clinical pharmacokinetics of acyclovir. *Clin Pharmacokinet* 1983; 8:187–201.
72. Van Dyke RB, Connor JD, Wyborny C, et al: Pharmacokinetics of orally administered acyclovir in patients with herpes progenitalis. *Am J Med* 1982; 73(1A):172–175.
73. Bryson YJ, Dillon M, Lovett M, et al: Treatment of first episodes of genital herpes simplex virus infection with oral acyclovir: A randomized double-blind controlled trial in normal subjects. *N Engl J Med* 1983; 308:916–921.
74. Blum RM, Liao SHT, de Miranda P: Overview of acyclovir pharmacokinetic disposition in adults and children. *Am J Med* 1982; 73(1A):186–192.
75. Hintz M, Connor JD, Spector SA, et al: Neonatal acyclovir pharmacokinetics in patients with herpesvirus infections. *Am J Med* 1982; 73(1A):210–214.
76. Laskin OL, Longstreth JA, Whelton A, et al: Effect of renal failure on the pharmacokinetics of acyclovir. *Am J Med* 1982; 73(1A):197–201.
77. Whitley RJ, Blum MR, Barton N, et al: Pharmacokinetics of acyclovir in humans following intravenous administration: A model for the development of parenteral antivirals. *Am J Med* 1982; 73(1A):165–171.
78. De Miranda P, Whitley RJ, Blum MR, et al: Acyclovir kinetics after intravenous infusion. *Clin Pharmacol Ther* 1979; 26:718–728.
79. Spector SA, Connor JD, Hintz M, et al: Single-dose pharmacokinetics of acyclovir. *Antimicrob Agents Chemother* 1981; 19:608–612.
80. Laskin OL, Longstreth JA, Saral R, et al: Pharmacokinetics and tolerance of acyclovir, a new anti-herpesvirus agent, in humans. *Antimicrob Agents Chemother* 1982; 21:393–398.
81. Corey L, Holmes KK: Genital herpes simplex virus infections: Current concepts in diagnosis, therapy, and prevention. *Ann Intern Med* 1983; 98:973–983.
81a. Meyer LJ, deMiranda P, Sheth N, et al: Acyclovir in human breast milk. *Am J Obstet Gynecol* 1988; 158:586–588.
82. De Miranda P, Good SS, Laskin OL, et al: Disposition of intravenous radioactive acyclovir. *Clin Pharmacol Ther* 1981; 30:662–672.
83. De Miranda P, Good SS, Krasny HC, et al: Metabolic fate of radioactive acyclovir in humans. *Am J Med* 1982; 73(1A):215–220.
84. Krasny HC, Liao SHT, de Miranda P, et al: Influence of hemodialysis on acyclovir pharmacokinetics in patients with chronic renal failure. *Am J Med* 1982; 73(1A):202–204.
85. Wade JC, Newton B, McLaren C, et al: Intravenous acyclovir to treat mucocutaneous herpes simplex virus infection after marrow transplantation: A double-blind trial. *Ann Intern Med* 1982; 96:265–269.
86. Mitchell CD, Bean B, Gentry SR, et al: Acyclovir therapy for mucocutaneous herpes simplex infections in immunocompromised patients. *Lancet* 1981; 1:1389–1391.
87. Chou S, Gallagher JC, Merigan TC: Controlled clinical trial of intravenous acyclovir in heart-transplant patients with mucocutaneous herpes simplex infections. *Lancet* 1981; 1:1392–1394.
88. Meyers JD, Wade JC, Mitchell CD, et al: Multicenter collaborative trial of intravenous acyclovir for the treatment of mucocutaneous herpes simplex virus infection in the immunocompromised host. *Am J Med* 1982; 73(1A):229–235.
89. Pass RF, Whitley RJ, Whelchel JD, et al: Identification of patients with increased risk of infection with herpes simplex virus after renal transplantation. *J Infect Dis* 1979; 140:487–492.
90. Meyers JD, Flournoy N, Thomas ED: Infection with herpes simplex virus and cell-mediated immunity after marrow transplant. *J Infect Dis* 1980; 142:338–346.
91. Spector SA, Hintz M, Wyborny C, et al: Treatment of herpes virus infections in immunocompromised patients with acyclovir by continuous intravenous infusion. *Am J Med* 1982; 73(1A):275–280.
92. Saral R: Management of mucocutaneous herpes simplex virus infections in immunocompromised patients. *Am J Med* 1988; 85(2A):57–60.
93. Straus SE, Smith HA, Brickman C, et al: Acyclovir for chronic mucocutaneous herpes simplex virus infection in immunosuppressed patients. *Ann Intern Med* 1982; 96:270–277.
94. Whitley RJ, Barton N, Collins E, et al: Mucocutaneous herpes simplex virus infections in immunocompromised patients: A model for evaluation of topical antiviral agents. *Am J Med* 1982; 73(1A):236–240.
95. Whitley RJ, Levin M, Barton N, et al: Infections caused by herpes simplex virus in the immunocompromised host: Natural history and topical acyclovir therapy. *J Infect Dis* 1984; 150:323–329.
96. Saral R, Burns WH, Laskin OL, et al: Acyclovir prophylaxis of herpes-simplex-virus infections: A randomized, double-blind, controlled trial in bone-marrow-transplant recipients. *N Engl J Med* 1981; 305:63–67.
97. Saral R, Ambinder RF, Burns WH, et al: Acyclovir prophylaxis against herpes simplex virus infection in patients with leukemia: A randomized, double-blind, placebo-controlled study. *Ann Intern Med* 1983; 99:773–776.
98. Prentice HG: Use of acyclovir for prophylaxis of herpes infections in severely immunocompromised patients. *J Antimicrob Chemother* 1983; 12(suppl B):153–159.
99. Fiddian AP: Prevention of herpes simplex virus infection in susceptible patients. *Infection* 1987; 15(suppl 1):S21–S25.
100. Gold D, Corey L: Acyclovir prophylaxis for herpes simplex infection. *Antimicrob Agents Chemother* 1987; 31:361–367.
101. Straus SE, Seidlin M, Takiff H, et al: Oral acyclovir to suppress recurring herpes simplex virus infections in immunodeficient patients. *Ann Intern Med* 1984; 100:522–524.
102. Gluckman E, Devergie A, Melo R, et al: Prophylaxis of herpes infections after bone marrow transplantation by oral acyclovir. *Lancet* 1983; 2:706–708.
103. Krusinski PA: Treatment of mucocutaneous herpes simplex infections with acyclovir. *J Am Acad Dermatol* 1988; 18:179–181.
104. Westheim AI, Tenser RB, Marks JG, Jr: Acyclovir resistance in a patient with chronic mucocutaneous herpes simplex infection. *J Am Acad Dermatol* 1987; 17:875–880.
105. Bean B, Fletcher C, Englund J, et al: Progressive mucocutaneous herpes simplex infection due to acyclovir-resistant virus in an immunocompromised patient: correlation of viral susceptibilities and plasma levels with response to therapy. *Diagn Microbiol Infect Dis* 1987; 7:199–204.
106. Spruance SL, Schnipper LE, Overall JC Jr, et al: Treatment of herpes simplex labialis with topical acyclovir in polyethylene glycol. *J Infect Dis* 1982; 146:85–90.
107. Raborn GW, Dip MS, McGaw WT, et al: Treatment of herpes labialis with acyclovir. *Am J Med* 1988; 85(2A):39–42.
108. Fiddian AP, Kinghorn GR, Goldmeir D, et al: Topical acyclovir in the treatment of genital herpes: A comparison with systemic therapy. *J Antimicrob Chemother* 1983; 12(suppl B):67–77.
109. Thin RN, Nabarro JM, Parker JD, et al: Topical acyclovir in the treatment of initial genital herpes. *Br J Vener Dis* 1983; 59:116–119.
110. Corey L, Nahmias AJ, Guinan ME, et al: A trial of topical acyclovir in genital herpes simplex virus infections. *N Engl J Med* 1982; 306:1313–1319.
111. Corey L, Benedetti JK, Critchlow CW, et al: Double-blind controlled trial of topical acyclovir in genital herpes simplex virus infections. *Am J Med* 1982; 73(1A):326–334.
112. Fiddian AP, Yeo JM, Clark AE: Treatment of herpes labialis. *J Infect* 1983; 6(suppl 1):41–47.
113. Kinghorn GR, Turner EB, Barton IG, et al: Efficacy of topical acyclovir cream in first and recurrent episodes of genital herpes. *Antiviral Res* 1983; 3:291–301.

114. Fiddian AP, Ivanyi L: Topical acyclovir in the management of recurrent herpes labialis. *Br J Dermatol* 1983; 109:321–326.

115. Van Vloten WA, Swart RN, Pot F: Topical acyclovir therapy in patients with recurrent orofacial herpes simplex infections. *J Antimicrob Chemother* 1983; 12(suppl B):89–93.

116. Reichman RC, Badger GJ, Guinan ME, et al: Topically administered acyclovir in the treatment of recurrent herpes simplex genitalis: A controlled trial. *J Infect Dis* 1983; 147:336–340.

117. Corey L, Fife KH, Benedetti JK, et al: Intravenous acyclovir for the treatment of primary genital herpes. *Ann Intern Med* 1983; 98:914–921.

118. Mindel A, Adler MW, Sutherlund S, et al: Intravenous acyclovir treatment for primary genital herpes. *Lancet* 1982; 1:697–700.

119. Corey L, Benedetti J, Critchlow C, et al: Treatment of primary first-episode genital herpes simplex virus infections with acyclovir: Results of topical, intravenous, and oral therapy. *J Antimicrob Chemother* 1983; 12(suppl B):79–88.

120. Nilsen AE, Aasen T, Halsos AM, et al: Efficacy of oral acyclovir in the treatment of initial and recurrent genital herpes. *Lancet* 1982; 2:571–573.

121. Bryson Y, Dillon M, Lovett M, et al: Treatment of first-episode genital HSV with oral acyclovir: Long term follow-up of recurrences: A preliminary report. *Scand J Infect Dis* 1985; 47(suppl):70–75.

122. Douglas JM, Critchlow C, Benedetti J, et al: A double-blind study of oral acyclovir for suppression of recurrences of genital herpes simplex virus infection. *N Engl J Med* 1984; 310:1551–1556.

123. Mindel A, Weller IV, Faherty A, et al: Prophylactic oral acyclovir in recurrent genital herpes. *Lancet* 1984; 2:57–59.

124. Halsos MA, Salo OP, Lassus A, et al: Oral acyclovir suppression of recurrent genital herpes: A double-blind, placebo-controlled, crossover study. *Acta Derm Venereol* 1985; 65:59–63.

125. Kinghorn GR, Jeavons M, Rowland M, et al: Acyclovir prophylaxis of recurrent genital herpes: Randomized placebo controlled crossover study. *Genitourin Med* 1985; 61:387–390.

126. Mindel A, Weller IV, Faherty A, et al: Acyclovir in first attacks of genital herpes and prevention of recurrences. *Genitourin Med* 1986; 62:28–32.

127. Sacks SL, Fox R, Levendusky P, et al: Chronic suppression for six months compared with intermittent lesional therapy of recurrent genital herpes using oral acyclovir: Effects of lesions and nonlesional prodromes. *Sex Transm Dis* 1988; 15:58–62.

128. Mindel A, Faherty A, Carney O, et al: Dosage and safety of long-term suppressive acyclovir therapy for recurrent genital herpes. *Lancet* 1988; 1:926–928.

129. Molin L, Back O, Frodin T, et al: Long-term twice-daily oral acyclovir therapy suppresses frequently recurrent genital herpes. *Scand J Infect Dis* 1987; 19:273–274.

130. Blom, Back O, Egelrud T, et al: Long-term oral acyclovir treatment prevents recurrent genital herpes. *Dermatologica* 1986; 173:220–223.

131. Straus SE, Seidlin M, Takiff HE, et al: Double-blind comparison of weekend and daily regimens of oral acyclovir for suppression of recurrent genital herpes. *Antiviral Res* 1986; 6:151–159.

132. Mertz GJ, Eron L, Kaufman R, et al: Prolonged continuous versus intermittent oral acyclovir treatment in normal adults with frequently recurring genital herpes simplex virus infection. *Am J Med* 1988; 85(2A):14–19.

133. Mattison HR, Reichman RC, Benedetti J, et al: Double-blind, placebo-controlled trial comparing long-term suppressive with short-term oral acyclovir treatment for management of recurrent genital herpes. *Am J Med* 1988; 85(2A):20–25.

134. Kinghorn GR: Long-term suppression with oral acyclovir of recurrent herpes simplex virus infections in otherwise healthy patients. *Am J Med* 1988; 85(2A):26–29.

135. Mostow SR, Mayfield JL, Marr JJ, et al: Suppression of recurrent genital herpes by single daily doses of acyclovir. *Am J Med* 1988; 85(2A):30–33.

136. Straus SE, Takiff H, Seidlin M, et al: Suppression of frequently recurring genital herpes: A placebo-controlled double-blind trial of oral acyclovir. *N Engl J Med* 1984; 310:1545–1550.

137. Ambinder RF, Burns WH, Lietman PS, et al: Prophylaxis: A strategy to minimize antiviral resistance. *Lancet* 1984; 1:1154–1155.

138. Lehrman SN, Hill EL, Rooney JF, et al: Extended acyclovir therapy for herpes genitalis: Changes in virus sensitivity and strain variation. *J Antimicrob Chemother* 1986; 18(suppl B):85–94.

139. Crumpacker CS: Significance of resistance of herpes simplex virus to acyclovir. *J Am Acad Dermatol* 1988; 18:190–195.

140. Selby PJ, Powles RL, Jameson B, et al: Parenteral acyclovir therapy for herpes virus infection in man. *Lancet* 1979; 2:1267–1270.

141. Serota FT, Starr SE, Bryan CK, et al: Acyclovir treatment of herpes zoster infections: Use in children undergoing bone marrow transplantation. *JAMA* 1982; 247:2132–2135.

142. Balfour HH Jr, Bean B, Laskin OL, et al: Acyclovir halts progression of herpes zoster in immunocompromised patients. *N Engl J Med* 1983; 308:1448–1453.

143. Meyers JD, Wade JC, Shepp DH, et al: Acyclovir treatment of varicella-zoster virus infection in compromised host. *Transplantation* 1984; 37:571–574.

144. Strommen GL, Pucino F, Tight RR, et al: Human infection with herpes zoster: Etiology, pathophysiology, diagnosis, clinical course, and treatment. *Pharmacotherapy* 1988; 8:52–68.

145. Straus SE, Ostrove JM, Inchauspe G, et al: NIH Conference: Varicella-zoster virus infections: Biology, natural history, treatment, and prevention. *Ann Intern Med* 1988; 108:221–237.

146. Huff JC: Antiviral treatment in chickenpox and herpes zoster. *J Am Acad Dermatol* 1988; 18:204–206.

147. Shepp DH, Danliker PS, Meyers JD: Treatment of varicella-zoster virus infection in severely immunocompromised patients: Randomized comparison of acyclovir and vidarabine. *N Engl J Med* 1986; 314:208–212.

148. Peterslund NA, Seyer-Hansen K, Ipsen J, et al: Acyclovir in herpes zoster. *Lancet* 1981; 2:827–830.

149. Peterslund NA, Esmann V, Ipsen J, et al: Oral and intravenous acyclovir are equally effective in herpes zoster. *J Antimicrob Chemother* 1984; 14:185–189.

150. Bean B, Braun C, Balfour HH Jr: Acyclovir therapy for acute herpes zoster. *Lancet* 1982; 2:118–121.

151. Esmann V, Ipsen J, Peterslund NA, et a: Therapy of acute herpes zoster with acyclovir in nonimmunocompromised host. *Am J Med* 1982; 73(1A):320–325.

152. Novelli VM, Marshall WC, Yeo J, et al: Acyclovir administered perorally in immunocompromised children with varicella-zoster infections. *J Infect Dis* 1984; 149:478.

153. McKendrick MW, Care C, Burke C, et al: Oral acyclovir in herpes zoster. *J Antimicrob Chemother* 1984; 14:661–665.

154. Wood MJ, McKendrick MW, McGill JI: Oral acyclovir for acute herpes zoster infections in immune-competent adults. *Infection* 1987; 15(suppl 1):S9–S13.

155. Wood MJ, McKendrick MW, McGill JI, et al: Oral acyclovir in acute herpes zoster. *Br Med J* 1987; 293:1529–1532.

156. Wassilew SW, Reimlinger S, Nasemann T, et al: Oral acyclovir for herpes zoster: A double-blind controlled trial in normal subjects. *Br J Dermatol* 1987; 117:495–501.

157. Wood MJ, Ogan PH, McKendrick MW, et al: Efficacy of oral acyclovir treatment of acute herpes zoster. *Am J Med* 1988; 85(2A):79–83.

158. Huff JC, Bean B, Balfour HH, et al: Therapy of herpes zoster with oral acyclovir. *Am J Med* 1988; 85(2A):84–89.

159. Cobo M: Reduction of the ocular complications of herpes zoster ophthalmicus by oral acyclovir. *Am J Med* 1988; 85(2A):90–93.

160. Levin MJ, Zaia JA, Hershey BJ, et al: Topical acyclovir treatment of herpes zoster in immunocompromised patients. *J Am Acad Dermatol* 1985; 13:590–596.

161. Vilde JL, Bricaire F, Leport C, et al: Comparative trial of acyclovir and vidarabine in disseminated varicella-zoster virus in-

fections in immunocompromised patients. *J Med Virol* 1986; 20:127–134.

162. Cohen PR, Beltrani VP, Grossman ME: Disseminated herpes zoster in patients with human immunodeficiency virus infection. *Am J Med* 1988; 84:1076–1080.

163. Drucker JL, Kinh DH: Management of viral infections in AIDS patients. *Infection* 1987; 15(suppl):S32–S35.

164. Whitley RJ: Antiviral treatment of a serious herpes simplex infection: Encephalitis. *J Am Acad Dermatol* 1988; 18:209–211.

165. Shaw GL, Langston AA: Herpes simplex encephalitis: The need for early diagnosis. *NC Med J* 1986; 47:17–18.

166. Nahmias AJ, Whitley RJ, Visintine AN, et al: Herpes simplex encephalitis: Laboratory examinations and their diagnostic significance. *J Infect Dis* 1982; 145:829–835.

167. Gutman LT, Wilfort CM, Eppes S: Herpes simplex virus encephalitis in children: Analysis of cerebrospinal fluid and progressive neurodevelopmental deterioration. *J Infect Dis* 1986; 154:415–421.

168. Kahlon J, Chatterjee S, Lakeman FD, et al: Detection of antibodies to herpes simplex virus in the cerebrospinal fluid of patients with herpes simplex encephalitis. *J Infect Dis* 1987; 155:38–44.

169. Lakeman FD, Koga J, Whitley RJ: Detection of antibodies to herpes simplex virus in cerebrospinal fluid from patients with herpes simplex encephalitis. *J Infect Dis* 1987; 155:1171–1178.

170. Whitley RJ, Alford CA, Hirsch MS, et al: Factors indicative of outcome in a comparative trial of acyclovir and vidarabine for biopsy-proven herpes simplex encephalitis. *Infection* 1987; 15(suppl):S3–S8.

171. Whitley RJ, Soong SJ, Dolin R, et al: Adenine arabinoside therapy of biopsy-proven herpes simplex encephalitis. *N Engl J Med* 1977; 297:289–294.

172. Whitley RJ, Soong SJ, Hirsch MS, et al: Herpes simplex encephalitis: Vidarabine therapy and diagnostic problems. *N Engl J Med* 1981; 304:313–318.

173. Whitley RJ: Treatment of human herpesvirus infections with special reference to encephalitis. *J Antimicrob Chemother* 1984; 14(suppl):57–74.

174. Skoldenberg B, Forsgren M, Alestig K, et al: Acyclovir versus vidarabine in herpes simplex encephalitis: Randomized multicentre study in consecutive Swedish patients. *Lancet* 1984; 2:707–711.

175. Whitley RJ, Alford CA, Hirsch MS, et al: Vidarabine versus acyclovir therapy in herpes simplex encephalitis. *N Engl J Med* 1986; 314:144–149.

176. Whitley RJ: Interim summary of mortality in herpes simplex encephalitis and neonatal herpes simplex infections: Vidarabine versus acyclovir. *J Antimicrob Chemother* 1983; 12(suppl B):105–112.

177. Kohl S: Herpes simplex virus encephalitis in children. *Pediatr Clin North Am* 1988; 35:465–483.

178. Deo EA, Sardesai SR: Herpes simplex encephalitis. *Am Fam Physician* 1988; 37:184–188.

179. Van Landingham KE, Marsteller HB, Ross GW, et al: Relapse of herpes simplex encephalitis after conventional acyclovir therapy. *JAMA* 1988; 259:1051–1053.

180. Arvin AM, Johnson RT, Whitley RJ, et al: Consensus: Management of the patient with herpes simplex encephalitis. *Pediatr Infect Dis J* 1987; 6:2–5.

181. Whitley RJ: Herpes simplex virus infections of the central nervous system: A review. *Am J Med* 1988; 85(2A):61–67.

182. Wade JC, Hintz M, McGuffin RW, et al: Treatment of cytomegalovirus pneumonia with high-dose acyclovir. *Am J Med* 1982; 73(1A):249–256.

183. Balfour HH Jr, Bean B, Mitchell CD, et al: Acyclovir in immunocompromised patients with cytomegalovirus disease: A controlled trial at one institution. *Am J Med* 1982; 73(1A):241–248.

184. Plotkin SA, Starr SE, Bryan CK: In vitro and in vivo responses of cytomegalovirus to acyclovir. *Am J Med* 1982; 73(1A):257–261.

185. Tyms AS, Scamans EC, Naim HM: The in vitro activity of acyclovir and related compounds against cytomegalovirus infections. *J Antimicrob Chemother* 1981; 8:65–72.

186. Spector SA, Tyndall M, Kelley E: Effects of acyclovir combined with other antiviral agents on human cytomegalovirus. *Am J Med* 1982; 73(1A):36–39.

187. Pagano JS, Datta AK: Perspective on interactions of acyclovir with Epstein-Barr and other herpes viruses. *Am J Med* 1982; 73(1A):18–26.

188. St. Clair MH, Furman PA, Lubbers CM, et al: Inhibition of cellular alpha and virally induced deoxyribonucleic acid polymerase by the triphosphate of acyclovir. *Antimicrob Agents Chemother* 1980; 18:741–745.

188a. Resnick L, Herbst JS, Ablashi DV et al: Regression of oral hairy leukoplakia after orally administered acyclovir therapy. *JAMA* 1988; 259:384–388.

189. Meyers JD, Reed EC, Shepp DH, et al: Acyclovir for prevention of cytomegalovirus infection and disease after allogeneic marrow transplantation. *N Engl J Med* 1988; 318:70–75.

190. Meyers JD: Management of cytomegalovirus infection. *Am J Med* 1988; 85(2A):102–106.

191. Reed EC, Meyers JD: Treatment of cytomegalovirus infection. *Clin Lab Med* 1987; 7:831–852.

192. Sullivan JL, Byron KS, Brewster FE, et al: Treatment of life-threatening Epstein-Barr infections with acyclovir. *Am J Med* 1982; 73(1A):262–266.

193. Hanto DW, Frizzera G, Gajl-Peczalska KJ, et al: Epstein-Barr virus-induced B-cell lymphoma after renal transplantation. *N Engl J Med* 1982; 306:913–918.

194. Pagano JS, Sixbey JW, Lin JC: Acyclovir and Epstein-Barr virus infection. *J Antimicrob Chemother* 1983; 12(suppl B):113–121.

195. Andersson J, Britton S, Ernberg I, et al: Effect of acyclovir on infectious mononucleosis: A double-blind, placebo-controlled study. *J Infect Dis* 1986; 153:283–290.

196. Andersson J, Skoldenberg B, Henle W, et al: Acyclovir treatment of infectious mononucleosis: A clinical and virological study. *Infection* 1987; 15(suppl 1):14–21.

197. Andersson J, Ernberg I: Management of Epstein-Barr virus infections. *Am J Med* 1988; 85(2A):107–115.

198. Crumpacker CS, Kowalsky PN, Oliver SA, et al: Resistance of herpes simplex virus to 9-[(2-hydroxy-1-(hydroxymethyl)ethoxy methyl] guanine: Physical mapping of drug synergism within the viral DNA polymerase locus. *Proc Natl Acad Sci USA* 1984; 81:1556–1560.

199. Frank KB, Cheng YC: Mutually exclusive inhibition of herpesvirus DNA polymerase by aphidicolin, phosphonoformate, and acyclic nucleoside triphosphates. *Antimicrob Agents Chemother* 1985; 27:445–448.

200. Connell EV, Cerruti RL, Trown PW: Synergistic activity of combinations of recombinant human alpha interferon and acyclovir, administered concomitantly and in sequence, against a lethal herpes simplex virus type 1 infection in mice. *Antimicrob Agents Chemother* 1985; 28:1–4.

201. Levin MJ, Leary PL: Inhibition of human herpesviruses by combination of acyclovir and human leukocyte interferon. *Infect Immun* 1981; 32:995–999.

202. Spector T, Averett DR, Nelson DJ, et al: Potentiation of antiherpetic activity of acyclovir by ribonucleotide reductase inhibition. *Proc Natl Acad Sci USA* 1985; 82:4254–4257.

203. Yarchoan R, Broder S: Development of antiretroviral therapy for the acquired immunodeficiency syndrome and related disorders: A progress report. *N Engl J Med* 1987; 316:557–564.

203a. Hollander H, Lifson AR, Moha M, et al: Phase I study of low-dose zidovudine and acyclovir in asymptomatic human immunodeficiency virus seropositive individuals. *Am J Med* 1989; 87:628–632.

204. Bach MC: Possible drug interaction during therapy with azidothymidine and acyclovir for AIDS [letter]. *N Engl J Med* 1987; 316:547.

205. Laskin OL, de Miranda P, King DH, et al: Effects of probenecid on the pharmacokinetics and elimination of acyclovir in humans. *Antimicrob Agents Chemother* 1982; 21:804–807.

206. Keeney RE, Kirk LE, Bridgen D: Acyclovir tolerance in humans. *Am J Med* 1982; 73(1A):176–181.

207. Wade JC, Meyers JD: Neurologic symptoms associated with parenteral acyclovir treatment after marrow transplantation. *Ann Intern Med* 1983; 98:921–925.

208. Quinn RP, Wolberg G, Medzihradsky J, et al: Effect of acyclovir on various murine in vivo and in vitro immunologic assay systems. *Am J Med* 1982; 73(1A):62–66.

209. Rooney JF, Felser JM, Ostrove JM, et al: Acquisition of genital herpes from an asymptomatic sexual partner. *N Engl J Med* 1986; 314:1561–1564.

210. Krasny HC, Petty BG: Metabolism of desciclovir, a prodrug of acyclovir, in humans after multiple oral dosing. *J Clin Pharmacol* 1987; 27:74–77.

211. Petty BG, Whitley RJ, Liao S, et al: Pharmacokinetics and tolerance of desciclovir, a prodrug of acyclovir, in healthy human volunteers. *Antimicrob Agents Chemother* 1987; 31:1317–1322.

212. Selby P, Powles RL, Blake S: Amino (hydroxyethoxymethyl) purine: A new well-absorbed prodrug of acyclovir. *Lancet* 1984; 2:1428–1430.

213. Krenitsky TA, Hall WW, de Miranda P, et al: 6-Deoxyacyclovir: A xanthine oxidase-activated prodrug of acyclovir. *Proc Natl Acad Sci USA* 1984; 81:3209–3213.

214. Whiteman PD: Tolerance and pharmacokinetics of A515U, acyclovir analogue, in healthy volunteers. *Proc BPS* 1984; 149P–150P.

215. Bruggeman CA, Engels W, Endert J: Treatment of experimental cytomegalovirus infections with acyclovir. *Arch Virol* 1987; 97:27–35.

216. Rees PJ, Selby P, Prentice HG, et al: A515U: A prodrug of acyclovir with increased oral bioavailability. *J Antimicrob Chemother* 1986; 18(suppl B):215–222.

217. Lundgren B, Ericson AC, Berg M, et al: Efficacy of the acyclic guanosine analog buciclovir [(R)-(3,4-dihydroxybutyl)guanosine] in experimental genital herpes. *Antimicrob Agents Chemother* 1986; 29:294–297.

218. Larsson A, Stenberg K, Ericson AC, et al: Mode of action, toxicity, pharmacokinetics and efficacy of some new antiherpes guanosine analogs related to buciclovir. *Antimicrob Agents Chemother* 1986; 30:598–605.

219. Datema R, Ericson AC, Field HJ, et al: Critical determinants of antiherpes efficacy of buciclovir and related acyclic guanosine analogs. *Antiviral Res* 1987; 7:303–316.

220. Meyers JD, Fluornoy N, Thomas ED: Nonbacterial pneumonia after allogeneic marrow transplantation: A review of ten years' experience. *Rev Infect Dis* 1982; 4:1119–1132.

221. Peterson PK, Balfour HH Jr, Marker SC, et al: Cytomegalovirus disease in renal allograft recipients: A prospective study of clinical features, risk factors, and impact on renal transplantation. *Medicine* 1980; 59:283–300.

222. Stagno S, Pass RF, Dworsky ME, et al: Congenital and prenatal cytomegalovirus infections. *Semin Perinatol* 1983; 7:31–42.

223. Macher AM, Reichert CM, Straus SE, et al: Death in the AIDS patient: Role of cytomegalovirus, letter. *N Engl J Med* 1983; 309:1454.

224. Armstrong D, Gold JWM, Dryjanski J, et al: Treatment of infections in patients with the acquired immunodeficiency syndrome. *Ann Intern Med* 1985; 103:738–743.

225. Drew WL, Conant MA, Miner RC, et al: Cytomegalovirus and Kaposi's sarcoma in young homosexual men. *Lancet* 1982; 2:125–127.

226. Pollard RB, Egbert PR, Gallagher JG, et al: Cytomegalovirus retinitis in immunosuppressed hosts. I. Natural history and effects of treatment with adenine arabinoside. *Ann Intern Med* 1980; 93:655–664.

227. Egbert PR, Pollard RB, Gallagher JG, et al: Cytomegalovirus retinitis in immunosuppressed hosts. II. Ocular manifestations. *Ann Intern Med* 1980; 93:664–670.

228. Fryd DS, Peterson PK, Ferguson RM, et al: Cytomegalovirus as a risk factor in renal transplantation. *Transplantation* 1980; 30:436–439.

229. Ho M, Dowling JN: Cytomegalovirus infection in transplant and cancer patients, in Remington JS, Swartz MN (eds): *Current Clinical Topics in Infectious Diseases*. New York, McGraw-Hill, 1980, pp 45–67.

230. Meyers JD, Spencer HC Jr, Watts JC, et al: Cytomegalovirus pneumonia after human marrow transplantation. *Ann Intern Med* 1975; 82:181–188.

231. Mintz L, Drew WL, Miner RC, et al: Cytomegalovirus infections in homosexual men. *Ann Intern Med* 1983; 99:326–329.

232. National Institutes of Health: Summary of a workshop on cytomegalovirus infections during organ transplantation. *J Infect Dis* 1979; 139:728–734.

233. Quinnan GV, Masur H, Rook AH, et al: Herpesvirus infections in the acquired immunodeficiency syndrome. *JAMA* 1984; 252:72–77.

234. Rubin RH, Cosimi AB, Tolkoff-Rubin NE, et al: Infectious disease syndromes attributable to cytomegalovirus and their significance among renal transplant recipients. *Transplantation* 1977; 24:458–464.

235. Collier AC, Meyers JD, Corey L, et al: Cytomegalovirus infections in homosexual men. Relationship to sexual practices, antibody to human immunodeficiency virus, and cell mediated immunity. *Am J Med* 1987; 82:593–601.

236. Jacobson MA, Mills J: Serious cytomegalovirus disease in the acquired immunodeficiency syndrome (AIDS). Clinical findings, diagnosis, and treatment. *Ann Intern Med* 1988; 108:585–594.

237. Visor GC, Lin LH, Jackson SE, et al: Stability of ganciclovir sodium (DHPG) in 5% dextrose or 0.9% sodium chloride injections. *Am J Hosp Pharm* 1986; 43:2810–2812.

238. Cheng YC, Grill SP, Dutschman GE, et al: Effects of 9-(1,3-dihydroxy-2-propoxymethyl) guanine, a new antiherpes virus compound on synthesis of macromolecules in herpes simplex virus-infected cells. *Antimicrob Agents Chemother* 1984; 26:283–288.

239. Frank KB, Chiou JF, Cheng YC: Interaction of herpes simplex virus-induced DNA polymerase with 9-(1,3-dihydroxy-2-propoxymethyl) guanine triphosphate. *J Biol Chem* 1984; 259:1566–1569.

240. Cheng YC, Grill SP, Dutchsman GE, et al: Metabolism of 9-(1,3-dihydroxy-2-propoxymethyl) guanine, a new antiherpes virus compound, in herpes simplex virus-infected cells. *J Biol Chem* 1983; 258:12460–12464.

241. Ashton WT, Karkas JD, Field AK, et al: Activation by thymidine kinase and potent antiherpetic activity of 2′-nor-2′-deoxyguanosine (2′-NDG). *Biochem Biophys Res Commun* 1982; 108:1716–1721.

242. Cheng YG, Huang ES, Lin JC, et al: Unique spectrum of activity of 9-(1,3-dihydroxy-2-propoxymethyl) guanine against herpesvirus in vitro and its mode of action against herpes simplex virus type 1. *Proc Natl Acad Sci USA* 1983; 80:2767–2770.

243. Field AK, Davies ME, DeWitt C, et al: 9-([2-hydroxy-1-(hydroxymethyl) ethoxy] methyl) guanine: A selective inhibitor of herpes group virus replication. *Proc Natl Acad Sci USA* 1983; 80:4139–4143.

244. Smee DF, Martin JC, Verheyden JPH, et al: Anti-herpes activity of the acyclic nucleotide 9-(1,3-dihydroxy-2-propoxymethyl) guanine. *Antimicrob Agents Chemother* 1983; 23:676–682.

245. Smith KO, Galloway KS, Kennell WL, et al: A new nucleoside analog: 9-([2-hydroxy-1-(hydroxymethyl) ethoxy] methyl) guanine, highly active in vitro against herpes simplex virus types 1 and 2. *Antimicrob Agents Chemother* 1982; 22:55–61.

246. Mar EC, Cheng YC, Huang ES: Effect of 9-(1,3-dihydroxy-2-propoxymethyl) guanine on human cytomegalovirus replication in vitro. *Antimicrob Agents Chemother* 1983; 24:518–521.

247. Tocci MJ, Livelli TJ, Perry HC, et al: Effects of the nucleoside analog 2′-nor-2′-deoxyguanosine on human cytomegalovirus replication. *Antimicrob Agents Chemother* 1984; 25:247–252.

248. Field HJ, Anderson JR, Efstathiou S: A quantitative study of the effects of several nucleoside analogues on established herpes encephalitis in mice. *J Gen Virol* 1984; 65:707–719.

249. Freitas VR, Smee DF, Chernow M, et al: Activity of 9-(1,3-dihydroxy-2-propoxymethyl) guanine compared with that of acyclovir against human, monkey, and rodent cytomegalovirus. *Antimicrob Agents Chemother* 1985; 28:240–245.

250. Eppstein DA, Marsh VY: Potent synergistic inhibition of herpes simplex virus-2 by 9-(1,3-hydroxy-2-propoxymethyl) guanine in combination with recombinant interferons. *Biochem Biophys Res Commun* 1984; 120:66–73.

251. Plotkin SA, Drew WL, Felsenstein D, et al: Sensitivity of clinical isolates of human cytomegalovirus to 9-(1,3-dihydroxy-2-propoxymethyl) guanine. *J Infect Dis* 1985; 152:833–834.

252. Shanley JD, Morningstar J, Jordan MC: Inhibition of murine cytomegalovirus lung infection and interstitial pneumonitis by acyclovir and 9-(1,3-dihydroxy-2-propoxymethyl) guanine. *Antimicrob Agents Chemother* 1985; 28:172–175.

253. Fletcher C, Sawchuk R, Chinnock B, et al: Human pharmacokinetics of the antiviral drug DHPG. *Clin Pharmacol Ther* 1986; 40:281–286.

253a. Fletcher CV, Balfour HH Jr: Evaluation of ganciclovir for cytomegalovirus disease. *DICP Ann Pharmacother* 1989; 23:5–12.

254. Jacobson MA, de Miranda P, Cederberg DM, et al: Human pharmacokinetics and tolerance of oral ganciclovir. *Antimicrob Agents Chemother* 1987; 31:1251–1254.

255. Shepp DH, Dandliker PS, de Miranda P, et al: Activity of 9-[2-hydroxy-1-(hydroxymethyl) ethoxymethyl] guanine in the treatment of cytomegalovirus pneumonia. *Ann Intern Med* 1985; 103:368–373.

256. Hecht DW, Snydman DR, Crumpacker CS, et al: Ganciclovir for treatment of renal transplant-associated primary cytomegalovirus pneumonia. *J Infect Dis* 1988; 157:187–190.

257. Holland GN, Sakamoto MJ, Hardy D, et al: Treatment of cytomegalovirus retinopathy in patients with acquired immunodeficiency syndrome: Use of the experimental drug 9-[(2-hydroxy-1-(hydroxymethyl) ethoxymethyl] guanine. *Arch Ophthalmol* 1986; 104:1794–1800.

258. Erice A, Jordan MC, Chace BA, et al: Ganciclovir treatment of cytomegalovirus disease in transplant recipients and other immunocompromised hosts. *JAMA* 1987; 257:3082–3087.

259. Masur H, Lane HC, Palestine A, et al: Effect of 9-(1,3-dihydroxy-2-propoxymethyl) guanine on serious cytomegalovirus disease in eight immunosuppressed homosexual men. *Ann Intern Med* 1986; 104:41–44.

260. Collaborative DHPG Study Group: Treatment of serious cytomegalovirus infection with 9-(1,3-dihydroxy-2-propoxymethyl) guanine in patients with AIDS and other immunodeficiencies. *N Engl J Med* 1986; 314:801–805.

261. Laskin OL, Stahl-Bayliss CM, Kalman CM, et al: Use of ganciclovir to treat serious cytomegalovirus infections in patients with AIDS. *J Infect Dis* 1987; 155:323–327.

262. Laskin OL, Cederberg DM, Mills J, et al: Ganciclovir for the treatment and suppression of serious infections caused by cytomegalovirus. *Am J Med* 1987; 83:201–207.

263. Drew WL, Buhles W, Erlich KS: Herpesvirus infections (caused by cytomegalovirus, herpes simplex virus, varicella-zoster virus): How to use ganciclovir (DHPG) and acyclovir, in Sande MA, Volberding PA (eds): *The Medical Management of AIDS*. Philadelphia, Saunders, 1988, pp 271–288.

263a. *Product Information: Cytovene (Ganciclovir Sodium)*. Palo Alto, Calif, Syntex Laboratories, 1990.

264. Henry K, Cantrill H, Fletcher C, et al: Use of intravitreal ganciclovir (dihydroxy propoxy methyl guanine) for cytomegalovirus retinitis in a patient with AIDS. *Am J Ophthalmol* 1987; 103:17–23.

265. Henry K, Cantrill H, Kish MA: Intravitreous ganciclovir for patients receiving zidovudine [letter]. *JAMA* 1987; 257:3066.

266. Kao GW, Peyman GA, Fiscella R, et al: Retinal toxicity of ganciclovir in vitrectomy infusion solution. *Retina* 1987; 7:80–83.

267. Debs RJ, Montgomery AB, Brunette EN, et al: Aerosol administration of antiviral agents to treat lung infections due to murine cytomegalovirus. *J Infect Dis* 1988; 157:327–331.

268. Rush J, Mills J: Effect of combinations of difluoromethylornithine (DFMO) and 9-[1,3-dihydroxy-2-propoxy) methyl] guanine (DHPG) on human cytomegalovirus. *J Med Virol* 1987; 21:269–276.

269. Nightingale SL: Treatment IND approved for ganciclovir. *JAMA* 1989; 261:350.

270. Lee WW, Benitez A, Goodman L, et al: Potential anticancer agents. XL. Synthesis of the B-anomer of 9-(D-arabinofuranosyl) adenine. *J Am Chem Soc* 1960; 82:2648–2649.

271. Bauer DJ: Antiviral Agents-I. The antiviral nucleosides, in *The Specific Treatment of Virus Disease*. Baltimore, University Park Press, 1977, pp 19–70.

272. Drach JC, Shipman D: The selective inhibition of viral DNA synthesis of chemotherapeutic agents: An indicator of clinical usefulness? *Ann NY Acad Sci* 1977; 284:396–409.

273. Müller WEG, Zahn RK, Bittlingmaier K, et al: Inhibition of herpesvirus DNA synthesis by 9-β-D-Arabinofuranosyladenine in vitro and in vivo. *Ann NY Acad Sci* 1977; 284:34–48.

274. Shipman C Jr, Smith SH, Carlson RH, et al: Antiviral activity of arabinosyladenine and arabinosylhypoxanthine in herpes simplex virus-infected KB cells. I. Selective inhibition of viral DNA synthesis in synchronized suspension cultures. *Antimicrob Agents Chemother* 1976; 9:120–127.

275. Shannon WM: Adenine arabinoside: Antiviral activity in vitro, in Pavan-Langston D, Buchanan RA, Alford CA Jr (eds): *Adenine Arabinoside: An Antiviral Agent*. New York, Raven Press, 1975, pp 1–43.

276. Brink JJ, LePage GA: Metabolic effects of 9-D-arabinosylpurines in ascites tumor cells. *Cancer Res* 1964; 24:312–318.

277. Müller WEG, Zahn RK, Beyer R, et al: 9-β-D-Arabinofuranosyladenine as a tool to study herpes simplex virus DNA replication in vitro. *Virology* 1977; 76:787–796.

278. LePage GA, Khaliq A, Gottlieb JA: Studies of 9-β-arabinofuranosyladenine in man. *Drug Metab Dispos* 1973; 1:756–759.

279. Kinkel AW, Buchanan RA: Human Pharmacology, in Pavan-Langston D, Buchanan RA, Alford CA Jr (eds): *Adenine Arabinoside: An Antiviral Agent*. New York, Raven Press, 1975, pp 197–204.

280. Whitley RJ, Alford C, Hess F, et al: Vidarabine: A preliminary review of its pharmacological properties and therapeutic use. *Drugs* 1980; 20:267–282.

280a. Trissel LA: *Handbook on Injectable Drugs*, ed 5. Bethesda, Md, American Society of Hospital Pharmacists, 1988, pp 695–696.

281. Glasko AJ, Chang T, Drach JC, et al: Species differences in the metabolic disposition of ara-A, in Pavan-Langston D, Buchanan RA, Alford CA Jr (eds): *Adenine Arabinoside: An Antiviral Agent*. New York, Raven Press, 1975, pp 111–133.

282. Arnoff GR, Szwed JJ, Nelson RL, et al: Hypoxanthine-arabinoside pharmacokinetics after adenine arabinoside administration to a patient with renal failure. *Antimicrob Agents Chemother* 1980; 18:212–214.

283. Poirier RH, Kinkel AW, Ellison AC, et al: Intraocular penetration of topical 3% adenine arabinoside, in Pavan-Langston D, Buchanan RA, Alford CA (eds): *Adenine Arabinoside: An Antiviral Agent*. New York, Raven Press, 1975, pp 307–312.

284. Ross AH, Julia A, Balakrishnan C: Toxicity of adenine arabinoside in humans. *J Infect Dis* 1976; 133(suppl):192–198.

285. Sacks SL, Smith JL, Pollard RB, et al: Toxicity of vidarabine (letter), *JAMA* 1979; 241:28–29.

286. Keeney RE: Human tolerance of adenine arabinoside, in Pavan-Langston D, Buchanan RA, Alford CA Jr (eds): *Adenine Arabinoside: An Antiviral Agent*. New York, Raven Press, 1975, pp 265–274.

287. Whitley RJ, Soong S, Dolin R, et al: Adenine arabinoside therapy of biopsy-proved herpes simplex encephalitis. *N Engl J Med* 1977; 297:289–294.

288. Whitley RJ, Ch'ien LT, Dolin R, et al: Adenine arabinoside

therapy of herpes zoster in the immunosuppressed. *N Engl J Med* 1976; 294:1193–1199.

289. Whitley RJ, Soong S, Dolin R, et al: Early vidarabine therapy to control the complications of herpes zoster in immunosuppressed patients. *N Engl J Med* 1982; 307:971–975.

290. Whitley RJ, Soong S, Hirsch MS, et al: Herpes simplex encephalitis. Vidarabine therapy and diagnostic problems. *N Engl J Med* 1981; 304:313–318.

291. Pollard RB, Egbert PR, Gallagher JG, et al: Cytomegalovirus retinitis in immunosuppressed hosts. 1. Natural history and effects of treatment with adenine arabinoside. *Ann Intern Med* 1980; 93:655–664.

292. Bassendine MF, Chadwick RG, Salmeron J, et al: Adenine arabinoside therapy in HB, Ag-positive chronic liver-disease—A controlled study. *Gastroenterology* 1981; 80:1016–1022.

293. Lauter CB, Bailey EJ, Lerner AM: Microbiologic assays and neurological toxicity during use of adenine arabinoside in humans. *J Infect Dis* 1976; 134:75–79.

294. Van Etta L, Brown J, Mastiri A, et al: Fatal vidarabine toxicity in a patient with normal renal function. *JAMA* 1981; 246:1703–1705.

295. Friedman HM, Grasela T: Adenine arabinoside and allopurinol—Possible adverse drug interaction (letter). *N Engl J Med* 1981; 304:423.

296. Ramos E, Timmons RF, Schimpff SC: Inappropriate antidiuretic hormone following adenine arabinoside administration. *Antimicrob Agents Chemother* 1979; 15:142–144.

297. Whitley RJ, Nahmias AJ, Soong S, et al: Vidarabine therapy of neonatal herpes simplex virus infection. *Pediatrics* 1980; 66:495–501.

298. Whitley RJ, Alford CA: Antiviral agents: Clinical status report. *Hosp Pract* 1981; 16:109–121.

299. Steele RW, Chapa IA, Vincent MM, et al: Effects of adenine arabinoside on cellular immune mechanisms in man, in Pavan-Langston D, Buchanan RA, Alford CA Jr (eds): *Adenine Arabinoside: An Antiviral Agent.* New York, Raven Press, 1975, pp 275–280.

300. Sloan BJ, Miller FA, McLean IW Jr: Treatment of herpes simplex virus types 1 and 2 encephalitis in mice with 9-β-D-arabinofuranosyladenine. *Antimicrob Agents Chemother* 1983; 3:74–80.

301. Zam ZS, Centifiano YM, Kaufman ME: The effect of adenine arabinoside on the immune response. *Progr Abstr Intersci Conf Antimicrob Agents Chemother* 1974; 14:139.

302. Dresner AJ, Seamans ML: Evidence of the safety and efficacy of adenine arabinoside in the treatment of herpes simplex epithelial keratitis, in Pavan-Langston D, Buchanan RA, Alford CA Jr (eds): *Adenine Arabinoside: An Antiviral Agent.* New York, Raven Press, 1975, pp 381–392.

303. Vidarabine (Vira-A): The Medical Letter on Drugs and Therapeutics 1977; 19:42–43.

304. Shannon WM: Adenine arabinoside: Antiviral activity in vitro, in Pavan-Langston D, Buchanan RA, Alford CA Jr (eds): *Adenine Arabinoside: An Antiviral Agent.* New York, Raven Press, 1975; pp 1–43.

305. Bryson Y, Connor JD, Sweetman L, et al: Determination of plaque inhibitory activity of adenine arabinoside (9-β-arabinofuranosyladenine) for herpesvirus using an adenosine deaminase inhibitor. *Antimicrob Agents Chemother* 1974; 6:98–101.

306. Fiala M, Chow AW, Miyasaki K, et al: Susceptibility of herpesvirus to three nucleoside analogues and their combinations and enhancement of the antiviral effect at acid pH *J Infect Dis* 1974; 129:82–85.

307. Shigeta S, Yokota T, Iwabuchi T, et al: Comparative efficacy of antiherpes drugs against various strains of varicella-zoster virus. *J Infect Dis* 1983; 147:576–584.

308. Marks MI: Variables influencing the in vitro susceptibilities of herpes simplex viruses to antiviral drugs. *Antimicrob Agents Chemother* 1974; 6:34–38.

309. Lemon SM, Bancroft WH: Lack of specific effect of adenine

arabinoside, human interferon, and ribavirin on the in vitro production of hepatitis B surface antigen. *J Infect Dis* 1979; 140:798–801.

310. Sloan BJ: Adenine arabinoside: Chemotherapy studies in animals, in Pavan-Langston D, Buchanan RA, Alford CA Jr (eds): *Adenine Arabinoside: An Antiviral Agent.* New York, Raven Press, 1975, pp 45–94.

311. Sidwell RW, Tolman RL, Huffman HJ, et al: Effect of 9-β-arabinofuranosyladenine-N-oxide-5'-phosphate (ara-A-OPICN 1255) on in vitro and in vivo DNA virus infections. *Prog Abstr Intersci Conf Antimicrob Agents Chemother.* American Society for Microbiology, Washington, DC, 1972, Abstract No 84.

312. Klein RJ, Friedman-Kien AE: Latent herpes simplex virus infections in sensory ganglia of mice after topical treatment with adenine arabinoside and adenine arabinoside monophosphate. *Antimicrob Agents Chemother* 1977; 12:577–581.

313. Soike KF, Felsenfeld AD, Gibson S, et al: Ineffectiveness of adenine arabinoside and adenine arabinoside 5'-monophosphate in simian varicella infection. *Antimicrob Agents Chemother* 1980; 18:142–147.

314. Ch'ien LT, Cannon NJ, Charamella LJ, et al: Effect of adenine arabinoside on severe herpesvirus hominis infections in man. *J Infect Dis* 1973; 128:658–663.

315. Ch'ien LT, Whitley JR, Charamella LJ, et al: Clinical and virologic studies with systemic administration of adenine arabinoside in severe, progressive, mucocutaneous herpes simplex infections, in Pavan-Langston D, Buchanan RA, Alford CA Jr (eds): *Adenine Arabinoside: An Antiviral Agent.* New York, Raven Press, 1975, pp 205–224.

316. Johnson MT, Luby JP, Buchanan RA: Treatment of varicella-zoster virus infections with adenine arabinoside. *J Infect Dis* 1975; 131:225–229.

317. Luby JP, Johnson MT, Buchanan R, et al: Adenine arabinoside therapy of varicella-zoster virus infections. Summary of phase II studies, in Pavan-Langston D, Buchanan RA, Alford CA Jr (eds): *Adenine Arabinoside: An Antiviral Agent.* New York, Raven Press, 1975, pp 237–245.

318. Ch'ien LT, Whitley RJ, Nahmias AJ, et al: Antiviral chemotherapy and neonatal herpes simplex virus infection: A pilot study-experience with adenine arabinoside. *Pediatrics* 1975; 55:678–685.

319. Whitley RJ, Ch'ien LT, Nahmias AJ, et al: Adenine arabinoside therapy of neonatal herpetic infections, in Pavan-Langston D, Buchanan RA, Alford CA Jr (eds): *Adenine Arabinoside: An Antiviral Agent.* New York, Raven, 1975, pp 225–235.

320. Abel R, Kaufman HE, Sugar J: Effect of intravenous adenine arabinoside on herpes simplex keratouveitis in humans, in Pavan-Langston D, Buchanan RA, Alford CA Jr (eds): *Adenine Arabinoside: An Antiviral Agent.* New York, Raven Press, 1975, pp 393–400.

321. Pavan-Langston D: Clinical evaluation of adenine arabinoside and idoxuridine in treatment of routine and idoxuridine-complicated herpes simplex keratitis, in Pavan-Langston D, Buchanan RA, Alford CA Jr (eds): *Adenine Arabinoside: An Antiviral Agent.* New York, Raven Press, 1975, pp 345–356.

322. O'Day DM, Poirier RH, Elliot JH: Adenine arabinoside: Therapy in complicated herpetic keratitis, in Pavan-Langston D, Buchanan RA, Alford CA Jr (eds): *Adenine Arabinoside: An Antiviral Agent.* New York, Raven Press, 1975, pp 357–369.

323. Baublis JV, Whitley RJ, Ch'ien LT, et al: Treatment of cytomegalovirus infections in children and adults, in Pavan-Langston D, Buchanan RA, Alford CA Jr (eds): *Adenine Arabinoside: An Antiviral Agent.* New York, Raven Press, 1975, pp 247–260.

324. Ch'ien LT, Cannon NJ, Whitley RJ, et al: Effect of adenine arabinoside on cytomegalovirus infections. *J Infect Dis* 1974; 130:32–39.

325. Rytel M, Kauffman HM: Clinical efficacy of adenine arabinoside in therapy of cytomegalovirus infections in renal allograft recipients. *J Infect Dis* 1976; 133:202–205.

326. Adams JG, Benson EA, Alexander ER, et al: Genital herpetic infection in men and women: Clinical course and effect of topical application of adenine arabinoside. *J Infect Dis* 1976; 133(suppl):A151–A159.

327. Goodman EL, Luby JP, Johnson MT: Prospective double-blind evaluation of topical adenine arabinoside in male herpes progenitalis. *Antimicrob Agents Chemother* 1975; 8:693–697.

328. Hyndiuk RA, Schultz RO, Hull DS: Herpetic keratitis—Clinical evaluation of adenine arabinoside and idoxuridine, in Pavan-Langston D, Buchanan RA, Alford CA Jr (eds): *Adenine Arabinoside: An Antiviral Agent.* New York, Raven Press, 1975, pp 331–335.

329. Laibson PR, Krachmer JH: Controlled comparison of adenine arabinoside and idoxuridine therapy of human superficial dendritic keratitis, in Pavan-Langston D, Buchanan RA, Alford CA Jr (eds): *Adenine Arabinoside: An Antiviral Agent.* New York, Raven Press, 1975; pp 323–330.

330. Coster DJ, McKinnon JR, McGill JI, et al: Clinical evaluation of adenine arabinoside and trifluorothymidine in the treatment of corneal ulcers caused by herpes simplex virus. *J Infect Dis* 1976; 133(suppl):A173–A177.

331. Whitley R, Miltz M, Haynes R, et al: Vidarabine therapy of varicella in immunosuppressed patients. *J Pediatrics* 1982; 101:125–131.

332. Whitley RJ, Alford CA Jr: Parenteral antiviral chemotherapy of human herpesviruses, in Nahmian A, Dowdle W, Schinzai R (eds): *The Human Herpesviruses: An Interdisciplinary Perspective.* New York, Elsevier Publishing Company, 1981, pp 478–490.

333. Braun P: The clinical management of suspected herpes virus encephalitis. A decision-analytic view. *Am J Med* 1980; 69:895–902.

334. Whitley RJ, Soong S, Linneman C, et al: Herpes simplex encephalitis. Clinical assessment. *JAMA* 1982; 247:317–320.

335. Barza M, Parker SG: The decision to biopsy, treat, or wait in suspected herpes encephalitis. *Ann Intern Med* 1980; 92:641–649.

336. Landry ML, Booss J, Hsiung GD: Duration of vidarabine therapy in biopsy-negative herpes simplex encephalitis. *JAMA* 1982; 247:332–334.

337. Whitley RJ, Ch'ien LT, Nahmias AJ, et al: Adenine arabinoside therapy of neonatal herpetic infections, in Pavan-Langston D, Buchanan RA, Alford CA Jr (eds): *Adenine Arabinoside: An Antiviral Agent.* New York, Raven Press, 1975, pp 225–235.

338. Whitley RJ, Nahmias AJ, Visintine AM, et al: The natural history of herpes simplex virus infection of mother and newborn. *Pediatrics* 1980; 66:489–494.

339. Bryson Y, Connor J, Hebbelwaite D: Pharmacology and efficacy of ara-A in neonatal and adults, in *Prog Abstr 19th Interscience Conf Antimicrob Agents Chemother.* Boston, American Society for Microbiology, October 1979, Abstract No 974.

340. Kraemer KG, Neiman PE, Reeves WC, et al: Prophylactic adenine arabinoside following marrow transplantation. *Transplant Proc* 1978; 10:237–240.

341. Marker SC, Howard RJ, Groth KE, et al: A trial of vidarabine for cytomegalovirus infection in renal transplant patients. *Arch Intern Med* 1980; 140:1441–1444.

342. Pollard RB, Smith JL, Neal A, et al: Effect of vidarabine on chronic hepatitis B virus infection. *JAMA* 1978; 239:1648–1650.

343. Koplan JP: Inefficacy of adenine arabinoside in the therapy of smallpox, in Pavan-Langston D, Buchanan RA, Alford CA Jr (eds): *Adenine Arabinoside: An Antiviral Agent.* New York, Raven Press, 1975, pp 261–263.

344. *HIV/AIDS Surveillance* Atlanta, Centers for Disease Control, March 1989.

345. Redfield RR, Burke DS: HIV infection: the clinical picture. *Sci Am* 1988; 259:90–98.

346. Barre-Sinoussi F, Chermann JC, Rey F, et al: Isolation of a T-lymphotropic retrovirus for a patient at risk for acquired immune deficiency syndrome (AIDS). *Science* 1983; 220:868–871.

347. Popovic M, Sarngadharan MG, Reed E, et al: Detection, isolation, and continuous production of cytopathic retroviruses (HTLV-III) from patients with AIDS and pre-AIDS. *Science* 1984; 224:497–500.

348. Gallo RC, Salahuddin SZ, Popovic M, et al: Frequent detection and isolation of cytopathic retroviruses (HTLV-III) from patients with AIDS and at risk for AIDS. *Science* 1984; 224:500–503.

349. Gallo RC, Montagnier L: AIDS in 1988. *Sci Am* 1988; 259:41–48.

350. Weber JN, Weiss RA: HIV infection: the cellular picture. *Sci Am* 1988; 259:100–109.

351. Fauci AS: Immunologic abnormalities in the acquired immunodeficiency syndrome (AIDS). *Clin Res* 1985; 32:491–499.

352. Fauci AS, Macher AM, Longo DL, et al: Acquired immunodeficiency syndrome: Epidemiologic, clinical, immunologic and therapeutic considerations. *Ann Intern Med* 1984; 100:92–106.

353. Fauci AS, Masur H, Gelmann EP, et al: The acquired immunodeficiency syndrome: An update. *Ann Intern Med* 1985; 102:800–813.

354. Ho DD, Rota TR, Hirsch MS: Infection of monocyte/macrophages by human T-lymphotropic virus type III. *J Clin Invest* 1986; 77:1712–1715.

355. Fauci AS: The human immunodeficiency virus: Infectivity and mechanisms of pathogenesis. *Science* 1988; 239:617–622.

356. Gallo RC, Streicher H: Human T-lymphotropic retroviruses (HTLV-I, II, and III): The biological basis of adult T-cell leukemia/lymphoma and AIDS. In Broder S (ed): *AIDS: Modern Concepts and Therapeutic Challenges.* New York, Marcel Dekker, 1987, p 4.

357. Gallo RC, Wong-Staal F: A human T-lymphotropic retrovirus (HTLV-III) as the cause of the acquired immunodeficiency syndrome. *Ann Intern Med* 1985; 103:679–689.

358. Minor J: AIDS update: Current treatment approaches. *Am Pharm* 1987; 27:552–558.

359. Haseltine WA, Terwilliger EF, Rosen CA, et al: Structure and function of human pathogenic retroviruses, in Gallo RC, Wong-Staal F (eds): *Retrovirus Biology: An Emerging Role in Human Diseases.* New York, Marcel Dekker, 1988.

360. Haseltine WA, Wong-Staal F: The molecular biology of the AIDS virus. *Sci Am* 1988; 259:52–62.

361. Waqar MA, Evans MJ, Manly KF, et al: Effects of 2′,3′-dideoxynucleosides on mammalian cells and viruses. *J Cell Physiol* 1984; 121:402–408.

362. Mitsuya H, Jarrett RF, Matsukura M, et al: Long-term inhibition of human T-lymphotropic virus type III/lymphadenopathy-associated virus (human immunodeficiency virus) DNA synthesis and RNA expression in T-cells protected by 2′,3′-dideoxynucleosides in vitro. *Proc Natl Acad Sci USA* 1987; 84:2033–2037.

363. Dahlberg JE, Mitsuya H, Blam SB, et al: Broad spectrum antiretroviral activity of 2′,3′-dideoxynucleosides. *Proc Natl Acad Sci USA* 1987; 84:2469–2473.

364. Lane HC, Masur H, Gelmann EP, et al: Therapeutic approaches to patients with AIDS. *Cancer Res* 1985; 45(suppl):4674s–4676s.

365. Broder S (ed): *AIDS: Modern Concepts and Therapeutic Challenges.* New York, Marcel Dekker, 1987.

366. Broder S, Fauci AS: Progress in drug therapies for HIV infection. *Public Health Rep* 1988; 103:224–229.

367. de Clerq E: Chemotherapeutic approaches to the treatment of the acquired immune deficiency syndrome (AIDS). *J Med Chem* 1986; 29:1561–1569.

368. Mitsuya H, Broder S: Strategies for antiviral therapy in AIDS. *Nature* 1987; 325:773–778.

369. Vogt MW, Hirsch MS: Treatment of human immunodeficiency virus infection. *Infect Dis Clin North Am* 1987; 1:323–336.

370. Yarchoan R, Mitsuya H, Broder S: AIDS therapies. *Sci Am* 1988; 259:110–119.

371. The chronology of AIDS research, commentary. *Nature* 1987; 326:435–436.

372. Dondero TJ: Human immunodeficiency virus infection in the United States: A review of current knowledge. *MMWR* 1987; 36(suppl S-6).

373. *Report of the Presidential Commission on the Human Immunodeficiency Virus Epidemic.* Washington, DC, Government Printing Office, 1988.

374. Curran JW, Jaffe HW, Hardy AM, et al: Epidemiology of HIV infection and AIDS in the United States. *Science* 1988; 239:610–616.

375. Heyward WL, Curran JW: The epidemiology of AIDS in the United States. *Sci Am* 1988; 259:72–81.

376. Mann JM, Chin J, Piot P, Quinn T: The international epidemiology of AIDS. *Sci Am* 1988; 259:82–89.

377. Piot P, Plummer FA, Mhalu FS, et al: AIDS: An international perspective. *Science* 1988; 239:573–579.

378. Bloom DE, Carliner G: The economic impact of AIDS in the United States. *Science* 1988; 239:604–610.

379. Mitsuya H, Popovic M, Yarchoan R, et al: Suramin protection of T cells in vitro against infectivity and cytopathic effect of HTLV-III. *Science* 1984; 266:172–174.

380. Hawking F: Suramin: With special reference to onchocerciasis. *Adv Pharmacol Chemother* 1978; 15:289–322.

381. Hawking F: Chemotherapy of filariasis. *Antibiot Chemother* 1981; 30:135–162.

382. de Clerq E: Suramin: A potent inhibitor of the reverse transcriptase of RNA tumor viruses. *Cancer Lett* 1979; 8:9–22.

383. de Clerq E: Suramin in the treatment of AIDS: Mechanism of action [erratum appears in *Antiviral Res* 1987; 7:185].

384. Ruprecht RM, Rossoni LD, Haseltine WA, et al: Suppression of retroviral propagation and disease by suramin in murine systems. *Proc Natl Acad Sci USA* 1985; 82:7733–7737.

385. Yarchoan R, Mitsuya H, Matsushita S, et al: Implications of the discovery of HTLV-III for the treatment of AIDS. *Cancer Res* 1985; 45(suppl):4684s–4688s.

386. Broder S, Yarchoan R, Collins JM, et al: Effects of suramin on HTLV-III/LAV infection presenting as Kaposi's sarcoma or AIDS-related complex. Clinical pharmacology and suppression of virus replication in vivo. *Lancet* 1985; 2:627–630.

387. Collins JM, Klecker RW Jr, Yarchoan R, et al: Clinical pharmacokinetics of suramin in patients with HTLV-III/LAV infection. *J Clin Pharmacol* 1986; 26:22–26.

388. Rollo IM: Miscellaneous drugs used in the treatment of protozoal infections, in Goodman LS, Gilman A (eds): *The Pharmacological Basis of Therapeutics*, ed 4. New York, MacMillan, 1970, pp 1144–1153.

389. Stein CA, Seville W, Yarchoan R, et al: Hypoadrenalism after suramin treatment. *Ann Intern Med* 1986; 104:286–287.

390. Cheson BD, Levine AM, Mildvan D, et al: Suramin therapy in AIDS and related disorders. Report of the US Suramin Working Group. *JAMA* 1987; 258:1347–1351.

391. Kaplan LD, Wolfe PR, Volberding PA, et al: Lack of response to suramin in patients with AIDS and AIDS-related complex. *Am J Med* 1987; 82:615–620.

392. Levine AM, Gill PS, Cohen J, et al: Suramin antiviral therapy in the acquired immunodeficiency syndrome. Clinical, immunological, and virologic results. *Ann Intern Med* 1986; 105:32–37.

393. Eeftinck Schattenkerk JK, Danner SA, Lange JM, et al: Persistence of human immunodeficiency virus antigenemia in patients with the acquired immunodeficiency syndrome treated with a reverse transcriptase inhibitor, suramin. *Arch Intern Med* 1988; 148:209–211.

394. Sandstrom EG, Kaplan JC: Antiviral therapy in AIDS. Clinical pharmacological properties and therapeutic experience to date. *Drugs* 1987; 34:372–390.

395. Yarchoan R, Weinhold K, Lyerly HK, et al: Administration of 3'-azido-3'-deoxythymidine, an inhibitor of HTLV-III/LAV replication, to patients with AIDS or AIDS-related complex. *Lancet* 1986; 1:575–580.

396. Product Information: Retrovir (Zidovudine). Research Triangle Park, NC, Burroughs Wellcome Co, 1990.

396a. Volberding PA, Lagakos SW, Koch MA, et al: Zidovudine in asymptomatic human immunodeficiency virus infection: A controlled trial in persons with fewer than 500 CD4-positive cells per cubic millimeter. *N Engl J Med* 1990; 322:941–949.

397. Sommadossi JP, Carlisle R: Toxicity of 3'-azido-3'-deoxythymidine and 9-(1,3-dihydroxy-2-propoxymethyl) guanine for normal human hematopoietic progenitor cells in vitro. *Antimicrob Agents Chemothr* 1987; 31:452–454.

398. Mitsuya H, Weinhold KJ, Furman PA, et al: 3'-azido-3'-deoxythymidine (BW A509U): An antiviral agent that inhibits the infectivity and cytopathic effect of human T-lymphotropic virus type III/lymphadenopathy-associated virus in vitro. *Proc Natl Acad Sci USA* 1985; 82:7096–7100.

399. Nakashima H, Matsui T, Harada S, et al: Inhibition of replication and cytopathic effect of human T-cell lymphotropic virus type III/lymphadenopathy-associated virus by 3'-azido-3'-deoxythymidine in vitro. *Antimicrob Agents Chemother* 1986; 30:933–937.

399a. Larder BA, Darby G, Richman DD: HIV with reduced sensitivity to zidovudine isolated during prolonged therapy. *Science* 1989; 243:1731–1734.

400. Klecker RW, Collins JM, Yarchoan R, et al: Plasma and cerebrospinal fluid pharmacokinetics of 3'-azido-3'-deoxythymidine: A novel pyrimidine analog with potential application for the treatment of patients with AIDS and related diseases. *Clin Pharmacol Ther* 1987; 41:407–412.

401. Yarchoan R, Brouwers P, Spitzer AR, et al: Response of human-immunodeficiency-virus-associated neurological disease to 3'-azido-3'-deoxythymidine. *Lancet* 1987; 1:132–135.

402. Horowitz JP, Chua J, Noel M: Nucleosides. V. The monomesylates of 1-(2'-deoxy-beta-D-lyxofuranosyl) thymine. *J Org Chem* 1964; 29:2076–2078.

403. Ostertag W, Roesler G, Krieg CJ, et al: Induction of endogenous virus and of thymidine kinase by bromodeoxyuridine in cell cultures transformed by Friend virus. *Proc Natl Acad Sci USA* 1974; 71:4980–4985.

404. Fischl MA, Richman DD, Grieco MH, et al: The efficacy of azidothymidine (AZT) in the treatment of patients with AIDS and AIDS-related complex. A double-blind, placebo-controlled trial. *N Engl J Med* 1987; 317:185–191.

405. Fiala M, Cone LA, Cohen N, et al: Responses of neurologic complications of AIDS to 3'-azido-3'-deoxythymidine and 9-(1,3-dihydroxy-2-propoxymethyl) guanine. I. Clinical features. *Rev Infect Dis* 1988; 10:250–256.

406. Dalakas MC, Yarchoan R, Spitzer R, et al: Treatment of human immunodeficiency virus-related polyneuropathy with 3'-azido-3'-deoxythymidine. *Ann Neurol* 1988; 23(suppl):S92–S94.

407. Yarchoan R, Thomas RV, Grafman J, et al: Long-term administration of 3'-azido-3'-deoxythymidine to patients with AIDS-related neurological disease. *Ann Neurol* 1988; 23(suppl):S82–S87.

408. Shaw GW, Harper ME, Hahn BH, et al: HTLV-III infection in brains of children and adults with AIDS encephalopathy. *Science* 1985; 177:177–181.

409. Ho DD, Rota TR, Schooley RT, et al: Isolation of HTLV-III from cerebrospinal fluid and neural tissues of patients with neurologic syndromes related to the acquired immunodeficiency syndrome. *N Engl J Med* 1985; 313:1493–1497.

410. Navia BA, Jordan BD, Price RW: The AIDS dementia complex: I. Clinical features. *Ann Neurol* 1986; 19:517–524.

411. Navia BA, Cho E-S, Petito CK, et al: The AIDS dementia complex: II. Neuropathology. *Ann Neurol* 1986; 19:525–535.

412. Gartner S, Markovits P, Markovitz DM, et al: The role of mononuclear phagocytes in HTLV-III/LAV infection. *Science* 1986; 233:215–219.

413. Richman DD, Fischl MA, Grieco MH, et al: The toxicity of azidothymidine (AZT) in the treatment of patients with AIDS and AIDS-related complex. A double-blind, placebo-controlled trial. *N Engl J Med* 1987; 317:192–197.

414. Eschbach JW, Egrie JC, Downing MR, et al: Correction of the anemia of end-stage renal disease with recombinant human erythropoietin. Results of a combined phase I and II clinical trial. *N Engl J Med* 1987; 316:73–78.

415. Golde DW, Gasson JC: Hormones that stimulate the growth of blood cells. *Sci Am* 1988; 259:62–70.

416. Clark SC, Kamen R: The human hemotopoietic colony-stimulating factors. *Science* 1987; 236:1229–1237.

417. Gasson JC, Weisbart RH, Kaufman SE, et al: Purified human granulocyte-macrophage colony-stimulating factor: direct action on neutrophils. *Science* 1986; 226:1339–1342.

418. Hammer SM, Gillis JM, Groopman JE, et al: In vitro modification of human immunodeficiency virus infection by granulocyte-macrophage colony-stimulating factor and gamma interferon. *Proc Natl Acad Sci USA* 1986; 83:8734–8738.

419. Golde DW, Baldwin GG, Gasson JC, et al: Granulocyte-macrophage colony-stimulating factor enhances neutrophil function in acquired immunodeficiency syndrome patients. *Proc Natl Acad Sci USA* 1988; 85:2763–2766.

420. Groopman JE, Mitsuyasu RT, Deleo MJ, et al: Effect of recombinant human granulocyte-macrophage colony-stimulating factor on myelopoiesis in the acquired immunodeficiency syndrome. *N Engl J Med* 1987; 317:593–598.

421. Gill PS, Rarick M, Brynes RK, et al: Azidothymidine associated with bone marrow failure in the acquired immunodeficiency syndrome (AIDS). *Ann Intern Med* 1987; 107:502–505.

422. Hagler DN, Frame PT: Azidothymidine neurotoxicity, letter. *Lancet* 1986; 2:1392–1393.

423. Bach MC: Zidovudine for lymphocytic interstitial pneumonia associated with AIDS, letter. *Lancet* 1987; 2:796.

424. Bessen LJ, Greene JB, Louis E, et al: Severe polymyositis-like syndrome associated with zidovudine therapy of AIDS and ARC. *N Engl J Med* 1988; 318:708.

425. Gorard DA, Henry K, Guiloff RJ: Necrotising myopathy and zidovudine. *Lancet* 1988; 1:1050–1051.

426. Furth PA, Kazakis AM: Nail pigmentation changes associated with azidothymidine (zidovudine). *Ann Intern Med* 1987; 107:350.

427. Spear JB, Kessler HA, Lehrman SN, et al: Zidovudine overdosage. *Ann Intern Med* 1988; 109:76–77.

428. Bach MC: Possible drug interaction during therapy with azidothymidine and acyclovir for AIDS, letter. *N Engl J Med* 1987; 316:547.

429. Surbone A, Yarchoan R, McAtee N, et al: Treatment of the acquired immunodeficiency syndrome (AIDS) and AIDS-related complex with a regimen of 3′-azido-2′,3′-dideoxythymidine (azidothymidine or zidovudine) and acyclovir. A pilot study. *Ann Intern Med* 1988; 108:534–540.

430. Yarchoan R, Perno CF, Thomas RV, et al: Phase I studies of 2′,3′-dideoxycytidine in severe human immunodeficiency virus infection as a single agent and alternating with zidovudine (AZT). *Lancet* 1988; 1:76–81.

431. Hartshorn KL, Vogt MW, Chou TC, et al: Synergistic inhibition of human immunodeficiency virus by azidothymidine and recombinant alpha A interferon. *Antimicrob Agents Chemother* 1987; 31:168–172.

432. Deyton LR, Kovacs JA, Masur H, et al: Phase I-II trial of zidovudine combined with lymphoblastoid interferon alpha in patients with AIDS and Kaposi's sarcoma, abstract. *Clin Res* 1988; 8:438A.

432a. Kovacs JA, Deyton L, Davey R, et al: Combined zidovudine and interferon-alfa therapy in patients with Kaposi's sarcoma and the acquired immunodeficiency syndrome (AIDS). *Ann Intern Med* 1989; 111:280–287.

433. Mitchell WM, Montefiori DC, Robinson WE Jr, et al: Mismatched double-stranded RNA (ampligen) reduces concentration of zidovudine (azidothymidine) required for in vitro inhibition of human immunodeficiency virus. *Lancet* 1987; 1:890–892.

434. Tochikura TS, Nakashima H, Kaneko Y, et al: Suppression of human immunodeficiency virus replication by 3′-azido-2′,3′-dideoxythymidine in various human hematopoietic cell lines in vitro: Augmentation of the effect by lentinan. *Jpn J Cancer Res* 1987; 78:583–589.

435. Vogt MW, Hartshorn KL, Furman PA, et al: Ribavirin antagonizes the effect of azidothymidine on HIV replication. *Science* 1987; 235:1376–1379.

436. Baba M, Pauwels R, Balzarini J, et al: Ribavirin antagonizes inhibitory effects of pyrimidine 2′,3′-dideoxynucleosides but enhances inhibitory effects of purine 2′,3′-dideoxynucleosides on replication of human immunodeficiency virus in vitro. *Antimicrob Agents Chemother* 1987; 31:1613–1617.

437. Mitsuya H, Broder S: Inhibition of the in vitro infectivity and cytopathic effect of human T-lymphotropic virus type III/lymphadenopathy-associated virus (HTLV-III/LAV) by 2′,3′-dideoxynucleosides. *Proc Natl Acad Sci USA* 1986; 83:1911–1915.

438. Mitsuya H, Matsukura M, Broder S: Rapid in vitro systems for assessing activity of agents against HTLV-III/LAV, in Broder S (ed): *AIDS: Modern Concepts and Therapeutic Challenges.* New York; Marcel Dekker, 1987, pp 303–333.

438a. Broder S (ed): Dideoxycytidine (ddC): A potent antiretroviral agent for human immunodeficiency virus infection. *Am J Med* 1990; 88(5B):1S–33S.

439. Cooney DA, Dalal M, Mitsuya H, et al: Initial studies on the cellular pharmacology of 2′,3′-dideoxycytidine, an inhibitor of HTLV-III infectivity. *Biochem Pharmacol* 1986; 35:2065–2068.

440. Starnes MC, Cheng Y-C: Cellular metabolism of 2′,3′-dideoxycytidine, a compound active against human immunodeficiency virus in vitro. *J Biol Chem* 1987; 262:988–991.

441. Kelley JA, Litterst CL, Roth JS, et al: The disposition and metabolism of 2′,3′-dideoxycytidine, an in vitro inhibitor of HTLV-III infectivity, in mice and monkeys. *Drug Metab Dispos* 1987; 15:595–601.

442. Kim CH, Marquez VE, Broder S: Potential anti-AIDS drugs: 2′,3′-dideoxycytidine analogues. *J Med Chem* 1987; 30:862–866.

443. Cooney DA, Ahluwalia G, Mitsuya H, et al: Initial studies on the cellular pharmacology of 2′,3′-dideoxyadenosine, an inhibitor of HTLV-III infectivity. *Biochem Pharmacol* 1987; 36:1765–1768.

444. Dalal M, et al: Cellular pharamcology of 2′,3′-dideoxyadenosine, an inhibitor of HTLV-III. *Proc AACR* 1987; 28:327.

445. Ahluwalia G, Cooney DA, Mitsuya H, et al: Initial studies on the cellular pharmacology of 2′,3′-dideoxyinosine, an inhibitor of HIV infectivity. *Biochem Pharmacol* 1987; 36:3797–3800.

446. Webb RR, Wos JA, Martin JC, et al: Synthesis of 2′,3′-dideoxyinosine. *Nucleosides Nucleotides* 1988; 7:147–153.

447. Schinazi RF, et al: Selective in vitro inhibition of human immunodeficiency virus (HIV) replication by 3′-azido-2′,3′-dideoxyuridine (CS-87), abstract. *J Cell Biol* 1987; 104(suppl):74.

448. Balzarini J, et al: Anti-retroviral activity of 3′-fluoro- and 3′-azido-substituted pyrimidine 2′,3′-dideoxynucleoside analogues. *Biochem Pharmacol* (in press).

449. Balzarini J, Pauwels R, Herdewijn P, et al: Potent and selective anti-HTLV-III activity of 2′,3′-dideoxycytidinene, the 2′,3′-unsaturated derivative of 2′,3′-dideoxycytidine. *Biochem Biophys Res Commun* 1986; 140:735–742.

450. Lin TS, Schinazi RF, Chen MS, et al: Antiviral activity of 2′,3′-dideoxycytidin-2′-ene (2′,3′-dideoxy-2′,3′-didehydrocytidine) against human immunodeficiency virus in vitro. *Biochem Pharmacol* 1987; 36:311–316.

451. Herdewijn P, Balzarini J, de Clerq E, et al: 3′-Substituted 2′,3′-dideoxynucleoside analogues as potential anti-HIV (HTLV-III/LAV) agents. *J Med Chem* 1987; 30:1270–1278.

452. Lin TS, Schinazi RF, Prusoff WH, et al: Potent and selective in vitro activity of 3′-deoxythymidine-2′-ene (3′-deoxy-2′,3′-didehydrothymidine) against human immunodeficiency virus. *Biochem Pharmacol* 1987; 36:2713–2718.

453. Ghazzouli L, et al: 2′,3′-Dideoxy-2′,3′-didehydrothymidine (D4T): A potent and selective agent against human immunodeficiency virus (HIV), abstract. Presented at Second International Conference on Antimicrobial Research. Williamsburg, Va, 1988.

454. Müller WEG: Mechanisms of action and pharmacology: Chemical agents, in Galasso GJ, Merigan TC, Buchanan RA (eds): *Antiviral Agents and Viral Diseases of Man.* New York, Raven Press, 1979, pp 77–149.

455. Smith RA, Wade MJ: Ribavirin: A broad spectrum antiviral agent, in Stapleton T (ed): *Studies with a Broad Spectrum Anti-*

viral Agent. Royal Society of Medicine Services International Congress and Symposium Series No. 108. London, Royal Society of Medicine Services, 1986.

456. Smith RA: Background and mechanisms of action of ribavirin, in Smith RA, Knight, Smith. *Clinical Applications of Ribavirin.* New York, Academic Press, 1984, pp 1–18.

457. Gilbert BE, Knight V: Biochemistry and clinical applications of ribavirin. *Antimicrob Agents Chemother* 1986; 30:201–205.

458. Wray SK, Gilbert BE, Knight V: Effects of ribavirin triphosphate on primer generation and elongation during influenza virus transcription in vitro. *Antiviral Res* 1985; 5:39–48.

459. Moss B, Martin SA, Ensinger M, et al: *Prog Nucleic Acid Res Mol Biol* 1976; 19:63–81.

460. Goswami BB, Charma OK, Borek E, et al: *Curr Chemother Immunol* 1982; 2:1075–1077.

461. Catlin DH, Smith RA, Samuels AI: ^{14}C-ribavirin: Distribution and pharmacokinetic studies in rats, baboons, and man, in Smith RA, Kirkpatrick W (eds): *Ribavirin: A Broad Spectrum Antiviral Agent.* New York, Academic Press, 1980, pp 83–98.

462. Ferrara EA, Oishi JS, Wannemacher RW, et al: Plasma disappearance, urine excretion, and tissue distribution of ribavirin in rats and rhesus monkeys. *Antimicrob Agents Chemother* 1981; 19:1042–1049.

463. Luskin OL, Longstreth JA, Hart CC, et al: Ribavirin disposition in high-risk patients for acquired immunodeficiency syndrome. *Clin Pharmacol Ther* 1987; 41:546–555.

464. Knight V, Wilson SZ, Quarles JM, et al: Ribavirin small-particle aerosol treatment of influenza. *Lancet* 1981; 2:945–949.

465. McClung HW, Knight V, Gilbert BE, et al: Ribavirin aerosol treatment of influenza B virus infection. *JAMA* 1983; 249:2671–2674.

466. Hall CB, Walsh EE, Hruska JF, et al: Ribavirin treatment of experimental respiratory syncytial virus infection. A controlled double-blind study in young adults. *JAMA* 1983; 249:2666–2670.

467. Hall CB, McBride JT, Walsh EE, et al: Aerosolized ribavirin treatment of infants with respiratory syncytial viral infection. A randomized double-blind study. *N Engl J Med* 1983; 308:1443–1447.

468. Hruska JF, Morrow PE, Suffin SC, et al: In vivo inhibition of respiratory syncytial virus by ribavirin. *Antimicrob Agents Chemother* 1982; 21:125–130.

469. Smith CB, Charette RP, Fox JP, et al: Lack of effect of oral ribavirin in naturally occurring influenza A virus (H1N1) infection. *J Infect Dis* 1980; 141:548–554.

470. Togo Y, McCraken EA: Double-blind clinical assessment of ribavirin (Virazole) in the prevention of induced infection with type B influenza virus. *J Infect Dis* 1976; 133(suppl):A109–A113.

471. Magnussen CR, Douglas RG Jr, Betts RF, et al: Double-blind evaluation of oral ribavirin (Virazole) in experimental influenza A virus infection in volunteers. *Antimicrob Agents Chemother* 1977; 12:498–502.

472. Cohen A, Togo Y, Khakoo R, et al: Comparative clinical and laboratory evaluation of the prophylactic capacity of ribavirin, amantadine hydrochloride, and placebo in induced human influenza type A. *J Infect Dis* 1976; 133(suppl):A114–A120.

473. Hillyard IW: The preclinical toxicology and safety of ribavirin, in Smith RA, Kirkpatrick W (eds): *Ribavirin: A Broad Spectrum Antiviral Agent.* New York, Academic Press, 1980, pp 59–71.

474. Centers for Disease Control: Assessing exposures of health-care personnel to aerosols of ribavirin-California. *MMWR* 1988, 37:560–563.

475. Rodriguez WJ, Dan Bui RH, Connor JD, et al: Environmental exposure of primary care personnel to ribavirin aerosol when supervising treatment of infants with respiratory syncytial virus infections. *Antimicrob Agents Chemother* 1987; 31:1143–1146.

476. Sidwell RW: Ribavirin: In vitro antiviral activity, in Smith RA, Kirkpatrick W (eds): *Ribavirin: A Broad Spectrum Antiviral Agent.* New York, Academic Press, 1980, pp 23–52.

477. Sidwell RW, Huffman JH, Khare GP, et al: Broad-spectrum activity of Virazole: 1-β-D-ribofuranosyl-1,2,4-triazole-3-carboxamide. *Science* 1972; 177:705–706.

478. Huffman JH, Sidwell RW, Khare GP, et al: In vitro effect of 1-β-D-ribofuranosyl-1,2,4-triazole-3-carboxamide (Virazole, ICN 1229) on deoxyribonucleic acid and ribonucleic acid viruses. *Antimicrob Agents Chemother* 1973; 3:235–241.

479. Allen LB, Wolf SM, Hintz CJ, et al: Effect of ribavirin on type 2 *Herpesvirus hominis* (HVH 2) in vitro and in vivo. *Ann NY Acad Sci* 1977; 284:247–253.

480. Sidwell RW, Simon LN, Witkowski JT, et al: Antiviral activity of Virazole: Review and structure-activity relationships, in Daikos GK (ed): *Proceedings of the Eighth International Congress on Chemotherapy,* 1973, Athens, Hellenic Society for Chemotherapy, 1974, vol 2, pp 889–903.

481. Katz E, Margalith E, Winer B: Inhibition of vaccinia virus growth by the nucleoside analoges of 1-β-D-ribofuranosyl-1,2,4-triazide-3-carboxamine (Virazole, ribavirin). *J Gen Virol* 1976; 32:327–330.

482. Toga Y: In vitro effect of Virazole against influenza viruses. *Antimicrob Agents Chemother* 1973; 4:641–642.

483. Hayden FG, Douglas RG Jr, Simons R: Enhancement of activity against influenza viruses by combinations of antiviral agents. *Antimicrob Agents Chemother* 1980; 18:536–541.

484. Burlington DB, Meiklejohn G, Mostow SR: Anti-influenza A activity of combinations of amantadine and ribavirin in ferret tracheal ciliated epithelium. *J Antimicrob Chemother* 1983; 11:7–14.

485. Kirshon B, Faro S, Zurawin RK, et al: Favorable outcome after treatment with amantadine and ribavirin in a pregnancy complicated by influenza pneumonia. A case report. *J Reprod Med* 1988; 33:399–401.

486. Hayden FG, Cote KM, Douglas RG Jr: Plaque inhibition assay for drug susceptibility testing of influenza viruses. *Antimicrob Agents Chemother* 1980; 17:865–870.

487. Stein DS, Creticos CM, Jackson GG, et al: Oral ribavirin treatment of influenza A and B. *Antimicrob Agents Chemother* 1987; 31:1285–1287.

488. Smee DF, Spendlove RS, Barnett BB, et al: Virus inhibitory effects of ribavirin in the presence of human serum and urine. Proceedings and abstracts of the 79th Annual Meeting of the American Society of Microbiology, 1979. Abstract No. A-63.

489. Smee DR, Sidwell RW, Barnett BB, et al: Bioassay system for determining ribavirin levels in human serum and urine. *Chemotherapy* 1981; 27:1–11.

490. Browne MJ: Comparative inhibition of influenza and parainfluenza virus replication by ribavirin in MDCK cells. *Antimicrob Agents Chemother* 1981; 19:712–715.

491. Hruska JF, Bernstein JM, Douglas RG Jr, et al: Effects of ribavirin on respiratory syncytial virus in vitro. *Antimicrob Agents Chemother* 1980; 17:770–775.

492. Allen LB, Fingal CM: Failure of type 1 herpes virus to develop resistance to ribavirin. *Antimicrob Agents Chemother* 1977; 12:120–121.

493. Huffman JH, Allen JB, Sidwell RW: Comparison of the development of resistant strains of type 1 herpes simplex virus to in vitro antiviral activity of 5-iodo-2'-deoxyuridine or ribavirin. *Ann NY Acad Sci* 1977; 284:233–238.

494. Sidwell RW, Robins RK, Hillyard IW: Ribavirin: An antiviral agent. *Pharmacol Ther* 1979; 6:123–146.

495. Appleyard G, Maber HB: Oxford JS, Williams JD (eds): *Chemotherapy and Control of Influenza.* New York, Academic Press, 1976, pp 49.

496. American Academy of Pediatrics Committee on Infectious Diseases: Ribavirin therapy of respiratory syncytial virus. *Pediatrics* 1987; 79:475–478.

497. Ribavirin and respiratory syncytial virus, editorial. *Lancet* 1986; 1:362–363.

498. Eggleston M: Clinical review of ribavirin. *Infect Control* 1987; 8:215–218.

499. Caramia G, Palazzini E: Efficacy of ribavirin aerosol treatment

for respiratory syncytial bronchiolitis in infants. *J Int Med Res* 1987; 15:227–233.

500. Rodriguez WJ, Kim JW, Brandt CD, et al: Aerosolized ribavirin in the treatment of patients with respiratory syncytial virus disease. *Pediatr Infect Dis J* 1987; 6:159–163.

501. Barry W, Cockburn F, Cornall R, et al: Ribavirin aerosol for acute bronchiolitis. *Arch Dis Child* 1986; 61:593–597.

502. Conrad DA, Christenson JC, Waner JL, et al: Aerosolized ribavirin treatment of respiratory syncytial virus infection in infants hospitalized during an epidemic. *Pediatr Infect Dis J* 1987; 6:152–158.

503. Outwater KM, Meissner HC, Peterson MB: Ribavirin administration to infants receiving mechanical ventilation. *Am J Dis Child* 1988; 142:512–515.

504. Frankel LR, Wilson CW, Demers RR, et al: A technique for the administration of ribavirin to mechanically ventilated infants with severe respiratory syncytial virus infection. *Crit Care Med* 1987; 15:1051–1054.

505. Hicks RA, Holson LC, Jackson MA, et al: Precipitation of ribavirin causing obstruction of a ventilation tube. *Pediatr Infect Dis* 1986; 5:707–708.

506. Salido-Rengell R, Nasser-Quiniones H, Briseno-Garcia B: Clinical evaluation of 1-β-D-ribofuranosyl-1,2,4-triazole-3-carboxamide (ribavirin) in a double-blind study during an outbreak of influenza. *Ann NY Acad Sci* 1977; 284:272–277.

507. Smith CB, Charette RP, Fox JP, et al: Lack of effect of oral ribavirin in naturally occurring influenza A virus (H1N1) infections. *J Infect Dis* 1980; 141:548–554.

508. Fernandez H: Ribavirin: A summary of clinical trials—Herpes genitalis and measles, in Smith RA, Kirkpatrick W (eds): *Ribavirin: A Broad Spectrum Antiviral Agent*. New York, Academic Press, 1980, pp 215–230.

509. Uylangco CV, Beroy GJ, Santiago LT, et al: A double-blind placebo-controlled evaluation of ribavirin in the treatment of acute measles. *Clin Ther* 1981; 3:389–396.

510. McCormick JB, King IJ, Webb PA, et al: Lassa fever. Effective therapy with ribavirin. *N Engl J Med* 1986; 314:20–26.

511. Denes AE, Ebert JW, Berquist KR, et al: Antiviral effects of virazole in chronic hepatitis B surface antigen seropositive chimpanzees. *Antimicrob Agents Chemother* 1976; 10:571–572.

512. Kende M, Lupton HW, Rill WL, et al: Enhanced therapeutic efficacy of poly(ICLC) and ribavirin combinations against Rift Valley fever virus infection in mice. *Antimicrob Agents Chemother* 1987; 31:986–990.

513. Prince GA, Hemming VG, Horswood RL, et al: Effectiveness of topically administered neutralizing antibodies in experimental immunotherapy of respiratory syncytial virus infection in cotton rats. *J Virol* 1987; 61:1851–1854.

514. Gruber WC, Wilson SZ, Throop BJ, et al: Immunoglobulin administration and ribavirin therapy: Efficacy in respiratory syncytial virus infection of the cotton rat. *Pediatr Res* 1987; 21:270–274.

515. Crumpacker C, Heagy W, Bubley G, et al: Ribavirin treatment of the acquired immunodeficiency syndrome (AIDS) and the acquired immunodeficiency syndrome-related complex (ARC). *Ann Intern Med* 1987; 197:664–674.

516. Davies WL, Grunert RR, Haff RF, et al: Antiviral activity of 1-adamantanamine (amantadine). *Science* 1964; 144:862–863.

517. Jackson GG, Muldoon RL, Akers LW: Serological evidence for prevention of influenzal infection in volunteers by an anti-influenzal drug, adamantanamine hydrochloride, in Sylvester JC (ed): *Antimicrobial Agents and Chemotherapy, 1963*. Ann Arbor, Mich, American Society of Microbiologists, 1964, p 703–707.

518. Hoffman CE, Neumayer EM, Haff RF, et al: Mode of action of the antiviral activity of amantadine in tissue culture. *J Bacteriol* 1965; 90:623–628.

519. Hoffman CE: Amantadine HC1 and related compounds, in Carter WA (ed): *Selective Inhibitors of Viral Functions*. Boca Raton, Fla, CRC Press, 1973, pp 199–211.

520. Ballowitz A, Kaslow RA: Use of amantadine in the United States, 1977–1982. *J Infect Dis* 1985; 151:372–373.

521. Zlydnikov DM, Kubar OI, Kovaleva TP, et al: Study of rimantadine in the USSR: A review of the literature. *Rev Infect Dis* 1981; 3:308–421.

522. Tilley JW, Kramer MJ: Aminoadamantane derivatives. *Prog Med Chem* 1981; 18:1–37.

523. Whitney JG, Gregory WA, Kaufer JC, et al: Antiviral agents I. Biocly(2.2.2)octan- and oct-2-enamines. *J Med Chem* 1969; 13:254–259.

524. Lundahl K, Schut J, Schlatmann JLMA, et al: Synthesis and antiviral activities of adamantane spiro compounds. 1. Adamantane and analogous spiro-3′-pyrrolidines. *J Med Chem* 1972; 15:129–132.

525. Tilley JW, Levitan P: Adamantylthiourea derivatives as antiviral agents. *J Med Chem* 1979; 22:1009–1010.

526. Al-Nakib W, Higgins PG, Willman J, et al: Prevention and treatment of experimental influenza A virus infection in volunteers with a new antiviral ICI 130, 685. *J Antimicrob Agents Chemother* 1986; 18:119–129

527. Beare AS, Hall TS, Tyrell DAJ: Protection of volunteers against challenge with A/Hong Kong/68 influenza virus by a new amantadine compound. *Lancet* 1972; 1:1039–1040.

528. Mathur A, Beare AS, Reed SE: In vitro antiviral activity and preliminary clinical trials of a new amantadine compound. *Antimicrob Agents Chemother* 1973; 4:421–426.

529. Appleyard G, Maber HB: A plaque assay for the study of influenza virus inhibitors. *J Antimicrob Chemother* 1(suppl):49–53.

530. Kato N, Eggers HJ: Inhibition of uncoating of fowl plaque virus by 1-adamantanamine hydrochloride. *Virology* 1969; 37:632–641.

531. Koff WC, Knight V: Effect of rimantadine on influenza virus replication. *Proc Soc Exp Biol Med* 1979; 160:246–253.

532. Koff WC, Knight V: Inhibition of influenza virus uncoating by rimantadine hydrochloride. *J Virol* 1979; 31:261–263.

533. Bukrinskaya AG, Vorkunova NK, Narmanbetova RA: Rimantadine hydrochloride blocks the second step of influenza virus uncoating. *Arch Virol* 1980; 66:275–282.

534. Bukrinskaaya AG, Vorkunova NK, Kornilayeva GV, et al: Influenza virus uncoating in infected cells and effect of rimantadine. *J Gen Virol* 1982; 60:49–59.

535. Bukrinskaya SG, Vorkunova NK, Pusharsdaya NL: Uncoating of rimantadine-resistant variant of influenza virus in the presence of rimantadine. *J Gen Virol* 1982; 60:61–66.

536. Richman DD, Hostetler KY, Yazaki PJ, et al: Fate of influenza A virion proteins after entry into subcellular fractions of LLC cells and the effect of amantadine. *Virology* 1986; 151:200–210.

537. Hay AJ, Zambon MC: Multiple actions of amantadine against influenza viruses, in *Antiviral Drugs and Interferon: The Molecular Basis of Their Activity*. Boston, Martinus Nijhoff, 1984, pp 301–315.

538. Hay AJ, Zambon MC, Wolstenholme AJ, et al: Molecular basis of resistance of influenza A viruses to amantadine. *J Antimicrob Chemother* 1986; 18:19–29.

539. White JK, Kielian M, Helenius A: Membrane fusion proteins of enveloped animal viruses. *Q R Biophys* 1983; 16:151–195.

540. Marsh M: The entry of enveloped viruses into cells by endocytosis. *Biochem. J* 1984; 218:1–10.

541. Lubeck MD, Schulman JL, Palese P: Susceptibility of influenza A viruses to amantadine is influenced by the gene coding for M protein. *J Virol* 1978; 28:710–716.

542. Hay, AJ, Kennedy NTC, Skehel JJ, Appleyard G: The matrix protein gene determines amantadine-sensitivity of influenza viruses. *J Gen Virol* 1979; 42:189–191.

543. Hay AJ, Wolstenholme AJ, Skehel JJ, et al: The molecular basis of the specific anti-influenza action of amantadine. *EMBO J* 1985; 4:3021–3024.

544. Belshe RB, Hall-Smith M, Hall CB, et al: Genetic basis of resistance to rimantadine emerging during treatment of influenza virus infection. *J Virol* 1988; 5:1508–1512.

545. Belshe RB, Powers B, Newman F, et al: Influenza virus resis-

tant to amantadine and rimantadine: results of one decade of surveillance. *J Infect Dis* 1988; in press.

546. Bean WJ, Threkeld SC, Webster RG: Biological potential of amantadine-resistant influenza A virus. *J Infect Dis* 1988; in press.

547. Zebedee SL, Lamb RA: Growth restriction of influenza A virus M2 protein: monoclonal antibody restriction of virus growth and detection of M2 in virions. *J Virol* 1988; 62:2762–2772.

548. Hay AJ: The mechanism of action of amantadine and rimantadine against influenza viruses, in Notkins AL, Oldstone MBA (eds): *Concepts in Viral Pathogenesis.* 1989, in press.

549. Warnick JE, Maleque MA, Bakry N, et al: Structure-activity relationships of amantadine: 1. Interaction of the N-alkyl analogues with the ionic channels of the nicotinic acetylcholine receptor and electrically excitable membrane. *Mol Pharmacol* 1982; 22:82–93.

550. Hayden FG, Hoffman HE, Spyker DA: Differences in side effects of amantadine hydrochloride and rimantadine hydrochloride relate to differences in pharmacokinetics. *Antimicrob Agents Chemother* 1983; 23:458–464.

551. Van Voris LP, Bartram J, Hoffman HE, et al: Comparative pharmacokinetics of rimantadine HC1 and amantadine HC1, in Program and Abstracts of the 23rd Interscience Conference on Antimicrobial Agents and Chemotherapy, Las Vegas, Oct 24–26, American Society for Microbiology, 1986.

552. Bleidner WE, Harmon JB, Hewes WE, et al: Absorption, distribution, and excretion of amantadine hydrochloride. *J Pharmacol Exp Ther* 1965; 150:484–490.

553. Hayden FG, Gwaltney JM Jr, Van de Casle RL, et al: Comparative toxicity of amantadine hydrochloride and rimantadine hydrochloride in healthy adults. *Antimicrob Agents Chemother* 1981; 19:226–233.

554. Van Voris LP, Betts RG, Hayden FG, et al: Successful treatment of naturally occurring influenza A/USSR/77 H₁N₁. *JAMA* 1981; 245:1128–1131.

555. Hayden FG, Minocha A, Spyker DA, et al: Comparative single-dose pharmacokinetics of amantadine hydrochloride in young and elderly adutls. *Antimicrob Agents Chemother* 1985; 28:216–221.

556. Schwab RS, et al: Amantadine in Parkinson's disease-review of more than two years' experience. *JAMA* 1972; 222:792–795.

557. Timberlake WH, Vance MA: Four years' treatment of patients with Parkinsonism using amantadine alone or with levodopa. *Ann Neurol* 1978; 3:119–128.

558. Aoki FY, Sitar DS, Ogilvie RI: Amantadine kinetics in healthy young subjects after long-term dosing. *Clin Pharmacol Ther* 1979; 26:729–736.

559. Greenblatt DJ, DiMascio A, Hormatz JS, et al: Pharmacokinetics and clinical effects of amantadine in drug-induced extrapyramidal symptoms. *J Clin Pharmacol* 1977; 17:704–708.

560. Horadam VW, Sharp JG, Smilack JD, et al: Pharmacokinetics of amantadine hydrochloride in subjects with normal and impaired renal function. *Ann Intern Med* 1981; 94:454–458.

561. Pacifici GM, Nardini M, Ferrari P, et al: Effect of amantadine on drug-induced parkinsonism: Relationship between plasma levels and effect. *Br J Clin Pharmacol* 1976; 3:883–889.

562. Aoki FY, Stiver HG, Sitar DS, et al: Prophylactic amantadine dose and plasma concentration-effect relationships in healthy adults. *Clin Pharmacol Ther* 1985; 37:128–136.

563. Endo Laboratories Inc: *Symmetrel: Amantadine Hydrochloride and Influenza A. Physician's Monograph.* Garden City, NY, E.I. Du Pont deNemours, 1977.

564. Smith CB, Purcell RH, Chanock RM: Effect of amantadine hydrochloride on parainfluenza type 1 virus infections in adult volunteers. *Am Rev Respir Dis* 1967; 95:689–690.

565. Fishaut M: Amantadine for severe influenza A pneumonia in infancy. *J Dis Child* 1980; 134:321.

566. Fahn S, Craddock G, Kumin G: Acute toxic psychosis from suicidal overdosage of amantadine. *Arch Neurol* 1971; 25:45–48.

567. Wu MJ, Ing TS, Soung LS, et al: Amantadine hydrochloride pharmacokinetics in patients with impaired renal function. *Clin Nephrol* 1982; 17:19–23.

568. Soung LS, Ing TS, Daugirdas JT, et al: Amantadine hydrochloride pharmacokinetics in hemodialysis patients. *Ann Intern Med* 1980; 93:46–49.

569. Ing TS, Daugiras JT, Soung LS, et al: Toxic effects of amantadine in patients with renal failure. *Can Med Assoc J* 1979; 120:695–698.

570. Aoki FY, Sitar DS: Amantadine kinetics in healthy elderly men: implications for influenza prevention. *Clin Pharmacol Ther* 1985; 37:137–144.

571. Hayden FG, Hall WJ, Douglas RG Jr, et al: Amantadine aerosols in normal volunteers: Pharmacology and safety testing. *Antimicrob Agents Chemother* 1979; 16:644–650.

572. Hayden FG, Hall WJ, Douglas RG Jr: Therapeutic effects of aerosolized amantadine in naturally acquired infection due to influenza A virus. *J Infect Dis* 1980; 141:535–542.

573. Knight V, Bloom K, Wilson SA, et al: Amantadine aerosol in humans. *Antimicrob Agents Chemother* 1979; 16:572–578.

574. Couch RB, Jackson GG: Antiviral agents in influenza—Summary of influenza workshop VIII. *J Infect Dis* 1976; 134:516–526.

575. Bryson YJ, Monahan C, Pollack M, et al: A prospective double-blind study of side effects associated with the administration of amantadine for influenza A virus prophylaxis. *J Infect Dis* 1980; 141:543–547.

576. Dolin R, Reichman RC, Madore HP, et al: A controlled trial of amantadine and rimantadine in the prophylaxis of influenza A infection. *N Engl J Med* 1982; 307:580–584.

577. Petterson RF, Helstrom P-E, Pentinen K, et al: Evaluation of amantadine in the prophylaxis of influenza A (H₁N₁) virus infection: A controlled field trial among young adults and high-risk patients. *J Infect Dis* 1980; 142:377–383.

578. Millet VM, Dreisbach M, Bryson YJ: Double-blind controlled study of central nervous system side effects of amantadine, rimantadine and chlorpheniramine. *Antimicrob Agents Chemother* 1982; 21:1–4.

579. Younkin SW, Betts RF, Roth FK, et al: Reduction in fever and symptoms in young adults with influenza A/Brazil/78 H₁N₁ infection after treatment wtih aspirin or amantadine. *Antimicrob Agents Chemother* 1983; 23:577–582.

580. Weitraub, M: Amantadine toxicity. *Drug Therapy* March 1976, pp. 181–185.

581. Postman JU, Van Tilburg W: Visual hallucinations and delirium during treatment with amantadine. *J Am Geriatr Soc* 1975; 23:212–215.

582. Casey DE: Amantadine intoxication reversed by physostigmine, letter. *N Engl J Med* 1978; 298:516.

583. α-Methyl-1-adamantanemethylamine HC1. *Supplemental Report.* Investigational brochure, Wilmington, Del, E.I. du Pont de Nemours, 1981.

584. α-Methyl-1-Adamantane-Methyamine HC1. Exp 126. *Oral Antiviral Agent.* Investigational brochure. E.I. du Pont de Nemours, 1971.

585. Wills RJ, Farolino DA, Choma N, et al: Rimantadine pharmacokinetics after single and multiple doses. *Antimicrob Agents Chemother* 1987; 31:826.

586. Anderson EL, Van Voris LP, Bartam J et al: Pharmacokinetics of a single dose of rimantadine in young adults and children. *Antimicrob Agents Chemother* 1987; 31:1140–1142.

587. Patriarca PA, Kater NA, Kendal AP, et al: Safety of prolonged administration of rimantadine hydrochloride in the prophylaxis of influenza A virus infections in nursing homes. *Antimicrob Agents Chemother* 1984; 26:101–103.

588. Dawkins AT, Gallager LR, Togo Y, et al: Studies on induced influenza in man. II. Double-blind study designed to assess the prophylactic efficacy of an analogue of amantadine hydrochloride. *JAMA* 1968; 203:93–97.

589. Rabinovich S, Baldini JT, Bannister R: Treatment of influenza. The therapeutic efficacy of rimantadine HC1 in a naturally occurring influenza A2 outbreak. *Am J Med Sci* 1969; 257:328–335.

590. Noble GR, Jones WE, Kaye HS, et al: Evaluation of amantadine and rimantadine side effects and efficacy in the prevention

of infection with influenza A/USSR/77 (H₁N₁) virus, in Program and Abstracts, 18th Interscience Conference on Antimicrobial Agents and Chemotherapy, Atlanta, Oct 1978, American Society for Microbiology, abstract No. 484.

591. Hayden RG, Zyldnikov DM, Iljenko VI, et al: Comparative therapeutic effect of aerosolized and oral rimantadine HC1 in experimental human influenza A virus infection. *Antiviral Res* 1982; 2:147–153.

592. Heider H, Adamczyk B, Prsber HW, et al: Occurrence of amantadine- and rimantadine-resistant influenza A virus strains during the 1980 epidemic. *Acta Virol* 1981; 25:396–400.

593. Wingfield WL, Pollack D, Grunert RR: Therapeutic efficacy of amantadine HC1 and rimantadine HC1 in naturally occurring influenza A2 respiratory illness in man. *N Engl J Med* 1969; 281:579–584.

594. Burlington DB, Meikeljohn G, Mostow SR: Anti-influenza A virus activity of amantadine hydrochloride and rimantadine hydrochloride in ferret tracheal ciliated epithelium. *Antimicrob Agents Chemother* 1982; 21:794–799.

595. Tsunoda A, Maassab HF, Cochran KW, et al: Antiviral activity of α-methyl-1-adamantanemethylamine hydrochloride. *Antimicrobial Agents and Chemotherapy*. Ann Arbor, Mich, American Society for Microbiology, 1965, pp 553–560.

596. McGahen JW, Neumayer EM, Grunert RR, et al: Influenza infections of mice. II. Curative activity of α-methyl-1-adamantane-methylamine HC1 (rimantadine HC1). *Ann NY Acad Sci* 1970; 173:557–567.

597. Pushkarskaya NL, Lvov ND, Kochemasova ZN: Comparative study on the inhibitory effect of rimantadine on the reproduction of epidemic strains of influenza A virus H₃N₂ and H₁N₁. *Acta Virol* 1981; 25:319–321.

598. Wallbank AM, Matter RE, Klinikowski NG: 1-Adamantanamine hydrochloride inhibition of Rous and Esk sarcoma viruses in cell culture. *Science* 1966; 152:1760–1761.

599. Skehel JJ, Hay AJ, Armstrong JA: On the mechanism of inhibition of influenza virus replication by amantadine hydrochloride. *J Gen Virol* 1977; 38:97–110.

600. Helenius A, Kartenbeck J, Simons K, et al: On the entry of Semliki Forest viruses into BHK-21 cells. *J Cell Biol* 1980; 84:404–420.

601. Koff WC, Elm JL Jr, Halstead SB: Suppression of dengue virus replication in vitro by rimantadine hydrochloride. *Am J Trop Med Hyg* 1981; 30:184–189.

602. Pfau CJ, Townbridge RS, Welsh RM, et al: Arenaviruses: Inhibition by amantadine hydrochloride. *J Gen Virol* 1972; 14:439.

603. Jansen EM, Liu O: Inhibitory effect of simple aliphatic amines on influenza virus in tissue culture. *Proc Soc Exp Biol Med* 1963; 112:456–459.

604. Helenius A, Marsh M, White J: Inhibition of Simliki Forset virus penetration by lysosmotropic weak bases. *J Gen Virol* 1982; 58:47–61.

605. Yoshimura A, Kuroda K, Kawasaki K, et al: Infectious cell entry mechanism of influenza virus. *J Virol* 1982; 43:284–292.

606. Daniels RS, Downie JC, Hay AJ, et al: Fusion mutants of the influenza virus haemagglutinin glycoprotein. *Cell* 1985; 40:431–439.

607. Scholtissek C, Faulkner GP: Amantadine-resistant and sensitive influenza A strains and recombinants. *J Gen Virol* 1979; 44:807–815.

608. Grunert RR, McGahen JW, Davies WL: The in vivo antiviral activity of 1-adamantanamine (amantadine). I. Prophylactic and therapeutic activity against influenza viruses. *Virology* 1965; 26:262–269.

609. Schulman JL: Effect of 1-amantadamine hydrochloride (amantadine HC1) and methyl-1-adamantanemethylamine hydrochloride (rimantadine HC1) on transmission of influenza virus infection in mice. *Proc Soc Exp Biol Med* 1968; 128:1173–1178.

610. Scott GH, Stephen EL, Berendt RF: Activity of amantadine, rimantadine and ribavirin against swine influenza in mice and squirrel monkeys. *Antimicrob Agents Chemother* 1978; 13:284–288.

611. Wilson SZ, Knight V, Wyde PR, et al: Amantadine and ribavirin aerosol treatment of influenza A and B infection in mice. *Antimicrob Agents Chemother* 1980; 17:624–648.

612. Bryans JT, Zent WW, Grunert RR, et al: 1-Adamantanamine hydrochloride prophylaxis for experimentally induced A/equine 2 influenza virus infection. *Nature* 1966; 212:1542–1544.

613. Easterday BC: Animal influenza, in Kilbourne ED (ed): *The Influenza Virus and Influenza*. New York, Academic Press, 1975; pp 449–481.

614. Lang G, Narayan O, Rouse BT: Prevention of malignant avian influenza by 1-adamantanamine hydrochloride. *Arch Gesamte Virusforsch* 1970; 38:171–184.

616. Webster RG, Kawaoka Y, Bean WJ, et al: Chemotherapy and vaccination: a possible strategy of the control of highly virulent influenza virus. *J Virol* 1985; 55:173–176.

617. Webster RG, Kawaoka Y, Bean WJ: Vaccination as a strategy to reduce the emergence of amantadine- and rimantadine-resistant strains of A/chick/Pennsylvania/83 (H₅N₂) influenza virus. *J Antimicrob Chemother* 1986; 18(suppl)B:157–164.

618. Smorodinstev AA, Zlydnikov DM, Kiseleva AM, et al: Evaluation of amantadine in artifically induced A2 and B influenza. *JAMA* 1970; 213:1148–1454.

619. Taylor-Dickenson PC, Chang T-W, Weinstein L: Effects of amantadine on influenza B and measles virus infection in children, in *Antimicrobial Chemotherapy*, Ann Arbor, Mich, American Society of Microbiology, 1967, p 521.

620. Togo Y, Hornick RB, Dawkins AT: Studies on induced influenza in man. *JAMA* 1968; 203:87–92.

621. Monto AS, Gunn RA, Bandy K, et al: Prevention of Russian influenza by amantadine. *JAMA* 1979; 241:1003–1007.

622. Oker-Blom N, Hovi T, Leinikki P, et al: Protection of man from natural infection with influenza A2 Hong Kong virus by amantadine: A controlled field trial. *Br Med J* 1970; 3:676–678.

623. Nafia I, Turcanu AG, Braun I, et al: Administration of amantadine for the prevention of Hong Kong influenza. *Bull WHO* 1970; 42:423–427.

624. Smorodintsev AA, Karpuhin GI, Zlydnikov DM, et al: The prophylactic effectiveness of amantadine hydrochloride in an epidemic of Hong Kong influenza in Leningrad in 1969. *Bull WHO* 1970; 42:865–872.

625. Muldoon RL, Stanley ED, Jackson GG: Use and withdrawal of amantadine chemoprophylaxis during epidemic influenza A. *Am Rev Respir Dis* 1976; 113:487–491.

626. Sears SD, Clements ML: Protective efficacy of low-dose amantadine in adults challenged with wild-type influenza A virus. *Antimicrob Agents Chemother* 1987; 10:1470–1473.

627. O'Donoghue JM, Ray CG, Terry DW Jr, et al: Prevention of nosocomial influenza infection with amantadine. *Am J Epidemiol* 1973; 93:276.

628. Atkinson WL, Arden NH, Patriarca PA, et al: Amantadine prophylaxis during an institutional outbreak of type A (H1N1) influenza. *Arch Intern Med* 1986; 146:1751–1756.

629. Galbraith AW, Oxford JS, Schild GC, et al: Protective effect of 1-adamantanamine hydrochloride in naturally occurring influenza A2 infections in the family environment. *Lancet* 1969; 2:1026–1028.

630. Clover RD, Crawford SA, Abell TD, et al: Effectiveness of rimantadine prophylaxis of children within families. *Am J Dis Child* 1986; 140:706.

631. Quarles JM, Couch RB, Cate TR, et al: Comparison of amantadine and rimantadine for prevention of type A (Russian) influenza. *Antiviral Res* 1981; 1:149–155.

632. LaMontagne JR, Gallasso GJ: Report of a workshop on clinical studies of the efficacy of amantadine and rimantadine against influenza virus. *J Infect Dis* 1978; 138:928–931.

633. Dolin R, Betts RF, Treanor JJ, et al: Rimantadine prophylaxis of influenza in the elderly. Program and Abstracts of the 23rd Interscience Conference on Antimicrobial Agents and Chemotherapy, Las Vegas, Oct 24–26, 1983, abstract No. 691, p 20.

634. Aoki FY, Sitar DS: Amantadine prophylaxis during an institu-

tional outbreak of type A influenza. *Arch Intern Med* 1987; 147:1189.

635. Payler DK, Purdham PA: Influenza A prophylaxis with amantadine in a boarding school. *Lancet* 1984; 1:502–504.

636. Rose HJ: Use of amantadine in influenza: a second report. *J R Coll Gen Pract* 1983; 33:651.

637. Galbraith AW, Oxford JS, Schild GC, et al: Study of 1-adamantanamine hydrochloride used prophylactically during the Hong Kong influenza epidemic in the family environment. *Bull WHO* 1969; 41:677–682.

638. Current status of amantadine and rimantadine as anti-influenza-A agents: memorandum from a WHO meeting. *Bull WHO* 1985; 63:51–56.

639. Arden NH, et al: The roles of vaccination and amantadine prophylaxis in controlling an outbreak of influenza-A (H3N2) in a nursing home. *Arch Intern Med* 1988; 148:865–868.

640. Patriarca PA, et al: Prevention and control of type A influenza infections in nursing homes. Benefits and costs of four approaches using vaccination and amantadine. *Ann Intern Med* 1987; 107:732–740.

641. Advisory Committee on Immunization Practices: Prevention and control of influenza. *MMWR* 1986; 35:317–331.

642. Centers for Disease Control: Recommendations for prevention and control of influenza: recommendations of the immunization practices advisory committee. *Ann Intern Med* 1986; 92:399–404.

643. Centers for Disease Control: Outbreaks of influenza among nursing home residents—Connecticut, United States. *MMWR* 1985; 34:479–492.

644. Use of amantadine in nursing homes for the control of influenza A. *Colo Med* 1987; 84:24.

645. Galbraith AW, Oxford JS, Schild GC, et al: Therapeutic effect of 1-adamantanamine hydrochloride in naturally occurring influenza A2/Hong Kong infection. *Lancet* 1971; 2:113–115.

646. Hornick RB, Togo Y, Mahler S, et al: Evaluation of amantadine hydrochloride in the treatment of A2 influenza disease. *Ann NY Acad Sci* 1970; 173:10–19.

647. Knight V, Fedson D, Baldini J, et al: Amantadine therapy of epidemic influenza A2/Hong Kong. *Infect Immun* 1970; 1:200–204.

648. Kitamoto O, Hirayama M, Ichida F, et al: Therapeutic effectiveness of amantadine hydrochloride in influenza A2 and influenza A Hong Kong — double blind studies. *Prog Antimicrob Anticancer Chemother* 1970; 2:65–70.

649. Galbraith AW: Therapeutic trials of amantadine (Symmetrel) in general practice. *J Antimicrob Chemother* 1975; 1(suppl):81–86.

650. Togo Y, Hornick RB, Felliti VJ, et al: Evaluation of therapeutic efficacy of amantadine in patients with naturally occurring A2 influenza. *JAMA* 1970; 211:1149–1156.

651. Baker LM, Paulshock MP, Lezzoni DG: The therapeutic efficacy of Symmetrel (amantadine hydrochloride) in naturally occurring influenza A2 respiratory illness. *J Am Osteopath Assoc* 1969; 68:1244–1250.

652. Kitamoto O: Therapeutic effectiveness of amantadine hydrochloride in naturally occurring Hong Kong influenza — Double blind studies. *Jpn J Tuberc Chest Dis* 1971; 17:1–7.

653. Hayden FG, Monto AS: Oral rimantadine hydrochloride therapy of influenza A virus H3N2 subtype infection in adults. *Antimicrob Agents Chemother* 1986; 29:339–

654. Hall CB, Dolin R, Gala CL, et al: Children with influenza A infection: treatment with rimantadine. *Pediatrics* 1987; 80:275–282.

655. Thompson J, Fleet W, Lawrence E, et al: A comparison of acetaminophen and rimantadine in the treatment of influenza A infection in children. *J Med Virol* 1987; 21:249–255.

656. Appleyard G: Amantadine-resistance as a genetic marker for influenza viruses. *J Gen Virol* 1977; 36:249–255.

657. Pemberton RM, Jennings, R, Potter CW, et al: Amantadine resistance in clinical influenza A (H3N2) and (H1N1) virus isolates. *J Antimicrob Chemother* 1986; 18(suppl B):135–140.

658. Quilligan JJ Jr, Hirayama M, Baernstein HD, Jr: The suppression of A2 amantadine in children by the prophylactic use of amantadine. *J Pediatr* 1966; 69:572–575.

659. Bryson YJ: The use of amantadine in children for prophylaxis and treatment of influenza A infections. *Pediatr Infect Dis* 1982; 1:44–46.

660. Castro DT: Amantadine hydrochloride: an agent for the prevention and treatment of influenza A infection. *J Pediatr Health Care* 1987; 1:51–53.

661. Finklea JK, Hennessey AB, Davenport FM: A field trial of amantadine chemoprophylaxis in respiratory disease. *Am J Epidemiol* 1967; 85:403–412.

662. Boezi JA: The antiherpes action of phosphonoacetate. *Pharmacol Ther* 1979; 4:231–243.

663. Oberg B: Antiviral effects of phosphonoformate (PFA, foscarnet sodium). *Pharmacol Ther* 1983; 19:387–415.

664. Sundquist B, Uberg B: Phosphonoformate inhibits reverse transcriptase. *J Gen Virol* 1979; 45:273–281.

665. Sarin PS, Taguchi Y, Sun D, et al: Inhibition of HTLV-III/LAV replication by foscarnet. *Biochem Pharmacol* 1985; 34:4075–4079.

666. Sandstrom EG, Byington RE, Kaplan JC, et al: Inhibition of human T-cell lymphotropic virus type III in vitro by phosphonoformate. *Lancet* 1985; 1:1480–1482.

667. Hirsch MS, Kaplan JC: Prospects for therapy for infections with human T-lymphotropic virus type III. *Ann Intern Med* 1985; 103:750–755.

668. Bergdahl S, Sonnerborg A, Larsson A, et al: Declining levels of HIV p24 antigen in serum during treatment with foscarnet. *Lancet* 1988; 1:1052.

669. Anon: Foscarnet. *Lancet* 1985; 2:648–649.

670. Spruance SL, Freeman DJ, Sheth NV: Comparison of foscarnet cream, acyclovir cream, and acyclovir ointment in the topical treatment of experimental cutaneous herpes simplex virus type 1 infection. *Antimicrob Agents Chemother* 1986; 30:196–198.

671. Wallin J, Lernestedt J-O, Ogenstad S, et al: Topical treatment of recurrent genital herpes infections with foscarnet. *Scand J Infect Dis* 1985; 17:165–172.

672. Barton SE, Munday PE, Kinghorn GR, et al: Topical treatment of recurrent genital herpes simplex viral infections with trisodium phosphonoformate (foscarnet): Double-blind, placebo-controlled multicentre study. *Genitourin Med* 1986; 62:247–250.

673. Klintmalm G, Lonngvist B, Oberg B, et al: Intravenous foscarnet for the treatment of severe cytomegalovirus infection in allograft recipients. *Scand J Infect Dis* 1985; 17:157–163.

674. Ringden O, Wilczak H, Lonngvist B, et al: Foscarnet for cytomegalovirus infections. *Lancet* 1985; 2:1503–1504.

675. Ringden O, Lonngvist B, Paulin T, et al: Pharmacokinetics, safety, and preliminary clinical experiences using foscarnet in the treatment of cytomegalovirus infections in bone marrow and renal transplant recipients. *J Antimicrob Chemother* 1986; 17:373–387.

676. Apperley JJ, Marcus RE, Goldman JM, et al: Foscarnet for cytomegalovirus pneumonitis. [letter] *Lancet* 1985; 1:1151.

677. Gaub J, Pedersen C, Poulsen AG, et al: The effect of foscarnet (phosphonoformate) on human immunodeficiency virus isolation, T-cell subsets and lymphocyte function in AIDS patients. *AIDS* 1987; 1:27–33.

678. Farthing CF, Dalgleish AG, Clark A, et al: Phosphonoformate (foscarnet): A pilot study in AIDS and AIDS related complex. *AIDS* 1987; 1:21–25.

679. Farthing CF, Anderson MG, Ellis ME, et al: Treatment of cytomegalo-virus pneumonitis with foscarnet (trisodium phosphonoformate) in patients with AIDS. *J Med Virol* 1987; 22:157–162.

680. Acheson JF, Shah SM, Spalton DJ, et al: Treatment of CMV retinitis in an AIDS patient. *Br J Ophthalmol* 1987; 71:810–816.

681. Weber JN, Thom S, Barrison I, et al: Cytomegalovirus colitis and oesophageal ulcerations in the context of AIDS: Clinical manifestations and preliminary report of treatment with foscarnet (phosphonoformate). *Gut* 1987; 28:482–487.

682. Jacobson MA, O'Donnell JJ, Mills J: Foscarnet treatment of cytomegalovirus retinitis in patients with the acquired immunodeficiency syndrome. *Antimicrob Agents Chemother* 1989; 33:736–741.

683. Walmsley SL, Chew E, Read SE, et al: Treatment of cytomegalovirus retinitis with trisodium phosphonoformate hexahydrate (foscarnet). *J Infect Dis* 1988; 157:569–572.

684. Stiehm ER, Kronenberg LH, Rosenblatt HM, et al: Interferon: Immunobiology and clinical significance. *Ann Intern Med* 1982; 96:80–93.

685. Murray HW, Rubin BY, Masur H, et al: Impaired production of lymphokines and immune (gamma) interferon in the acquired immunodeficiency syndrome. *N Engl J Med* 1984; 310:883–889.

686. Fauci AS, Rosenberg SA, Sherwin SA, et al: Immunomodulators in clinical medicine. *Ann Intern Med* 1987; 106:421–433.

687. Zoon KC: Human interferons: Structure and function. *Interferon* 1987; 9:1–12.

688. Herberman RB: Cancer therapy by biological response modifiers. *Clin Physiol Biochem* 1987; 5:238–248.

689. Fahey JL, Sarna G, Gale RP, et al: Immune interventions in disease [erratum appears in *Ann Intern Med* 1987; 106:783]. *Ann Intern Med* 1987; 106:257–274.

690. Douglas RM, Moore BW, Miles HB, et al: Prophylactic efficacy of intranasal alpha$_2$-interferon against rhinovirus infections in the family setting. *N Engl J Med* 1986; 314:65–70.

691. Vogt M, Hirsch MS: Prospects for the prevention and therapy of infections with the human immunodeficiency virus. *Rev Infect Dis* 1986; 8:991–1000.

692. Zarling JM, Eskra L, Borden EC, et al: Activation of human natural killer cells cytotoxicity for human leukemia cells by purified interferon. *J Immunol* 1979; 123:63–70.

693. Hartshorn KL, Hirsch MS: Interferons, in Peterson PK, Verhoef J (eds): *Antimicrobial Agents Annual.* Amsterdam, Elsevier, 1986, pp 371–383.

694. Cheeseman S, Rubin R, Steward J, et al: Controlled clinical trial of prophylactic human leukocyte interferon in renal transplantation. *N Engl J Med* 1979; 300:1345–1349.

695. Merigan TC, Rand KH, Pollard RB, et al: Human leukocyte interferon for the treatment of herpes zoster in patients with cancer. *N Engl J Med* 1978; 298:981–987.

696. Tyrell DA: Interferons and their clinical value. *Rev Infect Dis* 1987; 9:243–249.

697. Kuhls TL, Sacher J, Pineda E, et al: Suppression of recurrent genital herpes simplex virus infection with recombinant alpha interferon. *J Infect Dis* 1986; 154:437–442.

698. Strander HA: Interferon in the treatment of human papilloma virus. *Med Clin North Am* 1986; 70:(suppl):19–23.

699. Shindo M, Okuno T, Matsumoto M, et al: Serum 2′,5′-oligoadenylate synthetase activity during interferon treatment of chronic hepatitis B. *Hepatology* 1988; 8:366–370.

700. Muller R, Klein H, Vido I, et al: Antiviral treatment in chronic hepatitis B. Data of 5 prospective controlled randomized trials. *J Hepatol* 1986; 3(suppl 2):S217–S223.

701. Billiau A: The mode of action of interferons in viral infections and their possible role in the control of hepatitis B. *J Hepatol* 1986; 3(suppl 2):S171–S179.

702. Krown SE, Real FX, Cunningham-Rundles, et al: Preliminary observation on the effect of recombinant leukocyte interferon in homosexual men with Kaposi's sarcoma. *N Engl J Med* 1983; 308:1071–1076.

703. Ho DD, Hartshorn KL, Rota TR, et al: Recombinant human interferon alpha-$_a$ suppresses HTLV-III replication in vitro. *Lancet* 1985; 1:602–604.

704. Yamamoto JK, Barre-Sinoussi F, Bolton V, et al: Human alpha and beta interferon but not gamma suppress the in vitro replication of LAV, HTLV-III, and ARV-2. *J Interferon Res* 1986; 6:143–152.

705. Pitha PM, Wivel NA, Fernie BF, et al: Effect of interferon on murine leukemia virus infection. IV. Formation of non-infectious virus in chronically infected cells. *J Gen Virol* 1979; 42:467–480.

706. Rios A, Mansell PWA, Newell GR, et al: Treatment of acquired immunodeficiency syndrome related Kaposi's sarcoma with lymphoblastoid interferon. *J Clin Oncol* 1985; 3:506–512.

707. Volberding PA, Mitsuyasu Rt: Recombinant interferon alpha in the treatment of acquired immune deficiency syndrome related Kaposi's sarcoma. *Semin Oncol* 1985; 12:2–6.

708. Real FX, Oettgen HF, Krown SE: Kaposi's sarcoma and the acquired immunodeficiency syndrome. Treatment with high and low doses of recombinant leukocyte A interferon. *J Clin Oncol* 1986; 4:544–551.

709. Rinehart J, Malspeis L, Young D, et al: Phase I/II trial of human recombinant beta-interferon serine in patients with renal cell carcinoma. *Cancer Res* 1986; 46:5364–5367.

710. Vadhan-Raj S, Nathan CR, Sherwin SA, et al: Phase I trial of recombinant interferon gamma by 1-hour infusion. *Cancer Treat Rep* 1986; 70:609–614.

711. Spiegel RJ: Intron-A (interferon alfa-2b): Clinical overview. *Cancer Treat Rev* 1985; 12:5–16.

712. Horoszewicz JS, Leoung SS, Dolen J, et al: Human fibroblast interferon as a potential anticancer drug: Phase I studies on intravenous and intrathecal administration, in Serrou B, Rosenfeld C (eds): *International Symposium on New Trends in Human Immunology and Cancer Immunotherapy.* Paris, Doin, 1980, pp 908–919.

713. Bocci V: Pharmacokinetics of interferon. *Tex Rep Biol Med* 1982; 41:336–342.

714. Quesada JR, Talpaz M, Rios A, et al: Clinical toxicity of interferons in cancer patients. A review. *J Clin Oncol* 1986; 4:234–243.

715. Krown SE: Cytokines: Interferons and interferon inducers in cancer treatment. *Semin Oncol* 1986; 13:207–217.

716. Umeda T, Nijima T: Phase II study of alpha interferon on renal cell carcinoma. *Cancer* 1986; 58:1231–1235.

717. Cohen MC, Huberman MS, Nesto RW: Recombinant A$_2$ interferon-related cardiomyopathy. *Am J Med* 1988; 85:549–551.

7

Nosocomial Viral Infections

William M. Valenti

RESPIRATORY VIRUSES

INFLUENZA VIRUS

RESPIRATORY SYNCYTIAL VIRUS

PARAINFLUENZA VIRUSES

RHINOVIRUSES

ADENOVIRUSES

HERPESVIRUSES

VARICELLA-ZOSTER VIRUS
HERPES ZOSTER
HERPES SIMPLEX VIRUS
CYTOMEGALOVIRUS
EPSTEIN-BARR VIRUS

HEPATITIS

HEPATITIS A
HEPATITIS B
HEPATITIS B IN HEMODIALYSIS UNITS
HEPATITIS C

RUBELLA

MEASLES (RUBEOLA)

MUMPS

SLOW VIRUS INFECTION

GASTROENTERITIS VIRUSES

ROTAVIRUS
NORWALK GASTROENTERITIS VIRUS AND RELATED AGENTS

PICORNAVIRUSES

NONPOLIO ENTEROVIRUSES
POLIOVIRUSES

RHABDOVIRUS

ARENAVIRUSES

LYMPHOCYTIC CHORIOMENINGITIS (LCM)
LASSA FEVER
SMALLPOX

OTHER VIRUSES

MARBURG VIRUS
EBOLA VIRUS
PAPILLOMAVIRUSES
HUMAN IMMUNODEFICIENCY VIRUS

COHORT ISOLATION PRECAUTIONS

COMMUNICABLE DISEASE SURVEY

VISITOR POLICIES

PERSONNEL

EMPLOYEES WITH RESPIRATORY ILLNESSES
SPECIAL CONSIDERATIONS

CONCLUSION

The emergence of the acquired immunodeficiency syndrome (AIDS) epidemic has changed the discipline of infection control and caused us to rethink our infection control activities. In the past, the infection control emphasis for viral infections involved various aspects of hepatitis B and varicella control. Now, prevention of the human immunodeficiency virus (HIV) has become a major focus in health care. One change has been to employ universal blood and body fluid precautions or the body substance isolation approach, both of which treat the blood, body fluids, and needles from all patients the same way. This is an old philosophy of infection control that has taken a new name and emphasis in response to AIDS.

Other new issues in virology include the emergence of antiviral therapies in general, potential for use of the varicella vaccine in health care workers, and more widespread use of laser therapy for papilloma virus infections. Also, second-generation hepatitis B and polio vaccines have been developed and we are on our way to developing a variety of therapies for the HIVs.

The fields of infection control and virology continue to grow and come together as these new technologies are developed and our understanding of virology expands. The result of this union

Table 7–1

Rates of Nosocomial Virus Infection by Service, December 1977 to April 1979

	Pediatrics	Psychiatry	Medicine	Surgery	Gynecology	Total
Exogenous						
Respiratory syncytial virus	15*(37.5)†	—	—	—	—	15
Influenza A virus	1 (2.5)	5 (20.6)	2 (2.0)	—	—	8
Adenovirus	3 (7.5)	—	—	—	—	3
Parainfluenza	3 (7.5)	—	—	—	—	3
Rhinovirus	—	—	2 (2.0)	—	—	2
Rotavirus	2 (5.0)	—	—	—	—	2
Hepatitis, non-A, non-B	1 (2.5)	—	—	1 (0.8)	—	2
Echovirus	1 (2.5)	—	—	—	—	1
Coxsackievirus	1 (2.5)	—	—	—	—	1
Cytomegalovirus	—	—	—	1 (0.8)	—	1
Respiratory illness (not tested)	—	3 (12.3)	2 (2.0)	1 (0.8)	—	6
Subtotal	27 (67.4)	8 (32.9)	6 (5.9)	3 (2.5)	—	44
Endogenous						
Herpes simplex	—	2 (8.2)	4 (4.0)	3 (2.5)	1 (2.4)	10
Cytomegalovirus	2 (12.4)	—	3 (3.0)	2 (1.7)	—	7
Varicella-zoster	—	—	1 (1.0)	—	—	1
Subtotal	2 (5.0)	2 (8.2)	8 (7.9)	5 (4.1)	1 (2.4)	18
Total	29 (72.4)	10 (45.6)	14(13.8)	8 (6.6)	1 (2.4)	62

*Number of cases.

†Rate per 10,000 admissions per service.

Reproduced with permission from Valenti WM, et al: Nosocomial viral infections: I. Epidemiology and significance. Infect Control *1980; 1:33–37.*

is the time-honored infection control objective of improving patient care.

RESPIRATORY VIRUSES

Transmission of respiratory viruses in health care facilities is an annual event in temperate climates. Both patients and personnel appear to be at risk during the winter season, and the large numbers of health care personnel with acute respiratory illnesses become a major concern for infection control practitioners. Patients at greatest risk of acquiring nosocomial viral respiratory disease are pediatric patients,[1–5] patients in closed or semiclosed areas such as psychiatric units,[1] and patients in extended care facilities.[6]

Many health care facilities lack viral diagnostic facilities; therefore, it is essential that personnel have an understanding of the etiologic possibilities and the mechanisms of transmission of respiratory viruses to minimize their spread in the hospital. There are two major mechanisms of transmission of respiratory viruses. The first is by small-particle aerosols (10 μm median diameter) containing infectious virions. Aerosols produced by coughing, sneezing, or talking are capable of transmitting infection from one person to another over considerable distance (greater than 6 ft). Influenza virus and, perhaps, varicella and measles virus exhibit patterns of spread compatible with this mechanism. Other viral agents may be transmitted over shorter distances by mechanisms requiring close person-to-person contact, generally at a distance of less than 3 ft separating two persons. This method of transmission may occur when large droplets produced by coughing or sneezing contaminate the donor's hand, and infectious virus is transferred to

the skin or mucous membranes of a susceptible host. Thus, transmission occurs directly by hand-to-hand contact or indirectly by a contaminated fomite. In these latter cases infection of the susceptible host is a result of autoinoculation, with transfer of virus from hands to mucous membranes of the eye or nose. Rhinoviruses and respiratory syncytial virus exhibit patterns of spread compatible with close contact transmission.

Viral respiratory illnesses generally are classified based on the predominant anatomical site of involvement in the respiratory tract (Tables 7–1, 7–2, and 7–3). In addition to specific syndromes, epidemiologic data such as season of the year (Figures 7–1 and 7–2), geographic location, and type of patient population may also suggest specific viral etiologies in the absence of viral diagnostic facilities.

INFLUENZA VIRUS

Influenza A and B virus infections are among the most contagious diseases of man. They are characterized by explosive epidemics, and nosocomial transmission of influenza A[5–10] and B[11] has been well documented. Person-to-person transmission is thought to take place primarily by small-particle aerosols. These aerosols may account for the explosive nature of influenza outbreaks since, in a closed environment, one infected person can potentially infect large numbers of susceptibles. During an outbreak of influenza A at the New York Hospital during the pandemic of 1957 to 1958, 15 of 29 patients and 15 of 30 personnel on one hospital floor became infected, possibly from a single index case.[7] Influenza A virus infection may result in significant morbidity (eg, primary

Table 7–2
Viruses Associated with Respiratory Symptoms in Adults

Virus	Common Cold	Pharyngitis Civilian	Pharyngitis Military	Tracheo-bronchitis	Pneumonia Civilian	Pneumonia Military
Rhinovirus, 89 types	+ + + +*	+ +	+	+	+	+
Influenza A virus	+	+ +	+	+ + +	+ +	+ +
Influenza B virus	+	+ +	+	+ +	+	+
Coronavirus	+	+	+	+	+	+
Adenovirus types 4, 7	+	+	+ + + +	+	+	+ + + +
Adenovirus types 1, 2, 3, 5	+	+	+	+	+	+
Herpes simplex virus	—	+ +	+	—	—	—
Epstein-Barr virus	—	+	+	—	+	+
Respiratory synctial virus	+	+	+	+	—	—
Parainfluenza virus types 1, 2, 3	+	+ +	+	+	—	—
Group A coxsackievirus	+	+	+	+	+	+
Group B coxsackievirus	+	+	+	+	+	+
Echovirus	+	+	+	+	+	+
Poliovirus	+	+	+	+	—	—

*Relative frequency: + = occasional case; + + = small proportion of cases; + + + = substantial proportion of cases; + + + + = majority of cases.
Reproduced with permission from Valenti WM, et al: Nosocomial viral infections. II. Guidelines for prevention and control of respiratory viruses, herpesviruses, and hepatitis viruses. Infect Control 1980; 1:166.

Table 7–3
Viruses Associated with Respiratory Symptoms in Children

Virus	Common Cold	Pharyngitis	Tracheo-bronchitis	Laryngo-tracheo-bronchitis	Pneumonia	Bronchiolitis
Respiratory syncytial virus	+ + +*	+ +	+ + +	+ +	+ + + +	+ + + +
Parainfluenza virus type 3	+ + +	+ +	+ + +	+ +	+ + +	+ +
Parainfluenza virus type 2	+ + +	+ +	—	+	+	+
Parainfluenza virus type 1	+ + +	+ +	+ +	+ + + +	+ +	+
Influenza A virus	+	+ +	+ +	+ +	+ +	+
Adenovirus types 1, 2, 3, 5	+ +	+ +	+	+	+	+
Influenza B virus	+	+ +	+ +	+	+	+
Rhinovirus, 89 types	+ +	+ +	+	+	+	+
Coronavirus	+	+	+	+	—	—
Group A coxsackievirus	+	+	+	+	+	—
Group B coxsackievirus	+	+	+	+	+	—
Echovirus	+	+	+	+	+	—
Poliovirus	+	+	—	—	—	—

*Relative frequency; + = occasional case; + + = small proportion of cases; + + + = substantial proportion of cases; + + + + = majority of cases.
Reproduced with permission from Valenti WM, et al: Nosocomial viral infections. II. Guidelines for prevention and control of respiratory viruses, herpesviruses, and hepatitis viruses. Infect Control 1980; 1:166.

influenza pneumonia, secondary bacterial pneumonia) and mortality. It may also pose a significant risk to elderly and chronically ill institutionalized patients,[6] to patients in closed or semiclosed areas such as psychiatric units,[1] and to pediatric patients.[5]

Isolation Precautions

Current Centers for Disease Control (CDC) guidelines do not recommend a mask for influenza, because it is usually not possible to identify all infected patients. Respiratory isolation with masks for hospital personnel and private rooms for patients with proven or suspected influenza virus infection have been standard precau-

tions in the past. Despite this contradiction, it makes sense to consider hospitalized patients with febrile respiratory illness when influenza is prevalent in the community to have influenza until proved otherwise. In hospital outbreaks involving large numbers of people, patients with influenza should be cohorted in the same room or on the same hospital floor.[7] Shedding of virus may persist for as long as five days after the onset of symptoms in adults,[12] and for seven days or longer in children.[10] At the present time we maintain isolation precautions for patients with influenza virus infection for seven days or for the duration of clinical illness, whichever is longer. Amantadine may shorten the duration of

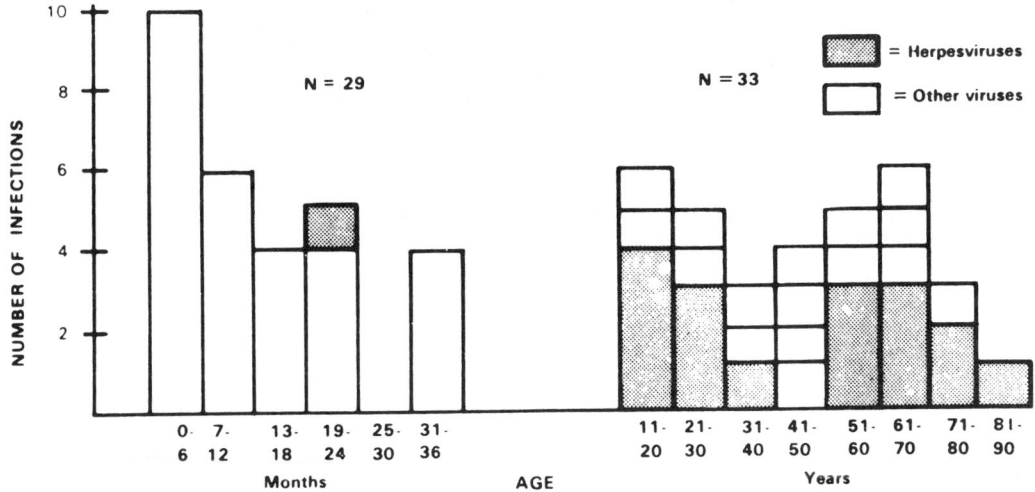

Figure 7–1. Nosocomial infections by age. (From Valenti WM, et al: Nosocomial viral infections: I. Epidemiology and significance. *Infect Control* 1980; 1:33–37. Used with permission).

infectivity and precautions could probably be discontinued earlier in these patients.

Immunization

Vaccination in the fall of each year of patients with chronic underlying illnesses and persons over the age of 65 should result in 60% to 90% protection against influenza A and B infections for many hospitalized patients.[13] Patients in extended care facilities are good candidates for vaccination.[14]

Although influenza virus infection in healthy young hospital

personnel is often benign and selflimited, hospital staff who have contact with patients should be vaccinated because of their high degree of exposure to influenza, and high risk of transmission of infection to hospitalized patients. Attempts at vaccinating hospital personnel are often unrewarding. Influenza vaccination programs directed at health care workers should include education about the purpose of vaccination and its side effects. While a significant association between influenza A/swine/New Jersey/vaccines in 1976 and Guillain-Barré syndrome was noted, a similar association has not been noted with subsequent vaccine formulations.[15]

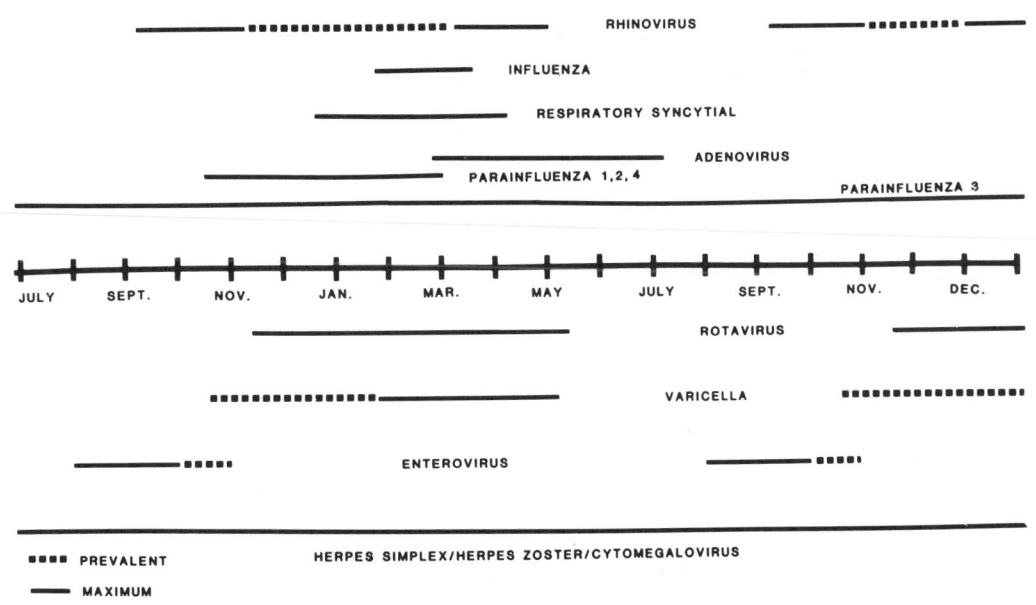

Figure 7–2. Period of greatest activity of commonly seen viruses.

Chemoprophylaxis

O'Donoghue et al have shown that amantadine hydrochloride is 80% effective in preventing nosocomial influenza A virus infection.[16] In addition, prophylactic amantadine plus vaccination are probably additive.[17,18] During periods of high prevalence of influenza virus infection in the hospital or community, amantadine may be used in unvaccinated hospital patients and personnel. Vaccination of susceptibles should also be done during an epidemic, in addition to amantadine use until an adequate serologic response to vaccine has occurred, generally about 2 weeks after vaccination. The usual dose of amantadine is 200 mg per day in either a single or divided dose. If susceptible personnel are not vaccinated, amantadine must be continued for the duration of the outbreak. Amantadine is not effective prophylactically for influenza B infection. In view of the problems with compliance when large numbers of people are taking amantadine, preexposure vaccination against influenza is the best preventive measure against the disease.

Other Considerations

During documented influenza outbreaks other control measures should be considered, depending on the severity of the outbreak: (1) curtailment or elimination of elective medical and surgical admissions (2) restriction of cardiovascular and pulmonary surgery, (3) restriction of hospital visitors, especially those with respiratory illnesses, and (4) work restriction for medical personnel with acute respiratory disease. Controlled studies to evaluate these measures have not been done to date. In addition, (3) and (4) above may be difficult to implement. It is often necessary to appeal to the common sense and good judgment of hospital personnel and visitors in restricting their contact in hospital. If personnel recovering from influenza must work, it is best to assign those personnel to areas of the hospital where influenza virus infections are prevalent.

RESPIRATORY SYNCYTIAL VIRUS

Respiratory syncytial virus (RSV) is the most common cause of lower respiratory tract disease in children less than 2 years of age[2] and may account for up to 50% of all hospital admissions for respiratory disease in this age group.[19] It is the most common nosocomial infection on our pediatric wards.[1,20,21] People in all age groups are potentially susceptible to RSV infection and, because immunity is incomplete and not permanent, reinfections occur throughout life.[22,23] RSV infections also occur in hospital personnel,[20,21] and in elderly chronically ill patients.[6] Generally, RSV infections occur in annual epidemics of 2 to 3 months' duration, often beginning in late December. Early studies by Chanock et al showed that approximately 59% of children admitted to the hospital with nonviral diseases showed serologic conversion to RSV while hospitalized during periods of RSV prevalence in the community.[24]

The primary mode of transmission of RSV requires close person-to-person contact. Spread is by direct inoculation of droplets or large particles or by self-inoculation after touching contaminated surfaces such as skin or fomites. Studies by Hall et al have elucidated the chain of transmission of RSV.[19,20,25] Patients infected with RSV shed large amounts of virus in their respiratory secretions

with a mean duration of shedding of six to seven days, and with a range of one to 21 days.[19] The virus can be recovered from the immediate environment of infected patients for prolonged periods of time. For example, RSV in nasal secretion from infected infants can be recovered for up to 30 minutes from contaminated skin, gowns, or paper tissues.[19] The virus appears to survive best on nonporous surfaces such as countertops and could be recovered for up to six hours from these surfaces.[19] Infectious virus can then be transferred from these environmental surfaces to hands, or from hand to hand.[25] Studies in volunteers have also demonstrated that infection can be initiated by instillation of RSV-containing fluid into the mucous membranes of the eyes or nose but not the mouth.[26] Spread by small-particle aerosols is less likely since nosocomial outbreaks are not as explosive as those of influenza virus, and studies in volunteers show that only subjects cuddling infected infants and touching contaminated surfaces became infected with RSV.[27] Subjects did not become infected if kept at more than 6 ft from an infected baby, suggesting that small-particle aerosol transmission is not a major route of transmission of RSV.[27]

The risk of nosocomial RSV infection has been correlated with the duration of hospitalization, and increases with each subsequent week of hospitalization. In one study, RSV infection was acquired by 45% of contact infants hospitalized for 1 week or more. The rate of RSV acquisition increased with each subsequent week of hospitalization until all infants hospitalized 4 weeks or more became infected.[20,28] The rate of infection was not related to underlying illness or age of the patient. Health care workers continue to play a major role in nosocomial RSV transmission. Recently, LeClair et al have shown that when health care workers wear masks and gowns, rates of nosocomial RSV transmission decrease.[29]

Isolation Precautions

During periods of RSV prevalence in the community, infants with respiratory illness who are admitted to the hospital should be placed in single rooms or cohorted with other infants with RSV illness. A clean gown should be worn for each contact with infected infants, and the gown should be changed after this contact.[29] To prevent cross-infection, hospital personnel caring for infected infants should not care for infants without respiratory illness, if at all possible. Although the risk of small-particle aerosol transmission of RSV is small, masks may prevent transmission of RSV via close contact.[29]

Immunizaton

There is no effective vaccine for RSV.

Special Considerations

Attempts to reduce nosocomial transmission of RSV should be directed toward hospital personnel. Education of health care workers should include special emphasis on both the mode of transmission of RSV and on the role of personnel in the chain of infection.

It may be necessary to curtail visits from family and friends who have respiratory illness during periods of RSV prevalence in the community. In the absence of locally generated data on RSV prevalence, one can assume its occurrence during December through March in the United States and Europe.

PARAINFLUENZA VIRUSES

Nosocomial transmission of parainfluenza types 1, 3, and 4a on pediatric services has been documented.[30, 31] Mufson et al have reported that 18% of infants who are well or infected with another respiratory pathogen at the time of admission to a children's hospital subsequently acquired nosocomial infections with parainfluenza type 3.[31] Infections in hospitals have also been reported in adult renal transplant patients[32] and in elderly institutionalized patients.[33] Details of transmission of parainfluenza virus have not been fully elucidated but transmission is believed to occur by close person-to-person contact or by large droplet spread (hand to hand or via fomites).[33] Infections with parainfluenza types 1 and 2 are seasonal, with the greatest activity occurring during the fall months. Epidemics with types 1 and 2 also occur approximately every 2 years, while infections with parainfluenza virus type 3 tend to occur throughout the year.

Isolation Precautions

Once again, handwashing is a key infection control strategy, especially in view of the proposed mechanism of transmission of parainfluenza virus. Precautions should be the same as those used for RSV since the mode of transmission is the same. Masks and gowns should be changed after each contact. Precautions should be maintained for the duration of the illness.

RHINOVIRUSES

Although rhinovirus infections are ubiquitous during the winter and spring months, they are relatively uncommon nosocomial pathogens.[1, 34] Rhinovirus may be a cause of significant morbidity in premature infants.

Large quantities of virus are present in nasal secretions and readily contaminate the hands of the infected individual. Virus transmission appears to take place directly from hand to hand or indirectly via fomites. From the recipient's hands, virus may be inoculated by touching mucous membranes of the nose and eyes.[35]

Once again, handwashing would appear to be the most effective way of minimizing transmission of rhinovirus.[36, 37]

Isolation Precautions

Generally, precautions other than handwashing are not recommended or necessary for patients with rhinovirus infection. However, cohorting of patients with infection in nurseries may be necessary on occasion.

ADENOVIRUSES

Adenovirus infection is common in the general population throughout the year. These viruses are quite stable and can be transmitted via a number of routes and cause a variety of illnesses. Adenoviruses are associated with conjunctivitis, keratoconjunctivitis, pharyngoconjunctival fever, pneumonia, and pertussislike syndrome. Respiratory transmission via aerosols occurs in all age groups,[38-40] and volunteer studies have shown that inhalation of small doses of virus can initiate acute respiratory illness, including pneumonia.[40] Fecal-oral transmission occurs but probably is more important in children than in adults.[38]

Hospital-acquired adenovirus infection has been reported in both patients and personnel.[41-45] Infections in neonates,[46] in pediatric patients,[42, 47] and in day care settings[48] account for many of the reported cases of nosocomial adenovirus infections. Although adenovirus pneumonia has been reported more frequently in military recruits, adenovirus can be the cause of sporadic pneumonia in up to 10% of pediatric patients admitted with pneumonia.[38] Transmission of adenovirus from patients with pneumonia to hospital personnel has occurred, with personnel developing conjunctivitis and pharyngoconjunctival fever. Adenovirus infections in immunocompromised hosts has led to speculation that adenoviruses, like herpesviruses, may be reactivated after primary infection.[49] Adenovirus has also been implicated as a cause of diffuse interstitial pneumonia in a renal transplant recipient.[50] All of these infections may have resulted from endogenous reactivation of adenovirus. Nosocomial transmission from staff with mild upper respiratory illness to immunocompromised patients may also have been involved.

An outbreak of epidemic keratoconjunctivitis due to adenovirus type 8, originating in a physician's office, has been reported.[51] Of 98 persons subjected to ophthalmic procedures, 21 of them developed infection. The physician's own eye infection probably served as a major source of virus with transmission to susceptible patients occurring by direct transfer of virus from the physician's hands and by indirect transfer of the virus via a Schiötz tonometer. A similar outbreak of keratoconjunctivitis was associated with a contaminated ophthalmic solution in an industrial health clinic.[52]

Recent evidence suggests that new types of adenovirus, called noncultivable adenoviruses (NCAV), are a frequent cause of sporadic diarrhea in children.[53, 54] Outbreaks of diarrhea among young children in a long-stay orthopedic ward suggest that these viruses can cause epidemic diarrhea and can act as nosocomial pathogens in addition to causing sporadic disease.[55, 56] Adenovirus type 3 associated with diarrhea has also been transmitted in premature nurseries.[46]

Isolation Precautions

Patients with adenovirus infection should be in private rooms if possible. Personnel should wear gowns and gloves when direct contact with skin and mucous membranes is anticipated. We also recommend a mask for personnel at all times. This is because available evidence suggests that airborne transmission of adenovirus takes place easily in closed populations and because of the apparent susceptibility of most adults to infection. Care must also be taken when handling secretions and contaminated articles. Because shedding of adenovirus may be variable and prolonged, these precautions should be maintained for the duration of clinical illness.

Immunization

No immunization is available.

Special Considerations

Adenoviruses are stable and survive for long periods of time. Special care must be given to the decontamination and sterilization of contaminated instruments such as tonometers. Thorough cleaning followed by steam sterilization (15 psi for 15 min at 121°C,

15 psi for 10 min at 126°C, or 29 psi for 3 min at 134°C) is recommended. The use of a disposable tonofilm to cover and preserve sterility of the tonometer has also been suggested but should not be a substitute for routine cleaning and disinfection.[57]

Handwashing between contacts cannot be overemphasized. Because personnel with conjunctivitis may present a hazard to patients, it is recommended that personnel with infectious conjunctivitis have no contact with patients in nurseries, obstetric units, or in the operating room until all drainage ceases.

HERPESVIRUSES

The members of the family *Herpetoviridae* include varicella-zoster virus (VZV), herpes simplex virus (HSV types 1 and 2), cytomegalovirus (CMV), and Epstein-Barr virus (EBV). Herpesvirus infections become latent or inactive after primary infection and can reactivate at a time remote from the primary infection.[58, 59] Infectious virus can be isolated in both primary and reactivated infections due to herpesviruses. Often primary infection is symptomatic while reactivation infection often is asymptomatic.[60] In the United States most individuals have come in contact with all the human herpesviruses (except for herpes simplex type 2) by age 50[61]; thus nosocomial infection is relatively infrequent. Transmission of the herpesviruses occurs from person to person and requires close personal contact for all except VZV. Of the herpesviruses, VZV is the most capable of nosocomial spread because of its transmission by direct contact or by small-particle aerosols. In addition, because of certain underlying diseases or chemotherapy, many hospitalized patients are susceptible to reactivation of herpesvirus infections. However, when herpesviruses are transmitted in the hospital, nosocomial transmission may be difficult to establish since all but HSV types 1 and 2 have prolonged incubation periods and illness often may develop after discharge.

In a 17-month period of careful virus surveillance, 20 cases of reactivation infection with herpesviruses were documented based on clinical criteria.[1] These cases represent reactivation of latent infection and not nosocomial transmission.

Varicella-Zoster Virus

VZV, the most contagious of the herpesviruses, is the etiologic agent of chickenpox and herpes zoster (shingles). Nosocomial transmission of chickenpox is well recognized,[62-65] and is a cause of mortality and serious morbidity in immunocompromised patients.[63, 66] The mechanism of transmission of varicella is primarily via small-particle aerosols and nosocomial spread by this route is well documented.[65] Epidemiologic evidence suggests that patients may shed varicella viruses prior to the onset of rash,[64] but this has never been proved by virus isolation.

Whenever possible, patients with uncomplicated chickenpox should not be admitted to the hospital since they present a hazard to susceptible patients and personnel. In addition, patients who develop chickenpox or who are exposed to chickenpox while hospitalized should be discharged, if possible. Severly ill patients who require hospitalization are exceptions.

Isolation Precautions

Nonimmune patients exposed to chickenpox or patients with active chickenpox should be isolated in a private room or cohorted. Universal precautions that prevent contact with secretions from patients' vesicles are recommended. Although the duration of contagion by the respiratory route is variable, the respiratory transmission of varicella decreases about five days after the onset of rash. Precautions should be continued until all skin lesions are completely dried and crusted.

The susceptible patient exposed to chickenpox who cannot be discharged from the hospital presents a problem with regard to restriction of activity and isolation precautions. Because of its high degree of communicability, personnel and patients in the same unit as a patient with chickenpox should be considered exposed.[67] Furthermore, patients with negative or unknown histories of chickenpox should be considered susceptible and will require isolation precautions until immunity can be proved. Because there are incomplete data on respiratory shedding of virus prior to the onset of the rash, precautions or cohorting of exposed individuals should be initiated on the tenth day after exposure. Ideally, immunity should be proved by varicella antibody testing. Unless immunity can be proved, these patients should remain isolated until discharged from the hospital or for 21 days, whichever occurs first.

Health care workers who are exposed to individuals with active varicella and who have negative or unknown histories of previous varicella infection should not work with susceptible patients from the tenth to the 21st day after exposure. Immunity should be proved by antibody testing in employees also. Otherwise, if large numbers of employees are involved, these precautions will result in a significant expense to the hospital due to time lost from work. In general, a history of previous chickenpox in an adult or child is felt to be a reliable index of immunity. The immune status in exposed individuals with negative or unknown histories of chickenpox should be confirmed. The most reliable tests for immunity are the fluorescent antibody to membrane antigen test (FAMA), and the immune adherence hemagglutination test (IAH); both tests are more reliable than complement fixation (CF) since these antibodies are thought to persist indefinitely. Skin testing for immunity to VZV has been described but is rarely done clinically.[69]

Prophylaxis

Varicella-zoster immune globulin (VZIG) is intended primarily for passive immunization of susceptible, immunocompromised children after significant exposure to chickenpox or herpes zoster. This group includes children with primary immunodeficiencies, neoplastic diseases, recipients of immunosuppressive therapy, and newborns of mothers who develop chickenpox within five days prior to delivery or 48 hours after delivery.[70] Available evidence suggests that if VZIG is administered within 96 hours of exposure, chickenpox can be prevented or modified in children with impaired immunity. The criteria for use of VZIG are shown in Table 7-4.

Varicella vaccine has been used in adults and might be useful as part of a preventive program for varicella in susceptible health care workers.[71]

Herpes Zoster

Transmission of virus from patients with herpes zoster to produce chickenpox occurs,[72] but less frequently than transmission of virus from patients with chickenpox. This may be due to the lower frequency of VZV in oral secretions of patients with herpes zoster than in patients with chickenpox.

Table 7–4
Indications and Guidelines for Use of Varicella-Zoster
Immune Globulin (VZIG) for Prophylaxis of
Chickenpox (Varicella)

1. One of the following underlying illnesses or
   conditions:
   a. Leukemia or lymphoma
   b. Congenital or acquired immunodeficiency
   c. Under immunosuppressive treatment
   d. Newborn of mother who had onset of
      chickenpox <5 d before delivery or within 48 h
      after delivery

and

2. One of the following types of exposure to
   chickenpox or zoster patient(s):
   a. Household contact
   b. Playmate contact (>1 h play indoors)
   c. Hospital contact (in same 2- to 4-bed room or
      adjacent beds in a large ward)
   d. Newborn contact (newborn of mother who had
      onset of chickenpox <5 d before delivery or
      within 48 h after delivery)

and

3. Negative or unknown prior history of chickenpox
   (see text)

and

4. Age of <15 yr, with administration to older
   patients on an individual basis (see ref 71)

and

5. Time elapsed after exposure is such that VZIG
   can be administered within 96 h

It is not entirely clear what precipitates zoster, but exposure to VZV has been suggested.[73]

Isolation Precautions

Localized herpes zoster requires precautions to guard against acquisition of infection by direct contact with secretions from vesicles and from secretion-contaminated articles. A private room is desirable, but not required.

Patients with disseminated herpes zoster should be cared for in the same way as patients with chickenpox. They require isolation precautions in a private room with negative air pressure.

Hospital personnel with negative or unknown histories of chickenpox should avoid contact with patients with localized or disseminated herpes zoster. In general, a positive history of chickenpox is felt to be a reliable index of previous disease in adults or children, as discussed under Varicella-Zoster Virus.

Gershon et al have shown that more than 95% of American-born women of childbearing age have detectable antibody to VZV.[74] Ross noted an 8% attack rate in historically susceptible adults with household exposure to chickenpox.[75] A negative or unknown history of chickenpox in adults is often unreliable. These data suggest that the risk to hospital personnel for varicella acquisition from patients is small but measurable. The pool of susceptible individuals, however small, represents a potential hazard for transmission of varicella both to susceptible patients and personnel.

Identification of individuals with negative or unknown histories using reliable screening tests (FAMA or IAH) at the time of employment is the ideal infection control measure. Since these tests may not be readily available, selective screening should be done as quickly as possible after exposure in order to minimize the disruption of patient services.

Herpes Simplex Virus

The use of acyclovir has made most infections with HSV more manageable. This drug is useful for both treatment and prevention of outbreaks of HSV infection of the skin and mucous membranes.

Reactivation of HSV type 1 infection frequently occurs spontaneously in healthy patients or personnel as well as in immunocompromised hosts. Individuals with reactivated HSV-1 infection rarely have intraoral lesions and often do not have labial lesions. Therefore, asymptomatic personnel potentially can transmit HSV-1 to susceptible patients. This transmission may explain the cluster of infections that have been described in burned patients,[76] or in immunocompromised patients.[77] Transmission of infection from hospital patients to personnel is well documented. Direct inoculation of HSV-1 on fingers of personnel after contact with the infected patient's mouth can result in herpetic whitlow.[78, 79] Herpetic whitlow can easily be mistaken for pyogenic paronychia and is often quite disabling to hospital personnel.[79] Herpetic whitlow can occur in immune or nonimmune individuals.[80] In addition, primary herpes simplex stomatitis and pharyngitis can occur in hospital personnel.[81, 82] Restriction endonuclease techniques have provided strong evidence that nosocomial transmission of HSV-1 occasionally occurs.[81–83] Also, a cluster of primary HSV stomatitis and pharyngitis has occurred due to transmission of HSV-1 to patients in a dental office from a dental hygienist with herpetic whitlow.[83]

Transmission of HSV-2 from mother to newborn infant has long been a concern on obstetric and newborn services. When genital herpes is present in a mother at term, as many as 40% to 60% of vaginally delivered infants will have clinically apparent infection with HSV-2.[84] Approximately 50% of these infants will have severe or fatal illness. The risk of neonatal infection may be lower as reported recently.[85] This risk can be minimized but not eliminated if delivery is by caesarian section and membranes remain unruptured or have been ruptured for less than six hours.[84] The risk of infection at birth is also less if the mother's infection is reactivated rather than primary.[84]

Although transmission of infection from mother to infant at the time of birth is well documented, evidence for postpartum transmission is only indirect. Infection control policies often lack uniformity from one institution to another.[85, 86] It is generally agreed, however, that certain precautions may be indicated, depending on the clinical status of the mother (see Isolation Precautions).

Isolation Precautions

Infection control recommendations for mothers with known, suspected, or inactive herpes simplex have been described in detail.[87]

Women With Proven or Clinically Suspected Genital Herpes Simplex.—These women may transmit virus postnatally to their offspring as well as to other close contacts. Therefore, personnel should observe universal or body substance isolation precautions, using gowns and gloves for direct contact with lesions containing virus. Soiled perineal pads, dressings, and linen should be handled the same way. The mother may care for her baby but she should be out of bed, must wash hands thoroughly prior to contact with the baby, and should wear a clean cover gown. The infant should be observed after birth for signs and symptoms of illness. Currently, there are no data regarding the use of the observation or isolation nursery for such infants after birth. The value of such a nursery for use in these cases is controversial and certainly nursery outbreaks of herpes simplex infection are uncommon. However, an observation nursery for these infants is recommended, and good technique including thorough handwashing should be emphasized. These precautions do not restrict mother-baby contact yet offer some degree of protection for other infants in the nursery.

Women With Active Nongenital Herpes Simplex.—Similar wound and skin precautions are reasonable for these women. A private room is not indicated. Mothers may care for their infants using the same precautions as noted for mothers with known or suspected genital herpes simplex with the addition of a mask or dressing to cover the lesions. The infant may be kept in the general newborn nursery without isolation after birth if there has been no maternal contact. After the first contact with the mother, the infant should be placed in the suspect or isolation nursery using precautions as noted previously for babies born to mothers with active genital herpes simplex.

Women With Clinically Inactive Herpes Simplex at Term.— No special precautions are necessary for either the mother or infant.

Special Considerations

The question of work restrictions for employees with herpes simplex infection is asked frequently. To determine restrictions in employees, it may be reasonable to distinguish between covered and uncovered active lesions of herpes simplex. Personnel who have exposed active lesions of herpes simplex should not work with pregnant women or newborn infants (term or preterm), burned patients, or immunocompromised hosts until all lesions have dried and crusted. These same restrictions apply to personnel with active herpetic whitlow. When working with patients, these employees should wear a glove on the involved hand. This may not be possible, however, since tight plastic gloves compress the painful lesion of whitlow. In these cases, infected employees may not be able to work until the lesion is dried and crusted. Personnel who have active genital herpes simplex or covered lesions of herpes simplex are not restricted from patient contact, but strict handwashing should be followed before and after patient contact.

Universal precautions to prevent herpetic whitlow include wearing gloves on both hands if direct contact with oral or pharyngeal secretions is anticipated.[79] Gloves should be worn routinely when suctioning patients or whenever contact with these herpes simplex lesions occurs.[79]

Cytomegalovirus

Cytomegalovirus, like other herpesviruses, requires close contact for spread. There has been a resurgence of concern over CMV risk to health care workers as patients with HIV infection or AIDS are admitted to hospitals, since most patients with AIDS also shed CMV. Evidence to date suggests that CMV infection is actually a sexually transmitted disease. The virus is found in cervical and vaginal secretions and in semen. In addition, the prevalence of CMV antibody has been found to be higher in homosexual men (96%) when compared to heterosexual men (57%).[88] It has also been shown to increase with years of sexual activity and is higher in prostitutes than in nuns.[89]

The potential for in-hospital transmission of CMV has long been a concern of hospital personnel because of its role in congenital malformations. Dworsky et al have shown that pediatric health care workers are not at increased risk of acquiring CMV from their patients.[90] In another setting, dialysis personnel failed to show any seroconversion after 2 years of follow-up.[91] Similar results were found in dialysis personnel in another institution after 2 years of contact.[92] Recent case reports have also demonstrated lack of transmission of CMV from patients to health care personnel by using restriction endonuclease techniques.[93, 94]

The risk of acquisition of CMV from blood transfusion has been established more clearly. This risk is reduced with leukocyte-poor blood,[95] and virtually eliminated if washed frozen red blood cells are used.[95] It can also be eliminated by screening potential blood donors for antibody to CMV and eliminating those with antibody. An important source of CMV is from patients undergoing renal transplantation.[96, 97] The majority of such patients have reactivation of endogenous CMV as a result of the transplant process or from associated immunosuppressive therapy. While these infections are not truly hospital-acquired, we have classified them as endogenous nosocomial infections.[1] A small number of transplant patients acquire CMV exogenously from the transplanted kidneys or from circulating cells present in the transplanted kidney.

Isolation Precautions

Congenital CMV Infection.—A recent review failed to show any way of identifying newborns with CMV by certain "risk factors" or clinical parameters. Therefore, the most reasonable approach to infection control in the nursery involves handling all patients with Universal Infection Control precautions (see Human Immunodeficiency Virus). Patients with congenital CMV infection are assigned to private rooms whenever possible. We suggest gloves for contact with secretions, excretions, soiled articles and soiled linens from patients. In our hospital, pregnant personnel are not restricted from caring for patients with CMV based on available data. Instead, hospital workers should be educated regarding the modes of transmission of CMV and the importance of better infection control techniques, including regular handwashing for all patients.

Acquired CMV Infection.—Careful handwashing is recommended before and after patient contact, but private room precautions are not used for patients with acquired CMV infection. Pregnant health care workers are not restricted from caring for patients with acquired CMV infection.

Special Considerations

At the present time, it is not recommended to perform routine screening of hospital personnel on newborn, pediatric, or dialysis or transplant services for antibody to CMV.

Patients undergoing renal transplantation and their donors or donor kidneys are tested for antibody to CMV prior to transplantation. Whenever possible, kidneys from antibody-negative donors are transplanted to antibody-negative recipients.

Epstein-Barr Virus

Epstein-Barr virus (EBV) is shed in high concentration from the oropharynx of infected patients. Although nosocomial transmission is relatively rare, infection has occurred through blood transfusion[98] and from blood contamination of dialysis equipment.[99]

HEPATITIS

Hepatitis A

Nosocomial hepatitis A has been known for many years to occur in institutions for the mentally retarded.[100] Crowded conditions and poor hygienic practices on the part of many patients in these institutions appear to be predisposing factors. Recently, it has been shown that as many as 80% of susceptible institutionalized patients may develop hepatitis A virus (HAV) infection as measured by seroconversion of antibody to HAV within 3 years of admission.[101, 102] This rate of seroconversion is considerably higher than the rate of seroconversion in noninstitutionalized adults or in child controls.

Transmission of HAV in general hospitals is uncommon. Nosocomial transmission from either personnel to patient or from patient to patient has not been reported. Infrequent transmission of HAV infection from patient to personnel has occurred.[103] Foodborne outbreaks have also occurred involving primarily hospital workers but also small numbers of patients.[100, 104]

Isolation Precautions

Precautions for the care of patients with hepatitis should follow the universal precautions–body substance isolation framework. Precautions should emphasize the importance of care in handling of bedpans, equipment, or instruments contaminated with feces. Infection control measures such as gowns, gloves, and masks are not required routinely but should be used whenever necessary to minimize contact with feces or material contaminated with feces. A private room is not required unless the patient is incontinent of feces.

Prophylaxis

Immune serum globulin (ISG) has been shown to be effective in preventing or modifying hepatitis A both before exposure and early in the incubation period. If given within 2 weeks of exposure, ISG will prevent 80% to 90% of HAV infection.

Hepatitis B

Nosocomial transmission of hepatitis B is thought to occur most often by parenteral exposure to hepatitis B surface antigen (HBs Ag)–positive blood. Transmission can occur from an acutely ill patient or, more likely, from an asymptomatic person who is positive for HBsAg and is unaware of it. The HBsAg carrier state accounts for the prolonged period of potential hepatitis B virus (HBV) infectivity of some patients even after the acute infection has resolved. The infectivity of blood is best correlated with the presence of either DNA polymerase or hepatitis B e antigen (HBeAg). However, for infection control purposes all blood that is positive for hepatitis B should be considered infectious. Although HBsAg has been detected in all body fluids, the frequency with which fluids other than blood contribute to hospital infection is probably low. The mechanisms of transmission, listed in order of ease of transmission, are listed below[105]:

1. Overt parenteral. Direct percutaneous inoculation by needles contaminated with serum or plasma (eg, transfusion of contaminated blood or blood products, contaminated needle stick).

2. Inapparent parenteral: (a) percutaneous inoculation of infective serum or plasma without overt needle puncture (eg, contamination of cutaneous cuts, abrasions, or lacerations); (b) contamination of mucosal surfaces by infected serum or plasma (eg, pipetting accidents, accidental ingestion, other direct contact with mucous membranes of the eye or mouth; (c) contamination of mucosal surfaces by infective secretions other than serum or plasma (eg, sexual activity); (d) transfer of infective material via a vector or inanimate environmental surfaces (eg, toothbrushes, toys, drinking cups, horizontal surfaces in hospitals).

Ample opportunity exists for transmission of hepatitis B in the hosptial to both patients and hospital personnel. Medical personnel who appear to be at highest risk are those working in dialysis units, emergency settings, hematology-oncology units, and certain laboratories.[106]

Health care workers appear to have a higher prevalence of markers for previous HBV infection than nonhospital personnel.[107–109]

Dienstag and Ryan have reviewed the prevalence of hepatitis B markers in hospital personnel by job category.[110] Emergency room nurses were found to have the highest prevalence of markers of previous HBV infection (30%). Other groups that appeared to be at high risk are surgical intensive care unit (ICU) nurses, phlebotomists, chemistry laboratory technicians, and surgical house officers. While this survey reflects the HBV status of employees in a large urban hospital, it also serves to underscore the fact that health care workers are at higher risk of HBV infection than the general population. In a large survey reported by Denes et al, evidence of prior HBV infection was higher among physicians practicing in urban communities, increased with the number of years in practice, and was highest among pathologists and surgeons.[108] When compared to dentists, physicians have a similar overall rate of positivity.[109] Nosocomial transmission of HBV from patients to personnel is well-known. Transmission of HBV from personnel to patients, however, rarely occurs, except in certain surgical settings. Epidemiologic data are available that show both transmission[111] and lack of transmission[112–114] from HBsAg-positive personnel to their patients.

In its guidelines for infection control in health care workers, the CDC does not recommend that HBsAg-positive employees be restricted from patient contact routinely.[115] Still, the issue of the HBsAg-positive health care worker presents a dilemma for the infection control professional. With maximum participation in hepatitis B vaccine programs by health care workers, this question becomes a moot point. The most important factors contributing to transmission of HBV from personnel to patients are probably the level and duration of antigenemia. It appears that patient care that does not involve contact with blood of infected personnel does not present a risk to patients.[112–114]

Table 7–5
Recommendations for Hepatitis B (HB) Prophylaxis Following Percutaneous Exposure

| Source | Exposed Person | |
	Unvaccinated	Vaccinated
HBsAg-positive	1. HBIG × I immediately* 2. Initiate HB vaccine† series	1. Test exposed person for anti-HBs 2. If inadequate antibody‡ HBIG × 1 immediately plus HB vaccine booster dose

Known source
  High risk
  HBsAg-positive
	1. Initiate HB vaccine series
	2. Test source for HBsAg
	 If positive, HBIG × 1
		1. Test source for HBsAg only if exposed is vaccine nonresponder; if source is HBsAg-positive, give HBIG × 1 immediately plus HB vaccine booster dose

Low risk HBsAg-positive	Initiate HB vaccine series	Nothing required
Unknown source	Initiate HB vaccine series	Nothing required

HBsAg = hepatitis B surface antigen; HBIG = hepatitis B immune globulin; SRU = sample ratio units; RIA = radioimmunoassay; EIA = enzyme immunoassay.
*HBIG dose 0.06 mL/kg intramuscularly (IM).
†HB vaccine dose 20μg IM for adults; 10μg IM for infants or children under 10 years of age. First dose within 1 week; second and third doses, 1 and 6 months later.
‡Less than 10 SRU by RIA, negative by EIA.

Isolation Precautions

Acute Hepatitis B.—A private room is not required routinely. However, the patient who is incontinent of feces or who is bleeding is managed best in a private room. While routine use of gowns, gloves, and masks is not required, any or all of these precautions should be used if patient contact may also involve contact with blood or other body fluids. Gowns, gloves, and masks are particularly important if there is to be direct contact with the patient from whom blood splashes or spills are likely to occur (eg, upper or lower gastrointestinal [GI] bleeding). Gloves should be used for direct contact with blood or blood-contaminated equipment such as intravenous (IV) catheters, drains, or soiled dressings. Precautions to avoid contact with feces or instruments that have been contaminated with feces should also be taken.

Prophylaxis

Preexposure Prophylaxis.—Hepatitis B vaccine is recommended for health care workers who have regular contact with blood or needles. Preexposure prophylaxis is the best strategy to prevent hepatitis B in health care workers. Either the plasma–derived vaccine (20 μg/mL) or the recombinant vaccine (10 μg/mL) can be used for the primary vaccine series in healthy adults.[116, 117]

The primary vaccine series consists of three injections given at 0, 1, and 6 months. As many as 10% to 15% of vaccines will fail to respond to this primary series. In that case, two additional doses of vaccine may be given one month apart, although this is not recommended by the CDC.[116] An additional 30% to 50% of nonresponders should respond to the two additional vaccine doses.

In general, it is not necessary to screen health care workers for hepatitis B antibodies prior to vaccination. Concerns regarding transmission of HIV in the plasma derived vaccine were raised shortly after the vaccine was introduced in 1982. In addition to screening all plasma donors for HIV, the vaccine manufacturing process inactivates HIV.[118] Concerns about vaccine safety should not be a reason to defer vaccination.

Postexposure Prophylaxis.—Employees who have had needle sticks or parenteral exposures to HBsAg–positive blood should receive hepatitis B immune globulin (HBIG) and the hepatitis B vaccine.[116] HBIG is a high–titer immune globulin to provide passive immunity initially while vaccine will induce active long-lasting immunity. Injections of HBIG and the first vaccine dose should be given at the same time and will not interfere with one another. The recommended dose of HBIG is 0.06 mL/kg.

The vaccine dose is 1 mL in normal healthy adults. The recommended vaccine dose for adults with any chronic underlying illness is twice the usual dose.

Hepatitis B vaccine-The vaccine has been shown to be safe, immunogenic, and effective in preventing hepatitis B.[119] Clinical trials in large numbers of homosexual men have shown that the vaccine is 100% effective in preventing hepatitis B infection in those who respond with antibody to HBV.[119] Recommendations regarding vaccination of high-risk groups of people in both the community and the hospital have been made. The decision facing the infection-control practitioner involves developing a vaccination program for health care workers that is suitable to the individual institution yet cost-effective.

Identification of high-risk groups may be one of the most arduous aspects of the vaccination program. In general, the easiest way to do this is to identify employees who have regular and frequent contact with blood and needles. Categorizing jobs from highest risk to lowest risk should identify health care workers who need to be vaccinated as a priority. Additional groups can be added as the program gets under way.

Mandatory vaccination of these high-risk individuals as a condition of employment is an issue that must also be addressed. While such a strategy is desirable, it may not be practical to implement and the legal ramifications of such a policy should be reviewed at the administrative level.

Voluntary vaccination of high-risk individuals is a more practical approach to vaccination. This strategy then places the burden on the infection-control practitioner in terms of "marketing" the vaccine to high-risk individuals.

Payment for vaccination may be a crucial factor in implementing a vaccine program. Once a health care facility has designated a group of employees as high risk, it would seem reasonable that the facility should also bear all or most of the financial responsibility for the vaccination program.

The decision not to offer vaccine may also be a viable alternative in some facilities. The decision not to offer vaccine is best based on the results of screening of employees that show a low prevalence or incidence of HBV markers in the population at risk.

When postvaccine antibody testing is done in health care workers, it should be done within 6 months of receiving the third dose. This will differentiate those who responded to the primary series from those who are considered primary nonresponders.

The need for booster doses of vaccine in vaccinated individuals has not been clarified as yet. Although it is not recommended by the Immunization Practices Advisory Committee,[116] some infection control programs are offering an additional booster of plasma or recombinant vaccine to individuals who are HBsAg-negative 5 to 7 years after completing the primary series.

Postvaccine testing may be helpful in deciding prophylactic treatment after percutaneous or needle exposures to HBsAg–positive blood in vaccine recipients. Unless that person has shown adequate levels of antibody in the past 12 months, serologic testing will need to be done after these accidents. A summary of recommended strategies is shown in Table 7–5.

As a reminder, vaccine should always be given in the deltoid rather than buttocks to ensure maximum antibody response.[120]

Special Considerations

Certainly one of the most important infection control measures for all forms of hepatitis is the education of hospital personnel. Hospital staff must be aware of the modes of transmission of hepatitis viruses and the importance of appropriate precautions in the care of such patients. Obtaining blood from patients with HBsAg presents one of the greatest hazards to hospital personnel. In some cases, large numbers of personnel have been exposed to blood containing HBsAg before the patient was known to be HBsAg-positive. For this reason, and because patients may have detectable HBsAg before the onset of illness, all blood should be considered infectious and should be handled appropriately. Special emphasis should be placed on avoiding contamination of skin and mucous membranes by blood spills from acutely ill patients who are HBsAg-positive. Employees should be encouraged to use precautions that will minimize contact with blood or blood-contaminated excretions and secretions at all times in the universal precautions-body substance isolation mode.

The issue of work restriction for the HBsAg-positive hospital worker is a controversial one. In general, it seems reasonable not to exclude personnel from routine patient contact who have HBsAg after they have recovered from their acute illness. Work accommodations for employees who are chronic HBsAg carriers should be made on an individual basis. The guidelines for employee health from the CDC emphasize that HBsAg-positive health care workers need not be restricted from patient contact routinely.[114]

Hepatitis B in Hemodialysis Units

Hepatitis B appears to be introduced into the dialysis unit by admission of HBsAg-positive patients, who probably acquire their infection from transfusion of HBsAg-positive blood. On the other hand, hemodialysis does not play a role in the spread of HAV infection.[121] The best strategy for hepatitis B control in dialysis settings should be hepatitis B vaccination of both dialysis patients and workers. It should be noted that to date, transmission of HBV infection from hemodialysis personnel to patients has not been reported. Transmission to personnel from either HBsAg-positive patients or from contaminated equipment or environmental surfaces, on the other hand, has been documented.[122] The greatest risk in such instances has been shown to be contact with blood or blood-contaminated materials and instruments.[122]

Isolation Precautions

Detailed discussion of these precautions are discussed in a CDC publication and are reviewed briefly here.

Patients.—Ideally, patients who are positive should undergo dialysis in a separate room or in another unit designated for hepatitis patients only. If this is not possible, the patient should undergo dialysis in an area removed from the mainstream of activity and should be separated from seronegative patients.

Personnel.—Whenever possible, patients who are HBsAg-positive should be dialyzed by personnel who are also seropositive (HBsAg-positive or anti-HBs-positive), or who have been vaccinated and who are immune to reinfection.

The hemodialysis unit infection control program should emphasize appropriate precautions in the care of patients and the handling of blood and secretions in the universal precautions mode. Dialysis equipment should not be shared by both HBsAg-positive and seronegative patients at any time. The CDC recommends that once they are vaccinated, dialysis patients should be screened for hepatitis B surface antibody (anti-HBs) to monitor their continued immunity. If their anti-HBs level falls below 10 sample ratio units/mL, they should receive a booster dose of vaccine.[116]

Surveillance

The use of hepatitis B vaccine for both dialysis patients and personnel is an important addition to an infection-control program in hemodialysis units. Vaccination offers the added advantage of providing immunity to HBV infection rather than merely monitoring its introduction into the hemodialysis unit.

Hepatitis C

Hepatitis C appears to be caused by more than one agent.[123] Available data suggest that transmission is primarily parenteral, through transfusions of blood or blood products.[124] Although nonparenteral transmission may occur,[125] these agents do not appear to be associated with a chronic carrier state. Hepatitis C has become the most common form of posttransfusion hepatitis since the advent of routine screening of donor blood for HBsAg and elimination of HBsAg-positive donors. At the present time there are no commercially available diagnostic tests for hepatitis C.

Isolation Precautions

Isolation precautions for patients with hepatitis C are similar to those for hepatitis B and should emphasize precautions when handling blood or blood contaminated articles.

RUBELLA

The introduction of rubella vaccine in 1969 has resulted in decreased numbers of cases of rubella in school-age children. The vaccine, however, has not decreased the incidence of rubella in older age groups as dramatically.[126] From 1976 to 1979, over 70% of reported cases occurred in persons 15 years of age or older.[126] In 1980, 46.6% of cases were over 15 years of age.[127] Orenstein et al reported an overall seronegativity rate of 14% among employees of hospitals for women and children.[128] In addition, outbreaks of rubella in hospitals have also been reported.[129–133] These outbreaks emphasize the potential for transmission of rubella in institutional settings and underscore the importance of immunity against rubella in order to protect patients and personnel. In general, efforts to vaccinate susceptible hospital personnel voluntarily have been disappointing.[130, 132, 133]

Isolation Procedures

The best strategy for rubella control in health care settings is to ensure that all health care workers are immune, regardless of age or sex. Employees who are susceptible to rubella should not care for patients with rubella. This restriction applies universally to all susceptible employees, not just pregnant women.

Screening and Immunization

The major purpose of the programs for rubella screening and immunization is eradication of the congenital rubella syndrome. Regulations regarding screening and immunization for rubella in hospital personnel vary widely. Such programs should be directed toward eliminating the risk of rubella to both pregnant patients and pregnant hospital personnel. Because of the change in the epidemiology of rubella since 1969, screening and immunization should be offered to both men and women to reduce the risk of epidemics in partially immune groups.[126] Documentation of vaccination is an acceptable waiver for screening of hospital personnel. The clinical history of previous illness is generally not considered a reliable indicator of immunity. Schoenbaum has outlined four possible strategies for rubella screening and immunization of hospital employees: (1) have a voluntary program for screening and immunize susceptibles voluntarily, (2) have a mandatory program of screening and either a voluntary or mandatory immunization program for susceptibles, (3) have a voluntary or mandatory immunization program without prescreening, and (4) do nothing.[134] Recently both the Advisory Committee on Infections Within Hospitals of the American Hospital Association and the CDC have recommended that "rubella immunization of susceptible personnel who may be in contact with pregnant patients remain obligatory.[126, 135] The epidemiology of rubella in hospitals certainly supports this recommendation.

Special Considerations

To prevent the transmission of rubella in outbreaks, those sus-
ceptible should be vaccinated promptly. It is not recommended, however, that pregnant women be vaccinated.[126, 136]

MEASLES (RUBEOLA)

Large hospital outbreaks of measles were common in the past, but with the advent of measles vaccination programs, nosocomial infection has decreased.[137]

Isolation Precautions

A single room (or cohort) is required and all susceptible personnel should wear a mask. We maintain mask precautions until seven days after onset of rash in known cases. When exposure to measles has occurred, masks should be used from the sixth to 21st day after exposure.

Special Considerations

"Modified Measles".—Measles that has been modified by immune serum globulin may often be overlooked or result in delays in diagnosis. Respiratory shedding of virus does occur in patients given immune serum globulin, and the mask precautions mentioned above should be instituted and maintained.

Atypical Measles.—The syndrome occurs after exposure to wild measles virus in persons who have been vaccinated with the inactivated measles vaccination that was used before 1965.[136, 138] The illness is characterized by fever, unusual skin rash, and pulmonary manifestations, and appears to be caused by an altered immune response in a previously sensitized host.[139] The illness is not thought to occur in those vaccinated after 1965 with live, attenuated vaccine, although such occurrences have been recorded.[140] Measles virus has not been isolated from patients with atypical measles. Because of this fact and the apparent pathogenesis of atypical measles, these patients are not thought to be infectious and special isolation precautions are not recommended.

MUMPS

Mumps virus is less contagious via the air than either measles or varicella (chickenpox), and infections in immunocompromised hosts have not been associated with the serious consequences that may follow measles or varicella.[141] Nosocomial transmission has been documented, but outbreaks are confined mostly to families, schools, and military personnel.

Isolation Precautions

Respiratory precautions and a private room are recommended, and presently we maintain precautions until the fifth day of illness at which time infectivity appears to decrease.

SLOW VIRUS INFECTION

Creutzfeldt-Jakob disease (CJD) is thought to be of viral origin with a long incubation period of 15 to 24 months. It does not appear to present excessive risks to hospital personnel. The disease has been reported to occur following corneal and dura mater transplantation,[142, 143] and through contaminated stereotactic electrodes used in previous neurosurgical procedures.[144]

Isolation Precautions

Once again, the universal precautions–body substance isolation strategy is adequate. To facilitate understanding by hospital personnel, it should be stressed that precautions for CJD are similar to those used for patients with hepatitis B.

Special Considerations

Additional precautions are recommended for handling specimens from patients with CJD and equipment and instruments used for these patients.[145] The details of such a policy are shown in Table 7–6.

GASTROENTERITIS VIRUSES

The two major causes of viral gastroenteritis were identified in the 1970s using immune electron microscopic examination of stool and by electron microscopic analysis of infected intestinal mucosa. The rotaviruses are a major cause of viral diarrhea in infants and children.[146, 147] The caliciviruslike agents (Norwalk gastroenteritis virus) generally cause gastroenteritis in older children and adults.[148]

Rotavirus

The human rotavirus (HRV; human reoviruslike agent or infantile gastroenteritis virus) is a major cause of gastroenteritis in infants and children during the winter in temperate climates.[149] Transmission is via the fecal-oral route. Kapikian et al showed that approximately half of all children admitted to hospitals in the winter months because of gastroenteritis are afflicted with human rotavirus.[150] Infants often are admitted to the hospital because of diarrhea and dehydration that may have been preceded by vomiting.[147] Children 6 to 24 months of age are most susceptible to HRV infection, and serum antibodies are rapidly acquired during this period. The majority of adults have such antibodies. However, the presence of serum antibodies does not protect completely against reinfection, and natural and experimental infections in adults do occur.[151, 152] Although adults may serve as a reservoir of infections despite the presence of preexisting antibody, the amount of virus shed is less than that shed by infected children.[152] Approximately 55% of adult contacts of children with rotavirus infection develop serologic evidence of infection.[152] Asymptomatic shedding also occurs. Using electron microscopy, Bolivar showed that while 25% of symptomatic students had rotavirus in their stool, 12% of asymptomatic students also had rotavirus in their stool.[153]

Isolation Precautions

Isolation precautions should emphasize care in handling feces and articles contaminated with feces.

Special Considerations

Rotaviruses are not readily isolated from tissue culture. The diagnosis is made by electron microscopic examination of stool or by serologic methods, enzyme-linked immunosorbent assay (ELISA), or counterimmunoelectrophoresis (CIE). Because these tests may not be available in some institutions, the infection control practitioner should be suspicious of rotavirus infection in infants who are admitted to the hospital for, or who become ill with, vomiting, diarrhea, dehydration, and fever during the winter months.

Norwalk Gastroenteritis Virus and Related Agents

Included in this group are the Norwalk, Hawaii, W, and Montgomery County agents. These agents are a major cause of viral gastroenteritis in children and adults and are associated with school,

Table 7–6
Infection Control Policy for Patients With Proven or Suspected Degenerative Neurologic Diseases, Including Creutzfeldt-Jakob Disease (CJD)

Because the agent of CJD is resistant to the usual methods of sterilization and disinfection, the following guidelines will assist hospital personnel who deal with the equipment and laboratory specimens from patients with any proven or suspected degenerative neurologic disease.

1. Disposable equipment: Disposable needles, instruments, etc, which have been in direct contact with the patient's *blood* or *tissue*, should be placed in the sharps bucket kept in the patient's room. This material should be taken to sterile supply each morning, where it should be autoclaved for one hour at 121°C and 15 psi (or equivalent).
2. Reusable equipment: Instruments from the autopsy suite and operating room, particularly material used in neurosurgical procedures that has come in direct contact with blood or tissue, should be separated from other instruments and equipment and sent to sterile supply, as noted in (1). This material may be placed in 5% sodium hypochlorite (Clorox) for two hours prior to sterilization, but should not be washed until *after* autoclaving.*
3. Operating room: Blood collected during surgical procedures should remain in closed collection bottles or containers. These containers should be placed in a plastic bag and sent to sterile supply as noted in (1).†
4. Laboratory precautions: Specimens sent to the laboratories should be labeled "biohazard" and handled in the usual manner. Blood, CSF, and tissue should be handled with gloves. Stool, urine, and saliva are not thought to transmit the disease. Spinal fluid counting chambers should be washed in the usual way after immersion in an iodophor (Betadine), phenolic (Lysol), or 5% sodium hypochlorite (Clorox) for two hours.
5. Decontamination of horizontal surfaces: Tables, floors, and countertops should be disinfected with an iodophor, phenolic, or 5% sodium hypochlorite preparation, followed by routine washing with soap and water.
6. Accidental needle punctures, etc: Percutaneous (through the skin) exposure to blood, CSF, or tissue should be handled as follows: Cleanse the wound with an iodophor, phenolic, or 0.5% sodium hypochlorite preparation. The skin should be cleansed, but care should be taken to avoid vigorous scrubbing or abrasion of skin.

*Equipment considered contaminated: phlebotomy needles; intravenous catheters or needles; cutdown instruments; tracheostomy kits; EEG electrodes; lumbar puncture needles; manometers and other instruments contaminated with CSF; spinal fluid counting chambers; surgical instruments and equipment in contact with brain, blood, or other tissues; laryngoscopes; endotracheal and tracheostomy tubes; suction catheters.
†Note: autoclave with slow exhaust must be used for decontamination of liquid.
Reproduced with permission from Valenti WM, et al: Nosocomial virus infections: III. Guidelines for prevention and control of exanthematous viruses, gastroenteritis viruses, picornaviruses and uncommonly seen viruses. Infect Control 1981; 2:42.

family, and community outbreaks. These agents probably are transmitted by fecal-oral spread. Nosocomial transmission has not been documented, but such transmission may occur in a manner similar to that of rotavirus.

Isolation Precautions

Since transmission is via the fecal-oral route, frequent handwashing and gloves for handling feces, bedpans, or feces-contaminated articles are the best infection-control recommendations.

Special Considerations

The Norwalk gastroenteritis–like agents cannot be isolated on viral culture. The only laboratory test presently available for identifying infected materials is immune electron microscopy, which is tedious and not widely available. When rotavirus and nonbacterial pathogens have been ruled out, patients can be classified as having "nonbacterial gastroenteritis other than rotavirus." Other agents, such as coronaviruslike agents, astrovirus, or noncultivatable adenoviruses also may be involved.

PICORNAVIRUSES

Of the three genera of the *Picornaviridae* family (*Enterovirus, Rhinovirus,* and *Calicivirus*), the enteroviruses are the most frequent causes of nosocomial infection. Included in the enterovirus group are coxsackieviruses A and B, echoviruses, polioviruses, and enterovirus types 68 to 71. Hepatitis A (enterovirus 72) is discussed above.

Enteroviruses cause sporadic disease throughout the year, but are most prevalent in the community during the summer and fall in temperate climates.[154, 155] Transmission of the virus is via the fecal-oral route, but droplet transmission has been described for coxsackie A21 and probably occurs with other enteroviruses as well.[155] Virus can be recovered easily from the oropharynx and rectum and may be shed for 1 month or more after infection. Enteroviruses also have been recovered from houseflies and cockroaches, but their role in transmission has never been documented. Transmission occurs in hosts with or without preexisting antibody.[155]

Nonpolio Enteroviruses

Infection is common in the general population, particularly among children, and results in a variety of illnesses. Patients may be asymptomatic or may have mild illness with fever, rash, upper respiratory, and/or GI symptoms. Symptomatic and severe disease occurs in newborn infants, particularly in full-term infants who may develop meningitis, encephalitis, myocarditis, and/or pericarditis in addition to the other symptoms mentioned. In older children, infection often is asymptomatic or benign. For these reasons, most of the reported nosocomial enterovirus infections have been outbreaks in neonatal units,[156–160] while nosocomial enterovirus acquisition among older children often is undetected.

Most nursery outbreaks involve the nonpolio enteroviruses. Often the virus is introduced into the nursery by an infected infant, and secondary transmission occurs from infant to infant via the hands of personnel. Infection also has been found in nursery personnel, suggesting that they may serve as sources of infection.[158]

The most consistent mode of acquisition of nonpolio entero-

viruses in infants is the mother.[158, 159] Transmission may take place before, during, or after delivery. In a study of 27 newborn infants with symptomatic infection, 30% had onset of symptoms within the first three days of life and 60% of the mothers were symptomatic at the time of delivery.[161] In a prospective study done during enterovirus season, Cherry et al demonstrated that two of 55 women were shedding virus at the time of delivery,[162] and one of these two transmitted virus to her child. Further epidemiologic studies are needed, however, to determine the frequency with which infected infants are introduced into the nursery and the risk they pose to other babies and personnel.

Isolation Precautions

Because of the potentially serious consequences of enterovirus infection in the newborn infant, precautions for the control of nosocomial enterovirus infection in the nursery are especially important. Ideally, infants with suspected or proven infection should be isolated in a private room or cohorted together. The cohort method of isolation may be useful in situations involving several infants and has proved to be an effective control measure in containing nursery outbreaks.[156] Enteric precautions for isolating infants, using gowns and gloves for direct contact, should be maintained. Gowns should be changed after each patient contact. The decision to close a nursery to new admission may be necessary, especially with prolonged outbreaks or if adequate cohort programs cannot be maintained. Handwashing before and after each patient contact obviously is required.

In the universal precautions–body substance isolation mode, careful handling of feces and secretions, as well as soiled objects and instruments, should be followed for all patients.

Prevention

Often a thorough maternal history is the best way to identify the infant at risk during the enterovirus season, and a mild febrile illness in the mother during the summer may warn of infection in the infant. Any infant born to a mother who is known to have had a recent febrile illness should be carefully observed after birth.

In addition, nursery personnel should be aware of their potential for infecting the newborn. While it may not be possible or necessary to identify employees with these nonspecific illnesses, reporting febrile, respiratory, or diarrheal illnesses to the occupational health service and careful handwashing are an important part of an in-service program for nursery personnel.

The attenuation of enterovirus disease by passive immunization has been suggested. Antibody does not protect against infection but appears to reduce the severity of disease and the duration of virus shedding. The administration of immune serum globulin in the setting of a sudden and particularly virulent nursery outbreak has been suggested by Cherry.[159]

Polioviruses

Poliovirus infection has become rare since the institution of widespread immunization programs, and nosocomial transmission of poliovirus is no longer a problem.

Virus shedding may follow vaccination with live, oral polio vaccine (OPV) for several weeks. In general, paralytic poliovirus infection today is associated with the use of live OPC, but this is rare.[163, 164] Cases occur in recipients of vaccine (recipient cases) or in their contacts (contact cases). The incidence of vaccine-induced paralysis in recipients is estimated to be 0.44 per million vaccinated.[165] In contacts the rate is 1.5 cases per million vaccinated.[165] Several community outbreaks of paralytic polio due to wild-type strains among groups of nonimmunized individuals were described recently.[166]

Isolation Precautions

Recently, a new, enhanced-potency inactivated polio vaccine (E-IPV) has been introduced. Asymptomatic children shedding poliovirus present a potential risk to certain high-risk patients, especially children with congenital immunodeficiency diseases (eg, agammaglobulinemia, hypogammaglobulinemia, combined immunodeficiency states). It is recommended that, as a precaution, unimmunized children or children with congenital or acquired immunodeficiency states not be placed in the same room as children who are known to be shedding poliovirus. The potential infection risk posed by the asymptomatic patient shedding enterovirus again underscores the importance of elevating infection control practices to a higher level in the universal precautions body–substance isolation mode.

Immunization

Because of the persistence of wild and vaccine strains of poliovirus, adequate immunity against polioviruses is essential and important for both pediatric patients and hospital personnel. Routine vaccination of adults currently is not recommended.[166]

Special Considerations

Enteroviruses are unusually stable and resist many commonly used disinfectants (eg, 70% alcohol, 5% Lysol, and 1% quarternary ammonium compounds). The most effective virucidal agent is 5% sodium hypochlorite solution, which may be used for surface decontamination, but it is corrosive to metal and stainless steel.

RHABDOVIRUS

Nosocomial rabies is uncommon. However, two cases of human-to-human transmission of rabies from corneal transplantation have been documented.[167, 168] Both donors had obscure neurologic illnesses, one resembling Guillain-Barré syndrome and the other, flaccid paralysis. Because of this atypical presentation, the diagnosis of rabies was not suspected prior to the death of either donor, and their tissues were considered acceptable for transplantation.

Hospital personnel also are at theoretical risk when exposed to patients with rabies. Often the diagnosis may not be suspected prior to death.[169] In an investigation of hospital personnel exposed to one such patient, many employees were unable to recall the extent of exposure 15 to 43 days earlier. Because of this and because of the long duration of hospitalization of the index case, 198 of 371 hospital employees were thought to have had probable significant rabies exposure and were advised to receive postexposure rabies prophylaxis.[169]

Laboratory personnel working with bat colonies and other potentially rabid animals also are at increased risk of this disease. Laboratory-associated rabies, presumably transmitted by aerosol-ization of laboratory virus strains, has been reported,[170] and resulted in revised safety recommendations for laboratory personnel working with rabies virus.[170]

Isolation Precautions

Strict isolation precautions are recommended for the duration of illness in patients with proven or suspected rabies.

Immunization

Human diploid cell rabies vaccine (HDCV) should be used for the following situations[171]:

1. Individuals with documented rabies exposure
2. Individuals with probable or possible exposure
3. Preexposure prophylaxis of laboratory workers working with bats or other potentially rabid animals

If HDCV is in short supply, duck embryo vaccine (DEV) may be substituted.

Postexposure prophylaxis of hospital personnel should be handled according to established recommendations.[171, 172] In addition local wounds should be cleansed with soap and water.[173] Preexposure prophylaxis of laboratory workers at high risk also should be undertaken. Personnel working with potentially rabid animals should not work with these animals until a complete series of vaccine is administered and satisfactory immunity has been demonstrated. Testing for immunity is not recommended until several weeks after the last booster dose of vaccine has been given.[171] Therefore, such vaccination programs are timeconsuming and require careful advance planning to ensure immunity of personnel prior to working with potentially rabid animals.

Special Considerations

The potential for transmission of rabies in transplanted tissues presents serious problems in evaluating potential donors. The Infection Control Committee of the Strong Memorial Hospital and the Rochester Area Eye Bank have jointly agreed to the following policy: "Corneas from individuals who have died with a diagnosis of dementia, encephalopathy, undiagnosed neurological illness, multiple sclerosis, conjunctivitis, or other viral diseases including hepatitis B, rabies, or Creutzfeldt-Jakob disease should not be utilized for the purposes of corneal transplantation. Corneas in such cases may be accepted for research purposes if they are labeled 'biohazard'."

ARENAVIRUSES

Lymphocytic Choriomeningitis (LCM)

This virus has been implicated as a cause of outbreaks of flulike illness with aseptic meningitis in laboratory workers and in other hospital personnel.[173] It is not known to be transmitted from person to person in hospital settings, however.

Isolation Precautions

No special isolation precautions are required for patients with LCM infection.

Lassa Fever

Lassa fever is a febrile viral illness associated with sore throat, headache, vomiting, diarrhea, and myalgias. Later features include hemorrhagic manifestations, rash, petechiae, shock, and death. The disease has been observed primarily in Nigeria and Liberia although serologic evidence of infection has been seen in other African countries.

Person-to-person spread is thought to occur via contact with blood, urine, and respiratory secretions.[174] Hospital outbreaks in Africa have involved personnel, patients and visitors.[174–176] In one of these outbreaks it was felt that spread of virus was airborne, as the index patient was in an open area where other patients subsequently became infected. No cases were noted in other areas of the hospital despite common nursing staff and equipment.

Isolation

Strict isolation precautions in a room with negative pressure are necessary for proven or suspected cases of Lassa fever. Details for the initial management of such cases are outlined in a CDC publication.[177]

Smallpox

Prior to the eradication of smallpox by the World Health Organization's Smallpox Eradication Program, outbreaks were reported in both hospital personnel and patients.[178] The virus is quite stable and can survive in crusts, fluid, or dried material for very long periods of time.[179] Transmission of smallpox occurs by direct or indirect contact with infectious material. Infected patients are able to transmit the disease to others from the onset of the exanthema until the last crust has been shed. Airborne transmission also occurs; this method of transmission appears to have caused the most recent laboratory-associated case, which occurred in a medical photographer working on the floor above a laboratory in which researchers were working with variola virus.[180]

Isolation Precautions

Patients with suspected cases of smallpox should be isolated, using strict isolation precautions, until all crusts have been shed.

Immunization

At present, smallpox vaccination is indicated only for laboratory workers who are using smallpox or related orthopox viruses (eg, monkeypox, vaccinia, etc).[181]

Special Considerations

In May 1980 WHO declared all countries free of smallpox. Nevertheless, stocks of smallpox virus remain in a few research and reference laboratories worldwide, presenting a small risk of smallpox in certain settings. Suspected cases must be reported immediately to local and state health authorities.

OTHER VIRUSES

Several uncommonly seen viruses also deserve mention. Marburg and Ebola virus disease have not been seen in the United States as yet. They have occurred in Africa in hospital personnel, especially in nurses, physicians, and laboratory workers.

Marburg Virus

Although infection with Marburg virus is rare, a number of cases in the world's literature have been hospital-acquired.[182, 183] The natural reservoir of Marburg virus is unknown, but the virus was first isolated from the African green monkey. A number of these animals were infected with Marburg virus; this resulted in an outbreak of disease in Marburg and Frankfurt, Germany. Person-to-person transmission of Marburg virus occurs as a result of contact with blood and probably with respiratory secretions and urine.

The most recent hospital-acquired case involved a nurse who cared for two patients infected with Marburg disease.[182] Exposure was thought to have taken place early in the care of one patient prior to the institution of isolation precautions. The diagnosis of Marburg virus disease should be considered in any febrile patient who has traveled recently in areas in Africa where this virus is endemic.

Isolation Precautions

Strict isolation precautions are necessary, and special attention should be given to handling blood and secretions and any articles contaminated with these body fluids.[177]

Special Considerations

Secondary contacts in the hospital should be identified and monitored for signs of illness. No vaccine is available currently. Although specific antiserum may be available for treatment of infected patients,[177] further trials are needed to evaluate its use.

Ebola Virus

Ebola virus infection is caused by a Marburg-like virus and produces similar symptoms. Its natural reservoir is also unknown. Two simultaneous epidemics occurred in southern Sudan and northern Zaire in 1976.[184, 185] In one hospital 76 of 230 staff members became ill, and 41 died. Transmission appears to require close personal contact. Since some patients who shared rooms with infected patients did not acquire the disease, it is presumed that aerosols do not play a major role in transmission of Ebola virus.

Isolation Precautions

Precautions are the same as for Marburg virus disease.[177] The efficacy of protective clothing in this disease apparently was demonstrated when a shortage of isolation materials in one hospital resulted in an increase in the number of new nosocomial cases.[184]

Papillomaviruses

The human papillomaviruses (HPV) are small, double-stranded DNA viruses. HPVs affect the skin and mucous membranes and cause warts and other benign tumors. The natural history of these tumors is variable; some regress spontaneously while others become malignant. There is good evidence to show that HPVs are sexually transmitted viruses. There is a high prevalence of HPV–associated malignancies in the male sexual partners of women with genital cancers.[186] Other studies have shown an association between squamous cell carcinomas and genital warts.[187, 188] These associations point to the importance of early detection and treatment of HPV-associated genital lesions.

Laser therapy or vaporization is a popular way of treating HPV condylomas, warts, and associated growths. Patients with laryngeal, cervical, and skin lesions may benefit from carbon dioxide (CO_2) laser therapy. The CO_2 laser generates a vapor or plume as it destroys the HPV–associated growths. Intact viral DNA has been shown to be liberated into the air with the vapor of laser-treated warts,[189] the significance of which is not clear at this time. As a first step, however, infection control and employee health personnel should be involved with laser safety programs in operation in their facilities.

With recent widespread availability of the laser, current safety practices are probably variable. The most practical solution for now is proper maintenance of equipment, including suction and exhaust apparatus. Until additional information is available, it also makes sense for operators to wear masks, gowns, gloves, and protective eyewear in the universal precautions mode as they would for any procedure that generated an aerosol.[189]

Human Immunodeficiency Virus (HIV)

The human immunodeficiency virus epidemic has presented numerous challenges to the health care system since its earliest descriptions. As our understanding of HIV and AIDS evolves, difficult questions are answered while new questions are raised. The central infection control issue here surrounds the potential for transmission of the virus to patients and to personnel in health care settings. Numerous strategies have been proposed to prevent this transmission.

Risk of Transmission

Health care workers seem to be at relatively low risk for acquiring HIV from their patients via accidental needle stick or other blood exposure. The risk is not zero, however. Currently, the CDC estimates that the risk of transmitting HIV from patients to health care workers via parenteral exposure to blood is less than 1%.[190] Most of the accidents that have resulted in HIV transmission from patients to health care workers have involved needle sticks. Prolonged contact with HIV–positive blood on nonintact skin or mucous membranes may also have transmitted virus, although less frequently than needle puncture. Also, several instances of HIV transmission in laboratory settings have been documented.[190]

The challenge for the health care industry involves developing strategies to reduce the risk of HIV transmission to patients and health care workers, just as strategies for risk reduction are being stressed to people in the community who are at risk of HIV infection. Some areas of concern in health care have been the risk of HIV transmission via infected health care workers to patients, from blood used for transfusion, from transplanted organs and tissues, and from injectable products such as hepatitis B and RhoGAM.[118, 192]

Education of Health Care Workers

Infection control education is based on an understanding of the mechanisms of infection transmission. Health care workers need a good understanding of the mechanisms of infection transmission. They need to know that the airborne route (e.g., influenza) is only one possible route of infection transmission from person to person. Other infectious agents are transmitted by the fecal-oral route (e.g.,

hepatitis A), the parenteral route (e.g., hepatitis B virus, HIV), or not at all (e.g., *Toxoplasma gondii*). This understanding forms the basis for all other elements of an infection-control program to prevent transmission of HIV and other bloodborne agents. In addition to having a good understanding of how HIV is transmitted, health care workers need to know how to apply this information in clinical settings when faced with an HIV/AIDS problem.[193]

New Strategies for Infection Control

The concept of universal precautions has been promoted by the CDC and adapted for use in most United States hospitals.[194] Universal precautions and another system called body substance isolation[195] are based on concepts of infection control that are really much older than the problems presented by AIDS. Basically, the universal precautions–body substance isolation mode requires that health care workers elevate their infection-control practices to a higher level. Since it is not possible to identify all patients who are infected with HIV or other bloodborne agents, health care workers are being taught to handle the blood, body fluids, and needles of all patients with the same degree of caution, regardless of the diagnosis. These two isolation systems tell us that we cannot be a purely diagnosis-driven system as we have in the past. Both systems are an attempt to minimize employee exposure to blood, body fluids, and needles of all patients. In doing so, health care workers will also minimize exposure to HIV.

The body substance isolation approach[195] is a bit broader in scope than universal precautions. The universal precautions system focuses on protection of health care workers by minimizing contact with blood or bloody body fluids[196] by the wearing of protective clothing. The body substance isolation system focuses on the use of barrier precautions (i.e., protective clothing). It upgrades the general level of barrier precautions used in routine patient care so that gloves are worn for contact with mucous membranes, nonintact skin, and moist body substances (including blood, urine, sputum, wound drainage, and other body fluids). The updated universal precautions guidelines are for blood and bloody body fluids.[196]

Recommendations for dental settings state that blood, saliva, and gingival fluid from all patients should be considered infective. As a minimum precaution, dental workers should wear gloves for contact with oral mucous membranes of all patients.[194] CDC guidelines provide more details on infection control in dental settings.[194] One could argue again that gloves should have been worn in dental settings before the HIV era because of the possibility of transmitting and acquiring other bloodborne and non-bloodborne agents (e.g., hepatitis B and HSV, respectively).

Disinfection-Sterilization

HIV is easily inactivated with standard household disinfectants and via the usual methods of sterilization. Hydrogen peroxide, ethanol, isopropyl alcohol, formaldehyde, household bleach, steam heat, dry heat, ethylene oxide, and soap and water can all be used in the appropriate setting.[197–199]

Extraordinary means of disinfection or sterilization are not necessary for reusable equipment. Reusable equipment should be reprocessed by first mechanical cleaning and removal of debris, blood, and tissue and then reprocessed via standard methods. It is not necessary to dedicate separate equipment such as brochoscopes or endoscopes for use exclusively in people with HIV/AIDS for infection-control purposes since proper cleaning and reprocessing will render this equipment safe for reuse.

HIV Testing in Health Care Settings

Testing programs for patients and health care workers should be part of the comprehensive strategy for prevention of HIV transmission in health care settings.[200] Otherwise, testing becomes awkward and controversial.

The testing program for donated blood is a program that is for the public health good. This program is not perfect, however, since seroconversion with HIV can take 6 weeks to 6 months or more. Therefore, a unit of blood can test negative in viremic patients who are tested during this "window" and have not yet seroconverted. HIV antigen testing may be positive earlier and eventually help close this window.

Similarly, the CDC recommends that donors of semen, organs, and tissues for transplantation should also be tested for HIV.[201] Tests for hospitalized donors should be done on samples taken before any transfusions to avoid situations in which transfusions might result in antibody loss due to hemodilution. There are additional recommendations for semen banks. Semen specimens from donors, other than donors involved in a mutually monogamous marriage or a relationship with the recipient, should be frozen for at least 6 months. Before frozen semen is used for artificial insemination, a blood sample taken at the time the semen was collected and again at least 6 months later should be tested for HIV antibody. Additional safeguards that should be applied to these donors include (1) no history of risk factors for HIV infection, and (2) a physical examination documented by a licensed physician at the time of donation that showed no obvious evidence of HIV infection. While these guidelines may be considered excessive by some health care workers, they represent the safest solution to this problem at the present time. This is another example, however, of how the AIDS epidemic has caused us to reassess our infection control priorities and elevate our practices to a higher level.

Testing programs for patients in other situations and for employees have been proposed as another mechanism to deal with HIV in health care settings. The CDC recommendations[194] state that HIV testing of patients should be done for (1) management of parenteral or mucous membrane exposures of health care workers, (2) patient diagnosis and management, and (3) counseling and serologic testing to prevent or control HIV transmission in the community. Testing programs for patients should include (1) informed consent for testing, (2) informing patients of test results with appropriate counseling for patients by trained individuals, (3) an assurance of confidentiality of test results, (4) assurance that infected patients will not be denied medical care, (5) a method of monitoring the program's efficacy in reducing the incidence of significant exposures of health care workers to HIV.

Practically speaking, testing as an adjunct to universal precautions is a good compromise here. For example, it is recommended that needle stick sources be tested for HIV antibody after a health care worker has a needle stick or accident involving skin or mucous membrane exposure to blood. This is probably more than most institutions are currently doing. On the other hand, the infection control model for hepatitis B tells us that serologic testing of patients and employees after exposure can be a helpful infection-control tool. At the present time, exposed employees should be followed up with serologic testing at the time of the accident and at three-month intervals for a total of 9 to 12 months. Although still unproven in humans, many facilities offer zidovudine prophylaxis to health care workers with parenteral HIV exposures. Doses range from 1,000–1,200 mg/day for 4 to 6 weeks.[202] In the meantime, moving toward a postexposure testing program seems to be a reasonable next step for testing activities in health care settings.

Testing prior to elective surgery has been proposed by some to ensure the safety of operating room personnel. The infection-control community and CDC have responded with universal precautions or body substance isolation contending that HIV testing of patients will not solve the problem. The solution lies somewhere between the surgical approach and the infection-control professional's response. Perhaps the best way to design a testing program is to look at it in the context of all of the infection-control strategies that are available in the health care settings for employee protection and safety. With this approach, testing and universal precautions become parts of a broader program.

When developing testing strategies for health care, it is important to decide how the results are to be used. HIV testing should be linked to health care and health information. The primary use of HIV testing should not be exclusion from health care, housing, insurance, or employment. It is clear that hospitals need to review their current HIV testing activities and ensure that they are reasonable, workable, and nondiscriminatory.

HIV-Seropositive Health Care Workers

The health care industry is probably not different than the rest of the work force and has HIV-positive workers at all levels. The CDC guidelines are equivocal on recommendations for the seropositive health care worker and leave the final decision to the individual institution.[194] There are enough scientific data on HIV transmission in health care settings to make some reasonable attempts at developing strategies to deal with the problem of the infected health care worker. The HIV-positive employee with patient contact does not appear to present an excessive risk of transmitting HIV to patients in most settings. Employees who perform invasive procedures need individual counseling and evaluation. Reassignment may work in some of these situations, but not for all. Realistically speaking, we will not know who most HIV-infected health care workers are. Likewise, it will not be possible to know who all of the HIV-infected patients are. Universal precautions again are a good first step toward attempting to deal with the problem of the HIV-infected health care worker. Clearly, the discipline of infection control has changed during the AIDS era. The infection-control program can be a valuable hospital resource by taking the lead to develop programs and policies that will protect health care workers from HIV infection and allow this new group of patients access to the health care system.

COHORT ISOLATION PRECAUTIONS

For the purpose of hospital epidemiology, a *cohort* is a group of individuals kept together to minimize contact between members of that cohort and other patients or personnel to decrease opportunities for transmission of infectious agents.

Cohort isolation programs have proved effective in controlling

Table 7–7
General Guidelines for Use of Cohort Isolation

1. Patients should be separated into cohorts of infected ("dirty") and noninfected ("clean") patients.
2. Only persons with proven or suspected infection should be admitted to the infected cohort.
3. All exposed (potentially infected) individuals should be included with the cohort of infected patients. In some instances, the potentially infected cohort may be separated into a third cohort.
4. The infected cohort should be closed to new, uninfected admissions and all new, uninfected admissions should be placed with the uninfected cohort.
5. Personnel working with the infected cohort should be immune to the illness in question by either previous history of illness or vaccination *whenever possible.*
6. Personnel should be assigned so that separate groups work with the infected and uninfected cohorts *whenever possible.* Crossover between cohorts should be discouraged to minimize the risk of cross-infection of the uninfected cohort.
7. Ideally, personnel should be separated for the duration of the cohort program, especially when viral illnesses are proven or suspected.
8. When personnel must work in both areas, they should work in the clean area first, then work in the dirty area.
9. The infected cohort area will be closed as patients are discharged from the hospital and may be used for new uninfected admissions after thorough cleaning of the area and its equipment.

Reproduced with permission from Valenti WM, et al: Nosocomial virus infections: IV. Guidelines for cohort isolation and other considerations. Infect Control *1981; 2:239.*

some nursery outbreaks of *Staphylococcus aureus*[203, 204] as well as those due to enteroviruses.[205, 206] Cohort isolation programs also have been used in hospital outbreaks of influenza on patient units other than nurseries.

A program of cohort isolation generally consists of two groups of people, an infected group and an uninfected group, that are separated from one another. Occasionally a third group, an exposed group of patients, is separated from the uninfected group and is cared for separately from the other two. This method of separation may involve the use of geographically distinct rooms or, if not available, physical separation in the same room. To ensure complete separation of cohorts, geographically separate rooms are preferable and should be used whenever possible. The separation of hospital staff often is overlooked, but this also is essential to maintain a successful cohort program. Obviously, it is not always possible to separate house staff and support personnel, but the nursing staff caring for infected and noninfected cohorts should be separated as much as possible, without disrupting services to patients. If possible, those caring for infected patients should be immune to the disease in question or receiving prophylaxis or vaccine. This immunity may be determined by prior infection or vaccination and may be identified by appropriate history of illness, vaccination, or antibody testing. In cohort programs for viral illness, especially respiratory viruses, the same groups of personnel ideally should care for the same cohort for the duration of isolation whenever possible. This plan will minimize the risk of transmission of infection to the uninfected cohort. Personnel who have recently recovered from the viral illness under consideration also may care for the infected cohort. In other cohort programs, for example, staphylococcal outbreaks in nurseries, personnel may work with different cohorts on different days but not during the same day.

It is also important to remember that separation of groups on the basis of symptoms alone will not guarantee that all members of the cohort have the same illness. It is desirable, therefore, to take appropriate steps to confirm the suspected diagnosis as quickly as possible to ensure proper cohorting of patients. More detailed guidelines for the use of cohort programs are presented in Table 7–7.

The cohort method of isolation may involve small numbers of patients and hospital staff, such as placing two patients with HIV disease in the same semiprivate room. Other uses of the cohort

method may involve restrictions of larger groups of patients and personnel. For example, outbreaks of respiratory viral infections, such as respiratory syncytial virus, are approached in this way.[21] Recently, this method was used during an outbreak of viral respiratory disease in an intensive care nursery (ICN) (Figure 7–3).[2, 207] When it was noted that there were eight cases of acute respiratory illness in newborn infants, these infants were moved to a separate area of the nursery (rooms A and B), and both the ICN and rooms A and B were closed to new admissions. New admissions were housed in clean rooms in the special care nursery (SCN), physically separate from the ICN. Separate nursing staff

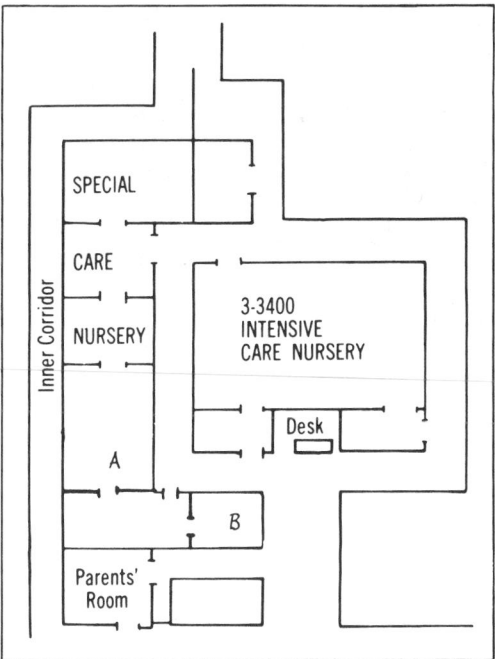

Figure 7–3. Floor plan of special care and intensive care nurseries. (From Valenti WM, et al: Nosocomial virus infections: III. Guidelines for prevention and control of exanthematous viruses, gastroenteritis viruses, picornaviruses and uncommonly seen viruses. *Infect Control* 1981; 2:38–49. Used with permission.)

236   *W.M. Valenti*

worked in each of these three areas, and crossover between areas was discouraged during shifts. House staff, other physicians, and support personnel could not be as easily restricted to one cohort area, but the importance of movement from uninfected to infected areas (and not the reverse) was emphasized strongly. The area housing the infected cohort (A and B) was opened for new admissions after all infected patients had been discharged from these rooms. Because of space limitations, the area housing the exposed, uninfected cohort of infants (ICN) was opened to new admissions when no new cases had been detected after the tenth day of isolation. An alternative to this method of cohort isolation would be to close the ICN to new admissions and maintain a cohort of infected and exposed babies together in the ICN. New admissions would then be assigned to SCN rooms. The major disadvantage of this two-cohort system might be the eventual underutilization of an ICN with highly specialized equipment that could not be used in the smaller SCN room.

In general, cohort programs using geographically separate areas of the same room are not recommended for the control of viral respiratory infections.

COMMUNICABLE DISEASE SURVEY

The purpose of the communicable disease survey ("contagion check") is to screen pediatric patients and visitors quickly to determine whether they are infected with or have been exposed to communicable diseases of any kind. The main concern of the survey is to prevent the introduction of varicella into the hospital, but other illnesses such as measles, mumps, and viral respiratory illnesses also should be considered. A contagion check should be done for every pediatric patient and child visitor and becomes especially important during periods of peak virus activity in the community.

Prior to the admission of a pediatric patient to the hospital, information regarding the child's immunization history, susceptibility to chickenpox, and history of recent exposure to chickenpox should be obtained. Questions that may yield additional helpful information are shown in Table 7–8 and may also be included in the communicable disease survey, especially for child visitors (see below). This survey is relatively uncomplicated and assists in screening patients who present potential hazards to both susceptible patients and personnel. Susceptible pediatric patients who have been exposed to proven or suspected viral illnesses are placed on precautions as previously noted[2, 87, 207].

VISITOR POLICIES

The child visitor to the hospital poses a unique set of questions and problems for the infection control practitioner.[208, 209] There is no doubt that child visitors to the hospital can be beneficial in certain instances. Unrestricted visits by children, however, can present definite infection control hazards to both susceptible patients and to personnel, especially in terms of virus transmission. Therefore, when formulating or revising visitor policies, infection control consultation is essential to set rational, minimum standards for visitors.

It is also important to remember that the issue of admittance of child visitors to patient units is only one aspect of visitor policies that must be considered. The movement of children on the patient

Table 7–8
Considerations for Communicable Disease Survey

Essential components
  Immunization history
    Measles, mumps, rubella
    Polio
    Diphtheria, pertussis, tetanus
  Has the child had or recently been exposed to chickenpox
Other considerations, especially for child visitors
  Has the child had or recently been exposed to
    Measles
    Mumps
    Rubella (German measles)
    Hepatitis
  Does the child have any of the following now or has the child had any of the following recently
    Streptococcal infection
    Cough, cold, or upper respiratory infection of any kind
    Diarrhea
    Vomiting
    Fever
    Rash
    Infection of any kind

Reproduced with permission from Valenti WM, et al: Nosocomial virus infection: IV. Guidelines for cohort isolation and other considerations. Infect Control 1981; 2:238.

unit and their contact with other patients (eg, in playrooms) also must be addressed when formulating or revising visitor policies.

Some authors have failed to note increases in infection rates on services with unrestricted visiting policies.[209] However, the possibility of transmission of varicella, respiratory syncytial virus, and influenza virus from visitors to susceptible personnel and patients is an important issue that cannot be ignored. Children under the age of 12 are not permitted to visit patients in the Strong Memorial Hospital without special permission from the head nurse on each patient unit. In these instances a communicable disease survey should be done (see Table 7–8) and child visitors under the age of 12 who have proven or suspected viral illnesses (or infections of any kind) should not visit in patient areas. Such a survey becomes especially important as visitation policies are relaxed in many institutions in an attempt to make immediate family members a more active part of the patient's hospitalization.

PERSONNEL

Employees With Respiratory Illnesses

Infection-control practitioners are asked frequently for guidelines regarding restriction from work of employees with viral illnesses. This issue becomes especially important during periods when respiratory viruses like influenza and respiratory syncytial virus are prevalent in the community. Because of the large numbers of employees with respiratory illnesses during the winter, it may not be possible to restrict all such employees from work. In general it is preferable that employees with febrile respiratory illnesses not work at least until they are afebrile. Because of staffing problems and other considerations, employees with respiratory illnesses who do work must observe certain minimum precautions. When work-

Table 7–9
Interaction of Factors in Nosocomial Transmission of Viruses

	Transmissibility	Susceptibility of Staff or Other Patients	Resultant Nosocomial Risk
Respiratory viruses			
Influenza	High	Variable*	High
Respiratory syncytial virus	High	High	High
Rhinovirus	Moderate	Moderate*	Moderate
Other (adenovirus, coronavirus)	Moderate	Moderate*	Moderate
Hepatitis B			
Needle sticks	High	High	High
Other exposure	Low	High	Low
Herpesviruses			
Herpes simplex type 1	Low	Moderate*	Low
Herpes simplex type 2	Very low	Moderate*	Very low†
Varicella (chickenpox) or disseminated zoster	High	Very low*	Low*
Herpes zoster (localized)	Moderate	Very low*	Very low
Epstein-Barr (EBV)	Very low	Very low*	Very low
Cytomegalovirus (CMV)	Low	Moderate*	Very low‡
Rubella	High	Moderate*	High
Human immunodeficiency virus (HIV)	Low	High	Low

*High in pediatric age groups.
†Except to newborn during delivery or after rupture of membranes.
‡Except for blood transfusion or organ transplantation.
Modified with permission from Valenti WM, et al: Nosocomial virus infections: IV. Guidelines for cohort isolation and other considerations. Infect Control 1981; 2:240.

ing with adult patients, careful handwashing and a mask should be considered for employees with respiratory illnesses. Hopefully this will minimize the transmission of viruses like influenza virus to susceptible patients. When caring for patients 2 years of age and under, an employee with a respiratory illness must also wear a gown to prevent transmission of respiratory syncytial virus and other viruses that appear to be transmitted, at least in part, by fomites. The most important control measure is prevention of infection by vaccination, if available. Influenza vaccination should be offered annually to hospital employees in an attempt to minimize the transmission of influenza infection to patients from personnel. Such a program, which has met with only a moderate degree of success in most hospitals, is considered to be an important aspect in the control of nosocomial influenza.

Special Considerations

The education of hospital personnel about mechanisms of transmission and the potential hazards of certain viruses should become the unifying theme in prevention and control of viruses in the hospital. It is important to emphasize that certain viral agents are more easily transmissible than others. For example, personnel may respond with extraordinary concern when caring for patients with CMV or HIV infection, while influenza vaccination programs and precautions for other more highly contagious viruses are often overlooked. Table 7–9 reviews briefly the relative risk of transmissibility of certain commonly seen viruses to hospital personnel and patients.

CONCLUSION

The relationship of virology to infection control has only re-

cently been appreciated. Until very recently, viral infections have traditionally been an enigma to most infection-control practitioners. The HIV epidemic underscores the importance of the relationship. Certainly the next few years should help clarify this relationship as further developments in antiviral chemotherapy and rapid viral diagnostic techniques occur. Health care facilities present a unique challenge to the virologist and infection control practitioner alike as they attempt to develop comprehensive programs for the prevention and control of nosocomial viral infections.

REFERENCES

1. Valenti WM, Menegus MM, Hall CB, et al: Nosocomial viral infections: I. Epidemiology and significance. *Infect Control* 1980; 1:33–37.
2. Valenti WM, Clarke TA, Hall CB, et al: Concurrent outbreaks of rhinovirus and respiratory synctial virus in an intensive care nursery: Epidemiology and associated risk factors. *J Pediatr* 1982; 100:722–726.
3. Mintz L, Ballard RA, Sniderman SH, et al: Nosocomial respiratory syncytial virus infections in an intensive care nursery. Rapid diagnosis by immunofluorescence. *Pediatrics* 1979; 64:149–153.
4. Hall CB: Nosocomial viral respiratory infections: Perennial weeds on pediatric wards. *Am J Med* 1981; 70:670–676.
5. Brachman PS: Epidemiology of nosocomial infections, in Bennett JV, Brachman PS (eds): *Hospital Infections*. Boston, Little, Brown, 1979, pp 17–34.
6. Mathur U, Bentley DW, Hall CB: Concurrent respiratory syncytial virus and influenza A infections in the institutionalized elderly and chronically ill. *Ann Intern Med* 1980; 93:49–52.
7. Bluemenfeld HL, Kilbourne ED, Louria DB, et al: Studies on influenza in the pandemic of 1957–1958. I. An epidemiologic, clinical serologic investigation of an intrahospital epidemic with a note on vaccine efficacy. *J Clin Invest* 1959; 38:199–212.
8. Boger WP, Frankel JW: Asian influenza: Isolated outbreak within a large closed population. *Am J Public Health* 1962; 52:834–840.

9. Hoffman PC, Dixon RE: Control of influenza in the hospital. *Ann Intern Med* 1977; 87:725–728.

10. Hall CB, Douglas RG Jr: Nosocomial influenza as a cause of intercurrent fever in infants. *Pediatrics* 1975; 55:673–677.

11. Van Voris LP, Belshe RB, Shaffer JL: Nosocomial influenza B in the elderly. *Ann Intern Med* 1982; 96:153–158.

12. Douglas RG Jr: Influenza in man, in Kilbourne ED (ed): *The Influenza Viruses and Influenza*. New York, Academic Press, 1975.

13. Parkman PD, Galasso GH, Top FH, et al: Summary of clinical trials of influenza vaccines. *J Infect Dis* 1976; 134:100–107.

14. Recommendations of the Immunization Practices Advisory Committee: Prevention and control of influenza. *MMWR* 1987; 36:373–387.

15. Hurwitz ES, Schonberger LB, Nelson DB, et al: Guillain-Barré syndrome and the 1978–79 influenza vaccine. *N Engl J Med* 1981; 304:1557–1561.

16. O'Donoghue JM, Ray CG, Terry DW, et al: Prevention of nosocomial influenza with amantadine. *Am J Epidemiol* 1973; 97:276–282.

17. Stanley ED, Muldoon RL, Akers LW, et al: Evaluation of antiviral drugs: The effect of amantadine on influenza in volunteers. *Ann NY Acad Sci* 1965; 130:44–51.

18. Muldoon RL, Stanley ED, Jackson GG: Use and withdrawal of amantadine chemoprophylaxis during epidemic influenza A. *Am Rev Respir Dis* 1976; 133:487–491.

19. Hall CB: The shedding and spreading of respiratory syncytial virus. *Pediatr Res* 1977; 11:236–239.

20. Hall CB, Douglas RG Jr, Geiman JM, et al: Nosocomial respiratory syncytial virus infections. *N Engl J Med* 1975; 293:1343–1346.

21. Hall CB, Geiman JM, Douglas RG Jr, et al: Control of nosocomial respiratory syncytial virus infections. *Pediatrics* 1978; 62:728–732.

22. Hall CB, Geiman JM, Biggar R, et al: Respiratory syncytial virus infections within families. *N Engl J Med* 1976; 294:414–419.

23. Henderson FW, Collier AM, Clyde WA, et al: Respiratory syncytial virus infections, reinfections and immunity: A prospective longitudinal study in young children. *N Engl J Med* 1979; 300:530–534.

24. Chanock RM, Kim HW, Vargosko AJ, et al: Respiratory syncytial virus I. Virus recovery and other observations during 1960 outbreak of bronchiolitis, pneumonia and respiratory diseases in children. *JAMA* 1961; 176:647–653.

25. Hall CB, Douglas RG Jr, Geiman JM: Possible transmission by fomites of respiratory syncytial virus. *J Infect Dis* 1980; 141:98–102.

26. Hall CB, Steinhoff MC, Douglas RG Jr: Infectivity of respiratory syncytial virus by various routes of inoculation. *Pediatr Res* 1979; 13:814A.

27. Hall CB, Douglas RG: Modes of transmission of respiratory syncytial virus. *J Pediatr* 1981; 99:100–103.

28. Hall CB, Kopelman AE, Douglas RG Jr, et al: Neonatal respiratory syncytial virus infection. *N Engl J Med* 1979; 300:393–396.

29. LeClair JM, Freeman J, Sullivan BF, et al: Prevention of nosocomial respiratory syncytial virus infections through compliance with glove and gown isolation precautions. *N Engl J Med* 1987; 317:329–341.

30. Gardner PS, Turk DC, Aherne WA, et al: Deaths associated with respiratory tract infection in childhood. *Br Med J* 1967; 4:316–320.

31. Mufson MA, Mocega HE, Krause HE: Acquisition of parainfluenza 3 virus infection by hospitalized children. I. Frequencies, rates and temporal data. *J Infect Dis* 1973; 128:141–147.

32. De Fabritis AM, Riggio RR, David DS, et al: Parainfluenza type 3 in a transplant unit. *JAMA* 1979; 241:384–385.

33. Centers for Disease Control: Parainfluenza outbreaks in extended-care facilities. *MMWR* 1978; 27:475–476.

34. Sims DG: A two year prospective study of hospital-acquired respiratory virus infection on pediatric wards. *J Hyg (Camb)* 1981; 86:335–342.

35. Gwaltney JM, Mosalski PB, Hendley JO: Hand to hand transmission of rhinovirus. *Ann Intern Med* 1978; 88:453–467.

36. Hendley JO, Mika LA, Gwaltney JM: Evaluation of virucidal compounds for inactivation of rhinovirus on hands. *Antimicrob Agents Chemother* 1978; 14:690–694.

37. Hendley JP, Wenzel RP, Gwaltney JM: Transmission of rhinovirus colds by self-inoculation. *N Engl J Med* 1973; 288:1362–1364.

38. Foy HM, Grayson JT: Adenoviruses, in Evans AS (ed): *Viral Infections of Humans: Epidemiology and Control* ed 2. New York, Plenum 1982, pp 67–84.

39. Ginsberg HS: Adenoviruses. *Am J Clin Pathol* 1972; 57:771–773.

40. Fox JP, Brandt CD, Wasserman FE, et al: The virus watch program: A continuing surveillance of viral infection in metropolitan New York families. VI. Observations of adenovirus infections. *Am J Epidemiol* 1969; 89:25–50.

41. Pingleton SK, Pingleton WW, Hill RH, et al: Type 3 adenoviral pneumonia occurring in a respiratory intensive care unit. *Chest* 1978; 73:554–555.

42. Straube RC, Thompson MA, VanDyke RB, et al: Adenovirus type 7b in a children's hospital. *J Infect Dis* 1983; 147:814–819.

43. Centers for Disease Control: Keratoconjunctivitis due to adenovirus-19-Canada. *MMWR* 1974; 23:185–186.

44. Laibson PR, Ortolan G, Dupre-Stachan S: Community and hospital outbreak of epidemic keratoconjunctivitis. *Arch Ophthalmol* 1968; 80:467–473.

45. Centers for Disease Control: Nosocomial outbreak of pharyngoconjunctival fever due to adenovirus, type 4-New York. *MMWR* 1978; 27:4.

46. Eichenwald HF, McCracken GH, Kindberg SJ: Virus infections of the newborn. *Prog Med Virol* 1967, 9:35–104.

47. Alpert G, Charney E, Fee M, et al: Outbreak of fatal adenoviral type 7a respiratory disease in a children's long–term care inpatient facility. *Am J Infect Control* 1986; 14:188–190.

48. Pacini DL, Collier AM, Henderson FW: Adenovirus infections and respiratory illnesses in children in group day care. *J Infect Dis* 1987; 156:920–927.

49. Wigger HF, Blank WA: Fatal hepatic and bronchial necrosis in adenovirus infection with thymic alymphoplasia. *N Engl J Med* 1977; 275:870–874.

50. Meyerowitz RL, Stalder H, Oxman MN, et al: Fatal disseminated adenovirus infection in a renal transplant recipient. *Am J Med* 1975; 59:591–597.

51. Dawson CR, Darrel R: Infections due to adenovirus type 8 in the United States. I. An outbreak of epidemic keratoconjunctivitis originating in a physician's office. *N Engl J Med* 1973; 268:1031–1034.

52. Sprague JB, Hierholzer JC, Currier RW, et al: Epidemic keratoconjunctivitis. *N Engl J Med* 1973; 289:1341–1346.

53. Appleton H, Buckley M, Robertson MH, et al: A search for faecal viruses in newborn and other infants. *J Hyg (Camb)* 1978; 81:279–282.

54. Middleton PJ, Azymanski MT, Petric PJ: Viruses associated with acute gastroenteritis in young children. *Am J Dis Child* 1977; 131:233–237.

55. Flewett TH, Bryden AS, Davies H: Epidemic viral enteritis in a long-stay children's ward. *Lancet* 1975; 1:4–5.

56. Richmond SJ, Caul EO, Dunn SM, et al: An outbreak of gastroenteritis in young children caused by adenoviruses. *Lancet* 1979; 1:1178–1180.

57. Jawetz E, Hanna L, Sonne M, et al: Laboratory infection with adenovirus type 8: Laboratory and epidemiologic observations. *Am J Hyg* 1979; 69:13–20.

58. Weller TH: The cytomegaloviruses: Ubiquitous agents with protean clinical manifestations *N Engl J Med* 1971; 285:203–214.

59. Weller TH: Varicella-herpes zoster virus, in Evans AS (ed): *Viral Infections of Humans: Epidemiology and Control* ed 2. New York, Plenum, 1982, pp 337–352.

60. Betts RF, Freeman RB, Douglas RG Jr, et al: Clinical manifesta-

tions of renal allograft derived primary cytomegalovirus infection. *Am J Dis Child* 1977; 131:759–763.

61. Wentworth BB, Alexander ER: Seroepidemiology of infections due to members of the herpes virus group. *Am J Epidemiol* 1971; 94:496–507.

62. Gustafson JL: An outbreak of nosocomial airborne varicella. *Pediatrics* 1982; 70:550–556.

63. Meyers JD, MacQuarrie MB, Merigan TC, et al: Nosocomial varicella-Part 1: Outbreak in oncology patients at a children's hospital. *West J Med* 1979; 130:196–199.

64. Gordon JE: Chickenpox: An epidemiological review. *Am J Med Sci* 1962; 244:362–389.

65. Leclair JM, Zaia JA, Levin MJ, et al: Airborne transmission of chickenpox in a hospital. *N Engl J Med* 1980; 302:450–453.

66. Morens DM, Bregman DJ, West CM, et al: An outbreak of varicella-zoster virus infection among cancer patients. *Ann Intern Med* 1980; 93:414–419.

67. Hayden GF, Meyers JD, Dixon RE: Nosocomial varicella Part II: Suggested guidelines for management. *West J Med* 1979; 130:300–303.

68. Zaia JA, Oxman MN: Antibody to varicella-zoster virus-induced membrane antigen: Immunofluorescence assay using monodisperse glutaraldehyde target cells. *J Infect Dis* 1977; 136:519–530.

69. Steele RF: Varicella-zoster in hospital personnel. Skin test reactivity to monitor susceptibility. *Pediatrics* 1980; 70:604–608.

70. Centers for Disease Control: Varicella-zoster immune globulin. *MMWR* 1981; 30:15, 16, 21–23.

71. Gershon AA, Steinberg SP, La Russa P, et al: Immunization of healthy adults with live attenuated varicella vaccine. *J Infect Dis* 1988; 158:132–137.

72. Berlin BS, Campbell T: Hospital–acquired chickenpox following exposures to herpes zoster. *JAMA* 1970; 211:1831–1833.

73. Palmer SR, Donald DE, Tillett H, et al: An outbreak of shingles? *Lancet* 1985; 2: 1108–1111.

74. Gershon AA, Baker R, Steinberg S, et al: Antibody to varicella-zoster virus in parturient women and their offspring during the first year of life. *Pediatrics* 1976; 58:692–696.

75. Ross AH: Modification of chickenpox in family contacts by administration of gamma globulin. *N Engl J Med* 1962; 267:369–376.

76. Foley FD, Greenwald KA, Nash MC, et al: Herpes virus infection in burned patients. *N Engl J Med* 1970; 282:652–656.

77. Naragi S, Jackson GG, Jonasson OM: Viremia with herpes simplex type 1 in adults. *Ann Intern Med* 1976; 85:165–169.

78. Stern J, Elek SD, Millar DM, et al: Herpetic whitlow, a form of cross-infection in hosptials. *Lancet* 1959; 2:871–874.

79. Greaves WL, Kaiser AB, Alford RH, et al: The problem of herpes whitlow among hospital personnel. *Infect Control* 1980; 1:381–385.

80. Blank H, Haines HG: Experimental reinfection with herpes simplex virus. *J Invest Dermatol* 1973; 61:223–225.

81. Hooton TM, Keenylside RG, Adams G, et al: Epidemiologic and laboratory evaluation of clusters of nosocomial herpes virus hominis infection in hospital personnel, in Program and Abstracts, 17th Interscience Conference on Antimicrobial Agents and Chemotherapy. New York, Oct 2–7, 1977, abstract No. 129.

82. Linnemann CC Jr, Buchman TG, Light IG, et al: Transmissions of herpes simplex virus type I in a nursery for the newborn: Identification of viral isolates by DNA fingerprinting. *Lancet* 1978; 1:964–966.

83. Manzella J, McConville J, Valenti WM, et al: An outbreak of herpes simplex virus stomatitis in a dental practice. *JAMA* 1984; 252: 2019–2022.

84. Nahmias AN, Josey WE, Naib ZM, et al: Perinatal risk associated with maternal genital herpes simplex virus infection. *Am J Obstet Gynecol* 1971; 110:825–837.

85. Prober GG: Mother-baby transmission of herpes simplex virus. *N Engl J Med* 1988; 318:887–891.

86. Kibrick S: Herpes simplex infection at term: What to do with mother, newborn, and nursery personnel. *JAMA* 1980; 243:159–160.

87. Valenti WM, Betts RF, Hall CB, et al: Nosocomial viral infections. II. Guidelines for prevention and control of respiratory viruses, herpesviruses, and hepatitis viruses. *Infect Control* 1980; 1:165–178.

88. Drew WL, Mintz L, Miner RC, et al: Prevalence of cytomegalovirus infection in homosexual men. *J Infect Dis* 1981; 143:188–192.

89. Weller TH: The cytomegaloviruses: Ubiquitous agents with protean manifestations. *N Engl J Med* 1971; 285:203–214, 267–274.

90. Dworsky ME, Welch K, Cassady G, et al: Occupational risk for primary cytomegalovirus infection among pediatric health care workers. *N Engl J Med* 1983; 309:950–953.

91. Betts RF, Cestero RVM, Freeman RB, et al: Epidemiology of cytomegalovirus infection in end stage renal disease. *J Med Virol* 1979; 4:89–96.

92. Tolkoff-Rubin NE, Rubin RH, Keller EE, et al: Cytomegalovirus infection in dialysis patients and personnel. *Ann Intern Med* 1978; 89:625–628.

93. Yow MD, Lakeman AD, Stagno S, et al: Use of restriction enzymes to investigate the source of primary cytomegalovirus infection in a pediatric nurse. *Pediatrics* 1982; 70:713.

94. Wilfert CM, Huang E, Stagno S: Restriction endonuclease analysis of cytomegalovirus deoxyribonucleic acid as an epidemiologic tool. *Pediatrics* 1982; 70:717–721.

95. Lang DJ, Ebert PA, Rodgers BM, et al: Reduction of post-transfusion cytomegalovirus infections following use of leukocyte-depleted blood. *Transfusion* 1977; 17:391–395.

96. Betts RF, Freeman RB, Douglas RG Jr, et al: Transmission of cytomegalovirus infection with renal allograft. *Kidney Int* 1975; 8:385–392.

97. Ho M, Suwansirikul S, Dowling JN, et al: The transplanted kidney as a source of CMV infection. *N Engl J Med* 1975; 293:1109–1112.

98. Turner AR, MacDonald RN, Cooper BA: Transmission of infectious mononucleosis by transfusion of pre-illness serum. *Ann Intern Med* 1972; 77:751–753.

99. Corey L, Stamm WE, Feorino PM, et al: HBsAg-negative hepatitis in a hemodialysis unit—relation to Epstein-Barr virus. *N Engl J Med* 1975; 293:1273–1278.

100. Matthew EB, Sietzman DE, Madden DL, et al: A major epidemic of infectious hepatitis in an institution for the mentally retarded. *Am J Epidemiol* 1973; 98:199–215.

101. Ward R, Krugman S, Giles JP, et al: Infectious hepatitis. Studies of its natural history and prevention. *N Engl J Med* 1958; 258:407–416.

102. Szmuness W, Purcell RH, Dienstag JL, et al: Antibody to hepatitis A antigen in institutionalized mentally retarded patients. *JAMA* 1977; 237:1702–1705.

103. Centers for Disease Control: Outbreak of viral hepatitis in the staff of a pediatrics ward-California. *MMWR* 1977; 26:77–78.

104. Meyers JD, Romm FJ, Then WS, et al: Foodborne hepatitis A in a general hospital. *JAMA* 1975; 231:1049–1053.

105. Favero MS, Maynard JE, Leger RT, et al: Guidelines for the care of patients hospitalized with viral hepatitis. *Ann Intern Med* 1979; 91:872–876.

106. Snydman DR, Bryan JA, Dixon RE: Prevention and control of nosocomial viral hepatitis, type B (hepatitis B). *Ann Intern Med* 1975; 83:838–845.

107. Lewis TJ, Alter HJ, Chalmers TC, et al: A comparison of the frequency of hepatitis B antigen and antibody in hospital and non-hospital personnel. *N Engl J Med* 1973; 289:647–651.

108. Denes AE, Smith JL, Maynard JE, et al: Hepatitis B infection in physicians: Results of a nationwide seroepidemiologic survey. *JAMA* 1978; 239:210–212.

109. Smith JL, Maynard JE, Berquist KR, et al: Comparative risk of hepatitis B among physicians and dentists. *J Infect Dis* 1976; 6:705–706.

110. Dienstag JL, Ryan DM: Occupational exposure to hepatitis B virus in hospital personnel: Infection or immunization? *Am J Epidemiol* 1982; 115:26–39.

111. Rimland D, Parkin WE, Miller GB, et al: Hepatitis B traced to

an oral surgeon. *N Engl J Med* 1977; 296:953–958.

112. Alter HJ, Chalmers TC, Freeman BM, et al: Health care workers positive for hepatitis B surface antigen: Are their contacts at risk? *N Engl J Med* 1975; 292:454–457.

113. Gerber MA, Lewin EB, Gerety MD, et al: The lack of transmission of type B hepatitis in a special care nursery. *J Pediatr* 1977; 91:120–122.

114. Meyers JD, Stamm WE, Kerr M, et al: Lack of transmission of hepatitis B after surgical exposure. *JAMA* 1978; 240:1725–1727.

115. Williams WW: *CDC Guideline for Infection Control in Hospital Personnel* US Dept of Health and Human Services publication no. (CDC)83–8314. Available from National Technical Information Service, US Dept Commerce, Springfield Va.

116. Recommendations of the Immunization Practices Advisory Committee: Update on hepatitis B prevention. *MMWR* 1987; 36:353–366.

117. Hollinger FB: Hepatitis B vaccines—to switch or not to switch. *JAMA* 1987; 257:2634–2636.

118. Francis DP, Feorino PM, McDougal S, et al: The safety of hepatitis B vaccine: inactivation of the AIDS virus during routine vaccine manufacture. *JAMA* 1986; 256:869–872.

119. Szmuness W, Stevens CE, Harley EJ, et al: Hepatitis B vaccine: Demonstration of efficacy in a controlled clinical trial in a high risk population in the United States. *N Engl J Med* 1980; 303:833–841.

120. Centers for Disease Control: Suboptimal response to hepatitis B vaccine given into the buttocks. *MMWR* 1987; 36:597–602.

121. Szmuness W, Dienstag JL, Purcell RH, et al: Hepatitis A and hemodialysis. *Ann Intern Med* 1977; 87:8–12.

122. Snydman DR, Bryan JA, Macon EJ, et al: Hemodialysis associated hepatitis: Report of an epidemic with further evidence on mechanisms of transmission. *Am J Epidemiol* 1976; 104:563–570.

123. Mosley JW, Redeker AG, Feinstone SM, et al: Multiple hepatitis viruses in multiple attacks of acute viral hepatitis. *N Engl J Med* 1977; 296:75–78.

124. Meyers JD, Dienstag JL, Purcell RH, et al: Parenterally transmitted non-A, non-B hepatitis: An epidemic reassessed. *Ann Intern Med* 1977; 87:57–59.

125. Centers for Disease Control: Enterically transmitted non-A, non-B hepatitis—Mexico. *MMWR* 1987; 36:597–602.

126. Advisory Committee on Immunization Practices: Rubella prevention. *MMWR* 1981; 30:37–42, 47.

127. Hethcote HW: Measles and rubella in the United States. *Am J Epidemiol* 1983; 117:2–18.

128. Orenstein WA, Heseltine PNR, LeGagnoux SJ, et al: Rubella vaccine and susceptible hospital employees. *JAMA* 1981; 245:711–737.

129. McLaughlin MC, Gold LH: The New York rubella incident: A case for changing hospital policy regarding rubella testing and immunization. *Am J Public Health* 1979; 69:287–289.

130. Heseltine PNR, Ripper M, Wohlford P: Nosocomial rubella—consequences of an outbreak and efficacy of a mandatory immunization program. *Infect Control* 1985; 6:371–374.

131. Centers for Disease Control: Exposure of patients to rubella by medical personnel. *MMWR* 1980; 27:123.

132. Polk BF, White JA, DeGirolami PC, et al: Outbreak of rubella among hospital personnel. *N Engl J Med* 1980; 303:541–545.

133. Fliegel PE, Weinstein WW: Rubella outbreak in a prenatal clinic: Management and prevention. *Am J Infect Control* 1982; 10:1, 29–33.

134. Schoenbaum SC: Rubella policies for hospitals and health workers, editorial. *Infect Control* 1981; 2:366, 416–417.

135. Advisory Committee on Infections Within Hospitals of the American Hospital Association: Recommendation for the control of rubella within hospitals, *Infect Control* 1981; 2:410–411.

136. Centers for Disease Control: Rubella vaccination during pregnancy—United States. *MMWR* 1987; 36:457–461.

137. Sienko DG, Friedman C, McGee HB, et al: A measles outbreak at university medical settings involving health care providers. *Am J Public Health* 1987; 77:1222–1224.

138. Nichols EM: Atypical measles syndrome: A continuing problem. *Am J Public Health* 1979; 69:160–162.

139. Immunization Practices Subcommittee: Measles prevention. *MMWR* 1987; 36:409–418, 423–426.

140. Cherry JD, Feigin RD, Lobes LA, et al: Atypical measles in children previously immunized with attenuated measles virus vaccine. *Pediatrics* 1972; 50:712–717.

141. Feldman HA: Mumps, in Evans AS (ed): *Viral Infections of Humans: Epidemiology and Control.* New York, Plenum, 1982, pp 419–440.

142. Duffy P, Wolf J, Collins G, et al: Possible person to person transmission of Creutzfeldt–Jakob disease (letter). *N Engl J Med* 1974; 290:692–693.

143. Centers for Disease Control. Update: Creutzfeldt-Jakob disease in a patient receiving a cadaveric dura mater graft. *MMWR* 1987; 36:324–325.

144. Bernoulli C, Siegfried J, Baumgartner G, et al: Danger of accidental person-to-person transmission of Creutzfeldt-Jakob disease by surgery. *Lancet* 1977; 1:478–479.

145. Gadjusek DC, Gibbs CJ, Asher DM, et al: Precautions in medical care of and in handling materials from patients with transmissible virus dementia (Creutzfeldt-Jakob disease). *N Engl J Med* 1977; 297:1253–1258.

146. Tallett S, MacKenzie C, Middleton P, et al: Clinical, laboratory and epidemiologic features of a viral gastroenteritis in infants and children. *Pediatrics* 1977; 60:217–222.

147. Cone R, Mohan K, Thouless M, et al: Nosocomial transmission of rotavirus infections. *Pediatr Infect Dis J* 1988; 7:103–109.

148. Davidson GP: Importance of a new virus in acute sporadic enteritis in children. *Lancet* 1975; 1:242–245.

149. DuPont HL, Portnoy BL, Conklin RH: Viral agents and diarrheal illness. *Ann Rev Med* 1977; 28:166–177.

150. Kapikian AZ, Kim HW, Wyatt RG, et al: Human reovirus-like agent as the major pathogen associated with "winter" gastroenteritis in hospitalized infants and young children. *N Engl J Med* 1976; 294:965–974.

151. Meurman OH, Laine MJ: Rotavirus epidemic in adults. *N Engl J Med* 1977; 296:1298–1299.

152. Kim HW, Brandt CD, Kapikian AZ, et al: Human reovirus-like agent infection occurrence in adult contacts of pediatric patients with gastroenteritis. *JAMA* 1977; 238:404–407.

153. Bolivar R, Conklin RH, Vollett JJ, et al: Rotavirus in travelers' diarrhea: Study of an adult student population in Mexico. *J Infect Dis* 1978; 137:324–327.

154. Phillips CA, Aronson MD, Tomkow J, et al: Enteroviruses in Vermont 1969–1978: An important cause of illness throughout the year. *J Infect Dis* 1980; 141:162–165.

155. Melnick JL: Enteroviruses, in Evans AS (ed); *Viral Infections in Humans: Epidemiology and Control.* New York, Plenum, 1976, pp 163–201.

156. Cramblatt HB, Haynes RD, Azimi PH, et al: Nosocomial infection with echovirus type 11 in handicapped and premature infants. *Pediatrics* 1973; 51:603–607.

157. Jones MJ, Kolb M, Votava HF, et al: Intrauterine echovirus type 11 infections. *Mayo Clin Proc* 1980; 55:509–511.

158. Gear JHS, Measroch V: Coxsackievirus infections of the newborn. *Prog Med Virol* 1973;15:42.

159. Cherry JD: Enteroviruses, in Remington JS, Klein JO (eds): *Infectious Diseases of the Fetus and Newborn Infant.* Philadelphia, Saunders, 1976, pp 367–413.

160. McDonald LL, St Gene JW, Arnold BH: Nosocomial infection with ECHO virus type 31 in neonatal intensive care unit. *Pediatrics* 1971; 47:995–999.

161. Lake AM, Lauer BA, Clark JC: Enterovirus infections in neonates. *J Pediatr* 1976; 89:787–791.

162. Cherry JD, Soriano F, Jahn CL: Search for perinatal viral infection. A prospective, clinical virologic and serologic study. *Am J Dis Child* 1968; 116:245.

163. Schonberger LB, McGowan JE, Gregg MB: Vaccine associated poliomyelitis in the United States 1961–1972. *Am J Epidemiol* 1976; 104:202–211.

164. Basilico FC, Bernat J: Vaccine associated polio-myelitis in a contact. *JAMA* 1978; 239:2275.

165. Nathanson N, Martin JR: The epidemiology of poliomyelitis: Enigmas surrounding its appearance, epidemicity and disappearance. *Am J Epidemiol* 1976; 110:672–692.

166. Centers for Disease Control: Poliomyelitis—Pennsylvania, Maryland. *MMWR* 1979; 28:49–50.

166. Robertson SE, Drucker JA, Fabre-Teste B, et al: Clinical efficacy of a new, enhanced–potency, inactivated poliovirus vaccine. *Lancet* 1988; 1:897–899.

167. Houff SA, Burton RC, Wilson RW, et al: Human-to-human transmission of rabies virus by corneal transplant. *N Engl J Med* 1979; 300:603–605.

168. Centers for Disease Control: Human-to-human transmission of rabies via a corneal transplant. *MMWR* 1980; 29:25–26.

169. Centers for Disease Control: Human rabies—Pennsylvania. *MMWR* 1979; 28:75–76.

170. Centers for Disease Control: Veterinary public health notes, July 1977.

171. Centers for Disease Control: Rabies prevention. *MMWR* 1980; 29:265–280.

172. Baer GM, Fishbein DB: Rabies postexposure prophylaxis. *N Engl J Med* 1987; 316:1270–1272.

172. Anderson LJ, Winkler WG: Aqueous quaternary ammonium compounds and rabies treatment. *J Infect Dis* 1979; 139:494–495.

173. VanZee BE, Douglas RG Jr, Betts RF, et al: Lymphocytic choriomeningitis in University Hospital personnel. *Am J Med* 1975; 58:803–809.

174. Buckley SM, Casals J: Lassa fever, a new viral disease of man from West Africa. *Am J Trop Med Hyg* 1973; 223:279–283.

175. Carey DE, Kempt GE, White HA, et al: Lassa fever, epidemiological aspects of the 1970 epidemic, Johannesburg, Nigeria. *Trans R Soc Trop Hyg* 1972; 66:402–408.

176. Monath TP, Martens PE, Patton R, et al: A hospital epidemic of Lassa fever in Zorzor, Liberia, March-April. *MMWR* 1972; 22:773–779.

177. Centers for Disease Control: Management of patients with suspected viral hemorrhagic fever. *MMWR* 1988; 37:1–16.

178. Wehrle PF, Posch J, Richter KH, et al: An airborne outbreak of smallpox in a German hospital and its significance with respect to other recent outbreaks in Europe. *Bull WHO* 1970; 43:669–679.

179. Downie AW: Poxvirus group, in Horsfall RL, Tamm I (eds): *Viral and Rickettsial Infections of Man,* ed 4. Philadelphia, Lippincott, 1965, pp 932–964.

180. Centers for Disease Control: Laboratory-associated smallpox. *MMWR* 1978; 27:319–320.

181. Centers for Disease Control: Smallpox vaccine. *MMWR* 1980; 29:417–420.

182. Gear JSS, Cassel GA, Gear AJ, et al: Outbreaks of Marburg virus disease in Johannesburg, *Br Med J* 1975; 4:489–493.

183. Martini GA, Surgert R (eds): *Marburg Virus Disease.* New York, Springer-Verlag, 1971.

184. Centers for Disease Control: Viral hemorrhagic fever—Sudan and Zaire. *MMWR* 1977; 26:209–210.

185. Editorial: After Marburg, Ebola. *Lancet* 1977; 1:581–582.

186. Barrasso R, De Brux J, Croissant O, et al: High prevalence of papillomavirus-associated penile intraepithelial neoplasia in sexual partners of women with cervical intraepithelial neoplasia. *N Engl J Med* 1987; 317: 916–923.

187. International Agency for Research on Cancer: Human papillomavirus and cervical cancer, *Lancet* 1988; 1:756–757.

188. Rando R: Human papillomaviruses: implications for clinical medicine. *Ann Intern Med* 1988; 108:628–630.

189. Garden JM, O'Banion K, Shelnitz L, et al: Papillomavirus in the vapor carbon dioxide laser-treated verrucae. *JAMA* 1988; 259:1199–1202.

190. Epidemiologic Notes and Reports: Update: Acquired immunodeficiency syndrome and human immunodeficiency virus infection among health care workers. *MMWR* 1988; 37:229–239.

191. Centers for Disease Control: 1988 Agent summary statement for human immunodeficiency virus and report on laboratory-acquired infection with human immunodeficiency virus. *MMWR* 1988; 37:1–22.

192. Centers for Disease Control: Lack of transmission of human immunodeficiency virus through Rh(d) immune globulin (human) *MMWR* 1987; 258:322–325.

193. Valenti WM, Anarella JP: A survey of hospital personnel on the understanding of AIDS. *Am J Infect Control* 1986; 14:60–63.

194. Centers for Disease Control: Recommendations for prevention of HIV transmission in health care settings. *MMWR* 1987; 36:1S–18S.

195. Lynch P, Jackson MM, Cummings J, et al: Rethinking the role of isolation practices in the prevention of nosocomial infections. *Ann Intern Med* 1987; 107:243–246.

196. Centers for Disease Control: Update: Universal precautions for prevention of transmission of HIV, hepatitis B and other bloodborne pathogens in health care settings. *MMWR* 1988; 37:377–387.

197. Spire B, Dormont D, Barre-Sinoussi F, et al: Inactivation of LAV by heat, gamma rays, and ultraviolet light. *Lancet* 1985; 1:188–189.

198. Spire B, Dormont D, Barre-Sinoussi F, et al: Inactivation of LAV by chemical disinfectants. *Lancet* 1984; 2:899–901.

199. Martin LS, McDougal S, Loskoski SL: Disinfection and inactivation of the human T lymphotropic virus type III/lymphadenopathy-associated virus. *J Infect Dis* 1985; 152:400–403.

200. Gerberding JL, Henderson DK: Design of rational infection control policies for human immunodeficiency virus infection. *J Infect Dis* 1987; 156:861–864.

201. Centers for Disease Control: Semen banking, organ and tissue transplantation, and HIV antibody testing. *MMWR* 1988; 37:1301–1305.

202. Henderson DK, Gerberding JL: Prophylactic zidovudine after occupational exposure to the human immunodeficiency virus: An interim analysis. *J Infect Dis* 1989; 160:321–327.

203. Frazer MJL: A study of neonatal infections in nurseries of a maternity hospital. *Arch Dis Child* 1948; 23:107–110.

204. Light IJ, Brackvogel MS, Walton RL, et al: An epidemic of *Staphylococcus aureus. Pediatrics* 1972; 49:15–20.

205. Cramblatt HB, Haynes RD, Azimi AM, et al: Nosocomial infection with echovirus type II in handicapped and premature infants. *Pediatrics* 1973; 51:603–607.

206. Brightman VJ, Scott TFM, Westphal M, et al: An outbreak of coxsackie B-5 virus infection in newborn nursery. *J Pediatr* 1966; 69:179–192.

207. Valenti WM, Hruska JF, Menegus MA, et al: Nosocomial virus infections: III. Guidelines for prevention and control of exanthematous viruses, gastroenteritis viruses, picornaviruses and uncommonly seen viruses. *Infect Control* 1981; 2:38–49.

208. Editorial: Why not child visitors? *Br Med J* 1968; 3:510.

209. Eton B: Visiting in maternity hospitals. *Br Med J* 1966; 2:304–306.

8

Introduction to Retroviruses

Rüdiger Hehlmann
Volker Erfle

Tumor viruses have been fascinating to scientists since their first discovery in animal tumors, not only as pathogenic agents but also as experimental models in the expectation that these viruses might allow us an insight into the mechanisms that underlie carcinogenesis. It is a consequence of research on tumor viruses that we are now beginning to understand better the complicated pathways leading to carcinogenesis.

Whereas viruses are an established natural cause of many animal neoplasms, the question of a possible role of viruses in human carcinogenesis remains unresolved. The viruses discussed most frequently as candidates for human carcinogenesis include the RNA tumor viruses (now often called by the more general name retroviruses, ie, reverse transcriptase–containing viruses), some members of the herpesvirus group, papovaviruses, adenoviruses, and hepatitis B virus. Members of the RNA tumor virus group have traditionally been considered to be the most likely candidates for the causation of some human cancers (leukemia, lymphoma, sarcoma, breast cancer), since viruses of this group are known to cause the same types of tumors in several vertebrate species. The discovery and characterization of oncogenes from retroviruses with the help of gene-cloning and DNA-sequencing techniques and the isolation of the first human retrovirus have supported the probable significance of these viruses for human carcinogenesis.

In addition, retroviruses have been found to be important veterinary and human pathogens beyond neoplastic disease. The realization that retroviruses may be natural genetic vectors for oncogenes has led to their use as genetic vectors for experimental and therapeutic purposes. This approach to retroviruses opens possibilities in modern molecular biologic and genetic research far beyond what was imagined only 10 years ago.

Since the DNA-containing tumor viruses are covered separately in individual chapters, this chapter will concentrate exclusively on retroviruses. Animal retroviruses are presented both systematically and in a more general way regarding their basic properties. Details are provided whenever this is necessary for the understanding of basic facts and mechanisms. In addition, the significance of retroviruses as models for the study of carcinogenesis, as vehicles for cellular genes, as promoters of cellular gene expression, as insertion mutagens, and as etiologic agents for veterinary and human disease will be discussed.

HISTORY

Detection of Retroviruses

The history of retroviruses is mainly that of RNA tumor viruses. After Ellermann and Bang's observation, in Copenhagen, of an ultrafiltrable agent in avian leukosis in 1908,[1] Peyton Rous, at the Rockefeller Institute in 1911, induced sarcomas in chickens with cell-free filtrates from sarcomas.[2] The virus isolated from the cell-free filtrates became the prototype of RNA tumor viruses and was termed Rous sarcoma virus (RSV). In 1914, Fujinami and Inamoto in Japan reported similar tumors which could be transmitted by ultrafiltrates to healthy chickens and ducks.[3] The virus isolated from these ultrafiltrates was designated Fujinami sarcoma virus (FSV). The significance of these observations was not recognized until much later; a Nobel Prize was awarded to Rous in 1966. In the 1930s, Jacob Furth found that erythroblastosis, myeloblastosis, and myelocytomatosis of chickens could be induced by different viruses.

When inbred mouse strains became available, Bittner, in 1936, demonstrated induction of mammary tumors through a milk factor.[4] He showed that newborn mice from a strain with a low mammary tumor incidence had a much higher incidence of tumors if they were removed from their mothers and foster-nursed by high-incidence mice and vice versa. The milk factor was later termed mouse mammary tumor virus (MMTV).

The first conclusive evidence for an etiologic role of viruses in murine leukemia came from Ludwik Gross in 1951.[5] He successfully transmitted leukemia in mice by inoculating very young mice of one mouse strain (C3H) with cell-free extracts of leukemias in mice of another strain (AKR). The viruses isolated from murine leukemias were subsequently designated murine leukemia viruses (MuLV). The different isolates were distinguished by the name of the scientists who discovered them first (eg, Gross MuLV). Another virus which causes myeloid leukemia in mice was isolated

by Graffi and coworkers from sarcoma filtrates in 1955.[6] It is referred to as the Graffi strain of murine leukemia virus (Graffi MuLV). In 1957, Friend obtained a filtrable agent from the spleen of a leukemic Swiss mouse which consistently produced erythroleukemia on serial transmission.[7] The virus is known as Friend MuLV. In 1959 Lieberman and Kaplan found leukemogenic activity in cell-free filtrates from radiation-induced leukemias of mice. The virus is referred to as radiation leukemia virus (Rad LV).[8] Soon Moloney (1960) and Rauscher (1962) described viral agents that also efficiently infected adult animals of most inbred strains of mice (Rauscher MuLV, Moloney MuLV).[9, 10]

The induction of murine sarcomas was linked to RNA tumor viruses through the isolates by Harvey (1964), Moloney (1966), Finkel, Biskis, and Jinkins (1966), and Kirsten and Mayer (1967).[11, 12] The viruses were designated murine sarcoma viruses (MuSV), strains Harvey, Moloney, Kirsten, and FBJ. Except for the Finkel, Biskis, and Jinkins (FBJ) virus, none of these murine sarcoma viruses was isolated from naturally occurring sarcomas, but from sarcomas which had developed in animals infected with MuLV.

Cat leukemias and sarcomas were shown to be associated with and transmitted by RNA tumor viruses since 1964 (feline leukemia viruses, feline sarcoma viruses). The different isolates were designated according to the scientists who described them first: Jarrett (1964), Kawakami and Theilen (1967), and Rickard (1969) described the respective strains of feline leukemia viruses (FeLV). The feline sarcoma virus (FeSV) isolates were first described by Snyder and Theilen (1969), Gardner and Arnstein (1970), and McDonough and Sarma (1971).[13, 14]

The existence of a bovine leukemia lymphosarcoma virus (BLV) had originally been deduced from seroepidemiologic observations in herds with bovine leukemia. The existence of such a virus was confirmed in 1969 by Miller and associates in cell culture studies.[15]

The first primate retrovirus was discovered in 1970 in a mammary carcinoma of a rhesus monkey (Mason-Pfizer monkey virus, MPMV).[16] Shortly thereafter (1971), a primate retrovirus was isolated from a fibrosarcoma of a woolly monkey by Theilen and Wolfe and their associates (simian sarcoma virus/simian sarcoma–associated virus [SiSV/SSAV]). This virus transforms cells in tissue culture and induces fibrosarcomas in infected marmoset monkeys.[17] In 1972, a related virus was isolated from spontaneous lymphosarcomas and leukemias of gibbon apes and was named gibbon ape leukemia virus (GaLV). GaLV induces granulocytic and lymphatic leukemias in gibbons.

Nononcogenic retroviruses were also isolated from normal (nontumorous) tissues and cells. These viruses are inducible from virus nonproducing cells with chemical and physical agents as was demonstrated in 1970 by Wallace Rowe in mouse cells and Peter Vogt in chicken cells.[18, 19] This led to the detection of the endogenous retroviruses that are inherited entities of normal cellular genomes. Endogenous retroviruses have been detected since then in most vertebrate species, for example, chickens, mice, rats, guinea pigs, minks, cats, pigs, and several primate species.

In 1970, a RNA-dependent DNA polymerase (reverse transcriptase) was identified in RNA tumor viruses by Howard Temin and also by David Baltimore.[20, 21] This enzyme is required to verify the replication of retroviruses via synthesis of a DNA intermediate and via its integration into the cellular genome. This detection was

Table 8–1
Taxonomy of Retroviruses

Family and Subfamily	Virus Group	Common Species (Abbreviation)
Retroviridae	Type C oncovirus group	
Oncovirinae	Mammalian	Murine C-type viruses
(RNA tumor		Murine leukemia viruses (MuLV)
virus group)		Murine sarcoma viruses (MuSV)
		Murine endogenous viruses
		Rat C-type viruses
		Hamster C-type viruses
		Feline C-type viruses
		Feline leukemia viruses (FeLV)
		Feline sarcoma viruses (FeSV)
		Feline endogenous viruses (RD114)
		Bovine C-type leukemia viruses (BLV)
		Porcine C-type viruses
		Primate C-type viruses
		Gibbon ape leukemia viruses (GaLV)
		Simian sarcoma virus (SiSv)
		Baboon endogenous viruses (BaEV)
		Simian T-lymphotropic virus (STLV)
		Human T cell lymphoma-leukemia virus
		(HTLV I and II)
	Avian	Avian C-type viruses
		Avian leukemia viruses (ALV)
		Avian sarcoma viruses (ASV)
		Avian reticuloendotheliosis viruses (REV)
		Avian endogenous viruses
	Reptilian	Viper C-type virus
	Type B oncovirus group	Mouse mammary tumor virus (MMTV)
	Type D oncovirus group	Mason-Pfizer monkey virus (MPMV)
		Simian immunodeficiency retrovirus
		type 1, 2 (SRV-1, -2)
		Langur endogenous virus (PO-1-Lu)
		Squirrel monkey endogenous virus (SMRV)
Lentivirinae		Visna-maedi virus
		Caprine arthritis encephalitis virus (CAEV)
		Equine infectious anemia virus (EIAV)
		Bovine immunodeficiency virus (BIV)
		Feline T-lymphotropic lentivirus
		(FTLV or FIV)
		Simian immunodeficiency virus (SIV)
		Human immunodeficiency virus (HIV-1, -2)
Spumavirinae		Foamy viruses of several animal species
		Human foamy virus (HFV)

a basic contribution to the knowledge of genetic information transfer and a Nobel Prize was awarded to both in 1975.

Another important discovery was the detection of oncogenes in RNA tumor viruses. Oncogenes are genes that mediate tumor induction in vivo and neoplastic transformation in vitro. In the early 1970s the first oncogene was detected in RSV by Peter Vogt, Peter Duesberg, and coworkers on the basis of biochemical and genetic analysis.[22, 23] The subsequent isolation of this oncogene (called src from *sarc*oma) in 1976, and the determination of its complete nucleotide sequence, in 1980, by Michael Bishop, Harold Varmus, and their associates, defined this oncogene and led to the detection of further oncogenes in retroviruses and also in transformed and normal vertebrate cells.[24, 25] A Nobel prize was awarded to Bishop and Varmus in 1989. A taxonomy of retroviruses is

presented in Table 8–1, a list of retroviral oncogenes in Table 8–2.

Search for Human Retroviruses
Electron Microscopy

The search for a human RNA tumor virus started soon after Ludwik Gross's discovery, in 1951, of the first mammalian leukemia virus in mice. In 1957, Leon Dmochowsky and coworkers first demonstrated by electron microscopy the presence of virus-like particles in the lymph nodes of two leukemic patients.[26] To obtain statistically significant results, studies of large numbers of patients were undertaken in the early 1960s. In some series particles were found in up to 34% of the samples studied, but other

Table 8–2
Retroviral onc Genes

Gene	Virus	Animal of Origin	Type of Tumor	Protein (mol wt × 10³)	Kinase Activity	Function of Related Proto-oncogene	Human Chromosomal Location
src	RSV	Chicken	Sarcoma	p60^{src}	+		1, 20
	B77	Chicken	Sarcoma	p60^{src}	+		
	rASV	Chicken, quail	Sarcoma	p60^{src}	+		
fps	FSV	Chicken	Sarcoma	p140$^{gag\text{-}fps}$	+		
	PRC II	Chicken	Sarcoma	p105	+		
	UR1	Chicken	Sarcoma	p150	+		
	16L	Chicken	Sarcoma	p142	+		
yes	Y73	Chicken	Sarcoma	p90$^{gag\text{-}yes}$	+		18
	ESV	Chicken	Sarcoma	p80	+		
ros	UR2	Chicken	Sarcoma	p68$^{gag\text{-}ros}$	+		
abl	A-MuLV	Mouse	Leukemia	p160$^{gag\text{-}abl}$	+		9
fes	ST-FeSV	Cat	Sarcoma	p90$^{gag\text{-}fes}$	+		15
	GA-FESV	Cat	Sarcoma	p110	+		
fgr	GR-FeSV	Cat	Sarcoma	P70$^{gag\text{-}actin\text{-}fgr}$	+		1
mos	Mo-MuSV	Mouse	Sarcoma	P37^{mos}	+		8
	Gz-MuSV	Mouse	Sarcoma	p37, 62			
mil	MH2	Chicken	Sarcoma	p75^{mil}	+		
raf	3611-MuSV	Mouse	Fibrosarcoma	p75^{raf}	+		3
Ki-ras	KI-MuSV	Rat	Sarcoma	p21$^{Ki\text{-}ras}$	+	GTP-binding	12(6)
Ha-ras	Ha-MuSV	Rat	Sarcoma	p21$^{Ha\text{-}ras}$	+	GTP-binding	11(x)
sis	SiSV	Monkey	Sarcoma	p28$^{env\text{-}sis}$	+	PDGF	22
erb A	AEV	Chicken	Leukemia	p75$^{gag\text{-}erb\text{-}A}$		T3 receptor	17
erb B	AEV	Chicken	Sarcoma	gp72$^{erb\text{-}B}$	+	EGF receptor	7
fms	MS-FeSV	Cat	Sarcoma	gp170^{fms}	+	CSF-1 receptor	5
kit	HZ4-FeSV	Cat	Sarcoma	p80$^{gag\text{-}kit}$		CSF-1-like receptor	4
myb	AMV	Chicken	Leukemia	p45$^{gag\text{-}myb}$			6
	E26	Chicken	Leukemia			Nuclear	
ets	E26	Chicken	Leukemia	p135$^{gag\text{-}myb\text{-}ets}$		Nuclear	11
myc	MC29	Chicken	Carcinomas, leukemias	p110$^{gag\text{-}myc}$		Nuclear, DNA-binding	8
	CM II	Chicken	Sarcoma	p90			
	MH2	Chicken	Leukemias, carcinomas, sarcoma	p100			
ski	SKV	Chicken	Carcinoma	p110$^{gag\text{-}ski}$		Nuclear	1
fos	FBJ-MuSV	Mouse	Osteosarcoma	p55^{fos}		Nuclear DNA binding (AP-1)	14
jun	ASV	Chicken	Sarcoma	p39^{jun}		Nuclear, DNA-binding (AP-1)	
rel	REV-T	Turkey	Lymphoma	p36$^{env\text{-}rel}$			

PDGF = platelet-derived growth factor; CSF-1 = mononuclear phagocyte colony-stimulating factor; EGF = epidermal growth factor; GR-FeSV = Gardner-Rasheed strain of FeSV; HZ4-FeSV = Hardy-Zuckerman strain of FeSV; for other abbreviations, see text. Data from references 67–73, 87–97, and 167–172.

large series failed to detect significant differences between leukemic and normal cell or plasma samples.

Similar large-scale studies were undertaken to associate RNA tumor viruses with human breast cancer. This was stimulated by the detection in human milk of particles resembling MMTV. The most extensive study was done by Dan Moore and associates in the late 1960s on milk samples from 101 American women at "high risk" for breast cancer, from 46 Parsi women in Bombay, who have a relatively higher incidence of breast cancer than the rest of the Bombay population, and from 181 control women. Particles resembling MMTV were reported in 39% of the Parsi milk samples, in 31% of the high-risk milk samples, and in 12% of the normal controls.[27]

Serology

Serologic studies done in parallel to the electron microscopic studies in the 1960s also yielded some evidence for footprints of human retroviruses. The techniques used were immunofluorescence reactions and virus neutralization tests. The human neoplasias investigated were mainly leukemias, sarcomas, and breast cancer.

Reverse Transcriptase and Viral RNA

The detection of an RNA-dependent DNA polymerase (reverse transcriptase) in retroviruses in 1970[20, 21] prompted the search for reverse transcriptase in human tumors and the subsequent detection of reverse transcriptase in some human leukemias,[28] lymphomas, breast carcinomas, and human milk samples. In some instances this reverse transcriptase was found to be associated with retroviruslike particles. In 1972, and in the following years, virus-related RNA was reported in some human leukemias, lymphomas, sarcomas, breast carcinomas, and a few other neoplasms.[29] Retrospectively, these findings have to be taken as early evidence for the existence and expression of human endogenous retroviruses (see Chapter 9).

Viral Isolates from Human Cells

The first retrovirus isolates that were claimed to be of human origin in 1971 and 1972 were soon characterized as nonprimate animal virus contaminants. Viral isolates from Robert Gallo's group in Bethesda, Peter Bentvelzen's group in the Netherlands, Werner Kirsten's group in Chicago, and Henry Kaplan and coworkers in Stanford during 1975 to 1977 remain of interest.[30–33] All these isolates are closely related to, or identical with, SiSV/SSAV, GaLV, or mixtures of these viruses with the endogenous baboon virus BaEV.[34–36] The first unambiguously human retroviruses were isolated, in 1980, from human T cell malignancies by Robert Gallo and coworkers.[34, 37, 38] Their detection became possible mainly because of improved growth conditions for human T cells by the detection and application of the human T cell growth factor (TCGF or interleukin-2).[39–41] Retroviruses became central targets of scientific and public interest with the detection that a retrovirus, the human immunodeficiency virus (HIV), was the cause of the acquired immunodeficiency syndrome (AIDS) (see Chapter 9).[42, 43]

BASIC PROPERTIES OF RETROVIRUSES

Morphology

By electron microscopy, retroviruses appear as almost spherical particles of approximately 100 nm diameter with an electron-dense nucleoid surrounded by an envelope consisting of one or two electron-dense membranes. On the basis of their morphologic fine structure, the viruses are subclassified into A-, B-, C-, and D-type particles.[44, 45] A-type particles (Figure 8–1) are intracellular and consist of two concentric electron-dense shells with an electron-lucent center. They may, in part, represent immature B-, C-, or D-type particles and thus far lack any demonstrable biologic activity. Their average diameter is 70 nm. B-type viruses (Figure 8–1) possess an eccentric, electrondense nucleoid, bud from the cell membrane, are extracellular, and average 105 nm in diameter. They are the causative agents of mammary carcinomas of mice. C-type viruses (Figure 8–2) possess a central electron-dense nucleoid, bud from the cell membrane, are extracellular, have a diameter of approximately 100 nm, and are the causative agents of leukemias, sarcomas, and sometimes carcinomas in various

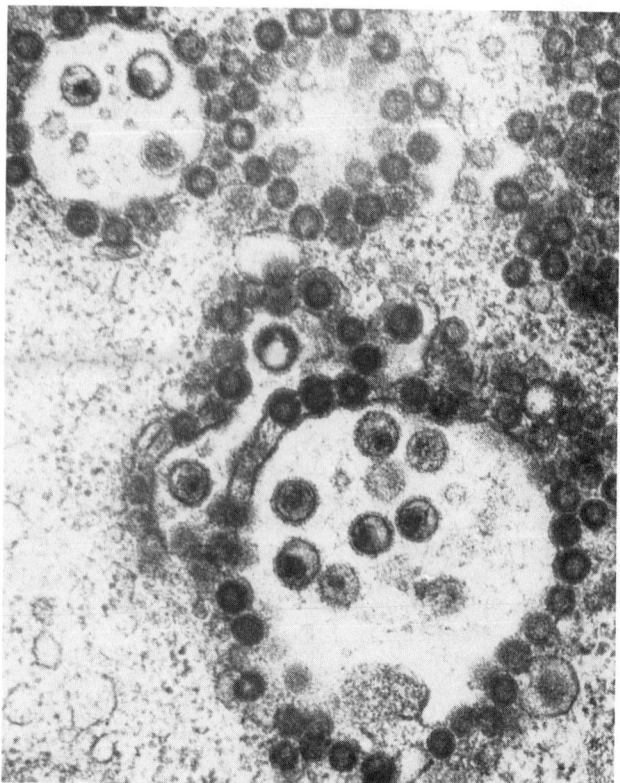

Figure 8–1. Electron micrograph depicting A– and B–type particles. Note the eccentric location of nucleoids in the larger B–type particles. Note also the electron-lucent centers of the smaller A–type particles. Original magnification approximately ×80,000. (*Courtesy of Dr. A. Goldfeder.*)

animal species. D-type viruses are somewhat similar to B-type viruses on serologic and biochemical grounds, but possess a central nucleoid.[45] These viruses have been detected, thus far, only in primate tissues and cell lines. B-, C-, and D-type viruses characteristically bud from the surfaces of their host cells (Figure 8–3), and this common property is generally accepted as the minimum criterion for their morphologic identification.

Modes of Transmission

Retroviruses are found to exist either as integral parts of their host cell genomes, in which case they are called *endogenous viruses,* or as independent extrachromosomal invaders of the cell, the so-called exogenous viruses. Endogenous viruses are stable components of host chromosomes, are replicated as parts of their host cell DNAs, and are transmitted vertically through the germ line from one generation to the next. They can be activated to form infectious retroviral particles by several chemical and physical agents, but usually are not pathogenic for their respective hosts. They are usually xenotropic, that is, they lost their capability to multiply in cells of their hosts of origin. Most vertebrate species appear to possess endogenous viruses. Transspecies infections of endogenous retroviruses in vivo are rare, but apparently do occur.

Exogenous retroviruses are transmitted horizontally by means of an infectious process, among individuals or also in utero or by milk. The complete genetic information of these viruses is not found as part of the genome of the species in which they cause disease. Lentiviruses and most oncogenic retroviruses are exogenous.

Structure and Replication

All retroviruses possess common structural features.[44, 46, 47] Their genetic information is contained in a high-molecular-weight 70S RNA which consists of two identical 35S RNA subunits linked by hydrogen bonds at their 5′ ends. Retroviral RNA resembles messenger RNA (mRNA) in that it has a cap structure consisting of m-GpppG at its 5′ terminus and a poly(A) sequence of approximately 200 residues at its 3′ terminus.

The RNA genomes of all replication-competent retroviruses contain three viral genes necessary for their replication: (1) the gag gene coding for the internal or core proteins of the viral particles; the gag-coded proteins consist of four or five proteins that are specific for each virus group (*group-specific antigens*); (2) the pol gene coding for the viral *pol*ymerase or reverse transcriptase; and (3) the env gene coding for the *env*elope glycoproteins and proteins. The sequence of these genes is 5′ gag-pol-env 3′.[48]

In addition, all retroviral RNA genomes carry noncoding terminal sequences: the terminally redundant R regions and the unique regions at the 5′ and 3′ ends next to the R regions called U5 and U3. These noncoding regions are duplicated during the formation of the DNA provirus in a complex process and form the domains called long terminal repeats (LTRs) at either end of the provirus (see below). The nucleotide sequences of most known retroviruses have been determined.[49–53]

Associated with the 70S RNA is a RNA-dependent DNA polymerase, the reverse transcriptase, which transcribes the viral RNA into DNA. Reverse transcriptases of mammalian retroviruses carry group-specific and interspecies determinants which help to identify the enzymes. The molecular weights (mol wt) of the mammalian C-type virus enzymes are about 70,000 daltons; the reverse transcriptases of avian retroviruses and B- and D-type viruses have higher molecular weights.

The structural proteins of retroviruses consist of essentially two groups, the inner core proteins and the envelope proteins and glycoproteins. The designation of retroviral proteins is by their molecular weights in thousands; a small p or gp before the number indicates whether it is a protein or a glycoprotein. The core proteins consist of four or five proteins encoded by the gag gene of the retroviral RNA which carries type-specific (eg, p12) and group-specific (eg, p30) determinants. In most retroviruses, one major

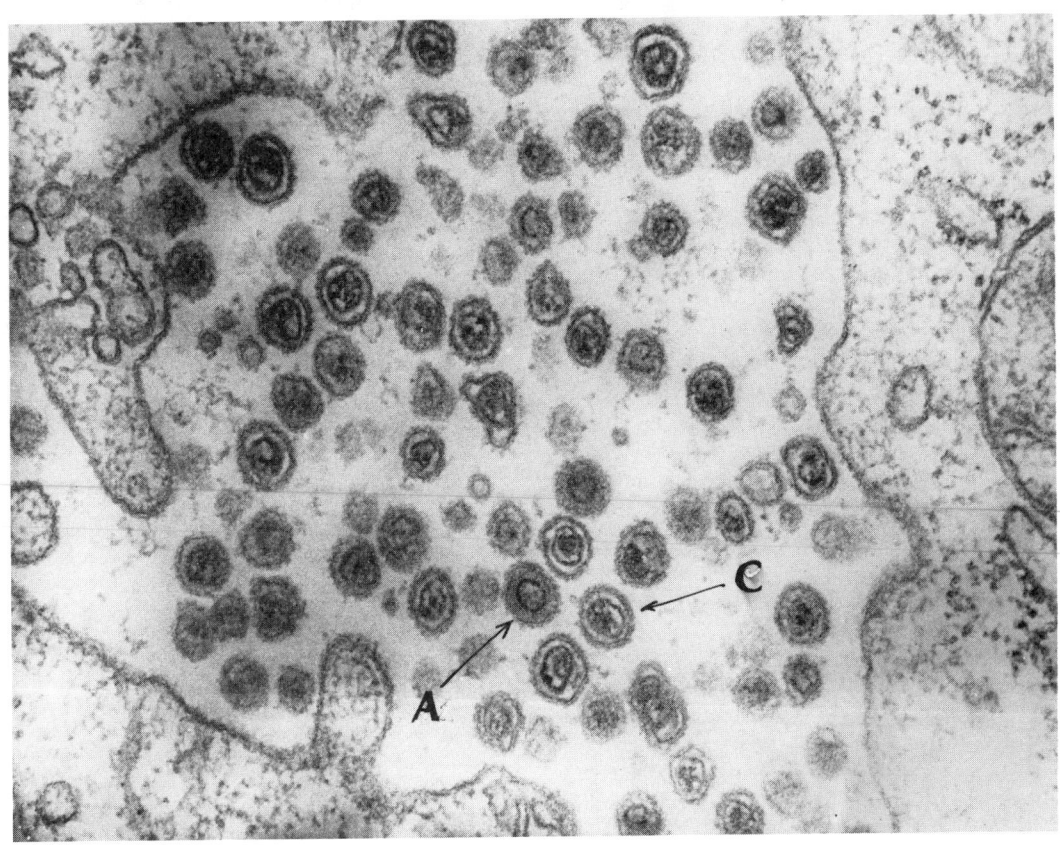

Figure 8–2. Electron micrograph depicting immature *(A)* and mature *(C)* C–type particles. Note the central location of the nucleoids in the mature particles. Original magnification approximately ×50,000. (Courtesy of Dr. A. Goldfeder.)

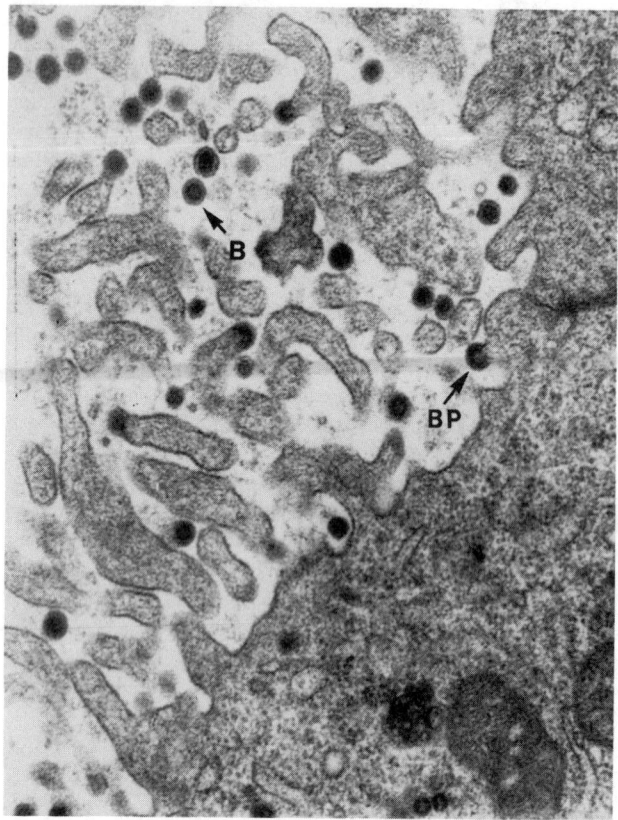

Figure 8–3. Electron micrograph of budding particles *(BP)* and some extracellular B–type particles *(B)* within intercellular spaces. Original magnification approximately ×44,000. (Courtesy of Dr. A. Goldfeder.)

internal core protein is present, the molecular weight of which ranges from 24,000 (eg, p24 of bovine leukemia virus [BLV]) to 30,000 daltons (eg, p30 of MuLV). The other core proteins are of lower molecular weights (for MuLV, eg, p10, p12, and p15).

The viral envelopes mainly consist of one or two glycoproteins with molecular weights ranging from 52,000 daltons for the gp52 of MMTV and 70,000 daltons for gp70 of MuLV to 120,000 daltons for the gp 120 of HIV. In addition, a smaller protein component (eg, p15E [E for envelope]) can be found in the envelopes of most mammalian C-type viruses representing the transmembrane protein of the virus. The envelope glycoproteins frequently carry, in addition to type- and group-specific determinants, interspecies determinants that allow the recognition of new related viruses by interspecies assays.

Retroviruses infect cells by adhesion to the cellular membrane at specific receptors. After penetration, the uncoated RNA is replicated as summarized in Figure 8–4. The first step of replication is the transcription of the viral RNA into DNA (reverse transcription). This step has been well analyzed and is illustrated in Figure 8–5. The transcription of retroviral RNA into DNA starts close to the 5′ terminus of the viral RNA molecule at the right (3′) boundary of the U5 region (see Figure 8–5) and is initiated by a host cell transfer RNA primer. Transcription proceeds through the short piece of RNA consisting of U5 and R, resulting in a short piece

of complementary DNA also called "strong stop" DNA, comes to a stop at the 5′ end of the RNA molecule, and then "jumps" to the 3′ terminus of the same, if circularized, or of another RNA molecule. This jump is facilitated by base paring of the region of the strong stop DNA that is complementary to R with the redundant R sequence at the 3′ terminus. Then the rest of the viral RNA is transcribed continuously in the 3′ → 5′ direction beginning with the U3 region, the resulting complementary minus(−)-strand DNA being synthesized in the 5′ → 3′ direction. Synthesis of complementary plus(+)-strand DNA is meanwhile initiated at the 5′ boundary of U3. The primer for this event is not known, but the priming site is always formed by a region ending in AATG. Extension of the positive-strand DNA occurs in a similar fashion as negative-strand DNA: After U3, R, and U5 of the negative-strand DNA and probably part of the linked primer transfer RNA (tRNA) have been transcribed, a duplex can be formed between the tRNA-binding site at the 3′ end of the negative strand and the sequences copied from the tRNA at the 3′ end of the positive strand. Synthesis of both strands then proceeds to completion and results in a double-stranded proviral DNA with the terminally redundant U3, R, and U5 regions (long terminal repeats) on either side of the provirus.

On the basis of nucleotide sequencing data, the LTRs, consisting of U3, R, and U5 (see above), were found to provide basic functions for regulation and expression of proviral genes (Table 8–3).[55] The U3 region in all LTRs contains a sequence closely related to the so-called TATAA box which is thought to promote initiation of transcription of eukaryotic genes.[56] Another common eukaryotic signal contained in the LTR is the AATAAA sequence for polyadenylation.

The proviral DNA is covalently incorporated into the host cellular genome (see Figure 8–4) by a mechanism not yet understood. It is not clear whether linear provirus DNA or circular forms are required for integration. The integration sites seem to be multiple and not dependent on certain host cell DNA sequences. Some

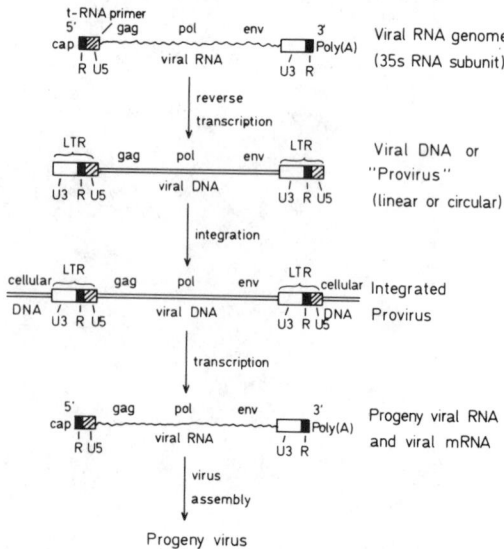

Figure 8–4. Replication of retroviral RNA. For details, see text.

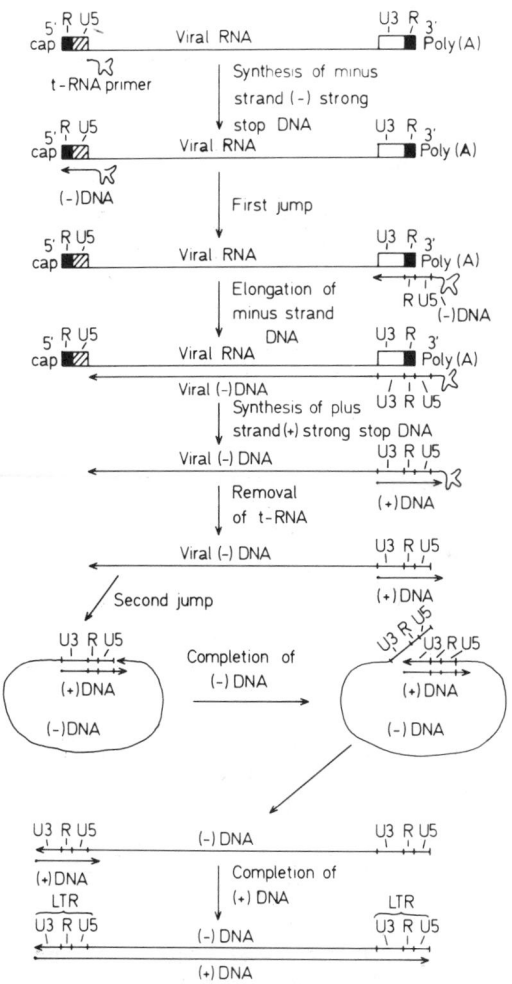

Figure 8–5. Model of reverse transcription. For details, see text.

sequence regions, however, seem to be preferred over others.[57] The proviral DNA is replicated with the cellular DNA as part of the host cell genome. Viral RNA synthesis is mediated by host RNA polymerase II, probably under the influence of the promoter region of the LTR. Viral RNA has to serve the twofold purpose of providing mRNA for viral protein synthesis and genomic RNA for incorporation into progeny virus. In the cytoplasm, several size classes of viral RNA can be observed, the 35S mRNA coding for all viral proteins and directing (eg, for MuLV) the synthesis of gag proteins and reverse transcriptase, and a 22S mRNA coding for the env gene products only (Figure 8–6). Viral RNA is first translated into precursor polyproteins which are subsequently cleaved into the viral structural proteins. The gag and env precursor proteins, for example, of MuLV, are cleaved into the p30, p15, p12, and p10 core proteins, and into the gp70 and p15 E envelope proteins, respectively. Assembly of RNA and viral proteins occurs in the cytoplasm near the cellular membrane. The details of the formation of complete viral particles leading to budding of retroviruses from the cell surface are largely unknown. The formation of progeny retrovirus is summarized in Figure 8–6.

Oncogenicity

The remarkable property of retroviruses which has given this virus group the name RNA tumor viruses is the capability of some retroviruses to cause tumors in various animal species and to mediate neoplastic transformation of cultured cells. The oncogenicity of retroviruses follows two patterns: (1) Some viruses induce tumors rapidly, that is, in 2 to 4 weeks and possess a gene called "oncogene" that is responsible for their capacity to induce tumors. (2) Other viruses do not possess oncogenes and induce tumors by other not yet fully recognized pathways. Oncogenesis by the second category of viruses in most instances is much slower and requires long latent periods (ie, several months) for tumor induction.

The genomes of most retroviruses that are rapidly oncogenic

Table 8–3
Structure of Various Long Terminal Repeats (LTRs)

| Virus | (+) Strand primer sequence | U3 | | | | R | U5 | | Binding site for tRNA primer |
		Inverted repeat sequence	Length (bp)	TATAA-box	Length (bp)	Length (bp)	Length (bp)	Inverted repeat sequence	
RSV	....	AATGTAGTCTTATGC..	230	..TATTTAG..........	23...	.. 21...	.. 80	.....GCAGAAGGCTTCATT	....
evl	....	AATGTAGTC..........	172	..TATATAA..........	23...	.. 21...	.. 80	............GGCTTCATT	....
SNV	....	AATGT..............	369	..TATAAG..........	21...	.160...	.100	................ACATT	....
MoMuLV	....	AATGAAAGACCCC	371	..AATAAAAG	21...	.139...	.. 75	.....GGGGTCTTTCATT	....
MMTV	....	AATGCCGC..........	1192	..TATAAAAG	24...	.. 13...	.122	............GCGGCAGC	....

Receptor binding site for glucocorticoid control of MMTV

AATAAA Poly (A) signal

Cap site   Poly (A) site

Initiation site for (+) DNA

Integration site

Integration site   Initiation site for (−) DNA

RSV = Rous sarcoma virus; SNV = spleen necrosis virus; MoMuLV = Moloney murine leukemia virus; MMTV = mouse mammary tumor virus; bp - base pairs.

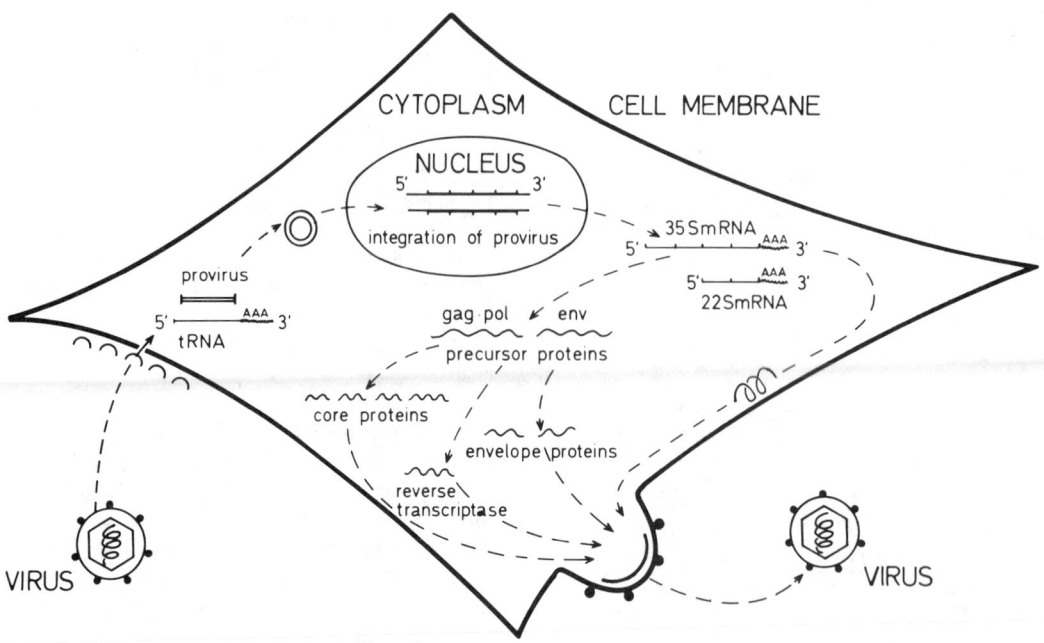

Figure 8–6. Infectious cycle of retroviruses. For details, see text.

possess oncogenes at the expense of replication genes.[58] They are therefore defective, and need the presence of a replication competent helper virus in order to replicate. The exceptions are RSV which possesses an oncogene in addition to a complete set of replication genes, and spleen focus-forming virus (SFFV) of the Friend murine leukemia virus complex (F-MuLV), which is defective but does not possess a detectable oncogene. Most remarkably, however, the 5′ and the 3′ ends of all defective viruses have been conserved and are homologous to those of their helper viruses.

On the basis of the gene products of the rapidly oncogenic retroviruses, several general structural patterns of these virus genes have been recognized. Viruses that have retained part of the gag gene (Δgag) immediately preceding the onc-specific information (X) synthesize a fused Δgag-X-polyprotein.[58] Examples are several avian viruses (FSV, Y73, UR2, most members of the MC29 group, avian erythroblastosis virus [AEV]; and E26), feline sarcoma viruses, and Abelson MuLV. Other viruses with different locations of their onc genes synthesize onc gene products without portions of viral structural proteins. Examples are RSV, avian myeloblastosis virus (AMV), Harvey and Kirsten MuSV, and probably also Moloney MuSV and simian sarcoma virus (SiSV).

ONCOGENES

Retroviral Oncogenes

Oncogenes are responsible for tumor induction by the acutely transforming retroviruses. Oncogenesis via viral oncogenes is rapid and predominates over all other cellular genes. More than 50 different oncogenes have been detected thus far, half of which are in retroviral genomes (see Table 8–2 for abbreviations). The best studied of these genes is the src gene of RSV.[59] The knowledge that a separate gene is involved in neoplastic transformation was

originally derived from observations with temperature-sensitive conditional mutants of RSV. When the RSV-transformed cells were maintained at a "permissive" temperature, they remained transformed. When the temperature was shifted to a higher "nonpermissive" temperature, the transformed cells regained normal morphology. By additional work with transformation-defective (td) mutants, it was possible to assign the transforming property to a fragment of RNA contained in wild-type RSV RNA, but missing from tdRSV RNA. These experiments led to the recognition that RSV, in addition to the three replication genes gag, pol, and env, possessed a fourth gene, called src, that was responsible for inducing transformation. RSV, thus far, is the only transforming retrovirus that has been found to contain an oncogene in addition to a complete set of replication genes.

Transformation Proteins

In RSV, the onc gene codes for a phosphoprotein of 60,000-dalton mol wt called pp60^{src}.[60, 61] pp60^{src} possesses protein kinase activity and specifically phosphorylates tyrosine, an uncommon amino acid to be phosphorylated under normal conditions. pp60^{src} was shown to be present in cells transformed by RSV or by src and is thought to be responsible for the transformation process. The molecular events by which pp60^{src} leads to and maintains the transformed state of the cell appear to be associated with the cytoskeleton. Transformation proteins from most other transforming avian viruses are fusion polyproteins of gag and onc-specific information (see above). Several of these polyproteins also have protein kinase activities that specifically phosphorylate tyrosine residues.

Not all transforming proteins, however, possess kinase activity. The transformation protein of avian myelocytomatosis virus MC29, for instance, has been described to possess DNA-binding activity.[58] This protein is not associated with the cell membrane; rather, it can be isolated from the cell nucleus. And the transformation protein of SiSV, p28[sis], is structurally related to a cellular growth factor, the platelet-derived growth factor (PDGF).[62, 63] This latter observation might represent a link between cellular events activated by retroviruses and events activated by hemopoietic growth factors.

Mouse sarcoma virus-transformed cells do not have a common transformation protein. A p37 protein in FBJ- and Moloney MuSV-transformed cells seems to be specific for transformation by these viruses. Both can be found phosphorylated, but neither contains protein kinase activity. Rat cells transformed by Kirsten or Harvey MuSV or by Rasheed rat sarcoma virus express p21 or p29 transformation proteins. The p21 contains a tyrosine phosphorylating kinase activity. Abelson leukemia virus-transformed cells express a single p160 Δgag-onc polyprotein which possesses tyrosine protein kinase activity. The feline sarcoma viruses, strains Gardner-Arnstein, Snyder-Theilen, and McDonough, also synthesize Δgag-X fusion proteins (p90, p110, gp170) that contain protein kinase activity.

As early as 1972 a protein was identified in feline oncornavirus-infected cells that was transformation-associated. It was designated FOCMA (*f*eline *o*ncornavirus-associated *c*ell *m*embrane *a*ntigen), because it was believed to be virus-induced. This protein now is found to be similar to or identical with the fes-gene-encoded p85 product of the Snyder-Theilen feline sarcoma virus.

The contribution of transformation proteins to the transformation process is not well understood. One possible model is suggested by observations in the RSV system. There the phosphorylated form of pp60[src] is found closely associated with the cytoskeleton component, vinculin, close to the inner plasmalemma of the cell membrane, while the nonphosphorylated form is found in the cytoplasm.[64] The transformation process appears to be closely interrelated with the breakdown of the cytoskeleton and the phosphorylation of vinculin. Vinculin is responsible, among other proteins, for the adhesion of cells to surfaces. Another model is derived from studies connecting pp60[src] with changes of phosphorylation of the membrane constituent phosphatidyl inositol.[65] Experiments with deletion mutants suggest that several functions of pp60[src] are required for oncogenesis (pleiotropic effect of pp60[src]).

Location and Function of Oncogene Products

Grouping of oncogenes currently is by location of their products in the cytoplasm or in the nucleus,[66] or by the function of their products[65] (see Table 8–2). The myc, myb, ski, fos, jun, and ets oncogene products are located in the cell nucleus and possess mostly DNA-binding properties, whereas those of most other oncogenes are located in the cytoplasm, in part associated with the cytoskeleton, such as the products of ras, src, erb B, ros fms, fes, fps, yes, mil, rof, mos, and abl.

Many oncogene products show kinase activity suggesting that phosphorylation is an important part of their function, although the substrates are largely unknown. A second group of oncogene products is closely related to, or identical with, growth factor receptors, such as the erb B product with the receptor for the epidermal growth factor (EGF),[67] the erb A product with the receptor for thyroid hormone (T$_3$),[68, 69] or the fms product with the

receptor for the mononuclear phagocyte growth factor, CSF-1.[70] The sis product closely corresponds to one chain of the human PDGF[71] and apparently acts by autocrine activation of PDGF receptors.[72] A fourth group of oncogene products (Ki-ras-, Ha-ras-p21) have guanosine 5′-triphosphate (GTP)-binding activity and are implicated in signal transduction from the cell surface to the nucleus, for example, via adenylatecyclase.[73] The products of the DNA-binding fos and jun proto-oncogenes finally have been identified in a protein complex that binds to a cellular sequence element referred to as the HeLa cell activator protein 1 (AP-1) binding site.[74–76] It has been suggested that oncogenes of the different groups might act in concert in the form of a cascade. Further work on oncogene function is expected to provide insights into more aspects of cellular growth and regulation than just those related to cancer. Indeed, the role of oncogenes in carcinogenesis beyond the rare events of retroviral infection has been challenged on the grounds that (a) proto-oncogenes differ from their retroviral counterparts and (b) carcinogenesis by oncogenes has been observed only in connection of oncogenes with retroviral genes and regulation sequences.[77, 78]

Origin of Retroviral Oncogenes

Retroviral onc genes (designated v-onc) are derived from progenitor DNA sequences of normal cells (designated c-onc or proto-onc).[25, 79] These sequences are thought to have been acquired by retroviruses upon passage through rodents, cats, chickens, or primates. The source of these new sequences has been traced in most cases to the genomes of the host animal through which the original virus was passed. This was shown first for src of RSV[24] by the hybridization of ^{3}H-src DNA with nuclear DNA of normal uninfected chickens. There appears to be a higher number of transforming retroviruses than of onc genes. The same or similar oncogenes have been observed in different viral isolates, for example, fps and fms in Fujinami sarcoma virus (FSV) and FeSV are closely related, or src and mos in RSV and Mo-MuSV. The designation of the individual onc genes follows three-letter codes adopted in 1981 (see Table 8–2).

The cellular progenitors of retroviral onc genes appear to be highly conserved during evolution. This conclusion can be drawn from the fact that sequences homologous to src are not only found in the DNAs of vertebrate species as diverse as chicken, calf, mouse, man, and salmon,[80] but also in the DNA of *Drosophila melanogaster*.[81] Similar observations have been made with sequences homologous to other onc genes. Evidence is accumulating that human DNA as well as the DNAs of all other vertebrate species contain progenitors of most onc genes analyzed. Examples are v-myc of avian myelocytomatosis virus MC29, v-myb of avian myeloblastosis, v-mos of Moloney murine sar v-has of Harvey MuSV, v-kis of Kirsten MuSV, v-bas of Balb MuSV, v-abl of Abelson murine leukemia virus, v-fes of feline sarcoma virus, v-sis of SiSV.[81–86]

Chromosomal Assignment of Oncogene Homologues

Chromosomal localization of the human oncogene homologues is important for the elucidation of their pathogenic potential in human disease. Chromosomal assignment has been accomplished for most oncogene homologues by means of the somatic cell hybrid technique. The human homologues of the transforming sequence of Abelson murine leukemia virus, c-abl; of the transforming sequence of feline sarcoma virus, c-fes; of Harvey MuSV, c-has; of myelocytomatosis virus MC29, c-myc; of Mo-MuSV, c-mos; of avian myeloblastosis virus, c-myb; and of SiSV, c-cis; have been assigned to the human chromosomes 9, 15, 11, 8, 8, 6, and 22, respectively (see Table 8–2).[87-97] Aberrations and translocations of these chromosomes (numbers 6, 8, 9, 15, 22) have been observed in chronic myelogenous leukemia, in Burkitt's lymphoma, and in acute leukemias.[94] The location of some human oncogene homologues (c-myc, c-mos, c-abl, c-myb) at the breakpoints of these chromosome translocations[87, 90, 94, 96, 97] suggests a causal relationship between chromosomal aberrations and oncogene activity in these neoplasms.

Cellular Oncogenes Detected and Isolated by Transfection

There is good evidence that the detection of oncogenes through retroviruses was a fortunate coincidence and that oncogenes do exist and can transform cells quite independently of retroviruses. In transfection studies DNA from chemically transformed and from normal fibroblasts and from several human tumors not associated with retroviruses was found to induce transformation of contact-inhibited NIH/3T3-mouse fibroblasts.[98-100] In several cases, the transforming sequences have been isolated by molecular cloning and characterized by hybridization and sequencing studies.[101] These studies showed that: (1) DNA of normal and transformed cells contain transforming sequences; (2) distinct types of tumors tend to be associated with distinct transforming sequences; and (3) some of these sequences are closely related to onc genes identified in retroviruses. The oncogenes isolated from the human bladder carcinoma lines EJ and T24, for example, are homologues of v-has, the onc gene of Harvey MuSV,[102-104] and the oncogenes isolated from lung and colon carcinomas are homologues of v-kis, the onc gene of Kirsten MuSV.[104] Nucleic acid sequence analysis has revealed that the transforming sequences of the EJ and T24 lines differ from the homologous sequences in normal human DNA by a single base exchange.[105-107]

It appears from these observations that oncogenes can act independently of retroviruses and that retroviruses rather serve as vehicles (vectors) for the transduction of cellular oncogenes.

Role of Oncogenes in Normal Cell Metabolism

The high degree of evolutionary conservation of most oncogenes suggests some important function of these genes in normal cell metabolism or development. Although relatively little is known yet about transcription of oncogenes in normal vertebrate cells, studies suggest participation of cellular oncogenes in normal developmental processes. Evidence stems from the observation of similarities between onc gene products and cellular growth factors or their receptors[67-72] and of expression of several cellular oncogene homologues during various stages of development.[108] In a study on human placentas and fetal tissues, a marked increase in expression of c-fos and c-fms was observed as compared to other normal human tissues.[109]

Retroviruses as Genetic Vectors

The recognition that retroviruses can serve as natural vectors for the transduction of cellular genes such as oncogenes led to the development of techniques to use retroviruses as experimental vehicles for the introduction of a variety of genes into eukaryotic cells.[110] A number of properties render retroviruses uniquely suitable for genetic transfer such as integration of proviruses into the host cell genome at high efficiency, stable association with the host cell, efficient expression of retroviral genes, broad host range of retroviruses, variability in the amount of genome to be incorporated into retroviruses with no minimum up to 15 kilobases (kb), etc.[111] Early examples of genes introduced by retroviral vectors include genes responsible for drug resistance, the growth hormone gene, and genes for interferons, globins, and immunoglobulins.[111, 112] The prospects are that possibly most genetic diseases are correctable with the help of retroviral vectors containing the desired genes.[113]

Retroviruses as Insertion Mutagens

Although preferred target sequences have been identified for retroviral integration into host cell DNA,[57] retroviral integration is poorly understood. Insertion sites apparently are highly variable and may include intragenic sites producing insertion mutations.[114] This has been shown by infection of mouse germ line cells with MuLV at various stages of development. The mutated phenotypes of the mouse offspring included hair pigmentation and a recessive collagen defect lethal to midgestational embryos. Retroviral infection, ultimately, might permit the detection of defined genes and the study of a wide variety of important genetic lesions.[115]

PATHOGENESIS

In Vivo and In Vitro Effects

Retroviruses as a rule are not cytopathogenic and do not kill their host cells.[41] An exception are members of the lentivirus group. Retroviral infection and replication in general is compatible with continued growth and may even confer a growth advantage on the infected cells. Retroviruses may induce various diseases in the infected host organisms in vivo and may transform cells in vitro by changing the growth and morphologic characteristics of the infected cells. Some examples for nontumor diseases induced by retroviruses are infectious anemia in horses, arthritis in goats, paralysis in wild mice, and osteopetrosis in chickens and mice. The neoplasias induced by retroviruses are mainly leukemias, lymphomas, and sarcomas, but include also various carcinomas. The susceptibility to infection and the development of disease is regulated by several host factors, including genetics and immunocompetence. Malignant transformation of cells in vitro is defined as abnormal "behavior" of cells with respect to morphology and growth regulation by neighboring cells. Transformed cells tend not to grow in monolayers, are not contact-inhibited, and do not spread on the culture flask surface as normal cells usually do. They rather round up, tend to pile up on top of one another, and grow in crisscross patterns (Figure 8–7). When injected into animals, transformed cells produce tumors, whereas nontransformed cells

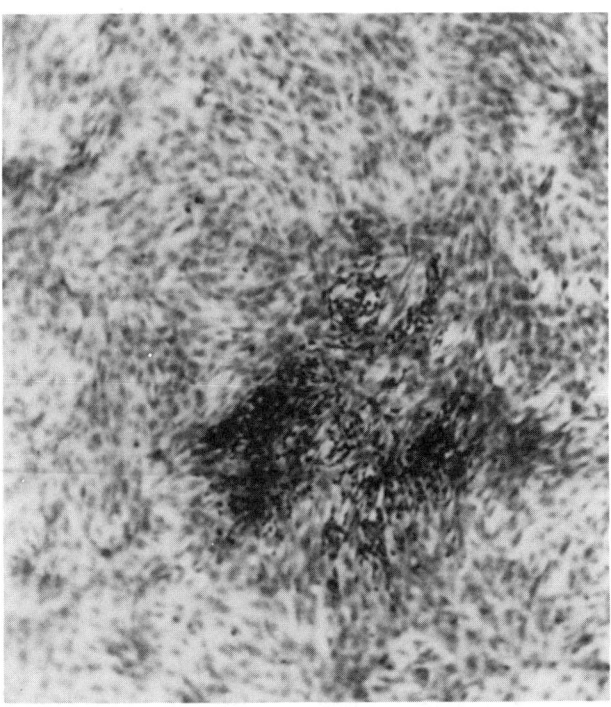

Figure 8–7. Focus of criss-crossed and piled–up transformed cells. Original magnification approximately ×125.

do not. The metabolism of transformed cells is changed from nontransformed cells, as indicated by increased carbohydrate uptake and altered enzyme activity.

The mechanisms by which retroviruses cause tumors in vivo and transform cells in vitro are subject to intense research efforts and have not yet been clarified. However, several possible mechanisms have evolved as the result of these efforts which might explain carcinogenesis and are compatible with present experimental data. The following section summarizes our current understanding of several possible mechanisms of carcinogenesis.

Possible Mechanisms of Carcinogenesis

Carcinogenesis as mediated by retroviruses appears to follow several pathways. Experimental support exists for several distinct theories of viral carcinogenesis. Clearly, the rapid induction of sarcomas or carcinomas by the rapidly transforming viruses which possess oncogenes is different from the slower induction of leukemia by the chronic leukemia viruses. The chronic leukemia viruses do not possess oncogenes but may utilize cellular oncogenes. Leukemogenesis by certain recombinant retroviruses, or via chronic mitogenic stimulation as a consequence of viral infection, may not be associated with oncogenes of either viral or cellular origin. A hypothetical second step, which could be DNA or chromosomal rearrangement, would be required for irreversible transformation or carcinogenesis.

Transformation by Virogene-Oncogene Recombinants (Acutely Transforming Viruses)

Several models have tried in the past to unify knowledge on carcinogenesis by viral onc genes.[116, 117]

1. In 1970 Temin proposed, in his protovirus hypothesis, that RNA tumor viruses evolved by de novo recombination of movable genetic elements in cells. Movable genetic elements, as observed in bacteria, yeast, and *Drosophila,* are always bounded by a small direct repeat of cellular DNA next to an inverted repeat of movable DNA element. Since DNA proviruses are also bounded by a few base pairs (bp) of direct repeat of cellular DNA next to a small inverted repeat of viral DNA as part of the LTR region, they resemble movable genetic elements. The acquisition and transduction of oncogenes by retroviruses would be similar to the incorporation of cellular genes into movable elements.[118]

2. The presence of oncogenes as part of viral genomes (virogenes) in the cells of most or all vertebrates was postulated by Huebner and Todaro in their oncogene-virogene theory in 1969.[117] The theory postulated that virogene and oncogene are normally repressed. The derepression of the oncogene, for example, by carcinogens, normal aging, or exogenous viruses, would result in neoplastic growth of cells according to this theory. Infectious (horizontal) transmission of the oncogene by retroviruses was thought to be a rare event. Although some revision is necessary, the theory correctly postulated the existence of oncogenes and oncogenesis via oncogenes.

But there still remain justified doubts whether oncogenesis by oncogenes is a common mechanism of carcinogenesis for naturally occurring neoplasias. What then is known, at present, about oncogenesis by oncogenes, and what is the evidence for and against it?

Oncogenes have been found in almost all acutely transforming retroviruses (sarcoma and acute leukemia viruses). The only known function of these oncogenes is malignant transformation. The transforming property of oncogenes was established by the use of temperature-sensitive conditional mutants and transformation-defective deletion mutants of RSV and AEV (see Oncogenes, above), and by transfection studies with onc genes isolated from a murine sarcoma virus and from cellular DNA. The transforming efficiency of the oncogenes could be markedly increased if they were ligated to LTR sequences.

Transformation by oncogenes is mediated by the protein products (transformation proteins) of the oncogenes, since presence and absence of transformation proteins correlate with transformed and nontransformed states of the cells. The action of some transformation proteins may be phosphorylation by kinase activity as, for example, reported for src, or DNA binding as reported for myc. One substrate for phosphorylation might be the cytoskeletal protein vinculin (see Transformation Proteins, above).

Since the cellular progenitor oncogene homologues present in normal cells are usually expressed at low levels, transformation has been assumed to be a quantitative problem due to an enhanced production of transformation proteins. If correct, this hypothesis assumes that cells normally control cellular oncogene homologues to prevent expression above a certain critical level. This assumption is supported by the observation that expression of oncogenes may be greatly enhanced after infection by acutely transforming retroviruses. Alternatively, it has been suggested that qualitative differences exist between retroviral oncogenes and their cellular progenitors. Evidence for this alternative comes from the observation that most cellular onc sequences are interrupted by several stretches of unrelated DNA (introns). Also, biologic activity does not occur following transfection with cellular DNA related to avian oncogenes (src or myc), even on ligation to LTR sequences. Furthermore, the discovery of point mutations as critical events for the acquisition of transforming properties as observed in the EJ and T24 bladder carcinoma oncogenes[105-107] argues for a mechanism of carcinogenesis by qualitative changes of cellular oncogenes.[23] In recognition of qualitative differences between viral and cellular oncogenes, it has been proposed that oncogenes play a role in normal cellular differentiation.

The sporadic isolation of oncogene-carrying viruses and the absence of horizontal spread of retroviruses with oncogenes suggest that *retroviral* onc genes are not a major cause of natural cancers. The location of oncogenes at critical points of chromosomal translocations associated with cancer suggests some role in carcinogenesis for *cellular* oncogene homologues (proto-oncogenes). In any case, the acutely transforming, oncogene-carrying retroviruses do represent excellent experimental models for the study of carcinogenesis.

Transformation by Promoter Insertion and Activation of Oncogenes (Chronic Leukemia Viruses)

An enhanced production of transformation proteins might also be the mechanism by which chronic leukemia viruses cause leukemia. Chronic leukemia viruses are nondefective, do not carry oncogenes, and induce leukemias after long latency periods. This leukemogenesis model assumes the insertion of retroviral promoter sequences adjacent to a cellular oncogene and the subsequent promotion of expression of this oncogene. A promoter insertion next to a cellular oncogene would be a rare recombinational event and would be consistent with a long latency period prior to tumor development. Evidence for this model has been obtained for leukemogenesis by chronic avian leukosis viruses (ALV).[119] It was shown that ALV proviral DNA is inserted adjacent to the cellular oncogene c-myc and that, as a consequence, expression of c-myc was stimulated 30- to 100-fold. It was further shown that enhanced expression of c-myc occurs with proviruses in any of three configurations: (1) on the 5′ side (upstream) of c-myc in the same transcriptional orientation, (2) on the 3′ side (downstream) of c-myc in the same orientation, and (3) upstream, in the opposite orientation.[120] As a consequence of these findings, the promoter insertion model would require several modes of transcriptional promotion to be valid.

Transformation by Recombination Among Nononcogenic Retroviruses

An entirely different mechanism of leukemogenesis has been suggested from observations in mice on highly leukemogenic retroviruses created by recombinational events in the env-gene region of the viruses.[121] The molecular events underlying leukemogenesis by these recombinant viruses are far from clear. It has, however, been suggested that the recombination in env might alter the antigenicity of the envelope glycoprotein (see below) and/or that the recombination includes part of the regulating sequences in the adjacent 3′ terminal region (U3). These alterations of antigenicity and/or regulating capacity are assumed to be responsible for leukemogenic potential.

Transformation by Chronic Mitogenic Stimulation

Retroviruses may be involved in leukemogenesis not by genetic mechanisms, as discussed above, but by cell surface signals mediated by retroviral antigens and antibodies. Models along this line could explain leukemia and lymphoma induction by the chronic leukemia viruses which require long latency periods.

The expression, for instance, of retroviral antigens on the surface of lymphocytes has been postulated as signals for some steps of differentiation. These antigens can be activated by certain mitogenic substances, and the proliferation of these activated cells can be blocked or activated by specific antiviral antibodies. The induction of a potent and specific antiviral antibody response that blocks the surface antigens could lead to a block of differentiation or proliferation and to an accumulation of undifferentiated cells.

Alternatively, it is assumed that the viral glycoprotein may act as a specific mitogen for certain hematopoietic progenitor cells.[122, 123] T cell lymphomas in mice may be a result of this process, and Friend MuLV–induced erythroleukemia may be caused by this mechanism. This might be similar to the mechanism that elicits the marked T cell response to Epstein-Barr virus (EBV)–infected B lymphocytes in infectious mononucleosis.

Induction of Irreversible Genetic Changes

Induction of irreversible genetic changes as a mechanism of oncogenesis requires a hypothetical second step for transition from the reversible polyclonal transformed or preleukemic state of tumor virus-infected cells to the state of irreversible, mostly monoclonal growth characteristic of malignant transformation. This second step was suggested by Klein, in 1980, to be permanent DNA or chromosomal rearrangement.[124] Indeed, characteristic chromosomal aberrations have been correlated with distinct malignant tumors of several species, and specific translocations have been identified in several virus- and non–virus-associated neoplasias. Examples include the 8;14 translocation in Burkitt's lymphoma, the 9;22 translocation in chronic myelogenous leukemia, the 14;48 translocation in follicular B cell lymphomas, and the trisomy of chromosome 15 in MuLV-induced T cell leukemias. The location of oncogenes at the breakpoints involved in chromosomal translocations (eg, the location of c-myc at the breakpoint of chromosome 8 in the 8;14 translocation in Burkitt's lymphoma[87, 96, 97] and the translocations of c-abl from chromosome 9 to chromosome 22, the Philadelphia chromosome, and c-sis from chromosome 22 to chromosome 9 in chronic myelogenous leukemia[85]) suggests a critical role of oncogenes at this step.

BIOLOGY OF RETROVIRUSES

Avian Retroviruses

Avian retroviruses (Table 8–4) were the first RNA tumor viruses to be discovered (Ellermann and Bang in 1908, and Rous in 1911, see above)[1, 2] and have been the model viruses with which most basic properties of the RNA tumor virus group have been explored.[47] On the basis of their biologic properties,[44] which are reflected by their genetic structures, these viruses consist of two large subgroups: the chronic lymphoid leukosis viruses (ALV or LLV), which induce neoplastic disease after a long latent period

Table 8–4
Avian C-Type Retroviruses

Strain Designation	Disease
Avian leukosis viruses (ALV)	Lymphocytic leukemia, lymphomatosis
Avian myeloblastosis virus (AMV)	Myeloblastosis
E26 myeloblastosis virus	Myeloblastosis, lymphomatosis, carcinomas
Avian erythroblastosis virus (AEV)	Erythroblastosis
MC29 ⎫	Lymphomatosis, kidney carcinoma
CM II ⎪ Avian myelocytomatosis viruses	Erythroblastosis,
MH2 ⎬	Lymphomatosis,
OK10 ⎭	Carcinomas
Reticuloendotheliosis viruses (REV)	Reticuloendotheliosis
Spleen necrosis virus (SNV)	Reticuloendotheliosis, spleen necrosis,
Rous sarcoma virus (RSV)	Fibrosarcomas, myxosarcomas,
(substrains: Prague, Carr-Zilber, Bryan,	Osteochondrosarcomas,
B 787, Schmidt-Ruppin, Harris, Mill-Hill,	Endotheliomas, hemangiomas,
Fujinami sarcoma virus)	Gliomas
PRC II sarcoma virus ⎫	
UR 1 sarcoma virus ⎪	
16 L sarcoma virus ⎬	
Y73 sarcoma virus	Fibrosarcomas
Esh sarcoma virus ⎪	
UR 2 sarcoma virus ⎭	
RAV-O endogenous virus	None
evl	None

of several months to 1 year and lack an onc gene, and the acutely transforming viruses (sarcoma viruses, acute leukemia viruses), which cause disease within a few weeks and do carry transformation genes (see Table 8–2). In addition, a third group of avian retroviruses, the reticuloendotheliosis viruses (REV), has been defined more recently which is not related to the avian leukemia or sarcoma viruses. One member of this group has been found to carry an onc gene (rel, see Table 8–2).

The LLVs are closely related to the avian sarcoma viruses, are nondefective for replication, possess the replication genes gag, pol, and env, but lack the transformation gene src. These viruses are oncogenic on their own, but in addition are frequently associated with defective sarcoma and leukemia viruses for which they serve as helper viruses for replication. The neoplasm caused by these viruses is predominantly chronic lymphoid leukosis. As a possible mechanism of oncogenesis by this virus group, activation of a cellular onc gene (eg, c-myc) by the inserted provirus has been suggested. Insertion of the virus adjacent to the c-myc, upstream or downstream (see Possible Mechanisms of Carcinogenesis, above), would provide the promoter sequences required for activation of the cellular oncogene and for malignant transformation.[119, 120]

In contrast to LLV, the acutely transforming viruses (except RSV) are defective for replication, possess onc genes, are rapidly oncogenic, and induce a variety of tumors (leukemias, sarcomas, carcinomas).[44] The type of neoplasm induced depends to a large extent on the viruses involved, but also on the target cells and on genetic factors of the host.

The avian sarcoma viruses mainly induce sarcomas, notably spindle cell sarcomas as initially described by Rous[2] and Fujinami and Inamoto.[3] By continuing serial passage in birds, however, various solid-tissue growths are induced; these include myxosar-

coma, osteochondrosarcoma, endothelioma, hemangioma, and gliomas. In addition, serial passage changed the species specificity of the virus, and RSV became infectious not only for many birds but for mammals, including primates and human tissue culture cell lines.[44, 46]

The spectrum of neoplasms induced by the acute leukemia viruses is generally broader than that of the sarcoma viruses. In addition to sarcomas, these viruses can induce different kinds of leukemias and also carcinomas. Three separate virus strains responsible for erythroblastosis, myeloblastosis, and myelocytomatosis had been recognized by Jacob Furth in the 1930s.[44] As the name implies, avian myeloblastosis virus (AMV) induces, in susceptible chickens, myeloblastosis with high numbers of myeloblasts in the peripheral blood[46]; rarely AMV may induce lymphomatosis, or carcinomas of the kidney, ovaries, or skin. Avian erythroblastosis virus (AEV) is responsible for erythroblastosis, lymphomatosis, and carcinoma of the kidney. Avian myelocytomatosis virus (MC29) induces myelocytomatosis, in addition to erythroblastosis, lymphomatosis, and carcinomas of liver and skin. The widest variety of carcinoma types have been observed with the Mill Hill strain 2 virus (MH2) of the myelocytomatosis group. MH2 induces leukemias, sarcomas, or carcinomas of the kidney, liver, pancreas, testis, or skin.

The different biologic properties of the acutely transforming viruses are reflected by different oncogenes. On the basis of oncogenes, seven subgroups have been defined (see Table 8–2): four subgroups of sarcoma viruses consisting of the src-containing RSV group, the fps group of FSV, PRCII, UR1, and 16L, the yes group consisting of Y73 and ESV, and the ros-containing UR2-sarcoma virus; and three subgroups of acute leukemia viruses which are the myc-containing group consisting of MC29-myelocytomatosis virus, MH2, CMII, and OK10, the erb-containing AEV, and the myb-containing group consisting of AMV and E26. Contrary to src, the onc genes of most of the other acutely transforming viruses are flanked by incomplete gag sequences leading to the onc gene products with the structure Δgag-X. The Δgag portion of the Δgag-X polyprotein has been used for identification of some of the onc gene products (see above).

The discoveries of many unique onc genes have demonstrated (1) that totally different onc genes may cause very similar or even identical tumors (src, fps, yes, and ros all cause sarcomas); (2) that certain onc genes have very specific oncogenic spectra like src, which almost exclusively causes sarcomas, or myb which almost exclusively causes acute leukemias; and (3) that some onc genes such as myc may induce many different neoplasms. The onc gene products are frequently phosphoproteins with kinase activity (eg, of src) and in one case a DNA-binding protein (ie, of myc) (see Table 8–2). Little is known about their role in transformation (see section on transformation proteins, above). Retroviral onc genes represent cellular genes (c-onc or proto-onc genes) and are present in normal uninfected cells. In the case of src, the cellular src locus has been cloned and compared by electron microscopic heteroduplex analysis to cloned src DNA from RSV, and most src-specific sequences appeared to be present in the cellular src locus. The cellular src sequence, however, is interrupted by six cellular sequences (introns) not related to src and is not linked to any other non-src retroviral sequences. Similar analysis exists for other avian onc genes (eg, c-myc). There is only preliminary evidence, to date, for a physiologic activity of these cellular onc genes. The levels of expression of these genes in normal cells are considerably lower (two- to 100-fold) than in virus-transformed cells. As in other species, the genomes of avian retroviruses are present in the genomes of their hosts as so-called endogenous viruses (eg, RAV-O) and may complement defective or mutant viruses to form again replication-competent progeny viruses. Models of viral carcinogenesis consistent with the data presently available are summarized above.

Murine C-Type Retroviruses

RNA tumor viruses have been isolated from a variety of tissues and tumors in mice[44, 126] (Table 8–5). Among the many isolates, some have been identified which induce abnormal proliferation of certain types of cells. Murine RNA tumor viruses can cause uncontrolled proliferation of hemopoietic cells (leukemia viruses) and can alter the growth appearance of fibroblasts (sarcoma viruses). Most isolates of the murine leukemia-sarcoma viruses have a long laboratory history and are referred to as exogenous viruses. Another group of murine retroviruses which has primarily no oncogenic potential and which can be isolated from normal tissues has been designated endogenous viruses.

Murine Leukemia Viruses (MuLV)

Since their first discovery in 1951,[5] a long list of MuLV isolates have been described. The viruses have been isolated from spontaneous, carcinogen-induced, or transplanted leukemias and lymphosarcomas. The various MuLV strains can induce a great variety of neoplastic changes of the reticuloendothelial system such as thymic leukemias (Moloney, Gross, or radiation leukemia viruses), B cell lymphomas (Abelson virus), erythroleukemias (Friend or Rauscher leukemia viruses), or myeloid leukemia (Graffi leukemia virus). The leukemia virus strains induce predominantly one of the leukemia types indicated above. But most of them have the potential to induce more than one type of leukemia. Some viral isolates have been found to be mixtures of several virus types with different biologic activities. The Friend leukemia virus complex, for example, consists of a polycythemia virus (SFFV$_{FVP}$), a virus which causes mild anemia (SFFV$_{FVA}$), and the replication-competent Friend virus (F-MuLV), which induces splenomegaly, hepatomegaly, and profound anemia, which all can be isolated simultaneously.

These exogenous leukemia virus strains are transmitted only with the syringe of the experimenter. Intraperitoneal injection has been proved a highly efficient route of inoculation. For some virus strains direct injections into the target tissues, such as the injection of radiation-induced leukemia virus (rad LV) into the thymus, has been shown to be superior to other routes of administration. No horizontal spread has been realized from virus-infected or diseased animals to healthy animals, even under conditions of permanent close contact. This is also the case for the transmission from the mother to the offspring.

The mouse is the most susceptible species for MuLVs. But under certain conditions the viruses can infect other rodents, for example, rats and hamsters. The immunoincompetent newborn mouse has been used to circumvent immunologic defense mech-

Table 8–5
Murine C-Type Retroviruses

Strain Designation	Disease
Gross MuLV Radiation MuLV Moloney MuLV }	T cell leukemias
Abelson MuLV	B cell leukemias (plasmacytoma)
Friend MuLV Rauscher MuLV }	Erythroleukemia, polycythemia
Graffi MuLV	Myelogenous leukemias
Moloney MuSV Kirsten MuSV* Harvey MuSV Gazdar MuSV Balb MuSV }	Fibrosarcomas, rhabdomyosarcomas
FBJ MuSV FBR MuSV	Periosteal sarcomas, osteosarcomas
Ecotropic endogenous viruses	Lymphomas, osteomas, osteoporosis, paralysis
Xenotropic endogenous viruses	None
Amphotropic endogenous viruses	None
Polytropic recombinant viruses	Lymphatic leukemias

MuLV = murine leukemia virus; MuSV = murine sarcoma virus; FBJ = Finkel, Biskis, Jinkins; FBR = Finkel, Biskis, Reilly. *Erythroleukemia.

anisms which prevent virus replication and the development of leukemia. Also, several genetic loci that affect the development of virus-induced leukemias in certain mouse strains have been identified. Studies in Gross virus-induced thymic leukemia and Friend virus-induced erythroleukemia have provided evidence that in each case the leukemia is controlled by three major genetic loci, Fv-1, Fv-2, and H-2. There is evidence that the Fv-1 locus confers dominant resistance to an early stage of virus infection and replication. In contrast, the Fv-2 locus affects the proliferative state of the target cell. The H-2 locus is responsible for the immunologic responses to the virus or the virus-infected cells.

Lymphoreticular tissues are the cell system for the replication of the MuLVs. There is strong evidence that the hemopoietic stem cell is the target cell for Rauscher MuLV. Other viruses have a preference for the thymus, such as radiation MuLV. The replication of MuLV in lymphoreticular tissue is followed by a viremic state and a marked immunosuppression characterized by depressed humoral and cellular immunity.

During the leukemia latency period, infected mice produce high levels of virus-neutralizing antibodies and also cytotoxic antibodies against virus-producing leukemic cells. According to the reactivity of the neutralizing antibodies, the exogenous MuLVs can be divided into two serologic groups, the Friend-Moloney-Rauscher (FMR) group and the Gross virus (G) group. Antibody levels decline when the mice start to develop leukemia. This phenomenon suggests that humoral immunity does not play a protective role. But active immunization or administration of passive immunity with specific antiserum prior to virus infection prevents virus replication and subsequent disease.

The development of the different types of leukemias induced by the prototype laboratory strains of murine leukemia viruses is rapid. The latency period ranges from 3 to 12 weeks and results in a progressive course of the disease and a fatal end. Most of the developing leukemias can be transplanted into healthy mice with reproduction of the disease. Several in vitro cell lines of these virus-induced leukemias and lymphomas have been established.

Most of the leukemias produce virus progeny which can transmit the disease to other mice. Some tumors are virus-free. This is mainly the case with tumors induced with helper-dependent virus types such as the SFFV in the Friend leukemia virus complex. The oncogenic component can be rescued by a replication-competent helper virus. Repeated passages of the leukemia viruses have potentiated the virulence of most isolates and have sometimes changed their pathogenic spectrum (compare also avian retroviruses).

The murine leukemia viruses can be grown in vitro in embryo cells or fibroblast cell lines of mice and also in cell lines of other mammalian species including human cell lines. The replication of the leukemia viruses in these cells normally does not produce cytopathic effects. Cell cultures of lymphoreticular cells such as bone marrow cells can be infected efficiently with the viruses, and these systems are often suitable in vitro models for the study of cell-virus interactions and mechanisms of viral transformation.

The exogenous murine leukemia viruses, obviously, are not good models for the viral etiology of spontaneous leukemias and lymphomas in mice or other mammals, but they have been proved to be important systems to elucidate basic mechanisms of malignant transformation of hematopoietic cells.

Abelson Murine Leukemia Virus (A-MuLV)

A-MuLV is a defective acute leukemia virus of mice which was isolated from a steroid-treated, Moloney MuLV-infected BALB/c mouse.[127] A-MuLV induces invariably fatal nonthymic lymphosarcomas 3 to 5 weeks after injection into neonatal mice. A-MuLV can be grown in cell cultures in vitro and requires a MuLV helper virus for replication. A-MuLV codes for only one protein with a molecular weight of 120,000 daltons (p120). This protein is phosphorylated and contains gag portions (p15, p12, part of p30) fused to the transformation-specific sequences of A-MuLV. The transformation-specific portion of the A-MuLV genome (abl) represents murine cellular sequences acquired by A-MuLV at the expense of most of the viral structural genes.

Murine Sarcoma Viruses (MuSV)

Murine sarcoma-inducing viruses were first isolated from sarcomas that had developed in mice or rats after infection with MuLVs. Moloney MuSV, for instance, originates from a mouse sarcoma, whereas Harvey and Kirsten MuSV come from sarcomas or osteosarcomas in rats. MuSVs could also be created in the laboratory by growing murine endogenous retroviruses in cell cultures of chemically induced sarcomas.

These experiments and the history of the best-known sarcoma viruses (Moloney, Harvey, Kirsten) indicate the genesis of sarcoma viruses by a recombination process between the genome of a replicating virus and cellular genomic material. The murine sarcoma viruses have lost parts of their genomes which are replaced by cellular genetic material. Therefore MuSVs cannot replicate without a so-called helper virus. The necessary functions for replication are mediated by the helper virus, and typical biologic characteristics like target cell specificity or serologic properties are determined by the helper virus. All mammalian replication-competent C-type retroviruses (nonmurine as well as murine) can function as helper virus for MuSV replication.

The MuSVs are not transmitted through natural routes (either horizontal or vertical). The only known route is by experimental inoculation. After inoculation into newborn or young adult mice, MuSVs are capable of inducing various types of tumors. Intramuscular injection of Moloney, Harvey, or Kirsten MuSV causes fibrosarcomas and rhabdomyosarcomas at the site of inoculation after a fairly short latency period of 1 to 2 months. Parosteal sarcomas and osteosarcomas develop after intraperitoneal administration of FBJ osteosarcoma virus. As observed with MuLV-induced leukemias, there is a mouse strain-dependent restriction of sarcoma development. Depending on the type of helper virus in the sarcoma virus complex, other mammals may be susceptible to sarcoma induction as well. Inoculation of newborn mice with Moloney MuSV leads to the progressive growth of sarcomas, whereas the tumor will regress sooner or later in adult mice if it appears at all. Moloney sarcoma has a strong transplantation antigenicity, and tumor regression is caused by high levels of humoral and cellular immune reactivities. Thus, sera and lymphocytes from mice with regressing tumors have virus-neutralizing activity and can protect animals against sarcoma development. These activities are absent from the sera of animals with progressing tumors.

Primary and secondary mouse embryo cell lines or contact-inhibited permanent mouse fibroblast cell lines are transformed by murine sarcoma viruses. Distinct areas in the cell sheet show morphologic changes which indicate loss of contact inhibition of growth (see Figure 8–7) (see section on laboratory diagnosis, below). These foci of transformed cells grow by cell division and through infection and transformation of neighboring cells. The transformed cells exhibit properties of tumor cells, including the induction of sarcomas after transplantation into healthy animals. Virus production in transformed cells is not a regular event. A considerable number of infected cells are virus nonproducers. They carry the sarcoma virus genome in their nuclear DNA; it can be rescued by superinfection with an appropriate helper virus.

Endogenous Murine Retroviruses

In every known laboratory strain of mice and also in several wild mouse populations, so-called endogenous retroviruses have been recognized. These viruses exist in a latent form as integrated provirus genomes in the nuclear DNA of every mouse cell and are transmitted via the germ line from generation to generation. The proviruses can be activated spontaneously during aging or experimentally by treatment with certain chemical and physical agents. Also, some herpesviruses and B cell mitogens can induce endogenous retroviruses. The most potent inducers are the halogenated pyrimidine analogues iododeoxyuridine and bromodeoxyuridine. The influence of these compounds, probably by direct interaction with DNA, gives rise to the production of complete infectious virus particles.

Three genetically different types of endogenous viruses are known in mice: ecotropic viruses, which only grow in mouse cells; xenotropic viruses, which do not replicate in mouse cells; and amphotropic viruses, which infect cells from mice and from other mammalian species. On the basis of host range, ecotropic viruses can be divided into two biologic subtypes: N-tropic viruses and B-tropic viruses. N-tropic viruses grow better in cells derived from *N*IH-Swiss mice, B-tropic viruses grow better in cells derived from *B*ALB/c mice. The biologic differences of these viruses are reflected by distinct type-specific antigenic determinants in the envelope glycoprotein gp70 and in the internal core protein p12. The in vivo expression of ecotropic and xenotropic virus is followed by an immune reaction. Most mouse strains develop precipitating and neutralizing antibodies. Amount and time of their appearance are determined by the genetics of the mouse strain. The antibodies are directed against the envelope proteins gp70 and probably also p15E.

The role of the endogenous viruses in physiologic or pathologic processes is not understood at the moment. Some authors attribute these viruses with important functions in immunologic reactions, differentiation, or embryogenesis. More data exist on their association with some spontaneous, chemical- or radiation-induced leukemias and sarcomas. From these tumors a variety of leukemogenic viruses have been isolated. The oncogenic principle of these isolates is not an acquired gene from cellular genetic material as in the sarcoma viruses (see Possible Mechanisms of Carcinogenesis, above). Ecotropic viruses from several mouse strains as well as wild mice have been shown to induce lymphomas of different cell lineages, osteomas, osteopetrosis, and paralysis.[128] A region at the 3′ end involving the env gene seems to be crucial for the oncogenic potential of some of the leukemia-inducing viruses. They seem to have emerged by recombination of the env genes of an ecotropic and a xenotropic virus. Some biologic

Table 8–6
Feline C-Type Retroviruses

Strain Designation	Disease
Jarrett 5 feline leukemia virus (FeLV)	
Kawakami-Theilen FeLV	B-cell lymphomas, T cell lymphomas, and leukemias
Rickard FeLV	
Snyder-Theilen feline sarcoma virus (FeSV)	
Gardner-Arnstein FeSV*	Fibrosarcomas
McDonough-Sarma FeSV	
Endogenous viruses (RD114, FeLV-related, etc)	None

*Melanoma

activities of these recombinant viruses are therefore those of ecotropic and xenotropic viruses (polytropic viruses).

The latency period of this type of oncogenic viruses is long (6–12 months) in contrast to that of the acute leukemia and sarcoma viruses. The type of leukemia induced resembles, in many respects, the spontaneous lymphocytic lymphomas appearing spontaneously in almost all laboratory mouse strains late in life. The activation of endogenous viruses by carcinogenic agents, the increased appearance of these viruses in chemical- and radiation-induced tumors, and the isolation of oncogenic isolates from these tumors support the idea of their basic involvement in carcinogenesis.

Feline Retroviruses

Feline leukemia and sarcoma viruses (FeLV, FeSV, Table 8–6) resemble the corresponding murine and primate viruses.[46, 47] FeLV, like MuLV and GaLV, is a replication-competent leukemia virus. Its proteins include the core proteins p15, p12, p30, and p10 (in 5′ → 3′ direction) and the envelope components gp70 and p15E. FeSV is defective, like the MuSVs and SiSV, and needs FeLV as a helper virus for replication.

Feline Leukemia Virus (FeLV)

Feline leukemia virus causes leukemia and lymphoma in cats and probably is the most frequent cause of death in that species. Feline leukemia and lymphoma occur in several forms. The most common forms, namely acute lymphoblastic leukemia, thymic lymphoma, and multicentric lymphoma appear to be T cell malignancies. In the alimentary form of lymphoma, the B lymphocyte appears to be the target cell. In addition, infection with FeLV may induce an immunosuppressed state that predisposes to lethal infections caused by cytopathic viruses, bacteria, and protozoan parasites.[114] Most field isolates of FeLV cause neoplastic disease under laboratory conditions, but not in all cats and only after prolonged latent periods. The mean incubation time for the development of FeLV-induced disease appears to be about 2 years. Selected virus strains, however, when injected into young cats less than 1 month of age, may cause disease much more rapidly in almost all infected animals. Viremia is present in the infected animals before manifestations of overt disease, and viremia may therefore be present in apparently healthy cats. High titers of infectious virus are found in the saliva of infected cats, and this presumably represents the main route of transmission. FeLV retains infectivity for several days if maintained in a moist state at temperatures below 25°C. There are three subgroups of FeLV (A, B, C), based on host range, interference, and virus neutralization. All field isolates contain FeLV of subgroup A.

Feline Sarcoma Virus (FeSV)

Feline sarcoma virus induces lethal multicentric fibrosarcomas that metastasize frequently. When inoculated into young cats, the incubation time is 2 weeks or less. When older cats are inoculated or when less virus is used, the cats tend to be more resistant. FeSV can induce fibrosarcomas in several species including dog, monkey, sheep, goat, and rabbit. The GA strain of FeSV induces malignant melanomas when the virus is inoculated by the intracutaneous or intraocular routes. In vitro, all FeSV strains transform susceptible cells. Cell clones nonproductively transformed with FeSV express the transformation-specific, FeSV-coded protein designated FOCMA (Feline Oncornavirus-Associated Cell Membrane Antigen). Cats resistant to tumor induction with FeSV develop high titers of anti-FOCMA antibodies.

Analysis of viral antigen expression in lymphoid tissues from cats with naturally occurring leukemia or lymphoma demonstrated that the extent of expression of viral-related proteins depended on transformation of the lymphoid target cells. Nonleukemic cells were regularly positive for viral gp70 and p30 expression and negative for FOCMA; leukemic or lymphoid tumor cells were regularly positive for FOCMA, but partly negative for the structural proteins of FeLV. This means that virus-negative leukemias can still be etiologically associated with FeSV-encoded FOCMA. This finding may be of significance for etiologic considerations of virus-negative leukemias in cats.

The genomic structure of FeSV resembles that of the other sarcoma viruses and of the acute leukemia viruses of mice and chickens. Most of the viral structural genes, except a portion of the gag gene, have been replaced by the transformation or onc gene. The ST and GA strains of FeSV have been found to possess identical onc genes which have been designated v-fes. The onc gene of MS-FeSV is different and has been designated v-fms (see Table 8-3); v-fes and v-fms are derived from normal cellular genes (c-fes and c-fms), like the other known onc genes. Sequences homologous to v-fes (c-fes) have been found to be highly conserved among vertebrates like the other onc genes and have been detected also in the human genome.

As transformation proteins, polyproteins have been identified designated Δgag-X consisting of a portion encoded by the transformation-specific (X) sequences linked to a portion coded for by gag sequences (Δgag). Antibodies reacting against the X portion of the molecules also react with FOCMA, suggesting that the transformation protein X and FOCMA share antigenic sites and may be identical.

Feline Endogenous Viruses

Endogenous viruses (RD114, CCC, FeLV related, etc) have been identified also in cats. RD114 does not cause any known disease and has no antigen or nucleic acid relatedness to FeLV or FeSV. It is, however, closely related to BaEV, suggesting previous transspecies infection or a common ancestor of the two viruses early in evolution.

Bovine Retroviruses

Bovine leukemia virus (BLV, Table 8-7) is a type C retrovirus that does not show antigenic or nucleic acid relatedness to any other known retrovirus.[15] Only the structural core protein p24 of human T-cell lymphoma virus (HTLV, see below) shows, by amino acid sequence analysis, some homology to the p24 of BLV. In particular, no group-specific or interspecies reactivities have been detected between BLV proteins and those of other mammalian C-type viruses. Otherwise, the genetic structure of BLV and structural protein composition much resemble the other C-type leukemia viruses. The viral structural proteins and glycoproteins possess molecular weights of 10,000 (p10), 12,000 (p12), 15,000 (p15), 24,000 (p24), 30,000 (gp30), and 51,000 (gp51) daltons. The glycoproteins constitute, as in the other retroviruses, the outer viral envelope.

BLV induces the enzootic form of bovine leukemia and lymphosarcoma (EBL) and persistent lymphocytosis (PL). EBL is a herd disease and should be distinguished from sporadic bovine leukosis (SBL) which is not associated with BLV or any other known virus. BLV infection and development of disease appear to depend on genetic and possibly also environmental factors, since certain herds have a much higher incidence than others and since not all infected animals of a given herd develop lymphosarcoma. BLV is transmitted horizontally and is exogenous to cattle, that is, the BLV genome is not present in the genomes of uninfected animals. BLV appears to infect only B lymphocytes. Free virus is difficult to identify in the animals, probably due to the good humoral antibody response elicited by the major core and envelope proteins of BLV. Tumor growth appears to be monoclonal. Animals having PL as a consequence of BLV infection are at much higher risk of developing leukemia than non-PL animals. The most probable route of transmission appears to be by milk or by whole cells, possibly through an insect vector. The presence of virus in saliva has not been confirmed. BLV can induce, under experimental conditions, lymphosarcoma in sheep, but tumor induction in other animals does not occur. The risk for man is probably best summarized by van der Maaten and Miller (1977),[129] who concluded in a detailed review of all available data on seroepidemiologic studies and nucleic acid analyses of human neoplastic tissues that "the risks to human health associated with BLV would seem to be at most minimal and perhaps nonexistent."

The origin of BLV is unclear. Epidemiologic studies point to the possibility that BLV originated from a region south of the Baltic Sea and spread from there mainly by movement of cattle. At present, EBL appears to be a worldwide problem, including most European countries, North and South America, Japan, and

Table 8-7
Bovine C-Type Retrovirus

Strain Designation	Disease
Bovine leukemia virus (BLV)	Leukemia, lymphosarcoma (enzootic form; EBL) Persistent lymphocytosis (PL)

Table 8–8
Nonhuman Primate C-Type Retroviruses

Strain Designation	Disease
Gibbon ape leukemia virus (GaLV) (substrains:GaLV$_{SF}$, GaLV$_{SEATO}$, GaLV$_H$, GaLV$_{BR}$)	Acute lymphoblastic leukemia, granulocytic leukemia, lymphosarcoma
Simian sarcoma virus (SiSV)	Fibrosarcomas
Simian sarcoma–associated virus (SSAV)	None
Baboon endogenous viruses (BaEV)	None
Stump-tailed monkey endogenous virus (MAC-1)	None
Rhesus monkey endogenous virus (MMC-1)	None
Owl monkey endogenous virus (OMC-1)	None
Simian T-lymphotropic viruses (STLV-I)	Malignant lymphoma

Africa (see below). Diagnosis originally was made by hematologic criteria but at present sensitive serologic assays for BLV antibodies are used (immunodiffusion, RIA, enzyme-linked immunosorbent assay [ELISA]). On the basis of serologic recognition of BLV infection and elimination of seropositive animals, eradication programs are being carried out in several European countries (see below). Prevention of BLV infection by immunization with inactivated BLV seems feasible but is still under experimental trial.

Primate C-Type Retroviruses

Infectious and oncogenic primate type C virus (Table 8–8) was first isolated from a spontaneous fibrosarcoma of a pet woolly monkey.[17] The isolate consists of a replication-defective sarcoma virus and an associated nondefective helper virus for which no oncogenic property has yet been detected. The viruses were designated simian sarcoma virus and simian sarcoma-associated virus (SiSV-1/SSAV-1).[17] The virus induces fibrosarcomas when inoculated into newborn marmosets and transforms fibroblasts in vitro.[17]

Tumor development is accompanied by the appearance of circulating antibodies against viral structural proteins and reverse transcriptase. No FOCMA-like antigen has been identified on the surface of SiSV-transformed cells or in the sera of tumor-carrying animals. In vitro, SiSV/SSAV can be grown in cells derived from many species including man, and cells can be transformed nonproductively by SiSV alone.

These viruses resemble the murine and feline leukemia-sarcoma viruses. Group-specific and interspecies reactivities exist among the corresponding proteins of SSAV, MuLV, and FeLV. MuLV can be used to rescue SiSV from cells nonproductively transformed by SiSV. The molecular weights of the proteins of SSAV are very similar to those of MuLV and FeLV (p10, p12, p15, p30, gp70), and considerable nucleic acid homology exists between SiSV/SSAV and some strains of MuLV. SiSV/SSAV are exogenous viruses for primates, that is, the viral genomes are not present in the genomes of normal primate cells. They are assumed to have emerged from an endogenous virus of wild mice.

The transforming sequence of SiSV, designated v-sis, has been identified, cloned, and sequenced. The cellular homologues of v-sis, designated c-sis, have been found to be highly conserved among vertebrates, like the other onc genes, and have been iden-

tified also in the human genome (see above). c-sis is located on human chromosome 22 and is translocated to chromosome 9 in chronic myelogenous leukemia.[125]

Primate C-type viruses very similar to SSAV have been isolated in several instances from leukemic gibbons. The virus, called gibbon ape leukemia virus (GaLV), induces myeologenous or lymphoblastic leukemias in gibbons, and appears, by seroepidemiologic data, to be the etiologic agent of naturally occurring leukemias in gibbons in captivity.[109, 130] The virus is present in high levels in saliva. An efficient immune response apparently prevents most of the exposed animals from developing leukemia. Four strains have been defined to date (see Table 8–8), and all four share most of their serologic and biochemical properties with SSAV.

Several endogenous C-type viruses have been isolated from primate tissues and cells, and the best-characterized virus is the endogenous virus of baboons, designated BaEV. Like the other endogenous viruses, BaEV is genetically transmitted through the germ line and has not been found to possess oncogenic properties. It is not related to the exogenous SiSV-GaLV group, but it is closely related to the endogenous cat virus RD114. BaEV is considered to be an example for a possible transspecies infection from an ancestor of the baboon to an ancestor of the cat earlier in evolution.

Simian T-Lymphotropic Viruses (STLV)

After the detection of the human T-lymphotropic viruses types I and II (HTLV-I and -II) in 1980 and 1981,[37, 38] related retroviruses have been detected in a variety of Asian and African Old-World monkeys.[131, 132] These viruses are of C-type morphology (Figure 8–8) and resemble the human counterparts in structure and biology. They are not endogenous in the species they were isolated from and are not related to the other known exogenous and endogenous retroviruses of monkeys (see Table 8–8). Healthy Old-World monkeys possess antibodies to HTLV-I with seropositivity rates ranging from 8% to 44% in the most extensively studied genus, *Macaca*. Antibodies to HTLV-I were detected in 11 of 13 macaques with malignant lymphoma or lymphoproliferative disease, but only in seven of 95 healthy macaques.[133] HTLV-I-related provirus was isolated from a seropositive baboon.[134] In analogy to the human viruses, the monkey viruses were called simian T-lymphotropic viruses type I or STLV-I (see Table 8–8) (not to be confused with SIV, viruses related to HIV). In Japan, the geographic distribution

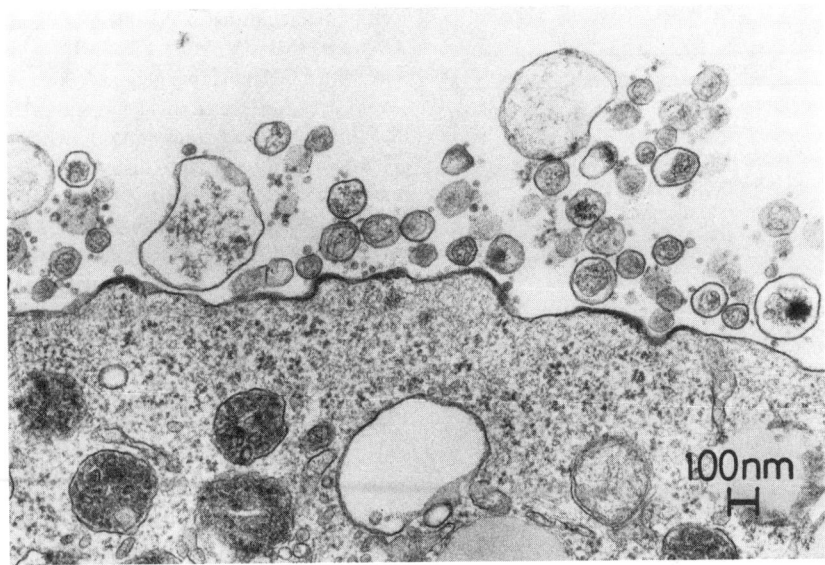

Figure 8–8. Electron micrograph of simian T lymphotropic virus type 1 (STLV–1). Note budding from cell surface and numerous viral particles of C–type morphology (central, spherical cores, absent or only short surface projections). Original magnification ×50,000. (Courtesy of Dr. H. Gelderblom.)

of seropositive macaques has not been found to be correlated with seropositivity in human populations, suggesting an independent origin for the human and the simian viruses.

Mouse Mammary Tumor Virus

MMTV (Table 8–9) was one of the first oncogenic viruses discovered.[44, 46] The virus has been isolated from milk and tumors of mammary carcinoma–bearing mice. Morphologically MMTV is a B-type virus with an eccentrically located core. In mammary carcinomas, the B-type extracellular particles are often associated with intracytoplasmic A-type particles which may be precursors of the former. The virus surface carries projections, so-called spikes. MMTV contains, like the other RNA tumor viruses, a high-molecular-weight RNA of 70S, a reverse transcriptase, envelope glycoproteins (gp52 and gp36), and several core proteins (p30, p28, p22, p18, p14, and p10).

Four major groups of MMTV are described: the endogenous virus of BALB/c mice (MMTV-O); the so-called milk factor from C3H mice (MMTV-S); the virus group MMTV-P isolated from the high mammary carcinoma–incidence mouse strains GR, RIII, and DD; and virus isolates from mammary carcinomas of mouse strains freed of MMTV in the milk by foster nursing (MMTV-L for low-oncogenic). These virus groups and strains can be distinguished by their in vivo host range and by the type of lesions they induce (see Table 8–9). Further differences can be detected by antigenic heterogeneity of their glycoproteins (gp52) and their core proteins p28 and p10 as well as in peptide maps of these three proteins. The RNAs of MMTV-S and MMTV-P share 95% sequence homology, whereas MTMV-L strains (viruses of low oncogenicity) lack some sequences of the highly oncogenic variants.

The MMTV genome is endogenous to mouse species. The number and the type of provirus copies vary from mouse strain to

mouse strain. Their expression is controlled by several genes like MTV-1, the germinal provirus of the MMTV-L viruses, and MTV-2, the gene for the release of the GR-mouse strain MMTV. Other genes like Imv regulate translational steps of provirus expression. Extrachromosomal transmission of the virus has been recognized via the milk and to some extent via infection of the female by her mate. The virus in the milk (so-called milk factor) is the cause of mammary carcinomas in the high-incidence mouse strains C3Hf, GR, and RIII. The latency period of these hormone-independent mammary tumors is relatively shorter (3–9 months). In the DNA of these tumors additional virus copies can be found integrated. Mammary tumors in low-incidence strains (BALB/c, C57 B1) have latency periods of more than 1 year.

MMTV expression can be stimulated by corticosteroid treatment of mice. The nucleotide sequences for this susceptibility are located within the viral LTR (see Table 8–3).[135] Besides the milk-borne exogenous MMTVs, an endogenous MMTV has been isolated from BALB/c mice; this virus also has a high capacity of

Table 8–9
Murine B-Type Retroviruses

Strain Designation	Disease
BALB/c-MTV (MMTV-0)	Mammary adenocarcinomas, adenoacanthomas
C3H-MTV (MMTV-S)	Hormone-independent type A mammary adenocarcinoma
GR-MTV R III-MTV } (MMTV-P) DD-MTV	Mammary gland plaques, hormone-dependent type B mammary adenocarcinoma
MMTV-L	Hyperplastic nodules, mammary carcinoma (long latency period)

Table 8–10

Primate D-Type Retroviruses

Strain designation	Disease
Mason-Pfizer monkey virus (MPMV) (related isolates: HeLA virus, AO virus)	Immunodeficiency, lymphadenopathy, simian acquired immunodeficiency syndrome (AIDS)
Simian immunodeficiency retroviruses Types 1, 2 (SRV-1, -2)	Immunodeficiency, simian AIDS
Langur endogenous virus (PO-1-Lu)	None
Squirrel monkey endogenous virus (SMRV)	None

inducing mammary carcinomas after injection into recipient mice. This virus seems to be genetically controlled in the low-incidence BALB/c strain. The induction of mammary carcinomas by experimental infection with endogenous MMTV is controlled by host genetic factors. The genes responsible for susceptibility or resistance to exogenous virus are not yet identified, but the histocompatibility loci seem to be involved to some extent.

Mice naturally expressing MMTV in their mammary glands or mice infected with exogenous MMTV elicit humoral antibodies that are directed against the envelope glycoprotein gp52. The highest antibody levels could be detected in animals with mammary carcinomas. Cytotoxic antibodies and cellular immune reactions are present as consequences of virus exposure. Vaccination with MMTV prior to expression of endogenous MMTV or prior to infection with exogenous virus prevents viral replication and subsequent tumor development.

MMTV can infect cell cultures of mink and cat to a limited extent, but no satisfactory in vitro bioassay has been established. In vitro propagation of MMTV is possible in cell lines from mammary carcinomas of several mouse strains after treatment with insulin and hydrocortisone.

Type D Retroviruses

Type D viruses (Table 8–10) consist of two groups of primate retroviruses: (1) the Mason-Pfizer monkey virus (MPMV) and related viruses, including SRV-1 and -2[136–138] and the Langur virus (PO-1-Lu); and (2) the squirrel monkey retrovirus (SMRV) and related viruses.[42] On morphologic and biochemical grounds these viruses are neither B-type nor C-type and thus have been designated D-type. MPMV, an exogenous virus, was isolated from a spontaneous mamma carcinoma of a female rhesus monkey (*Macaca mulatta*). PO-1-Lu, an endogenous virus, was isolated by cocultivation of the lung of a spectacled langur (*Presbytis obscuris*) with bat and with human cells. Both the rhesus and the langur are Old-World monkeys. Viruses morphologically similar to MPMV were isolated from a variety of human cell lines including the HeLa and AO cell lines. SMRV, also an endogenous virus, was isolated from tissue of a New-World monkey (squirrel monkey, *Saimiri sciurens*).

All type D viruses are associated with intracytoplasmic A particles that represent immature virus particles. They have an ec-

centric nucleoid that is complete at the time of budding. All type D viruses (MPMV, PO-1-Lu, SMRV) contain a reverse transcriptase with a molecular weight of 80,000 to 90,000 daltons. It prefers Mg^{2+} over Mn^{2+} as a divalent cation. Under high-salt conditions the SMRV-reverse transcriptase switches from Mg^{2+} to $Mn.^{2+}$ This peculiarity is used to distinguish the Old-World viruses from the New-World viruses (ie, MPMV and PO-1-Lu from SMRV).

MPMV predominantly infects primate cells. PO-1-Lu has also a somewhat restricted host range and replicates best in human and bat cells. SMRV has a broad host range. PO-1-Lu and SMRV are xenotropic and do not replicate in cells of their hosts of origin. In vitro, MPMV is of questionable oncogenicity since it has not been possible to induce tumors with MPMV in monkeys. However, high titers of neutralizing and precipitating antibodies against structural proteins suggest that effective immune surveillance might control tumor induction. When inoculated with MPMV, neonatal rhesus monkeys did not develop tumors but developed severe lymphadenopathy, weight loss, thymic atrophy, and immunodeficiency (simian AIDS). Simian AIDS is also caused by the simian immune deficiency retroviruses SRV-1 and -2. Nucleotide sequence analyses of MPMV, SRV-1 and SRV-2 show only 6% to 18% differences in the predicted amino acid sequences.[137–139]

Of the MPMV genome, 20% is present in the rhesus monkey genome and in that of related Old-World monkeys. Gene sequences partially homologous to the endogenous langur virus are found multicopied in langur and in related Old-World monkeys, suggesting that MPMV may be derived from an endogenous langur virus. SMRV-related sequences are exclusively found in squirrel monkeys and not in any Old- or New-World monkey or in any other animal species tested.

The protein composition of MPMV and PO-1-Lu is similar. They contain two glycoproteins, gp68 and gp20. The gp68 is located on the outer virus envelope membrane. Core structural proteins are p27, p14, p12, and p10. Additional virion-associated glycoproteins depend on the host cell in which the virus is propagated. The protein pattern of SMRV is distinct from that of the MPMV/PO-1-Lu group. It is composed of one glycoprotein, gp75, and the core proteins p36, p20, and p10. Serologically, all three viruses contain determinants in their glycoproteins that cross-react with one another as well as with the C-type BaEV gp70 as detected by an interspecies competition RIA.

Lentiviruses

The name *lentiviruses* (slow viruses) reflects one of the basic properties of this group of retroviruses, namely the "slow" chronic courses of the diseases they cause. The prototype lentivirus, *visna-maedi virus,* causes in sheep a progressive pneumonia associated with wasting and a form of subacute encephalomyelitis that leads to clinical paresis 0.5 to 8.0 years after infection.[140,141] The Icelandic word *visna* denotes "wasting," *maedi,* "shortness of breath."

In 1933, visna-maedi virus was inadvertently introduced into the Icelandic sheep population by the importation of 20 apparently latently infected rams from Germany. The epidemic was recognized in the early 1940s by the Icelandic physician Sigurdsson who showed that the disease was caused by a transmissable agent and who succeeded in growing the virus in cultured choroid plexus cells of sheep. Attempts at therapy and vaccination failed, and the

Table 8–11
Lentiviruses

Strain Designation	Disease
Visna-maedi virus	Progressive pneumonia, encephalitis and wasting of sheep
Caprine arthritis encephalitis virus (CAEV)	Proliferative synovitis and arthritis of goats, demyelinating encephalomyelitis and chronic interstitial pneumonia of goats and sheep
Equine infectious anemia virus (EIAV)	Infectious anemia of horses
Bovine immunodeficiency virus (BIV)	Immunodeficiency of cattle (bovine AIDS)
Feline T-lymphotropic lentivirus (FTLV or FIV)	Immunodeficiency of cats (feline AIDS)
Simian immunodeficiency viruses (SIV)	
SIV$_{MAC}$ SIV$_{MNE}$ SIV$_{SM}$	Immunodeficiency of macaques (simian AIDS)
SIV$_{AGM}$ SIV$_{MND}$	No disease observed
Human immunodeficiency viruses (HIV-1, -2)	Human AIDS, HIV disease

AIDS = acquired immunodeficiency syndrome; HIV = human immunodeficiency virus.

disease was finally eradicated by replacement of the total Icelandic sheep population during the years 1944 to 1965.[142, 143]

The morphology of visna-maedi virus and of the other lentiviruses (Table 8–11) is characterized by the cylindrical shape of their cores (Figure 8–9). Most other retroviruses have spherical cores.

Lentiviruses are probably transmitted between animals via cells (macrophages, monocytes) or their secretions. Free virus is hardly detectable. The routes of entry of visna-maedi virus are the respiratory and the gastrointestinal (GI) tracts. Housing animals closely together favors virus transmission. Insects have been shown to be a rare but existing vector for the transmission of equine infectious anemia virus (EIAV).[144]

After infection, visna-maedi virus replicates at the site of entry, usually the lung, and subsequently spreads via the blood or the spinal fluid. Target cells are primarily of monocyte-macrophage lineage. The infected animals mount a humoral and cell-mediated immune response which is effective against free virus but probably does not eradicate infected cells.[145] Immune surveillance of the host is complicated by antigenic variation of the virus, and this antigenic drift may be one explanation for the persistence of viral infection.[146] The infected animals develop symptoms during the second year after infection and die after a protracted and progressive course. In vitro, infected cells rapidly produce progeny and degenerate, in the presence of or without fusion, within three days. In contrast, viral replication in vivo is focal and unproductive. Synthesis of viral RNA, antigens, and virus is found in 1% or less of choroid plexus cells of infected animals.

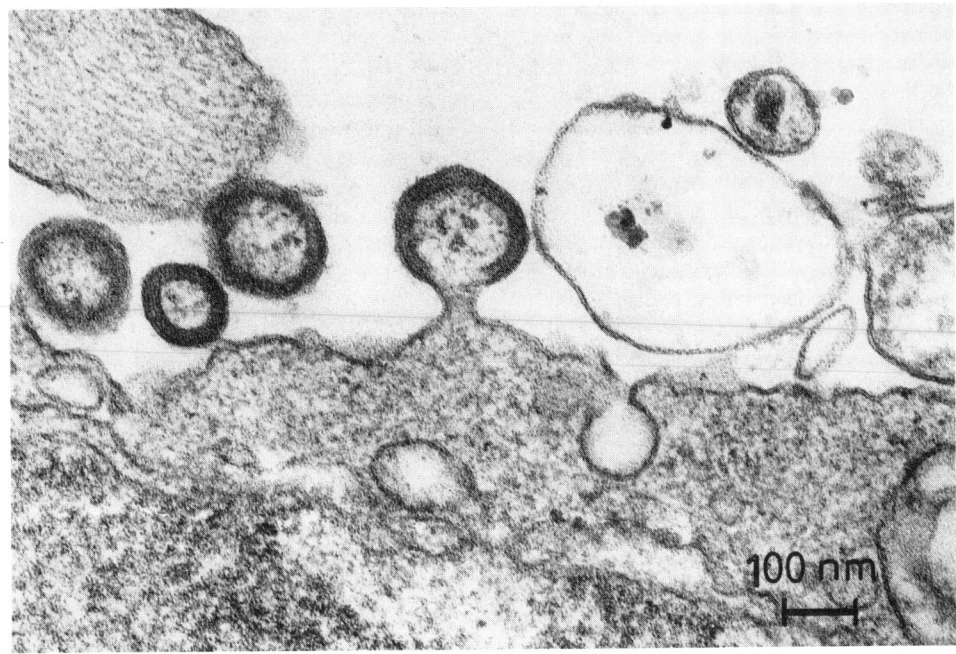

Figure 8–9. Electron micrograph of visna-maedi virus. Note budding particles with still electron–lucent centers and one mature virion with a cylindrical core. Original magnification ×110,000. (Courtesy of Dr. H. Gelderblom.)

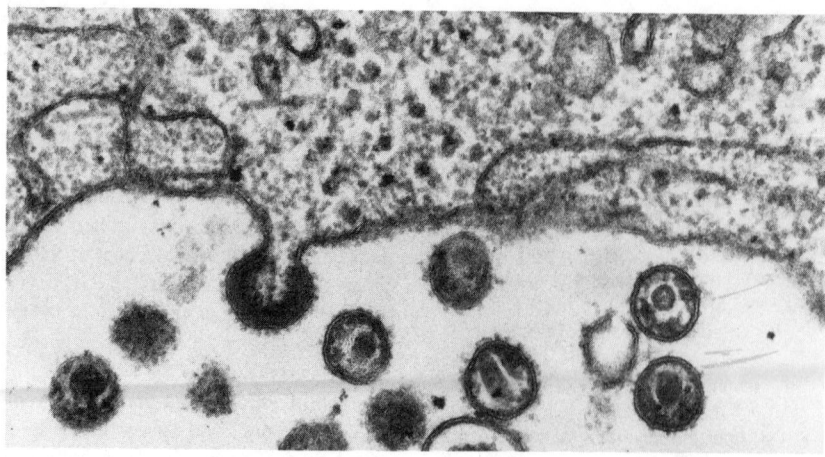

Figure 8–10. Electron micrograph of simian immunodeficiency virus (SIV_{agm}). Note budding and cylindrical cores of mature virions. Original magnification ×96,000. (Courtesy of Dr. H. Gelderblom.)

Restricted gene expression appears to be a central property of lentivirus infections which may remain asymptomatic during the normal life span of the animal. Lentivirus infections of sheep are widespread in the United States and in Germany as documented by the presence of antibodies, but apparently remain largely asymptomatic. This points to the relevance of the susceptibility of the animals or of other cofactors favoring infection and development of disease.

Another lentivirus, *caprine arthritis encephalitis virus* (CAEV), primarily causes inflammation of the synovia and arthritis in goats.[147] The most common and severe localizations are in the carpal joints. In young animals neurologic disease may be dominant. Some animals also develop pneumonia and inflammation of the mammary glands. The disease develops insidiously, and the course is slowly progressive as in other lentiviral infections.

Equine infectious anemia (EIA), which was first described in France in 1843, is a chronic relapsing anemia with fever which is caused by a third lentivirus, *equine infectious anemia virus* (EIAV).[148] Target cells of EIAV are the macrophages. Periodic viral replication leads to an immunologically mediated disease with fever and severe anemia. The hallmark of EIA is periodic remissions. The recurrences of acute disease usually decrease in severity and frequency, leading to an inapparent virus carrier state in the older animals. EIAV, like other lentiviruses, persists for life in the infected animals. Visna-maedi virus, CAEV, and EIAV are related viruses which share, in addition to biologic properties, cross-reacting antigenicity.

Analysis of the genome organization and nucleotide sequencing studies of visna virus, HIV, and other immunodeficiency viruses confirmed that also HIV and most other immunodeficiency viruses belong to the lentivirus group.[146, 149–151]

The detection and characterization of human immunodeficiency viruses in 1983 and 1984[42, 43] prompted the detection of related immunodificiency viruses in several animal species. The best known are the *simian immunodeficiency viruses* (SIV, formerly STLV-III) (Figure 8–10 and Table 8–11). Many strains of SIV have been isolated and characterized[151–158] and the complete nucleotide sequences of two of them, SIV_{MAC} and SIV_{AGM}, have been elucidated.

The genome of SIV_{MAC} is 9643 nucleotides,[159] that of SIV_{AGM} 9170 nucleotides long.[155] SIV_{MAC} causes a syndrome similar to AIDS in rhesus macaques. In contrast, SIV_{AGM} is associated with inapparent infection in several monkey species including African green monkeys and mangabeys. SIV_{MAC} is closely related to HIV-2 (see Chapter 9) by antigenicity and nucleic acid sequence homology,[156] suggesting that HIV-2 might have evolved by transspecies infection from monkey to man. SIV_{AGM} is about equally distantly related to HIV-1 and HIV-2.[155]

Immunodeficiency viruses have also been found in cattle and in cats. A bovine retrovirus causing immunodeficiency in cattle was described 20 years ago, but attracted little attention at that time. Genome analysis confirmed that it belongs to the same group as HIV and SIV and led to its designation *bovine immunodeficiency virus* or BIV.[159] From domestic cats which were seronegative for FeLV, but showed an immunodeficiency-like syndrome, a T-lymphotropic retrovirus was isolated which is not related to FeLV or to HIV.[160] Morphology and anion requirement of its reverse transcriptase suggest that the virus belongs to the lentivirus family. The name *feline T-lymphotropic lentivirus* (FTLV) was proposed, but further characterization of the virus and its genome structure is required.

Spumaviruses

Spumaviruses or foamy viruses are a group of retroviruses that are not associated with any known disease. They were called foamy viruses, because they induce, in cell culture, syncytia with nu-

Table 8–12
Spumaviruses

Strain Designation	Disease
Simian foamy viruses (9 serotypes)	None
Foamy viruses of cats, cattle, hamsters	None
Human foamy virus (HFV)	None

merous vacuoles which have a foamy appearance. Foamy viruses have been described in several animal species including monkeys, cats, cattle, and hamsters. Also, one human strain has been isolated and molecularly characterized (Table 8–12) (see Chapter 9).

EPIDEMIOLOGY

Most retroviruses appear to be ubiquitous. Retroviruses have been detected in virtually all vertebrate species investigated. Some retroviruses are genetically transmitted as endogenous viruses; other retroviruses are infectious and are transmitted horizontally. Most horizontally transmitted infectious viruses have pathogenic effects on their hosts. Epidemiologic studies help to clarify the route of transmission of infectious viruses and to reach etiologic conclusions. On the basis of epidemiologic data, measures for prevention, treatment, and eradication of a given virus-induced disease can be devised. Prior to epidemiologic field studies, it is useful to determine whether a retrovirus is endogenous or exogenous for a given animal species.

Epidemiologic studies have been particularly valuable in the past for the evaluation of two retrovirus-induced neoplasias: feline leukemia and enzootic bovine leukemia and lymphosarcoma. They also have helped to establish leukemia of gibbon apes as a disease induced by the retrovirus GaLV, and seroepidemiologic studies, at present, are investigating the worldwide association of the human T cell leukemia retrovirus (HTLV) with human T cell malignancies.

Avian Leukemia Viruses (ALV)

Chronic lymphoid leukemia or lymphomatosis is caused by ALV after a long latent period in susceptible chickens.[44] ALV-induced leukemia or lymphomatosis is a major cause of death of infected chickens, is very common in commercial flocks of the United States, and is responsible for heavy losses to the poultry industry. The virus is not genetically inherited, but transmitted horizontally or congenitally to the fertilized egg. In addition to genetic factors, resistance to ALV is determined by an immune response to the virus. Viremic chickens are at high risk for development of disease. The significance of the acutely transforming avian retroviruses for naturally occurring disease is unknown.

Murine Leukemia Viruses (MuLV)

The best known spontaneous leukemia in mice, the T cell leukemia in AKR mice, has an incidence of almost 10% in this species.[44] All AKR mice have been found to express ecotropic endogenous retroviruses in most organs and in high titers. Antibody formation is absent. Horizontal transmission of the leukemogenic viruses from diseased or virus-expressing animals to healthy animals from other strains has not been observed.

Wild mice in several areas of California develop lymphoma or paralysis with great frequency (18% and 12%, respectively). Those mice which develop one or both of these diseases have high serum levels of viral core proteins and express high titers of infectious virus in tissues. Antibodies are lacking. Virus from high frequency expressor mice is transmitted via the milk to the progeny or to litters from other mouse strains which also develop lymphomas

and/or paralysis. In contrast, wild mice foster-nursed by virus-free laboratory mice do not show virus infection and remain disease-free.

Feline Leukemia Viruses (FeLV)

The epidemiology of FeLV-induced leukemia is like that of other retrovirus-induced leukemias in that it does not follow the classic pattern expected for a typical infectious disease.[46, 47] The reasons are several; FeLV is ubiquitous, infecting most cats at some time in their lifetime. Only a small proportion of the infected animals develop overt leukemia. The incubation periods are variable and prolonged. The same virus may cause different pathologic forms of the disease.

About 2% of transiently infected cats develop persistent viremia, and about 30% of viremic animals ultimately develop leukemia or lymphoma. Healthy viremic cats provide the major source of infectious virus for further infections. Infectious virus is excreted in the saliva, and this is thought to be the major route for transmission. Feline leukemia and lymphoma may occur in clusters, when cats are housed closely together.

Infected cats develop an active immune response to the virus envelope glycoprotein gp70 and thereby eliminate infectious virus. Virus producer cells expressing viral envelope proteins on their surfaces also can be eliminated in this way. Further immune responses to viral proteins useful in seroepidemiologic studies are those to the viral core proteins p10, p12, p15, and p30, to the viral reverse transcriptase, and to the FeSV-encoded FOCMA (see above). The levels of antibody to FOCMA are closely correlated with resistance to development of leukemia.

Bovine Leukemia Viruses (BLV)

BLV is the etiologic agent of EBL and lymphosarcoma (see above). The virus is transmitted horizontally in most instances, but possibly also congenitally from the cow.[15] The mechanism for transmission is unclear, but insect vectors and the transmission of lymphocytes containing the virus may play a role. The major envelope glycoprotein of BLV, gp51, elicits a good cytotoxic immune response, probably neutralizing free virus and eliminating BLV-producing lymphocytes.

According to present understanding, BLV most probably originated from East Prussia and Poland at the southern Baltic seacoast, spreading from there by export of cattle to North America. Massive movements of cattle during and after World War I spread BLV to Russia and to Western Europe. BLV and EBL have further been reported in Japan, Israel, Africa, and South America. The incidence of EBL varies within herds and within geographic areas. In North America, up to 70% of animals have been reported BLV antibody–positive in some herds. Eradication programs based on hematologic diagnosis were only partly successful since healthy BLV-infected carriers were not detected. More recently, eradication programs based on serologic diagnosis of BLV carriers have been started in Denmark and West Germany. The assays used are immunodiffusion, RIA, and ELISA for antibodies to BLV structural proteins. In Lower Saxony (Germany), the incidence of BLV infection dropped as the result of such programs from 11% of all animals to less than 3% within little more than 1 year.

Gibbon Ape Leukemia Viruses (GaLV)

Information on GaLV almost exclusively comes from gibbon apes in captivity. GaLV induces myelogenous and lymphoid leukemias in gibbon apes under experimental conditions.[117, 130] The virus is transmitted rapidly and efficiently among gibbons held in captivity. GaLV is excreted in saliva in high levels. The animals mount an active immune response against the virus which prevents the development of leukemia in most infected animals. It is unclear whether GaLV is a major cause of leukemia for free-living gibbon apes in their natural habitats.

Lentiviruses

Serologic testing for antibodies against the core protein p30, which carries antigenic determinants shared by the lentiviruses visna-maedi virus, CAEV, and EIAV, shows that lentivirus infection is common in sheep and goats in the United States. Prevalence of visna virus infection is increasing with age and reaches 80% to 85% in animals older than 7 years. A similar level of infection has been found in adult goats for infection with CAEV. CAEV infection is widespread also in goats in Western Europe and Australia.[140, 141, 147] Horizontal transmission is the primary source of infection in sheep, probably via virus-contaminated colostrum and milk. Inhalation of droplets containing virus-infected cells has also been implicated. No hosts other than sheep and goats have been identified for these viruses. This explains why eradication programs such as the slaughter of all infected flocks in Iceland were successful.

LABORATORY DIAGNOSIS OF INFECTION

Electron Microscopy

The morphology of mature viruses as well as of viruses in cells during different steps of maturation can be analyzed by electron microscopy and immune electron microscopy. Viral components accumulate at the cell membrane, assemble to immature particles, and bud from the cell membrane into the culture medium as mature viruses. The developing nucleoids can be seen in the electron microscope as electron-dense particles. Using antibodies to viral components that are coupled to electron-dense molecules like ferritin, it is possible to make serologic reactions visible in the electron microscope. The bound antibodies appear as black dots accumulated in certain areas of the cell surface or cytoplasm.

Biochemical Test Systems

Detection of Virus Particles by RNA Labeling

RNA tumor viruses can be detected in cell cultures by demonstration of their characteristic high-molecular-weight genomic RNA. The RNA is radioactively labeled by cell culture labeling with a radioactive RNA precursor like ^{3}H-uridine. Subsequently the 70S RNA is identified by velocity centrifugation in 10% to 30% glycerol or 5% to 20% sucrose gradients or by density centrifugation in a cesium chloride gradient. The radioactively labeled RNA can also be detected within the cell by in situ hybridization. The RNA is located visually by the densely populated black silver grains on the film representing radioactively labeled RNA. The RNA can be easily localized in different compartments of the cell.

Reverse Transcriptase Assay

Cells productively infected with retroviruses shed these viruses into the cell culture medium. The cell culture supernatant is centrifuged at 100,000 g to yield a microsomal precipitate. This precipitate contains the viruses which can be demonstrated by testing the precipitate for the presence of reverse transcriptase. Reverse transcriptase is characteristic for RNA tumor viruses and transcribes RNA into DNA. For the detection and characterization of reverse transcriptase activity, synthetic RNA homopolymers containing a short DNA primer sequence are used as template. Radioactively labeled deoxynucleotide triphosphates are added as substrate and are incorporated into the newly synthesized DNA. The usual sequence of preference for the templates by the reverse transcriptase is poly rA:oligo dT_{10-12} > poly rC:oligo dG_{10-12} > poly mrC:oligo dG_{10-12} > natural RNA > poly dA:oligo dT_{10-12}. The activity is dependent on the presence of divalent cations like Mg^{2+} or Mn^{2+}. The reverse transcriptases of avian, bovine, and human C-type viruses, B-type and D-type viruses prefer Mg^{2+}, whereas the reverse transcriptases of the other mammalian C-type viruses, such as murine, feline, and primate C-type viruses, prefer Mn^{2+}. Thus reverse transcriptase assay allows detection and also limited identification of retroviruses.

Simultaneous Detection Assay

The detection of complete virus particles in tumors, other tissues, or cultured cells is possible by the simultaneous detection assay. This assay demonstrates the presence of RNA and reverse transcriptase in the microsomal fraction of cellular extracts. With the microsomal fraction a radioactive reverse transcription product is prepared. The phenol-extracted radioactively labeled DNA reaction product is still attached to its high-molecular-weight viral RNA template by hydrogen bonds and can be identified by subsequent glycerol sedimentation centrifugation.

Molecular Hybridization

The presence of viral information in cellular RNA or DNA as well as the degree of relatedness of different RNA tumor viruses can be determined by molecular hybridization. Molecular hybridization uses the principle of the formation of hydrogen bonds between complementary nucleotides like A-T or -U and G-C. The more that complementary nucleotides occur, the more that hydrogen bonds form, and the stronger the hybridization and the more related the nucleic acids are. Using large amounts of cellular DNA and small amounts of radioactive viral DNA or RNA, it is possible to quantitate the viral information present in the cellular DNA. The complementary sequences of cellular and viral nucleic acids will form a hybrid. The hybrid formation can be analyzed by different procedures (autoradiography of Southern or Northern blots, Cs_2SO_4 density centrifugation, digestion by single-strand-specific nuclease, hydroxyapatite chromatography), depending on the nature of the hybrids. The formed hybrid is characterized by thermal dissociation. With increasing homology of the hybridized nucleic acid strands, higher temperatures are necessary to dissociate the hybrids. By comparison of thermal dissociation profiles, the degree of relatedness of the nucleic acids can be determined. This basic principle can now be applied in different hybridization techniques such as liquid hybridization, Southern blot hybridization, in situ hybridization, and the polymerase chain reaction.[160–162]

Serologic Test Systems

Immunofluorescence and Immunoperoxidase Staining

For the in situ detection of viral proteins, two methods are used: the immunofluorescence and the immunoperoxidase staining techniques. In both cases first a viral antigen-specific antibody is applied. Then a second, anti-IgG antibody is added which is labeled either with fluorescein or with an enzyme (peroxidase, alkaline phosphatase, β-galactosidase, etc) that catalyzes a color reaction. The fluorescein-mediated detection has to be performed in the dark. Only the fluorescing image of the cell can be seen in the fluorescence microscope. The immunoperoxidase technique works similarly but can be evaluated with a regular light microscope.[163] This has the advantage that more cellular details can be recognized. Both techniques allow the localization of intracellular antigens.

Detection of Antibodies

The method most frequently used for the detection of antibodies is the ELISA with whole disrupted virus or with an antigenic substructure.[165] In the antibody-ELISA antigen is coated onto a solid phase, mostly microtiter plates or plastic balls, and the serum to be tested is then allowed to react with the fixed virus antigen. The antigen-antibody complex is then monitored by an anti-IgG antibody to which an enzyme is covalently bound (mostly horseradish peroxidase or alkaline phosphatase) that gives a color reaction on addition of substrate.

For confirmation of ELISA results and for the determination of the antigen specificity of the antibodies, western blot analysis is the method of choice.[166] In western blotting the proteins of whole disrupted virus are electrophoretically separated and, after transfer to a cellulose strip (the ''blotting'' step), reacted with the antibodies. Antigen-antibody complexes are detected by addition of an enzyme-bound antihuman antibody and a subsequent color reaction as described above for the ELISA.

Other techniques for the detection of antiviral antibodies are the radioimmune precipitation with disrupted virus and immunofluorescence or immunoperoxidase tests[164] with virus-producing cells which may be used alternatively (see below). Also, by the use of cell culture techniques, antibodies with defined functions such as neutralizing antibodies can be detected.

Characterization of Antibodies

For characterization of humoral immune responses the radioimmunoprecipitation (RIP) or the double immunodiffusion techniques are generally used. In RIP assays radioactively labeled virus is bound by viral antigen-specific antibody which is precipitated by an excess of anti-IgG antibody. The radioactivity in the precipitate after subtraction of nonspecific binding is analyzed by polyacrylamide gel electrophoresis under denaturing conditions and by subsequent autoradiography. The exposed film shows the darkened bands where the radioactivity was located, allowing a correlation of labeled virus with immune-precipitated antibody.

The double immunodiffusion test is less sensitive and requires larger test specimens. It is used, for example, to detect BLV carriers among cattle suspected to be BLV-infected. Antibodies and antigens are applied to a semisolid agar plate. The antigen fills the center well, while different animal sera are instilled into the wells arranged in a circle around the center well. Viral antigen and antibody migrate in the semisolid medium toward each other and form a precipitation line at the point of molar equilibrium. Each precipitation line corresponds to one viral protein. Precipitation lines that continue from well to well without a break indicate that identical reagents are precipitated.

Detection of Viral Antigens

For the detection of viral antigens, the competition RIA or the ELISA can be used. In RIA, first the uncharacterized, unlabeled protein is reacted with a limiting amount (50% binding of radioactively labeled antigen) of viral antigen-specific antibody. In a second step radioactive viral protein is added to bind the remaining free antibody. An excess of anti-IgG antibody precipitates the viral antigen-antibody complexes. The radioactivity in the precipitate is then determined. The presence of homologous proteins will reduce the radioactivity in the precipitate due to competition for binding sites; heterologous (unrelated) proteins will not decrease the bound radioactivity.

In the antigen-ELISA a solid phase (microtiter plates, tubes, plastic balls) is coated with an antigen-specific antibody. To this antibody the homologous antigen (or the unknown antigen) is bound. The same antigen-specific antibody, but coupled to an enzyme (peroxidase, alkaline phosphatase) is bound to the antigen-antibody complex on the solid phase, yielding a sandwichlike structure. The enzyme then catalyzes a color reaction that can be measured.

Biologic Test Systems

In Vivo Assays for Retroviruses

Early research on RNA tumor viruses used animals as the only available test subjects for viral infectivity. The viral activity was measured by the appearance of tumors, for example, leukemias or sarcomas. Several parameters including tumor incidence, death rate, or the latent period of the development of the disease have been shown to be related to the viral dose. These tests are time-consuming because of the time needed for tumor development, which varies from weeks for avian or murine sarcomas and acute leukemias (eg, Rauscher leukemia) to months and years for lymphoblastic leukemias.

In vivo tests were subsequently developed with a shortened time requirement to detect viral replication. For example, the induction of antibodies has been used to detect viral replication prior to tumor development. The time of antibody appearance and the antibody titer can be correlated to the virus titer. Widely used assay systems include serologic methods that detect viral antigens in the target organs of virus replication or of later tumor development. The spleen antigen test for murine leukemia viruses screens for the presence of virus-related proteins in tissue extracts several days after virus inoculation. A more refined system is the preparation of single-cell suspensions of the organs, and the consecutive evaluation of the percentage of cells containing virus antigen by immunofluorescence. Both determine the titer of infecting retrovirus accurately. With virus isolates that are not adapted to growth in cell cultures, these test systems reveal better results than in vitro tests. They also correlate with tumor-inducing capacity of the virus preparations.

Other rapid and sensitive in vivo assays include the spleen

weight assay and the spleen focus assay. The spleen weight assay is based on the induction of splenomegaly after inoculation of a retrovirus such as Friend or Rauscher MuLV. Two to three weeks after virus inoculation, the spleen weights of the inoculated mice are measured and correlated to virus dilutions. In the spleen focus assay the animals are sacrificed nine to ten days after infection with Rauscher or Friend virus and examined for macroscopically visible yellow-white lesions that develop on the spleen surface. The focus count is directly proportional to the virus dose. A similar system has been used for avian sarcoma viruses which counts ectodermal lesions on the chicken embryo chorioallantoic membrane. This assay was the direct predecessor of the in vitro transformation focus assay in chicken embryo fibroblasts.

In Vitro Assays

Tissue culture assay systems for RNA tumor viruses have the advantage over in vitro systems of being faster, less expensive, and more suitable for the determination of titration patterns. The main disadvantage is the necessity for correlation of the in vitro effects with tumorigenesis in vivo. The reliability of the results obtained in in vitro assays is dependent on the selection of suitable cell cultures and of media and sera free of inhibiting factors, for example, antibodies or virus-lysing lipoproteins. Optimal conditions for virus adsorption and penetration must be used. Polycations such as diethylaminoethyl (DEAE)-dextran or polybrene increase the efficiency of viral infection up to 80-fold. Further improvement of infection can be achieved by cocultivation of the indicator cell cultures with virus-producing cells or tissues instead of virus suspensions (infectious center assay). The infection of cell cultures with RNA tumor viruses can be detected either by cytologic changes or by screening of the cultures for viral components with serologic or biochemical methods.

Focus Assay.—Sarcoma viruses of avian, murine, feline, or primate origin cause morphologic changes in secondary embryo fibroblasts or permanent fibroblast tissue culture cell lines, and these changes are defined as in vitro oncogenic transformation. The ''transformed'' cell phenotype is characterized by changed morphology, increased population density, loss of contact inhibition and multilayered growth, capacity to grow in semisolid agar, and immortalized growth behavior in tissue culture lines. The areas of growth change (focus) consist of rounded or elongated cells which tend to pile up within the flat, contact-inhibited growth pattern of the surrounding cells (Figure 8–11). The foci can be counted in unstained cultures or after staining with Giemsa.

The focus assay for mammalian and avian sarcoma viruses can be used as a quantitative assay. Unlike avian RSV, a replication-competent sarcoma virus, the mammalian sarcoma viruses are helper-dependent for replication. Therefore a one-hit titration pattern (in which one virus particle is sufficient for transformation of one cell) can only be obtained in the presence of an excess of a nontransforming helper virus, for example, a leukemia virus.

Plaque Assay.—Leukemia viruses generally do not produce detectable cytopathologic changes in vitro. The observation of syncytia formation in RSV-transformed rat cells (XC cells) after contact with murine leukemia virus-infected mouse embryo cells has led to an assay system (XC plaque assay) with wide application

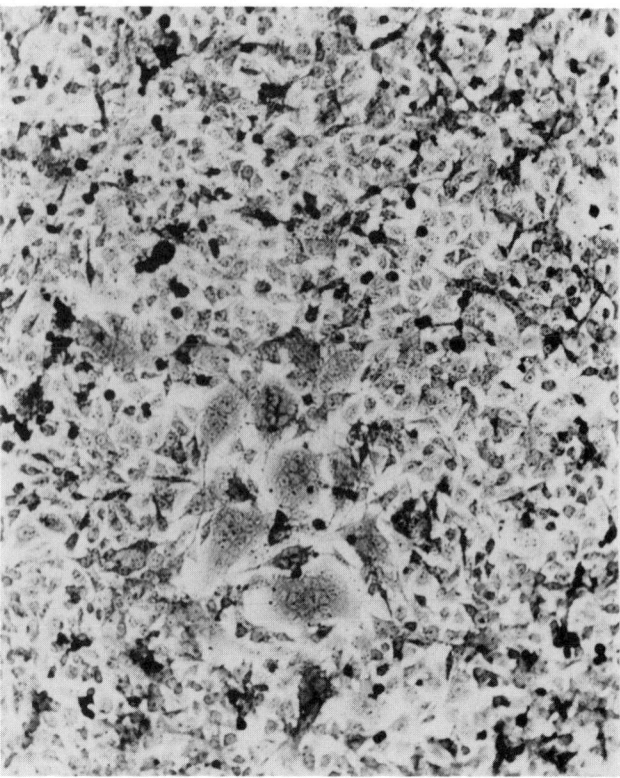

Figure 8–11. XC plaque consisting of several multinucleated giant cells. Original magnification approximately ×125.

in work with MuLVs. This phenomenon was also utilized for similar tests with feline, bovine, and simian C-type viruses. Virus-infected cells are inactivated by UV irradiation two to three days after infection and then cocultivated with the indicator cells (XC cells, KC cells). Some days later, areas of several (at least four to five) multinucleated syncytium cells develop that can be easily counted after staining of the cell sheet (see Figure 8–8). These tests can be performed as end point dilution assays. In susceptible cells the number of plaques is directly proportionate to the virus inoculum, and the titration pattern is uniformly one transformed focus corresponding to one infecting particle.

Nonsyncytial cytopathic effects in mouse cells, such as the appearance of rounded cells, have been observed with MuLV, and this property is useful to assay for some retroviruses. A widely used assay of this kind is the mink cell focus assay for the detection of recombinant leukemia viruses from spontaneous mouse leukemias. Similar effects have been described for avian leukosis viruses.

Several cell lines from mouse, cat, or mink have been transformed with Mo-MuSV, and cell clones have been selected which harbor the sarcoma genome without expression of the entire virus (S + L cells). The sarcoma genome can be rescued by superinfection with replication-competent MuLV and results in transformation foci similar to those described in the sarcoma virus focus assay. These tests are quantitative and have been performed with a variety of replication-competent mammalian C-type viruses including FeLV and BaEV.

Avian myeloblastosis virus (AMV) induces morphologic transformation of chicken hematopoietic cells in vitro. A more accurate assay has been established with chicken yolk sac macrophages which are transformed by AMV and form foci of myeloblasts. A similar test for Friend MuLV is based on the induction of erythroid colonies with bone marrow cells.

The in vitro infection by retroviruses that have no known in vitro cytopathologic effect can be determined by immunologic or biochemical assays. As the result of a virus-productive infection by a retrovirus, viral proteins, enzymes, and RNA are synthesized, and practically any of these components lends itself to qualitative and quantitative determinations by appropriate methods. These methods are described above and only some general remarks are included here.

Immunologic assays require a specific antiserum for detection of the virus under question. These assays are therefore limited to known viruses or to related new isolates. They can be used as end point dilution assays (COMUL, COFAL, COCAL test) using complement fixation, RIA, and ELISA, or also as plaque assays for virus titration using immunofluorescence or immunoperoxidase staining. These assays have been successfully used in research related to a variety of retroviruses.

Biochemical methods including specific nucleic acid probes for in situ hybridization have the same major range of application as the serologic test systems. Radioactive labeling of RNA coupled with density centrifugation, assaying of reverse transcriptase in cell culture supernatants, and electron microscopy are the best known methods used to study in vitro infectivity of uncharacterized retroviruses. The major disadvantage to these methods is the problem of establishing quantitative assay systems.

PREVENTION AND TREATMENT

No effective treatment exists for most retrovirus-induced diseases. Prevention therefore is the mainstay of measures to control retrovirus-induced neoplasias. In addition, eradication of some retroviral diseases has been attempted by eradication of infected animals. As in other viral diseases, prevention is best accomplished by active or passive immunization of animals at risk for the disease. The feasibility of this approach has been demonstrated in several retroviral diseases. The development of Friend MuLV-induced murine leukemia could be, under laboratory conditions, successfully prevented by immunization with inactivated whole Friend MuLV or purified MuLV gp70 envelope glycoprotein.[166] Similar results were obtained in preventing EBL by immunization with inactivated BLV.[15] In both cases, an active immune response was elicited in the vaccinated animals preventing, after subsequent infection with viable virus, the development of disease. Similar trials in feline leukemia were less successful since purified FeLV gp70 was poorly immunogenic in cats. Good protection, however, was accomplished in cats by immunization, prior to infection with FeLV or FeSV, with FOCMA-containing lymphoma cells inactivated by heat or by other measures.

Passive immunization has been carried out in mice prior to infection with Friend MuLV using antiserum to MuLV gp70.[166] Significant protection against tumor development was accomplished if infection occurred during a limited time interval after immunization.

Attempts of active immunization have been carried out in human leukemia using Rauscher MuLV as immunogen. This approach was chosen under the assumption of a viruslike agent similar to Rauscher MuLV in human leukemias. No difference in clinical response as compared to a control group was observed.

Immunotherapy with cat sera containing high levels of antibodies to gp70 and FOCMA has been tried in cats infected with FeLV or FeSV and in cats with naturally occurring lymphomas.[47] The treatment was successful if given within 1 to 2 weeks of virus inoculation. In naturally occurring lymphomas, remissions could be induced in about 50% of the animals, if the antiserum dose was repeated 6 to 8 times over 2 weeks.

Eradication programs have been successfully established for BLV and EBL in several countries (see above) and for visna-maedi virus in Iceland. Diseased animals and infected carrier animals as detected by sensitive serologic tests for viral proteins are eliminated from the herds. The percentage of BLV-infected animals has been lowered significantly by these measures, in one instance from 11% to less than 3% within 1 year.[15] In Iceland an eradication program of visna-maedi virus-infected sheep was carried out from 1944 to 1965. Sheep in Iceland are now free of visna-maedi virus.

REFERENCES

1. Ellerman V, Bang O: Experimentelle Leukämie bei Hühnern. *Zentralbl Bakteriol 1 Abt Orig A* 1908; 46:595.
2. Rous PA: Sarcoma of the fowl transmissible by an agent separable from the tumor cells. *J Exp Med* 1911; 13:397.
3. Fujinami A, Inamoto K: Über Geschwülste bei japanischen Haushühnern, insbesondere über einen transplantablen Tumor. *Zeitschr Krebsforsch* 1914; 14:94–119.
4. Bittner JJ: Some possible effects of nursing on the mammary gland tumor incidence of mice. *Science* 1936; 84:162–163.
5. Gross L: ''Spontaneous'' leukemia developing in C3H mice following inoculation in infancy, with AK leukemic extracts, or AK embryos. *Proc Soc Exp Biol Med* 1951; 76:27.
6. Graffi A, Beilka H, Fey F, et al: Gehäuftes Auftreten von Leukämien nach Injektion von Sarkomfiltraten. *Wien Klin Wochenschr* 1955; 105:61.
7. Friend C: Cell-free transmission in adult Swiss mice of a disease having the character of a leukemia. *J Exp Med* 1957; 105:307–318.
8. Lieberman M, Kaplan HS: Leukemogenic activity of filtrates from radiation-induced lymphoid tumors of mice. *Science* 1959; 130:387–388.
9. Moloney JB: Biological studies on lymphoid leukemia virus extracted from sarcoma S37. I. Origin and introductory investigations. *J Natl Cancer Inst* 1960; 24:933–951.
10. Rauscher FJ: A virus-induced disease of mice characterized by erythrocytopoiesis and lymphoid leukemia. *J Natl Cancer Inst* 1962; 29:515–543.
11. Moloney JB: A virus-induced rhabdomyosarcoma of mice. *Natl Cancer Inst Monogr* 1966; 22:139–142.
12. Finkel MP, Biskis BO, Jinkins PB: Virus induction of osteosarcomas in mice. *Science* 1966; 151:698–701.
13. Jarret WFH, Martin WB, Crighton GW, et al: Leukemia in the cat: Transmission experiments with leukemia (lymphosarcoma). *Nature* 1964; 202:566–568.
14. Snyder SP, Theilen GH: Transmissible feline fibrosarcoma. *Nature* 1969; 221:1074–1075.
15. Burny A, Bex F, Chantrenne H, et al: Bovine leukemia virus involvement in enzootic bovine leukosis. *Adv Cancer Res* 1978; 28:251–311.
16. Chopra HS, Mason MM: A new virus in a spontaneous mammary tumor of a rhesus monkey. *Cancer Res* 1970; 30:2081–2086.

17. Wolfe LG, Deinhardt F, Theilen GH, et al: Induction of tumors in marmoset monkeys by simian sarcoma virus, type I (lagothrix): A preliminary report. *J Natl Cancer Inst* 1971; 47:1115–1120.

18. Rowe WP, Hartley JW, Lander MR, et al: Noninfectious AKR mouse embryo cell lines in which each cell has the capacity to be activated to produce infectious murine leukemia virus. *Virology* 1971; 46:866–876.

19. Weiss RA, Friis RR, Katz E, et al: Induction of avian tumor viruses in normal cells by physical and chemical carcinogens. *Virology* 1971; 46:920–938.

20. Temin HM, Mizutani S: RNA-dependent DNA polymerase in virions of Rous sarcoma virus. *Nature* 1970; 226:1211–1213.

21. Baltimore D: RNA-dependent DNA polymerase in virions of RNA tumor viruses. *Nature* 1970; 226:1209–1211.

22. Duesberg PH, Vogt PK: Differences between the ribonucleic acids of transforming and nontransforming avian tumor viruses. *Proc Natl Acad Sci USA* 1970; 67:1673–1680.

23. Duesberg PH: Retroviral transforming genes in normal cells? *Nature* 1983; 304:219–226.

24. Stéhelin D, Varmus HE, Bishop JM, et al: DNA related to the transforming gene(s) of avian sarcoma viruses is present in normal DNA. *Nature* 1976; 260:170–173.

25. Bishop JM: The molecular biology of RNA tumor viruses: A physician's guide. *N Engl J Med* 1980; 303:675–682.

26. Dmochowski L, Grey CE: Studies on submicroscopic structure of leukemias of known or suspected viral origin: A review. *Blood* 1958; 13:1017–1042.

27. Moore DH, Charney J, Kramarsky B, et al: Search for a human breast cancer virus. *Nature* 1971; 229:611–615.

28. Gallo RC, Yang SS, Ting RC: RNA-dependent DNA polymerase of human acute leukemic cells. *Nature* 1970; 228:927–929.

29. Hehlmann R: RNA tumorviruses and human cancer. *Curr Top Microbiol Immunol* 1976; 73:141–215.

30. Gallagher RE, Gallo RC: Type-C RNA tumor virus isolated from cultured human acute myelogenous leukemia cells. *Science* 1975; 187:350–353.

31. Nooter K, Aarson AM, Bentvelzen P, et al: Isolation of infectious C-type oncornavirus from human leukemic bone marrow cells. *Nature* 1975; 256:595–597.

32. Panem S, Prochownik EV, Reale FR, et al: Isolation of type C virions from a normal human fibroblast strain. *Science* 1975; 189:297–299.

33. Kaplan HS, Goodenow RS, Epstein AL, et al: Isolation of a type C RNA virus from an established human histiocytic lymphoma cell line. *Proc Natl Acad Sci USA* 1977; 74:2564–2568.

34. Gallo RC, Wong-Staal F, Ruscetti F: Viruses and adult leukemia-lymphoma of man and relevant animal models, in Bloomfield CD (ed): *Adult Leukemias*. The Hague, Martinus Nijhoff, 1982, pp 1–41.

35. Hehlmann R, Schetters H, Erfle V: Current understanding of viral etiology in leukemia, in *Leukemia, Recent Developments in Diagnosis and Therapy. Recent Results in Cancer Research*. Berlin, Springer Verlag, 1984, pp 1–24.

36. Pimentel E: Human oncovirology. *Biochim Biophys Acta* 1979; 560:169–216.

37. Poiesz BJ, Ruscetti FW, Gazdur AF, et al: Detection and isolation of type C retrovirus particles from fresh and cultured lymphocytes of a patient with cutaneous T-cell lymphoma. *Proc Natl Acad Sci USA* 1980; 77:7415–7419.

38. Poiesz BJ, Ruscetti FW, Reitz MS, et al: Isolation of a new type C retrovirus (HTLV) in primary uncultured cells of a patient with Sézary T-cell leukemia. *Nature* 1981; 294:268–271.

39. Morgan DA, Ruscetti FW, Gallo RC: Selective in vitro growth of T lymphocytes from normal human bone marrows. *Science* 1976; 193:1007–1008.

40. Mier JW, Gallo RD: Purification and some characteristics of human T-cell growth factor from phytohemagglutinin-stimulated lymphocyte-conditioned media. *Proc Natl Acad Sci USA* 1980; 77:7415–7419.

41. Poiesz BJ, Ruscetti FW, Mier JW, et al: T-cell lines established from human T-lymphocytic neoplasias by direct response to T-cell growth factor. *Proc Natl Acad Sci USA* 1980; 77:6815–6819.

42. Barré-Sinoussi F, Chermann JC, Rey F, et al: Isolation of a T-lymphotropic retrovirus from a patient at risk for acquired immune deficiency syndrome (AIDS). *Science* 1983; 220:868–871.

43. Popovic M, Sarngadharan MG, Read E, et al: Detection, isolation, and continuous production of cytopathic retroviruses (HTLV–III) from patients with AIDS and pre–AIDS. *Science* 1984; 224:497–500.

44. Gross L:*Oncogenic Viruses* ed 3. Oxford, Pergamon, 1983.

45. Fine D, Schochetman G: Type D primate retroviruses: A review. *Cancer Res* 1978; 38:3123–3139.

46. Klein G (ed): *Viral Oncology*. New York, Raven Press, 1980.

47. Weiss RA, Teich N, Varmus HE, et al: The molecular biology of tumor viruses, part II, RNA tumor viruses. Cold Spring Harbor, NY, *Cold Spring Habor Laboratory*. 1982.

48. Wang LH: The gene order of avian RNA tumor viruses derived from biochemical analyses of deletion mutants and viral recombinants. *Annu Rev Microbiol* 1978; 32:561–593.

49. van Beveren C, van Straaten F, Galleshaw JA, et al: Nucleotide sequence of the genome of a murine sarcoma virus. *Cell* 1981; 27:97–108.

50. Reddy EP, Smith MJ, Aaronson SA: Complete nucleotide sequence and organization of the Moloney sarcoma virus genome. *Science* 1981; 214:445–450.

51. Shinnick TM, Lerner RA, Sutcliffe JG: Nucleotide sequence of Moloney murine leukemia virus. *Nature* 1981; 293:543–548.

52. Moore R, Dixon M, Smith R, et al: Complete nucleotide sequence of a milk-transmitted mouse mammary tumor virus: Two frameshift suppression events are required for translation of gag and pol. *J Virol* 1987; 61:480–490.

53. Ono M, Toh H, Miyata T, et al: Nucleotide sequence of the Syrian hamster intracisternal A-particle gene: Close evolutionary relationship of type A particle gene to types B and D oncovirus genes. *J Virol* 1985; 55:387–394.

54. Giboa E, Mitra SW, Goff S, et al: A detailed model of reverse transcription and tests of crucial aspects. *Cell* 1979; 18:93–100.

55. Temin HM: Function of the retrovirus long terminal repeat. *Cell* 1982; 28:3–5.

56. Breathnach R, Chambon P: Organization and expression of eukaryotic split genes coding for protein. *Annu Rev Biochem* 1981; 50:349–383.

57. Shih C-C, Stoye JP, Coffin JM: Highly preferred targets for retrovirus integration. *Cell* 1988; 53:531–537.

58. Bister K, Duesberg PH: Genetic structure and transforming genes of avian retroviruses. *Adv Viral Res* 1982; 1:3–42.

59. Czernilofsky AP, Levinson AD, Varmus HE, et al: Nucleotide sequence of a sarcoma virus oncogen (src) and proposed amino acid sequence for gene product. *Nature* 1980; 287:198–203.

60. Brugge JS, Erikson RL: Identification of a transformation-specific antigen induced by an avian sarcoma virus. *Nature* 1977; 269:1673–1680.

61. Hunter T, Sefton BM: Tranforming gene product of Rous sarcoma virus phosphorylates tyrosine. *Proc Natl Acad Sci USA* 1980; 77:1311–1315.

61. Donner P, Greiser-Wilcke J, Moelling K: Nuclear localization and DNA binding of the transforming gene product of myelocytomatosis virus. *Nature* 1982; 296:262–266.

62. Waterfield MD, Scrace GT, Whittle N, et al: Platelet-derived growth factor is structurally related to the putative transforming protein p28^{sis} of simian sarcoma virus. *Nature* 1983; 304:35–39.

63. Doolittle RF, Hunkapillar MW, Hood LE, et al: Simian sarcoma virus onc gene, v-sis, is derived from the gene (or genes) encoding a platelet-derived growth factor. *Science* 1983; 221:275–277.

64. Nigg EA, Sefton BM, Hunter T, et al: Immunofluorescent localization of the transforming protein of Rous sarcoma virus with antibodies against a synthetic src peptide. *Proc Natl Acad Sci USA* 1982; 79:5322–5326.

65. Bauer H: RNA-Tumorviren und ihre Onkogene. *AIFO* 1986; 1:583–590.

66. Weinberg RA: The action of oncogenes in the cytoplasm and nucleus. *Science* 1985; 230:770–776.

67. Downward J, Yarden Y, Mayes E, et al: Close similarity of epidermal growth factor reception and v–erb–B oncogene protein sequences. *Nature* 1984; 307:521–527.

68. Sap J, Munoz A, Damm K, et al: The c-erb-A protein is a high-affinity receptor for thyroid hormone. *Nature* 1986; 324:635–640.

69. Weinberger C, Thompson CC, Ong ES, et al: The c-erb-A gene encodes a thyroid hormone receptor. *Nature* 1986; 324:641–646.

70. Sherr CJ, Rettenmier CW, Sacca R, et al: The c-fms proto-oncogene product is related to the receptor for the mononuclear phagocyte growth factor, CSF-1. *Cell* 1985; 41:665–676.

71. Robbins KC, Antoniades HN, Devare SG, et al: Structural and immunological similarities between simian sarcoma virus gene product(s) and human platelet-derived growth factor. *Nature* 1983; 305:605–608.

72. Keating MT, Williams LT: Autocrine stimulation of intracellular PDGF receptors in v-sis-transformed cells. *Science* 1988; 239:914–916.

73. de Vos AM, Tong L, Milburn MV, et al: Three-dimensional structure of an oncogene protein: catalytic domain of human c-H-ras p21. *Science* 1988; 239:888–893.

74. Bohmann D, Bos TJ, Admon A, et al: Human protooncogene c-jun encodes a DNA binding protein with structural and functional properties of transcription factor AP-1. *Science* 1987; 238:1386–1392.

75. Rauscher III FJ, Cohen DR, Curran T, et al: Fos-associated protein p39 is the product of the jun proto-oncogene. *Science* 1988; 240:1010–1016.

76. Franza BR, Rauscher FJ III, Josephs SF, et al: The fos complex and fos–related antigens recognize sequence elements that contain AP–1 binding sites. *Science* 1988; 239:1150–1153.

77. Duesberg P: Retroviral transforming genes in normal cells? *Nature* 1983; 304:219–226.

78. Duesberg P: Retroviruses as carcinogens and pathogens: expectations and reality. *Cancer Res* 1987; 47:1199–1220.

79. Graf T, Stèhelin D: Avian leukemia viruses. Oncogenes and genome structure. *Biochem Biophys Acta* 1982; 218:801–806.

80. Spector DH, Varmus HE, Bishop JM: Nucleotide sequences related to the transforming gene of avian sarcoma virus are present in DNA of uninfected vertebrates. *Proc Natl Acad Sci USA* 1978; 75:4102–4106.

81. Shilo BZ, Weinberg RA: DNA sequences homologous to vertebrate oncogenes are conserved in *Drosophila melanogaster*. *Proc Natl Acad Sci USA* 1981; 78:6789–6792.

82. Groffen J, Heisterkamp N, Grosveld F, et al: Isolation of human oncogene sequences (v-fes homolog) from a cosmid library. *Science* 1982; 216:1136–1138.

83. Bergmann DG, Souza LM, Baluda MA: Vertebrate DNAs contain nucleotide sequences related to the transforming gene of avian myeloblastosis virus. *J Virol* 1981; 40:450–455.

84. Watson R, Oskarsson M, vande Woude GF: Human DNA sequence homologous to the transforming gene (mos) of Moloney murine sarcoma virus. *Proc Natl Acad Sci USA* 1982; 79:4078–4082.

85. Chang EH, Gonda MA, Ellis RW, et al: Human genome contains four genes homologous to transforming genes of Harvey and Kirsten murine sarcoma viruses. *Proc Natl Acad Sci USA* 1982; 79:4848–4852.

86. Dalla Favera R, Gelmann EP, Gallo RC, et al: A human onc gene homologous to the transforming gene (v-sis) of simian sarcoma virus. *Nature* 1981; 292:31–35.

87. Dalla Favera R, Bregni M, Erikson J, et al: Human c-myc onc gene is located on the region of chromosome 8 that is translocated in Burkitt lymphoma cells. *Proc Natl Acad Sci USA* 1982; 79:7824–7828.

88. Dalla Favera R, Franchini G, Martinotti S, et al: Chromosomal assignment of the human homologues of feline sarcoma virus and avian myeloblastosis virus onc genes. *Proc Natl Acad Sci USA* 1982; 79:4714–4717.

89. Dalla Favera R, Gallo RC, Giallongo A, et al: Chromosomal localization of the human homolog (c-sis) of the simian sarcoma virus onc gene. *Science* 1982; 218:686–688.

90. deKlein A, van Kessel A, Grosveld G, et al: A cellular oncogene is translocated to the Philadelphia chromosome in chronic myelocytic leukemia. *Nature* 1982; 300:765–767.

91. Heisterkamp N, Groffen J, Stephenson JR, et al: Chromosomal localization of human cellular homologues of two viral oncogenes. *Nature* 1982; 299:747–749.

92. McBride OW, Swan DC, Santos E, et al: Localization of the normal allele of T24 human bladder carcinoma oncogene to chromosome 11. *Nature* 1982; 300:773–774.

93. Prakash K, McBride OW, Swan DC, et al: Molecular cloning and chromosomal mapping of a human locus related to the transforming gene of Moloney murine sarcoma virus. *Proc Natl Acad Sci USA* 1982; 79:5210–5214.

94. Rowley JD: Human oncogene locations and chromosome aberrations. *Nature* 1983; 301:290–291.

95. Swan DC, McBride OW, Robbins KC, et al: Chromosomal mapping of the simian sarcoma virus onc gene analogue in human cells. *Proc Natl Acad Sci USA* 1982; 79:4691–4695.

96. Taub R, Kirsch L, Morton C, et al: Translocation of the c-myc gene into the immunoglobulin heavy chain locus in human Burkitt lymphoma and murine plasmacytoma cells. *Proc Natl Acad Sci USA* 1982; 79:7837–7841.

97. Neel BG, Jhanwar SC, Chaganti RSK, et al: Two human c-onc genes are located on the long arm of chromosome 8. *Proc Natl Acad Sci USA* 1982; 79:7842–7846.

98. Shih C, Shilo BZ, Goldfarb MP, et al: Passage of phenotypes of chemically transformed cells via transfection of DNA and chromatin. *Proc Natl Acad Sci USA* 1979; 76:5714–5718.

99. Shilo BZ, Weinberg RA: Unique transforming gene in carcinogen-transformed mouse cells. *Nature* 1981; 289:607–609.

100. Cooper GM, Okenquist S, Silverman L: Transforming activity of DNA of chemically transformed and normal cells. *Nature* 1980; 284:418–421.

101. Cooper GM: Cellular transforming genes. *Science* 1982; 218:801–806.

102. Parada LF, Tabin CJ, Shih C, et al: Human EJ bladder carcinoma oncogene is homologue of Harvey sarcoma virus ras gene. *Nature* 1982; 297:474–478.

103. Santos E, Tronick SR, Aaronson SA, et al: T24 human bladder carcinoma oncogene is an activated form of the normal human homologue of Balb- and Harvey-MSV transforming genes. *Nature* 1982; 298:343–347.

104. Der CJ, Krontiris TG, Cooper GM: Transforming genes of human bladder and lung carcinoma cell lines are homologous to the ras genes of Harvey and Kirsten sarcoma viruses. *Proc Natl Acad Sci USA* 1982; 79:3637–3640.

105. Tabin CJ, Bradley SM, Bargmann CI, et al: Mechanism of activation of a human oncogene. *Nature* 1982; 300:143–149.

106. Reddy EP, Reynolds RK, Santos E, et al: A point mutation is responsible for the acquisition of transforming properties by the T24 human bladder carcinoma oncogene. *Nature* 1982; 300:149–152.

107. Taparowsky E, Suard Y, Fasano I, et al: Activation of the T24 bladder carcinoma transforming gene is linked to a single amino acid change. *Nature* 1982; 300:762–765.

108. Müller R, Tremblay JM, Adamson ED, et al: Tissue and cell type-specific expression of two human c-onc genes. *Nature* 1983; 304:454–456.

109. Kawakami TG, Buckley PM, McDowell TS, et al: Antibodies to simian C–type virus antigen in sera of gibbons (*Hylobates sp.*) *Nature* 1973; 246:105–107.

110. Varmus H: Retroviruses. *Science* 1988; 240:1427–1435.

111. Coffin J: Genome structure, in Weiss R, et al (eds): *RNA Tumorviruses*. Cold Spring Harbor, NY, Cold Spring Harbor Laboratory, 1985, vol 2, pp 17–73.

112. Doehmer J, Borinaga M, Vale W, et al: Introduction of rat growth hormone gene into mouse fibroblasts via a retroviral DNA

vector: expression and regulation. *Proc Natl Acad Sci USA* 1982; 79:2268–2272.

113. Nichols E: *Human Gene Therapy.* Cambridge, Mass, Harvard University Press, 1988.

114. Jaenisch R: Transgenic animals. *Science* 1988; 240:1468–1474.

115. Favor J, Strauss PG, Erfle V: Molecular characterization of a radiation–induced reverse mutation at the dilute locus in the mouse. *Genet Res* 1987; 50:219–223.

116. Temin HM: The protovirus hypothesis: Speculations on the significance of RNA-directed DNA synthesis for normal development and for carcinogenesis. *J Natl Cancer Inst* 1971; 46:3–7.

117. Huebner RJ, Todaro GJ: Oncogenes of RNA tumor viruses as determinants of cancer. *Proc Natl Acad Sci* 1969; 64:1087–1094.

118. Temin HM: Origin of retroviruses from cellular moveable genetic elements. *Cell* 1980; 21:599–600.

119. Hayward WS, Neel BG, Astrin SM: Activation of a cellular oncogene by promotor insertion in ALV–induced lymphoid leukosis. *Nature* 1981; 290:475–480.

120. Payne GS, Bishop JM, Varmus HE: Multiple arrangements of viral DNA and an activated host oncogene in bursal lymphomas. *Nature* 1982; 295:209–214.

121. Hartley JW, Wolford NK, Old LJ, et al: A new class of murine leukemia virus associated with development of spontaneous lymphomas. *Proc Natl Acad Sci USA* 1977; 74:789–792.

122. McGrath MS, Weissman IL: AKR leukemogenesis: Identification and biological significance of thymic lymphoma receptors for AKR retroviruses. *Cell* 1979; 17:65–75.

123. Ihle JN, Enjuances L, Lee JC, et al: The immune response to C-type viruses and its potential role in leukemogenesis. *Curr Top Microbiol Immunol* 1982; 101:31–49.

124. Klein G: The role of gene dosage and genetic transpositions in carcinogenesis. *Nature* 1981; 294:313–318.

125. Groffen J, Heisterkamp N, Stephenson JR, et al: c-sis is translocated from chromosome 22 to chromosome 9 in chronic myelocytic leukemia. *J Exp Med* 1983; 158:9–15.

126. Scolnick EM: Hyperplastic and neoplastic erythroproliferative diseases induced by oncogenic murine retroviruses. *Biochim Biophys Acta* 1982; 651:273–283.

127. Risser R: The pathogenesis of Abelson virus lymphomas of the mouse. *Biochim Biophys Acta* 1982; 651:213–244.

128. Leib-Mösch C, Schmidt J, Etzerodt M, et al: Oncogenic retrovirus from spontaneous osteomas. II. Molecular cloning and genomic characterization. *Virology* 1986; 150:96–105.

129. van der Maaten MJ, Miller JM: Current assessment of human health hazards associated with bovine leukemia virus in *Origins of Human Cancer.* Cold Spring Harbor, NY, Cold Spring Harbor Laboratory, 1977, pp 1223–1234.

130. Kawakami TG, Sun L, McDowell TS: Natural transmission of gibbon leukemia virus. *J Natl Cancer Inst* 1978; 61:1113–1115.

131. Miyoshi I, Yoshimoto S, Fujishita M, et al: Natural adult T-cell leukemia virus infection in Japanese monkeys. *Lancet* 1982; 2:658.

132. Hunsmann G, Schneider J, Schmitt J, et al: Detection of serum antibodies to adult T–cell leukemia virus in non-human primates and in people from Africa. *Int J Cancer* 1983; 32:329–332.

133. Homma T, Kanki PJ, King Jr NW, et al: Lymphoma in macaques: association with virus of human T lymphotropic family. *Science* 1984; 225:716–718.

134. Guo H-G, Wong–Staal F, Gallo RC: Novel viral sequences related to human T–cell leukemia virus in T-cells of a seropositive baboon. *Science* 1984; 223:1195–1197.

135. Scheidereit C, Geisse S, Westphal HM, et al: The glucocorticoid receptor binds to defined nucleotide sequences near the promoter of mouse mammary tumor virus. *Nature* 1983; 304:749–752.

136. Daniel MD, King NW, Letvin NL, et al: A new type D retrovirus isolated from macaques with an immunodeficiency syndrome. *Science* 1984; 223:602–605.

137. Power MD, Marx PA, Bryant ML, et al: Nucleotide sequence of SRV-1, a type D simian acquired immune deficiency syndrome retrovirus. *Science* 1986; 231:1567–1572.

138. Thayer RM, Power MD, Bryant ML, et al: Sequence relation-

ships of type D retroviruses which cause simian acquired immunodeficiency syndrome. *Virology* 1987; 157:317–329.

139. Sonigo P, Barker C, Hunter E, et al: Nucleotide sequence of Mason-Pfizer monkey virus: an immunosuppressive D-type retrovirus. *Cell* 1986; 45:375–385.

140. Haase AT: Pathogenesis of lentivirus infections. *Nature* 1986; 322:130–136.

141. Nathanson N, Georgsson G, Palsson PA, et al: Experimental visna in Icelandic sheep: the prototype lentiviral infection. *Rev Infect Dis* 1985; 7:75–82.

142. Sigurdsson B, Palsson PA, Grimson H: Visna, a demyelinating transmissible disease of sheep. *J Neuropathol Exp Neurol* 1957; 16:389–403.

143. Sigurdsson B: Maedi, a slow progressive pneumonia of sheep: an epizootiological and a pathological study. *Br Vet J* 1954; 110:225–270.

144. Möhlmann H: Ansteckende Blutarmut der Pferde, in Röhrer H (ed): *Handbuch der Virusinfektionen bei Tieren.* Jena, Gustav Fischer Verlag, 1968, pp 627–719.

145. Kennedy-Stoskopf S, Narayan O: Neutralizing antibodies to visna lentivirus: mechanism of action and possible role in virus persistence. *J Virol* 1986; 59:37–44.

146. Payne SL, Fang F-D, Lin C-P, et al: Antigenic variation and lentivirus persistence: variations in envelope gene sequences during EIAV infection resemble changes reported for sequential isolates of HIV. *Virology* 1987; 161:321–331.

147. Narayan O, Cork LC: Lentiviral diseases of sheep and goats: chronic pneumonia, leukoencephalomyelitis, and arthritis. *Rev Infect Dis* 1985; 7:89–98.

148. Cheevers WP, McGuire T: Equine infectious anemia virus: immunopathogenesis and persistence. *Rev Infect Dis* 1985; 7:83–88.

149. Gonda MA, Wong-Staal F, Gallo RC, et al: Sequence homology and morphologic similarity of HTLV-III and visna virus, a pathogenic lentivirus. *Science,* 1985; 227:173–177.

150. Sonigo P, Alizon M, Staskus K, et al: Nucleotide sequence of the visna lentivirus: relationship to the AIDS virus. *Cell* 1985; 42:369–382.

151. McClure MA, Johnson MS, Feng D-F, et al: Sequence comparisons of retroviral proteins: relative rates of change and general phylogeny. *Proc Natl Acad Sci USA* 1988; 85:2469–2473.

152. Daniel MD, Letvin NL, King NW, et al: Isolation of T-cell tropic HTLV-III-like retrovirus from macaques. *Science* 1985; 228:1201–1204.

153. Kanki PJ, Alroy J, Essex M: Isolation of T-lymphotropic retrovirus related to HTLV-III/LAV from wild-caught African green monkeys. *Science* 1985; 230:951–954.

154. Benveniste RE, Morton WR, Clark EA, et al: Inoculation of baboons and macaques with simian immunodeficiency virus Mne, a primate lentivirus closely related to human immunodeficiency virus type 2. *J Virol* 1988; 62:2090–2101.

155. Fukasawa M, Miura T, Hasegawa A, et al: Sequence of simian immunodeficiency virus from African green monkey, a new member of the HIV/SIV group. *Nature* 1988; 333:457–461.

156. Chakrabarti L, Guyader M, Alizon M, et al: Sequence of simian immunodeficiency virus from macaque and its relationship to other human and simian retroviruses. *Nature* 1987; 328:543–547.

157. Fultz PN, McClure HM, Anderson DC, et al: Isolation of a T-lymphotropic retrovirus from naturally infected sooty mangabey monkeys *(Cercocebus atys)*. *Proc Natl Acad Sci USA* 1986; 83:5286–5290.

158. Murphey-Corb M, Martin LN, Rangan SRS, et al: Isolation of an HTLV-III-related retrovirus from macaques with simian AIDS and its possible origin in asymptomatic mangabeys. *Nature* 1986; 321:435–437.

159. Gonda MA, Braun MJ, Carter SG, et al: Characterization and molecular cloning of a bovine lentivirus related to human immunodeficiency virus. *Nature* 1987; 330:388–391.

160. Pederson NC, Ho EW, Brown ML, et al: Isolation of a T-lymphotropic virus from domestic cats with an immunodeficiency-like syndrome. *Science* 1987; 235:790–793.

161. Southern EM: Detection of specific sequences among DNA frag-

ments separated by gel electrophoresis. *J Mol Biol* 1975; 98:503–517.

162. Harper ME, Marselle LM, Gallo RC, et al: Detection of lymphocytes expressing human T-lymphotropic virus type III in lymph nodes and peripheral blood from infected individuals by in situ hybridization. *Proc Natl Acad Sci USA* 1986; 83:772–776.

163. Mullis K, Faloona F, Scharf S, et al: Specific enzymatic amplifications of DNA in vitro: the polymerase chain reaction. *Cold Spring Harbor Symp Quant Biol* 1986; 51:263–273.

164. Mellert W, Erfle V, Hehlmann R: HTLV-III/LAV-Antikörpertest: Indirekte Immunoperoxidasefärbung. *AIFO* 1986; 1:105–107.

165. Erfle V, Mellert W: Human T-lymphotropic virus III/lymphadenopathy-associated virus antibodies, in Bergmeyer (ed): *Methods of Enzymatic Analysis*. VCH Weinheim, West-Germany, Verlagsgesellschaft, vol 10, pp 469–483.

166. Hunsmann G, Moenning V, Schäfer W: Properties of mouse leukemia viruses IX. Active and passive immunization of mice against Friend leukemia with isolated viral gp71 glycoprotein and its corresponding antiserum. *Virology* 1975; 66:327–329.

167. Tronick SR, Popescu NC, Cheah MSC, et al: Isolation and chromosomal localization of the human fgr proto-oncogene, a distinct member of the tyrosine kinase gene family. *Proc Natl Acad Sci USA* 1985; 82:6595–6599.

168. Barker PE, Rabin M, Watson M, et al: Human c-fos oncogene mapped within chromosomal region 14q21 → q31. *Proc Natl Acad Sci USA* 1984; 81:5826–5830.

169. Dayton AI, Selden JR, Laws G, et al: A human c-erb A oncogene homologue is closely proximal to the chromosome 17 breakpoint in acute promyelocytic leukemia. *Proc Natl Acad Sci USA* 1984; 81:4495–4499.

170. Marshall C: Human oncogenes, in Weiss R, et al (eds): *RNA-Tumorviruses*. Cold Spring Harbor, NY, Cold Spring Harbor Laboratory, 1985, vol 2, pp 487–558.

171. Besmer P, Murphy JE, George PC, et al: A new acute transforming feline retrovirus and relationship of its oncogene v-kit with the protein kinase gene family. *Nature* 1986; 320:415–421.

172. Chabot B, Stephenson DA, Chapman VM, et al: The protooncogene c-kit encoding a transmembrane tyrosine kinase receptor maps to the mouse W locus. *Nature* 1988; 335:88–89.

9

Human Retroviruses

Rüdiger Hehlmann

HUMAN IMMUNODEFICIENCY VIRUSES (HIV-1,-2)

CLINICAL FEATURES OF HIV INFECTION
EPIDEMIOLOGY OF HIV INFECTION
LABORATORY DIAGNOSIS OF INFECTION
THERAPY AND VACCINE DEVELOPMENT

**HUMAN T CELL LYMPHOMA-LEUKEMIA VIRUSES
(HTLV-I,-II)**

HUMAN ENDOGENOUS RETROVIRUSES

HUMAN FOAMY VIRUS (HFV)

For many years the existence of retroviruses of humans had been heavily debated. Analogy to animal retroviral systems and so-called retroviral footprints in human neoplastic disease, particularly human leukemias and breast cancer, and in embryonic tissues had long suggested that retroviruses in man not only do exist but may be important pathogens. Scientific attention initially focused on the oncogenic retroviruses because they were thought to answer the question of human carcinogenesis. The fact that another group of retroviruses, the lentiviruses, caused widespread disease among several animal species such as sheep, goats, and horses (see Chapter 8) was not generally recognized.

The detection of a first human retrovirus, human T-lymphotropic virus type I (HTLV-I) in adult T cell leukemia and lymphoma did not come as a surprise to most human retrovirologists. HTLV-I was detected almost simultaneously by two independent groups, and a second human retrovirus, HTLV-II, was isolated shortly thereafter from a patient with hairy cell leukemia. The detection of human immunodeficiency virus (HIV), however, and the realization that HIV, the causative agent of acquired immunodeficiency syndrome (AIDS), was a retrovirus moved these viruses to the center of public and scientific interest. The isolation of HIV led to an enormous expansion of retrovirus research in all fields which included the search for, and detection of similar viruses in animal systems (see Chapter 8).

In the shadow of these spectacular retrovirus isolations, another development in human retrovirology, namely, the detection of endogenous retroviral sequences in the human genome, remained almost unnoticed. The observations that these viral-related sequences represent probably more than 0.5% of the human genome and contain regulation elements point to the potential role these sequences might play in cellular evolution, differentiation, and carcinogenesis.

The identification of human oncoviruses and lentiviruses has spurred interest also in a third retrovirus subgroup, the spumaviruses. Although human spumaviruses exist, no disease has been associated yet with these viruses. In this chapter, the human retrovirus groups and the endogenous retroviral sequences (Table 9–1) are described in the order of their apparent medical relevance.

HUMAN IMMUNODEFICIENCY VIRUSES (HIV-1,-2)

In 1981 the Centers for Disease Control (CDC) published two reports describing cases of *Pneumocystis carinii* pneumonia and Kaposi's sarcoma in previously healthy, young male homosexuals.[1, 2] *Pneumocystis carinii* pneumonia until then was mainly known to occur in immunodepressed patients after organ transplantation, after cancer chemotherapy, or in genetic immunodeficiency states. It soon was recognized that these male homosexuals had severe immunodeficiencies with a profound depression of so-called T4 helper lymphocytes. Shortly thereafter, the same kind of immunodeficient state was recognized in intravenous (IV) drug users, transfusion recipients, hemophiliacs, and newborn infants of IV drug-dependent mothers. In late 1982 the name acquired immunodeficiency syndrome (AIDS) was coined for the syndrome. Tracing of contacts of patients with the syndrome by researchers of the CDC soon established that AIDS was an infectious disease, transmitted by sexual intercourse, blood, and/or blood products.

Table 9–1
Human Retroviruses

Type of Virus	Associated Disease
Oncoviruses	
Human T-lymphotropic virus type I (HTLV-I)	Adult T-cell leukemia-lymphoma T-cell malignancies, tropical spastic paraparesis
Human T-lymphotropic virus type II (HTLV-II)	Unknown
Lentiviruses	
Human immunodeficiency virus type 1 (HIV-1, substrains HTLV-III, LAV-1, ARC)	Immunodeficiency, neurologic disorders, acquired immunodeficiency syndrome (AIDS)
Human immunodeficiency virus type 2 (HIV-2)	Immunodeficiency, AIDS
Spumaviruses	
Human foamy virus (HFV)	Unknown
Endogenous retroviral sequences	
Sequences related to C-type animal retroviruses	Unknown, expression in leukemias
Sequences related to A-, B-, and D-type animal retroviruses	Unknown, expression in breast cancer

LAV = lymphadenopathy-associated virus; ARV = AIDS-related retrovirus.

Identification of HIV

The search for an etiologic agent initially included agents such as cytomegalovirus (CMV) and Epstein-Barr virus (EBV), but subsequently concentrated on retroviruses, since the recently detected human T cell leukemia virus (HTLV) also infected T helper lymphocytes. T-lymphotropic retroviruses were found in AIDS patients and patients with lymphadenopathy by several laboratories in 1983 and 1984.[3–5] The main problem in isolating and characterizing the AIDS-associated retrovirus was the peculiarity that patient lymphocytes in vitro died rapidly. Only with continued supply of peripheral blood lymphocytes was it possible to demonstrate reverse transcriptase activity as evidence for retroviruses in the tissue culture supernatant. This finding led to the first publication by the French group (around L. Montagnier) of a retrovirus isolated from a patient with lymphadenopathy in 1983.[4] In early 1984 a permanent cell line was identified by an American group (around R. Gallo) that allowed the in vitro propagation of the AIDS-associated retrovirus without lysis of the cells[3] and subsequently its characterization and the production of antisera for seroepidemiologic studies.

The virus was initially named lymphadenopathy-associated virus (LAV) by the French group, human T-lymphotropic virus type III (HTLV-III) by Gallo and colleagues, and AIDS-related virus (ARV) by Levy and coworkers.[5] In 1986 a unifying nomenclature for immunodeficiency viruses was proposed and the virus was renamed human immunodeficiency virus, abbreviated HIV. Animal immunodeficiency viruses were renamed accordingly: SIV for simian immunodeficiency virus, BIV for bovine immunodeficiency virus, etc. The availability of virus from permanent cell cultures allowed the growth of HIV in quantities sufficient for both the establishment of serologic test systems for epidemiologic studies and for the molecular characterization of the virus.

In 1986, a second immunodeficiency virus was identified in West Africa which also causes AIDS but does not cross-react serologically with HIV in screening tests.[6,7] It therefore was designated HIV-2, and the first HIV was subsequently renamed HIV-1. The designations HIV and HIV-1 will be used interchangeably in this chapter.

Basic Properties

From seroepidemiologic studies it became clear that HIV was already widespread among apparently healthy individuals, that a long incubation period existed, and that infection with the virus must have preceded clinical symptoms by years (see below). These properties and morphologic studies suggested that the virus was a member of the lentivirus family, a subgroup of retroviruses with long incubation times (Table 9–2). This taxonomic assignment was later confirmed by the genome organization and by nucleic acid sequencing results. Lentiviruses are cytopathic, that is, they destroy their host cells, and thereby are distinguished from the noncytopathic, transforming oncogenic retroviruses (see Chapter 8). Special features of lentiviruses include a long latent period, a chronic course, and CNS involvement.

Virus composition and structure in most respects correspond to those of other retroviruses: core proteins; envelope proteins, including a transmembrane protein; reverse transcriptase with endonuclease, protease, and RNase H. Differences between transforming retroviruses and HIV can be recognized in the virus morphology (Figure 9–1) and genome structure of HIV (Figure 9–2). HIV characteristically shows, by electron microscopy, a cylindrical core within the viral envelope in contrast to the oncogenic retroviruses which show spherical cores.[8,9] Cylindrical cores are a feature also of other lentiviruses (compare visna-maedi

Table 9–2
Lentivirus Group of Retroviruses

Strain Designation	Associated Disease
Human immunodeficiency virus type 1 (HIV-1)	Acquired immunodeficiency syndrome (AIDS)
Human immunodeficiency virus type 2 (HIV-2)	AIDS
Simian immunodeficiency virus (SIV$_{MAC}$)	Simian AIDS (in rhesus macaques)
Simian immunodeficiency virus (SIV$_{AGM}$)	None (African green monkeys)
Feline immunodeficiency virus (FIV, feline T-lymphotropic virus [FTLV])	Feline AIDS
Bovine immunodeficiency virus (BIV)	Persistent lymphocytosis, CNS lesions, wasting (cattle)
Visna-maedi virus / Caprine arthritis encephalitis virus (CAEV)	Pneumonia, encephalitis, wasting (sheep, goats,) arthritis (CAEV, goats)
Equine infectious anemia virus (EIAV)	Fever, anemia (horses)

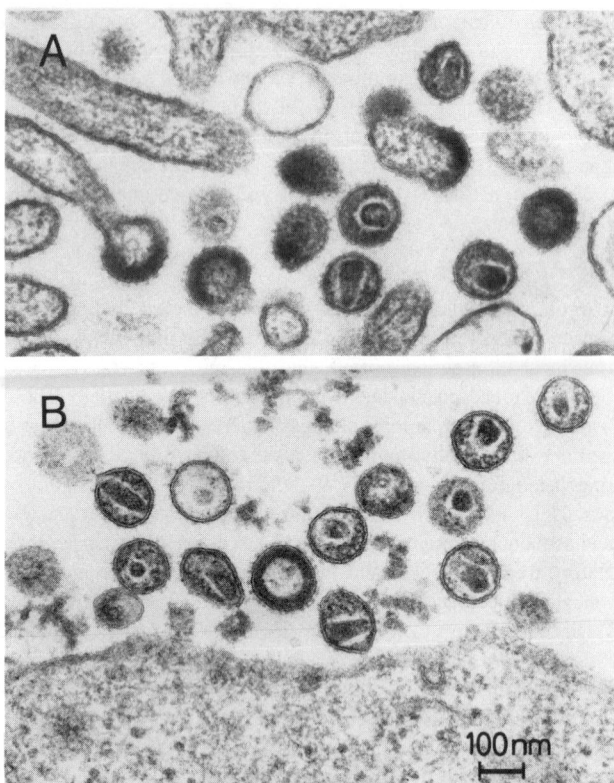

Figure 9–1. Electron micrographs of (a) human immunodeficiency virus type 1 (HIV-1) (human T-lymphotropic virus type III [HTLV-2 B]) and (b) HIV-2. Note the cylindrical cores apparent in several virions in (a) and (b). In (a) a budding virus is visible. Visualization of virion cores in budding particles depends on cutting level. Magnification × 92,000. (Courtesy of Dr H. Gelderblom, Berlin.)

virus, Chapter 8). The HIV genome contains, in addition to the three known structural genes gag, pol, and env, genes for at least six additional proteins which induce antibodies in infected persons and of which at least four fulfill regulation functions. The genes are called by three-letter codes[10]: tat, rev (formerly art/trs), vif (formerly sor), nef (formerly 3'orf), vpr (formerly R), and vpu,[11] the latter in HIV-1 only. Of these genes, tat and rev are of special interest since viral replication without the products of these genes apparently is not possible, or at very low levels only. They are obvious targets for therapeutic intervention.

Of the structural genes, gag codes for the core proteins p24, p17, and p15, which are cleared from a p55 precursor protein by the viral protease. The RNA-dependent DNA polymerase (reverse transcriptase) is encoded by the pol gene which also codes for the protease (p16) and the integrase/endonuclease (p31). The viral polymerase exists in two forms, p66 and p51. Associated with the polymerase is RNase H, which specifically degrades RNA in RNA-DNA hybrids.[12] The envelope proteins are responsible for virus adsorption and seem to be important for the cytopathic effect of HIV. They are encoded by the env gene and consist of gp160 and its two subunits, gp120 and gp41. gp120 is the outer membrane part of the envelope protein which forms the knobs on the virus surface, gp41 the transmembrane part by which gp120 is fixed to

the viral membrane. gp120 binds to the CD4 receptors of T helper lymphocytes and other cells and mediates adsorption of HIV to the cell surface. The gene composition of HIV-1 and HIV-2 has been confirmed by determination of the complete nucleotide sequences. The genome of HIV-1 consists of about 9200 (HTLV-III 9213, ARV-2 9265) nucleotides,[13–16] the HIV-2 genome of 9671 nucleotides.[17]

Regulation of Virus Replication

Replication of HIV is controlled by the long terminal repeat (LTR) which acts in *cis* on the same nucleic acid molecule and by regulation genes which act in *trans* by diffusible products. The mechanisms of action of the regulation genes tat (transactivator of transcription) and rev (regulator of expression of virion proteins) are illustrated in Figure 9–3. The tat product acts in trans both on the transcriptional and a posttranscriptional level.[18, 19] Tat stimulates a several hundred– to one thousand–fold increase of virus transcription and protein synthesis. Part of this regulational effect of tat is mediated by sequences of the viral LTR region to which the tat product binds, the so-called tat acceptor region (TAR).[20] The TAR sequences are located in the R region of the HIV-LTR downstream of the starting point for RNA synthesis, the cap site (see Figure 9–3). Without binding of the tat protein to TAR, no measurable virus RNA synthesis occurs. The tat gene is therefore called the master switch of virus replication. The factors that contribute to switching on the tat gene are not known in detail.

Unlike tat, which regulates the synthesis of all proteins, rev selectively regulates the viral structural genes gag, pol, and env by a posttranscriptional regulation mechanism that was unknown in molecular biology until found in HIV.[21–23] RNA is amply synthesized, but only selectively translated. REV was identified by unusual phenotypes of tat gene mutants and was called initially art for antirepression transactivator or trs for transregulator of splicing. The unusual feature is that rev selectively regulates the synthesis of the structural proteins but not of the regulation proteins. The reason for this unusual regulation pattern are probably repressor sequences (CRS, or cis-acting repressor sequences) in the structural genes which are derepressed by binding of rev to antirepressor sequences (CAR, or cis-antirepressor). In support of this model is that the repressor sequences CRS are found only in the structural genes but not in the regulator genes.

Some information also exists on the regulatory functions of vif (virion infectivity factor) and of nef (negative factor). Nef-minus mutants with deletions in the nef gene show a more pronounced cytopathic effect and lead to a fivefold higher virus production than wild-type virus.[24] It is speculated that the function of nef is to downregulate virus replication and the cytopathic effect of the virus in order not to destroy the host cell too quickly.

In contrast, vif-minus mutants are less or not at all infectious, although much virus is produced.[25, 26] Vif consequently influences virus infectivity and transmission positively. It is unclear whether the vif gene product functions as a not yet identified part of the virus envelope via an early role during viral penetration, through proviral DNA synthesis, or by another mechanism.

The vpu gene product encodes a 16-kilodalton (kd) protein and is thought to have a role in assembly or maturation of progeny virion.[27] Finally, the function of the vpr gene product is still unknown.

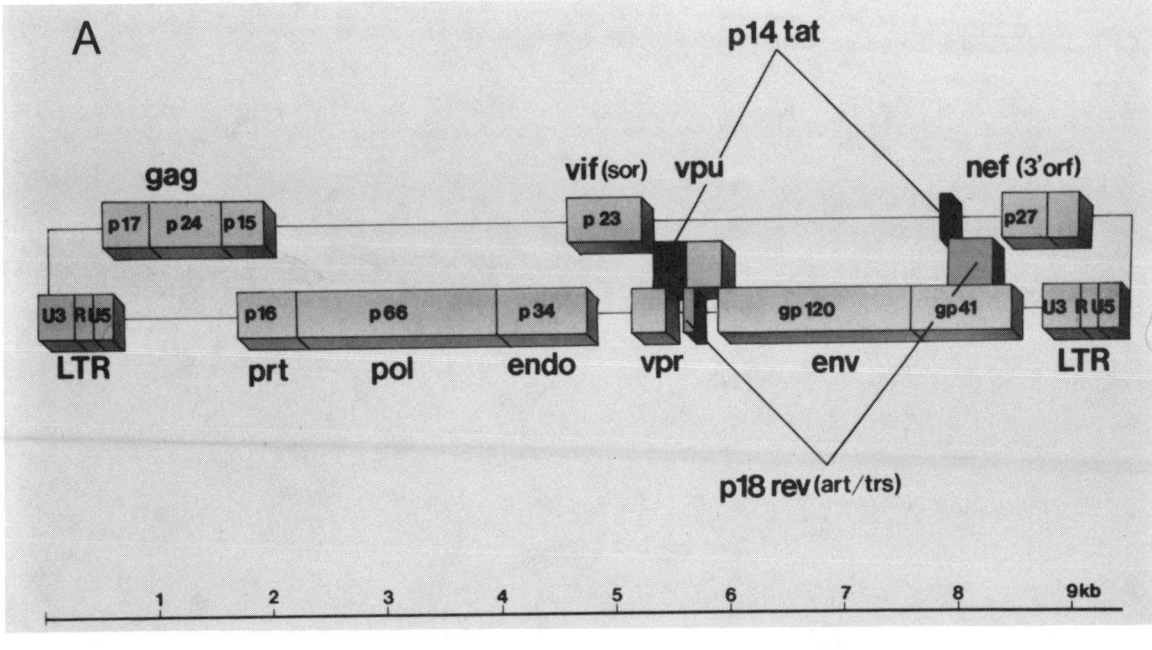

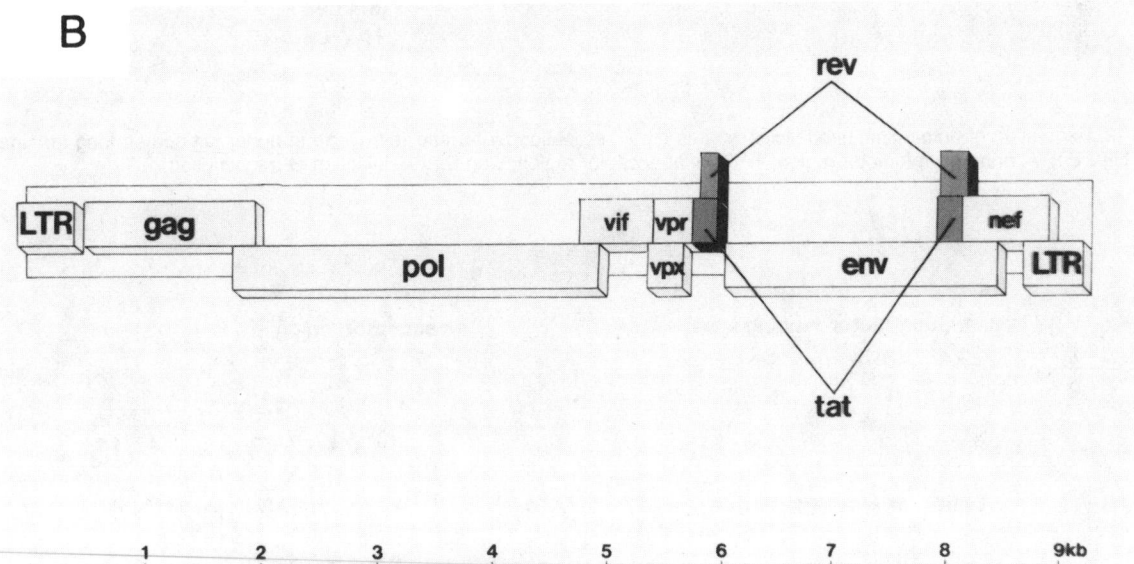

Figure 9–2. Genome organization of human immunodeficiency virus type 1 (a) ((HIV-1) and (b) HIV-2.

Additional regulators are located in the U3 region of the HIV-LTR (Figure 9–4).[28] Besides the TAR sequences these are the binding sites for the transcription factors Sp1 and kappa B.[29, 30] Furthermore, in the U3 region of the LTR, sequences are present that are homologous to interleukin-2 and to gamma interferon, and also a negative regulatory element (NRE) which binds nef.

The regulatory proteins tat, rev, and nef may determine the incubation time for disease progression. In vitro findings and observations with patients indicate that cofactors such as antigens, mitogens, and infectious cofactors possibly modulated by genetic factors also may play an important role.[31–33] These factors might activate HIV-infected cells, for example, via transcription factors

and activation of regulators, and thereby lead to a stimulation of HIV replication and to progression of the disease.

Replication Cycle

The first step of infection is the binding of gp120 to the CD4 receptor of the cell (Figure 9–5). The binding is mediated, as shown in experiments with minus mutants, by three highly conserved regions of the carboxyl end of the gp120 molecule; it is a binding reaction of high affinity.[34–36] The next important step is the fusion of the virus and cell membranes which is mediated by the amino end of the gp41 molecule.[37–39] This end of gp41 is freed probably by a conformational change of gp120 after its binding to

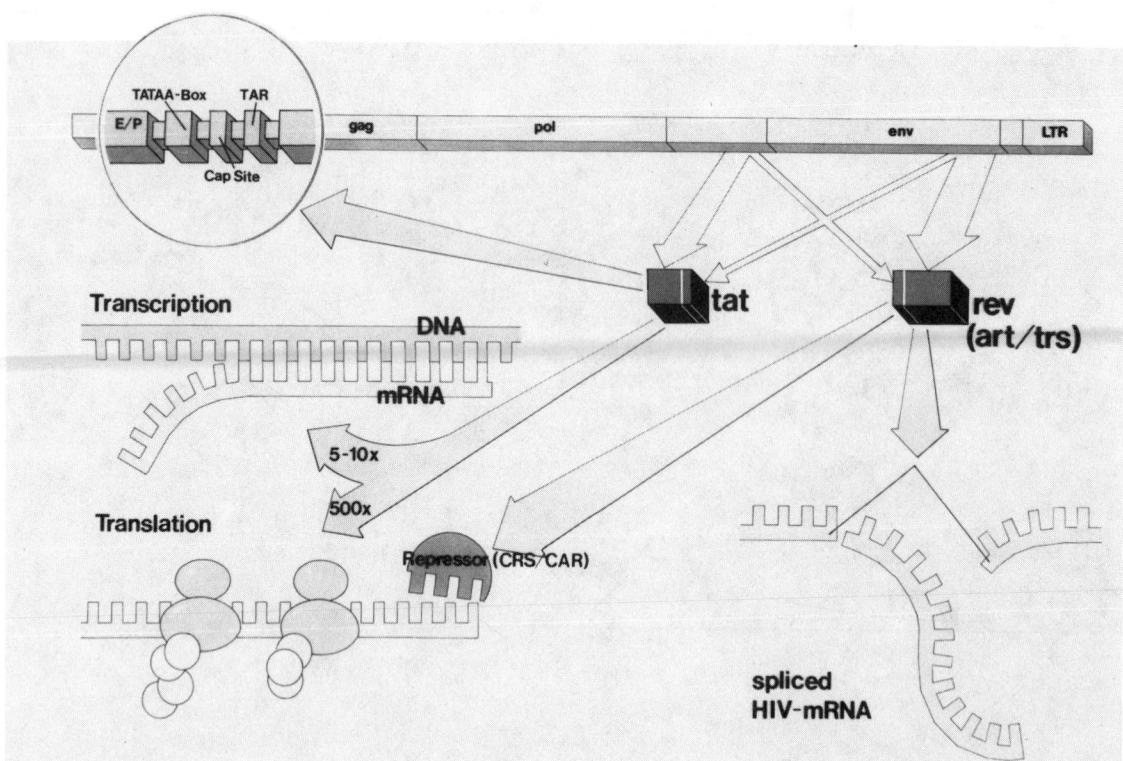

Figure 9–3. Regulation of human immunodeficiency virus (HIV) replication by tat and rev. Circle in upper left corner: long terminal repeat (LTR) of HIV. E/P = enhancer/promoter region; TAR = tat acceptor region; Cap Site = initiation of transcription.

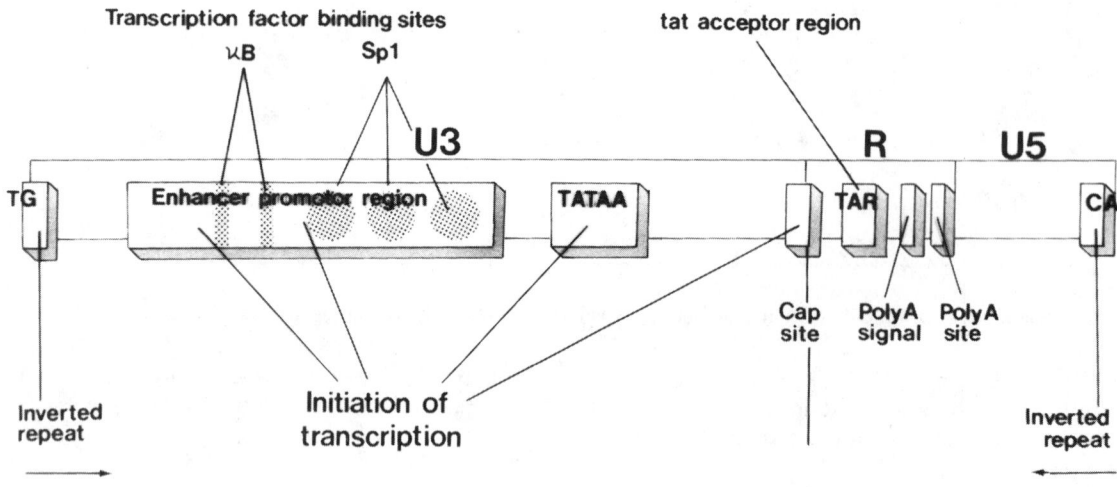

Figure 9–4. (LTR) of human immunodeficiency virus (HIV) with transcription factor binding sites, tat acceptor region, and cap site.

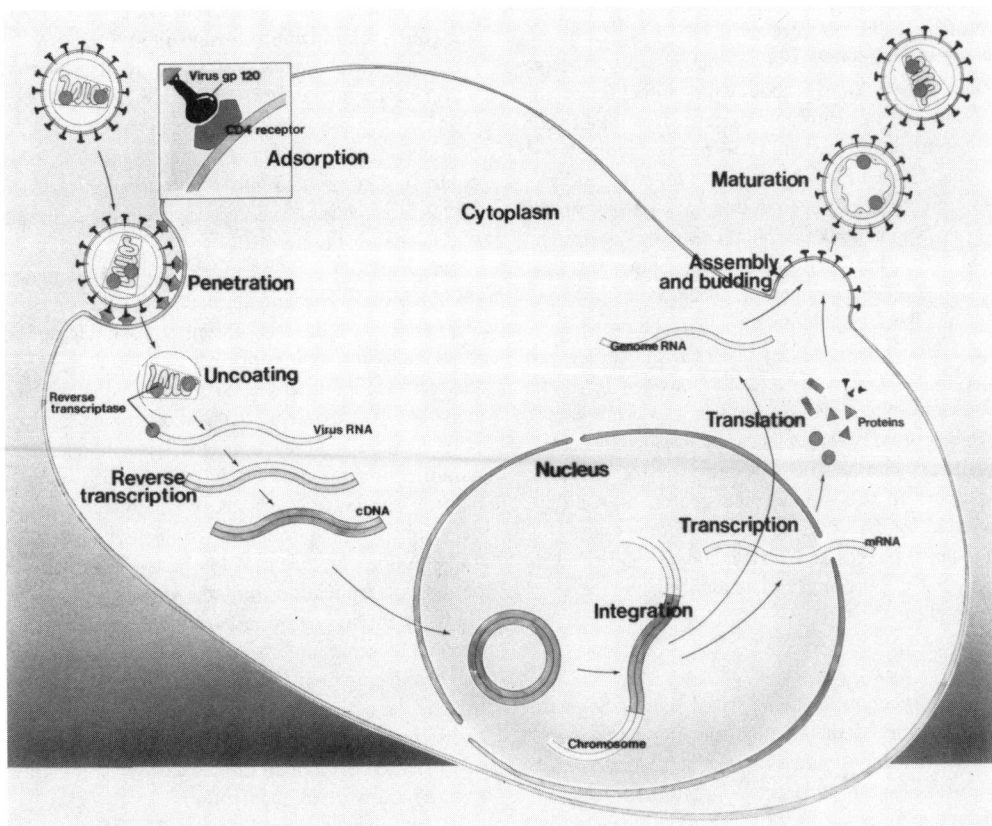

Figure 9–5. Replication cycle of human immunodeficiency virus (HIV) with adsorption to the CD4 receptor, reverse transcription, assembly, budding, and maturation.

CD4. The free amino end of gp41 can then intrude into the lipid layer of the cell membrane (which occurs at an angle of about 60 degrees) and thereby mediate penetration of the virus into the cell. Uncoating, reverse transcription, provirus synthesis and integration, and subsequent synthesis and maturation of virus progeny as shown in Figure 9–5 occur as known from other retroviruses. HIV-infected cells, like other retrovirus-infected cells, express retroviral envelope proteins on their cell surfaces.

Pathogenesis

Besides the CD4-positive T lymphocytes,[40] the target cells for HIV infection in vivo include monocytes and macrophages,[41, 42] including the Langerhans cells of the skin and dendritic cells[43]; cells in the brain such as macrophages, microglial cells, astrocytes, and endothelial cells[44]; B lymphocytes; cells of the intestinal mucosa[45]; and cells of the cervical endothelium.[46] In vitro studies have confirmed the in vivo target cells and indicate that additional cell types can be infected such as fibroblasts.[47, 48] Current understanding of HIV infection suggests that the primary target cells are the monocytes, which are not destroyed by the virus and probably serve as a permanent virus reservoir.[41, 42] This reservoir might be activated under certain conditions (radiation, mitogens) similar to what we know from lysogenic bacteriophages. Hidden in the macrophages, HIV probably can pass the blood-brain barrier (the so-called Trojan horse mechanism).

The cytopathic effect of HIV has been analyzed in T helper lymphocytes in vitro and consists in part of cell fusion with formation of syncytia and subsequent cell death.[49, 50] Syncytia are recognizable in tissue culture as bubblelike structures. Frequently, however, infected lymphocytes die without formation of syncytia.[51] In vitro, syncytia formation possibly depends on the numbers of gp120 molecules and of CD4 receptors on the cell surfaces.[49, 50] In the presence of a high CD4 density, for example, on T helper lymphocytes, formation of syncytia occurs and cell death follows. Cells with few CD4 receptors, such as monocytes, macrophages, or glia cells, are infected latently, and can carry the virus genome without being destroyed. Macrophages infected in vitro also form giant cells but do not succumb to lysis. It is assumed that via syncytia formation one infected cell, with the help of the HIV gp120 and gp41 molecules expressed on its surface, can infect and kill several hundred uninfected CD4 receptor–carrying cells.

In spite of the detailed knowledge on viral structure and regulation, very little is known about the mechanisms by which the virus exerts its pathogenicity in vivo. There is some evidence that the penetration of HIV particles perturbs the cell membrane, which possibly is the first step of its disintegration.[52] Extremely low levels of viral expression and infiltration in infected individuals (expression in only 1 in 10^4–10^5 lymphocytes, proviral DNA in only 1 in 10^2–10^3 lymphocytes) have cast doubt on whether HIV is sufficient to cause AIDS.[53, 54] Low levels of virus expression are observed, however, in other lentivirus infections (see Chapter 8).

The relevance of the CD4 cell tropism of HIV for infection is established only for the immune system, that is, the T helper lymphocytes. Much less is known about virus infection of the brain and the pathogenesis of neurologic disease. It is established that the nervous sytem is infected in HIV-infected individuals, frequently early in the course of the disease.[55-61] Direct and indirect evidence for HIV infection has been found in all parts of the nervous system (brain, spinal cord, peripheral nervous system, and cerebrospinal fluid). This has been shown by in situ hybridization,[55] immunohistochemical examination, electron microscopy, virus isolation,[56-61] and demonstration in the spinal fluid of specific anti-HIV antibodies autochthonously synthesized in the nervous system.[62, 63] Using monoclonal anti-CD4 antibodies it has been shown that neurons and glial cells also possess CD4 receptors.[64] Human glia cells and neuroblastoma cells can be infected by certain HIV variants in vitro.[44] The genetic variability of HIV may be responsible for changes in cell tropism and neuropathogenicity. This view is supported by the isolation of HIV variants with different tropisms for macrophages and T lymphocytes and of virus strains of which the pathogenicity correlates with the aggressiveness of the clinical course.[42, 60, 61, 65]

Course of HIV Infection

The course of HIV infection is characterized by a long phase of inapparent infection and by the terminal development of immunodeficiency. The first sign of infection may be the appearance of IgM antibodies in the serum of infected individuals.[66, 67] HIV antigen can be detected in a portion of these individuals a few days earlier.[67] IgG antibodies in amounts sufficient to be detected by antibody screening assays (eg, enzyme-linked immunosorbent assay [ELISA]) appear in most infected persons after about 3 to 12 weeks. IgG antibodies to individual viral components may be detected, however, much earlier.[68, 69] Viral antigen, in general, is not detectable any longer in the serum after the appearance of IgG antibodies. Antibodies against most viral proteins can be demonstrated by western blots in the serum of infected persons. Of particular diagnostic relevance are antibodies against the core (p24) and the envelope proteins (gp41, gp120, gp160). Antibodies against these proteins can be detected in most infected persons throughout the course of infection at high titers (anti-env > anti-core).[70, 71] Anti-core antibodies decline and may disappear with the manifestation of immunodeficiency (decline of CD4 lymphocytes) and with the beginning of symptoms, simultaneously with the reappearance of HIV antigen and infectious virus in the serum.[70, 71] In contrast, anti-env antibody titers remain high also during the final stages of infection. The course of viral and immunologic markers is depicted in Figure 9–6.

Neutralizing antibodies are frequently detected in infected individuals early after infection.[72-74] The titers mostly range between 1:20 and 1:200. Low or absent neutralizing antibodies have been associated with a poorer prognosis. Recently it has been observed that serolatency may be much longer than 12 weeks. With more sensitive assay systems using recombinant antigens and with the polymerase chain reaction (PCR) technique[75-77] that allows the amplification of viral DNA by many orders of magnitude (see below), serolatency periods of several years duration have been determined.[69, 78] It seems possible that virus dose and mode of transmission play a role. A low virus dose might require prolonged periods of replication until the quantity of virus is sufficient to elicit an antibody response in the infected individual that is detectable by screening assays. Several features of HIV pathogenesis and of the course of HIV infection remain unclear. These features include the extremely long incubation period and the determinants of its duration. In addition, it is unusual for an infectious agent that disease develops in the presence of humoral immunity and in spite of a low level of infection.

It has been proposed that epidemiology and course of HIV-infection are consistent also with the simultaneous action of two pathogens, e.g. HIV, and a member of the herpes virus group. CMV, EBV, HSV, and human herpes virus type 6 (HHV-6) with its tropism for T4-helper lymphocytes all have been suggested as candidates for a second agent. Present data, however, are most consistent with the assumption that co-factors such as other viruses, genetic predisposition, mitogens, or still unknown co-factors accelerate HIV replication and disease progress, which ultimately lead to the decline and collapse of immune surveillance. With AIDS, medicine is confronted with an infectious disease that pos-

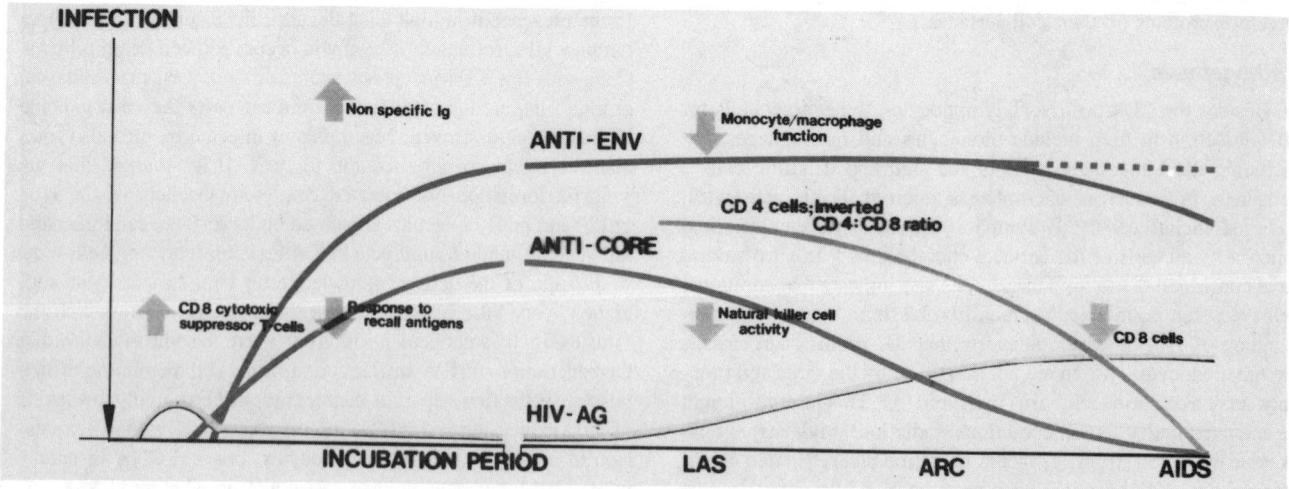

Figure 9–6. Course of immunologic and viral markers during human immunodeficiency virus (HIV) infection.

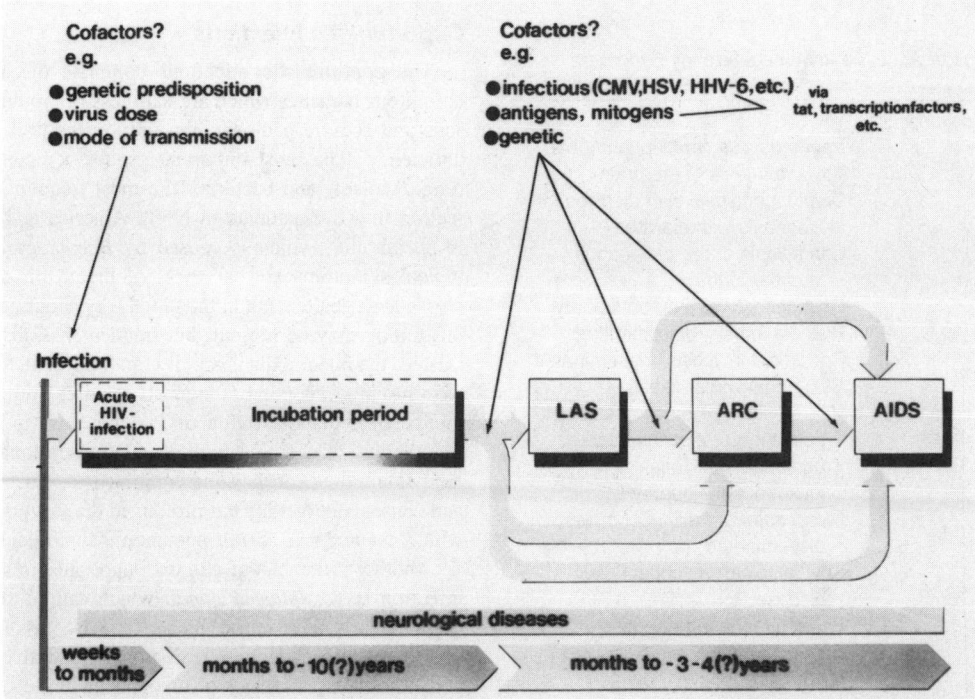

Figure 9–7. Course of human immunodeficiency virus (HIV) infection with clinical stages and possible sites of action of cofactors.

sesses several extremely unusual previously not observed features implying a new hitherto unknown mechanism of pathogenesis.

Clinical Features of HIV Infection

AIDS exhibits numerous unusual manifestations and characteristics. The clinical picture can be highly variable depending on whether the first manifestations are opportunistic infections or tumors, neurologic changes such as meningitis, encephalitis with alterations of personality and behavior and subsequent dementia, or other signs and symptoms such as skin diseases, disturbances of hemopoiesis, age-specific manifestations as in children, or geographic variations such as wasting.

The natural course of the HIV infection is summarized schematically in Figure 9–7. A few weeks after infection with HIV, roughly coinciding with seroconversion, about 10% of the patients present with an acute flulike or mononucleosislike syndrome which may be accompanied by fever, sore throat, enlarged lymph nodes, skin rash, joint aches, and general malaise. Rarely, disturbances of the central and peripheral nervous system may occur. All these symptoms resolve in a few days to weeks. An asymptomatic phase, the incubation period, follows, and this is of variable duration (months to more than 10 years, median 8–10 years, see below).

At the end of the incubation period a number of signs and symptoms may appear which do not fulfill the definition of AIDS or other defined HIV-associated syndromes. These include slight immunologic, dermatologic, hematologic, and neurologic changes. Later, typical skin diseases, deficits of the peripheral and central nervous systems, and cytopenias may appear as well as disturbances of cell-mediated immunity such as decrease of the number of T helper lymphocytes and decline of the immunologic skin reactivity accompanied by a reactive increase of B lymphocytes

with lymphadenopathy and hyperimmunoglobulinemia. In addition, constitutional symptoms, such as fever, weight loss, night sweats, and diarrhea may develop. Defined AIDS prestages include the development of generalized lymphadenopathy (Lymphadenopathy syndrome or LAS) and the appearance of constitutional symptoms (AIDS-related complex or ARC).

The lymphadenopathy syndrome (synonym: generalized lymphadenopathy, GLP) is defined as:[79] enlargement of lymph nodes to 1 cm or more at two or more body regions which persists longer than 3 months without any other recognizable cause other than HIV infection.

AIDS-related complex is defined by: fever, weight loss, night sweats, or chronic diarrhea of more than 1 month's duration in the presence of disturbances of cell-mediated immunity and in the absence of any other recognizable cause other than HIV infection. These definitions may be in part overlapping and are not mutually exclusive.

The first manifestation of HIV infection may be noted at any disease stage. As indicated in Figure 9–7 the different stages may or may not occur consecutively, the transitions occurring slowly or rapidly after weeks, months, or years. Infection, transition to the symptomatic phase, and disease progression are probably influenced by cofactors; evidence exists for other viruses or infections, stress situations, or genetic predisposition as cofactors.[31–33] It is not possible to predict which patient will develop symptoms and disease progression. Poor prognostic factors indicating disease progression include a decrease of the absolute number of CD4 lymphocytes, an increase of HIV antigen in the serum, a decline of HIV core antibodies,[70 71] and increased serum levels of neopterin and beta$_2$-microglobulin.[370] In the majority of infected persons the course of the infection is characterized by a continuous deterioration of the immunologic parameters and increasing symptoms.

Table 9–3

Indicator Diseases of Acquired Immunodeficiency Syndrome (AIDS)*

Opportunistic infections	
Protozoal	*Pneumocystis carinii* pneumonia
	Toxoplasmosis of the brain
	Cryptosporidiosis with diarrhea
	Isosporiasis with diarrhea
Fungal	Candidiasis of the esophagus, trachea, lungs
	Cryptococcosis, extrapulmonary
	Histoplasmosis, disseminated
	Coccidioidomycosis, disseminated
Viral	Cytomegalovirus disease
	Herpes simplex virus infection, persisting or disseminated
	Progressive multifocal leukoencephalopathy
Bacterial	*Mycobacterium avium* complex, disseminated
	Any "atypical" mycobacterial disease
	Extrapulmonary tuberculosis
	Salmonella septicemia, recurrent
	Multiple or recurrent pyogenic bacterial infections

Opportunistic neoplasias
  Kaposi's sarcoma
  Primary lymphoma of
    the brain
  Other non-Hodgkin's
    lymphomas
Others
  HIV wasting syndrome
  HIV encephalopathy
  Lymphoid interstitial
    pneumonia

Manifestations of human immunodeficiency virus (HIV) infection defining AIDS according to criteria of Centers for Disease Control.

The diagnosis of AIDS is established with the appearance of opportunistic infections, or of certain neoplasias, such as Kaposi's sarcoma, primary lymphoma of the brain, and other non-Hodgkin's lymphomas (Table 9–3).

For the definition of AIDS the surveillance criteria of the CDC in Atlanta are generally recognized.[80] These criteria were based solely on clinical findings until August 1987 and defined as AIDS all diseases moderately suggestive of an acquired immunodeficiency. This condition is fulfilled in the presence of certain defined opportunistic infections and tumors as listed in Table 9–3. In September 1987 this definition was revised and additional disease manifestations were included such as extrapulmonary tuberculosis, HIV encephalopathy, wasting syndrome, and lymphoid interstitial pneumonia, if the HIV antibody test is positive.[81]

For a better evaluation of the clinical course of the HIV infection and for better comparability, several staging systems of HIV infection were proposed. The two most popular and relevant classification systems are those of the CDC (stages I-IV), which is based on clinical criteria,[80] and of the Walter Reed Army Center (WR stages 0–6), which uses clinical and immunologic criteria.[82]

Opportunistic Infections

The opportunistic infections comprise diseases with mostly ubiquitous parasites which are harmless in immunocompetent persons and acquire pathogenicity only in the presence of immunodeficiency. The most important groups of agents are: protozoa, fungi, viruses, and bacteria. The most frequent opportunistic infection in AIDS patients in North America and Western Europe is pneumonia, which is caused by *Pneumocystis carinii*.[83] The typical symptoms are shortness of breath on exertion with decreased oxygen tension in the blood, dry cough, and fever. A lung infiltration may be present, but frequently is absent initially. Untreated, the pneumonia is rapidly fatal, but with therapy, the short-term prognosis is good. Diagnosis requires bronchoscopy and the microscopic demonstration of *Pneumocystis* in the lavage fluid. The therapy of choice is high-dose IV co-trimoxazol. Alternatives are pentamidine, or dapsone combined with trimethoprim. Rapid and consequent therapy has prolonged the survival of most patients with *Pneumocystis carinii* pneumonia significantly.[84]

Another protozoan of clinical importance in patients with HIV infection is *Toxoplasma gondii* which causes toxoplasmosis and is particularly relevant because of its CNS involvement. The frequency of toxoplasmosis is regionally variable and appears to depend on the prevalence of toxoplasma in the general population which, for instance, is much higher in Western Europe than in the United States (about 70% vs about 30%). Like *Pneumocystic carinii* pneumonia, toxoplasmosis can be successfully treated if the diagnosis is made early, for example, by the combination of pyrimethamine and a sulfonamide. A third protozoan, *Cryptosporidium*, frequently causes intractable diarrhea for which virtually no therapy exists.

The most important fungal infection (thrush) and the second most frequent opportunistic infection in AIDS patients is caused by *Candida albicans*. Thrush of the oral cavity is observed in about 25% of patients with LAS, 60% of patients with ARC, and in an even higher percentage of AIDS patients. Candidiasis of the esophagus is a CDC criterion defining AIDS.[56] Therapy is relatively simple with amphomoronal solution or ketoconazol tablets. Of further clinical relevance is infection with the fungus *Cryptococcus neoformans*[85] which, if untreated, is fatal in all cases. Clinical symptoms are mostly related to a meningitis or encephalitis. Early diagnosis by demonstration of antigens or fungus (brown color effect on Guizotia creatinine agar,[85]) in the spinal fluid and subsequent therapy with a combination of amphotericin B and flucytosine improve the prognosis.

The most frequent opportunistic viral infections are those caused by cytomegalovirus (CMV), herpes simplex virus (HSV), and varicella-zoster virus (VZV). The important clinical symptoms of CMV infection are retinitis, colitis with severe diarrhea, and, less frequently, pneumonitis and hepatitis.[86] Treatment has recently become possible with DHPG (gancyclovir). Treatment of herpes simplex and varicella-zoster infections is best accomplished with acyclovir, a compound that has been successfully used for the same infections in immunocompetent individuals.

An increasing problem are infections with mycobacteria. In North America and Western Europe infections with the so-called atypical mycobacteria, for example, *M avium-intracellulare, M kansasii,* etc., dominate. In the developing countries, particularly in Central Africa, the classic *M tuberculosis* is more frequent. Whereas classic tuberculosis in AIDS patients is well treatable, no therapy exists for atypical mycobacterioses.

A complete description of all opportunistic infections that define AIDS is beyond the scope of this chapter. The spectrum of disease manifestations is extremely manifold, frequently unusual, and new variants of the courses of infections are continuously being recognized. Multi-infections at the same time frequently complicate diagnosis and management of the opportunistic infections. Not unusually, an isolated infectious agent is not the cause of the observed symptoms.

Opportunistic Tumors

The most frequent opportunistic tumor, *Kaposi's sarcoma,* is observed in about 20% of patients with AIDS.[87] For unknown reasons Kaposi's sarcoma is observed mostly in homosexuals. Its relative incidence is declining.[88] Kaposi's sarcoma is a vascular, brownish-blueish-reddish tumor, which in its characteristic form is easily identifyable. In 30% to 40% of patients, the mucosal membranes, most frequently the oral cavity and larynx, and internal organs, most frequently the esophagus, stomach, and intestines, are affected. In most cases, no treatment is required. Cytostatic treatment is impeded by the dilemma that optimal dosage cannot be given in the presence of immunodeficiency. Certain advances have been made by the introduction of systemic alpha interferon treatment.[89] Excision, local treatment with vincristine and/or laser irradiation are the mainstay of palliative therapy. Less than 5% of AIDS patients die of Kaposi's sarcoma because most patients succumb to opportunistic infections first.

Malignant lymphomas of HIV-infected patients differ from other known lymphomas by their localization, degree of malignancy, and response to therapy.[90, 91] HIV-associated lymphomas are primarily found outside of the lymphatic system, particularly in the brain, bone marrow, gastrointestinal (GI) tract, and skin. The majority of HIV-associated lymphomas are of high-grade malignancy. Their response to therapy is much poorer than that of the classic lymphomas. Chemotherapy induces remissions in a lower percentage of cases, and if remissions are induced, they are mostly of short duration.

The pathogenesis both of Kaposi's sarcoma and of HIV-associated lymphomas is uncertain. In the case of the lymphomas pathogenesis may be related to the impairment of the T cell system and the reactive proliferation of the B lymphatic system.

Neurologic Manifestations

A high percentage of HIV-infected patients shows neurologic changes that are not explained by opportunistic infections or tumors.[92–95] The spectrum of symptoms reaches from slight neuropsychological abnormalities—disturbances of memory, mood, and behavior—to organic psychoses and complete dementia. In almost all cases a continuous deterioration is observed. The most relevant clinical entities are acute meningoencephalitis, subacute encephalitis, chronic aseptic meningitis, vacuolating myelopathy, and peripheral neuropathy. The most frequent neurologic disorder is subacute encephalitis (synonyms: AIDS encephalopathy, AIDS dementia complex). About two thirds of all AIDS patients exhibit signs and symptoms of this most severe neurologic manifestation of HIV infection (changes of cerebrospinal fluid, abnormal neuropsychological tests, subcortical abnormalities on cranial MRI). Post mortem, in 90% of AIDS cases histologic evidence of a subacute encephalitis is found.[96]

It is still unclear to what extent the signs and symptoms of the immunodeficiency and of the neurologic manifestations are causally and temporarily related. Figure 9–8 summarizes the present knowledge on the time course of neurologic manifestations in HIV infection. It is unclear whether genetic variants of HIV with different

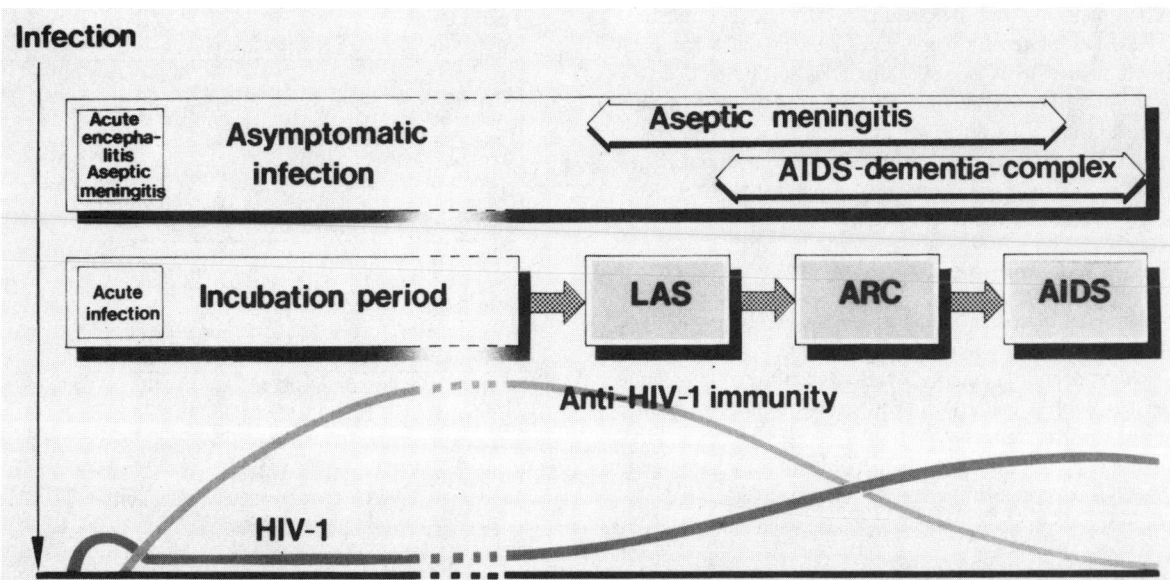

Figure 9–8. Course of human immunodeficiency virus (HIV) encephalopathy correlated with clinical stages, with HIV immunity, and with HIV antigenemia.

cell tropism (eg, prefer macrophages) or other factors, such as genetic predisposition of the host or other infections, are involved.

Dermatologic Manifestations

In all stages of HIV infection characteristic skin manifestations can be observed which frequently may be the first symptoms that lead the patient to medical attention. Herpes zoster may be an early clinical sign.[97] Other skin manifestations may be common skin diseases with different disease characteristics (younger age, more severe course). Examples are the seborrheic eczema that occurs in 40% of patients with LAS and in 70% of AIDS patients, and which is much more frequent in HIV-infected patients than in the normal population. Allergic exanthemas are more frequent in HIV patients, particularly after certain drugs, such as co-trimoxazol. Psoriasis may have a much more severe course in HIV patients. But also manifestations specific for HIV infection are observed, for example, an itching maculopapular eruption[98] or oral hairy leukoplakia at the sides of the tongue.[99] Other skin diseases (in addition to those mentioned under opportunistic infections) which may be of importance in HIV infection are condyloma acuminatum, verruca vulgaris, molluscum contagiosum, acnelike exanthemas of the forehead and back, and others.

Manifestations in Children and During Pregnancy

In children the clinical spectrum of HIV infection differs from that observed in adults. The typical opportunistic infections of adults are less frequent; bacterial infections dominate. In about 50% of children a pneumonia is observed which is called lymphoid interstitial pneumonia. It has been suggested that this pneumonia is directly caused by HIV. In addition, failure to thrive, weight loss, and neurologic symptoms are noted. HIV transmission to the fetus has been observed as early as the 15th week of pregnancy.[100] Prenatal HIV infection may cause a specific embryopathy in the majority of infected children.[101] The characteristic defects are small stature, high forehead, short flat nose, pronounced philtrum, microcephaly, thick lips, and hypertelorism. Whereas the transmission of HIV to children by blood and blood products has been virtually eliminated in Western Europe and North America, the number of infected newborns from HIV-infected mothers (mostly from the risk group of IV drug users) is rising steadily. The transmission rate from infected mothers to their offsprings is estimated to be 50%.[102, 103] There is evidence that a pregnancy also favors progression of HIV disease of the mother.

Epidemiology of HIV Infection

The main goal of epidemiology is the careful observation and description of the course and spread of disease to provide clues for the development of countermeasures. According to the picture evolving it is evident that HIV infection spread unrecognized in the 1960s and 1970s. Retrospectively, AIDS cases have been identified as occurring in Europe and in the United States in the early 1970s.[104] The earliest unambiguously identified HIV antibody-positive serum stems from Kinshasa, Zaire, and dates back to 1959.[105]

The epidemic has spread worldwide, and the numbers of AIDS patients reported to the World Health Organization (WHO) by June 1988 amounted to 100,000 worldwide. WHO assumes that because of underreporting the number is two- to three-fold higher.

The WHO estimates of all HIV-infected persons amount to 5 to 10 million. Reliable estimates about incidence and prevalence of HIV infection do not exist because of the lack of representative data. The long incubation period initially led to an underestimate of the manifestation rate of clinical AIDS. It is still unclear to what extent the mode of transmission, virus dose, cofactors, and genetic predisposition influence the infection and incubation period. Studies on the course of the disease and calculations of the median incubation period, however, allow the conclusion that the proportion of infected persons who finally develop AIDS is significantly higher than initially assumed and may approach 99%. The average survival time from the diagnosis of AIDS is less than 1 year.

Seroconversion

The interval between infection and seroconversion was generally assumed to last about 3 to 12 weeks. Recently, serolatency periods of many months and up to several years have been recognized in some patients.[66, 67, 76] The implications of these observations are far-reaching.

Incubation Period

The duration of the incubation period, that is, the interval from infection to clinically manifest immunodeficiency, is not predictable in individual cases. On the basis of the incubation periods of transfusion-induced AIDS cases that were reported to the CDC[106] and of AIDS cases in homosexuals or hemophiliacs with known seroconversion dates,[107, 108] median incubation periods were calculated by mathematical models. The predictions range between 7.8 and 15 years around a mean of 8 to 10 years (see Table 9–4a). According to the longest observation studies (about 10 years) the median incubation period is 10 to 12 years[107, 108] (range: a few months to more than 14 years) if a manifestation rate close to 100% is assumed.

Table 9–4a
Median Incubation Periods (Calculated)

Lui et al, 1986[109]	4.5 (2.6–14.2) yr
May and Anderson, 1987[110]	8–10 yr
Rees, 1987[111]	15 yr
Medley et al, 1987[112]	8.2 yr
Lui et al, 1988[113]	7.8 (4.2–15.0) yr
Goedert et al, 1988[107]	10 yr (observed)
Hessol et al, 1988[108]	10 yr (observed)
Costagliola et al, 1989[371]	5.3 (4.4–8.9) yr

Table 9–4b
Manifestation Rates of Acquired Immunodeficiency Syndrome (AIDS)

No. of Patients	Observation Time (yr)	AIDS Incidence	Study
44	5	45%	Goedert et al, 1987[117]
42	5	39%	
154	9	42%	Goedert et al, 1988[107]
84	6	18%	Eyster et al, 1987[118]
155	7.4	36%	Hessol et al, 1987[119]
181	10	48%	Hessol et al, 1988[108]
82	6	25%	Ward et al, 1987[120]
59	4.5	29%	Helm et al, 1987[121]

Table 9–5
Cumulative AIDS Cases by Transmission Group as Reported to World Health Organization (WHO)

Transmission Group	United States (1/4/88)		France (3/31/88)		United Kingdom (3/31/88)		West Germany (3/31/88)		Italy (3/31/88)		Belgium (3/31/88)	
Homosexual	32,138	(64%)	2138	(59%)	1199	(84%)	1390	(73%)	352	(20%)	89	(26%)
Intravenous (IV) drug user*	12,237	(24%)	551	(15%)	48	(3%)	194	(10%)	1,132	(65%)	8	(2%)
Heterosexual	1987	(4%)	355	(10%)	48	(3%)	60	(3%)	71	(4%)	184	(55%)
Transfusion recipient	1144	(2%)	259	(7%)	14	(2%)	49	(3%)	31	(2%)	26	(8%)
Hemophiliac	494	(1%)	37	(1%)	84	(6%)	104	(5%)	44	(3%)	0	
Mother to child	750	(1.5%)	75	(2%)	13	(1%)	20	(1%)	59	(3%)	11	(3%)
Others	1515	(3%)	213	(6%)	10	(1%)	89	(5%)	47	(3%)	18	(5%)
Totals	50,265	(100%)	3628	(100%)	1429	(100%)	1906	(100%)	1736	(100%)	336	(100%)

*Including IV drug users and homosexuals.
Data from Centers for Disease Control[122] and WHO Report No. 17.[123]

Manifestation Rate

The percentage of infected persons who finally develop AIDS (manifestation rate) increases with the duration of the infection by an average of 5% to 7% per year.[114] In several studies[115, 116] it was determined that the AIDS incidence was 0% to 2% during the first 2 years after seroconversion, increased to about 5% during the third to fifth years, and reached a plateau of 8% to 10% per year during years 6 to 10. The manifestation rates were similar in transfusion recipients and homosexuals and ranged between 18% and 45% after 5 to 7 years (Table 9–4b). In one study with a long observation period, 48% had developed AIDS after 10 years.[108] Only 23% were still without symptoms.

Modes of Transmission

HIV is transmitted by sexual contact. In addition, HIV can be transmitted parenterally by blood, blood products, contaminated needles and syringes, or from the mother to her newborn infant. The knowledge on the modes of transmission is mainly derived from epidemiologic observations. The main transmission groups in the United States and five West European countries are depicted in Table 9–5. Other theoretical ways of transmission such as by saliva or insects do not play a role in the epidemiology of HIV infection.[124] Transmission frequency by sexual contact can be reduced by the use of condoms.[125]

Infectivity

Evidence is increasing that infectivity of HIV-infected individuals varies during the course of infection. It appears that infectivity is correlated with viremia and is greater very early after infection before the appearance of antibodies and later in the course after the development of symptomatic immunodeficiency.[116, 126]

Risk Groups

Male homosexuals (and bisexuals) constitute the largest proportion of HIV-infected persons in most countries of Western Europe and in North America. Main risk factors for HIV infection in male homosexuals as determined by cohort studies are anal intercourse, particularly receptive, and high numbers of partners.[127–129]

Evidence is increasing that *heterosexual* transmission of HIV

occurs, particularly in developing nations, and may be associated with other sexually transmitted diseases (particularly those causing genital ulcers). Heterosexual transmission of HIV is increasing in the United States. HIV transmission can occur from man to woman or from woman to man. The number of contacts necessary for HIV transmission is not yet known, but probably depends on the infectivity of the index cases.

Prostitutes, particularly IV drug-dependent prostitutes, can be an important multiplicator of the epidemic. The infection rate of prostitutes in different countries and large cities ranges from 0% in some European and American cities to almost 90% in some African cities (Table 9–6).

Numerous studies have demonstrated that HIV is transmitted by *blood transfusions, clotting factors,* and by *contaminated needles and syringes*. Blood transfusions as a cause of infection have been virtually eliminated in Western Europe and North America since the introduction of HIV antibody screening tests in 1985. In developing countries, however, blood transfusions continue to be an important cause of HIV transmission, particularly in Central Africa because of the high degree of infection of the donors and the lack of financial resources to test donors for HIV antibodies. Clotting factors no longer cause HIV infections since HIV inactivation steps have been included in their production process since 1984. The most serious danger for a continued distribution of HIV to the general population in the industrial countries presently comes from HIV-infected *IV drug users*. IV drug users represent the largest AIDS patient groups in Italy (65%) and Spain (54%) and the second largest groups in the United States and in the majority of Western European countries (see Table 9–5). Estimates of the number of IV drug users in the United States amount to about 750,000, and in the Federal Republic of Germany, including West Berlin, 50,000 to 100,000, mostly in the large cities. The HIV infection rates of IV drug users have increased considerably worldwide and exceed 60% in some groups and cities (Table 9–7).

The increase in HIV-infected, mostly drug-dependent mothers is paralleled by an increase of *HIV-infected newborns*. The transmission frequency from infected mothers to their newborn infants is approximately 50%.[102, 103]

Medical personnel are not considered a risk group per se but nosocomial HIV infections may occur. By April 1988, 22 HIV transmission cases by needle injuries and contacts with blood of HIV-infected persons had been described worldwide.[179, 180] Considering the number of needle injuries (1176 reported to the CDC by Dec 31, 1987) the risk of HIV infection by a single needle exposure appears to be small. The risk increases, obviously, with the number of exposures.

Table 9–6
Prevalence of Human Immunodeficiency Virus (HIV) Infection in Various Groups of Prostitutes

City/Country (yr)	Anti-HIV–Positive (Positive/Total) (%)	Reference
United States		
Atlanta (1987)	1/92 (1.1)	130
Miami (1987)	47/252 (18.7)	130
Drug users (1987)	29/63 (46)	131
No drugs (1987)	8/27 (30)	131
Prison (1987)	5/22 (23)	131
Escort service (1987)	0/25 (0)	131
Newark (1987)	32/56 (57.1)	130
Colorado Springs (1987)	1/71 (1.4)	130
Las Vegas (1987)	0/34 (0)	130
Brothel (1987)	0/535 (0)	132
Prison (1987)	23/370 (6.2)	132
Los Angeles (1987)	8/184 (4.3)	130
San Francisco (1987)	9/146 (6.2)	130
New York		
Drug users (1987)	7/13 (54)	133
No drugs (1987)	5/65 (7)	133
South America		
Rio de Janeiro (1988)	4/177 (2)	134
	7/113 (6.2)	135
Africa		
Nairobi, Kenya (1985)	384/535 (65)	136
(1987)	(>85)	136
Meigangu, Cameroon (1986)	18/221 (8.1)	137
Accra, Ghana (1986)	1/98 (1)	138
Ngoma, Rwanda (1985)	29/33 (88)	139
Abidjan and Tortiya, Ivory Coast (1985)	109/232 (47)	140
Asia		
Tamilnadu, India (1986)	30/1025 (2.9)	141
(1988)	33/1277 (2.6)	142
Delhi (1988)	22/73 (30)	143
Madras (1988)	37/831 (4.5)	144
Thailand (1988)	20/19,873 (0.1)	145
Europe		
Pordenone, Italy (1986)	10/14 (71)	146
Athens (1985)	12/200 (6)	147
Paris (1985)	0/56 (0)	148
London (1985)	0/50 (0)	148
Zurich (1986)	15/123 (12)	149
Munich (1984)	0/101 (0)	150
Munich (1984–1985)	0/187 (0)	151
Munich, Stuttgart, Berlin, Heidelberg, Frankfurt, Kiel (1985–1986)	17/2000 (0.85)	152
Nuremberg (1986)	0/399 (0)	153

Table 9–7
Prevalence of Human Immunodeficiency Virus (HIV) Infection in Various Groups of Intravenous Drug Users

City/Country (yr)	Anti-HIV–Positive (Positive/Total) (%)	Reference
United States*		
New York		
Queens (1981–1985)	23/56 (41)	156
Manhattan (1984)	147/290 (51)	157
Manhattan (1984)	50/86 (58)	158
Harlem, Brooklyn (1984)	292/585 (50)	159
(1986)	171/280 (61)	159
Bronx (1986)	169/498 (34)	152
Baltimore (1986)	53/184 (29)	159
New Bedford, Mass (1986)	27/114 (24)	157
New Haven (1986)	38/171 (22)	160
San Antonio (1986)	2/106 (2)	159
Fresno, San Diego (1986)	6/413 (1.5)	159
Asia		
Thailand (1985)	(0)	145
(1986)	(1)	145
(1988)	(16)	145
Europe		
Valencia (1983)	6/58 (11)	160
Rome (1986)	40/120 (33)	162
(1986)	(80)	163
Naples (1986)	23/164 (14)	163
Milan (1979)	0/16 (0)	164
(1980)	0/59 (0)	164
(1981)	4/108 (0)	164
(1982)	23/108 (21)	164
(1983)	53/157 (34)	164
(1984–1985)	94/271 (35)	164
(1987)	439/646 (67.9)	165
Turin (1985)	90/320 (28)	166
Italy		
North (1986–1987)	(54)	163
Central (1986–1987)	18,000 (39)	163
South (1986–1987)	(26)	163
Palermo (1987)	468/684 (68.4)	167
London (1985)	15/236 (6.4)	164
Edinburgh (1985)	40/106 (38)	168
(1986)	100/191 (52)	169
(1988)	96/171 (56)	170
Glasgow (1986)	59/960 (6.1)	171
Yugoslavia (1987)	286/652 (43.9)	172
Sweden (1987)	347/7000 (5.3)	173
Bern (1984)	28/75 (37)	174
Zurich (1984)	69/141 (49)	175
West Germany (1983)	13/129 (10)	176
(1984)	33/188 (18)	176
(1985)	146/610 (24)	176
West Berlin (before 1982)	0/45 (0)	177,178
(1982)	3/17 (18)	177,178
(1983)	11/33 (30)	177,178
(1984)	18/69 (26)	177,178
(1985)	32/82 (39)	178
(1986)	58/89 (67)	178

*For review, see Centers for Disease Control[154] and Hehlmann.[155]

Incidence and Prevalence of HIV Infection

No reliable data exist on the incidence and prevalence of HIV infection in the general population. Several cohort studies were started in 1984 to determine the incidence of HIV infection among groups of homosexual men. The multicenter AIDS cohort study (MACS) recruited 4933 homosexuals from Los Angeles, Baltimore, Chicago, and Pittsburgh from April 1984 until March 1985.[127, 128] The incidence of new HIV infections initially was 4% per year, then dropped to less than 2% per year in early 1987. The dropout rate from the study was, however, considerable (27%) by 1987 and limits the interpretability of the data. In the US Army an incidence of 0.077% per year was determined by mandatory testing from 1985 to 1987.[189] Prevalence data are also available on selected population groups.[154, 155] The prevalence of HIV infections in homosexuals in the United States ranges from 20% to 70% in some urban centers. In Europe, prevalences around 30% were determined in homosexual groups in some cities as early as 1984.[183] Among 963,077 applicants for military service in the United States the prevalence was 0.15% (0.16% in men, 0.06% in women) during the period 1985 to 1987.[183–185] On the basis of studies of samples from HIV risk groups and from the general population, the total prevalence of HIV-infected persons has been estimated in several countries. The prevalence of HIV infections in the United States was estimated to be 1 to 1.5 million in June 1988; in the Federal Republic of Germany, 30,000 to 100,000 in early 1987.

The Worldwide Distribution of AIDS

The worldwide distribution of AIDS is shown in Table 9–8. As of June 30, 1988, 40 countries from four continents (America, Africa, Europe, Australia) had reported more than 100 AIDS cases to WHO.

Africa.—AIDS is a new disease in most areas of Central and East Africa and has been spreading there since the late 1970s and early 1980s.[137, 186, 187] HIV infection is not recognizably limited to certain risk groups. The male-female ratio in Africa is 1:1 in contrast to Western Europe and North America where the ratio at present (1988) is around 13:1. The extent of infection of the general population is considerable in some regions, mainly in large cities but also in some rural areas. In Kinshasa (Zaire) the prevalence of HIV infection was 7% in pregnant women in early 1988, 6.8% in blood donors, and 3% to 5% in workers and their wives.[115, 116] The seropositivity rate of blood donors in Kigali (Uganda) was 18% in 1984; the same percentage was determined for blood donors in Lusaka (Zambia) in 1986.[137] High rates of infection are reported also from Rwanda, Burundi, Kenya, Tanzania, Congo, and Malawi. The highest infection rates are found in prostitutes (see Table 9–6) and in patients with sexually transmitted diseases.

Caribbean and South America.—High numbers of AIDS cases are reported from Haiti and from other islands of the Caribbean area.[188–190] The transmission is homosexual and heterosexual. The male-female sex ratio in Haiti is 4:1, suggesting that heterosexual transmission is important. In South America the largest number of AIDS cases is reported from Brazil,[134, 135] mostly from Sao Paolo and Rio de Janeiro. Of particular concern is the

Table 9–8
Summary of the 40 Countries That Reported More than 300 Acquired Immunodeficiency Syndrome (AIDS) Cases to World Health Organization (WHO) by December 31, 1989

Country	Date of Report	No. of Cases
United States	12/31/89	117,781
Brazil	12/30/89	9,555
France	9/30/89	8,025
Uganda	4/15/89	7,375
Kenya	6/30/89	6,004
Tanzania	12/31/89	5,627
Italy	12/31/89	5,307
Zaire	12/31/88	4,636
West Germany	12/31/89	4,306
Spain	9/30/89	3,965
Mexico	1/11/89	3,427
Canada	12/31/89	3,288
United Kingdom	11/30/89	2,779
Malawi	6/30/88	2,586
Zambia	10/30/89	2,417
Burundi	6/30/89	2,355
Haiti	9/30/89	2,331
Rwanda	8/31/89	1,806
Australia	12/27/89	1,596
Congo	12/9/87	1,250
Switzerland	12/31/89	1,159
Zimbabwe	9/30/89	1,148
Dominican Republic	9/30/89	1,084
Ghana	10/31/89	1,077
Netherlands	12/31/89	1,074
Ivory Coast	9/30/89	1,010
Central African Republic	12/31/88	662
Venezuela	9/30/89	619
Colombia	9/30/89	589
Belgium	9/30/89	563
Burkina Faso	3/31/89	555
Denmark	12/31/89	518
Trinidad and Tobago	3/31/89	509
Argentina	9/30/89	497
Honduras	9/30/89	415
Bahamas	9/30/89	392
Sweden	12/31/89	378
Austria	12/31/89	369
Portugal	12/31/89	348
South Africa	12/15/89	332

fact that a sizable number of blood donations test HIV-positive (0.36% in Rio de Janeiro in early 1987).

Asia and Australia.—The prevalence of HIV infection in Asia is still low. As of June 1988 a total of 243 AIDS cases had been reported from 36 Asian countries. Most cases stem from Japan (n = 66) and Israel (n = 58). Transmission was primarily by students from Africa and by contacts of Asian business people with IV drug users or homosexuals abroad. The epidemiology of AIDS in Australia and New Zealand is similar to that of the other industrial countries of North America and Western Europe.

Epidemiologic Models

For prognostic estimates of the future course of the epidemic epidemiologic models have been developed.[191, 192] All models show that the epidemic will continue to spread. The prognostic reliability of the models, however, depends on the quality of the data available, which is limited. On the basis of such models WHO predicts 56,000 AIDS cases in Western Europe by the end of 1989. Similar projections by the CDC predict 365,000 AIDS cases in the United States by 1992.

HIV-2

Since 1986 retroviral isolates from West Africa have been described that are closely related to the monkey retrovirus, simian immunodeficiency virus (SIV), but do not, or only very little, cross-react with HIV.[6, 7, 17] These isolates have therefore been termed HIV-2, HIV-2 is still rare in North America and Western Europe.[193, 194] HIV-2 infected persons come from West Africa or are contacts of West Africans. Also, HIV-2 causes an immunodeficiency syndrome like AIDS, although some reports suggest that the pathogenicity of HIV-2 is less than that of HIV-1.

Origin of HIV

Several hypotheses regarding the origin of HIV have been developed: (1) mutation of older viruses, (2) transmission of animal viruses (eg, SIV) to man, and (3) transmission by an isolated, remote section of the population (eg, by change of sexual behavior and mobility). Available data, at present, favor the third possibility.[195, 196]

Laboratory Diagnosis of Infection

Antibody Tests

The method most frequently used for the screening of blood and serum samples for HIV antibodies is the ELISA using disrupted whole virus or defined virus antigens.[197] ELISA is a solid-phase assay in which the antigen is coated onto a solid phase, usually the surface of microtiter plates or plastic balls, and the patient's serum is added and antibody then binds to the fixed antigens. The antigen-antibody complex is detected by a second antihuman antibody to which an enzyme is covalently bound, typically horseradish peroxidase or alkaline phosphatase, that gives a color reaction on addition of substrate. Specificity and sensitivity of the presently available commercial assay systems are close to 100%, but false-positive and false-negative reactions occur. To exclude false-positive test results, confirmation tests are carried out such as western blotting, immunofluorescence, or immunoperoxidase cell tests,[197] or radioimmunoprecipation. The standard remains western blotting in which the proteins of whole disrupted virus are electrophoretically separated and, after transfer to a cellulose strip (the "blotting" step), reacted with the patient's serum.[198] Antigen-antibody complexes are detected by addition of an enzyme-bound antihuman antibody and a subsequent color reaction as described above for ELISA. The advantage of Western blotting is that serologic reactivity to individual viral proteins can be detected. Nonspecific reactions can be recognized by a pattern not characteristic of HIV proteins. To exclude "technically" false-negative test results, sensitivities of assay systems are being improved by the use of purified antigens or recombinant antigens. Not detectable are "biologically" false-negative reactions, if the individual is HIV-infected but does not (yet) possess anti-HIV antibodies. For these cases, nucleic acid tests are available.

Antigen Test

Monoclonal antibodies against viral antigens, at present mostly anti-p24, are used for the detection of viral antigens. In some cases HIV antigen can be detected in HIV antibody-negative persons, for example, early after infection. The disadvantage of the antigen test is that it is less sensitive than the antibody tests and therefore only of limited use for the diagnosis of HIV-infected persons that are antibody-negative.

Virus Isolation

Isolation of infectious virus from HIV-infected persons is possible by cocultivation of patient's lymphocytes with fresh peripheral blood cells of healthy donors or with suitable continuous tissue culture cell lines, for example, from T-lymphomas. Demonstration of virus is accomplished by reverse transcriptase assays, serological tests, or by changes in the growth pattern of the indicator cells. Virus isolation is tedious and time-consuming (weeks) and is successful in only about 70% to 90% of cases. Recently, virus isolation rates up to 100% have been reported.[372, 373] Virus isolation is mainly used for characterization purposes of the virus, or in cases in whom the diagnosis is in doubt, such as in infants of seropositive mothers.

Tests for Nucleic Acids

Viral nucleic acids can be detected in viral-infected cells by in situ hybridization with the help of radioactively labeled viral DNA probes.[199] The presence and location of viral nucleic acids (mostly RNA) is visualized by autoradiography if sufficient quantities of replicating virus are present. Recently, the demonstration of proviral DNA at low concentrations has become possible by the amplification of viral DNA with the help of the polymerase chain reaction technique (PCR).[75–77] Presynthesized oligonucleotides of viral specificity (conserved regions) are hybridized to the proviral DNA and the DNA chains elongated by DNA polymerase. Proviral DNA can thus be amplified by many orders of magnitude permitting the detection of viral DNA at concentrations down to one copy in 10^5 to 10^6 cells.

Therapy

Therapy of HIV is complicated by the fact that the HIV genome is incorporated in the host genome and may remain there in a dormant state for prolonged periods until it is reactivated. This property of HIV implies that an effective therapy must be directed against both free virus and virus-infected cells. A number of substances with anti-HIV activity in vitro have been described, but only a few drugs exhibit anti-HIV activity in vivo at tolerable toxicities. Anti-HIV substances can be grouped according to their viral target structures and their mechanisms of action. The main groups of substances are reverse transcriptase inhibitors, nucleoside analogues, interferons, active lipids, and soluble CD4 receptor.

The first group of substances to be used in vivo were inhibitors of the viral reverse transcriptase. The best-known member of this group is suramin known from its antitrypanosomal activity in sleeping sickness.[200] Its high toxicity and low activity preclude its further use in HIV-infected patients. Other substances of this group still under clinical trial are foscarnet, HPA-23, D-penicillamine, and others.

The compounds with greatest clinical relevance are nucleoside analogues that prevent the synthesis of proviral DNA. The best known member of this group is azidothymidine (AZT, Retrovir, zidovudine). Zidovudine has a definite effect on HIV infection and viremia in vivo, reduces the number of opportunistic infections, and prolongs the lives of certain patients with ARC and AIDS.[201] Its toxicity consists mainly of cytopenias resulting in transfusion-dependent anemia in 25% of cases.[202] Base analogues currently under clinical evaluation are dideoxycytidine (DDC), dideoxyadenosine, dideoxyinosine (DDI), and ribavirin, among others.[203, 204]

Additional substances of potential use in HIV therapy are alpha and beta interferon[205]; the xanthates, which interfere with viral membrane synthesis[206]; peptide T, an octapeptide corresponding to a constant region of the HIV envelope protein,[207, 208]; active phospholipids (the best-known is AL 721)[206]; double-stranded RNA[210]; dextran sulfate[211]; fusidic acid[212, 213]; and others. The synthesis of soluble recombinant CD4 receptor[214–218] offers the possibility of blocking the HIV gp120 molecules on the viral surface in order to prevent viral adsorption to the target cells and thus abolish HIV infectivity. For most of these substances, however, clinical experience is still lacking.

Cytopenias secondary to HIV infection alone, or due to zidovudine toxicity may respond to treatment with recombinant granulocyte or granulocyte-macrophage colony-stimulating factors (G-CSF or GM-CSF). Initial clinical trials are promising.[219]

Development of Vaccines

The difficulties facing the development of an AIDS-vaccine are, in large part, similar to those encountered in antiviral drug development.[220, 221] Host defense mechanisms have to provide protection both against free virus and against virus-infected cells. Several examples of other retroviral infections indicate that a *humoral immune response* (neutralizing antibodies) may be protective. One example is feline leukemia, in which the presence of neutralizing antibodies against feline leukemia virus (FeLV) correlates with protection against disease. Another example are rhesus monkeys which survive infection with SIV$_{MAC}$ in direct correlation with the magnitude of the humoral response. The observation that neutralizing anti-HIV antibodies in man do not prevent progression of HIV disease and that the induction of neutralizing antibodies in chimpanzees by HIV gp160 does not prevent infection with HIV argues against the possibility that neutralizing antibodies are sufficient for protection against infection with HIV. Individuals with high neutralizing antibody titers, however, seem to have a longer disease-free interval.

In addition to humoral immunity *cell-mediated immune responses* may be important. Cellular immune responses are effective by several mechanisms such as:

- Antibody-dependent cellular cytotoxicity (ADCC) in which effector cells (lymphocytes, macrophages) with Fc receptors for immunoglobulins bind and kill immunoglobulin-coated target cells that express viral genes
- Lymphokine-activated natural killer cytolytic activity
- Cytotoxic T lymphocyte activity, which is specific for HIV-1 proteins and recognizes and lyses virally infected cells and thereby limits cell-to-cell spread of the virus

The role of these mechanisms in the protection against HIV infection, and their relevance for anti-HIV vaccination are still unclear.

Another obstacle to the development of an effective HIV vaccine may be the high genetic variability of HIV which results in considerable diversity of HIV isolates. The genetic variation is due to variations primarily in the envelope gene of HIV. In certain regions of the envelope gene the degree of variation may be as high as 50% in some isolates.[15, 222] Such a variability may prevent protection by a single vaccine and necessitate the combination of several antigens. Conserved regions exist in the gp120 molecule and in the amino terminal part of gp41 which are recognized by HIV sera. Neutralizing antibodies can be induced with peptides representing these regions.[223] The main types of approaches to an AIDS vaccine presently under consideration are:

- Live attenuated HIV
- Whole inactivated HIV
- Live recombinant viruses (vaccinia, adenovirus)
- Synthetic peptides (envelope, p17 core)
- Recombinant DNA products (gp120, gp160)
- Native envelope and/or core proteins
- Anti-idiotypes
- Passive immunization

Live attenuated viruses, which induce both humoral and cellular immunity, are well established for a variety of viral diseases. Retroviruses, however, have a high rate of genetic mutation. In addition, retroviral genetic information can, integrated in the host genome, persist for the lifetime of the host with unpredictable consequences. It is therefore not likely that live attenuated HIV will be acceptable as a human vaccine. The same problem may be true for *whole inactivated viral vaccines.* In addition, with lentiviruses vaccine-induced enhancement of disease has been observed. Also antibody-dependent enhancement of HIV infection has been described.[224]

Live recombinant viruses, such as vaccinia or adenovirus recombinants, have been developed for HIV vaccination. Their advantage is a high immunogenicity, since viral replication results in large quantities of HIV antigens. Also, extensive experience exists with the application of vaccinia virus and its humoral and cellular immune responses. A disadvantage of this approach is possible adverse effects observed after inoculation of vaccinia virus.

Synthetic peptides can be designed such that neutralizing and T cell epitopes are included.[223, 225] The problems with synthetic peptides are related to the tertiary structures which may be different from those of native proteins and thus may not represent the epitopes of interest.

Another promising approach to the development of an AIDS vaccine appears to be the production of *recombinant viral antigens.*

Recombinant antigens can be produced in large amounts at reasonable costs. This approach has been successfully applied to the production of a recombinant hepatitis B vaccine. For the production of recombinant antigens the expression vector systems may be of importance, since the glycosylation pattern that is specific for the expression system may be important for antigenicity and depends on the choice of the vector system. The viral antigens that are considered the most likely candidates for a successful induction of humoral and cellular immunity are the env gene products gp160, gp120, and gp41. In addition, the membrane-associated p17 core protein is being evaluated for its induction of protective immunity.

An alternative approach is the production of *anti-idiotypic antibodies*. Their usefulness has been demonstrated for vaccination against several infectious agents. Also, *passive immunization* may be of use in preventing HIV infection, for instance, in medical personnel after needle stick injuries or in newborn infants of HIV-infected mothers.

A major obstacle in the production of a safe and effective vaccine is the lack of a readily available animal model. Thus far chimpanzees and gibbons are the only animal species that can be infected with HIV. No disease has been observed after several years. The number of chimpanzees available for vaccine testing is limited and the costs are high. In chimpanzees neutralizing humoral and cell-mediated immune responses against HIV can be induced with various env gene product preparations. On challenge with high-dose HIV, however, no protection could be observed in these animals.[226] Recently, it was shown that rhesus macaques can be infected with HIV-2, but also in macaques no disease developed. Rhesus macaques can also be infected with SIV$_{MAC}$ and subsequently develop an immunodeficiency syndrome resembling AIDS. Like HIV infection, SIV infection results in depletion of CD4 lymphocytes. Thus the rhesus SIV$_{MAC}$ model may be suitable for resolving some general problems of HIV vaccine development. Other models may be animals infected by other lentiviruses such as visna-maedi virus–infected sheep, caprine arthritis encephalitis virus (CAEV)–infected goats, equine infectious anemia virus (EIAV)–infected horses, bovine immunodeficiency virus (BIV)-infected cows, or feline T-lymphotropic virus–infected cats. In addition, transgenic mice have been produced that carry the complete HIV provirus in their cell genomes and show clinical evidence of HIV infection.[227] Of interest is that rabbits seem to be susceptible to HIV-1 infection.

Suitable vaccine candidates ultimately have to be tested in clinical trials of human volunteers. Phase 1 trials have to determine that the candidate vaccine is safe. Only small numbers of volunteers are needed. Phase 2 trials are conducted with larger numbers of volunteers and determine the optimal dosage that is safe and induces immunity. Finally, in phase 3 trials, protection against disease by the candidate vaccine is evaluated. Phase 3 trials have to be conducted on a sample size that is sufficiently large to allow significant results on protection from infection or disease. At present (July 1988) several phase 1 trials with recombinant purified viral antigens and vaccinia recombinant viruses are in progress in Africa, the United States, and Western Europe.[228, 229]

HUMAN T CELL LYMPHOMA-LEUKEMIA VIRUSES (HTLV-I, -II)

In 1980 an entirely new approach to the question of human leukemia viruses became possible with the successful propagation of human T lymphocytes with the help of a growth factor, called T cell growth factor (TCGF) or interleukin-2 (IL-2).[230, 231] Long-term cultivation of T lymphocytes from patients with neoplasia of T cells (mycosis fungoides, Sézary syndrome) yielded retroviruses of C-type morphology that were unrelated to all previously known retroviruses.[232–233] Similar viruses were isolated from patients with adult T cell leukemia (ATL), which is endemic in Japan,[235–237] and comparative studies of the different isolates from mycosis fungoides and T cell leukemias showed that they represent virtually identical viruses.[238] The viruses were designated human T cell lymphoma virus (HTLV) and adult T cell leukemia virus (ATLV). In 1982, a second virus more distantly related to HTLV was isolated from a patient with hairy cell leukemia and designated HTLV-II.[239, 240]

Basic properties

HTLV-I and -II share most properties such as density, morphology, a 70S RNA, reverse transcriptase, and structural proteins with all other replication-competent C-type retroviruses.[232] The electron micrograph of Figure 9–9 shows C-type morphology. The sizes of some of the structural proteins (p24, p42) are different from those of other retroviruses. The major HTLV core protein (p24) was shown to be serologically distinct from the core proteins of all previously described viruses.[241] Its amino acid sequence is in part homologous to only that of the major core protein p24 of BLV.[242] This relationship, however, is not detectable by conventional serologic or nucleic acid hybridization assays. A close re-

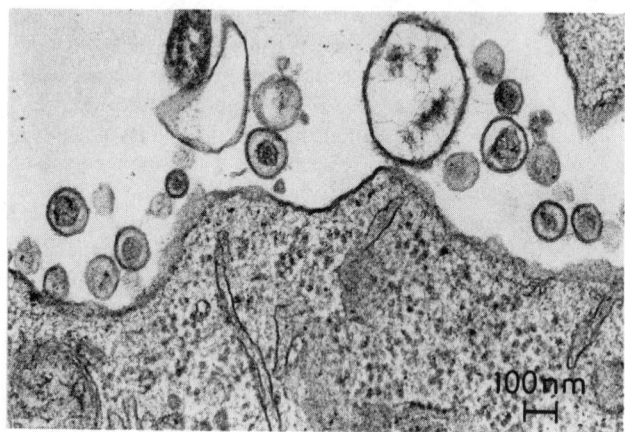

Figure 9–9. Electron micrograph of human T cell leukemia virus type I (HTLV-I). Note C-type morphology (central core, no or only short surface projections). Magnification × 75,000. *(Courtesy of Dr H. Gelderblom, Berlin.)*

Table 9–9
Human T-Cell Leukemia (HTLV) Group of Retroviruses

Strain designation	Disease
Human T-cell leukemia virus type I (HTLV-I)	Adult T cell leukemia, tropical spastic paraparesis
Human T-cell leukemia virus type II (HTLV-II)	Unknown
Simian T-cell leukemia viruses (STLV-I)	Malignant lymphoma
Bovine leukemia virus (BLV)	Persistent lymphocytosis, leukemia, lymphosarcoma

lationship exists to similar viruses of monkeys called STLV-I that were discovered subsequently and can cause malignant lymphomas in monkeys. HTLV, BLV, and STLV-I are therefore classified in one group as shown in Table 9–9. The glycoprotein gp68 was identified as the major env-gene product.[243] Cocultivation of HTLV- or ATLV-producing cell lines with leukocytes from adult peripheral blood and umbilical cord blood resulted in transformation of the leukocytes and expression of HTLV or ATLV antigens by these cells.[244, 245] The transformed cell lines exhibited T cell and non-T, non-B cell surface properties. HTLV is not an endogenous human virus and was not transmitted through the germ line of the patient from whom HTLV was first isolated since HTLV sequences were present in the DNA of T cells, and absent from B cells of this patient.[246]

The complete nucleotide sequences of HTLV-I (9032 bases) and HTLV-II (8952 bases) have been determined.[247, 248] The genome organization of HTLV-I and -II resembles more that of HIV than those of the other mammalian C-type oncoviruses since it contains genes for two regulation proteins, tax (transactivator of viral proteins) and rex (regulation of expression of virion proteins), which act in trans, similar to tat and rev of HIV-1 and -2 (Figure

9–10).[249–253] The tax product has a molecular weight of about 40 kd and regulates all viral genes. The rex product has an apparent molecular weight of about 27 kd and initiates expression of virion proteins only (253). The HTLV-I tax gene product has been demonstrated to regulate IL-2 receptor gene expression through a nuclear factor-kappa B–like factor.[249–251] This is of interest in the context of the T4 helper lymphocyte tropism of the HTLVs.

Clinical Features of HTLV-I Infection

Two kinds of disease manifestations have been associated with HTLV-I: adult-T cell leukemia-lymphoma (ATL) and a myelopathy also called tropical spastic paraparesis (TSP). The evidence implicating HTLV-I as the etiologic agent of ATL includes the association of ATL with anti-HTLV-I antibodies,[254–257] the isolation of the virus,[236, 337] the finding of monoclonal integrated proviral sequences in leukemic cells of patients with ATL,[258, 259] and epidemiologic data associating leukemia and regions endemic for HTLV-I infection.[260–262] ATL, in the majority of cases, is a rapidly fatal disease that was first described in Japan in 1977, but it is prevalent also in the West Indies and in Africa. ATL is characterized by diffuse lymph node infiltration, hypercalcemia, leukemia, skin infiltrates, and a positive HTLV-I antibody test.[263, 264]

The association of HTLV-I with TSP was discovered in 1985 while screening blood donors for HTLV-I antibodies in Martinique, West Indies.[265] More than 75% of patients with TSP were found to possess antibodies against HTLV-I by ELISA and western blot.[266–268] The evidence suggesting a causal relationship between HTLV-I and TSP is supported by the isolation of HTLV-I from blood and spinal fluid of patients with TSP[269, 270, 341] and by cloning of HTLV-I provirus from a case with TSP.[271] A chronic neurologic disorder identical with TSP was found subsequently also in the other regions endemic for HTLV-I such as Africa and southwestern Japan where TSP was named HTLV-I–associated myelopathy (HAM).[272, 273] Clinically, TSP resembles multiple sclerosis (MS), but lacks the intracranial nerve signs and remissions characteristic of MS. Initial symptoms are bilateral weakness and stiffness of

Table 9–10
Human Endogenous Retroviral Sequences

Designation	Related to	Structure	Copy No.	Chromosomal Localization	Expression	References
4–1	C-type MuLVs	Provirus	Multiple	Dispersed	RNA: env LTR	329–332
51–1		gag-pol				333–335
ERV1	BaEV,Mo-MuLV	No 5′LTR	1	18	gag-related proteins	336–340
ERV3		Provirus	1	7	RNA: env, flanking cellular sequences	341–343
S71	SSAV	gag-pol-LTR	1	18	Related proteins, RNA	344–345 290
HLM-2	MMTV	"Mosaic" provirus(?)	Multiple	1(5,7,8, 11,14,17)	RNA	346,347
HM-16	MMTV	pol	Multiple	—	RNA	348
HERV-K	MMTV IAP	Provirus	Multiple	—	RNA	349–351
HBL	BaEV	LTR-related	Multiple	—	—	
RTVL-H	—	LTR~6 kb-LTR	Multiple	—	—	352,353,466

MuLV = murine leukemia virus; BaEV = baboon endogenous virus; MoMuLV = Moloney MuLV; SSAV = simian sarcoma–associated virus; MMTV = mouse mammary tumor virus; IAP = intracisternal A particle of hamster; LTR = long terminal repeat.

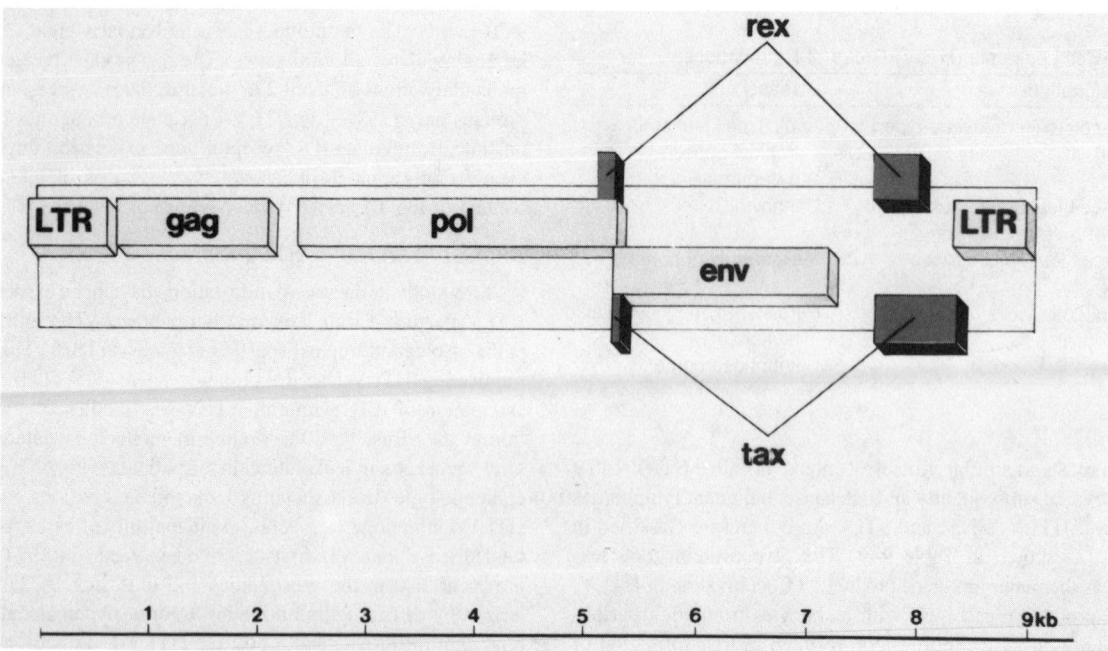

Figure 9–10. Genome organization of human T cell leukemia viruses types I and II (HTLV-I, -II).

the lower extremities.[267, 268] The course is slowly progressive, usually with bladder involvement, but shows considerable variations. On examination spastic paraparesis is found with hyperactive deep tendon reflexes, mainly of the lower extremities. Some patients may show abnormalities of the spinal fluid (protein and cells increased), of nerve conduction, and of cranial scanning on magnetic resonance imaging (MRI).[274, 275]

Pathogenesis

Both HTLV-I and HTLV-II were found to transform suitable target cells in vitro. Both viruses have a tropism for CD4-positive T helper lymphocytes, but also other cells can be infected. In contrast to HIV, the receptor for binding of HTLV is not exactly known. It is assumed that the transforming properties of HTLV-I are directly responsible for the induction of leukemia or lymphoma. Very little is known on the pathogenesis of the neurologic disorder. By analogy to HIV, it appears possible that HTLV-I infects cells of the spinal cord. Alternatively, HTLV-I could chronically infect and activate its CD4 target lymphocytes which then would evoke a chronic inflammatory reaction leading to neuronal damage and demyelination. Since ATL and TSP are only rarely observed in the same patient, HTLV-I-infected lymphocytes have been suggested to be either transformed or chronically activated or, much more commonly, neither, as for example, in healthy carriers.

Epidemiology

Seroepidemiologic studies, initially based on immunoprecipitation tests for antibodies against the HTLV structural proteins p19 and p24, then on ELISAs with whole disrupted virus, showed the presence of HTLV antibodies clustered in certain geographic areas.[260–262] Clusters were found especially in southwestern Japan. In Japan, 6% to 37% of 473 healthy individuals from various regions were positive for HTLV antibodies.[260] The higher prevalences were found in the southwestern areas. The islands around Okinawa have HTLV-I antibody rates of up to 15% for the entire population. In Kagoshima 16% of the population have HTLV-I antibody.[272] The rates increase with age and are higher in women. Among Hawaiian-born offspring of Japanese migrants to Hawaii, HTLV-I antibody rates of up to 20% have been reported.

Prevalence data for HTLV-I antibody show that HTLV-I is endemic also in the West Indies and neighboring countries (Jamaica, Trinidad, Colombia)[256, 258, 262, 264, 266] and in Africa,[276] including the Seychelles. In Jamaica, island-wide prevalence is about 6%. Elsewhere in the Caribbean area rates of 1% to 4% are observed. Clusters and sporadic cases positive for HTLV antibodies or virus have been reported also in several areas of the United States,[257,263] in South America,[266] in Israel, among the Eskimo populations of Canada and Greenland, and in southern Italy.

It has been estimated by presently available data that the *incidence of T cell malignancies* in HTLV-infected persons is about 1 to 2 in 1000.

Transmission of HTLV seems to essentially follow the same routes as that of HIV (sexual contact, mother to infant, blood transfusion, sharing of contaminated needles).[277] Blood transfusions have been identified as a major mode of transmission in Japan.[272] After routine screening of blood donors for HTLV-I antibodies the rate of seroconversions declined from about 9% in 1981–1985 to 0.1% in 1986–1987 in surveyed groups of recipients. In the United States screening of 39,898 blood donors yielded an HTLV-I prevalence of 0.025% with a range from 0% to 0.1% at various locations. HTLV-I seems to be endemic at a low prevalence in the black populations of the southeastern United States.[278]

Transmission among IV drug users is of increasing importance in the United States. Prevalence in IV drug users varies widely according to location. In the New York area prevalences of 11%

(4/37) among black and of 5% (1/19) among white IV drug users were detected in blood samples collected in 1981 and 1982.[157] In a hemodialysis center four of nine IV drug users (44%) tested positive.[276] A high prevalence was determined in a population of drug users in New Orleans.[280] Other transmission routes are sexual contact[281] and transmission from the mother to her newborn infant.

An incubation time of 15 to 20 years has been suggested for the development of ATL. This means that with an ATL incidence of 1 to 2 in 1000 HTLV-I–infected persons the lifetime risk for a carrier to develop ATL would be 1 in 20 over 50 years. The observed risks are lower and closer to 1 in 100. Taken together HTLV-I seems to be less readily transmitted and causes disease at a lower rate than HIV.

Laboratory Diagnosis

Detection of infection rests primarily on the detection of HTLV-I antibodies with screening tests, mainly ELISA, using whole disrupted virus similar to the assay systems described above for HIV. Also, positive HTLV-I screening tests have to be confirmed by an independent test system, western blotting, to exclude false-positive reactions. In addition, tests for viral antigen, infectious virus, and viral DNA are carried out, but mainly on an investigative basis. All blood donations in the United States are screened for HTLV-I; positive units are not administered to patients.

Therapy and Vaccination

No therapy or vaccination is available for HTLV-I infection. It is probable, however, that advances made in the therapy of HIV infection are applicable also to infection with HTLV-I. In the absence of an effective therapy or vaccination, countermeasures, at present, have to concentrate on prevention via information campaigns for groups at risk and through testing of blood donors. Screening programs for HTLV-I have been started in endemic areas in Japan and are being considered in Jamaica and for certain high-risk areas also in the United States.

HUMAN ENDOGENOUS RETROVIRUSES

One of the unique features of retroviruses is their ability to integrate their genetic information in the genomes of their host cells, including the germ line, and to persist there as proviruses. Proviruses, which are contained in the germ line of a given species and are inherited from generation to generation like cellular genes, are called endogenous retroviruses. Although the function or biologic role of endogenous retroviruses still remains to be elucidated, they have been detected in almost all vertebrate species examined, including man.[282]

The most relevant properties of endogenous, genetically transmitted retroviruses are:

- Persistance in cellular DNA
- Germ line transmission
- Transposonlike structure
- Activation by mutagens, carcinogens, mitogens, DNA viruses, aging
- Expression as antigen or infectious virus

The transposonlike structure enables retroviruses to integrate at any position of the cellular genome.[283] Endogenous retroviruses

can be activated by certain chemicals such as mutagens or carcinogens or by mitogens, radiation, and other mechanisms such as DNA viruses or aging to express antigens or to form infectious virus particles. Their biologic relevance is unknown but may include involvement in physiologic processes such as embryogenesis, differentation, or protection against superinfection by related retroviruses similar to observations made with exogenous retroviruses in some animal systems. They might also be involved in carcinogenesis by several mechanisms, for example, via recombination events with exogenous retroviruses (see below).

Experimental evidence has pointed to the existence of human endogenous retroviruses for many years. This evidence included electron microscopic visualization of retroviruslike particles in human placentas and embryonal or neoplastic tissues, cells, and cell lines, and the detection of so-called retroviral footprints in human tissues or body fluids such as reverse transcriptase activity, cytoplasmic RNA, or proteins related to those of known animal retroviruses.[284] For the interpretation of some of the evidence implicating the existence of human endogenous retroviruses, the concept of "molecular mimicry" has to be considered,[285] that is, common sequences of two proteins might be fortuitous or they may constitute similar structural or functional elements of these proteins as a site of convergent evolution. Some evidence for such a concept stems from a region of homology in a human autoimmune protein and in retroviral p30 gag antigen.[286]

Human leukemias were, without doubt, the human neoplasias studied most extensively for their possible association with retroviruses. Retrospectively, the early evidence for retroviruses obtained in human leukemias has to be taken as evidence for human endogenous retroviruses. Much of this evidence was based on the knowledge that retroviruses of closely related species share nucleic acid homologies, exhibit cross-reacting antigenicity, and therefore can be used as probes.

The presence of a reverse transcriptase in at least some of the human leukemias has been demonstrated by several independent laboratories. The reverse transcriptase purified from human leukemic cells and tissues (eg, spleen) possesses a molecular weight of 70,000 daltons which is characteristic of the reverse transcriptases of mammalian C-type retroviruses.[287, 288] It shows a serologic relationship with the reverse transcriptases of simian sarcoma-associated virus (SSAV) and of murine leukemia viruses (MuLVs) and prefers the synthetic templates dT-rA and dG-rC (dG-rCm) diagnostic for reverse transcriptases. In some instances the polymerase was found associated with 70S RNA and/or viruslike particles.[289] The existence of SSAV- or MuLV-related RNA in some human leukemias has been observed also by molecular hybridization. The RNA had a high molecular weight and possessed poly(A) sequences similar to retroviral RNA.[289]

Some human leukemias showed antigens related to the structural proteins p30 and gp70 of the primate retroviruses SSAV and baboon endogenous virus (BaEV).[290, 291] Corresponding antibodies reactive with the internal core proteins (p30) of SSAV, BaEV, and MuLV were reported in human sera and exudate fluids.[292, 293] Antibodies in human sera that reacted with the envelope glycoprotein gp70 of SSAV were shown to be directed, in part, against the sugar moieties of the glycoproteins.[294–296] Several successful isolations of retroviruses from cultured human leukemic and embryonic cells were reported which showed an RNA and antigenic relationship with SSAV and BaEV.[297–300] In some instances infectivity of the isolated particles was demonstrated. The interpretation that these isolates represent laboratory contaminations is acceptable for only some isolates.

Retroviruslike structures have also been detected in human *placentas*[301–303] and embryonic cells.[304–308] Complete particles were observed by electron microscopy. Some of the viral components discovered were serologically related to SSAV and BaEV. Other particles detected in amnion cells or in HeLa cells resembled the D-type Mason-Pfizer monkey virus (MPMV), a retrovirus originally isolated from a mammary tumor of a rhesus monkey.[309–315]

Retroviruses have been associated also with some human breast cancers, osteosarcomas, and melanomas. Although in these areas research efforts have been less intensive than in leukemia, evidence exists for an association of retroviruses with *human breast cancer*. In a number of human breast cancer specimens retroviral-related RNA has been reported with sequence homology to the RNAs of mouse mammary tumor virus (MMTV) or of MPMV. A reverse transcriptase has been described in breast cancer tissue and in milk of women at risk for breast cancer with properties of retroviral reverse transcriptases.[316] The enzyme possesses the characteristic molecular weight of 70,000 daltons and cross-reacts serologically with the reverse transcriptase of MPMV[316] and, in some instances, is found in viruslike particles associated with a high-molecular-weight RNA.

Electron microscopic search for particles in breast cancer and in human milk yielded evidence for B-type viruslike particles which, however, has been challenged on technical grounds. Attempts to grow retroviruses from human breast cancer tissue were successful in some cases.[317, 318] Particles obtained from the human breast cancer cell line T47D possess the properties of retroviruses (morphology, density, reverse transcriptase, 70S RNA), and show serologic cross-reactivity with MMTV.[319]

Another line of evidence for retroviral components in human breast cancer came from the detection of antigens that cross-react with MMTV envelope proteins. In about 40% of human breast cancers antigens have been found that cross-react with the envelope glycoprotein gp52 of MMTV.[320, 321] This antigen appears to be specific for breast cancer and was not found in normal breast tissue or in nonmalignant breast lesions. A protein with similar antigenic properties has been isolated from human milk.[322]

In human *sarcomas*, virus-related RNA has been detected with sequence homologies to the RNAs of MuLV, feline sarcoma virus (FeSV), and SSAV. A reverse transcriptase has been purified from human osteosarcomas that cross-reacts serologically with the reverse transcriptase of BaEV.[323, 324] Viruslike particles containing a 70S RNA complexed to a reverse transcriptase and to viral antigens have been observed in cell cultures from human sarcomas.[325]

From human *melanomas* a reverse transcriptase has been partially purified that is associated with a 70S RNA and cross-reacts serologically with the reverse transcriptase of BaEV.[326, 327] In some instances cultured human melanomas yielded particles with properties of retroviruses.[328]

In summary the evidence strongly suggests that some human leukemias and breast cancers contain nucleic acids, proteins, and/or viral particles related to known animal retroviruses, in particular SSAV, BaEV, and MMTV. Retroviruses related to SSAV, BaEV, and MMTV probably do occur but this appears to be a rare event. Thus far no epidemiologic or causal relationship has been shown between these viruses or viral components and the development of human neoplasms.

The existence of human endogenous retroviruses has become generally accepted since the detection and characterization of multiple, more or less related *endogenous retroviral sequences* in the human genome (Table 9–10).[329–332, 336–340, 344–352] These sequences have been identified by low-stringency hybridization with probes derived either from cloned primate endogenous retroviruses related to known retroviruses or from other known animal retroviruses. Human endogenous retroviral sequences can be divided into four major families based on relationship to the Moloney MuLV strain (clones 4-1, 51-1), to BaEV (clones ERV1, ERV3), to SSAV (clone S71), and to MMTV (clones HLM-2, HM16, HERV-K). In addition, some less well-characterized retroviral sequences containing LTR-like features have also been described (for details, see summary in Table 9–10).

Evidence for the expression of these endogenous retroviral sequences has been detected on RNA and on protein levels.[333–335, 341–343, 353–355] Although some of the human endogenous retroviral sequences represent full-length proviruses (4-1, ERV-3, HERV-K), nucleotide sequencing revealed that the majority is replication-defective. For example, 4-1 contains numerous stop codons for translation of proteins dispersed over most of the proviral sequence (Figure 9–11). The existence of these multiple stop codons might indicate that endogenous retroviral sequences are of sufficient biologic significance as to warrant an efficient inhibition of translation to prevent virus replication and/or genetic expression. Another example, HERV-K, however, contains several open reading frames (ORFs), coinciding with retroviral genes suggesting that this provirus may be functional (Figure 9–12).

Two intrinsic features of retroviruses make it likely that endogenous retroviral sequences may be involved in carcinogenesis. The first is the LTR which contains all signal sequences including enhancer elements required for initiation of transcription. Therefore the LTR is able to activate adjacent cellular genes which may in turn be involved in carcinogenesis (promotor insertion model, Figure 9–13). Indeed, some cases of neoplastic disease have been reported in which activation of cellular oncogenes was observed to be a result of proviral integration.[354, 355] Chromosomal translocation may also lead to LTR-directed transcription of genes involved in carcinogenesis. Alternatively, activation of the LTR itself could be induced by proteins acting in trans, which in turn are switched on by environmental factors (heat, carcinogens etc). Furthermore, mutation within human endogenous LTR-like sequences may also result in their activation.

The second retroviral feature making endogenous sequences potential factors of carcinogenesis is associated with the env gene (Figure 9–14). p15E-related proteins have been shown to possess immunosuppressive activity and may therefore promote certain later steps required for carcinogenesis.[356–360] Another line of evidence for a role of the env gene in carcinogenesis is the fact that the env gene is the site of recombination between endogenous

Stop codon   Frame shift

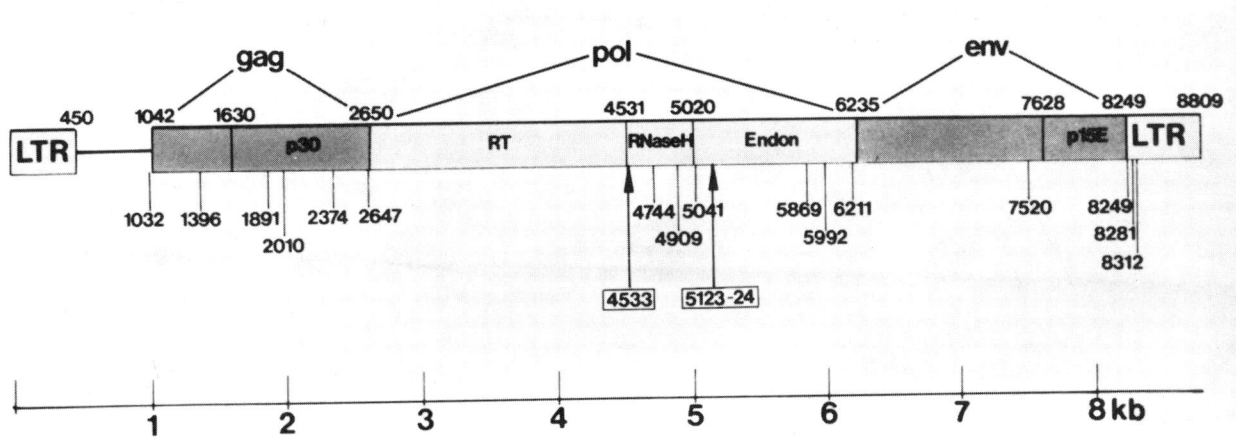

Figure 9–11. Genome organization of human endogenous provirus 4-1. Note stop codons (*bars*) and frame shifts (*boxes*). Numbers indicate positions of nucleotides.

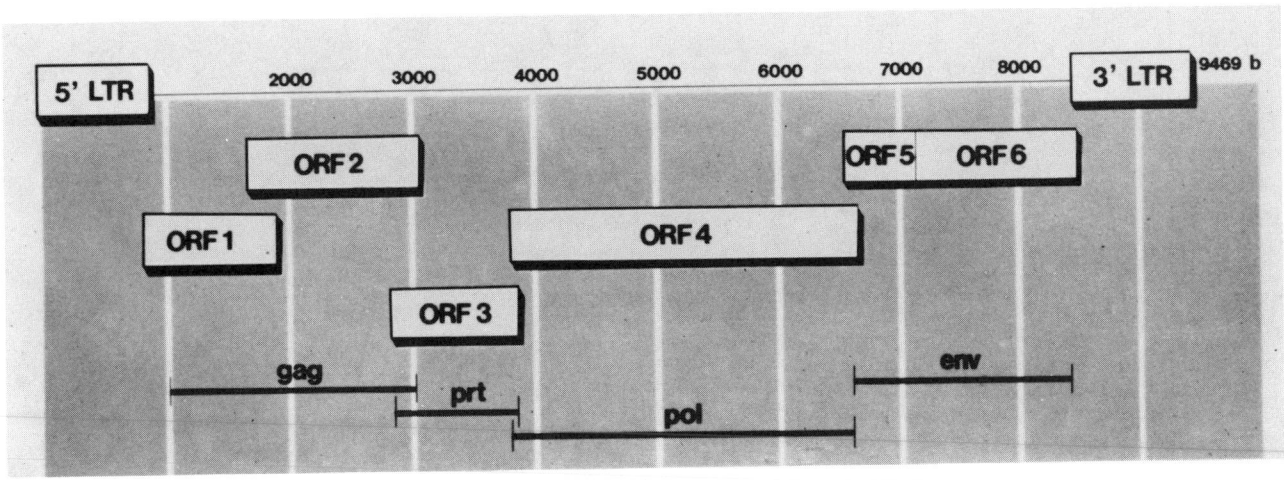

Figure 9–12. Genome organization of human endogenous provirus HERV-K10. Note open reading frames (ORFs).

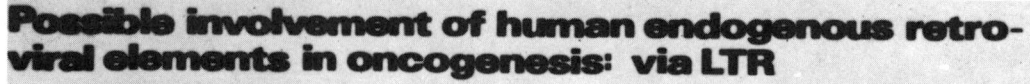

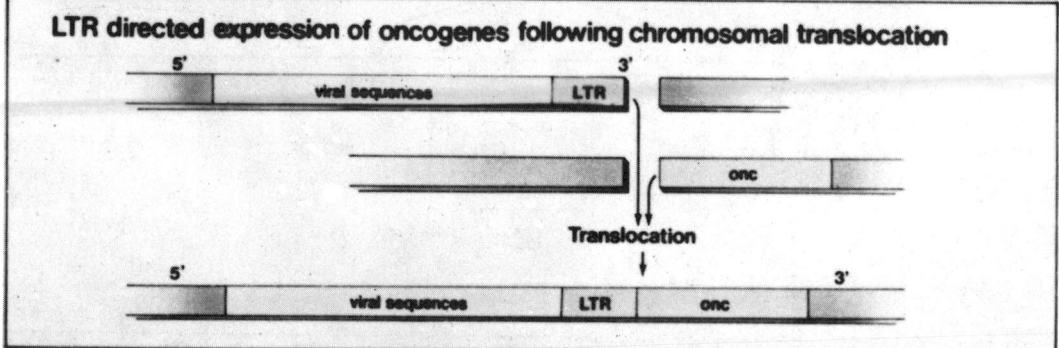

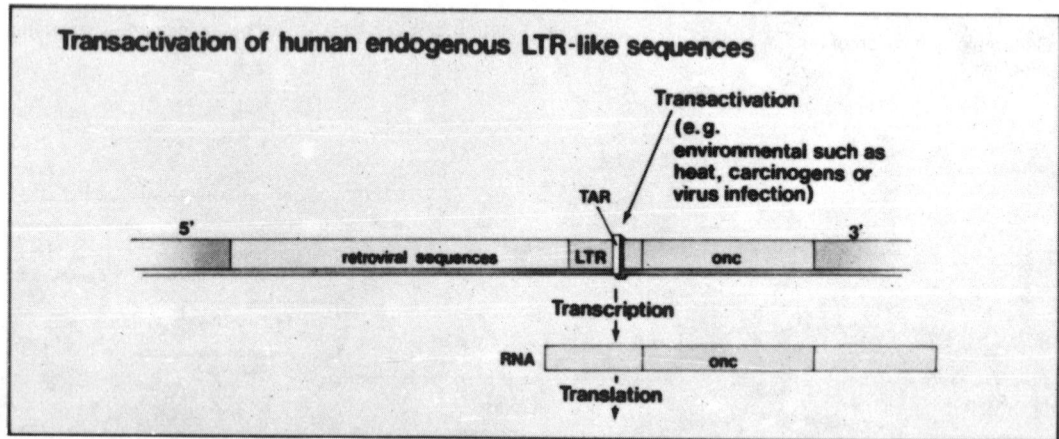

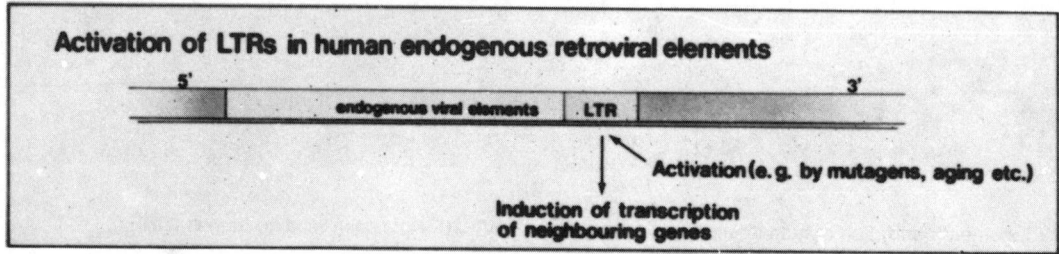

Figure 9–13. Model of long terminal repeat (LTR)–directed carcinogenesis.

Possible involvement of human endogenous retro-viral elements in oncogenesis: via env

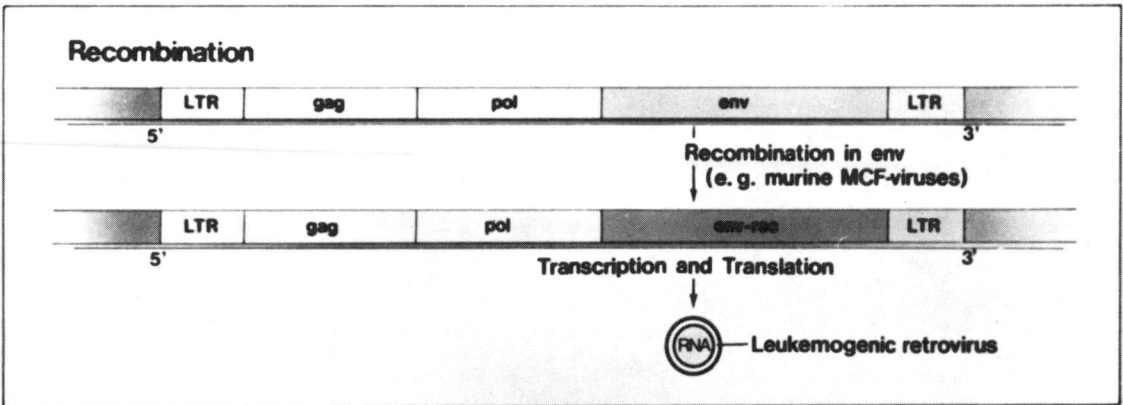

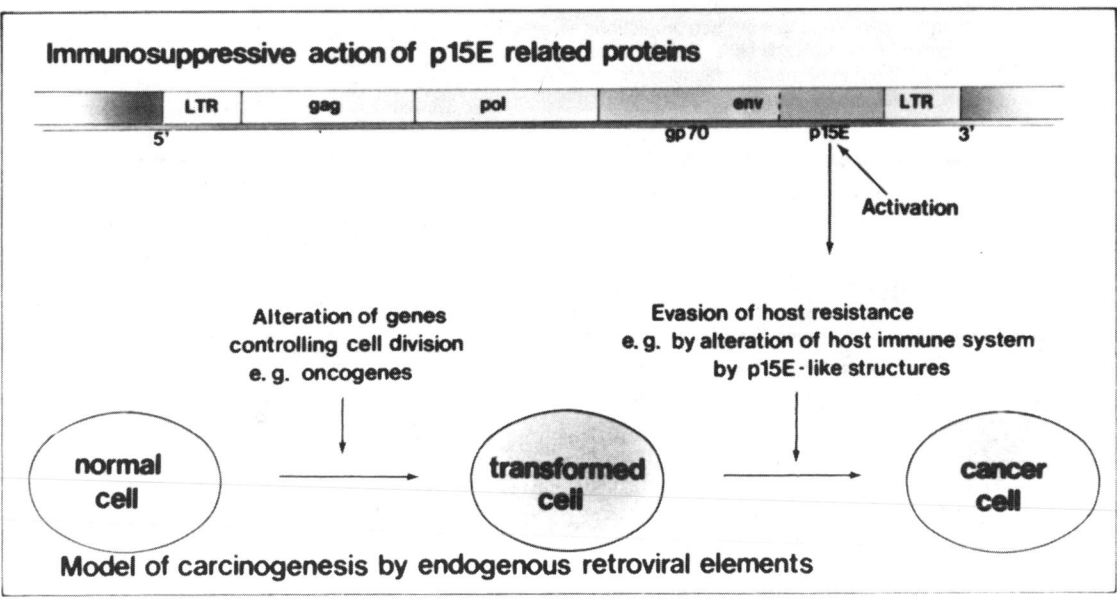

Figure 9–14. Model of env gene–mediated carcinogenesis.

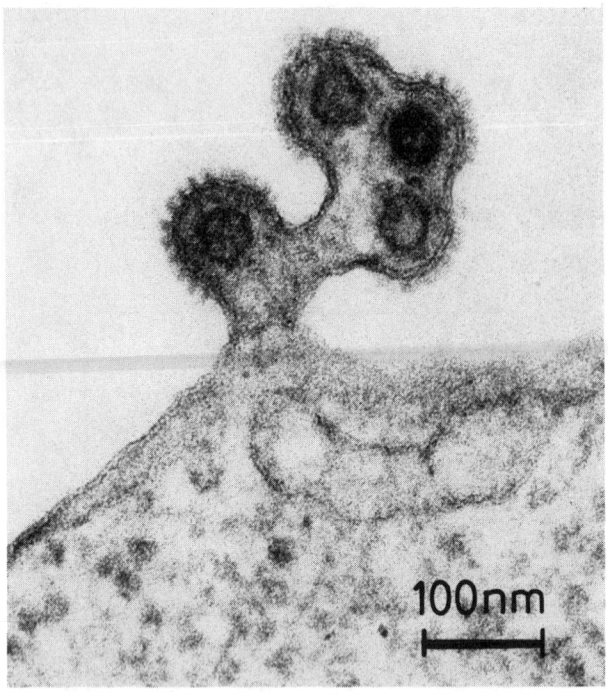

Figure 9–15. Electron micrograph of budding human foamy virus. Note that the envelope is studded with prominent surface projections about 12 nm in length. The central core is clearly separated from the envelope and measures about 50 nm in diameter. Magnification × 200,000. *(Courtesy of Dr H. Gelderblom, Berlin.)*

ecotropic and xenotropic retroviruses leading to the generation of highly leukemogenic viruses such as mink cell focus (MCF)–forming viruses in mice.[361–365]

HUMAN FOAMY VIRUS (HFV)

Although human foamy virus was among the first human viruses to be found to possess a reverse transcriptase, thereby fulfilling the definition of a human retrovirus, little attention was given to this virus group since no recognizable disease is associated with it.[366] The name "foamy virus" is derived from a growth peculiarity in tissue culture: they induce multinucleated giant cells with vacuoles which give the syncytia a foamy appearance. The first isolate stemmed from a cultured nasopharyngeal carcinoma. Other isolates were made from a cluster of patients with de Quervain thyroiditis.[367] But no causal relation has been established. The structure of HFV is shown in Figure 9–15. Characteristic features are the prominent surface projections and the clearly separated central core.[367]

The genome organization and nucleotide sequence of HFV have been determined recently. The genome is little more than 12,000 nucleotides long and has the common retroviral genes gag, pol, and env. There are four additional ORFs, three at the 3′ end called bel-1, -2, and -3, and one (called S1) between pol and env.[368, 369]

The 5′ half of the HFV genome containing gag and pol resembles mammalian C-type oncoviruses. The HFV reverse transcriptase prefers Mn^{2+} to Mg^{2+} for optimal activity similar to mammalian

C-type viruses. The 3′ half of the HFV genome resembles more that of lentiviruses mainly because of the three ORFs, between env and the 3′ LTR.

Foamy viruses have also been reported in monkeys, cats, cattle, and hamsters. Nine distinct serotypes of simian foamy viruses are known which have been noted particularly in chimpanzees. HFV is related to one of the chimpanzee strains.

Little is known on the epidemiology of HFV. Five percent seropositivity has been found in some populations of East Africa and some Pacific islands. No disease has been associated yet with HFV seropositivity or seroconversion.

REFERENCES

Human Immunodeficiency Viruses (HIV-1, -2)

1. Centers for Disease Control: *Pneumocystis* pneumonia—Los Angeles. *MMWR* 1981; 30:250–252.
2. Centers for Disease Control: Kaposi's sarcoma and *Pneumocystis* pneumonia among homosexual men—New York City and California. *MMWR* 1981; 30:305–308.
3. Popovic M, Sarngadharan MG, Reed E, et al: Detection, isolation, and continuous production of cytopathic retroviruses (HTLV-III) from patients with AIDS and pre-AIDS. *Science* 1984; 224:497–500.
4. Barré-Sinoussi F, Chermann JC, Rey F, et al: Isolation of a T-lymphotropic retrovirus from a patient at risk of acquired immune deficiency syndrome (AIDS). *Science* 1983; 220:868–871.
5. Levy JA, Hoffman AD, Kramer SM, et al: Isolation of lymphocytopathic retroviruses from San Francisco patients with AIDS. *Science* 1984; 225:840–842.
6. Clavel F, Guétard D, Brun-Vezinet F, et al: Isolation of a new human retrovirus from West African patients with AIDS. *Science* 1987; 233:343–346.
7. Clavel F, Mansinho K, Chamaret S, et al: Human immunodeficiency virus type 2 infection associated with AIDS in West Africa. *N Engl J Med* 1986; 316:1180–1185.
8. Gelderblom H, Pauli G: LAV/HTLV-III. Vergleich mit anderen Retroviren und Einordnung in die Subfamilie der Lentivirinae. *AIFO* 1986; 1:61–72.
9. Gelderblom HR, Özel M, Hausmann EHS, et al: Fine structure of human immunodeficiency virus (HIV), immunolocalization of structural proteins and virus-cell relation. *Micron Microsc* 1988; 19:41–60.
10. Gallo RC, Wong-Staal F, Montagnier L, et al: HIV/HTLV gene nomenclature. *Nature* 1988; 333:504.
11. Cohen EA, Terwilliger EF, Sodroski JG, et al: Identification of protein encoded by the vpu gene of HIV-1. *Nature* 1988; 334:532–534.
12. Hansen J, Schulze T, Mellert W, et al: Identification and characterization of HIV-specific RNaseH by monoclonal antibody. *EMBO* 1988; 7:239–243.
13. Wain-Hobson S, Sonigo P, Danos O, et al: Nucleotide sequence of the AIDS virus, LAV. *Cell* 1985; 40:9–17.
14. Ratner L, Haseltine W, Patarca R, et al: Complete nucleotide sequence of the AIDS virus, HTLV-III. *Nature* 1985; 313:227–284.
15. Alizon M, Wain-Hobson S, Montagnier L, et al: Genetic variability of the AIDS virus: Nucleotide sequence analysis of two isolates from African patients. *Cell* 1986; 46:63–74.
16. Desai SM, Kalyanaraman US, Casey JM, et al: Molecular cloning and primary nucleotide sequence analysis of a distinct human immunodeficiency virus isolate reveal significant divergence in its genomic sequences. *Proc Natl Acad Sci USA* 1986; 83:8380–8384.
17. Guyader M, Emerman M, Sonigo P, et al: Genome organization and transactivation of the human immunodeficiency virus type 2. *Nature* 1987; 326:662–669.

18. Sodroski J, Rosen C, Wong-Staal F, et al: Trans-acting transcriptional regulation of human T-cell leukemia virus type III long terminal repeat. *Science* 1985; 227:171–173.
19. Goh WC, Rosen C, Sodroski J, et al: Identification of a protein encoded by the transactivator gene tat III of human T-cell lymphotropic retrovirus type III. *J Virol* 1986; 59:181–184.
20. Rosen CA, Sodroski JG, Haseltine WA: Location of cis-acting regulatory sequences in the human T-cell lymphotropic virus type III long terminal repeat. *Cell* 1985; 41:813–823.
21. Sodroski J, Goh WC, Rosen C, et al: A second post-transcriptional trans-activator gene required for HTLV-III replication. *Nature* 1986; 321:412–417.
22. Feinberg MB, Jarrett RF, Aldovini A, et al: HTLV-III expression and production involve complex regulation at the levels of splicing and translation of viral RNA. *Cell* 1986; 46:807–817.
23. Knight DM, Flomerfelt FA, Ghraveb J: Expression of the art/trs protein of HIV and study of its role in viral envelope synthesis. *Science* 1987; 236:837–840.
24. Luciw PA, Cheng-Mayer C, Levy JA: Mutational analysis of the human immunodeficiency virus: The orf-B region down-regulates virus replication. *Proc Natl Acad Sci USA* 1987; 84:1434–1438.
25. Fisher AG, Ensoli B, Ivanoff L, et al: The sor gene of HIV-1 is required for efficient virus transmission in vitro. *Science* 1987; 237:888–893.
26. Strebel K, Daugherty D, Clouse K, et al: The HIV "A" (sor) gene product is essential for virus infectivity. *Nature* 1987; 328:728–730.
27. Strebel K, Klimkait T, Martin MA: A novel gene of HIV-1, vpu, and its 16-kilodalton product. *Science* 1988; 241:1221–1223.
28. Starcich B, Ratner L, Josephs SF, et al: Characterization of long terminal repeat sequences of HTLV-III. *Science* 1985; 227:538–540.
29. Jones KA, Kadonaga JT, Luciw PA, et al: Activation of the AIDS retrovirus promoter by the cellular transcription factor, Sp 1. *Science* 1986; 232:755–759.
30. Nabel G, Baltimore D: An inducible transcription factor activates expression of human immunodeficiency virus in T-cells. *Nature* 1987; 326:711–713.
31. Gendelman HE, Phelps W, Feigenbaum L, et al: Trans-activation of the human immunodeficiency virus long terminal repeat sequence by DNA viruses. *Proc Natl Acad Sci USA* 1986; 83;9759–9763.
32. Mosca JD, Bednarik DP, Raj NBK, et al: Herpes simplex virus type-1 can reactivate transcription of latent human immunodeficiency virus. *Nature* 1987; 325:67–70.
33. Steel CM, Ludlam CA, Beatson D, et al: HLA haplotype A1 B8 DR3 as a risk factor for HIV-related disease. *Lancet* 1988; 1:1185–1188.
34. Kowalski M, Potz J, Basiripour L, et al: Functional regions of the envelope glycoprotein of human immunodeficiency virus type 1. *Science* 1987; 237:1351–1355.
35. Lasky LA, Nakamura G, Smith DH, et al: Delineation of a region of the HIV type 1 gp120 glycoprotein critical for interaction with the CD4-receptor. *Cell* 1987; 50:975–985.
36. McDougal JS, Kennedy MS, Sligh JM, et al: Binding of HTLV-III/LAV to T4+ T cells by a complex of the 110 K viral protein and the T4 molecule. *Science* 1986; 231:382–385.
37. Matthews TJ, Weinhold KJ, Lyerly HK, et al: Interaction between the human T-cell lymphotropic virus type III$_B$ envelope glycoprotein gp120 and the surface antigen CD4: Role of carbohydrate in binding and cell fusion. *Proc Natl Acad Sci USA* 1987; 84:5424–5428.
38. Stein BS, Gowda SD, Lifson JD, et al: pH-independent HIV entry into CD4-positive T-cells via virus envelope fusion to the plasma membrane. *Cell* 1987; 49:659–668.
39. Lifson JD, Feinberg MB, Reyes GR, et al: Induction of CD4-dependent cell fusion by the HTLV-III/LAV envelope glycoprotein. *Nature* 1986; 323:725–728.
40. Seligmann M, Pinching AJ, Rosen FS, et al: Immunology of human immunodeficiency virus infection and the acquired immunodeficiency syndrome—an update. *Ann Intern Med* 1987; 107:234–242.
41. Gartner S, Markovits P, Markovitz DM, et al: The role of mononuclear phagocytes in HTLV-III/LAV infection. *Science* 1986; 233:215–219.
42. Popovic M, Gartner S: Isolation of HIV-1 from monocytes but not T-lymphocytes. *Lancet* 1987; 2:916.
43. Niedecken H, Lutz G, Bauer R, et al: Langerhans cell as primary target and vehicle for transmission of HIV. *Lancet* 1987; 2:519–520.
44. Cheng-Mayer C, Rutka JT, Rosenblum ML, et al: Human immunodeficiency virus can productively infect cultured human glial cells. *Proc Natl Acad Sci USA* 1987; 84:3526–3530.
45. Nelson JA, Wiley CA, Reynolds-Kohler C, et al: Human immunodeficiency virus detected in bowel epithelium from patients with gastrointestinal symptoms. *Lancet* 1988; 1:259–262.
46. Pomerantz RJ, de la Monte SM, Donegan SP, et al: Human immunodeficiency virus (HIV) infection of the uterine cervix. *Ann Intern Med* 1988; 108:321–327.
47. Levy JA, Cheng-Mayer C, Dina D, et al: AIDS retrovirus (ARV-2) clone replicates in transfected human and animal fibroblasts. *Science* 1986; 232:998–1001.
48. Mellert W, Kleinschmidt A, Schmidt J, et al: Productive infection of human fibroblasts and osteoblast-like cells with HIV-1. *AIDS Res Hum Retroviruses,* in press.
49. Lifson JD, Reyes GR, McGrath MS, et al: AIDS retrovirus induced cytopathology: Giant cell formation and involvement of CD4 antigen. *Science* 1986; 232:1123–1127.
50. Sodroski J, Goh WC, Rosen C, et al: Role of the HTLV-III/LAV envelope in syncytium formation and cytopathicity, *Nature* 1986; 322:470–474.
51. Somasundaran M, Robinson HL: A major mechanism of human immunodeficiency virus-induced cell killing does not involve cell fusion. *J Virol* 1987; 61:3114–3119.
52. Lynn WS, Tweedale A, Cloyd MW: Human immunodeficiency virus (HIV-1) cytotoxicity: perturbation of the cell membrane and depression of phospholipid synthesis. *Virology* 1988; 163:43–51.
53. Duesberg PH: Retroviruses as carcinogens and pathogens: expectations and reality. *Cancer Res* 1987; 47:1199–1220.
54. Duesberg P: HIV is not the cause of AIDS, *Science.* 1988; 241:514–517.
55. Shaw GM, Harper ME, Hahn BH, et al: HTLV-III infection in brains of children and adults with AIDS encephalopathy. *Science* 1985; 227:177–182.
56. Ho DD, Rota TR, Schooley RT: Isolation of HTLV-III from cerebrospinal fluid and neural tissues of patients with neurologic syndromes related to the acquired immunodeficiency syndrome. *N Engl J Med* 1985; 313:1493–1497.
57. Levy JA, Shimabukuro J, Hollander H, et al: Isolation of AIDS-associated retroviruses from cerebrospinal fluid and brain of patients with neurological symptoms. *Lancet* 1985; 2:586–588.
58. Gartner S, Markovits P, Markovitz DM, et al: Virus isolation from and identification of HTLV-III/LAV-producing cells in brain tissue from a patient with AIDS. *JAMA* 1986; 256; 2365–2371.
59. Koenig S, Gendelman E, Orenstein JM, et al: Detection of AIDS virus in macrophages in brain tissue from AIDS patients with encephalopathy. *Science* 1986; 233:1089–1093.
60. Rübsamen-Waigmann H, Becker WB, Helm EB, et al: Isolation of variants of lymphadenopathic retroviruses from the peripheral blood and cerebrospinal fluid of patients with ARC or AIDS. *J Med Virol* 1986; 19:335–344.
61. Koyanagi Y, Miles S, Mitsuyasu RT, et al: Dual infection of the central nervous system by AIDS viruses with distinct cellular tropism. *Science* 1987; 236:819–823.
62. Resnick L, di Marzo-Veronese F, Schüpbach J, et al: Intra-blood-brain-barrier synthesis of HTLV-III-specific IgG in patients with neurologic symptoms associated with AIDS or AIDS-related complex. *N Engl J Med* 1985; 314:1498–1504.
63. Goudsmit J, Epstein LG, Paul DA, et al: Intra-blood-brain barrier synthesis of human immunodeficiency virus antigen and antibody

in humans and chimpanzees. *Proc Natl Acad Sci USA* 1987; 84:3876–3880.

64. Funke I, Hahn A, Rieber EP, et al: The cellular receptor (CD4) of the human immunodeficiency virus is expressed on neurons and glial cells in human brain. *J Exp Med* 1987; 165:1230–1235.
65. Asjö B, Morfeldt-Manson L, Albert J, et al: Replicative capacity of human immunodeficiency virus from patients with varying severity of HIV infection. *Lancet* 1986; 2:660–662.
66. Joller-Jemelka HI, Joller PW, Müller F, et al: Anti-HIV IgM antibody analysis during early manifestations of HIV-infections. *AIDS* 1987; 1:45–47.
67. v Sydow M, Gaines H, Parry JV, et al: Early diagnosis of primary HIV infections. Abstracts. Fourth International Conference on AIDS, 1988, No. 3511.
68. Allain JP, Laurian Y, Paul DA, et al: Serological markers in early stages of human immunodeficiency virus infection in haemophiliacs. *Lancet* 1986; 2:1233–1236.
69. Ranki A, Valle SL, Krohn M, et al: Long latency precedes overt seroconversion in sexually transmitted human immunodeficiency virus infection. *Lancet* 1987; 2:589–593.
70. Lange J, Hiusmann DA, de Wolf F, et al: Persistent HIV antigenaemia and decline of HIV core antibodies associated with transition to AIDS. *Br Med J* 1986; 293:1459–1462.
71. Hehlmann RA, Fischer A, Matuschke A, et al: Development of HIV-markers during the later stages of HIV-infection. *AIFO* 1987; 2:441–447.
72. Weiss RA, Clapham PR, Cheingsong-Popov R, et al: Neutralization of human T-lymphotropic virus type III by sera of AIDS and AIDS-risk patients. *Nature* 1985; 316:69–72.
73. Robert-Guroff M, Brown M, Gallo RC: HTLV-III-neutralizing antibodies in patients with AIDS and AIDS-related complex. *Nature* 1985; 316:72–74.
74. Ho DD, Sarngadharan MG, Hirsch MS, et al: Human immunodeficiency virus neutralizing antibodies recognize several conserved domains on the envelope glycoproteins. *J Virol* 1987; 61:2024–2028.
75. Mullis K, Faloona F, Scharf S, et al: Specific enzymatic amplification of DNA in vitro: the polymerase chain reaction. *Cold Spring Harbor Symp Quant Biol* 1986; 6:263–273.
76. Marx JL: Multiplying genes by leaps and bounds. *Science* 1988; 240:1408–1410.
77. Kwok S, Mack DH, Mullis KB, et al: Identification of human immunodeficiency virus sequences using in vitro enzymatic amplification and oligomer cleavage detection. *J Virol* 1987; 61:1690.
78. Wolinsky S, Rinaldo C, Farzedegan H, et al: Polymerase chain reaction (PCR) detection of HIV provirus before HIV seroconversion. Presented at Fourth International Conference on AIDS, 1988, abstract No. 1099, 1646.
79. Centers for Disease Control: Persistent, generalized lymphadenopathy among homosexual males. *MMWR* 1982; 31:249–251.
80. Centers for Disease Control: CDC classification for human T-lymphotropic virus type III/lymphadenopathy associated virus infections. *MMWR* 1986; 35:334–339.
81. Centers for Disease Control: Revision of the CDC surveillance case definition for acquired immunodeficiency syndrome. *MMWR* 1987; 36(suppl):1S–15S.
82. Redfield R, Wright DC, Tramont EC: The Walter Reed staging classification for HTLV-III/LAV infection. *N Engl J Med* 1986; 314:131–132.
83. Meuwissen JHTH, Tauber I, Leeuwenberg ADEM, et al: Parasitologic and serologic observations of infection with pneumocystis in humans. *J Infect Dis* 1977; 136:43–49.
84. Rothenberg R, Woelfel M, Stoneburner R, et al: Survival with the acquired immunodeficiency syndrome. Experience with 5833 cases in New York City. *N Engl J Med* 1987; 317:1297–1302.
85. Staib F: Kryptokokkose bei AIDS aus mykologisch-diagnostischer und epidemiologischer Sicht. *AIFO* 1987; 2:363–382.
86. Jahn G, Mach M, Fleckenstein B: Cytomegalovirus and AIDS. *AIFO* 1988; 3:59–72.
87. Ziegler JL, Templeton AC, Vogel CL: Kaposi's sarcoma: a comparison of classical, endemic, and epidemic forms. *Semin Oncol* 1984; 11:47–52.
88. Des Jarlais DC, Stoneburner R, Thomas P, et al: Declines in proportion of Kaposi's sarcoma among cases of AIDS in multiple risk groups in New York City. *Lancet* 1987; 2:1024–1025.
89. Abrams DI, Volberding PA: Alpha interferon therapy of AIDS-associated Kaposi's sarcoma. *Semin Oncol* 1986; 13(suppl. 2):43–47.
90. Ziegler JL, Beckstaed JA, Volberding PA, et al: Non-Hodgkin's lymphoma in 90 homosexual men. *N Engl J Med* 1984; 311:565–570.
91. Levine AM: Non-Hodgkin's lymphomas and other malignancies in the acquired immune deficiency syndrome. *Semin Oncol* 1987; 14(suppl 3):34–39.
92. Gabuzda DH, Hirsch MS, Neurologic manifestations of infection with human immunodeficiency virus. *Ann Intern Med* 1987; 107:383–391.
93. Grant I, Atkinson JH, Hesselink JR, et al: Evidence for early central nervous system involvement in the acquired immunodeficiency syndrome (AIDS) and other human immunodeficiency virus (HIV) infections. *Ann Intern Med* 1987; 107:828–836.
94. Price RW, Brew B, Sidtis J, et al: The brain in AIDS: Central nervous system HIV-1 infection and AIDS dementia complex. *Science* 1988; 239:586–592.
95. Levy RM, Bredesen DE: Central nervous system dysfunction in acquired immunodeficiency syndrome. *J AIDS* 1988; 1:41–64.
96. Petito CK, Eun-Sook Cho, Lemann W, et al: Neuropathology of acquired immunodeficiency syndrome (AIDS): An autopsy review. *Neuropathol Exp Neurol* 1986; 45:635–646.
97. Friedman-Kien AE, Lafleur F, Gendler E, et al: Herpes zoster: a possible early clinical sign of acquired immunodeficiency syndrome in high risk individuals. *J Am Acad Dermatol* 1986; 14:1023–1028.
98. Colebunders R, Mann JM, Francis H, et al: Generalized papular pruritic eruption in African patients with human immunodeficiency virus infection. *AIDS* 1987; 1:117–121.
99. Greenspan D, Greenspan JS, Conant M, et al: Oral "hairy" leukoplakia in male homosexuals: evidence of association with both papillomavirus and a herpes group virus. *Lancet* 1984; 2:1564–1571.
100. Sprecher S, Soumenkoff G, Puissant F, et al: Vertical transmission of HIV in 15-week fetus. *Lancet* 1986; 2:288–289.
101. Marion RW, Wiznia AA, Hutcheon RG, et al: Human T-cell lymphotropic virus type III (HTLV-III) embryopathy. *AJDC* 1986; 140:638–640.
102. Semprini AE, Vucetich A, Pardi G, et al: HIV infection and AIDS in newborn babies of mothers positive for HIV antibody. *Br Med J* 1987; 294:610.
103. Mok JQ, De Rossi A, Ades AE, et al: Infants born to mothers seropositive for human immunodeficiency virus. Preliminary findings from a multicentre European study. *Lancet* 1987; 1:1164–1167.
104. Froland SS, Jenum P, Lindboe CF, et al: HIV-1 infection in Norwegian family before 1970. *Lancet* 1988; 1:1344–1345.
105. Nahmias AJ, Weiss J, Yao X, et al: Evidence for human infection with an HTLV-III/LAV-like virus in Central Africa, 1959. *Lancet* 1986; 1:1279–1280.
106. Peterman TA, Jaffe HW, Feorino PM, et al: Transfusion-associated acquired immunodeficiency syndrome in the United States. *JAMA* 1985; 254:2913–2917.
107. Goedert JJ, Eyster ME, Friedman RM, et al: AIDS rates, markers and cofactors. Abstracts. Fourth International Conference on AIDS, 1988, No. 4144.
108. Hessol N, Rutherford G, Lifson AR, et al: The natural history of HIV infection in a cohort of homosexual and bisexual men: A decade of follow-up. Abstracts. Fourth International Conference on AIDS, 1988, No. 4096.
109. Lui K-J, Lawrence DN, Morgan WM, et al: A model-based approach for estimating the mean incubation period of transfusion-

associated acquired immunodeficiency syndrome. *Proc Natl Acad Sci USA* 1986; 83:3051–3055.

110. May RM, Anderson RM: Transmission dynamics of HIV-infection. *Nature* 1987; 326:137–142.

111. Rees M: The sombre view of AIDS. *Nature* 1987; 326:343–345.

112. Medley GF, Anderson RM, Cox DR, et al: Incubation period of AIDS in patients infected via blood transfusion. *Nature* 1987; 328:719–721.

113. Lui KJ, Darrow WW, Rutherford III GW: A model-based estimate of the mean incubation period for AIDS in homosexual men. *Science* 1988; 240:1333–1335.

114. Brodt HR, Helm EB, Werner A, et al: Spontanverlauf der LAV/HTLV-III-Infektion. *Dtsch Med Wochenschr* 1986; 111:1175–1180.

115. Hehlmann R: Editorial: IVth International AIDS Conference. *AIFO* 1988; 3:427–430.

116. Frösner G: Epidemiology, parts I and II. Report from the IVth International Conference on AIDS. *AIFO* 1988; 3:460–468, 503–510, 516–523, 573–579.

117. Goedert JJ, Landesman SH, Eyster ME, et al: AIDS incidence in pregnant women, their babies, homosexual men, and hemophiliacs. Abstracts. Third International Conference on AIDS, 1987, TP.56.

118. Eyster ME, Gail MH, Ballard JO, et al: Natural history of human immunodeficiency virus infections in hemophiliacs: effects of T-cell subsets, platelet counts, and age. *Ann Intern Med* 1987; 107:1–6.

119. Hessol N, Rutherford G, O'Mally PM, et al: The natural history of human immunodeficiency virus in a cohort of homosexual and bisexual men: A 7-year prospective study. Abstracts. Third International Conference on AIDS, 1987, M3.1.

120. Ward JW, Deppe D, Perkins H, et al: Risk of disease in recipients of blood from donors later found infected with human immunodeficiency virus (HIV). Abstracts. Third International Conference on AIDS 1987, M3.5.

121. Helm EB, Brodt R, Wegner R, et al: Spontanverlauf der HIV-Infektion. Eine Bilanz 5 Jahre nach den ersten AIDS-Erkrankungen in Frankfurt/Main. *AIFO* 1987; 2:567–572.

122. Centers for Disease Control: Update: acquired immunodeficiency syndrome (AIDS)—worldwide. *MMWR* 1988; 37:286–295.

123. WHO Report No. 17: AIDS Surveillance in Europe (situation by 31th March 1988). *AIFO* 1988; 3:530–535.

124. Rozenbaum W, Gharakhanian S, Cardon B, et al: HIV-transmission by oral sex. *Lancet* 1988; 1:1395.

125. Fischl MA, Dickinson GM, Segal A, et al: Heterosexual transmission of human immunodeficiency virus (HIV): Relationship of sexual practices to seroconversion. *Abstracts. Third International Conference on AIDS, 1987.* THP. 92.

126. Goedert JJ, Eyster ME, Biggar RJ: Heterosexual transmission of human immunodeficiency virus (HIV): Association with severe T4-cell depletion in male hemophiliacs. *Abstracts. Third International Conference on AIDS, 1987* W.2.6.

127. Kingsley LA, Detels R, Kaslow R, et al: Risk factors for seroconversion to HIV among male homosexuals. Results from the multicenter AIDS cohort study. *Lancet* 1987; 1:345–349.

128. Kaslow RA, Phair JP, Friedman HB, et al: Infection with the human immunodeficiency virus: clinical manifestations and their relationship to immune deficiency. A report from the Multicenter AIDS Cohort Study. *Ann Intern Med* 1987; 107:474–480.

129. Winkelstein W, Lyman DM, Padian N, et al: Sexual practices and risk of infection by the human immunodeficiency virus. *JAMA* 1987; 257:321–325.

130. Centers for Disease Control: Antibody to human immunodeficiency virus in female prostitutes. *MMWR* 1987; 36:157–161.

131. Fischl MA, Dickinson GM, Flanagan S, et al: Human immunodeficiency virus (HIV) among female prostitutes in South Florida. *Abstracts. Third International Conference on AIDS, 1987,* W.2.2.

132. Padian N, Carlson J, Browning R, et al: Human immunodeficiency virus (HIV) infection among prostitutes in Nevada. *Abstracts. Third International Conference on AIDS, 1987,* WP.53.

133. Wallace JI, Christonikos N, Mann J: HIV Exposure in New York City streetwalkers (prostitutes). *Abstracts. Third International Conference on AIDS,* 1987, THP 55.

134. Cortes E, Lix L, Detels R, et al: Seroprevalence of HIV-1, HIV-2, and HTLV-I in high-risk Brazilians. *Abstracts. Fourth International Conference on AIDS, 1988,* No. 5067.

135. Castello-Branco L, Carvalho MIL, Castilho EA, et al: Frequency of antibody to human immunodeficiency virus (HIV) in male and female prostitutes in Rio de Janeiro, Brazil. *Abstracts. Fourth International Conference on AIDS, 1988,* No. 5144.

136. Plummer FA, Simonsen JN, Ngugi EN, et al: Incidence of human immunodeficiency virus (HIV) infection and related disease in a cohort of Nairobi prostitutes. *Abstracts. Third International Conference on AIDS, 1987,* M.8.4.

137. Anonymous: AIDS in Africa. *AIFO* 1987; 2:5–25.

138. Neequaye AR, Neequaye J, Mingle JA, et al: Preponderance of females with AIDS in Ghana. *Lancet* 1986; 2:978.

139. van de Perre Ph, Clumeck N, Carael M, et al: Female prostitutes. A risk group for infection with human T-cell lymphotropic virus type III. *Lancet* 1985; 2:524–527.

140. Denis F, Gershy-Damet G, Lhuillier M, et al: Prevalence of human T-lymphotropic retroviruses type III (HIV) and type IV in Ivory Coast. *Lancet* 1987; 1:408–411.

141. John TJ, Babu PG, Jayakumari H, et al: Prevalence of HIV infection in risk groups in Tamilnadu, India. *Lancet* 1987; 1:160–161.

142. Babu PG, John TJ, Moses H: Current prevalence of HIV-infection in Tamilnadu, Southern India. *Abstracts. Fourth International Conference on AIDS, 1988,* No. 5511.

143. Seth P, Sharma UK, Malaviya AN, et al: Serosurveillance of human immunodeficiency virus (HIV) infection in North India. *Abstracts. Fourth International Conference on AIDS, 1988,* No. 5507.

144. Solomon S, Sunderaman DR, Babu G, et al: Quantitative estimation of HIV antibodies in prostitutes. *Abstracts. Fourth International Conference on AIDS, 1988,* No. 5512.

145. Thongcharoen P, Wasi C, Wangroongsarb Y: HIV infection in Thailand. *Abstracts. Fourth International Conference on AIDS, 1988,* No. 5523.

146. Tirelli U, Vaccher E, Sorio R, et al: HTLV-III antibodies in drug-addicted prostitutes used by US soldiers in Italy. *JAMA* 1986; 256:711–712.

147. Papaevangelou G, Roumeliotou-Karayannis A, Kallinikos G, et al: LAV/HTLV-III infection in female prostitutes. *Lancet* 1985; 2:1018.

148. Barton SE, Underhill GS, Gilchrist C, et al: HTLV-III antibody in prostitutes. *Lancet* 1985; 2:1424.

149. Lüthy R, Ledergerber B, Täuber M, et al: Prevalence of HIV-antibodies among prostitutes in Zürich, Switzerland. *Klin Wochenschr* 1987; 65:287–288.

150. Hunsmann G, Schneider J, Bayer H, et al: Seroepidemiology of HTLV-III (LAV) in the Federal Republic of Germany. *Klin Wochenschr* 1985; 63:233–235.

151. Erfle V, Hehlmann R, Mellert W, et al: Prevalence of antibodies to HTLV-III in AIDS risk groups in West Germany. *Cancer Res* 1985; 45(suppl):4627s–4629s.

152. Schultz S, Milberg JA, Kristal AR, et al: Female-to-male transmission of HTLV-III. *JAMA* 1986; 255:1703–1704.

153. Smith GL, Smith KF: Lack of HIV infection and condom use in licensed prostitutes. *Lancet* 1986; 2:1392.

154. Centers for Disease Control: Human immunodeficiency virus infection in the United States: a review of current knowledge. *MMWR* 1987; 36(suppl 5–6):1–48.

155. Hehlmann R: Epidemiologie der HIV-Infektion. *Internist* 1988; 29:112–123.

156. Robert-Guroff M, Weiss SH, Giron JA, et al: Prevalence of antibodies to HTLV-I, -II, and -III in intravenous drug abusers from an AIDS endemic region. *JAMA* 1986; 255:3133–3137.

157. Marmor M, Des Jarlais DC, Cohen H, et al: Risk factors for infection with human immunodeficiency virus among intravenous drug abusers in New York City. *AIDS* 1987; 1:39–44.

158. Centers for Disease Control: Antibodies to a retrovirus etiologically associated with acquired immunodeficiency syndrome (AIDS) in populations with increased incidences of the syndrome. *MMWR* 1984; 33:377–379.
159. Lange WR, Primm BJ, Tennant FS, et al: The geographic distribution of human immunodeficiency virus (HIV) antibodies in parenteral drug abusers (PDAs). Abstracts. Third International Conference on AIDS, 1987, TP.54.
160. D'Aquila R, Williams AB, Petersen LR: HIV-seroprevalence among Connecticut intravenous drug users in 1986. *Abstracts. Third International Conference on AIDS, 1987,* THP 44.
161. Rodrigo JM, Serra MA, Aguilar E, et al: HTLV-III antibodies in drug addicts in Spain. *Lancet* 1985; 2:156–157.
162. Gradilone A, Zani M, Barillari G, et al: HTLV-I and HIV infection in drug addicts in Italy. *Lancet* 1986; 2:753–754.
163. Luzi G, Aiuti F, Rezza G, et al: Italian HIV infection updated. *Nature* 1987; 328:385–386.
164. Ferroni P, Geroldi D, Galli C, et al: HTLV-III antibody among Italian drug addicts. *Lancet* 1985; 2:52–53.
165. Zerboni R, Cusini M, Carminati G, et al: Trend of sexually transmitted HIV infection in Milan, Italy. *Abstracts. Fourth International Conference on AIDS, 1988,* No. 4174.
166. Conte ID, Lucchini A, Colombo S, et al: HIV infection in drug addicts: an epidemiological study in Turin, North Italy. *Abstracts. Third International Conference on AIDS, 1987,* MP 40.
167. Accurso V, Mancuso S, Mitra ME, et al: The epidemiology of HIV infection in Sicily: our experience. *Abstracts. Fourth International Conference on AIDS, 1988,* No. 4170.
168. Peutherer JF, Edmond E, Simmonds P, et al: HTLV-III antibody in Edinburgh drug addicts. *Lancet* 1985; 2:1129–1130.
169. Brettle RP, Bisset K, Burns S, et al: Human immunodeficiency virus and drug misuse: the Edinburgh experience. *Br Med J* 1987; 295:421–424.
170. Robertson JR, Skidmose CA, France AJ, et al: 1985 epidemic of HIV infection in Edinburgh IVDA: 3 years on. *Abstracts. Fourth International Conference on AIDS, 1988* No. 4528.
171. Follett EAC, Wallace LA, McCruden EAB: HIV and HBV infection in drug abusers in Glasgow. *Lancet* 1987; 1:920.
172. Sonja Z, Jevtovic DJ, Fridman V, et al: Two years of experience with HIV infection in Belgrade (Yugoslavia). *Abstracts. Fourth International Conference on AIDS, 1988,* No. 4179.
173. Böttiger M, Forsgren M, Grillner L, et al: Monitoring of HIV infection among i.v. drug users in Stockholm. *Abstracts. Fourth International Conference on AIDS, 1988,* No. 4709.
174. Mortimer PP, Vandervelde EM, Jesson WJ, et al: HTLV-III antibodies in Swiss and English intravenous drug abusers. *Lancet* 1985; 2:449–450.
175. Joller-Jemelka JI, Wilhelm U, Steffen R, et al: Virale Hepatitis und AIDS-assoziierte HTLV-III/LAV-Virusinfektionen bei Drogenabhängigen. *Schweiz Med Wochenschr* 1985; 115:1114–1119.
176. Zoulek G, Gürtler L, Eberle J, et al: Zunahme der Prävalenz von Antikörpern gegen LAV/HTLV-III bei Drogenabhängigen in der Bundesrepublik Deutschland. *Dtsch Med Wochenschr* 1986; 111:567–570.
177. Harms G, Laukamm-Josten U, Bienzle U, et al: Risk factors for HIV-infection in German i.v. drug abusers. *Klin Wochenschr* 1987; 65:376–379.
178. Harms G, Bienzle U, Schneider V, et al: HIV-Antikörperprevalenz bei Berliner i.v.-Drogenabhängigen. *AIFO* 1987; 2:392–393.
179. Centers for Disease Control: Update: acquired immunodeficiency syndrome and human immunodeficiency virus infection among health-care workers. *MMWR* 1988; 37:229–239.
180. Centers for Disease Control: Update: Human immunodeficiency virus infections in health-care workers exposed to blood of infected patients. *MMWR* 1987; 36:285–289.
181. McNeil JG, Wann F, Burke D, et al: A direct estimation of the rate of new HIV-infections in US Army personnel. *Abstracts. Fourth International Conference on AIDS, 1988,* No. 4641.
182. Hehlmann R, Kreeb G, Erfle V, et al: Antibodies to HTLV-III in patients with acquired immunodeficiency of lymphadenopathy

syndrome in West Germany. *Lancet* 1984; 2:1094.
183. Brundage J, Burke DS, Gardner LI, et al: Temporal trends of prevalence and incidence of HIV infection among civilian applicants for U.S. military service: Analysis of 18 months of serological screening data. *Abstracts. Third International Conference on AIDS, 1987,* T.7.1.
184. Burke DS, Brundage JF, Herbold JR, et al: Human immunodeficiency virus infections among civilian applicants for United States military service, October 1985 to March 1986. *N Engl J Med* 1987; 317:131–136.
185. Centers for Disease Control: Trends in human immunodeficiency virus infection among civilian applicants for military service—United States. October 1985–December 1986. *MMWR* 1987; 36:157–161.
186. Quinn TC, Mann JM, Curran JW, et al: AIDS in Africa: An epidemiologic paradigm. *Science* 1986; 2:955–963.
187. Fleming AF: AIDS in Africa—an update. *AIFO* 1988; 3:116–138.
188. Lange WR, Jaffe JH: AIDS in Haiti. *N Engl J Med* 1987; 316:1409–1410.
189. Koenig RE, Pittaluga J, Bogart M, et al: Prevalence of antibodies to the human immunodeficiency virus in Dominicans and Haitians in the Dominican Republic. *JAMA* 1987; 257:631–634.
190. Bartholomew C, Saxinger WC, Clark JW, et al: Transmission of HTLV-I and HIV among homosexual men in Trinidad. *JAMA* 1987; 257:2604–2608.
191. González J, Koch M: On the role of the transients for the prognostic analysis of AIDS and the anciennity distribution of AIDS patients. *AIFO* 1986; 1:621–630.
192. Downs AM, Ancelle RA, Jager HC, et al: AIDS in Europe: Current trends and short-term predictions estimated from surveillance data, January 1981–June 1986. *AIDS* 1987; 1:53–57.
193. Staszewski S, Stille W, Werner A, et al: HIV-2-Infektion auch in Deutschland. *Dtsch Med Wochenschr* 1987; 112:487.
194. Centers for Disease Control: AIDS due to HIV-2-infection—New Jersey. *MMWR* 1988; 37:33–35.
195. Nzilambi N, de Cock KM, Forthal DN, et al: The prevalence of infection with human immunodeficiency virus over a 10-year period in rural Zaire. *N Engl J Med* 1988; 318:276–279.
196. Flahault A, Valleron AJ: The global spread of AIDS: potential role of air transport. A mathematical model based on the Rvacher-Longini approach. *Abstracts. Fourth International Conference on AIDS, 1988,* No. 4684.
197. Mellert W, Erfle V, Hehlmann R: HTLV-III/LAV-Antikörpertest: Indirekte Immunperoxidasefärbung. *AIFO* 1986; 1:105–107.
198. Erfle V, Mellert W: Human T-lymphotropic virus III/lymphadenopathy-associated virus antibodies, in: Bergmeyer (ed): *Methods of Enzymatic Analysis.* VCH Verlagsgesellschaft, Weinheim, West Germany, 1986, vol 10, pp 469–483.
199. Harper ME, Marselle LM, Gallo RC, et al: Detection of lymphocytes expressing human T-lymphotropic virus type III in lymph nodes and peripheral blood from infected individuals by in situ hybridization. *Proc Natl Acad Sci USA* 1986; 83:772–776.
200. Cheson BD, Levine AM, Mildvan D, et al: Suramin therapy in AIDS and related disorders. Report of the US suramin working group. *JAMA* 1987; 258:1347–1351.
201. Fischl MA, Richman DD, Griego MH, et al: The efficiency of azidothymidine (AZT) in the treatment of patients with AIDS and AIDS-related complex. *N Engl J Med* 1987; 317:185–191.
202. Richman DD, Fischl MA, Griego MH, et al: The toxicity of azidothymidine (AZT) in the treatment of patients with AIDS and AIDS-related complex. *N Engl J Med* 1987; 317:192–197.
203. Yarchoan R, Perno CF, Thomas RV, et al: Phase-1 studies of 2',3'-dideoxycytidine in severe human immunodeficiency virus infection as a single agent and alternating with zidovudine (AZT). *Lancet* 1988; 1:76–81.
204. Crumpacker C, Heagy W, Bubley G, et al: Ribavirin treatment of the acquired immunodeficiency-syndrome-related complex (ARC). *Ann Intern Med* 1987; 107:664–674.
205. Yamamoto IK, Barré-Sinoussi F, Bolton V, et al: Human alpha-

and beta-interferon but not gamma-interferon suppress the in vitro replication of LAV, HTLV-III and ARV-2. *Interferon Res* 1986; 6:143–152.

206. Meller W, Amtmann E, Erfle V, et al: Inhibition of HIV-1 replication by an antiviral xanthate compound in vitro. *AIDS Res Hum Retroviruses* 1988; 4:71–81.

207. Pert CB, Hill JM, Ruff MR, et al: Octapeptides deduced from the neuropeptide receptor-like pattern of antigen T4 in brain potently inhibit human immunodeficiency virus receptor binding and T-cell infectivity. *Proc Natl Acad Sci USA* 1986; 83:9254–9258.

208. Wetterberg L, Alexius B, Sääf J, et al: Peptide T in treatment of AIDS. *Lancet* 1987; 1:159.

209. Sarin PS, Gallo RC, Sherr DI, et al: Effect of a novel compound (AL 721) on HTLV-III infectivity in vitro. *N Engl J Med* 1985; 313:1289–1290.

210. Montefiori DC, Mitchell WM: Antiviral activity of mismatched double-stranded RNA against human immunodeficiency virus in vitro. *Proc Natl Acad Sci* 1987; 84:2985–2989.

211. Mitsuya H, Looney DJ, Kuno S, et al: Dextran sulfate suppression of viruses in the HIV family: inhibition of virion binding to CD4+ cells. *Science* 1988; 240:646–649.

212. Faber V, Dalgleish AG, Newell A, et al: Inhibition of HIV replication in vitro by fusidic acid. *Lancet* 1987; 2:827–828.

213. Lloyd G, Atkinson T, Sutton PM: Effect of bile salts and of fusidic acid on HIV-1 infection of cultured cells. *Lancet* 1988; 1:1418–1421.

214. Smith DH, Byrn RA, Marsters SA, et al: Blocking of HIV-1 infectivity by a soluble, secreted form of the CD4 antigen. *Science* 1987; 238:1704–1707.

215. Fisher RA, Bertonis JM, Meier W, et al: HIV infection is blocked in vitro by recombinant soluble CD4. *Nature* 1988; 331:76–78.

216. Hussey RE, Richardson NE, Kowalski M, et al: A soluble CD4 protein selectively inhibits HIV replication and syncytium formation. *Nature* 1988; 331:78–81.

217. Deen KC, McDougal JS, Inacker R, et al: A soluble form of CD4 (T4) proteins inhibits AIDS virus infection. *Nature* 1988; 331:82–84.

218. Traunecker A, Lüke W, Karjalainer K: Soluble CD4 molecules neutralize human immunodeficiency virus type 1. *Nature* 1988; 331:84–86.

219. Groopman J, Mitsuyasu RT, de Leo MJ, et al: Effect of recombinant human granulocyte-macrophage colony-stimulating factor on myelopoiesis in the acquired immunodeficiency syndrome. *N Engl J Med* 1987; 317:593–598.

220. Koff WC, Hoth DF: Development and testing of AIDS vaccines. *Science* 1988; 241:426–432.

221. Clements ML: AIDS vaccines. Principles and practice of infectious diseases. Submitted for publication.

222. Willey RL, Rutledge RA, Dias S, et al: Identification of conserved and divergent domains within the envelope gene of the acquired immunodeficiency syndrome retrovirus. *Proc Natl Acad Sci USA* 1986; 83:5038–5042.

223. Ho DD, Kaplan JC, Rackauskas IE, et al: Second conserved domain of gp 120 is important for HIV infectivity and antibody neutralization. *Science* 1988; 239:1021–1023.

224. Robinson WE Jr, Montefiori DC, Mitchell WM: Antibody-dependent enhancement of human immunodeficiency virus type 1 infection. *Lancet* 1988; 1:790–794.

225. Modrow S, Hahn BH, Shaw GM, et al: Computer-assisted analysis of the envelope protein sequences of seven HTLV-III/LAV isolates: Prediction of antigenic epitopes in conserved and variable regions. *J Virol* 1987; 61:570–578.

226. Berman PW, Groopman JE, Gregory T, et al: Human immunodeficiency virus type 1 challenge of chimpanzees immunized with recombinant envelope glycoprotein gp120. *Proc Natl Acad Sci USA* 1988; 85:5200–5204.

227. Leonard JM, Abramczuk J, Pezen D, et al: Expressions of an infectious HIV provirus in transgenic mice. *Abstracts. Fourth International Conference on AIDS,* 1988, No. 3107.

228. Zagury D, Léonard R, Fouchard M, et al: Immunization against AIDS in humans. *Nature* 1987; 326:249–250.

229. Zagury D, Bernard J, Cheynier R, et al: A group specific anamnestic immune reaction against HIV-1 induced by a candidate vaccine against AIDS. *Nature* 1988; 332:728–731.

Human T Cell Lymphoma-Leukemia Viruses (HTLV-I, -II)

230. Morgan DA, Ruscetti FW, Gallo RC: Selective in vitro growth of T-lymphocytes from normal human bone marrows. *Science* 1976; 193:1007–1008.

231. Mier JW, Gallo RC: Purification and some characteristics of human T-cell growth factor from phytohemagglutinin-stimulated lymphocyte-conditioned media. *Proc Natl Acad Sci USA* 1980; 77:6134–6138.

232. Poiesz BJ, Ruscetti FW, Mier JW, et al: T-cell lines established from human T-lymphocytic neoplasias by direct response to T-cell growth factor. *Proc Natl Acad Sci USA* 1980; 77:6815–6819.

233. Poiesz BJ, Ruscetti FW, Gazdur AF, et al: Detection and isolation of type C retrovirus particles from fresh and cultured lymphocytes of a patient with cutaneous T-cell lymphoma. *Proc Natl Acad Sci USA* 1980; 77:7415–7419.

234. Poiesz BJ, Ruscetti FW, Reitz MS, et al: Isolation of a new type C retrovirus (HTLV) in primary uncultured cells of a patient with Sézary T-cell leukemia. *Nature* 1981; 294:268–271.

235. Hinuma Y, Nagata K, Hanaoka M, et al: Adult T-cell leukemia: Antigen in an ATL cell line and detection of antibodies to the antigen in human sera. *Proc Natl Acad Sci USA* 1981; 78:6476–6480.

236. Miyoshi I, Kubonishi I, Yoshimoto S, et al: Type C virus particles in a cord T-cell line derived by cocultivating normal human cord leukocytes and human leukemic T-cells. *Nature* 1981; 294:770–771.

237. Yoshida M, Miyoshi I, Hinuma Y: Isolation and characterization of retrovirus from cell lines of human adult T-cell leukemia and its implication in the disease. *Proc Natl Acad Sci USA* 1982; 79:2031–2035.

238. Popovic M, Reitz Jr MS, Sarngadharan MG, et al: The virus of Japanese adult T-cell leukemia is a member of the human T-cell leukemia virus group. *Nature* 1982; 300:63–66.

239. Kalyanaraman VS, Sarngadharan MG, Robert-Guroff M, et al: A new subtype of human T-cell leukemia virus (HTLV-II) associated with a T-cell variant of hairy cell leukemia. *Science* 1982; 218:571–573.

240. Rosenblatt JD, Golde DW, Wachsman W, et al: A second isolate of HTLV-II associated with atypical hairy-cell leukemia. *N Engl J Med* 1986; 315:372–377.

241. Kalyanaraman VS, Sarngadharan MG, Poiesz B, et al: Immunological properties of a type C retrovirus isolated from cultured human T-lymphoma cells and comparison to other mammalian retroviruses. *J Virol* 1981; 38:906–915.

242. Oroszlan S, Sarngadharan MG, Copeland TD, et al: Primary structure analysis of the major internal protein p24 of human type C T-cell leukemia virus. *Proc Natl Acad Sci USA* 1982; 79:1291–1294.

243. Schneider J, Yamamoto N, Hinuma Y, et al: Precursor polypeptides of adult T-cell leukemia virus: detection with antisera against isolated polypeptides gp68, p24 and p19. *J Gen Virol* 1984; 65:2249–2258.

244. Miyoshi I, Yoshimoto S, Kubonishi I, et al: Transformation of normal human cord lymphocytes by co-cultivation with a lethally irradiated human T-cell line carrying type C virus particles. *Gann* 1981; 72:997–998.

245. Yamamoto N, Okada M, Koyanagi Y, et al: Transformation of human leukocytes cocultivated with an adult T-cell leukemia virus producer cell line. *Science* 1982; 217:737–739.

246. Gallo RC, Mann D, Broder S, et al: Human T-cell leukemia-lymphoma virus (HTLV) is in T but not B lymphocytes from a patient with cutaneous T-cell lymphoma. *Proc Natl Acad Sci USA* 1982; 79:5680–5683.

247. Seiki M, Hattori S, Hirayama Y, et al: Human adult T-cell leukemia virus: Complete nucleotide sequence of the provirus genome integrated in leukemia cell DNA. *Proc Natl Acad Sci USA* 1983; 80:3618–3622.
248. Schimotohno K, Takahashi Y, Schimizu N, et al: Complete nucleotide sequence of an infectious clone of human T-cell leukemia virus type II: an open reading frame for the protease gene. *Proc Natl Acad Sci USA* 1985; 82:3101–3105.
249. Siekevitz M, Feinberg MB, Holbrook N, et al: Activation of interleukin 2 and interleukin 2 receptor (Tac) promotor expression by the trans-activator (tat) gene product of human T-cell leukemia virus, type I. *Proc Natl Acad Sci USA* 1987; 84:5389–5393.
250. Leung K, Nabel GJ: HTLV-I transactivator induces interleukin-2 receptor expression through an NF-kappa B-like factor. *Nature* 1988; 333:776–778.
251. Ruben S, Poteat H, Tan T-H, et al: Cellular transcription factors and regulation of IL-2 receptor gene expression by HTLV-I tax gene product. *Science* 1988; 241:89–92.
252. Rosenblatt JD, Cann AJ, Slamon DJ, et al: HTLV-II transactivation is regulated by the overlapping tax/rex nonstructural genes. *Science* 1988; 240:916–919.
253. Hidaka M, Inoue J, Yoshida M, et al: Post-transcriptional regulator (rex) of HTLV-1 initiates expression of viral structural proteins but suppresses expression of regulatory proteins. *EMBO J* 1988; 7:519–523.
254. Kalyanaraman VS, Sarngadharan MG, Bunn PA, et al: Antibodies in human sera reactive against an internal structural protein of human T-cell lymphoma virus. *Nature* 1981; 294:271–273.
255. Kalayanaraman VS, Sarngadharan MG, Nakao Y, et al: Natural antibodies to the structural core protein (p24) of the human T-cell leukemia (lymphoma) retrovirus found in sera of leukemia patients in Japan. *Proc Natl Acad Sci USA* 1982; 79:1653–1657.
256. Catovsky D, Rose M, Goolden AWG, et al: Adult T cell lymphoma-leukemia in blacks from the West Indies. *Lancet* 1982; 1:639–643.
257. Minamoto GY, Gold JWM, Scheinberg DA, et al: Infection with human T-cell leukemia virus type I in patients with leukemia. *N Engl J Med* 1988; 318:219–222.
258. Clark JW, Gurgo C, Franchini G, et al: Molecular epidemiology HTLV-I-associated non-Hodgkin's lymphomas in Jamaica. *Cancer* 1988; 61:1477–1482.
259. Kuo TT, Sato H, Dunn P, et al: Presence of HTLV-I proviral DNA in patients with adult T-cell leukemia/lymphoma in Taiwan. *Cancer* 1988; 62:702–704.
260. Hinuma Y, Komoda H, Chosa T, et al: Antibodies to adult T-cell leukemia-virus-associated antigen (ATLA) in sera from patients with ATL and controls in Japan: A nation-wide sero-epidemiologic study. *Int J Cancer* 1982; 29:631–635.
261. Robert-Guroff M, Nakao Y, Notake K, et al: Natural antibodies to human retrovirus HTLV in a cluster of Japanese patients with adult T-cell leukemia. *Science* 1982; 215:975–978.
262. Blattner WA, Saxinger C, Clark J, et al: Human T-cell leukemia/lymphoma virus-associated lymphoreticular neoplasia in Jamaica. *Lancet* 1983; 2:61–64.
263. Dosik H, Denic S, Patel N, et al: Adult T-cell leukemia/lymphoma in Brooklyn. *JAMA* 1988; 259:2255–2257.
264. Gibbs WN, Lofters WS, Campbell M, et al: Non-Hodgkin lymphoma in Jamaica and its relation to adult T-cell leukemia-lymphoma. *Ann Intern Med* 1987; 106:361–368.
265. Gessain A, Barin F, Vernant JC, et al: Antibodies to human T-lymphotropic virus type-I in patients with tropical spastic paraparesis. *Lancet* 1985; 2:407–409.
266. Rodgers-Johnson P, Gajdusek DC, Morgan OStC, et al: HTLV-I and HTLV-III antibodies and tropical spastic paraparesis. *Lancet* 1985; 2:1247–1248.
267. Brew BM, Price RW: Another retroviral disease of the nervous system: chronic progressive myelopathy due to HTLV-I. *N Engl J Med* 1988; 318:1195–1197.
268. Broder S: Pathogenic human retroviruses. *N Engl J Med* 1988; 318:243–245.
269. Jacobson S, Raine CS, Mingioli ES, et al: Isolation of an HTLV-1-like retrovirus from patients with tropical spastic paraparesis. *Nature* 1988; 331:540–543.
270. Bhagavati S, Ehrlich G, Kula RW, et al: Detection of human T-cell lymphoma/leukemia virus type I DNA and antigen in spinal fluid and blood of patients with chronic progressive myelopathy. *N Engl Med* 1988; 318:1141–1147.
271. Reddy EP, Mettus RV, De Freitas E, et al: Molecular cloning of human T-cell lymphotropic virus type I-like proviral genome from the peripheral lymphocyte DNA of a patient with chronic neurologic disorders. *Proc Natl Acad Sci USA* 1988; 85:3599–3603.
272. Osame M, Iszumos S, Igata A, et al: Blood transfusion and HTLV-I associated myelopathy. *Lancet* 1986; 2:104–105.
273. Roman GC, Osame M: Identity of HTLV-I-associated tropical spastic paraparesis and HTLV-I-associated myelopathy. *Lancet* 1988; 1:651.
274. Tournier-Lasservé E, Gout O, Gessain A, et al: HTLV-I, brain abnormalities on magnetic resonance imaging, and relation with multiple sclerosis. *Lancet* 1987; 2:49–50.
275. Mattson DH, Mc Farlin DE, Mora C, et al: Central-nervous-system lesions detected by magnetic resonance imaging in an HTLV-1 antibody positive symptomless individual. *Lancet* 1987; 2:49.
276. Saxinger W, Blattner WA, Levine PH, et al: Human T-cell leukemia virus (HTLV-I) antibodies in Africa. *Science* 1984; 225:1473–1476.
277. Ueda K, Kusuhara K, Tokugawa K: Transmission of HTLV-1. *Lancet* 1988; 1:1163–1164.
278. Williams AE, Fang CT, Slamon DJ, et al: Seroprevalence and epidemiological correlates of HTLV-I infection in U.S. blood donors. *Science* 1988; 240:643–646.
279. Stam L, Dosik H, Levine P: Human T-cell leukemia virus (HTLV-I) seropositivity in patients with renal failure. *Am Soc Artif Intern Organs* 1986; 15:73.
280. Weis SH, Saxinger WC, Ginzburg HM, et al: Human T-cell lymphotropic virus type I (HTLV-I) and HIV prevalence among US drug abusers, *Proc Am Soc Clin Oncol* 1987; 6-4.
281. Rezza G, Titti F, Rossi GB, et al: Sex as a risk factor for HTLV-I spread among intravenous drug abusers. *Lancet* 1988; 1:713.

Human Endogenous Retroviruses

282. Weiss RA, Teich N, Varmus HE, (eds): *RNA Tumor Viruses. Supplement: Endogenous retroviruses.* Cold Spring Harbor NY, Cold Spring Harbor Laboratory, 1985.
283. Shimotohno K, Mizutani S, Temin HM: Sequence of retrovirus resembles that of bacterial transposable elements. *Nature* 1980; 285:550–554.
284. Hehlmann R, Brack-Werner R, Leib-Mösch C: Human endogenous retroviruses. *Leukemia* 1988; 2:167–177S.
285. Fujinami RS, Oldstone MBA, Wroblewska Z, et al: Molecular mimicry in virus infection: crossreaction of measles virus phosphoprotein or of herpes simplex virus protein with human intermediate filaments. *Proc Natl Acad Sci USA* 1983; 80:2346–2350.
286. Query CC, Keene JD: A human autoimmune protein associated with U1 RNA contains a region of homology that is crossreactive with retroviral p30 gag antigen. *Cell* 1987; 51:211–220.
287. Witkin SS, Ohno T, Spiegelmann S: Purification of RNA-instructed DNA-polymerase from human leukemic spleens. *Proc Natl Acad Sci USA* 1975; 72:4133–4136.
288. Chandra P, Steel LK: Purification, biochemical characterization and serological analysis of cellular deoxy-ribonucleic acid polymerases and a reverse transcriptase from spleen of a patient with myelofibrotic syndrome. *Biochem J* 1977; 167:315–523.
289. Hehlmann R, Schetters H, Leib-Mösch C, et al: Current understanding of viral etiology in leukemia, in Thiel E, Thierfelder S (eds): *Recent Results in Cancer Research.* Heidelberg, Springer Verlag, 1984, vol 93, pp 1–28.
290. Hehlmann R, Schetters H, Erfle V, et al: Detection and biochemical characterization of antigens in human leukemic sera that

crossreact with primate C-type viral p30 proteins. *Cancer Res* 1983; 43:392–399.

291. Hehlmann R, Erfle V, Schetters H, et al: Antigens and circulating immune complexes related to the primate retroviral glycoprotein SiSVgp70: Indicators of early mortality in human acute leukemias and chronic myelogenous leukemias in blast crises. *Cancer* 1984; 54:2927–2935.

292. Herbrink P, Moen JET, Brouwer J, et al: Detection of antibodies crossreactive with type-C RNA tumor viral p30 protein in human sera and exudate fluids. *Cancer Res* 1980; 40:166–173.

293. Kurth R, Mikschy U: Human antibodies reactive with purified envelope antigens of primate type-C tumor viruses. *Proc Natl Acad Sci USA* 1978; 75:5692–5696.

294. Barbacid M, Bolognese D, Aaronson SA: Humans have antibodies capable of recognizing oncoviral glycoproteins: Demonstration that these antibodies are formed in response to cellular modification of glycoproteins rather than as consequences of exposure to virus. *Proc Natl Acad Sci USA* 1980; 77:1617–1621.

295. Snyder HW Jr, Fleissner E: Specificity of human antibodies to oncovirus glycoproteins: Recognition of antigen by natural antibodies directed against carbohydrate structures. *Proc Natl Acad Sci USA* 1980; 77:1622–1626.

296. Löwer J, Davidson EA, Teich NM, et al: Heterophil antibodies recognize oncornavirus envelope antigens: epidemiological parameters and immunological specificity of the reaction. *Virology* 1981; 109:409–417.

297. Gallagher RE, Gallo RC: Type-C RNA tumor virus isolated from cultured human acute myelogenous leukemia cells. *Science* 1975; 187:350–353.

298. Nooter K, Aarson AM, Bentvelzen P, et al: Isolation of infectious C-type oncornavirus from human leukemic bone marrow cells. *Nature* 1975; 256:595–597.

299. Panem S, Prochownik EV, Reale FR, et al: Isolation of type C virions from a normal human fibroblast strain. *Science* 1975; 189:297–299.

300. Kaplan HS, Goodenow RS, Epstein AL, et al: Isolation of type C RNA virus from an established human histiocytic lymphoma cell line. *Proc Natl Acad Sci USA* 1977; 74:2564–2568.

301. Kalter SS, Helmke JR, Herberling RL, et al: C-type particles in normal human placentas. *J Natl Cancer Inst* 1973; 50:1081–1084.

302. Sawyer MH, Nachlas NE Jr, Panem S: C-type viral antigen expression in human placenta. *Nature* 1978; 275:62–64.

303. Dirksen ER, Levy JA: Virus-like particles in placentas from normal individuals and patients with systemic lupus erythematosus. *J Natl Cancer Inst* 1977; 59:1187–1192.

304. Boller K, Frank H, Löwer J, et al: Structural organization of unique retrovirus-like particles budding from human teratocarcinoma cell lines. *J Gen Virol* 1983; 63:2549–2559.

305. Löwer R, Löwer J, Frank H, et al: Human teratocarcinomas cultured in vitro produce unique retrovirus-like viruses. *J Gen Virol* 1984; 65:887–898.

306. Bronson D, Saxinger WC, Ritzi DM, et al: Production of virions with retrovirus morphology by human embryonal carcinoma cells in vitro. *J Gen Virol* 1984; 65:1043–1051.

307. Larsson E, Nilsson BO, Sundstrom P, et al: Morphological and microbiological signs of endogenous C-virus in human oocytes. *Int J Cancer* 1981; 28:551–557.

308. Mondal H, Hofschneider PH: Isolation and characterization of retrovirus-like elements from normal human fetuses. *Int J Cancer* 1982; 30:281–287.

309. Parks WP, Gilden RV, Bykovsky AF, et al: Mason-Pfizer virus characterization: a similar virus in a human amniotic cell line. *J Virol* 1973; 12:1540–1547.

310. Gelderblom H, Bauer H, Ogura H, et al: Detection of oncornavirus-like particles in HeLa cells. I. Fine Structure and comparative morphological classification. *Int J Cancer* 1974; 13:246–253.

311. Bauer H, Daams JH, Watson KF, et al: Oncornavirus-like particles in HeLa cells. II. Immunological characterization of the vi-

rus. *Int J Cancer* 1974; 13:254–261.

312. Watson KF, Mölling K, Gelderblom H, et al: Oncornavirus-like particles in HeLa cells. III. Biochemical characterization of the virus. *Int J Cancer* 1974; 13:262–267.

313. Ilyin KV, Bykovsky AF, Zhdanov VM: An oncornavirus isolated from human cancer cell line. *Cancer* 1973; 32:89–96.

314. Bukrinskaya AG, Miller GG, Lebedeva EN, et al: Intracellular virus-specific structures and RNAs in oncornavirus-producing human cells. *J Virol* 1974; 13:478–487.

315. Bukrinskaya AG, Miller GG, Lebedeva EN, et al: Properties of intracytoplasmic A particles isolated from oncornavirus-producing human cells. *J Virol* 1974; 14:924–933.

316. Ohno T, Spiegelman S: Antigenic relatedness of the DNA polymerase of human breast cancer particles to the enzyme of the Mason-Pfizer monkey virus. *Proc Natl Acad Sci USA* 1977; 74:2144–2148.

317. Furmanski P, Longley C, Fouchey D, et al: Normal human mammary cells in culture: Evidence for oncornavirus-like particles. *J Natl Cancer Inst* 1974; 52:975–976.

318. Keydar I, Chen L, Karby S, et al: Establishment and characterization of a cell line of human breast carcinoma origin. *Eur J Cancer* 1979; 15:659–670.

319. Keydar I, Ohno T, Nayak R, et al: Properties of retrovirus-like particles produced by a human breast carcinoma cell line: Immunological relationship with mouse mammary tumor virus proteins. *Proc Natl Acad Sci USA* 1984; 81:4188–4192.

320. Mesa-Tejada R, Keydar I, Ramanarayanan M, et al: The detection in human breast carcinomas of an antigen immunologically related to a group-specific antigen of the mouse mammary tumor virus. *Proc Natl Acad Sci USA* 1978; 75:1529–1533.

321. Ohno T, Mesa-Tejada R, Keydar I, et al: The human breast carcinoma antigen is immunologically related to the polypeptide of the group-specific glycoprotein of the mouse mammary tumor virus. *Proc Natl Acad Sci USA* 1979; 76:2460–2464.

322. Dion AS, Farwell DC, Pomenti AA, et al: A human protein related to the major envelope protein of murine mammary tumor virus: Identification and characterization. *Proc Natl Acad Sci USA* 1980; 77:1301–1305.

323. Ebener U, Welte K, Chandra P: Purification and biochemical characterization of a virus-specific reverse transcriptase from human osteosarcoma tissue. *Cancer Lett* 1979; 7:179–188.

324. Welte K, Ebener U, Chandra P: Serological characterization of a purified reverse transcriptase from osteosarcoma of a child. *Cancer Lett* 1979; 7:189–195.

325. Zurcher C, Brinkhof J, Bentvelzen P, et al: C-type virus antigens detected by immunofluorescence in human bone tumor cultures. *Nature* 1975; 254:457–459.

326. Chandra P, Balikcioglu S, Mildner B: Biochemical and immunological characterization of a reverse transcriptase from human melanoma tissue. *Cancer Lett* 1978; 5:299–310.

327. Balda BR, Hehlmann R, Cho JR, et al: Oncornavirus-like particles in human skin cancers. *Proc Natl Acad Sci USA* 1975; 72:3697–3700.

328. Parsons PG, Klucis E, Gross PD, et al: Oncornavirus-like particles in malignant melanoma and control biopsies. *Int J Cancer* 1976; 18:757–763.

329. Martin MA, Bryan T, Rasheed S, et al: Identification and cloning of endogenous retroviral sequences present in human DNA. *Proc Natl Acad Sci USA* 1981; 78:4892–4896.

330. Repaske R, O'Neill RR, Steele PE, et al: Characterization and partial nucleotide sequence of endogenous type C retrovirus segments in human chromosomal DNA. *Proc Natl Acad Sci USA* 1983; 80:678–682.

331. Repaske R, Steele PE, O'Neill RR, et al: Nucleotide sequence of a full-length human endogenous retroviral segment. *J Virol* 1985; 54:764–772.

332. Steele PE, Martin MA, Rabson AB, et al: Amplification and chromosomal dispersion of human endogenous retroviral sequences. *J Virol* 1986; 59:545–550.

333. Rabson AB, Steele PE, Garon CF, et al: mRNA transcripts related to full-length endogenous retroviral DNA in human cells. *Nature* 1983; 306:604–607.

334. Rabson B, Hamagishi Y, Steele PE, et al: Characterization of human endogenous retroviral envelope RNA transcripts. *J Virol* 1985; 56:176–182.

335. Gattoni-Celli S, Kirsch K, Kalled S, et al: Expression of type C-related endogenous retroviral sequences in human colon tumors and colon cancer cell lines. *Proc Natl Acad Sci USA* 1986; 83:6127–6131.

336. Bonner TI, O'Connell C, Cohen M: Cloned endogenous retroviral sequences from human DNA. *Proc Natl Acad Sci USA* 1982; 79:4709–4713.

337. O'Brien SJ, Bonner TI, Cohen M, et al: Mapping of an endogenous retroviral sequence to human chromosome 18. *Nature* 1983; 303:74–77.

338. O'Connell C, O'Brien SJ, Nash WG, et al: ERV3, a full-length human endogenous provirus: Chromosomal localization and evolutionary relationships. *Virology* 1984; 138:225–235.

339. Cohen M, Powers M, O'Connell C, et al: The nucleotide sequence of the env gene from the human provirus ERV3 and isolation and characterization of an ERV3-specific cDNA. *Virology* 1985; 147:449–458.

340. Renan MJ, Reeves BR: Chromosomal localization of human endogenous retroviral element ERV1 to 18q22 → q23 by in situ hybridization. *Cytogenet Cell Genet* 1987; 44:167–170.

341. Suni J, Nävänen A, Wahlström T, et al: Human placental syncytiotrophoblastic M_r 75,000 polypeptide defined by antibodies to a synthetic peptide based on a cloned human endogenous retroviral DNA sequence. *Proc Natl Acad Sci USA* 1984; 81:6197–6201.

342. Wahlström T, Närvänen A, Suni J, et al: M_r 75,000 protein, a tumor marker in renal adenocarcinoma reacting with antibodies to a synthetic peptide based on a cloned human endogenous retroviral nucleotide sequence. *Int J Cancer* 1985; 36:379–382.

343. Kato N, Pfeifer-Ohlsson S, Kato M, et al: Tissue-specific expression of human provirus ERV3 mRNA in human placenta: Two of the three ERV3 mRNAs contain human cellular sequences. *J Virol* 1987; 61:2182–2191.

344. Leib-Mösch C, Brack R, Werner T, et al: Isolation of an SSAV-related endogenous sequence from human DNA. *Virology* 1986; 155:666–677.

345. Brack-Werner R, Barton DE, Werner T, et al: Human SSAV-related endogenous retroviral element: LTR-like sequence and chromosomal localization to 18q21. *Genomics* 1989; 4:68–75.

346. Callahan R, Drohan W, Tronick S, Schlom J: Detection and cloning of human DNA sequences related to the mouse mammary tumor virus genome. *Proc Natl Acad Sci USA* 1982; 79:5503–5507.

347. Horn T, Huebner K, Croce C, et al: Chromosomal locations of members of a family of novel endogenous human retroviral genomes. *J Virol* 1986; 58:955–959.

348. Deen KC, Sweet RW: Murine mammary tumor virus pol-related sequences in human DNA: Characterization and sequence comparison with the complete murine mammary tumor virus pol gene. *J Virol* 1986; 57:422–432.

349. Ono M: Molecular cloning and long terminal repeat sequences of human endogenous retrovirus genes related to types A and B retrovirus genes. *J Virol* 1986; 58:937–944.

350. Ono M, Yasunaga MT, Miyata T, et al: Nucleotide sequence of human endogenous retrovirus genome related to the mouse mammary tumor virus genome. *J Virol* 1986; 60:589–598.

351. Ono M, Kawakami M, Ushikubo H: Stimulation of expression of the human endogenous retrovirus genome by female steroid hormones in human breast cancer cell line T47D. *J Virol* 1987; 61:2059–2062.

352. Mager DL, Henthorn PS: Identification of a retrovirus-like repetitive element in human DNA. *Proc Natl Acad Sci USA* 1984; 81:7510–7514.

353. McClain K, Wilkowski C: Activation of endogenous retroviral sequences in human leukemia. *Biochem Biophys Res Commun* 1985; 133:945–950.

354. Canaani E, Dreazen O, Klar A, et al: Activation of the c-mos oncogene in a mouse plasmacytoma by insertion of an endogenous intracisternal A-particle genome. *Proc Natl Acad Sci USA* 1983; 80:7118–7122.

355. Goodwin G, Rottman FM, Callaghan T, et al: c-erbB activation in avian leukosis virus-induced erythroblastosis: Multiple epidermal growth factor receptor mRNAs are generated by alternative RNA processing. *Mol Cell Biol* 1986; 6:3128–3133.

356. Cianciolo GJ, Phipps D, Snyderman R: Human malignant and mitogen-transformed cells contain retroviral p15E-related antigen. *J Exp Med* 1984; 159:964–969.

357. Snyderman R, Cianciolo GJ: Immunosuppressive activity of the retroviral envelope protein p15E and its possible relationship to neoplasia. *Immuno Today* 1984; 5:240–244.

358. Cianciolo GJ, Copeland TD, Oroszlan S, et al: Inhibition of lymphocyte proliferation by a synthetic peptide homologous to retroviral envelope proteins. *Science* 1985; 230:453–455.

359. Schmidt DM, Sidhu NK, Cianciolo GJ, et al: Recombinant hydrophilic region of murine retroviral protein p15E inhibits stimulated T-lymphocyte proliferation. *Proc Natl Acad Sci USA* 1987; 84:7290–7294.

360. Thiel HJ, Schwarz H, Fischinger P, et al: Role of antibodies to murine leukemia virus p15E transmembrane protein in immunotherapy against AKR leukemia: A model for studies in human acquired immunodeficiency syndrome. *Proc Natl Acad Sci USA* 1987; 84:5893–5897.

361. Hartley J, Wolford NK, Old LJ, et al: A new class of murine leukemia virus associated with development of spontaneous lymphomas. *Proc Natl Acad Sci USA* 1977; 74:789–792.

362. Chattopadhyay SK, Lander MR, Gupta S, et al: Origin of mink cytopathic focus-forming (MCF) viruses: Comparison with ecotropic and xenotropic murine leukemia virus genomes. *Virology* 1981; 113:465–483.

363. Blatt C, Mileham K, Haas M, et al: Chromosomal mapping of the mink cell focus-inducing and xenotropic env gene family in the mouse. *Proc Natl Acad Sci USA* 1983; 80:6298–6302.

364. Ruta M, Bestwick R, Machida C, et al: Loss of leukemogenicity caused by mutations in the membrane glycoprotein structural gene of Friend spleen focus-forming virus. *Proc Natl Acad Sci USA* 1983; 80:4704–4708.

365. Evans H, Cloyd MW: Friend and Moloney murine leukemia viruses specifically recombine with different endogenous retroviral sequences to generate mink cell focus-forming viruses. *Proc Natl Acad Sci USA* 1985; 82:459–463.

Human Foamy Virus (HFV)

366. Weiss RA: Foamy retroviruses: a virus in search of a disease. *Nature* 1988; 333:497–498.

367. Werner J, Gelderblom H: Isolation of foamy virus from patients with de Quervain thyroiditis. *Lancet* 1979; 2:258–259.

368. Flügel RM, Rethwilm A, Maurer B, et al: Nucleotide sequence analysis of the env gene and its flanking regions of the human spumaretrovirus reveals two novel genes. *EMBO J* 1987; 6:2077–2084.

369. Maurer B, Bannert H, Darai G, et al: Analysis of the primary structure of the long terminal repeat and the gag and pol genes of the human spumaretrovirus. *J Virol* 1988; 62:1590–1597.

370. Fahey JL, Taylor JMG, Detels RL, et al: The prognostic value of cellular and serologic markers in infection with HIV-1. *N Engl J Med* 1990; 322:166–172.

371. Castagliola D, Mary JR, Brouard N, et al: Incubation time for AIDS from French transfusion-associated cases. *Nature* 1989; 338:768–769.

372. Ho DD, Mondgil T, Alam M: Quantitation of human immunodeficiency virus infection. *N Engl J Med* 1989; 321:1621–1625.

373. Coombs RW, Collier AC, Allain JP, et al: Plasma viremia in human immunodeficiency virus infection. *N Engl J Med* 1989; 321:1626–1631.

374. Centers for Disease Control: AIDS and HIV infection in the United States: 1988 update. *MMWR*, 1989, vol 38, No. S-4.

10

Influenza Viruses

Alan J. Hay
Robert B. Belshe
Edwin L. Anderson
Geoffrey J. Gorse
T. Ulf Westblom

The influenza viruses, which belong to the family *Orthomyxoviridae*, are important viruses with regard to the epidemiology of worldwide respiratory disease. These viruses have been causing recurrent epidemics of febrile respiratory disease every 1 to 3 years for at least 400 years, as far as can be discerned.[1, 2] Pandemics, or epidemics of worldwide influenza-related illness, have occurred every 10 to 20 years, and have accounted for up to 21 million deaths.[3] In addition to mortality, influenza viruses account for major morbidity in children and adults and can place the elderly at high risk for serious complications. The cost that can be attributed to these illnesses is certainly in the billions of dollars.[4] The importance of these viral infections makes infuenza one of the most heavily investigated worldwide diseases.

Recent work has led to new insights regarding the epidemiology of these viruses, indicating that animal reservoirs may play a large role in the shifting of antigenic structures of viruses. With the advent of new, more rapid diagnostic techniques, the emphasis upon accurate and rapid diagnosis of influenza virus infections is increasing. Simple methods of antigen detection are being developed (see Chapters 4, 5), so that therapy of illness or preventive epidemiologic measures can be instituted. Until recently, influenza vaccines typically consisted of purified inactivated virus or viral subunits. However, live attenuated vaccines appear to hold promise for the future, not only to provide long-term immunity, but also to provide a high margin of safety. Perhaps as this new information becomes available, influenza illnesses will become less of a burden to the world's population.

HISTORY

Written history suggests that influenza has not changed since the classical era. The characteristic abrupt onset of fever, cough, and myalgias lasting only a few days with more persistent weakness and depression affecting a large part of the population was described by Hippocrates in the fifth century BC. The earliest reference in English records occurred in 1170.[5] The epidemic behavior of the illness enables medical historians to identify influenza in accounts of the Middle Ages. The illness arose in the fall months and rapidly spread through the winter. People of all ages and races became affected. And while many were ill, deaths mainly occurred in the elderly and those otherwise chronically ill. An epidemic arising in Africa and spreading to Europe in 1510 was very likely influenza; the disease "attacked at once and raged all over Europe not missing a family and scarce a person." Mary Queen of Scots was one of the victims of the 1562 Edinburgh epidemic:

> Immediately upon the Queene's arrival here, she fell acquainted with a new disease that is common in this towne, called here the newe acquayntance, which passed also throughe the whole courte, neither sparinge lordes, ladyes, nor damoysells, not so much as either Frenche or English. It is a plague in their heades that have yet with a great cough, that remayneth with some longer, with others shorter tyme as yt findeth apte bodies for the nature of the disease. The Queene kept her bed six days. There was no appearance of danger nor manie that die of the disease except some olde folkes.[6]

The "newe acquayntance" was one of many terms used to describe influenza at the time. Other names included *petite peste,* the "jolly rout," *Galanterie-Krankheit* and *grippe.*[7] The term "influenza" was first used by the Italians in 1358 and referred to the influence of either the stars or the cold weather. The term was later adopted by the English during the 1782 epidemic.[7]

Increased international travel, beginning with the colonization of the New World, undoubtedly increased the rate of spread of influenza. One of the first examples may be the explosive epidemic that occurred at Isabela, the first city of the New World, on December 9, 1493. The day before, 1500 men and domestic animals had landed from the ships of Columbus's second voyage. The disease had an extremely high mortality among the natives and was characterized by high fever, prostration, and respiratory symptoms. The mode of spread and the very short incubation time of this illness makes it highly likely to have been influenza.[8] A century later the first known pandemic occurred, starting in Asia in 1580 and spreading to Africa and Europe as well as the New World.

The eighteenth and nineteenth centuries were characterized by a dramatic increase in international travel. But, more importantly for the historian, reliable record-keeping became an established means of chronicling the times on nearly all continents. During this 200-year span, 16 pandemics have been described.[9] A study of these pandemics reveals a fairly consistent pattern of behavior which is pertinent to the modern endeavors to reduce the dissemination of and mortality due to influenza. The disease could arise in any part of the world at any time of the year, but wide dissemination was generally recognized during the winter months. Furthermore, while the attack rate may have been very high, the case-fatality ratio was relatively low and variable (Table 10–1).

The pandemics of the twentieth century have been better chronicled and tell essentially the same story as those previously described. The living witnesses to the great pandemic of Spanish influenza (1918–1919), and the subsequent Asian (1957) and Hong Kong (1968) pandemics, provide the modern historian with a detailed accounting. More importantly to the seroarchaeologists of contemporary medicine, survivors of these and interval epidemics also serve as biologic witnesses, allowing a more precise understanding of the behavior of the influenza viruses and their subtypes. Although the pandemic of 1918 to 1919 was the single greatest epidemic in history of any kind,[3] the more interesting history of the search for the cause of influenza was being written at the time.

In regard to the etiology of influenza, the medical thinking of sixteenth century Italy survived essentially unchanged into the nineteenth century. An epidemic in Philadelphia was felt to be "exclusively of atmospheric origin." Although the germ theory was finding acceptance in the latter half of the century, influenza was still felt to be caused by bad air according to the popular miasmatic theory. Germany was the center of modern medical thought and practice at the time of the pandemic of 1889 to 1890, and it was there that Richard Pfeiffer discovered a bacterium in the throats of many patients with influenza.[10] Although the concept was not entirely correct, it certainly served a useful purpose. Large portions of the medical community were not entirely convinced and held a contagiomiasmatic theory of dissemination. An authoritative text published in 1910 devoted 60 pages to influenza, accepting "Pfeiffer's influenza bacillus" as its etiology, but allowed that there was much debate, and "that about 1500 physicians were in favor of, 1100 against this view of contagion.[11] During the pandemic of Spanish influenza, attempts to reproduce the disease by placing drops of "bacillus" culture into the noses of human volunteers were unsuccessful. Concurrent attempts to reproduce the disease in humans and in animals after passing infected secretions through bacterial filters met with a similar lack of success. Although Koch's postulates had not been fulfilled, most physicians accepted the infectious nature of influenza, and assigned a bacterial etiology to it. A text published in 1928, entitled *Filterable Viruses,* which devoted individual chapters to poliomyelitis, foot-and-mouth disease, and bacteriophagy, had only one line to describe influenza as a "bacterial disease."[12] This is where the definition of influenzal etiology may have stood for a long time had it not been for the curious (and perhaps erroneous) observation of the frequent coincidence of animal and human illness.

Occasional epidemics of human influenza were associated with, or even preceded by outbreaks of "distemper" in horses or influenza in swine in certain localities. In 1918, J.S. Koen, a veterinarian in Ford Dodge, Iowa, believed he was observing a disease in pigs which was the same as Spanish influenza, and averred that "It looked like 'flu,' and until it was proved it was not 'flu,' I shall stand by that diagnosis."[13] Ten years later, Richard Shope at the Rockefeller Institute for Comparative Pathology at Princeton, who was cognizant of Koen's observations, instilled mucus secretions from pigs with influenza into the noses of healthy pigs and was able to transmit the disease in this fashion. More importantly, pigs also became ill when secretions were first passed through bacterial filters, thus establishing the first reliable evidence that influenza was caused by a filterable virus, at least in pigs.[14]

In 1933, two years after the publication of Shope's findings, influenza was epidemic in England. Christopher Andrewes, Wilson Smith, and Patrick Laidlow, at the National Institute of Medical Research in London were attempting to infect ferrets with

Table 10–1
History of Influenza

Years	Onset	Dissemination	Comments
1729–1730		European, with a high attack rate and appreciable mortality	Regarded as a new disease in London; 1000 deaths per week in September
1732–1733	Connecticut (October) Moscow (November)	Worldwide	Overall mortality tripled in London at peak of outbreak
1742–1743		European	London and Rome experienced high attack rates
1761–1762	Western Hemisphere in 1761	European in 1762	Mortality in Europe variable
1767		North America, Europe	England apparently spared
1775–1776		Near and Far East, Europe	Little mortality in England
1781–1782	China (autumn)	Worldwide	Very high attack rate everywhere; high mortality even into summer
1788–1789		North America, Europe	Mild illness with hardly any deaths in England
1800–1802	Russia (October) China (September)	China, Europe, South America	Mild illness and little mortality
1830–1833	China (January)	Worldwide	Death rate quadrupled in England during worst 2 wk
1836–1837		Europe, Africa, Australia	Probably a recurrence of previous pandemic
1847–1848	Russia (March)	Western Hemisphere, Europe	"The great influenza" in England; high mortality
1850–1851		Western Hemisphere, Australia, Germany	Probably a recurrence of previous pandemic
1857–1858	Panama (August)	Western Hemisphere, Europe	Many deaths in Rome, but only a slight epidemic in Scotland
1873–1875		North America, Europe	England apparently spared
1889–1890	Bukhara (May)	Worldwide	"Asiatic influenza" spread westward involving North America in December; attack rate 40%–50%; 0.5–1.2% mortality in Germany

Adapted from Beveridge.[9]

human influenza. Smith himself was ill with influenza and washings from his throat were filtered and inoculated into the noses of the animals. Until then they had been injecting filtered material parenterally without success. By the time Smith had recovered from his illness, the ferrets had become ill with sneezing, discharge from nose and eyes, and raised temperature. They also observed that when ferrets were preanesthetized in order to make them more tractable, the illness was more severe.[15] For the first time, a filterable virus had been demonstrated in a case of influenza in man, and the modern era of understanding influenza and influenza virus began.

Dramatic medical advances in the study of influenza have been made in a relatively short period of time. Influenza B virus, distinct from influenza A, was isolated in 1940 by Francis,[16] and influenza C virus in 1950 by Taylor.[17] The cultivation of virus in embryonated hens' eggs in 1936 by Burnet,[18] and the discovery of the hemagglutination phenomenon by Hirst in 1941,[19] led to the development of inactivated vaccines and methods for the measurement of type-specific antibody. Worldwide surveillance has enabled the (partial) anticipation of epidemics due to certain subtypes of influenza, and type-specific vaccines have been made available to selected populations since the mid-1950s.[20] Other attempts at prevention and treatment include the use of amantadine in chemoprophylaxis and therapy. The last chapter in the history of influenza has yet to be written, as health officials attempt to control the dissemination of the virus and search for more effective therapy of the infection.

GENERAL FEATURES OF INFLUENZA VIRUS

Influenza viruses are enveloped RNA viruses and have been classified into three groups—types A, B, and C—based on differences in the serologic cross-reactivity of their nucleoprotein (NP) and matrix (M1) protein components. These internal antigens of strains belonging to each type fail to cross-react with viruses of the other two. The influenza A viruses can be further divided into subtypes based on the antigenic properties of their hemagglutinin (HA) and neuraminidase (NA) surface antigens. To date, 13 distinct HA subtypes and nine NA subtypes have been identified (Table 10–2). Although the HAs of B viruses also show extensive variation in antigenicity, subtypes of neither B- nor C-type viruses have been distinguished. The strain designations for influenza viruses contain the antigenic type based on the NP antigen (A, B, or C), the host of origin (if not specified, the virus is of human origin), geographic origin, strain number, and year of isolation (eg, influenza A/California/10/78[H1N1]).

The three virus types are also distinguished by a number of structural and biologic characteristics. Although all three virus types are associated with disease in man, there are differences in the severity of disease and the host range of these viruses. Type B and C viruses infect predominantly humans and have been iso-

Table 10–2
Present-Day and Historical Classification of Influenza A Virus Antigens

Current WHO Classification	1971 WHO Classification	Pre-1971 Designation*	Vernacular Name*
Hemagglutinin subtypes			
H1	H0		PR8
	H1	A0	FM1
	Hsw 1		Swine
H2	H2	A1	Singapore, Asian
H3	H3	A2	Hong Kong
	Heq 2		
	Hav 7		
H4	Hav 4		
H5	Hav 5		
H6	Hav 6		
H7	Heq 1		
	Hav 1		
H8	Hav 8		
H9	Hav 9		
H10	Hav 2		
H11	Hav 3		
H12	Hav 10		
H13			
Neuraminidase subtypes			
N1	N1		
N2	N2		
N3	Nav 2		
	Nav 3		
N4	Nav 4		
N5	Nav 5		
N6	Nav 1		
N7	Neq 1		
N8	Neq 2		
N9	Nav 6		

WHO = World Health Organization.
**Refers to whole virus with the indicated hemagglutinin.*

lated only infrequently from animals.[21, 22] Type A viruses on the other hand can cause epidemics in a variety of animals, in particular horses and pigs, as well as birds.[23] This wider host range of influenza A viruses is related to their greater epidemiologic significance, and in particular provides the basis for the occurrence of viruses with the ability to cause major pandemics.

Whereas a very limited number of subtypes of influenza A viruses infect mammalian species, for example, three in humans and two in pigs and horses, all known subtypes of HA and NA have been isolated from aquatic birds—hence the suggestion that the latter represent a reservoir of potential "novel" animal and human subtypes.[23–27] Ducks, in particular, are the major reservoir in which different virus subtypes cocirculate causing asymptomatic infections by replicating in cells lining the intestinal tract and shedding high concentrations of virus in the feces. Evidence in support of avian-to-mammalian transfer has been acquired in recent years from serologic and RNA sequence comparisons. For example, two outbreaks of disease in harbor seals in 1977–1978 and 1982–1983 were caused by viruses closely related to viruses normally only detected in birds.[28, 29] The first was caused by an H7N7 virus closely related to fowl plague virus which also caused conjunctivitis in an investigator[30] and the second was caused by an H4N5 strain. H13N2 and H13N9 viruses isolated from the lungs and hilar nodes of a pilot whale are closely related in H13 subtype to viruses only previously isolated from gulls.[31, 32] The high mortality among mink in Sweden in 1984 was caused by a highly virulent H10N7 virus which again was closely related to strains previously identified only in avian species.[33] Of particular significance to human disease are the observed similarities between the H3 hemagglutinins of A/Hong Kong/68, the cause of the most recent pandemic, and various duck isolates including, for example, A/duck/Ukraine/63 and A/duck/Hokkaido/8/80.[27]

STRUCTURE AND REPLICATION

Genome

The genomes of all three types of influenza viruses are composed of discrete segments of single-stranded RNAs of negative polarity (ie, of opposite sense to messenger RNA [mRNA]), ranging in size from approximately 900 to 2400 nucleotides.[34–37] A and B viruses both have eight segments, a number of which exhibit a high degree of homology between the two virus types. Influenza C viruses, on the other hand, have only seven segments.[36,37] The noncoding sequences at the ends of the RNAs of all three types have certain features in common.[37–39] Conserved sequences of 10 to 13 nucleotides at the 5' and 3' termini of the various genome segments show a high degree of similarity among all three virus types, presumably reflecting their role in binding the polymerase and the initiation of RNA transcription. Segment-specific sequences within ten to 20 nucleotides of the 3' and 5' ends may have a role to play in the selection and packaging of the genome into virions.[38, 40] Of interest in this regard also is the partial sequence complementarity between the two ends of each segment which promotes panhandle formation[41] and a circular conformation of the ribonucleoprotein (RNP) normally seen in the electron microscope as a double helix with a loop at one end.[42] It has been suggested that the feature is of importance in the production of the incomplete mRNA transcripts.

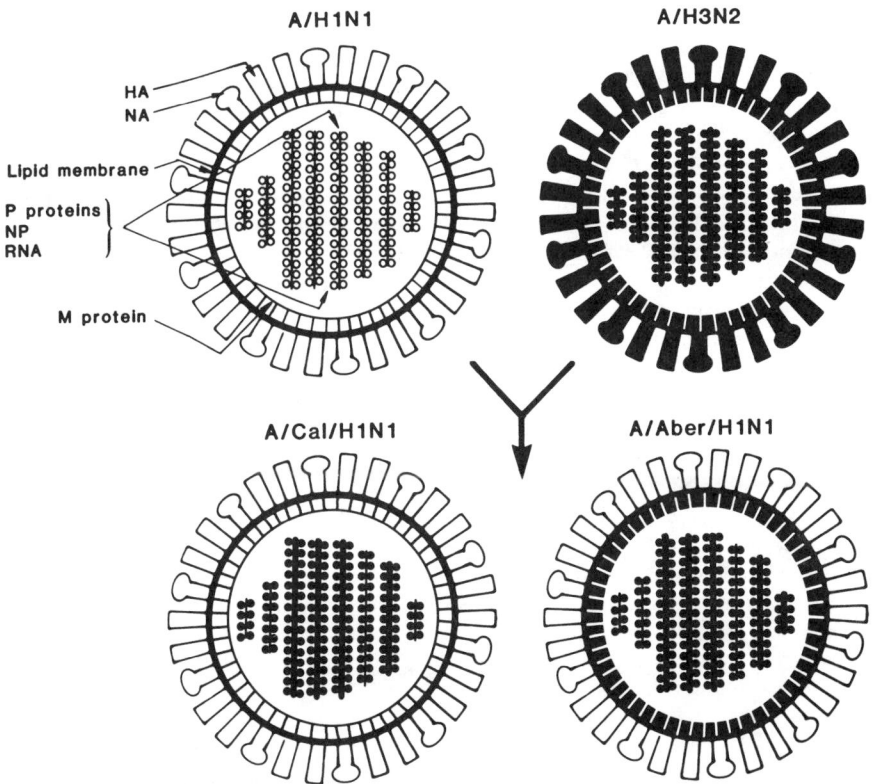

Figure 10–1. Schematic diagram of influenza A virus and gene derivation of the H1N1 recombinants A/Cal/10/78 and A/Aberdeen/v1340/78. Influenza A virus particles are characterized by spikes on the surface consisting of hemagglutinin (*rectangles*) and neuraminidase (*mushrooms*), by a host-derived lipid membrane, an underlying matrix (M) protein layer, and by the ribonucleoprotein (RNP) complexes which are composed of eight RNA segments associated with the nucleoprotein (NP) (*circles*) and the three polymerase (P) proteins (*circles*). The diagram also shows the genotype of A/Cal/10/78 virus which derives the NP and the three P genes through recombination (reassortment). The remaining four genes (*light bars* in RNP) and the corresponding proteins are derived from an H1N1 subtype parent. The A/Aberdeen/v1340/78 H1N1 recombinant derives a fifth gene from an H3N2 parent (*heavy bar* for the RNA segment and *filled rectangle* for the M protein). The appearance of A/Cal- and A/Aberdeen-like strains in the population proves that recombination (reassortment) of genes among human influenza viruses occurs in nature. (*Reproduced with permission from Palese P, Young JF: Variation of influenza A, B and C viruses. Science 1982; 215:1468–1474.*)

One consequence of the segmented nature of the virus genome is that it affords the ready reassortment of genes of two viruses during mixed infection of a cell, producing a large number of the possible 254 reassortant genomes among the progeny. This occurs both in vivo[43] and in vitro[44] and has been very useful in defining the products of the particular genes and in identifying the genetic basis of certain phenotypes, for example, host range, virulence, and drug resistance. Its importance epidemiologically is seen in the occurrence of new virus strains (Figure 10–1), in particular those responsible for major pandemics[23] (see below).

The nucleotide sequences of all eight genes of a number of strains of both A- and B-type viruses have been determined and a high degree of homology between some of the corresponding genes of A and B viruses has been noted.[45] The essential features of their replication are also similar; thus the ensuing discussion regarding influenza A viruses is generally applicable to influenza B viruses. Influenza C viruses, which have received increased attention only recently, show a greater divergence in their characteristics from the other two types, as discussed below.

Replication

The replication of influenza viruses was described in detail in Chapter 3; thus only certain essential features are considered in the present discussion. Table 10–3 lists the genome segments of influenza A viruses and the proteins they encode.

The three largest genes encode the components PB1, PB2, and PA of the RNA transcriptase[46] which is associated with the virus RNP and is responsible for initiating infection by transcribing the infecting genome into mRNAs. Two particularly notable features of influenza virus RNA synthesis are that it occurs in the nuclei of infected cells and mRNA production requires host cell-derived RNA primers. The PB2 component has a cap 1-binding specificity[47, 48] and is responsible for binding the 5′ termini of host cell nuclear pre-mRNAs from which are derived the ten to 15 nucleotide primers, cleaved by a virion-associated endonuclease.[49–56] Transcription is then initiated from the penultimate C residue of the genome RNA by addition of a complementary G to the 3′ end of the primer, and is terminated some 20 to 30 nucleotides before the 5′ end of the template, followed by the addition of poly(A)sequences. PB1 contains the nucleotide-binding site[52, 57] while the role of PA has yet to be defined. The complementary RNA templates for genome replication are quite distinct from the corresponding mRNAs in that they are exact genome complements with no additional 3′ poly(A) or 5′ heterogeneous sequences.[58, 59] Initiation of their synthesis therefore does not invoke a primer and the poly(A)addition signal is ignored. The factors responsible for the switch from mRNA to template RNA synthesis, as well as those necessary for the production of progeny genome RNAs have yet to be identified. It is evident, however, that the nucleoprotein, the product of gene 5, can promote readthrough of the poly(A)signal and is continually required for the production of both template and genome RNPs.[60-62] It is the major structural component associated with the virus genome and is present in approximately one molecule per 20 nucleotides.[63, 64]

The mRNAs of the two smallest genes undergo splicing to form mRNAs for additional gene products.[65, 66] The matrix or M1 protein is the major virus structural component located on the inside of the lipid envelope.[67, 68] The product M2 of the spliced mRNA of gene 7[69] is an integral component of the virus envelope present in only very low levels[70, 71] and appears to have a role in the assembly and uncoating of virus particles.[72] Of particular interest is the observation that it is the target of the specific anti-influenza A drugs, amantadine and rimantadine[73-75] (see Chapter 6). The two products NS1 and NS2[76-78] of gene 8 of A and B viruses and gene 7 of influenza C are not components of virus particles and their functions, presumed to be associated with RNA replication, have yet to be identified.

One difference between A and B viruses is in a second gene product, NB of the NA gene of B viruses, translated from the first AUG, seven nucleotides upstream from that initiating synthesis of NA.[79-81] This protein may be analogous to the M2 protein of influenza A viruses. The product of the spliced mRNA of gene 7 of B viruses has not yet been detected in infected cells, but from its proposed amino acid sequence would appear to have different properties from the M2 of influenza A viruses.[82, 83] A further difference seen in the coding of the M gene of influenza C virus is that the principle membrane protein product is translated from a spliced mRNA.[84]

The main difference between influenza C viruses on the one hand and influenza A and B viruses on the other is in their surface glycoproteins. Whereas the receptor-binding and receptor-destroying activities of A and B viruses are provided by the distinct HA and NA components, respectively, encoded by genes 4 and 6, in the case of influenza C a single glycoprotein possesses both activities[85, 86]; hence the difference in number of genes. Whether or not as a consequence of this, C viruses exhibit a more defined surface morphology with the spikes formed into regular hexagonal arrays.[87, 88] The different recognition specificity of the influenza C glycoprotein for 9-*O*-acetyl-*N*-acetyl neuraminic acid also distinguishes these viruses from types A and B.[89]

Hemagglutinin

The hemagglutinin (HA) is the major surface component of the virus and protrudes as triangular-shaped spikes (16 × 5 nm) from the lipid envelope. The key role this protein plays, not only in initiating virus infection but also in determining the pathogenicity and tissue tropism of virus strains, as well as being the target of neutralizing antibody, has made it the focus of detailed structure-function analyses.[90] The primary sequences of six of the 13 subtype

Table 10–3
Influenza A Virus Genome and Polypeptides

RNA segment (Nucleotide Length)	Polypeptide (Amino Acid Length)	Molecules per Virion (approx)	Function
1 (2341)	PB2 (759)	15	Transcriptase component, capped RNA primer binding site
2 (2341)	PB1 (757)	15	Transcriptase component, nucleotide binding site
3 (2233)	PA (716)	15	Transcriptase component, chain elongation
4 (1778)	HA (566)	500	Binding to sialic acid containing cell receptor, membrane fusion
5 (1565)	NP (498)	1000	Ribonucleoprotein
6 (1413)	NA (454)	100	Removal of sialic acid; virus release
7 (1027)	M_1 (252)	3000	Major structural component; surrounds viral core
	M_2 (97)	20–60	Minor structural component; role in virus entry; target of amantadine action
8 (890)	NS_1 (230)	—	Nonstructural protein, function not identified
	NS_2 (121)	—	Nonstructural protein, function not identified

HAs have been determined[45] and the three-dimensional structure of the H3 hemagglutinin has been elucidated by x-ray crystallographic analysis at 3-Å resolution.[91]

The native molecules are trimers, 135 Å in length, composed of identical glycopolypeptide subunits. These are synthesized as single polypeptide chains which are cleaved by an arginine-specific protease into disulfide-linked HA1 and HA2 subunits prior to insertion into the host cell plasma membrane. An additional carboxypeptidase activity is responsible for the removal of the single Arg, or in some viruses the connecting peptide containing several basic amino acids between HA1 and HA2. Although the uncleaved molecule has receptor-binding activity, cleavage to HA1 and HA2 is essential to generate the "fusion" mediating N-terminus of HA2 and hence virus infectivity. Furthermore, the susceptibility of the molecule to intracellular proteolytic cleavage has been shown to be an important determinant of the pathogenicity of H5 and H7 avian viruses. An essential feature of these HAs is the connecting peptide containing a sequence of two to six basic amino acids which facilitates cleavage in a variety of cell types, including cells in culture.[92–94] Other features of HA structure in the vicinity of the cleavage site are also important determinants of this phenotype. For example, a mutation which removed an attachment site for a carbohydrate side chain which normally "masked" the cleavage site was responsible for the generation of a highly virulent virus in chickens.[95] Amino acid changes which destabilize this region of the molecule can also promote cleavage of the H3 HA in tissue culture cells in the absence of exogenous proteases.[96] The viruses which infect mammals, all of which possess a single arginine between HA1 and HA2, are produced in an infectious form only in the superficial cells of the respiratory tract. The synergistic action of bacterial proteases in activating the HA of otherwise noninfectious virus and causing the dissemination of infection to the lungs of mice may explain the development of fatal influenza pneumonia in animals and man.[97, 98]

The HA molecule shown schematically in Figure 10–2, A and B contains two principal domains, a membrane distal globular head composed exclusively of HA1 and the membrane proximal stalk containing the N- and C-terminal segments of HA1 in conjunction with HA2. A triple-standard coiled coil formed between the long α helices of HA2 of the three subunits provides the principal interactions to stabilize the trimer. Other interactions involving the N-terminus of HA2 located at the trimeric interface and between the globular domains of HA1 are important in maintaining the stability of the native structure. The sequence of hydrophobic amino acids near the C-terminus of HA2 is responsible for anchoring the molecule in the lipid membrane. The six N-linked oligosaccharide chains present on the H3 hemagglutinin are mainly located on the lateral surfaces of the molecule.[91, 99] The variation in the number and location of carbohydrate moieties among influenza A subtypes and among strains within a subtype can significantly influence the antigenicity, stability, and receptor-binding properties of the HA, as well as proteolytic cleavage. Sequence homology between the HA2 components of various subtype HAs, of greater than 50%, is higher than for HA1 (approximately 40%), which contains the variable antigenic sites.

Of particular importance to the functions of the molecule are the receptor binding sites on the top and the N-terminal "fusion peptide" of HA2 buried in the interior of the stalk. These are both involved in mediating virus entry into cells: in attaching the virus to sialic acid containing glycopeptide or glycolipid receptors on susceptible cells and in mediating fusion of the virus envelope with the endosomal membrane, which results in the release of the viral RNP core.

Receptor Binding Site

Direct identification of the receptor-binding site has come from recent x-ray crystallographic analyses of hemagglutinins complexed with sialyllactose, a trisaccharide receptor analogue.[100] It is located on the membrane distal surface of each hemagglutinin subunit and consists of a pocket of conserved amino acids surrounded by residues observed to vary with changes in antigenicity. The proximity of these antibody-binding sites suggests that antibodies neutralize virus infectivity by preventing binding to the cell receptor, as observed in the inhibition of hemagglutination. Since the sialic acid moiety occupies the entire pocket, it is evident that it is the predominant component of the cell receptor.

Of particular interest to the epidemiology of influenza A viruses is the observed variation in receptor-binding specificities of different virus strains both within and between subtype, and in particular in viruses of the same subtype which infect different species. Differences in receptor-binding specificities occur in regard to both the nature of the sialic acid moiety and the type of linkage, either α 2–6 or α 2–3, to the penultimate galactose of the oligosaccharide chain.[101, 102]

For example, a change within the binding site at amino acid 155 from threonine to tyrosine correlates with an increase in affinity for N-glycolyl neuraminic acid, normally bound with only low affinity by most HAs.[103] A common feature of H3 human isolates is the strong preference for binding to NeuAcα 2–6 Gal sequences whereas avian and equine H3 isolates bind preferentially to NeuAcα 2–3 Gal. The main structural determinant of this difference in specificity was identified as the nature of amino acid 226 located in the receptor-binding pocket.[104] Leucine 226 specified the preference of the human H3 viruses for the α2–6 linkage, whereas substitution by glutamine 226 in mutants selected by passage in the presence of the horse serum inhibitor α2 macroglobulin exhibited a marked increase in affinity for the α2–3 linkage and corresponding reduction in affinity for the α2–6 linkage. Selection in the reverse direction of NeuAcα2–6 Gal variants of A/duck/Ukraine/1/63 (H3N7), a close relative of the Hong Kong virus, was again mediated by the opposite change in amino acid 226, glutamine to leucine.[105] Whereas this specific variation was stable to passage in MDCK cells, a single passage in chick embryos results in reversion to the NeuAcα2–3 Gal-specific phenotype. This provides a striking example of host-mediated selection based on receptor-binding specificities.

The importance of the nature of amino acids 226 and 228 in the receptor-binding site in restricting host range and tissue tropism was demonstrated by analyses of avian virus reassortants containing the H3 hemagglutinin.[106] These viruses do not normally replicate in ducks. However, mutants with changes in HA at residues 226 (leucine to glutamine) and 228 (serine to glycine) to those present in the avian sequence replicated in both bursa and intestine, whereas alteration in only amino acid 226 allowed replication solely in the bursa. Furthermore, the isolation from pigs in China

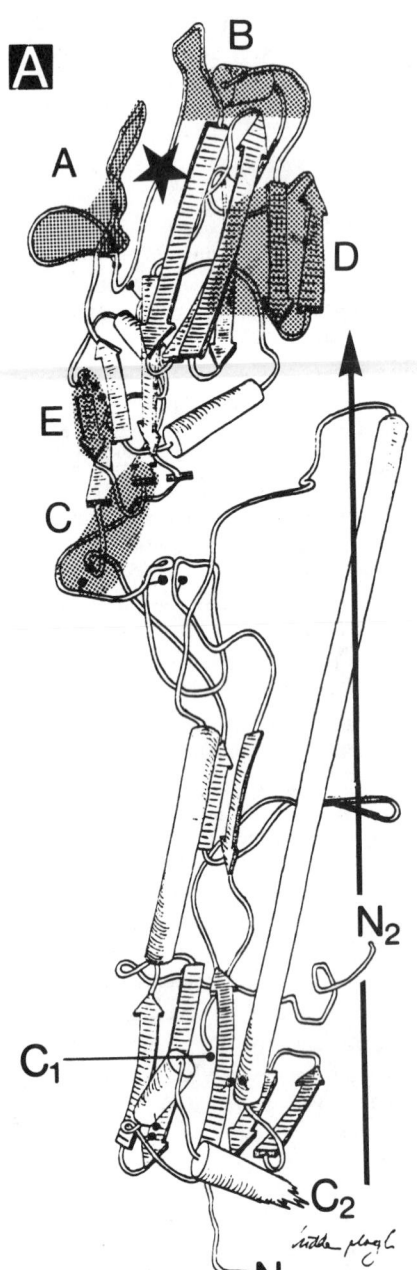

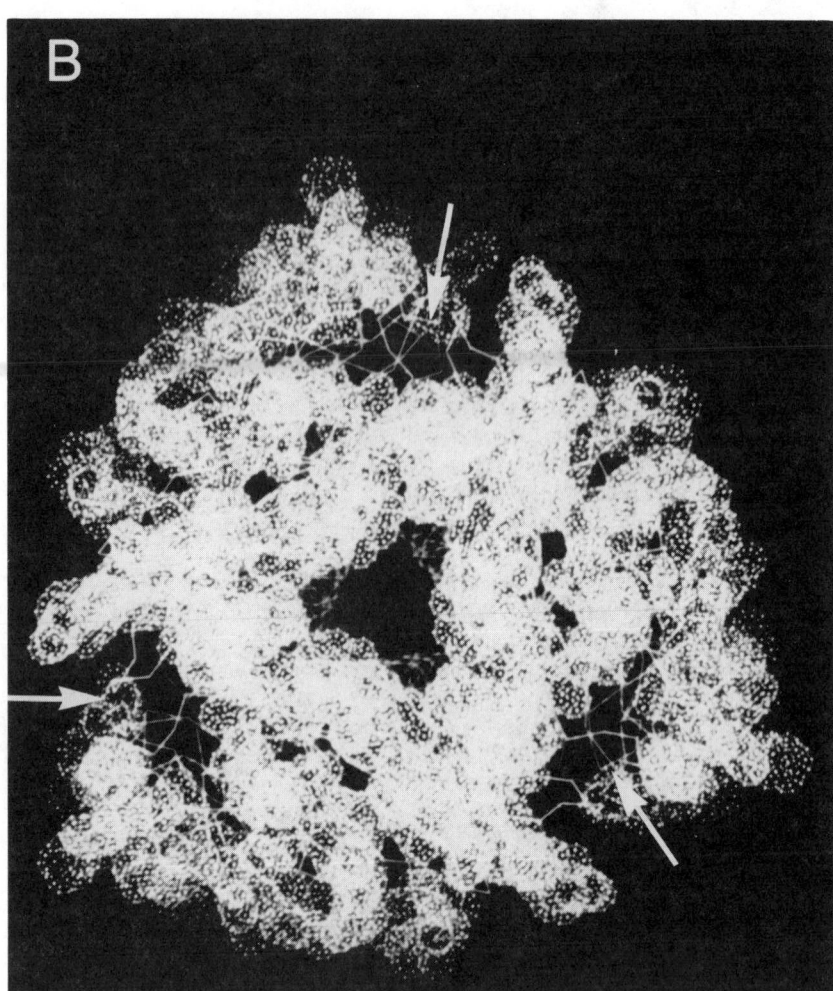

Figure 10–2. A. Schematic diagram of the three-dimensional structure of the influenza virus hemagglutinin monomer[91]. The arrows represent β strands and the cylinders α helices. The N-termini of HA1 (N1) and HA2 (N2) and the C-terminus of HA 1 (C1) are indicated, as is the point (C2) close to the viral membrane and cleaved by bromelain to release the soluble ectodomain of the protein used for crystallization. The protein extends 135 nm from the viral membrane. The location of the threefold axis of symmetry in the trimer is indicated, as are the locations of the receptor-binding site (*star*); the five antibody-binding sites (*shaded areas*, A–E, indicated by amino acid changes in natural strains and monoclonal antibody–selected variants of A/Hong Kong/68 (H3N2); and the fusion peptide at the N-terminus of HA2.[144] B. Top view of an α-carbon trace of the HA trimer. Dotted spheres indicate the variable amino acids in the H3 hemagglutinin positioned around conserved residues which line the three receptor-binding pockets (*arrows*).

of viruses containing either the "human" or the "avian" combination of amino acids 226 and 228 has evident implications for interspecies transfer and the generation of the Hong Kong pandemic strain.[107]

The molecular basis of this difference in specificity of binding is not evident from comparative crystallographic analyses of HA receptor complexes of the mutant and wild-type viruses since there are only small adjustments within the binding site and no direct interactions between the linkage atoms and the side chain at position 226. Rather, it may be due to small but significant alterations in conformation extending outside the binding site, also indicated

by the differential binding of monoclonal antibodies to the mutant and wild-type proteins.[108] The converse of this is also true, namely, that certain antibody-selected variants[109–111] and natural isolates[112, 113] with substitutions in amino acids close to the binding pocket have altered receptor-binding characteristics. Furthermore, amino acid differences at more remote sites on the HA molecule, for example, near the trimer interface, have also been observed to alter the specificity and affinity of receptor interaction.[114] Other examples of host cell-mediated selection of variants of both A and B viruses differing in both antigenicity and in the specificity and affinity for receptors on cells of mammalian versus avian origin have demonstrated the influence of alterations in amino acids in the vicinity of the receptor-binding site[115, 116] and the presence and nature of associated carbohydrate side chains.[117, 118]

Membrane Fusion

The next step in virus infection following virus binding and endocytosis by the cell involves fusion between the virus membrane and that of the endocytic vesicle.[119, 120] Acidification by proton pumps associated with these cellular compartments provides the acidic environment (pH between 5 and 6) required to trigger an irreversible conformational rearrangement in the structure of the HA and the consequent hemagglutinin-mediated fusion reaction.[121] A detailed understanding of the mechanism whereby this occurs is not yet available; however, current evidence is consistent with the idea that the N-terminus of HA2, which becomes exposed as a result of the structural alterations, interacts with the vesicular membrane to bring the two surfaces together and facilitates, by local destabilization, the merging of the two lipid bilayers. Hence the absolute requirement for cleavage of HA and consequent generation of the N-terminus of HA2 for virus infectivity. The amino acid sequence of this fusion peptide is highly conserved in both A- and B-type viruses and exhibits a high degree of homology with the equivalent peptides of certain other fusogenic viruses.[119] Oligopeptides with similar amino acid sequences inhibit membrane fusion activity apparently by interacting with the target membrane.[122]

Changes in the biochemical,[123–125] ultrastructural,[126] and antigenic[127–130] properties of the low pH form of HA have indicated that the conformational change involves extensive rearrangements in the tertiary structure of both stem and head regions with partial dissociation of contacts between monomers, without any gross change in secondary structure. Studies of mutants selected for their ability to promote fusion at elevated pH have indicated that this phenotype results from amino acid changes which destabilize either the location of the N-terminus of HA2 or the intersubunit interactions of the HA trimer at neutral pH.[131–132] The significance of variations in the pH optimum of fusion of closely related human and avian virus strains over a range of 5.5 to 6.2 has yet to be elucidated.[90] Differences between natural variants have also been noted; for example, two viruses recovered from the original isolate of A/duck/Ukraine/63 had pH optima of 5.5 and 5.9, respectively,[131] and two variants of X-31 differed by 0.2 pH unit.[133]

Changes in pH optima may also accompany selection of altered growth characteristics such as at lower temperature in the case of cold-adapted variants, or adaptation to grow in MDCK cell culture.[96] The concomitant variation in antigenicity, the affinity and specificity of receptor binding, and the pH optimum of fusion noted with certain variants selected using monoclonal antibodies further emphasizes the importance of all three phenotypes in the epidemiology of influenza viruses.

Neuraminidase

The neuraminidase is responsible for catalyzing the removal of terminal sialic acid residues from oligosaccharides and hence the elimination of the HA receptors on the surface of infected cells, thereby facilitating the release and preventing the aggregation of progeny viruses. It may also have a role in penetrating the mucin

in the respiratory tract and permitting access to the susceptible target epithelial cells.

The molecule is a tetramer of identical disulfide-linked subunits (molecular weight 60,000) with circular fourfold symmetry. It is composed of a box-shaped head (100 × 100 × 60 Å) attached by a slender stalk to the virus membrane. A hydrophobic sequence of approximately 30 amino acids near the N-terminus anchors the molecule to the virus membrane with the conserved N-terminal hexapeptide localized internally. A further 40 to 50 hypervariable amino acids make up the heavily glycosylated stem region while the remaining C-terminal portion forms the head which contains a further three to four carbohydrate side chains. Released by pronase cleavage, the soluble "heads" have been crystallized and the structures of both N2 and N9 NAs and the enzyme-substrate complexes of N2 (A/Tokyo/3/67) determined by x-ray analysis to 3-Å resolution.[123–136] The polypeptide is folded into six topologically identical four-stranded antiparallel beta sheets arranged in a propeller formation. The catalytic site on the top surface of each subunit is a large pocket lined by nine acidic, six basic and three hydrophobic amino acids strictly conserved in all influenza A and B virus neuraminidases and encircled by strain-variable amino acid residues which go to form overlapping antigenic determinants forming a nearly continuous surface across the top of the monomer.

The N9 neuraminidase in contrast to that of most other subtypes appears to possess a second sialic acid binding site which is responsible for its unusual hemagglutinating activity.[135] The identity of this site as well as the biologic significance of this latter activity is still in doubt.

In spite of the 70% difference in amino acid sequence between the NAs of influenza A and B viruses, the conservation of key residues, in particular the charged and hydrophobic amino acids lining the sialic acid binding pocket and several of the cysteines involved in disulfide formation, suggests a similar overall structure and configuration of the active site of the influenza B molecule.[137]

Influenza C Glycoprotein

The single influenza C glycoprotein encompasses all three activities, the receptor-binding and low pH membrane fusion activities of the HA and the receptor-destroying activity of the NA of influenza A and B viruses.[85, 86] It resembles the HA in many biochemical properties and is a trimer of similar size and shape[88] which requires proteolytic cleavage for virus infectivity. The specificity of receptor binding for 9-O-acetyl-N-acetyl neuraminic acid[89] is, however, quite distinct from that of A and B virus HAs, as is the 9-O-acetylesterase receptor-destroying activity.[138] Results of antibody and chemical inhibition studies indicate that the two activities are associated with different functional sites on the molecule.[139, 140]

VARIATION AND EPIDEMIOLOGY

Antigenic Variation

Influenza remains a major disease of man, primarily due to the considerable antigenic variation displayed by these viruses. This property is an important factor contributing to the difficulties in the long-term control of influenza by vaccination. Thus continuous monitoring of the antigenicity of virus isolates is necessary to ensure the inclusion in vaccines of variants closely related to the viruses in circulation.[141] Hemagglutinin inhibition tests using convalescent ferret antisera, which is highly strain-specific, are used to indicate the relationships between viruses isolated in different years. The antigenic changes in the surface glycoproteins is the result of two processes referred to as antigenic drift and antigenic shift.[23] The former is characterized by the gradual accumulation of mutations in the genes and the consequent cumulative changes in antigenic structure of the two glycoproteins. This allows the virus to circumvent the existing immunity in a segment of the population on a year-to-year basis. Antigenic shift, on the other hand, describes the appearance of a virus with a complete change in antigenic properties to which there is no immunologic experience and generally gives rise to pandemics. Such alterations may involve only the hemagglutinin, as in 1968, or both the hemagglutinin and neuraminidase proteins, as in 1957. The hemagglutinin is of predominant importance since it is antibodies against this component which neutralize virus infectivity and prevent virus infection. Antibodies against the neuraminidase, although not neutralizing, do interfere with the systemic spread of virus in chickens,[142] and reduce both the pulmonary virus titer and extent of lung lesions in mice,[143] hence reducing the severity of the disease.

Hemagglutinin

The antigenic determinants on the hemagglutinins of the two influenza A subtypes currently circulating, H3 since 1968 and H1 since 1977, have been defined by identifying the amino acid changes in the HAs of sequential natural isolates and antigenic variants selected by growth in the presence of monoclonal antibodies. This has been achieved by nucleotide sequence analysis of the HA genes of these viruses.[144–153] The variation occurs predominantly in the HA1 glycopeptide, 73 out of the 328 residues (22%) of the H3 HA having changed between 1968 and 1986 as compared to only 12 out of the 221 residues (5%) of HA2. These changes are distributed over the surface of the molecule and cluster into five distinguishable hypervariable antibody-binding sites, A to E (see Figure 10–2), surrounding the conserved receptor-binding pocket, which is inaccessible to antibody.[144] The distribution of sites on the H1 HA is similar.[148] The coincidence between the changes in natural isolates and those selected under antibody pressure confirm the immunologic significance of the five sites. Furthermore, crystallographic analyses of mutant HAs have shown that the structural changes are localized to the vicinity of the substituted amino acid indicating that the antibody binds to this region.[154] In addition to alterations in charge or side chain length, amino acid changes which result in addition of carbohydrate side chains may also alter antigenicity.[155]

Antigenic drift therefore generally occurs as a result of the accumulation of sequential changes from year to year at a fairly constant rate of approximately 1.1% per year for the H3 hemagglutinin between 1968 and 1986.[145, 147] The lower level of silent mutations of approximately 0.3% per year argues in favor of the positive selection of antigenic mutants by antibody pressure. Differences in the rate of change in H1 hemagglutinins of 1.4% per year between 1950 and 1957 and 0.8% per year between 1977 and 1983 may reflect differences in the level of immunity in the population.[151] In this regard analyses of the variety of H3 antibody

specificities in postinfection human sera obtained between 1969 and 1971 and in 1978 have shown that during the early experience of the H3 subtype different sera contained antibodies with different ranges of specificities, whereas the later sera contained a broad range of antibodies.[156] It has been suggested that the broader specificity of sera in 1978 may have contributed to the decrease in incidence of the disease since 1975.

Although the processes involved in antigenic drift are not yet understood, it has been suggested that epidemic strains of H3N2, such as occurred in 1972 and 1975 with the potential to infect the majority of the population, would result from changes in at least three antigenic regions. These may arise by sequential changes at each site during reinfections of partially immune individuals by antigenic variants changed in only one or two sites. The high frequency of antigenic change is likely also to be linked to the infrequent antigenic shifts which interrupt any tendency to reach an "antigenic equilibrium" similar to that attained by less variable viruses. Since changes which alter antigenicity also affect the receptor-binding and membrane fusion activities of the HA and hence various biologic characteristics of the virus, for example, virulence and host range, it is evident that these last-named characteristics will impose constraints on the degree of antigenic variability. It has been suggested that this may account for the occurrence of "terminal" strains and the relatively low level of influenza in recent years caused by the later main-line H3N2 viruses.[109]

In the past 60 years, three different subtype strains of influenza A virus have caused pandemics in man. The H1N1 (swine) viruses probably appeared in 1918 and were responsible for 20 million deaths in that year. These viruses continued to circulate until 1957, at which time they were supplanted by the H2N2 (Asian) viruses. These strains had both hemagglutinin and neuraminidase proteins that were serologically distinct from the H1N1 viruses. The H2N2 viruses were prevalent until 1968, at which time another shift occurred with the introduction of the H3N2 (Hong Kong) strains which have continued to circulate to this date. In this case, only the hemagglutinin changed. The new virus in each case replaced the previous epidemic strain. In contrast, the H1N1 virus, which reappeared in 1977, did not replace the H3N2 subtypes and both subtypes have continued to cocirculate in the human population.

As discussed previously, the nature of the virus genome predisposes these viruses to undergo genetic reassortment during a mixed infection. Instances have been observed during cocirculation of two virus strains in both human[157, 158] and avian[43] populations. Thus in 1978 the appearance of A/Cal/10/78 and A/Aberdeen/V1340/78 evidently resulted from mixed infections by the current H3N2 and and H1N1 viruses (see Figure 10–1), the former deriving four genes and the latter five genes from the H3N2 parent while the remaining genes, including those for the surface glycoproteins, were from the H1N1 parent virus.

Evidence indicates that the new H2N2 and H3N2 pandemic strains arose through reassortment of genes from different strains.[159] Sequence analyses of the genes coding for the H1, H2, and H3 hemagglutinins showed that the differences among the consecutive subtypes were too great to be attributable to drift during a 1-year transition. The amino acid sequence homologies between their HA1s was 58% for H1 and H2 and 36% for H2 and H3 subtypes.[160, 161] Nucleic acid hybridization studies have suggested that the human H2N2 viruses derived four genes (RNA segments 1, 5, 7, and 8) from a preceding human H1N1 strain and the remaining four genes, including those coding for the hemagglutinin and neuraminidase, from an as yet unidentified animal H2N2 virus through reassortment.[162] A similar comparison of the genes from the H2N2 and H3N2 viruses indicated that with the exception of the HA gene the remaining seven genes were derived from the preceeding H2N2 human strain. Initial serologic indications[163–165] that the HA was closely related to the HAs of A/duck/Ukraine/63 and A/equine/Miami/63 were subsequently borne out by protein and nucleic acid sequence comparisons.[166–168] The closest sequence homologies are with A/duck/Ukraine/63, and more recent data have indicated a closer relationship still with recent duck isolates, for example, A/duck/Hokkaido/8/80, which suggests that the human H3 gene may have been derived from a member of the duck H3 lineage.

Although it is therefore apparent that the virus arose by genetic reassortment, the origin of the actual viruses involved and the site of reassortment is not known. Pigs have been proposed as the most likely host in view of their tolerance for infection by both human or avian viruses.[107] As discussed earlier in relation to the receptor-binding specificities of these viruses, the process would also involve selection of mutants with altered host range. Although there would appear to be the potential for new pandemic strains deriving genes from viruses with one of the additional ten hemagglutinin subtypes, the appearance of only three human subtypes, H1, H2, and H3 to date, indicates that interspecies transfer is highly restricted. It is apparent that in addition to characteristics of the HA, such as receptor-binding specificity, properties of NP, M, and the polymerase components are also important in determining the growth characteristics of viruses in different host species.

The latest antigenic shift involved the reintroduction into the human population of an H1N1 virus, closely related in antigenicity and RNA sequence homology to H1N1 strains infecting humans in 1950.[169, 170] The susceptibility to infection mainly of young people of less than 25 years demonstrated the immunity of adults who had experienced a similar virus during the previous pandemic period. Moreover, this partial susceptibility of the population may be responsible for the continued cocirculation of the H3N2 subtype. The source of the "dormant" virus strain which remained largely unchanged for 27 years has yet to be determined. The observations of H3 antibodies in sera obtained from aged individuals prior to the 1968 H3N2 pandemic and H2 antibodies in sera of people born prior to 1887[171] suggest the recycling of only a limited number of hemagglutinin subtypes in the viruses which infect man.

Distinct antigenic variants of influenza B viruses cocirculate, although antigenic shift among these viruses and different subtypes have not been observed. The antigenic structure of the B hemagglutinin has been analyzed in a similar manner to that described and by reference to the influenza A molecule. The locations of amino acid substitutions in monoclonal antibody-selected variants and differences between natural strains have identified at least two immunodominant regions corresponding roughly to sites A and B in the influenza A HA (see Figure 10–2).[172, 173] Since antigenically similar viruses have been isolated many years apart, the nature of the relationships between different virus strains and the process of antigenic variation is not well understood.

Neuraminidase

The nucleotide sequences of several neuraminidases of different subtypes of influenza A have been determined. The similarity in the numbers of amino acid changes in the proposed antigenic sites of the N2 NA between 1968 and 1975 as occurred in the HAs of these human virus isolates indicate a similar rate of antigenic drift.[136, 174] Seventy-three amino acid substitutions accumulated in the N2 NA between 1957 and 1979 at a rate of 0.7% per year. In contrast to the amino acid sequence homology of 87% between these N2 neuraminidases, the homology between N1 and N2 neuraminidases was 41%[175]—similar to that observed between, for example, the H2 and H3 hemagglutinin subtypes. The evidence therefore supports the idea that as for the hemagglutinin the appearance of a "novel" neuraminidase in the 1957 Asian influenza virus was the result of genetic reassortment.

Studies using monoclonal antibodies have distinguished four antigenic regions, two on the enzyme-active face, monoclonal antibodies against which can inhibit enzyme activity; and two others, more remote from the catalytic site on the side or bottom face of the tetramer.[176, 177] Amino acid substitutions in escape mutants selected using the former are located on the rim of the substrate binding cavity.[178] Structural analysis of one such escape mutant showed that as for HA monoclonal antibody variants, the single amino acid substitution caused only local adjustments to the structure of the molecule.[179] Three-dimensional x-ray analysis of a neuraminidase-antibody complex suggests that antibodies which bind to this region do not block access of the substrate but appear to inhibit activity by causing distortion of the catalytic site.[180] In regard to the protection afforded by these antibodies directed against different regions of the molecule, it was observed in studies of passive immunity that monoclonal antibodies directed against one of the more distant epitopes, while not inhibiting enzyme activity in vitro, were most effective in reducing virus replication and disease symptoms in chickens.[142] The clustering of amino acid differences between the N9 NAs of isolates from different hosts, terns and whales, at the base of the tetramer suggests there may be positive selection for changes in this region of the molecule.[181]

Variation in Nonsurface Proteins

In addition to the changes in the hemagglutinin and neuraminidase surface proteins, a more limited variation (less than 10% in nucleotide sequence) occurs in the genes coding for the other virus proteins. Variation in these components is much less important immunologically although most, and in particular the NP, do provide important cross-reactive, type-specific determinants in class I major histocompatibility complex (MHC)-restricted cytotoxic T cell killing of virus-infected cells, which plays an important role in limiting the spread of infection. Variation in these nonsurface proteins is therefore unlikely to result from immunologic selection pressure; rather it may reflect selection for changes in certain other characteristics such as virion stability, host range, transmission, or tissue tropism of the virus. Furthermore, considerations of the influence of these genes on virulence is important in relation to devising suitable live vaccine strains.

Minor antigenic variation in the nucleoproteins of type A viruses has been observed with both polyclonal and monoclonal antibodies.[182, 183] RNA-RNA hybridization analysis has defined five, largely species-specific, groups of nucleoproteins (NPs).[184] The clear differentiation of viruses infecting human and avian hosts was confirmed by nucleotide sequence analysis.[185] The data obtained are consistent with a linear pathway of evolution and the continuous accumulation of mutations in human epidemic strains from 1934 to 1972 and conservation during antigenic shifts in 1957 and 1968. The importance of the NP in determining host range and the attenuation of avian viruses in primates has been demonstrated by the inability of the NP of human viruses to complement a temperature-sensitive (*ts*) defect in the corresponding protein of avian strains,[186] and the growth restriction in monkeys imposed by an avian-derived NP in reassortants with a human influenza A virus.[187, 188] The similarities between the NP genes of human and most swine isolates correlates with the ready transmission of H3N2 viruses from humans to pigs. Furthermore, the detection of swine isolates containing NPs with characteristics of both human and avian groups lends support to the idea that pigs provide the site for genetic reassortment in the generation of new human pandemic strains.

The M gene encoding both the matrix and M2 proteins is also an important determinant of growth potential and host range.[187] Again, human and avian strains are distinguishable on a basis of nucleotide sequences.[189] The greater divergence in amino acid sequence of M2 as compared to M1 suggests that it is an important determinant of host range.[189, 190] It also appears that the incompatibility between HA and M gene products reflected in the inability to isolate certain reassortants is related to the function of M2.[72] Variation in antigenicity of the matrix protein is less than that for the nucleoprotein and no differences were detectable by monospecific heterogeneous antisera. Monoclonal antibodies detected three distinct epitopes on the matrix protein, two of which underwent antigenic variation, although in a very limited number of virus strains, only three out of 26 animal and human influenza A isolates over a period of 49 years.[191] The observation of two antigenically distinct H3N2 viruses cocirculating in 1968 points to genetic dimorphism also noted more recently within a local community.[75] Also, an antigenic distinction between the 1977 H1N1 strain, A/USSR/90/77, and the closely related 1950 virus (A/Fort Warren/1/50) is in marked contrast to the lack of antigenic difference between the HA and NP components.

Differences in polymerase components also clearly influence the ability of viruses to replicate in mammalian cells. The PA gene was shown to discriminate between the abilities of two avian influenza A viruses to replicate in BHK cells[192] while replacement of the PB1 gene of a human virus by that of an avian strain was responsible for the restricted growth in MDCK cells and attenuation of the reassortant viruses for monkeys.[188] Reversion of the avirulent, *ts* phenotype of a cold-adapted variant of B/Ann Arbor/1/66 was shown to be due to a mutation in the PA protein.[193]

In contrast to the high degree of homology in amino acid sequence (approximately 95%) of the polymerase components of different influenza A strains, the degree of homology between A and B viruses is of the order of 60% for PB1 and 40% of PA. In view of the strict requirements of compatibility between virus gene products and host cell factors for efficient virus replication, the lack of intertypic genetic reassortment between A and B viruses is not surprising.

A clear distinction between avian and human influenza A strains is again evident in the sequences of their NS genes as determined by RNA-RNA hybridization analysis.[194] Although nucleotide sequence analyses of several human isolates show a gradual drift of approximately 2.2% to 3.4% per 10 years from 1933,[195, 196] more extensive variation is seen in the size of the NS1 proteins, between 202 and 237 amino acids, depending on the location of the stop codon.[197] The degree of variation which can be tolerated without affecting the functional integrity of the protein is indicated by examples of both type A and B viruses in which internal deletions of ten or 13 nucleotides in the NS gene cause the production of truncated molecules of 124 and 127 amino acids, respectively.[197]

Evolution of A, B, and C Viruses

It is evident from the preceding discussion that human influenza A viruses evolve gradually during antigenic drift in their HA and NA components as a result of accumulation of mutations in their genes. The gradual variation in the NS gene over the last 50 years can be depicted as a linear evolutionary tree,[196] supporting the hypothesis that several of the virus genes were preserved during the antigenic shifts which involved the introduction by genetic reassortment of novel HA and NA genes. Within a particular subtype, variation in the HA and NA components follows a similar pattern. Thus influenza A viruses in humans evolve through a series of successive variants, one of which tends to dominate during an epidemic period, although a significant degree of microheterogeneity exists among the viruses infecting local populations[198, 199] and is also seen in viruses isolated from individual patients.[200, 201] The two cocirculating virus subtypes infecting horses undergo a similar process of antigenic drift to that seen with human subtypes, although at a significantly slower rate.[168] In contrast, antigenic and genetic analyses of duck viruses isolated between 1977 and 1985 showed that their hemagglutinins were highly conserved and that viruses of different lineages cocirculate.[27] A similar contrast has been noted between the antigenic drift of the N2 neuraminidase of human viruses and the antigenic conservation of the N2 of duck isolates.

Analysis of the variation in the glycoprotein and NS genes of influenza C viruses indicate that in contrast to the situation with influenza A viruses, these viruses are characterized by the presence within the population of many cocirculating strains belonging to multiple evolutionary lineages.[202, 203] The rate of nucleotide substitution in the NS gene is some fivefold lower than for the influenza A virus gene,[196] indicating the slower evolution of influenza C viruses. Evidence of genetic reassortment among influenza C viruses isolated from pigs[204] raises questions as to the importance of this mechanism of genetic variation in the human viruses and the relationships between the viruses infecting pigs and humans.

The nature and rate of evolution of influenza B viruses appear to fall somewhere between those of A and C viruses. Comparisons of the sequences of a number of HA and NS genes of influenza B viruses isolated between 1940 and 1987 indicate that multiple evolutionary lineages can coexist for considerable periods of time with sequential evolution within subsets of virus strains.[205, 206] The pattern of antigenic variation is therefore rather complex, and antigenically distinct influenza B viruses can cocirculate during a single epidemic while antigenically similar viruses have been isolated many years apart.

CLINICAL ASPECTS

An outbreak of influenza virus infection can be a gradual event during interpandemic periods, or it may be explosive—in crowded situations, when there is close contact among susceptible persons, or when antibody levels are low. Younger children, especially those of preschool age, tend to suffer the most morbidity and the highest attack rates. School-age children appear to be the early disseminators of virus during epidemics, with subsequent transmission to adults and preschool children during the later stages of epidemics.[4] In settings such as large institutions or college or university campuses, the duration of an outbreak lasts between 2 and 6 weeks.[207-209] In small populations such as aboard a ship or an airliner, outbreaks can be explosive and can last from a few days to 2 weeks.[210, 211] In rural settings, the outbreak may be of a much longer duration.[212] Attack rates depend on many factors: ages of the patients, proximity of exposure to infected persons, prior vaccination history, and prevailing serum antibody titers among the population's age groups.

Transmission of influenza viruses from person to person is thought to occur through several mechanisms. Small-particle aerosols appear to be partially responsible for transmission of infection virus from one person to another.[210, 213, 214] These aerosols are produced while talking, coughing, or sneezing. Influenza virus survives best when humidities and temperatures are low, making winter an ideal time for transmission of the virus.[215] In addition to small-particle aerosols, dried secretions (with infectious virus) on fomites also may be responsible for transmission of influenza viruses. It has been demonstrated that influenza A and B viruses remain viable and infectious for up to 24 hours on hard, smooth surfaces, and for up to four to six hours on more porous surfaces.[216] Other respiratory viruses also have been shown to survive on fomites.[217] Since large amounts of influenza viruses—up to 30 to 70 $\log_{10}$ TCID$_{50}$ (50% tissue culture infections dose)—are shed in respiratory secretions for long periods, especially in children,[218] it is not surprising that fomites might play an important role in transmission of influenza.

Once virus is inoculated into the respiratory tract, and not prevented from adsorbing into epithelial cells, replication takes place over a four- to six-hour period. Additional epithelium is infected after virus is released from dying cells, and once cytotoxicity occurs, symptoms begin. Incubation periods in influenza infections are usually 18 to 72 hours, but may be as long as four days.[219, 220] During the incubation period, infectious virus is shed.[221] The amount of virus shed from the respiratory tract in naturally acquired influenza does not necessarily correlate with the degree of clinical illness, but the degree of cell-mediated cytotoxicity may be related in some way to the degree of illness.[222] However, the relationship of cell-mediated cytotoxicity to recovery from, or pathogenesis of, influenza virus infection is not yet well defined (see Immunity and Immunoprophylaxis, below).

Influenza A virus infection has a fairly typical clinical course. The onset usually is abrupt, with systemic symptoms predomi-

Table 10–4

Comparison of Symptoms in Uncomplicated Influenza A, B, and C Virus Infections

Symptom	Incidence (%) in Indicated Influenza Type		
	Type A	Type B	Type C
Myalgia, arthralgia	60–80	60–80	50
Headache	90	75	80–100
Chills	70–90	55–80	
Rhinorrhea	25	80	90
Cough	75	80–90	50
Sore throat	44	40–70	60–100
Gastrointestinal	10–25	10–45*	0

Increased in younger children, especially diarrhea.

nating early in the illness.[223] Table 10–4 compares and contrasts the symptoms seen in different types of influenza virus infections. Chills and feverishness are frequent, but headache and myalgia are usually most severe and troublesome. Respiratory symptoms are also seen with varying frequency and seem to become more prominent later in the illness. Physical signs include fever, which can be up to 41°C, is almost always present, and last two to three days.[224] Conjunctivitis, nasal discharge, hyperemic mucous membranes, and scattered pulmonary rhonchi and rales can be detected in small numbers of patients. Illnesses associated with influenza A/USSR/77 strains appear to have been less severe than previously described infections with H3N2 viruses, although Douglas's summary of symptoms related to changes in surface antigens of the virus support the case that symptoms and physical findings in influenza A virus infections have not varied greatly over the years.[223] Other specific syndromes, which may not be systemic, and which may be specifically seen in children (see below), are also seen during influenza A outbreaks in adults. In addition, many subclinical cases occur. A confounding problem during influenza virus outbreaks is the fact that other viruses may cause similar illness.[219, 220, 224, 225]

Some authors have felt that influenza B infections may be somewhat milder than those associated with influenza A, but recent investigations[226-228] support the contention that influenza B virus infection can be severe and incapacitating. Influenza B-associated illnesses are discussed below. In general, influenza A and B illnesses cannot be distinguished from one another. Gastrointestinal (GI) symptoms, especially diarrhea in children, tend to be observed more frequently in influenza B than in influenza A. However, this is not a distinguishing finding.

Influenza C illness tends to be a less severely symptomatic illness, compared to influenza A and B infection.[223] Children tend to be more susceptible to influenza C infection.[229-231] Although influenza C illnesses have been characterized in the past as afebrile upper respiratory illnesses, studies have been able to document fever, nasal discharge, and cough.[232] The high rate of seropositivity to influenza C seen in older children and adults would support the contention that this illness usually is mildly symptomatic or subclinical. Reinfection has been demonstrated to occur in both children and adults.[232] Nevertheless, a small percentage (1.4%) of afebrile upper respiratory illnesses may be caused by influenza C virus.[233] As with other respiratory viruses, influenza C virus is able to cause outbreaks in populations with close interpersonal contact.[232]

Complications of Influenza Virus Infection

A number of complications of influenza A and B virus infections can occur in all age groups. (Table 10–5) Among these complications, the pulmonary ones are the most important. It has been shown that influenza virus infections, in patients with both normal pulmonary function and preexisting lung disease, can cause alterations in small airways function and bronchial reactivity.[234, 235] These changes may last for 3 to 4 weeks and may be ameliorated with amantadine therapy.[235] In addition, the syndrome of primary influenzal pneumonia is well described.[236, 237] Primary viral pneumonia can occur in young healthy adults, and appeared to do so during the 1918 to 1919 outbreak. Since 1918, however, primary influenza viral pneumonia has been thought to occur primarily in persons with cardiovascular disease, underlying lung disease, and in the elderly. The mortality rate for patients with this type of pneumonia is high, and long-term sequelae are frequent and include development of diffuse pulmonary fibrosis.[238] In patients who succumb to influenza pneumonia, a hemorrhagic pneumonia with diffuse hyaline membranes lining alveoli and terminal bronchioles is seen. Both influenza A and B viruses have been associated with primary influenzal pneumonia, but it is thought that the B virus causes this complication less often.

In addition to primary influenzal pneumonia, a well-recognized complication of influenza virus infections is secondary bacterial pneumonia. A biphasic illness is often seen, with recurrence of fever after a period of improvement. Cough, fever, and sputum production are usually seen. Pathogens isolated in this syndrome of secondary pneumonia include staphylococci, *Streptococcus pneumoniae*, and *Haemophilus influenzae*. In addition, mixed influenza-bacterial pneumonia can also occur, and coinfections with *Mycoplasma pneumoniae* and *Legionella* sp have been described.[239] Influenzal pneumonia does not necessarily have to occur during epidemics. Influenza virus can be isolated from a significant percentage of patients routinely hospitalized for pneumonia.[240]

The mechanisms underlying increased risk for patients with influenza for bacterial pneumonia are not clear but have been elucidated somewhat. A review of this subject by Couch is an excellent summary.[241] Based on human and animal data, it appears that there is increased adherence of bacteria (particularly staphylococci, *Haemophilus* spp, and *Pneumococcus*) in the pharynx of patients with naturally acquired influenzal illness.[242] Impairment of neutrophil chemotaxis and a detrimental effect on the phagocytic and bactericidal capacities of pulmonary macrophages result in poor pulmonary clearance of staphylococci and other bacteria.[243–245]

Table 10–5
Potential Complications of Influenza A and B Virus Infections

Pneumonia	Reye syndrome
Myocarditis	Guillain-Barré syndrome
Pericarditis	Hematologic disorders
Meningitis	Myositis
Encephalitis	Acute myoglobinuric renal failure

In addition, reduced mucociliary clearance has also been documented after influenza infection.[246] Other effects of influenza virus infection on the immune system include possible depression of lymphocyte function, decreased numbers of circulating T cells, and a decrease in T cell blastogenesis, but reports are conflicting regarding these effects (see Immunity and Immunoprophylaxis, below).

Other complications of influenza virus infection include myositis with myoglobinuria and elevated serum creatine phosphokinase (CPK) levels following influenza A or B infection.[247] Renal failure occur in association with the myoglobinuria,[248] but renal failure following influenza A infection does not necessarily have to be associated with myoglobinuria.[249] Influenza infections also can be complicated by myocarditis and pericarditis, but these infections are rare.[250, 251]

The neurologic sequellae of influenza have been well publicized recently, with the increased incidence of Guillain-Barré syndrome following swine flu vaccination. Vaccination with inactivated influenza A/New Jersey/76 (swine flu vaccine) was associated with Guillain-Barré syndrome in 1 in 100,000 vaccinees. Most vaccinees recovered, but 1 in 10 afflicted died from this complication. The association of influenza vaccine with Guillain-Barré syndrome has not been observed since the swine antigen was removed from the vaccine. However, etiologic association of encephalitis, Guillain-Barré, and transverse myelitis has not been proved. Reye syndrome, a complication of both influenza B and influenza A viral infections, is discussed in Chapter 45.

Nosocomial Influenza Virus Infections

An extensive review of nosocomial viral infections can be found in Chapter 7. Among these nosocomial viral infections, influenza virus is an important cause of such infections in both children and adults. Numerous reports have been published detailing outbreaks of influenza A or influenza B infections in adults.[219, 225, 252–254] Even nosocomial influenza virus infections can be found concurrently with other viral infections.[225] Influenza virus infections also are an important cause of hospital-associated intercurrent illnesses in infants and neonates.[220, 255, 256] Influenza virus infections are also an important cause of illness in nursing homes and geriatric facilities.[220, 225, 228, 252, 257] In addition to being responsible for morbidity and mortality in hospitalized or institutionalized patients, these illnesses are costly, approaching the cost in dollars of some types of nosocomial infections caused by bacteria.[219]

Influenza in Children

Influenza virus infection produces significant morbidity and mortality in children as well as in adults. The highest attack rates occur in school-age children with secondary spread to family members. During outbreaks of respiratory infection, influenza viruses may exceed all other agents in their rates of isolation.

Influenza virus outbreaks occur as discrete epidemics and supplant the other major respiratory disease viruses in the community.[258] Influenza virus has been the most important cause of respiratory illnesses that bring children to ambulatory care. In the 1975 to 1976 outbreaks of influenza A in Houston, influenza virus was isolated more frequently than respiratory syncytial virus, and many infants were hospitalized with lower respiratory disease.[258]

Attack rates of influenza in preschool children of 35% and in school children of 62% have been reported.[259] Fifty percent or more of the affected children were less than 9 years of age and two thirds of influenza isolates were from patients 19 or less. Children under 5 years are at highest risk because of the constant infusion of susceptible individuals and the greater propensity of younger children to develop lower respiratory disease.[260] In another outbreak of influenza in Houston, 30% of influenza isolates were from children less than 5 years of age, an age group constituting less than 10% of the total population.[4] In an outbreak in Nashville, one third of infants and young children in the surveillance population were infected with influenza A.[261]

Data are sparse to support the impression that influenza infections in children are frequently associated with fatal illness. These deaths have not been apparent in the calculation of excess mortality of influenza epidemics, the traditional method for detecting deaths in excess of those expected. One explanation may be the observation that the frequency of lower respiratory tract disease in children does not vary from year to year despite the introduction of new influenza viruses. Therefore, deaths attributable to influenza virus would be detected only if a virulent and explosive influenza epidemic occurred. Consequently, a more direct measurement of deaths due to influenza infection is needed.[259]

The peak incidence of viral lower respiratory disease occurs in infants less than 1 year of age.[262] Large quantities of virus are shed in respiratory secretions of young children infected with influenza virus, in contrast to lesser amounts from adults. This implies that children are particularly effective in transmission of influenza.[263] The earlier occurrence of influenza in young children than in the general population suggests that children may be important in initial community spread of influenza. The introduction of influenza virus into a susceptible population of school children appears to be the most efficient method for community-wide dissemination. Further evidence for this conclusion is the observation that influenza becomes epidemic after school opens and school vacation can interrupt or abort epidemics.[260] In general, the younger the child, the higher the titer of virus shed and the longer the shedding.[264] Longitudinal studies indicate that children are the introducers into and the disseminators within families of influenza virus.[265] The best approach to the control of epidemic influenza may be to immunize healthy school children, college students, and other healthy young populations.[260]

Respiratory airway infections in children can be classified as upper respiratory, laryngotracheobronchitis (croup), tracheobronchitis, and pneumonia.[266] Influenza virus has been associated with all these clinical categories. The most common presentation is an undifferentiated febrile illness involving only the upper airway. Fever tends to be high (> 39°C) and creates diagnostic and therapeutic problems for physicians treating young infants. Older children and adolescents tend to have typical influenza with fever, cough, headache, myalgia, and sore throat (see Tables 10–4 and 10–6). Because the systemic symptoms are often overlooked, influenza in younger children is indistinguishable from that due to other respiratory viruses (respiratory syncytial virus, parainfluenza virus, rhinovirus, or adenovirus). Sixteen to fifty-two percent of children have been reported to develop lower airway disease when infected with influenza A.[259] Laryngotracheobronchitis and pneumonia were the most frequent forms of lower airway involve-

Table 10–6

Frequency of Symptoms and Signs of Proven Influenza A (H2N2) in Children (0–14 Years of Age) and Adults

Symptoms or Signs	Percent with Symptom or Sign	
	Children (n = 45)	Adults (n = 30)
Sudden onset	66*	46
Systemic symptoms		
Feverishness	93	71
Headache	81	72
Anorexia	69*	37
Malaise	68	67
Chilliness	37	64†
Myalgia	33	62†
Respiratory symptoms		
Cough	86	90
Nasal discharge	67	82
Sore throat	62	62
Nasal obstruction	54	52
Sneezing	38	67†
Hoarseness	22	37
Sputum production	19	41†
Other symptoms		
Abdominal pain	31*	0
Vomiting	26*	7
Nausea	23*	4
Diarrhea	2	0
Maximum temperature		
≤37.7°C	11	13
37.8–38.8°C	29	58†
≥38.9°C	60*	29
Other		
Conjunctival abnormalities	61	56
Pharyngeal injection	60	68
Nasal injection, edema	50	64
Nasal discharge	38	20
Cervical adenopathy	38*	8
Rhonchi, rales	2	0
Pharyngeal exudate	1	0

*Significantly more frequent in children (P < .05, Fisher's exact test).
†Significantly more frequent in adults (P < .05, Fisher's exact test).
Modified with permission from Jordan WS, Denny FW, Badger GR, et al: Am J Hyg 1958; 68:190.

ment.[258] In contrast to older children and adolescents, infants and young children infected with influenza often have nausea, vomiting, and diarrhea, in addition to airway disease.[261]

Influenza A and B viruses each produce significant airway disease. Influenza A has been associated with the greater morbidity but has also been the more frequent cause of epidemics. Influenza B has produced epidemics that resulted in the same amount of school absenteeism but not the amount of lower airway disease or excess mortality observed in influenza A.[264] Influenza B virus has been implicated in severe airway and neurologic disease.[227] Type C influenza has been an infrequent cause of epidemic disease.[231, 232]

Complications that range in seriousness from otitis media to Reye syndrome often occur in patients with influenza or after clinical symptoms of infection have subsided. Otitis media is a frequent complication of viral respiratory infection; in an outbreak of influenza A, 41% of pediatric patients developed this complication.[261] Bacterial pneumonia following influenzal lower respiratory disease is a well-recognized, but infrequently documented and reported, complication. Myositis has occurred in children in association with epidemics of influenza. Calf pain was severe enough to limit walking and CPK was elevated. The illness was self-limited, and no sequelae were reported.[267, 268] Toxic shock syndrome, with a high mortality, has been associated with influenza infection.[269] The most serious complication of influenza is Reye syndrome, an entity characterized by encephalopathy and fatty changes in the liver. Reye syndrome was first linked to influenza B infection in 1973 but subsequently has been shown to follow influenza A infections as well (see Chapter 45).[264] Reye syndrome has been epidemiologically linked to salicylate use since the early 1980s. The reported incidence of Reye syndrome has declined in recent years at the same time that salicylate use among children has decreased.[270] National surveillance for Reye syndrome began in 1977 and the peak incidence of this illness was 0.88 per 100,000 population less than 18 years of age in 1980. The incidence in 1986 was 0.16.[271]

Mortality Associated With Influenza

In addition to the morbidity previously described for influenza illnesses, there is a substantial degree of mortality that can be attributed to this virus. As mentioned previously, over 20 million deaths due to influenza occurred worldwide during the 1918 to 1919 pandemic, and many deaths due to influenza or its complications occur each year. A system in the United States for sur-

veying cases of influenza in 121 cities has been in effect since 1962[272] and has been thought to be an accurate predictor and indicator of epidemic activity of influenza. This system has been based on the determination of excess mortality due to pneumonia and influenza, compared to baseline mortality. With some recent refinements in the calculations, much more accurate forecasting can be accomplished (Figure 10–3).[273] However, the extensive epidemiologic surveillance in Houston by Glezen[274] has demonstrated that for the years 1974 to 1981 influenza virus infections had been epidemic during each respiratory disease season, with coincident peaks of acute respiratory illness among the population. Much of the "normal" wintertime increase in the baseline of mortality (see Figure 10–3) has included deaths which in fact have been related to influenza. When outbreaks in reporting cities are not occurring at the same time or are not widespread, the "epidemic threshold" may not be exceeded. Others have agreed that mortality due to pneumonia and influenza is underestimated.[275]

It is clear, however, that certain patient populations are at increased risk for mortality due to influenza.[276] Persons 45 to 64 years old with underlying high-risk disease and persons over 65 years old with or without high-risk underlying disease are at increased risk for death due to pneumonia or influenza during influenza A outbreaks (Table 10–7). Outbreaks of influenza B infections also are associated with excess mortality.[277] These findings have major implications for vaccination programs aimed at high-risk populations, although immunization rates for these populations are not good.[278] A multifaceted program for immunization

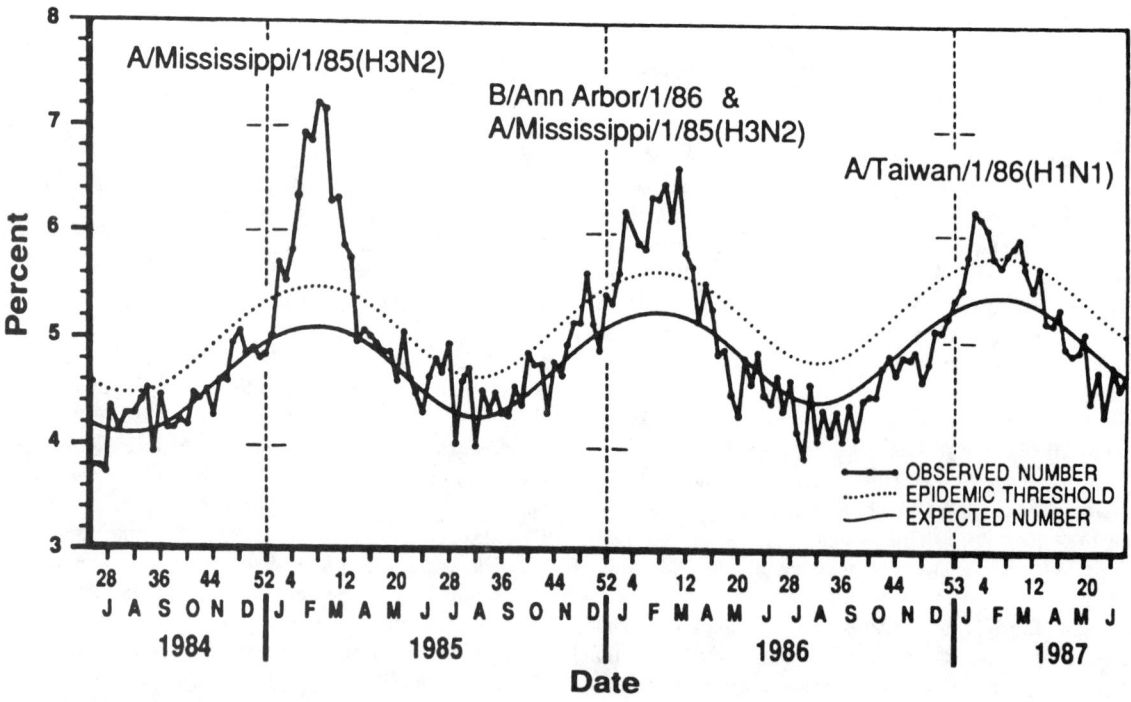

Figure 10–3. Pneumonia and influenza (P & I) deaths as a percentage of total deaths in the United States, July 1984–June 1987. P & I deaths include all deaths for which pneumonia is listed as a primary or underlying cause or for which influenza is listed on the death certificate. Based on reports to Centers for Disease Control from 121 US cities. (*Reproduced with permission from Centers for Disease Control: Influenza— United States, 1986–87 season.* MMWR *1988; 37:469.*)

Table 10–7
Categories of Patients at High Risk for Death Due to Pneumonia or Influenza During 1968 to 1969 and 1972 to 1973 Influenza A Outbreaks

High-Risk, (HR) Category	Deaths per 100,000 Population
Cardiovascular	104
Pulmonary	240
Cardiovascular and diabetes	1040
Cardiovascular and pulmonary	920
Age ≥ 45	
Without HR	4
With 1 HR	157
With ≥ 2HR	615
Age ≥ 65	
Without HR	9
With 1 HR	217
With ≥ 2 HR	797

Adapted from Barker and Mullooly.[276]

of large numbers of high risk patients and the children who spread the influenza viruses,[259] as well as timely chemoprophylaxis and chemotherapy, might be expected to make some impact on influenza virus-related mortality.[274]

In order to prevent influenza illnesses, accurate forecasting techniques must be available. However, accurate prediction of influenza activity for a specific influenza season has been a difficult task. Recent epidemiologic observations by Glezen et al have established the concept of the "herald wave."[260] The herald wave consists of a small cluster of influenza illnesses seen in the late winter or spring—the latter half of the epidemic period—which were caused by different influenza viruses from those which had caused the epidemic illnesses.[260, 279] The herald waves consisted of only 0.4% to 2.0% of the respiratory illnesses that were examined for viral etiology by these workers and required continuous and consistent surveillance in a large population. When the viruses were of different types (A and B), the herald wave was easy to recognize, but when they were antigenically similar, and of the same type, it was more difficult to detect.[260]

LABORATORY DIAGNOSIS OF INFLUENZA

The isolation of influenza viruses in tissue culture remains the standard by which other diagnostic techniques are measured (Table 10–8). In the past, influenza virus isolation was accomplished by inoculation of specimens either onto primary monkey kidney cells or into both the allantoic and amniotic sacs of embryonated eggs. Seven- to eight-day-old embryonated eggs were felt to be superior for the growth of influenza C viruses whereas 13- to 15-day-old eggs were optimal for the isolation of influenza A and B.[280, 281] More recently, it has been shown that several continuous cell lines, including LLC-MK2, GMK-AH-1 (green monkey kidney), and BSC-1 cells, were equivalent to primary rhesus or cynomologous monkey kidney cells in supporting the growth of influenza A or B viruses.[282] The addition of trypsin to the media of continuous cell lines increases the rate of isolation.[283] Influenza C viruses are best isolated in LLC-MK2 cells. Titers of influenza C virus grown in LLC-MK2 cells are tenfold higher than when the virus was isolated in embryonated eggs.[284]

In many instances, influenza viruses cause no cytopathic effects in tissue culture. Hemadsorption of infected monolayers at room temperature with guinea pig or chicken erythrocytes serves to identify cultures infected with influenza A or B. Hemadsorption of erythrocytes to cell monolayers is more sensitive for detecting infection than is testing for hemagglutination in the virus-containing media.[281] Influenza C viruses will agglutinate chicken cells at 4°C but not at room temperature. At room temperature, influenza C viruses are eluted from erythrocytes by virtue of a receptor-destroying enzyme unique to this virus.[285]

Neutralizing antibody (NT) titers correlate best with protection from infection. NT assays are difficult and expensive to perform and are not suited for mass screening. They have been supplanted by easier-to-perform tests, including complement fixation (CF), hemagglutination inhibition (HI), and enzyme immunoassay (EIA) (Table 10–9).

Historically, the assay of CF antibodies has been used to retrospectively establish the diagnosis of influenza. Influenza has two complement-fixing antigens. Antibody to the S antigen (nucleocapsid) usually appears within the first week of illness and may be detected for 3 to 6 months. S antigen is type-specific and varies little between strains of influenza A. The V antigen represents the membrane-associated (HA and NA) antigens. Antibody to this component appears somewhat later in illness, usually around the end of the third week, but may remain detectable for up to 2 years. V antigen is strain-specific, and assay for CF antibody to V antigen must be carried out using an influenza strain homologous for the hemagglutinin.[285]

Due to its relative complexity, the CF test has been primarily used for large-scale surveys and not for the diagnosis of sporadic

Table 10–8
Viral Isolation and Identification Techniques for Influenza Virus

Virus Types	Host		Hemagglutination Characteristics, Species, and Temperature (C)					
	Embryonated Egg	Tissue Culture	Chick		Guinea Pig		Human Type O	
			4°	22°	4°	22°	4°	22°
A	+	+/−	+	+	+	+	+	+
B	+	+	+	+	+	+	+	+
C	+	−*	+	−	−	−	−	−

*Reported to be isolated on LLC-MK2 cells.
Adapted from Hsiung.[293]

Table 10–9
Rate of Serodiagnosis of Influenza Virus Infection by CF, HI, NI, ELISA, or NT*

Virus	CF	HI	NI	ELISA	NT	Ref.
A	89	67				286
A	78	93				287
A	47	55		58		288
A		75	75	88		289
A				74†	74	290
		100		100‡		290
B		77		87		291

CF = complement fixation; HI = hemagglutination inhibition; NI = neutralization inhibition; ELISA = enzyme-linked immunosorbent assay; NT = neutralizing antibody titers.
*Number positive by test or by tissue culture expressed as percent.
†Two-step ELISA.
‡One-step ELISA.

cases of influenza. Moreover, antibody responses to the S antigen are often poor in childhood. Adults tend to have high CF titers; these persist for long periods of time and frequently do not show significant rises following infection.[292] For these reasons, most laboratories utilize the HI test for the serologic diagnosis of influenza.

The HI test is based on the ability of antihemagglutinin antibody to inhibit the ability of influenza virus to agglutinate erythrocytes. The test is simple and rapid and may be carried out with a minimum of reagents and at low cost. Sera frequently contain nonspecific inhibitors of hemagglutination. To remove these inhibitors, sera are heated to 56°C for 30 minutes and treated with either receptor-destroying enzyme, trypsin and periodate, or kaolin. Occasionally, naturally occurring agglutinins in serum will cause agglutination of the erythrocytes; in these cases the serum can be adsorbed with erythrocytes of the same species used in the test.[293] HI antibody is of long duration and titers correlate well with the titer of neutralizing antibody. Tissue culture–grown antigen is superior to egg-grown antigen for use in HI assays to detect influenza B antibodies.[296] This is due to a single amino acid change that occurs in the receptor region of the HA of influenza B when grown in avian cells compared to mammalian cells.

Single radial hemolysis (SRH) has been used in some centers to measure antibody directed against influenza virus.[288, 295, 296] In this test, suspensions of influenza virus are prepared in agarose gels. Test sera are dropped in a central well and allowed to diffuse overnight. Zones of opalescence surrounding the well are correlated with the presence of antibody. Delem and Jovanovic have used SRH to determine the 50% protective titer of antibody against influenza virus infection.[295] Nevertheless, SRH remains a technique limited to research centers.

EIAs, including the enzyme-linked immunosorbent assay (ELISA), and radioimmunoassay (RIA), have been used increasingly to determine the serologic response to influenza virus. When ELISA, using ether-treated virus, was compared to CF and HI, it was found that the sensitivity of the test was greater than CF but less than that of HI.[297] ELISA could not distinguish among viruses with different hemagglutinins. Purification of the constituent polypeptides of influenza virus has allowed the development of specific EIA procedures which will measure antibody directed against the

M protein,[298] neuraminidase,[299] RNP, or hemagglutinin.[290] These specific immunoassays have proved to be more sensitive than CF and HI in the measurement of protective antibody against the virus and may become the preferred method for examining the serologic response to influenza virus infection. EIA has also proved more sensitive than HI in the diagnosis of influenza B[291] and influenza C[300] infections.

The rapid diagnosis of influenza infection by immunofluorescent (IF) antibody techniques was first reported by Liu over 30 years ago[301] (Table 10–10). The sensitivity of IF is usually greater than 80%, and its specificity approaches 100%. In general, EIA techniques have not proved quite as sensitive as IF (see Table 10–10). This may reflect the relative insensitivity of EIA for detecting small amounts of virus in nasal mucus. Yolken et al have developed a sensitive assay for the detection of neuraminidase in nasal secretions.[292] Using this technique, they have achieved a sensitivity of 75% as compared to tissue culture isolation.

CHEMOPROPHYLAXIS AND CHEMOTHERAPY OF INFLUENZA

With the rapidly changing epidemiology of influenza virus infections as a stimulus, chemotherapy and chemoprophylaxis of influenza has become an important investigative field. Amantadine hydrochloride was the first agent to be demonstrated to possess efficacy for therapy and prevention of influenza A virus infection (see Chapter 6). Other agents, including rimantadine hydrochloride, other amantadine derivatives, ribavirin, and isoprinosine have shown variable efficacy in prevention and/or therapy of influenza A. Ribavirin has some efficacy against influenza B virus infection. Little is known about the susceptibility of influenza C virus—in vitro or in vivo—to antiviral agents.

Influenza A Virus

Amantadine hydrochloride is the standard agent for prophylaxis and therapy of influenza A virus infections (Chapter 6 discusses this agent in detail). Numerous investigators have demonstrated the prophylactic efficacy of amantadine in naturally acquired influenza A.[308–312] Protection rates have varied in different studies, but important variables appear to be whether or not prophylaxis is begun early enough in the outbreak, the magnitude of the out-

Table 10–10
Sensitivity and Specificity of Rapid Diagnostic Tests for Influenza*

(IF)		(EIA)		
Sensitivity	Specificity	Sensitivity	Specificity	Reference
78	100			302
		53	97	303
80	100			304
—	—†	100	98	305
96	99			306
		75	97‡	307

*All specimens tested were positive by tissue culture.
†Only tissue culture–positive, IF-positive specimens were tested.
‡Fluorometric assay to detect neuraminidase.

break, and the underlying immunity of the population.[311, 312] Nevertheless, a protection rate of 75% is reasonable to estimate. In addition, amantadine's protection may be additive to that of vaccine. Prophylaxis with 200 mg of amantadine per day for 5 to 6 weeks or for the duration of the influenza A outbreak is not recommended for all persons. However, elderly persons with chronic underlying disease, institutionalized persons, staff and patients in hospital, close contacts of an index case, and patients who cannot receive influenza vaccine due to sensitivity to egg protein may benefit from prophylaxis with amantadine during an influenza A outbreak. Additionally, in the event of an outbreak of an unexpected type of influenza A virus for which there is no vaccine, it might be considered for use in these same high-risk populations or in special groups among the general population. Alternatively, amantadine hydrochloride 200 mg per day (in patients with normal renal function) can be administered for ten to 14 days after vaccine administration to protect patients while antibody is developing. It is possible that in the future lower doses might be found to be equally efficacious.

Rimantadine also has been shown to be effective in prevention of influenza A infections.[310, 311, 313–315] A dose of 100 mg twice a day has been effective in most studies, with demonstration of similar efficacy to that of amantadine; lower daily doses may have the same efficacy with fewer side effects.[316, 317] Untreated contacts of recipients of rimantadine, and possibly amantadine, may also be protected. Rimantadine has a longer half-life and causes fewer side effects, compared with amantadine. Other antiviral agents have not been shown consistently to be effective in prophylaxis of influenza A virus infections.

Amantadine can be used for therapy of uncomplicated influenza A virus infections. Definite but limited therapeutic efficacy has been shown for most strains of influenza A,[224, 318–327] and therapy may improve ability to return to work or school.[217] The recommended dose is 200 mg per day for five days, but 100 mg per day may be as effective and perhaps less toxic.[317, 327] In addition, adding aspirin (or acetaminophen for children) to amantadine during the first 24 hours of illness might result in more rapid defervescence.[327] Whether amantadine might be helpful in serious or complicated influenza is not known, but oral amantadine hydrochloride in a dose of 5 mg/kg/d, if it is tolerated, might be reasonable in these cases. Aerosolized amantadine has been used successfully in several studies, but whether it will be practical and useful in uncomplicated or complicated influenza A virus infections remains to be proved.[328–330]

Rimantadine also is effective for therapy of uncomplicated influenza A infection in doses of 150 to 250 mg per day,[224, 325, 331] and it causes fewer central nervous system side effects than amantadine.[224, 316, 317, 332] Aerosolized rimantadine also might be promising as therapy for influenza A infection, but further investigation needs to be performed with this preparation.[333]

Rimantadine- and amantadine-resistant viruses are readily generated in the laboratory by cultivating influenza A in the presence of low concentrations of amantadine or rimantadine.[334] The emergence of resistance is due to a genetic change in RNA segment 7 encoding the matrix and M2 proteins of the virus. The genetic changes have been limited to codons corresponding to amino acids 27, 30, 31, and 34 in the transmembrane portion of the M2 protein. More than 120 isolates of resistant influenza A characterized to date have one and only one of these changes. The consistent finding that amino acid alterations at residues 27, 30, 31, or 34 in the transmembrane portion of the M2 protein are associated with resistance to the action of both amantadine and rimantadine indicate that these compounds have the same mechanism of action; also, the site of drug action likely involves the transmembrane portion of M2. The greater activity of rimantadine versus amantadine may correlate to the site of action of these drugs in the membrane and the greater lipid solubility of rimantadine. The partition coefficient between octanol and H_2O, Poct/H_2O, is 1.0 for rimantadine but 0.1 for amantadine (V. Toome, Dept of Chemistry, Hoffmann-La Roche, Inc, Nutley, NJ, unpublished observations, 1988). Therefore, the greater antiviral activity of rimantadine compared to amantadine may be a result of higher concentrations of rimantadine within membranes due to its higher lipid solubility.

Naturally occurring resistant influenza A occurs in tissue culture–grown virus populations with a frequency of 1 in 10^3 to 1 in 10^4.[334] The emergence of resistant influenza A virus during drug treatment with rimantadine indicates that these variants occur in nature. In the absence of amantadine or rimantadine, these variants do not emerge as the predominant species. To date the emergence of resistant influenza A has been documented primarily in young children undergoing therapy with rimantadine. This may be due to the large quantities of virus shed by children undergoing primary influenza A virus infection compared with adults who have previously been infected with influenza A. Resistant viruses are transmissible and can cause typical influenza. Treatment of influenza with amantidine also results in shedding of resistant virus. There is no reason to expect that rimantadine treatment would result in the emergence of resistance more often than amantadine.

The universal susceptibility of all types of naturally occurring influenza A isoalted from man and animals suggests that resistance will be found only in those individuals that are treated with drug. Studies on the function of the M2 protein may reveal the reason for natural selection of the susceptible phenotype of influenza A in nature. It has been suggested that the epidemiology of influenza A virus will prevent the widespread emergence of resistance.[334] Natural selection of antigenic variants each few years and the disappearance of previous variants may prevent the emergence of viruses with genetic changes in both RNA segment 4 encoding hemagglutinin and RNA segment 7 encoding M2.

Two targets of specific antiviral action have been identified in cell culture at drug concentrations comparable to those attained in vivo. The relative importance of these targets depends on the virus strain. The replication of most influenza virus is blocked due to the action of amantadine and rimantadine preventing uncoating of viral RNA from the ribonucleoprotein complex of influenza virus during entry into the cell. Certain avian H7 viruses are inhibited by amantadine and rimantadine, inhibiting virus maturation in the cell cytoplasm. Synthesis of viral components is largely unaffected, and the block to virus production is a direct consequence of structural modification to the virus HA. Investigations of this phenomenon have been largely responsible for our current understanding of the action amantadine and rimantadine and the function of the target M2 protein.[334a] Since the same amino acid changes in M2 abolish susceptibility to both the early and late actions of these compounds, inhibition of the two processes shares a common mechanism directed against the function of M2.

The alteration to HA resulting from amantadine treatment of chick cells infected with Rostock virus (H7N1) was shown to correspond to the conformational change induced by exposure to an acidic pH of less than 5.5. The properties of the HA were indistinguishable from the low pH form. The structural modification occurs late in the transport pathway and probably coincident with proteolytic activation of HA.

After insertion into the plasma membrane, HA becomes refractory to drug action. Uncleaved HA_0 does not undergo an equivalent irreversible conformational change on exposure to low pH, and the HA of relatively few subtypes are susceptible to intracellular proteolytic cleavage. Since changes in the primary sequence of the M2 protein alone can eliminate these effects, it is apparent that amantadine or rimantadine do not interact directly with HA but, rather, interfere with interactions between the two proteins. This suggests that the M2 protein is capable of regulating the pH of the environment to which the HA is exposed. This conclusion is based on the two principal observations: first, that in MDCK cells the pH at which the HA undergoes the conformational transition is important in determining the drug-susceptibility of a series of virus mutants; and second, a number of reagents that elevate the pH of intracellular vesicular compartments antagonize the specific actions of amantadine and rimantadine.

Since inhibition of M2 function appears to cause a reduction in pH, the net effect of the protein itself must be to raise it. M2 serves to protect the HA in infections, apparently by influencing the pH of certain compartments of the exocytic pathway. We conclude from these observations that the M2 protein can either directly or indirectly promote the reduction in the transmembrane pH gradient of acidic vesicles.

It is most likely that drug action directed against virus uncoating is effected by a similar mechanism. The dissociation of matrix protein under acidic conditions provides a motive for the acidification of the virion interior. The postulate is that the M2 protein, in response to the acidity of the endosome, promotes the transfer of protons across the viral membrane, causing the acidification and consequent destabilization of the internal matrix structure.

Certain structural characteristics of the M2 protein are consistent with its formation of an ion channel, although there is as yet no direct evidence of this function. The M2 protein has been shown to exist as disulfide-linked tetramers; whether these form part of a larger multimeric structure is not known.[9] Furthermore, the transmembrane domains of M2 proteins can form amphophilic α-helices. The location of the amino acid substitutions that confer amantadine/rimantadine resistance on the hydrophilic face is consistent with direct interaction of drug with this region of the postulated "aqueous" pore. In this regard, the action of amantadine and rimantadine against influenza A viruses is analogous to the anticholinergic activity of amantadine in blocking the ionic channel of the nicotinic acetylcholine receptor during treatment of Parkinson's disease with this drug.[334b]

A number of other antiviral agents have been tested in the therapy of influenza A virus infections. Oral ribavirin does not appear to be particularly useful, nor does isoprinosine to a great degree.[335–339] However, aerosolized ribavirin may be a promising future modality for therapy of influenza A.[340]

Influenza B Virus

Little success has been achieved in the chemotherapy and chemoprophylaxis of influenza B virus infections. Neither amantadine nor rimantadine appear to be prophylactically or therapeutically effective. However, ribavirin, via the aerosolized route, recently has been shown to have a definite therapeutic effect.[341] The application of this type of therapy remains to be defined, but it holds some promise for treatment of children or adults hospitalized with serious systemic respiratory disease caused by influenza B. Until effective oral antiviral agents are developed, epidemiologic measures and vaccination should be used for prevention of influenza B infections, and general supportive measures should be used for therapy.

Influenza C Virus

Although influenza C virus infection may occasionally be a significant problem as far as clinical illness is concerned, little knowledge is available regarding possible therapy of this influenzal illness. Until more is learned about possible efficacious agents, general and symptomatic supportive measures would seem to suffice.

Immunity and Immunoprophylaxis

Although both humoral and cell-mediated immunity to influenza are stimulated during infection, it is immunoglobulin directed against the HA antigen that correlates best with protection from infection and illness. During infection with influenza, antibodies against several viral antigens appear in serum and in nasal secretions. Antibody can be first demonstrated against HA antigen within the first week of illness. Thereafter HI antibody increases for 14 to 21 days after illnesses onset and may persist for years.[342]

Several lines of evidence suggest that antibody to HA is primarily responsible for immunity to influenza viruses. Investigations in experimental animal hosts have demonstrated that passively transferred serum from mice immunized with whole virus or purified HA will protect recipient mice from infection following challenge with influenza A.[343] Protection is also correlated to the appearance of antibody in respiratory secretions so that the location of anti-HA antibody is important in determining the immune status to influenza. Antibody directed against one other surface antigen, NA, also confers protection against infection in animals, but more anti-NA was required than anti-HA antibody to confer protection. Antibody directed against internal virus proteins, NP or M, did not confer protection in animal experiments.[344]

Clinical observations in experimental or naturally occurring influenza in man support the role of antibody to HA as the major determinant of immunity; antibody to NA also confers some degree of protection against infection or illness. Protection from live virus challenge in children and young adults has been associated with serum IgG antibody to HA, and serum HAI antibody to the challenge virus strain.[345–348] Serum HI antibody in titer of 1:32 or 1:40 is generally associated with protection from infection. In a study of over 1000 volunteers experimentally challenged with influenza A/H3N2 or influenza B, the titer of serum antibody associated

Table 10–11
Comparison of Infection Rates and Prechallenge Titers Among 1032 Volunteers Challenged With Influenza A or B Virus

Virus Designation*	Infection Rate in Percent in Volunteers with the Given HAI Serum Antibody Titer (Reciprocal)								Titer (Reciprocal) Associated with ≥ 50% Reduction in Infection
	<6	6	12	24	48	96	≥192		
A2/Hong Kong/1/68	89	50	35	30	20	1	—		6–12
A2/Hong Kong/68-like		75	82	77	42	18	10	3	24–48
Pre-A2/Hong Kong/68		68	92	67	55	32	23	0	48–96
B/England/13/75		54	51	37	18	9	10	3	12–24

*Virus designation and data adapted from Hobson et al.[349]

with 50% reduction of infection was from 1:12 to 1:48 (Table 10–11).[349] Complete protection from infection was not present even at titers of 1:192 or greater. However, HI titer of 1:96 was associated with at least 80% reduction of experimental infections. Furthermore, HI antibody is believed to modify or prevent illness if infection does occur. In addition, transplacentally acquired antibody to influenza A virus confers a degree of protection against infection.[350] Anti-NA antibody is probably less important than anti HA antibody in protecting from infection. However, anti-NA antibody does reduce the occurrence of illness.[351]

Functionally, anti-HA antibody is believed to prevent virus from attaching to cells and therefore prevents initiation of infection. The number of antibody molecules necessary to neutralize an influenza virus particle is not known, but anti-HA antibody is probably the same as neutralizing antibody. Anti-NA antibody is believed to cross-link budding viruses from cells and inhibit virus release.[352]

The antigenic diversity among influenza A hemagglutinins complicates the analysis of the protective effect of antibody. The concept of multiple antigenic determinants on the hemagglutinin molecule, some of which cross-react with other influenza hemagglutinins and some of which are strain-specific, is useful in understanding the role of antigenic variation of influenza in causing disease.[352] Viruses which are related but circulated in man several decades apart, for example, the H1N1 viruses previous to 1952 and H1N1 of the late 1970s and 1980s, were sufficiently similar to result in significant protection from serious illness for persons infected with H1N1 over two decades earlier. In addition, vaccination with related H1 viruses, that is, swine flu vaccine, another H1 virus, resulted in antibody increase to the H1N1 viruses which reappeared in the late 1970s. Therefore primary infection with a given hemagglutinin subtype (H1, H2, or H3) results in strain-specific antibody for that particular hemagglutinin, and these antibodies may cross-react with related subtypes of influenza. Strain-specific antibody probably has the greatest activity in preventing infection and disease, but cross-reacting antibody also may be somewhat efficacious. Antigenic drift of influenza A (H3N2), which re-emerged in 1968, has periodically resulted in diminished vaccine efficacy because of reduced strain cross-reactivity, such as between A/Port Chalmers/1/73 and A/Victoria/3/75 and between A/Mississippi/1/85 and A/Sichaun/2/87.[353, 354] When infection with another virus of the same hemagglutinin subtype occurs, antibody increase to the cross-reactive antigen may occur, resulting in a "booster effect". Also, antigenic drift of the neuraminidase surface glycoprotein has been less extensive than the HA, and anti-

body response to neuraminidase glycoprotein may provide protection from illness.[353–355] Using a sensitive EIA to test for antibody, cross-reactions may be detected between H1 and H3 antibody.[356] However, these antibodies probably do not provide protection from infection or illness caused by heterotypic viruses.

Secretory antibody is at least equal to and possibly more important than circulating antibody in prevention of influenza.[346, 348, 357, 358] Sufficient antibody in either serum or nasal secretions is capable of conferring resistance. Cross-protection in mice infected with influenza A virus to homotypic viral challenge correlates with local secretory IgA in lung washings.[359] Neutralizing IgA antibody and, to a lesser extent, IgG antibody is present in nasal wash specimens taken from volunteers who are resistant to challenge with influenza A. In the lungs, IgG may make up the majority of immunoglobulin in secretions, with IgA present in lesser amounts. Influenza A virus-stimulated serum IgA antibody to HA appears to be of mucosal origin and nasal wash IgA antibody is polymeric, secretory, and primarily of the IgA1 subclass.[360] Anti-HA IgG nasal wash antibody appears to be mainly derived from the serum by a process of passive transudation.[361] Rat anti-HA secretory IgA antibody prevents the attachment of neutralized virus, while neither monomeric IgA or IgG have an effect on this process or on subsequent stages of infection by which virion RNA accumulates in nuclei.[362]

Nasal wash antibody appears shortly after infection, and the largest amounts are present 14 to 21 days after onset of infection. Thereafter the antibody wanes and does not persist as long as serum antibody. Secretory antibody is believed to confer a broader range of protection against influenza strains, whereas circulating antibody may be more strain-specific in preventing influenza. The secretory immune response is best stimulated by infection; parenteral vaccination results in principally a circulatory antibody response, with only small increases in secretory antibody. These observations have important implications for vaccine development (see below).

The cell-mediated immune response is considered to be an important factor in the pathogenesis of and recovery from influenza viral infections.[363–368] In contrast, less is known about the cellular immune response to influenza virus following vaccination with either parenteral inactivated or intranasal live virus.[369–372] Infection with virulent influenza virus in the host decreases lymphocyte transformation in response to mitogens in vitro. The abnormality is detectable within two or three days after infection and may persist for at least 4 weeks. Live attenuated vaccine may alter lymphocyte transformation to mitogenic stimulation, but the studies which have been done are contradictory.[366, 373, 374]

Infection of macrophages with influenza A virus significantly decreases their ability to enhance the lymphocyte transformation response of either infected or uninfected lymphocytes in vitro.[375] Presumably the defect occurs in processing and presenting the mitogen to the lymphocytes.[376] Possible conclusions from these studies include: (1) Viremia (a rare event in influenza infection) and infection of circulating monocytes in vivo may inhibit the immune response to influenza virus by circulating T lymphocytes; (2) viral infection may affect certain T cell subpopulations quantitatively, leading to altered lymphocyte transformation responses. The latter possibility is supported by the finding of lymphopenia primarily comprised of decreased T cell numbers following influenza infection.[377] Viremia has been documented in severe influenzal infection, and some investigators have demonstrated normal and others reduced cellular immune responsiveness during natural or experimental influenza virus infections of varying severity.[368, 374, 378–384] Cutaneous anergy has also been reported in patients with wild-type influenza infection as well as after infection with attenuated virus strains.[373, 384]

Thus, influenza infection may suppress lymphocyte responsiveness to mitogen stimulation in vitro, perhaps on the basis of dysfunction of the infected monocytes. This effect is not universally found in all studies and may be dependent on severity of the viral infection. This immunosuppressive effect is evidenced as well by suppression of skin test–delayed hypersensitivity during severe influenza infection. Inactivated influenza vaccines do not suppress lymphocyte transformation in response to mitogens but do stimulate lymphocyte transformation responses to viral antigen challenge in vitro as does infection with attenuated influenza virus.[368, 370, 371, 374, 375, 383, 385] Serum hemagglutination inhibition antibody titer has been correlated with in vitro lymphocyte transformation response to viral antigen in some studies, but not in others.[368, 371, 373] The amount of viral antigen needed to induce cell-mediated immunity seems to be less than that required to induce a humoral response. In addition, the lymphocyte transformation response is demonstrable earlier than a rise in serum antibody titers after infection.[374] This suggests a role for cellular immunity in the initial defense against influenza virus infection and subsequent recovery.

The role for cellular immunity in recovery from influenza virus infection has been further suggested by studies of cytotoxic T cells and natural killer (NK) cells.[365,386] Cytotoxic T cells recognize viral antigens as well as histocompatibility leukocyte antigens (HLA) class I and class II on the surfaces of infected cells and kill these infected cells. Virus-infected target cells expressing certain HLA antigens (HLA-A1, A9, and -B8) are less susceptible to lysis by HLA-matched cytotoxic T cells than target cells which matched the cytotoxic cells at other HLA loci.[387] Influenza A virus-specific cytotoxicity cross-reactive among influenza A virus subtypes is usually due to CD8 + cytotoxic T cells and is HLA class I-restricted.[365, 386, 388–394] Subtype-specific cytotoxic T cells (CD4 +) make up a smaller proportion of the total number of cytotoxic T cells and are HLA class II-restricted.[365, 390] The principal target antigens of CD8 + cross-reactive cytotoxic T cells are influenza A virus nucleoprotein, polymerase, PB2 and matrix protein.[365, 393] The NK cell is a lymphocyte effector cell which can be detected

in the circulation of nonimmune mice and humans. Its activity is not virus-specific and can be detected early during viral infections. NK cells may provide an early defense against virus infection in the nonimmune host.

While humoral immunity (antibody directed against specific viral hemagglutinin) is known to protect humans as well as laboratory animals from subsequent influenza infection of the same subtype, administration of hyperimmune serum in animals with established viral infection does not effect recovery.[386] However, adoptive transfer of influenza-specific cytotoxic T lymphocytes and of influenza-immune splenic T cells has protected recipient syngeneic mice challenged with influenza virus, and has also enhanced recovery from infection and resolution of pneumonia,[386, 395] reduced influenza virus replication in lung tissue, and reduced mortality.[396, 397] Studies in humans have also suggested a role for HLA-restricted virus-specific T cells in recovery from influenza virus infection.[386, 394] NK cells appear earlier during influenza infection and alone are unable to clear virus from mouse lung tissue. The presence of the cytotoxic T cells is required for viral clearance; however, NK cells may limit virus replication and spread prior to the augmentation of the cytotoxic T cell responses. In addition, the clearance of virus-infected host cells by these cytotoxic cells may contribute to the clinical severity of influenza pneumonia by inducing further damage to host tissue beyond that produced by the virus itself. Thus the cellular immune system may, in addition to clearing virus from infected tissue, also worsen the histopathologic changes in the infected lung tissue.

Antibody-dependent cellular cytotoxicity (ADCC) mediated by antibody occurs after natural and live attenuated influenza A virus infection and after inactivated virus vaccination in at least young adults and children.[398, 399]

ADCC antibody titer may increase sooner than HAI antibody titer and remain elevated longer postvaccination.[398] It may mediate an early host response to virus infection since the Fc + effector cells (K cells) do not have to be induced. The clinical significance of ADCC to the host undergoing natural infection is not known.

Interferon has primary antiviral effects on cells and also acts through the regulation of certain immune functions. Interferon most likely serves as the earliest host response to viral infection by inducing an antiviral state in host cells and by enhancing cytotoxic lymphocyte activity. Type 1 interferon has been detected in nasopharyngeal washings and serum within 24 to 48 hours of onset of natural infection as well as following experimental intranasal inoculation of wild-type influenza virus.[383, 400–406] Intranasal inoculation of either live attenuated influenza strains or inactivated influenza virus produces lower titers of type 1 interferon than those produced by natural infection. This is presumably due to diminished or absent viral replication.[372, 401, 407, 408] Unfortunately, interferon-induced heterologous resistance to other respiratory viruses following intranasal inoculation of live attenuated viruses, a theoretical advantage over parenteral inactivated vaccines, has not been a reproducible finding.[401, 407]

Alpha interferon (a subtype of type 1 interferon) is produced in vitro by peripheral blood mononuclear leukocytes obtained from volunteers previously vaccinated with inactivated or live attenuated influenza A vaccine.[374, 383] The titer of interferon, when the peripheral blood mononuclear leukocytes were stimulated in vitro with inactivated influenza A virus, did not correlate with serum

HI antibody titer, prior history of influenza-like illness, or nasal vaccine virus shedding. This reflects the fact that production of alpha interferon does not depend on prior exposure to the inducer, and also the way in which influenza virus antigen was presented to the peripheral blood mononuclear leukocytes in vitro.

Alpha interferon as well as beta interferon (another subtype of type 1 interferon) have greater antiviral activity than gamma interferon (type 2 or immune interferon). Alpha and beta interferon seem to be mediators of innate immunity. In contrast, gamma interferon (type 2) and other lymphokines are products of cells responding to immune stimuli, and therefore are presumed to be active in acquired immunity.[409] Production of interferons usually accompanies blastogenesis occurring in association with immune responses to antigens and mitogens; however, blast transformation is not a prerequisite for production of gamma or other interferons.[410, 411]

Cell-mediated immunity is affected in several ways by interferon. Interferon enhances target-specific T cell cytotoxicity, the cytotoxic phase of the mixed lymphocyte reaction, spontaneous and NK cell activity, and expression of cell surface antigens.[409, 410, 412] Gamma interferon (and to a lesser degree, type 1) has macrophage activating effects and enhances the bactericidal and antiviral functions of macrophages.[409] In response to influenza virus antigens presented by infected autologous cells, gamma and alpha interferons are produced in vitro by peripheral blood mononuclear leukocytes obtained from volunteers who had received either live attenuated or inactivated influenza A virus vaccine.[413] Mononuclear leukocytes from adults who were not recently exposed to influenza antigens (either not infected or not vaccinated) produced lower levels of gamma interferon after exposure to several influenza virus strains in vitro.[413] The level of gamma interferon production was similar for any one lymphocyte donor after stimulation by any of the live virus strains used (H1N1, H3N2, or influenza B/Hong Kong/5/72). Thus lower titers of interferon were produced in the absence of recent antigenic stimulation, but titers were not dependent on the hemagglutinin and neuraminidase type or subtype. Stimulation of peripheral blood mononuclear leukocytes with inactivated whole virus vaccines and purified hemagglutinin antigens in vitro induced low levels of interferon or none, compared to those levels induced by live influenza virus.[413] This may indicate that, in humans, live intact virus is necessary for gamma interferon induction, although a recent study using a murine model showed that cells exposed to intact, noninfectious influenza virus were recognized by class I-restricted anti-influenza cytotoxic T lymphocytes. The cells processed the intact exogenous proteins for recognition by the cytotoxic cells.[414] The influenza virus antigenic determinants which stimulate gamma interferon production may be the same determinants which activate cytotoxic T lymphocytes.[413, 415] The level of anti-influenza cytotoxicity has correlated with in vitro gamma interferon production.[416]

Infection with wild-type influenza virus induces alpha interferon production in nasopharyngeal washings and serum. This may simply reflect viral replication only and may not affect recovery from influenza infection. Alternatively, alpha interferon may reflect initial nonspecific host defense against viral infection. Gamma interferon and anti-influenza, HLA class I- and HLA class II-restricted cytotoxic T lymphocytes are produced in response to in vitro exposure of peripheral blood mononuclear leukocytes to influenza virus. Interferon and cytotoxic T cell activity may serve an integral and vital part in the immune response of the host to influenza virus infection.

Inactivated Vaccines

Influenza vaccines have been available since the late 1940s. These vaccines have always been in an inactivated form. Vaccines for either type A, type B, or both usually have been available for vaccination before the influenza season. The types included in these vaccines have been antigenically similar to those types isolated during the previous winter's influenza season. Since 1978, when the H3N2 and H1N1 viruses began to cocirculate, each of these A virus types, and the prevalent type B virus, have been included in each year's vaccine. Amounts of viral antigens have varied through the years, but in recent years, the antigen in some vaccines has been increased in an attempt to achieve a better antibody response. However, previous experience with the antigen resulted in a sufficient response with lesser amounts of vaccine antigen, and two doses of a smaller mass of antigen seemed to be sufficient for adequate immunization in persons with no previous immunity.[417, 418]

Gross, et al[419] found that in healthy ambulatory elderly patients who have been previously immunized, a booster dose one month after the first dose (using either split virus or whole virus vaccine) does not enhance serum HAI antibody responses. Repeated vaccination annually or at six-month intervals of adults does not result in a significant increase in the proportion of individuals with protective levels of serum antibody or in the proportion of individuals with fourfold serum antibody rises.[420, 421]

Influenza virus vaccines are prepared after embryonated hen's eggs are infected with a particular strain, after which allantoic fluid is harvested, inactivated with formalin, and purified. Several types of preparations can be created at this point. The purified virus preparation can be left alone, thus creating "whole virus" vaccines. "Subvirion" or "split virus" vaccines, which consist of fragments of virus, including the hemagglutinin, neuraminidase, and internal components, are created by disrupting the whole virus with ether or tri-*n*-butyl phosphate.[422]

In general, influenza vaccines are well tolerated. However, these vaccines are known to cause certain side effects. Local mild discomfort is to be expected in 25% to 50% of patients for one to two days. Fever, malaise, myalgia, or other systemic symptoms occur in 1% to 2% of vaccine recipients, but in the pediatric population, fever may occur in up to 40%. These reactions begin six to 12 hours after vaccination and can persist for one to two days.[423] In children, split virus vaccines are less reactogenic than whole virus vaccines (the same holds true in young adults with no prior exposure to the antigen) but in adults, there appears to be little difference in reaction rates between the split virus vaccines and whole virus vaccines.[422, 424] During the 1976 National Immunization Program, an excess rate of Guillain-Barré syndrome occurred among vaccinees compared to those who did not receive vaccine.[425] However, subsequent vaccines have not been associated with a risk of Guillain-Barré syndrome.[426, 427] Immediate, presumably allergic, reactions may occur, but are extremely rare. They probably result from sensitivity to a vaccine component such as residual egg protein.[423]

The antigenicity of influenza vaccines has been tested extensively. Most vaccines have been shown to be satisfactorily immunogenic in patients with normal host immunity. "Protective" titers of HI antibody can be expected after vaccine administration in anywhere from 75% to 90% of persons, depending on whether or not they have been "primed." In children, two doses may be necessary. Levels of antibody wane over an 8- to 12-month period.[428] In patients with underlying diseases such as malignant diseases, chronic cardiac diseases, rheumatic diseases, and chronic renal disease, serologic response to influenza vaccines may be less than satisfactory, especially in those with malignant diseases. In general, influenza vaccines are safe in these populations and do not exacerbate the underlying disease.[429, 430] However, patients who are receiving active chemotherapy or glucocorticoids do not respond adequately to these vaccines.[428, 431] It is known that immunosuppressive agents reduce cell-mediated responses of peripheral blood mononuclear leukocytes such as lymphocyte transformation (^{3}H thymidine uptake) and lymphokine (interferon and interleukin-2) production in vitro in response to influenza virus, Newcastle disease virus, and mitogens.[411, 432, 433] It is recommended that patients with malignant diseases receive influenza vaccines between courses of chemotherapy in order to maximize their immune response and therefore their protection against influenza infection. Simultaneous administration of influenza and pneumococcal vaccines is safe and effective.[434]

Efficacy rates of influenza vaccines have varied, depending on the population in question and the drift of the epidemic influenza type away from the vaccine antigen. A vaccine efficacy rate of 60% to 80% is a reasonable expectation, although lower rates have been reported. Multiple vaccinations may improve efficacy rates.[421, 435] Patriarca et al[436] reviewed vaccine efficacy studies conducted in nursing homes between 1972 and 1985 and estimated that 27% of residents who receive influenza vaccine are fully protected against symptomatic infection. It has been clearly shown that inactivated influenza vaccines reduce attack rates and ameliorate illness.[437, 438] At 3 years after vaccination, little protective efficacy is observed for influenza B vaccines.[437] For influenza A vaccines, protective immunity may last for two epidemic seasons, and even if antigenic drift has occurred, a previously administered vaccine may provide some protection.[439, 440] In elderly persons, influenza A virus vaccines have been shown to result in reduction in hospitalization and mortality. Influenza B vaccines may be less effective in the elderly, but in explosive outbreaks, attack rates may be higher and, therefore, vaccine efficacy might appear to be reduced. Nevertheless, the need for active immunization programs for the elderly and high-risk patients cannot be overemphasized. Physicians and hospitals should attempt to develop influenza vaccine programs that attempt to achieve high rates of vaccination in appropriate populations. Hopefully, improved inactivated vaccines will become available, or else live attenuated vaccines will be used in the future to achieve high rates of efficacy, long duration of protection, and safe vaccine administration.

Live Attenuated Vaccines

Live attenuated vaccines have been studied in attempts to stimulate secretory antibody by intranasal vaccination. The resulting immunity may afford superior efficacy against a range of related hemagglutinins and longer duration of immunity.

The segmented genome of influenza virus provides not only for the occurrence in nature of major antigenic changes when recombinant (reassortant) viruses arise by dual infection with a human and an animal virus, but also for a mechanism to generate attenuated viruses for vaccine use. In the case of vaccine production, advantage can be taken of this segmented genome. Attenuated "master strains" that have predictable growth properties can be used as donors of genes coding for internal viral proteins and nonstructural proteins. There are six such genes. To these six genes are combined the two genes coding for the desired hemagglutinin and neuraminidase. The result is an attenuated virus with predictable biologic behavior and with the selected hemagglutinin and neuraminidase subtype. These reassortant viruses are produced by dual infection of tissue culture cells and selection of the progeny virus for desired genotype. This process can be simplified by laboratory manipulation such as culturing at restrictive temperature and with antisera added to inhibit production of undesired reassortants.

Several master strains carrying genes that result in attenuated biologic activity have been developed. These include host-range mutants selected by serial passage in tissue culture; ts mutants selected following chemical mutagenesis for reduced growth at 39°C; cold-adapted viruses which have been adapted to grow at 25°C, and in the process acquired ts lesions; and lastly, wild-type avian viruses that are nonpathogenic for man.[441] Of the donor strains, the cold-adapted viruses have been the most extensively studied.[442, 443]

Cold-adapted recombinants are generated by dual infection of tissue culture at 25°C with the cold-adapted donor strain in excess, but with antibody to the H and N of the cold-adapted donor strain added to the media. The progeny virus that has genes coding for cold-adapted internal proteins and nonstructural proteins, but with the new hemagglutinin and neuraminidase, is preferentially selected. Plaque-to-plaque purification is performed, and the cloned populations are genotyped by polyacrylamide gel electrophoresis to confirm the composition of the resulting vaccine seed virus.

The polymerase gene of the cold-adapted parent specifies the cold-adapted phenotype and the PB2 and PB1 genes independently specify the ts phenotype. The polymerase, M, PB2, and PB1 genes of the cold-adapted donor virus each contribute to the attenuation phenotype.[444] The finding that four genes encode for the attenuation phenotype may partially explain the phenotypic stability of these viruses during replication in humans.[444]

Evaluation of several vaccines derived from the cold-adapted influenza A/Ann Arbor/6/60 (H2N2) virus has yielded encouraging results to date.[348, 445–454]

Cold recombinant H1N1 and H3N2 vaccines have been shown to be highly attenuated in seronegative children and adults, and in older adults with chronic obstructive pulmonary disease and other chronic diseases, most of whom have had prior experience with influenza viruses.[447, 448, 452, 455] The vaccines stimulate secretory antibody as well as serum antibody to HA.[348] The live cold-adapted virus vaccines induce a better secretory IgA antibody to HA response than does inactivated virus vaccine administered parenterally.[446, 448] The amount of intranasal vaccine virus required to infect seronegative adults is approximately 10^5 to 10^6 TCID$_{50}$; seronegative children require ten- to 100-fold less virus to result in infection with vaccine virus.[449, 455] In the older high-risk adult population, infection rates with cold-adapted virus strains are at least 60%,[448, 456] although possibly lower rates may be observed in the healthy elderly.[457, 458] The rate of response may be increased if both parenteral inactivated virus vaccine and intranasal cold-adapted vaccine of the same subtype are given together compared with response to either administered alone.[457, 458] Cell-mediated immunity, measured by lymphocyte transformation and by influenza A virus-specific cytotoxic T lymphocyte activity, is stimulated by cold-adapted virus infection.[366, 374, 387, 388, 459] Bivalent cold recombinant vaccines (H1N1 and H3N2) may be given to children without ill effect or interference among the viruses, although reassortment between hemagglutinin and neuraminidase components of H1N1 and H3N2 vaccine viruses occurred, giving rise to H3N1 and H1N2 viruses in 25% of plaques picked from virus plated with original nasal secretions.[460] Preliminary efficacy studies indicate that the cold recombinant vaccines prevent infection following experimental or natural challenge with related strains, and may be more effective than inactivated virus vaccine.[443, 449, 451, 452] It remains to be shown how broad and how durable is the immunity that results from these vaccines.

REFERENCES

1. Hirsch A: *Handbook of Geographical and Historical Pathology.* Creighton C (trans). London, New Sydenham Society, 1883, vol 1, pp 7–17.
2. Thomson D, Thomson R: Influenza. *Ann Pickett-Thomson Res Lab* 1993; 9:4–11.
3. Crosby AW: *Epidemic and Peace.* 1918, part IV. Westport, Conn, Greenwood Press, 1976.
4. Glezen WP, Couch RB: Interpandemic influenza in the Houston area, 1974–1976. *N Engl J Med* 1978; 298:587–592.
5. Burnet M, White DO: *National History of Infectious Disease,* ed 4. London, Cambridge University Press, 1972, p 203.
6. Thompson T (ed): *Annals of Influenza.* London, Sydenham Society, 1852; pp 58–60.
7. Levin ML: An historical account of "the influence" (influenza). *Md State Med J* 1978; 27:58–62.
8. Guerra F: Cause of death of the American Indians. *Nature* 1987; 326:449–450.
9. Beveridge WIB: *Influenza: The Last Great Plague.* New York, PROSIT, 1977.
10. Pfeiffer R: Die Aetiologie der Influenza. *Z. Hyg Infekt-Krankh* 1893; 13:357–386.
11. Fürbringer P: Influenza in Wilson JC (ed): *Modern Clinical Medicine: Infectious Diseases.* New York, Appleton, 1910, pp
12. Rivers TM (ed): *Filterable Viruses.* Baltimore, Williams & Wilkins, 1928.
13. Koen JS: A practical method for field diagnosis of swine diseases. *Am J Vet Med* 1919; 14:468–470.
14. Shope RE: Swine influenza. III. Filtration experiments and etiology. *J Exp Med* 1931; 54:373–385.
15. Smith W, Andrewes CH, Laidlow PP: A virus obtained from influenza patients. *Lancet* 1933; 2:66–68.
16. Francis T Jr: A new type of virus from epidemic influenza. *Science* 1940; 92:405–408.
17. Taylor RM: A further note on 1233 (influenza C) virus. *Arch Gesamte Virusforsch* 1951; 4:485–500.
18. Burnet FM: Influenza virus on the developing egg. *Brit J Exp Pathol* 1936; 17:282–293.
19. Hirst GK: The agglutination of red cells by allantoic fluid of chick embryos infected with influenza virus. *Science* 1941; 94:22–23.
20. Francis T Jr: The current status of the control of influenza. *Ann Intern Med* 1955; 43:534–538.
21. Kilbourne ED: *Influenza.* New York, Plenum 1987, p 235.
22. Guo Y, Jin F, Wang P, et al: Isolation of influenza C virus from pigs and experimental infection of pigs with influenza C virus. *J Gen Virol* 1983; 64:177–182.
23. Webster RG, Laver WG, Air GM, et al: Molecular mechanisms of variation in influenza viruses. *Nature* 1982; 296:115–121.
24. Shortridge KF: Asian influenza A viruses of southern China and Hong Kong: Ecological aspects and implications for man. *Bull WHO* 1982; 60:129–135.
25. Alexander D, Daniels R, Easterday BC, et al: Molecular epidemiology of influenza viruses: memorandum from a WHO meeting. *Bull WHO* 1987; 65:161–165.
25a. Nestorowicz A, Kawaoka Y, Bean WJ, et al: Molecular analysis of the hemagglutinin genes of Australian H7N7 influenza viruses: role of passerine birds in maintenance or transmission? *Virology* 1987; 160:411–418.
26. Scholtissek C: Molecular aspects of the epidemiology of virus disease. *Experientia* 1987; 43:1197–1201.
27. Kida H, Kawaoka Y, Naeve CW, et al: Antigenic and genetic conservation of H3 influenza virus in wild ducks. *Virology* 1987; 159:109–119.
28. Webster RG, Hinshaw VS, Bean WJ, et al: Characterization of an influenza A virus from seals. *Virology* 1981; 113:712–724.
29. Hinshaw VS, Bean WJ, Webster RG, et al: Are seals frequently infected with avian influenza viruses? *J Virol* 1984; 51:863–865.
30. Webster RG, Geraci J, Petursson G, et al: Conjunctivitis in human beings caused by influenza A virus of seals, letter. *N Engl J Med* 1982; 304:911.
31. Hinshaw VS, Bean WJ, Geraci JR, et al: Characterization of two influenza A viruses from a pilot whale. *J Virol* 1986; 58:655–656.
32. Kawaoka Y, Chambers TM, Sladen WL, et al: Is the gene pool of influenza viruses in shorebirds and gulls different from that in wild ducks? *Virology* 1988; 163:247–250.
33. Feldmann H, Kretzschmar E, Klingeborn B, et al: The structure of serotype H10 hemagglutinin of influenza A virus: comparison of an apathogenic avian and mammalian strain pathogenic for mink. *Virology* 1988; 165:428–437.
34. McGeoch D, Fellner P, Newton C: Influenza virus genome consists of eight distinct RNA species. *Proc Natl Acad Sci USA* 1976; 73:3045–3049.
35. Palese P: The genes of influenza virus. *Cell* 1977; 10:1–10.
36. Palese P, Racaniello VR, Desselberger U, et al: Genetic structure and genetic variation of influenza viruses. *Philos Trans R Soc Lond (Biol)* 1980; 288:299–305.
37. Desselberger U, Racaniello VR, Zazra JR, et al: The 3' and 5' terminal sequences of influenza A, B, and C viruses are highly conserved and show partial inverted complementarity. *Gene* 1980; 8:315–328.
38. Skehel JJ, Hay AJ: Nucleotide sequences at the 5'-termini of influenza virus RNAs and their transcripts. *Nucleic Acids Res* 1978; 5:1207–1219.
39. Robertson JS: 5' and 3' terminal nucleotide sequences of the RNA genome segments of influenza virus. *Nucleic Acids Res* 1979; 6:3745–3757.
40. Stoeckle MY, Shaw MW, Choppin PW: Segment-specific and common nucleotide sequences in the noncoding regions of influenza B virus genome RNAs. *Proc Natl Acad Sci USA* 1987; 84:2703–2707.
41. Hsu M-T, Parvin JD, Gupta S, et al: Genomic RNAs of influenza viruses are held in a circular conformation in virions and in infected cells by a terminal panhandle. *Proc Natl Acad Sci USA* 1987; 84:8140–8144.
42. Jennings PA, Finch JT, Winter G, et al: Does the higher order structure of the influenza virus ribonucleoprotein guide sequence rearrangements in influenza viral RNA? *Cell* 1983; 34:619–627.
43. Webster RG, Campbell CH, Granoff A: The in vivo production of new influenza A viruses. I. Genetic recombination between avian and mammalian influenza viruses. *Virology* 1971; 44:317–328.

44. Tumova B, Pereira HG: Genetic interaction between influenza A viruses of human and animal origin. *Virology* 1965; 27:253–261.

45. Lamb RA: The genes and proteins of influenza viruses, in Krug RM (ed): *The Influenza Viruses*. New York, Plenum 1989 (in press).

46. Kato A, Mitzumoto K, Ishihama A: Purification and enzymatic properties of an RNA polymerase-RNA complex from influenza virus. *Virus Res* 1985; 3:115–127.

47. Blaas D, Patzelt E, Kuechler E: Identification of the cap binding protein of influenza virus. *Nucleic Acids Res* 1982; 10:4803–4812.

48. Ulmanen I, Broni BA, Krug RM: Role of two of the influenza virus core P proteins in recognizing cap 1 structures (m^7GpppNm) on RNAs and in initiating viral RNA transcription. *Proc Natl Acad Sci USA* 1981; 78:7355–7359.

49. Plotch SJ, Bouloy M, Krug RM: Transfer of 5′ terminal cap of globin mRNA to influenza viral complementary RNA during transcription *in vitro*. *Proc Natl Acad Sci USA* 1979; 76:1618–1622.

50. Beaton AR, Krug RM: Selected host cell capped RNA fragments prime influenza viral RNA transcription *in vivo*. *Nucleic Acids Res* 1981; 9:423–426.

51. Krug RM, Broni B, Bouloy M: Are the 5′ ends of influenza viral mRNAs synthesized in vivo donated by host mRNAs? *Cell* 1979; 18:329–334.

52. Braam J, Ulmanen I, Krug RM: Molecular model of a eukaryotic transcription complex: functions and movements of influenza P proteins during capped RNA-primed transcription. *Cell* 1983; 34:609–618.

53. Ploch SJ, Bouloy M, Ulmanen I, et al: A unique cap (m^7GpppXm)-dependent influenza virion endonuclease cleaves capped RNAs to generate the primers that initiate vial RNA transcription. *Cell* 1981; 23:847–858.

54. Ulmanen I, Broni BA, Krug RM: Influenza virus temperature-sensitive cap (m^7GpppNm)-dependent endonuclease. *J Virol* 1983; 45:27–35.

55. Hay AJ, Abraham G, Skehel JJ, et al: Influenza virus messenger RNAs are incomplete transcripts of the genome RNA. *Nucleic Acids Res* 1977; 4:4197–4209.

56. Robertson JS, Schubert M, Lazzarini RA: Polyadenylation sites for influenza virus mRNA. *J Virol* 1981; 38:157–163.

57. Romanos MA, Hay AJ: Identification of the influenza virus transcriptase by affinity labelling with pyridoxal 5′-phosphate. *Virology* 1984; 132:110–117.

58. Hay AJ, Skehel JJ, McCauley J: Characterization of influenza virus RNA complete transcripts. *Virology* 1982; 116:517–522.

59. Hay AJ, Skehel JJ, McCauley J: Structure and synthesis of influenza virus complementary RNAs. *Philos Trans R Soc Lond (Biol)* 1980; 288:341–348.

60. Beaton AR, Krug RM: Synthesis of the templates for influenza virion RNA replication *in vitro*. *Proc Natl Acad Sci USA* 1984, 81:4682–4686.

61. Beaton AR, Krug RM: Transcription antitermination during influenza viral template RNA synthesis requires the nucleocapsid protein and the absence of a 5′ capped end. *Proc Natl Acad Sci USA* 1986; 83:6282–6286.

62. Shapiro GI, Krug RM: Influenza virus RNA replication *in vitro*: synthesis of viral template RNAs and virion RNAs in the absence of an added primer. *J Virol* 1988; 62:2285–2290.

63. Pons MW, Schulze IT, Hirst GK, et al: Isolation and characterization of the ribonucleoprotein of influenza virus. *Virology* 1969; 39:250–259.

64. Kingsbury DW, Webster RG: Some properties of influenza virus nucleocapsids. *J Virol* 1969; 4:219–225.

65. Lamb RA, Lai C-J, Choppin PW: Sequences of mRNAs derived from genome RNA segment 7 of influenza virus: colinear and interrupted mRNAs code for overlapping proteins. *Proc Natl Acad Sci USA* 1981; 78:4170–4174.

66. Lamb RA, Lai C-J: Sequence of interrupted and uninterrupted mRNAs and cloned DNA coding for the two overlapping nonstructural proteins of influenza virus. *Cell* 1980; 21:475–485.

67. Ye Z, Pal R, Fox JW, et al: Functional and antigenic domains of the matrix (M_1) protein of influenza A virus. *J Virol* 1987; 61:239–246.

68. Lamb RA, Lai C-J: Conservation of the influenza virus membrane protein (M_1) amino acid sequence and an open reading frame of RNA segment 7 encoding a second protein (M_2) in H1N1 and H3N2 strains. *Virology* 1981; 112:746–751.

69. Lamb RA, Choppin PW: Identification of a second protein (M_2) encoded by RNA segment 7 of influenza virus. *Virology* 1981; 112:729–737.

70. Lamb RA, Zebedee SL, Richardson CD: Influenza virus M_2 protein is an integral membrane protein expressed on the infected-cell surface. *Cell* 1985; 40:627–633.

71. Zebedee SL, Lamb RA: Influenza virus M_2 protein: monoclonal antibody restriction of virus growth and detection of M_2 in virions. *J Virol* 1988; 62:2762–2772.

72. Hay AJ: The mechanism of action of amantadine and rimantadine against influenza viruses, in Notkins AL, Oldstone MBA (eds): *Concepts in Viral Pathogenesis*. 1989, pp 361–367.

73. Hay AJ, Wolstenholme AJ, Skehel JJ, et al: The molecular basis of the specific anti-influenza action of amantadine. *EMBO J* 1985; 4:3021–3024.

74. Hay AJ, Zambon MC, Wolstenholme AJ, et al: Molecular basis of resistance of influenza A viruses to amantadine. *J Antimicrob Chemother* 1986; 18(suppl B):19–29.

75. Belshe RB, Hall Smith M, Hall CB, et al: Genetic basis of resistance to rimantadine emerging during treatment of influenza virus infection. *J Virol* 1988; 62:1508–1512.

76. Lamb RA, Choppin PW: Segment 8 of the influenza virus genome is unique in coding for two polypeptides. *Proc Natl Acad Sci USA* 1979; 76:4908–4912.

77. Briedis DJ, Lamb RA: Influenza B virus genome: sequences and structural organization of RNA segment 8 and the mRNAs coding for the NS_1 and NS_2 proteins. *J Virol* 1982; 42:186–193.

78. Nakada S, Graves PN, Palese P: The influenza C virus NS gene: evidence for a spliced mRNA and a second NS gene product (NS2 protein). *Virus Res* 1986; 4:263–273.

79. Shaw MW, Choppin PW, Lamb RA: A previously unrecognized influenza B virus glycoprotein from a bicistronic mRNA that also encodes the viral neuraminidase. *Proc Natl Acad Sci USA* 1983; 80:4879–4883.

80. Williams MA, Lamb RA: Determination of the orientation of an integral membrane protein and sites of glycosylation by oligonucleotide-directed mutagenesis: influenza B virus NB glycoprotein lacks a cleavable signal sequence and has an extracellular NH_2-terminal region. *Mol Cell Biol* 1986; 6:4317–4328.

81. Williams MA, Lamb RA: Polylactosaminoglycan modification of a small integral membrane glycoprotein, influenza B virus NB. *Mol Cell Biol* 1988; 8:1186–1196.

82. Briedis DJ, Lamb RA, Choppin RW: Sequence of RNA segment 7 of the influenza B virus genome: partial amino acid homology between the membrane proteins (M_1) of influenza A and B viruses and conservation of a second open reading frame. *Virology* 1982; 116:581–588.

83. Hiebert SW, Williams MA, Lamb RA: Nucleotide sequence of RNA segment 7 of influenza B/Singapore/222/79: maintenance of a second large open reading frame. *Virology* 1986; 155:747–751.

84. Yamashita M, Krystal M, Palese P: Evidence that the matrix protein of influenza C virus is coded for by a spliced mRNA. *J Virol* 1988; 62:3348–3355.

85. Herrler G, Durkop I, Becht H, et al: The glycoprotein of influenza C virus is the haemagglutinin, esterase and fusion factor. *J Gen Virol* 1988; 69:839–846.

86. Vlasak R, Krystal M, Nacht M, et al: The influenza C virus glycoprotein (HE) exhibits receptor-binding (haemagglutinin) and receptor-destroying (esterase) activities. *Virology* 1987; 160:419–425.

87. Herrler G, Nagele A, Meier-Ewert H, et al: Isolation and structural analysis of influenza C virion glycoproteins. *Virology* 1981; 113:439–451.

88. Hewat EA, Cusack S: Low resolution structure of the influenza C glycoprotein determined by electron microscopy. *J Mol Biol* 1984; 175:175–193.

89. Rogers GN, Herrler G, Paulson JC, et al: Influenza C virus uses 9-*O*-acetyl-N-acetylneraminic acid as a high affinity receptor determinant for attachment to cells. *J Biol Chem* 1986; 261:5947–5951.

90. Wiley DC, Skehel JJ: The structure and function of the HA membrane glycoprotein of influenza virus. *Annu Rev Biochem* 1987; 56:365–394.

91. Wilson IA, Skehel JJ, Wiley DC: Structure of the haemagglutinin membrane glycoprotein of influenza virus at 3A resolution. *Nature* 1981; 289:366–373.

92. Kawaoka Y, Webster RG: Sequence requirements for cleavage activation of influenza virus hemagglutinin expressed in mammalian cells. *Proc Natl Acad Sci USA* 1988; 85:324–328.

93. Kawaoka Y, Nestorowicz A, Alexander DJ, et al: Molecular analyses of the hemagglutinin genes of H5 influenza viruses: origin of a virulent turkey strain. *Virology* 1987; 158:218–227.

94. Webster RG, Rott R: Influenza A virus pathogenicity: the pivotal role of hemagglutinin. *Cell* 1987; 50:665–666.

95. Deshpande KL, Fried VA, Ando M, et al: Glycosylation affects cleavage of an H5N2 influenza virus hemagglutinin and regulates virulence. *Proc Natl Acad Sci. USA* 1987; 84:36–40.

96. Rott R, Orlich M, Klenk H-D, et al: Studies on the adaptation of influenza viruses to MDCK cells. *EMBO J* 1984; 3:3329–3332.

97. Tashiro M, Ciborowski P, Klenk H-D, et al: Role of staphylococcus protease in the development of influenza pneumonia. *Nature* 1987; 325:536–537.

98. Barbey-Morel CL, Oeltmann TN, Edwards KM, et al: Role of respiratory tract proteases in infectivity of influenza A virus. *J Infect Dis* 1987; 155:667–672.

99. Ward CW, Dopheide TAA: Completion of the amino acid sequence of a Hong Kong influenza haemagglutinin heavy chain: sequence of cyanogen bromide fragment CN1. *Virology* 1980; 103:37–53.

100. Weis W, Brown JH, Cusack S, et al: Structure of the influenza virus haemagglutinin complexed with its receptor, sialic acid. *Nature* 1988; 333:426–431.

101. Rogers GN, Paulson JC: Receptor determinants of human and animal virus isolates: differences in receptor specificity of the H3 hemagglutinin based on species of origin. *Virology* 1983; 127:361–373.

102. Suzuki Y, Nagao Y, Kato H, et al: Human influenza A virus hemagglutinin distinguishes sialyloligosaccharides in membrane-associated gangliosides as its receptor which mediates the adsorption and fusion processes of virus infection. *J Biol Chem* 1986; 261:17057–17061.

103. Anders EM, Scalzo AA, Rogers GN, et al: Relationship between mitogenic activity of influenza viruses and the receptor binding specificity of their haemagglutinin molecules. *J Virol* 1986; 60:476–482.

104. Rogers GN, Paulson JC, Daniels RS, et al: Single amino acid substitutions in influenza haemagglutinin change receptor binding specificity. *Nature* 1983; 304:76–78.

105. Rogers GN, Daniels RS, Skehel JJ, et al: Host-mediated selection of influenza virus receptor variants. *J Biol Chem* 1985; 260:7362–7367.

106. Naeve CW, Hinshaw VS, Webster RG: Mutations in the hemagglutinin receptor-binding site can change the biological properties of an influenza virus. *J Virol* 1984; 51:567–569.

107. Kida H, Shortridge KF, Webster RG: Origin of the hemagglutinin gene of H3N2 influenza viruses from pigs in China. *Virology* 1988; 162:160–166.

108. Daniels RS, Douglas AR, Skehel JJ, et al: Antigenic analyses of influenza virus haemagglutinins with different receptor-binding specificities. *Virology* 1984; 138:174–177.

109. Underwood PA: Receptor binding characteristics of strains of the influenza Hong Kong subtype, using a periodate sensitivity test. *Arch Virol* 1985; 84:53–61.

110. Underwood PA, Skehel JJ, Wiley DC: Receptor-binding characteristics of monoclonal antibody-selected antigenic variants of influenza virus. *J Virol* 1987; 61:206–208.

111. Yewdell JW, Caton AJ, Gerhard W: Selection of influenza A virus adsorptive mutants by growth in the presence of a mixture of monoclonal antihemagglutinin antibodies. *J Virol* 1986; 57:623–628.

112. Carroll SM, Higa HH, Paulson JC: Different cell surface receptor determinants of antigenically similar influenza virus hemagglutinins. *J Biol Chem* 1981; 16:8357–8363.

113. Both GW, Cheng HS, Kilbourne ED: Hemagglutinin of swine influenza virus: A single amino acid change pleiotropically affects viral antigenicity and replication. *Proc Natl Acad Sci USA* 1983; 80:6996–7000.

114. Daniels RS, Jeffries S, Yates P, et al: The receptor-binding and membrane-fusion properties of influenza virus variants selected using anti-haemagglutinin monoclonal antibodies. *EMBO J* 1987; 6:1459–1465.

115. Robertson JS, Bootman JS, Newman R, et al: Structural changes in the haemagglutinin which accompany egg adaptation of an influenza A (H1N1) virus. *Virology* 1987; 160:31–37.

116. Katz JM, Naeve CW, Webster RG: Host cell-mediated variation in H3N2 influenza viruses. *Virology* 1987; 156:386–395.

117. Robertson JS, Naeve CW, Webster RG, et al: Alterations in haemagglutinin associated with adaptation of influenza B virus to growth in eggs. *Virology* 1985; 143:166–174.

118. Deom CM, Caton AJ, Schulze IT: Host cell-mediated selection of a mutant influenza A virus that has lost a complex oligosaccharide from the tip of a hemagglutinin. *Proc Natl Acad Sci USA* 1986; 83:3771–3775.

119. White J, Kiellan M, Helenius A: Membrane fusion proteins of enveloped animals viruses. *Q Rev Biophys* 1986; 16:151–195.

120. Wharton SA: The role of influenza virus haemagglutinin in membrane fusion. *Microbiol Sci* 1987; 4:119–124.

121. Skehel JJ, Bayley PM, Brown EB, et al: Changes in the conformation of influenza virus haemagglutinin at the pH optimum of virus-mediated membrane fusion. *Proc Natl Acad Sci USA* 1982; 79:968–972.

122. Richardson CD, Choppin PW: Oligopeptides that specifically inhibit membrane fusion by paramyxoviruses: studies on the site of action. *Virology* 1983; 131:518–532.

123. Graves PN, Schulman JL, Young JF, et al: Preparation of influenza virus subviral particles lacking the HA1 subunit of hemagglutinin: unmasking of cross-reactive HA2 determinants. *Virology* 1983; 126:106–116.

124. Daniels RS, Douglas AR, Skehel JJ, et al: Studies of the influenza virus haemagglutinin in the pH5 conformation, in Laver WG (ed): *The Origin of Pandemic Influenza Viruses*. New York, Elsevier, 1983, pp 1–7.

125. Wharton SA, Ruigrok RWH, Martin SR, et al: Conformational aspects of the acid-induced fusion mechanisms of influenza virus haemagglutinin. *J Biol Chem* 1988; 263:4474–4480.

126. Ruigrok RWH, Wrigley NG, Calder LJ, et al: Electron microscopy of the low pH structure of influenza virus haemagglutinin. *EMBO J* 1986; 5:41–49.

127. Yewdell JW, Gerhard W, Bachi T: Monoclonal antihemagglutinin antibodies detect irreversible antigenic alterations that coincide with the acid activation of influenza virus A/PR/834-mediated hemolysis. *J Virol* 1983; 48:239–248.

128. Daniels RS, Douglas AR, Skehel JJ, et al: Analyses of the antigenicity of influenza haemagglutinin at the pH optimum for virus-mediated membrane fusion. *J Gen Virol* 1983; 64:1657–1661.

129. Webster RG, Brown LE, Jackson DC: Changes in the antigenicity of the haemagglutinin molecule of H3 influenza virus at acidic pH. *Virology* 1983; 126:587–599.

130. White JM, Wilson IA: Anti-peptide antibodies detect sites in a protein conformational change: low pH activation of the influenza virus haemagglutinin. *J Cell Biol* 1987; 105:2887–2896.

131. Daniels RS, Downie JC, Hay AJ, et al: Fusion mutants of the influenza virus haemagglutinin glycoprotein. *Cell* 1985; 40:431–439.

132. Gething M-J, Doms RW, York D, et al: Studies on the mechanism of membrane fusion: site-specific mutagenesis of the haemagglutinin of influenza virus. *J Cell Biol* 1986; 102:11–23.

133. Doms RW, Gething M-J, Henneberry J, et al: Variant influenza virus hemagglutinin that induces fusion at elevated pH. *J Virol* 1986; 57:603–613.

134. Varghese JN, Laver WG, Colman PM: Structure of the influenza virus glycoprotein antigen neuramaminidase at 2.9 Å resolution. *Nature* 1983; 303:35–40.

135. Baker AT, Varghese JN, Laver WG, et al: Three-dimensional structure of neurmaninidase of subtype N9 from an avian influenza virus. *Proteins* 1987; 2(2):111–117.

136. Colman PM, Varghese JN, Laver WG: Structure of the catalytic and antigenic sites in influenza virus neuraminidase. *Nature* 1983; 303:41–44.

137. Wei K, Els MC, Webster RG, et al: Effects of site-specific mutation on structure and activity of influenza virus B/Lee/40 neuraminidase. *Virology* 1987; 156:253–258.

138. Herrler G, Rott R, Klenk H-D, et al: The receptor-destroying enzyme of influenza C virus is neuraminate-*O*-acetylesterase. *EMBO J* 1985; 4:1503–1506.

139. Herrler G, Klenk H-D: The surface receptor is a major determinant of the cell tropism of influenza C virus. *Virology* 1987; 159:102–108.

140. Muchmore EA, Varki A: Selective inactivation of influenza C esterase. A probe for detecting 9-*O*-acetyated sialic acids. *Science* 1987; 236:1293–1295.

141. Chakraverty P, Cunningham P, Shen GZ, et al: Influenza in the United Kingdom 1982–1985. *J Hyg Camb* 1986; 97:347–358.

142. Webster RG, Reay PA, Laver WG: Protection against lethal influenza with neuraminidase. *Virology* 1988; 164:230–237.

143. Schulman JL, Khakpour M, Kilbourne ED: Protective effects of specific immunity to viral neuraminidase on influenza virus infection of mice. *J Virol* 1968; 2:778–786.

144. Wiley DC, Wilson IA, Skehel JJ: Structural identification of the antibody-binding sites of Hong Kong haemagglutinins and their involvement in antigenic variation. *Nature* 1981; 289:373–378.

145. Both GW, Sleigh MJ, Cox NJ, et al: Antigenic drift in influenza virus H3 haemagglutinin from 1968 to 1980. Multiple evolutionary pathways and sequential amino acid changes at key antigenic sites. *J Virol* 1983; 48:52–60.

146. Skehel JJ, Daniels RS, Douglas AR, et al: Antigenic and amino acid sequence variations in the haemagglutinins of type A influenza viruses recently isolated from human subjects. *Bull WHO* 1983; 61:671–676.

147. Stevens DJ, Douglas AR, Skehel JJ, et al: Antigenic and amino acid sequence analysis of the variants of H1N1 influenza virus in 1986. *Bull WHO* 1987; 65:177–180.

148. Caton AJ, Brownlee GG, Yewdell JW, et al: The antigenic structure of the influenza virus A/PR/8/34 haemagglutinin (H1 subtype). *Cell* 1982; 31:417–427.

149. Daniels RS, Douglas AR, Skehel JJ, et al: Antigenic and amino acid sequence analyses of influenza viruses of the H1N1 subtype isolated between 1982 and 1984. *Bull WHO* 1985; 63:273–277.

150. Raymond FL, Caton AJ, Cox NJ, et al: Antigenicity and evolution amongst recent influenza viruses of H1N1 subtypes. *Nucleic Acid Res* 1983; 11:7191–7203.

151. Raymond FL, Caton AJ, Cox NJ, et al: The antigenicity and evolution of influenza H1 haemagglutinin from 1950–1957 and 1977–1983: Two pathways from one gene. *Virology* 1986; 148:275–287.

152. Laver WG, Air GM, Webster RG, et al: Antigenic drift in type A influenza virus: Sequence differences in the haemagglutinin of Hong Kong (H3N2) variants selected with monoclonal hybridoma antibodies. *Virology* 1979; 98:226–237.

153. Laver WG, Air GM, Webster RG: Mechanism of antigenic drift in influenza virus. Amino acid sequence changes in an antigenically active region of Hong Kong (H3N2) influenza virus hae-

magglutinin. *J Mol Biol* 1981; 145:339–361.

154. Knossow M, Daniels RS, Douglas AR, et al: Three-dimensional structure of an antigenic mutant of the influenza virus haemagglutinin. *Nature* 1984; 311:678–680.

155. Skehel JJ, Stevens DJ, Daniels RS, et al: A carbohydrate side chain on haemagglutinins of Hong Kong influenza viruses inhibits recognition by a monoclonal antibody. *Proc Natl Acad Sci USA* 1984; 81:1779–1783.

156. Wang M-L, Skehel JJ, Wiley DC: Comparative analyses of the specificities of anti-influenza haemagglutinin antibodies in humans sera. *J Virol* 1986; 57:124–128.

157. Young JF, Palese P: Evolution of human influenza A viruses in nature: recombination contributes to genetic variation of H1N1 strains. *Proc Natl Acad Sci USA* 1979; 76:6547–6551.

158. Bean WJ, Cox NJ, Kendal AP: Recombination of human influenza A viruses in nature. *Nature* 1980; 284:638–640.

159. Palese P, Young JF: Variation of influenza A, B and C viruses. *Science* 1982; 215:1468–1474.

160. Gething M-J, Bye J, Skehel JJ, et al: Cloning and DNA sequence of double-stranded copies of haemagglutinin genes from H2 and H3 strains elucidates antigenic shift and drift in human influenza virus. *Nature* 1980; 287:301–306.

161. Winter G, Fields S, Brownlee GG: Nucleotide sequence of the haemagglutinin gene of a human influenza virus H1 subtype. *Nature* 1981; 292:72–75.

162. Scholtissek C, Rohde W, Von Hoyningen V, et al: On the origin of the human influenza virus subtypes H2N2 and H3N2. *Virology* 1978; 87:13–20.

163. Coleman MT, Dowdle WR, Pereira HG, et al: The Hong Kong/68 influenza A2 variant. *Lancet* 1968; 2:1384–1413.

164. Waddell GH, Tiegland MB, Sigel MM: A new influenza virus associated with equine respiratory disease. *J Am Vet Med Assoc* 1963; 143:587–590.

165. Laver WG, Webster RG: Studies on the origin of pandemic influenza, III. Evidence implicating duck and equine influenza viruses as possible progenitors of the Hong Kong strain of human influenza. *Virology* 1973; 51:383–391.

166. Ward CW, Dopheide TA: Evolution of the Hong Kong influenza A subtype. Structural relationship between the haemagglutinin from A/duck/Ukraine/63 (Hav7) and the Hong Kong (H3) haemagglutinins. *Biochem J* 1981; 195:337–340.

167. Fang R, Min Jou W, Huylebroeck D, et al: Complete structure of A/duck/Ukraine/63 influenza haemagglutinin gene: animal virus as progenitor of human H3 Hong Kong 1968 influenza haemagglutinin. *Cell* 1981; 25:315–323.

168. Daniels RS, Skehel JJ, Wiley DC: Amino acid sequences of haemagglutinins of influenza viruses of the H3 subtype isolated from horses. *J Gen Virol* 1985; 66:457–464.

169. Kendal AP, Noble GR, Skehel JJ, et al: Antigenic similarity of influenza A (H1N1) viruses from epidemics in 1977–1978 to 'Scandinavian' strains isolated in epidemics of 1950–1951. *Virology* 1978; 89:632–636.

170. Scholtissek C, Von Hoyningen V, Rott R: Relatedness between the new 1977 epidemic strains (H1N1) of influenza and human influenza strains isolated between 1947 and 1957. *Virology* 1978; 89:613–617.

171. Mulder J, Masurel N: Pre-epidemic antibody against the 1957 strain of Asiatic influenza in the serum of older persons living in the Netherlands. *Lancet* 1958; 1:810–814.

172. Hovanec DL, Air GM: Antigenic structure of the hemagglutinin of influenza virus B/Hong Kong/8/73 as determined from gene sequence analysis of variants selected with monoclonal antibodies. *Virology* 1984; 139:384–392.

173. Berton MT, Naeve CW, Webster RG: Antigenic structure of the influenza B virus hemagglutinin: nucleotide sequence analysis of antigenic variants selected with monoclonal antibodies. *J Virol* 1984; 52:919–927.

174. Martinez C, Del Rio L, Portela A, et al: Evolution of the influenza virus neuraminidase gene during drift of the N2 subtype. *Virology* 1983; 130:539–545.

175. Van Rompuy L, Min Jou W, Huylebroeck D, et al: Complete nu-

cleotide sequence of a human influenza neuraminidase gene of subtype N2 (A/Victoria/3/75). *J Mol Biol* 1982; 161:1–11.

176. Webster RB, Brown LE, Laver WG: Antigenic and biological characterization of influenza virus neuraminidase (N2) with monoclonal antibodies. *Virology* 1984; 135:30–42.

177. Webster RG, Air GM, Metzger DW, et al: Antigenic structure and variation in an influenza virus N9 neuraminidase. *J Virol* 1987; 61:2910–2916.

178. Air GM, Els MC, Brown LE, et al: Location of antigenic sites on the three-dimensional structure of the influenza N2 virus neuraminidase. *Virology* 1985; 145:237–248.

179. Varghese JN, Webster RG, Laver WG, et al: Structure of an escape mutant of glycoprotein N2 neuraminidase of influenza virus A/Tokyo/3/67 at 3Å. *J Mol Biol* 1988; 200:201–203.

180. Colman PM, Laver WG, Varghese JN, et al: Three-dimensional structure of a complex of antibody with influenza virus neuraminidase. *Nature* 1987; 326:358–362.

181. Air GM, Webster RG, Colman PM, et al: Distribution of sequence differences in influenza N9 neuraminidase of tern and whale viruses and cyrstallization of the whale neuraminidase complexed with antibodies. *Virology* 1987; 160:346–354.

182. Schild GC, Oxford JS, Newman RW: Evidence for antigenic variation in influenza A nucleoprotein. *Virology* 1979; 93:569–573.

183. Van Wyke KL, Hinshaw VS, Bean WJ, et al: Antigenic variation of influenza A virus nucleoprotein detected with monoclonal antibodies. *J Virol* 1980; 35:24–30.

184. Bean WJ: Correlation of influenza A virus nucleoprotein genes with host species. *Virology* 1984; 133:438–442.

185. Buckler-White AJ, Murphy BR: Nucleotide sequence analysis of the nucleoprotein gene of an avian and a human influenza virus strain identifies two classes of nucleoproteins. *Virology* 1986; 155:345–355.

186. Scholtissek C, Burger H, Kistner O, et al: The nucleoprotein as a possible major factor in determining host specificity of influenza H3N2 viruses. *Virology* 1985; 147:285–294.

187. Tian S-F, Buckler-White AJ, London WT, et al: Nucleoprotein and membrane protein genes are associated with restriction of replication of influenza A/Mallard/NY/78 virus and its reassortants in squirrel monkey respiratory tract. *J Virol* 1985; 53:771–775.

188. Snyder MJ, Buckler-White AJ, London WT, et al: The avian influenza virus nucleoprotein gene and a specific constellation of avian and human virus polymerase genes each specify attenuation of avian-human influenza A/Pintail/79 reassortant viruses for monkeys. *J Virol* 1987; 61:2857–2863.

189. Buckler-White AJ, Naeve CW, Murphy BR: Characterization of a gene coding for M proteins which is involved in host range restriction of an avian influenza A virus in monkeys. *J Virol* 1986; 57:697–700.

190. Markushin S, Ghiasi H, Sokolov N, et al: Nucleotide sequence of RNA segment 7 and the predicted amino sequence of M1 and M2 proteins of FPV/Weybridge (H7N7) and WSN (H1N1) influenza viruses. *Virus Res* 1988; 10:263–272.

191. Van Wyke W, Yewdell JW, Reck LJ, et al: Antigenic characterization of influenza A virus matrix protein with monoclonal antibodies. *J Virol* 1984; 49:248–252.

192. Almond JW: A single gene determines the host range of influenza virus. *Nature* 1977; 270:617–618.

193. Donabedian AM, DeBorde DC, Cook S, et al: A mutation in the PA protein gene of cold-adapted B/Ann Arbor/1/66 influenza virus associated with reversion of temperature sensitivity and attenuated virulence. *Virology* 1988; 163:444–451.

194. Scholtissek C, Von Hoyningen-Huene V: Genetic relatedness of the gene which codes for the nonstructural (NS) protein of different influenza A strains. *Virology* 1980; 102:13–20.

195. Krystal M, Buonagurio D, Young JF, et al: Sequential mutations in the NS genes of influenza virus field strains. *J Virol* 1983; 45:547–554.

196. Buonagurio DA, Nakada S, Parvin JD, et al: Evolution of human influenza A viruses over 50 years: rapid, uniform rate of change in NS gene. *Science* 1986; 232:980–982.

197. Norton GP, Tanaka T, Tobita K, et al: Infectious influenza A and B virus variants with long carboxyl terminal deletions in the NS1 polypeptides. *Virology* 1987; 156:204–213.

198. Oxford JS, Salum S, Corcoran T, et al: An antigenic analysis using monoclonal antibodies of influenza A (H3N2) viruses isolated from an epidemic in a semi-closed community. *J Gen Virol* 1986; 67:265–274.

199. Six HR, Webster RG, Kendal AP, et al: Antigenic analysis of H1N1 viruses isolated in the Houston metropolitan area during four successive seasons. *Infect Immun* 1983; 42:453–458.

200. Katz JM, Webster RG: Antigenic and structural characterization of multiple subpopulations of H3N2 influenza virus from an individual. *Virology* 1988; 165:446–456.

201. De Jong JC, De Ronde-Verloop FM, Veenendaal-Van Herk TM, et al: Antigenic heterogeneity within influenza A(H3N2) virus strains. *Bull WHO* 1988; 66:47–55.

202. Buonagurio DA, Nakada S, Desselberger U, et al: Noncumulative sequence changes in the hemagglutinin genes of influenza C virus isolates. *Virology* 1985; 146:221–232.

203. Buonagurio DA, Nakada S, Fitch WM, et al: Epidemiology of influenza C virus in man. Multiple evolutionary lineages and low rate of change. *Virology* 1986; 153:12–21.

204. Yuanji G, Desselberger U: Genome analysis of influenza C viruses isolated in 1981/82 from pigs in China. *J Gen Virol* 1984; 65:1857–1872.

205. Yamashita M, Krystal M, Fitch WM, et al: Influenza B virus evolution: co-circulating lineages and comparison of evolutionary pattern with those of influenza A and C viruses. *Virology* 1988; 163:112–122.

206. Bootman JS, Robertson JS: Sequence analysis of the hemagglutinin of B/Ann Arbor/1/86, an epidemiologically significant variant of influenza B virus. *Virology* 1988; 166:271–274.

207. Sobal J, Loveland FD: Infectious disease in a total institution: A study of the influenza epidemic of 1978 MA college campus. *Public Health Rep* 1982; 97:66–72.

208. Pons VG, Canter J, Dolin R: Influenza A/USSR/77 (H1N1) on a university campus. *Am J Epidemiol* 1980; 111:23–30.

209. Layde PM, Engelberg AL, Dobbs HI, et al: Outbreak of influenza A/USSR/77 at Marquette University. *J Infect Dis* 1980; 142:347–352.

210. Moser MR, Bender JR, Margolis HS, et al: An outbreak of influenza aboard a commercial airliner. *Am J Epidemiol* 1979; 110:1–6.

211. Ksiazek TG, Olson JG, Irving GS, et al: An influenza outbreak due to A/USSR/77-like (H1N1) virus aboard a US Navy ship. *Am J Epidemiol* 1980; 112:487–494.

212. Retaillian HF, Storch GA, Curtis AC, et al: The epidemiology of influenza B in a rural setting in 1977. *Am J Epidemiol* 1979; 109:639–649.

213. Alford RH, Kasel JA, Gerone PJ, et al: Human influenza resulting from aerosol inhalation. *Proc Soc Exp Biol Med* 1966; 122:800.

214. Little JW, Douglas RG Jr, Hall WJ, et al: Attenuated influenza produced by experimental intranasal inoculation. *J Med Virol* 1979; 3:177–180.

215. Hemmes JH, Winkler KC, Kool SM: Virus survival as a seasonal factor in influenza and poliomyelitis. *Nature* 1960; 188:430–431.

216. Bean B, Moore BM, Sterner D, et al: Survival of influenza viruses on environmental surfaces. *J Infect Dis* 1982; 146:47–51.

217. Hall CB, Douglas RG Jr, Geiman JM: Possible transmission by fomites of respiratory syncytial virus. *J Infect Dis* 1980; 141:98–102.

218. Douglas RG Jr, Betts RF: Influenza virus, in Mandell GL, Douglas RG Jr, Bennett JE (eds): *Principles and Practice of Infectious Diseases.* New York, Wiley, 1979, pp 1135–1167.

219. Van Voris LP, Belshe RB, Shaffer JL: Nosocomial influenza B virus infection in the elderly. *Ann Intern Med* 1982; 96:153–158.

220. Hall CB, Douglas RG Jr: Nosocomial influenza infection as a cause of intercurrent fevers in infants. *Pediatrics* 1975; 55:673–677.

221. Murphy BR, Baron S, Chalhub EG, et al: Temperature sensitive

mutants of influenza virus. IV. Induction of interferon in the nasopharynx by wild-type and a temperature-sensitive recombinant virus. *J Infect Dis* 1973; 128:488–493.

222. Reichman RC, Pons VG, Murphy BR, et al: Cell-mediated cytotoxicity following influenza infection and vaccination in humans. *J Med Virol* 1979; 4:1–14.

223. Douglas RG Jr: Influenza in man, in Kilborne ED (ed): *Influenza Viruses and Influenza*. New York, Academic Press, 1975, pp 395–447.

224. Van Voris LP, Betts RF, Hayden FG, et al: Successful treatment of naturally occurring influenza A/USSR/77 H1N1. *JAMA* 1981; 245:1128–1131.

225. Mathur U, Bentley DW, Hall CB: Concurrent respiratory syncytial virus and influenza A infections in the institutionalized elderly and chronically ill. *Ann Intern Med* 1980; 93:49–52.

226. Clark PS, Feltz ET, List-Young B, et al: An influenza B epidemic within a remote Alaska community. Serologic, epidemiologic and clinical considerations. *JAMA* 1970; 214:507–512.

227. Baine WB, Luby JP, Martin SM: Severe illness with influenza B. *Am J Med* 1980; 68:181–189.

228. Hall WN, Goodman RA, Noble GR, et al: An outbreak of influenza B in an elderly population. *J Infect Dis* 1981; 144:297–302.

229. O'Callaghan RJ, Gohd RS, Lebat DD: Human antibody to influenza C virus: Its age-related distribution and distinction from receptor analogues. *Infect Immun* 1980; 30:500–505.

230. Homma M, Ohyama S, Katagivi S: Age distribution of the antibody to type C influenza virus. *Microbiol Immunol* 1982; 26:639–642.

231. Dykes AC, Cherry JD, Nolan CE: A clinical, epidemiologic, serologic, and virologic study of influenza C virus infection. *Arch Intern Med* 1980; 140:1295–1298.

232. Katagiri S, Ohizumi A, Homma M: An outbreak of type C influenza in a children's home. *J Infect Dis* 1983; 148:51–56.

233. Mogabgab WJ: Viruses associated with upper respiratory illnesses in adults. *Ann Intern Med* 1963; 59:306–322.

234. Hobbins TE, Hughes TP, Rennels MB, et al: Bronchial reactivity in experimental infections with influenza virus. *J Infect Dis* 1982; 146:468–471.

235. Little JW, Hall WJ, Douglas RG Jr, et al: Amantadine effect on peripheral airways abnormalities in influenza. *Ann Intern Med* 1976; 85:177–182.

236. Louria DB, Blumenfeld HL, Ellis JT, et al: Studies on influenza in the pandemic of 1957–1958. II. Pulmonary complications of influenza. *J Clin Invest* 1959; 38:213–265.

237. Martin LM, Kunin CM, Gottlieb LS, et al: Asian influenza A in Boston, 1957–1958. II. Severe staphylococcal pneumonia complicating influenza. *Arch Intern Med* 1959; 103:532–542.

238. Winterbauer RH, Ludwig WR, Hammar SP: Clinical course, management, and long-term sequelae of respiratory failure due to influenza viral pneumonia. *Johns Hopkins Med* 1977; 141:148–155.

239. Renner ED, Helms CM, Johnson W, et al: Coinfections of *Mycoplasma pneumoniae* and *Legionella pneumophila* with influenza A virus. *J Clin Microbiol* 1983; 17:146–148.

240. Kimball AM, Foy HM, Gomez MK, et al: Isolation of respiratory syncytial and influenza viruses from the sputum of patients hospitalized with pneumonia. *J Infect Dis* 1983; 147:181–184.

241. Couch RB: The effects of influenza on host defenses. *J Infect Dis* 1981; 144:284–291.

242. Fainstein V, Musher DM, Cate TR: Bacterial adherence to pharyngeal cells during viral infection. *J Infect Dis* 1980; 141:172–176.

243. Nugent KM, Pesanti EL: Effect of influenza infection on the phagocytic and bactericidal activities of pulmonary macrophages. *Infect Immun* 1979; 26:651–657.

244. Nugent KM, Pesanti EL: Staphylococcal clearance and pulmonary macrophage function during influenza infection. *Infect Immun* 1982; 38:1256–1262.

245. Warshauer D, Goldstein E, Akers T: Effect of influenza viral infection on the ingestion and killing of bacteria by alveolar macrophages. *Ann Rev Respir Dis* 1977; 15:269–277.

246. Camner P, Jarstrand C, Philipson K: Tracheobronchial clearance in patients with influenza. *Am Rev Respir Dis* 1973; 108:131–135.

247. Kessler HA, Trenholme GM, Vogelzang NJ, et al: Elevated creatine phosphokinase levels associated with influenza A/Texas/1/77 infection. *Scand J Infect Dis* 1983; 15:7–10.

248. Cunningham E, Kohli R, Venuto RC: Influenza-associated myoglobinuric renal failure. *JAMA* 1979; 242:2428–2429.

249. Shenouda A, Hatch FE: Influenza A viral infection associated with acute renal failure. *Am J Med* 1976; 61:697–702.

250. Englblom E, Ekfors JO, Meurman OH: Fatal influenza A myocarditis with isolation of virus from the myocardium. *Acta Med Scand* 1983; 213:75–78.

251. Finland M, Parker F, Barnes M, et al: Acute myocarditis in influenza A infections. *Am J Med Sci* 1945; 207:455–468.

252. Mathur U, Bentley DW, Hall CB, et al: Influenza A/Brazil/78 (H1N1) infection in the elderly. *Am Rev Respir Dis* 1981; 123:633–635.

253. Kapila R, Lintz DI, Tecson FT, et al: A nosocomial outbreak of influenza A. *Chest* 1977; 71:576–579.

254. McDougal BA, Hodges GR, Lewis HD, et al: Nosocomial influenza A infection. *South Med J* 1977; 70:1023–1024.

255. Bauer CR, Elie K, Spence L, et al: Hong Kong influenza in a neonatal unit. *JAMA* 1973; 223:1233–1235.

256. Brocklebank JT, Court SDM, McQuillan J, et al: Influenza-A infection in children. *Lancet* 1972; 2:497–500.

257. Silverstone FA, Libow LS, Duthie E, et al: Outbreak of influenza B, 1980, in a geriatric long term care facility, abstract. *Gerontologist* 20(pt 20):200, 1980.

258. Glezen WP, Paredes A, Taber LH: Influenza in children: Relationship to other respiratory viruses. *JAMA* 1980; 243:1345–1349.

259. Glezen WP: Consideration of the risk of influenza in children and indications for prophylaxis. *Rev Infect Dis* 1980; 2:408–420.

260. Glezen WP, Couch RB, Six HR: The influenza herald wave. *Am J Epidemiol* 1982; 116:589–598.

261. Wright PF, Thompson T, Karzon DT: Differing virulence of H1N1 and H3N2 influenza strains. *Am J Epidemiol* 1980; 112:814–819.

262. Glezen WP, Denny FW: Epidemiology of acute lower respiratory disease in children. *N Engl J Med* 1973; 288:498–505.

263. Wright PF, Ross KB, Thompson J, et al: Influenza A infections in young children; Primary natural infection and protective efficacy of live-vaccine-induced or naturally acquired immunity. *N Engl J Med* 1977; 296:829–834.

264. LaMontagne JR: Summary of a workshop on influenza B viruses and Reye's syndrome. *J Infect Dis* 1980; 142:452–465.

265. Fox TP, Cooney MK, Hall CE, et al: Influenza virus infections in Seattle families, 1975–1979. II. Pattern of infection in invaded households and relation of age and prior antibody to occurrence of infection and related illness. *Am J Epidemiol* 1982; 116:228–242.

266. Glezen WP, Loda FA, Clyde WA, et al: Epidemiology patterns of acute lower respiratory disease of children in a pediatric group practice. *J Pediatr* 1971; 78:397–407.

267. Farrell MK, Partin JC, Bove KE, et al: Epidemic influenza myopathy in Cincinnati in 1977. *J Pediatr* 1980; 96:545–551.

268. Dietzman DE, Schaller JG, Ray G, et al: Acute myositis associated with influenza B infection. *Pediatrics* 1976; 57:225–258.

269. MacDonald KL, Osterholm MT, Craig CW, et al: Toxic shock syndrome; a newly recognized complication of influenza and influenza-like illness. *JAMA* 1987; 257:1053–1058.

270. Hurwitz ES, Barrett MJ, Bregman D, et al: Public Health Service study of Reye's Syndrome and medications. Report of the main study. *JAMA* 1987; 257:1905–1911.

271. Centers for Disease Control: Reye syndrome surveillance—United States, 1986. *MMWR* 1987; 36:689–691.

272. Choi K, Thacker SB: Improved accuracy and specificity of forecasting deaths attributed to pneumonia and influenza. *J Infect Dis* 1981; 144:606–608.

273. Influenza—United States 1986–87 season. *MMWR* 1988; 37:466–475.

274. Glezen WP: Prevention of influenza-related morbidity and mortality. *Arch Intern Med* 1982; 142:25–26.

275. Barker WH, Mullooly JP: Underestimation of the role of pneumonia and influenza in causing excess mortality. *Am J Public Health* 1981; 71:643–645.

276. Barker WH, Mullooly JP: Pneumonia and influenza deaths during epidemics. Implications for prevention. *Arch Intern Med* 1982; 142:85–89.

277. Nolan TF, Goodman RA, Hinman AR, et al: Morbidity and mortality associated with influenza B in the United States, 1979–1980. A report from the Centers for Disease Control. *J Infect Dis* 1980; 142:360–362.

278. Barker WH, Mullooly JP: Influenza vaccination of elderly persons: Reduction in pneumonia and influenza hospitalizations and deaths. *JAMA* 1980; 244:2547–2549.

279. Glezen WP, Couch RB, Taber LH, et al: Epidemiologic observations of influenza B virus infections in Houston, Texas, 1976–1977. *Am J Epidemiol* 1980; 111:13–22.

280. Smith TF, Reichrath L: Comparative recovery of 1972–1973 influenza virus isolates in embryonated eggs and primary rhesus monkey kidney cell cultures after one freeze-thaw cycle. *Am J Clin Pathol* 1974; 61:579–584.

281. Jackson GG, Muldoon RL (eds): Viruses causing common respiratory infections in man. *Univ of Chicago Press* 1975, chap 5.

282. Frank AL, Couch RB, Griffis CA, et al: Comparison of different tissue cultures for isolation and quantitation of influenza and parainfluenza viruses. *J Clin Microbiol* 1979; 10:32–36.

283. Nerome K, Ishida M, Nakayama M: Established cell line sensitive to influenza C virus. *J Gen Virol* 1979; 43:257–259.

284. Glezen WP: Influenza C virus infection. *Arch Intern Med* 1980; 140:1278.

285. Lief FS, Heinie W: Methods and procedures for use of complement fixation technique in type- and strain-specific diagnosis of influenza. *Bull WHO* 1959; 20:411–420.

286. Kalter SS, Casey HL, Jensen KE, et al: Evaluation of laboratory diagnostic procedures with A/Asian influenza. *Proc Soc Exp Biol Med* 1959; 100:367–370.

287. Oker-Blom N, Hovi T, Leinikki P, et al: Protection of man from natural infection with influenza A2 Hong Kong virus by amantadine: A controlled field trial. *Br Med J* 1970; 3:676–678.

288. Schild GC, Henry-Aymard M, Pereira HG: A quantitative, single-radial diffusion test for immunological studies with influenza virus. *J Gen Virol* 1972; 16:231–236.

289. Murphy BR, Tierney EL, Barbour BA, et al: Use of the enzyme-linked immunosorbent assay to detect serum antibody responses of volunteers who received attenuated influenza A virus vaccines. *Infect Immun* 1980; 29:342–347.

290. Murphy BR, Phelan MA, Nelson DL, et al: Hemagglutinin-specific enzyme-lined immunosorbent assay for antibodies to influenza A and B viruses. *J Clin Microbiol* 1981; 13:554–560.

291. Turner R, Lathey JL, Van Voris LP, et al: Serological diagnosis of influenza B virus infection. Comparison of an enzyme-linked immunosorbent assay and the hemagglutination inhibition test. *J Clin Microbiol* 1982; 15:824–829.

292. Kendall AP, Dowdle WR: Influenza virus, in Rose NR, Friedman H, Fahey JL (eds): *Manual of Clinical Immunology*, ed 3, Washington DC, American Society for Microbiology, 1986, pp 515–520.

293. Hsiung GD: *Diagnostic Virology*. New Haven, Conn, Yale University Press, 1982, pp 38–40.

294. Turner R, Lathey JL, Van Voris LP, et al: Serological diagnosis of influenza B virus infection. Comparison of an enzyme-linked immunosorbent assay and the hemagglutination inhibition test. *J Clin Microbiol* 1982; 15:824–829.

295. Delem A, Jovanovic D: Correlation between rate of infection and preexisting titer of serum antibody as determined by single radial hemolysis during an epidemic of influenza A/Victoria/3/75, *J Infect Dis* 1978; 137:194–196.

296. do Nascimento JP, Chaves JRS, Pereira MS: Single radial haemolysis: a sensitive test for the detection of antibody to Influenza B virus. *Rev Microbiol* 1982; 13:65–69.

297. Hammond GW, Smith SJ, Noble GR: Sensitivity and specificity of enzyme immunoassay for serodiagnosis of influenza A virus infections. *J Infect Dis* 1980; 141:644–651.

298. Khan MW, Bucher DJ, Koul AK, et al: Detection of antibodies to influenza virus M protein by an enzyme-linked immunosorbent assay. *J Clin Microbiol* 1982; 16:813–820.

299. Khan MW, Gallagher M, Bucher D, et al: Detection of influenza virus neuraminidase-specific antibodies by an enzyme-linked immunosorbent assay. *J Clin Microbiol* 1982; 16:115–122.

300. Troisi CL, Monto AS: Comparison of enzyme-linked immunosorbent assay and hemagglutination inhibition in a seroepidemiological study of influenza type C infection. *J Clin Microbiol* 1981; 14:516–521.

301. Liu C: Rapid diagnosis of human influenza infection from nasal smears by means of fluorescein labeled antibody. *Proc Soc Exp Biol Med* 1956; 92:883–887.

302. McQuillin J, Gardner PS, McGuckin R: Rapid diagnosis of influenza by immunofluorescent techniques. *Lancet* 1970; 2:690–695.

303. Harmon MW, Pawlik KM: Enzyme immunoassay for direct detection of influenza type A and adenovirus antigens in clinical specimens. *J Clin Microbiol* 1982; 15:5–11.

304. Hers JF Ph, Leiden MD, der Kuip LV, et al: Rapid diagnosis of influenza/experience in a winter outbreak. *Lancet* 1968; 1:510–511.

305. Sarkkinen HK, Halonen PE, Salmi AA: Detection of influenza A virus by radioimmunoassay and enzyme-immunoassay from nasopharyngeal specimens. *J Med Virol* 1981; 7:213–220.

306. Gardner PS: Rapid virus diagnosis. *J Gen Virol* 1977; 36:1–29.

307. Yolken RH, Torsch VM, Berg R, et al: Fluorometric assay for measurement of viral neuraminidase—application to the rapid detection of influenza virus in nasal wash specimens. *J Infect Dis* 1980; 142:516–523.

308. Monto AS, Gunn RA, Bandy K, et al: Prevention of Russian influenza by amantadine. *JAMA* 1979; 241:1003–1007.

309. Oker-Blom N, Hovi T, Leinikki P, et al: Protection of man from natural infection with influenza A2 Hong Kong virus by amantadine: A controlled field trial. *Br Med J* 1970; 3:676–678.

310. Dolin R, Reichman RC, Madore HP, et al: A controlled trial of amantadine and rimantadine in the prophylaxis of influenza A infection. *N Engl J Med* 1982; 307:580–584.

311. Quarles JM, Couch RB, Cate TR, et al: Comparison of amantadine and rimantadine for prevention of type A (Russian) influenza. *Antiviral Res* 1981; 1:149–155.

312. Muldoon RL, Stanley ED, Jackson GG: Use and withdrawal of amantadine chemoprophylaxis during epidemic influenza A. *Am Rev Respir Dis* 1976; 113:487–491.

313. Dawkins AT, Gallager LR, Togo Y, et al: Studies on induced influenza in man. II. Double-blind study designed to assess the prophylactic efficacy of an analogue of amantadine hydrochloride. *JAMA* 1968; 203:93–97.

314. Noble GR, Jones WE, Kaye HS, et al: Evaluation of amantadine and rimantadine side effects and efficacy in the prevention of infection with influenza A/USSR/77 (H1N1) virus. In Program and Abstracts of the Atlanta, 18th Interscience Conference on Antimicrobial Agents and Chemotherapy, Oct 1978, American Society for Microbiology, abstract No. 484.

315. Zlydnikov DM, Kubar OI, Kovaleva TP, et al: Study of rimantadine in the USSR: A review of the literature. *Rev Infect Dis* 1981; 3:408–421.

316. Hayden FG, Gwaltney JM, Van de Castle RL, et al: Comparative toxicity of amantadine hydrochloride and rimantadine hydrochloride in healthy adults. *Antimicrob Agents Chemother* 1981; 19:226–233.

317. Hayden FG, Hoffman HE, Spyker DA: Differences in amantadine hydrochloride and rimantadine hydrochloride side effects relate to differences in pharmacokinetics. *Antimicrob Agents Chemother* 1983; 23:458–464.

318. Galbraith AW, Oxford JS, Schild GC, et al: Therapeutic effect of 1-adamantanamine hydrochloride in naturally occurring influenza A2/Hong Kong infection. *Lancet* 1971; 2:113–115.

319. Hornick RB, Togo Y, Mahler S, et al: Evaluation of amantadine hydrochloride in the treatment of A2 influenzal disease. *Ann NY Acad Sci* 1970; 173:10–19.

320. Knight V, Fedson D, Baldini J, et al: Amantadine therapy of epidemic influenza A2/Hong Kong. *Infect Immun* 1970; 1:200–204.

321. Kitamoto O, Hirayama M, Ichida F, et al: Therapeutic effectiveness of amantadine hydrochloride in influenza A2 and influenza A Hong Kong—double blind studies. *Prog Antimicrob Anticancer Chemother* 1970; 2:65–70.

322. Little JW, Hall WJ, Douglas RJ Jr, et al: Amantadine effect on peripheral airways abnormalities in influenza. *Ann Intern Med* 1976; 85:177–182.

323. Galbraith AW: Therapeutic trials of amantadine (Symmetrel) in general practice. *J Antimicrob Chemother* 1975; 1(suppl):81–86.

324. Togo Y, Hornick RB, Felliti VJ, et al: Evaluation of therapeutic efficacy of amantadine in patients with naturally occurring A2 influenza. *JAMA* 1970; 211:1149–1156.

325. Wingfield WL, Pollack D, Grunert RR: Therapeutic efficacy of amantadine HCl and rimantadine HCl in naturally occurring influenza A2 respiratory illness in man. *N Engl J Med* 1969; 281:579–584.

326. LaMontagne JR, Galasso GJ: Report of a workshop on clinical studies of the efficacy of amantadine and rimantadine against influenza virus. *J Infect Dis* 1978; 138:928–931.

327. Younkin SW, Betts RF, Roth FK, et al: Reduction in fever and symptoms in young adults with influenza A/Brazil/78 H1N1 infection after treatment with aspirin or amantadine. *Antimicrob Agents Chemother* 1983; 23:577–582.

328. Hayden FG, Hall WJ, Douglas RG Jr, et al: Amantadine aerosols in normal volunteers: Pharmacology and safety testing. *Antimicrob Agents Chemother* 1974; 16:644–650.

329. Hayden FG, Hall WJ, Douglas RG Jr: Therapeutic effects of aerosolized amantadine in naturally acquired infection due to influenza A virus. *J Infect Dis* 1980; 141:535–542.

330. Knight V, Bloom K, Wilson SZ, et al: Amantadine aerosol in humans. *Antimicrob Agents Chemother* 1979; 16:572–578.

331. Rabinovich S, Baldini JT, Bannister R: Treatment of influenza. The therapeutic efficacy of rimantadine HCl in a naturally occurring influenza A2 outbreak. *Am J Med Sci* 1969; 257:328–335.

332. EI du Pont de Nemours & Co, Inc: α-Methyl-1-adamantanemethylamine HCl. Supplemental report. Investigational brochure, December 1981; Wilmington, Del, EI du Pont.

333. Hayden FG, Zylidnikov DM, Iljenko VI, et al: Comparative therapeutic effect of aerosolized and oral rimantadine HCl in experimental human influenza A virus infection. *Antiviral Res* 1982; 2:147–153.

334. Belshe RB, Burk B, Newman F, et al: Influenza A virus resistant to amantadine and rimanatadine: Results of one decade of surveillance. *J Infect Dis* 1989; 195:430–435.

334a. Hay AJ: The mechanism of action of amantadine and rimantadine against influenza viruses, in Notkins AL, Oldstone MBA (eds): *Concepts in Viral Pathogenesis Ill.* New York, Springer-Verlag, 1989, pp 361–367.

334b. Warnick JE, Maleque MA, Bakry N, et al: Structure-activity relationships of amantadine: I. Interaction of the *N*-alkyl analogues with the ionic channels of the nicotinic acetylcholine receptor and electrically excitable membrane. *Mol Pharmacol* 1982; 22:82–93.

335. Smith CB, Charette RP, Fox JP, et al: Lack of effect of oral ribavirin in naturally occurring influenza A virus (H1N1)

infection. *J Infect Dis* 1980; 141:548–554.

336. Magnussen CR, Douglas RG Jr, Betts RF, et al: Double-blind evaluation of oral ribavirin (Virazole) in experimental influenza A virus infection in volunteers. *Antimicrob Agents Chemother* 1977; 12:498–502.

337. Salido-Rengel R, Nasser-Quiniones H, Briseno-Garcia B: Clinical evaluation of 1-β-D-ribofuranosyl-1,2,4-triazole-3-carboxamide (ribavirin) in a double-blind study during an outbreak of influenza. *Ann NY Acad Sci* 1977; 284:272–277.

338. Khakoo RA, Wilson GW, Waldman RH, et al: Effect of inosiplex (Isoprinosine) on induced human influenza A infection. *J Antimicrob Chemother* 1981; 7:389–397.

339. Betts RF, Douglas RG Jr, George SD, et al: Isoprinosine in experimental influenza A infection in volunteers. In Abstracts of the 78th Annual Meeting of the American Society for Microbiology Las Vegas, American Society for Microbiology, Oct. 1978, abstract No. A75.

340. Knight V, Wilson SZ, Quarles JM, et al: Ribavirin small-particle aerosol treatment of influenza. *Lancet* 1981; 2:945–949.

341. McClung HW, Knight V, Gilbert BE, et al: Ribavirin aerosol treatment of influenza B virus infection. *JAMA* 1983; 249:2671–2674.

342. Potter CW, Oxford JS: Determinants of immunity to influenza in man. *Br Med Bull* 1979; 35:69–74.

343. Fayekas de St. Groth S, Donelly M: Studies in experimental immunology of influenza. IV. Protective value of active immunization. *J Exp Biol Med Sci* 1950; 28:61.

344. Virelizier JL: Host defenses against influenza virus: the role of antihemagglutinin antibody. *J Immunol* 1975; 115:434–437.

345. Belshe RB, Van Voris LP, Bartram J, et al: Live attenuated influenza A virus vaccines in children: results of a field trial. *J Infect Dis* 1984; 150:834–840.

346. Johnson PR, Feldman JM, Thompson JD, et al: Immunity to influenza A virus infection in young children: a comparison of natural infection, live cold-adapted vaccine, and inactivated vaccine. *J Infect Dis* 1986; 154:121–127.

347. Clements ML, Betts RF, Tierney EL, et al: Resistance of adults to challenge with influenza A wild-type virus after receiving live or inactivated virus vaccine. *J Clin Microbiol* 186; 23:73–76.

348. Clements ML, O'Donnell S, Levine MM, et al: Dose response of A/Alaska/6/77 (H3N2) cold-adapted reassortant vaccine virus in adult volunteers: Role of local antibody in resistance to infection with vaccine virus. *Infect Immun* 1983; 40:1044–1051.

349. Hobson P, Curry RL, Beare AS, et al: The role of serum haemagglutination-inhibiting antibody in protection against challenge infection with influenza A2 and B viruses. *J Hyg Camb* 1972; 70:767–777.

350. Puck JM, Glezen WP, Frank AL, et al: Protection of infants from infection with influenza A virus by transplacentally acquired antibody. *J Infect Dis* 1980; 142:844–849.

351. Murphy BR, Kasel JA, Chanock RM: Association of serum antineuraminidase antibody with resistance to influenza in man. *N Engl J Med* 1972; 286:1329–1332.

352. Kilbourne ED: Influenza as a problem in immunology. *J Immunol* 1978; 120:1447–1452.

353. Centers for Disease Control: Antigenic variation of recent influenza A (H3N2) viruses. *MMWR* 1988; 37:38–47.

354. Centers for Disease Control: Influenza—United States. *MMWR* 1988; 37:207–209.

355. Monto AS, Kendal AP: Effect of neuraminidase antibody on Hong Kong influenza. *Lancet* 1973; 1:623–625.

356. Murphy BR, Tierney EL, Barbour BA, et al: Use of enzyme-linked immunosorbent assay to detect serum antibody responses of volunteers who received attenuated influenza A virus vaccines. *Infect Immun* 1980; 29:342–347.

357. Clements ML, Betts RF, Murphy BR: Advantage of live attenuated cold-adapted influenza A virus over inactivated vaccine for A/Washington/80 (H3N2) wild-type virus infection. *Lancet* 1984; 1:705–708.

358. Clements ML, Betts RF, Tierney EL, et al: Serum and nasal

wash antibodies associated with resistance to experimental challenge with influenza A wild-type virus. *J Clin Microbiol* 1986; 24:157–160.

359. Liew FY, Russell SM, Appleyard G, et al: Cross-protection in mice infected with influenza A virus by the respiratory route is correlated with local IgA antibody rather than serum antibody or cytotoxic T cell reactivity. *Eur J Immunol* 1984; 14:350–356.

360. Brown TA, Murphy BR, Radl J, et al: Subclass distribution and molecular form of immunoglobulin A hemagglutinin antibodies in sera and nasal secretions after experimental secondary infection with influenza A virus in humans. *J Clin Microbiol* 1985; 22:259–264.

361. Wagner DK, Clements ML, Reimer CB, et al: Analysis of immunoglobulin G antibody responses after administration of live and inactivated influenza A vaccine indicates that nasal wash immunoglobulin G is a transudate from serum. *J Clin Microbiol* 1987; 25:559–562.

362. Taylor HP, Dimmock NJ: Mechanism of neutralization of influenza virus by secretory IgA is different from that of monomeric IgA or IgG. *J Exp Med* 1985; 161:198–209.

363. Zykov MP, Smorodintsev AA, Alexandrova GI, et al: The present and future of specific prophylaxis of influenza and other acute viral respiratory diseases. *Am Rev Respir Dis* 1974; 110:537–541.

364. Nai-Ki M, Yong-He Z, Ada GL, et al: Humoral and cellular responses of mice to infection with a cold-adapted influenza A virus variant. *Infect Immun* 1982; 38:218–225.

365. Rouse BT, Norley S, Martin S: Antiviral cytotoxic T lymphocyte induction and vaccination. *Rev Infect Dis* 1988; 10:16–33.

366. Gorse GJ, Belshe RB: Stimulation of cellular immune responses with live-attenuated influenza A virus vaccine in older adults, in Program and Abstracts of the 28th International Conference on Antimicrobial Agents and Chemotherapy, Los Angeles, Oct. 1988, American Society for Microbiology, abstract No. 404.

367. Chow TC, Beutner KR, Ogra PL: Cell-mediated immune responses to the hemagglutinin and neuraminidase antigens of influenza A virus after immunization in humans. *Infect Immun* 1979; 25:103–109.

368. Cate TR, Kelly JR: Hong Kong influenza antigen sensitivity and decreased interferon response of peripheral lymphocytes, in Hobby GL (ed): *Antimicrobial Agents and Chemotherapy—1970.* Bethesda, Md, American Society for Microbiology, 1971, pp 156–160.

369. Cate TR, Couch RB: Live influenza A/Victoria/75 (H3N2) virus vaccines: reactogenicity, immunogenicity and protection against wild-type virus challenge. *Infect Immun* 1982; 38:141–146.

370. Dolin R, Murphy BR, Caplan EA: Lymphocyte blastogenic responses to influenza virus antigens after influenza infection and vaccination in humans. *Infect Immun* 1978; 19:867–874.

371. Shapira-Nahor O, Morag A, Levy R, et al: Cellular response in humans following vaccination with Gripax influenza virus. *J Med Virol* 1982; 10:75–80.

372. Danielescu G, Barbu C, Sorodoc Y, et al: The presence of interferon and type A immunoglobulins in the nasopharyngeal secretions of volunteers immunized with an inactivated influenza vaccine. *Acta Virol* 1975; 19:245–249.

373. Kantzler GB, Lauteria SF, Cusumano CL, et al: Immunosuppression during influenza virus infection. *Infect Immun* 1974; 10:996–1002.

374. Lazar A, Okabe N, Wright PF: Humoral and cellular immune responses of seronegative children vaccinated with a cold-adapted influenza A/HK/123/77 (H1N1) recombinant virus. *Infect Immun* 1980; 27:862–866.

375. Roberts NJ, Steigbigel RT: Effect of in vitro virus infection on response of human monocytes and lymphocytes to mitogen stimulation. *J Immunol* 1978; 121:1052–1058.

376. Roberts NJ, Diamond ME, Douglas RG, et al: Mitogen responses and interferon production after exposure of human macrophages to infections and inactivated influenza viruses. *J Med Virol* 1980; 5:17–23.

377. Criswell BS, Couch RB, Greenberg SB, et al: The lymphocyte response to influenza in humans. *Am Rev Respir Dis* 1979; 120:700–704.

378. Kauffman CA, Linnemann CC Jr, Tan JS, et al: Cell-mediated immunity in humans during viral infection: dermal hypersensitivity and in vitro lymphocyte proliferation during mild viral respiratory infections. *Infect Immun* 1974; 10:757–761.

379. Buckley CE, Zitt MJ, Cate TR: Two categories of lymphocyte unresponsiveness to phytohemagglutinin. *Cell Immunol* 1973; 6:140–148.

380. Dolin R, Richman DD, Murphy BR, et al: Cell-mediated immune responses in humans after induced infection with influenza A virus. *J Infect Dis* 1977; 135:714–719.

381. Kauffman CA, Linnemann CC Jr, Schiff GM, et al: Effect of viral and bacterial pneumonias on cell-mediated immunity in humans. *Infect Immun* 1976; 13:78–83.

382. Jarstrand C, Wasserman J: Mitogen stimulation of lymphocytes from patients with epidemic influenza. *Scand J Infect Dis* 1976; 8:7–11.

383. Lazar A, Wright PF: Cell-mediated immune response of human lymphocytes to influenza A/USSR (H1N1) virus infection. *Infect Immun* 1980; 27:867–871.

384. Reed WP, Olds JW, Kisch AL: Decreased skin-test reactivity associated with influenza. *J Infect Dis* 1972; 125:398–402.

385. Ruben FL, Jackson GG, Gotoff SP: Humoral and cellular response in humans after immunization with influenza vaccine. *Infect Immun* 1973; 7:594–596.

386. Ennis, A: Some newly recognized aspects of resistance against and recovery from influenza. *Arch Virol* 1982; 73:207–217.

387. Ennis FA, Rook AH, Hua QY, et al: HLA-restricted virus-specific cytotoxic T-lymphocyte responses to live and inactivated influenza vaccines. *Lancet* 1981; 2:887–891.

388. Reichman RC, Pons VG, Murphy BR, et al: Cell-mediated cytotoxicity following influenza, infection and vaccination in humans. *J Med Virol* 1979; 4:1–14.

389. Biddison WE, Shaw S, Nelson DL: Virus specificity of human influenza virus-immune cytotoxic T cells. *J Immunol* 1979; 122:660–664.

390. Kaplan DR, Griffith K, Braciale VL, et al: Influenza virus-specific human cytotoxic T cell clones: Heterogeneity in antigenic specificity and restriction by class II MHC products. *Cell Immunol* 1984; 88:193–206.

391. Lamb JR, Eckels DD, Lake P, et al: Antigen-specific human T lymphocyte clones: Induction, antigen specificity and MHC restriction of influenza virus-immune clones. *J Immunol* 1982; 128:233–238.

392. McMichael AJ, Askonas BA: Influenza virus-specific cytotoxic T cells in man; induction and properties of the cytotoxic cell. *Eur J Immunol* 1978; 8:705–711.

393. McMichael AJ, Michie CA, Gotch FM, et al: Recognition of influenza A virus nucleoprotein by human cytotoxic T lymphocytes. *J Gen Virol* 1986; 67:719–726.

394. McMichael AJ, Gotch FM, Noble GR, et al: Cytotoxic T cell immunity to influenza. *N Engl J Med* 1983; 309:13–17.

395. Wells MA, Ennis FA, Albrecht P: Recovery from a viral respiratory infection. II. Passive transfer of immune spleen cells to mice with influenza pneumonia. *J Immunol* 1981; 126:1042–1046.

396. Kuwano K, Scott M, Young JF, et al: HA2 subunit of influenza A H1 and H2 subtype viruses induces a protective cross-reactive cytotoxic T lymphocyte response. *J Immunol* 1988; 140:1264–1268.

397. Lukacher AC, Braciale VL, Braciale TJ: In vivo effector function of influenza virus-specific cytotoxic T lymphocyte clones is highly specific. *J Exp Med* 1984; 160:814–826.

398. Hashimoto G, Wright PF, Karzon DT: Antibody-dependent cell-mediated cytotoxicity against influenza virus-infected cells. *J Infect Dis* 1983; 148:785–794.

399. Vella S, Rocchi G, Resta S, et al: Antibody reactive in antibody-dependent cell-mediated cytotoxicity following influenza virus vaccination. *J Med Virol* 1980; 6:203–211.

400. Green JA, Charetti RP, Yeh TJ, et al: Presence of interferon in

acute and convalescent sera of humans with influenza or an influenza-like illness of undetermined etiology. *J Infect Dis* 1982; 145:837–841.

401. Murphy BR, Baron S, Chalhub EG, et al: Temperature-sensitive mutants of influenza virus. IV. Induction of interferon in the nasopharynx by wild type and a temperature sensitive recombinant virus. *J Infect Dis* 1973; 128:488–493.

402. Richman DD, Murphy BR, Baron S, et al: Three strains of influenza virus (H3N2): Interferon sensitivity in vitro and interferon production in volunteers. *J Clin Microbiol* 1976; 3:223–226.

403. McIntosh K: Interferon in nasal secretions from infants with viral respiratory tract infections. *J Pediatr* 1978; 93:33–36.

404. Ray CG, Gravelle CR, Chinn TDY: Circulating interferon in infants and children with acute respiratory illness. *J Pediatr* 1967; 71:27–32.

405. Jao RL, Wheelock EF, Jackson GG: Production of interferon in volunteers infected with Asian influenza. *J Infect Dis* 1970; 121:419–426.

406. Gresser I, Dull HB: A virus inhibitor in pharyngeal washings from patients with influenza. *Proc Soc Exp Biol Med* 1974; 115:192–196.

407. Murphy BR, Richman DD, Chalhub EG, et al: Failure of attenuated temperature-sensitive influenza A (H3N2) virus to induce heterologous interference in humans to parainfluenza type I virus. *Infect Immun* 1975; 12:62–68.

408. Rytel MW: Induction of interferon in man by vaccines. *Proc Soc Exp Biol Med* 1975; 149:266–270.

409. Neta R, Salvin SB: Interferons and lymphokines. *Tex Rep Biol Med* 1981–82; 41:435–442.

410. Stiehm ER, Kronenberg LH, Rosenblatt HM, et al: Interferon: Immunobiology and clinical significance. *Ann Intern Med* 1982; 96:80–93.

411. Gorse GJ, Kopp WC: Modulation by immunosuppressive agents of peripheral blood mononuclear cell responses to influenza A virus. *J Lab Clin Med* 1987; 110:592–601.

412. Johnson HM: Effect of interferon on antibody formation. *Tex Rep Biol Med* 1981–82; 41:411–419.

413. Ennis FA, Meager A: Immune interferon produced to high levels by antigenic stimulation of human lymphocytes with influenza virus. *J Exp Med* 1981; 154:1279–1289.

414. Yewdell JW, Bennink JR, Hosaka Y: Cells process exogenous proteins for recognition by cytotoxic T lymphocytes. *Science* 1988; 239:637–640.

415. Farrar WL, Johnson HM, Farrer JJ: Regulation of the production of immune interferon and cytotoxic T lymphocytes by interleukin 2. *J Immunol* 1981; 126:1120–1125.

416. Yamada YK, Meager A, Yamada A, et al: Human interferon alpha and gamma production by lymphocytes during the generation of influenza virus-specific cytotoxic T lymphocytes. *J Gen Virol* 1986; 67:2325–2334.

417. Cate TR, Couch RB, Kasel JA, et al: Clinical trials of monovalent influenza A/New Jersey/76 virus vaccines in adults: Reactogenicity, antibody response, and antibody persistence. *J Infect Dis* 1977; 136:S450–S455.

418. Betts RF, Douglas RG Jr: Comparative study of reactogenicity and immunogenicity of influenza A/New Jersey/8/76 (Hsw1N1) virus vaccines in normal volunteers. *J Infect Dis* 1977; 136:S433.

419. Gross PA, Weksler ME, Quinnan GV Jr, et al: Immunization of elderly people with two doses of influenza vaccine. *J Clin Microbiol* 1987; 25:1763–1765.

420. Powers RD, Hayden FG, Samuelson J, et al: Immune response of adults to sequential influenza vaccination. *J Med Virol* 1984; 14:169–175.

421. Keitel WA, Cate TR, Couch RB: Efficacy of sequential annual vaccination with inactivated influenza virus vaccine. *Am J Epidemiol* 1988; 127:353–364.

422. Gross PA, Ennis FA: Influenza vaccine: split-product versus whole-virus types—how do they differ? *N Engl J Med* 1977; 296:567–568.

423. Centers for Disease Control: Prevention and control of influenza. *Ann Intern Med* 1987; 107:521–525.

424. Wright PF, Dolin R, LaMontagne JR: Summary of clinical trials of influenza vaccines. II. *J Infect Dis* 1976; 134:633–638.

425. Schonberger LB, Bregman DJ, Sullivan-Bolyai JZ, et al: Guillain-Barré syndrome following vaccination in the National Influenza Immunization Program, United States, 1976–1977. *Am J Epidemiol* 1979; 110:105–123.

426. Murwitz ES, Schonberger LB, Nelson DB, et al: Guillain-Barré syndrome and the 1978–79 influenza vaccine. *N Engl J Med* 1981; 304:1557–1561.

427. Centers for Disease Control. Influenza vaccines 1982–1983. *MMWR* 1982; 31:349–353.

428. Ortbals DW, Liebhaber H, Presant CA, et al: Influenza immunization of adult patients with malignant diseases. *Ann Intern Med* 1977; 87:552–557.

429. Herron A, Dettleff G, Hixon B, et al: Influenza vaccination in patients with rheumatic diseases. Safety and efficacy. *JAMA* 1979; 242:53–56.

430. Ortbals DW, Marks ES, Liebhaber H: Influenza immunization in patients with chronic renal disease. *JAMA* 1978; 239:2562–2565.

431. Gross PA, Lee H, Wolff JA, et al: Influenza immunization in immunosuppressed children. *J Pediatr* 1978; 92:30–35.

432. Gorse GJ, Slater LM, Kaplan HS, et al: Inhibition of interferon yield by vincristine. *Proc Soc Exp Biol Med* 1984; 175:309–313.

433. Cesario TC, Slater L, Poo W, et al: The effect of hydrocortisone on the production of gamma interferon and other lymphokines by human peripheral blood mononuclear cells. *J Interferon Res* 1986; 6:337–347.

434. DeStefano F, Goodman RA, Noble GR, et al: Simultaneous adminstration of influenza and pneumococcal vaccines. *JAMA* 1982; 247:2551–2554.

435. Gross PA, Quinnan GV, Rodstein M, et al: Association of influenza immunization with reduction in mortality in an elderly population: a prospective study. *Arch Intern Med* 1988; 148:562–565.

436. Patriarca PA, Arden NH, Koplan JP, et al: Prevention and control of type A influenza infections in nursing homes. Benefits and costs of four approaches using vaccination and amantadine. *Ann Intern Med* 1987; 107:732–740.

437. Eickhoff TC: Immunization against influenza: rationale and recommendations. *J Infect Dis* 1971; 123:446–454.

438. Foy HM, Cooney MK, Allan ID, et al: Influenza B virus vaccines in children and adults: Adverse reactions, immune response and observations in the field. *J Infect Dis* 1981; 143:700–706.

439. Mieklejohn G, Eickhoff TC, Graves P, et al: Antigenic drift and efficacy of influenza virus vaccines, 1976–1977. *J Infect Dis* 1978; 138:618–624.

440. Stiver HG, Graves P, Eikhoff JC, et al: Efficacy of "Hong Kong" vaccine in preventing "England" variant influenza A in 1972. *N Engl J Med* 1973; 289:1267–1271.

441. Tyrrell DA: Using the genetics of influenza virus to make live attenuated vaccines. *Lancet* 1978; 1:196–197.

442. Maassab HF, Kendal AP, Abrams GD, et al: Evaluation of a cold-recombinant influenza virus vaccine in ferrets. *J Infect Dis* 1982; 146:780–790.

443. Wright PF, Okabe N, McKee KT, et al: Cold-adapted recombinant influenza A virus vaccines in seronegative young children. *J Infect Dis* 1982; 146:71–79.

444. Snyder MH, Betts RF, DeBorde D, et al: Four viral genes independently contributed to attenuation of live influenza A/Ann Arbor/6/60 (H2N2) cold-adapted reassortant virus vaccines. *J Virol* 1988; 62:488–495.

445. Belshe RB, Van Voris LP, Bartram J, et al: Efficacy of cold recombinant influenza A/Washington/H3N2 vaccine (CR-48) in young children. *Program and Abstracts of the 23rd International Conference on Antimicrobial Agents and Chemotherapy.* Washington DC, Oct 1983 American Society for Microbiology, abstract no. 683.

446. Clements ML, Murphy BR: Development and persistence of local and systemic antibody responses in adults given live attenuated or inactivated influenza A virus vaccine. *J Clin Microbiol* 1986; 23:66–72.

447. Gorse GJ, Belshe RB, Munn NJ: Safety of and serum antibody

response to cold-recombinant influenza A and inactivated trivalent influenza virus vaccines in older adults with chronic disease. *J Clin Microbiol* 1986; 24:336–342.

448. Gorse GJ, Belshe RB, Munn NJ: Local and systemic antibody responses in high-risk adults given live-attenuated and inactivated influenza A virus vaccines. *J Clin Microbiol* 1988; 26:911–918.

449. Belshe RB, Van Voris LP: Cold-recombinant influenza A/California/10/78 (H1N1) virus vaccine (CR-37) in seronegative children: infectivity and efficacy against investigational challenge. *J Infect Dis* 1984; 149:735–740.

450. Feldman S, Wright PF, Webster RG, et al: Use of influenza A virus vaccines in seronegative children: live cold-adapted versus inactivated whole virus. *J Infect Dis* 1985; 152:1212–1218.

451. Johnson PR, Feldman S, Thompson JM, et al: Immunity to influenza A virus infection in young children: a comparison of natural infection, live cold-adapted vaccine, and inactivated vaccine. *J Infect Dis* 1986; 154:121–127.

452. Clements ML, Betts RF, Murphy BR: Advantage of live attenuated cold-adapted influenza A virus over inactivated vaccine for A/Washington/80 (H3N2) wild-type virus infection. *Lancet* 1984; 2:705–708.

453. Clements ML, Betts RF, Tierney EL, et al: Resistance of adults to challenge with influenza A wild-type virus after receiving live or inactivated virus vaccine. *J Clin Microbiol* 1986; 23:73–76.

454. Wright PF, Karzon DT: Live attenuated influenza vaccines. *Prog Med Virol* 1987; 34:70–88.

455. Belshe RB, Van Voris LP, Bartram J, et al: Live attenuated influenza A virus vaccines in children: results of a field trial. *J Infect Dis* 1984; 150:834–840.

456. Gorse GJ, Belshe R: Immunogenicity and safety of live-attenuated influenza A/Korea/1/82 (H3N2), CR–59 virus vaccine in chronically ill older adults. Program and abstracts of the 90th annual meeting of the American Society for Microbiology, Washington, DC, May 1990, No. E48.

457. Clements ML, Powers D, Sears S, et al: Systemic and local antibody responses in the elderly to live or inactivated influenza vaccines or both, in Program and Abstracts of the 28th International Conference on Antimicrobial Agents and Chemotherapy, Los Angeles, Oct. 1988, American Society for Microbiology, abstract No. 420.

458. Powers DC, Sears SD, Murphy BR, et al: Systemic and local antibody responses in elderly subjects given live or inactivated influenza A virus vaccines. *J Clin Microbiol* 1989; 27:2666–2671.

459. Karpovich LG, Kalashnikova TV, Dzagurov SG, et al: Blastogenic lymphocyte response as indicator of cell-mediated immunity in humans vaccinated with live and inactivated influenza vaccines. *Acta Virol* 1983; 27:511–517.

460. Wright PF, Bhargava M, Johnson PR, et al: Simultaneous administration of live, attenuated influenza A vaccines representing different serotypes. *Vaccine* 1985; 3:305–308.

11

Parainfluenza Viruses

Peter F. Wright

HISTORY

STRUCTURE AND BIOLOGY OF PARAINFLUENZA
    VIRUSES

EPIDEMIOLOGY

TRANSMISSION

COURSE OF INFECTION

PATHOGENESIS

CLINICAL SYMPTOMS

IMMUNOLOGIC RESPONSE

LABORATORY DIAGNOSIS

PREVENTION AND TREATMENT

The human parainfluenza viruses are a group of four related single-stranded RNA paramyxoviruses collectively responsible for a major component of acute respiratory illness in childhood. An understanding of the basic and clinical aspects of the parainfluenza viruses lagged somewhat behind the rapidly accumulating knowledge of influenza virus infections. However, a sufficiently detailed picture of parainfluenza virus molecular biology and clinical behavior can now be painted to establish their importance as a cause of human disease.[1-5]

HISTORY

In the fall of 1955, the first human parainfluenza viruses were isolated from children with croup.[6, 7] They were referred to as CA (croup-associated) viruses and caused syncytial cytopathic effects in monkey kidney and human amnion cells. Subsequently, two distinct viruses were isolated from children with acute respiratory disease which were identified by hemadsorption with guinea pig red blood cells. These were referred to as type 1 and 2 hemadsorption viruses. With final classification as parainfluenza viruses,

hemadsorption virus type 2 became parainfluenza type 1, CA virus became parainfluenza type 2, and hemadsorption virus type 1 became parainfluenza type 3.[8] Parainfluenza type 4 was subsequently discovered and found to have two distinct subtypes designated types A and B.[9, 10] A number of viruses antigenically related to the human parainfluenza viruses have been isolated from animals including Sendai virus (mice), simian virus 5 and 41 (monkeys), shipping fever virus (cattle) (Table 11–1).

STRUCTURE AND BIOLOGY OF PARAINFLUENZA VIRUSES

The parainfluenza viruses are spherical, 125 to 250 nm in diameter, enveloped RNA viruses.[11] The purified viruses have a composition of 74% protein, 19% lipid, 6% carbohydrate, and 1% RNA. The outer envelope is comprised of proteins and lipids. The lipids reflect the surface membrane composition of the cell of replication, but the proteins are specified by the virus. Two glycoproteins protrude from the envelope as 10-nm spikes. One of these spike proteins has both hemagglutinin and neuraminidase activities, the HN protein; the other protein mediates cell fusion and hemolytic properties of the virus and is referred to as the F protein. Each of these proteins has recently been sequenced.[12, 13] The activities of these proteins are described in greater detail subsequently. The inner layer of the envelope is formed by a nonglycosylated protein responsible for maintaining structural integrity, the M or matrix protein. Within the envelope is the nucleocapsid, and RAN-nucleoprotein structure which is a loosely coiled, flexible, helical structure with a length of 1 μm. The RNA is of a negative polarity, is single-stranded, and has a molecular weight of 5×10^6 daltons. Also contained within the core of the virus is an RNA-dependent RNA polymerase (the transcriptase necessary to convert the negative-stranded RNA to a template for replication).

Viral replication follows a rather classic pattern for negative-strand RNA viruses.[14] Viral entry into cells is initiated by hem-

Table 11–1
Parainfluenza Viruses

Nomenclature of Human Types		Related Animal Viruses
Present	Original	
Parainfluenza type 1	Hemadsorption type 2 (HA-2)	Sendai (mouse)
Parainfluenza type 2	Croup-associated (CA)	Simian virus 5 (monkey)
		Simian virus 41 (monkey)
Parainfluenza type 3	Hemadsorption type 1 (HA-1)	Shipping fever (cow)
Parainfluenza type 4a		
Parainfluenza type 4b		

agglutinin binding to receptors on susceptible cells.[15] The neuraminidase activity, unlike influenza virus, is contained in the same glycoprotein as the hemagglutinin. It can reverse the attachment of virus to target cell, but its precise role in replication is not understood.[16, 17] Viral entry into the cell is facilitated by the F protein. To become active, the F protein must be cleaved by a host cell enzyme into two disulfide-bonded subunits (F_1 and F_2). The newly generated N-terminus of F_1 has an amino acid sequence that is hydrophobic and highly conserved among different parainfluenza viruses.[18, 19] Synthetic amino acid analogues of this area will inhibit the functions ascribed to the F protein of viral penetration, cell fusion, and hemolysis. Failure of a cell to have the appropriate proteolytic enzymes leads to production of noninfectious virus and failure to sustain multiple replicative cycles.

Once viral attachment and penetration have occurred, transcription of the viral RNA is initiated by the virion's RNA-dependent RNA polymerase. There is a single promoter region with sequential transcription of genes which are ordered from the 3' end: $NP = P = H = F_0 = HN = L$.[20] It is thought that the monocistronic messenger RNAs (mRNAs) are formed by cleavage of the transcript of the entire genome.[14] Viral polypeptides and genome copies are then generated in the cytoplasm with total replication occurring over a three- to five-hour period. There is no requirement for cellular DNA synthesis as demonstrated by the lack of inhibition by dactinomycin. Viral glycoproteins are inserted through the cell plasma membrane and virus release occurs by budding. Defective interfering particles are formed which can inhibit replication of infective virus. These particles appear to be either of the copy-back type or to have large portions of the internal genome deleted with 3'- and 5'- terminal sequences intact.[21, 22] Parainfluenza viruses with fully cleaved F proteins have the capacity to initiate cell fusion, which may facilitate cell-to-cell spread of virus. Inactivated Sendai virus can initiate fusion between cells and is used in cocultivation to rescue fastidious viruses.

EPIDEMIOLOGY

Parainfluenza viruses are ubiquitous, having been isolated from many areas of the world.[23] They are most commonly recovered in association with respiratory illness in young children, having a particular association with laryngotracheobronchitis or croup. Epidemiologic surveys indicate that parainfluenza type 3 virus is often experienced in the first year of life with 50% of children being seropositive by 12 months of age while parainfluenza types 1 and 2 are agents which cause disease in the preschool child.[24–26] Data

from a prospectively followed population of children at Vanderbilt University support this concept (Fig 11–1).

Parainfluenza type 3 is more endemic in the community that are types 1 and 2, which occur as epidemics in the fall (Fig 11–2). In the early epidemiologic studies it was suggested that parainfluenza types 1 and 2 alternated years (Table 11–2). This pattern has not been clear in recent years. Reinfections occur not infrequently with all the parainfluenza viruses, although the illness seen on reinfection is less severe. Nosocomial spread of parainfluenza infection in hospitalized pediatric patients probably occurs with great frequency, with one fifth of hospitalized children under 18 months acquiring infection with parainfluenza type 3.[27] The interruption of such spread has proved difficult with other respiratory viruses.

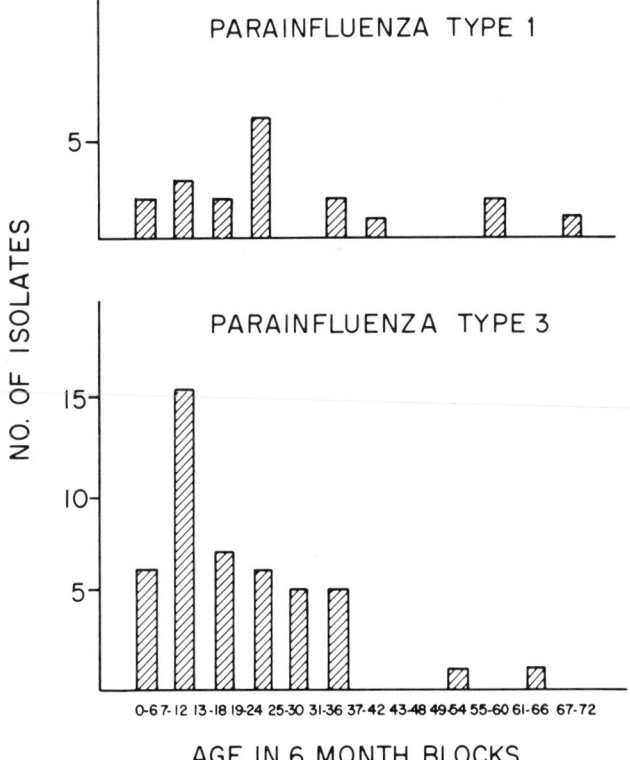

Figure 11–1. Age-related incidence of parainfluenza types 1 and 3.

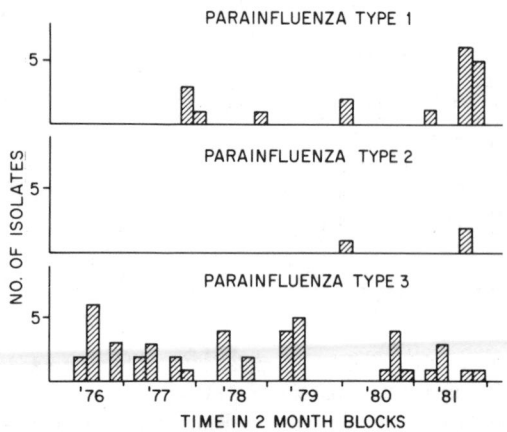

Figure 11–2. Seasonal occurrence of parainfluenza types 1, 2, and 3.

A molecular epidemiologic study of the nucleotide sequence of the hemaggutinin-neuraminidase gene of parainfluenza type 3 from six isolates from 1957 to 1983 reveals little variability. There is not the progressive drift in nucleotide sequences seen with influenza.[28]

TRANSMISSION

In humans, parainfluenza infections are primarily transmitted by the respiratory route. A number of recent studies have suggested that hand contamination with nasal secretions may be an important link in the spread of rhinoviruses and respiratory syncytial virus (RSV).[29, 30] Presumably the same mode of transmission may also be operative with the parainfluenza viruses.

COURSE OF INFECTION

Initial replication of parainfluenza viruses is within the epithelial cells lining the upper respiratory tract, and there is little evidence of viremia or spread to extrarespiratory sites.[31] In experimental infection, the incubation period is two days in adults.[32, 33] The illness in adults is characterized as coldlike with signs and symptoms confined to the upper respiratory tract. A study performed at Vanderbilt, in which young children were infected with an incompletely attenuated intranasal vaccine, has given a detailed picture of the replication pattern of parainfluenza type 3.[34] Preexisting serum antibody was an important determinant of whether infection occurred with intranasal vaccine (Table 11–3). In seronegative children, virus was shed for up to, but not beyond, 11 days (Fig 11–3). The duration of virus shedding with several other respiratory viruses in young children is similar. The pattern of eight to 11 days of virus shedding is probably quite representative of not only parainfluenza, but RSV and influenza as well. Particularly in immunocompromised patients, longer periods of virus shedding have been observed, suggesting that the termination of respiratory virus shedding is immunologically mediated. When vaccinees that were shedding virus were compared to uninfected or uninoculated vaccinees, a significant increase in respiratory symptomatology was seen with virus shedding (Table 11–4). Symptoms correlated as well with the titer of virus shed in the children shedding virus. A similar correlation of shedding with clinical symptoms was seen with natural parainfluenza type 1 infection by Hall et al.[35] These observations would suggest that illness was directly related to the amount of virus shed as opposed to being mediated by the host response.

PATHOGENESIS

Studies in animals have defined some of the important host

Table 11–2
Recovery of Parainfluenza Viruses From Total Group of Respiratory Disease Inpatients and Outpatients During Odd-Numbered as Compared to Even-Numbered Years (October 1957–June 1972)

Years	Number Tested	Patients with Isolates of Indicated Serotype (%)				
		Type 1	Type 2	Type 3	Type 4	Total
Odd-numbered	7918	1.5	2.4	4.1	0.2	8.2
Even-numbered	8613	4.7	0.3	2.9	0.5	8.3

Data courtesy of C. D. Brandt, H. W. Kim, R. M. Chanock, and R. W. Parrott.

Table 11–3
Serologic Response of Young Children to Intranasal Inoculation With Experimental Parainfluenza Type 3 Vaccine

Serologic Status	Number Studied	Virus Recovered	Serum Antibody Response		
			Hemagglutination Inhibition	Neutralizing	Complement Fixation
Seropostive	8	0	1/8	0/8	1/8
Seronegative	8	7	7/8	7/8	6/8
Controls	5	0	0/5	0/5	0/5

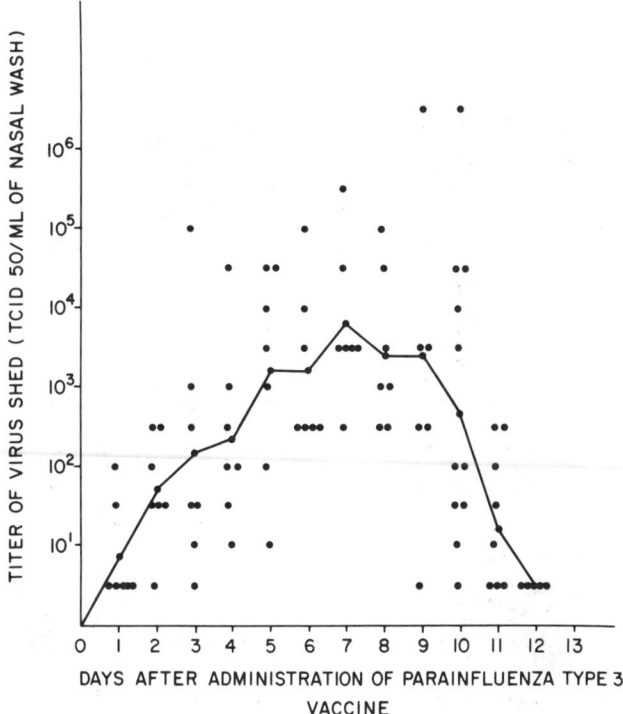

Figure 11–3. Pattern of virus shedding with parainfluenza type 3 vaccine. TCID50 = 50% tissue culture infective dose.

for secondary bacterial infection in parainfluenza virus infection.

Immunization of cotton rats with vaccinia expressing either the hemagglutinin-neuraminidase or the fusion glycoprotein have been carried out. Immunization with either of the individual vectors provided significant protection, although levels of neutralizing antibody and suppression of intranasal replication were greater with the hemagglutinin-neuraminidase construct.[38] When purified glycoproteins were systemically administered as immunogens, neither protein individually provided protection. However when both glycoproteins were given simultaneously, partial protection was seen on challenge.[39] Of interest, the administration of these glycoprotein preparations intranasally induced complete protection.[40]

Parainfluenza virus infections in hamsters have provided another model for studying pathogenesis.[41] Hamsters infected with parainfluenza viruses develop recognizable pathologic changes in the lung which are not altered by passive administration of serum antibody.[42] T cell functions have been investigated to the extent of demonstrating T cell cytotoxicity in the early stages, days 3 to 4, of infection, although whether this may be a protective mechanism interrupting intracellular replication and cell-to-cell spread of virus or whether it may mediate mucosal damage remains to be determined.[43] Ferrets may be infected readily with parainfluenza virus,[44] and this model may provide information on the relative importance of local and systemic immunity. Organ culture systems of animal and human origin also have been established.[45, 46] In both systems viral replication and cytologic alterations were noted.

defense mechanisms in recovery from parainfluenza virus infections. In mice, Sendai virus replication initially occurs in mucosal cells lining the respiratory tract.[36] There is subsequent destruction of mucosal layers with infiltration by mononuclear cells in the submucosa. Viral growth reaches a maximum titer at three to four days after infection and is not detectable after day 8. Interferon appears early in the course of the infection, but serum antibody is not detected until day 8. If animals are treated with cyclophosphamide, the lymphocytic infiltration and antibody production are blocked and the animals progress to a fatal pneumonia in spite of normal levels of interferon production. The role that T cell immunity may play was evaluated in thymectomized, bone marrow-reconstituted mice whose T cell depletion led to increased pneumonitis but not as severe an illness as seen in the cyclophosphamide-treated animals. The role of Sendai infection in limiting alveolar macrophage killing of *Staphylococcus aureus* in mice has been investigated.[37] A defect in intracellular killing of the staphylococcus was demonstrated. This provides a potential explanation

CLINICAL SYMPTOMS

The spectrum of respiratory illness caused by the parainfluenza virus is wide, in spite of the classic association in children with laryngotracheobronchitis.[21] In adults the illnesses are predominantly confined to the upper respiratory tract, although pneumonia has been described.[47, 48] Surveillance, at Vanderbilt, of a population of young children who had viral cultures taken during respiratory illnesses revealed the broad spectrum of illness with parainfluenza types 1 and 3 and is shown in Table 11–5. A comparison of illness between these two strains suggests a very comparable illness pattern with the exception of otitis media, which occurred significantly more frequently with type 3 than with parainfluenza type 1.

With epidemics of parainfluenza virus, laryngotracheobronchitis, or croup, is the predominant form of illness that leads to hospitalization. Work by Brandt et al has defined the strong association of each of the parainfluenza strains with this illness, which often leads to severe respiratory embarrassment in the young

Table 11–4
Symptomatic Days During Shedding* of Parainfluenza Type 3 Vaccine

	Rhinorrhea	Cough	Fever	Total with Illness
Infected, 8 children	8 (11%)	22 (31%)	0	30 (42%†)
Uninfected, 13 children	1 (0.9%)	6 (5 %)	4 (34%)	12 (10%)

*Days 2 to 6 postvaccination.
†Percent of total days of observation; with indicated symptom.

Table 11–5

Comparison of Illness in Pediatric Outpatients
With Parainfluenza Types 1 and 3

Characteristic	Type 1	Type 3
Number of patients	19	46
Fever		
101°F (38.3°C)	13 (68%)	32 (67%)
103°F (39.4°C)	6 (32%)	13 (28%)
Coryza	16 (84%)	39 (85%)
Cough	18 (94%)	38 (83%)
Pharyngeal erythema	11 (58%)	24 (52%)
Hoarseness	7 (37%)	11 (24%)
Wheezing	2	4
Anorexia	6	17
Irritability	7	21
Vomiting	2	9
Diarrhea	3	4
Clinical diagnoses		
Uncomplicated URI	9	11
Pharyngitis	3	5
Otitis	3 (16%)	21 (46%)
	$P < .05$	
Croup	3	3
Bronchiolitis	1	1
Pneumonia	—	2
Exanthema	—	1
Fever without source	—	2

URI = upper respiratory infection.

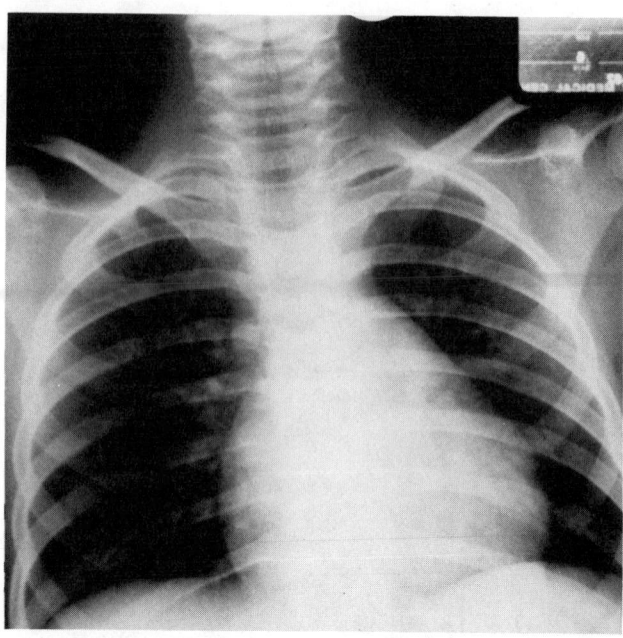

Figure 11–4. Radiographic "steeple sign" of subglottic narrowing in croup.

child[49] (Table 11–6). Other viruses, including influenza A and B and RSV, and *Mycoplasma* can cause a clinically indistinguishable illness.[24, 50] Croup characteristically begins with upper respiratory symptoms of rhinitis and sore throat with low-grade fever. Over a period of days, the illness progresses to hoarseness and increasing respiratory compromise. Patients present to the physician with tachypnea, stridor, and intercostal retractions secondary to subglottic edema. The area of compromise can be appreciated radiographically as a "steeple sign" of subglottic narrowing (Fig 11–4). The clinical syndrome of croup must be distinguished from epiglottiditis—a more acute medical emergency caused by *Haemophilus influenzae*. More recently, a third clinical syndrome, bacterial tracheitis, has been described which clinically resembles croup. It is caused by a bacterial infection, usually *Staphylococcus aureus,* which forms a pseudomembrane in the laryngeal area.[51]

Bacterial tracheitis is almost certainly a superinfection imposed on an initial viral infection, as in several patients we have demonstrated cultural or serologic evidence of simultaneous parainfluenza or influenza infection.

A number of respiratory viruses now have been associated with chronic and progressive pneumonia in immunocompromised patients. Parainfluenza virus type 3 appears to be particularly frequent in patients with severe combined immunodeficiency and in these patients may take the form of a giant cell pneumonia.[52–58] Parainfluenza viruses may be triggers for episodes of wheezing in asthmatic children and exacerbate chronic bronchitis.[59–61] Loughlin and Taussig have suggested that children with croup may be identifiable in later life as having small airway disease with bronchoconstriction on exercise.[62]

Parainfluenza viruses have rarely been implicated as causes of

Table 11–6

Recovery of Parainfluenza Viruses by Illness Syndrome at Children's Hospital National Medical Center (October 1957–June 1972)

Illness Category	Number Tested	Mean Age (months)	Percent of Patients Yielding Virus of Indicated Type					
			Type 1	Type 2	Type 3	Type 4a	Type 4b	Total
Pneumonia	2236	24.8	1.3	0.4	1.9	0.09	0.04	3.7*
Bronchiolitis	1523	8.3	1.1	0.3	2.8	0.1	0.1	4.5
Croup	994	23.7	16.5	9.6	6.2	0.2	0.0	32.5
Pharyngitis-bronchitis	1704	31.8	1.2	0.5	1.9	0.2	0.06	3.8
Total inpatient respiratory	6457	22.5	3.6	1.8	2.8	0.1	0.06	8.3*
Inpatient control	2871	35.9	0.3	0.2	0.2	0.03	0.0	0.7

*There was one dual type 1–type 2 infection.
Data courtesy of C. D. Brandt, H. W. Kim, R. M. Chanock, and R. H. Parrott.

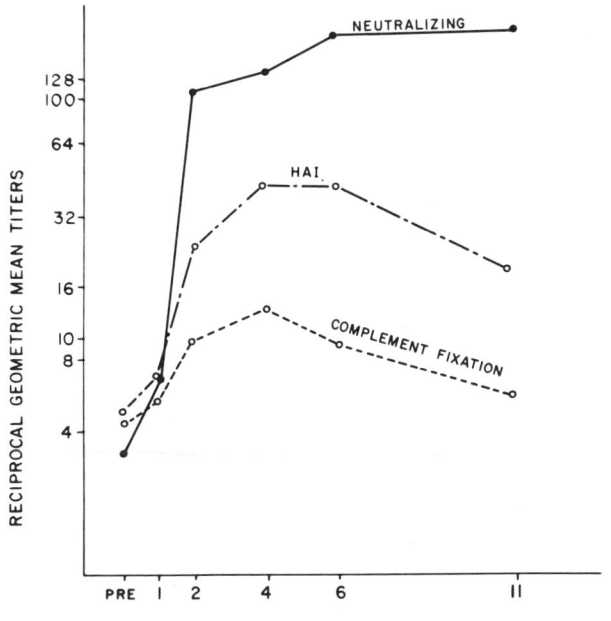

WEEKS AFTER ADMINISTRATION OF PARAINFLUENZA TYPE 3

Figure 11–5. Serum immune response to parainfluenza type 3 vaccine.

parotitis.[63, 64] An association with multiple sclerosis has been reported, but remains unproven.[65, 66] There is a report of the detection of parainfluenza type 3 and SV-5 antigens in the osteoclasts of patients with Paget's disease.[67]

IMMUNOLOGIC RESPONSE

Both serum and local antibodies are found after parainfluenza virus infection.[68] Serum antibody is readily demonstrated by neutralizing, complement fixation, or hemagglutinin-inhibiting antibody after primary infection, as shown in Figure 11–5, which demonstrates the immune response to the partially attenuated parainfluenza strain administered intranasally at Vanderbilt. In tissue culture systems antibody to HN protein inhibits hemagglutinating and neuraminidase activity and blocks penetration into the cell. Antibody to the F protein inhibits cell fusion and hemolyzing activity. Antibodies to the F protein inhibit cell-to-cell spread of parainfluenza viruses after initiation of a limited infection; antibodies to HN protein do not inhibit this spread of virus, which may have implications in human disease. The lack of an antigenic F protein after formalin inactivation of measles and RSV vaccines has been suggested as a cause for the paradoxical sensitization from these vaccines.[16] Recent work by Kasel, who followed the development of antibody in young children, suggested that antibody responses to components of the virus other than HN protein, particularly to fusion protein, may be important in determining protection and were only seen after several infections with parainfluenza viruses.[69]

During primary infection with partially attenuated parainfluenza vaccine, neutralizing antibody in the nasal secretions was not demonstrable.[34] A similar experience was reported with natural parainfluenza types 1 and 2;[70] however, when an enzyme-linked immunosorbent assay (ELISA) was utilized, IgA antibody was detectable in secretions after infection.[70] The importance of the secretory immune system in protection against parainfluenza virus infection was emphasized by Smith et al, who showed a strong correlation of the level of secretory antibody with susceptibility to experimental infection in adults.[71] The relatively poor secretory antibody response in the young child may be a factor in reinfection with parainfluenza virus. We have demonstrated reinfections in four children with parainfluenza type 3 among the viral isolates from approximately 200 children who had viral cultures performed with each respiratory illness.

LABORATORY DIAGNOSIS

Parainfluenza viruses are most readily isolated in primary rhesus or cynomologous monkey kidney cells.[72] An alternative continuous line is LLC-MKC with trypsin incorporated into the media as described by Frank et al.[73] Virus is shed in the upper respiratory tract and most efficiently recovered by a nasal washing or suction technique.[74] Material should be promptly inoculated and tubes examined for cytopathic effect and hemadsorption with 0.1% guinea pig red blood cells at five and ten days. Blind passage may uncover additional low-titered isolates. Full identification of the virus may be accomplished by hemagglutinin inhibition or hemadsorption inhibition. The latter often proves to give the clearest answer. Immunofluorescent staining of infected cells also offers a way of confirming and identifying isolates. Variability of presently available reagents is considerable. Serologic diagnosis of infection may be accomplished by neutralization or hemagglutinin inhibition or complement fixation.[72, 75] Heterotypic rises in antibody titer occur not infrequently, making interpretation of serologic responses more difficult.[76] Type 3 heterotypic rises often occur after type 1 infection and occasionally after type 2 and mumps infection. The animal parainfluenza viruses react extensively with the human strains.

PREVENTION AND TREATMENT

Development of vaccines against parainfluenza viruses has not received the priority accorded influenza or RSV. A successful approach with any one of the respiratory viruses might well lead to more rapid developments in the parainfluenza field. Inactivated and live attenuated vaccines have been developed and administered in human trials without demonstrable success.[68–76] Inactivated vaccines were first administered in conjunction with inactivated respiratory RSV vaccine trials.[77–88] Enhanced RSV disease was seen among RSV vaccine on natural reexposure, but no such adverse effect was seen in the parainfluenza virus recipients.

There is renewed interest in two approaches to live parainfluenza vaccines. The first is the utilization of a bovine parainfluenza virus type 3 as a human immunogen. Recent studies in primates have demonstrated the attenuation of such strains and their ability to protect against challenge with a human parainfluenza virus type 3.[84] The second is the utilization of cold-adapted vaccines to provide a satisfactory measure of attenuation.[85, 86]

The demonstration of the importance of fusion protein in the spread of parainfluenza virus has led to efforts to develop antiviral components using synthetic analogues of the critical N-terminus of the F_1 fusion polypeptide. Inhibition is amino acid sequence–

specific and is influenced by peptide length with longer peptides being more active. Inhibition of both viral replication and cell fusion by these synthetic analogues may be through blocking cell receptors.[89]

Treatment of parainfluenza virus infections is primarily symptomatic, but importantly includes very close observation for respiratory failure and the potential need for intubation and mechanical respiratory assistance.[90] Racemic epinephrine appears, in some children, to offer temporary relief of symptoms.[91] The temporary nature of this relief should be stressed, and children requiring such treatment should be observed in the hospital. The clinically observed beneficial effects of cold and humidity in shrinking mucosal swelling and loosening secretions are established. Cool mist is routinely employed in patient management.

Of the antiviral drugs, amantadine or its derivatives are not effective in vitro against parainfluenza, nor was amantadine effective against parainfluenza type 1 experimental infection.[92] Interferon is produced in respiratory secretions during parainfluenza virus infections,[93] but its therapeutic role is not established. Ribavirin is a nucleoside consisting of D-ribose attached to a 1,2,4-triazole carboxamide that has antiviral activity against a range of DNA and RNA viruses. It inhibits parainfluenza viruses at a minimal inhibiting concentration of 0.01 to 0.1 mg/mL. It increases survival against parainfluenza types 1 and 3 in rodent models but has not been evaluated in clinical trials.[94]

REFERENCES

1. Chanock RM, Bell JA, Parrott RH: Natural history of parainfluenza infection. *Perspect Virol* 1961; 2:126–139.
2. Clarke SKR: Parainfluenza virus infections. *Postgrad Med J* 1973; 49:792–797.
3. Dowrham MAPS, McQuillin J, Gardner PS: Diagnosis and clinical significance of parainfluenza virus infection in children. *Arch Dis Child* 1974; 49:8–15.
4. Gardner PS, McQuillin J, McGuckin R, et al: Observations on clinical and immunofluorescent diagnosis of parainfluenza virus infections. *Br Med J* 1971; 2:7–12.
5. Jackson GG, Muldoon RL: Viruses causing common respiratory infection in man. II. Enteroviruses and paramyxoviruses. *J Infect Dis* 1973; 123:409–451.
6. Chanock RM: Association of a new type of cytopathogenic myxovirus with infantile croup. *J Exp Med* 1956; 104:555–576.
7. Chanock RM, Parrott RH, Cook K, et al: Newly recognized myxoviruses from children with respiratory diseases. *N Engl J Med* 1958; 258:207–213.
8. Andrews CH, Bang FB, Chanock RM, et al: Parainfluenza viruses 1, 2, and 3: Suggested names for recently described myxoviruses. *Virology* 1959; 8:129–130.
9. Gardner SD: The isolation of parainfluenza 4 sub-types A and B in England and serological studies of their prevalence. *J Hyg Camb* 1969; 67:540–545.
10. Kilgore GE, Dowdle WR: Antigenic characterization of parainfluenza 4A and 4B by the hemagglutination-inhibition test and distribution of HI antibody in human sera. *Am J Epidemiol* 1970; 91:306–316.
11. Waterson AP, Hurrell JMW: The fine structure of the parainfluenza viruses. *Arch Virusforsch* 1962; 12:138–142.
12. Elango N, Coligan JE, Jambou RC, et al: Human parainfluenza type 3 virus hemagglutinin-neuraminidase glycoprotein: nucleotide sequence of mRNA and limited amino acid sequence of the purified protein. *J Virol* 1986; 57:481–489.
13. Spriggs MK, Olmstead RA, Venkatesan S, et al: Fusion glycoprotein of human parainfluenza type 3: nucleotide sequence of the gene, direct identification of the cleavage-activation site, and comparison with other paramyxoviruses. *Virology* 1986; 152:241–251.
14. Choppin PW, Compans RW: Reproduction of paramyxoviruses, in Fraenkel H, Wagner RF (eds): *Comprehensive Virology,* ed 4. New York, Plenum, 1975, pp 95–178.
15. Scheid A, Caliguiri LA, Compans RW, et al: Isolation of paramyxovirus glycoproteins. Association of both hemagglutinating and neuraminidase activities with the larger SV5 glycoprotein. *Virology* 1972; 50:640–652.
16. Chopping PW, Richardson CD, Merz DC, et al: Functions of surface glycoproteins of myxoviruses and paramyxoviruses and their inhibition. Adhesion and microorganism pathogenicity. *Ciba Found Symp* 1981; 80:252–269.
17. Choppin PW, Scheid A: The role of viral glycoproteins in adsorption, penetrations and pathogenicity of viruses. *Rev Infect* 1980; 2:40–61.
18. Hsu M-c, Scheid A, Choppin PW: Activation of the Sendai virus fusion protein (F) involves a conformational change with exposure of a new hydrophobic region *J Biol Chem* 1981; 256:3557–3563.
19. Merz DC, Scheid A, Choppin PW: Immunological studies of the functions of paramyxovirus glycoproteins. *Virology* 1981; 109:94–105.
20. Shioda T, Iwasaki K, Shibuta H: Determination of the complete nucleotide sequence of the Sendai virus genome RNA and the predicted amino acid sequence of the F,HN and L proteins. *Nucleic Acids Res* 1986; 14:1545–1563.
21. Amesse LS, Pridgen CL, Kingsbury DW: Sensai virus DI RNA species with conserved virus genome termini and extensive internal deletions. *Virology* 1982; 118:17–27.
22. Kolakofsky D: Isolation and characterization of Sendai virus DI-RNAs. *Cell* 1976; 8:547–555.
23. Bisno AL, Barratt NP, Swanston SW, et al: An outbreak of acute respiratory disease in Trinidad associated with parainfluenza viruses. *Am J Epidemiol* 1970; 91:68–77.
24. Glezen WP, Denny FW: Epidemiology of acute lower respiratory disease in children. *N Engl J Med* 1973; 288:498–505.
25. Foy HM, Cooney MK, Maletzsky AJ, et al: Incidence and etiology of pneumonia, croup and bronchiolitis in pre-school children belonging to a prepaid medical care group over a four-year period. *Am J Epidemiol* 1973; 97:80–92.
26. Monto AS: The Tecumseh study of respiratory illness. V. Patterns of infection with the parainfluenza viruses. *Am J Epidemiol* 1973; 97:338–348.
27. Mufson MA, Mocega HE, Krause HE: Acquisition of parainfluenza 3 virus infection by hospitalized children. I. Frequencies, rates and temporal data. *J Infect Dis* 1973; 128:141–147.
28. van Wyke Coelingh KL, Winter CC, Murphy BR: Nucleotide and deduced amino acid sequence of the hemagglutinin-neuraminidase genes of the human type 3 parainfluenza viruses isolated from 1957 to 1983. *Virology* 1988; 162:137–143.
29. Hall CB, Douglas RG Jr: Modes of transmission of respiratory syncytial virus. *J Pediatr* 1981; 99:100–103.
30. Hendley JP, Wenzel RP, Gwaltney JM Jr: Transmission of rhinovirus colds by self-inoculation. *N Engl J Med* 1973; 288:1361–1364.
31. Rocchi G, Arangio-Ruiz G, Giannini V, et al: Detection of viremia in acute respiratory disease of man. *Acta Virol* 1970; 14:405–407.
32. Tyrrell DAJ, Bynoe ML, Birkum K, et al: Inoculation of human volunteers with parainfluenza viruses 1 and 3 (HA2 and HA1) *Br Med J* 1959; 2:909–1011.
33. Kapikian AZ, Chanock RM, Reichelderfer TE, et al: Inoculation of human volunteers with parainfluenza virus types 3. *JAMA* 1961; 178:537–541.
34. Wright PF, Meguro H, Thompson J, et al: Live parainfluenza type 3 vaccine in children. *Pediatr Res* 1977; 11:509.
35. Hall CB, Geiman JM, Breese BB, et al: Parainfluenza viral infections in children: Correlation of shedding with clinical manifestations. *J Pediatr* 1977; 91:194–198.

36. Heath RB: The pathogenesis of respiratory viral infection. *Postgrad Med J* 1979; 55:122–127.

37. Jakab GJ, Green GM: Defect in intracellular killing of *Staphylococcus aureus* within alveolar macrophages in Sendai virus-infected murine lungs. *J Clin Invest* 1976; 57:1533–1539.

38. Spriggs MK, Murphy BR, Prince GA, et al: Expression of the F and HN glycoproteins of human parainfluenza virus type 3 by recombinant vaccinia viruses: contributions of the individual proteins to host immunity. *Virology* 1987; 61:3416–3423.

39. Ray R, Glaze BJ, Compans RW: Role of the individual glycoproteins of human parainfluenza type 3 in the induction of a protective immune response. *Virology* 1988; 62:783–787.

40. Ray R, Glaze BJ, Moldoveanu Z, et al: Intranasal immunization of hamsters with envelope glycoproteins of human parainfluenza virus type 3. *J Infect Dis* 1988; 157:648–654.

41. Buthala DA, Soret MG: Parainfluenza type 3 virus infection in hamsters. Virologic, serologic and pathologic studies. *J Infect Dis* 1964; 114:226–231.

42. Glezen WP, Fernald GW: Effect of passive antibody on parainfluenza virus type 3 pneumonia in hamsters. *Infect Immun* 1976; 14:212–216.

43. Henderson FW: Anti-viral cytotoxic lymphocyte response in hamsters with parainfluenza virus type 3 infection. *Adv Exp Med Biol* 1981; 134:215–219.

44. Metzgar DP, Gower TA, Larson EJ, et al: The effect of parainfluenza virus type 3 on newborn ferrets. *J Biol Stand* 1974; 2:273–282.

45. Klein JD, Collier AM: Pathogenesis of human parainfluenza type 3 virus infection in hamster tracheal organ culture. *Infect Immun* 1974; 10:883–888.

46. Craighead JE, Brennan BJ: Cytopathic effects of parainfluenza virus type 3 in organ cultures of human respiratory tract tissue. *Am J Pathol* 1968; 52:287–300.

47. Wenzel RP, McCormick DP, Beam WE Jr: Parainfluenza pneumonia in adults. *JAMA* 1972; 221:294–295.

48. Bloom HH, Johnson KM, Jacobsen R, et al: Recovery of parainfluenza viruses from adults with upper respiratory illness. *Am J Hyg* 1961; 74:50–59.

49. Brandt CD, Kim HW, Chanock RM, et al: Parainfluenza virus epidemiology *Pediatr Res* 1974; 8:422.

50. Parrott RH, Kim MW, Vargosko AJ, et al: Serious respiratory tract illness as a result of Asian influenza and influenza B infections in children. *J Pediatr* 1962; 62:205–213.

51. Jones R, Santos JI, Overall JC: Bacterial tracheitis. *JAMA* 1979; 242:721–726.

52. Craft AW, Reid MM, Gardner PS, et al: Virus infections in children with acute lymphoblastic leukemia. *Arch Dis Child* 1979; 54:755–759.

53. Delage G, Brochu P, Pelletier M, et al: Giant-cell pneumonia caused by parainfluenza virus. *J Pediatr* 1979; 94:426–429.

54. Fishaut M, Tubergen D, McIntosh K: Cellular response to respiratory viruses with particular reference to children with disorders of cell-mediated immunity. *J Pediatr* 1980; 96:179–180.

55. Gross PA, Green RH, Curnen MGM: Persistent infection with parainfluenza type 3 virus in man. *Am Rev Respir Dis* 1973; 108:891–898.

56. Jarvis WR, Middleton PJ, Gelfand EW: Parainfluenza pneumonia in severe combined immunodeficiency disease. *J Pediatr* 1979; 94:423–425.

57. Karp D, Willis J, Wilfert C: Parainfluenza virus II and the immunocompromised host. *Am J Dis Child* 1974; 127:592–593.

58. DeFabritus AM, Riggio RR, David SD, et al: Parainfluenza type 3 in a transplant unit. *JAMA* 1979; 241:384–386.

59. McIntosh K, Ellis EF, Hoffman LS, et al: The association of viral and bacterial respiratory infections with exacerbations of wheezing in young asthmatic children. *J Pediatr* 1973; 82:578–590.

60. Minor TE, Baker JW, Dick EC, et al: Greater frequency of viral respiratory infections in asthmatic children as compared with their nonasthmatic siblings. *J Pediatr* 1974; 85:472–477.

61. Stark JE, Heath RB, Curwen MP: Infection with influenza and parainfluenza viruses in chronic bronchitis. *Thorax* 1965; 20:124–127.

62. Loughlin GM, Taussig LM: Pulmonary function in children with a history of laryngotracheobronchitis. *J Pediatr* 1979; 94:365–369.

63. Zoller LM, Mufson MA: Acute parotitis associated with parainfluenza type 3 virus infection. *Am J Dis Child* 1970; 119:147–148.

64. Cullen SJ, Baublis JW: Parainfluenza type 3 parotitis in two immunodeficient children. *J Pediatr* 1980; 96:437–438.

65. Koprowski H, ter Meulen V: Multiple sclerosis and parainfluenza I virus: History of the isolation of the virus and expression of phenotypic differences between the isolated virus and Sendai virus. *J Neurol* 1975; 208:175–190.

66. Norrby E, Link H, Olsson JE, et al: Comparison of antibodies against different viruses in cerebrospinal fluid and serum samples from patients with multiple sclerosis. *Infect Immun* 1974; 10:688–694.

67. Basle MF, Russell WC, Goswami KKA, et al: Paramyxovirus antigens in osteoclasts from Paget's bone tissue detected by monoclonal antibodies. *J Gen Virol* 1985; 66:2103–2110.

68. Chanock RM, Wong DC, Huebner RJ, et al: Serologic response of individuals infected with parainfluenza viruses. *Am J Public Health* 1970; 50:1858–1865.

69. Tyeryar FJ: Report of a workshop on respiratory syncytial virus and parainfluenza viruses. *J Infect Dis* 1983; 184:588–598.

70. Yanagihara R, McIntosh K: Secretory immunological response in infants and children to parainfluenza virus types 1 and 2. *Infect Immun* 1979; 30:23.

71. Smith CB, Purcell RH, Bellanti JA, et al: Protective effect of antibody to parainfluenza type 1 virus. *N Engl J Med* 1966; 275:1145–1152.

72. Chanock RM: Parainfluenza viruses, in Lennette EH, Schmidt NJ (eds): *Diagnostic Procedures for Viral and Rickettsial and Chlamydial Infections.* ed 5. New York, American Public Health Assoc, 1967, pp 611–632.

73. Frank AL, Couch RB, Griffis CA, et al: Comparison of different tissue cultures for isolation and quantitation of influenza and parainfluenza viruses. *J Clin Microbiol* 1979; 10:32–36.

74. Hall CB, Douglas RG: Clinically useful method for the isolation of respiratory syncytial virus. *J Infect Dis* 1975; 131:1–5.

75. Frank AL, Puck J, Hughes BJ, et al: Microneutralization test for influenza A and B and parainfluenza 1 and 2 viruses that uses continuous cell lines and fresh serum enhancement. *J Clin Microbiol* 1980; 12:426–432.

76. Lennette EH, Jensen FW, Guenther RW, et al: Serologic responses to parainfluenza viruses in patients with mumps virus infection. *J Lab Clin Med* 1963; 61:780–788.

77. Kim HW, Canchola JG, Vargosko AJ, et al: Immunogenicity of inactivated parainfluenza type 1, type 2 and type 3 vaccines in infants. *JAMA* 1966; 196:819–824.

78. Sweet BH, Tyrell AA, Potash L, et al: Repiratory virus vaccine. III. Pentavalent respiratory syncytial parainfluenza *Mycoplasma pneumonia* vaccine. *Am Rev Respir Dis* 1966; 94:340–349.

79. Chin J, Magoffin RL, Shearer LA, et al: Field evaluation of a respiratory syncytial virus vaccine and a trivalent parainfluenza virus vaccine in a pediatric population. *Am J Epidemiol* 1969; 89:449–463.

80. Fulginiti VA, Amer J, Eller JJ, et al: Parainfluenza virus immunization. IV. Simultaneous immunization with parainfluenza types 1, 2, and 3 aqueous vaccines. *Am J Dis Child* 1967; 114:26–28.

81. Fulginiti VA, Eller JJ, Sieber OF, et al: Respiratory virus immunization. I. A field trial of two inactivated respiratory vaccines; an aqueous trivalent parainfluenza virus vaccine and an alum-precipitated respiratory syncytial virus vaccine. *Am J Epidemiol* 1969; 89:435–448.

82. Vella PP, Weibel RE, Woodhour AF, et al: Respiratory virus vaccine. VIII. Field evaluation of trivalent parainfluenza virus vaccine among preschool children in families, 1967–1968. *Am*

Rev Respir Dis 1969; 99:526–541.

83. Wigley FM, Fruchtman MH, Waldman RH: Aerosol immunization of humans with inactivated parainfluenza type 2 vaccine. *N Engl J Med* 1970; 283:1250–1253.

84. van Wyke Coelingh KL, Winter CC, Tierney EL, et al: Attenuation of bovine parainfluenza virus type 3 in nonhuman primates and its ability to confer immunity to human parainfluenza virus type 3 challenge. *J Infect Dis* 157; 157:655–662.

85. Belshe RB, Hissom RK: Cold adaptation of parainfluenza virus type 3: Induction of three phenotypic markers. *J Med Virol* 1982; 10:235–242.

86. Crookshanks RF, Belshe RB: Evaluation of cold adapted and temperature sensitive mutants of parainfluenza virus type 3 (para 3) in weanling hamsters. *J Med Virol* 1984; 13:243–249.

86a. Heilman CA: From the National Institute of Allergy and Infectious Diseases and the World Health Organization: Respiratory syncytial and parainfluenza viruses. *J Infect Dis* 1990; 161:402–406.

87. Gutekunst DE, Paton IM, Volenec FJ: Parainfluenza-3 vaccine in cattle: Comparative efficacy of intranasal and intramuscular routes. *J Am Vet Med Assoc* 1969; 155:1879–1885.

88. Potash L, Lees RS, Greenberger JL, et al: A mutant of parainfluenza type 1 virus with decreased capacity for growth at 38C and 39C. *J Infect Dis* 1970; 121:640–647.

89. Choppin PW, Richison CD, Mertz DC, et al: The functions and inhibition of the membrane glycoprotein of paramyxoviruses and myxoviruses and the role of the measles virus M protein in subacute sclerosing panencephalitis. *J Infect Dis* 1981; 143:352–362.

90. Newth CJ, Levinson H, Byron AC: The respiratory status of children with croup. *J Pediatr* 1972; 81:1068–1073.

91. Gardner HG, Powell KR, Roden VJ, et al: The evaluation of racemic epinephrine in the treatment of infectious croup. *Pediatrics* 1973; 52:52–55.

92. Smith CB, Purcell RH, Chanock RM: Effect of amantadine hydrochloride on parainfluenza type 1 virus infections in adult volunteers. *Am Rev Respir Dis* 1967; 95:689–690.

93. McKintosh K: Interferon in nasal secretions from infants with viral respiratory infections. *J Pediatr* 1978; 93:33–36.

94. Chang T-W, Heel RC: Ribavirin and inosiplex: A review of their present status in viral diseases. *Drugs* 1981; 22:111–128.

Mumps Virus

Mark D. Tolpin

The word "mumps" probably derives from the British verb "to mump," which means "to grimace or grin."[1] Thus, the name of the disease likely refers to the marked parotid swelling (Fig 12–1) which is the most common physical manifestation of infection with this virus. In fact, until modern virologic and serologic methods showed that mumps virus could cause illness without parotitis and that other viruses could cause parotitis, mumps virus infection was known as "epidemic parotitis." The mumps virus is the most common cause of parotitis, and mumps infections often occur in local outbreaks. Other viruses, such as the coxsackie, parainfluenza, lymphocytic choriomeningitis, influenza A, echo- and possibly herpes simplex and varicella-zoster viruses, also cause parotid swelling.[2, 3]

During childhood, mumps is generally a self-limited febrile disease with manifestations that are frequently multisystemic. The incidence of permanent residua is quite low. Approximately 30% of all mumps infections are subclinical.[4–6] Postpubescent children and adults tend to have more overt, clinically apparent multiple organ involvement.[6] In addition to parotitis and other salivary gland inflammation, mumps virus can also cause aseptic meningitis, meningoencephalitis, orchitis, and pancreatitis.[1] When mumps orchitis occurs in postpubescent males, it can result in varying degrees of testicular dysfunction.[7] Less commonly encountered complications of mumps include oophoritis, mastitis, thyroiditis, myocarditis, nephritis, arthritis, and endolymphatic labyrinthitis with eighth nerve deafness.[1, 5, 8]

HISTORY

In 1934, Johnson and Goodpasture published a study in which they showed that the saliva of four patients with "epidemic parotitis" could produce a nonsuppurative parotitis when it was inoculated into the parotid glands of *Macaca* rhesus monkeys.[9] These affected monkey parotid glands were then extracted and filtered. The filtrate was shown to cause parotitis when it was inoculated into the parotid glands of additional, previously uninfected monkeys. In this way, Koch's postulates were fulfilled, and the agent of mumps was shown to be filterable (ie, a virus).

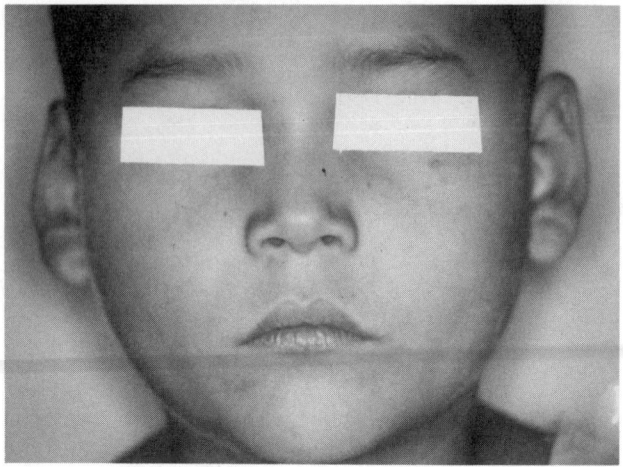

Figure 12–1. Mumps parotitis, showing asymmetric involvement of parotid glands. Parotid swelling is seen to push the pinnae away from the head. *(Photograph courtesy of Dr. Leon LeBeau.)*

The mumps virus was subsequently propagated in embryonated chicken eggs. This development allowed the production of mumps antigen for use in both a serologic complement fixation test and a skin test for delayed hypersensitivity to mumps.[10, 11] Formalin inactivation of the mumps virus was accomplished, and studies using this inactivated virus as an immunizing agent were performed. Although immunization with this preparation protected most susceptible individuals from developing overt disease during live virus challenge, the duration of this effect was relatively short-lived. As a result, inactivated mumps virus was never widely used for vaccination purposes from the time of its introduction in 1950 until the time that its use was discontinued in 1978.[10–12, 112]

Attenuation of the mumps virus by in vitro passage was noted by Enders in the mid-1940s. He speculated that this phenomenon would prove useful in the development of an attenuated mumps vaccine.[10] With the development of tissue culture techniques for propagation of mumps virus in vitro, a live attenuated mumps vaccine was prepared and licensed in 1967. Immunization with the Jeryl Lynn strain of attenuated mumps virus provides long-term protection in over 90% of susceptible individuals from clinically apparent mumps infection.[5, 13–15] With the advent of this vaccine, the prevention of mumps and hence its complications and sequelae became feasible.

STRUCTURE AND BIOLOGY OF MUMPS VIRUS

Mumps virus is a paramyxovirus. It is therefore related to the parainfluenza, measles, and Newcastle disease viruses, and is somewhat more distantly related to respiratory syncytial influenza virus.

The mumps virion is often spherical, although pleomorphism including filamentous forms has also been reported (Fig 12–2).[16, 17] The spherical virion has a diameter of 120 to 200 nm. The virus's genetic information is encoded on unsegmented, negative-stranded RNA. In the infected cell, positive-stranded messenger RNA (mRNA) is transcribed from the virion RNA by virion RNA polymerase(s). The core of the virion is helical and contains the RNA

genome surrounded by capsid protein; RNA-dependent RNA polymerase is also present. This ribonucleoprotein core is surrounded by an envelope consisting of a lipid membrane that contains glycoprotein projections. There are two glycoproteins present in this envelope. One of them has both hemagglutination and neuraminidase functions, and the other has hemolysin and fusion factor properties.[1, 18]

During infection of tissue culture cells, all paramyxoviruses produce cytoplasmic inclusions that contain viral nucleocapsid antigen and appear eosinophilic when stained with hematoxylin and eosin. Unlike other paramyxoviruses, mumps also produces these inclusions in the nucleoplasm of the infected cell.[17] This nucleocapsid antigen, when obtained from lysates of infected cells, is known as ''soluble antigen.'' The soluble antigen of mumps virus contains antigenic sites that are similar to or the same as some nucleocapsid antigenic sites of certain other paramyxoviruses. Therefore, antibodies directed to the nucleocapsid antigens of other paramyxoviruses (most notably the parainfluenza and Newcastle disease viruses) will often cross-react with mumps soluble antigen in serologic assays.[18]

The two surface glycoproteins of mumps virus are expressed on the cell membranes of infected cells. Cells in which mumps virus is actively replicating, therefore, acquire the ability to hemadsorb red blood cells to their cell membranes from the viral hemagglutinin glycoprotein (see Fig 12–2). The other (ie, hemolysin-fusion factor) glycoprotein causes the cell membranes of mumps virus-infected cells to fuse with the cell membranes of adjacent cells, thereby creating multinucleated giant cells (Fig 12–3). In this way, mumps virus can spread from cell to cell without first having to leave the primarily infected cell as a complete viral particle.[1, 16]

Mumps virus matures at the cell membrane of the infected cell. Once the cell membrane is laden with viral glycoprotein, filamentous aggregates of viral nucleocapsid form in the peripheral

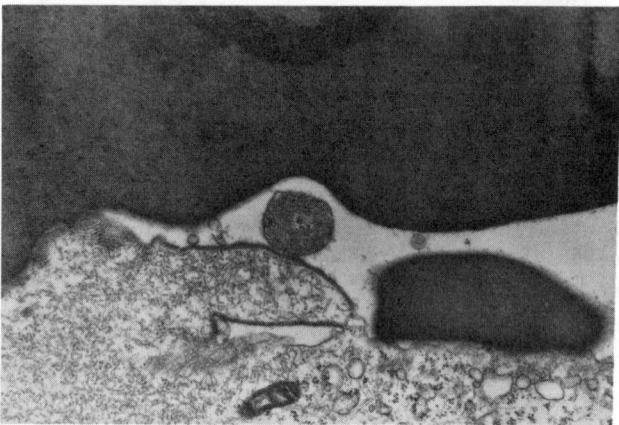

Figure 12–2. Electron micrograph of spherical mumps virion (*center*). The virus is seen between a chick embryo fibroblast (*bottom*) in which mumps virus is replicating, and a red blood cell (*top*) that is hemadsorbed to both the mumps virion and the infected chick embryo fibroblast's cell membrane. *(From Due-Nguygen H: Hemadsorption of mumps virus examined by light and electron microscopy. J Virol 1968; 2:494–506. Reproduced with permission.)*

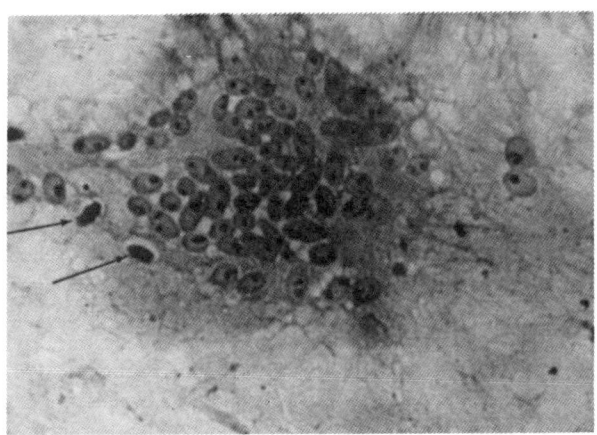

Figure 12–3. Chick embryo fibroblast tissue culture infected with mumps virus. Multinucleated giant cell *(center)* with occasional pyknotic nuclei surrounded by clear halo *(arrows)* is illustrated. *(From Due-Nguyen H: Hemadsorption of mumps virus examined by light and electron microscopy. J. Virol 1968; 2:494–506. Reproduced with permission.)*

cytoplasm of the cell and separate into complete viral cores. The complete viral particle then buds from the cell membrane. The viral envelope therefore consists of the viral glycoproteins embedded in a lipid membrane derived from the infected cell.[17]

EPIDEMIOLOGY

The mumps virus has a worldwide distribution and is endemic in urban areas. There are no known immunologic differences among the various strains of mumps virus, and natural infection with wild-type mumps virus or immunization with attenuated mumps virus vaccine provide long-lasting immunity.[5, 14, 18]

In the United States, the incidence of mumps infections increases during the late winter months and peaks during March and April.[1, 5, 18] In at least some regions of the world, there appear to be year-to-year variations in the incidence of mumps activity. The research unit of the Royal College of General Practitioners observed triennial peaks of mumps activity in 1964, 1967, and 1970 in the United Kingdom. During the years following these peaks (ie, 1965, 1968, and 1971), the level of mumps activity was usually low.[19]

Mumps became a nationally notifiable disease in the United States in 1968. However, mumps is likely to be underreported because: (1) it may be an asymptomatic infection, (2) it may lack the characteristic finding of parotitis, (3) it may not be of sufficient severity to warrant medical attention, or (4) it may not be reported by the examining physician. Additionally, patients with severe complications of mumps may be more likely to be reported than those without complications. Nevertheless, the reported mumps data allow comparison of disease frequency from year to year.

An attenuated mumps vaccine was licensed for distribution in the United States in 1967.[15] In 1976, approximately 50% of children 1 to 10 years old had received this vaccine. Vaccine use was much less in most other parts of the world, including the United Kingdom, and the incidence of mumps in various countries is a reflection of the use of the vaccine.[4, 6, 20]

In the United States from 1976 to 1980 the median annual number of mumps cases reported was 16,777. During the early 1980s, the number of mumps cases reported in the United States has fallen markedly: 8449 cases were reported in 1980 and 4729 were reported in 1981.[21] By 1984 the incidence of mumps had dropped to 1.3 per 100,000 people (a total of 3021 cases reported).[22] The widespread administration of the live attenuated mumps vaccine following the 1977 ACIP recommendation for routine mumps vaccination in the United States was responsible, at least in part, for this decline in the incidence of reported mumps cases. By 1985, a record low of 2982 cases of mumps was reported.[112] However, in 1986 and 1987, the number of reported cases increased (7790 and 12,848, respectively, with a provisional total of 4730 in 1988). At the same time, the peak incidence age shifted from 5 to 9 year olds to older age ranges. The most dramatic increases were seen in 10 to 14 year olds (almost a sevenfold increase relative to 1967–1971) and 15 to 19 year olds (over eightfold greater than during the 1967–1971 reporting period).[112] During 1987, the incidence of reported mumps cases per 100,000 population was 1.1 in the District of Columbia and the 14 states that required proof of mumps immunization for public school attendance as opposed to 11.5 in the states without mumps immunization requirements.[112] Hence, the recent increase in reported mumps cases in the United States likely resulted from inadequate vaccination rather than vaccine failures. In fact, 20 years of data indicate that both humoral immunity and protection persist following live attenuated mumps vaccine administration.[112]

Man is the only known host for the mumps virus in nature.[5] The virus still primarily infects young children during their early to middle school years, with the highest incidence (about 60%) of mumps infection occurring in children 5 to 14 years old.[2, 14, 15, 18, 112] Hence, the potential for day care center outbreaks of mumps exists if the children are unimmunized.[23] High school and college outbreaks of mumps have also been reported in recent years.[112]

A significant proportion of the adult population has escaped infection by the mumps virus during childhood. In the United States, approximately 20% of the adult population is estimated to have ''no detectable immunity to mumps.''[25] The susceptibility of adults to mumps may relate to decreased communicability of the virus as compared to measles.[6] This susceptible postpubescent population is at risk of the increased severity and higher complication rate seen in mumps infection within this age group.[6] In fact, prior to 1979, in the United States, approximately 15% of the reported mumps cases occur in either adolescents or adults.[14, 15] As noted previously, this figure increased to almost one third of the reported cases from 1985 to 1987.[112] With a 20% susceptibility in the adult population, mumps infection can occur during pregnancy. The incidence of mumps infection during pregnancy in the United States was previously estimated to be between 1 in 1000 and 1 in 30,000.[1, 26, 27] However, this figure may be on the rise.

The age-specific attack rates of mumps per 1000 population seen in the United Kingdom during the period from 1969 to 1971 has been determined. For individuals from 15 to 44 years of age, the attack rate was 1.6 for males and 1.9 for females. In the age range from 5 to 14 years, the attack rates were 29.2 and 27.6 for males and females, respectively.[19] Mumps virus infection is a rare occurrence in children under the age of 9 months.[1, 2, 18]

PATHOGENESIS OF MUMPS VIRUS INFECTION

During mumps infection, the virus is shed heavily in respiratory secretions. Transmission, therefore, is accomplished by means of droplet infection and possibly also by fomites.[1, 18] Mumps virus has also been recovered from the urine of infected individuals.[28] Hence, transmission of the virus by contact with contaminated urine is theoretically possible.

The average incubation period for mumps is 18 days, with a range of 12 to 25 days.[5, 18] Symptoms manifested in the prodromal period of the disease include fever, anorexia, myalgia, and malaise. Parotitis, when it occurs, becomes clinically apparent from one to seven days after onset of the prodrome. The swollen parotid glands may be tender, with pain being referred to as an earache. The parotid glands continue to enlarge for two to three days, and then the swelling regresses. At the height of the swelling, the parotid glands may completely fill the area between the angle of the mandible and the ear lobe, thus pushing the lower portion of the pinna away from the head (see Fig 12–1). Reddening and swelling of Stensen's ducts is usually present in mumps parotitis. Parotid swelling is usually bilateral, although one gland may begin swelling a day or two earlier than the other gland; therefore the progress of the parotitis may be asynchronous. Swelling of the submaxillary and sublingual salivary glands sometimes occurs in mumps; these glands are rarely enlarged in the absence of parotid involvement. The swollen salivary glands may be quite tender to palpation. Salivary gland involvement in mumps usually lasts for 1 week or less.[1, 2, 5, 18] An elevation in serum amylase levels usually accompanies the parotid swelling. The serum amylase levels fall as the parotitis subsides.[29]

In addition, there is evidence that a large number of individuals with parotitis have cerebrospinal fluid (CSF) pleocytosis without other evidence of central nervous system (CNS) disease. In one study of 372 hospitalized patients with mumps parotitis, 63% showed an increased WBC count in their CSF. Over half of those patients with a CSF pleocytosis had no CNS symptoms.[30] In another study of 40 hospitalized patients with mumps parotitis, many subjects had a CSF pleocytosis without other evidence of CNS disease.[31]

Use of parotitis as the major diagnostic criterion for mumps infection may be misleading. Approximately 30% of primary mumps virus infections are subclinical. Therefore, many unimmunized individuals who have no history of parotitis still have had mumps infections at some time during their lives.[5, 14, 32, 33] Likewise, clinically apparent mumps virus infection can occur without demonstrable parotitis. In one series of 51 patients with mumps-related aseptic meningitis and meningoencephalitis, only 24 (47%) had parotitis.[29] In a British study in which 2707 upper respiratory specimens obtained from patients with nonspecific illnesses were cultured for viruses, mumps virus was isolated from nine patients.[34] Finally, mumps is not the only virus that can cause parotid swelling; coxsackie, echovirus, parainfluenza (types 1 and 3), lymphocytic choriomeningitis, influenza A, and possibly herpes simplex and varicella-zoster viruses have also been shown to cause this clinical finding.[2, 3] Because lasting immunity to mumps virus follows natural mumps virus infection or mumps vaccine, cases of parotitis following a documented mumps infection or immunization are quite likely caused by these other viruses rather than by the mumps virus. This statement is valid irrespective of whether one, both, or neither parotid was involved during the documented mumps virus infection.

Other causes of parotid swelling are suppurative parotitis (usually unilateral; pus can be expressed from the affected gland's parotid duct), calculus, pneumoparotitis, intraparotid hemorrhage, parotid tumor, sarcoidosis, and Sjögren syndrome. Parotid pain is occasionally associated with administration of bretylium, clonidine, guanethidine, vincristine, or vinblastine. Frank parotid swelling can occur in patients receiving penicillamine, succinylcholine, insulin, phenylbutazone, oxyphenylbutazone, methimazole, methyldopa, or iodine compounds such as potassium iodide or radiocontrast media. In addition, facial cellulitis and anterior cervical lymphadenitis can be confused with parotid swelling.[1] Mumps-associated salivary gland swelling can occur in the absence of any prodrome and without other clinical manifestations of mumps infection. In this form, mumps can be mistaken for other diseases of the parotid gland.[2] Because of these diagnostic possibilities, recurrent or persistent parotid swelling is an indication for otolaryngologic consultation.

Individuals incubating mumps virus have been shown to be contagious before their infection becomes clinically apparent.[18, 33] Viremic spread of the virus occurs during early incubation and not thereafter.[18, 28] Virus can be recovered from the infected individual's saliva up to seven days before the onset of parotitis, and salivary shedding of mumps virus then continues for up to nine days after the onset of parotitis.[18, 33] Viruria also occurs, and mumps virus has been recovered from the urine of infected patients from six days before to 15 days into their clinical illness.[2, 28] As a result of these patterns of virus shedding, isolation of a mumps patient at the time that his or her parotitis becomes clinically apparent will not prevent secondary spread of the virus to susceptible contacts. Respiratory isolation of both the index case and all of that person's contacts is necessary in order to prevent tertiary spread of the virus.[5, 33]

In uncomplicated mumps infection, the peripheral white blood cell count is usually between 4000 and 16,000. There is usually a predominance of lymphocytes; lymphocytopenia can occur. Serum amylase concentrations are often elevated while parotitis is present. These laboratory abnormalities usually persist for 1 week or less. The erythrocyte sedimentation rate is usually normal in uncomplicated mumps. Interestingly, a CSF pleocytosis is found in approximatley half of patients with uncomplicated mumps infection.[18]

Complications of mumps infection often result from viral infection of the tissues and organs outside the upper respiratory tract. The most frequently affected organs are the testicle, the brain, the meninges, and the pancreas. Involvement of the ovaries, labyrinth, thyroid, kidney, heart, joints, thymus, liver, spleen, mammary and vulvovaginal glands, epididymis, prostate, spinal cord, cranial nerves, lung, and gastrointestinal tract has also been reported.[1, 18, 20, 32, 35, 36] Those organs infected directly by the mumps virus show histologic changes that are similar to the ones found in mumps virus-infected parotid glands: both perivascular and interstitial edema and an inflammatory exudate of mononuclear cells.[1]

COMPLICATIONS

Complications of mumps virus infection can occur during the acute, convalescent, or postconvalescent phases. The overall incidence of mumps-related complications is higher in the postpubescent population than in the prepubescent population; it is also higher in the male population than in the female population. In a British study, the complication rate per 1000 cases of mumps was 2.8 in individuals less than 14 years of age and 47.1 in individuals 15 years of age or older; the overall complication rate was 8.6 per 1000 cases of mumps. In contrast to the equal incidence of mumps infection in both sexes, 72% of these observed complications occurred in males.[19] Occasional deaths related to complications of mumps infection have been reported.[20, 37] About 50% of mumps-associated deaths occur in individuals 20 years of age and older.[112] The major complications of mumps infections are discussed individually below.

Central Nervous System Complications of Mumps Infection

Clinically apparent CNS involvement during mumps infection occurs in about 15% of cases reported to the Centers for Disease Control in the United States.[14, 15] The symptoms range from slight headache and listlessness to seizures and altered states of consciousness; the preponderance of patients have less severe symptoms. Complications specifically include meningitis, encephalitis, meningoencephalitis, and, rarely, Reye syndrome.

Mumps meningoencephalitis is associated with the presence of mumps virus in the patient's CNS.[29] Clinically apparent mumps disease of the CNS can occur in patients with or without parotitis. If parotitis is present, CNS symptoms usually occur after the onset of parotid swelling—most frequently with an interval of eight to ten days between the involvement of these two sites.[18] However, CNS symptoms have been noted to precede parotitis by one to eight days in up to 18% of patients with mumps meningoencephalitis.[29, 38] In the United States and Britain, approximately half the patients with mumps meningoencephalitis have no evidence of parotitis during their disease.[29, 38, 39]

The clinical spectrum of mumps meningoencephalitis is well illustrated in the series of 51 children of Azimi et al.[29] Symptoms included fever (94%), vomiting (84%), nuchal rigidity (71%), lethargy (69%), parotid swelling (47%), headache (47%), convulsions (18%), abdominal pain (14%), sore throat (8%), diarrhea (8%), and delerium (6%). In these patients, fever was noted to persist as long as seven days, with an average duration of 3.1 days. Recovery had occurred by the time the fever resolved. The incidence of frank encephalitis with CNS involvement has been recorded as 35% in one American series and 4% in a British series.[29, 39] About 18% of patients in whom symptoms of encephalitis predominate have seizures.[18] The average case-fatality rate in mumps encephalitis is 1.4%.[112]

In the absence of parotitis, the meningoencephalitis of mumps is clinically indistinguishable from the "aseptic meningitis" of the enteroviruses, syphilis, lymphocytic choriomeningitis, and other agents.[1] CSF findings in mumps meningoencephalitis vary widely depending on the form and severity of the CNS involvement. White blood cell counts in CSF have been reported to range between 6 and 2200 per microliter, with a predominance of lymphocytes in about three fourths of cases and a polymorphonuclear leukocyte predominance in the remainder. CSF WBC counts are less than 500 per microliter in about two thirds of the cases.[29] Abnormally low CSF glucose concentrations have been reported during the CNS disease in up to 31% of patients.[29, 38] Elevated CSF protein concentrations were found in 39% of patients in one series.[29] In another series of hospitalized patients, the CSF pleocytosis of mumps meningoencephalitis was shown to persist for up to 5 weeks after hospital admission.[38]

Mumps meningoencephalitis occurs year round. In one study conducted prior to the widespread use of mumps vaccine in the United States, the incidence of mumps meningoencephalitis was reported to peak during the spring and summer months.[29] At that time, as now, the incidence of uncomplicated mumps peaked during the late winter and early spring. Whether this disparate peak in the incidence of mumps meningoencephalitis in the United States has persisted into the era of widespread immunization against mumps is not known. In Great Britain, serologic studies have revealed a similar spring-summer annual peak for mumps meningoencephalitis without parotitis; however, in patients with both parotitis and meningoencephalitis, the peak incidence occurred during the months of November, December, and January.[39] Although there is no sex predilection for mumps infection, mumps-caused CNS disease has a male predominance, with male-to-female ratios of up to 3:1 reported.[20, 29, 39] Reported permanent residua associated with severe mumps encephalitis include psychomotor retardation, eighth nerve deafness, various types of paralysis, and perhaps hydrocephalus.[18, 20, 30, 39, 40]

Mumps Orchitis

Mumps orchitis has been described as "the classic example of testicular dysfunction secondary to a specific infection."[7] It is the most common mumps complication brought to the attention of physicians in postpubescent males, accounting for 44% of the complications observed in one British study.[18, 19] While mumps orchitis has been observed in adults of all ages and in children as young as 3 years, it is most commonly observed during adolescence and young adulthood. About 20% to 30% of postpubescent males infected with mumps develop orchitis.[14, 18, 32, 36, 112] In the absence of parotitis, care must be taken to distinguish mumps orchitis from testicular torsion.[1]

Mumps orchitis is usually unilateral.[4] Some degree of testicular atrophy occurs in one third to one half of affected testicles.[36] Clinically apparent bilateral testicular atrophy in varying degrees occurs in only about 10% of individuals with mumps-related testicular atrophy, and in most cases, only one gonad is severely damaged.[7, 18] As a result, infertility secondary to mumps orchitis is a rare phenomenon.[14]

Mumps-related testicular atrophy has never been shown to cause either impotence or feminization.[36] Coppage and Cooner demonstrated normal plasma testosterone levels in three individuals who had severe bilateral testicular atrophy, azoospermia, and infertility resulting from mumps orchitis.[41]

In individuals who develop parotitis with mumps infection, orchitis usually becomes clinically apparent three to seven days after the parotid swelling has subsided.[18] During the acute phase, the affected gonad displays an imflammatory response characterized by marked swelling, warmth, and pain (Fig 12–4). If clincally apparent testicular atrophy occurs, it becomes noticeable as the orchitis subsides.

Histologically, atrophic testes show patchy damage to the seminiferous tubules. Some seminiferous tubules may appear normal, while others show varying degrees of arrest of spermatogenesis. These changes result from patchy destruction of the seminiferous epithelium; the Leydig cells are usually both histologically normal and functional. Azoospermia results when the damage is extensive and bilateral.[7]

There is no evidence for direct damage of the seminiferous epithelium by the mumps virus. In fact, the most likely site of mumps virus replication is in the interstitial cells. Therefore, Steinberger has postulated the following two possible mechanisms for the damage within the seminiferous tubules: The seminiferous epithelium may sustain direct damage from the elevated temperature and the edema-related pressure elevation during the acute orchitis; in addition, direct damage to the interstitium of the gonad by the mumps virus may alter the physiologic and anatomical relationship of the interstitial cells to the seminiferous tubules, thereby resulting in damage to the seminiferous epithelium.[7] The suggestion that mumps orchitis is "a relatively frequent finding in the history of patients who develop germ cell tumors of the testes" has not been supported by published data.[42]

Administration of nonsteroidal analgesics, injection of the spermatic cord with anesthetics, and incision of the tunica albuginea are all said to relieve the pain of mumps orchitis; however, no controlled studies have been done. While orchitis symptoms can also be diminished or relieved by hydrocortisone or ACTH, use of these agents should be avoided if possible. They do not shorten the course of the patient's disease and, in fact, may potentiate the parotitis. In addition, administration of steroids may increase the incidence of secondary infection.[18]

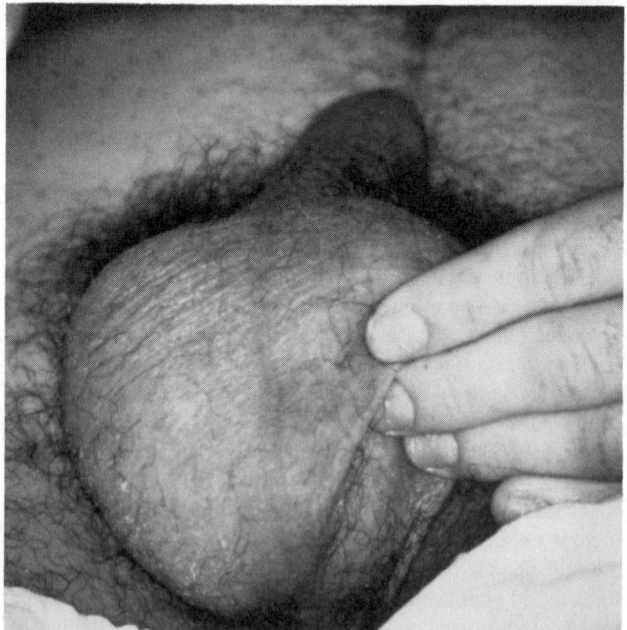

Figure 12–4. Mumps orchitis: testicular swelling is seen. (Photograph courtesy of Dr. Leon LeBeau.)

Pancreatic Effects of Mumps Virus Infection

Mumps-induced pancreatitis is a late effect of mumps infection. Because it is usually diagnosed on the basis of mild clinical symptoms, the incidence of reported mumps pancreatitis varies widely from series to series; figures ranging from less than 1% to 15% can be found in the literature.[19, 20, 43] Approximately one third of the reported cases of mumps pancreatitis have occurred in the absence of demonstrable parotitis.[18, 43] When parotitis is present, pancreatitis usually develops days or even weeks after the parotid involvement occurs. Pancreatitis is more commonly associated with mumps infection in the young adult than in the young child.[43]

Histologically, an acute inflammatory response is seen in the interstitium of the affected exocrine pancreas. A mononuclear cell infiltrate with serous edema and associated swelling is present. There may be varying degrees of necrosis and/or degeneration or compression of the exocrine epithelial cells; the islets of Langerhans may be similarly affected in some cases.[43] This histologic picture looks similar to that seen in salivary glands infected with mumps virus; however, the presence of mumps virus in affected pancreatic tissue has yet to be definitively documented.[43–45]

In 1927, Gundersen published a study in which he noted a periodicity in the death rate from acute-onset childhood diabetes mellitus. These peaks occurred 2 to 4 years after peaks in the incidence of epidemic parotitis (ie, mumps). He noted that epidemic parotitis was associated with acute pancreatitis, and he speculated that mumps infection could thereby cause diabetes mellitus.[46] Similar observations were reported almost 50 years later by Sultz et al. Peaks and troughs in reported new cases of juvenile diabetes mellitus followed respective peaks and troughs in mumps activity by 4 years.[47]

Many case reports purporting to establish mumps as an etiologic agent of diabetes mellitus have appeared in the medical literature for almost a century. In most of these cases, the evidence rests upon a close temporal relationship (varying from a few days to more than a month) between the subject's clinical parotitis or exposure to parotitis and clinical presentation with permanent diabetes mellitus or transient hyperglycemia.[36, 43, 45, 48–50] Most of these case reports have no serologic or virologic evidence establishing antecedent mumps virus infection.[36, 48, 49] In a controlled, serologic study published in 1969 by Gamble et al, no relationship between diabetes mellitus and antecedent mumps virus infection was found; there was, however, a relationship between coxsackie B4 infection and diabetes mellitus in this study.[51] Gamble, as cited by Yoon, subsequently (in 1980) reported that a small number of childhood diabetes may result from recent antecedent mumps infection.[52] Craighead's conclusion about mumps as an etiologic agent of diabetes therefore seems warranted: ". . . if indeed mumps plays a direct role in the pathogenesis of diabetes mellitus, this sequence of events must occur rarely."[43]

Hearing Loss and Mumps Infection

Deafness secondary to endolymphatic labyrinthitis is a rare complication of mumps virus infection. The exact incidence of mumps-related deafness varies from study to study, but is between 0.02 and 0.3%.[18, 20, 30] In the United States, the estimated frequency is 0.5 to 5.0 per 100,000 reported mumps cases.[112] This hearing loss is severe and of sudden onset. While it is usually unilateral, bilateral cases have been reported. Males and females are affected with equal frequency, and mumps-associated deafness most commonly occurs in children and young adults.[53] Tinnitus and vertigo may be present. This hearing loss has been reported to occur in both the acute and convalescent phases of mumps infection. Parotitis may or may not be present, and the patient's mumps virus infection need not be symptomatic. When parotitis is present, deafness usually occurs about 1 week after the onset of parotitis.[53] In most case reports, mumps is implicated as the cause of this process only on a temporal basis. There is, however, some serologic data linking antecedent mumps virus infection to hearing loss of sudden onset.[54] Although some individuals show subsequent improvement of their hearing tests, others do not.[8, 54]

In 1960, Lindsay et al published their histopathologic findings on the inner ear of a child who, 4 years previously, had suffered sudden onset of bilateral deafness following parotitis. They described atrophy of the stria vascularis, the tectorial membrane, and the organ of Corti. These changes were focal and were most pronounced in the lower middle and basal coils. Since pathologic changes were found only in structures within the endolymphatic system of the cochlea, they termed the condition "endolymphatic labyrinthitis."[8]

Strauss and Davis have theorized that this condition arises from passage of the mumps virus into the endolymph either by means of hematogenous spread or by direct extension into the inner ear from a mumps-infected CNS.[55] Although there is a hamster model of mumps viral spread to the cochlea following intracerebral inoculation, one study of humans revealed no correlation between mumps meningitis and deafness.[53] Because mumps virus has never been found in the human inner ear (either histologically or by means of viral isolation), the pathogenesis of this condition in humans remains unclear.

Mumps-Associated Thyroiditis

Subacute throiditis has been reported as a complication following mumps infection in some studies.[20, 32] Evidence for an association of thyroiditis and mumps virus infection was first reported by Eylan and Zmucky in 1957.[56] They reported their findings in 15 cases of subacute thyroiditis that occurred during an epidemic of parotitis in Israel. Using the complement fixation serology for antibody against the V antigen of mumps (ie, the viral surface antigens), they found antimumps antibody titers of 1:80 or greater in a majority of their patients with subacute thyroiditis. They documented a fourfold change in antimumps antibody titer in five patients. Thyroid biopsies were done in two of these five patients, and in both cases a paramyxoviruslike isolate was obtained from cultures of the tissue in both infant hamsters and embryonated eggs.[56] One may, therefore, infer that mumps virus can replicate in thyroid tissue. However, whether mumps virus infection of the thyroid causes subacute thyroiditis or merely brings previously undiagnosed cases to medical attention remains unclear. Since that time, only occasional case reports of thyroiditis associated with mumps infection have appeared in the literature.[32, 57]

In 1964, Leboeuf and Bongiovanni[58] reported a 12% incidence of antithyroid antibodies in children with serologically documented acute or recent mumps virus infection. However, their reported percentages of antithyroid antibodies in recent parainfluenza virus-infected, adenovirus-infected, and control populations were 40%, 20%, and 6%, respectively.[58] The case for mumps virus causing subacute thyroiditis either by direct infection of the thyroid or by stimulation of antithyroid antibody production, therefore, is not strong.

Mumps-Associated Arthritis

Migratory polyarthritis is a rare complication of mumps virus infection; it occurs in approximately 0.4% of mumps cases.[18, 59, 60] The onset of arthritis follows parotitis, when present, by a reported mean of ten to 14 days.[18, 60] Arthritic complaints persist an average of 12 days; however, patients have been reported to remain symptomatic for as long as 6 months.[18, 60, 61] The large joints (ie, knees, ankles, and shoulders) are most frequently affected; however, involvement of the wrists, hands, temporomandibular joints, and cricoarytenoid joint have also been reported.[18, 60] Complaints of arthritis following mumps virus infection are most frequently encountered during the third decade of life. The youngest reported patient in one series of 19 subjects was 5 years of age.[60, 62] The complication of mumps virus infection has a male predominance with a reported male-to-female ratio of approximately 5:1.[60, 62] Other organ systems, such as testes and pancreas, are often symptomatically involved in these patients. Rheumatoid factor has been reported to be present transiently in acute mumps-associated arthritis.[60] In two cases in which synovial fluid was aspirated from acutely affected joints, the fluid was found to be clear and yellow.[60]

Mumps-associated migratory polyarthritis is a self-limited phenomenon that resolves without residual joint damage or recurrence.[59, 60] Symptoms do not appear to respond to aspirin treatment. However, ACTH has been reported to diminish the symptoms but not the duration of the complaints. One case of mumps-associated cricoarytenoid arthritis was reported to resolve with steroid therapy.[60] In our review article, a 2-week course of prednisone or nonsteroidal (but not salicylate) anti-inflammatory agent therapy (with an additional 2-week course if symptoms subsequently recur) is suggested.[61] Whether mumps-associated arthritis is a direct result of viral replication in the synovium or is an immunologic or autoimmune phenomenon remains to be determined.[59, 60]

Renal Complications of Mumps Infection

Viruria is a common finding in mumps infection; the virus has been isolated from urine as early as 6 days before the onset of parotitis.[2] Mumps virus is isolable from the urine of 72% of patients during the first five days of mumps parotitis, and from between 75% and 100% of adult patients during the first 14 days after the onset of parotitis.[63, 64] Transient subclinical renal dysfunction has been reported in 100% of 20 adults following the onset of their mumps parotitis. These findings included proteinuria in 20%, microscopic hematuria in 40%, and a mild transient decrease in glomerular filtration rate associated with viruria in 85%.[64]

Cases of symptomatic nephritis following mumps are unusual. In most cases, the relationship of the nephritis to mumps is based solely upon a temporal association; parotitis is followed a short time thereafter by symptomatic presentation of the nephritis.[65–67] Although deaths due to frank renal failure have been occasionally reported in this syndrome, it is unclear whether these individuals had underlying renal disease of another etiology prior to their mumps virus infection.[65]

Case reports associating mumps infection with other disorders of the kidney have appeared in the literature. Paroxysmal cold hemoglobinuria and acute tubular necrosis following parotitis with serologic evidence of mumps virus infection have each been reported.[68, 69]

Oophoritis in Mumps Infection

Clinical series from the United States, United Kingdom, and Germany indicate that the incidence of oophoritis in women with acute mumps ranges from 0.5% to 7.0%.[19, 20, 32, 70] The diagnosis of this condition is almost always based on the presence of pelvic pain in a female patient with clinically apparent mumps. However, evidence that the mumps virus actually replicates in ovarian tissue has yet to be more firmly established.[44] Although Prinz and Taubert have suggested that mumps infection during late childhood or early adolescence could play a role in female infertility, there are no controlled data in mumps oophoritis cases to support this contention.[70]

Mumps Myocarditis

Mumps myocarditis is a rarely reported complication of mumps infection.[18, 20, 37, 71] ECG changes, either with or without associated congestive heart failure, usually occur five to ten days after the onset of symptoms of mumps infection.[71] Fatalities have been reported.[37, 71] In one case report, mumps virus was isolated from the patient's myocardium at the time of autopsy, and mumps antigen was subsequently demonstrated in the myocardial tissues by means of indirect immunofluorescence.[37] The pathologic finding seen in this condition is probably a direct effect of viral replication within the myocardium.

Miscellaneous Rare Complications of Mumps Infection

Mastitis is an occasionally encountered complication of mumps infection. Its occurrence is not surprising since mumps virus proliferates in glandular tissue and since mumps virus can be isolated from the milk of infected humans.[72] Mastitis usually occurs after mumps parotitis has resolved. Although it is somewhat uncomfortable, breast involvement following mumps infection is self-limited and appears to cause no permanent residua.[18, 32] It is possible that mumps virus could be transmitted by breast feeding since infants born to susceptible mothers would be seronegative.

Transient abnormalities in liver function tests are sometimes seen during acute mumps infection.[18] However, clinically apparent hepatitis is rarely reported in epidemiologic surveys of mumps infection.[20]

A high frequency of gastritis symptoms was reported in one series of mumps cases, but not in other series.[32] Whether in fact these symptoms actually resulted from pancreatitis or oophoritis or whether actual gastritis is associated with some mumps outbreaks remains unclear.

A wide range of CNS problems are occasionally attributed to mumps infection. Johnson has cited three cases of hydrocephalus occurring after resolution of clinically apparent mumps infection in children. This observation is especially interesting because non-laboratory-adapted human isolates of mumps virus, when inoculated intrathecally into newborn hamsters, can cause hydrocephalus secondary to aqueductal stenosis.[40, 73] Serologically diagnosed mumps infection has occasionally been reported as the antecedent viral infection preceding the onset of Reye syndrome.[74]

Segmental involvement of the spinal cord has been noted as a rare complication following mumps infection.[18] In one series, four of ten patients with Bell's palsy showed serologic (complement fixation test using assays with both soluble and viral antigens on one serum specimen per patient) evidence compatible with recent mumps virus infection; however, none of these patients had manifested parotitis, and no control population was studied.[54] Other instances of cranial nerve paralysis have been reported.[18]

Mumps Virus Infection in Pregnancy

As previously stated, about 20% of adults have no serologic evidence of previous mumps infection; many of these individuals therefore are presumed to be susceptible to mumps.[25] In fact, approximately one third of clinically apparent cases of mumps occur during the childbearing years of adolescence and adulthood.[112] The attack rate for primary mumps infection during pregnancy has been reported to be between 0.3 and 10 cases per 10,000 pregnancies in the United States during the mid-1960s.[1, 26, 27] However, the attack rate in pregnancy depends on the prevalence of mumps in the general population. As a result, the questions of whether intrauterine mumps infection can occur, and if so, whether intrauterine mumps virus infection of the fetus causes congenital abnormalities, have been of great concern.

Evidence in experimentally infected animals suggests that mumps virus can cross the placenta and infect the fetus. Ferm and Kilham administered mumps virus intravenously (IV) to pregnant hamsters and showed that the virus grew well in the uterus and placenta. However, in this experimental host, penetration of the placenta by mumps virus with subsequent infection of the fetus was a rare phenomenon. There was no evidence of fetal wastage or reabsorption or congenital malformations, and mumps virus was recovered from the fetal material of only one animal.[75]

St Geme et al produced experimental mumps infection during pregnancy in *Macaca mulata* monkeys.[76] Five monkeys were given mumps virus IV during their first trimester, and the placental and fetal tissues were harvested 1 week later. Mumps virus was recovered from the fetal tissue of two monkeys and from the placental tissue of three. When the interval between administration of virus and harvest of fetal tissue was extended to 2 weeks, mumps virus was recoverable from neither the fetuses nor the placenta.[76] Yamauchi et al have also shown that the attenuated Jeryl Lynn mumps virus, when administered to pregnant women, can disseminate and cause placental, but not fetal, infection.[77] These findings suggest that mumps viremia during early gestation in humans could cause a short-lived mumps infection of both the placenta and fetus.

Unfortunately, it would be difficult to document intrauterine mumps virus infection in the postpartum infant. When mumps virus was administered to *M mulata* monkeys during their first trimester, the resulting infants reacted to mumps skin test antigen; however, the neutralizing antibody to mumps virus in these infant monkeys appeared to be completely maternal.[76] Similarly, of 12 young children who had been exposed in utero to mumps virus during the St George's Island, Alaska, epidemic, 83% had a positive reaction to mumps skin test antigen. None of these patients had demonstrable neutralizing antibody to mumps virus.[78] Since an individual's response to mumps skin test antigen is not a reliable indicator of exposure to mumps virus, and since the fetus does not appear to respond serologically to intrauterine mumps virus exposure, there is no way of reliably determining whether an infant has undergone a gestational mumps virus infection.[14, 15, 79, 80]

In a prospective study of fetal mortality during symptomatic maternal viral infection, Siegel et al showed a statistically significant increase in fetal deaths when mumps infection occurred during the first trimester.[81] The incidence of spontaneous abortion occuring in association with first trimester mumps infection may be as high as 27%.[112] Over 60% of these mumps-related fetal deaths occurred within 2 weeks after the clinical onset of mumps in the mother. Fetal mortality was not increased when maternal mumps occurred during the second or third trimester or during the postnatal period.[81] This mumps-related increase in first-trimester fetal mortality could be related to the chromosomal fragmentation that mumps virus is known to cause in vitro.[82] Prospective studies comparing the offspring of mothers who had clinically apparent mumps during gestation to the offspring of mothers with no apparent infection during pregnancy have failed to show any difference in the incidence of infants with low birth weight, mental retardation, or congenital anomalies between these two groups.[83–85]

Although mumps infection during gestation does not appear to cause congenital anomalies with sufficient regularity to be detected in prospective studies, occasional reports have appeared purporting to link maternal mumps infection with certain birth defects, including corneal opacities, chorioretinitis, and primary endocardial fibroelastosis (EFE).[86, 87] Evidence for a cause-and-effect relationship between maternal mumps infection and these congenital anomalies is scant. Robertson et al inoculated the laboratory-adapted Enders strain of mumps virus over the blastoderm of chicken embryos that had not yet reached Hamburger-Hamilton lens stage 18.[88] The resulting chicks had a 43% to 87% incidence of lenticular cataracts. No other anomalies were noted. The authors noted that the lens was the only organ consistently exhibiting abnormal development following inoculation of the mumps virus.[87] It should be noted that the ocular anomalies attributed to gestational mumps infection in humans (ie, corneal opacities and chorioretinitis) are different from the lenticular anomalies found in the experimental host described above. Moreover, ocular anomalies such as corneal opacities, chorioretinitis, and cataracts are relatively common congenital defects with myriad causes, and there are very few reported cases of these types of eye pathologic changes in infants whose mothers had mumps virus infections during pregnancy. Therefore, it is likely that gestational mumps virus infection is not responsible for ocular anomalies in humans.

The case for congenital mumps infection causing EFE is based on reports that a positive response to mumps skin test antigen is seen in children with clinical, but not tissue, evidence of EFE.[89–91] There are two major problems with this evidence. As described above, the mumps skin test is an unreliable predictor of either immunity or exposure to mumps virus. False-positives and false-negatives have been reported.[80, 92] The mumps skin test antigen has been judged so unreliable in predicting immunity to mumps virus that its use is no longer indicated for this purpose.[15] In addition, one cannot reliably diagnose EFE on the basis of clinical findings; tissue evaluation is the only way to definitely diagnose EFE.[71]

The problems associated with use of clinical criteria to diagnose EFE and mumps skin test antigen to implicate intrauterine mumps virus infection as a cause of EFE are illustrated by the findings of Gersony et al.[79] Four children with an antemortem clinical diagnosis of EFE died and were subsequently autopsied. Two of these patients did not have tissue findings diagnostic of EFE; both had had positive mumps skin tests ante mortem. The other two patients did have EFE diagnosed at autopsy; neither of these children had had a positive reaction to mumps skin test antigen.

Several studies have shown a high frequency of reactivity to mumps skin test antigen in babies with clinically diagnosed EFE.[89–91] Vosburgh et al confirmed the association of mumps skin test reactivity with clinically diagnosed EFE and showed that this high frequency of skin test reactivity did not occur in children with other forms of congenital heart disease and normal age-matched children who had not previously had mumps.[90] However, other studies from the United States and the United Kingdom found few or no children with clinically diagnosed EFE that exhibited a positive skin test response to mumps antigen.[79, 93] Because of reliance on clincial criteria to diagnose EFE, it is entirely possible that many of the children reported to have EFE in all of the above-mentioned series did not have this congenital heart lesion. Furthermore, clinical evidence for gestational mumps exposure in infants with EFE is lacking. Only one mother of an infant with EFE has been reported to have had clinically apparent mumps infection during pregnancy.[89]

Mumps Infection in the Immunocompromised Host

Data on mumps infection are available for patients with hematologic malignancies. In a series of 21 children with either acute leukemia or lymphosarcoma who acquired symptomatic mumps infection, clinically apparent aseptic meningitis was found in two. Both of these patients had rapid and uneventful recoveries. None of the 21 patients was seriously ill, and no residua were noted.[92] Although mumps has not been reported to cause severe or unusual disease in patients with leukemia or lymphoma, the duration of symptoms and viral shedding may be prolonged.[94] Isolation of immunocompromised patients from exposure to individuals with active mumps virus infection is advised.[92, 94]

HOST IMMUNE RESPONSE TO MUMPS INFECTION

Humoral Immunity

In contrast to many viral diseases, mumps may be diagnosed serologically during the acute phase of the illness. Because of the long incubation period of mumps, evidence of an immune response to the virus is often present at the time that the patient becomes ill. Complement-fixing antibodies directed to the S antigen (ie, soluble nucleoprotein) are present and detectable during the acute phase of the disease. Levels of complement-fixing antibody to the S antigen of mumps remain high during the convalescent phase of the disease, begin to fall during late convalescence, and are undetectable within a few months after the acute mumps infection has resolved. In contrast, complement-fixing antibodies to the V antigen (ie, the surface glycoprotein antigens of whole mumps virion) are often undetectable during the acute phase of mumps infection, rise and peak during the convalescent period, and begin to fall slowly thereafter. Anti-V complement-fixing antibodies usually persist for years following the acute illness.[11]

Neutralizing antibody is detectable as early as two days after the onset of parotitis in some individuals. Levels of neutralizing antibody to mumps virus peak 2 to 4 weeks after the onset of parotitis.[33] This neutralizing antibody response to natural mumps virus infection is more rapid than that observed following immunization with the live attenuated mumps vaccine. In mumps-seronegative individuals who receive live mumps vaccine, neutralizing antibodies become detectable from 5 to 7 weeks following vaccination.[77]

Immunity to clinically apparent mumps infection correlates best with a neutralizing antibody titer of 1:8 or greater. Most individuals have clinically apparent mumps infection only once during their lives and maintain low, but protective, levels of neutralizing antibody thereafter.[14, 18, 95, 96] The natural tendency of neutralizing antibody to decline gradually to nonprotective levels over time may be offset by booster effects from repeated exposures to and subclinical infections by mumps virus during the individual's lifetime.[95] Therefore, if mumps virus were eradicated from a geographic region by means of widespread vaccination, it is possible that the immunity of the residents would gradually wane, and they would eventually be capable of developing clinically apparent mumps infection if the virus were reintroduced into the environment.[97]

Virus-specific IgM is initially made in response to a primary mumps infection. This IgM response is short-lived. A brief interferon response—detectable in both serum and saliva during the first three days of illness—also occurs.[18] During convalescence, antimumps IgG is synthesized, and virus-specific IgG persists thereafter. The booster response elicited during subsequent subclinical mumps reinfections is almost always IgG alone. When the level of past immunity is extremely low, however, a primary IgM booster response followed by a lasting IgG booster response may occur.[95]

Cell-Mediated Immunity

During acute infection with mumps virus, lymphocytopenia has occasionally been noted. A transient decrease in the level of skin hypersensitivity to tuberculin antigen can also occur during acute mumps. The lymphoproliferative response to mumps antigen peaks at ten to 15 days following the onset of clinically apparent mumps virus infection in humans. This lymphoproliferative response is detectable for many years after mumps virus infection and is more long-lived than that seen with certain other viruses. During infection with polio, rubella, herpes simplex virus, or vaccinia, the respective, virus-specific lymphoproliferative response peaks ten to 15 days following onset of symptoms, then rapidly declines to low levels, and becomes undetectable several weeks thereafter. Lymphoid cells harvested from individuals with serologic and lymphoproliferative evidence of immunity to mumps virus also react in vitro with cytotoxicity to mumps virus-infected target cells.[98]

As noted above, immunologic protection from clinically ap-

parent mumps disease correlates with neutralizing antibody titers of 1:8 or greater in individuals who have either had a natural mumps infection or have received live attenuated mumps vaccine.[95, 96] However, administration of human immune serum globulin or hyperimmune human antimumps serum globulin to susceptible individuals following mumps exposure does not protect these persons from symptomatic mumps virus infection.[5, 10, 14, 32, 97, 99] It is therefore likely that the neutralizing antibody response to mumps virus reflects the level of cell-mediated immunity in the individual and that the cell-mediated immune response to the virus is crucial to lasting protection against repeated, clinically apparent mumps virus infection.

LABORATORY DIAGNOSIS OF MUMPS INFECTION

Isolation of the Mumps Virus from Clinical Specimens

Isolation of mumps virus from clinical specimens may be helpful in distinguishing mumps virus infection from more severe or treatable viral or bacterial infections. Viral isolation is helpful in patients who have mumps but no parotitis. Mumps virus can be isolated from urine during the period from six days before to 15 days after the onset of parotitis.[2, 63, 64] The virus can also be isolated from the patient's saliva from seven days before until nine days after the onset of salivary gland enlargement.[18] Because of this prolonged period of viral shedding, there is a reasonable chance of successfully isolating mumps virus from saliva and urine obtained during the acute or early convalescent phases of mumps infection. The virus can also be isolated from the spinal fluid of patients with meningoencephalitis.[29]

Mumps virus is readily isolated in various tissue culture cell lines. The most commonly used are Vero, human embryonic kidney, and chick embryo fibroblast cells; grivet renal cells, HEp-2 cells, and HeLa cells have also been used.[1, 14, 16, 33, 77] Monolayers infected with mumps virus invariably hemadsorb; sometimes, giant cell formation characteristic of paramyxoviruses occurs, but this is not a regular feature and cannot be relied upon for identification.[16, 18, 33] The giant cells caused by mumps virus infection of monolayers characteristically have some pyknotic nuclei that are surrounded by a clear or whitish-appearing halo (see Fig 12–3).[16] In the absence of cytopathic effect, cells infected with mumps virus can be detected by indirect immunofluorescence. Mumps virus can also be grown in the allantoic cavity of embryonated hen's eggs. This method of propagation is still occasionally used to prepare large quantities of mumps virus for research purposes.

Complement-Fixation Serology

The early complement-fixation tests utilized an extract from infected monkey parotid glands as the viral antigen.[10] This serologic assay was later refined and characterized by Henle et al, who described two different complement-fixation tests for antibody to mumps virus, one using the soluble or S antigen (ie, viral nucleoprotein), and the other using the viral or V antigen (ie, whole mumps virus, hence the glycoproteins of the virus as antigen).[11] Serum specimens obtained during acute mumps disease had high titers of antibody directed to the S antigen but absent or low titers to the V antigen. Sera obtained during early convalescence showed high titers of antibody directed to both the S and V antigens, and specimens obtained from individuals with a past history of mumps virus infection showed low or absent antibody to the S antigen and persistence of antibody to the V antigen.[11]

The complement-fixation assays for antibody to mumps virus are not reliable for determining whether an individual is immune to clinically apparent mumps virus infection and, therefore, should not be used to screen individuals for immunity.[12] In addition, V and especially S antigen cross-react with parainfluenza viral and other antigens.[5, 15] Since parainfluenza viruses can also cause parotitis, use of the mumps complement-fixation test in parainfluenza disease may lead to a false diagnosis of mumps virus infection.[3] The complement-fixation tests for antimumps antibody can be used to diagnose mumps-related illness allowing for these limitations. Titers of acute and convalescent sera should be compared, since an increase in titer of antibody to the V antigen of mumps virus is probably somewhat more specific than relying on an acute positivity in the assay utilizing the S antigen. Unfortunately, much of the older serologic evidence linking antecedent mumps virus infection to some of its rarer complications (such as deafness, thyroiditis, and Bell's palsy) is based on S and V antigen complement-fixation serologic studies using a single serum specimen.

Hemagglutination-Inhibition Test

This serologic assay is based on the ability of antimumps antibody to bind to the glycoproteins of the mumps virus, thereby blocking the ability of the glycoprotein with hemagglutinin activity to bind to and agglutinate red blood cells. As in the case of the complement-fixation assays, antibodies directed to other paramyxoviruses are capable of causing false-positive serologic tests.[5, 12, 96] This assay cannot be relied on for determining whether an individual is susceptible to mumps virus disease.[96] A rise in mumps hemagglutination-inhibition titer between acute and convalescent specimens can be used to diagnose mumps infection, but anamnestic responses may occur during parainfluenza virus infections.[5, 12]

Viral Neutralization Test

This assay is based on the ability of antimumps antibody to bind to and inhibit the function of antigenic sites on the mumps virus that are responsible for the ability of the virus to adsorb to and penetrate the cell membrane of a susceptible host cell. If neutralizing antibody directed to mumps virus is present in a patient's serum, mumps virus incubated in that serum will be incapable of infecting susceptible tissue culture cells. This assay is very specific for antibody directed to mumps virus, and therefore a rise in antimumps neutralizing titer between acute and convalescent specimens is diagnostic for mumps virus infection. In addition, the neutralizing antibody test for antimumps antibody is highly reliable for determining immunity to mumps virus. Titers of 1:8 or greater indicate complete resistance to development of symptomatic mumps infection. This is a somewhat complex assay that requires a tissue culture laboratory and takes approximately 1 week to generate results. As a result, it is somewhat inconvenient to perform and is not widely available.[5, 12, 15, 95, 96]

Other Assays for Antimumps Antibody

In recent years, an enzyme-linked immunosorbent assay (ELISA) for IgG antibody to mumps virus has been developed, as well as radioimmunoassay (RIA) and immunofluorescence (IF) assays. A radial hemolysis test for antibody to mumps virus has also been developed and tested. These assays are highly specific and reliable for diagnosing both mumps infection (by rise or fall in titer between paired acute and convalescent serum specimens) and for determining whether a patient is immune to symptomatic infection by mumps virus.[15] Mumps-specific IgM in serum can be detected by ELISA or indirect IF in 80% to 85% of symptomatic patients during the first week of illness. These assays can be run in a short time and do not require a tissue culture laboratory. Single radial immunodiffusion, hemolysis inhibition, and mixed hemadsorption assays for antibody to mumps virus have also been developed.

Mumps Skin Test

In 1946, Enders published a report that included a description of a mumps skin test for delayed-type hypersensitivity (DTH) cell-mediated immunity to mumps virus.[10] The skin test reagent consisted of formalinized mumps virus that had been grown in the allantoic cavity of embryonated chicken eggs. Enders showed that those individuals who had the largest diameter of erythematous reaction to the skin test 24 hours after intradermal injection had the lowest attack rate of clinically apparent mumps following exposure. However, some subjects who had very large reactions to the skin test (>15 mm in diameter) still acquired symptomatic mumps infection on subsequent exposure.[10] Similar observations were made 20 years later by Meyer et al.[96] Initially, it was thought that individuals who reacted well to the mumps skin test but acquired symptomatic mumps infection following exposure to the virus were actually reacting to either avian antigens from the allantoic fluid or to adventitious avian viruses in the skin test preparation. As a result, a control skin test consisting of formalin-treated allantoic fluid that did not contain mumps virus was also applied at the time of mumps skin testing. Use of this control antigen, however, did not substantially help to reduce the incidence of false-positive reactions to the mumps skin test.[80, 101] The lack of complete correlation between diameter of mumps skin test reaction and susceptibility to symptomatic mumps virus infection was also ascribed to variable potency of different lots of the mumps skin test antigen and to cross-reaction of the mumps skin test in patients with cell-mediated immunity to the parainfluenza viruses.[26]

The correlation between neutralizing antibody and skin test reactivity is better in adolescents and adults than in children.[80, 97] Only 60% of children with a positive mumps skin test have neutralizing antibody to mumps virus.[80] These frequent false-positive reactions may reflect cross-reactivity of skin test antigens with parainfluenza virus antigens. Some children may have neutralizing antibody to mumps virus but lack skin test reactivity.

The validity of erythema induced by injected mumps antigens as a measure of DTH to mumps antigens is unknown because findings of DTH, such as induration and perivascular lymphocytic infiltration, have not been determined. The mumps skin test is unreliable for detecting immunity to mumps; it is, therefore, not an approved test for determining whether a patient is immune to mumps virus.[15]

Method of Rapid Viral Diagnosis

Lindeman et al have described an IF assay that is capable of detecting mumps antigen in cells obtained from the spinal fluids of patients with mumps meningoencephalitis.[102] Use of this test can rapidly distinguish patients with mumps meningoencephalitis from patients with meningitis or encephalitis caused by other bacterial, fungal, and viral agents.[102]

ELISA and RIA methods are coming into more widespread use in rapid viral diagnosis. Using these assays, it may be possible to detect mumps virus antigens in the urine and saliva of individuals who are shedding the virus.

PREVENTION AND TREATMENT OF MUMPS VIRUS INFECTION

Mumps Virus Vaccine

In 1946, Enders attempted immunoprophylaxis of mumps virus infection using a formaldehyde-inactivated suspension of mumps virus from infected salivary glands of monkeys. Monkeys immunized with this material were protected against developing parotitis as a result of live mumps virus challenge. Seronegative institutionalized children immunized with this formalinized virus suspension and subsequently challenged orally or by instillation into Stensen's duct with live mumps virus were also protected.[10]

A formalin-inactivated vaccine prepared from chick embryo-grown mumps virus was subsequently produced and made commercially available. Inactivated mumps vaccine was licensed in the United States from 1950 through 1978.[112] It provided protection against symptomatic mumps virus infection in approximately 80% of susceptible individuals. The immunity it imparted could be boosted by repeated injections. However, the protection imparted by a dose of this vaccine lasted no longer than 1 year.[96] Use of formalin-inactivated mumps virus vaccine would have required that the individual be reimmunized every 6 to 12 months. As a result of both its short duration and relatively low level (ie, 80%) of protection, inactivated mumps vaccine was unsuitable for clinical use. It is no longer produced or marketed.[14, 15, 92, 112]

In his 1946 paper, Enders noted that the mumps virus was attenuated by passage through eggs and speculated that this method could be used to produce a live attenuated mumps vaccine.[10] However, tissue culture passage of mumps virus was required to achieve attenuation satisfactory for use in a live vaccine. The Jeryl Lynn strain of mumps virus (named after the child from whom this mumps strain was isolated) was first partially attenuated in embryonated hen eggs, then further attenuated and prepared for vaccine by passage in chick embryo fibroblast cell culture.[13]

The Jeryl Lynn live attenuated mumps vaccine has very few markers of attenuation. It is as neurovirulent in corticosteroid-treated *Macaca* rhesus monkeys as wild-type mumps virus. The attenuated mumps virus vaccine is, however, distinguishable in tissue culture; the Jeryl Lynn vaccine strain is capable of inducing higher levels of interferon production than wild-type mumps virus does in vitro.[103]

In field trials of the Jeryl Lynn attenuated mumps vaccine, the rate of neutralizing antibody seroconversion was between 96.9% and 100% in susceptible children and 92.6% in susceptible adults.[13, 104] This vaccine protected susceptible individuals from illness upon subsequent challenge with or exposure to wild-type mumps virus approximately 95% of the time.[13, 105] There was no increased incidence of fever or other clinical findings during the postimmunization period in those subjects receiving the Jeryl Lynn attenuated mumps vaccine when compared to subjects who received placebo.[3, 104, 105]

In one series, the seroconversion rate following administration of the Jeryl Lynn vaccine was studied in babies under 1 year of age and was found to be lower than that observed in older individuals. It was postulated that low levels of maternal antibody might prevent the establishment of infection by vaccine virus in young children, thereby preventing seroconversion in this population.[13] Based on this finding and on the observation that children under 9 to 12 months of age rarely contract clinically apparent mumps virus infection, the American Academy of Pediatrics has recommended that attenuated mumps virus vaccine be given to children 12 months of age or older.[13] However, the trivalent measles, mumps, rubella vaccine should not ordinarily be given to children under 15 months of age. In this way, the immunizing efficacy of the attenuated measles component of the vaccine is optimized.[5, 14, 15]

Children who were given 0.01 to 0.02 mL per pound of human immune serum globulin (ISG) at the time that they received the attenuated mumps vaccine responded serologically to the vaccine as did children who had received only vaccine.[13] The quantities of ISG usually administered to patients are substantially larger than the amount used in this study. There is a possibility that mumps-specific antibody contained in standard doses of ISG could interfere with the immune response to attenuated mumps vaccine. As a result, it has been recommended that mumps vaccine not be given to any patient during the period from 2 weeks before until 3 months after that individual has received a dose of ISG.[5, 14, 15, 112]

When the Jeryl Lynn attenuated mumps vaccine was mixed with live attenuated measles vaccine and the combination inoculated into volunteers, the serologic response to each virus was found to be the same as when the two attenuated viruses were administered individually at different times.[13] Similarly encouraging results were obtained with a mixture of the mumps and rubella attenuated vaccine strains and with a mixture of the measles, mumps, and rubella attenuated vaccine strains.[33, 106, 107]

Because mumps is generally considered to be a "relatively benign disease," the attenuated mumps vaccine has not seen widespread, international use. In many developed Western nations only selected, high-risk populations are immunized.[20]

Live attenuated mumps vaccine may be administered to any immunocompetent child over 12 months of age. Any individual immunized prior to 1 year of age should be reimmunized.[112] To prevent orchitis and oophoritis in children approaching puberty, and in adolescents and adults, the mumps vaccine should be administered to individuals in these age categories if they have no history of previous mumps virus disease or immunization to mumps. This is advisable even though most unimmunized people born before 1957 probably were naturally infected.[112] Live attenuated mumps vaccine should not be given to pregnant or most immunocompromised individuals.[14, 15]

The Jeryl Lynn strain of attenuated mumps virus vaccine was licensed for distribution in December 1967. As of 1988, more than 84 million doses had been administered in the United States.[15, 112] By 1976, approximately 50% of the children from 1 to 10 years of age had received this mumps vaccine, and the annual recorded incidence of mumps virus infection had dropped to about one third of its pre-1967 level.[6] With this drop in the incidence of mumps virus infection came a proportional drop in the number of mumps-related deaths, although the case-fatality ratio stayed constant.[108] The widespread use of mumps virus vaccine and its subsequent success in reducing the incidence of mumps in the United States until 1986 (see ''Epidemiology'' section) probably resulted from the administration of the Jeryl Lynn attenuated mumps virus in a single immunization that also contains the attenuated measles and rubella vaccine viruses (MMR). As a component of MMR, mumps vaccine administration is both convenient and economical. In fact, for reasons of cost and convenience to the patient, use of trivalent rather than the individual vaccines is recommended for primary immunization against measles, mumps, and rubella.[5]

Neutralizing antibody to mumps virus becomes detectable 5 to 7 weeks after administration of the vaccine to a seronegative patient.[77] Although the neutralizing antibody titers obtained with the vaccine are somewhat lower than those seen following natural mumps virus infection, the protection imparted by the vaccine appears to be long-lasting. Some early recipients of the vaccine have now been followed for 20 years, and their resistance to clinically apparent mumps virus infection has persisted throughout that period.[15, 112] Therefore, no booster dose is required.

When neutralizing antibody titers of a vaccine recipient are followed serially, periodic boosts in antibody titer are seen. This phenomenon may be caused by subclinical infections with wild-type mumps virus encountered in the environment and may explain the long-lived resistance to symptomatic disease imparted by the attenuated mumps virus vaccine or primary mumps virus infection.[107] Removal of wild-type mumps virus from a population by widespread use of mumps virus vaccine could prevent these booster exposures and might lead to a gradual decline in the population's level of immunity. As a result, development of susceptibility in previously vaccinated individuals could occur.[97]

The Jeryl Lynn live attenuated mumps vaccine does not contain penicillin and, therefore, may be administered to individuals with penicillin allergies.[14, 15] However, since this vaccine does contain traces of neomycin, the vaccine is contraindicated in individuals with a history of anaphylactic reaction to topical or systemic neomycin.[14, 15, 104, 112] Neomycin contact dermatitis without anaphylaxis does not contraindicate the use of mumps vaccine.[112] Although the vaccine virus is grown in chick embryo fibroblasts, no allergic reactions ever have been reported in individuals with allergies to chicken or feathers; therefore use of the mump of MMR vaccine in this patient population is not contraindicated.[14, 15, 112] However, individuals with a history of anaphylactic reactions following ingestion of eggs should not receive mumps vaccine unless it is administered using a published protocol and with informal consent.[112]

''Live mumps vaccine given after exposure may not provide protection.''[14] The protective neutralizing antibody response to the live attenuated mumps vaccine is slow to develop.[77]

Meyer et al have shown that the formalin-inactivated mumps vaccine, administered to susceptible individuals within three days of exposure to an index case of mumps, neither protected the recipients from developing clinically apparent mumps virus infection nor altered the severity of the symptoms.[96] However, immunization of susceptible patients with live attenuated vaccine at the time of mumps exposure is not contraindicated. Should the individual not contract mumps infection as a result of that exposure, she or he will be protected against disease resulting from subsequent exposures to wild-type mumps virus.[14, 15]

Reactions associated with administration of live attenuated mumps virus vaccine are rare. They include fever, parotitis, allergic reactions such as rash pruritus, and purpura, and CNS effects (febrile seizures, unilateral nerve deafness, and encephalitis).[5, 14, 15, 109] Many of these reported reactions are not etiologically related to the mumps vaccine, but rather temporally related (ie, occurring within 30 days of administration of the vaccine). In fact, the CNS reactions observed in one study were more common in the control population than in the recipients of live attenuated mumps virus vaccine.[5, 14, 15] There is no evidence that administration of the mumps vaccine to previously immunized or infected individuals results in any untoward reactions; therefore, there is no contraindication to reimmunization (whether intentional or inadvertent).[112]

Administration of live attenuated mumps virus vaccine is contraindicated during pregnancy.[5, 14, 15, 40, 77] Yamauchi et al administered the Jeryl Lynn attenuated mumps vaccine to three pregnant women who were scheduled for saline induction abortions.[77] When, ten days thereafter, the abortions were performed, the virus was recovered from the placentas of two of the subjects. However, the virus was not recovered from the fetal tissues in any of these three cases.[77] The contraindication to mumps vaccine use in pregnancy is based on the consideration that intrauterine mumps infection might have a low-level potential for teratogenicity, and that the vaccine virus could conceivably pass from the placenta to the fetus. Vaccinated women should avoid pregnancy for 3 months after immunization.[112] However, should mumps vaccine be inadvertently administered to a pregnant woman, this should not be considered an indication for termination of pregnancy.[112]

Attenuated mumps virus vaccine, either alone or in MMR, can be given with either the diphtheria-tetanus-pertussis (DTP) or trivalent oral poliovirus (OPV) vaccine without decreasing the efficacy of any of the vaccines used. No studies have been done on administering mumps or MMR vaccine with both DTP and OPV together. However, this combination should be administered if all of these immunizing agents are needed and if there is uncertainty as to whether the patient will return for follow-up visits. Whether the efficacy of immunization with live attenuated mumps vaccine is inhibited by simultaneous administration of vaccines other than the above is unknown.[5]

Use of the live attenuated mumps virus vaccine is contraindicated in most immunosuppressed patients, because the virus could conceivably: (1) undergo prolonged infection and replication during which the virus could revert to unattenuated, wild-type, (2) establish persistent infection, and (3) disseminate and cause severe systemic disease. For this reason, the live attenuated mumps virus vaccine should not be given to individuals with most immunodeficiency disorders, patients with malignancies, or most patients receiving immunosuppressive therapy.[14, 15, 92, 94] The following exceptions apply. All asymptomatic HIV-infected children should receive MMR on schedule (i.e., at age 15 months).[112] If one elects to administer measles vaccine to symptomatic HIV-infected children, it should be administered as MMR.[112] Leukemics in remission who have not received chemotherapy for at least 3 months (and in whom additional chemotherapy is not anticipated for the foreseeable future) may receive mumps vaccine.[112] Individuals receiving short-term (less than 2 weeks) systemic, local, or topical corticosteroid treatment may receive mumps vaccine.[112]

Individuals with acute viral illnesses might produce enough interferon to prevent the replication of live attenuated mumps virus if mumps vaccine were administered during the acute illness. As a result, the immunogenicity of the vaccine (and hence its protective effect) could be adversely affected. For this reason, the live attenuated mumps virus vaccine should not be administered to individuals during severe, intercurrent febrile illnesses. However, since the frequency of mild upper respiratory illness in young children is extremely high, withholding immunization from this category of patient is impractical and could result in the patient's never being immunized. Therefore, mild upper respiratory illness is not a contraindication to the administration of the live attenuated mumps virus vaccine.[14, 15]

Passive Immunization of Susceptible Individuals Following Exposure to Mumps Virus

Administration of ISG to susceptible children shortly after their exposure to mumps virus does not lower the attack rate of mumps virus disease.[10] Hyperimmune antimumps globulin (MIG) did not alter either the attack rate or the rate of complications secondary to mumps virus infection.[30]

When ISG is administered to adults shortly after the onset of their parotitis, the incidence of mumps orchitis remains unaltered.[110] There are conflicting reports in the literature as to whether administration of MIG to adults shortly after the onset of parotitis prevents the subsequent development of orchitis.[110, 111] Since MIG is not efficacious in preventing symptomatic mumps infection following exposure to the virus, and since its use following the development of mumps parotitis probably does not alter the complication rate of the disease, MIG is no longer commercially available.[5] Administration of ISG does nothing to prevent either mumps infection or mumps-related complications. Therefore, administration of ISG is contraindicated for preventing either mumps infection or the complications thereof.[5, 14, 15]

SUMMARY: APPROACH TO PREVENTION AND TREATMENT OF MUMPS VIRUS

1. *Routine immunization.* For economy, administer combined measles, mumps, and rubella vaccine (MMR) to children at 15 months of age. Live attenuated mumps virus vaccine may be administered to children 12 months of age or older. Prepubescent children, adolescents, and adults who have no history of mumps virus infection and have not received mumps vaccine should also be immunized; immunization of susceptible adults whose occupations increase their risk of exposure to mumps virus (such as hospital personnel) is especially important. Do not administer any

live attenuated vaccine—including mumps vaccine—to pregnant women or to most people with immunodeficiencies or most patients on immunosuppressive therapy. Asymptomatic HIV-infected children should receive MMR at 15 months of age. See the "Mumps Virus Vaccine" section for other immunocompromised individuals who may qualify for mumps immunization. Mumps vaccine should not be given to patients who recently (ie, within 3 months) received immune serum globulin (ISG) or transfusions of blood or blood products.

2. *Immunoprophylaxis of susceptible individuals exposed to wild-type mumps virus.* Passive immunization does not protect from illness. ISG should not be used. Active immunization of susceptible individuals following exposure to mumps virus will probably not prevent them from contracting the disease. However, use of the vaccine is not contraindicated in this patient population, since it will ensure future immunity if natural infection does not occur as a result of this exposure.

3. *Prevention of nosocomial spread of mumps virus.* Patients and hospital personnel without a history of either mumps virus infection or mumps vaccination who are exposed to the index case up to seven days before the clinical presentation of the index case may already be infected and incubating mumps virus disease. Both the index case and susceptible patients exposed to the index case should be placed in respiratory isolation. Exposed susceptible individuals should also receive mumps vaccine. It may be advisable to exclude susceptible, exposed hospital personnel from contact with susceptible patients.

4. *Mumps virus infection during pregnancy.* Mumps occurring during the first trimester of pregnancy may cause an increased rate of spontaneous abortion. Intrauterine mumps infection most likely can occur. To date, there is little evidence that intrauterine mumps infection causes congenital defects.

5. *Treatment of symptomatic mumps virus infection.* Treat significant pain and fever symptomatically with analgesics and antipyretics. See specific complications discussed earlier.

REFERENCES

1. Young NA: Chickenpox, measles and mumps, in Remington JS, Klein JO (eds): *Infectious Diseases of the Fetus and Newborn Infant.* Philadelphia, Saunders, 1976, pp 521–586.
2. Batsakis JG, McWhirter JD: Nonneoplastic diseases of the salivary glands. *Am J Gastroenterol* 1972; 57:226–247.
3. Brill SJ, Gilfillan RF: Acute parotitis associated with influenza type A. *N Engl J Med* 1977; 296:1391–1392.
4. Dudgeon JA: The control of diphtheria, tetanus, poliomyelitis, measles, rubella and mumps. *Practitioner* 1975; 215:299–309.
5. Klein JO (ed): Mumps, in *Report of the Committee on Infectious Diseases,* ed 19. Evanston, Ill, American Academy of Pediatrics, 1982, pp 142–145.
6. Meyer HM Jr, Hopps HE, Parkman PD: Appraisal and reappraisal of viral vaccines. *Adv Intern Med* 1980; 25:533–560.
7. Steinberger E: The etiology and pathophysiology of testicular dysfunction in man. *Fertil Steril* 1978; 29:481–491.
8. Lindsay JR, Davey PR, Ward PH: Inner ear pathology in deafness due to mumps. *Ann Otol Rhinol Laryngol* 1960; 69:918–935.
9. Johnson CD, Goodpasture EW: An investigation of the etiology of mumps. *J Exp Med* 1934; 59:1–20.
10. Enders JF: Mumps: Techniques of laboratory diagnosis, tests for susceptibility, and experiments on specific prophylaxis. *J Pediatr* 1946; 29:129–142.

11. Henle G, Harris S, Henle W: Reactivity of various human sera with mumps complement fixation antigens. *J Exp Med* 1948; 88:133–147.
12. Habel K: Vaccination of human beings against mumps: Vaccine administration at start of epidemic. I. Incidence and severity of mumps in vaccinated and control groups. *Am J Hyg* 1951; 54:295–311.
13. Hilleman MR, Buynak EB, Weibel RE, et al: Live, attenuated mumps-virus vaccine. *N Engl J Med* 1968; 278:227–233.
14. Public Health Service Advisory Committee on Immunization Practices: Mumps vaccine. *MMWR.* 1977; 26:393–394.
15. The Immunization Practices Advisory Committee (ACIP). Mumps vaccine. *MMWR* 1980; 29:87–94.
16. Due-Nguyer H: Hemadsorption of mumps virus examined by light and electron microscopy. *J Virol* 1968; 2:494–506.
17. Howe C, Morgan C, Hsu KC: Recent virologic applications of ferritin conjugates. *Prog Med Virol* 1969; 11:307–353.
18. Lerner AM: Guide to immunization against mumps. *J Infect Dis* 1970; 122:116–121.
19. Research Unit of the Royal College of General Practitioners: The incidence and complications of mumps. *J R Coll Gen Pract* 1974; 24:545–551.
20. The Association for the Study of Infectious Disease: A retrospective survey of the complications of mumps. *J R Coll Gen Pract* 1974; 24:552–556.
21. Gregg MB (ed): Summary—Cases of specified notifiable diseases, United States. *MMWR* 1982; 30:640.
22. Bart KJ, Orenstein WA, Himnan AR: The virtual elimination of rubella and mumps from the United States and the use of combined measles, mumps and rubella vaccines (MMR) to eliminate measles. *Dev Biol Stand* 1986; 65:45–52.
23. The Child Day Care Infectious Disease Study Group: Public health considerations of infectious diseases in child day care centers. *J Pediatr* 1984; 105:683–701.
24. Cherry JD: The 'new' epidemiology of measles and rubella. *Hosp Pract* 1980; 15(7):49–57.
25. Barrett-Connor E: Infections and pregnancy: A review. *South Med J* 1969; 62:275–284.
26. St Geme JW Jr, Davis CWC, Noren GR: An overview of primary endocardial fibroelastosis and chronic viral cardiomyopathy. *Perspect Biol Med* 1974; 17:495–505.
27. Horstmann DM: Viral infections in pregnancy. *Yale J Biol Med* 1969; 42:99–112.
28. Utz JP: Viruria in man, an update. *Prog Med Virol* 1974; 17:77–90.
29. Azimi PH, Cramblett HG, Haynes RE: Mumps meningoencephalitis in children. *JAMA* 1969; 207:509–512.
30. Bang HO, Bang J: Involvement of the central nervous system in mumps. *Acta Med Scand* 1943; 113:487–505.
31. Finkelstein H: Meningoencephalitis in mumps. *JAMA* 1938; 111:17–19.
32. Reed D, Brown G, Merrick R, et al: A mumps epidemic on St George Island, Alaska. *JAMA* 1967; 199:113–117.
33. Brunell PA, Brickman A, O'Hare D, et al: Ineffectiveness of isolation of patients as a method of preventing the spread of mumps: Failure of the mumps skin-test antigen to predict immune status. *N Engl J Med* 1968; 279:1357–1361.
34. Hope-Simpson RE, Higgins PG: A respiratory virus study in Great Britian: Review and evaluation. *Prog Med Virol* 1969; 11:354–407.
35. Branson D: Timely topics in microbiology: Virology 1968–1969. *Am J Med Technol* 1970; 36:174–183.
36. Levy NL, Notkins AL: Viral infections and diseases of the endocrine system. *J Infect Dis* 1971; 124:94–103.
37. Brown NJ, Richmond SJ: Fatal mumps myocarditis—England. *MMWR* 1980; 29:425.
38. Wilfert CM: Mumps meningoencephalitis with low cerebrospinal-fluid glucose, prolonged pleocytosis and elevation of protein. *N Engl J Med* 1969; 280:855–859.
39. Johnstone JA, Ross CAC, Dunn M: Meningitis and encephalitis

40. Johnson RT: Effects of viral infection on the developing nervous system. *N Engl J Med* 1972; 287:599–604.
41. Coppage WS Jr, Cooner AE: Testosterone in human plasma. *N Engl J Med* 1965; 273:902–907.
42. Merrin C: Seminoma. *Urol Clin North Am* 1977; 4:379–392.
43. Craighead JE: The role of viruses in the pathogenesis of pancreatic disease and diabetes mellitus. *Prog Med Virol* 1975; 19:161–214.
44. Weller TH, Craig JM: The isolation of mumps virus at autopsy. *Am J Pathol* 1949; 25:1105–1115.
45. Notkins AL: Virus-induced diabetes mellitus: Brief review. *Arch Virol* 1977; 54:1–17.
46. Gundersen E: Is diabetes of infectious origin? *J Infect Dis* 1927; 41:197–202.
47. Sultz HA, Hart BA, Zielezny M, et al: Is mumps virus an etiologic factor in juvenile diabetes mellitus? *J Pediatr* 1975; 86:654–656.
48. Dacou-Voutetakis C, Constantinidis M, Moschos A, et al: Diabetes mellitus following mumps: Insulin reserve. *Am J Dis Child* 1974; 127:890–891.
49. Hinden E: Mumps followed by diabetes. *Lancet* 1962; 1:1381.
50. McCrae WM: Diabetes mellitus following mumps. *Lancet* 1963; 1:1300–1301.
51. Gamble DR, Kinsley ML, Fitzgerald MG, et al: Viral antibodies in diabetes mellitus. *Br Med J* 1969; 3:627–630.
52. Yoon JW: Viruses in the pathogenesis of type I diabetes. *Curr Probl Clin Biochem* 1983; 12:11–44.
53. Davis LE, Johnsson L-G: Viral infections of the inner ear: Clinical, virologic and pathologic studies in humans and animals. *Am J Otolaryngol* 1983; 4:347–362.
54. Saunders WH, Lippy WH: Sudden deafness and Bell's palsy: A common cause. *Ann Otol Rhinol Laryngol* 1960; 63:830–837.
55. Strauss M, Davis GL: Viral disease of the labyrinth: I. Review of the literature and discussion of the role of cytomegalovirus in congenital deafness. *Ann Otol* 1973; 82:577–583.
56. Eylan E, Zmucky R: Mumps virus and subacute thyroiditis. *Lancet* 1957; 1:1062–1063.
57. Felix-Davies D: Autoimmunization in subacute thyroiditis associated with evidence of infection by mumps virus. *Lancet* 1958; 1:880–883.
58. Leboeuf G, Bongiovanni AM: Thyroiditis in childhood. *Adv Pediatr* 1964; 13:183–212.
59. Gold HE, Boxerbaum B, Leslie HJ Jr: Mumps arthritis. *Am J Dis Child* 1968; 116:547–548.
60. Hyer FH, Gottlieb NL: Rheumatic disorders associated with viral infection. *Semin Arthritis Rheum* 1978; 8:17–31.
61. Gordon SC, Lauter CB: Mumps arthritis: A review of the literature. *Rev Infect Dis* 1984; 6:338–344.
62. Caranasos GJ, Felker JR: Mumps arthritis. *Arch Intern Med* 1967; 119:394–402.
63. Utz JP, Szwed CF, Kasel JA: Clinical and laboratory studies of mumps: II. Detection and duration of excretion of virus in urine. *Proc Soc Exp Biol Med* 1958; 99:259–261.
64. Utz JP, Houk VN, Alling DW: Clinical and laboratory studies of mumps: IV. Viruria and abnormal renal function. *N Engl J Med* 1964; 270:1283–1286.
65. Hughes WT, Steigman JA, Delong HF: Some implications of fatal nephritis associated with mumps. *Am J Dis Child* 1966; 111:297–301.
66. Reimann HA: Nephropathy and viruses. *Postgrad Med J* 1968; 44:853–860.
67. Eknoyan G, Dillman RO: Renal complications of infectious diseases. *Med Clin North Am* 1978; 52:979–1003.
68. Colley EW: Paroxysmal cold haemoglobinuria after mumps. *Br Med J* 1964; 1:1552–1553.
69. Dastur F: Mumps and acute tubular necrosis. *Practitioner* 1968; 201:796–797.
70. Prinz W, Taubert HD: Mumps in pubescent females and its effect

on later reproductive function. *Gynaecologia* 1968; 167:23–27.

71. Lansdown ABG: Viral infections and diseases of the heart. *Prog Med Virol* 1978; 24:70–113.
72. Kilham L, Margolis G: Problems of human concern arising from animal models of intrauterine and neonatal infections due to viruses: A review. *Prog Med Virol* 1975; 20:113–143.
73. Johnson RT, Johnson KP, Edmonds CJ: Virus-induced hydrocephalus: Development of aqueductal stenosis in hamsters after mumps infection. *Science* 1967; 157:1066–1067.
74. Roe CR, Schonberger LB, Gelbach SH, et al: Enzymatic alterations in Reye's syndrome: Prognostic implications. *Pediatrics* 1975; 55:119–126.
75. Ferm VH, Kilham L: Mumps virus infection of the pregnant hamster. *J Embryol Exp Morphol* 1963; 11:659–665.
76. St Geme JW Jr, Peralta H, Van Pelt LF: Intrauterine infection of the Rhesus monkey with mumps virus: Abbreviated viral replication in the immature fetus as an explanation for split immunologic recognition after birth. *J Infect Dis* 1972; 126:249–256.
77. Yamauchi T, Wilson C, St Geme JW Jr: Transmission of live, attenuated mumps virus to the human placenta. *N Engl J Med* 1974; 290:710–712.
78. Aase JM, Noren GR, Reddy DV, et al: Mumps-virus infection in pregnant women and the immunologic response of their offspring. *N Engl J Med* 1972; 286:1379–1382.
79. Gersony WM, Katz SL, Nadas AS: Endocardial fibroelastosis and the mumps virus. *Pediatrics* 1966; 37:430–434.
80. St Geme JW Jr, Yamauchi T, Eisenklam EJ, et al: Immunologic significance of the mumps virus skin test in infants, children and adults. *Am J Epidemiol* 1975; 101:253–263.
81. Siegel M, Fuerst HT, Peress NS: Comparative fetal mortality in maternal virus diseases: A prospective study on rubella, measles, mumps, chickenpox and hepatitis. *N Engl J Med* 1966; 274:768–771.
82. Stich HF, Yohn DS: Viruses and chromosomes. *Prog Med Virol* 1970; 12:78–127.
83. Blattner RJ, Williamson AP, Heys FM: Role of viruses in the etiology of congenital malformations. *Prog Med Virol* 1973; 15:1–41.
84. Siegel M: Congenital malformations following chickenpox, measles, mumps, and hepatitis: Results of a cohort study. *JAMA* 1973; 226:1521–1524.
85. Siegel M, Fuerst HT: Low birth weight and maternal virus diseases. *JAMA* 1966; 197:680–684.
86. Elizan TS, Fabiyi A: Congenital and neonatal anomalies linked with viral infections in experimental animals. *Am J Obstet Gynecol* 1970; 106:147–165.
87. Swan C, Tostevin AL, Moore B, et al: Congenital defects in infants following infectious diseases during pregnancy. *Med J Aust* 1943; 2:201–210.
88. Robertson GG, Williamson AP, Blattner RJ: Origin and development of lens cataracts in mumps-infected chick embryos. *Am J Anat* 1964; 115:473–486.
89. Noren GR, Adams P, Anderson RC: Positive skin reactivity to mumps virus antigen in endocardial fibroelastosis. *J Pediatr* 1963; 62:604–606.
90. Vosburgh JB, Diehl AM, Liu C, et al: Relationship of mumps to endocardial fibroelastosis. *Am J Dis Child* 1965; 109:69–73.
91. Shone JD, Armas SM, Manning JA, et al: The mumps antigen skin test in endocardial fibroelastosis. *Pediatrics* 1966; 37:423–429.
92. Feldman S, Cox F: Viral infections and haematological malignancies. *Clin Haematol* 1976; 5:311–328.
93. Dudgeon JA: Infective causes of human malformations. *Br Med Bull* 1976; 32:77–83.
94. Levine AS, Schimpff SC, Graw RG Jr, et al: Hematologic malignancies and other marrow failure states: Progress in the management of complicating infections. *Semin Hematol* 1974; 11:141–202.
95. Chang TW: Recurrent viral infection (reinfection). *N Engl J Med* 1971; 284:765–773.
96. Meyer MB, Stifler WC Jr, Joseph JM: Evaluation of mumps vaccine given after exposure to mumps, with special reference to exposed adult. *Pediatrics* 1966; 37:304–315.
97. St Geme JW Jr: Therapeutic control of viral infections: Chemotherapy, interferon and gamma gobulin, in Gluck L (ed): *Current Problems in Pediatrics.* Chicago, Year Book Medical Publishers, 1979.
98. Woodruff JF, Woodruff JJ: T lymphocyte interaction with viruses and virus-infected tissues. *Prog Med Virol* 1975; 19:120–160.
99. Stiehm ER: Standard and special human immune serum globulins as therapeutic agents. *Pediatrics* 1979; 63:301–319.
100. Grandien M, Olding-Stenkvist E: Rapid diagnosis of viral infections in the central nervous system. *Scan J Infect Dis* 1984; 16:1–8.
101. Vicens CN, Nobrega T, Joseph JM, et al: Evaluation of tests for measurement of previous mumps infection and analysis of mumps experience by blood group. *Am J Epidemiol* 1966; 84:371–381.
102. Lindeman J, Müller WK, Versteeg J, et al: Rapid diagnosis of meningoencephalitis, encephalitis: Immunofluorescent examination of fresh and in vitro cultured cerebrospinal fluid cells. *Neurology* 1974; 24:143–148.
103. Kantoch M: Markers and vaccines. *Adv Virus Res* 1978; 22:259–325.
104. Roth A: Immunization with live attenuated mumps virus vaccine in Honolulu: A field trial. *Am J Dis Child* 1968; 115:459–460.
105. Sugg WC, Finger JA, Levine RH, et al: Field evaluation of live virus mumps vaccine. *J Pediatr* 1968; 72:461–466.
106. Walters VW, Miller SA, Jackson JE, et al: A field trial with live measles-mumps-rubella vaccine. *Clin Pediatr* 1975; 14:928–933.
107. Weibel RE, Buynak EB, McLean AA, et al: Persistence of antibody after administration of monovalent and combined live attenuated measles, mumps and rubella virus vaccines. *Pediatrics* 1978; 61:5–11.
108. Hayden GF, Preblud SR, Orenstein WA, et al: Current status of mumps and mumps vaccine in the United States. *Pediatrics* 1978; 62:965–969.
109. Healy CE: Mumps vaccine and nerve deafness. *Am J Dis Child* 1972; 123:612.
110. Gellis SS, McGuinnes AC, Peters M: A study on the prevention of mumps orchitis by gamma globulin. *Am J Med Sci* 1945; 210:661–664.
111. Pollock TM: Human immunoglobulin in prophylaxis. *Br Med Bull* 1969; 25:202–207.
112. Recommendations of the Immunization Practices Advisory Committee (ACIP): Mumps prevention. *MMWR* 1989; 38:388–400.

Measles Virus

John F. Modlin

HISTORY

Nomenclature

According to different authorities, the English word "measles" is either derived from the Latin *misellus* (diminutive of *miser,* miserable) or from the Teutonic word *mazer.*[1,2] Measles is a more specific term than "morbilli" (diminutive of *morbus* [Latin], dis-ease), a word applied throughout Western recorded history to measles, but also to other rash illnesses such as smallpox. The use of "rubeola," another Latin term often used for measles, has been discouraged due to confusion with "rubella."

Historical Notes

The origins of measles as a human disease are lost in antiquity. Black has postulated that measles first appeared among the Middle Eastern river valley civilizations after 2500 BC, because human populations large enough to sustain virus transmission among susceptibles did not exist before then.[3] The first written account of measles is generally attributed to the tenth-century Arabian physician Rhazes, although he quoted other accounts of measles dating to the seventh century AD.[2] Through the Middle Ages, measles and smallpox were often confused and considered the same disease. However, by 1629 measles was separated from smallpox by the parish clerks of London in the annual "bills of mortality."[2] Repeated epidemics of measles occurred in London in the seventeenth and eighteenth centuries. During an outbreak in 1670, Thomas Sydenham wrote the first clear and accurate clinical description of measles in the English language.[4]

Caulfield has written a scholarly account of the episodic outbreaks of measles in colonial America.[5] He quotes the diary of John Hull, a mintmaster, who chronicled an early epidemic in Boston in September 1657 which caused mild disease despite the high attack rate. "Scarce any house escaped: only through the goodness of God, scarce any died of it." Subsequent epidemics in New England were not so kind, as evidenced by Cotton Mather's heart-rending account of the measles epidemic of 1713 that claimed the lives of six members of his own household.[5] Early epidemics in the New World were separated by many years and affected persons of all ages. These epidemics would spread through a largely susceptible population following the landing of imported cases aboard ships bearing immigrants from England. As the population increased, and the number of landings increased in frequency, the interval between epidemics decreased and only the younger persons born since the previous epidemic became ill. By 1795, the population of Philadelphia was large enough that measles had become endemic.

Like colonial America, the Faeroe Islands were sufficiently isolated from European civilization in the nineteenth century so that outbreaks of measles in the islands were separated by several generations. In 1846, Peter Panum, a Danish medical student, was sent to aid with an epidemic among the islands' inhabitants during which 75% of the Faeroese became ill with measles within a 5-month period. The detailed studies of Panum demonstrated person-to-person transmission of measles, a constant incubation period of 13 to 14 days from exposure to onset of rash, a high attack rate among closely exposed persons, limitation of infectivity to persons with acute illness, higher mortality among adults, and lifelong immunity for the island inhabitants over 65 years old who had been infected during the previous measles epidemic in 1781.[6] These careful observations form the basis of much of what we know about measles today.

Although Panum's studies confirmed that measles was transmitted from person to person, the infectious nature of measles had been demonstrated nearly 90 years earlier in Edinburgh by Home, who transmitted measles to 15 persons with the blood of an acutely ill patient.[7] Hektoen confirmed Home's discovery in 1905.[7] Six years later, Goldberger and Anderson isolated and passed the virus of measles in rhesus and cynomolgous monkeys.[8] Enders and Peebles were the first to report unequivocal isolation of measles virus in tissue culture.[9] They originally isolated the virus from blood and throat washings of five patients in primate kidney cell cultures and confirmed their findings by complement fixation and neutralization with convalescent sera.

The adaptation of cultured measles virus to embryonated chicken eggs[10] in Enders's laboratory led to attenuation of measles virus by multiple passage in cultured chicken embryo cells[11] and ultimately to development of the live attenuated measles virus vaccines. Widespread use of these vaccines has dramatically reduced the incidence of measles in the United States[12] and other developed countries and has heralded the possible elimination of endemic measles in the United States in the 1980s.[13]

PROPERTIES OF THE VIRUS

Classification

Measles virus is a member of the family *Paramyxoviridae* and the genus *Morbillivirus*.[14] The other morbilliviruses, canine distemper virus and rinderpest, a virus of ungulants, share common nucleocapsid and envelope antigens with measles virus and produce similar pathologic changes in their natural hosts.[15, 16]

Physical and Biologic Characteristics

Measles virions are pleomorphic particles that range from 120 to 250 nm in diameter[17] (Figure 13–1). The envelope is covered with projecting peplomers of hemagglutinin. A tightly coiled helical nucleocapsid composed of protein and the single-stranded RNA genome is enclosed within the envelope.

Electron microscopy and physicochemical studies have revealed many details of the structure and function of each of the components of the measles virion. The nucleocapsid is approximately 17 nm in diameter and 1 μm in length.[18, 19] The major

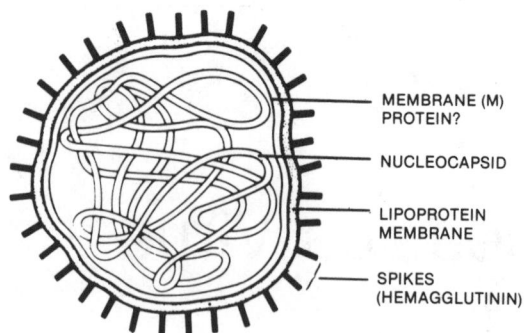

Figure 13–1. Schematic figure of the measles virion. (From Morgan EM, Rapp F: Measles virus and its associated diseases. *Bacteriol Rev* 1977; 41:636. Reproduced with permission.)

component of the nucleocapsid is a polypeptide with a molecular weight of 60,000.[20, 21] The subunits of this polypeptide are spirally arranged around the RNA genome. Measles virus RNA accounts for approximately 5% of the weight of the nucleocapsid[22] and has a molecular weight of 6.2×10^6 dalton.[19, 20] The negative-strand RNA genome codes for at least six, and possibly as many as nine[23] polypeptides including the nucleocapsid (N) protein, the RNA polymerase (P), matrix (M) protein, fusion (F) protein, and hemagglutinin (H).[21, 22, 24] The nucleotide sequence for the entire measles virus genome has been determined and the position of each gene has been resolved.[25–26]

The viral envelope is a lipoprotein membrane 10 to 20 nm in thickness which contains proteins associated with the hemagglutinating, hemolyzing, and membrane fusion properties. Measles viruses avidly attach to the cell membranes and agglutinate the erythrocytes of Old-World monkeys over a wide range of temperature and pH conditions,[27–28] but virus does not elute spontaneously, lacking the neuraminidase activity found in other paramyxoviruses. The hemagglutinin activity is mediated by the 69,000-dalton hemagglutinin (H) glycoprotein residing with the peplomers on the envelope membrane.[29, 30]

The hemagglutinin can be extracted and purified while retaining erythrocyte agglutinating activity.[30, 31] Although hemagglutination appears to be necessary for the hemolytic activity of measles virus, hemolysis is a separate function residing with the envelope F protein. The F protein plays a role in virus penetration into the host cell and promotes fusion of measles virus–infected cell membranes.[32, 33] Measles virus M protein is a nonglycosylated structural protein that forms the inner surface of the viral envelope. M protein promotes the alignment of viral nucleocapsids with the portion of the cell membrane containing viral-coded glycoproteins prior to budding and release of mature virions from the infected cell.[33]

Measles virus is relatively thermolabile; the half-life for infectivity is two hours at 37°C and three to five days at 25°C.[34] Rapid inactivation occurs at 50°C. When a protein source is added to the maintenance medium, measles virus remains stabile at −70°C with little loss of titer.[35] Infectivity is retained over a pH range of 5.0 to 10.5,[35] but the virus is easily inactivated by lipid solvents (ether, chloroform) and ultraviolet, beta, or gamma radiation.[24, 35] In artificially created aerosols measles virus survives better in low humidity.[36]

Replication Cycle

Replication of measles virus within the host cell is similar to replication of other paramyxoviruses. Attachment of the virion to the cell membrane occurs via a specific affinity between a viral envelope membrane protein, probably the hemagglutinin, and a host cell membrane receptor. Penetration of the viral genome into the cell requires fusion of the viral envelope with the cell membrane, an event that appears to be dependent on cleavage of the viral envelope F protein by a host cell enzyme and subsequent fusion activity by the activated F protein.[33]

Viral RNA synthesis begins within 24 hours of penetration of the measles virus genome into the host cells.[37, 38] Both the cytoplasm and the nucleus appear to support virus transcription and translation.[38] The anticomplementary RNA of measles virus is first transcribed into a complementary (positive) RNA message. RNA polymerase activity has not been specifically identified for measles virus, but a nucleocapsid-associated RNA polymerase has been demonstrated in some of the paramyxoviruses and is assumed to be present within the measles virion.[31, 39] The positive RNA segment serves as a template for both replication of the negative-stranded viral genome and for translation of the gene message into viral proteins. Progeny RNA strands are then rapidly encased in capsid protein. However, the specific mechanisms and sequences of these processes have not been fully characterized for measles virus.[40]

During the later stages of viral replication, segments of cell membrane acquire viral-coded proteins and the morphologic characteristics of the viral envelope.[41] The assembled nucleocapsids align themselves near the cell membrane and are then released from the cell by budding, acquiring a "coat" of cell membrane complete with viral proteins. The M protein appears to play a critical role in the release of mature virions.

Host Range and Cytopathology

Man is the natural host for measles virus, although other primates are susceptible to naturally transmitted measles infection. Rhesus monkeys have acquired measles from humans and transmitted infection to other monkeys in captivity.[42] Monkey infection is similar to human infection, albeit generally milder.[43] Unadapted measles virus is not infectious for subprimate animals, but tissue culture-adapted strains will replicate and produce cytopathologic changes when given intracranially to young mice, rats, or hamsters.[44]

Primary cell cultures of monkey kidney and human kidney remain the most sensitive means of recovering measles virus from clinical specimens.[45] Isolates which have been recovered in primary kidney cells can often be adapted to other laboratory cell lines such as continuous primate cells (eg, Vero, HeLa), human amnion, and dog kidney,[46] as well as the amniotic sac of embryonated chicken eggs.[47]

Specific virus cytopathic effect (CPE) generally appears in vitro after six to ten days in culture, but may appear sooner or later depending on the inoculum size (Fig 13–2). The characteristic CPE caused by measles virus is the formation of syncytia (giant cells) due to fusion of the cell membranes of adjacent infected cells. In stained monolayers, eosinophilic inclusions can be found in both the cytoplasm and the nucleus of infected cells. Electron micrographs demonstrate that these inclusions are large aggregates of measles virus nucleocapsids.[19] With repeated passage of undiluted virus, a second type of CPE may occur in the absence of giant cell formation.[48, 49] This alternate type of CPE is characterized by the development of spindle-shaped cells with long cytoplasmic processes (stellate cells). It is associated with low titers of infectious virus but high hemagglutinin activity.[50] Measles virus also may be detected in tissue culture by hemadsorption of monkey erythrocytes onto cell monolayers.[51, 52]

Naturally Occurring and Laboratory-Adapted Variants

Naturally occurring, epidemiologically distinct measles virus strains are now known to differ phenotypically. Studies with panels of monoclonal antibodies generally confirm the conservation of epitopes among diverse strains of measles virus for most of the structural proteins and the RNA polymerase.[53] The exception is the M protein which appears to exhibit considerable antigenic variation among different measles virus strains.[53]

The Edmonston measles virus strain is a widely studied laboratory variant which is the parent strain for the live attenuated measles virus vaccines. The Edmonston strain was derived from a wild measles isolate by sequential passage in human kidney, human amnion, and chicken embryos.[54] The further attenuated strains of measles virus currently used in live measles vaccines have been passed additional times in chicken embryo cells.[55, 56] The attenuated vaccine strains can be differentiated in the laboratory from wild-type measles virus by their ability to grow in chick cells, slow growth in human kidney cells, and ability to induce interferon production in vitro.[57]

A number of other measles virus variants have been induced in the laboratory by altering the physical or biologic conditions for replication. These include a number of temperature-sensitive (*ts*) mutants selected for loss of a specific biologic function (ie, hemadsorption, syncytia formation) or for ability to synthesize a specific virion component at an elevated temperature.[58, 59] These

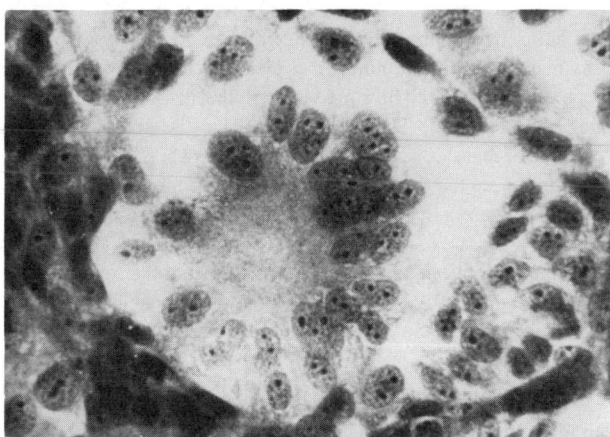

Figure 13–2. "Giant cell" syncytial formation induced by measles virus in monkey kidney cell culture. (From Morgan EM, Rapp F: Measles virus and its associated diseases. *Bacteriol Rev* 1977; 41:636–666. Reproduced with permission.)

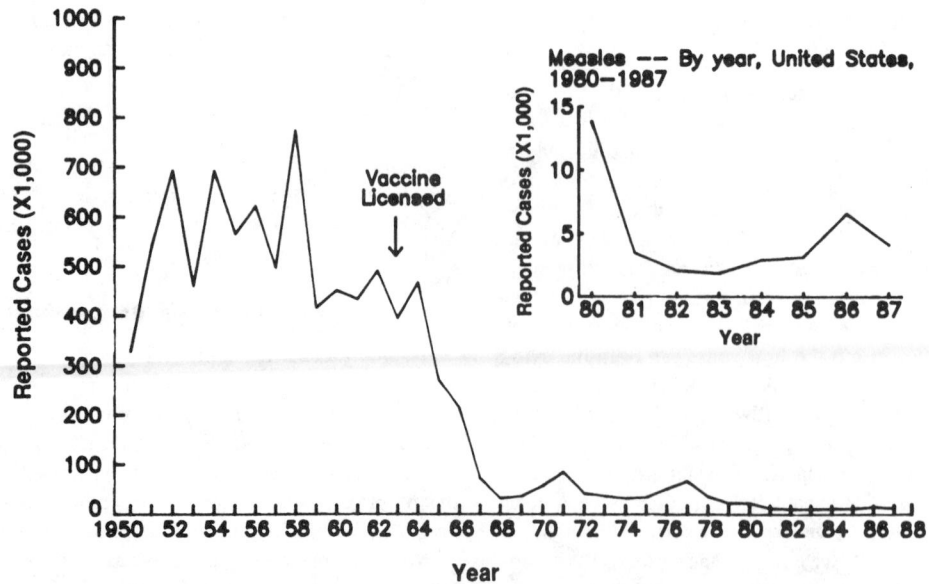

Figure 13–3. Reported measles cases in the United States, 1951–1987. (From Centers for Disease Control: Measles—United States, 1987. *MMWR* 1988; 37:527–531. Reproduced with permission.)

mutants strains have proved valuable to molecular biologists who study the relationships between structure and function of the measles virus components.

EPIDEMIOLOGY

Source of Data

In the United States, data from measles cases reported to local healthy departments are forwarded to state health departments and subsequently to the Centers for Disease Control (CDC). Completeness of reporting has varied widely by location and time. Prior to the availability of measles vaccine, it is estimated that from 15%[60] to 50%[61, 62] of cases were reported to health authorities, with higher percentages during epidemic periods.[61] Since measles was endemic in urban America, and since 90% to 95% of the population had antibody to measles by age 15, a reasonable approximation of the true number of measles cases can be made by extrapolation from the birth rate or from the size of the population under 15 years old. These estimates place the completeness of reporting of measles cases in the prevaccine era at 25% to 50%.[62, 63] Although there are no similar data regarding reporting efficiency in the vaccine era, public health authorities believe that a higher proportion of cases is now reported, similar to the way in which reporting of poliomyelitis improved after introduction of polio vaccine.[13]

Secular Trends

From 1912 to 1959, 200,000 to 600,000 cases of measles were reported annually in the United States, and the morbidity rate remained relatively constant at 200 to 500 cases per 100,000 population per year.[64] With the introduction of measles vaccine in 1963, the annual number of reported cases fell rapidly (Fig 13–3). The decline accelerated following the distribution of measles

vaccine to local health departments through a federal assistance program beginning in 1966, leading to a low of 22,231 reported cases of measles by 1968.[65] Moderate increases in reported measles occurred during brief periods of the 1970–1971 and 1976–1977.[65, 66] In 1978, the US Public Health Service announced a program aimed at eliminating indigenous measles in the United States by October 1982.[67] With the institution of this program, reported measles fell to a record low level in 1983 when only 1497 cases were reported in the United States.[68] While low levels of measles incidence continue to be reported, the goal of interruption of indigenous measles transmission in the United States has yet to be achieved. In 1987, a provisional total of 3655 cases were reported to the CDC representing an incidence of 1.5 cases per 100,000 population, or a 99% reduction in incidence compared with the prevaccine era.[68] Many parts of the United States remain free of measles cases for long periods, while small outbreaks continue to occur in diverse geographic locations among both partially and fully immunized populations (see Microepidemiology).

Geographic Distribution

Measles occurs in all parts of the world inhabited by man. Climate and natural boundaries influence the occurrence of measles only to the extent that they limit social intercourse and the opportunities for contact between susceptible and contagious individuals.

Seasonal Incidence

Although measles may occur at any time of the year, in endemic areas measles incidence exhibits marked seasonal variation. In temperate climates, measles morbidity ebbs during summer, increases in October and November coincident with the onset of cooler weather and the opening of schools, and rises to a peak between February and April. Seasonal trends occur at all latitudes, although there is a tendency toward higher and narrower winter peak incidence curves at southern latitudes, perhaps due to the shorter duration of the cold season.[69] The reason(s) for the marked seasonal variation in measles is unknown. The opportunity for transmission that occurs with the opening of schools and indoor congregation during colder weather have been cited as probable factors,[61] in addition to the enhanced ability of the measles virus to survive at the lower humidity levels prevalent indoors during the winter.[36]

Age-Specific Incidence

Measles is uncommon in the first 6 months of life because of the protection conferred by passively acquired maternal antibody. Beyond the first year of life, there is no evidence that susceptibility to measles virus varies with age, and therefore age of infection is determined largely by opportunity for contact with a contagious person. Prior to the introduction of measles vaccine, exposure and subsequent infection usually occurred early in life. In the United State, 50% of children experienced infection before their fifth birthday,[63] and 95% had antibody to measles by 15 years of age.[66]

Within 15 years of the introduction of measles vaccine, the age-specific incidence of measles dramatically shifted upward as the overall incidence of measles declined.[66, 70] By 1979, the majority of reported measles cases occurred in persons over 10 years old, with 30% to 35% of all cases occurring in the 10- to 14-year-old age group and 25% occurring in persons aged 15 years and older.[70] Epidemiologic investigations of measles cases among teenagers and young adults revealed that most had not been immunized or had received measles vaccine before 12 months of age. These individuals had maintained their susceptibility through years of declining measles activity in the community.[66] Most cases in the United States now occur in (largely unvaccinated) children under 5 years of age and among teenagers; school-age children and older adults have lower rates of measles.[68]

Macroepidemiology

Over the years, many theories[3, 71–78] and mathematical models[79] have been developed to explain the epidemic nature of measles. The basic fact underlying all of these theories is that measles transmission depends on the number of susceptible individuals in a population and their opportunities for contact with the disease. It has been estimated that a "community" of at least 200,000 persons is necessary to introduce a sufficient number of susceptibles into the population via birth in order to maintain continuous measles transmission.[3, 73] Accordingly, in smaller communities the supply of susceptibles would be exhausted, and measles would fade out until reintroduction from the outside. In addition, the introduction of measles vaccination greatly increases the critical size of the population required to sustain measles transmission, depending on the proportion of the population immunized.[76, 77]

History records many measles outbreaks among populations that are largely or wholly susceptible by virtue of geographic isolation.[5, 6, 61, 80] These "virgin-soil" epidemics are characterized by rapid spread of measles through the population with high attack rates and significant morbidity in all age groups, including adults and very young infants. One such outbreak in Greenland in 1951 affected 99.9% of the 4000 inhabitants in less than 6 weeks.[81]

Forty-five percent developed complications such as pneumonia or heart failure, and significant mortality occurred among infants less than 1 year old (4.6%) and persons over 55 years old (15.9%).

In contrast, most parts of the world are populous enough to support continuous (endemic) transmission of measles. Prior to the introduction of measles vaccine, the outbreaks of measles that occurred annually during winter months affected children of school age and younger. In urban areas, the annual peak reached epidemic levels every 2 to 3 years,[69] and the mean age of measles cases was 5 to 6 years.[82, 83] In rural areas the interval between epidemic years was longer,[69] and the mean age of measles cases was older than in urban areas.[61]

Microepidemiology

Measles is a highly contagious disease that is transmitted with high efficiency via the respiratory route. Within family settings, introduction of measles into the household results in infection of nearly 100% of susceptibles. Frequently, younger siblings are infected as a result of measles in a school-age child,[84] leading to the observation that secondary cases have a lower mean age than primary cases,[85] and that mean age of measles is inversely related to the number of siblings of the child.[84, 86]

In the prevaccine era, measles occurred in any setting that brought susceptible persons into close contact. In Western societies, the elementary school provided an important source of exposure and transmission of measles,[61, 87] Limited outbreaks also occurred among military recruits and college students as well, despite the fact that a high proportion of the population were immune.[61, 88] With the advent of measles vaccine and the subsequent introduction of school immunization laws, the importance of the preschool and elementary school classroom as a source of measles transmission dramatically declined.[89] However, occasional outbreaks continue to occur in day care centers and among adolescents and young adults in secondary schools[90] and colleges.[91, 92] Military recruits now receive universal measles immunization, a policy that has effectively prevented the occasional outbreaks that recently occurred in this population.[93] Other settings such as physicians' offices and hospitals that bring together young children, adolescents, and young adults are important settings for measles transmission as well.[94, 95]

Recently, measles outbreaks have occurred in classrooms in which virtually 100% of the students had previously been immunized according to current recommendations.[90, 96] The small percentage (ie, 4%–5%) of students who fail to develop an immune response to measles vaccine appears to play an important role in the spread of measles in these highly immune populations. Therefore, alternative measles immunization strategies may be required in order to achieve the goal of elimination of indigenous transmission of measles virus in the United States.[97]

HUMAN DISEASE CAUSED BY MEASLES VIRUS

Clinical Pathophysiology

Transmission

A person with measles is capable of transmitting infection from as early as three days prior to onset of symptoms until the rash desquamates.[61] Infectivity is maximal during the prodrome and diminishes rapidly with onset of the rash. Measles virus is spread by direct contact with respiratory secretions and by exposure to aerosols created by coughing and sneezing.[98] The primary portal of entry and site of initial virus replication is the respiratory tract epithelium. Studies with live measles vaccine virus suggest that aerosolization is the most efficient means of transmitting measles,[99] but direct intranasal inoculation also results in infection.[100] The amount of infectious virus (inoculum size) required to produce human infection is so low that the minimum human infectious dose cannot be detected in monkey kidney cell culture.[99]

Incubation Period

Symptoms of measles first appear nine to 11 days after exposure. Sometimes the incubation period is measured from exposure to onset of rash, which is ten to 14 days for 80% of measles cases. However, rash occurring up to 19 days after exposure is well documented.[81] The incubation period may be longer for children under 2 years of age[101] and following administration of immune serum globulin.[61] Conversely, onset of rash occurs in less than ten days in 6% of naturally exposed persons.[101] The incubation period is also shortened when the respiratory epithelium is bypassed by parenteral administration of wild measles virus or attenuated measles vaccine virus.[99, 102]

No symptoms attributable to measles occur during the incubation period, but blood counts taken during this period may reveal a leukopenia due to a diminished number of circulating lymphocytes.[100, 103] The abnormal blood counts reflect the fact that the incubation period is a time of active virus replication and proliferation. Experience with measles virus infections in nonhuman primates[104–112] strongly supports the concept that the pathogenesis of measles is similar to the ectromelia (mousepox) virus model in mice.[113] These studies indicate that minimal replication of virus occurs at the primary site of infection followed by lymphatic spread of measles virus to regional lymphoid tissue.[109] Low titers of virus can be found in the blood as early as three days following infection, primarily in the leukocyte fraction.[114–116] An early (primary) viremia leads to infection of reticuloendothelial tissue throughout the body, including tonsils, lymph nodes, spleen, gastrointestinal (GI) lymphoid tissue, and lung. During this period, multinucleated giant cells, the histologic hallmark of measles, can be demonstrated in many tissues.[105] Release of virus from these tissues results in a higher-grade (secondary) viremia and heralds the onset of clinical disease.

Prodrome

The prodromal phase of measles consists of fever plus signs and symptoms of upper respiratory tract infection, including cough, profuse coryza, and conjunctivitis (Figure 13–4). Fever is minimal at first, but progresses in a stepwise manner to reach 102 to 105°F (39–40.5°C) over three or four days.[117] During the prodrome, the respiratory symptoms become progressively more severe, and Koplik's spots appear on the buccal mucosa. Koplik's spots are clusters of pinpoint bluish-white lesions with surrounding erythema that are usually observed opposite the upper molars.[118] When carefully sought, they are found in more than 80% of measles cases.[61] Their presence is a useful diagnostic sign in the preeruptive phase of measles, since they do not occur in any other illness.

High titers of measles virus are found in nasopharyngeal se-

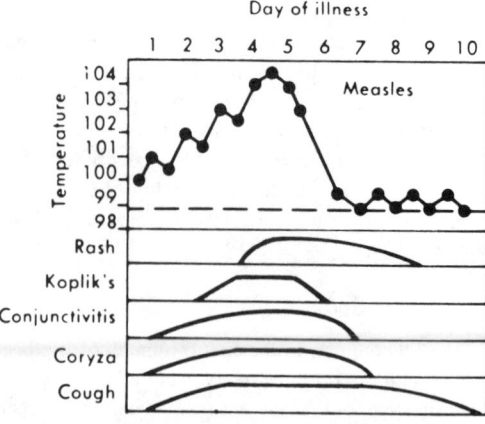

Figure 13–4. Representative time course of the common symptoms and signs of measles in normal children. (From Krugman S, Katz SL (eds): *Infectious Diseases of Children*, St Louis, Mosby, 1977, p 133. Reproduced with permission.)

cretions and urine during the prodrome.[119] Pathologic studies of sacrificed monkeys[104–108] and of humans dying during this period[120] show extensive giant cell formation in respiratory epithelium and in reticuloendothelial tissue.

Rash

The rash of measles appears when virus titers peak in blood and nasopharyngeal secretions. Characteristically, the erythematous macular eruption begins near the hairline on the neck, then spreads rapidly to involve the face and upper trunk. Over the next two to three days, the rash extends to the distal extremities as discrete maculopapular lesions, while becoming confluent on the upper parts of the body. The fever peaks on the second or third day of the rash, and then diminishes rapidly by lysis, signaling clinical improvement. During convalescence, the rash fades rapidly, although a brownish epidermal desquamation may occur in cases where the rash has been extensive. Respiratory symptoms improve, but a dry cough may persist for several weeks.

Light and electron microscopic examination of the measles exanthema and enanthema (Koplik's spots) show focal edema, mononuclear cell infiltration surrounding the dermal capillaries, occasional giant cells, and measles virus nucleocapsids within the capillary endothelial cells.[121, 122] With the appearance of the rash, measles virus rapidly disappears from blood and is rarely recovered after the second day of the rash. The disappearance of virus from blood corresponds with the appearance of humoral antibody.[123] Since some immunodeficient children with measles do not develop an exanthema,[124] it has been postulated that the exanthema and Koplik's spots are inflammatory lesions that are dependent on the immune response accompanying the appearance of antibody.[2, 121]

Immune Response

Specific humoral antibody, local secretory antibody, lymphocyte responsiveness, and increased serum interferon activity can be demonstrated following natural infection or administration of attenuated measles vaccine virus. Infection with natural or attenuated virus has also been shown to suppress nonspecific lymphocyte responsiveness. However, the relative importance of each of these phenomena in the protection against reinfection, the immune response to acute disease, and the pathogenesis of the clinical disease are not fully understood.

Antibody Response

Serum measles antibodies have been detected by neutralization, complement fixation (CF), hemagglutinin inhibition (HI), indirect fluorescent antibody (IFA), and enzyme-linked immunosorbent assay (ELISA) techniques. The CF test lacks sensitivity compared with the other methods and is rarely used today in the United States. The HI and neutralization tests are both reliable indicators of past infection (and therefore immunity), but the HI test has become the widely accepted standard clinical method for detection of antibodies to measles virus becasue it is the least cumbersome of the two methods.[125, 126] Plaque neutralization[127] and ELISA[128] detect lower concentrations of measles antibodies than the HI test, but the use of these methods has been mostly confined to research laboratories. HI antibody is directed against the viral hemagglutinin. Antibody specific for the viral hemolysin[129] and complement-dependent cytotoxic antibody[130] have also been demonstrated following natural infection.

Antibody to measles virus can first be detected in serum shortly after onset of the rash in naturally infected persons[123] or 11 to 14 days following administration of live attenuated measles vaccine.[126] The first antibodies detected following primary infection or vaccination are IgM antibodies, which persist for 3 to 6 weeks.[131, 132] IgG antibodies appear later than IgM antibodies, peak in 2 to 6 weeks, and gradually decline to low, but persistent, levels for life. During reinfection, a boost in titer of IgG antibody occurs in serum, but IgM antibody does not reappear.[133] Immune children who are exposed to natural measles maintain higher levels of antibody as a result of subclinical reinfections than do immune children who do not have opportunities for reinfection.[126] Both natural infection and infection with attenuated vaccine virus also induce specific secretory IgA antibody in nasal secretions.[134]

Lymphocyte-Mediated Immunity

Lymphocytes from persons immune to measles transform in the presence of measles virus antigen[135, 136] and kill measles virus-infected tissue culture cells.[137] Measles virus-specific lymphocyte-mediated immunity can be demonstrated less commonly in previously vaccinated persons than in persons with past natural infection.[136]

Infectious measles virus and viral antigen are found in a significant proportion of circulating T lymphocytes during natural infection.[138] Measles virus produces productive infection of T lymphocytes in vitro, resulting in reduced T cell proliferation, but normal lymphokine production.[139] These in vitro phenomena correlate with the observed lymphopenia, reversed T4 cell number, and transient loss of skin test reactivity that occur during acute measles[138, 139] and following the administration of live attenuated measles vaccine.[140] The altered T cell immunity of acutely infected persons has not been convincingly linked to susceptibility to other pathogens.

Interferon

Interferon is stimulated by measles virus both in cell culture[141] and in human infection.[142] In vaccine recipients, interferon appears six to seven days postimmunization, and peaks at ten to 11 days, during, or shortly after, the expected period of maximum vaccine virus replication.[142]

Immunity to Reinfection

Infection with measles virus confers lifelong immunity to symptomatic reinfection. There are poorly documented reports of measles occurring in previously infected persons[143]; however, if second clinical attacks occur, they are very rare. In contrast, subclinical reinfection is well documented among children with either vaccine-induced or natural immunity.[126, 144] Subclinical reinfection is characterized by absence of an IgM antibody response[144] and an anamnestic IgG antibody response.[145]

The immunologic determinants of immunity to reinfection are not fully understood. It is apparent that humoral antibody alone can be protective, since transplacentally acquired antibody in infants and immune serum globulin administration to older children[146] will prevent or modify illness in the susceptible host. There are rare reports of disease occurring in the presence of preexisting antibody to measles.[143, 145, 147] These cases have occurred in children who had received killed measles vaccine[143, 145] or in immunocompromised children with passively administered immunoglobulin.[147]

Recovery From Natural Infection

Recovery from measles infection appears to depend on an adequate cell-mediated immune (CMI) response. Patients with poor CMI due to the acquired immunodeficiency syndrome (AIDS),[147, 148] congenital immunodeficiency syndromes,[149] immunosuppressive chemotherapy,[124] and malnutrition[150] have severe, sometimes fatal, measles virus infections. Serum antibody and interferon responses are temporally related to recovery from measles, but the significance of their role in recovery is unknown. Patients with isolated agammaglobulinemia, and otherwise normal persons who have undetectable antibody responses to measles, handle acute infection in the normal fashion and are immune to clinical reinfection.[151, 152]

Diagnosis

Diagnosis of Acute Infection

The majority of measles cases are diagnosed on clinical grounds alone. The presence of upper respiratory symptoms, Koplik's spots, and the characteristic rash, in combination with a history of exposure compatible with the incubation period, is sufficient to make a clinical diagnosis. In some cases the Koplik's spots may be missed, or the disease may be mild enough to be confused with other causes of rash illness. Mild disease often occurs in infants who have passively acquired maternal antibody. In parts of the developed world where measles incidence has dropped to very low levels, physicians may have little experience with measles and thus may be uncomfortable relying on clinical findings alone. In the United States, advisory committees recommend that clinically suspected cases be confirmed by laboratory testing.[153, 154]

Laboratory confirmation is based on identification of measles virus in specimens from the acutely infected patient or on serologic evidence of measles infection. Measles virus may be identified by isolation of infectious virus in cell culture from nasopharyngeal secretions up to one or two days after onset of the rash[123] and from buffy coat blood and urine for one or two days longer.[2, 119] Failure to recover virus in cell culture does not rule out the diagnosis. Measles virus antigen has also been demonstrated in cells collected from the nasopharyngeal secretions of acutely infected patients by fluorescent antibody (FA) techniques.[155, 156] This technique is comparable to virus isolation in sensitivity[156] and has the advantage of providing a rapid result. Unfortunately, the availability of laboratories capable of virus isolation and FA procedures is somewhat limited.

Serologic techniques represent the most sensitive means of diagnosing acute measles infection. A positive diagnosis depends on demonstration of a fourfold or greater rise in antibody titer between serum drawn during the acute stage of the illness and a convalescent phase serum drawn ten to 21 days later. This method is more frequently used than virus identification methods. It has the advantage of increased sensitivity and wider availability, but has the disadvantage of requiring weeks for a definitive result.

Determination of Immune Status

In clinical practice, a history of measles or a history of administration of live measles vaccine after 12 months of age is adequate evidence of immunity to measles. For research and epidemiologic purposes, the only meaningful evidence of immunity is the presence of antibody to measles. Although the HI test is the most widely used technique, it may fail to detect very low levels of antibody to measles virus which are demonstrable by more sensitive methods such as enhanced neutralization[127] or ELISA.[128]

Complications

In the normal host, measles infection can be complicated by secondary pyogenic bacterial infections of the upper and lower respiratory tracts, giant cell pneumonia, acute measles encephalitis, and very rarely by CNS disorders such as subacute sclerosing panencephalitis (SSPE).

Pneumonia

During acute measles, the lung may be secondarily infected by bacteria such as *Streptococcus pneumoniae, Staphylococcus aureus* or *Neisseria meningitidis*,[157] and perhaps by adenoviruses.[158] In addition, measles virus directly infects the pulmonary parenchyma, producing (Hecht's) giant cell pneumonia.

From 25% to 50% of children admitted to hospital will have clinical or roentgenographic evidence of pneumonia.[60, 159, 160] Unfortunately, most reports have inadequately distinguished viral and bacterial causes of measles-related pneumonia. Therefore, the incidence, natural history, and relative proportion of bacterial and viral causes of measles pneumonia are poorly understood. In all likelihood, these factors depend on the population studied. Most authorities agree that measles virus is the dominant cause of pneumonia in young children,[60, 158, 161] while among adults secondary bacterial infection is common.[162] Children with underlying cardiac or chronic pulmonary disorders seem especially susceptible to measles pneumonia.[161, 162] Mortality rates for measles pneumonia vary according to the population surveyed. During an outbreak of measles in St Louis in the early 1970s, six (9%) of 66 cases of pneumonia were fatal among children admitted to hospital.[60] Many children, and the majority of adults,[163] who die of measles pneu-

monia have underlying lymphoreticular malignancies or immunodeficiency syndromes. Fatal measles pneumonia has also been described during simultaneous infection with chickenpox.[164]

Other Respiratory Complications

Bacterial otitis media is a common complication of measles, occurring in 5% to 15% of cases.[165] Less frequent complications include bacterial cervical lymphadenitis, laryngotracheobronchitis (croup), and bronchiolitis. Bronchiectasis in children has often been ascribed to previous measles infection.[166]

Tuberculosis

Measles has been linked to progression of disease and death in persons with tuberculosis during virgin-soil epidemics.[167] The risk of reactivation of tuberculosis may be limited to adults, since measles has been shown to have little effect on children with tuberculosis.[167, 168] There is no indication that measles vaccine presents a risk to tuberculin-positive persons. However, depression of cutaneous sensitivity to tuberculin commonly occurs with natural measles infection[169, 170] and with administration of measles vaccine.[170–172] Loss of skin test reactivity begins during the incubation period,[170] and extends for 1 to 4 weeks after the rash of natural measles and for a shorter duration following measles vaccine.[169, 170] Cutaneous anergy to tuberculin has been correlated with depression of tuberculin-induced lymphocyte proliferation in vitro.[172]

Encephalitis

Measles encephalitis is an acute inflammatory reaction in the CNS temporally associated with measles infection. Encephalitis complicates approximately one per 1000 cases of measles,[173–175] a rate that was comparable to the incidence of bacterial meningitis in the prevaccine era. With the introduction of measles vaccine, the incidence of measles encephalitis declined in parallel with the declining incidence of measles. Currently, fewer than five cases are reported annually to the CDC.[175] The risk of encephalitis rises with the age of the measles case, resulting in the highest incidence in school-age children.[176, 177] However, there is no relationship between the severity of the acute measles illness and the risk of encephalitis. Administration of immune serum globulin during the incubation period reduces, but does not totally eliminate, the risk of encephalitis.[178, 179]

Onset of encephalitis during the incubation period is well documented, but rare.[178] CNS symptoms usually appear from two to seven days after the eruption of the rash,[174, 176] at the time that the patient is usually beginning to recover from measles.[180] Onset of encephalitic symptoms is heralded by abrupt recurrence of fever and appearance of headache, lethargy, irritability, and confusion. Half of children with measles encephalitis will have generalized seizures, but seizures do not correlate with prognosis unless they are prolonged or difficult to control.[174, 180] Although the majority of patients improve and return to normal after two to three days, approximately 30% of cases progress to a comatose state which may persist for days to weeks. Other clinically distinct syndromes have been reported to occur together with cerebritis and also as isolated syndromes. These include cerebellar ataxia,[180] transverse myelitis,[181, 182] optic neuritis,[180, 183] Bell's palsy,[184] and Guillain-Barré syndrome.[185, 186]

The characteristic laboratory finding in measles encephalitis is a CSF with a lymphocytic pleocytosis in the range of 10 to 500 WBC per microliter (10% of cases will have fewer than 10 WBC/ μL[174]), elevated protein content, and normal glucose concentration. Electroencephalography inevitably shows diffuse or focal slow-wave changes. EEG abnormalities may persist for weeks following clinical recovery. Attempts to recover infectious measles virus from CSF or biopsied brain tissue are virtually always unsuccessful.

Ten to fifteen percent of measles encephalitis cases are fatal[174, 175] and one fourth of survivors can be expected to have permanent CNS sequelae such as mental retardation, personality disorders, seizures, deafness, hemiplegia, or paraplegia.[187]

The pathophysiology of acute measles encephalitis is not completely understood. Biopsy or postmortem examination of brains from encephalitis cases shows generalized vascular congestion; hemorrhage, perivascular infiltration with macrophages, lymphocytes, and plasma cells; and a variable degree of perivenous demyelination.[188, 189] Cytoplasmic and intranuclear inclusions and multinucleated giant cells are sometimes found in brain tissue,[190] but measles virus has only rarely been recovered from somewhat atypical measles encephalitis cases.[176, 191, 192] Because infectious virus, viral antigen,[193] and intrathecal measles antibody synthesis[194] cannot be demonstrated in the great majority of cases, postinfectious measles encephalitis is thought to be similar to experimental allergic encephalitis of mice, which is an acute demyelinating process with a host lymphoproliferative response directed against myelin basic protein.[194]

Other CNS syndromes have been described in association with recent measles infection. Several reports document the occurrence of an acute, invariably fatal encephalitis 5 weeks to 6 months following recovery from measles.[195–198] With one exception,[195] all cases have occurred in immunosuppressed patients, most in remission from reticuloendothelial malignancies. Measles has also been shown to precede a "toxic encephalopathy," which is now recognized as Reye syndrome.[199]

Other Complications

Myocardial deaths have been reported during the prodrome[200] and acute phase of measles,[201] and also months later secondary to residual cardiac fibrosis of the conducting system.[202] Although measles myopericarditis is well documented, it is a rare complication of measles. Degan found only two cases of myopericarditis and two additional cases of pericarditis in 100 autopsied patients dying during acute measles.[203] In contrast, evidence of subclinical cardiac involvement during measles is common. Electrocardiographic abnormalities have been noted in 19% of children with otherwise uncomplicated measles.[204] They occur from two to 20 days after onset of the rash, persist for up to seven days, and are unrelated to age or severity of the rash and fever.[204, 205]

Thrombocytopenic purpura is a rare complication of measles. Diffuse intravascular coagulation is responsible for the clinical picture of thrombocytopenia, purpuric lesions, and generalized hemorrhagic tendency known in the past as "hemorrhagic" or "black" measles. About 25% of reported children with hemorrhagic measles have died.[206]

The Stevens-Johnson syndrome (erythema multiforme exudativum) has also been reported to occur during measles.[207]

Subacute Sclerosing Panencephalitis

Subacute sclerosing panencephalitis (SSPE) is a very rare degenerative disease in children and adolescents characterized by the insidious onset of mental deterioration and motor dysfunction. Inevitably SSPE progresses to convulsions, coma, emaciation, and death. Although SSPE was first described in the United States by Dawson in 1933,[208] the same pathologic entity had been known in Europe as subacute sclerosing leukoencephalitis (van Bogaert's disease)[209] and also as nodular panencephalitis of Pette and Doring.[210] In 1965, Bouteille et al first demonstrated measles viruslike nucleocapsids in electron micrographs of postmortem brain tissue from SSPE patients.[211] The link between SSPE and measles was strengthened by the demonstration of measles virus antigen in biopsied SSPE brain tissue by immunofluorescence[212, 213] and ultimately proved by recovery of measles virus after prolonged cocultivation of SSPE brain tissue with permissive cell lines.[214, 215]

Epidemiology

SSPE occurs 2 to 3 times more frequently in males than females, and 3 to 4 times more frequently in whites than blacks in the United States.[216] Eighty-five percent of cases first develop symptoms between 5 and 14 years of age. For unexplained reasons, children who come from rural areas and children who have measles at a very young age have higher risks of developing SSPE.[216, 217] The "incubation period" from acute measles to onset of neurologic symptoms varies from several months to many years (mean 7.0 years).[218, 219] There is no evidence that the severity of the original measles epidose is related to the risk of SSPE.

Well-documented cases of SSPE have occurred in children whose only measles infection has been via administration of live attenuated measles vaccine virus.[219, 220] However, retrospective surveillance data from CDC indicate that the risk of SSPE following measles vaccination (0.5–1.1 cases/10^6 vaccine doses distributed) is considerably smaller than the estimated risk among children naturally infected with measles (5.2–9.7 cases/10^6 measles cases).[219] Interestingly, the mean incubation period for measles vaccine-related cases is significantly shorter than that following natural measles.[219]

Clinical Features

The first sign of SSPE is the insidious onset of intellectual deterioration. This may take the form of an unexplained decline in school performance, emotional lability, personality change, forgetfulness, poor attention span, or difficulty sleeping.[221, 222] On occasion, visual disturbances resulting from chorioretinitis are early complaints.[223, 224] Clumsiness and gait disturbances occur, sometimes resulting from myoclonic seizures. These movement disturbances are sudden repetitive flexion movements of one or more extremities that occur as often as every 5 to 10 seconds. They represent true myoclonic seizures but do not interfere with the patient's state of consciousness and usually disappear with sleep.

Progression of the illness is heralded by the appearance of frank neurologic signs and symptoms in addition to the myoclonus. Intellectual function rapidly deteriorates; involuntary movements progress, with the appearance of dystonia and extrapyramidal dysfunction; and cranial nerve abnormalities, such as dysphagia, develop. The final stage of SSPE is characterized by cortical blindness, complete absence of intellectual function, decerebrate posturing, generalized wasting, and loss of bowel and bladder control. Cessation of the myoclonic seizures is not unusual in advanced stages of SSPE. Abnormalities of vital signs such as hyperthermia, irregular pulse, blood pressure, and respiratory activity are indicative of hypothalamic dysfunction and impending death. Most patients die of progressive disease 6 months to 3 years after onset (mean 24 months). Rare cases have been reported with a fulminant course resembling acute encephalitis.[225, 226] On the other hand, some patients' courses are marked by prolonged remission.[227–230] Survival for 8 years or longer is well documented.[227]

The EEG and CSF measles antibody titer determination help confirm the diagnosis of SSPE. The highly characteristic EEG pattern consists of synchronous paroxysmal bursts of 2- to 3-per-second high-voltage waves followed by flattening of background activity ("suppression bursts").[231] The CSF cell count, glucose, and protein are usually normal, but CSF IgG is elevated as determined by quantitative CSF immunoelectrophoresis or reflected by a first-zone colloidal gold curve. The elevated CSF IgG is secondary to high titers of measles antibody, which is not normally detectable in CSF, even in persons convalescing from measles and acute postinfectious measles encephalitis.[232]

SSPE has been treated with numerous therapeutic procedures, antiviral drugs, and biologic agents, but none have effectively altered the course of the disease.

Pathology

Microscopic examination of postmortem brain tissue shows vascular congestion and perivascular infiltration by lymphocytes and plasma cells.[233, 234] These changes are present throughout the brain but are most prominent in the cortex and basal ganglia. Demyelination is a frequent finding and may be extensive in cases of long duration.[234] Intranuclear inclusions, the pathologic hallmark of SSPE, are seen in neurons and glial cells[235] (Figure 13–5). Histochemical staining[235, 236] and electron microscopy[211, 237]

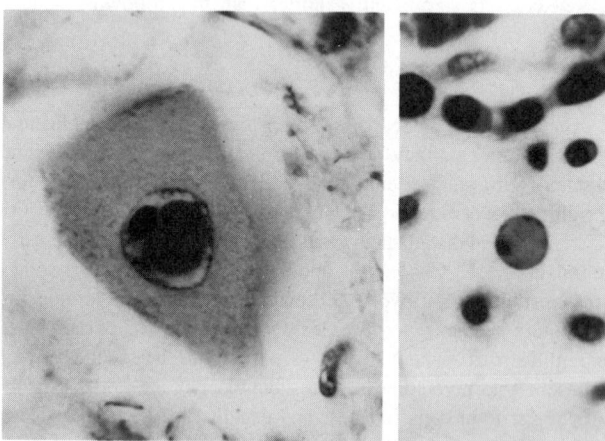

Figure 13–5. Large, eosinophilic intranuclear body in brain of patient with subacute sclerosing panencephalitis. (From Parker JC, et al: Uncommon morphologic features of subacute sclerosing panencephalitis [SSPE]. *Am J Pathol* 1970; 61:275. Reproduced with permission.)

confirm that the intracellular inclusions are aggregates of viral nucleocapsids.

Pathogenesis

There has been extensive investigation into general host immune status[238, 239] and the immune response to persistent measles virus infection of the CNS[240–244] in patients with SSPE. These studies have produced no convincing evidence that SSPE patients have a preexisting immunologic abnormality or that the humoral or CMI response to measles virus is aberrant.

Measles viruses are only recovered from SSPE patients after prolonged cocultivation of brain tissue with permissive cell lines. These SSPE isolates cannot be distinguished from viruses recovered from patients with acute measles by infectivity for cell culture, CPE, plaque size, host cell range, neurovirulence for animals, or by routine electron microscopy.[245] However SSPE measles virus isolates seem to lack the ability to produce the M protein both in vitro[246, 247] and in vivo,[248–249] probably secondary to a mutation in the M protein gene leading to abnormal translation of the mRNA transcript encoding the M protein. Serum and CSF specimens from SSPE patients lack antibody to the M protein as well.[250–251] The loss of M protein is associated with the development of a nonproductive, highly cell-associated measles virus infection of the CNS that is possibly protected from immune surveillance.[252, 253]

SSPE virus has been passed in several animal species, including subhuman primates,[254] but no single animal model adequately duplicates the features of human SSPE. The two most extensively studied animal models are the ferret[255] and the weanling hamster.[256]

Measles in the Altered Host
Immunosuppressed Host

Measles in the patient with altered immunity due to chemotherapy, malignancy, or immunodeficiency may be clinically aberrant, prolonged, and fatal. Severe measles has been reported in children with leukemia,[124, 257] dysgammaglobulinemia,[258] reticuloendotheliosis,[259] nephrotic syndrome,[260] and also in adults with bone marrow dyscrasias.[261, 262] Children infected with the human immunodeficiency virus (HIV) appear to be susceptible to severe and sometimes fatal measles infection, even though they may have previously received live measles vaccine or recent immunoglobulin infusion.[147, 148] In immunocompromised patients, mortality is caused by giant cell pneumonia which may occur at any time from the incubation period[124] up to a year following the rash.[257] Characteristically, measles virus is shed from the respiratory tract for prolonged periods.[124, 263] In some patients, giant cell pneumonia has occurred in the absence of rash.[147, 259] Live measles vaccine has also been responsible for fatal giant cell pneumonia in immunodeficient children.[258, 263]

A chronic, often fatal, generalized encephalitis has been described in a small number of children with disorders of lymphocyte-mediated immunity.[195–197, 264–266] Immunosuppressive measles encephalitis develops an average of 4 to 6 weeks after acute measles infection with acute or subacute onset of progressive neurologic deterioration and seizures. At least one case followed administration of further attenuated measles vaccine after onset of symptoms of acute leukemia.[266] As in SSPE, the CSF is usually acellular, but there may be an increase in protein concentration. The majority of children have succumbed, although complete recovery has been observed.[265, 266] A diffuse encephalitis is found at postmortem examination with intranuclear and cytoplasmic inclusions. Measles virus has been recovered from CSF in some patients[266] and evidence of measles virus replication in brain tissue has been noted by electron microscopy and by IF antibody staining.

Measles in Pregnancy

Pregnancy is associated with a slight increase in maternal morbidity and mortality.[81, 267] Giant cell pneumonia is the principal cause of death in gestational measles. There is no evidence that maternal measles leads to congenital anomalies.[267–269] However, acute measles induces labor in 22% to 37% of pregnant women, resulting in a high rate of spontaneous abortion and premature delivery.[267, 268, 270, 271] There is some evidence that the measles virus can infect the fetus in utero, although it is not known if fetal infection is related to premature labor.[271–272] Infants delivered during the mother's incubation often develop a measles rash simultaneously with the mother, suggesting transplacental infection late in gestation.[267, 272] While some infants with perinatally acquired measles infection have mild illnesses, others develop severe disease with pneumonia.[267] The mortality is approximately 15%.[272]

Atypical Measles

Shortly after the introduction of killed measles vaccine, reports appeared describing a severe, clinically atypical measles infection among prior recipients of one or more doses of killed vaccine.[273–277]

Even though there are well-documented reports of atypical measles occurring in children who received only live attenuated measles vaccine,[278] the principal risk is among the estimated 600,000 recipients of killed measles vaccine.[279] The actual risk of atypical measles has not been defined among killed measles vaccine recipients, although Rauh and Schmidt noted that eight cases occurred among 125 killed measles vaccine recipients who had household exposure to natural measles.[273] Atypical measles syndrome has been reported up to 16 years after immunization with killed vaccine.[280] Because killed vaccine was available in the United States only from 1963 to 1967, the age of patients with atypical measles syndrome has steadily increased so that recent cases have occurred exclusively among adolescents and young adults.[280–284]

Following exposure and the usual incubation period, the patient with atypical measles experiences sudden onset of high fever and a two- or three-day prodrome of dry cough, pleuritic chest pain, and myalgias. Headache is often prominent at this time and abdominal pain may be severe enough to mimic appendicitis.[274] Koplik's spots are not seen. The atypical measles rash begins on the extremities, involving both the palms and soles, and spreads centrally to the trunk. The rash consists of discreet, maculopapular skin lesions that frequently become petechial or vesicular[274] (Figure 13–6). Many patients develop peripheral edema.

Conjunctivitis and coryza are not prominent, but involvement of the lower respiratory tract is common. Most patients with atypical measles syndrome experience some dyspnea and have evidence of pneumonia on physical examination. The chest x-ray may reveal

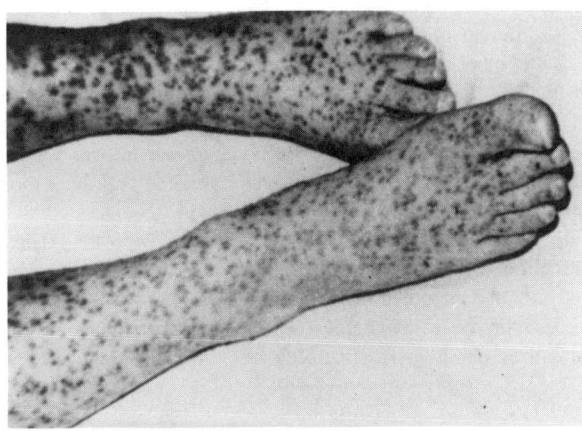

Figure 13–6. Rash of the atypical measles syndrome on the lower extremities of a young adult patient. (From Annunziato D, et al: Atypical measles syndrome: Pathologic and serologic findings. *Pediatrics* 1982; 70:203. Reproduced with permission.)

unilateral or bilateral infiltrates, hilar adenopathy, or pleural effusions[285, 286] (Figure 13–7). At least two cases of pneumonia have occurred in patients without rash.[287, 288] Infrequent findings include hepatomegaly[273] and peripheral neuropathy.[275, 282]

Leukopenia is common early in the clinical illness, while a small proportion of patients develop eosinophilia during convalescence.[274] Because measles virus has not been recovered from patients with atypical disease, laboratory diagnosis depends on demonstration of a rise in measles serum antibody titer. Characteristically, measles HI antibody is absent at the beginning of the rash, but then rises to extraordinary levels during the acute illness. HI titers of 1:1280 or greater are expected, and titers of 1:10,000 or greater are not unusual. The differential diagnosis of atypical measles includes rickettsial infection,[289] meningococcemia, and Henoch-Schönlein purpura. Epidemiologic studies suggest that patients with atypical measles are not contagious.

Recovery within four to seven days is the general rule. Several authors have noted that residual nodular lesions may persist on radiologic examination for several months after resolution of symptoms.[285, 290]

The pathophysiology of atypical measles is unknown. Skin biopsies from acutely ill patients bear histologic similarity to both the delayed hypersensitivity and Arthus reaction.[281] Killed vaccine induces antibody to the viral hemagglutinin, but not to the viral hemolysin,[291] and acute sera from atypical measles cases show a similar pattern.[281, 291] However, the importance of this observation in the pathogenesis of the atypical measles syndrome is speculative.

It is uncertain whether atypical measles will continue to occur in the United States. Although there are many killed measles vaccine recipients who have remained susceptible to measles into adulthood, the incidence of atypical measles can be expected to decline because of the diminishing risk of exposure to natural measles. Rare cases among live vaccine recipients may continue to occur.

Measles in the Underdeveloped World

The clinical and epidemiologic character of measles is considerably different in the underdeveloped world than in the United States and other developed nations. The severe, persistent disease and high mortality caused by measles is often attributed to underlying malnutrition,[150, 292–294] although recent data strongly suggest that the intense exposure of secondary cases in overcrowded households with large numbers of small children may be a more important factor.[295–298]

Most clinical data on severe measles come from the African continent,[150, 292–301] although measles similarly affects disadvantaged children in other parts of the world.[302, 303] Most data on measles reported from underdeveloped countries are gathered from hospitalized children. At least 50% of children hospitalized with

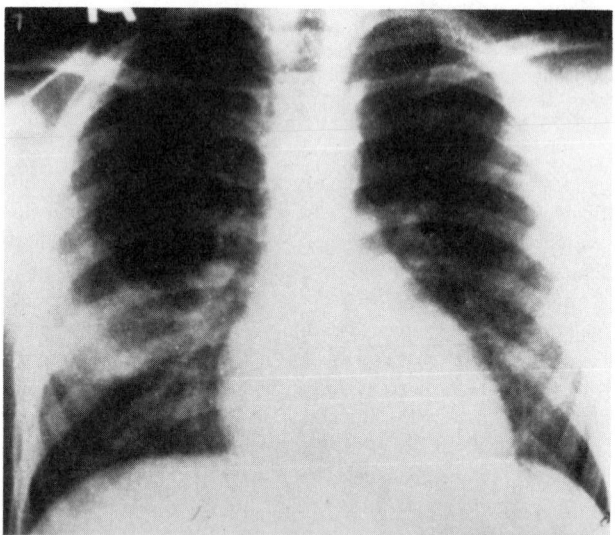
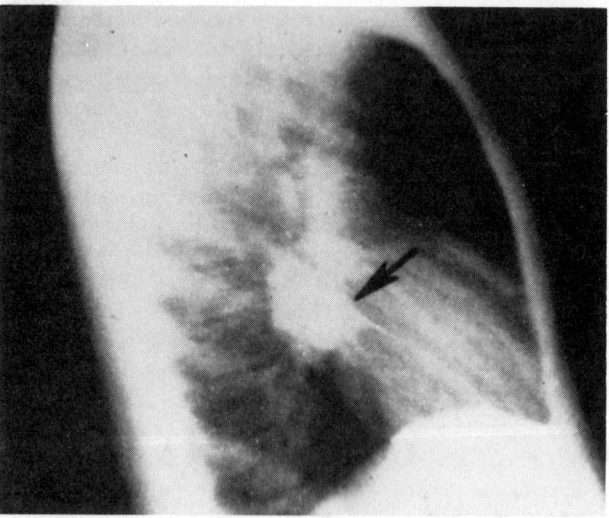

Figure 13–7. Chest roentgenogram showing a nodular pulmonary lesion in a patient with the atypical measles syndrome. (From Laptook A, et al: Pulmonary lesions in atypical measles. *Pediatrics* 1978; 62:42. Reproduced with permission.)

measles are less than 2 years old.[150] Although some children are hospitalized because of severe, fulminant measles alone, approximately two thirds have serious localized complications. The most frequent complications are pneumonia, gastroenteritis, and croup, all of which may be fatal.[292] Ulcerative stomatitis, purulent keratoconjunctivitis, and extensive epidermal desquamation are also common.[150, 292, 293] By limiting oral intake of food, severe measles may aggravate preexisting protein–calorie malnutrition and lead to excessive weight loss, especially in young children.[292, 294] The mortality rate for hospitalized children generally ranges from 5% to 25%,[300] but may be much higher for children under 1 year of age.[301]

Immunization Programs in Underdeveloped Countries

The Expanded Immunization Program (EPI) of the World Health Organization (WHO) recommends immunization against measles for children in developing countries at 9 months of age. It has been shown that passively acquired maternal antibody protects infants in underdeveloped countries for a shorter duration than infants born in developed nations.[303] Thus infants under 1 year of age in underdeveloped countries not only become susceptible to measles earlier, but are also more likely to respond to measles immunization.[303, 304] In these settings, from 80% to 85% of 9-month-old infants can be expected to seroconvert to routinely used measles vaccines.[303–305] The high frequency of concurrent respiratory and GI illnesses or malnutrition does not appear to affect the seroconversion rate or the rate of vaccine-associated adverse effects.[305, 306]

The inclusion of measles vaccine in the EPI recommendations has resulted in vaccine coverage of 50% to 90% in many of the target areas.[296, 307, 308] Measles vaccine efficacy of 78% to 90% has been observed and additional reductions in mortality among unimmunized children may have resulted by reducing the secondary household attack rate.[308] While measles continues to occur in both immunized and unimmunized children in the tropics, immunized children have a much lower attack rate, have milder disease, and are less likely to transmit measles.[309]

PREVENTION AND CONTROL

Prophylaxis

Postexposure Prophylaxis

Immune serum globulin (ISG) given intramuscularly (IM) in a dose of 0.25 mL/kg (up to 15 mL) will prevent or modify measles infection in normal children when administered up to six days after exposure.[146] ISG is especially useful for measles contacts who are under 12 months of age because of the higher risk of complications in this age group. ISG recipients who do not develop measles should receive measles vaccine 3 months later, or when they reach 15 months of age. Intravenous immune globulin (IVIG), which also contains a high titer of measles antibody, should be at least as effective as ISG, although there are no controlled data regarding the efficacy of IVIG in the prevention or modification of measles. However, fatal measles infection has occurred in at least one patient with HIV infection receiving regular doses of IVIG.[147]

Although conclusive data do not exist, most authorities feel that live attenuated measles vaccine will also prevent natural measles if given within 72 hours of exposure.[153, 310] This concept is based on observations that children vaccinated after exposure to measles experience the same incidence of rash and fever as unexposed children receiving vaccine.[310, 311]

Measles Vaccines

Live attenuated measles vaccine (Edmonston B strain) and killed measles vaccine were each introduced for general use in 1963. Because killed vaccine produced only short-term protection and was also linked to the atypical measles syndrome, it was withdrawn from distribution in 1967. The Edmonston B vaccine proved highly immunogenic, but was associated with unacceptably high reaction rates when given alone. After the introduction of the live, further attenuated (Schwartz, Moraten) strains in 1967, use of Edmonston B vaccine declined. Since 1970, the only measles vaccines available in the United States have been the live, further attenuated vaccines. Other measles vaccines derived from the original Edmonston A and Edmonston B strains are used in other parts of the world. One of these, the Edmonston-Zagreb strain, is currently undergoing evaluation for use in underdeveloped countries because of its potential for immunization of young infants with passively acquired maternal antibody.

Inactivated (Killed) Measles Vaccine

Killed measles vaccines were prepared by formalin inactivation of the Edmonston strain of measles virus.[312] During field trials, it was found that children who received the killed vaccine lost measles antibody rapidly and that protection conferred by killed vaccine waned over 3 years in half of recipients.[313, 314] Upon exposure to natural measles, many killed vaccine recipients acquired clinical infection, and some developed the atypical measles syndrome.[273, 315] Subsequently, many children who received only killed vaccine were revaccinated with live attenuated measles vaccine and 30% to 50% of these children developed extensive local reaction at the site of the live vaccine injection.[316, 317] Live vaccine did not completely protect against subsequent development of atypical measles in these children.[318]

Live Attenuated Measles Vaccine (Edmonston B)

The Edmonston vaccine strain is the product of multiple passage of wild measles virus through human kidney cells, human amnion cells, chick embryos, and cultured chick embryo cells.[319] Early clinical trials among institutionalized and home-dwelling children demonstrated seroconversion rates of greater than 95%, persistence of antibody, and protection against natural infection.[99, 100, 102, 320–324] However, the vaccine also caused a high incidence of fever (67%–80%), rash (25%–50%), and febrile convulsions (2%) among recipients.[102, 323, 325] Subsequently, it was shown that simultaneous administration of ISG significantly reduced the risk of side effects while having little effect on the immune response to the vaccine.[325–327]

Live, Further Attenuated Vaccines

Schwartz[55] and Moraten[56] strains of live measles vaccine were derived by additional passage of the Edmonston B strain in chick embryo cell culture. The advantage of these vaccine strains is the lower incidence of side effects in the immediate postvaccination period. From 5% to 20% of live, further attenuated vaccine recipients develop fever and/or rash from five to 12 days after vaccination.[55, 56] Most febrile responses occur from six to eight days after vaccination, and virtually all are transient and mild. A transient fall in the platelet count (averaging 36%) was reported in the majority of recipients of Edmonston B vaccine.[328] Transient petechiae and purpura were rarely reported.[329, 330] The risk of thrombocytopenia and other hematologic sequelae following administration of the further attenuated vaccines is unknown.

Very rare neurologic complications of measles vaccine are reported. Landrigan and Witte reviewed 59 cases of encephalitis occurring within a month of receipt of live measles vaccine; three fourths of these cases developed between six and 15 days after vaccination.[331] From these data, they estimated the risk of encephalitis to be approximately one case per million vaccinees. Rare cases of SSPE may occur in one per million measles vaccine recipients.[219]

At least 95% of susceptible persons develop antibody to measles following administration of live attenuated measles vaccine[153]; however, rates of 98% to 100% have been observed in recent trials.[332]

Peak levels of antibody are reached in 4 to 6 weeks. In general, postimmunization antibody titers are slightly lower than following natural infection, but then decline at the same rate.[332] Persistence of detectable measles antibody has been measured for at least 14 years following immunization.[333] There is good evidence that subclinical reinfection resulting from exposure to natural disease in the community maintains higher levels of antibody after immunization.[333] A recent serologic survey of Massachusetts schoolchildren found measles antibody in more than 98%.[334] Most authorities believe that protection for most vaccinees will extend through life.

Observations made during the original field trials,[102, 323, 324] and subsequently during community outbreaks of measles,[335–343] place vaccine efficacy in the range of 91% to 99% in adequately immunized children. Lower rates for vaccine efficacy are observed for children who received vaccine at less than 12 months[337, 339, 342] or who received improperly handled vaccine.[335]

Until 1977, infants were routinely given measles vaccine at 12 months of age. Several studies indicated that 12-month-old infants had lower seroconversion rates or reduced vaccine efficacy when compared with infants immunized at 15 months of age.[344] The rate of seroconversion is even lower for many infants who received live measles vaccines before 12 months of age.[345–347] In 1977, the recommended age for routine measles immunization was raised to 15 months of age.[348] An increasing number of women of childbearing age have immunity to measles from immunization rather than natural infection. It has been shown that the infants of vaccine-immune mothers are born with lower levels of passively acquired antibody which would make them susceptible to measles at an earlier age than infants of women with past natural infection.[349] Whether the wider window of susceptibility will pose a significant risk to infants in the future remains to be determined.

In addition to age of vaccination, primary measles vaccine failure has been attributed to vaccine inadvertently inactivated as a result of faulty storage and handling,[335, 350, 351] and to errant administration of ISG with further attenuated vaccines.[126, 351]

Further attenuated measles vaccine is recommended for all persons older than 15 months who are susceptible to measles. Although it is available as a single agent, measles vaccine is usually administered in combination with live mumps virus and live rubella virus vaccines (MMR). In general, individuals are considered susceptible to measles unless they were born before 1957 (ie, were of school age when measles vaccine was introduced), or unless they have had physician-diagnosed measles, received live measles vaccine at after 12 months of age, or have serologic evidence of immunity. Live measles vaccines are contraindicated in pregnant women and in persons with altered immunity. Allergy to eggs, chickens, or feathers does not constitute a risk to measles vaccine recipients. However, very rare hypersensitivity reactions may occur to the mumps component of MMR in persons with serious egg protein allergy.[352]

In recent years, some authorities have suggested routine revaccination of children prior to entering school at age 5 or 6 years.[353] Revaccination has been viewed as an opportunity to assure primary immunization in previous vaccine failures, rather than boosting preexisting immunity. So far, the national advisory committees have hesitated to recommend routine revaccination as public policy.[332] There are no contraindications to revaccination.

Live, Further Attenuated Vaccines

Edmonston-Zagreb Strain.—The Edmonston-Zagreb vaccine strain has been derived from the parent Edmonston B strain by 19 passages in human diploid cells.[354] Studies in several tropical nations indicate that the Edmonston-Zagreb strain is more immunogenic than the Schwarz strain in infants under 1 year of age who still possess passively acquired maternal antibody.[354-357] Seroconversion rates of 62% to 100% have been achieved in 4- to 6-month-old infants in several developing countries, depending on dose and route of administration.[355-357] The Edmonston-Zagreb strain is an excellent candidate for immunization of young infants in underdeveloped regions where as many as 27% of measles cases occur before 9 months of age,[307] the age at which measles vaccine is now recommended.

Administration of measles vaccine by aerosolization has also been explored as a means of enhancing the immune response of young infants in tropical areas.[355, 356, 358] However, there appear to be several important barriers that this approach must overcome in order to be practical, including malfunctioning of the aerosolization equipment and the increased cold chain requirements.[354]

Outbreak Control

As the incidence of measles wanes, the definition of what constitutes an "outbreak" shrinks as well. In most communities in the United States today, a single case of measles may be considered an outbreak. In such cases, the danger of spread is proportional to the number of susceptible persons having contact with an active case. Control measures for measles outbreaks consist of prompt administration of live measles vaccine to all susceptible persons within the local epidemiologic sphere and exclusion of unvaccinated children from the classroom or day care center. ISG should be given to all contacts who are less than 12 months of age. Any case of suspected measles should be promptly reported to the local public health authority.

Measles Eradication

The successful effort of WHO in eradicating smallpox worldwide has engendered speculation among public health authorities that measles can be similarly controlled. Measles shares several features with smallpox that make the disease a potential candidate for eradication.[67] These include the easily recognizable clinical syndrome, transmission only during the acute phase of illness, absence of a carrier state, lack of a nonhuman reservoir in nature, and the induction of lifelong immunity following clinical disease. In addition, there is the availability of a safe vaccine that produces long-term immunity.

The rationale and strategy for elimination of measles in the United States and other parts of the world has been articulated by Hinman and his colleagues at the CDC.[13, 67, 359] The concept of measles control developed from experiences in West Africa in the 1960s where annual measles vaccination campaigns targeted at greater than 90% of the susceptible population successfully interrupted measles transmission for variable periods. One country, Gambia, remained free of measles for at least 4 years.[360]

Contemporary attempts to eliminate measles in the United States have been less successful. A CDC-based effort to eradicate measles was launched in 1967,[361] but faltered after a few years due to a lack of commitment of resources at both the federal and state levels.[65] In 1978, a renewed effort was initiated at the federal level with a goal of eliminating domestic transmission of measles by October 1982.[67] While indigenous transmission of measles has not been fully interrupted, considerable success has been achieved in reducing reported cases to record low levels in the United States.[68] The cornerstones of this program include maintenance of high levels of immunity in the population by immunization, surveillance for susceptibility to measles, and surveillance and rapid response to measles outbreaks. Emphasis has been placed on enactment and rigorous enforcement of school immunization laws; encouragement of immunization requirements for day care centers, nursery schools, colleges, and the military; and establishment of active surveillance systems in state and local health departments. Furthermore, special attempts have been made to respond to outbreaks of summertime measles when the prospects for interrupting the chain of human-to-human transmission is greatest. Day care centers may be an important link in the maintenance of measles during the summer.[359]

There are several epidemiologic and practical problems that stand in the way of measles elimination efforts in the United States. Even when virtually 100% of the population receives measles vaccine, there will be enough susceptible persons to permit continued measles transmission because of the primary vaccine failure rate as high as 3% to 5%. Even if elimination of measles transmission is achieved in the United States, there will be the constant threat of outbreaks occurring through introduction of measles into the United States by travelers from other countries. Measles elimination programs require considerable expenditures of public resources and some will always question whether measles control should continue to have a high priority for public health funds.

REFERENCES

1. Wilson GS: Measles as a universal disease. *Am J Dis Child* 1962; 103:219–223.

2. Black FL: Measles, in Evans AS (ed): *Viral Infections of Humans*. NY, Plenum, 1976, pp 248–297.

3. Black FL: Measles endemicity in insular populations: Critical community size and its evolutionary implication. *Theor Popul Biol* 1965; 11:207–211.

4. Courrie JD (ed): *Selected Works of Thomas Sydenham*. New York, William Wood, 1922.

5. Caulfield E: Early measles epidemics in America. *Yale J Biol Med* 1943; 15:531–556.

6. Panum PL: Observations made during the epidemic of measles on the Faroe Islands in the year 1846. *Med Classics* 1939; 3:829–886.

7. Hektoen L: Experimental measles. *J Infect Dis* 1905; 2:238–255.

8. Goldberger J, Anderson JF: An experimental demonstration of the presence of the virus of measles in the mixed buccal and nasal secretions. *JAMA* 1911; 57:476–478.

9. Enders JF, Peebles TC: Propagation in tissue cultures of cytopathic agents for patients with measles. *Proc Soc Exp Biol Med* 1954; 86:272–286.

10. Milovanovic MV, Enders JF, Mitus A: Cultivation of measles virus in human amnion cells and in developing chick embryo. *Proc Soc Exp Biol Med* 1957; 95:120–127.

11. Katz SL, Milovanovic MV, Enders JF: Propagation of measles virus in cultures of chick embryo cells. *Proc Soc Exp Biol Med* 1958; 97:23–29.

12. Elimination of indigenous measles—United States. *MMWR* 1982; 31:517–519.

13. Hinman AR, Brandling-Bennett AD, Bernier RH, et al: Current features of measles in the United States: Feasibility of measles elimination. *Epidemiol Rev* 1980; 2:153–170.

14. Fenner F: Second report of the international committee on taxonomy of viruses. *Intervirology* 1976; 7:4–115.

15. Imagawa DT: Relationships among measles, canine distemper and rinderpest viruses. *Prog Med Virol* 1968; 110:160–193.

16. Orvell C, Norrby E: Further studies on the immunologic relationships among measles, distemper and rinderpest viruses. *J Immunol* 1974; 113:1850–1858.

17. Waterson AP, Cruickshank JG, Laurence GD, et al: The nature of measles virus. *Viorology* 1961; 15:379–382.

18. Norrby ECJ, Magnusson P: Some morphological characteristics of the internal component of measles virus. *Arch Gesamte Virusforsch* 1965; 7:443–447.

19. Nakai T, Shand FL, Howatson AF: Development of measles virus in vitro. *Virology* 1969; 30:50–67.

20. Hall WW, Martin SJ: Purification and characterization of measles virus. *J Gen Virol* 1973; 19:175–188.

21. Waters DJ, Bussell RH: Polypeptide composition of measles and canine distemper viruses. *Virology* 1973; 55:554–557.

22. Waters DJ, Hersh RF, Bussell RH: Isolation and characterization of measles nucleocapsid from infected cells. *Virology* 1972; 48:278–281.

23. Udem SA, Cook KA: Isolation and characterization of measles virus intracellular nucleocapsid RNA. *J Virol* 1984; 49:57–65.

24. Schluederberg A: Measles virus RNA. *Biochem Biophys Res Commun* 1971; 42:1012–1015.

25. Crowley J, Dowling P, Menonna J, et al: Molecular cloning of 99% of measles virus genome, positive identification of 5′ end clones, and mapping of the L gene region. *Intervirology* 1987; 28:65–77.

26. Crowley JC, Dowling PC, Menonna J, et al: Sequence variability and function of measles virus 3′ and 5′ ends and intercistronic regions. *Virology* 1988; 164:498–506.

27. Rosen L: Hemagglutination and hemagglutination-inhibition with measles virus. *Virology* 1961; 13:139–141.

28. Norrby E: Hemagglutination by measles virus: I. The production of hemagglutinin in tissue culture and the influence of different conditions on the hemagglutinating system. *Arch Gesamte Virusforsch* 1962; 12:153–163.

29. Hall WW, Martin SJ: The biochemical and biological characteristics of the surface components of measles virus. *J Gen Virol* 1974; 22:363–374.

30. Hall WW, Martin SJ: Structure and functional relationships of the envelope of measles virus. *Med Microbiol Immunol* 1974; 160:143–154.

31. Norrby E: Hemagglutination by measles virus: 4. A simple procedure for production of high potency antigen for hemagglutination inhibition (HI) tests. *Proc Soc Exp Biol Med* 1962; 111:814–818.

32. Morgan EM, Rapp F: Measles virus and its associated diseases. *Bacteriol Rev* 1977; 41:636–666.

33. Choppin PW, Richardson CD, Merz DC: The functions and inhibition of the membrane glycoproteins of paramyxoviruses and myxoviruses and the role of the measles virus M protein in subacute sclerosing panencephalitis. *J Infect Dis* 1981; 143:352–363.

34. Black FL: Growth and stability of measles virus. *Virology* 1959; 7:184–192.

35. Musser SJ, Underwood GE: Studies on measles virus: II. Physical properties and inactivation studies of measles virus. *J Immunol* 1960; 85:292–297.

36. de Jong JG, Winkler KC: Survival of measles virus in air. *Nature* 1964; 201:1054–1055.

37. Portner A, Bussell RH: Measles virus ribonucleic acid and protein synthesis: Effects of 6-azauridine and cycloheximide on virus replication. *J Virol* 1973; 11:46–53.

38. Fournier JG, Rozenblatt S, Bouteille M: Localization of measles virus nucleic acid sequences in infected cells by in situ hybridization. *Biol Cell* 1983; 49:287–290.

39. Mountcastle WE, Choppin PW: A comparison of the polypeptides of four measles virus strains. *Virology* 1977; 78:463–474.

40. Kingsbury DW: The molecular virology of paramyxoviruses. *Med Microbiol Immunol* 1974; 160:73–83.

41. Nakai M, Imagawa DT: Electron microscopy of measles virus replication. *J Virol* 1969; 3:187–197.

42. Meyer HM, Brooks BE, Douglas RD, et al: Ecology of measles in monkeys. *Am J Dis Child* 1962; 103:307–313.

43. Peebles TC, McCarthy K, Enders JF, et al: Behavior of monkeys after inoculation of virus derived from patients with measles and propagated in tissue culture together with observations on spontaneous infections of these animals by an agent exhibiting similar antigenic properties. *J Immunol* 1957; 78:63–74.

44. Griffin DE, Mullinex J, Narayan O, et al: Age dependence of viral expression: Comparative pathogenesis of two rodent-adapted strains of measles virus in mice. *Infect Immun* 1974; 9:690–695.

45. Enders JF: Measles virus. *Am J Dis Child* 1962; 103:282–287.

46. Matumoto M: Multiplication of measles virus in cell cultures. *Bacteriol Rev* 1966; 30:152–176.

47. Enders JF, Peebles TC, McCarthy K, et al: Measles virus: A summary of experiments concerned with isolation, properties and behavior. *Am J Public Health* 1957; 47:275–282.

48. Oddo FG, Flaccomio R, Sinatra A: "Giant-cell" and "strand-forming" cytopathic effect of measles virus lines conditioned by serial propagation with diluted or concentrated inoculum. *Virology* 1967; 13:550–553.

49. McCarthy K: Measles in laboratory hosts and tissue culture systems. *Am J Dis Child* 1962; 103:314–319.

50. Parfanovich M, Hammarskjold B, Norrby E: Synthesis of virus-specific RNA in cells infected with two different variants of measles virus. *Arch Gesamte Virusforsch* 1971; 35:38–44.

51. Kohn A: Hemadsorption by measles syncytia. *Nature* 1962; 193:1088–1089.

52. Rosanoff EI: Hemagglutination and hemadsorption of measles virus. *Proc Soc Exp Biol Med* 1961; 106:563–567.

53. Sheshberadaran H, Chen SN, Norrby E: Monoclonal antibodies against five structural components of measles virus: I. Characterization of antigenic determinants on nine strains of measles virus. *Virology* 1983; 128:341–353.

54. Enders JF, Katz SL, Holloway A: Development of attenuated measles virus vaccines. *Am J Dis Child* 1962; 103:335–340.

55. Schwartz A: Preliminary tests of a highly attenuated measles vaccine. *Am J Dis Child* 1962; 103:386–389.

56. Hilleman MR, Buynak EB, Weibal RE, et al: Development and evaluation of the Moraten measles virus vaccine. *JAMA* 1968; 206:587–590.

57. Enders JF, Katz SL, Grogan E, et al: Markers for Edmonston measles virus. *Am J Dis Child* 1962; 103:473–474.

58. Bergholz CM, Kiley MP, Payne FF: Isolation and characterization of temperature-sensitive mutants of measles virus. *J Virol* 1975; 16:192–202.

59. Haspel MV, Duff R, Rapp F: Isolation and preliminary characterization of temperature-sensitive mutants of measles virus. *J Virol* 1975; 16:1000–1009.

60. Cherry JD, Feigan RD, Lobes LA, et al: Urban measles in the vaccine era: A clinical epidemiologic, and serologic study. *J Pediatr* 1972; 81:217–230.

61. Gordon JE, Ingalls TH: Modern measles. *Am J Med Sci* 1954; 228:334–361.

62. Chapin CV: Measles in Providence, RI. *Am J Hyg* 1925; 5:635–655.

63. Hedrich AW: The corrected average attack rate from measles among city children. *Am J Hyg* 1930; 11:576–600.

64. Langmuir AD: Medical importance of measles. *Am J Dis Child* 1962; 103:224–226.

65. Conrad JL, Wallace R, Witte JJ: The epidemiologic rationale for the failure to eradicate measles in the United States. *Am J Public Health* 1971; 61:2304–2310.

66. Cherry JD: The ''new'' epidemiology of measles and rubella. *Hosp Pract* 1980; 15:49–57.

67. Hinman AR: Brandling-Bennett AD, Nieburg PI: The opportunity and obligation to eliminate measles from the United States. *JAMA* 1979; 242:1157–1167.

68. Centers for Disease Control: Measles—United States, 1987. 1988; 37:527–531.

69. Wells MW: The seasonal patterns of measles and chicken pox. *Am J Hyg* 1944; 40:279–317.

70. Age characteristics of measles cases—United States. *MMWR* 1980; 29:526–528.

71. Hamer WH: Epidemic disease in England—the evidence of variability and persistency of type. *Lancet* 1906; 1:733–739.

72. Abbey H: An examination of the Reed-Frost theory of epidemics. *Hum Biol* 1952; 24:201–233.

73. Bartlett MS: The critical community size for measles in the United States. *J R Stat Soc* 1960; 123:34–44.

74. Hope-Simpson RE: Infectiousness of communicable diseases in the household (measles, chicken pox, and mumps). *Lancet* 1952; 2:549–554.

75. Matumoto M: Mechanism of perpetuation of animal viruses in nature. *Bacteriol Rev* 1969; 33:404–418.

76. Griffiths DA: The effects of measles vaccination on the incidence of measles in the community. *J R Stat Soc* 1973; 136:441–449.

77. Yorke JA, Nathanson N, Pianigiani G, et al: Seasonality and the requirements for perpetuation and eradication of viruses in populations. *Am J Epidemiol* 1979; 109:103–123.

78. London WP, Yorke JA: Recurrent outbreaks of measles, chicken pox and mumps: I. Seasonal variation in contact rates. *Am J Epidemiol* 1973; 98:453–468.

79. London WP, Yorke JA: Recurrent outbreaks of measles, chicken pox and mumps. II. Systematic differences in contact rates and stochastic effects. *Am J Epidemiol* 1973; 98:469–482.

80. Christensen PE, Schmidt H, Jensen O, et al: An epidemic of measles in southern Greenland, 1951: Measles in virgin soil. I. *Acta Med Scand* 1952; 144:313–322.

81. Christensen PE, Schmidt H, Bang HO, et al: Measles in virgin soil: II. The epidemic proper. *Acta Med Scand* 1952; 144:430–449.

82. Collins SD: Age incidence of specific causes of illness. *Public Health Rep* 1935; 50:1404–1427.

83. Wilson EB, Worcester J: Contact with measles. *Proc Natl Acad Sci USA* 1941; 27:7–13.

84. Wright GP, Wright HP: The influence of social condition upon diphtheria, measles, tuberculosis and whopping cough in early childhood in London. *J Hyg* 1942; 42:451–473.

85. Aycock WL, Eaton P: A comparison between multiple cases of measles, scarlet fever, and infantile paralysis. *Am J Hyg* 1925; 5:733–741.

86. Wilson EB, Bennett C, Allen M, et al: Measles and scarlet fever in Providence, RI. *Proc Am Philos Soc* 1939; 80:357–476.

87. Cheeseman EA: Epidemics in schools. London, Medical Research Council Special Report, series No. 271, 1950.

88. Black FL: A nationwide serum survey of United States military recruits, 1962: III. Measles and mumps antibodies. *Am J Hyg* 1964; 80:304–307.

89. Robbins KB, Brandling-Bennett AD, Hinman AR: Low measles incidence: Association with enforcement of school immunization laws. *Am J Public Health* 1981; 71:270–274.

90. Gustafson TL, Lievens AW, Brunell PA, et al: Measles outbreak in a fully immunized secondary–school population. *N Engl J Med* 1987; 316:771–774.

91. Measles vaccination reactions among college students—North Carolina, Massachusetts. *MMWR* 1980; 29:549–551.

92. Krouse PJ, Cherry JD, Deseda-Tous J, et al: Epidemic measles in young adults. *Ann Intern Med* 1979; 90:873–876.

93. Measles—U.S. military. *MMWR* 1981; 30:314–316.

94. Davis RM, Orenstein WA, Frank JA, et al: Transmission of measles in medical settings. *JAMA* 1986; 255:1295–1298.

95. Watkins NM, Smith RP Jr, St. Germain DL, et al: Measles (rubeola) infection in a hospital setting. *Am J Infect Control* 1987; 15:201–206.

96. Nkowane BM, Bart SW, Orenstein WA, et al: Measles outbreak in a vaccinated school population: epidemiology, chains of transmission and the role of vaccine failures. *Am J Public Health* 1987; 77:434–438.

97. Levy DL: The future of measles in highly immunized populations: A modeling approach. *Am J Epidemiol* 1984; 120:39–48.

98. Riley EC, Murphy G, Riley RL: Airborne spread of measles in a suburban elementary school. *Am J Epidemiol* 1978; 107:421–432.

99. Kress S, Schluederberg AE, Hornick RB, et al: Studies with live, attenuated measles-virus vaccine: II. Clinical and immunologic response of children in an open community. *Am J Dis Child* 1961; 101:701–707.

100. Black FL, Sheridan SE: Studies on an attenuated measles-virus vaccine: IV. Administration of vaccine by several routes. *N Engl J Med* 1960; 263:165–169.

101. Stillerman M, Thalhimer W: Attack rate and incubation period of measles. *Am J Dis Child* 1944; 67:15–21.

102. Katz SL, Enders JF, Holloway A: Use of Edmonston attenuated measles strain. *Am J Dis Child* 1962; 103:340–344.

103. Benjamin B, Ward SM: Leukocytic response to measles. *Am J Dis Child* 1932; 44:921–963.

104. Blake FG, Trask JD: Studies on measles: I. Susceptibility of monkeys to the virus of measles. *J Exp Med* 1921; 33:385–422.

105. Sergiev PG, Ryazantseva NE, Shroit IG: The dynamics of pathological processes in experimental measles in monkeys. *Acta Virol* 1960; 4:265–273.

106. Kamahora J, Nii S: Pathological and immunological studies of monkeys infected with measles virus. *Arch Gesamte Virusforsch* 1965; 16:161–167.

107. Yamanouchi K, Egashira Y, Uchida N, et al: Giant cell formation in lymphoid tissues of monkeys inoculated with various strains of measles virus. *Jpn J Med Sci Biol* 1970; 23:131–145.

108. Nii S, Kamahora J, Takahashi M, et al: Experimental pathology of measles in monkeys. *Biken J* 1964; 6:271–297.

109. Ono K, Iwa N, Kato S, et al: Demonstration of viral antigen in giant cells formed in monkeys experimentally infected with measles virus. *Biken J* 1970; 13:329–337.

110. Grist NR: The pathogenesis of measles: Review of the literature and discussion of the problem. *Glas Med J* 1950; 31:431–441.

111. Robbins FC: Measles: Clinical features. *Am J Dis Child* 1962; 103:266–273.

112. Kempe CH, Fulginiti VA: The pathogenesis of measles virus infection. *Arch Gesamte Virusforsch* 1965; 16:103–128.

113. Fenner F: The pathogenesis of the acute exanthems. *Lancet* 1948; 2:915–920.

114. Gresser I, Chany C: Isolation of measles virus from the washed leukocytic fraction of blood. *Proc Soc Exp Biol Med* 1963; 113:695–697.

115. Peebles TC: Distribution of virus in blood components during the viremia of measles. *Arch Gesamte Virusforsch* 1967; 22:43–47.

116. Berg RB, Rosenthal MS: Propagation of measles virus in suspensions of human and monkey leukocytes. *Proc Soc Exp Biol Med* 1961; 106:581–585.

117. Krugman S, Ward R, Katz SL: *Infectious Diseases of Children*, ed 6, St. Louis, Mosby, 1977.

118. Koplik H: The diagnosis of the invasion of measles from a study of the exanthema as it appears on the buccal mucous membrane. *Arch Pediatr* 1896; 13:918–922.

119. Gresser I, Katz SL: Isolation of measles virus from urine. *N Engl J Med* 1962; 263:452–454.

120. Sherman FE, Ruckle G: In vivo and in vitro cellular changes specific for measles. *Arch Pathol* 1958; 65:587–599.

121. Kimura A, Tosaka K, Nakao T: Measles rash: I. Light and electron microscopic study of skin eruptions. *Arch Virol* 1975; 47:295–307.

122. Suringa DWR, Bank LJ, Ackerman AB: Role of measles virus in skin lesions and Koplik's spots. *N Engl J Med* 1970; 283:1139–1142.

123. Ruckle G, Rogers KD: Studies with measles virus: II. Isolation of virus and immunological studies in persons who have had the natural disease. *J Immunol* 1957; 78:341–355.

124. Mitus A, Enders JF, Craig JM, et al: Persistence of measles virus and depression of antibody formation in patients with giant-cell pneumonia after measles. *N Engl J Med* 1959; 261:882–889.

125. Fulginiti VA, Kempe CH: A comparison of measles neutralizing and hemagglutination inhibition antibody titers in individual sera. *Am J Epidemiol* 1965; 82:135–142.

126. Krugman S, Giles JP, Friedman H, et al: Studies on immunity to measles. *J Pediatrics* 1965; 66:471–488.

127. Albrecht P, Ennis FA, Saltzman EJ, et al: Persistence of maternal antibody in infants beyond 12 months: Mechanism of measles vaccine failure. *J Pediatr* 1977; 91:715–718.

128. Weigle KA, Murphy MD, Brunell PA: Enzyme-linked immunosorbent assay for evaluation of immunity to measles virus. *J Clin Microbiol* 1984; 19:376–379.

129. Norrby E, Gollmar Y: Appearance and persistence of antibodies against different virus components after regular measles infection. *Infect Immun* 1972; 6:240–247.

130. Kibler R, ter Meulen V: Antibody-mediated cytotoxicity after measles virus infection. *J Immunol* 1975; 114:93–98.

131. Schluederberg A: Immunoglobulins in viral infections. *Nature* 1965; 205:1232–1233.

132. Lievens AW, Brunell PA: Specific immunoglobulin M enzyme-linked immunosorbent assay for confirming the diagnosis of measles. *J Clin Microbiol* 1986; 24:391–394.

133. Schluederberg A: Modification of immune response by previous experience with measles. *Arch Gesamte Virusforsch* 1965; 16:347–350.

134. Bellanti JA, Sanga RL, Klutinis B, et al: Antibody responses in serum and nasal secretions of children immunized with inactivated and attenuated measles-virus vaccines. *N Engl J Med* 1969; 280:628–633.

135. Graziano KD, Ruckdeschel JC, Mardiney MR: Cell-associated immunity to measles (rubeola). *Cell Immunol* 1975; 15:347–359.

136. Gallagher ME, Welliver R, Yamanaka T, et al: Cell-mediated immune responsiveness to measles. *Am J Dis Child* 1981; 135:48–51.

137. Labowskie RJ, Edelman R, Rustigian R, et al: Studies of cell-mediated immunity to measles virus by in vitro lymphocyte-mediated cyto-toxicity. *J Infect Dis* 1974; 129:233–239.

138. Whittle HC, Dossetor J, Oduloju A, et al: Cell mediated immunity during natural measles infection. *J Clin Invest* 1978; 62:678–684.

139. Dagan R, Phillip M, Sarov I, et al: Cellular immunity and T-lymphocyte subsets in young children with acute measles. *J Med Virol* 1987; 22:175–182.

140. Fireman P, Friday G, Kumatz J: Effect of measles vaccine on immunologic responsiveness. *Pediatrics* 1969; 43:264–272.

141. De Mayer E, Enders JF: An interferon appearing in cell cultures infected with measles virus. *Proc Soc Exp Biol Med* 1961; 107:573–578.

142. Petralli JK, Merigan TC, Wilbur JR: Circulating interferon after measles vaccination. *N Engl J Med* 1965; 273:198–201.

143. Watson GI: Serological studies on second attacks of measles and rubella. *Lancet* 1965; 1:80–81.

144. Linneman CC, Hegg ME, Rotte TC, et al: Measles IgM response during reinfection of previously vaccinated children. *J Pediatr* 1973; 82:798–801.

145. Linneman CC, Rotte TC, Schiff GM, et al: A seroepidemiologic study of a measles epidemic in a highly immunized population. *Am J Epidemiol* 1972; 95:238–246.

146. Ordman CW, Jennings CG, Janeway CA: XII. The use of concentrated normal human serum gamma globulin (human immune serum globulin) in the prevention and attenuation of measles. *J Clin Invest* 1944; 23:541–549.

147. Markowitz LE, Chandler FW, Roldan EO, et al: Fatal measles pneumonia without rash in a child with AIDS. *J Infect Dis* 1988; 158:480–486.

148. Centers for Disease Control: Measles in HIV-infected children. *MMWR* 1988; 37:183–186.

149. Nahmias AJ, Griffith D, Salsburg C, et al: Thymic aplasia with lymphopenia, plasma cells, and normal immunoglobulins. *JAMA* 1967; 201:729–734.

150. O'Donovan C: Measles in Kenyan children. *East Afr Med J* 1971; 48:526–532.

151. Good RA, Zak SJ: Disturbances in gamma globulin synthesis as experiments in nature. *Pediatrics* 1956; 18:109–149.

152. Ruckdeschel JC, Graziano KD, Mardiney MR: Additional evidence that the cell-associated immune system is the primary host defense against measles. *Cell Immunol* 1975; 17:11–18.

153. Centers for Disease Control: Measles prevention. *MMWR* 1987; 36:409–418, 423–425.

154. *Report of the Committee on Infectious Diseases (Redbook)*, ed 20. Evanston, Ill, American Academy of Pediatrics, 1986.

155. McQuillain J, Bell TM, Gardner PS, et al: Application of immunofluorescence to a study of measles. *Arch Dis Child* 1976; 51:411–419.

156. Fulton RE, Middleton PJ: Comparison of immunofluorescence and isolation techniques in the diagnosis of respiratory viral infections of children. *Infect Immun* 1977; 10:92–101.

157. Lucke B: Postmortem findings in measles-bronchopneumonia and other acute infections. *JAMA* 1918; 70:2006–2011.

158. Pather M, Wesley AG, Schonland M, et al: Severe measles-associated pneumonia treated with assisted ventilation. *South Afr Med J* 1976; 50:1600–1603.

159. Kohn JL, Koiransky H: Successive roentgenograms of the chest of children during measles. *Am J Dis Child* 1929; 38:258–270.

160. Weinstein L, Franklin W: The pneumonia of measles. *Am J Med Sci* 1949; 217:314–324.

161. O'Donovan C, Barua KN: Measles pneumonia. *Am J Trop Med Hyg* 1973; 22:72–77.

162. Olson RW, Hodges GR: Measles pneumonia. *JAMA* 1975; 232:363–365.

163. Sobonya RE, Hiller FC, Pingleton W, et al: Fatal measles (rubeola) pneumonia in adults. *Arch Pathol Lab Med* 1978; 102:366–371.

164. Lobes LA, Cherry JD: Fatal measles pneumonia in a child with chicken-pox pneumonia. *JAMA* 1973; 223:1143–1144.

165. Cherry JD: Measles, in Feigan RD, Cherry JD (eds): *Textbook of Pediatric Infectious Diseases*. Philadelphia, Saunders, 1981, pp 1210–1231.

166. Field CE: Bronchiectasis in childhood: I. Clinical survey of 160 cases. *Pediatrics* 1949; 4:21–46.

167. Christensen PE, Schmidt H, Bang HO, et al: An epidemic of measles in southern Greenland, 1951: Measles in virgin soil: III. Measles and tuberculosis. *Acta Med Scand* 1952; 144:450–454.

168. Nalbant JP: The effect of contagious diseases on pulmonary tuberculosis and on the tuberculin reaction in children. *Am Rev Tuberc* 1937; 36:773–777.

169. Helms S, Helms P: Tuberculin sensitivity during measles. *Acta Tuberc Scand* 1958; 35:166–171.

170. Starr S, Berkovich S: Effects of measles, gamma-globulin-modified measles and vaccine measles on the tuberculin test. *N Engl J Med* 1964; 270:386–391.

171. Mellman WJ, Wetton R: Depression of the tuberculin reaction by attenuated measles virus vaccine. *J Lab Clin Med* 1963; 61:453–458.

172. Zweiman B, Pappagianis D, Maibach H, et al: Effect of measles immunization on tuberculin hypersensitivity and in vitro lymphocyte reactivity. *Int Arch Allergy Appl Immun* 1971; 40:834–841.

173. Hoyne AL, Slotkowski EL: Frequency of encephalitis as a complication of measles. *Am J Dis Child* 1947; 73:554–558.

174. La Boccetta AC, Tornay AS: Measles encephalitis: Report of 61 cases. *Am J Dis Child* 1964; 107:247–255.

175. Measles encephalitis—United States, 1962–1979. *MMWR* 1981; 30:362–364.

176. McLean DM, Best JM, Smith PA, et al: Viral infections of Toronto children during 1965: II. Measles encephalitis and other complications. *Can Med Assoc J* 1966; 94:905–910.

177. Ehrengut W: Measles encephalitis: Age disposition and vaccination. *Arch Gesamte Virusforsch* 1965; 16:311–314.

178. Holliday PB: Pre-eruptive neurological complications of the common contagious diseases—rubella, rubeola, roseola and varicella. *J Pediatr* 1950; 36:185–198.

179. Greenberg M, Pellitteri O, Eisenstein DT: Measles encephalitis: I. Prophylactic effect of gamma globulin. *J Pediatr* 1955; 46:642–647.

180. Tyler HR: Neurological complications of rubeola (measles). *Medicine* 1957; 36:147–167.

181. Box CR: A case of acute ascending paralysis occurring as a complication of measles and terminating in recovery. *Lancet* 1921; 1:222–223.

182. Aarli JA: Nervous complication of measles. *Eur Neurol* 1974; 12:79–93.

183. Meadows SP: Discussion on the neuro-ophthalmological aspects of failure of vision in children. *Proc R Soc Med* 1954; 47:494–499.

184. Pollack MA, Grose C, Friend H: Measles associated with Bell's palsy. *Am J Dis Child* 1975; 129:747.

185. Berkovich S, Schneck L: Ascending paralysis associated with measles. *J Pediatr* 1964; 64:88–93.

186. Lidin-Janson G, Strannegard O: Two cases of Guillain-Barré syndrome and encephalitis after measles. *Br Med J* 1972; 2:572–575.

187. Meyer E, Byers RK: Measles encephalitis. *Am J Dis Child* 1952; 84:543–579.

188. Miller HG, Stanton JB, Gibbons JL: Para-infectious encephalomyelitis and related syndromes: A critical review of the neurological complications of certain specific fevers. *Q J Med* 1956; 25:427–505.

189. Adams RD, Kubik CS: The morbid anatomy of the demyelinative diseases. *Am J Med* 1952; 12:510–546.

190. Adams J, Baird C, Filloy L: Inclusion bodies in measles encephalitis. *JAMA* 1966; 195:290–297.

191. Foreman ML, Cherry JD: Isolation of measles virus from the cerebrospinal fluid of a child with encephalitis following measles vaccination. Presented to the American Pediatric Society, 1967.

192. ter Meulen V, Muller D, Kackell Y, et al: Isolation of infectious measles virus in measles encephalitis. *Lancet* 1972; 2:1172–1175.

193. Gendelman HE, Wolinsky JS, Johnson RT, et al: Measles encephalomyelitis: Lack of evidence of viral invasion of the central nervous system and quantitative study of the nature of demyelination. *Ann Neurol* 1984; 15:353–360.

194. Johnson RT, Griffin DE, Hirsch RL, et al: Measles encephalomyelitis—clinical and immunologic studies. *N Engl J Med* 1984; 310:137–141.

195. Lyon G, Ponsot G, Lebon P: Acute measles encephalitis of the delayed type. *Ann Neurol* 1977; 2:322–327.

196. Murphy JV, Yunis EJ: Encephalopathy following measles infection in children with chronic illness. *J Pediatr* 1976; 88:937–942.

197. Aicardi J, Goutieres F, Arsenio-Nunes M-L, et al: Acute measles encephalitis in children with immunosuppression. *Pediatrics* 1977; 59:232–239.

198. Agamanolis DP, Tan JS, Parker DL: Immunosuppressive measles encephalitis in a patient with a renal transplant. *Arch Neurol* 1979; 36:686–690.

199. Ferraro A, Scheffer IH: Toxic encephalopathy in measles. *Arch Neurol Psychiatry* 1935; 27:1209–1225.

200. Cohen NA: Myocarditis in prodromal measles. *Am J Clin Pathol* 1963; 40:50–53.

201. Finkle HE: Measles myocarditis. *Am Heart J* 1964; 67:679–683.

202. Giustra FX: Final report on a case of myocarditis following measles. *Am J Dis Child* 1954; 87:615.

203. Degan JA: Visceral pathology in measles. *Am J Med Sci* 1937; 194:104–111.

204. Goldfield M, Boyer NH, Weinstein L: Electrocardiographic changes during the course of measles. *J Pediatr* 1955; 46:30–35.

205. Ross LJ: Electrocardiographic findings in measles. *Am J Dis Child* 1952; 83:282–291.

206. Hudson JB: Weinstein L, Chang T-W: Thrombocytopenic purpura in measles. *J Pediatr* 1956; 48:48–56.

207. Maretic Z, Stihovic L, Ogrizak M, et al: Stevens-Johnson syndrome in the course of measles. *J Trop Med Hyg* 1965; 68:50–52.

208. Dawson JR: Cellular inclusions in cerebral lesions of lethargic encephalitis. *Am J Pathol* 1933; 9:7–17.

209. van Bogaert L: Une leuko-encephalite sclerosante subaigue. *J Neurol Neurosurg Psychiatry* 1945; 8:101–120.

210. Pette H, Doring G: Über einheimische Panencephalitis vom Charakter der Encephalitis japonica. *Dtsch Z Nervenheilk* 1939; 149:7–44.

211. Bouteille M, Fontain C, Vedrenne C, et al: Sur un cas d'encéphalitis subaiguë a inclusions: Étude anatomoclinique et ultrastructurale. *Rev Neurol* 1965; 118:454–458.

212. Connolly JH, Allen IV, Hurwitz LJ, et al: Measles-virus antibody and antigen in subacute sclerosing panencephalitis. *Lancet* 1967; 1:542–544.

213. Freeman JM, Magoffin RL, Lennette EH, et al: Additional evidence of the relationship between subacute inclusion-body encephalitis and measles virus. *Lancet* 1967; 2:129–131.

214. Payne FE, Baublis JV, Itabashi HH: Isolation of measles virus from cell cultures of brain from a patient with subacute sclerosing panencephalitis. *N Engl J Med* 1969; 281:585–589.

215. Horta-Barbosa L, Fuccillo DA, London WT, et al: Isolation of measles virus from brain cell cultures of two patients with subacute sclerosing panencephalitis. *Proc Soc Exp Biol Med* 1969; 132:272–277.

216. Modlin JF, Halsey NA, Eddins DL, et al: Epidemiology of subacute sclerosing panencephalitis. *J Pediatr* 1979; 94:231–236.

217. Canal N, Torck P: An epidemiological study of subacute sclerosing leukoencephalitis in Belgium. *J Neurol Sci* 1964; 1:380–389.

218. Jabbour JT, Duenas DA, Sever JL, et al: Epidemiology of subacute sclerosing panencephalitis. *JAMA* 1972; 220:959–962.

219. Modlin JF, Jabbour JT, Witte JJ, et al: Epidemiological studies of measles, measles vaccine and subacute sclerosing panencephalitis. *Pediatrics* 1977; 59:505–512.

220. Cho CT, Lansky LJ, D'Souza BJ: Panencephalitis following measles vaccination. *JAMA* 1973; 224:1229.

221. Freeman JM: The clinical spectrum and early diagnosis of Dawson's encephalitis. *J Pediatr* 1969; 75:590–603.

222. Jabbour JT, Garcia JH, Lemmi H, et al: Subacute sclerosing panencephalitis: A multidisciplinary study of eight cases. *JAMA* 1969; 207:2248–2254.

223. Font RL, Jenis EH, Tuck KD: Measles maculopathy associated with subacute sclerosing panencephalitis. *Arch Pathol* 1973; 96:168–174.

224. Robb RM, Walters GV: Ophthalmic manifestations of subacute sclerosing panencephalitis. *Arch Ophthalmol* 1970; 83:426–435.

225. Case records of the Massachusetts General Hospital. *N Engl J*

Med 1974; 291:141–149.

226. Murphy JV, Yunis EJ, Turner M: Rapidly progressive subacute sclerosing panencephalitis. Presented to the Third Annual Meeting of the Child Neurology Society, Madison, Wisc, Oct 10–12, 1974.

227. Landau WM, Luse SA: Relapsing inclusion encephalitis (Dawson type) of either years; duration. *Neurology* 1962; 8:660–676.

228. Kennedy CA: A ten year experience with subacute sclerosing panencephalitis. *Neurology* 1968; 18(pt 2):58–59.

229. Resnick JS, Engel WK, Sever JL: Subacute sclerosing panencephalitis: Spontaneous improvement in a patient with elevated antibody in blood and spinal fluid. *N Engl J Med* 1968; 279:124–129.

230. Cobb WA, Morgan-Hughes JA: Nonfatal subacute sclerosing leukoencephalitis. *J Neurol Neurosurg Psychiatry* 1968; 31:115–123.

231. Markand O, Panszi JG: The EEG in subacute sclerosing panencephalitis. *Arch Neurol* 1975; 32:719–726.

232. Sever JL, Krebs H, Ley A, et al: Diagnosis of subacute sclerosing panencephalitis: The value and availability of measles antibody determinations. *JAMA* 1974; 228:604–607.

233. Parker JC, Klintworth GK, Graham DG, et al: Uncommon morphologic features of subacute sclerosing panencephalitis (SSPE). *Am J Pathol* 1970; 61:275–292.

234. Greenfield JH: Infectious disease of the central nervous system, in Blackwood W, McMenemey WH, Meyer A, et al (eds): *Greenfield's Neuropathology*, London, Arnold Ltd, 1963, p 206.

235. Herndon RM, Rubenstein LJ: Light and electron microscopy observation on the development of viral particles in the inclusions of Dawson's encephalitis (subacute sclerosing panencephalitis). *Neurology* 1968; 18:(pt 2):8–20.

236. Tans J, Wyers H: Inclusion body encephalitis. *Folia Psychiatr Neurol Neurochir (Neerland)* 1955; 58:438–455.

237. Tellez-Nagel I, Harter DH: Subacute sclerosing leukoencephalitis: Ultrastructure of intranuclear and intracytoplasmic inclusions. *Science* 1966; 154;899–901.

238. Blaese RM, Hofstrand H: Immunocompetence of patients with SSPE. *Arch Neurol* 1975; 32:494–495.

239. Sell KW, Ahmed A: Humoral and cellular immune responses in patients with SSPE. *Arch Neurol* 1975; 32:496.

240. Link H, Panelius M, Salmi AA: Immunoglobulins and measles antibodies in subacute sclerosing panencephalitis. *Arch Neurol* 1973; 28:23–30.

241. Salmi AA, Norrby E, Panelius M: Identification of different measles virus-specific antibodies in the serum and cerebrospinal fluid from patients with subacute sclerosing panencephalitis and multiple sclerosis. *Infect Immun* 1972; 6:248–254.

242. Thurman GB, Ahmed A, Strong DM, et al: Lymphocyte activation in subacute sclerosing panencephalitis virus and cytomegalovirus infections. *J Exp Med* 1973; 138:839–846.

243. Barbosa LH, Blaese MR, Hamilton R: Lymphocytotoxicity assay for evaluating cellular immune function to SSPE measles virus. *Arch Neurol* 1975; 32:499.

244. Kreth HW, Kackell M, ter Meulen V: Demonstration of in vitro lymphocyte-mediated cytotoxicity against measles virus in subacute sclerosing panencephalitis. *J Immunol* 1975; 188:1042–1046.

245. Horta-Barbosa L, Fuccillo DA, Hamilton R, et al: Some characteristics of SSPE measles virus. *Proc Soc Exp Biol Med* 1970; 134:17–21.

246. Hall WW, Kiessling W, ter Meulen V: Membrane proteins of subacute panencephalitis and measles viruses. *Nature* 1978; 272:460–462.

247. Wechler SL, Fields BN: Differences between the intracellular polypeptides of measles and subacute sclerosing panencephalitis virus. *Nature* 1978; 272:458–460.

248. Hall WW, Choppin PW: Measles virus proteins in the brain tissue of patients with subacute sclerosing panencephalitis. *N Engl J Med* 1981; 304:1152–1155.

249. Johnson KP, Norrby E, Swoveland P, et al: Experimental sub-

acute sclerosing panencephalitis: Selective disappearance of measles virus matrix protein from the central nervous system. *J Infect Dis* 1981; 144:161–169.

250. Hall WW, Lamb RA, Choppin PW: Measles and subacute sclerosing panencephalitis virus proteins: Lack of antibodies to the M protein in patients with subacute sclerosing panencephalitis. *Proc Natl Acad Sci* 1979; 76:2047–2051.

251. Wechler SL, Weiner H, Fields BN: Immune response in subacute sclerosing panencephalitis: Reduced antibody response to the matrix protein of measles virus. *J Immunol* 1979; 123:884–889.

252. Carrigan DR: Round cell variant of measles virus: Mechanisms involved in the establishment of defective viral infection of the central nervous system. *Virology* 1986; 155:614–624.

253. Haase AT, Gantz D, Eble B, et al: Natural history of restricted synthesis and expression of measles virus genes in subacute sclerosing panencephalitis. *Proc Natl Acad Sci USA* 1985; 82:3020–3024.

254. Albrecht P, Burnstein T, Klutch MJ, et al: Subacute sclerosing panencephalitis experimental infection in primates. *Science* 1977; 195:64–66.

255. Katz M, Rorke LB, Masland WS, et al: Subacute sclerosing panencephalitis: Isolation of a virus encephalitogenic for ferrets. *J Infect Dis* 1970; 121:188–195.

256. Byington DP, Johnson KP: Experimental subacute sclerosing panencephalitis in the hamster: Correlation of age with chronic inclusion-cell encephalitis. *J Infect Dis* 1972; 126:18–26.

257. Siegal MM, Walker TK, Ablin AR: Measles pneumonia in childhood leukemia. *Pediatrics* 1977; 60:38–40.

258. Mawhinney H, Allen IV, Beare JM, et al: Dysgammaglobulinemia complicated by disseminated measles. *Br Med J* 1971; 2:380–381.

259. Enders JF, McCarthy K, Mitus A, et al: Isolation of measles virus at autopsy in cases of giant-cell pneumonia without rash. *N Engl J Med* 1959; 261:875–881.

260. Meadow SR, Weller RO, Archibald RWR: Fatal systemic measles in a child receiving cyclophosphamide for nephrotic syndrome. *Lancet* 1969; 2:876–878.

261. Koffler D: Giant cell pneumonia. *Arch Pathol* 1964; 78:267–273.

262. McConnell EM: Giant cell pneumonia in an adult. *Br Med J* 1969; 2:288–289.

263. Mitus A, Holloway A, Evans AE, et al: Attenuated measles vaccine in children with acute leukemia. *Am J Dis Child* 1962; 103:413–418.

264. Roos RP, Graves MC, Wollman RL, et al: Immunologic and virologic studies of measles inclusion body encephalitis in an immunosuppressed host: The relationship to subacute sclerosing panencephalitis. *Neurology* 1981; 31:1263–1270.

265. Pedersen FK, Schiotz PO, Valerius NH, et al: Immunosuppressive measles encephalopathy. *Acta Pediatr Scand* 1978; 67:109–112.

266. Valmari P, Lanning M, Tuokko H, et al: Measles virus in the cerebrospinal fluid in postvaccination immunosuppressive measles encephalopathy. *Pediatr Infect Dis* 1987; 6:59–63.

267. Dyer I: Measles complicating pregnancy. *South Med J* 1940; 33:601–604.

268. Jespersen CS, Littauer J, Sagild U: Measles as a cause of fetal defects: A retrospective study of ten measles epidemics in Greenland. *Acta Pediatr Scand* 1977; 66:367–372.

269. Siegel M: Congenital malformations following chickenpox, measles, mumps, and hepatitis. *JAMA* 1973; 226:1521.

270. Siegel M, Fuerst HT: Low birth weight and maternal viral diseases: A prospective study of rubella, measles, mumps, chickenpox, and hepatitis. *JAMA* 1966; 197:88.

271. Gazela E, Karplus M, Liberman JR, et al: The effect of maternal measles on the fetus. *Pediatr Infect Dis* 1985; 4:203–204.

272. Kohn JL: Measles in newborn infants (maternal infection). *J Pediatr* 1933; 3:176–180.

273. Rauh LW, Schmidt R: Measles immunization with killed virus vaccine. *Am J Dis Child* 1965; 109:232–237.

274. Fulginiti VA, Eller JJ, Downie AW, et al: Altered reactivity to

measles virus. *JAMA* 1967; 202:1075–1080.

275. Nader PR, Horwitz MS, Rousseau J: Atypical exanthem following exposure to natural measles: Eleven cases in children previously inoculated with killed vaccine. *J Pediatr* 1968; 72:22–28.
276. Gokiert JG, Beamish WE: Altered reactivity to measles virus in previously vaccinated children. *Can Med Assoc J* 1970; 103:724–727.
277. McLean DM, Kettyls GDM, Hingston J, et al: Atypical measles following immunization with killed measles vaccine. *Can Med Assoc J* 1970; 103:743–744.
278. Cherry JD, Feigan RD, Lobes LA, et al: Atypical measles in children previously immunized with attenuated measles virus vaccines. *Pediatrics* 1972; 50:712–717.
279. Brodsky AL: Atypical measles. *JAMA* 1972; 222:1415–1416.
280. Fulginiti VA, Helfer RE: Atypical measles in adolescent siblings 16 years after killed measles virus vaccine. *JAMA* 1980; 244:804–806.
281. Annunziato D, Kaplan MH, Hall WW, et al: Atypical measles syndrome: Pathologic and serologic findings. *Pediatrics* 1982; 70:203–209.
282. Martin DB, Weiner LB, Nieburg PI, et al: Atypical measles in adolescents and young adults. *Ann Intern Med* 1979; 90:877–881.
283. Welliver RC, Cherry JD, Holtzman AE: Typical, modified and atypical measles. *Arch Intern Med* 1972; 137:39–47.
284. Weiner LB, Corwin RM, Nieburg PI, et al: A measles outbreak among adolescents. *J Pediatr* 1977; 90:17–20.
285. Laptook A, Wind E, Nussbaum M, et al: Pulmonary lesions in atypical measles. *Pediatrics* 1978; 62:42–46.
286. Editorial: Pneumonia in atypical measles. *Br Med J* 1971; 2:235.
287. Young LW, Smith DI, Glasgow LA: Pneumonia of atypical measles: Residual nodular lesions. *Am J Roentgenol* 1970; 110:439–448.
288. Norrby E, Lagercrantz R, Gard S: Measles vaccination: VII. Following-up studies in children immunized with four doses of inactivated vaccine. *Acta Paediatr Scand* 1969; 58:261–267.
289. Horwitz MS, Grose C, Fisher M: Atypical measles rash mimicking Rocky Mountain spotted fever. *N Engl J Med* 1973; 289:1203–1204.
290. Haas EJ, Wendt VE: Atypical measles 14 years after immunization. *JAMA* 1976; 236:1050.
291. Norrby E, Enders-Ruckle G, ter Meulen V: Difference in the appearance of antibodies to structural components of measles virus after immunization with inactivated and live virus. *J Infect Dis* 1975; 132:262–269.
292. Morley D, Woodland M, Martin WJ: Measles in Nigerian children. *J Hyg* 1963; 16:115–134.
293. Scheifele DW, Forves CE: Prolonged giant cell excretion in severe African measles. *Pediatrics* 1972; 50:867–873.
294. Hayden RJ: The epidemiology and nature of measles in Nairobi before the impact of measles immunization. *East Afr Med J* 1974; 51:199–205.
295. Aaby P: Malnutrition and overcrowding/intensive exposure in severe measles infection: Review of community studies. *Rev Infect Dis* 1988; 10:478–491.
296. Lamb WH: Epidemic measles in a highly immunized rural West African (Gambian) village. *Rev Infect Dis* 1988; 10:457–462.
297. Aaby P, Bukh J, Lisse IM, et al: Overcrowding and intensive exposure as determinants of measles mortality. *Am J Epidemiol* 1984; 120:49–63.
298. Aaby P, Bukh J, Lisse IM, et al: Measles vaccination and reduction in child mortality: A community study from Guinea-Bissau. *J Infect* 1984; 8:13–21.
299. Morley DC, Martin WJ, Allen I: Measles in East and Central Africa. *East Afr Med J* 1967; 44:497–508.
300. Whittle HC, Bradley-Moore A, Fleming A, et al: Effects of measles on the immune response of Nigerian children. *Arch Dis Child* 1973; 43:753–756.
301. Hull HF, Williams PJ, Oldfield F: Measles mortality and vaccine efficacy in rural West Africa. *Lancet* 1983; 1:972–975.
302. John TJ: Measles in India, a neglected problem. *Indian J Pediatr*

1983; 50:399–403.

303. Halsey NA, Boulos R, Mode F, et al: Response to measles vaccine in Haitian infants 6 to 12 months old: Influence of maternal antibodies, malnutrition, and concurrent illnesses. *N Engl J Med* 1985; 313:544–549.
304. Saha SM, Aggarwal RK, Sood DK, et al: Seroconversion in different age groups after measles vaccination. *Indian J Pediatr* 1985; 52:303–305.
305. Ndikuyeze A, Munoz A, Stewart J, et al: Immunogenicity and safety of measles vaccine in ill African children. *Int J Epidemiol* 1988; 17:448–455.
306. Baer CL, Bratt DE, Edwards R, et al: Response of mildly to moderately malnourished children to measles vaccination. *West Indian Med J* 1986; 35:106–111.
307. Taylor WR, Mambu RK, ma-Disu M, et al: Measles control efforts in urban Africa complicated by high incidence of measles in the first year of life. *Am J Epidemiol* 1988; 127:788–794.
308. Dabis F, Sow A, Waldman RJ, et al: The epidemiology of measles in a partially vaccinated population in an African city: Implications for immunization programs. *Am J Epidemiol* 1988; 127:171–178.
309. Aaby P, Bukh J, Leerhoy J, et al: Vaccinated children get milder measles infection: A community study from Guinea-Bissau. *J Infect Dis* 1986; 154:858–863.
310. Measles Vaccines Committee to the Medical Research Council: Vaccination against measles: A study of clinical reactions and serological responses of young children. *Br Med J* 1965; 1:817.
311. Ruuskanen O, Salmi TT, Halonen P: Measles vaccination after exposure to natural measles. *J Pediatr* 1978; 93:43–46.
312. Warren J, Gallian MJ: Concentrated inactivated measles-virus vaccine. *Am J Dis Child* 1966; 103:418–423.
313. Fulginiti VA, Kempe CH: Measles exposure among vaccine recipients. *Am J Dis Child* 1963; 106:450–461.
314. Winkelstein W, Karzon DT, Rush D, et al: A field trial of inactivated measles virus vaccine in young school children. *JAMA* 1965; 194:494–498.
315. Karzon DT, Rush D, Winkelstein W: Immunization with inactivated measles virus vaccine: Effect of booster dose and response to natural challenge. *Pediatrics* 1965; 36:40–50.
316. Scott TF, Bonanno DE: Reactions to live-measles-virus vaccine in children previously inoculated with killed-virus vaccine. *N Engl J Med* 1967; 277:248–250.
317. Fulginiti VA, Arthur JH, Pearlman DS, et al: Altered reactivity to measles virus. *Am J Dis Child* 1967; 115:671–676.
318. Chatterji M, Markad M: Failure of attenuated viral vaccine in prevention of atypical measles. *JAMA* 1977; 238:2635.
319. Enders JF, Katz SL, Milovanovic MB: Studies on an attenuated measles-virus vaccine: I. Development and preparation of the vaccine: Technics for assay of effects of vaccination. *N Engl J Med* 1960; 263:153–159.
320. Katz SL, Enders JF, Holloway A: Studies on attenuated measles-virus vaccine. II. Clinical, virologic and immunologic effects on vaccine in institutionalized children. *N Engl J Med* 1960; 263:159–161
321. Katz SL, Enders JF: Immunization of children with a live, attenuated measles virus. *Am J Dis Child* 1959; 98:605–607.
322. Kempe CH, Ott EW, St Vincent L, et al: Studies on an attenuated measles-virus vaccine: III. Clinical and antigenic effects of vaccine in institutionalized children. *N Engl J Med* 1960; 263:162–165.
323. Katz SL, Kempe CH, Black FL, et al: Studies on an attenuated measles-virus vaccine. VIII. General summary and evaluation of the results of vaccination. *N Engl J Med* 1960; 263:180–184.
324. McCrumb FR, Kress S, Saunders E, et al: Studies with live attenuated measles vaccine. I. Clinical and immunologic responses in institutionalized children. *Am J Dis Child* 1961; 101:689–700.
325. Weibel R, Halenda R, Stokes J, et al: Administration of Enders live measles virus vaccine with human immune globulin. *JAMA* 1962; 180:1086–1094.
326. McCrumb FR, Hornick RB, Kress S, et al: Studies with live at-

tenuated measles-virus vaccine. III. Development of a practical method of large-scale immunization. *Am J Dis Child* 1961; 101:708–712.

327. Martin CM, Manfredonia SJ, Webb NC, et al: Controlled trial of live measles vaccine. *Am J Dis Child* 1963; 100:267–279.

328. Oski FA, Naiman JL: Effect of live measles vaccine on the platelet count. *N Engl J Med* 1966; 275:352–356.

329. Wilhelm DJ, Paegle RD: Thrombocytopenic purpura and pneumonia following measles vaccination. *Am J Dis Child* 1967; 113:534–537.

330. Alter HJ, Scanlon RT, Schechter GP: Thrombocytopenic purpura following vaccination with attenuated measles virus. *Am J Dis Child* 1968; 115:111–113.

331. Landrigan PJ, Witte JJ: Neurologic disorders following live measles vaccination. *JAMA* 1973; 223:1459–1462.

332. Brunell PA: Measles vaccine—one or two doses? *Pediatrics* 1988; 81:722–724.

333. Krugman S: Present status of measles and rubella immunization in the United States: A medical progress report. *J Pediatr* 1977; 90:1–12.

334. Orenstein WA, Hermann K, Albrecht P, et al: Immunity against measles and rubella in Massachusetts school children. *Dev Biol Stand* 1986; 65:75–83.

335. Lerman SJ, Gold E: Measles in children previously vaccinated against measles. *JAMA* 1971; 216:1311–1314.

336. Shasby DM, Shope TC, Downs H, et al: Epidemic measles in a highly vaccinated population. *N Engl J Med* 1977; 296:585–589.

337. Baratta RO, Ginter MC, Price MA, et al: Measles (rubeola) in previously immunized children. *Pediatrics* 1970; 46:375–402.

338. Wyll SA, Witte JJ: Measles in previously vaccinated children. *JAMA* 1975; 216:1306–1310.

339. Currier RW, Hardy GE, Conrad, JC: Measles in previously vaccinated children. *Am J Dis Child* 1972; 124:854–857.

340. Schluederberg A, Lamm SH, Landrigan PJ, et al: Measles immunity in children vaccinated before one year of age. *Am J Epidemiol* 1973; 97:402–409.

341. McCormick JB, Halsey NA, Rosenberg R: Measles vaccine efficacy determined from secondary attack rates during a severe epidemic. *J Pediatr* 1977; 90:13–16.

342. Marks JS, Halpin TJ, Orenstein WA: Measles vaccine efficacy in children previously vaccinated at 12 months of age. *Pediatrics* 1978; 62:955–960.

343. Shelton JD, Jacobson JE, Orenstein WA, et al: Measles vaccine efficacy: Influence of age at vaccination vs duration of time since vaccination. *Pediatrics* 1978; 62:961–964.

344. Orenstein WA, Markowitz L, Preblud SR, et al: Appropriate age

for measles vaccination in the United States. *Dev Biol Stand* 1986; 65:13–21.

345. Yeager AS, Davis JH, Ross LA, et al: Measles immunization. *JAMA* 1977; 237:347–351.

346. Krugman RD, Rosenberg R, McIntosh K, et al: Further attenuated live measles vaccines: The need for revised recommendations. *J Pediatr* 1977; 91:766–767

347. Linneman CC, Dine MD, Roselle GA, et al: Measles immunity after revaccination: Results in children vaccinated before 10 months of age. *Pediatr* 1974; 85:512–514.

348. *Report of the Committee on Infectious Diseases (Redbook).* Evanston, Ill, American Academy of Pediatrics, 1977.

349. Lennon JL, Black FL: Maternally derived measles immunity in era of vaccine-protected mothers. *J Pediatr* 1986; 108:671–676.

350. Krugman RD, Meyer BC, Enterline JC, et al: Impotency of live virus vaccines as a result of improper handling in clinical practice. *J Pediatr* 1974; 85:512–514.

351. Hayden GF: Measles vaccine failure: A survey of causes and means of prevention. *Clin Pediatr* 1979; 18:155–167.

352. American Academy of Pediatrics: Committee on Infectious Diseases: Redbook update. *Pediatrics* 1982; 70:819–822.

353. Krugman S: Measles immunization: New recommendations. *JAMA* 1977; 237:366.

354. Markowitz LE, Bernier RH: Immunization of young infants with Edmonston-Zagreb measles vaccine. *Pediatr Infect Dis* 1987; 6:809–812.

355. Khanum S, Uddin N, Garelick H, et al: Comparison of Edmonston-Zagreb and Schwarz strains of measles vaccine given by aerosol or subcutaneous injection. *Lancet* 1987; 1:150–153.

356. Sabin AB, Flores Arechiga A, Fernandez de Castro J, et al: Successful immunization of infants with and without maternal antibody by aerosolized measles vaccine: II. Vaccine comparisons and evidence for multiple antibody response. *JAMA* 1984; 251:2363–2371.

357. Whittle HC, Mann G, Eccles M, et al: Effects of dose and strain of vaccine on success of measles vaccination of infants aged 4–5 months. *Lancet* 1988; 1:963–966.

358. Sabin AB, Albrecht P, Takeda AK, et al: High effectiveness of aerosolized chick embryo fibroblast measles vaccine in seven-month-old and older infants. *J Infect Dis* 1985; 152:1231–1237.

359. Hinman AR: World eradication of measles. *Rev Infect Dis* 1982; 4:933–936.

360. Millar JD: Theoretical and practical problems in measles control, in *CDC Smallpox Eradication Report* 1970; vol 4, pp 175–176.

361. Sencer DJ, Dull HB, Langmuir AD: Epidemiologic basis for eradication of measles in 1976. *Public Health Rep.* 1967; 32:253–256.

Respiratory Syncytial Virus

Robert B. Belshe
Maurice A. Mufson

The first description of pneumonia in children believed to be of viral etiology was published by Goodpasture et al in 1939.[1] Subsequently, Adams reported the occurrence of pneumonia in 32 infants with nine associated deaths which had occurred in January,

February, and March of 1937.[2] This outbreak was a nosocomial epidemic in a newborn nursery and the disease was characterized by cough, dyspnea, and cyanosis in the affected infants. The lungs from each of the deceased infants that were examined cytopathologically exhibited cytoplasmic inclusion bodies in the bronchial epithelial cells. Most likely, this represented the first detailed description of a nosocomial respiratory syncytial virus (RSV) outbreak and the first pathologic description of infants dying from severe RSV infection. RSV remains the most important cause of lower respiratory illness in infants. In Naples, Italy, in 1978 to 1979, a "mystery disease" (il male oscuro) was responsible for approximately 60 infant deaths; the disease was shown to be caused primarily by RSV.[3] This event directed the public's attention to RSV as the most common cause of severe respiratory infection in infants.

HISTORY

RSV was first isolated in 1956 from chimpanzees when an epidemic of viral respiratory disease occurred among a colony in captivity.[4] Initially, the virus was termed chimpanzee coryza agent because of the purulent rhinorrhea that was prominent in infected chimpanzees. One of the animal handlers became ill and developed a similar illness; the authors speculated that chimpanzee coryza agent was principally a disease of man and that the chimpanzee colony had acquired the agent from man. The following year Chanock and coworkers recovered a virus from infants ill with lower respiratory disease.[5] The virus was subsequently shown to be identical to that of chimpanzee coryza agent. The new agent was named respiratory syncytial virus to connote not only the clinical manifestations of infection but also the characteristic syncytial cytopathologic finding in infected tissue cultures (Figure 14–1). The isolation of RSV from ill infants ushered in an era of extensive study of the epidemiology of viral respiratory disease in infants and young children.

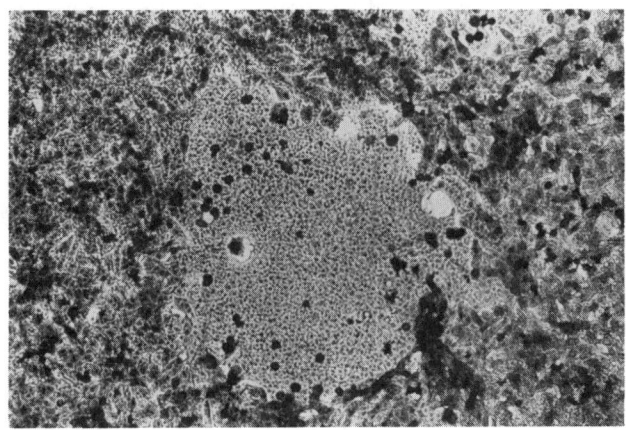

Figure 14–1. Characteristic syncytia formation by respiratory syncytial virus in HEp-2 cells.

CLASSIFICATION, STRUCTURE, AND REPLICATION OF RSV

RSV is related to the parainfluenza viruses. However, there are several distinctions that have led to its being placed in the genus *Pneumovirus*. RSV exhibits fusion activity, but it does not have the hemagglutination, hemadsorption, hemolytic, or neuraminidase activity associated with some of the other paramyxoviruses.[6] It is a pleomorphic, enveloped virus with a diameter of 300 to 350 nm exhibiting both spherical and filamentous forms (Figure 14–2). Within the envelope is a helical nucleocapsid with a diameter of 13.5 nm and a helix pitch of 6.5 nm.[7] On the surface of the virion are 12- to 15-nm spikes. These spikes have been partially purified and consist of two glycoproteins.

The genome of RSV is a single-stranded RNA in negative sense of approximately 15,000 nucleotides. It encodes ten messenger RNAs (mRNA) and each mRNA encodes a single polypeptide. The RSV proteins that appear to be related with other paramyxoviruses include the nucleocapsid protein (N); the phosphoprotein (P); the large protein (L), believed to have polymerase activity; the matrix protein (M); the attachment glycoprotein on the envelope (G); and the fusion glycoprotein (F) on the envelope. Several other RSV proteins have been identified but their function is not yet fully described. These include the envelope-associated 22-kilodalton (kd) protein (22K), nonstructural proteins 1B and 1C, and the small hydrophobic protein 1A. The viral gene order has been determined to be 3'-1C - 1B - N - P - M - 1A - G - F - 22K - L -5".[8–12] Unlike other paramyxoviruses, the intergenic regions are not conserved in sequence and in length.[8] Furthermore, there is no intergenic region between 22K and L and these messages overlap by 153 nucleotides. It has been postulated that the 22K gene end signal acts as an attenuator within the L gene which might modulate transcription of this gene independently from other viral genes.[8]

The G and F proteins are envelope-associated proteins; the G protein may be responsible for viral attachments to cells and F is the putative fusion protein of RSV. Unlike the attachment protein of other paramyxoviruses, the G protein of RSV is smaller and heavily glycosylated, including not only N-linked, but also O-linked sugar moieties. The F protein shows many similarities to the homologous protein of other paramyxoviruses; proteolytic cleavage of the F protein breaks the disulfide-linked complex of a 48K F_1 fragment and a 20K F_2 fragment.[12] Both the G and F glycoproteins of RSV play a role in immune protection.

The structure of G has been deduced from nucleotide sequence data on complementary DNA (cDNA) clones.[13, 14] The protein is 298 amino acids long, which gives a molecular mass of 32,588 daltons. A single 23-amino-acid-long hydrophobic domain has been interpreted to allow membrane insertion of 41 residues from the NH_2 terminus. Heavy glycosylation with both the N- and O-linked sugars[12–14] is the cause of the apparent molecular mass of 90 kd of the G protein.

For the three decades since its discovery, RSV has been considered to represent a single homogeneous serotype. In the early 1960s, cross-neutralization tests with animal hyperimmune sera demonstrated subtle differences between some RSV isolates, but no corresponding differences were observed with serum specimens from infants and thus they were not considered to be of any relevance.[15–17] With the advent of monoclonal antibodies, the antigenic variation of RSV could be assessed again. Now RSV can be separated into two subgroups based on characteristic reaction patterns with collections of monoclonal antibodies.[18, 19] The two subgroups of RSV are designated as subgroup A and subgroup B. The Long strain is the prototype of subgroup A, and strain CH18537, the first strain found to differ antigenically from the Long strain, is the prototype of subgroup B. The widely used A2 strain is a subgroup A strain also.[20]

The two subgroups of RSV show different properties in several structural proteins, the G, F, N, M, and P proteins.[18–21] The major antigenic differences between the two subgroups occur in the G proteins, which share only one of six epitopes, and in the F proteins, which show differences in one epitope.[19] The size of the F protein cleavage products and the P protein also differ between the two subgroups.[20, 21] The molecular weight of the F_1 cleavage product is 48 kd in subgroup A and 46 to 47 kd in subgroup B strains; the size of the F_2 cleavage product is 18 to 20 kd in subgroup A strains and 18.5 to 20 kd in subgroup B strains.[20] The size of the P protein is 36 kd in subgroup A strains, but only 34

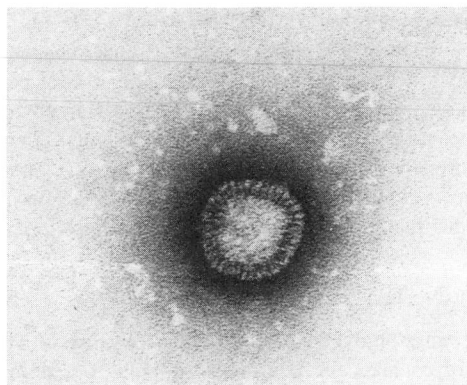

Figure 14–2. Electron micrograph of respiratory syncytial virus. Glycoprotein spikes are evident on the viral envelope (original magnification × 150,000). *(Photo courtesy of Dr Bruce Fernie.)*

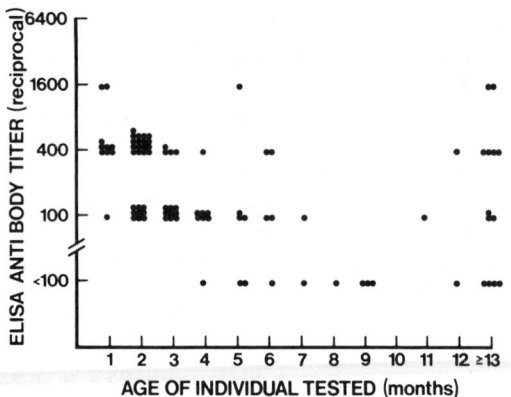

Figure 14–3. Respiratory syncytial virus (RSV) antibody titer as measured by enzyme-linked immunosorbent assay in the acute phase serum of infants and young children with RSV disease by age. *(Adapted from Richardson et al.[30])*

kd in subgroup B strains.[20] The size of the G protein also differs between the two subgroups.[22] Two variants of subgroup B strains, designated B1 and B2, have been described. All B2 strains had G proteins of molecular weight 92–95K; however, B1 strains exhibited marked variation in the size of the G protein, ranging from 81–95K.[22a]

RSV replicates optimally in HeLa and HEp-2 cell lines; Chang liver, WI-38, KB, monkey kidney, and BEK cells support growth of the virus also. After a two-hour adsorption period, there is an eclipse phase of approximately six to 12 hours and a logarithmic growth phase that lasts another 12 to 24 hours.[23] Peak quantities of infectious virus are seen in the supernatant of infected cells between two and three days after infection. Intracytoplasmic viral antigen may be detected by fluorescent antibody techniques as early as seven hours following infection; cell-free virus appears three to five hours later, but up to 90% of the virus remains cell-associated.[23] Continued high multiplicity passage of RSV generates defective-interfering (DI) particles. These DI particles decrease both cytopathic effects and the yield of infectious virus.[24]

On the basis of complementation group analysis, Wright et al reported three mutually exclusive complementation groups of temperature-sensitive (ts) mutants derived from the A2 strain of RSV.[25] One of the A2 strain ts mutants, ts-2, is a plaque morphology mutant that does not fuse cells to form syncytia. The ts-2 mutant is defective in adsorption and/or penetration under nonpermissive conditions (growth temperature of 39°C); after a brief period of adsorption at permissive temperature, the infected cells may be "shifted up" to nonpermissive temperature and viral growth will proceed normally.[26] Loss of the ts phenotype by ts-2 is associated with a reacquisition of fusion activity. On this basis, Belshe et al proposed that the ts defect resides in the fusion protein.[26, 27]

EPIDEMIOLOGY

Early studies on the epidemiology of RSV relied on the measurement of complement-fixing (CF) antibody to determine the prevalence of RSV infections. However, neutralizing antibody, measured by tube dilution or plaque reduction assay, is more sensitive for detecting low levels of antibody.[28, 29] More recently,

enzyme-linked immunosorbent assay (ELISA) has been used in seroepidemiologic studies.[30]

The CF technique, although relatively insensitive for determining past infections with RSV, revealed that up to 50% of adults in all areas of the world manifested CF antibody to RSV. The more sensitive plaque reduction assay has revealed that 100% of adults tested have antibody to RSV.[31] Studies on the serologic epidemiology of RSV have been done on peoples of western and northern Europe, the United States, Oceania, the Arctic, Taiwan, Jamaica, Trinidad, India, Japan, Scandinavia, South Africa, Central Africa, and other areas.[32–46] Uniformly, these studies have shown antibody to be present in a high proportion of adults, and antibody prevalence in adults varies depending on the technique for determining antibody to RSV rather than on the population studied. Serologic epidemiology studies done in the United States and in Japan have revealed that most infants less than 6 months of age possess maternal antibody. Antibody wanes by 6 to 12 months of age as detected by the neutralization technique or ELISA (Figure 14–3). By 1 and 2 years of age, 50% to 75% of children have circulating antibody to RSV, and by 4 years of age, at least 80% of children have developed antibody.

Epidemiologic investigation of RSV infections based on culturing viruses from the respiratory tract has revealed that in all northern climates epidemics of RSV occur annually. In general, epidemics occur in the winter or spring months. In a study involving over 5000 patients with respiratory disease in Washington, DC, RSV was recovered in each of 13 years of study during epidemics that occurred annually during the winter months (Figure 14–4).[34] Annual epidemics have occurred in small towns and communities as well as large cities.[47] In tropical climates, some investigators have reported epidemics of RSV infections during the rainy season. In Trinidad-Tobago, this occurred on an annual basis.[37] In other equatorial regions including Chandigarh, India, the virus

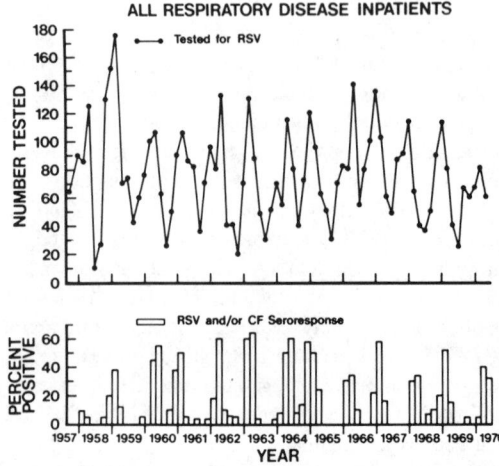

Figure 14–4. Respiratory syncytial virus infection in all patients who were hospitalized for respiratory disease, by 2-month intervals, from October 1957 to June 1970. (Reproduced with permission from Kim HW, et al: Epidemiology of respiratory syncytial virus infection in Washington, D.C. I. Importance of the virus in different respiratory tract disease syndromes and temporal distribution of infection. *Am J Epidemiol* 1973; 98:216–225.)

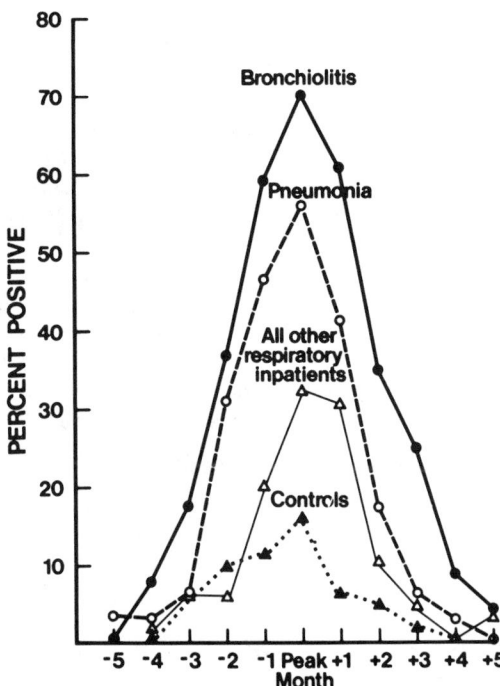

Figure 14–5. Frequency of respiratory syncytial virus (RSV) infection as indicated by isolation of RSV and/or complement-fixing (CF) antibody response by month of RSV epidemic. Peak month refers to the month in which RSV was most frequently isolated from respiratory disease inpatients. (Reproduced with permission from Brandt CD, et al: Epidemiology of respiratory syncytial virus infection in Washington, DC: III. Composite analysis of eleven consecutive yearly epidemics. *Am J Epidemiol* 1973; 98:355–364.)

has been found to occur in up to 8 months of the year, although periods of epidemic activity were detected.[48] Children in West Bengal tended to be infected during the postmonsoon season.[39] In South Africa, RSV epidemics occurred principally during their autumn months of May, June, and July.[49]

In temperate climates, epidemics of RSV occur in sharp peaks. A composite epidemic curve from 11 years of consecutive RSV disease at Children's Hospital in Washington, DC, revealed that 82% of RSV isolates were obtained during the three midepidemic months (Figure 14–5).[50] Low levels of RSV activity occur between epidemics, but RSV is rarely isolated in August and September.

Bronchiolitis occurs most commonly at 2 months of age.[51] Thereafter, the frequency of children hospitalized with this clinical syndrome rapidly decreases, and bronchiolitis is uncommon after 12 months of age (Figure 14–6). This pattern of RSV bronchiolitis is observed in Europe as well as the United States.[52] Similarly, RSV pneumonia occurs most frequently at 2 months of age and gradually decreases in occurrence during the first 2 years of life (Figure 14–7).

The risk of hospitalization from lower respiratory disease has been estimated in five studies (Table 14–1). Area of residence (urban or rural) was found to influence the rate of hospitalization from RSV disease in England but not in the United States.[52] Other possible risk factors for hospitalization include low socioeconomic status and low antibody level in umbilical cord blood.[53] When evaluated in a prospective study, breast feeding did not exert a protective influence from RSV infection.[54]

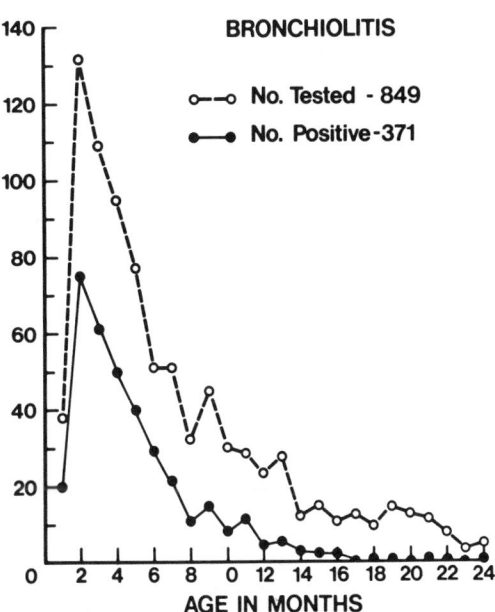

Figure 14–6. Occurrence of respiratory syncytial virus (RSV) bronchiolitis by age during the first 2 years of life. Infection was indicated by isolation of RSV and/or complement-fixing (CF) antibody response (January 1960–June 1970). (Reproduced with permission from Parrott RH, et al: Epidemiology of respiratory syncytial virus infection in Washington, DC: II. Infection and disease with respect to age, immunologic status, race, and sex. *Am J Epidemiol* 1973; 98:289–300.)

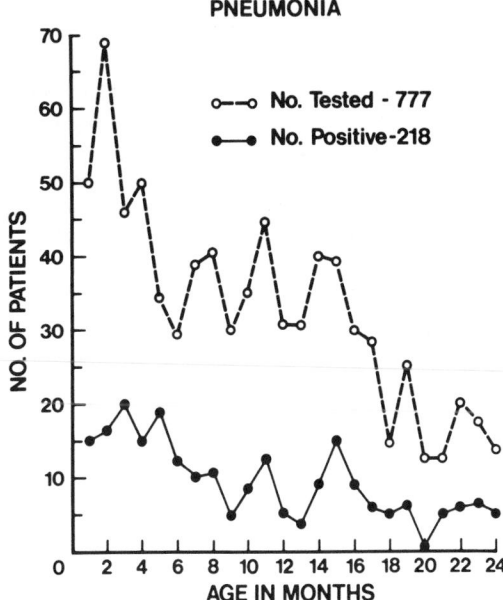

Figure 14–7. Occurrence of respiratory syncytial virus (RSV) pneumonia by age during the first 2 years of life. Infection was indicated by isolation of RSV and/or serum complement-fixing (CF) antibody response (January 1960–June 1970). (Reproduced with permission from Parrott RH, et al: Epidemiology of respiratory syncytial virus infection in Washington, DC: II. Infection and disease with respect to age, immunologic status, race, and sex. *Am J Epidemiol* 1973; 98:289–300.)

Table 14-1
Risk of Hospitalization with Respiratory Syncytial Virus Infection Among Children Less than 12 Months Old

Rate per 1000 Infants/Year	Country (Location)	Reference
5.8–11.1	Sweden	86
9–38*	England (Newcastle)	52
2.8–9.2	United States (Houston)	53
12†	United States (Huntington, WVa)	114
10‡	United States (Washington, DC)	34

Urban greater than rural.
†No difference between urban and rural.
‡Bronchiolitis only.

The nursery school, day care center, and family unit are common grounds for RSV transmission. Epidemic RSV may be severe in homes for infants, and transmission occurs to most children within nursery schools.[55–59] There is a high degree of penetrance of illness in children infected in these situations; asymptomatic infection of young children is not the usual event.[60] The attack rate of RSV in isolated Arctic communities was also high among infants 2 to 5 months old.[44] Seventy-five percent of this group became infected in one epidemic.

Among families, spread of RSV is common.[61, 62] In an extensive study by Hall et al, members of 44% of families became infected during one epidemic.[61] Overall 22% of family members were involved. However, among RSV-positive families, 46% of individuals became infected. The highest attack rate, 62%, occurred in infants living in RSV-positive families; 38% to 47% of older children or adults became infected. Families residing in the city were infected prior to families living outside the city. Admission to hospital of city infants preceded admission to hospital of noncity infants and paralleled the pattern of spread of RSV from city families to suburban families.

Subgroup Epidemiology

With the advent of monoclonal antibodies and the recognition of two subgroups of RSV, the epidemiology of this infection is being reexamined to ascertain the relative occurrence of the two subgroups. Among five epidemics of RSV in Huntington, West Virginia, from 1981 to 1986, subgroup A strains occurred, on the average, 3 times as often as subgroup B strains.[63] In each of the 5 years, subgroup A and B strains occurred together throughout the duration of the epidemic. Hendry and coworkers also reported the occurrence of strains of both subgroups during two epidemics of RSV: 1981–1982 and 1983–1984.[64] Åkerlind and Norrby[65] reported that subgroup A and B strains occurred together in Stockholm during 1984, the one year they tested 12 strains of RSV. Annual epidemics of RSV in temperate climates occur during the winter and early spring. In the Northern Hemisphere, RSV epidemics start early in alternate years, and the peak months are December and January; the epidemic starts late in other years, and

the peak months are March and April. The occurrence of the subgroup A and B strains of RSV follow this pattern.[63, 66]

Subgroup A and subgroup B strains of RSV were recovered during all five epidemic years (Figure 14–8). The number of subgroup B strains isolated each year was relatively constant and ranged between seven and 12. The recovery of subgroup A strains was also relatively constant, with more than 30 strains isolated each epidemic year, except in 1984–1985. The 1984–1985 season was unique in that only three subgroup A strains were isolated. The total reisolation of RSV in this epidemic year was 15 of 23 strains. As a result, the ratio of occurrence of subgroup A/B strains in this year was reversed to 1:4, compared with the other years in which the ratio varied from 3:1 to 6:1. The epidemic of 1984–1985 was the smallest epidemic of RSV, even though approximately the same number of infants and children were tested in that year as in other epidemic years.[63]

The pattern of RSV epidemics in Huntington, West Virginia tended to follow the pattern of the peak occurrence, alternating early and late in successive years, a pattern first described by Chanock and his associated in studies among infants and children in Washington, DC.[31] Both subgroup A and subgroup B strains followed this pattern of occurrence, and the epidemic of 1984–1985, which was predominantly an epidemic of subgroup B strains, did not vary from that pattern.[63]

The demographic characteristics of infants and children with subgroup A and subgroup B RSV infections were similar (Table 14–2). Males were more often infected with RSV than were females, and the proportion of males to females was similar in subgroup A and subgroup B infections. The distribution by age of infants and children was also similar between the two subgroups. No difference between subgroup A and subgroup B was detected in the proportion of children admitted to the hospital for RSV infection. The clinical categorization of the illnesses associated with subgroup A and subgroup B strains appeared to differ between the two subgroups of RSV. Fewer children with subgroup B infections developed bronchiolitis compared with children with subgroup A infections.[63]

TRANSMISSION OF RSV

RSV is most efficiently transmitted by close contact with an infected infant. Among seven adults caring for infected infants for two to four hours, five became infected.[67] Among ten adults who touched surfaces contaminated with secretions from infected infants and who then autoinoculated their conjunctival or nasal membranes, four became infected. In another study, none of 14 adults sitting at a distance of greater than 6 ft from RSV-infected infants became infected.[68] These studies suggest that fomites are responsible for transmission of RSV to adults. RSV can be recovered from countertops for up to six hours and from other surfaces such as cloth gowns and paper tissue for up to 45 minutes and from skin for up to 20 minutes.[68]

The infectivity of RSV varied according to route of inoculation in experimental infections of adults.[69] Infection by the oral route did not occur frequently. Infection by intranasal or conjunctival inoculation was accomplished by a dose of $10^{5.2}$ $TCID_{50}$ (50% tissue culture infectious dose) in adult volunteers. Aerosol administration as little as $10^{2.7}$ $TCID_{50}$ infected adult volunteers.

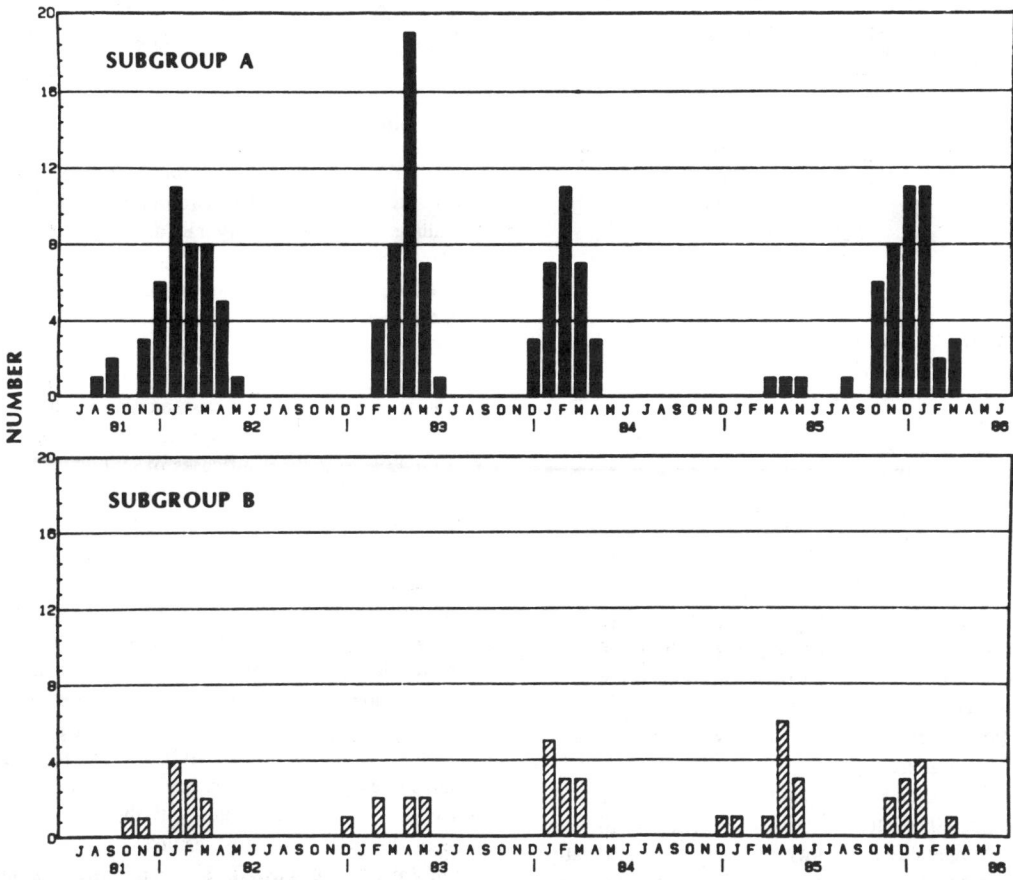

Figure 14–8. Temporal distribution of subgroup A *(solid bars)* and subgroup B *(hatched bars)* strains of respiratory syncytial virus in Huntington, West Virginia, 1981–1986. (Reproduced with permission from Mufson MA, et al: Respiratory syncytial virus epidemics: variable dominance of subgroups A and B strains among children, 1981–1986. *J Infect Dis* 1988; 157:143–148.)

Table 14–2

Demographic Characteristics of Infants and Children Infected with Respiratory Syncytial Virus (RSV), According to Subgroup

	No. with Indicated RSV		
Characteristic	Subgroup A (n = 155)*	Subgroup B (n = 51)	Subgroup Affiliation Not Defined (n = 24)
Gender			
Males	92	32	12
Females	63	19	12
Age (mo)			
0–6	87	16	14
6–12	23	12	5
13–24	23	13	2
25–36	13	5	2
37–48	5	2	0
49+	4	3	1
Illness			
Upper respiratory tract infection	32	17	9
Laryngotracheobronchitis	19	10	4
Bronchiolitis	47	6	5
Pneumonia	57	18	6
Inpatient	131	39	18
Ambulatory patient	24	12	6

*There were 160 patients in subgroup A, but clinical information was only available for 155 of them. Reproduced with permission from Mufson MA, et al: Respiratory syncytial virus epidemics: Variable dominance of subgroup A and B strains among children, 1981–1986. J Infect Dis 1988; 157:143–148.

Table 14–3
Recovery of Respiratory Syncytial Virus (RSV) by Illness Syndrome at Children's Hospital, Washington, DC, January 1960 to July 30, 1976*

Illness Category	No. of Children Tested	RSV Recovered	
		No.	Percent
Pneumonia	2132	217	10.2
Bronchiolitis	1546	400	25.9
Croup	988	37	3.7
Pharyngitis-bronchitis	1601	69	4.3
Total inpatient respiratory	6267	723	11.5
Outpatient respiratory	10,150	738	7.3
Total respiratory	16,417	1461	8.9
Control children without respiratory disease	7586	17	0.2

Data courtesy of Dr Robert Parrott.

Quantitation and duration of viral shedding has been studied in chimpanzees and in infants. In experimental infection of chimpanzees, it was shown that chimpanzees inoculated intranasally with RSV began shedding on day 2 and virus shedding peaked by day 4; greater than 10^6 plaque-forming units per milliliter of nasal swab specimens appeared during the peak shedding of virus.[70] Shedding of virus occurred intermittently for long periods in experimental infection; greater than 20 days of virus shedding has been shown in chimpanzees.

Hospitalized infants shed a large quantity of virus during early illness.[71] Some infants shed greater than 10^6 $TCID_{50}$ per milliliter of nasal wash specimen. The quantity of virus shed gradually decreased through day 11 of hospitalization. However, some infants were found to be shedding virus for longer than 3 weeks.[72] This long duration of shedding may account for the occasional report of children with more than one infection with RSV within a short time; the second illness may represent infection with another pathogen but associated with prolonged shedding of RSV from the first illness. Significantly greater quantities of virus are shed by younger infants compared with older infants. Infants with lower respiratory infection shed virus for a longer time than infants with upper respiratory infection. Infants with radiographic evidence of consolidation shed more virus than infants without consolidation.[72]

DISEASES CAUSED BY RSV

Among children, the clinical syndromes caused by RSV include febrile upper respiratory disease, bronchiolitis, pneumonia, and bronchitis (Table 14–3). Croup is uncommonly associated with RSV infection. Otitis media may be primarily caused by RSV, or secondary bacterial infection of the middle ear may follow or occur simultaneously with RSV infection. Among the different patient groups, RSV may have an atypical presentation. The clinical manifestations of RSV in neonates are different from those among older infants. Diseases sometimes attributed to RSV infection of infants and children include sudden infant death syndrome (SIDS) and neurologic diseases (see below). In older children and adults, heart disease has been reported, but the significance of this is not known. Among elderly patients, RSV pneumonia occurs and some

reports suggest that rarely other diseases may be caused by RSV. Immunocompromised hosts may develop severe RSV respiratory disease.

Bronchiolitis

RSV is the major cause of bronchiolitis and pneumonia in early infancy and childhood. These two clinical syndromes represent a continuum of lower respiratory tract disease, and it is often difficult to differentiate RSV pneumonia and bronchiolitis. Frequently, characteristic findings of these two clinical entities may coexist within the same patients.

Table 14–4 compares the clinical, laboratory, and roentgenographic findings of RSV bronchiolitis with RSV pneumonia. Bronchiolitis is second only to pneumonia as the most common manifestation of RSV lower respiratory tract illness. It is estimated that from 43% to 90% of all cases of childhood bronchiolitis are due to RSV. The remainder are due to parainfluenza, adenovirus, *Mycoplasma pneumoniae,* or other agents. There is a seasonal occurrence of bronchiolitis, primarily during the winter and early spring months and simultaneous with the annual RSV epidemic.

Children that develop bronchiolitis usually have previous upper respiratory illness for two or three days, and this is characterized by rhinitis, low-grade fever, and cough. Cardinal signs of bronchiolitis include wheezing and hyperaeration of the lungs. In addition to wheezing, rales and rhonchi are frequently detected on auscultation. Children who are dyspneic and moderately hypoxic may have chest wall retractions and nasal flaring. Pharyngitis or conjunctivitis often is associated with this clinical syndrome. The course of the disease usually results in improvement of clinical signs in three to four days despite continued viral shedding for 2 to 3 weeks. The patient may continue to have a degree of hypoxemia secondary to mismatched ventilation-perfusion of the lungs several weeks after the acute illness.[73] The severity of hypoxemia has been correlated with the duration of viral shedding, occurrence of apnea, respiratory rate, young age, and percentage of immature neutrophils.[73]

Pulmonary function abnormalities persist for months or years after an episode of acute bronchiolitis. Stokes et al found that of 22 infants followed up for 12 months after acute bronchiolitis, 75% had pulmonary function abnormalities including hyperinflated lungs, increased thoracic gas volumes, and recurrent cough and wheezing attacks.[74] Children who had clinical and radiologic evidence of bronchiolitis at a young age and who remained symptom-free during the subsequent 10 years had residual parenchymal and/or airway disease.[75] The majority of these patients continued to have abnormal oxygen tension or reduced volume of isoflow or a reduced residual volume-total lung capacity ratio. Almost a third of these patients had abnormal values for all three pulmonary function indicators.

Treatment of patients with RSV bronchiolitis is directed against the virus with aerosolized ribavirin and symptomatic relief (see Chapter 6, and under Chemotherapy of RSV Infection, below). Neither antibiotics, theophylline, nor corticosteroids have therapeutic effect.[76–79] Humidified oxygen and intravenous (IV) hydration should be maintained. Aerosolized bronchodilators may benefit children over 18 months old, but generally are of no benefit to younger children.

Table 14–4
Comparison of Epidemiologic, Clinical, and Laboratory Parameters of Bronchiolitis and Pneumonia Caused by Respiratory Syncytial Virus (RSV) Infection

Parameters	Bronchiolitis	Viral Pneumonia	Reference
Incidence	Second most common clinical syndrome among children hospitalized with RSV infection	Most common manifestation of lower respiratory disease caused by RSV among hospitalized children	50, 90
Age	Peak incidence at age 2 mo	Most common in infants < 12 mo old	51
History	Prior upper respiratory illness	Prior upper respiratory illness, poor feeding, listlessness	87, 88
Symptoms and signs			
Fever	Fever may or may not be present; if present, usually low-grade < 39°C (102°F)	Fever common during initial and later phases of illness	
Respiratory	Dyspnea, tachypnea, chest wall retractions	Dyspnea with retractions and nasal flaring more commonly seen in younger infants and children	
	Rales and rhonchi (predominantly expiratory)	Rales and rhonchi	
	Wheezing, hyperinflation of lungs are hallmarks of bronchiolitis	Occasional intermittent wheezes	
	Thoracic cavity may have an increased anterior → posterior diameter		
	Cough	Cough usually nonproductive or minimally productive; may be severe and paroxysmal	
Clinical course	Improvement usually seen within 3 to 4 d	Duration of illness 7–21 d	
	Viral shedding may continue despite clinical improvement		
	Hypoxemia of prolonged duration	Hypoxemia of prolonged duration	
Laboratory data			
White blood cell count	WBC count highly variable; frequently elevated; usually neutrophilia with immature forms	WBC count highly variable; frequently elevated; usually neutrophilia with immature forms	Dansby KN, Belshe RB, unpublished data, 1984
Pulmonary function	Increased lung volume		74, 75, 89
	Increased expiratory resistance		
	Increased pulmonary flow resistance		
	If arterial hypoxia severe, there may be accompanying hypercapnia and acidosis		
Roentgenographic findings	Hyperinflation with or without areas of segmental or subsegmental atelectasis	Interstitial or peribronchial infiltration with areas of hyperaeration	91–93
	Infiltrates due to atelectasis	Common to find 2- or 3-lobe involvement	
		Rarely see consolidation or atelectasis	
Treatment	Aerosolized ribavirin	Aerosolized ribavirin	173a, 174–178, 178a
	Humidified oxygen	Judicious use of antibiotics for superimposed bacterial infections	76–79, 179–185
	Adequate hydration		
	Symptomatic therapy		
	Antibiotics, theophylline, and corticosteroids have no therapeutic value		

Wheezing in children is a common diagnostic problem for the pediatrician, and recurrent wheezing is seen frequently following acute bronchiolitis in infancy. Atopy may predispose RSV-infected infants to bronchiolitis.[80, 81] However, not all studies are in agreement on this association.[82] Recurrent wheezing was observed in 56% of children with bronchiolitis, and 43% had wheezing on at least five occasions.[81] In children with asthma, wheezing attacks are precipitated by documented viral infection in only 40% of wheezing episodes.[83] Differentiating bronchiolitis from asthma is difficult and arbitrary at times. Both syndromes manifest bronchiolar hyperreactivity; generally first episodes of wheezing in young infants are called "bronchiolitis." Recurrent wheezing is usually diagnosed as asthma regardless of pathogenesis.[84, 85]

Pneumonia

RSV has been implicated in causing 5% to 40% of pneumonia in infants and young children admitted to hospital. During RSV epidemics, the occurrence of pneumonia parallels that of bronchiolitis. During 11 years of study in an outpatient pediatric population in North Carolina, RSV was the second most common cause of pneumonia (26% positive cultures) among ambulatory children less than 7 years old.[86]

Fever is commonly observed during the initial phase of the illness. However, the fever may be low grade or disappear by the time of hospitalization. Cough, rhinitis, dyspnea, and wheezing are common. Rales and rhonchi are heard on auscultation (see Table 14–4). Pneumonia is generally distinguished from bronchiolitis on the basis of the chest roentgenogram (see below[87–89]). (Dansby KN, Belshe RB, unpublished observations, 1984).

The influence of rapid viral diagnosis of RSV infection on the clinical treatment of children with lower respiratory disease was studied by Carlsen and Orstavik.[90] Widespread use of immunofluorescence (IF) to confirm RSV infection resulted in a significant reduction in the number of children receiving antibiotics (80% before use of IF to 38% after wide use of IF). Also, the median hospital stay was reduced by three days, from nine to six days. Specific antiviral therapy with ribavirin is effective in severe lower respiratory disease (see Chemotherapy of RSV Infection below, and Chapter 6, Antiviral Drug Therapy).

Roentgenographic Findings in RSV Infection

The roentgenographic findings in children with viral respiratory disease has been examined.[91–93] Bronchial wall thickening, peribronchial shadows, and perihilar streaking are common findings in viral lower respiratory disease. Often multiple lobes are involved. Air trapping commonly occurs in patients with RSV infection, but this finding may be seen also in parainfluenza or adenovirus infections. Pleural effusion, pneumothorax, pneumatocele, or lung abscesses are characteristic of staphylococcal pneumonia or other bacterial lower respiratory disease and are not often associated with viral respiratory infections.

The chest roentgenogram findings are highly variable in infants with RSV infection, and they range from normal to extensive pneumonia with multiple areas of consolidation. Diffuse interstitial pneumonia is the most common finding, and hyperinflation of the lung is frequently found. Consolidation may occur in either bacterial or viral pneumonia. Needle aspiration of consolidated lung

tissue may reveal RSV alone with no bacterial involvement.[92] Upper lobe pneumonia occurs frequently in RSV infection.[92] Clinical correlation is low between the diagnosis of bronchiolitis and radiologic findings of air trapping in the lungs. Consolidation was found less often in RSV infection than among children with other lower respiratory infections.[91] Peribronchial thickening did not occur more often in RSV infection compared to other infections. Air trapping was more frequently found in children under 6 months of age if RSV infection was present.[91]

Other Primary RSV Infections of the Respiratory Tract

Croup is an uncommon manifestation of RSV illness, and less than 5% of all croup illnesses are caused by RSV. Lewis et al investigated the role of respiratory viruses in the etiology of pertussis syndrome.[94] RSV may be implicated in occasional cases of whooping cough, although adenovirus is the most frequently isolated virus in this syndrome.[94, 95]

RSV and Otitis Media

Most investigators have considered the significance of RSV in otitis media to be antecedent viral infection with secondary bacterial infection. In a review of 663 middle ear effusions cultured for viruses, Klein and Teele found that only 4.4% of the cultures were positive for viruses.[96] RSV was the most frequent virus isolated. In a recent study, the viral or bacterial etiology of 103 cases of acute otitis media was investigated.[97] Middle ear fluid cultures were positive for bacteria in 66% of children, and only three (0.04%) of 74 cultures were positive for virus. These data suggest that acute otitis media is generally a bacterial disease. However, antecedent viral infection may predispose to the bacterial disease. In the three virus-positive cultures, each was also associated with a bacterial pathogen.

Concurrent RSV infection has been found in up to 40% of children with otitis media during RSV epidemics.[98] It is not known if RSV replicates in the middle ear or is conducted mechanically from the nasopharynx to the middle ear. It is believed that RSV destroys the middle ear epithelium, thereby allowing bacterial pathogens to invade the submucosal space.[99–101]

RSV and Sudden Infant Death Syndrome (SIDS)

The occurrence of SIDS correlates to the presence of viruses causing epidemic respiratory disease in pediatric populations.[102] No definite cause-and-effect relationship has been shown. During periods of epidemic respiratory virus disease, there was an increase in the number of SIDS cases. However, other factors, including neurologic development, may be more important in causing SIDS. RSV may play a role in some cases due to the frequent occurrence of bronchiolitis in the community and SIDS cases.[103, 104] Acute viral respiratory disease and death may occur at home and be confused with other syndromes causing sudden infant death.

Neonatal RSV Infections

RSV infection in neonates may be atypical in clinical manifestations and may not be suspected by the clinician due to the absence of the usual signs and symptoms of respiratory disease.

RSV-infected infants less than 3 weeks of age tended to have upper respiratory infection, lethargy, irritability, and poor feeding; infants over 3 weeks of age tended to have retractions and rales, as well as manifestations of upper respiratory infection during RSV infection.[105] Apnea may occur in RSV-infected neonates.[106]

RSV and Neurologic Disease

Although viruses have been implicated in aqueductal stenosis, RSV was not implicated as a cause of hydrocephalus.[107] In a search for a viral etiology of amyotrophic lateral sclerosis (ALS), serologic markers of RSV infection did not differ comparing ALS patients with controls.[108] RSV has rarely been associated with Reye syndrome.[109]

RSV and Heart Disease

The risk of severe RSV infection in infants with congenital heart disease is significantly greater than the risk in infants without congenital heart disease.[110] Infants with congenital heart disease and RSV infection also have a significantly higher mortality rate compared with matched controls. The functional cardiac abnormality associated with an unfavorable outcome is pulmonary hypertension (75% mortality). Affected infants die of irreversible hypoxia. It has been suggested that elective hospital admission of infants with congenital heart disease be avoided during peak periods of RSV infection due to the high mortality associated with nosocomial infections in this group.[110]

Only rarely has RSV been implicated in acute myocarditis and acquired conduction defects.[111, 112] Furthermore, in these few cases, the cardiac manifestations surfaced several days or weeks after RSV infection. The high frequency of primary and recurrent RSV infection in children and adults may indicate that the few case reports of RSV-induced heart disease are the result of coincidence rather than cause and effect. It has been suggested, but not proved, that the myocarditis and cardiac arrhythmias may be responsible for sudden death in some infants with RSV infection.

RSV and Immunocompromised Hosts

Children who are immunosuppressed for treatment of malignancy or with immunodeficiency syndromes are more susceptible to severe RSV illness. Children with acute lymphocytic leukemia (ALL) and documented RSV infection mount a CF antibody response in only 29% of cases.[113] Serologic tests are less sensitive than virus isolation techniques for confirming RSV infection in this group. The titer of CF antibody did not correlate with the severity of illness in ALL, indicating that antibody was not a moderator of illness. Fatal RSV infection may occur in adults who are immunocompromised.[114]

Fatal RSV Infections

Death from RSV is usually associated with underlying illness. In a recent survey of children with RSV in West Virginia, only children with RSV infection and underlying diseases required mechanical ventilation due to respiratory failure.[115] The underlying diseases in these patients included three children born prematurely who had respiratory distress syndrome and subsequent pulmonary fibrosis, and one child with amyotonia congenita. Two of these four infants died. In the United Kingdom, 13 RSV deaths were reviewed; nine had congenital or acquired abnormalities.[52]

Nosocomial RSV Infections

Nosocomial infections with RSV commonly cause serious illness in children less than 12 months of age. Up to 40% of infants develop pneumonia with nosocomial RSV infection. The risk of acquiring nosocomial RSV infection correlates directly with the length of hospitalization.[116] Infants hospitalized when RSV is prevalent in the community are at risk of acquiring the virus in hospital. RSV is believed to be spread by hand-to-eye or hand-to-nose routes. Hospital staff are responsible for most of the nosocomial transmission of RSV. The nosocomial infection rate was over 30% during community RSV epidemics in some studies.[116, 117] The frequency of nosocomial infections may be related to the design of the hospital ward and the age of the patients. Those less than 12 months of age are most susceptible of RSV infection. Infants admitted with lower respiratory tract disease shed the virus in high titers and for prolonged periods. Strict handwashing and use of gloves for handling infectious secretions is indicated to reduce the spread of RSV from patients to staff and from staff to patients. Masks are not necessary when handling infected children.[116]

RSV Infection in Adults

Most adults readily become infected with RSV, and in the majority of instances, an upper respiratory tract infection is the predominant clinical feature.[118] Fever may be associated with the upper respiratory infection. Loss of work time is common among infected adults. Abnormal pulmonary function tests persist for up to 8 weeks following RSV infections in adults.[119] The role of RSV in pneumonia in normal civilian adults has been evaluated and antibody response was not detected significantly more frequently among adults with pneumonia compared with those without respiratory infection.[120] However, in certain populations more severe infection occurs. These populations include the elderly, the military, and immunocompromised patients. In 1977, an outbreak of RSV occurred in a chronic care facility.[121] Fifteen of 77 residents aged 57 to 98 years (mean age 84 years) were infected. Seven of the 15 infected patients developed pneumonia, and six were hospitalized; none died. Among military populations, RSV may cause febrile respiratory disease. Of 553 US Special Forces troops in Vietnam, 97 had acute febrile respiratory disease during the 6 months of one study.[122] RSV was the second (nine of 97 illnesses) most common virus implicated after adenovirus (20 of 97 illnesses). Among the military of the Netherlands, ten of 91 persons with pneumonia illnesses had RSV infection.[123] Immunocompromised adults may get severe RSV infections, and these are often nosocomially acquired. Studies of diabetic patients have failed to associate RSV infection as an etiology for this condition.[124]

IMMUNITY TO INFECTION WITH RSV

Infection with RSV does not confer long-lasting protection against subsequent reinfection; however, only the first, and occasionally the second, infection is life-threatening. Primary infection does not necessarily protect against subsequent reinfection, but it does lessen the severity of illness as the child grows older.[60]

Adults are not completely immune to RSV infection, although the usual clinical syndrome is that of a common cold. Occasionally, adult infections may be severe; RSV has been shown to cause epidemics in nursing homes[125] and may be confused with influenza in veteran's hospitals.[126] Chimpanzee infection experiments have shown that chimpanzees who are infected with RSV are protected against reinfection with the same strain of virus for several months, but the immunity wanes, and rechallenge results in symptomatic infection.[70]

Reinfection with RSV occurs commonly. As virtually all older children and adults possess neutralizing antibody to RSV, infections in these groups reflect reinfection. Among children who had repeated infections of RSV at least 1 year apart, second infections with strains of either subgroup A or B did not potentiate illness, and infection with subgroup A strains provided some degree of homologous protection from a second infection.[66]

Second infections with the homologous subgroup were detected as often as second infections with the alternate subgroup. Of 13 children tested, six had two infections of the same subgroup and seven had two infections with different subgroups. During the first infection, ten of the 13 children had subgroup A strains, which represented a 3:1 ratio of A/B strains. By contrast, subgroup B strains occurred more often during second infections. Of the ten children who had subgroup A strains during their first infection, six has B strains and four had A strains during the second infection. This finding represents significantly more subgroup B strains than expected by chance. Thus, infection with A strains appeared to confer immunity to second infections with strains of the same subgroup, at least as reflected in the occurrence of second infections in the 2 years after the first infection. No second infections were identified within the interval of a single annual epidemic.[66]

Second infections were not more severe than first infections with either subgroup of RSV, and lower respiratory illness occurred as often during second infections as during first infections. Reinfection with RSV has not been associated with more severe illness in children. Thus, there was no evidence of immunopathologic amplification of illness in cases of two consecutive infections with strains of different RSV subgroups. These observations on consecutive infections with RSV represent different circumstances than the potentiation of disease observed after the administration of killed RSV vaccine (see below).

The factors that protect against reinfection are being elucidated. Secretory immunity to RSV probably plays a predominant role in early elimination of the virus from the respiratory tract. The development of secretory IgA antibody to RSV corresponds with elimination of the virus from respiratory secretions.[127] IgA antibody appears early in illness and is initially cell-bound to respiratory epithelial cells.[104] Cell-free IgA antibody appears somewhat later and temporally correlates with disappearance of the virus.[127] Clearance of virus from infected cotton rat lungs was mediated by the $F(ab')_2$ portion of antibody to RSV; this observation suggested that complement-independent, cell-independent neutralization was the major mechanism of clearance of virus from lungs.[127a]

Humoral immunity may have a partial role in preventing the severe lower respiratory disease seen with RSV infection. Prince and coworkers have shown that it is possible to prevent RSV involvement of the lower respiratory tract in cotton rats by xenobiosis.[128] An immune animal providing circulating antibody to a nonimmune animal protected the nonimmune animal from infection. Similarly, intramuscular (IM) injection of live RSV or passive administration of immune sera protected susceptible cotton rats from pulmonary, but no nasal, RSV infection. In humans, maternal antibody does not protect against illness but may lessen the severity of disease.[129]

The relative contributions of anti-F and anti-G antibodies to host immunity have been determined using vaccinia virus (VV) recombinants expressing either F or G glycoproteins of RSV.[130] Both F- and G-expressing recombinants (VV-F or VV-G) stimulated protective antibodies in cotton rats; however, VV-F stimulated more complete resistance than VV-G. Data suggest that the antibodies to both F and G are responsible for protection but that the relative contributions of F outweigh those of G.[130, 131] Studies in mice have confirmed that antibodies to F and G are protective, but antibodies to the P phosphoprotein and the 22K protein did not induce neutralizing antibody.[132]

The recognition of two subgroups of RSV have led to studies comparing protection conferred by G or F proteins versus the homologous and heterologous subgroup RSV. Mice or cotton rats vaccinated with recombinant VV expressing the G glycoprotein of RSV (subgroup A) were protected against challenge only with homologous subgroup A RSV. In contrast the F glycoprotein (subgroup A) induced protection against both homologous (subgroup A) and heterologous (subgroup B) viruses.[133–135]

Recombinant VVs carrying the N (nucleoprotein) gene of RSV also induce a modest amount of protection in mice.[136] The observation that cytotoxic T cells specific to RSV recognize viral nucleoprotein suggests that cytotoxic T cells may be important in immunoprophylaxis against RSV. It has been shown that RSV-specific major histocompatibility complex (MHC)-restricted cytotoxic T cells in both human and mouse recognize cells expressing the nucleoprotein N but not the major glycoprotein G of RSV.[137] T helper cells recognized F and G glycoproteins but no nonstructural proteins in one study.[138] The combination of neutralizing antibodies, antibodies directed against surface glycoproteins, and cytotoxic T cells directed against nucleoproteins may be efficacious in protection from disease.

The degree of antigenic relatedness between subgroups A and B of RSV has been determined from antibody responses induced in cotton rats following infection with RSV.[139] Protein-specific ELISA assays of the antibody responses induced by infection demonstrated that there was a high degree of relatedness between the F glycoproteins of the RSV subgroups A and B. In contrast, the G glycoproteins were distantly related. Neutralizing antibodies indicated an intermediate degree of relatedness in the cotton rats infected with one of the two subgroups of RSV. Immunity induced against the F glycoprotein of subgroup A conferred a similar degree of protection following challenge with RSV of subgroups B or A. In comparison, immunity against the G glycoprotein of subgroup A induced by VV recombinant conferred less complete protection against the heterologous subgroup B virus.[139]

It has been postulated that breast feeding, through the delivery of antiviral IgA to the infant, may serve to protect suckling infants from infection. Specific anti-RSV IgA is present in colostrum, and mothers who became infected with RSV exhibited a rise in the level of antiviral IgA in their milk.[140] Although children who are admitted to hospital with RSV infection are less likely to have

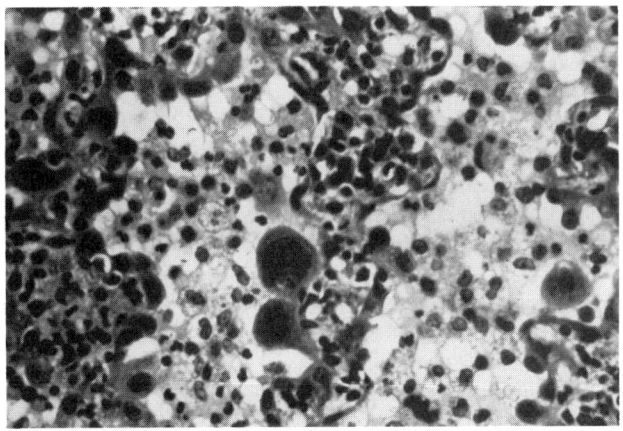

Figure 14–9. Fusion of alveolar cells to form syncytia is evident in respiratory syncytial virus-infected cebus monkey lung.

been breast-fed than hospitalized infants who do not have RSV, socioeconomic factors may account for this observation.[141] In prospective studies, breast feeding had no effect on the occurrence of RSV infection.[54, 142]

The role of cell-mediated immunity (CMI) in causing or preventing RSV disease is not known. CMI toward RSV is present in the cord blood lymphocytes of most infants.[143] It is not known how long this immunity persists. Kim et al have shown that CMI to RSV was increased in children after vaccination with the formalin-inactivated vaccine[144] (see below, Vaccines to Prevent RSV Infection). This killed vaccine induced CMI, but it did not protect against RSV infection and increased severity of disease was noted in the children when they became naturally infected.

PATHOGENESIS

The pathogenesis of RSV infection has been studied experimentally in both the cotton rat and infant ferret experimental hosts. In the ferret, infection is age-dependent.[145, 146] Newborn ferrets inoculated intranasally develop nasal and pulmonary infection. The virus reaches its highest titers in the lungs within two to four days after infection, but it may not be cultured for more than two to four days' duration from this site. Nasal shedding occurs for a longer time, and virus may be recovered for ten to 14 days. Adult ferrets are resistant to pulmonary infection with RSV, but RSV readily infects the upper respiratory tract of adult ferrets.

Cotton rats are susceptible to RSV infection at all ages, although infant rats are most susceptible to disease and shed the highest quantities of virus. The viral shedding pattern of cotton rats is similar to that of ferrets. Virus may be isolated from the nose as early as 24 to 48 hours after infection, and peak titers are shed at five days after inoculation. RSV may be recovered from the trachea and lungs for as long as seven days and from the nasal turbinates for nine to 14 days.[146]

The cytopathology of infection reflects a tropism for the luminal epithelial cells of both the cotton rat and ferret. Virus replication in the upper respiratory tract is localized to the epithelial cells. Infected cells exhibit ballooning of their cytoplasm, and syncytia may be observed. Ferrets and cotton rats differ in the localization of viral antigen in the lungs. In the ferret, viral antigen is localized

in the pulmonary alveolar cells, whereas in the cotton rat the virus is found in the bronchiolar epithelial cells.[146]

Studies with adult volunteers have shown the incubation period of RSV infection to be three to seven days, depending on the inoculum titer.[68] Transmission of natural infection is by autoinoculation into the eye or nose. Small-particle aerosols do not appear to be an important route of transmission. In the child, virus is shed for prolonged periods. Of infants naturally infected with RSV, 92% to 100% continued to shed virus for their first seven days of hospitalization; some infants shed for as long as 21 days.[72]

Peribronchiolar lymphocytic infiltration is seen in the initial stages of bronchiolar infections. Luminal epithelial cells are shed into the bronchioles as they die, occasionally obstructing the lumina. Airway obstruction in bronchiolitis is greatest on expiration. This may result in hyperinflation of the infant's lung and air trapping. Pathologic findings in fatal RSV pneumonia include necrosis of the tracheobronchiolar epithelium, peribronchiolar lymphocytic infiltration, interstitial pneumonitis, atelectasis, and emphysema (see below).

RSV PATHOLOGY

RSV affects the epithelial cells of the respiratory tract. Cytoplasmic, perinuclear inclusion bodies in the ciliated epithelial cells are among the cytopathic effects.[147–149] By electron microscopy, the perinuclear inclusion bodies produced by RSV infection are composed of dense intertwining nucleocapsids. The ciliated cells swell, protrude into the lumen, and lose their cilia. Progeny viral particles bud from the luminal aspect of the ciliated cells. RSV infection produces a fusion of the infected cell membrane with cell membranes of adjacent epithelial cells, thus forming a giant cell with multiple nuclei. Similar findings occur in experimentally infected cebus monkeys (Figure 14–9). Giant cell formation may be noted in human lungs at autopsy in some cases. Inclusions occur in bronchiolar as well as alveolar epithelium.

Histologically, necrosis of the bronchiolar epithelium occurs 18 to 24 hours after onset of the infection. Host response is indicated by peribronchial infiltration of lymphocytes with occasional plasma cells and macrophages. The submucosa and adventitia appear edematous and congested. There is no damage to elastic fibers or muscle. Mucus secretion is increased and forms thick plugs of cellular debris within the bronchiolar lumen. These plugs occlude small bronchioles and are responsible for airway obstruction in acute bronchiolitis. Collapsed subsegments of lung may be seen.[150]

IMMUNOPATHOGENESIS OF SEVERE RSV DISEASE

Several features associated with severe lower respiratory disease due to RSV suggest an immune-mediated pathogenesis. The administration of a formalin-inactivated RSV vaccine to children resulted in high levels of antibody, but the vaccine-induced antibody did not prevent infection.[151] During subsequent natural RSV infection, vaccinees had higher rates of virus isolation and shed higher titers of the virus than controls.[152] Lower respiratory disease was more frequent in vaccine than control infants. The development of the cotton rat as an experimental host for RSV infection has led to detailed studies of the pulmonary pathologic changes augmented by prior IM inoculation of formalin-inactivated virus.[153] Cotton rats immunized with formalin-inactivated RSV or the clinically tested RSV lot 100 vaccine resulted in augmented pulmonary pathologic changes when the cotton rats were challenged with live intranasal RSV. An increase in neutrophils and lymphocytes infiltrating the lungs was noted compared to unimmunized cotton rats. In contrast, there was no enhancement of pulmonary pathologic changes if cotton rats were initially inoculated IM with live RSV. The pathologic changes observed were suggestive of a type 3 (Arthus) immunopathologic process. The authors postulated that selected epitopes on the surface glycoproteins, F or G or both, were modified due to the formalin. Furthermore, a neutralizing antibody response was not stimulated in cotton rats by the lot 100 RSV vaccine.[153]

Serum from infants immunized with the lot 100 vaccine have now been assayed for antibodies to the F and G glycoproteins and neutralizing antibody.[154] Infants 2 to 6 months of age developed high-titered antibodies to the F glycoprotein but had poor response to the G glycoprotein following immunization with the lot 100 RSV vaccine. These data support the concept that treatment of RSV with formalin altered epitopes of the G glycoprotein and possibly also the F glycoprotein. When these children became naturally infected, they had a relatively low level of neutralizing antibody response compared with individuals of the same age who had not been immunized and who were undergoing RSV infection.[154] Three factors could possibly have contributed to potentiated disease in these children: (1) The augmented pathologic process may have been due to a pulmonary Arthus reaction caused by nonfunctioning antibodies; (2) the poor antibody response to the G glycoprotein in the formalin-inactivated vaccine may have been insufficient to provide resistance to natural RSV infection; and (3) the relatively reduced neutralizing antibody response of infants to natural RSV infection may also have contributed to their enhanced disease by delaying clearance of virus from the respiratory tract.[154]

Immunopathologic mechanisms may be responsible for some manifestations of naturally occurring RSV disease in infants. The level of maternal neutralizing antibody has been correlated with protection from pneumonia. However, there is no relationship between the maternal antibody titers and the development of bronchiolitis.[130, 153] Antibody directed against the F protein of other paramyxoviruses is necessary in order to prevent cell-to-cell spread of virus. Anti-F antibody may be absent in some children. The absence of this antibody may make them more susceptible to severe RSV infection. This mechanism could also explain the severe disease associated with the inactivated vaccine since anti-F glycoprotein antibody was not stimulated by the other killed paramyxovirus vaccines, measles or mumps. The common factors might be the lack of sufficient quantity of anti-F antibody to prevent spread of the virus.

An initial asymptomatic "sensitizing" RSV infection has been proposed to predispose to bronchiolitis. Little evidence exists for this mechanism. In one study, IgE was identified bound to exfoliated nasopharyngeal cells in most children with RSV infection and cell-bound IgE was seen only during the acute phase of mild illness.[155] The continued presence of IgE appeared to be correlated with the more severe forms of disease, pneumonia with wheezing, or bronchiolitis. Nasopharyngeal anti-RSV IgE antibody titers tended

to increase through the infant's illnesses; peak titers correlated with the degree of hypoxia.[156] Whether previous sensitization was necessary for this phenomenon is not known.

Several studies cast doubt on the "prior sensitizing infection" theory.[51, 53, 60] If sensitization is required for severe disease, older children who had been infected during the previous epidemic should develop bronchiolitis during the initial stage of the epidemic, whereas younger children with no exposure to the virus would not become severely ill. However, this is not the case. The incidence of pneumonia, bronchiolitis, and upper respiratory infection parallel one another during RSV epidemics, and the peak incidence of bronchiolitis occurs at 2 months of age, a time when previous RSV infection is not likely.

CMI has been suggested to contribute to RSV-induced bronchiolitis. As mentioned above, children who receive the inactivated RSV vaccine developed CMI to RSV, but this did not protect them or diminish severity of illness. Specific T lymphocyte transformation response develops in children with RSV infection.[157, 158] This response was more frequent in younger children; 78% of infants less than 6 months of age had a positive T lymphocyte response as compared with only 46% responses in those more than 6 months of age. The investigators suggested that the CMI response in infants with bronchiolitis was related to the pathogenesis of RSV disease. Antibody-dependent, cell-mediated cytotoxicity (ADCC), an effector arm of the cell-mediated immune response, has been suggested to cause wheezing and bronchiolitis seen in children with severe disease.[157] ADCC has been shown to appear in respiratory secretions during acute RSV infection.[159] However, Meguro et al have shown no correlation between age, severity of disease, or type of disease and the level of ADCC antibody.[160]

LABORATORY DIAGNOSIS OF RSV INFECTION

With widespread use of the specific antiviral therapy, ribavirin, the laboratory diagnosis of RSV infection is increasing in importance. Many laboratories now use rapid diagnostic tests with traditional tissue culture methods for confirmation. The diagnosis of RSV infection is best confirmed by isolation of the virus from respiratory secretions. Nasal wash specimens offer the highest yield for isolation; swab specimens of the nasopharynx and throat are also adequate if purulent rhinorrhea is present. Due to the lability of RSV to freezing, thawing, and pH change, specimens should be inoculated onto tissue culture as soon as possible. One- or two-day-old HEp-2 cells are the most sensitive cell line for growing RSV. Other cell lines, including human diploid fibroblasts, heteroploid lines, and monkey kidney cells, can be used, but they are not as sensitive as HEp-2 cells. Viral cytopathic effects (CPE) include large syncytia with eosinophilic intracytoplasmic inclusions. These develop after two to seven days of incubation. Occasionally, the culture must be "blind-passaged" once prior to the CPE becoming evident.[161]

Techniques for the rapid diagnosis of RSV infection are now available in most large hospitals and medical centers. The indirect immunofluorescent antibody technique was first described by Gardner et al.[162] Processing of the nasal epithelial cell specimens can be done rapidly and diagnosis can be confirmed within a few hours. The use of a direct immunofluorescent assay is also sensitive.[163]

Table 14–5
Serologic Response of Patients with Respiratory Syncytial Virus (RSV) Infections as Measured by CF, Plaque Reduction, and ELISA techniques

Age of Patients (mo)	No. with Increase* in Antibody Titer by Indicated Technique/No. Tested		
	CF	Plaque Reduction	ELISA
1–3	1/49	1/47[†]	25/49
4–6	9/19	11/19	18/19
7–12	9/10	9/10	9/10
13–24	6/9	8/9	8/9
≥ 25	3/4	3/4	3/4
Total	28/91	32/89	63/91

CF = complement fixation; ELISA = enzyme-linked immunosorbent assay.
*Fourfold or greater rise.
[†]Two children in this age group could not be tested by the plaque reduction technique, since heparinized plasma was collected instead of serum and heparin inactivates RSV. Each of these children had a serologic response detectable by ELISA.
(Reproduced with permission from Richardson LS et al: Enzyme-linked immunosorbent assay for measurement of serological response to respiratory syncytial virus infection. Infect Immun 1978; 20:660–664.)

ELISA has proved useful in the diagnosis of RSV infection; this technique proved approximately 85% sensitive and greater than 95% specific when compared with virus isolation in the detection of RSV.[164] Hendry and McIntosh have modified this ELISA to utilize commercially available reagents.[165] They found that sensitivity and specificity of the ELISA was similar to immunofluorescence. More importantly, "mistreatment of samples" through prolonged storage at room temperature had little effect on ELISA reactivity. Positive nasopharyngeal specimens retained their reactivity even when mailed to the processing laboratory. Commercial ELISA tests are now available that are highly sensitive and specific for RSV infection.[166–169]

Other techniques, including electron microscopy to detect viral particles,[170] radioimmunoassay to detect viral nucleocapsid,[171] or reverse passive hemagglutination (RPH)[172] to detect viral antigen, have been developed. Of these, RPH was the most sensitive and compared favorably with immunofluorescence and virus isolation.

Serologic methods have proved useful in the retrospective diagnosis of RSV infection. Richardson et al developed an ELISA for measuring the IgG antibody response to RSV infection and compared the sensitivity of three serologic methods.[30] ELISA proved 100-fold more sensitive than CF and two- to fourfold more sensitive than plaque reduction neutralization in detecting antibody. The sensitivity of CF, plaque reduction, and ELISA at detecting fourfold antibody increase was age-dependent (Table 14–5). ELISA was more sensitive than CF or plaque reduction in infants less than 7 months old. Among older infants or children, these three methods were equally sensitive and detected fourfold antibody increase in over three fourths of RSV culture–positive children.

Complement-fixing antibodies to RSV are a relatively insensitive indicator of immune status since CF antibody wanes after infection. Tube dilution neutralization remains the most sensitive test in detecting seropositive individuals.[28] Low levels of antibody were detected by tube neutralization among vaccinees who did not develop antibody after parenteral administration of live RSV vaccine. This antibody was not detected by ELISA. Site-directed serology using synthetic polypeptides of 15 amino acids in length

has been used to partially define immunogenic sites on the G glycoprotein.[173]

CHEMOTHERAPY OF RSV INFECTION

Ribavirin (1-β-D-ribofuranosyl-1,2,4-triazole-3-carboxamide, Virazol) is a synthetic nucleoside. Its structure is similar to that of guanosine and inosine. In the United States the drug is available only for aerosol administration. The American Academy of Pediatrics Committee on Infectious Diseases has published a summary of recommendations for ribavirin therapy of RSV infections.[174] It is recommended that infants hospitalized with lower respiratory disease caused by RSV infection be considered for the treatment of ribavirin aerosol. Infants that might particularly benefit from treatment would include:

1. Infants at high risk for severe or complicated RSV infection. These infants include those with congenital heart disease, bronchopulmonary dysplasia, or other chronic lung conditions; premature infants and infants with immunodeficiency are also at risk for complicated RSV infection.
2. Infants hospitalized with RSV lower respiratory disease who are severely ill, particularly those children with low PaO_2 levels (<65 mm Hg) or those with increased $PaCO_2$ levels.
3. Infants that are hospitalized and do not appear particularly severely ill but that are at increased risk of progression to severe disease because of their young age (<6 wk) or those with multiple congenital anomalies or neurologic or metabolic diseases.

Ribavirin is administered by aerosol in an oxygen hood or mask from a solution containing 20 mg of ribavirin per milliliter of water. The drug manufacturer provides the small-particle aerosol generator. The aerosol is administered for 12 to 20 hours continuously daily for three to seven days. Infants who are on mechanical ventilators require special care in administering the drug, since precipitation of ribavirin within the ventilator tubes has led to complications of mechanical ventilation.[175] Techniques for administering the drug during mechanical ventilation have been published.[176, 177] Incidental exposure of nursing personnel and other hospital workers will occur during treatment; however, persons working around infants receiving continuous ribavirin therapy have been examined and no ribavirin has been detected in the serum or urine of these individuals.[178]

Clinical trials of treating infants hospitalized with RSV infection with ribavirin have demonstrated efficacy.[179–184] In controlled studies, ribavirin has been associated with greater clinical improvement than placebos. Infants generally improve by the third day but it may require longer for significant improvement to occur in some infants.

Ribavirin aerosol particles (diameter 1–2 μm) reach the lower respiratory tract. There is little systemic absorption by this route and no significant toxicity was observed in any of the controlled trials. Oral ribavirin is associated with anemia, however, and at present this route for drug administration is not approved for use in the United States.[180] The combination of ribavirin with immunoglobulin has potential for effective therapy and human studies with IV gamma globulin are being conducted.[185]

In vitro, RSV is interferon-sensitive; however, RSV infection stimulates nasal interferon production in less than 5% of children.[187] Moreover, only small quantities of interferon are produced and the concentration of interferon does not relate to recovery from infection.[188] Few adults with RSV infection produce interferon, and only in low titers that do not affect viral shedding.[189] In vitro, RSV has been shown to be a poor inducer of interferon.[190] Additionally, RSV-induced interferon is somewhat virus-specific, that is, RSV-induced interferon is more active in inhibiting RSV plaque formation than in inhibiting other viruses.[128, 191] It appears that interferon does not play a major role in recovery from infection with RSV. Whether therapy with topical or systemic interferon is beneficial has yet to be determined.

VACCINES TO PREVENT RSV INFECTION

The history of attempts at immunoprophylaxis with vaccines to prevent RSV infections has paralleled that of vaccine technology in general. Initial attempts at immunoprophylaxis were made with inactivated vaccines. Further attempts at prevention of RSV infection have included live attenuated intranasal vaccine and live parenteral RSV vaccination. To date, none of these strategies have proved efficacious or satisfactory for general use.

Inactivated RSV vaccines have been given to infants in attempts to prevent infection with this virus. Initially a fourfold concentrated, inactivated, alum-precipitated RSV vaccine was given to 53 infants. Twenty of the vaccinees subsequently became ill with naturally acquired infection, and nine required hospitalization because of lower respiratory illness.[192] The antibody response of these children to the inactivated vaccine was poor, and initially an association was not made between the killed vaccine and potentiation of illness during subsequent natural infection. Several other killed RSV vaccines were tested.[193-195] A 100-fold concentrated, inactivated, alum-precipitated vaccine (lot 100) was administered to children.[196] The vaccine induced CF antibodies in most children and neutralizing antibody in half the children; in addition, CMI was stimulated. Of 31 children given the lot 100 vaccine, 18 required hospitalization for subsequent naturally occurring RSV lower respiratory infection in one study.[193] The vaccine is believed to have potentiated the illness of some of these children. Several theories have been proposed on the mechanism of potentiation. Analogous to killed measles vaccine, the killed RSV vaccine may have failed to protect infants and resulted in augmented disease due to lack of immune response to one or both RSV glycoproteins. (See Immunopathogenesis of Severe RSV Disease, above.)

Several live RSV vaccines have been developed and tested. These have included a cold-adapted RSV vaccine which was shown to be attenuated in adults and older children when administered intranasally.[197] However, the vaccine was insufficiently attenuated when given to young children; some evidence of lower respiratory infection occurred in a few vaccinees given the cold-adapted RSV vaccine.[198]

Subsequent efforts have dealt with the production of *ts* mutants of RSV. Among a group of *ts* mutants of RSV, two have been tested as candidate vaccines in adults and children.[199, 200] The first vaccine to be tested was designated *ts*-1. The purpose of the intranasal administration of this vaccine was to produce infection localized to the upper respiratory tract and induce protective se-

cretory IgA immunity. The *ts* mutants are believed to replicate at the cooler upper airway temperatures but not at the warmer lower airway temperatures. When administered to adults and older children, *ts*-1 was noninfectious.[199] When *ts*-1 was given to young children in a high dose (10^4 to 10^5 TCID$_{50}$ per child), some children manifested mild upper respiratory infection, and one child developed otitis media.[201] In addition, revertant virus, that is, virus that has lost the *ts* property, was shed by some children.[202] When low-dose vaccine (10^2 TCID$_{50}$ per child) was administered to young children, untoward effects were not detected.[203] Children who were given *ts*-1 and subsequently became naturally infected with wild-type RSV did not manifest evidence of severe disease. Nevertheless, the occurrence of otitis media and the shedding of revertant virus by the group given high-dose *ts*-1 led to the search for more attenuated *ts* mutants. The *ts* mutant *ts*-2, in addition to being temperature-sensitive, manifested altered plaque morphology. The defect is believed to reside in the F glycoprotein and results in nonsyncytial plaque formation. The mutant was highly attenuated when administered to chimpanzees; however, when administered to seronegative infants, the vaccine was overly attenuated and did not infect the majority of vaccinees even when a dose of 10^6 TCID$_{50}$ was given.[200] Thus, to date the *ts* mutants have not been satisfactorily developed for general use.

Live RSV has been injected subcutaneously in attempts to induce serum neutralizing antibody against the appropriate antigens.[204, 205] Parenterally administered live RSV induces neutralizing antibody, and this is protective in small animals.[206] These observations led to clinical trials with parenteral live RSV vaccine. The vaccine was prepared from wild-type RSV that had been serially passaged a small number of times in WI-38 cells (5 to 10 times depending on the lot number). The vaccine had no markers of attenuation and was believed to be attenuated by route of administration. When evaluated in the field trial, the vaccine induced low levels of antibody, one-tenth that produced by natural infection; however, no effect on the occurrence of natural disease was detected nor was the severity of disease augmented.[207]

Future directions in attempts to prevent RSV illness in young children are aimed at purifying or synthesizing subunit vaccines such as purified surface glycoprotein. Studies on the immunology of RSV have pointed to both F and G glycoproteins as important immunogens (see Immunity to Infection with RSV, above). Current efforts at immunoprophylaxis will take advantage of the new understanding of immunity induced by F and G subunits and A and B subgroups of RSV. A subunit vaccine could be administered intranasally and/or subcutaneously. Also, infectious, but highly attenuated, live RSV mutants may allow the live attenuated vaccine to be given topically to the respiratory tract.

REFERENCES

1. Goodpasture EW, Auerback SH, Swanson HS, et al: Virus pneumonia of infants secondary to epidemic infections. *Am J Dis Child* 1939; 57:997–1011.
2. Adams JM: Primary virus pneumonitis with cytoplasic inclusion bodies: Study of an epidemic involving thirty-two infants with nine deaths. *JAMA* 1941; 116:925–933.
3. Visiting experts find the ''mystery disease'' of Naples is a common virus. *Science* 1979; 203:980–981.
4. Morris JA, Blount RE Jr, Savage RE: Recovery of a cytopatho-

genic agent from chimpanzees with coryza. *Proc Soc Exp Biol Med* 1956; 92:544–549.

5. Chanock R, Roizman B, Myers R: Recovery from infants with respiratory illness of a virus related to chimpanzee coryza agent (CCA): I. Isolation, properties and characterization. *Am J Hyg* 1957; 66:281–290.

6. Richman AV, Pedreira FA, Tauraso NM: Attempts to demonstrate hemagglutination and hemadsorption by respiratory syncytial virus. *Appl Microbiol* 1971; 21:1099–1100.

7. Berthiaume L, Joncas J, Pavilanis V: Comparative structure, morphogenesis and biological characteristics of the respiratory syncytial (RS) virus and the pneumonia virus of mice (PVM). *Arch Gesamte Virusforsch* 1974; 45:39–51.

8. Collins PL, Dickens LE, Buckler-White A, et al: Nucleotide sequences for the gene junctions of human respiratory syncytial virus reveal distinctive features of intergenic structure and gene order. *Proc Natl Acad Sci USA* 1986; 83:4594–4598.

9. Collins PL, Wertz GW: cDNA cloning and transcriptional mapping of nine polyadenylated RNA's encoded by the genome of respiratory syncytial virus. *Proc Natl Acad Sci USA* 1983; 80:3208–3212.

10. Collins PL, Huang YT, Wertz GW: Identification of a tenth mRNA of respiratory syncytial virus and assignment of polypeptides to the 10 viral genes. *J Virol* 1984; 49:572–578.

11. Dickens LE, Collins PL, Wertz GW: Transcriptional mapping of human respiratory syncytial virus. *J Virol* 1984; 52:364–369.

12. Fernie BF, Gerin JL: Immunochemical identification of viral and nonviral proteins of the respiratory syncytial virus virion. *Infect Immun* 1982; 37:243–249.

13. Satake M, Coligan JE, Elango N, et al: *Nucleic Acids Res* 1985; 13:7795–7812.

14. Wertz G, Collins PL, Huang Y, et al: *Proc Natl Acad Sci USA* 1985; 82:4075–4079.

15. Coates HV, Kendrick L, Chanock RM: Antigenic differences between two strains of respiratory syncytial virus. *Proc Soc Exp Biol Med* 1963; 112:958–964.

16. Wulff H, Kidd P, Wenner HA: Respiratory syncytial virus: observations on antigenic heterogeneity. *Proc Soc Exp Biol Med* 1964; 115:240–243.

17. Doggett JE, Taylor-Robinson D: Serological studies with respiratory syncytial virus. *Arch Gesamte Virusforsch* 1964; 15:601–608.

18. Anderson LJ, Hierholzer JC, Tsou C, et al: Antigenic characterization of respiratory syncytial virus strains with monoclonal antibodies. *J Infect Dis* 1985; 151:626–633.

19. Mufson MA, Örvell C, Rafnar B, et al: Two distinct subtypes of human respiratory syncytial virus. *J Gen Virol* 1985; 66:2111–2124.

20. Norrby E, Mufson MA, Sheshberadaran H: Structural differences between subtype A and B strains of respiratory syncytial virus. *J Gen Virol* 1986; 67:2721–2729.

21. Giminez HB, Hardman N, Kier HM, et al: Antigenic variation between human respiratory syncytial virus isolates. *J Gen Virol* 1986; 67:863–870.

22. Walsh EE, Brandriss MW, Schlesinger JJ: Immunological differences between the envelope glycoproteins of two strains of human respiratory syncytial virus. *J Gen Virol* 1987; 68:2169–2176.

22a. Åkerlind B, Norrby E, Örvell C, et al: Respiratory syncytial virus: Heterogeneity of subgroup B strains. *J Gen Virol* 1988; 69:2145–2154.

23. Levine S, Hamilton R: Kinetics of the respiratory syncytial virus growth cycle in HeLa cells. *Arch Gesamte Virusforsch* 1969; 28:122–132.

24. Treuhauft MW, Beem MO: Defective interfering particles of respiratory syncytial virus. *Infect Immun* 1982; 37:439–444.

25. Wright PF, Ghapure MA, Chanock RM: Genetic studies of respiratory syncytial virus temperature-sensitive mutants. *Arch Gesamte Virusforsch* 1973; 41:238–247.

26. Belshe RB, Richardson LS, Schnitzer TJ, et al: Further characterization of the complementation group B temperature-sensitive mutant of respiratory syncytial virus. *J Virol* 1977; 24:8–12.

27. Walsh EE, Hruska J: Monoclonal antibodies to respiratory syncytial virus proteins: Identification of the fusion protein. *J Virol* 1983; 27:171–177.

28. Belshe RB, Van Voris LP, Mufson MA, et al: Comparison of enzyme-linked immunosorbent assay and neutralization techniques for measurement of antibody to respiratory syncytial virus: Implications for parenteral immunization with live virus vaccine. *Infect Immun* 1982; 37:160–165.

29. Mills J, Van Kirk JE: Wright PF, et al: Experimental respiratory syncytial virus infection of adults. *J Immunol* 1971; 107:123–130.

30. Richardson LS, Yolken RH, Belshe RB, et al: Enzyme-linked immunosorbent assay for measurement of serological response to respiratory syncytial virus infection. *Infect Immunol* 1978; 20:660–664.

31. Chanock RM, Kim HW, Brandt CD, et al: Respiratory syncytial virus, in Evans AS (ed):*Viral Infections of Humans, Epidemiology and Control.* New York, Plenum, ed 2, 1982, pp 471–485.

32. Fransen H, Heigl Z, Wolontis S, et al: Infections with viruses in patients hospitalized with acute respiratory illness, Stockholm 1963–1967. *Scand J Infect Dis* 1969; 1:127–136.

33. Achong BG, Epstein MA: Preliminary seroepidemiological studies on the human syncytial virus. *J Gen Virol* 1978; 40:175–181.

34. Kim HW, Arrobio JO, Brandt CD, et al: Epidemiology of respiratory syncytial virus infection in Washington, DC: I. Importance of the virus in different respiratory tract disease syndromes and temporal distribution of infection. *Am J Epidemiol* 1973; 98:216–225.

35. Miles JAR, Macnamara FN, Mitchell R, et al: A serological study on the occurrence of some respiratory infections in Fiji. *Hum Biol Oceania* 1973; 2:79–96.

36. Lee GC, Huang YT: A serological survey of antibodies to selected respiratory viruses on Taiwan. *J Formosan Med Assoc* 1975; 74:541–547.

37. Spence L, Barratt N: Respiratory syncytial virus associated with acute respiratory infections in Trinidadian patients. *Am J Epidemiol* 1968; 88:257–266.

38. Kloene W, Bang FB, Chakraborty SM, et al: A two-year respiratory virus survey in four villages in West Bengal, India. *Am J Epidemiol* 1970; 92:307–320.

39. Hillis WD, Cooper MR, Bang FB, et al: Respiratory syncytial virus infection in children in West Bengal. *Indian J Med Res* 1971; 59:1354–1364.

40. Sobeslavsky O, Sebikari SRK, Harland PSEG, et al: The viral etiology of acute respiratory infections in children in Uganda. *Bull WHO* 1977; 55:625–631.

41. Ogunbi O: Bacteriological and viral aetiology of bronchiolitis and bronchipneumonia in Lagos children. *J Trop Med Hyg* 1970; 73:138–140.

42. Jennings R: Adenovirus, parainfluenza virus and respiratory syncytial virus antibodies in the sera of Jamaicans. *J Hyg Camb* 1972; 70:523–529.

43. Muller HK, Ball G, Epstein MA, et al: The prevalence of naturally occurring antibodies to human syncytial virus in East African populations. *Virology* 1980; 47:399–406.

44. van Rooyen E: Serologic surveys of Arctic populations and some virus diseases of interest. *Arch Environ Health* 1968; 17:547–554.

45. Golubjatnikov R, Allen VD, Olmos-Blancarte MP, et al: Serologic profile of children in a Mexican highland community: Prevalence of complement-fixing antibodies to *Mycoplasma pneumoniae,* respiratory syncytial virus and parainfluenza viruses. *Am J Epidemiol* 1975; 101:458–464.

46. Doggett JE: Antibodies to respiratory syncytial virus in human

sera from different regions of the world. *Bull WHO* 1965; 32:849–853.

47. Belshe RB, Van Voris LP, Mufson MA: Impact of viral respiratory diseases on infants and young children in a rural and urban area of southern West Virginia. *Am J Epidemiol* 1983; 117:467–474.

48. Agarwal SC, Bardoloi JNS, Mehta S: Respiratory syncytial virus infection in infancy and childhood in a community in Chandigarh. *Indian J Med Res* 1971; 59:19–25.

49. Joosting ACC, Harwin RM, Orchard M, et al: Respiratory viruses in hospital patients on the Witwatersrand. *S Afr Med J* 1979; 55:403–409.

50. Brandt CD, Kim HW, Arrobio JO, et al: Epidemiology of respiratory syncytial virus infection in Washington DC: III. Composite analysis of eleven consecutive yearly epidemics. *Am J Epidemiol* 1973; 98:355–364.

51. Parrott RH, Kim HW, Arrobio JO, et al: Epidemiology of respiratory syncytial virus infection in Washington, DC: II. Infection and disease with respect to age, immunologic status, race, and sex. *Am J Epidemiol* 1973; 98:289–300.

52. Sims DG, Downham MAPS, McQuillin J, et al: Respiratory syncytial virus infection in north-east England. *Br Med J* 1976; 1095–1098.

53. Glezen WP, Paredes A, Allison JE, et al: Risk of respiratory syncytial virus infection for infants from low-income families in relationship to age, sex, ethnic group, and maternal antibody level. *J Pediatr* 1981; 98:708–715.

54. Van Voris LP, Belshe RB, Mufson MA: Failure of breast feeding to protect against respiratory syncytial virus infection. *Clin Res* 1979; 27:652A.

55. Goldson EJ, McCarthy JT, Welling MA, et al: A respiratory syncytial virus outbreak in a transitional care nursery. *Am J Dis Child* 1979; 133:1280–1282.

56. Kapikian AZ, Bell JA, Mastrota FM, et al: An outbreak of febrile illness and pneumonia associated with respiratory syncytial virus infection. *Am J Hyg* 1961; 74:234–248.

57. Sterner G, Wolontis S, Both B, et al: Respiratory syncytial virus, an outbreak of acute respiratory illness in a home for infants. *Acta Paediatr Scand* 1966; 55:273–279.

58. Berglund B, Mantyjarvi R: Respiratory infections in children in a nursery in Finland. *Ann Paediatr Fenn* 1966; 12:143–149.

59. Aitken CJD, Moffat MAJ, Sutherland JAW: Respiratory illness and viral infection in an Edinburgh nursery. *J Hyg Camb* 1967; 65:25–36.

60. Henderson FW, Collier AM, Clyde WA Jr, et al: Respiratory-syncytial-virus infections, reinfections and immunity: A prospective, longitudinal study in young children. *N Engl J Med* 1979; 300:530–534.

61. Hall CB, Geiman JM, Biggar R, et al: Respiratory syncytial virus infections within families. *N Engl J Med* 1976; 294:414–419.

62. Hurrell GD: Viruses in families. *Lancet* 1971; 1:769–774.

63. Mufson MA, Belshe RB, Örvell C, et al: Respiratory syncytial virus epidemics: Variable dominance of subgroup A and B strains among children, 1981–1986. *J Infect Dis* 1988; 157:143–148.

64. Hendry RM, Talis AL, Godfrey E, et al: Concurrent circulation of antigenically distinct strains of respiratory syncytial virus during community outbreaks. *J Infect Dis* 1986; 153:291–297.

65. Åkerlind B, Norrby E: Occurrence of respiratory syncytial virus (RS) subtype A and B strains in Sweden. *J Med Virol* 1986; 19:241–247.

66. Mufson MA, Belshe RB, Örvell C, et al: Subgroup characteristics of respiratory syncytial virus strains recovered from children with two consecutive infections. *J Clin Microbiol* 1987; 25:1535–1539.

67. Hall CB, Douglas RG Jr: Modes of transmission of respiratory syncytial virus. *J Pediatr* 1981; 99:100–103.

68. Hall CB, Douglas RG Jr, Geiman JM: Possible transmission by fomites of respiratory syncytial virus. *J Infect Dis* 1980; 141:98–102.

69. Hall CB, Douglas RG Jr, Schnabel KC, et al: Infectivity of respiratory syncytial virus by various routes of inoculation. *Infect Immun* 1981; 33:779–783.

70. Belshe RB, Richardson LS, London WT, et al: Experimental respiratory syncytial virus infection of four species of primates. *J Med Virol* 1977; 1:157–162.

71. Hall CB, Douglas RG Jr, Geiman JM: Quantitative shedding patterns of respiratory syncytial virus in infants. *J Infect Dis* 1975; 132:151–156.

72. Hall CB, Douglas RG Jr, Geiman JM: Respiratory syncytial virus infections in infants: Quantitation and duration of shedding. *J Pediatr* 1976; 89:11–15.

73. Hall CB, Hall WJ, Speers DM: Clinical and physiological manifestations of bronchiolitis and pneumonia. *Am J Dis Child* 1979; 133:798–802.

74. Stokes GM, Milner AD, Hodges IGC, et al: Lung function abnormalities after acute bronchiolitis. *J Pediatr* 1981; 98:871–874.

75. Kattan M, Keens TG, Lapierre JG, et al: Pulmonary function abnormalities in symptom-free children after bronchiolitis. *Pediatrics* 1977; 59:683–688.

76. Connolly JH, Field CMB, Glasgow JFT, et al: A double blind trial of prednisolone in epidemic bronchiolitis due to respiratory syncytial virus. *Acta Paediatr Scand* 1969; 58:116–120.

77. Brooks LJ, Cropp GJA: Theophylline therapy in bronchiolitis: A retrospective study. *Am J Dis Child* 1981; 135:934–936.

78. Rutter N, Milner AD, Hiller EJ: Effect of bronchodilators on respiratory resistance in infants and young children with bronchiolitis and wheezing bronchitis. *Arch Dis Child* 1975; 50:719–722.

79. Field CMB, Connolly JH, Murtagh G, et al: Antibiotic treatment of epidemic bronchiolitis—A double-blind trial. *Br Med J* 1966; 1:83–85.

80. Twiggs JT, Larson LA, O'Connell EJ, et al: Respiratory syncytial virus infections. *Clin Pediatr* 1981; 20:187–190.

81. Rooney JC, Williams HE: The relationship between proved viral bronchiolitis and subsequent wheezing. *J Pediatr* 1971; 79:744–747.

82. Sims DG, Gardner PS, Weightman D, et al: Atopy does not predispose to RSV bronchiolitis or postbronchiolitis wheezing. *Br Med J* 1981; 282:2086–2088.

83. McIntosh K, Ellis EF, Hoffman LS, et al: The association of viral and bacterial respiratory infections with exacerbations of wheezing in young asthmatic children. *J Pediatr* 1973; 82:578–590.

84. McIntosh K: Bronchiolitis and asthma: Possible common pathogenetic pathways. *J Allergy Clin Immunol* 1976; 57:595–604.

85. Gurwitz D, Mindorff C, Levison H: Increased incidence of bronchial reactivity in children with a history of bronchiolitis. *J Pediatr* 1981; 98:551–555.

86. Murphy TF, Henderson FW, Clyde WA Jr, et al: Pneumonia: An eleven-year study in a pediatric practice. *Am J Epidemiol* 1981; 113:12–21.

87. Simpson H, Matthew DJ, Habel AH, et al: Acute respiratory failure in bronchiolitis and pneumonia in infancy, modes of presentation and treatment. *Br Med J* 1974; 2:632–636.

88. Elderkin FM, Gardner PS, Turk DC, et al: Aetiology and management of bronchiolitis and pneumonia in childhood. *Br Med J* 1965; 2:722–727.

89. Hall WJ, Hall CB: Clinical significance of pulmonary function tests. *Chest* 1979; 76:458–465.

90. Carlsen KH, Orstavik I: Respiratory syncytial virus infection in Oslo 1972–1978: II. Clinical and laboratory studies. *Acta Paediatr Scand* 1980; 69:723–729.

91. Simpson W, Hacking PM, Court SDM, et al: The radiological findings in respiratory syncytial virus infection in children. II: The correlation of radiological categories with clinical and virological findings. *Pediatr Radiol* 1974; 2:155–160.

92. Rice RP, Loda F: A roentgenographic analysis of respiratory syncytial virus pneumonia in infants. *Radiology* 1966; 87:1021–1027.

93. Osborne D: Radiologic appearance of viral disease of the lower respiratory tract in infants and children. *Am J Roentgenol* 1978; 130:29–33.

94. Lewis FA, Gust ID, Bennett NM: On the aetiology of whooping cough. *J Hyg Camb* 1973; 71:139–144.

95. Pereira MS, Candeias JAN: The association of viruses with clinical pertussis. *J Hyg Camb* 1971; 69:399–403.

96. Klein JO, Teele DW: Isolation of viruses and mycoplasmas from middle ear effusions: A review. *Ann Otol Rhinol Laryngol* 1976; 85(suppl):140–144.

97. Douglas RM, Miles H, Hansman D, et al: Microbiology of acute otitis media. *Med J Aust* 1980; 1:263–266.

98. Berglund B, Salmivalli A, Toivanen P, et al: Isolation of respiratory syncytial virus from middle ear exudates of infants. *Arch Dis Child* 1966; 41:554–555.

99. Berglund B, Salmivalli A, Grönroos JA: The role of respiratory syncytial virus in otitis media in children. *Acta Otolaryngol* 1967; 63:445–454.

100. Berglund B, Salmivalli A, Toivanen P: Isolation of respiratory syncytial virus from middle ear exudates of infants. *Acta Otolaryngol* 1966; 61:475–487.

101. Grönroos JA, Vihma L, Salmivalli A, et al: Coexisting viral (respiratory syncytial) and bacterial (pneumococcus) otitis media in children. *Acta Otolaryngol* 1968; 65:505–517.

102. Uren EC, Williams AL, Jack I, et al: Association of respiratory virus infection with sudden infant death syndrome. *Med J Aust* 1980; 1:417–419.

103. Ferris JAJ, Aherne WA, Locke WS, et al: Sudeen and unexpected deaths in infants: Histology and virology. *Br Med J* 1973; 2:439–442.

104. Gardner PS, McQuillin J, Court SDM: Speculation on pathogenesis in death from respiratory syncytial virus infection. *Br Med J* 1970; 1:327–330.

105. Hall CB, Kopelman AE, Douglas RG Jr, et al: Neonatal respiratory syncytial virus infection. *N Engl J Med* 1979; 300:393–396.

106. Bruhn FW, Mokrohisky ST, McIntosh K: Apnea associated with respiratory syncytial virus infection in young infants. *J Pediatr* 1977; 90:382–386.

107. Johnson RT, Johnson KP: Hydrocephalus as a sequela of experimental myxovirus infections. *Exp Mol Pathol* 1969; 10:68–80.

108. Cremer NE, Oshiro LS, Norris FH, et al: Cultures of tissues from patients with amyotrophic lateral sclerosis. *Arch Neurol* 1973; 29:331–333.

109. Griffin N, Keeling JW, Tomlinson AH: Reye's syndrome associated with respiratory syncytial virus infection. *Arch Dis Child* 1979; 54:74–76.

110. MacDonald NE, Hall CB, Suffin SC, et al: Respiratory syncytial virus infection in infants with congenital heart disease. *N Engl J Med* 1982; 307:397–400.

111. Bairan AC, Cherry JD, Fagan LF, et al: Complete heart block and respiratory syncytial virus. *Am J Dis Child* 1974; 127:264–265.

112. Giles TD, Gohd RS: Respiratory syncytial virus and heart disease: A report of two cases. *JAMA* 1976; 236:1128–1130.

113. Brugman S, Hutter JJ Jr: Respiratory syncytial virus (RSV) pneumonitis in acute leukemia. *Am J Pediatr Hematol Oncol* 1980; 2:371–374.

114. Englund JA, Sullivan CJ, Jordan C, et al: Respiratory syncytial virus infection in immunocompromised adults. *Ann Intern Med* 1988; 109:203–208.

115. Belshe RB, Van Voris LP, Mufson MA, et al: Epidemiology of severe respiratory syncytial virus infection in Huntington, West Virginia. *W Va Med J* 1981; 77:49–52.

116. Hall CB, Douglas RG Jr, Geiman JM, et al: Nosocomial respiratory syncytial virus infection. *N Engl J Med* 1975; 293:1343–1346.

117. Hall CB, Douglas RG Jr: Nosocomial respiratory syncytial viral infections: Should gowns and masks be used? *Am J Dis Child* 1981; 135:512–515.

118. Mills J, Van Kirk JE, Wright PF, et al: Experimental respiratory syncytial virus infection of adults. *J Immunol* 1971; 107:123–130.

119. Hall WJ, Hall CB, Speers DM: Respiratory syncytial virus infection in adults: Clinical, virologic and serial pulmonary function studies. *Ann Intern Med* 1978; 88:203–205.

120. Mufson MA, Chang V, Gill V, et al: The role of viruses, mycoplasmas and bacteria in acute pneumonia in civilian adults. *Am J Epidemiol* 1967; 86:526–544.

121. Kakler K, Keairnes HW, Symons J, et al: Respiratory syncytial virus—Missouri. *MMWR* 1977; 26:351.

122. Sanford JP: Acute respiratory disease in the United States Army in the Republic of Vietnam, 1965–1970. *Yale J Biol Med* 1975; 48:179–184.

123. Hers JFP, Masurel N, Gans JC: Acute respiratory disease associated with pulmonary involvement in military servicemen in the Netherlands: A serologic and bacteriologic survey, January 1967 to January 1968. *Am Rev Respir Dis* 1969; 100:499–506.

124. Madden DL, Fuccillo DA, Traub RG, et al: Juvenile onset diabetes mellitus in pregnant women: Failure to associate with Coxsackie B1-6, mumps, or respiratory syncytial virus infections. *J Pediatr* 1978; 92:959–960.

125. Mathur U, Bentley DW, Hall CB: Concurrent respiratory syncytial virus and influenza A virus infections in the institutionalized elderly and chronically ill. *Ann Intern Med* 1980; 93:49–52.

126. Van Voris LP, Belshe RB, Shaffer JL: Nosocomial influenza B virus infection in the elderly. *Ann Intern Med* 1982; 96:153–158.

127. McIntosh K, Masters H, Orr I, et al: Secretory antibody following respiratory syncytial virus infection in infants. *Pediatr Res* 1976; 10:389.

127a. Prince GA, Hemming VG, Horswood RL, et al: Mechanism of antibody-mediated viral clearance in immunotherapy of respiratory syncytial virus infection of cotton rats. *J Virol* 1990; 64:3091–3092.

128. Tyeryar FJ: Report of a workshop on respiratory syncytial virus and parainfluenza viruses. *J Infect Dis* 1983; 148:588–598.

129. Lamprecht CL, Krause HE, Mufson MA: Role of maternal antibody in pneumonia and bronchiolitis due to respiratory syncytial virus. *J Infect Dis* 1976; 134:211–217.

130. Olmsted RA, Elango N, Prince GA, et al: Expression of the F glycoprotein of respiratory syncytial virus by a recombinant vaccinia virus: Comparison of the individual contributions of the F and G glycoproteins to host immunity. *Proc Natl Acad Sci USA* 1986; 83:7462–7466.

131. Elango N, Prince GA, Murphy BR, et al: Resistance to human respiratory syncytial virus (RSV) infection induced by immunization of cotton rats with a recombinant vaccinia virus expressing the RSV G glycoprotein. *Proc Natl Acad Sci USA* 1986; 83:1906–1910.

132. Routledge EG, Willcocks MM, Samson ACR, et al: The purification of four respiratory syncytial virus proteins and their evaluation as protective agents against experimental infections in BALB/c mice. *J Gen Virol* 1988; 69:293–303.

133. Stott EJ, Taylor G, Ball LA, et al: Immune and histopathological responses in animals vaccinated with recombinant vaccinia viruses that express individual genes of human respiratory syncytial virus. *J Virol* 1987; 61:3855–3861.

134. Stott EJ, Ball LA, Young KK, et al: Human respiratory syncytial virus glycoprotein G expressed from a recombinant vaccinia virus vector protects mice against live-virus challenge. *J Virol* 1986; 60:607–613.

135. Wertz GW, Stott EJ, Young KKY, et al: Expression of the fusion protein of human respiratory syncytial virus from recombinant vaccinia virus vectors and protection of vaccinated mice. *J Virol* 1987; 61:293–301.

136. King AMQ, Stott EJ, Langer SJ, et al: Recombinant vaccinia viruses carrying the N gene of human respiratory syncytial virus: Studies of gene expression in cell culture and immune response in mice. *J Virol* 1987; 61:2885–2890.

137. Bangham CRM, Openshaw PJM, Ball LA, et al: Human and murine cytotoxic T cells specific to respiratory syncytial virus recognize the viral nucleoprotein (N), but not the major glycoprotein (G), expressed by vaccinia virus recombinants. *J Immunol* 1986; 137:3973–3977.

138. Openshaw PJM, Pemberton RM, Ball LA, et al: Helper T cell recognition of respiratory syncytial virus in mice. *J Gen Virol* 1988; 68:305–312.

139. Johnson PR Jr, Olmsted RA, Prince GA, et al: Antigenic relatedness between glycoproteins of human respiratory syncytial virus subgroups A and B: Evaluation of the contributions of F and G glycoproteins to immunity. *J Virol* 1987; 61:3163–3166.

140. Fishaut M, Murphy D, Neifert M, et al: Bronchomammary axis in the immune response to respiratory syncytial virus. *J Pediatr* 1981; 99:186–191.

141. Downham MAPS, Scott R, Sims DG, et al: Breast-feeding protects against respiratory syncytial virus infections. *Br Med J* 1976; 2:274–276.

142. Frank AL, Taber LH, Glezen WP, et al: Breast-feeding and respiratory virus infection. *Pediatrics* 1982; 70:239–245.

143. Sieber OF: Immunologic factors in infectious diseases of the airways and lung in infants and young children with particular emphasis on bronchiolitis: Comments. *Pediatr Res* 1977; 11:230.

144. Kim HW, Leikin SL, Arrobio J, et al: Cell-mediated immunity to respiratory syncytial virus induced by inactivated vaccine or by infection. *Pediatr Res* 1976; 10:75–78.

145. Prince GA, Porter DD: The pathogenesis of respiratory syncytial virus infection in infant ferrets. *Am J Pathol* 1976; 82:339–350.

146. Prince GA, Jensen AB, Horswood RL, et al: The pathogenesis of respiratory syncytial virus infection in cotton rats. *Am J Pathol* 1978; 93:771–783.

147. Aherne W, Bird T, Court SDM, et al: Pathological changes in virus infections of the lower respiratory tract in children. *J Clin Pathol* 1970; 23:7–18.

148. Collier AM: Injury of respiratory epithelium. *Environ Health Perspect* 1980; 35:83–88.

149. Naib ZM, Steward JA, Dowdle WR, et al: Cytological features of viral respiratory tract infections. *Acta Cytol* 1968; 12:162–171.

150. Gardner PS, McQuillin J, Court SDM: Speculation on pathogenesis in death from respiratory syncytial virus infection. *Br Med J* 1970; 1:327–330.

151. Kim HW, Canchola JG, Brandt CD, et al: Respiratory syncytial virus disease in infants despite prior administration of antigenic inactivated vaccine. *Am J Epidemiol* 1969; 89:422–434.

152. Chanock RM: Control of acute mycoplasma and viral respiratory disease. *Science* 1977; 169:248–256.

153. Prince GA, Jenson AB, Hemming VG, et al: Enhancement of respiratory syncytial virus pulmonary pathology in cotton rats by prior intramuscular inoculation of formalin-inactivated virus. *J Virol* 1986; 57:721–728.

154. Murphy BR, Prince GA, Walsh EE, et al: Dissociation between serum neutralizing and glycoprotein antibody responses of infants and children who received inactivated respiratory syncytial virus vaccine. *J Clin Microbiol* 1986; 24:197–202.

155. Welliver RC, Kaul TN, Ogra PL: The appearance of cell-bound IgE in respiratory-tract epithelium after respiratory-syncytial-virus infection. *N Engl J Med* 1980; 303:1198–1202.

156. Welliver RD, Wong DT, Sun M, et al: The development of respiratory syncytial virus-specific IgE and the release of histamine in nasopharyngeal secretions after infection. *N Engl J Med* 1981; 305:841–846.

157. Scott R, Kaul A, Scott M, et al: Development of in vitro correlates of cell-mediated immunity to respiratory syncytial virus infection in humans. *J Infect Dis* 1978; 137:810–817.

158. Scott R, DeLandazuri MO, Gardner PS, et al: Human antibody-dependent cell-mediated cytotoxicity against target cells infected with respiratory syncytial virus. *Clin Exp Immunol* 1977; 28:19–26.

159. Cranage MP, Gardner PS, McIntosh K: In vitro cell-dependent lysis of respiratory syncytial virus-infected cells mediated by antibody from local respiratory secretions. *Clin Exp Immunol* 1981; 43:28–35.

160. Meguro H, Kervina M, Wright PF: Antibody-dependent cell-mediated cytotoxicity against cells infected with respiratory syncytial virus: Characterization of in vitro and in vivo properties. *J Immunol* 1979; 122:2521–2526.

161. Fulginiti VA, Stahl M: Parainfluenza and respiratory syncytial viruses, in Lennette EH, Spaulding EH, Trucent JP (eds): *Manual of Clinical Microbiology*, ed 2, Washington, DC, American Society for Microbiology, 1974; pp 686–694.

162. Gardner PS, Grandien M, McQuillin J: Comparison of immunofluorescence and immunoperoxidase methods for viral diagnosis at a distance: A WHO collaborative study. *Bull WHO* 1978; 56:105–110.

163. Minnich LL, Ray CG: Comparison of direct and indirect immunofluorescence staining of clinical specimens for detection of respiratory syncytial virus antigen. *J Clin Microbiol* 1982; 15:969–970.

164. Chao RK, Fishaut M, Schwartzman JD, et al: Detection of respiratory syncytial virus in nasal secretions from infants by enzyme-linked immunosorbent assay. *J Infect Dis* 1979; 139:483–486.

165. Hendry RM, McIntosh K: Enzyme-linked immunosorbent assay for detection of respiratory syncytial virus infection: Development and description. *J Clin Microbiol* 1982; 16:324–328.

166. Masters HB, Weber KO, Groothuis JR, et al: Comparison of nasopharyngeal washings and swab specimens for diagnosis of respiratory syncytial virus by EIA, FAT, and cell culture. *Diagn Microbiol Infect Dis* 1987; 8:101–105.

167. Ahluwalia G, Embree J, McNicol P, et al: Comparison of nasopharyngeal aspirate and nasopharyngeal swab specimens for respiratory syncytial virus diagnosis by cell culture, indirect immunofluorescence assay, and enzyme-linked immunosorbent assay. *J Clin Microbiol* 1987; 25:763–767.

168. Chonmaitree T, Bessette-Henderson BJ, Hepler RE, et al: Comparison of three rapid diagnostic techniques for detection of respiratory syncytial virus from nasal wash specimens. *J Clin Microbiol* 1987; 25:746–747.

169. Kumar ML, Super DM, Lembo RM, et al: Diagnostic efficacy of two rapid tests for detection of respiratory syncytial virus antigen. *J Clin Microbiol* 1987; 25:873–875.

170. Joncas JH, Berthiaume L, Williams R, et al: Diagnosis of viral respiratory infections by electron microscopy. *Lancet* 1969; 1:956–959.

171. Hoffman EJ, Ford EC, Chanock RM, et al: A radioimmunoprecipitation test for antibody to the ribonucleoprotein of respiratory syncytial virus. American Society for Microbiology. 1976, abstract No. 5305.

172. Cranage MP, Stott EJ, Nagington J, et al: A reverse passive haemagglutination test for the detection of respiratory syncytial virus in nasal secretions from infants. *J Med Virol* 1981; 8:153–160.

173. Norrby E, Mufson MA, Alexander H, et al: Site-directed serology with synthetic peptides representing the large glycoprotein G of respiratory syncytial virus. *Proc Natl Acad Sci USA* 1987; 84:6572–6576.

174. American Academy of Pediatrics Committee on Infectious Diseases: Ribavirin therapy of respiratory syncytial virus. *Pediatrics* 1987; 79:475.

175. Hicks RA, Olson LC, Jackson MA: Precipitation of ribavirin causing obstruction of a ventilation tube. *Pediatr Infect Dis* 1986; 5:707–708.

176. Frankel LR, Wilson CW, Demers RR, et al: A technique for the administration of ribavirin to mechanically ventilated infants with severe respiratory syncytial virus infection. *Crit Care Med* 1987; 15:1051.

177. Outwater KM, Meissner HC, Peterson MB: Ribavirin administration to infants receiving mechanical ventilation. *Am J Dis Child* 1988; 142:512.

178. Rodriguez WJ, Dang Bui RH, Connor JD, et al: Environmental exposure of primary care personnel to ribavirin aerosol when supervising treatment of infants with respiratory syncytial virus infections. *Antimicrob Agents Chemother* 1987; 31:1143–1146.
179. Hall CB, Walsh EE, Hruska JR, et al: Ribavirin treatment of experimental respiratory syncytial viral infection, a controlled double-blind study in young adults. *JAMA* 1983; 249:2666–2670.
180. Gilbert BE, Knight V: Biochemistry and clinical applications of ribavirin. *Antimicrob Agents Chemother* 1986; 30:201–205.
181. Barry W, Cockburn F, Cornall R, et al: Ribavirin aerosol for acute bronchiolitis. *Arch Dis Child* 1986; 61:593–597.
182. Rodriguez WJ, Kim HW, Brandt CD, et al: Aerosolized ribavirin in the treatment of patients with respiratory syncytial virus disease. *Pediatr Infect Dis* 1987; 6:159–163.
183. Caramia G, Palazzini E: Efficacy of ribavirin aerosol treatment for respiratory syncytial virus bronchiolitis in infants. *J Int Med Res* 1987; 15:227–233.
184. Conrad DA, Christenson JC, Waner JL, et al: Aerosolized ribavirin treatment of respiratory syncytial virus infection in infants hospitalized during an epidemic. *Pediatr Infect Dis* 1987; 6:152–158.
185. Prince GA, Hemming VG, Horswood RL, et al: Effectiveness of topically administered neutralizing antibodies in experimental immunotherapy of respiratory syncytial virus infection in cotton rats. *J Virol* 1987; 61:1851–1854.
186. Gruber WC, Wilson SZ, Throop BJ, et al: Immunoglobulin administration and ribavirin therapy: Efficacy in respiratory syncytial virus infection of the cotton rats. *Pediatr Res* 1987; 21:270.
187. Hall CB, Douglas RG Jr, Simons RL, et al: Interferon production in children with respiratory syncytial influenza and parainfluenza virus infections. *J Pediatr* 1978; 93:28–32.
188. McIntosh K: Interferon in nasal secretions from infants with viral respiratory tract infections. *J Pediatr* 1978; 93:33–36.
189. Hall CB, Douglas RG, Jr, Simons RL: Interferon production in adults with respiratory syncytial viral infection. *Ann Intern Med* 1981; 94:53–55.
190. Chonmaitree T, Roberts NJ Jr, Douglas RG Jr, et al: Interferon production by human mononuclear leukocytes: Differences between respiratory syncytial virus and influenza viruses. *Infect Immun* 1981; 32:300–303.
191. Roberts NJ Jr: Different effects of influenza virus, respiratory syncytial virus, and Sendai virus on human lymphocytes and macrophages. *Infect Immun* 1982; 35:1142–1146.
192. Parrott RH, Kim HW, Arrobio JO, et al: Respiratory syncytial and parainfluenza virus vaccines: Experience with inactivated respiratory syncytial and parainfluenza virus vaccines in infants. *Pan Am Health Org Sci Pub* 1967; 147:35–41.
193. Potash L, Tytell AA, Sweet BH, et al: Respiratory virus vaccines: I. Respiratory syncytial and parainfluenza virus vaccines. *Am Rev Respir Dis* 1966; 93:536–548.
194. Sweet BH, Tytell AA, Potash L, et al: Respiratory virus vaccines: III. Pentavalent respiratory syncytial-parainfluenza-*Mycoplasma pneumoniae* vaccine. *Am Rev Respir Dis* 1966; 94:340–349.
195. Chin J, Magoffin RL, Shearer LA, et al: Field evaluation of a respiratory syncytial virus vaccine and a trivalent parainfluenza virus vaccine in a pediatric population. *Am J Epidemiol* 1969; 89:449–463.
196. Kapikian AZ, Mitchell RH, Chanock RM, et al: An epidemiologic study of altered clinical reactivity to respiratory syncytial (RS) virus infection in children previously vaccinated with an inactivated RS virus vaccine. *Am J Epidemiol* 1969; 89:405–421.
197. Friedewald WT, Forsyth BR, Smith CB, et al: Low-temperature-grown RS virus in adult volunteers. *JAMA* 1968; 204:690–694.
198. Kim HW, Arrobio JO, Pyles G, et al: Clinical and immunological response of infants and children to administration of low-temperature adapted respiratory syncytial virus. *Pediatrics* 1971; 48:745–755.
199. Wright PF, Mills J, Chanock RM: Evaluation of a temperature-sensitive mutant of respiratory syncytial virus in adults. *J Infect Dis* 1971; 124:505–511.
200. Wright PF, Belshe RB, Kim HW, et al: Administration of a highly attenuated, live respiratory syncytial virus vaccine to adults and children. *Infect Immun* 1982; 37:397–400.
201. Kim HW, Arrobio JO, Brandt CD, et al: Safety and antigenicity of temperature sensitive (ts) mutant respiratory syncytial virus (RSV) in infants and children. *Pediatrics* 1973; 52:56–64.
202. Hodes DS, Kim HW, Parrott RH, et al: Genetic alteration in a temperature-sensitive mutant of respiratory syncytial virus after replication in vivo (37972). *Proc Soc Exp Biol Med* 1974; 145:1158–1164.
203. Wright PF, Shinozaki T, Fleet W, et al: Evaluation of live, attenuated respiratory syncytial virus vaccine in infants. *J Pediatr* 1976; 88:931–936.
204. Buynak EB, Weibel RE, McLean AA, et al: Live respiratory syncytial virus vaccine administered parenterally (40112). *Proc Soc Exp Biol Med* 1978; 157:636–642.
205. Buynak EB, Weibel RE, Carlson AJ, et al: Further investigations of live respiratory syncytial virus vaccine administered parenterally (40433). *Proc Soc Exp Biol Med* 1979; 160:272–277.
206. Prince GA, Potash L, Horswood RL, et al: Intramuscular inoculation of live respiratory syncytial virus induces immunity in cotton rats. *Infect Immun* 1979; 23:723–728.
207. Belshe RB, Van Voris LP, Mufson MA: Parenterally administered live respiratory syncytial virus vaccine: Results of a field trial. *J Infect Dis* 1982; 145:311–319.

Coronaviruses

Maurice A. Mufson

Coronaviruses of humans are pathogens of the respiratory tract and possibly also of the gastrointestinal (GI) tract. Viruses belonging to the genus *Coronavirus* had been recognized as pathogens of a variety of animals many years before the first coronaviruses of humans were isolated and identified.[1] Among animals, coronaviruses cause diverse diseases affecting the pulmonary, GI, renal, or central nervous systems; these infections in domestic animals have important economic consequences. By contrast, the first human coronaviruses were isolated less than 20 years ago and required special organ culture procedures and unique variations in tissue culture techniques. In man, coronaviruses cause acute respiratory tract disease, predominantly common cold illnesses, bronchitis, and to a much less extent, pneumonia, and possibly gastroenteritis. Coronaviruses cause 5% to 15% of acute upper respiratory tract illnesses in children. Coronaviruslike particles can be visualized in specimens of feces of persons with diarrheal illnesses and appear to be associated with these illnesses.[2, 3]

HISTORY

The isolation and characterization of human coronaviruses in the early 1960s concluded an era of discovery of many new viruses that was made possible by advances in tissue and organ culture techniques, including the development of new cell lines from human tissues, the availability of antibiotics, and the application of new methods for recognizing virus growth in the absence of cytopathic changes in cells. Coronaviruses were isolated from respiratory secretions of adults with common colds by two groups of investigators at nearly the same time.[4] In England, Tyrrell and Bynoe isolated a virus, designated strain B814, using human embryonic trachea organ cultures.[5] Hamre and Procknow, in the United States, recovered five viruses, including 229E, in tissue cultures of human embryonic kidney and diploid fibroblast cells.

The ultrastructural features of strains 229E and B814 appeared similar to several animal viruses, including infectious bronchitic virus and mouse hepatitis virus, and subsequently these viruses (and other animal viruses, including bovine coronavirus, transmissible gastroenteritis virus of swine, feline infectious peritonitis virus, and turkey coronavirus) were classified as a new genus, *Coronavirus*.[6, 7] The successful passage in mouse brain of strains from one group of human coronaviruses and the development of antibody assay procedures fostered the investigation of the role of these viruses in human respiratory tract disease.[1] Coronaviruses cause a significant proportion of acute upper respiratory tract illnesses and exacerbations of chronic bronchitis, but they cause only a small number of viral pneumonias.[1]

CLASSIFICATION AND STRUCTURE

Coronavirus comprises the single genus of the family ***Coronaviridae,*** which includes the human coronaviruses and numerous animal viruses.[1, 8, 9] These viruses are enveloped, pleomorphic particles of approximately 80 to 120 nm in diameter, with linear plus-stranded RNA genome of approximate molecular weight of 6×10^6. The RNA genome is capped at the 5' end and contains a poly (A) sequence at the 3' end. The plus-strand genome comprises the template for producing a negative-strand RNA which enables transcription of the genomic RNA and six nested subgenomic (a 3' coterminal set) messenger RNAs (mRNA). These code for the major polypeptides of the virus.[8, 9]

Coronaviruses replicate in the cell cytoplasm and mature by budding through endoplasmic reticulum. Strain 229E and other strains similar to it grow in human diploid fibroblast cells, producing cytopathic effects. Certain strains of human coronaviruses isolated using embryonic trachea organ cultures, for example, strains OC38 and OC43, have been adapted to growth in mouse brain and cause encephalitis in experimental infection of mice. The prototypic human coronaviruses exhibiting antigenic relatedness form "subgroups," namely strains 229E and LP, strains OC43 and OC38, and strain B814.[1] Human coronavirus strain OC43 is closely related to mouse hepatitis virus (MHC, strain A59), bovine coronavirus, and hemagglutinating porcine encephalomyelitis coronavirus.

Human coronavirus OC43 possesses four major virion proteins: a surface peplomeric glycoprotein (P), hemagglutinin (H), nucleoprotein (N), and matrix protein (M).[8] The peplomeric protein, which comprises the clublike projections of the corona, has a molecular weight of 190 kilodaltons (kd); it is glycosylated and cleaves into two subunits of nearly identical size, 110 kd and 90 kd, but these subunits consist of different amino acid composition.[10] The peplomeric protein is comparable to the E2 glycoprotein of MHV and bovine coronavirus, and monoclonal antibodies to peplomeric protein of these two animal coronaviruses neutralizes the virion.[11, 12] The hemagglutinating glycoprotein has a molecular weight of 130 kd and is a dimer (or homodimer in animal coronaviruses) of disulfide-bonded 65-kd subunits. It is comparable to the E3 protein of MHV. Nonhemagglutinating strains of human coronaviruses, such as strain 229E, do not contain this protein. The nucleoprotein is a phosphorylated protein of 55 kd. Monoclonal antibodies to the nucleoprotein do not neutralize the virus. The smallest virion protein is the M protein of 26 kd.

EPIDEMIOLOGY

Coronavirus infections occur sporadically and worldwide. Outbreaks of acute respiratory tract disease associated with coronavirus infections may exhibit a winter and spring pattern of occurrence. Although strains 229E and OC43 can circulate in a community at the same time, apparently one of these infections will predominate during each outbreak, and cycles of individual strains occur during subsequent outbreaks.

Coronavirus infections of the respiratory tract occur mainly among children and, to a lesser extent, among adolescents and adults.[1] These viruses may account for 5% to 15% of upper respiratory tract illnesses of children and adults. However, few pneumonia illnesses are associated with coronavirus infection. The proportion of persons with antibody to coronaviruses 229E and OC43 (the only two strains for which adequate antigens can be prepared for antibody tests) increases with advancing age. By age 30, greater than two thirds of persons possess antibody to corona-

virus strains OC43 and 229E. Reinfections are common; as many as four fifths of coronavirus infections occur in persons with pre-existing antibody.

TRANSMISSION

Although no direct evidence exists on the mode of transmission of human coronaviruses, it seems likely that they spread by the respiratory route in large droplets and possibly by aerosols from infected to noninfected persons. The rapidity of spread of coronaviruses during outbreaks also suggests these mechanisms as the means of spread. In volunteers, infection of the upper respiratory tract was produced by intranasal instillation of coronavirus 229E.[13]

DISEASES CAUSED BY CORONAVIRUSES

Human coronaviruses mainly cause acute upper respiratory tract illness (common colds) and, on occasion, febrile upper respiratory tract illness, pneumonia, and exacerbations of chronic bronchitis. The patterns of clinical features of respiratory tract diseases caused by coronaviruses are not sufficiently characteristic to permit differentiation on clinical grounds alone. Although the diagnosis of coronavirus respiratory disease can be suspected by the clinician, it can be confirmed only by laboratory diagnostic tests. Since coronaviruses account for a sizable proportion of colds, and some instances of exacerbations of chronic bronchitis, the clinician should be cognizant of these infections.

Common Cold

The incubation period of colds associated with coronavirus infection is three days, as determined in experimentally infected volunteers.[13] The main clinical features of naturally occurring coronavirus colds are coryza, rhinorrhea, and nasal congestion; sore throat; and pharyngeal erythema.[14] These symptoms and signs occur in more than two thirds of persons with coronavirus colds. Cough, headache, fever, and cervical adenitis develop less often. The severity of illness appears unrelated to the presence of pre-existing antibody. In volunteers given strain 229E by intranasal administration, more severe colds were associated with greater secretory and IgE levels.[13] Coronavirus colds usually abate within 1 week. The signs and symptoms of respiratory illness do not appear to be different for the two coronavirus strains 229E and OC43.

Pneumonia

Very infrequently, pneumonia may be associated with coronavirus infection.[15–17] In a single study among infants less than 18 months of age, coronavirus infection was deteced in 8.3% of infants with pneumonia. These infants experienced an atypical pneumonia that was clinically indistinguishable from other viral pneumonias.[15] The findings included fever, cough, restlessness, and anorexia, and pulmonary findings of an atypical pneumonia. Pneumonia associated with coronavirus infection has been observed uncommonly among military recruits.[16] The illnesses were characterized by cough, sore throat, malaise, headache, and hoarseness in at least two thirds of cases and fever and rales in one half of cases. Pleural reactions occurred in one third of cases. Several cases have been reported recently of community-acquired pneumonia associated with coronavirus infection (strain OC43) among children and adults.[17]

Exacerbations of Chronic Bronchitis

Coronavirus infection has been associated with exacerbations of chronic bronchitis.[18] In one longitudinal evaluation of infections in chronic bronchitis patients, coronavirus infections (determined by antibody assays) were detected in 6% of exacerbations.[18] It seems reasonable to expect that persons with chronic bronchitis will experience infections with many viral respiratory pathogens, including coronaviruses, and that these infections will exacerbate their fragile pulmonary status. No data exist to suggest a special role of coronaviruses in exacerbations of chronic bronchitis.

Other Diseases

Human enteric coronaviruses have been observed in the stools of children and adults with diarrheal illnesses or gastroenteritis, and in the stools of infants with neonatal necrotizing enterocolitis.[19, 20] The frequency of observation was similar from persons with or without diarrheal illnesses or gastroenteritis.[20] Coronavirus-like particles in stool specimens were visualized by electron microscopic procedures in nearly 70% of persons with gastroenteritis in one study of 862 stool specimens.[3] Most virus-positive persons had high amounts of homogeneous populations of virus in their stool specimens. Coronavirus was isolated from stool specimens in all months, with a slightly higher prevalence in September. However, seasonal occurrence of coronavirus was not statistically significant. No control persons were tested. Among more than 2000 persons mainly admitted with gastroenteritis to one hospital in Melbourne, Australia, between January 1980 and September 1985, 34 persons were positive for coronavirus-like particles detected by electron microscopic examination of stool.[20a] Twenty-six of these 34 persons had diarrhea as the major sign of illness. They were drawn from three groups: intellectually handicapped persons from institutions, recent overseas travellers to developing communities, and some homosexuals. It appeared that excretion of the virus was related to poor hygiene.

During an outbreak of neonatal necrotizing enterocolitis among premature and full-term newborns, coronavirus-like particles were observed by electron microscopic procedures significantly more often in stools of ill infants than in control infants.[21] Twenty-three (72%) of 32 patients with neonatal necrotizing enterocolitis were positive for enteric coronaviruses, compared with only three (11.5%) of 26 control patients. All seven virus-positive newborns with neonatal necrotizing enterocolitis tested for antibody rises by immune electron microscopy developed high antibody levels during convalescence, but only one of six virus-negative control patients developed high antibody levels. Other bacterial and viral pathogens were not detected. At least four deaths occurred among the ill newborns. These findings suggest that coronavirus-like particles may be pathogenic for the human GI tract, as they are in lower animals. In pigs and cattle, coronaviruses infect the GI tract and produce enteritis.

IMMUNITY

Antibody develops in response to naturally occurring or experimental coronavirus infection. The purified surface projections of the virus elicit a neutralizing antibody response. Volunteers challenged with strain 229E developed such antibody rises, but only one volunteer developed antibody to membrane antigen and four volunteers developed antibody to ribonucleoprotein.[12]

Little, if any, antibody cross-reaction occurs between strains 229E and CO43. Usually, persons infected with one of these coronaviruses will develop antibody only to the infecting strain, even if they had preexisting antibody to the other strain. Neutralizing antibody develops in nearly all infected persons; however, hemagglutination-inhibition and complement-fixing antibodies develop in less than one half of persons with coronavirus infections. Serum antibody persists for long periods. Reinfections occur commonly, and it appears that serum antibody plays only a minor role in moderating the severity of acute upper respiratory illnesses. The role of secretory antibody in coronavirus infections remains to be investigated.

PATHOGENESIS

Our understanding of the pathogenesis of coronaviruses for the respiratory tract is derived only from the experimental infection of volunteers. No laboratory animal has been infected by the respiratory route, although strain OC43 has been adapted to growth in suckling mouse brain.

In volunteers challenged with coronaviruses by intranasal instillation into the nose and throat, infection and illness ensue after an incubation period of three days.[13] The volunteer becomes ill with an acute upper respiratory illness and sheds virus in the respiratory secretions. The infection involves only the upper respiratory tract. Usually it lasts 1 week.

LABORATORY DIAGNOSIS

Isolation of virus using human embryonic trachea cultures or visualization of virus by electron microscopic procedures remains a research tool. Viral RNA of coronavirus 229E can be detected in nasal washings of infected persons using RNA:RNA hybridization.[21a] This technique is sensitive and specific and it provides a rapid means for the diagnosis of coronavirus 229E infection. For practical purposes, the laboratory diagnosis of coronavirus infections is limited to the detection of an antibody rise in paired sera taken during the acute and convalescent phases of illness. Antibody can be measured only to strains 229E and OC43 because adequate antigens can be made for these two coronavirus strains. Specific coronavirus antibody can be measured by several different procedures including neutralization,[22] complement fixation,[1] enzyme-linked immunosorbent assay,[23] single radial hemolysis,[24] immune-adherence hemagglutination,[25] and immunofluorescence.[26] Antibody to strain OC43 can be measured also by hemagglutination inhibition.[14]

COMMENT

Although human coronaviruses cause a significant number of acute respiratory tract illnesses in children and adults, the difficulty in recognizing these illnesses on clinical grounds or in establishing a laboratory diagnosis impedes their study in a major way, except by a few research investigators. Consequently, progress in understanding coronavirus infections, epidemic patterns, and clinical syndromes has been slow. The two prototype strains of human coronaviruses exhibit little antigenic relatedness. No vaccine for human coronaviruses has been tested or is under consideration at this time; however, tests of live animal coronavirus vaccines are under way.

REFERENCES

1. McIntosh K: Coronaviruses, in Fields BN, Knipe DM, Chanock RM, et al (eds): *Virology*. New York, Raven Press, 1985, pp 1323–1330.
2. Battaglia M, Passarani N, Di Matteo A, et al: Human enteric coronaviruses: Further characterization and immunoblotting of viral proteins. *J Infect Dis* 1987; 155:140–143.
3. Payne CM, Ray CG, Bordiun V, et al: An eight-year study of the viral agents of acute gastroenteritis in humans: Ultrastructural observations and seasonal distribution with a major emphasis on coronavirus-like particles. *Diagn Microbiol Infect Dis* 1986; 5:39–54.
4. Weiner LP: Coronaviruses: a historical perspective. *Adv Exp Med Biol* 1987; 218:1–5.
5. Tyrrell DAJ, Bynoe ML: Cultivation of a novel type of common-cold virus in organ cultures. *Br Med J* 1965; 1:1467–1470.
6. Hamre D, Procknow JJ: A new virus isolated from the human respiratory tract. *Proc Soc Exp Biol Med* 1966; 121:190–193.
7. Coronaviruses. *Nature* 1968; 220:650.
8. Hogue BG, Brian DA: Structural proteins of human respiratory coronavirus OC43. *Virus Res* 1986; 5:131–144.
9. Sawicki SG, Sawicki DL: Coronavirus minus-strand RNA synthesis and effect of cycloheximide on coronavirus RNA synthesis. *J Virol* 1986; 57:328–334.
9a. Jouvenne P, Richardson CD, Schreiber SS, et al: Sequence analysis of the membrane portion gene of human coronavirus 229E. *Virology* 1990; 174:608–612.
9b. Raabe T, Siddell SG: Nucleotide sequence of the gene encoding the membrane protein of human coronavirus 229E. *Arch Virol* 1989; 107:323–328.
10. Sturman LS, Holmes KV: The molecular biology of coronaviruses. *Adv Virus Res* 1983; 28:35–112.
11. Schmidt I, Skinner M, Siddell S: Nucleotide sequences of the gene encoding the surface projection glycoprotein of coronavirus MHV-JHM. *J Gen Virol* 1987; 68:47–56.
12. MacNaughton MR, Hasony HJ, Madge MH, et al: Antibody to virus components in volunteers experimentally infected with human coronavirus 229E group viruses. *Infect Immun* 1981; 31:845–849.
13. Callow KA, Tyrrell DA, Shaw RJ, et al: Influence of atopy on the clinical manifestations of coronavirus infection in adult volunteers. *Clin Allergy* 1988; 18:119–129.
14. Kaye HS, Dowdle WR: Seroepidemiologic survey of coronavirus (strain 229E) infections in a population of children. *Am J Epidemiol* 1975; 101:238–244.
15. McIntosh K, Chao RK, Krause HE, et al: Coronavirus infection in acute lower respiratory tract disease in infants. *J Infect Dis* 1974; 130:502–507.
16. Wenzel RP, Hendley JO, Davies JA, et al: Coronavirus infections in military recruits: Three year study with coronavirus strains OC43 and 229E. *Am Rev Respir Dis* 1974; 109:621–624.
17. Riski H, Hovi T: Coronavirus infections of man associated with diseases other than the common cold. *J Med Virol* 1980; 6:259–265.
18. Gump DW, Phillips CA, Forsyth BR, et al: Role of infection in chronic bronchitis. *Am Rev Respir Dis* 1976; 113:465–474.
19. Caul EO, Ashley CR, Egglestone SI: Recognition of human enteric coronaviruses by electron microscopy. *Med Lab Sci* 1977; 34:259–263.
20. Clarke SKR, Caul EO, Egglestone SI: The human enteric coronaviruses. *Postgrad Med J* 1979; 55:135–142.
20a. Marshall JA, Thompson WL, Gust ID: Coronavirus-like particles in adults in Melbourne, Australia. *J Med Virol* 1989; 29:238–243.
21. Chany C, Moscovici O, Lebon P, et al: Association of coronavirus infection with necrotizing enterocolitis. *Pediatrics* 1982; 69:209–214.
21a. Myint S, Siddell S, Tyrrell D: Detection of human coronavirus 229E in nasal washings using RNA:RNA hybridisation. *J Med Virol* 1989; 29:70–73.
22. Gerna G, Cattaneo E, Cereda PM, et al: Human coronavirus OC43 serum-inhibition and neutralizing antibody by a new plaque-reduction assay. *Proc Soc Exp Biol Med* 1980; 163:360–366.
23. Kraaijeveld CA, Reed SE, MacNaughton MR: Enzyme-linked immunosorbent assay for the detection of antibody in volunteers experimentally infected with human coronavirus strain 229E. *J Clin Microbiol* 1980; 12:493–497.
24. Hierholzer JC, Tannock GA: Quantitation of antibody to non-hemagglutinating viruses by single radial hemolysis: Serological test for human coronaviruses. *J Clin Microbiol* 1977; 5:613–620.
25. Gerna G, Achilli G, Cattaneo E, et al: Determination of coronavirus 229E antibody by an immune-adherence hemagglutination method. *J Med Virol* 1978; 2:215–223.
26. McIntosh K, McQuillan J, Reed SR, et al: Diagnosis of human coronavirus infection by immunofluorescence: Method and application to respiratory disease in hospitalized children. *J Med Virol* 1978; 2:341–346.

16

Rhinoviruses

Roland A. Levandowski

HISTORY

STRUCTURE AND BIOLOGY

EPIDEMIOLOGY

PATHOGENESIS

TRANSMISSION
INFECTION
IMMUNOLOGY

LABORATORY DIAGNOSIS

VACCINE-INDUCED IMMUNITY

ANTIVIRAL AGENTS

REMAINING PROBLEMS

The major cause of mild upper respiratory disease in man is the rhinovirus, a member of the family ***Picornaviridae***.[1, 2] It is responsible for the syndrome known as the common cold, together with other viruses such as adenoviruses, coronaviruses, myxoviruses, and paramyxoviruses. Illness related to rhinovirus infection is predominated by symptoms and signs of nasal discharge and obstruction. While it is considered by many a mere nuisance, the worldwide occurrence of the common cold, its frequent appearance in otherwise healthy individuals, and its rightly perceived economic importance in terms of employee absenteeism and physician visits in industrial countries have made it the subject of extensive investigation in the twentieth century.

Rhinoviruses were first isolated in the mid-1950s. Since that time over 100 individual serotypes have been identified in sporadic rhinovirus infection.[3–5] Partly because of the profusion of individual serotypes, control of rhinoviruses is an unrealized goal. Nevertheless, investigations of the pathogenesis, immunologic consequences, and prevention of rhinovirus infections continue and offer hope of one day eliminating this ubiquitous illness.

HISTORY

The true nature of the common cold has only recently been unraveled, although undoubtedly it has plagued mankind for centuries. The name given to the syndrome is derived from the nineteenth-century belief that "a cold is a diseased state brought on by the body being exposed to cold, or having its heat abstracted suddenly by cold air, a draught of air, damp, or other means."[6] Thus, the term initially encompassed any dysfunction thought to result from chilling of the body, but eventually "common cold" came to mean acute upper respiratory tract disease or, more specifically, acute coryza.

In spite of this mistaken popular belief, the infectious etiology of the common cold was established early in this century. In 1914, cell-free filtrates obtained from the nasal secretions of an individual with acute coryza caused an identical acute illness in 30% to 40% of the volunteers inoculated intranasally with the secretions.[7] Although a nonbacterial etiology was postulated, in the 1930s various bacteria were investigated as possible contributors to the common cold.[8] The viral etiology of the common cold was proved in 1953, when a virus was successfully isolated in tissue culture after inoculation of nasal secretions from a patient with acute coryza.[9] The isolate did not produce a cytopathic effect in primary embryonic lung tissue culture, but tissue culture-passaged virus did reproduce illness in inoculated volunteers. Other similar viruses (variously called Salisbury agents, coryzaviruses, mild upper respiratory illness [muri] viruses, and echo-rhino-coryza [ERC] agents) were soon isolated.[10–12] The development of tissue cultures such as human diploid fibroblast cell lines and identification of the special conditions necessary for virus replication allowed propagation and laboratory investigation of these viruses. The name rhinovirus was eventually chosen in recognition of the role of the virus in producing disease of the nasal passages and upper airways.[13] Subsequently, over the next decade and a half, numerous other rhinoviruses were collected and identified, and a numbering

Table 16–1

Cesium Chloride (CsCl) Buoyant Density, Native (D) or Inactive (C) Antigenic Reactivity, Capsid Protein Content, RNA Content, Replication Capability and Cell Attachment Capability of Rhinovirus Particles

Particle Type	CsCl Buoyant Density (g/mL)	Antigenic Reactivity	Capsid Proteins*	RNA Content	Replication Potential	Cellular Attachment
Infectious virion	1.38–1.42	D	1, 2, 3, 4 (trace 0)	+	+	+
Empty capsid	1.29	D or C	0, 1, 3	−	−	+ or −
Acid-inactivated	1.31–1.395	C	1, 2, 3	+	−	−
Heat-inactivated	Not done	C	1, 2, 3	−	−	−

*Rhinovirus capsid proteins: 0 = polypeptide precursor (VP_0) to capsid proteins VP_2 and VP_4; 1 = VP_1, 2 = VP_2, 3 = VP_3, 4 = VP_4; see text.
(Data from Korant et al,[27] Rueckert[30] and Lonberg-Holm et al.[41])

system based on neutralization with specific antisera was developed.[2, 5, 14–23]

STRUCTURE AND BIOLOGY

Rhinoviruses are the most numerous group in the ***Picornaviridae*** family, which includes other human and animal viruses such as enteroviruses, cardioviruses, and aphthoviruses. In common with other picornaviruses, the rhinovirus virion with a total molecular weight (mol wt) of approximately 8×10^6 daltons consists of a 30-nm-diameter nonenveloped nucleocapsid that surrounds a linear segment of single-stranded RNA with an approximate molecular weight of 2×10^6 daltons.[24–26] The nucleocapsid is an icosahedral 5:3:2 arrangement of capsomers that are composed mainly of four structural polypeptides (VP_1, VP_2, VP_3, and VP_4).[27] Traces of a fifth (VP_0) are present, but VP_0 is mostly cleaved to its products, VP_2 and VP_4, in the complete virion. All the structural proteins are derived from the posttranslational cleavage of a large polypeptide precursor. Although proteases of both host- and virus-specified origin participate in the process, the cleavage of VP_0 to its products appears to be catalyzed by RNA in the maturing virion.[27–29]

For some time, the symmetry of the icosahedron was explained by 32 capsomers made of different proportions of the four structural proteins. However, more recent evidence suggests that the icosahedron of the rhinovirus is composed of 60 identical capsomers of about 100,000 daltons arranged as 12 groups of five.[30]

The study of picornaviruses by x-ray crystallography in combination with protein sequencing has provided a powerful method to identify the nature of the folding and spatial arrangement of the proteins in the viral capsid (VP_1, VP_2, and VP_3 with exterior and interior projections, and VP_4 confined to the interior), and surprisingly suggests that human rhinoviruses and other animal picornaviruses may have evolved from a precursor that also produced certain plant viruses.[31, 32] In common with these plant viruses, each of the major picornaviruses capsid proteins (VP_1, VP_2, and VP_3) is folded into a structure termed an eight-stranded antiparallel beta barrel. The same studies indicate the presence of a 25-Å depression oriented around the fivefold axis in the surface of the capsid. This depression is potentially the site of virus-receptor interaction, and is surrounded by sites specific for neutralizing antibody attachment.[32a, 33] At the base of the depression a pocket extending into the capsid and surrounded by hydrophobic residues has been determined to be the site of binding of a number of related chemical compounds that interfere with picornavirus replication by preventing the uncoating of RNA.[32, 34, 34a] Of the potential modes of action for the prevention of uncoating, the more likely mechanism based on accumulating data appears to be a decrease in the flexibility of the viral capsid proteins with stabilization of virion structure. Although another possibility is that the compounds prevent capsid swelling and opening by occupying an ion channel to the interior of the virion, the process seems less likely because the putative ion channel has not been identified by careful analysis of data that provide a resolution of structures on the order of 3 Å. Interestingly, a single amino acid change in the hydrophobic pocket may be sufficient to produce resistance to some of the compounds.[34]

The viral RNA segment codes for approximately 7500 nucleotides.[35] The native (plus) strand serves as a monocistronic template for production of the large polypeptide precursor.[35–39] By convention, the single open reading frame of the genome is divided into three coding regions termed P1, P2, and P3.[39] P1 codes for the structural proteins VP1–VP4. The P2 region includes a functional protease which cleaves the P1 product from the nascent polypeptide during translation.[39a] The P3 region encodes a second protease with specificity for the peptide bonds within the structural proteins.[39b] Also in the P3 segment is the RNA-dependent RNA polymerase gene. The open reading frame is preceded at the 5' end by 500–600 nucleotides which are highly conserved among picornaviruses, but are not translated and appear to direct the site of translation initiation which does not require capping like other messenger RNAs.[39c] Attached to the 5' end of the genome is a small P3-encoded peptide (VPg) which possibly functions to anchor RNA during transcription of the genome.[39d] Although naked RNA is capable of infecting cells, it is much less efficient than the whole virion.

Rhinoviruses replicated in tissue culture produce multiple particle types which can be identified by cesium chloride centrifugation and by immunologic properties (Table 16–1).[27] Fully infectious virions sediment with a buoyant density of approximately 1.40 g/mL in CsCl. The reversible binding of cesium by rhinovirions is responsible for their greater buoyant density as compared with enteroviruses which have a density of 1.34 g/mL.[30] Other rhinovirus particles sediment at different densities in CsCl. "Empty capsids" consist of VP_0, VP_1, and VP_3 but lack RNA and sediment with a density of 1.29 g/mL. Particles of density intermediate between infectious virions and empty capsids include the RNA-containing particles that lack one or more of the structural proteins in the capsid such as "slow component" which lacks VP$_4$.[27] Empty capsids and slow component lack infectivity. However, such particles are responsible for the bulk of tissue culture-derived viral antigens, and the ratio of infectious to noninfectious particles is approximately 1:1000.

The infectious and noninfectious particles are immunologically distinct and have been designated as D (dense or native virion) and C (coreless virion) antigens. Fully infectious virions are always antigenically D. Noninfectious particles lacking VP$_4$ (such as slow component) are antigenically C. Empty capsids can be of either C or D antigenicity.

Chemical and physical agents have various effects on rhinoviruses. Rhinoviruses are resistant to inactivation by organic solvents including ether and chloroform by virtue of the absence of a lipid envelope around the virion.[3] They also resist inactivation by 70% to 95% ethanol, 5% phenol, and trichlorofluoroethane.[39] Rhinovirus infectivity is retained over a fairly wide range of temperature, but varies somewhat from strain to strain. At $-70°C$, the virion retains infectivity almost indefinitely. At 20 to 37°C, inactivation occurs over a period of days. At 50 to 56°C, however, inactivation of a variable degree occurs in minutes to hours. Some serotypes are completely inactivated at 56°C. Infectivity is inconsistently temperature-stabilized by cationic substances such as MgCl$_2$.[41] Electron micrographs of heat-inactivated rhinovirus particles demonstrate strands of protein-coated RNA with extensively degraded empty capsids.[25] The loss of infectivity by 100-fold or greater after exposure to pH 3 for three hours at room temperature is a characteristic of all rhinoviruses tested and differentiates them from the enteroviruses, which are acid-stable.[13] Both acid- and heat-inactivated rhinoviruses lack VP$_4$,[27, 42] which is important (but not entirely necessary) for attachment of the virion to cell membrane receptor sites.[35, 43]

Under usual conditions human rhinoviruses replicate only in cells of primate origin. This appears to relate not only to the presence of correct membrane receptors but also to the potential for penetration and replication after receptor interactions occur. Recently it has been shown that a small subgroup of human rhinoviruses (Table 16–2) attach to cells of murine origin.[44] A strain of rhinovirus serotype 2 has been adapted by serial passages in murine and human cells to permit replication in mice, although the replication appears highly inefficient.[45, 45a] In addition to a mouse cell receptor attachment site, mouse adaptation of a human rhinovirus requires a mutation in the P2 region of the genome. Otherwise, attempts to infect animals other than closely related primates such as chimpanzees have proved futile.[46]

A number of types of tissue cultures have been found useful for propagation of rhinoviruses. These include the noncontinuous cell lines of monkey kidney, human fetal kidney, human fetal tonsil, and human diploid lung fibroblast as well as the continuous epidermoid tumor cell lines HeLa, KB, and HEp-2.[1, 10–12, 16, 25, 47] Human diploid lung fibroblasts are most frequently used for primary isolation of rhinovirus from virion-containing nasal secretions. Certain rhinovirus-permissive strains of HeLa cells (sometimes called HeLa R, HeLa [Rhino], HeLa-O, HeLa-Ohio, or M-HeLa), however, produce higher virus yields (10^7–10^8 plaque-forming units [PFU]/10^6 cells) and may be more sensitive to infection than human diploid lung fibroblast.[16, 27, 48–50] Organ cultures such as human fetal trachea and nasal polyp have also been used for rhinovirus study.[46, 51]

Infection of cells follows a definite sequence. The rhinovirus must contact cell membrane receptors. These surface receptors are incompletely defined. However, studies with HeLa cells indicate that two different proteins, each of approximately 450 kilodaltons (kd) mol wt (possibly pentameric structures of subunits of 90 kd), serve as the receptors for the rhinoviruses.[52, 53] One of these receptors has been identified as intercellular attachment molecule 1 (ICAM-1), which is ubiquitous in distribution on leukocytes and other cells and has important interleukocyte signalling functions in the immune response.[53a, 53b, 53c] Once receptor attachment has occurred, the viral particle releases its RNA into the cell. The precise mechanism for viral uncoating and RNA entrance is unclear but seems to involve endocytosis with a pH-dependent conformational change in the internalized viral capsid and subsequent release of viral RNA from the endosome.[35, 43, 54] The intracellular presence of the viral genome quickly inhibits normal cellular functions, and replication of viral RNA and protein begins in the cytoplasm of the cell. The sequence of events from attachment of the virion to release of new infectious virus occurs over a five- to eight-hour period. Cell-free virus in the tissue culture media and cell-associated virus rise simultaneously in nearly identical titer.[55]

There are presently more than 100 individual rhinovirus serotypes recognized by specific neutralizing antibodies.[4, 5, 23] Early studies of RNA homology suggested little similarity between the few rhinovirus serotypes evaluated.[56] However, firmer data from the complete genomic sequencing of several different picornaviruses suggest that variability in RNA sequence is greatest in regions which translate into antigenic sites for neutralization and that conservation of significant portions of structural and nonstructural proteins occurs not only among rhinoviruses, but also among rhinoviruses and enteroviruses.[33, 36, 57, 58, 58a] Other studies suggest further relatedness of rhinovirus serotypes and indicate the possibility of reduction of serotype diversity into broader categories. Cell membrane receptor studies with HeLa cells indicate at least two groups of rhinoviruses based on competitive binding assays with multiple rhinovirus serotypes and with a monoclonal antibody directed at the ICAM-1 receptor on HeLa cells.[44, 59] The two rhinovirus groups are unequal in number of serotypes with the majority (approximately 90%) belonging to the group that bind only to cells of human or closely related primate origin (see Table 16–2).

Members of the two receptor groups overlap when the susceptibility of rhinovirus serotypes is compared by testing a battery of

Table 16–2
Human Rhinovirus Serotypes Which Bind to Two Mutually Exclusive Receptor Proteins on HeLa Cells

Receptor 1*	Receptor 2
1A, 1B, 2, 29–31, 44, 47, 49, 62	3–28, 32–43, 45, 46, 48, 50–52, 54–61, 63–81, 83–86, 88, 89

*Bind to human and mouse cells
Data from Colonno et al.[44]

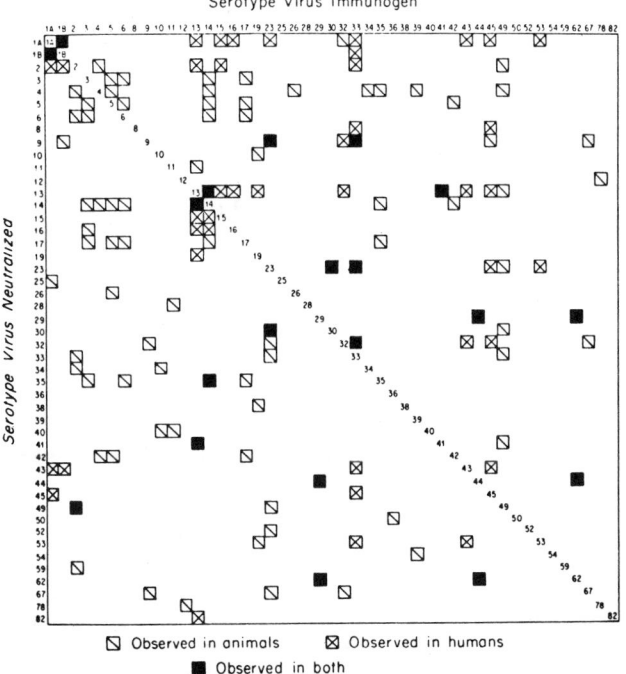

Serotype Virus Immunogen

Serotype Virus Neutralized

☒ Observed in animals   ☒ Observed in humans
■ Observed in both

Figure 16–1. Cross neutralization of 47 rhinoviruses arranged by serotype numbers. (From Fox JP: Is a rhinovirus vaccine possible? *Am J Epidemiol* 1976; 103:345–354. Reproduced with permission.)

antiviral chemicals that bind to the hydrophobic pocket at the base of the putative receptor depression in the surface of the virion.[34a] By relative inhibitory potencies it is noted that there are two fairly distinct groups with approximately two thirds of the serotypes (including all with mouse cell receptor binding capability) in one group. The serotypes in the larger group appear to account for an unexpectedly high frequency of naturally acquired rhinovirus infections in a review of several published studies. In addition, antiviral susceptibility is related to the conservation of amino acid sequences of capsid proteins and nonstructural proteins. The combined receptor binding and antiviral susceptibility studies suggest an evolution of human rhinoviruses that resulted in divergence among serotypes in the hydrophobic pocket and in the receptor binding site as independent sequential events.

The serotypes represented in the smaller receptor group echo to some degree earlier work examining tissue tropism.[13, 16, 55] It was noted in those studies that most rhinovirus serotypes replicated in cells of human origin (H strains), while about 10%, including serotypes 1A, 1B, 2, 14, 15, 17, 31, 39, 44, and 47, could infect cells of both human and monkey origin (M strains).[5, 16] Subsequent studies showed this division to be largely inoculum-related, since larger viral inocula permitted several H strains to infect or adapt to monkey kidney cells.[60] Other studies have shown neutralizing antibody cross-reactivity of variable degree among certain strains of rhinoviruses (Figure 16–1).[17, 61–63] If the data generated with human sera are excluded from consideration (because of the uncontrollable possibility of exposure to multiple rhinovirus serotypes during the lifetime of the human donor), the cross-neutralization pattern interestingly anticipates the presence of the

two HeLa receptor groups, since over 80% of the cross-neutralizations occur with sera raised against strains within the same receptor group.

The defined neutralizing antibody cross-reactivity has led to the postulate that rhinovirus ecology involves antigenic shift and drift.[5, 63] This concept is supported by several other observations. Rhinovirus serotypes are numbered in more or less chronologic order of recovery in tissue culture. (Serotypes 1A and 1B denote the first clearly established rhinoviruses which serologically are closely related strains that were recovered in the United States and Great Britain by different investigators.[3]) Epidemiologic investigations have shown that higher-numbered serotypes have replaced lower-numbered serotypes as the predominant strains circulating in communities in more recent years.[1, 2, 21, 22] Although individual strains of specific serotypes may be found in successive years, incomplete neutralization of later strains by antibody to earlier strains is noted.[64] In addition, some of the untypable strains submitted as new prototypes appear to be variants of earlier lower-numbered strains.[22] Consistent with these observations, studies with rhinovirus neutralization escape mutants raised in the presence of monoclonal antibodies indicate that four virion surface areas on the three external capsid proteins (VP_1, VP_2, and VP_3) are neutralizing antigenic sites, and that only a single amino acid substitution can permit escape from neutralization in some instances.[33] However, a practical limit may exist to the number of permissible wild-type viruses since fewer and fewer truly new serotypes are being identified.[23]

EPIDEMIOLOGY

Rhinovirus colds occur worldwide.[15, 55, 65–67] All populations and all age groups within populations include members susceptible to many of the rhinovirus serotypes. Infection has been well documented in climatic conditions ranging from tropic to arctic.[68–70] Outbreaks of rhinovirus infection occur everywhere but they have been investigated most extensively in industrially developed countries such as Great Britain and the United States, where viral respiratory illnesses account for the major proportion of all acute illnesses.[1, 2, 18, 22, 55]

Surveys in the United States and Great Britain indicate that the common cold occurs at a rate of almost one per person per year. Actually, some individuals never have colds while others experience four, five, or more colds per year.[1, 2, 15, 55, 71] Physiologic and constitutional factors account for the apparent susceptibility of some individuals since, under volunteer conditions, these individuals experience cold symptoms even after inoculation with noninfectious material. Multiple episodes of rhinoviral infection are well documented.[2, 72] Overall, rhinoviruses account for 20% to 45% of the viruses isolated from cold victims under natural conditions. This may underestimate the total contribution of rhinoviruses to the common cold since the season of the year, the methods of collection of nasal secretions, and the type and number of tissue cultures used can greatly affect the rate of isolation.[1, 2]

Rhinovirus inoculation of unscreened volunteers results in infection in 50% to 90%, but definitive symptoms of the common cold occur in only 30% to 50%.[73–75] These data suggest that infections without overt illness may occur. Such infections are of potential importance for protection of individuals from rhinovirus infections and illnesses. Isolation for 6 weeks or longer in the Antarctic, for example, has been noted to result in more severe illness in volunteers after rhinovirus inoculation than seen in volunteers not protected from social contacts.[70] Explanations for the protective effect of inapparent infections include nonspecific mechanisms such as local interferon production and viral interference. Rhinovirus shedding in nasal secretions may be prolonged for 2 to 3 weeks in as many as 20% of individuals after an illness.[1] In addition, sequential subclinical infections with second rhinoviruses have been documented in children as soon as two to five days after initial infections.[72]

Seasonal variations in the incidence of rhinovirus infection are well-known. While sporadic infection occurs all year long, distinct peaks of infection occur, usually in fall and spring.[1, 2, 22] In some years the fall incidence exceeds that of spring. In other years the reverse is true, although some variation is caused by observer and technical variables.[1] Whether seasonal variation is due to factors directly affecting the virus or to social patterns with effects on virus transmission is unknown at present. However, the effects of environmental changes in temperature and humidity have not been found to be important factors affecting the susceptibility of hosts.[76, 77] Although it was believed that chilling of the body predisposed to infection, studies of volunteers exposed to various temperatures lower than body temperature show no effect on the rate of infection or the severity of symptoms. Efficient spread of rhinovirus infection has been documented under cold weather conditions in Alaska and Antarctica[69, 70] as well as in the tropics during warm weather.[68]

Susceptibility to rhinovirus infection is present from infancy through adulthood. In general, the family group forms the unit of infection.[78–80] Other social groups, including those produced by employment, appear to be much less important. Children have the highest incidence of symptomatic rhinovirus infection. Children less than 1 year of age experience 1.5 to 3 times as many infections as older children or adults. Mothers have a slightly higher incidence of colds than fathers, possibly because of the mother's more extensive contact with children. However, female susceptibility is partly related to the menstrual cycle with peak susceptibility at midcycle.[76] Children 5 years old or younger are probably responsible for initiating infection in other family members in 60% to 70% of the instances. Mothers are responsible for initiating about two thirds of the remaining infections and fathers for about 10%. An inverse relation between age and the development of infection from contact with a previously infected family member has been noted. This correlates directly with the increasing prevalence of antibody to specific rhinovirus serotypes as age increases.[1, 81] Of interest, the more family members in a given family, the more rhinovirus serotypes documented as a cause of infection during any observation period.[1] This is in accord with early observations of common cold epidemiology and may partly explain the occurrence of multiple rhinovirus infections in some individuals and none in others.[78, 79]

In all locations sampled, multiple rhinovirus serotypes circulate at one time.[1, 2, 18, 22, 67, 69] Increased frequency of naturally occurring rhinovirus colds has been associated with as few as two and as many as 20 distinct serotypes. Usually a few serotypes predominate during cold season with the most recently discovered serotypes more prevalent.

PATHOGENESIS

Transmission

Potential modes of transmission of rhinovirus infection include the inhalation of aerosolized droplets and the self-inoculation of virus from contaminated inanimate objects or the secretions of infected individuals by way of the hands. Although infection by virus-containing experimentally generated aerosols is efficient, spread by an aerosol under the conditions of daily life has not been uniformly documented.[82, 83] Aerosols produced by normal coughing and sneezing come mainly from oral secretions which consistently yield lower titers of virus than nasal secretions.[83, 84] In addition, aerosolized particles are limited in their range of transfer since sneezing and coughing at Petri dishes by infected volunteers results in little rhinovirus transfer or recovery.[84, 85] A number of studies with volunteers have demonstrated the difficulty of transfer of infection by the aerosol route from cold donors prevented from making direct contact with susceptible recipients.[74, 75, 83, 86] However, studies done by arranging the close proximity of rhinovirus-infected donors shedding virus maximally with susceptible recipients restrained to preclude hand-to-face contact indicate that aerosol transmission may be considerable under proper circumstances of duration and intensity of exposure.[87] Virus in substantial amount can be found on inanimate objects for a few hours after handling by infected individuals.[82, 88] However, indirect spread of virus via inanimate objects appears to be another inefficient mode of transmission.

Self-inoculation through person-to-person contact is a major mechanism of rhinovirus transmission. Part of the human condition is a tendency for frequent contact of fingers with nasal and oral orifices. Studies have revealed extensive redistribution of nasal and oral secretions over the hands and clothing.[85, 88] Investigations have shown transfer of rhinovirus infection to up to 75% of volunteers by exposure to rhinovirus cold donors during hand-to-hand contact of as little as 10 seconds duration.[85] In sharp contrast, aerosolized secretions produced by coughing, sneezing, talking loudly, and singing resulted in an efficiency of transfer of less than 5% in the same studies. Forms of intimate contact such as kissing are less well studied, but evidence suggests kissing to be an ineffective method of transfer of infection.[86] This is consistent with the inefficient transfer of rhinovirus infection by pharyngeal inoculation as compared with intranasal.[88]

Risk factors that may influence the transmission and establishment of infection are identified to some extent. Studies done in married couples point out that transfer is greater when a larger number of infectious units are present in secretions.[86] The presence of virus on the hands and anterior nares increases risk and reflects the amount of virus present in nasal secretions. Duration of exposure also is important, since exposure to smaller quantities of virus over a long period appears to produce infection. Persons who possess specific serum neutralizing antibody to a rhinovirus prior to exposure are less likely to acquire infection, and if infected, are less likely to shed large quantities of virus in the course of

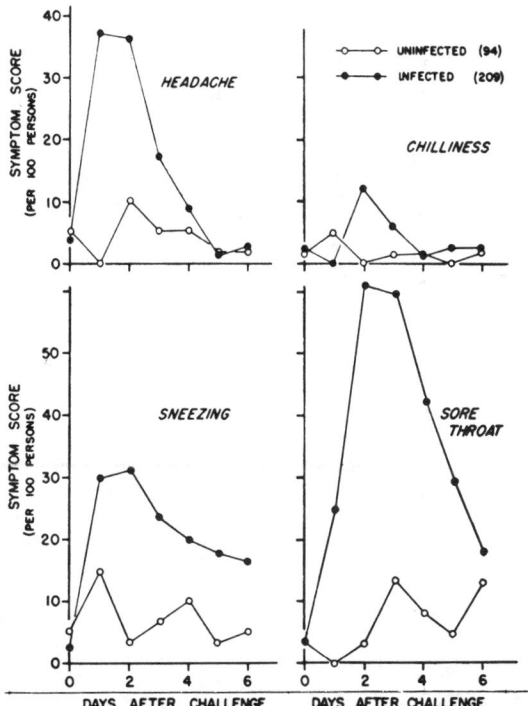

Figure 16–2. Early common cold symptoms in experimentally infected volunteers compared with concomitant uninfected controls. (From Jackson GG, et al: Transmission of the common cold to volunteers under controlled conditions: I. The common cold as a clinical entity. *Arch Intern Med* 1958; 101:267–278. Reproduced with permission.)

disease.[81] These observations indicate that seronegative persons may experience symptoms of greater severity with more virus shedding and can be responsible for increased transmission rates.

Infection

Infection occurs after rhinovirus particles contact the appropriate epithelial cells of the conjunctival or respiratory tract mucosa. The pathology of the infected ciliated epithelial cells is not known, but infected ciliated cells are sloughed from the nasal mucosa.[89] The 24- to 72-hour incubation period that precedes symptoms and peak virus shedding and the fact that less than 1 $TCID_{50}$ (50% tissue culture infectious dose) can cause infection and cold symptoms in susceptible hosts indicates the sensitivity of the human nasal mucosa to infection and suggests spread of infection from small initial foci.[75, 90] After introduction by way of conjunctival or pharyngeal inoculation, rhinovirus is recovered initially from the posterior nasopharynx and later from the more anterior mucosal sites, which suggests that virions are first deposited posteriorly by mucociliary processes and spread antegrade as replication of the virus proceeds.[91]

Although relatively large quantities of virus are swallowed, rhinoviruses lack the ability to replicate effectively in the gastrointestinal (GI) tract.[92] Rhinoviruses in low titer have been recovered in stool specimens on occasion, possibly as a result of the passage of unaltered virus through the GI tract.[67] Factors other than gastric acid, such as pancreatic proteolytic enzymes, may account for the failure of rhinoviruses to replicate, since stomach

contents from volunteers do not routinely inactivate rhinoviruses, and virus is not readily recovered from stool after the gastric juices are bypassed.[92] Recovery of rhinoviruses from other nonrespiratory sites is also unusual. Two instances of recovery of a rhinovirus from heart blood at necropsy are reported,[93] but no documentation of rhinoviremia in live hosts exists.

Local and, to a lesser degree, systemic manifestations contribute to the rhinovirus common cold[73] (Figures 16–2 and 16–3). The cold syndrome is readily recognized when profuse nasal discharge, obstruction to airflow through nasal passages, sneezing, sore throat, and cough are present. Variability is observed in the relative contribution of these symptoms to the total subjective experience of a cold. For example, some rhinoviruses produce pharyngeal and lower respiratory symptoms more frequently than others. Symptoms related to a particular virus tend to be in the same pattern from person to person, although the overall severity of the individual experience is somewhat variable.[55]

Among the earliest symptoms of local mucosal damage and irritation are sneezing and sore throat which reach their peak by about two to three days after inoculation in volunteers. Later local symptoms of nasal discharge and obstruction peak at about three to four days, tend to be more persistent, and exceed other symptoms in severity. Nasal discharge tends to be clear and watery at the onset but usually becomes mucopurulent and tenacious after several days. This is not related to bacterial infection or colonization since the microflora of rhinovirus-infected and uninfected

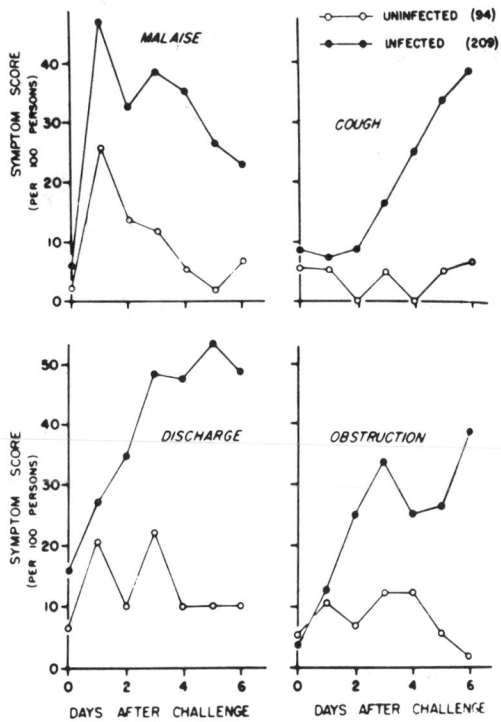

Figure 16–3. Later common cold symptoms in experimentally infected volunteers compared with concomitant uninfected controls. (From Jackson GG, et al: Transmission of the common cold to volunteers under controlled conditions: I. The common cold as a clinical entity. *Arch Intern Med* 1958; 101:267–278. Reproduced with permission.)

volunteers retain the same type and distribution of organisms.[73] Other symptoms contribute less to the illness. Headache and chilliness occur early and resolve quickly, while malaise and cough tend to begin later. Fever and rigors are distinctly unusual accompaniments of the rhinovirus common cold.[73] Generally, symptoms peak by three to five days and resolve in about seven to ten days, although occasionally cough or nasal discharge may persist for longer.

At the same time that symptoms become apparent, rhinovirus shedding has already begun. Viral shedding in previously nonimmune susceptible volunteers appears as early as 24 hours after intranasal inoculation of virus and peak titers of 500 to 1000 $TCID_{50}$/mL of virus in nasal secretions are found by 48 to 96 hours when symptoms are becoming maximal. Some nonimmune volunteers and other immune subjects exhibit low levels of viral shedding (10–50 $TCID_{50}$/mL) that peaks later (7–10 days after viral inoculation) in the absence of symptoms. Some subjects may shed virus in low titer for several weeks after inoculation.[74, 75]

An explanation for the unusual limitation of rhinovirus illness to the upper respiratory tract has been that rhinoviruses grow best at the lower temperatures of the nasal passages. However, it is clear that rhinovirus infection can sometimes affect other respiratory sites, including the lower airways. Sinusitis and otitis media have been found in association with rhinovirus infection.[94, 94a] Although this might be partly related to mucosal edema with narrowing or closure of the ostia of the paranasal sinuses, in some instances rhinoviruses have been recovered from maxillary sinus fluid obtained by a method that circumvents contamination of the specimen by nasal secretions. This suggests that sinusitis may be caused by direct infection of the epithelium that lines the sinuses. Bronchopneumonia, tracheobronchitis, and bronchiolitis have been noted in association with naturally acquired infection in children, although an actual causal relationship for the rhinovirus has not been documented.[67, 95] Adults also exhibit lower airway infection and disease if the mode of transmission is altered. Inhalation of a rhinovirus in small-particle aerosols of 0.2 to 3.0 μm aerodynamic diameter capable of deposition in the lungs results in symptoms of tracheobronchitis.[96] Under such circumstances coughing, chest pain, and tracheal tenderness are the predominant symptoms instead of the coryza that follows administration of the same rhinovirus as solution placed directly on the nasal mucosa or as droplets large enough to impact on the upper airways.

Subclinical changes in pulmonary physiology have been noted in naturally occurring and volunteer rhinovirus infection. A reduction in ventilatory frequency-dependent compliance has been documented in healthy nonsmoking adults.[97] Smokers with preexisting abnormalities of closing volume develop significant worsening of this parameter of airway function during rhinovirus infection.[98] Abnormalities of pulmonary mucociliary clearance, including regional retention of aerosols and slowed whole lung clearance, have been found in natural and experimental rhinovirus infection in individuals without a history of smoking or preexisting lung disease.[99] However, the ciliated epithelium of the trachea appears to be unaffected since the rate of tracheal transport of mucus labeled with a radioactive aerosol is unchanged during rhinovirus infection.[100] Whether any of these changes reflects direct virus-induced lower airway disease or reflex responses to upper airway disease remains to be determined. However, these obser-

vations help to explain the consequences of rhinovirus infection in patients with chronic bronchitis and asthma. In both groups exacerbation of airway abnormalities has been shown.[72, 101, 102]

Individuals with allergic rhinitis are more susceptible to rhinovirus infection.[76] Asthmatic children experience respiratory infections more frequently than their siblings, and about half of their symptomatic rhinovirus infections result in asthmatic attacks. Exacerbation of asthma does not appear to be caused by any particular serotype since 14 of 21 serotypes isolated in one study were linked to asthmatic attacks.[102] Similarly, bronchitic exacerbations with increased sputum production and airflow obstruction in association with rhinovirus infection have been noted.[101]

Immunology

Symptoms of the common cold may partly be a direct result of respiratory epithelial injury caused by the virus.[75] Support for this includes the observation that the onset of symptoms generally appears at a time when peak virus shedding and (by inference) infection of the maximal number of cells has occurred. However, asymptomatic infection and symptomatic infection with small quantities of virus in the nasal secretions of nonimmune individuals are well-documented phenomena.[1, 74] The contributions of the immune system and inflammatory mediators to the syndrome are now being scrutinized. The involvement of cellular functions in the activation of the inflammatory response is suggested by a number of studies. In peripheral blood, the acute response to rhinovirus infection includes an increase in neutrophils and a reduction in circulating lymphocytes of several types, but predominantly of the T helper phenotype.[103] Both granulocytes and lymphocytes increase in nasal secretions at a time corresponding to peak symptoms and to the changes noted in the peripheral blood, which suggests that the mucosal inflammation and leukocyte fluxes are related.[104] The large numbers of exfoliated granulocytes may be a result of local chemoattraction, since fibroblasts infected by a rhinovirus in vitro produce a chemoattractant protein distinct from the progeny virions.[105]

Local interferon production plays an important role in the progress of rhinovirus infection. The interferon produced is predominantly acid-resistant (and possibly alpha or leukocyte-derived) interferon and its appearance coincides with a reduction of shedding of virus in nasal secretions.[106] This type of interferon is also the major product of peripheral blood lymphocytes exposed to a rhinovirus in vitro, and is associated with the induction of cells with natural killer (NK) functional activity.[107] The timing of appearance or relative quantity of interferon may be critical, since exacerbation of symptoms rather than amelioration has been noted in some instances after administration of an interferon inducer and in some studies with alpha or gamma interferon produced by recombinant DNA technology.[108, 109, 109a] Nasal obstruction and the secretion of up to 15 g of nasal fluid per day[75] strongly suggest a role for vasoactive mediators. The presence of kinins in association with symptomatic rhinovirus infection has been demonstrated, and may be important in the local inflammatory cascade, since nasal obstruction, sore throat, and rhinorrhea are induced by nasal application of bradykinin.[110]

Parallel with the increased production of nasal secretions, protein concentrations in the nasal secretions rise by three- to fivefold.

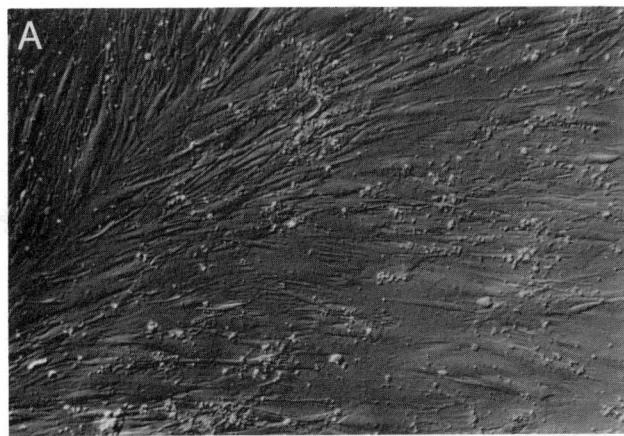
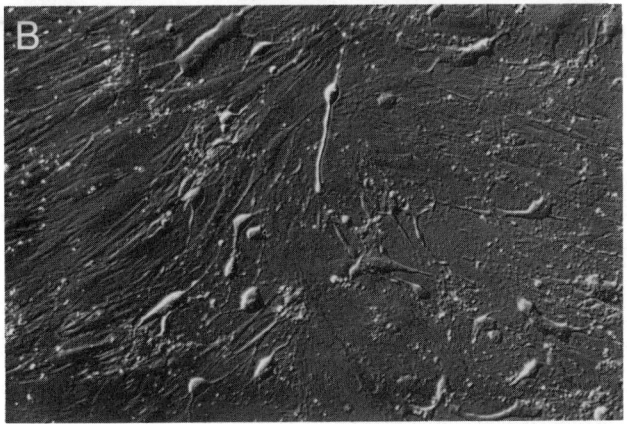

Figure 16–4. Rhinovirus cytopathic effect (CPE) in human diploid fibroblast tissue culture (MRC–5 cell line). **A,** uninfected cell monolayer. **B,** CPE 24 hours after inoculation with 100 TCID$_{50}$ (50% tissue culture infective dose) rhinovirus serotype 2 (strain HGP, original magnification × 100).

A number of globulin species are included, but secretory IgA predominates, with somewhat lesser quantities of IgG in both the presence and absence of infection.[111, 112] The nasal IgA fraction accounts for the majority of type-specific neutralizing activity against an infecting rhinovirus.[112, 113] Specific neutralizing antibody in serum is both IgA and IgG, with the latter the predominant immunoglobulin. Specific nasal IgA antibody probably plays an important role in protection from recurrent infection by the same rhinovirus serotype.[74, 114] The presence of nasal antibody usually denotes serum antibody,[115] but the effects of the two are difficult to dissociate.

Immunologic evidence of rhinovirus infection includes the development of serum and nasal secretion neutralizing antibodies and expansion of peripheral blood lymphocyte populations with specificity for the infecting strain within 3 to 6 weeks after the exposure.[75, 116, 117] Not all infected individuals demonstrate a fourfold or greater rise in neutralizing antibody between acute and convalescent phase sera after infection documented by the shedding of a rhinovirus.[63, 90, 115, 118] As the level of serum antibody increases, however, the risk of acquiring homotypic rhinovirus infection diminishes. Studies in volunteers show that in order to increase the infection and the antibody response rates upon rechallenge, an increase of viral inoculum proportional to the level of antibody at the time of rechallenge is required.[90] Virus shedding occurs later and at lower titers in immune than in inexperienced hosts. If illness occurs in immune hosts, however, symptom severity is unaffected by antibody status.[75] The duration of protection against infection and illness is limited and begins to fade by 18 months after infection.[116]

LABORATORY DIAGNOSES

Rhinovirus infection cannot be recognized specifically by the resulting clinical syndrome. The possibility that an infection is caused by a rhinovirus is greatest when nasal obstruction and discharge predominate, although many upper respiratory symptoms can be produced. Rhinovirus infection is documented by recovery of the virus from secretions or by demonstration of a fourfold or greater increase in serum neutralizing antibody.

Nasal wash specimens maximize virus recovery in adults. Nasopharyngeal swabs in children are more practical. Nasal washing is done by introduction of 5 to 10 mL of phosphate-buffered saline, or Hanks' or Earle's buffered salt solutions into each of the nares of the subject with the neck hyperextended. As much as possible of the solution and secretion are recovered when the subject tilts forward to drain the nares. Swabs are obtained by inserting cotton-tipped applicators through the nasopharynx. The swab is immersed in a vial of 1 to 2 mL of salt solution, agitated, and squeezed against the side of the vial to express as much nasal secretion as possible from the applicator. Specimens obtained by throat gargle are less useful for culture of rhinoviruses, but other viruses that cause the common cold are often recovered.

Immediate inoculation of secretions onto tissue culture is not always practical. After the addition of a drop of albumin of gelatin to stabilize viruses, specimens can be placed at 4°C for inoculation of tissue cultures within four to 24 hours or held at −70°C until their use. The yield is best when secretions are inoculated directly onto tissue culture tubes of human diploid fibroblasts. Primary monkey kidney also will support replication of most rhinoviruses and yields several other common respiratory viruses as well. HeLa cells of a strain permissive for rhinoviruses appear to be more sensitive for the isolation of rhinoviruses from clinical specimens in some studies. Their use may increase rhinovirus recovery.[16, 41, 50]

Incubation of cells for rhinovirus replication is best in media buffered to pH 7.0 to 7.2 at 33°C.[55] The use of roller drums at 12 revolutions per hour amplifies cytopathic effects (CPE). The rapidity of appearance of CPE partly depends on the number of infectious particles in the inoculum. CPE is usually found within 24 hours when the ratio of virions to cells equals or exceeds 1.[27] CPE from most clinical specimens that contain relatively few infectious virions appears after a longer incubation (5–7 d). Foci of cellular rounding and disintegration in tissue cultures is the initial evidence of CPE, but extensive areas of the cell monolayer eventually exhibit the same appearance and slough (Figure 16–4A,B).

Identification of an isolated virus involves several steps. Presumptive evidence of a rhinovirus is provided by the appearance of CPE in the appropriate clinical setting. Further evidence is provided by chloroform or ether resistance of the virus and by acid lability with a 100-fold or greater decrease in virus titer after exposure of the virus to pH 3 to 5 for three hours.[13] Testing for acid lability requires an initial titer of 10^3 PFU or better, which may be attained after two or three passages in tissue culture, especially when virus is adapted to and replicated in HeLa cells.[16] Specific identification of serotype is done with neutralizing antibody. The use of intersecting pools of hyperimmune sera is the least cumbersome method, and results can be confirmed with single specific sera.[119] Considering previous experience, nontypable rhinoviruses will occasionally be found.[1-5, 20-22, 67]

Demonstration of an antibody response requires some knowledge of the responsible rhinovirus. Antibody has serotype specificity with occasional cross-reactivities.[61-63] The logistics of attempting to conduct antibody assays in all persons with common colds would require an enormous expenditure of time and money, in view of the large number of distinct viruses and serotypes. The only practical method to identify sporadic rhinovirus infection in a community is isolation of virus from the nasopharyngeal secretions. Neutralization of the virus done later with the acute and convalescent sera can be used as supportive evidence.

Neutralization tests for virus identification can be done by either macro or micro method, although the latter is becoming more popular because of its conservation of materials.[49, 81, 120, 121] Generally, 20 antibody units are mixed with 32 to 100 $TCID_{50}$ of the unknown virus each in equal volume. (Antibody units are determined with 1 unit taken as the end point neutralization of 30 to 300 $TCID_{50}$.[16]) The antibody-virus mixture and virus not exposed to antibody (to serve as a control) are incubated at room temperature for one to two hours prior to inoculation of volumes of solution containing equal quantities of virus onto tissue cultures. Serum controls to test for nonspecific CPE caused by the test serum are included. The tissue cultures are incubated at 33°C until a specified degree of CPE (usually near total) occurs in the virus control. If no CPE is noted in the antibody-virus mixture, the virus has been neutralized.

Quantification of infectious virions can be carried out in one of two ways. The titer can be determined by inoculation of tenfold dilutions of virus onto tissue cultures to determine end point dilution and to calculate $TCID_{50}$ by a statistical method such as the method of Reed and Muench.[122] Somewhat more technically demanding, but a more direct measure of the number of infectious virions, is determination of the number of PFU per unit of solution.[123] The total number of virions (infectious and noninfectious) can be estimated by spectrophotometry.[27]

Once a virus has been isolated, whether or not it has been identified by neutralization, the serum of the subject can be tested for neutralizing activity against the virus. Neutralization is carried out as above. However, the titer of virus used for neutralization is more critical here, and the sensitivity of the test is greatly improved by the use of less than 32 $TCID_{50}$, usually 3.2 to 10 $TCID_{50}$.[120] The end point of twofold dilutions of serum is taken as the last dilution to completely inhibit CPE and constitutes the antibody titer for the serum specimen.

Newer methods may permit some improvement in the speed and ease of diagnosing rhinovirus infection. Enzyme immunoassays have been developed for a number of common respiratory viruses. Initial studies with enzyme immunoassays suggest the feasibility of rhinovirus antigen detection in infected secretions.[124, 125] The relatively short time required for these tests (3–48 h) offers a substantial advantage to laboratory diagnosis if sensitivity and specificity can be optimized to permit identification of rhinoviruses of all serotypes. As it is being applied in many areas of clinical virology, the procedure known as polymerase chain reaction (PCR) can amplify nucleic acid sequences from a theoretical limit of one infectious unit. PCR may be useful in a number of ways for identifying rhinovirus infection. Because of the great sensitivity of PCR, it is possible to detect small quantities of a rhinovirus directly from a nasal secretion.[125a] The presence in the genome of conserved and variable segments of RNA (for example in the 5' nontranslated region) suggests that it may be possible to identify a rhinovirus and determine its serotype in one procedure if initial observations are correct in indicating that unique products for each serotype can be discerned readily with restriction endonucleases after amplification of the genome with primers common to all serotypes.[125b] The development of a method for the detection of serum or secretion antibodies other than neutralization could also be useful by reducing time requirements and allowing a recognition of rhinoviruses in more generic terms.[126]

VACCINE-INDUCED IMMUNITY

No vaccine is commercially available for clinical applications. However, vaccines for a number of rhinovirus serotypes have been produced and tested.[5, 114, 127-129] Rhinovirus vaccines have been inactivated by formalin after replication of virus to higher titer in tissue culture and have usually been administered by intramuscular (IM) injection in an adjuvant preparation. Close to 100% of vaccinees have developed a rise in serum neutralizing antibody to the homotypic serotype after single or multiple injections.[114, 128, 129] Serum antibody has also been elicited by intranasal administration of formalin-inactivated virus solution.[129]

Despite typically brisk immunologic responses, vaccines have been less than 100% effective in protecting volunteers from infection and illness. Vaccine made from rhinovirus serotype 1A was administered parenterally to children just before an outbreak of rhinovirus 1A respiratory illness.[127] In that instance, children who were not vaccinated had a much higher frequency of colds and serologic evidence of infection after the outbreak. In another study, vaccine produced from rhinovirus serotype 2 protected volunteers from colds and reduced virus shedding after inoculation with the homotypic virus but not after inoculation with rhinovirus serotype 1A.[128] In the homotypic virus challenge, increases in serum antibody in many volunteers who did not shed virus suggested an inapparent infection that boosted the vaccine-induced immunity. After intranasal administration of rhinovirus serotype 13 inactivated with formalin, significantly fewer vaccinated volunteers (33%) became ill upon challenge with the homotypic rhinovirus than did unvaccinated volunteers (>80%).[129] The same rhinovirus administered parenterally did not markedly reduce the number of volunteers who shed virus or became ill following challenge with a small virus inoculum selected to mimic natural infection.[114] However, the degree and duration of virus shedding and the severity of illness were all significantly less in vaccinated individuals.

Although favorable results have been noted in studies of immunoprophylaxis, obstacles unrelated to vaccine potency remain.[63] The ability to provide protection against the array of naturally occurring strains may be impossible. Even though a few strains predominate in a given location during each rhinovirus season, the predominant strains have tended to change to previously unrecognized strains. The frequent appearance of heterotypic antibody responses after rhinovirus infection or vaccination and the defined cross-reactivities of some rhinoviruses offer a strategy of incorporating rhinoviruses selected by cross-reactions into vaccines. As an indication of multivalent vaccine feasibility, two decavalent vaccines have been developed and tested.[5] Neither vaccine elicited a response in any individual to more than 40% of the serotypes included in the vaccine, possibly because of suboptimal antigenic loads of some serotypes. Nevertheless, cross-reactions with other rhinoviruses not included in the vaccine were also demonstrated. Heterotypic antibody responses are elicited from animals immunized with small peptides synthesized from the known sequences of rhinovirus structural proteins.[129a, 129b] Although the sera from immunized animals neutralize a variety of rhinovirus serotypes to a greater or lesser extent, the ability of such immunogens to prevent infection and illness are unknown. Difficulties in incorporating adequate quantities of multiple rhinovirus antigens, unknown interferences, and insufficient data on the duration of immunologic responses and protection after vaccination make it unlikely that these problems will be solved in the near future.

ANTIVIRAL AGENTS

A number of chemical compounds have been identified with significant in vitro inhibitory activity against rhinoviruses.[130–140a] Many are unacceptable because of limited spectrum of activity, potential for undesirable side effects, or inability to prevent infection or illness in man.[130–133, 140] Among drugs with any clinical efficacy, none appears to be effective if administered after infection is established, but the results suggest that there is a reason for encouragement that chemical inhibitors of rhinovirus infection with activity against all serotypes can be developed. Several drugs appear to inhibit rhinovirus replication when the drug is administered prior to infection.[134, 135, 138, 139, 140a] A major failure of several antiviral compounds with high in vitro activity appears to be the delivery to, and penetration of, target tissues because of compound hydrophobicity. Promising approaches to improve accumulation of drug at the tissue site of action include incorporation of the compound in a carrier molecule or in liposomes.[140a, 140b] While no drug is past the investigational stage, potential uses of prophylactic agents would be for individuals at high risk of developing more severe clinical syndromes, such as asthmatic children, chronic bronchitics, and those with a known exposure to a rhinovirus.

Several studies have been done to investigate the effects of topically applied interferon and its inducers on rhinovirus infection.[106, 108, 109, 109a, 141–147c] Administration of preformed alpha interferon prevents infection and illness, but available evidence suggests the need for application of several million units of interferon to inhibit infection and reduce symptoms.[141, 143, 147, 147a] Although the in vitro inhibitory activity of alpha, beta, and gamma interferons for rhinoviruses is similar, results are variable when beta or gamma interferon is administered as a prophylactic remedy for rhinovirus infection. In a volunteer study, beta interferon effectively reduced illness severity although it did not prevent rhinovirus infection or reduce rhinovirus shedding.[147b] However, in field trials, beta interferon was ineffective in reducing either the frequency of rhinovirus infection or related illnesses.[147c] In a volunteer study, gamma interferon application not only failed to prevent rhinovirus infection, but was associated with increased illness severity as compared with placebo.[109a]

Studies in families indicate a reduction in the number of secondary infections and colds after prophylactic administration of alpha interferon intranasally to family members exposed to a rhinovirus. However, other respiratory viruses associated with colds do not appear to be as easily inhibited by interferon. In addition, adverse reactions including varying degrees of nosebleed and symptoms suggestive of a cold such as nasal obstruction have been noted in 5% to 10% of individuals after intranasal application of alpha interferon. Biopsy studies indicate a possible immunopathogenesis, since large numbers of T lymphocytes, particularly T helper cells, accumulate in the nasopharyngeal mucosa after interferon administration.[147, 147b]

Among interferon inducers, a propanediamine derivative applied intranasally has been shown to be very effective in increasing nasal interferon titers.[106, 108, 142] Reduced viral shedding and less severe symptoms were produced when multiple doses of the inducer were administered beginning the day before viral challenge with 1 $TCID_{50}$.[108] The same compound, however, appeared less effective when a larger inoculum of virus was used or if the inducer was administered after initiation of infection or illness.

Vitamin C (ascorbic acid) and zinc compounds deserve mention only because of lay awareness of these as potential cold remedies. In spite of the fact that no studies have been reported to show any direct antiviral effect of ascorbic acid, it has been suggested that amounts of one to 10 g per day orally can prevent the common cold (not necessarily caused by rhinovirus). No study done with appropriate controls has shown more than a moderate benefit in naturally occurring colds, and no consistent or persistent effect has been found in a comparison of studies.[148] A trial of ascorbic acid given prophylactically to volunteers at a dose of 3 g per day for two weeks prior to intranasal challenge with rhinovirus serotype 44 failed to prevent cold symptoms or infection.[149] Although zinc ions are capable of inhibiting viral enzymatic functions,[150] controlled trials including trials in volunteers challenged with a rhinovirus demonstrate no efficacy of zinc preparations in preventing viral respiratory infection or illness.[151, 152] Thus, an initial report suggesting a beneficial effect of zinc gluconate lozenges can be attributed to a placebo effect related to the fact that zinc has a distinct, unpleasant flavor.[153] There is no satisfactory evidence to support the administration of ascorbic acid or zinc preparations for prevention of rhinoviral (or any other) common cold.

The identification of the receptor on HeLa cells (ICAM-1) for the majority of rhinovirus serotypes and the development of a monoclonal antibody specific for that receptor suggest the potential for prevention of rhinovirus infection by interference with the attachment of the virion to a susceptible cell. In tissue culture the anti-receptor antibody appears to have a much greater affinity for the receptor than rhinoviruses, since the anti-receptor antibody can displace rhinoviruses from cells after many minutes.[44] However, no significant effect in either prevention of infection or prevention of illness was achieved in a preliminary study in which the anti-receptor antibody was administered intranasally before rhinovirus challenge, although a delay in the onset of virus shedding and symptoms was noted.[154] The receptor molecule itself has been produced in a soluble form by recombinant DNA technology, and it effectively inhibits the replication of rhinoviruses that bind to ICAM-1 but not other picornaviruses.[154a] Presumably, it should be possible to reproduce the inhibitory effect for the other rhinovirus receptor. Although the approach to prevention of infection is intriguing, future development also depends on elucidating the nature and function of the receptor(s) for rhinoviruses in the nasopharyngeal tissues.

Presently available measures for treatment of the common cold are for symptomatic relief. The careful administration of nasal decongestants such as pseudoephedrine can be helpful when nasal obstruction and watery discharge are present.[154b] Adequate hydration to reduce the viscosity of mucus and nasal washing with a buffered salt solution to remove tenacious secretions are simple and afford some relief during the later stages of a cold. Aspirin, which is commonly recommended, does not reduce nasal symptoms, although its use may give modest relief from constitutional symptoms.[155] Aspirin has no antiviral action and under experimental conditions may prolong viral shedding, presumably by suppressing natural mechanisms that control virus replication. Nasal vasoconstrictors may afford some reduction of symptoms, but overuse can produce a rebound vasodilation and habituation. Histamine release is not apparent during rhinovirus infections and antihistaminic agents are ineffective for reversing symptoms.[110, 156] The role of kinins and agents to inhibit kinin formation and effects remains to be demonstrated. Antibacterial agents are unnecessary and ineffective in uncomplicated colds.

Education and awareness of mechanisms of rhinovirus transmission can be helpful in preventing spread of rhinoviruses in adults, but inapparent or asymptomatic infections negate this approach to some extent. Certainly, personal hygiene is important to avoid contact with contaminated secretions. Recent studies have demonstrated the efficacy of iodinated or acidified scrubs in inactivating rhinovirus on the hands of ill individuals and preventing spread of virus to susceptible persons.[157, 158] This offers at least one avenue of preventing spread of rhinoviruses to those who experience the most severe symptoms such as asthmatics and bronchitics.

REMAINING PROBLEMS

Although much is known about the common cold and the rhinoviruses, there is much left to learn to be able to effectively control this problem. The identification of rhinovirus infection is limited to cumbersome techniques which require days to weeks to document infection. A rapid, consistent, and readily available method to demonstrate rhinoviral antigens present in small amounts in nasal secretions would certainly be helpful. Indeed, it will probably be necessary if antiviral agents are to be administered to patients in a timely fashion. The immunology, pathogenesis, and events that lead to symptoms after rhinovirus infection of the respiratory epithelium of the nasal passages are far from clear. The continuing development and deployment of antiviral agents and immunoprophylaxis are in great part dependent on further exploration of these phenomena, as well as on identifying rhinovirus interrelationships and evolution.

REFERENCES

1. Fox JP, Cooney MK, Hall CE: The Seattle virus watch: V. Epidemiologic observations of rhinovirus infections, 1965–1969, in families with young children. *Am J Epidemiol* 1975; 101:122–142.
2. Phillips CA, Melnick JL, Grim CA: Rhinovirus infections in a student population: Isolation of five new serotypes. *Am J Epidemiol* 1968; 87:447–456.
3. Kapikian AZ, Conant RM, Hamparian VV, et al: Rhinoviruses: A numbering system. *Nature* 1967; 213:761–762.
4. Kapikian AZ, Conant RM, Hamparian VV, et al: A collaborative report: Rhinoviruses—extension of the numbering system. *Virology* 1971; 43:524–526.
5. Hamory BH, Hamparian VV, Conant RM, et al: Human responses to two decavalent rhinovirus vaccines. *J Infect Dis* 1975; 132:623–629.
6. Hayward J: *Taking Cold: The Cause of Half Our Diseases.* London, Henry Turner, 1877.
7. Kruse W: Die Erreger von Husten und Schnupfen. *Munch Med Wochenschr* 1914; 61:1547.
8. Thomson D, Thomson R (eds): The common cold with special reference to the part played by streptococci, pneumococci, and other organisms, in *Annals of the Pickett-Thomson Research Laboratory,* Vol III. London, Bailliere, Tindall, Cox, 1932.
9. Andrewes CH, Chaproniere DM, Gompels AEH, et al: Propagation of common cold virus in tissue cultures. *Lancet* 1953; 2:546–547.
10. Price, WH: The isolation of a new virus associated with respiratory clinical disease in humans. *Proc Natl Acad Sci USA* 1956; 42:892–896.
11. Pelon W, Mogabgab WJ, Phillips IA, et al: A cytopathogenic agent isolated from naval recruits with mild respiratory illness. *Proc Soc Exp Biol Med* 1957; 94:262–267.
12. Mogabgab WJ, Pelon W: Problems in characterizing and identifying an apparently new virus found in association with mild respiratory disease in recruits. *Ann NY Acad Sci* 1957; 67:403–412.
13. Tyrrell DAJ, Chanock RM: Rhinoviruses: A description. *Science* 1963; 141:152–153.
14. Hamparian VV, Leagus MB, Hilleman MR: Additional rhinovirus serotypes. *Proc Soc Exp Biol Med* 1964; 116:976–984.
15. Hamre D, Connelly AP Jr, Procknow JJ: Virologic studies of acute respiratory disease in young adults: III. Some biologic and serologic characteristics of seventeen rhinovirus serotypes isolated October, 1960 to June, 1961. *J Lab Clin Med* 1964; 64:450–460.
16. Conant RM, Hamparian VV: Rhinoviruses: Basis for a numbering system: I. HeLa cells for propagation and serologic procedures. *J Immunol* 1968; 100:107–113.
17. Conant RM, Hamparian VV: Rhinoviruses: Basis for a numbering system: II. Serologic characterization of prototype strains. *J Immunol* 1968; 100:114–119.
18. Gwaltney JM Jr, Hendley JO, Simon G, et al: Rhinovirus infections in an industrial population: III. Number and prevalence of serotypes. *Am J Epidemiol* 1968; 87:158–166.
19. Hamre D: Rhinoviruses, in Melnick JL (ed): *Monographs in Virology.* Basel, Karger, 1968, vol 1.
20. Cooney MK, Hall CE, Fox JP: The Seattle virus watch: III. Evaluation of isolation methods and summary of infections detected by virus isolations. *Am J Epidemiol* 1972; 96:286–305.
21. Monto AS, Cavallaro JJ: The Tecumseh study of respiratory illness: IV. Prevalence of rhinovirus serotypes, 1966–1969. *Am J Epidemiol* 1972; 96:352–360.
22. Calhoun AM, Jordan WS Jr, Gwaltney JM Jr: Rhinovirus infections in an industrial population: V. Change in distribution of serotypes. *Am J Epidemiol* 1974; 99:58–64.
23. Hamparian VV, Colonno RJ, Cooney MK, et al: A collaborative report: rhinoviruses—extension of the numbering system from 89 to 100. *Virology* 1987; 159:191–192.

24. Mayor HD: Picornavirus symmetry. *Virology* 1964; 22:156–160.
25. McGregor S, Mayor HD: Biophysical studies on rhinovirus and poliovirus: I. Morphology of viral ribonucleoprotein. *J Virol* 1968; 2:149–154.
26. McGregor S, Mayor HD: Biophysical and biochemical studies on rhinovirus and poliovirus: II. Chemical and hydrodynamic analysis of the rhinovirus. *J Virol* 1971; 7:41–46.
27. Korant BD, Lonberg-Holm K, Noble J, et al: Naturally occurring and artificially produced components of three rhinoviruses. *Virology* 1972; 48:71–86.
28. Lawrence C, Thach RE: Identification of a viral protein involved in posttranslational maturation of the EMC virus capsid precursor. *J Virol* 1975; 15:918–928.
29. Arnold E, Luo M, Vriend G, et al: Implications of the picornavirus capsid structure for polyprotein processing. *Proc Natl Acad Sci USA* 1987; 84:21–25.
30. Rueckert RR: On the structure and morphogenesis of picornaruses, in Fraenkel-Conrat H, Wagner RR (eds): *Comprehensive Virology*. New York, Plenum, 1976, vol 6, pp 131–213.
31. Rossman MG, Arnold E, Erickson JW, et al: Structure of a human common cold virus and functional relationship to other picornaviruses. *Nature* 1985; 317:145–153.
32. Smith TJ, Kremer MJ, Luo G, et al: The site of attachment in human rhinovirus 14 for antiviral agents that inhibit uncoating. *Science* 1986; 233:1286–1293.
32a. Rossman MG, Palmenberg AC: Conservation of the putative receptor attachment site in picornaviruses. *Virology* 1985; 164:373–382.
33. Sherry B, Mosser AG, Colonno RJ, et al: Use of monoclonal antibodies to identify four immunogenic neutralization immunogens on a common cold picornavirus, human rhinovirus 14. *J Virol* 1986; 57:246–257.
34. Badger J, Minor I, Kremer MJ, et al: Structural analysis of a series of antiviral agents complexed with human rhinovirus 14. *Proc Natl Acad Sci USA* 1988; 85:3304–3308.
34a. Andries K, Dewindt B, Snoeks J, et al: Two groups of rhinoviruses revealed by a panel of antiviral compounds present sequence divergence and differential pathogenicity. *J Virol* 1990; 64:1117–1123.
35. Levintow L: The reproduction of picornaviruses, in Fraenkel-Conrat H, Wagner RR (eds): *Comprehensive Virology*. New York, Plenum, 1974, vol 2, 109–169.
36. Jacobson MF, Asso J, Baltimore D: Further evidence on the formation of poliovirus proteins. *J Mol Biol* 1970; 49:657–669.
37. Baltimore D: Expression of animal virus genomes. *Bacteriol Rev* 1971; 35:235–241.
38. Stanway G, Hughes PJ, Mountford RC, et al: The complete nucleotide sequence of a common cold virus: Human rhinovirus 14. *Nucleic Acid Res* 1984; 12:7859–7875.
39. Rueckert RR, Wimmer E: Systematic nomenclature of picornavirus proteins. *J Virol* 1984; 50:957–959.
39a. Sommergruber W, Zorn M, Blaas D, et al: Polypeptide 2A of human rhinovirus type 2: Identification as a protease and characterization by mutational analysis. *Virology* 1989; 169:68–77.
39b. Wanoff L, Towatari T, Ray J, et al: Expression and site-specific mutagenesis of the poliovirus 3C protease in *E. coli. Proc Natl Acad Sci USA* 1986; 83:5392–5396.
39c. Rivera VM, Welsh JD, Maizel JV Jr: Comparative sequence analysis of the 5' noncoding region of the enteroviruses and rhinoviruses. *Virology* 1988; 165:42–50.
39d. Semler BL, Anderson CL, Hanecak R, et al: A membrane-associated precursor to poliovirus VPg identified by immunoprecipitation with antibodies directed against a synthetic heptapeptide. *Cell* 1982; 28:405–412.
40. Hamparian VV, Ketler A, Hilleman MR: Recovery of new viruses (coryzavirus) from cases of common cold in human adults. *Proc Soc Exp Biol Med* 1961; 108:444–453.
41. Dimmock NJ, Tyrrell DAJ: Some physicochemical properties of rhinoviruses. *Br J Exp Pathol* 1964; 45:271–280.
42. Lonberg-Holm K, Yin FH: Antigenic determinants of infective and inactivated human rhinovirus type 2. *J Virol* 1973; 12:114–123.
43. Lonberg-Holm K, Philipson L: Early interaction between animals viruses and cells, in Melnick JL (ed): *Monographs in Virology*. Basel, Karger, 1974.
44. Colonno RJ, Callahan PL, Wong WJ: Isolation of a monoclonal antibody that blocks attachment of the major group of human rhinoviruses. *J Virol* 1986; 57:7–12.
45. Yin FH, Lomax NB: Establishment of a mouse model for human rhinovirus infection. *J Gen Virol* 1986; 67:2335–2340.
45a. Lomax NB, Yin FH: Evidence for the role of the P2 protein of human rhinovirus in its host range change. *J Virol* 1989; 63:2396–2399.
46. Stott EJ, Killington RA: Rhinoviruses. *Annu Rev Microbiol* 1972; 26:503–524.
47. Haff RF, Wohlsen B, Force EE, et al: Growth characteristics of two rhinovirus strains in WI-26 and monkey kidney cells. *J Bacteriol* 1966; 91:2339–2342.
48. Stott EJ, Tyrrell DAJ: Some improved techniques for the study of rhinoviruses using HeLa cells. *Arch Gesamte Virusforsch* 1968; 23:236–244.
49. Monto AS, Bryan ER: Microneutralization test for detection of rhinovirus antibodies. *Proc Soc Exp Biol Med* 1974; 145:690–694.
50. Lewis FA, Kennet ML: Comparison of rhinovirus-sensitive HeLa cells and human embryo fibroblasts for isolation of rhinoviruses from patients with respiratory disease. *J Clin Microbiol* 1976; 3:528–532.
51. Hamory BH, Hendley JO, Gwaltney JM Jr: Rhinovirus growth in nasal polyp organ culture. *Proc Soc Exp Biol Med* 1977; 155:577–582.
52. Tomassini JE, Collono RJ: Isolation of a receptor protein involved in attachment of human rhinoviruses. *J Virol* 1986; 58:290–295.
53. Mischak H, Neubauer C, Kuechler E, et al: Characteristics of the minor group receptor of human rhinoviruses. *Virology* 1988; 163:19–25.
53a. Greve JM, Davis G, Meyer AM, et al: The major human rhinovirus receptor is ICAM-1. *Cell* 1989; 56:839–847.
53b. Staunton DE, Merluzzi VJ, Rothlein R, et al: A cell adhesion molecule, ICAM-1, is the major surface receptor for rhinoviruses. *Cell* 1989; 56:849–853.
53c. Tomassini JE, Graham D, DeWitt CM, et al: cDNA cloning reveals that the major group rhinovirus receptor on HeLa cells is intercellular adhesion molecule 1. *Proc Natl Acad Sci USA* 1989; 86:4907–4911.
54. Neubauer C, Frasel L, Kuechler E, et al: Mechanism of entry of human rhinovirus 2 into HeLa cells. *Virology* 1987; 158:255–258.
55. Tyrrell DAJ: Common cold viruses. *Int Rev Exp Pathol* 1962; 1:209–242.
56. Yin FH, Lonberg-Holm K, Chan SP: Lack of a close relationship between three strains of human rhinoviruses as determined by their RNA sequences. *J Virol* 1973; 12:108–113.
57. Jenkins O, Booth JD, Minor PD, et al: The complete nucleotide sequence of coxsackie B4 and its comparison to other members of the picornaviridae. *J Gen Virol* 1987; 68:1835–1848.
58. Hughes PJ, North C, Jellis CH, et al: The nucleotide sequence of human rhinovirus 1B: Molecular relationships within the rhinovirus genus. *J Gen Virol* 1988; 69:49–58.
58a. Hughes PJ, North C, Minor PD, et al: The complete nucleotide sequence of coxsackievirus A21. *J Gen Virol* 1989; 70:2943–2952.
59. Lonberg-Holm K, Crowell RL, Philipson L: Unrelated animal viruses share receptors. *Nature* 1976; 259:679–681.
60. Douglas RG Jr, Cate TR, Couch RB: Growth and cytopathic effect of "H" type rhinoviruses in monkey kidney tissue culture. *Proc Soc Exp Biol Med* 1966; 123:238–241.
61. Cooney MK, Kenny GE, Tam R, et al: Cross relationships

among 37 rhinoviruses demonstrated by virus neutralization with potent monotypic rabbit antisera. *Infect Immun* 1973; 7:335–340.

62. Cooney MK, Wise JA, Kenny GE, et al: Broad antigenic relationships among rhinovirus serotypes revealed by cross-immunization of rabbits with different serotypes. *J Immunol* 1975; 114:635–639.

63. Fox JP: Is a rhinovirus vaccine possible? *Am J Epidemiol* 1976; 103:345–354.

64. Stott EJ, Walker M: Antigenic variation among strains of rhinovirus type 51. *Nature* 1969; 224:1311–1312.

65. Kjersgaard R, Lindbom G, Dinter Z, et al: The etiology of respiratory tract infections in military personnel: 5. The recovery of ECHO 28 from cases with minor illness. *Acta Pathol Microbiol Scand* 1963; 59:537–542.

66. Kawana R, Yoshida S, Matsumoto I, et al: Rhinoviruses isolated from Japanese children with common cold. *Jpn J Microbiol* 1966; 10:127–128.

67. Stott EJ, Eadie MB, Grist NR: Rhinovirus infections of children in hospital: Isolation of three possibly new rhinoviruses serotypes. *Am J Epidemiol* 1969; 90:45–52.

68. Monto AS, Johnson KM: A community study of respiratory infections in the tropics: II. The spread of six rhinovirus isolates within the community. *Am J Epidemiol* 1968; 88:55–68.

69. Wulff H, Noble GR, Maynard JE, et al: An outbreak of respiratory infection in children associated with rhinovirus types 16 and 29. *Am J Epidemiol* 1969; 90:304–311.

70. Holmes MJ, Reed SE, Stott EJ, et al: Studies of experimental rhinovirus type 2 infections in polar isolation and in England. *J Hyg Camb* 1976; 76:379–393.

71. Jackson GG, Dowling HF, Muldoon RL: Present concepts of the common cold. *Am J Public Health* 1962; 52:940–945.

72. Minor TE, Dick EC, Peterson JA, et al: Failure of naturally acquired rhinovirus infections to produce temporal immunity to heterologous serotypes. *Infect Immun* 1974; 10:1192–1193.

73. Jackson GG, Dowling HF, Spiesman IG, et al: Transmission of the common cold to volunteers under controlled conditions: I. The common cold as a clinical entity. *Arch Intern Med* 1958; 101:267–278.

74. Douglas RG Jr, Cate TR, Gerone PJ, et al: Quantitative rhinovirus shedding patterns in volunteers. *Am Rev Respir Dis* 1966; 94:159–167.

75. Douglas RG Jr: Pathogenesis of rhinovirus common colds in human volunteers. *Ann Otol Rhinol Laryngol* 1970; 79:563–571.

76. Dowling HF, Jackson GG, Inouye T: Transmission of the experimental common cold in volunteers: II. The effect of certain host factors upon susceptibility. *J Lab Clin Med* 1957; 50:516–525.

77. Dowling HF, Jackson GG, Spiesman IG, et al: Transmission of the common cold to volunteers under controlled conditions: III. The effects of chilling of the subjects upon susceptibility. *Am J Hyg* 1958; 68:59–65.

78. Lidwell OM, Sommerville T: Observations on the incidence and distribution of the common cold in a rural community during 1948 and 1949. *J Hyg Camb* 1951; 49:365–381.

79. Badger GF, Dingle JH, Feller AE, et al: A study of illness in a group of Cleveland families. *Am J Hyg* 1953; 58:31–40,41–46,174–178.

80. Lidwell OM, Williams REO: The epidemiology of the common cold. *J Hyg Camb* 1961; 59:309–319,321–334.

81. Mufson MA, Ludwig WM, James HD, et al: Effect of neutralizing antibody on experimental rhinovirus infection. *JAMA* 1963; 186:132–138.

82. Reed SE: An investigation of the possible transmission of rhinovirus colds through indirect contact. *J Hyg Camb* 1975; 75:249–258.

83. Gwaltney JM Jr, Hendley JO: Rhinovirus transmission: One if by air, two if by hand. *Am J Epidemiol* 1978; 107:357–361.

84. Buckland FE, Tyrrell DAJ: Experiments on the spread of colds: I. Laboratory studies on the dispersal of nasal secretions. *J Hyg Camb* 1964; 62:365–377.

85. Gwaltney JM Jr, Moskalski PB, Hendley JO: Hand-to-hand transmission of rhinovirus colds. *Ann Intern Med* 1978; 88:463–467.

86. D'Alessio DJ, Peterson JA, Dick CR, et al: Transmission of experimental rhinovirus colds in volunteer married couples. *J Infect Dis* 1976; 133:28–36.

87. Dick EC, Jennings LC, Mink KA, et al: Aerosol transmission of rhinovirus colds. *J Infect Dis* 1987; 156:442–448.

88. Hendley JO, Wenzel RP, Gwaltney JM Jr: Transmission of rhinovirus colds by self-inoculation. *N Engl J Med* 1973; 288:1361–1364.

89. Turner RB, Hendley JO, Gwaltney JM Jr: Shedding of infected ciliated epithelial cells in rhinovirus colds. *J Infect Dis* 1982; 145:849–853.

90. Hendley JO, Edmondson WP Jr, Gwaltney JM Jr: Relation between naturally acquired immunity and infectivity of two rhinoviruses in volunteers. *J Infect Dis* 1972; 125:243–248.

91. Winther B, Gwaltney JM Jr, Mygind N, et al: Sites of rhinovirus recovery after point inoculation of the upper airway. *JAMA* 1986; 256:1763–1767.

92. Cate TR, Douglas RG Jr, Johnson KM, et al: Studies on the inability of rhinovirus to survive and replicate in the intestinal tract of volunteers. *Proc Soc Exp Biol Med* 1967; 124:1290–1295.

93. Urquhart GED, Stott EJ: Rhinoviraemia. *Br Med J* 1970; 4:28–30.

94. Hamory BH, Sande MA, Sydnor A Jr, et al: Etiology and antimicrobial therapy of acute maxillary sinusitis. *J Infect Dis* 1979; 139:197–202.

94a. Arola M, Ziegler T, Ruuskanen O, et al: Rhinovirus in acute otitis media. *J Pediatr* 1988; 113:693–695.

95. Mufson MA, Krause HE, Mocega HE, et al: Viruses, *Mycoplasma pneumoniae,* and bacteria associated with lower respiratory tract disease among infants. *Am J Epidemiol* 1970; 91:192–202.

96. Cate TR, Couch RB, Fleet WF, et al: Production of tracheobronchitis in volunteers with rhinovirus in a small-particle aerosol. *Am J Epidemiol* 1965; 81:95–105.

97. Blair HT, Greenberg SB, Stevens PM, et al: Effects of rhinovirus infection on pulmonary function of healthy human volunteers. *Am Rev Respir Dis* 1976; 114:95–102.

98. Fridy WW Jr, Ingram RH Jr, Hierholzer JC, et al: Airways function during mild viral respiratory illnesses: The effect of rhinoviruses on cigarette smokers. *Ann Intern Med* 1974; 80:150–155.

99. Lourenco RV, Stanley ED, Gatmaitan B, et al: Abnormal deposition and clearance of inhaled particles during upper respiratory viral infections. *J Clin Invest* 1971; 50:62a.

100. Garrard CS, Levandowski RA, Gerrity TR, et al: The effects of acute respiratory virus infection upon tracheal mucus transport. *Arch Environ Health* 1985; 40:322–325.

101. Stenhouse AC: Rhinovirus infection in acute excerbations of chronic bronchitis: A controlled prospective study. *Br Med J* 1967; 3:461–463.

102. Minor TE, Dick EC, Baker JW, et al: Rhinovirus and influenza type A infections as precipitants of asthma. *Am Rev Respir Dis* 1976; 113:149–153.

103. Levandowski RA, Ou DW, Jackson GG: Acute phase decrease of T lymphocyte subsets in rhinovirus infection. *J Infect Dis* 1986; 153:743–748.

104. Levandowski RA, Weaver CW, Jackson GG: Nasal secretion leukocyte populations determined by flow cytometry during acute rhinovirus infection. *J Med Virol* 1988; 25:423–432.

105. Turner RB: Rhinovirus infection of human embryonic lung fibroblasts induces the production of a chemoattractant for polymorphonuclear leukocytes. *J Infect Dis* 1988; 157:346–350.

106. Panusarn C, Stanley ED, Dirda V, et al: Prevention of illness from rhinovirus infection by a topical interferon inducer. *N Engl J Med* 1974; 291:57–61.

107. Levandowski RA, Horohov DW: Natural killer cell activity is induced by rhinovirus. Presented at the 28th Interscience Con-

ference on Antimicrobial Agents and Chemotherapy. Los Angeles, Cal, Oct 23–26, 1988.

108. Stanley ED, Jackson GG, Dirda VA, et al: Effect of a topical interferon inducer on rhinovirus infections in volunteers. *J Infect Dis* 1976; 133(suppl):A121–A127.

109. Douglas RM, Albrecht JK, Miles HB, et al: Intranasal interferon alpha-2 prophylaxis of natural respiratory virus infection. *J Infect Dis* 1985; 151:731–736.

109a. Higgins PG, Al-Nakib W, Barrow GI, et al: Recombinant human interferon-γ as prophylaxis against rhinovirus colds in volunteers. *J Interferon Res* 1988; 8:591–596.

110. Naclerio RM, Proud D, Lichtenstein LM, et al: Kinins are generated during experimental rhinovirus colds. *J Infect Dis* 1988; 157:133–142.

111. Anderson TO, Riff LJM, Jackson GG: Immunoelectrophoresis of nasal secretions collected during a common cold: Observations which suggest a mechanism of seroimmunity in viral respiratory infections. *J Immunol* 1962; 89:691–697.

112. Rossen RD, Butler WT, Cate TR, et al: Protein composition of nasal secretion during respiratory virus infection. *Proc Soc Exp Biol Med* 1965; 119:1169–1176.

113. Rossen RD, Douglas RG Jr, Cate TR, et al: The sedimentation behavior of rhinovirus neutralizing activity in nasal secretion and serum following the rhinovirus common cold. *J Immunol* 1966; 97:532–538.

114. Douglas RG Jr, Couch RB: Parenteral inactivated rhinovirus vaccine: Minimal protective effect. *Proc Soc Exp Biol Med* 1972; 133:899–902.

115. Cate TR, Rossen RG, Douglas RG Jr, et al: The role of nasal secretion and serum antibody in the rhinovirus common cold. *Am J Epidemiol* 1966; 84:352–363.

116. Jackson GG, Dowling HF, Akers LW, et al: Immunity to the common cold from protective serum antibody: Time of appearance, persistence, and relation to reinfection. *N Engl J Med* 1962; 266:791–796.

117. Levandowski RA, Pachucki CT, Rubenis M: Specific mononuclear cell response to rhinovirus. *J Infect Dis* 1983; 148:1125.

118. Fleet WF, Couch RB, Cate TR, et al: Homologous and heterologous resistance to rhinovirus common cold. *Am J Epidemiol* 1965; 82:185–196.

119. Kenney GE, Cooney MK, Thompson DJ: Analysis of serum pooling schemes for identification of large numbers of viruses. *Am J Epidemiol* 1970; 91:439–445.

120. Douglas RG Jr, Fleet WF, Cate TR, et al: Antibody to rhinovirus in human sera: I. Standardization of a neutralization test. *Proc Soc Exp Biol Med* 1968; 127:497–502.

121. Fleet WF, Douglas RG Jr, Cate TR, et al: Antibody to rhinovirus in human sera: II. Heterotypic response. *Proc Soc Exp Biol Med* 1968; 127:503–509.

122. Reed LJ, Muench H: Simple method of estimating 50 percent endpoints. *Am J Hyg* 1938; 27:493–497.

123. Fiala M, Kenney GE: Enhancement of rhinovirus plaque formation in human heteroploid cell cultures by magnesium and calcium. *J Bacteriol* 1966; 92:1710–1715.

124. Levandowski RA: Nitrocellulose dot-blot immunoassay for rapid detection of rhinovirus. *Clin Res* 1986; 34:923A.

125. Dearden CJ, Al-Nakib W: Direct detection of rhinoviruses by an enzyme-linked immunosorbent assay. *J Med Virol* 1987; 23:179–189.

125a. Gama RE, Hughes PJ, Bruce CB, et al: Polymerase chain reaction amplification of rhinovirus nucleic acids from clinical material. *Nucleic Acids Res* 1988; 16:9346.

125b. Torgersen H, Skern T, Blaas D: Typing of human rhinoviruses based on sequence variations in the 5′ non-coding region. *J Gen Virol* 1989; 70:3111–3116.

126. Barclay WS, Al-Nakib W: An ELISA for the detection of rhinovirus specific antibody in serum and nasal secretions. *J Virol Methods* 1987; 15:53–64.

127. Price WH: Vaccine for the prevention in humans of cold like symptoms associated with the JH virus. *Proc Natl Acad Sci USA* 1957; 43:790–795.

128. Andrewes CH, Tyrrell DAJ, Stones PB, et al: Prevention of colds by vaccination against a rhinovirus. *Br Med J* 1965; 1:1344–1349.

129. Perkins JC, Tucker DN, Knopf HLS, et al: Evidence for protective effect of an inactivated rhinovirus vaccine administered by the nasal route. *Am J Epidemiol* 1969; 90:319–326.

129a. McCray J, Werner G: Different rhinovirus serotypes neutralized by antipeptide antibodies. *Nature* 1987; 329:736–738.

129b. Francis MJ, Hastings GZ, Sangar DV, et al: A synthetic peptide which elicits neutralizing antibody against rhinovirus type 2. *J Gen Virol* 1987; 68:2687–2691.

130. Tamm I, Eggers HJ: Differences in the selective virus inhibitory action of 2-(α-hydroxybenzyl)-benzimidazole and guanidine HCl. *Virology* 1962; 18:439–447.

131. Gwaltney JM Jr: Rhinovirus inhibition by 3-substituted triazinoindoles. *Proc Soc Exp Biol Med* 1970; 133:1148–1154.

132. Reed SE, Bynoe ML: The antiviral activity of isoquinolone drugs for rhinoviruses in vitro or in vivo. *J Med Microbiol* 1970; 3:346–352.

133. Shannon WM, Arnett G, Schabed FM: 3-Deazauridine: Inhibition of ribonucleic acid virus-induced cytopathogenic effect in vitro. *Antimicrob Agents Chemother* 1972; 2:159–163.

134. Jackson GG: A perspective from controlled investigations on chemotherapy for viral respiratory infections. *J Infect Dis* 1976; 133(suppl):A83–A92.

135. Reed SE, Craig JW, Tyrrell DAJ: Four compounds active against rhinovirus: Comparison in vitro and in volunteers. *J Infect Dis* 1976; 133(suppl):A128–A135.

136. DeLong DC, Reed SE: Inhibition of rhinovirus replication in organ cultures by a potential antiviral drug. *J Infect Dis* 1980; 141:87–91.

137. Selway JWT, Bauer DJ: In vitro studies with 4′, 6-dichloroflavan, a new anti-rhinovirus compound. Presented at the 20th Interscience Conference on Antimicrobiol Agents and Chemotherapy. New Orleans, Sept 22–24, 1980.

138. Levandowski RA, Pachucki CT, Rubenis M, et al: Topical enviroxime against rhinovirus infection. *Antimicrob Agents Chemother* 1982; 22:1004–1007.

139. Phillpotts RJ, Jones RW, DeLong DC, et al: The activity of enviroxime against rhinovirus infection in man. *Lancet* 1981; 1:1342–1344.

140. Al-Nakib W, Willman J, Higgins PG, et al: Failure of intranasally administered 4′, 6-dichloroflavan to protect against rhinovirus infection in man. *Arch Virol* 1987; 92:255–260.

140a. Al-Nakib W, Higgins PG, Barrow GI, et al: Suppression of colds in human volunteers challenged with rhinovirus by a new synthetic drug (R61837). *Antimicrob Agents Chemother* 1989; 33:522–525.

140b. Wyde PR, Six HR, Wilson SZ, et al: Activity against rhinoviruses, toxicity, and delivery in aerosol of enviroxime in liposomes. *Antimicrob Agents Chemather* 1988; 32:890–895.

141. Merigan TC, Hall TS, Reed SE, et al: Inhibition of respiratory virus infection by locally applied interferon. *Lancet* 1973; 1:563–567.

142. Waldman RH, Ganguly R: Effect of CP-20, 961, an interferon inducer, on upper respiratory tract infection due to rhinovirus type 21 in volunteers. *J Infect Dis* 1978; 138:531–535.

143. Greenberg SB, Harmon MW, Couch RB, et al: Prophylactic effect of low doses of human leukocyte interferon against infection with rhinovirus. *J Infect Dis* 1982; 145:542–546.

144. Hayden FG, Gwaltney JM Jr: Intranasal interferon α2 for prevention of rhinovirus infection and illness. *J Infect Dis* 1983; 148:543–550.

145. Douglas RM, Moore BW, Miles HB, et al: Prophylactic efficacy of intranasal alpha 2-interferon against rhinovirus infections in the family setting. *N Engl J Med* 1986; 314:65–70.

146. Hayden FG, Albrecht JK, Kaiser DL, et al: Prevention of natural colds by contact prophylaxis with intranasal alpha 2-interferon. *N Engl J Med* 1986; 314:71–75.

147. Hayden FG, Winther B, Donowitz GR, et al: Human nasal mucosal responses to topically applied recombinant leukocyte A in-

terferon. *J Infect Dis* 1987; 156:64–72.

147a. Monto AS, Schwartz SA, Albrecht JK: Ineffectiveness of post-exposure prophylaxis of rhinovirus infection with low-dose intranasal alpha 2b interferon in families. *Antimicrob Agents Chemother* 1989; 33:387–390.

147b. Sperber SJ, Levine PA, Innes DJ, et al: Tolerance and efficacy of intranasal administration of recombinant beta serine interferon in healthy adults. *J Infect Dis* 1988; 158:166–175.

147c. Sperber SJ, Levine PA, Sorrentino JV, et al: Ineffectiveness of recombinant interferon-beta serine nasal drops for prophylaxis of natural colds. *J Infect Dis* 1989; 160:700–705.

148. Coulehan JL: Ascorbic acid and the common cold: Reviewing the evidence. *Postgrad Med* 1979; 66:153–160.

149. Schwartz AR, Togo Y, Hornick RB, et al: Evaluation of the efficacy of ascorbic acid in prophylaxis of induced rhinovirus 44 infection in man. *J Infect Dis* 1973; 128:500–505.

150. Korant BD, Kaver JC, Butterworth BE: Zinc ions inhibit replication of rhinoviruses. *Nature* 1974; 248:588–590.

151. Douglas RM, Miles HB, Moore BW, et al: Failure of effervescent zinc acetate lozenges to alter the course of upper respiratory tract infections in Australian adults. *Antimicrob Agents Chemother* 1987; 31:1263–1265.

152. Farr BM, Connor EM, Betts RF, et al: Two randomized controlled trials of zinc gluconate lozenge therapy of experimentally induced rhinovirus colds. *Antimicrob Agents Chemother* 1987; 31:1183–1187.

153. Eby GA, Davis DR, Halcomb WW: Reduction in duration of common colds by zinc gluconate lozenges in a double-blind study. *Antimicrob Agents Chemother* 1984; 25:20–24.

154. Hayden FG, Gwaltney JM Jr, Colonno RJ: Modification of experimental rhinovirus colds by receptor blockade. *Antiviral Res* 1988; 9:233–247.

154a. Marlin SD, Staunton DE, Springer TA, et al: A soluble form of intercellular adhesion molecule-1 inhibits rhinovirus infection. *Nature* 1990; 344:70–72.

154b. Sperber SJ, Gwaltney JM Jr, Sorrentino JV, et al: Pseudoephedrine alone or combined with ibuprofen as treatment for experimental rhinovirus colds. Presented at the 27th Interscience Conference on Antimicrobial Agents and Chemotherapy, New York, 1987.

155. Stanley ED, Jackson GG, Panusarn C, et al: Increased virus shedding with aspirin treatment of rhinovirus infection. *JAMA* 1975; 231:1248–1251.

156. Gaffey M, Gwaltney JM Jr, Sastre A, et al: Intranasally and orally administered antihistamine treatment of experimental rhinovirus colds. *Am Rev Respir Dis* 1987; 136:556–560.

157. Gwaltney JM Jr, Moskalski PB, Hendley JO: Interruption of experimetnal rhinovirus transmission. *J Infect Dis* 1980; 142:811–815.

158. Dick EC, Hossain SU, Mink KA, et al: Interruption of transmission of rhinovirus colds among human volunteers using viricidal paper handkerchiefs. *J Infect Dis* 1986; 153:352–356.

17

Polioviruses and Other Enteroviruses

David M. Morens
Mark A. Pallansch
Melinda Moore

The enteroviruses are a group of at least 67 recognized members of the picornavirus family *pico* [small] + *rna* [ribonucleic acid] + *virus*. The enteroviruses include the polioviruses (three types), the coxsackie A viruses (23 types), the coxsackie B viruses (six types), the echoviruses (31 types), and four recently identified enteroviruses which, because of changes in nomenclature, are not placed into any of the other four established groups.

Ironically, despite their name, enteroviruses are not commonly associated with enteric signs such as nausea, vomiting, or diarrhea. Their name simply reflects the fact that the human alimentary tract is the predominant site of replication and the viruses were first isolated from enteric specimens. These viruses are, however, recognized causes of paralytic poliomyelitis, aseptic meningitis-encephalitis, myocarditis, pleurodynia, hand-foot-and-mouth disease, conjunctivitis, and numerous other syndromes associated with extraintestinal target organs.

Confusion about enteroviruses also arises from the fact that single enterovirus serotypes can produce multiple distinct clinical syndromes; for example, coxsackievirus B5 and severe neonatal disease, childhood pleurodynia, adult myocarditis, meningitis, rash, and febrile illness, etc. Conversely, distinctive clinical syndromes may be independently associated with many different enterovirus types.[1] What is more, such associations are not always predictable: a given virus type may "behave" differently (clinically and epidemiologically) in different places at different times. Echovirus 9, for example has been associated primarily with aseptic meningitis in some outbreaks and with exanthematous disease in others.

A third source of confusion is that asymptomatic ("silent") infections are well recognized for virtually all enteroviruses, including polioviruses, and such infections may be highly prevalent under most circumstances. Therefore, isolation of an enterovirus from the alimentary tract does not necessarily imply an etiologic role in the disease.

A final confusing aspect of enterovirus disease is that both the nature and severity of symptoms may vary with age. Such variations are seen for different virus types and different clinical syndromes, but not always in the same direction: For example, whereas coxsackievirus B disease may be more severe in neonates, poliomyelitis is often more severe in adults.[2, 3]

The polioviruses are the best known of the enteroviruses both because of their association with paralytic poliomyelitis, and because of the proven effectiveness of type-specific vaccines and the public health vaccination programs to deliver them. Yet other enteroviruses are more prevalent, but only occasionally cause paralysis and death. From a public health point of view, the polioviruses deserve special consideration. But in attempting to understand the many complex aspects of enterovirus epidemiology, pathogenesis, and host immune responses, it is more natural to consider polioviruses and other enteroviruses together rather than separately. For the purpose of most of the following discussions the reader is advised to consider the polioviruses as an important subset of the enteroviruses whose most distinguishing feature is the increased frequency with which they are associated with paralysis.

HISTORY

Many of the clinical diseases now known to be caused by enteroviruses were described long before the viruses themselves were identified. Others are newly appreciated. In some cases recognition of "new" disease has led to isolation and identification of "new" enteroviruses. Poliomyelitis was well recognized before a viral etiology was suspected or polioviruses themselves were isolated.[4, 5] Pleurodynia,[6] myocarditis,[7] and herpangina[8] were described in the late nineteenth and early twentieth centuries, well before their enterovirus etiologies were discovered. On the other hand, the appearance in 1954 of the Boston exanthema led to the identification of a new enterovirus, echovirus 16.[9, 10] A pandemic of acute hemorrhagic conjunctivitis (AHC; first called Apollo 11 disease because it was identified at the time of the first manned moon landing) spread from Africa and southeast Asia during 1969 to 1973 and resulted in the discovery of enterovirus 70, the "original" agent of AHC;[4, 11–15] later outbreaks of AHC in southeast Asia from 1970 to 1975 led to the discovery of yet another cause of AHC, a variant of coxsackievirus A24.[11–13]

The foundation for such discoveries, however, had been laid in the United States decades before, when fear of poliomyelitis led to an unprecedented effort by the scientific community, the public, and government to end polio epidemics. Ironically, however, the successful products of those endeavors—vaccines capable of preventing poliomyelitis—have led to such complacency in much of the developed world that a generation has now grown up unaware of the fear associated with the word "polio" during the pre-vaccine era. As one author states, without exaggeration:

> These outbreaks were accompanied by a great deal of emotional terror . . . not the mass hysteria which characterized the black Plague of the fourteenth century but a quiet dread in the minds of parents, who live with the fear that at any time . . . poliomyelitis could paralyze or kill their children.[16]

Most Americans over 40 today can remember that mothers often kept children indoors during the summer months, refusing to let them swim or engage in activities involving contact with crowds of children or, in extreme cases, refusing to let them play outside of the house at all. A mania for cleanliness developed and grew; households were cleaned and recleaned; bottles, toys, and inanimate objects were boiled, steamed, or otherwise disinfected; newspapers, magazines, radios, and televisions stressed sanitation; school systems initiated mandatory courses in hygiene; posters of crippled children seemed to be everywhere, and the "iron lung" became a symbol of dread for millions (Fig 17–1). During an epidemic in New York in which thousands of people died,

> Long impatient queues gathered at railroad and ferry ticket windows. Thousands of parents urged their children through turnstiles to crowded ferries and trains, seeking to leave a city seemingly beset by some biblical disaster. Only a few could escape, for there were guards at the city's gates, stolidly turning back those who could not show signed certificates proving that they were free of the devastating germs.[17]

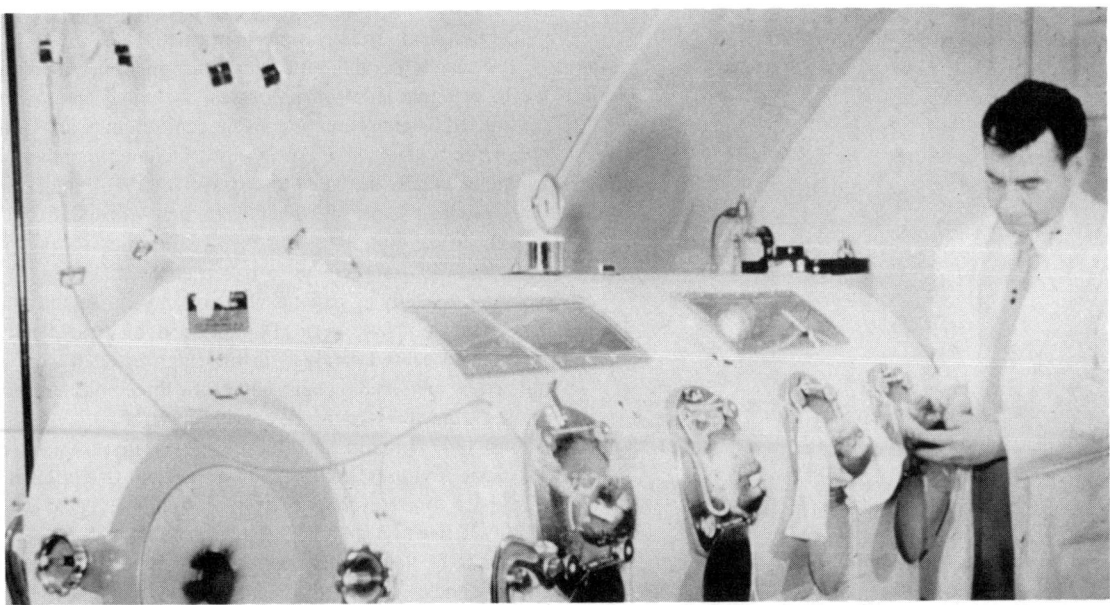

Figure 17-1. The "iron lung", a negative pressure mechanical ('Drinker') ventilator used to treat poliomyelitis patients with paralysis of respiratory muscles.

In some instances, persons fleeing the affected city were turned away by armed vigilante groups in unaffected cities. Parents carrying ill children into hospitals were arrested for exposing the public on city streets. A newspaper article documenting the degree of official hysteria inspired by poliomyelitis describes the city's response to a possibly ill child as follows:

> Three policemen entered [the woman's] house by cutting the screen covering a window on the first floor, breaking their way into the room where [she] stood with the baby in her arms. Stealing up behind her they seized her arms. Their revolvers were drawn . . . [Her] screams attracted neighbors to the house, but before they could enter two of the policemen held her while the third pulled the child from her arms and passed him through the window . . . .[17]

Evidence of crippling paralytic disease has been known since ancient times,[4] including an Egyptian stele showing an adult with probable history of paralytic poliomyelitis (Fig 17–2), and bone changes in the skeleton of an Egyptian who died about 3700 B.C. The ancient annals of Ulster, Ireland record the occurrence of an epidemic of a "pestilence that is called baccach (lameness)" in 708 A.D. However, poliomyelitis (*polio* [gray] + *myel* [spinal cord] + *itis* [inflammation of]) was not characterized as a specific disease until over a thousand years later. Though cases of paralytic disease in Asian and European children living in Asia had been reported as early as 1761,[18] it was not until 1793 that directly observed cases were described unequivocally by Underwood.[19] Badham reported the first poliomyelitis outbreak (four cases from one small town) in 1835.[20] Heine is generally credited with the best early written description of poliomyelitis as a distinct clinical disease in 1840.[21] Epidemics of poliomyelitis swept the United States beginning in Louisiana in 1891 and in Vermont in 1894[22, 23] and into the twentieth century, often beginning on the East Coast and spreading westward.[4, 24] In the first well-studied epidemic in

America, the death rate was said to be 13.5%, with more than 25% of the survivors suffering permanent paralysis.[22] In the United States poliomyelitis was the most prevalent acute nonbacterial epidemic disease of the central nervous system (CNS) during the first half of the twentieth century.[25] In large part because of poliomyelitis and other infectious diseases of childhood, the New York City Health Department established a Division of Child Hygiene in 1908, the first such agency of its kind, and a model for maternal and child health (MCH) programs that survive today.

In 1920 a wealthy New Yorker who was soon to play a key role in the conquest of poliomyelitis took his family for an island vacation. One morning, after a day of strenuous physical activity, he awoke with a fever, and was soon paralyzed with poliomyelitis. But although permanently crippled, Franklin Delano Roosevelt was determined to remain in public office and, four years later, he went before the nation to make the Democratic Party's nominating speech for the presidency. The drama of a political leader conquering a severe handicap struck a responsive chord in the American people, and in 1924 poliomyelitis became imprinted on the nation's consciousness.

Roosevelt's personal efforts on behalf of poliomyelitis began soon thereafter, when he purchased a resort in Warm Springs, Georgia to treat crippled persons, mostly victims of poliomyelitis. Roosevelt himself visited frequently, exercising his atrophied legs and thighs in the warm water (Figure 17–3). After his election as president, he instituted yearly "President's Birthday Balls" (1934) in cities around the country to raise money for poliomyelitis research, spearheaded by the slogan: "Dance so that others may walk." In those days, there was little precedent for media-driven fund-raising events, nor for private disease-specific granting agencies. But using the National Tuberculosis Association, founded in 1890, as a loose model, Roosevelt set up in 1938 the National Foundation for Infantile Paralysis (NFIP). To fund it, show busi-

Figure 17–2. An Egyptian stele (c 1500 B.C.) depicting the priest Ruma, 18th dynasty, with flaccid paralysis of the leg, probably due to poliomyelitis. Presumably the condition was sufficiently common in ancient Egypt for artisans to be aware of and accurately represent it. Note the muscle atrophy, shortening of the leg, the position of the arched foot as it steps upon the ground, and the staff, used as a crutch or cane. The stele is from Copenhagen's Carlsberg Glyptothek.

ness personality Eddie Cantor suggested that the slogan "March of Dimes" be used in a campaign in which radio stations would ask listeners to send their dimes directly to the president in the White House. Within three days after Roosevelt's birthday in 1938, so much money had been sent that countless mailbags blocked the corridors of the White House, interfering with the functioning of the government. The problem of funding poliomyelitis research had been dramatically solved, though it was not clear how long it might take scientists to find a cure or prevention.

On the scientific front, a landmark event in the history of poliomyelitis had been the description by Landsteiner and Popper (1909) of transmission of poliomyelitis to monkeys by intraperitoneal inoculation of filtered stool from a patient with paralytic disease.[26] The next major breakthrough did not come for 40 years: in 1949 Enders, Weller, and Robbins reported propagation of poliovirus type 2 in human embryonic tissues.[27] Their work earned them a Nobel Prize and led to development of poliomyelitis vac-

cines. Use of living cells for isolation of viruses has since become the mainstay of viral diagnosis, a development without which modern clinical virology would not exist.

The search for other viral agents that might cause poliomyelitis led to recognition of other viruses, including enteroviruses not neutralized by antiserum or convalescent serum to any of the three poliovirus types. These new viruses included members of what would eventually be called the coxsackievirus A and B and echovirus groups, some of which were first isolated from patients thought to have poliomyelitis.[28, 29] Before the success of Enders et al in 1949, suckling mice had been routinely used for virus isolation. In studying patients with poliomyelitis in the small town of Coxsackie, New York, Dalldorf and Sickles identified two viruses that caused paralysis in suckling mice and were not neutralized by antiserum against any of the three polioviruses.[30] Both viruses were from young boys with onset of paralytic disease in August 1947. In retrospect, these were the first isolated strains of coxsackie A viruses[30] although, ironically, the two original patients were later found to have been concurrently infected with polioviruses.[31] Because the clinical significance of these new viruses was yet to be determined, Dalldorf suggested that they be named after the locale of the first recognized human cases,[32] a practice now commonly used for naming newly discovered viruses.

Coxsackie B viruses were first isolated by Melnick and coworkers (1949) in suckling mice using specimens obtained from patients with suspected nonparalytic poliomyelitis.[33] Subsequently, Curnen et al (1949) isolated coxsackie B viruses from patients

Figure 17–3. Franklin Delano Roosevelt, President of the United States of America from 1933 to 1945, relaxing at poolside in Warm Springs, Georgia. Note the atrophy of the calf and thigh muscles of both legs, a result of denervation due to destruction of lower motor neurons. The president walked with leg braces and crutches, and even drove an automobile specially outfitted with hand controls. (Photograph courtesy of Little White House Historic Site, Georgia Department of Natural Resources.)

with pleurodynia and nonspecific febrile illness following accidental laboratory infection.[34] The worldwide distribution of these viruses was recognized by 1952 through reports from Alaska, Canada, England, France, the Netherlands, and Sweden.[35–40] Within 5 years the etiologic relationship of coxsackieviruses to clinical disease was well documented.[41]

The echoviruses, too, were discovered fortuitously during studies of poliomyelitis, but only once tissue culture techniques for cultivating polioviruses had been developed. In 1951, Robbins et al recovered viruses not neutralized by poliovirus antiserum and not pathogenic for infant mice.[29] Similar viruses were isolated from healthy children.[42, 43] At first these were truly "viruses in search of disease." They were referred to as "enteric viruses", or "orphan viruses" because of their (then) undocumented relationship to human disease.[43, 44] The term "echoviruses" was eventually adopted, derived from an acronym reflecting their origin and (incorrectly presumed) relationship to human disease,[44] *enteric cytopathogenic human orphan viruses*. In later years their association with a variety of human disease syndromes was extensively documented.

PHYSICAL AND BIOPHYSICAL PROPERTIES OF ENTEROVIRUSES

Virion Structure

The enteroviruses form a genus of the *Picornaviridae* family, which also includes rhinoviruses, hepatitis A virus, aphthoviruses (foot-and-mouth disease viruses), and the cardioviruses (agents related to mouse encephalomyocarditis virus and Mengo virus). Although quite diverse in host range and tissue tropism, the picornaviruses share a common structure and genome strategy. Picornaviruses are nonenveloped, icosahedral, 30 nm in diameter, containing a genome of single-stranded RNA of the positive, messenger RNA (mRNA) sense. Because the structural details of picornaviruses are difficult to determine by electron microscopy (Figure 17–4), biophysical approaches have been most informative. A major advance in studies on the structure of enteroviruses occurred with the solution of the crystal structure of poliovirus to a resolution of 0.29 nm.[45] The viruses consist of 60 subunits, each subunit containing four polypeptides which result from proteolytic cleavage of a single polyprotein precursor.[46] Although the molecular weights and amino acid compositions of the corresponding polypeptides differ among the picornaviruses and among enterovirus serotypes, the sizes of the four major virion polypeptides of poliovirus type 1 (Mahoney strain) are probably representative: VP1, 33,500; VP2, 30,000; VP3, 26,400; VP4, 7400. In addition, one small noncapsid protein, VPg, is covalently attached to the 5' end of the virion RNA. From the three-dimensional structure of the poliovirion, it is evident that VP1 constitutes a majority of the amino acid residues on the virion surface. VP2 and VP3 are also partially exposed on the surface while VP4 is completely internal. Crystal structures of at least two other picornaviruses have been determined, and while differing in detail, are similar to the poliovirus structure.

The information concerning the surface of the virion has been particularly useful in understanding the neutralization of poliovirus by antibodies. These efforts have culminated recently with the three-dimensional description of the neutralizing determinants on

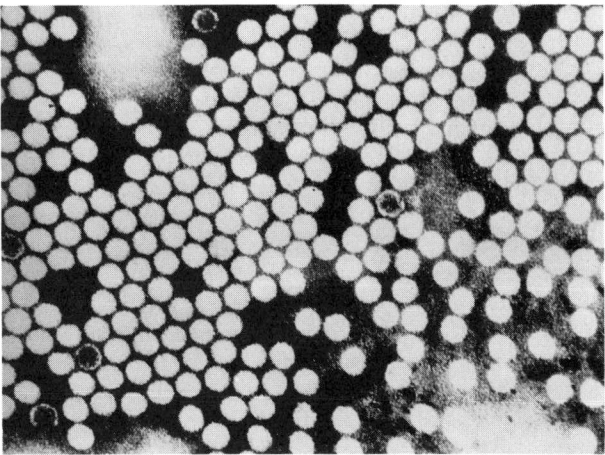

Figure 17–4. Electron micrograph of poliovirus particles. Enteroviruses cannot be distinguished from one another morphologically on the basis of electron micrography.

type 1 poliovirus.[47] From these studies using monoclonal antibodies and genomic sequencing of neutralization-resistant mutants, three antigenic sites have been identified, sites 2, 3A, and 3B. These sites involve all three of the larger capsid proteins, and two of the sites (3A and 3B) are shared between two different polypeptides. Studies of type 3 poliovirus have also identified a fourth antigenic site on VP1 (site 1),[48] which appears to be nonimmunogenic for type 1 poliovirus. All four of these sites are seen in human rhinovirus 14. It should be emphasized that all enteroviruses will almost certainly contain multiple neutralizing antigenic sites, each differing in their degree of antigenicity. In addition, there are other sites that elicit an immune response which is nonneutralizing, adding further complexity to the antigenic structure of enteroviruses.

Genomic Structure

Picornaviruses are among the simplest viruses in terms of genetic complexity and size. The RNA for many enteroviruses has now been cloned and complete genomic sequences obtained, including all three serotypes of poliovirus,[49] coxsackieviruses B1,[50] B3,[51] B4,[52] and part of A21.[53] The RNA from all the sequenced enteroviruses are similar in length, about 7400 nucleotides, and have identical genomic organizations. The virion RNA is infectious and serves as mRNA for viral protein synthesis. The RNA is translated in a single open reading frame into one large polyprotein which is then processed through proteolytic cleavage into more than 25 protein products and intermediates which contain the viral functions. In addition to the virion structural proteins, the viral RNA also encodes for two protease activities, a viral replicase, and the genome-linked protein VPg. Replication of the viral RNA occurs exclusively in the cytoplasm of the infected cell. Enterovirus infection rapidly inhibits host-specific macromolecular synthesis and redirects the host ribosomal system for the exclusive production of viral proteins by causing the modification of host protein synthesis initiation factors. In cell culture an infectious cycle is complete in about six to eight hours, with production of up to 10^5 virus particles per infected cell. However, only 0.1% to 5.0% of the particles are infectious in cell culture.

RNA hybridization studies have shown the following levels of genomic homology[54]: (1) among all enteroviruses, 5% or more; (2) between group types (eg, polioviruses and coxsackie A viruses), less than 20%; and (3) within groups, 30% to 50%. Genomic heterogeneity exists between strains of the same enterovirus serotype. The examination of genomic homologies has been extended by hybridization experiments using cloned enterovirus probes.[55, 56] From these experiments differences in relatedness could be demonstrated both among the major groups, but also within groups, and these differences varied depending on which region of the genome was examined. For example, probes from the capsid region are much less cross-reactive, while probes from the replicase region show a higher degree of homology between serotypes within a group. By using large probes from the replicase and protease regions, some homologies could be demonstrated among the polioviruses, coxsackie B viruses, and most of the echoviruses.

Enteroviruses have a buoyant density of 1.34 g/mL in cesium chloride, are relatively heat-labile (unless stabilized by magnesium chloride), and are resistant to acid pH (pH 3–5 for 1–3 hours), and to many common laboratory disinfectants (sodium hypochlorite, 70% alcohol), ether, deoxycholate, and other lipid solvents.[4, 57–60]

Enteroviruses are inactivated by various physical factors and chemicals[4, 61] including:

Physical:

- Drying
- Extreme heat (50°C for 1 h, except when stabilized by $MgCl_2$)
- Light (in the presence of vital dyes, such as neutral red, acridine orange, and proflavine)

Chemical (in the absence of organic matter with which viruses may associate and derive protection against inactivation):

- Formaldehyde, 0.3%
- HCl, 0.1 N
- Free residual chlorine, 0.3 to 0.5 ppm
- Other halogens: free residual bromine or iodine (approximately 0.5 ppm × 10 min contact time)

Enteroviruses can be stored for years at −70°C and for extended periods at −20°C (standard freezer temperature) with little or no decrease in infectivity.[4, 62] Although inadvisable for routine storage, enteroviruses in solution may be viable for weeks when stored at 4°C (standard refrigerator temperature), and for days at room temperature.

Host Range

Man is the natural host for all "human" enteroviruses. Although serologically distinct picornaviruses with the same physical properties as enteroviruses have been found in many animals, human beings do not usually have recognizable infections with "animal" enteroviruses. However, some animals are susceptible to infection with human enteroviruses, including primates for polioviruses, mice (and, subclinically, some monkeys) for coxsackieviruses A and B, and monkeys (subclinically) for echo-

viruses. Interestingly, at least one human enterovirus (coxsackievirus B5) is closely related antigenically to the porcine enterovirus causing swine vesicular disease, with about 50% genetic homology.

Each enterovirus type has been propagated in vivo and/or in vitro. As a rule of thumb the "diagnostic laboratory host range" of the enteroviruses can be described as follows[4]:

- Polioviruses: tissue culture
- Coxsackie A viruses:
  - A9: tissue culture, adult mice
  - All others: suckling mice and selected tissue culture
- Coxsackie B viruses: tissue culture, suckling mice
- Echoviruses: tissue culture
- Enteroviruses 68 to 71: tissue culture

The following distinctive outcomes of coxsackie A and coxsackie B virus infections in suckling mice form the basis for classification of agents into one or the other of these two groups[4, 63]:

Coxsackie A viruses. Flaccid paralysis; severe, extensive degeneration of skeletal muscle (sparing the tongue, heart, and CNS), with or without renal lesions
Coxsackie B viruses. Spastic paralysis and tremors associated with encephalomyelitis, focal myositis, necrosis of brown fat pads, myocarditis, hepatitis, acinar cell pancreatitis

The cytopathic effect (CPE) of enteroviruses propagated in cell culture is characteristic, as will be described later.

Antigenic Relationships

The antigenic relationships among enteroviruses are generally consistent with their taxonomic classification, based originally on their effects in suckling mice or cell culture. Many enteroviruses are apparently antigenically related to one another. Polioviruses 1 and 2 share common antigens. Antigenic relationships also exist between coxsackieviruses A3 and A8, A11 and A15, A13 and A18; and echoviruses 6 and 30 and 12 and 29. When virions are disrupted by heating, and particularly in the presence of detergent, antigens are revealed which are shared broadly among many enteroviruses,[64] although antibodies reacting with these antigens are generally non-neutralizing.

In addition to the 67 original—or prototype—strains, antigenic variants of several enteroviruses have been identified. The origin of such variants is not clear, but they may result from mutation or antigenic drift.[4] Genetic recombination may occur, but its biologic significance is not proven. One type of variant is the prime strain, identified for many enteroviruses, including coxsackievirus A17, echoviruses 1 to 6, 9, 11, 29, and 30, and enterovirus 70.[65–68] A prime strain bears the following relationship to the prototype strain[4, 66]: (1) antibody to the prototype strain neutralizes the prime strain poorly, or not at all; (2) antibody to the prime strain neutralizes the prime strain and the prototype strain equally well; (3) the prototype and prime strains share complement-fixing (CF) antigens. A prime strain thus has a broader antigenic spectrum than its corresponding prototype, and also elicits a broader spectrum of neutralizing antibodies.

Intratypic variants have also been identified for some of the enteroviruses, including coxsackieviruses A24, B1 to 4, B6; echoviruses 4, 9, and 33; and enterovirus 70.[69-76] Such variants generally have a narrower antigenic spectrum than their corresponding prototype strains and thus cannot be classified as prime strains.

The accepted prototype enterovirus strains are maintained in the American Type Culture collection (ATCC), Rockville, Maryland and in World Health Organization (WHO) Collaborating Reference Laboratories. They have been formally approved as being prototype strains by the International Committee on the Taxonomy of Viruses. Reference enterovirus strains can be obtained from the WHO reference centers or from ATCC. Reference antisera are obtained through WHO, Geneva, or directly from the WHO Collaborating Center Virus Reference and Research, Copenhagen, by prior arrangement.

The extent to which enterovirus antigenic drift occurs is not known; however, comparison of recent versus prototype isolates of certain enteroviruses (eg, coxsackievirus B5) reveals changes in the polypeptide sequences. When such evidence is considered in light of (1) the existence of many multiply related enteroviruses, (2) prime strains, (3) intratypic variants, and (4) relatedness of human and animal enteroviruses, it is tempting to speculate that such antigenic instability as exists may reflect adaptive genetic instability.

Taxonomic Classification

The enteroviruses are members of the picornaviruses, one of 15 RNA virus families of the known animal viruses. Officially classified as such in 1963, the picornaviruses include four subgroups of different densities in cesium chloride: the aphthoviruses, the cardioviruses, the enteroviruses, and the rhinoviruses. Because different enterovirus types and other unrelated microorganisms may cause the same syndromes, enteroviruses cannot be identified or classified purely on the basis of clinical manifestations.

Classification of enteroviruses began in 1955, when a committee of the NFIP adopted the term "echovirus" as a group designation, and 2 years later formally classified into the enterovirus family the polioviruses, coxsackie A viruses, coxsackie B viruses, and echoviruses.[44] Subsequently, Rosen and colleagues recommended that new enterovirus types be numbered sequentially rather than placed into one of the four existing groups on the basis of mouse or tissue culture pathology, the boundaries of which were sufficiently indistinct to cause several instances of misclassification.[4] Hence, the four most recently accepted virus types have been designated enteroviruses 68 to 71. Hepatitis A virus, which is discussed separately in Chapter 18, was proposed for classification as enterovirus 72 by the International Committee on Taxonomy of Viruses.[77] The proposal is based on the distinct similarities between the physical properties of hepatitis A virus and the enteroviruses. Subsequently, the complete genomic sequence of hepatitis A virus has been obtained, and there is little homology with other enteroviruses.[78] Based upon more recent information, it is therefore appropriate that hepatitis A be considered a distinct picornavirus, possibly even a unique genus within the *Picornaviridae*. Other probable enteroviruses await further study and formal classification.

The human enteroviruses now include the following 67 numbered types (exclusive of variants):

- 3 Polioviruses: types 1 to 3
- 23 Coxsackie A viruses: types 1 to 34 (except A23, which was found to be the same as echovirus 9)
- 6 Coxsackie B viruses: types 1 to 6
- 31 Echoviruses: types 1 to 34 (except: echovirus 8—deleted because of identity with echovirus 1; echovirus 10—reclassified as reovirus type 1; and echovirus 28—reclassified as rhinovirus type 1A)
- 4 Other enteroviruses: types 68 to 71

EPIDEMIOLOGY

Sources of Information about Enterovirus Epidemiology

Information about enterovirus epidemiology and about epidemics is published widely in the scientific literature: a literature search going back only a few years will reveal literally hundreds of articles in many languages. In recent years, poliomyelitis epidemics on Taiwan (1982) and in Finland (1984–1985) have been extensively documented, in part because of the implications for national vaccination policies.[79, 80]

In addition to the general medical and scientific literature, descriptions of cases, clusters, outbreaks, and occasional reviews, enterovirus surveillance information is provided by a variety of sources, including:

Global
> *Weekly Epidemiologic Record*, published by WHO in split English/French format. (Also available, *WHO Quarterly Report*, and *WHO Annual Reports on Virus Isolations*.) Address: WHO, 1211 Geneva 27, Switzerland (WHO regional offices also publish periodic reports)

National
> *Morbidity and Mortality Weekly Report (MMWR)*; annual *Poliomyelitis Surveillance Report*; and *Enterovirus Surveillance Report*, all published by the US Centers for Disease Control (US Public Health Service). Address: CDC, Atlanta, GA 30333
>
> *Canada Diseases Weekly Report/Rapport hebdomadaire des maladies au Canada*, published by the Canadian Department of National Health and Welfare in split English/French format. Address: Bureau of Communicable Disease Epidemiology, Laboratory Centre for Disease Control, Tunney's Pasture, Ottawa, Ont, Canada K1A OL2
>
> *Communicable Disease Report (CDR)* (weekly, quarterly, and annually), published by the Public Health Laboratory Service for the United Kingdom. Address: PHLS Communicable Disease Surveillance Centre, 61 Colindale Avenue, London NW9 5EQ, England
>
> *Communicable Disease Intelligence*, published by the Australian Department of Health. Address: Environmen-

tal Health Branch, Dept of Health, PO Box 100, Woden, ACT 2606 Australia

State/Local

In the United States, jurisdictional health departments publish periodic newsletters which may have important information about enteroviruses, for example, *California Morbidity, Wisconsin Epidemiologic Bulletin, Minnesota Department of Health Disease Control Newsletter,* etc. For addresses, check with the state, county, or city health department

Other

In addition, alone, or in cooperation with local health departments, some universities publish similar surveillance information, for example, *Infectious Disease Newsletter.* Address: University of Rochester Medical Center, Box MED, 601 Elmwood Avenue, Rochester, NY 14642

General Epidemiologic Considerations

The ability to propagate some enteroviruses in cell culture simplifies epidemiologic investigations. Nevertheless, understanding of enterovirus epidemiology requires appreciation of the strengths and weaknesses of the laboratory systems used and the methods of specimen collection, transportation, and storage (discussed below). Enterovirus excretion (or "carriage") does not necessarily imply association with disease, since most such excretion is asymptomatic. This word of caution applies particularly to developing countries where enteroviruses are ubiquitous and childhood infections commonplace and characteristically silent.

In addition to recognizing the critical distinction between enterovirus infection and disease, the epidemiologist must distinguish between active and passive case finding and know how to make, or avoid making, assumptions about data generated therefrom. Surveillance systems usually depend on passive case finding of enterovirus disease. That is, the surveillance system is likely to "hear about" a case if it is easily recognizable and diagnosed by someone who decides to report it. Not surprisingly, such surveillance systems overestimate the true proportion of serious complications, particularly those of the CNS. In the United States, for example, the only "notifiable" enteroviral diseases (ie, those for which the physician making the diagnosis is required to notify the local health department) are poliomyelitis, aseptic meningitis, and encephalitis; the last two are only reportable by diagnostic category (ie, encephalitis, meningitis) rather than by etiology (eg, echovirus meningitis). WHO established in 1963 a system for surveillance of viral neurologic diseases other than those of arbovirus etiology. The first 10-year surveillance report, covering 1967 to 1976, summarized 59,281 reports from over 30 countries on five different continents.[81] As of 1975, 119 WHO Virus Reference Centres and other national laboratories in 47 countries were participating in diagnosis and reporting to the WHO Virus Unit, Geneva. Such "complication-based" surveillance is the most accessible but the least representative of all surveillance data.

Another type of surveillance is exemplified by the Virus Watch studies conducted in various United States cities in the early 1960s.[82–84] These studies depended on active surveillance of enteroviral infections, with regular visits and virologic sampling of subjects in selected households over long periods of time. While difficult and extremely expensive, such prospective cohort studies avoid many of the pitfalls of passive surveillance and allow interpretations about both infection and disease incidence.

Epidemiologic studies are often designed to supply information about either the incidence of infection or disease, or prevalence, usually determined by a one-time survey of disease or of the presence of serum antibody to designated enterovirus types. To determine incidence, the number of new cases of infection (or, in some cases, disease) in a population is established over a specified time interval. For example, the incidence of poliomyelitis in the United States in 1979 was 0.01 per 100,000 persons per year.[85] This type of study is greatly improved by laboratory confirmation of cases. Incidence studies generally rely on virus isolation and/or documentation of a rise or fall of specific serum antibodies (seroconversion). To determine prevalence, the number of cases of the infection (or disease) is established at a single point in time, laboratory documentation likewise improving the overall quality of the data. An important type of prevalence study useful in studying enteroviruses is the serosurvey, in which the proportion of persons with antibody titers at or above some predetermined minimum level is sought. For example, the prevalence of detectable poliovirus antibodies in a population of clinic attendees during the 1979 United States poliomyelitis outbreak was between 78% and 89% for each of the three poliovirus types.[85]

Finally, enterovirus activity in populations may be either sporadic or epidemic. Certain enterovirus types are associated with both sporadic and epidemic disease occurrence, although they may be limited to one or the other.[4] The reported incidence or prevalence of a given enterovirus disease may be actually and/or artifactually increased in an outbreak situation when there is a sudden focus of attention that improves diagnosis and reporting of cases, but this may also increase reporting of "noncases." The clinician should ideally maintain a high index of suspicion for sporadic cases as well as outbreak-associated cases of enteroviral diseases.

Geographic and Seasonal Distribution

In temperate climates enteroviruses are characteristically "summer" viruses. In fact, the naturally occurring (wild) enteroviruses (when compared with the live attenuated polioviruses of the oral poliomyelitis vaccine) have a distinct seasonal pattern of circulation that varies by geographic area. In tropical and semitropical areas circulation tends to be year round,[4] or associated with the rainy season.[86] In temperate areas enteroviruses are most prevalent in the summer and fall, although outbreaks may continue into the winter until they "burn out."[4] In the United States, 10 years of surveillance indicated that 82% of enterovirus isolations were made during the five summer-fall months of June to October.[87] In a 6-year study of viral CNS disease, 85% of enteroviral disease, compared with 12% to 26% of diseases due to other viral agents, occurred between June and November.[88] The United States 10-year surveillance summary also indicated that polioviruses (mostly vaccine strains) were isolated year round, reflecting the routine administration of poliomyelitis vaccine to children. Knowledge of the seasonal pattern of enterovirus activity, especially in temperate climates, is a very important clue to diagnosis.

Socioeconomic and Urban-Rural Considerations

Enteroviruses are more prevalent among persons of lower socioeconomic status living in urban areas. In a study utilizing active surveillance of healthy children for enterovirus infections in West Virginia during 1951 to 1953, the rate of isolations among children in a lower socioeconomic setting was 2 to 7 times higher than among children in a higher socioeconomic setting[89]; these results may have been confounded by the greater number of persons per household and per room in the lower socioeconomic groups. A similar study in Ghana during 1971 to 1973 further indicated that isolations were significantly more frequent from children in areas with poorer sanitation and in urban areas, during both the rainy and dry seasons.[90] Other data from a prospective cohort study of newborns in Rochester, New York, suggest that socioeconomic status is also a predictor of neonatal infection.[91]

Enterovirus infection rates appear to be greater for nonwhites than for whites, probably reflecting socioeconomic and other confounding variables rather than strictly ethnic characteristics.[92-95] Nevertheless, some studies that controlled for socioeconomic status revealed that enterovirus infections were more frequent in nonwhites.[92, 94, 95]

Paradoxically, poliomyelitis and perhaps some nonpolio enterovirus (NPEV) diseases tend to be "diseases of development."[4] In the case of poliomyelitis, improvement in a country's hygienic and socioeconomic conditions leads to a "transition phase" in disease experience characterized by a delay in age at first infection and a temporary increase in the paralysis-to-infection ratio, before vaccination programs successfully reduce the incidence of paralysis to its ultimate low level. Before introduction of poliovirus vaccine into the United States and other developed countries, paralytic poliomyelitis was disproportionately a disease of the middle and upper socioeconomic classes, a reflection of delay in age at infection to an older age when paralysis was a more frequent complication; a delay occasioned, ironically, by improved hygiene. The infant mortality rate, a general indicator of a country's level of health development, may be inversely correlated with the incidence of poliomyelitis.[4, 96]

Age

Age is one of the most important determinants of outcome of enterovirus infections. Different age groups have different susceptibilities to infection, different clinical manifestations and degrees of severity, and different prognoses following enterovirus infection. Nevertheless, certain generalizations are possible.

Young children are probably the most important transmitters of enteroviruses: in one study echovirus 9 disease attack rates in children were found to be 50% to 70% compared with 17% to 33% in adult age groups.[97] Age-specific attack rates of echovirus 30 per 1000 persons during an outbreak in the United Kingdom in 1966 ranged from 19.70 (for children 0–9 years) to 7.11, 4.85, 4.73, 1.50, and 0.00 for the succeeding 10-year age cohorts, respectively.[98]

Severity of disease in infected persons may also be strikingly age-related. With poliovirus infection, adults are more likely to be severely affected, tending to acquire paralytic poliomyelitis rather than nonparalytic poliomyelitis (poliovirus aseptic meningitis), abortive illness, or asymptomatic infection.[2, 3] On the other hand, coxsackie B virus infection is clearly more severe in newborns than in older children and adults, often causing fulminant "viral sepsis" with myocarditis, encephalitis, hepatitis, and sometimes death.[99-101] For the most part, diseases associated with coxsackie A viruses and echoviruses are milder in children than in adults.[1, 97, 102, 103] Exceptions include coxsackievirus A16, which tends to be more severe in younger than in older persons.[104]

More specific information about the age distribution of various enterovirus diseases is summarized in Table 17–1. Childhood poliomyelitis appears to be more common in developing nonindustrialized countries, in which control through vaccination has not yet been achieved, than in wealthier industrialized countries. Encephalitis and aseptic meningitis due to NPEVs appear to be most frequent among those 5 to 14 years old[95, 105-107] while carditis is commonly seen in adults and neonates. In a 10-year surveillance summary from the United States,[87] adults tended to be "overrepresented" among cases of severe disease (paralysis, encephalitis, meningitis, carditis) when compared with the age distribution of the enterovirus-infected population as a whole. In another study,[118] the mean age among patients with coxsackievirus B meningitis (7.7 years) or pericarditis (9.9 years) was greater than the mean age of patients with coxsackievirus B gastroenteritis (1.3 years).

In mice, susceptibility is related to age at infection, virus and strain type, and principal target organ.[119] In humans the fetus and newborn are more susceptible to serious complications of coxsackie B viruses than are adults.[120] The different age susceptibilities and different tissue tropisms have been postulated to result from differences in the relative abundance of cell receptor sites.[121, 122] In mice there are marked differences in the abundance of sedimentable receptor site material at different ages and in different tissues.[121] Human cell receptors are discussed elsewhere.

Sex Distribution

Enterovirus diseases, and possibly also enterovirus infections, occur more frequently in males than in females.[4, 87, 92, 94, 107, 109, 110, 114, 123-130] Exceptions have been described.[6, 111b, 115, 131]

A summary of the sex distribution of various enteroviral diseases as reported in the literature is presented in Table 17–2. The male-female ratio appears to range generally between about 1.5 and 2.5:1; that is, approximately 60% to 70% of such diseases occur in males. Male predominance tends to be greater for the more severe disease, for example, CNS disease or carditis, than for less severe disease, for example, pleurodynia, hand-foot-and-mouth disease (HFM), respiratory disease, rash, or undifferentiated febrile illness.

The reasons for the apparent predominance of enteroviral infections among males is obscure. Based on a study of healthy children, Gelfand et al suggested the following possibilities[94]: (1) longer duration of virus excretion in males than in females (leading to more complete ascertainment of infected males than of infected females); (2) higher virus titers in the feces of males (with the same improvement in ascertainment among males); or (3) more frequent infections in males due to greater exposure (parental treatment and play habits of little boys and, later, greater activity among older boys). That human myopericarditis is more common in adolescent and adult males than in females, except pregnant and postpartum females,[135a] could reflect endocrine effects.

Table 17–1

Summary of Enteroviral Agents, Associated Clinical Syndromes, and Age Groups Affected

Syndrome	Agent	Setting
Poliomyelitis	P1	UK, 1947–1956
	P1–P3	United States, 1962–1968 (N = 1373)
		United States, 1969–1979 (N = 187)
Encephalitis	All	United States, 1970–1979 (N = 1687)
Aseptic meningitis	E4	Australia, 1956–1957 (N = 82)
	E9	1960–1961 (N = 62)
	E6	1960–1961 (N = 165)
	B1–B4	1960–1961 (N = 95)
	B5	1960–1961 (N = 54)
	E19	UK, 1975 (N = 290)
	All	United States, 1970–1979 (N = 5407)
	E4	New York, 1956
	E4, B5	Baltimore, 1967 (N = 202)
	E9	Hawaii, 1967 (N = 174)
	E7	New Haven, 1979 (N = 13)
Aseptic meningitis and others	E19	UK, 1974 (N = 268)
Viral neurologic disease	A	WHO surveillance, 1967–1976
	B	
	Echoviruses	
	Polioviruses	
Carditis		
M, Pe	All	United States, 1970–1979 (N = 78)
M, Pe	All	Wisconsin, 1957–1976
M	B5	Finland (N = 18)
Pleurodynia		Sylvest's original description, 1935
Acute hemorrhagic conjunctivitis	EV70	Thailand, 1974
Respiratory disease	All	United States, 1970–1979 (N = 1082)
Undifferentiated fever	All	United States, 1970–1979 (N = 326)
Rash disease	All	United States, 1970–1979 (N = 195)
Hand-foot-and-mouth disease	EV71	Japan, 1978 (N = 2374)
Mixed	All	United States, 1970–1979 (N = 18,152)
	E19	New Zealand, 1975–1976 (N = 33)
	E24	W. Germany, 1978 (N = 46)
		E. Germany, 1977
	B	Montreal, 1972 (N = 26)

(Continued)

Incidence and Prevalence

Incidence data about diseases caused by particular enterovirus types is often based on active or passive case findings and computation of attack rates, using population estimates at a given point in time. For example, the age-specific attack rates of illness during an echovirus 4 aseptic meningitis outbreak in an Iowa community in 1955, determined by house-to-house survey, ranged from 46 to 308 per 1000 population during the six weeks of the epidemic, with an overall attack rate of 191 per 1000.[136]

Better incidence data may be derived from prospective longitudinal surveillance of a defined population, or a sample of the population, in which the occurrence of disease and/or infection can be more reliably determined. This type of study is exemplified by the Virus Watch program in United States cities in the 1960s,[82–84] in which specimens from subject children were obtained every 2 weeks for virologic evaluation. Although these children

could have had infections not detected through biweekly sampling, these studies probably came closer than any others to estimation of true attack rates of enterovirus infections.

Less useful is information based on passive case finding. Typically, these data are reported by laboratories testing specimens submitted by clinicians for diagnosis, and may include the total number of specimens examined, and the number positive for the virus in question. For example, Kelen and Labzoffsky reported data from a 10-year period in Ontario, Canada, showing an overall 11% virus isolation rate among 21,698 specimens tested, with enteroviruses constituting 82% of all positive specimens.[137] Another method of passive case finding is surveillance for only "positive" laboratory specimens. For example, 10 years of data from WHO surveillance for viral neurologic disease revealed that 56% of all reported "virus-positive" cases were found to be enteroviruses.[81] Since such data indicate neither how many ill persons were not reported, nor how many ill persons had negative labo-

Table 17–1 (Cont.)

Proportion of Patients Affected per Age Group		
Children	Adults	Reference
67% 0–15 yr	33% ≥ 16 yr	5
78% 0–14 yr	20% ≥ 15 yr	85
56% 0–14 yr	45% ≥ 15 yr	85
60% 0–14 yr	40% ≥ 15 yr	CDC*
Peak in 5–14 yr		105
Peak in 5–9 yr		
Peak in 5–9 yr	Smaller peak in 25–29 yr	
Peak in 0–4 yr		
Peak in 5–9 yr		
Peak in 5–15 yr -and-	Mothers (20–29 yr)	106
70% 0–14 yr	30% ≥ 15 yr	CDC*
63% 5–14 yr		107
43–56 per 10^5 among 0–14 yr	6–35 per 10^5 among ≥ 15 yr	95
108–126 per 10^5 among < 1 yr	3–9 per 10^5 among ≥ 11 yr	108
55% 0–11 mo		109
50% 0–7 yr	Few > 35 yr	110
74% 0–14 yr	26% ≥ 15 yr	81
73% 0–14 yr	28% ≥ 15 yr	
71% 0–14 yr	29% ≥ 15 yr	
97% 0–14 yr	3% ≥ 15 yr	
48% 0–14 yr	52% ≥ 15 yr	CDC*
33% 0–15 yr	67% ≥ 16 yr	111a
	Mean age = 28 yr	112
60% 0–14 yr	40% ≥ 15 yr	6
	Mostly adults 20–49 yr	113
89% 0–14 yr	11% ≥ 15 yr	CDC*
87% 0–14 yr	13% ≥ 15 yr	CDC*
87% 0–14 yr	13% ≥ 15 yr	CDC*
80% 0–4 yr (most 2–4 yr)		114
56% 0–9 yr (including 26% < 1 yr)	16–20% ≥ 21 yr	87
48% 0–5 mo		115
24% 0.11 mo		116
76% 1–14 yr		
60% ≥ 6 yr		117
Mean age = 7.3 yr		118

*Unpublished data, 1981.
M = myocarditis; Pe = pericarditis; P = poliovirus type 1, 2, or 3; A = coxsackievirus A type; B = coxsackievirus B type; E = echovirus type; EV = enterovirus type.

ratory tests, the information is mostly of qualitative value, though it may be useful in indicating trends.

Various studies have suggested that certain enteroviruses occur predominantly in epidemic form, whereas others are identified only in sporadic cases.[4] When a particular strain is predominant in a community, there may be a tendency for other strains to be excluded,[5, 134] although large communities with summer enteroviral disease typically support cocirculation of several different types simultaneously and in no particular pattern.

Transmission

Enteroviruses can be isolated from both the lower and upper alimentary tract and can be transmitted both by the fecal-oral and respiratory routes.[4, 24] Fecal-oral transmission may predominate in areas with poor sanitary conditions, while respiratory transmission may be important in more developed areas.[24] It is believed that almost all enteroviruses (except, possibly, enterovirus type 70) can

be transmitted by the fecal-oral route; however, it is not known whether most are also transmitted by the respiratory route. Respiratory spread may result from passage of viruses from the bloodstream into the saliva or from virus replication in upper respiratory tract tissues during the early phase of infection. For at least one syndrome, acute hemorrhagic conjunctivitis (AHC), transmission may be exclusively mediated by direct contact with contaminated hands or fomites.[138] Enteroviruses, especially polioviruses, are regularly found in sewage[33, 139] and have been isolated from flies,[4, 33] leading to a suspicion that houseflies (*Musca domestica*) and various filth flies may be vehicles of mechanical transmission.

However, most enteroviruses are transmitted from person to person, either via fecal-oral contact or exposure to respiratory aerosols or secretions. It is also likely that enteroviruses are transmitted in the same manner as are other viruses causing the common cold—that is, by hand contact with secretions (eg, on the hand of another person), and autoinoculation to the mouth, nose, or eyes. There is no evidence that venereal transmission is important, al-

Table 17–2

Summary of Sex Distribution of Enteroviral Syndromes Associated with Various Enterovirus Types

Syndrome	Agent	Location	Sex Distribution (M/F Ratio)		Reference
Paralysis	A7	Scotland, 1959 (N = 37)		1.8:1	132
Aseptic meningitis (AM)	E4	New York, 1956	< 20 yr	1.6:1	107
			≥ 20 yr	0.8:1	
	E4	Scotland, 1971–1972 (N = 194)	Overall M < F		127
			< 1 yr	1.9:1	
			10–14 yr	2:1	
	E6	New York, 1955 (N = 92)	< 20 yr	2.5:1	126
			≥ 20 yr	1:1	
	E7	New Haven, 1979 (N = 13)		3.3:1	109
	E9	Ohio, 1967–1968 (N = 196)		2.7:1	124
	E9	New Mexico, 1959 (N = 49)		1.5:1	125
	E9	Hawaii, 1967		1.2–4.1:1	⌐108
	E4, B5	Baltimore, 1967 (N = 202)		1.4:1	95
AM only	E4	Kentucky, 1964 (N = 255)		0.6:1	111b
AM + minor illness				2.6:1	
Mostly AM	E3	Toronto, 1970, (N = 29)		0.8:1	
AM	B	Washington, DC, 1955–1960 (N = 114)		2.0:1	133
AM	Mixed	Toronto, 1965 (N = 26)		1.6:1	134
All		United States, 1970–1979 (N = 5543)		1.5:1	CDC*
Encephalitis	All	United States, 1970–1979 (N = 1777)		1.8:1	CDC*
Carditis (M, Pe)					
M	B5	Finland, 1968 (N = 18)		2:1	112
M, Pe	B	Washington, DC, 1955–1960 (N = 9)		3.5:1	133
M	B	Scotland, 1966–1968 (N = 30)		2.0:1	128
P	B	Scotland, 1966–1968 (N = 30)		3.6:1	128
M + Pe	B	Australia, 1962–1969 (N = 42)		1.5:1	129
P only		(N = 20)		5.7:1	
M, Pe	All	United States, 1970–1979 (N = 81)		2.0:1	CDC*
Pleurodynia	B3	Singapore, 1974 (N = 21)		1.6:1	135
	B3	Oxford, 1951 (N = 262)		0.8:1	131
	B	Washington, DC, 1955–1960 (N = 38)		5.3:1	133
Acute hemorrhagic conjunctivitis	EV70	Thailand, 1974		1.9:1	113
Hand-foot-and-mouth disease	EV71	Japan, 1978		1.2:1	114
Boston exanthema	E16	Boston, 1954 (N = 18)		0.4:1	10
Respiratory disease	All	United States, 1970–1979 (N = 1131)		1.4:1	CDC*
Rash disease	All	(N = 207)		1.0:1	
Undifferentiated fever	All	(N = 321)		1.4:1	
Mixed	E19	New Zealand, 1975–1976 (N = 33)		1:1	115
	E19	UK, 1974 (N = 268)		1.6:1	110
	B	Montreal, 1972 (N = 26)		2.7:1	118
	A	Wisconsin, 1957–1976 (N = 1529)		1.8:1	111a
	B			1.1:1	
	All	United States, 1970–1979 (N = 17,343)		1.5:1	CDC*

M = myocarditis; Pe = pericarditis; P = poliovirus type; A = coxsackievirus A type; B = coxsackievirus B type; E = echovirus type; EV = enterovirus type.
* Unpublished data, 1981.

though certain sexual practices, particularly those of some homosexual men (eg, analingus, rectal intercourse, and "fisting") would seem likely to increase transmission. However, enterovirus infections do not appear to be highly prevalent in persons with acquired immunodeficiency syndrome (AIDS) or other illnesses associated with the human immunodeficiency virus (HIV), suggesting that such infections, if they occur, are transient and either mild or inapparent. Direct bloodstream inoculation, usually by laboratory accidents, including needle sticks and shattered glass vials, may result in enterovirus infection, but neither blood transfusion nor mosquito or insect bites appear to transmit infection. Documentation of biologic transmission of a strain of coxsackievirus A6, originally isolated from mosquitoes, to infant mice is of questionable significance. On theoretical grounds, acquisition of enterovirus infection from drinking contaminated water is possible, yet such occurrences are rarely documented. Nevertheless, swimming pool outbreaks have been occasionally documented, suggesting that swallowing of contaminated pool water may account for transmission. However, there is no proof that this type of transmission actually occurs. Food-borne acquisition of echovirus type 4, in some cases causing aseptic meningitis, has been documented on at least one occasion (CDC, unpublished data, 1976), but food-borne transmission is thought to be an uncommon cause of enterovirus infection. Likewise, survival of enteroviruses on vegetable food crops exposed to contaminated water or fertilizer has not been proved to be associated with transmission of infection.

Transmission within households has been well studied for both polioviruses and NPEVs. Transmission also occurs within the neighborhood and community. Nosocomial transmission, typically in newborn nurseries, has also been well documented, including transmission of various coxsackieviruses of group A, group B, and the echoviruses.[99, 100, 102, 109, 140–159] Laboratory-acquired infections are occasionally documented.

Enteroviruses are generally introduced into the family by small children,[160] although in some outbreaks of AHC young adults make up the majority of index cases. Intrafamily transmission may be rapid[161] and relatively complete, depending on (1) duration of virus excretion, (2) household size, (3) number of siblings, (4) socioeconomic status, (5) immunity status of household members, and other risk factors.[4, 136, 162] Transmission has been generally found to be greatest in large families of lower socioeconomic status with more 5- to 9-year-old children and apparent serologic susceptibility to the virus type studied. Not surprisingly, infections in different family members may result in different clinical manifestations.[10, 141, 163, 164]

Household secondary attack rates in susceptible members may be greatest for the agents of AHC (enterovirus type 70 and coxsackievirus A24 variant), and for the polioviruses, and of lesser magnitude for the coxsackieviruses and echoviruses. In some studies, secondary attack rates may be 90% or more, although they are typically lower.[84, 165] New York Virus Watch data indicate that enterovirus infections were more frequent among 2- to 9-year-old children[84] and that secondary coxsackievirus infections were more frequent in mothers (78%) than in fathers (47%). In the same study, coxsackieviruses spread to 76% of exposed susceptibles versus 25% of exposed persons who had detectable antibody to the infecting type; echoviruses infected 43% of susceptibles and only one person with antibody.[84] The greater spread of polioviruses

and coxsackieviruses may derive from longer periods of viral excretion.[4, 165]

Observations of household transmission of various enteroviruses is summarized in Table 17–3, documenting that many infected contacts do not become ill[104, 107, 126, 164, 166] and that the extent of secondary transmission varies with different enteroviruses.[131, 167, 168]

Like many other viruses, enteroviruses can be rapidly transmitted within institutions when circumstances permit, for example, crowding, poor hygiene, contaminated water, etc. School teams or activity groups and institutionalized ambulatory retarded children or adults may be at special risk. Despite crowding, enterovirus transmission is not usually accelerated to a noticeable degree in institutions where good sanitation is usual (eg, university dormitories or military barracks).

Of great interest is the existence of poliovirus-susceptible enclaves (usually religious groups) in countries with otherwise high prevalences of poliovirus immunity. Despite the barrier of millions of immune persons, poliovirus outbreaks have recently occurred in some of these enclaves,[169–171] suggesting that herd immunity may be of only limited value in protecting groups of susceptible persons who have regular contact with each other, and raising questions about the risks that such groups may pose to the community at large.

Enteroviruses occasionally cause nosocomial outbreaks, particularly in hospital nurseries, where hospital staff may mediate transmission (see Perinatal and Neonatal Enteroviral Infection). Enterovirus type 70 is highly transmissible and may cause outbreaks in ophthalmology clinics when instruments (eg, tonometers) are inadequately cleaned between patients. An apparent outbreak of coxsackievirus A1 in bone marrow transplant recipients, including fatal cases, has been reported.[172]

Enteroviruses in the Environment

Although human enteroviruses have been isolated from various environmental sources, man is thought to be the only important natural reservoir.[4, 173] There is not known to be any extra-human "reservoir" or focus of "overwintering"; in small closed populations transmission may be explosive, but quickly dies out, and the viruses disappear completely. Long-term carriage of enteroviruses (beyond a few weeks) does not normally occur. Since viruses cannot replicate outside of living cells, infectious enterovirus particles can only decrease in number in the environment. But enteroviruses are so hardy that they can survive for months in favorable environmental conditions such as neutral pH, moisture, and low temperatures, especially in the presence of organic matter, which protects against inactivation.[173]

Although there is little evidence that enteroviruses found in the environment are of public health importance,[173] concern has been expressed about the possible dangers of contaminated sources of water and of shellfish intended for consumption. Recreational swimming water has been investigated in several studies: enteroviruses have been isolated from swimming and wading pools in the absence of fecal coliforms and in the presence of "recommended" levels of free residual chlorine.[61, 174, 175] Although outbreaks of adenovirus pharyngoconjunctival fever and Norwalk-like viral gastroenteritis have been attributed to swimming pool

Table 17–3
Household (HH) Transmission of Enterovirus Infections: Primary and Secondary Infection Rates

Setting	Agent	Descriptions of Study	Results	Reference
United States, AM outbreak, 1956	B5	61 families studied (154 persons)	B5 infection rates: with AM—75%; minor illness—71%; asymptomatic HH contacts—43%; asymptomatic non-HH contacts—30%	164
UK, AM outbreak, 1975	E19	Families of AM patients studied	40% of contacts infected with E19 (of these, 32% symptomatic, 68% asymptomatic)	166
New York, AM outbreak, 1955	E6	Families of AM patients studied	Ill: 55% in 0–19 yr, 33% in ≥ 20 yr; well: 16% overall	126
Iowa, AM outbreak, 1955	E4	House-to-house survey	Multiple cases of illness in 36% of HH (more spread in larger HH)	136
New York, AM outbreak, 1956	E4	71 families of AM patients studied	11% of HH had multiple AM cases	107
Sweden, outbreak of AM, rash, 1972	E18	6 families studied (27 persons)	85% of persons shown to be infected	167
Oxford, pleurodynia outbreak, 1951	B3	Approximately 262 persons	34% of cases = only case in HH (ie, heavy HH infections not the rule)	131
Baltimore, HFM outbreak, 1968	A16	Families of HFM patients studied	Cases: 80% with A16; asymptomatic contacts: 44% with A16 (53% of positive contacts were adults)	CDC*
England, outbreak of illness, 1977	B1	Boys' boarding school, 800 students, 11–19 yr	18% of serologically susceptibles infected; transmission associated with dormitories, not classrooms	168

AM = aseptic meningitis; A = coxsackievirus A type; B = coxsackievirus B type; E = echovirus type; HFM = hand-foot-and-mouth disease.
*Unpublished data, 1969.

transmission, no such outbreaks have been documented for enteroviruses. However, in one study the relative risk of enterovirus infection among Wisconsin children was significantly higher for beach swimmers, especially for those less than 4 years old.[176] In a 1972 outbreak at a boy's camp in Vermont, coxsackievirus B5 was isolated from the unchlorinated lake swimming area, but the outbreak itself was explained by person-to-person transmission.[176a]

Enteroviruses have been found in surface and ground waters throughout the world.[173] In the tropics, virus survival is longer in ground water because it is cooler than surface water. As in water from swimming pools, these viruses are often found even after chlorination and in the absence of fecal coliforms. In industrialized countries enterovirus transmission from potable water is apparently uncommon but is a constant source of concern for public health investigators since the usual conditions under which city drinking water is chlorinated (residual chlorine concentrations of 0.2–0.4 ppm in water of pH 7.0 for 10 min) may be insufficient to completely inactivate enteroviruses.

Enteroviruses have been isolated from raw or partly cooked mollusks and crustacea and their overlying waters.[173, 178, 179] Shellfish rapidly concentrate many viruses, including enteroviruses, and these may survive in oysters for 3 weeks at temperatures of 1 to 21°C.[173] Depuration in clean, warm, flowing water removes 99.9% of viruses in 24 hours.[173] Such cleansing is important, as some enteroviruses can survive in shellfish that have been stewed, fried, baked, or steamed,[173] and in any case hepatitis A and Norwalk-like gastroenteritis have both been acquired by ingestion of contaminated shellfish. To date there has not been an outbreak of enterovirus disease attributed to consumption of shellfish. However, food-borne transmission has been documented: a 1976 outbreak of aseptic meningitis in Mechanicsburg, Pennsylvania, attributed to echovirus type 4, was apparently caused by consumption of contaminated coleslaw at a large picnic (CDC, unpublished data, 1976).

The poliomyelitis literature is replete with investigation of polioviruses in sewage. In industrialized countries in the prevaccine era, these studies have shown a distinct seasonality, but an absence of seasonality is apparent today in countries widely using live attenuated poliovirus vaccine. Today enteroviruses are still more prevalent in sewage from areas with low socioeconomic conditions or large proportions of young children.[173] Sewage workers have been shown to have a higher prevalence of serum antibodies to enteroviruses than highway maintenance workers,[180] consistent with an occupational risk. Enteroviruses can be inactivated by proper sewage treatment, but such treatment should be carefully performed and evaluated. Practical methods for developing countries include waste stabilization ponds (water temperature > 25°C and holding time > 30 days), sludge drying beds, or composting.[173]

Soil and crops also provide conditions favorable to enteroviruses, which survive well in sludge and remain on the surface of sludge-treated soil and even on crops.[173] Because of this, it is recommended that when night soil or sludge is used agriculturally, drying periods of three to five days be allowed between applications.[173] Air samples from aerosolized spray irrigants using contaminated effluents have also been found to contain enteroviruses.[173, 181] Protective facewear may be desirable for workers involved in or downwind of such irrigation.

To prevent transmission from potential fomite sources, as in hospitals or day care centers, it is recommended to clean articles first and then disinfect them.[182] Cleaning can be accomplished with soap and water, and disinfection with any high (preferably)- or intermediate-level germicide. The best of these is sodium hypochlorite, 5% disinfectant solution for 30 seconds.[183]

Molecular Epidemiology of Enteroviruses

Study of the molecular variation of viral proteins or nucleic acid is capable of contributing significant epidemiologic information on viral diseases. Restriction endonuclease analysis of DNA viruses, notably herpes simplex virus (HSV) and cytomegalovirus (CMV), has been successfully applied to prove transmission from one individual to another and to infer common-source acquisition. For the enteroviruses, and in particular poliovirus, three types of molecular studies have been used to generate epidemiologic information: analysis of antigenic variation of virion proteins using monoclonal antibodies; examination of changes in the viral genome using oligonucleotide fingerprinting; and direct analysis of genomic variation using nucleic acid sequencing.

All three approaches have been utilized in addressing the classic problem of differentiating wild and vaccine-derived poliovirus. Early attempts at differentiation of wild from vaccine polioviruses were insensitive. Typically, poliovirus isolates were grown at low (35.5°C) and high (39.9°C) temperatures with the assumption that temperature-sensitive vaccine polioviruses would not grow at the higher temperature. However, it was eventually learned that roughly 30% of the wild viruses would not grow at such temperatures either, making interpretation problematic. Another test intended to differentiate between wild and vaccine viruses depended on cross-absorbed antibody. Separate aliquots of hyperimmune serotype-specific antisera were reacted with either wild or vaccine virus to absorb cross-reacting antibodies. The two resulting sera could then be used in neutralization tests to determine which serum neutralized an unknown virus better. More recently, investigators have distinguished between wild and vaccine polioviruses using cross–absorbed rabbit IgG in an enzyme-linked immunosorbent assay (ELISA) test.[184, 184a]

With the discovery of the procedure for producing monoclonal antibodies, production of vaccine-specific antibodies soon followed. There now exists a significant collection of these monoclonal antibodies which are capable of uniquely recognizing the Sabin vaccine strains.[185, 186] These antibodies have also been used to demonstrate changes in the antigenic properties of vaccine virus excreted by a primary vaccinee, such that the virus became antigenically less vaccinelike.[187] This antigenic drift to a less vaccinelike virus helps explain some of the difficulties in using antigenic tests to differentiate wild from vaccine virus. In addition to specificity for vaccine virus, monoclonal antibodies have also been

produced with specificities for various wild polioviruses, and these panels have been used to study antigenic variation in single outbreaks,[188] and among multiple outbreaks over several years.[189] The large antigenic diversity and plasticity of wild polioviruses is evident in all of these studies. During a 1984–1985 poliomyelitis epidemic in Finland, wild poliovirus type 3 isolates were shown to differ significantly from strains used to produce the inactivated vaccine in Finland[188, 190] and strains isolated sequentially from the same individuals exhibited antigenic drift of VP1 epitopes as determined by epitope–reactive monoclonal antibodies.[188] It thus appears that enteroviruses may undergo continuous antigenic drift in natural host populations, although it is not known whether this occurs in response to the selection pressures of gut immunity. Among the other enteroviruses, similar studies have shown large numbers of antigenic variants among coxsackievirus B4 isolates using monoclonal antibodies[192] and a significant difference in the stability of neutralizing epitopes between isolates of this virus.[193] All studies looking at antigenic properties of enteroviruses emphasize the significant variation observable at individual epitopes, and this in the face of serotype stability.

At about the same time that monoclonal antibodies were first being produced, oligonucleotide mapping was first applied to the study of poliovirus. The current technique for oligonucleotide mapping is relatively straightforward and is discussed in detail in Chapter 2. Such patterns appear to be characteristic for given strains of virus and have been referred to as fingerprints (Figure 17–5). Studies of wild and vaccine polioviruses have revealed many fascinating aspects of poliovirus molecular epidemiology.[195–197] First, fingerprints of poliovirus strains that are epidemiologically distinct, that is, those that are isolated sporadically or from persons in different epidemics, are unequivocally different. Secondly, poliovirus genomes appear to spontaneously and randomly mutate during replication in humans, resulting in variation in fingerprint types isolated during epidemics, presumably reflecting single and multiple generations of person-to-person transmission. Investigation of one epidemic where contact tracing was possible revealed that the fingerprint changed during infection of each case or contact, attesting to the remarkable rapidity of poliovirus evolution.[195] However, changes do not appear so rapidly that it is impossible to detect related strains. In one instance, an unsuspected epidemiologic link was established when it was discovered that wild poliovirus type 1 isolates from apparently unrelated fatal cases in New York and Ohio had similar fingerprints.[195]

Fingerprinting studies have also been done with vaccine polioviruses.[195] Patterns for the live attenuated (Sabin) type 1 poliovirus vaccine and for the prototype Mahoney strain from which it was derived are quite similar. However, as is the case with wild viruses, vaccine viruses predictably change during human infection.

Several studies using oligonucleotide fingerprinting have examined isolates of enterovirus 70 (EV70), one of two principal agents of epidemic acute hemorrhagic conjunctivitis, described below. Fingerprints of isolates obtained from multiple sites worldwide during the 1981–1982 pandemic showed that all of the isolates were very closely related, supporting a single agent as the etiology of the global outbreak.[198] Further studies demonstrated that the changes in the genome of EV70 were progressive, with increased numbers of changes with time over a 10-year period.[199] Quantitative analysis of these fingerprint data suggested a common

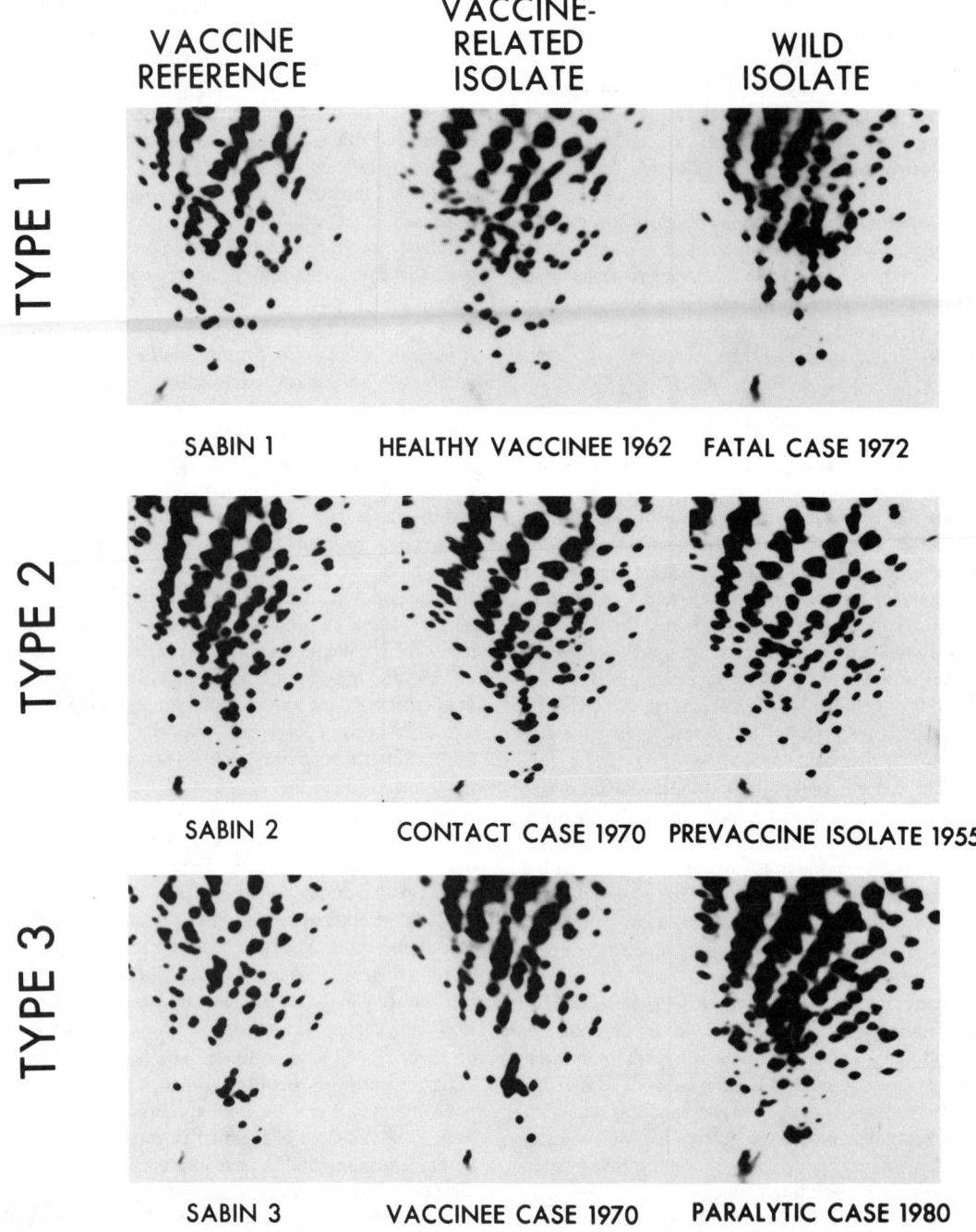

Figure 17–5. Two-dimensional oligonucleotide fingerprint analysis of the virion RNA molecules of closely and distantly related poliovirus isolates. Radiolabeled virion RNA is digested with ribonuclease T_1, which specifically cleaves at guanosine residues (about 23% of the nearly 7500 total base residues in poliovirus RNA). The oligonucleotide fragments are then separated by two-dimensional electrophoresis in polyacrylamide gels and visualized by autoradiography. For each fingerprint, first-dimension separation (*left to right*) is according to oligonucleotide composition and second-dimension separation (*bottom to top*) according to oligonucleotide chain length. The larger, structurally unique, oligonucleotides (representing a random sample of 10%–15% of the total RNA sequences) are distributed into patterns or "fingerprints" highly characteristic of a specific overall RNA sequence.

Vaccine-related isolates (*center column*) have fingerprints that are very similar to the respective oral vaccine reference strains (*left column*). Wild isolates from each of the three serotypes have fingerprints (*right column*) that are entirely distinct from the vaccine-related group, indicating a lack of close genetic relatedness. Because polioviruses undergo rapid evolution during replication in humans, new sequences are constantly being produced in nature. Thus, wild strains of the same serotype from different epidemics have quite distinct fingerprints. Similarities in fingerprints (i.e., >25% of oligonucleotide spots shared) indicate the existence of genetic and epidemiologic relationships between isolates. (Figure courtesy of Olen M. Kew.)

origin for all EV70 isolates with an estimated date of origin of 1966 to 1967, likely in West Africa, two or three years prior to the first known pandemic of this disease.[199, 200]

A recent report of several serial isolates of both coxsackieviruses A4 and A15 from a chronically infected child demonstrated serial base changes in the viral genomes, by oligonucleotide fingerprinting,[201] that appeared to evolve continuously over many months, suggesting that under these conditions, at least, genomic drift may occur. Nevertheless, all of the isolates of each virus were serologically indistinguishable by cross–neutralization.

Both monoclonal antibodies and oligonucleotide fingerprinting are limited by their ability to show similarities and small differences only among relatively closely related viruses. However, neither technique is able to detect any patterns among seemingly unrelated virus isolates. Recently, the technique of genomic nucleic acid sequencing has been applied to the study of wild poliovirus type 1 isolates from different parts of the world.[202] By analyzing the random mutations that occur in the genome of different polioviruses, not only were closely related viruses easily detected, but more distantly related viruses clustered into distinct geographic groupings of endemic circulation. In addition, epidemiologic links were extended beyond those of other techniques. Once a catalogue of wild virus genome sequences is accumulated, it will be possible to identify viral isolates as to their likely geographic origin, and thus provide a useful tool for eradication efforts in the developing world.

PATHOPHYSIOLOGY

Pathology

The classic gross and histologic pathologic picture of paralytic poliomyelitis, first described by Charcot and Joffroy in 1870,[203] includes extensive involvement of the large anterior horn cells of the spinal cord at the level of paralysis, often in the cervical or lumbar areas innervating the limbs. The changes may be severe. In fatal cases there may be involvement of the brainstem motor nuclei (bulbar poliomyelitis) or nerve cells of the motor cortex or thalamus and hypothalamus. In some cases, a variable proportion of cells in several of these areas may be affected simultaneously. The earliest histologic change is vascular engorgement, followed by perivascular infiltration with lymphocytes and to a lesser extent polymorphonuclear neutrophils, plasma cells, and microglia. Cell damage is due to a cytolytic effect of polioviruses. The infected nerve cells swell, undergo satellitosis, and are phagocytosed by mononuclear cells. Under the electron microscope, reduplication of cytoplasmic membranes is the earliest sign of poliovirus infection (based on studies in monkeys), followed by increase in ribosomal granules, and perinuclear rimming by endoplasmic reticulum. With particularly virulent strains that result in extensive infection, presumably analogous to human poliomyelitis, there is loss of all cytoplasmic organelles, excepting mitochondria, and the variable appearance of crystalline arrays of cytoplasmic viruses, nuclear granules, and cytoplasmic vacuoles. Virus destruction results in wallerian degeneration of axons and axon sheaths, followed by atrophy of the area and astrocytic scarring. The clinical result is flaccid paralysis of the limb innervated by the affected nerves, and eventual disuse atrophy of muscles no longer stimulated by the nerve cells.

The pathologic picture of disease with other enteroviruses is more variable and less understood. Based on experience with cases of adult and infantile carditis, severe neonatal disease, and various other syndromes, it appears that enteroviruses may cause gross or microscopic focal infection of cells of various target organs. At the microscopic level it appears that focal infection is followed by infiltration of inflammatory cells, perhaps including polymorphonuclear leukocytes early on but always reverting to mononuclear cell predominance, and in severe cases profound cell damage, necrosis, atrophy, and scarring occur. Crystalline arrays of enteroviruses may be seen, particularly in infected muscles (Figure 17–6). In monkeys paralyzed by polioviruses, in situ hybridization techniques have revealed viral RNA in motor neurons and their processes, and in polymorphonuclear and small neural cells, with less extensive cellular destruction and fewer inflammatory cells after infection with attenuated Sabin type 1 strain than with wild virus.[203a] Other information about the pathologic appearance of specific enterovirus disease syndromes is presented in the context of discussion about them (see below).

Pathogenesis

The upper respiratory tract, particularly the oropharynx, is the portal of entry for most enteroviruses. Virus infects the mucosal tissues of the pharynx and/or the gut, finally entering the bloodstream and gaining access to cells of the reticuloendothelial system and of specific target organs, such as the meninges and spinal cord, myocardium, and skin. Pharyngeal replication and viremia occur during the incubation period, that is, before development of illness.[204] Enteroviruses can generally be recovered from the pharynx during the first week of illness and from the stool for several days (up to 30 or more days) after illness onset.[205] Infection of the lower alimentary tract occurs because enteroviruses can survive both the acid and proteolytic environment of the stomach and the alkaline environment of the duodenum.[206]

At the molecular level, poliovirus particles adsorb to cell surface receptors and, apparently, lose the structural polypeptide VP_4. An eclipse period of variable duration follows, during which time virions are internalized, uncoated, and begin to replicate viral RNA and synthesize RNA-coded proteins on cytoplasmic membranes of host cells. Within two to four hours of infection, the cell's own protein synthesis has been supplanted by virus-coded protein synthesis. The mechanism for host-protein shutoff is slowly being elucidated, at least for poliovirus. Recent work has established that one of the viral proteases induces the cleavage of one of the eukaryotic initiation factors resulting in a translation system incapable of translating normal cellular mRNA.[207] The polioviral mRNA, which has a different "un-capped" end, can still be translated. Virus-coded proteins also directly inhibit synthesis of cellular RNA apparently by inactivation of specific transcription factor TFIIIC.[208] Inhibition of host cell DNA synthesis is presumed to result indirectly from effects of virus infection on host protein synthesis.

Virus protein synthesis occurs entirely within the host cell cytoplasm, as evidenced by the fact that replication is unaffected by cell enucleation. (However, cytologic changes of infection with echoviruses 22 and 23 have been shown to include such late nuclear changes as nucleolar disintegration and loss of intranuclear structure.) Polyribosomes containing mRNA from the virion attach to cell membranes and begin producing protein. Each molecule of viral mRNA contains only one initiation site, all of the individual polypeptides resulting from subsequent proteolysis.

Virus RNA serves not only as a template for protein translation, but also for RNA replication, which begins immediately after infection, peaks at three to four hours, and is usually complete within eight hours. Despite a large effort, the details of RNA replication have not been fully described. Transcription begins at the 3' (poly[A]tail) end of the infecting viral RNA and proceeds in the normal 5'–to-3' direction of synthesis to generate a complementary RNA (cRNA). In the next step, which is dependent on a "host factor," the progeny strand synthesis is primed and a new strand of viral RNA is made. Processing of the viral RNA is completed with the covalent addition of the VP_g protein to the 5' end of the RNA, either as part of the priming step, or subsequently.

Assembly of whole virions occurs on cell membranes in the host cell cytoplasm. As noted, viral RNA codes for one large precursor polypeptide. After the capsid protein region has been cleaved from the remainder of the polyprotein, this capsid protein precursor is further cleaved into three proteins followed by self-association into pentameric structures, five "sets" of three polypeptides. In the case of poliovirus, this results in five sets of VP0, VP1, and VP3. Twelve of the pentameric structures then continue

to assemble in a reversible process into a capsid-like structure which contains no RNA, an empty procapsid. An unstable provirion is formed when viral RNA associates with the procapsid, and, very rapidly, VP0 undergoes proteolytic transformation to VP2 and VP4, resulting in mature infectious virions. These virions are released by cell lysis and may cause infection of other nearby or distant host cells. The molecular biology of picornavirus infections has been reviewed elsewhere.[210]

The polioviruses have the most specific extraintestinal target cell range: the CNS, especially anterior horn cells of the spinal cord, but also dorsal root ganglia, certain brainstem centers, cerebellum, spinal sensory columns, and occasionally the cerebral motor cortex.[2, 4]

A classic question dealing with the pathogenesis of poliovirus is what viral factor is responsible for neurovirulence. Recent progress in this area has been possible using molecular biologic techniques to identify several potential sites conferring neurovirulence of the virus. Most work has used comparisons between the attenuated Sabin oral vaccine viruses and their virulent parents or natural virulent revertents. Studies using artificially generated recombinant viruses between vaccine and wild strains and examination of natural vaccine revertents has demonstrated a multifactorial viral contribution with a change in the 5' noncoding region and another in the VP3 capsid protein being associated with attenuation.[211, 212]

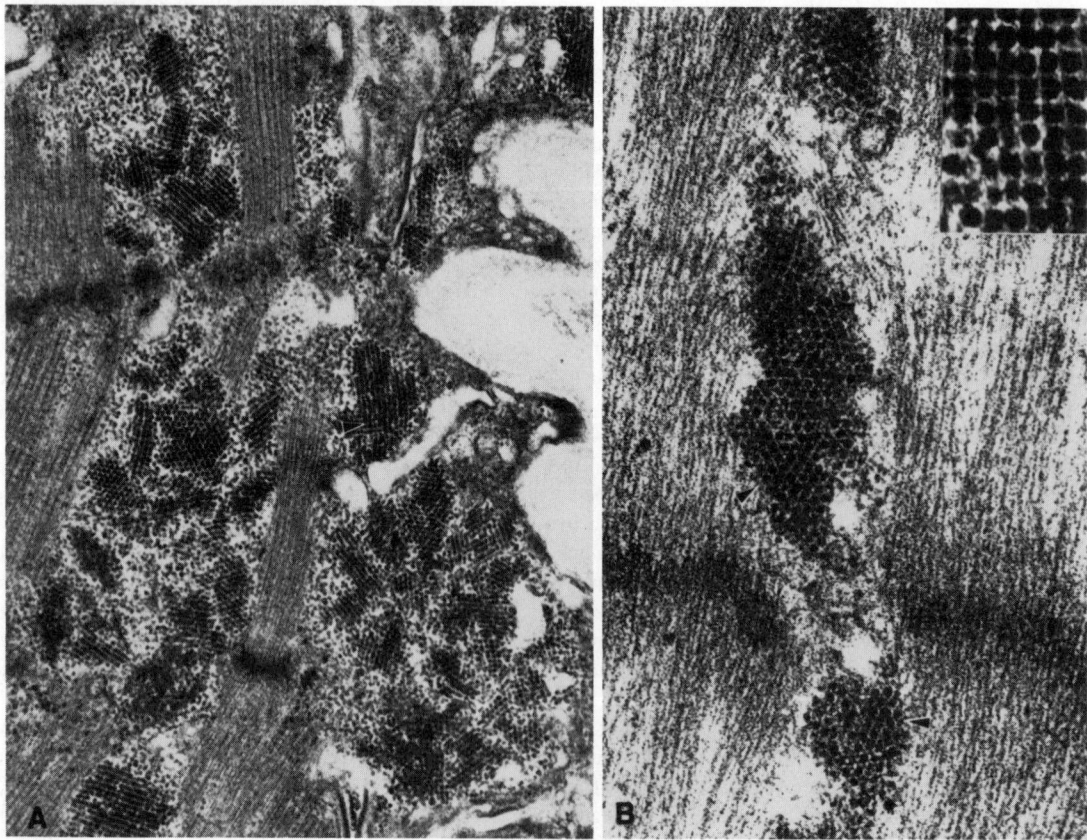

Figure 17–6. Crystalline assay of enteroviruses in human skeletal muscle cells (*arrowheads*) obtained from a patient with polymyositis. The viruses are probably coxsackievirus A9. Original magnification: **A,** × 55,000; **B,** × 100,000; **B inset,** × 245,000. (Photographs courtesy of Joseph L. Melnick.)

Since other changes or differences other than these are seen in these experiments, it is not clear if these two changes are solely sufficient for attenuation. Further refinement of the factors responsible for neurovirulence of poliovirus can be expected in the near future. Coxsackieviruses and echoviruses have more diverse extragastrointestinal organ tropism and can usually or occasionally be recovered from cerebrospinal fluid (CSF), urine, skin ulcers, vesicle fluid, conjunctival scrapings, pericardial fluid, and muscle. In postmortem specimens, they may be found in myocardium, liver, CNS tissues, spleen, and lung. Of uncertain significance is the fact that some enteroviruses have been found to replicate in peripheral blood leukocytes.[213]

Polioviruses initially replicate in the pharynx and gut. After entering the bloodstream, they gain access to the CNS from the bloodstream at the level of the medulla oblongata or from passage at the capillary level to lower motor neuron fibers, traveling subsequently along nerve fibers into the CNS. Polioviruses may also gain direct access to the CNS via exposed nerves in the oropharynx of tonsillectomized children,[4] resulting in a greater risk of bulbar poliomyelitis.[214-219] CNS involvement can lead to permanent damage caused by destruction of anterior horn cells, or to transient loss of function, probably due to local edema associated with inflammation.[4] Polioviruses may infect the myocardium but only rarely cause necrotizing myocarditis.

That circulating antibody may limit the spread of virus from the primary site of replication to susceptible target organs is suggested by experiments with adult mice (usually unaffected by coxsackievirus infection) in which those treated with cyclophosphamide to block the humoral antibody response developed myocarditis and pancreatitis.[220] As discussed later, viremia precedes poliomyelitis, and circulating type-specific antibody can therefore prevent bloodstream spread of virus and resulting poliomyelitis even in the face of alimentary tract poliovirus infection.

Incubation Period

The incubation period is defined as the time between acquisition of infection and onset of disease. For enteroviruses (including polioviruses) this period varies greatly, with a range of one to 35 days.[4, 5, 14, 62, 67, 75, 97, 221-223] Shorter incubation periods (eg, 2–3 days) are typical when upper respiratory symptoms predominate. The shortest incubation periods, reported for AHC due to EV70 or to coxsackievirus A24 variant, are 12 to 30 hours.[4, 224] Other viruses associated with short incubation periods include echovirus 11, one to three days[67]; echovirus 20, mean 2.5 days[222]; coxsackievirus A9, two to 12 days[226]; and echovirus 9, two to 20 days.[74] These incubation periods were mostly documented during human volunteer challenge studies. The incubation period also varies by clinical syndrome,[5] and has been observed to be relatively shorter in children than in adults.

Factors Affecting Severity of Disease

One of the striking features of most enteroviral infections is the wide spectrum of associated clinical manifestations, ranging from asymptomatic infections to rapidly progressive disease and death. Host factors associated with increased clinical severity in animal and human studies include the following: preexisting immunodeficiency, particularly of immunoglobulins, very young and very old age, male sex, chronic undernutrition, corticosteroid treatment, physical exertion, hypoxia, cold, irradiation, tonsillectomy, pregnancy, adrenal-related endocrine changes, and (possibly) hypercholesterolemia.[1-4, 99, 101, 110, 111, 214-219, 221, 225-247]

As noted, age is one of the most important determinants of severity of enterovirus disease, the incidence of some syndromes being greatest in neonates and young infants,[1, 100, 110, 227] and others in older children and adults.[2, 3, 111, 221, 245]

Studies of undernutrition and infection in mice revealed that more severe disease developed when marasmus was induced in (normally resistant) postweanling mice who were subsequently challenged with coxsackievirus B3,[4, 228, 230] apparently because of marked but reversible atrophy of lymphoid tissue. The adverse effect of chronic undernutrition on disease was reversed or blunted by resumption of a normal diet at the time of inoculation of virus[230] or by transfer of immune spleen lymphocytes to the marasmic host.[228]

Although anecdotal reports had suggested an association in prior decades (development of poliomyelitis in Roosevelt after unusually intense physical activity), it was not until the 1940s that physical exertion was identified as a risk factor associated with a higher incidence or a greater extent of paralysis.[242-244] Laboratory studies in the 1940s showed that monkeys experimentally infected with polioviruses and made to swim to exhaustion developed more severe paralysis,[246] and that mice infected with coxsackievirus A9 or B3 and made to swim to exhaustion had higher virus titers in their myocardium or higher mortality rates.[232, 234, 235, 247] There are at least two case reports of patients who purposely underwent vigorous exercise during the early phase of an enteroviral infection and developed severe disease one day to 1 month later; one of these patients died.[233, 248] Hypoxia may be an important mechanism of enhancement of severity associated with physical exertion.[235, 236] Another factor implicated in experimental models is cold stress[101, 238]; infected mice subjected to cold have higher virus titers in target organs and higher mortality rates.

Tonsillectomy-adenoidectomy has been reported as a risk factor for the development of bulbar (vs purely spinal) poliomyelitis,[214-219] possibly because of a corresponding decrease in local secretory antibody (increasing the chances for infection) or exposure of nerve endings. Pregnancy and parturition may also be associated with greater risk of paralysis with poliovirus infection or greater risk of myocarditis with coxsackievirus B infection.[249, 250]

Animal experiments have detected seasonal and circadian rhythmicity associated with variations in clinical severity of enterovirus infections, consistent with an endocrine effect.[231, 240] Finally, in one study, serum cholesterol was implicated as a risk factor, based on increased severity of disease in experimentally hypercholesterolemic mice infected with coxsackievirus B5. Disease severity allegedly resulted from altered leukocyte response.[241]

IMMUNOLOGIC RESPONSE

Alimentary or respiratory tract infection allowing local enterovirus replication is a necessary first step in elicitation of an immunologic response in the host. Exposure to an enterovirus does not always result in infection. Infection may depend on the virus inoculum,[251] the presence of cell receptors, local cross-reacting or type-specific antibody, or other poorly understood conditions in the alimentary (or respiratory) tract. Experiments in mice suggest that there are two distinct resistance mechanisms at the gut level: an intestinal barrier and a virus clearance mechanism,[206] neither of which is present at birth. That receptors are different for different enteroviruses is suggested by the fact that development of human-mouse hybrid cells resistant to poliovirus are still susceptible to other enteroviruses. By using mouse-human cell lines it has been possible to localize a cellular receptor for poliovirus to human chromosome 19.[252] Further work on enteroviral receptors has identified and partially purified the coxsackie B receptor on HeLa cells,[253] and recently monoclonal antibodies to this receptor have been produced,[254] increasing the prospects for further progress in this area.

Alimentary tract infection provokes a secretory immune response with secretory IgA antibody detectable within 2 to 4 weeks.[255–258] IgA-deficient patients have been shown to respond with local IgG and IgM antibody.[256] Secretory IgA (sIgA) appears to be effective in preventing or limiting the alimentary tract excretion of the polioviruses,[255] although such immunity may be only partial or transient. In fact, elicitation of local gut immunity is regarded as a major advantage of orally administered live poliovirus vaccine versus parenterally administered inactivated virus vaccine. Nasopharyngeal or gut sIgA induced by wild or live vaccine poliovirus infection can prevent replication to the extent that a second dose of oral vaccine given too soon afterward may not result in the desired infection.[255] Recent reports suggest that inactivated poliovaccines may also elicit measurable secretory antibody,[259, 260] including neutralizing antibody to VP1, VP2, and VP3, although the VP3 response may be incomplete.[260a]

Humoral immunity to enteroviruses is mediated by circulating IgG and IgM. IgM antibody to a specific enterovirus type appears shortly after initial infection and persists for 6 to 8 weeks.[226, 258, 261] As is the case with most virus infections, IgG appears later and persists longer, undoubtedly for years after infection. Like infection with influenza viruses, flaviviruses (eg, dengue), and other groups of related viruses with apparent antigenic overlap, reinfection with enteroviruses (with the same or a related type) may provoke a "secondary-type" (anamnestic) serologic response, with prompt rises of IgG to high titers often associated with concurrent titer rises to other related enteroviruses, that is, a heterotypic response.[4, 262] Type-specific neutralizing antibody appears within several days of onset of infection and is long-lasting. CF antibody is variable and transient, being type-specific only in association with a first enterovirus infection, and enterovirus group-specific with subsequent infections with different types. Hemagglutination-inhibiting (HI) antibodies preventing agglutination of virus–adsorbed human blood group O erythrocytes are more persistent, but can only be detected with those virus types that hemagglutinate: all or some strains of coxsackieviruses A20, A21, A24; B1, B3, B5 and B6; echoviruses 3, 6, 7, 11, 12, 13, 19, 20, 21, 24, 25, 29, 30 and 33.

Circulating antibody is crucial in preventing hematogenous spread of virus to target organs, for example, of poliovirus to the CNS. Circulating antibody to polioviruses is thus considered to prevent paralytic disease with the virus type against which antibody is directed, although it does not prevent virus replication in the gut. There is evidence that production of local antibody within the CNS may occur, although serum antibody may also cross the blood-brain barrier in the presence of meningeal irritation.[4, 255, 263]

The presence of neutralizing serum antibody against the polioviruses would ideally imply lifelong immunity.[4] However, some persons without detectable antibody may also be immune, as has been demonstrated by elicitation of a secondary-type serum antibody response upon rechallenge with live poliovirus vaccine.[264] Thus, failure to detect neutralizing antibody in serum cannot be accepted as conclusive evidence for susceptibility. Infection with any serotype of poliovirus, whether or not associated with disease, thus probably induced lifelong type–specific immunity.[265]

The nature of immunity to the NPEVs is not as well established as that of the polioviruses.[266] Infection with NPEVs may not produce immunity in all cases.[251] Although such occurrences could be attributed to within-type strain differences of enteroviruses causing sequential infections, persons with preexisting and, presumably, type-specific serum neutralizing antibody to a challenge virus may also become reinfected.[67, 84, 266] Some studies have shown that persons with higher preexisting titers are less likely to become reinfected or to demonstrate titer rises.[266, 267] Household studies in the New York Virus Watch program indicated that reinfection rates among persons thought to be immune (on the basis of having type-specific serum antibody) were higher for coxsackieviruses than for echoviruses, with an estimated 50% coxsackievirus reinfection rate among children under 10 years old, 10% in teens and adults, or about 25% overall.[90]

Transplacentally acquired maternal IgG antibody to the polioviruses and certain NPEVs[4, 59, 268] may not protect the infant against gut colonization (infection) or illness,[99, 268] but epidemiologic evidence suggests that protection against serious complications indeed occurs. Unfortunately, maternal IgG may hinder active immunization by vaccine, as may breast-feeding. On the other hand, breast-feeding appears to correlate with protection from postnatal enterovirus infection. The postneonatal incidence of poliomyelitis and infection with most other NPEVs is low and begins to increase in infants over 6 months of age, at about the same time that passively acquired antibody has waned to low or undetectable levels. Studies of human gamma globulin prophylaxis during the 1950s suggested that passive serum antibody could prevent or modify poliomyelitis.[269] The material used was of very high titer[270] and thus likely not comparable to transplacentally acquired IgG from mothers today, especially in the industrialized world, where vaccine–induced maternal immunity is typical. Postexposure prophylaxis with gamma globulin, successful with rabies, hepatitis, varicella, and some other viral diseases, may be of little practical value for poliovirus infection since viremia and spread to the CNS occurs early in the course of infection.

CLINICAL CHARACTERISTICS AND SYNDROMES
General Considerations

The diverse clinical manifestations of enterovirus infections reflect infecting serotype or strain, infecting dose, virulence, tissue tropism, age, sex, portal of entry, level of physical activity of the host, and other factors.

In evaluating reported enterovirus-associated syndromes, it is important to establish criteria for disease causality so that the clinician may be aided in diagnosis, and the investigator in determining the validity of claims of disease causality. Kilbourne in

1952 proposed the following criteria for associating enteroviruses with disease:[271]

- Isolation of the virus from a clinically involved parenteral tissue source (eg, CSF from a patient with meningitis)
- Recovery of the virus from an alimentary tract specimen and/or concomitant type-specific seroconversion
- Disease distinct enough to be recognized by the clinician and (preferably) not associated with other pathogens (eg, pleurodynia)
- Absence of other pathogens known to cause the same syndrome (eg, bacterial or fungal agents in cases of meningitis)
- Disease reproducible in man by the agent in question, or the occurrence of similar disease associated with the agent in different locations and at different times
- Agent present in cases, but not in appropriately matched controls (epidemiologic association)

Lerner et al later established criteria for determining the strength of association between viral infection and myocarditis,[226] a system which, with necessary modification, may be useful for determining associations between enteroviruses and disease syndromes in general:

High-order association. Virus isolated from the myocardium, endocardium, or pericardial fluid; or type-specific viral antigen demonstrated in any of these tissues (eg, by immunofluorescent staining).

Moderate-order association. Virus isolated from an alimentary tract source (pharynx or stool), and concomitant fourfold or greater rise in specific antibody (neutralizing, HI, or CF); or isolation from the alimentary tract, associated with a single specific IgM titer greater than or equal to 1:32 (neutralizing or HI). A moderate-order association becomes a high-order association if the agent is associated with disease in cases but not controls, or if the agent produces similar disease in mice.

Low-order association. Virus isolated from the alimentary tract,

or a fourfold or greater rise in specific antibody (neutralizing, HI, or CF), or specific IgM titer greater than or equal to 1:32 (neutralizing or HI). A low-order association becomes a moderate-order association if the agent is associated with disease in cases but not controls, or if the agent produces similar disease in mice.

Excluding asymptomatic cases and mild or nonspecific illnesses, the following clinical syndromes are typically associated with the various enterovirus groups: (1) polioviruses: paralytic and nonparalytic poliomyelitis; (2) coxsackie A viruses: enanthemas (eg, herpangina), exanthemas (eg, hand-foot-and-mouth disease), and respiratory tract illnesses; (3) coxsackie B viruses: carditis, pleurodynia, neonatal disease, aseptic meningitis–encephalitis; (4) echoviruses: aseptic meningitis–encephalitis, febrile illness with or without rash, and neonatal disease; and (5) enteroviruses 68 to 71: distinct for each virus.

The various clinical syndromes associated with the four major enterovirus groups are presented in Table 17–4. As can be seen, most of these syndromes are associated with viruses of all or most of the enterovirus groups. However, some virus-syndrome associations are relatively distinct as pleurodynia–coxsackie B viruses, herpangina–coxsackie A viruses, and others. Coxsackie B viruses have the most varied reported clinical spectrum. It should be noted here that neither Table 17–4 nor the clinical summaries (see later) associating diseases with various enterovirus types purport to be either exhaustive or complete. The reported associations between enterovirus types and specific syndromes are those familiar to the authors and cited in the medical literature available to them. Undoubtedly, some existing associations have not been reported, and others reported overlooked. On the other hand, some reported associations may be coincidental rather than causal. Such associations of disease syndromes with specific viruses should therefore be considered as guidelines for help in solving clinical and epidemiologic problems, rather than as definitive of disease causality.

Viruses such as coxsackievirus A9, echovirus 9, the coxsackie B viruses, and many others cause infections of different organ systems and of variable severity. This may be due to one or more of the following factors: (1) multiple tissue tropisms; (2) ease of laboratory identification (more virus identifications from the wide

Table 17–4

Summary of Clinical Syndromes Associated with Major Enterovirus Groups*

Syndrome	Polioviruses	Coxsackie A	Coxsackie B	Echoviruses
Paralytic disease	+	+	+	+
Encephalitis–meningitis	+	+	+	+
Carditis	+	+	+	+
Neonatal disease	−	−	+	+
Pleurodynia	−	−	+	−
Herpangina	−	+	−	−
Rash disease	−	+	+	+
Acute hemorrhagic conjunctivitis (AHC)†	−	+	−	−
Respiratory infections	+	+	+	+
Undifferentiated fever	+	+	+	+
Diabetes/pancreatitis	−	−	+	−
Orchitis	−	−	+	−
Disease in immunodeficient patients	+	+	−	+

*As reported in the literature, proven, or frequently reported associations.
†Only coxsackievirus A24 variant and enterovirus type 70 are associated with AHC.

range of specimens submitted); and (3) greater prevalence of the virus (a virus that is more prevalent is more likely to be associated with uncommonly occurring syndromes than would be a less prevalent virus). In support of the latter hypothesis, 10 years of United States surveillance based on isolations reported to CDC by state health department laboratories revealed that the most frequently reported enteroviruses were those thought to exhibit the broadest clinical spectrum.[87] On the other hand, the relative infrequency of reported coxsackievirus A disease in the same surveillance system is probably due largely to the absence of suckling mice for isolation in many laboratories, resulting in an apparently "narrower" disease spectrum for each coxsackievirus A type. In laboratories using suckling mice for virus isolation, coxsackie A viruses are found with greater frequency.[272, 273]

Asymptomatic Infections

A striking feature of most enteroviruses is the high rate of asymptomatic infection. Best documented in this regard are the polioviruses, for which subclinical infection is the overwhelming rule.[4, 5, 245, 265] As noted, age is an important determinant of whether or not infection will be clinically apparent.[162, 274] Within each of the major enterovirus groups, a wide range of asymptomatic infection rates may be observed; for example, approximately 15% for echovirus 9 versus 67% for echovirus 11.[251, 275] As a rule of thumb, asymptomatic infection is apparently most common for the polioviruses (90%–95%), followed by the echoviruses and coxsackieviruses (about 50%).[84]

Mixed Infections

Concurrent infection with two or more enteroviruses has been observed,[4, 102, 118, 271, 276, 277] and may be more common than is generally appreciated, though it can be difficult to document by standard techniques for isolation and identification. Infection with one enterovirus may interfere with replication of the second, perhaps because of interferon production, competition for receptor sites, or competition for the host cell's replicative machinery. Such an interference phenomenon has been invoked as a possible explanation for the lower efficacy of live poliovirus vaccine in developing countries,[278–280] although other studies suggested such interference cannot be implicated.[278–281] Mixed enterovirus infections are observed more frequently in tropical climates and in populations of lower socioeconomic status.

SPECIFIC CLINICAL SYNDROMES

Poliomyelitis

The public health significance of poliomyelitis is underscored by the prodigious work undertaken by outstanding scientists over a period of many decades. Because of space limitations, it is not possible to review the volumes of extant polio data. The interested reader is referred to excellent reviews which have appeared since the late 1940s.[2, 3, 245, 282–285] Those endeavors that directly led to vaccine development are highlighted later in the chapter.

Much of the history of poliomyelitis has been discussed earlier in the chapter, including evidence for its existence in ancient times, recognition as a distinct clinical entity by European physicians in the late 1700s and early 1800s,[19–21] and the recognition of epidemics in the late 1800s.[23, 286] In 1891, Medin described a major Swedish epidemic[286] followed in 1896 by Caverly's classic description of the Vermont epidemic of 1894; the world's largest recognized epidemic up to that time, with 132 cases.[22] Caverly also advanced the critical concept that paralytic poliomyelitis is a comparatively rare complication of a common infection.[22] In 1905, the "incubation period" of poliomyelitis, the degree of contagiousness, and the existence of subclinical cases were recognized by Wickman.[287] The next significant event in the history of poliomyelitis was the discovery in 1908 that the disease was caused by a transmissible agent,[26] which heralded the modern era of poliovirus research culminating in the first successful polio vaccine 46 years later, in 1954. The classic comprehensive clinical description of poliomyelitis was published in 1912.[288]

Descriptive terms for paralytic poliomyelitis were not generally in use before the middle 1800s. The term "infantile paralysis" appears to have been introduced at about that time, while "acute anterior poliomyelitis" is said to have been used first by Erb in 1875.[289] Poliomyelitis has also been called Heine-Medin disease. Today, confusing terms are used by lay and medical persons alike to describe poliovirus infections, including the ambiguous term "polio," which can refer to the virus itself, to infections that do not result in paralysis, to paralytic infections, to bulbar paralytic–encephalitis infections, and to post–illness states of neurologic impairment. In this text we use the term "polio" as an adjective or combining form to specify the causative agent, the poliovirus. The term "poliomyelitis" refers to clinically apparent poliovirus infection of the anterior horn cells; "paralytic poliomyelitis" specifies permanent nerve damage, whereas "nonparalytic poliomyelitis" describes cases of full recovery. Nonparalytic poliovirus infections without even transient evidence of anterior horn cell involvement are referred to simply as poliovirus infections, or are described by prominent clinical features, for example, polioencephalitis.

Although the incidence of poliomyelitis has decreased markedly in the United States since the early 1960s, an annual average of about 12 cases are still recorded, of which approximately seven are associated with live virus vaccines.[290, 291] No indigenous wild viruses have been detected in the United States since 1979.[291] In the developing world, poliomyelitis is still a major problem, particularly for countries that have begun economic transitions, as is described later in discussing immunization policy.

The incubation period of poliomyelitis is commonly six to 20 days, with a range of three to 35 days.[2, 184, 245, 292] Polioviruses 1, 2, and 3 are acquired either by the fecal–oral route or from respiratory secretions of an infected person. Infection results in one of four outcomes[2, 5, 245]:

1. *Inapparent infection* (90%–95%): Virus may be recovered from the throat or stool, but the patient is asymptomatic.
2. *"Abortive illness"* (4%–8%): Also known as "minor illness." Three basic syndromes associated with this form of poliovirus infection include upper respiratory tract infection, gastroenteritis, and influenzalike illness.
3. *Nonparalytic poliomyelitis* (1%–2%): The patient may have prodromal illness compatible with abortive illness as described above, followed by invasion of the CNS and illness similar to aseptic meningitis, often accompanied by back pain and muscle spasms.

Figure 17–7. A young Marshallese child with bilateral leg braces. A devastating epidemic struck the Marshall Islands in 1963.[292] A high percentage of children were permanently paralyzed. This photograph was taken in 1967, about one year after the epidemic. (Figure courtesy of Robin Smith.)

4. *Paralytic poliomyelitis–polioencephalitis* (0.1%–2%): Disease usually consists of a prodromal illness (similar to the abortive illness described above), which may be biphasic (especially in children); meningeal irritation; and eventual onset of asymmetric flaccid paralysis (involvement of the whole muscle), or paresis (involvement of only some muscle groups) due to spinal and/or bulbar damage. Common constitutional symptoms include sore throat, rhinorrhea, vomiting, diarrhea, headache and malaise. Stiff neck may develop and pleocytosis is common, occurring in up to 90% of cases. Early in the course of spinal paralytic poliomyelitis older patients may complain of pain or muscle cramping in one or more limbs, followed by onset of weakness over the ensuing 48 hours. Bulbar paralysis may involve any combination of cranial nerves and/or the medullary respiratory center. Paralytic poliomyelitis is divided into three types on the basis of the site of involvement: spinal, bulbar, and bulbospinal. In addition, polioencephalitis leads to paralysis in some, but not all, cases. Bulbar paralysis without limb involvement is more common in children than in adults. Adults with bulbar involvement generally have limb paralysis as well. The likelihood that poliovirus infection will result in paralysis is increased by the following factors: extremes of age, "triple seronegativity" (absence of serum antibodies to all three poliovirus types), pregnancy, tonsillectomy, recent intramuscular (IM) inoculation, other trauma, fatigue, and possibly a high infecting dose of virus.

A recent set of criteria for retrospectively diagnosing poliomyelitis has been published.[293] These include a history of acute

onset, absence of progression after initial paralysis, normal sensation, muscle weakness and atrophy, absent or diminished deep tendon reflexes, and shortened limb or diminished growth in both limbs. In some studies about 3% of patients had involvement of all four limbs, 30% had involvement of both legs, 26% had involvement of only one limb (usually a leg), and the remainder had mixed upper and lower limb involvement.[2, 295, 296] Cases with lower limb paralysis constitute the majority of patients seen in most physical therapy clinics.

Older persons and infants are generally most severely paralyzed. Previous tonsillectomy may predispose to bulbar involvement,[214–219] and recent inoculation or trauma may predispose to paralysis in the traumatized limb.[2, 297–303] Physical exertion following the onset of CNS signs or symptoms may increase the severity of CNS involvement.[242–244]

Polioviruses have been isolated from the stool as early as 19 days before onset of illness, and as late as 3 months afterward. The mean duration of virus excretion is approximately 5 weeks after onset of illness. The mean duration of excretion following immunization with oral poliovirus vaccine (OPV) may also be about 5 weeks, beginning roughly two days after vaccination, an important consideration when evaluating laboratory isolations of polioviruses from young infants, many of whom will have recently received trivalent oral polio vaccine (TOPV) as part of the routine well-baby visit.

A paralyzed patient may die, recover completely, or have any degree of residual neurologic deficit. Because, historically, the presence of a residual deficit 60 days after onset was deemed a useful factor to distinguish disease caused by polioviruses from that caused by NPEVs, it has become a criterion of the US Public Health Service for accepting as valid a reported case of paralytic poliomyelitis.[85] A 13-year-review of the 203 cases officially reported in the United States between 1969 and 1981 revealed that residual paralysis was minor in 11% and significant or severe in 79%. Ten percent of cases were fatal.[304] In 1989, CDC outlined a new classification system for cases of paralytic poliomyelitis according to epidemic criteria (endemic, epidemic, imported or occurring in immunodeficient persons) and to recent prior OPV exposure.[304a]

In earlier times, poliomyelitis was treated with bleeding, blistering, purges, and electric shock. In modern times, treatment is essentially supportive. Bed rest is encouraged, with limitation of physical exertion during the acute phase of illness. Patients with paralysis may benefit from hot packs or analgesics to relieve pain. Mechanical ventilation may be necessary. Electrical stimulation of muscles may also be beneficial.[2] Of real importance is prevention and treatment of complications, such as bacterial infections (pneumonia or urinary tract infection), myocarditis or cardiac failure, or respiratory failure due to bulbar paralysis. Patients with residual paralysis may require physical rehabilitation, including physical therapy, bracing (Figure 17–7), or corrective surgery. A multidisciplinary team approach is optimal, provided there is overall coordination of patient care by a primary physician who assumes responsibility for developing a close ongoing relationship with the patient.

Hospitalized patients with poliomyelitis or uncomplicated poliovirus infection should be placed in standard enteric isolation as defined by the US Department of Health and Human Services publication, *Guideline for Isolation Precautions in Hospitals.*[305]

Because of the fear that still surrounds poliomyelitis, hospital staff may need to be educated about the minimal risks of acquisition of poliovirus infection and subsequent poliomyelitis. Routine se-rologic screening of hospital personnel is not necessary, except in those who perform laboratory work with enteroviruses or who work in a diagnostic virology laboratory (see below).

Poliomyelitis: Clinical and Epidemiological Summary

	References

FIRST DESCRIPTION: Badham (1834) — 20
OCCURRENCE: Worldwide; occurs as peri-odic outbreaks in developing countries with "pockets" of susceptibles; mostly as sporadic cases in industrialized countries and other areas with effective vaccination programs

ASSOCIATED AGENTS:
Occurrence
  Commonly associated Polioviruses 1–3
Etiologic Role Proven   Polioviruses 1–3

AGE DISTRIBUTION:
Usual Age Range   In endemic areas over 90% under 4–5 yr; average age of patients in-creases with improvement in hygienic and so-cioeconomic conditions — 2
Clinical Differences by Age: Yes: adults are considered by many more likely to be severely affected, paralyzed — 284

SEX DISTRIBUTION: Males > females

CLINICAL:
Signs/Symptoms
Common
Prodrome: common, may be biphasic (espe-cially children); anorexia, headache, sore throat, vomiting, irritability; onset abrupt in chil-dren, gradual in adults; prodrome precedes major illness by 1–7 d (average 3–4 d; shorter in younger patients) — 2, 3, 245, 284

Paralytic disease: preceding symptoms include irritability, restlessness, emotional lability, hy-peresthesia, stiffness, pain, especially of the back, neck, and limbs (pain is often the first symptom in adults), weakness or flaccid asymmetric paralysis, affecting one or more limbs (especially lower limbs) and occasionally cranial nerves or brainstem centers
Less Common
Polioencephalitis

Clinical Course   Paralysis develops over 24–48 h, rarely progresses after deferves-cence. Recovery period, as percent of total re-covery a patient will ever have: 60% by 3 mo, 80% by 6 mo, 100% by 2 yr

Complications
  Common
  Residual paralysis: minor, significant, or severe
  Uncommon
  Death: 5% overall; 2.5% in children; 30% in adults; 25%–75% with bulbar paralysis

  Myocarditis, pulmonary edema

  Respiratory failure (due to bulbar paralysis), requiring mechanical ventilation

  Bacterial infection (especially pulmonary or urinary tract)

DIAGNOSIS
Differential Diagnosis
Nonparalytic: Nonpolio enterovirus (NPEV) aseptic meningitis–meningoencephalitis, mumps, partially treated bacterial meningitis, tuberculous (TB) meningitis, lymphocytic cho-riomeningitis (LCM), arboviral encephalitis, pertussis encephalopathy, leptospirosis, trichi-nella meningitis, etc.

Paralytic: Guillain-Barré syndrome, polyneuri-tis, heavy metal poisoning, postinfectious en-cephalitis, trichinosis, cerebrovascular accident, syphilis, multiple sclerosis, pseudobul-bar palsy, spinal epidural abscess, spinal cord tumor, etc.

Key to Clinical Recognition   Fever and asym-metric flaccid paralysis, especially in an un-vaccinated child or adult

Specimens for Viral Isolation   Stool, throat, CSF is rarely positive

LABORATORY FINDINGS:
Peripheral WBC count: normal or slightly ele-vated

CSF: may be completely normal. WBC pleocy-tosis generally found (25–500, occasionally 1000–2000 cells/μL); may be neutrophil pre-dominance early, especially with nonparalytic poliomyelitis. Protein normal or slightly ele-vated (usually < 100 mg/dL). Glucose usually $\geq$ 50% serum glucose.

(Continued.)

Poliomyelitis: Clinical and Epidemiological Summary *(cont.)*

PATIENT MANAGEMENT:
Nonparalytic disease: Bed rest, decreased physical exertion

  Supportive: relief of fever, headache, back pain, muscle spasm

Paralytic disease: Bed rest, decreased physical exertion, "hot packs" to help relieve muscle pain; analgesics; electrical stimulation of muscles

  Supportive treatment and treatment of complications: Physical rehabilitation, including bracing, corrective surgery, etc.

The Postpolio Syndrome

The so-called postpolio syndrome is a newly appreciated complication of poliomyelitis that is probably of multiple etiologies. The hallmark of the syndrome, which may affect as many as 20% to 80% of the hundreds of thousands of surviving poliomyelitis victims in the United States, is exacerbation of muscle disability years after acute illness and stabilization of neuromuscular deficit. Following acute poliomyelitis, it usually takes a matter of months for the lower motor neuron deficit and denervation-associated flaccid paralysis to stabilize. Thereafter, the patient normally achieves a plateau and can, with optimal treatment, exercise regimens, orthotic appliances, etc, maintain residual muscle function for years or decades. The postpolio syndrome is often noted about 30 to 40 years after acute poliomyelitis, although the interval is variable. It is believed by some that men are as much as 10 times more likely to be affected than women. Other risk factors appear to include severity of initial deficit, and poliomyelitis onset early in childhood. Cardinal symptoms include those that reflect diminished muscle capacity—weakness, fatigue, exercise intolerance, and muscle and joint pain. Fasciculations may be noted. Some patients note weight gain, probably as a result of decreased physical activity. In severely affected patients, falls, bone demineralization, and fractures may occur. Patients with marked involvement of respiratory muscles may experience dyspnea, increased pulmonary infections, and cognitive and sleep disturbances. Studies by some investigators have suggested that postpolio syndrome is of at least two distinctive types, reflecting different etiologies.[306-311] The first group of patients, which is the largest group and which includes many persons who were severely affected by their initial bout of poliomyelitis, is characterized by deterioration in the same muscles involved initially, conceivably as a result of the normal loss of motor neurons with age, exacerbated by chronic overexertion of remaining muscles. The second group of patients, apparently much smaller than the first, includes persons who generally had less severe involvement initially, but who have then gone on to experience later deterioration in muscles not thought to have been involved initially, a syndrome also referred to as "late progressive postpolio muscular atrophy." Studies of these patients have suggested an active process with perimysial and perivascular lymphocytic infiltration of muscles, nonspecific immunologic abnormalities, and signs of active denervation of group atro-

phy.[307, 312, 313] In both groups of patients, the prognosis is guardedly optimistic, with restabilization of disease the rule. Other conditions, like amyotrophic lateral sclerosis, must be ruled out. Treatment is nonspecific, symptomatic, and preventive. Although patients may benefit from aerobic training programs, extreme physical exertion must be avoided, and weight control is also critical, especially for persons with leg involvement. New orthotic appliances may be necessary as well.

Paralysis Caused by Nonpolio Enteroviruses

Clinical syndromes indistinguishable from poliomyelitis may result from infection with many enteroviruses, a fact that is not well appreciated because NPEV-associated paralysis is much less common. When confronted with a case of paralytic disease in a country with a high poliovirus immunization rate, the physician must consider both polioviruses and NPEV-associated paralysis and take appropriate steps to make the diagnosis, including obtaining proper specimens (discussed in a later section) for isolation in cell culture and suckling mice.

As indicated in the accompanying summary, many enteroviruses have been associated with paralysis, some no doubt based on questionable interpretations. Nevertheless, a number of NPEVs can cause paralysis, and it is probable that others for which an association has not yet been established may also be causes of paralytic disease. Cases are sporadic and sufficiently rare to preclude accurate estimates of incidence. Although unproven, the possibility that EV70 (discussed in the section on conjunctivitis, below) may be associated with paralysis is of great concern, because the efficient transmission of this virus has resulted in large epidemics and even pandemics. It appears probable that enterovirus type 71 causes poliomyelitis-like disease with a relatively high frequency.[314-316] In one epidemic,[314] a large-scale paralysis outbreak was documented.

The clinical picture is similar to that of poliomyelitis. After a nonspecific prodromal course of fever and constitutional symptoms lasting one to two days, there is onset of flaccid paralysis progressing over another one to two days. Unlike poliomyelitis, there is rarely bulbar involvement, and the prognosis is better than in poliomyelitis since most patients recover completely. Management of patients is symptomatic, with an emphasis on avoidance of physical exertion, usually including strict bed rest.

Paralytic Disease (Nonpolio Enteroviruses, NPEVs): Clinical and Epidemiological Summary

	References		References
FIRST DESCRIPTION: Coxsackieviruses A and B first isolated from patients thought to have paralytic poliomyelitis	30, 32, 317	Lower extremity involvement in 71% (vs 94% for poliomyelitis in one United States study)	
Coxsackievirus A7 in USSR, 1952 (later in Scotland), alleged to be "poliovirus type 4"	132, 318	Mild paresis: echoviruses 4, 6, 9; moderate to severe paresis: echovirus 11	
OCCURRENCE: Paralysis associated with NPEVs tends to occur as rare sporadic cases, although the epidemic occurrence of enterovirus (EV) 71–associated paralysis was reported from Bulgaria in 1975. Coxsackievirus A7 has been shown to cause flaccid paralysis in experimental inoculation of rhesus monkeys. Possible association with epidemic acute hemorrhagic conjunctivitis (EV70)	319, 320	Spinal paralysis: coxsackieviruses A7, 9; B2–5	
		Less Common Bulbar involvement (less common with NPEVs than polioviruses)	
		Greater severity with coxsackievirus A7, especially in children < 1 year old	
ASSOCIATED AGENTS: *Occurrence*		Spastic paralysis (upper motor neuron)	
Commonly associated: Echoviruses 3, 4, 6, 9, 11; coxsackieviruses B2–5; coxsackievirus A7; EV71	1, 4, 314–316, 319, 321–328	*Clinical Course* Complete recovery in nearly 100% of cases, though residual deficit after 60 d occasionally reported	275, 332
Less commonly associated: Echoviruses 1, 2, 7, 13, 16, 18, 19, 20, 30; coxsackieviruses B1, 6; coxsackieviruses A2, 4, 7, 8, 9, 10, 16		*Complications* Common None	
Etiologic Role Proven Echoviruses 2, 4, 6, 9, 11; coxsackieviruses A4, 7, 9; EV71	1, 314–316, 319, 327, 329–341	Uncommon Death (coxsackievirus A7)	1
AGE DISTRIBUTION: *Usual Age Range* Mostly children < 12 years (50% are 5–9 yr)	332, 333	DIAGNOSIS: *Differential Diagnosis* Poliomyelitis (see differential diagnosis of poliomyelitis); botulism	
Clinical Differences by Age? May be more severe at extremes of age	132	*Key to Clinical Recognition* Localized paralytic disease often following prodromal illness, especially during enterovirus outbreak	
SEX DISTRIBUTION: M/F ratio 1.8:1 in one study of coxsackievirus A7	132	*Specimens for Viral Isolation* (*isolation establishes etiologic role) *CSF (early specimens more likely to yield virus); stool; throat	
CLINICAL: *Signs/Symptoms* Common		LABORATORY FINDINGS: Generally compatible with viral CNS infection—see Aseptic Meningitis, below	
Prodromal illness may or may not be biphasic: fever, malaise, headache, nausea, abdominal pain followed by major illness 1–2 d later	5, 87, 132, 275, 304, 322, 323, 328, 332, 334, 335	PATIENT MANAGEMENT: Bed rest; decreased physical exertion; supportive care (see Poliomyelitis)	
Poliomyelitislike syndrome: flaccid paralysis (lower motor neuron), generally less severe than that due to polioviruses, maximum paralysis within 48–72 h			

Aseptic Meningitis–Encephalitis

Perhaps the best-known syndrome associated with NPEV infection is aseptic meningitis (AM), outbreaks of which occur every year (during the summer and fall) in developed countries with temperate climates.[336] In fact, there is probably no enterovirus type for which AM is the most common manifestation of infection: community or institutional AM outbreaks are actually outbreaks of enteroviral infections in which most cases are associated with different syndromes or are asymptomatic, nonspecific, or mild. Outbreaks of AM indicate widespread community transmission of one or more enteroviruses, underscoring the need to maintain a high index of suspicion for other syndromes associated with the same enteroviruses. AM outbreaks may be recognized in camps, schools, and occasionally on school sports teams, probably reflecting close personal contact of large numbers of persons, sometimes combined with improper sanitary conditions or practices. Most cases of AM are diagnosed in school-age children or in young infants and toddlers. Knowledge of the seasonal pattern of enteroviruses which may be highly predictable in some locales, and of the clinical picture is crucial to establishing the diagnosis.

In the older child and adult, diagnosis of AM is usually straightforward: a prodrome of two to three days of nonspecific febrile illness is typically followed by headache, nausea and vomiting, irritability, and meningeal signs. In the infant, the clinical picture is not so pronounced. Meningeal signs may not be present, but the infant may become irritable, disinterested in feeding, and, in more severe cases, floppy, hypotonic, pale, and grunting. Depending on the virus causing the illness (and seen especially with echovirus infection), a rash may be present. The diagnosis should be suspected on clinical-epidemiologic grounds and must be investigated by lumbar puncture. The diagnosis can then be confirmed by ruling out bacterial, mycobacterial, fungal, and protozoal organisms and by culturing the virus from the CSF or stool. Although many NPEVs can be isolated with relative ease from the CSF, others causing AM are only rarely recovered from this source. Before culture results are available, the diagnosis is suggested by consideration of the clinical picture and examination of the CSF, which usually reveals a moderate pleocytosis, normal or slightly elevated protein, and normal glucose. Pleocytosis is typically mononuclear; a left shift may be present early in illness, but usually changes rapidly to mononuclear cell predominance. Persistence of a left shift in cells of the CSF is not typical of enterovirus aseptic meningitis and should raise suspicion of untreated or partially treated bacterial meningitis.

Treatment is supportive and should probably include restricting physical activity. In older children and adults the prognosis is good with complete resolution following a recovery phase, which may be prolonged. The prognosis in infants, especially neonates, may be more guarded. Studies[337, 339, 340] have suggested that some infants who survive may be at risk of brain damage or motor damage that may not become apparent until the child's general development has progressed to the point where such deficits are recognizable—as long as 5 years later, when the child begins school. Other studies have suggested an excellent prognosis.[340, 341] Although the frequency and extent of neurologic damage following infantile enteroviral aseptic meningitis is not accurately known, the fact that even a minority of such children can have permanent problems argues for caution in counseling parents.

Since enteroviral encephalitis is regarded as part of the spectrum of AM, it will not be discussed separately. In many cases the decision to call an enterovirus infection of the CNS AM or encephalitis is somewhat arbitrary, based on those signs and symptoms the physician feels are most important. Oftentimes, evidence of both is present. Encephalitis is likely to be diagnosed when there are changes in mental status or evidence of cerebral involvement, including somnolence, lethargy, seizures, etc. In general, however, there is a tendency for physicians to diagnose AM in children, and encephalitis in adults. The differential diagnosis of enteroviral encephalitis is lengthy; it is particularly important to rule out HSV encephalitis, since treatment is available. The course is relatively benign in the vast majority of adult cases, but instances of residual neurologic damage and death have been reported.

Aseptic Meningitis: Clinical and Epidemiological Summary

	References		References
FIRST DESCRIPTION: Wallgren (1925)	358	*Etiologic Role Proven* Echoviruses 1, 3, 7, 9, 11, 11', 19, 22, 24, 27, 30, 31, 33; coxsackieviruses A1, 2, 4–7, 9, 10, 14, 16, 22, 24; coxsackieviruses B3, 5; EV71	1, 98, 106, 321, 362, 364–367
OCCURRENCE: Aseptic meningitis occurs worldwide both in epidemics (echoviruses 3, 4, 6, 9, 11, 16, 30; coxsackieviruses A7, 9; B5) and as sporadic cases	1, 95, 359		
		AGE DISTRIBUTION:	
		Usual Age Range Peak generally 5–15 yr, although cases and outbreaks among infants have been reported	95, 111, 334, 368
ASSOCIATED AGENTS: *Occurrence* Commonly associated Echoviruses 3, 4, 6, 7, 9, 11 11'; coxsackievirus A9; coxsackieviruses B1–5; enterovirus 71 (EV71); polioviruses 1–3	1, 4, 105, 106, 115, 117, 221, 336, 360, 361	*Clinical Differences by Age?* Yes: Infants present with irritability, lethargy; older patients present with fever, meningeal signs	109, 117, 125, 366, 369, 370
Less commonly associated Echoviruses 1, 2, 5, 14, 16, 18, 19, 22, 24, 27, 30, 31, 33; coxsackieviruses A1–8, 10, 11, 14, 16–18, 22, 24; coxsackievirus B6	362, 363	SEX DISTRIBUTION: M/F ratio generally 1.5–2.5:1	95, 107–109, 111, 124–126, 134

(Continued)

Aseptic Meningitis *(cont.)*

	References
CLINICAL:	
Signs/Symptoms	
Common	
Prodrome of 2–3 d in approximately two thirds, biphasic course in approximately 25% of those (otherwise onset may be abrupt)	1, 368, 370–373
Fever (≥ 90%), headache (45%), nausea/ vomiting (42%–83%), meningeal signs (51%– 89%), anorexia (26%–37%), sore throat, respiratory symptoms	
Less Common	
Gastrointestinal symptoms, especially echoviruses and especially young patients; rash (5%–42%), especially youngest patients; myalgias (2%–34%); photophobia (6%–12%); drowsiness; conjunctivitis	
Clinical Course Short benign course in most patients, lasting 5–10 d (long convalescent periods reported, especially in adults)	
Complications	
Common	
Children < 1 yr at time of infection may be at risk of long-term physical or mental impairment (16%–50% reported)	1, 337, 339, 340
Uncommon	
Febrile seizure; paresis, paralysis; lethargy, coma	4, 124, 321, 368, 371, 374, 375

	References
DIAGNOSIS:	
Differential Diagnosis Mumps, lymphocytic choriomeningitis, leptospirosis, arboviral disease, toxoplasmosis, bacterial meningitis, parameningeal infection, tuberculous meningitis, syphilis, *Mycoplasma* infection, cryptococcosis, listeriosis, etc	88, 360, 371, 376
Key to Clinical Recognition Meningitis following respiratory prodrome, especially in child 5– 15 yr old during local enterovirus season; rash suggests echoviruses, myalgias suggest coxsackie B viruses	
Specimens for Viral Isolation (*isolation establishes etiologic role) *CSF (early specimens more likely to yield virus); stool; throat	
LABORATORY FINDINGS:	
Peripheral WBC often normal, but may be depressed or elevated	363
CSF: WBC can be normal to moderately elevated, reported range 0–5500 (mostly 10– 2000); polymorphonuclear leukocytosis may predominate early and mononuclear leukocytosis later in course. Protein can be normal or elevated (< 40 in 33%–45%, 40–80 in 42%, > 80 in 12%). Glucose generally ≥ 50% serum glucose, although hypoglycorrhachia reported. Culture bacteriologically sterile.	5, 371, 372 / 372 / 373, 377
PATIENT MANAGEMENT:	
Supportive care; decrease physical exertion, especially at first indication of CNS involvement (especially for polioviruses; theoretical for nonpolio enteroviruses)	

Encephalitis: Clinical and Epidemiological Summary

	References
OCCURRENCE: Worldwide, commonly during outbreaks of aseptic meningitis or other enteroviral disease	
ASSOCIATED AGENTS:	
Occurrence	
Commonly associated Echoviruses 9, 18; coxsackievirus A9; coxsackievirus B5	1, 374
Less commonly associated Echoviruses 2, 3, 4, 6, 7, 11 14, 19, 25; coxsackieviruses A2, 4, 5, 6; coxsackieviruses B1–4	

	References
Etiologic Role Proven Echoviruses 2, 9, 25; coxsackieviruses A2, 4, 9; coxsackievirus B5	1, 74, 378
AGE DISTRIBUTION: Same as Aseptic Meningitis	
SEX DISTRIBUTION: Same as Aseptic Meningitis	
CLINICAL:	
Signs/Symptoms	
Common	

(Continued)

Encephalitis *(cont.)*

	References
Fever, tremor, twitch, dizziness, psychiatric symptoms, somnolence, stupor, seizure (generalized or focal)	
Often associated with meningitis (ie, meningoencephalitis)	
Less common Rash, coma, cerebellar ataxia, choreiform movement, paresthesias	
Clinical Course Generally benign, though may be fulminant in severe neonatal systemic disease	
Complications Common None	
Uncommon Guillain-Barré syndrome—coxsackieviruses A2, 5, 6, 9; echoviruses 6, 7, 22; certain coxsackie B viruses	1, 62, 100, 379, 380
Paralysis, urinary retention	
Bulbar, cranial nerve involvement, nystagmus	

	References
Residual neurologic deficit (physical, intellectual)	
Postinfectious hypothalamic dysfunction	
DIAGNOSIS: *Differential Diagnosis* Arboviral encephalitis, postinfectious encephalomyelitis, mumps, lymphocytic choriomeningitis, herpes simplex virus encephalitis, tuberculous meningitis, measles, varicella, infectious mononucleosis	81, 88, 105, 377, 382
Key to Clinical Recognition Association with cases of aseptic meningitis during local enterovirus season	
Specimens for Viral Isolation (*isolation establishes etiologic role) *CSF; stool; throat	
LABORATORY FINDINGS: EEG abnormalities during acute illness	
PATIENT MANAGEMENT: Supportive; decrease physical exertion, especially at earliest signs of CNS involvement (theoretical)	

Enterovirus Infections in Pregnancy

Pregnancy may be associated with enhanced severity and maternal death in poliovirus or coxsackievirus B infection.[249, 250] Effects of maternal infection on the developing fetus are not as clear. Since transplacental transmission of enteroviruses may occur,[339–344] there is concern that enterovirus infections, especially during the first trimester of pregnancy, may result in congenital malformation.

Despite negative reports,[1, 345, 346] there is arguable evidence for the following associations[346]: coxsackievirus B2 or B4, urogenital anomalies; coxsackievirus B3 or B4, cardiovascular anomalies; coxsackievirus A9, digestive system malformations; and several different coxsackievirus B infections, cardiovascular malformations.

The mothers reported in these studies were often only asymptomatically infected. Anomalous infants were of lower birth weight and more likely to be males than were matched controls. There has been no evidence for the teratogenicity of polioviruses.[99] Because of incomplete evidence for untoward effects of congenital enterovirus infection, it is not accepted practice to recommend abortion for women with proven enterovirus infection in the first trimester.

It has been suggested that infection later in pregnancy may lead to abortion or stillbirth.[1, 99, 120, 342, 347, 348] Evidence supporting a role for enteroviruses in fetal death includes case reports,[348, 349] controlled studies of pregnancy outcomes,[99] observations of otherwise inexplicable seasonal increases in spontaneous abortions,[328] and

stillborns found with virologic and histologic evidence of enteroviral myocarditis.[120, 343] Pregnant mice experimentally infected with coxsackievirus B3 or B4 experience greater fetal wastage or runting.[340, 344] But most mid- or late-trimester infections do not result in human fetal wastage.[253] In utero infection near term may or may not be associated with illness in the neonate.[147, 350–352]

In recent years, several cases of severe or fatal congenital enterovirus infections have been reported.[353–355] In one such case, it was alleged that a live polio vaccine was responsible.[353] In typical case reports, fetuses are infected in the third trimester and die in utero. Presumably such fetal deaths are rare, but if, in fact, the placenta is not an effective barrier to enteroviruses, widespread circulation of enteroviruses in open populations could result in multiple fetal infections. Other data suggest that enterovirus colonization of the cervix of pregnant women during the third trimester is a cause of perinatal, and possibly congenital infection.[356] One group of investigators has drawn attention to a temporal association between community enterovirus circulation and increased numbers of stillbirths.[357] Given the relative frequency and severity of neonatal enterovirus infections, the question of fetal infection bears closer scrutiny.

Perinatal, Neonatal Enteroviral Infection

Infants, particularly neonates, are of the age group most susceptible to serious consequences of enterovirus infections. Although the term "severe neonatal enteroviral disease" applied without reference to a specific organ system or physical sign may at first appear to be nonspecific and ambiguous, serious enterovirus disease in infancy is a distinctive and dramatic condition which all pediatricians and other physicians dealing with infants must be able to recognize. Other terms, such as "viral sepsis" and "neonatal virosis," are less scientific, but more descriptive and more evocative of the illness. The earliest description of encephalomyocarditis neonatorum[383a, 383b] is also descriptive of many of these cases.

In general, serious complications of infantile enterovirus infection are inversely correlated with age. But there is no "magic" cutoff point in the neonatal (ie, less than one month) or infancy period beyond which risk is notably decreased. Many pediatricians note that serious enteroviral diseases appear to be less common after 2 months of age or so, roughly the same age beyond which severe infections with enteric and other bacterial pathogens are less likely to occur, possibly reflecting maturation of host defenses. It is becoming increasingly apparent that perinatal enterovirus infections include cases in which the infant was congenitally infected shortly before birth, either from ascending cervical infection or via hematogenous spread from maternal blood, across the placenta; at birth, presumably via exposure to virus from the mother's cervix or fecal material; or after birth, via nosocomial transmission.[156, 384-388] Accordingly, the day of life at which infant disease is noted may give a clue to the source of infection.

Illness in the neonate is usually first noted by the second to 12th day of life in an otherwise healthy baby who may suddenly become irritable or refuse feeding. The temperature may be normal, decreased, or elevated, and is not a particularly good indicator of disease severity. Illness onset may be abrupt or subacute, followed several days later by fulminant disease. Depending on the virus (though particularly common with echoviruses), a pink macular or maculopapular rash may appear over most of the body. During infection with coxsackie B viruses, which may result in particularly severe disease, rash is generally absent. In some cases infants who die suddenly without symptoms or signs of enterovirus disease are found to have been infected with enteroviruses at autopsy, on the basis of culture results and histology. The signs of serious disease in a neonate are likely to be nonspecific and difficult to recognize, reflecting the limited repertoire of the baby's immature physical and physiologic functions. Multisystem disease may present as apparent "sepsis." When myocarditis predominates, tachycardia, respiratory difficulty, weak cry, cyanosis, mottling, and organomegaly may be seen. Tachypnea and grunting respirations may be noted. Cyanosis and marked respiratory difficulty predict a poor prognosis. In one report[387] neonatal enterovirus infection presented as a suspected surgical emergency. The differential diagnosis must always include bacterial sepsis, meningitis or other bacterial infection, and congenital viral infection, including CMV and particularly HSV infection, for which there may be specific treatment. After obtaining appropriate bacterial and viral cultures, the infant is usually placed on broad-coverage parenteral antibiotics. Death is usually due to either carditis, meningoencephalitis, or hepatic-adrenal failure,[157, 386, 387-389] although evidence of overwhelming multisystem viral disease may be found at autopsy. Carditis or meningoencephalitis alone may also be seen in these infants.[388-390] A milder clinical course with more favorable outcome may also be seen, but it is unclear whether this is due to maternal antibody, less virulent strains, or to some other cause.[157, 390] In one prospective study of 586 newborns, 12.8% acquired enterovirus infection in the first month of life, but only 21% of these required hospitalization.[87] Although there is no proven treatment, human immunoglobulin is being given with increasing frequency (see below). Since nosocomial transmission of enteroviruses within the nursery has been well documented,[156-159, 390-392] it is essential that all infected infants be isolated from other babies. In general, such nursery cross-infections tend to be associated with milder diseases than those associated with maternal-fetal or maternal-infant transmission.[157]

Neonatal Disease: Clinical and Epidemiological Summary

	References		References
FIRST DESCRIPTION: Encephalomyocarditis neonatorum due to Coxsackie B viruses first described in South Africa, 1953	383a	*Etiologic Role Proven* Coxsackieviruses B1–5; echoviruses 1, 3, 6, 7, 9, 11, 15, 17–19; coxsackieviruses A4, 16	1, 99, 100, 134, 143, 145, 370, 391, 392, 397–404
OCCURRENCE: Reported worldwide especially as outbreaks in premature and newborn nurseries (coxsackieviruses B1–5; echoviruses 5, 6, 11, 11', 17–19, 22, 31); sporadic cases also occur (eg, echoviruses 9, 19, 20)	1, 95, 96, 142, 144, 148, 149, 151, 152, 354, 365, 366, 383, 384, 390, 391, 392–394	AGE DISTRIBUTION:	
		Usual Age Range Premature or full-term neonates and infants (coxsackievirus A disease usually beyond neonatal period)	153, 398
ASSOCIATED AGENTS:		*Clinical Differences by Age?* Premature babies may be more severely ill than full-term neonates	143
Occurrence Commonly associated: Coxsackieviruses B1–5; echoviruses 9, 11, 14, 18, 19, 22	1, 99, 395, 396		
Less commonly associated: Echoviruses 1–7, 11; 15–17, 21, 31; coxsackieviruses A4, 9, 16		SEX DISTRIBUTION: M/F ratio approximately 1–2.6:1	144, 154, 405, 406

(Continued)

Neonatal Disease *(cont.)*

	References
CLINICAL:	
Signs/Symptoms	
Most often normal at birth, with onset of severe illness in 2–12 d (infection usually acquired after birth, although in utero infections reported); onset 0–7 d (48%), 8–14 d (32%), 15–21 d (16%)	1, 4, 5, 99–101, 142, 144, 154, 155, 342, 398, 407–409
Presentation with fever or temperature instability, irritability, lethargy, poor feeding, vomiting	
Myocarditis (most common) may present with abrupt onset, rapid course; subacute phase 1–7 d, then cardiac failure; subclinical infection (found at necropsy)	389
Myocarditis appears with tachycardia, tachypnea, dyspnea, mottling, cyanosis, hepatosplenomegaly, and occasionally associated CNS symptoms or jaundice	
Common	91, 390
Asymptomatic or mild disease (eg, echoviruses 5, 9, 17, 18, 20, 22)	
Respiratory disease: upper or lower tract (e.g., pneumonia)	
Diarrheal illness	
Benign arrhythmias	
Clinical Course Ill babies may develop disseminated multisystem disease and die within 3–7 d; disease generally more severe with coxsackie B viruses than echoviruses or coxsackie A viruses; as many as 83% with neonatal coxsackievirus B infection have been reported to have severe disease	342, 351, 370, 410, 411

	References
Complications	
Common	
Death, generally due to myocarditis, hepato-adrenal failure or multisystem failure with or without diffuse intravascular coagulation (up to 50%–76% mortality); survival after severe neonatal multisystem disease or carditis is uncommon	100, 101, 147, 383, 386, 387
DIAGNOSIS:	
Differential Diagnosis Bacterial sepsis	
Key to Clinical Recognition Neonate within first 1–2 wk of life with illness resembling sepsis, especially if associated with rash or with mild illness in mother during week before delivery	
Older infants with a variety of signs and symptoms associated with enteroviruses	
Specimens for Viral Isolation (*isolation establishes etiologic role) *CSF; *tissue from heart, brain, spinal cord, meninges, lung, kidney, liver, spleen; stool	
LABORATORY FINDINGS:	
ECG diffuse ST-T wave changes, conduction defects, etc.	
PATIENT MANAGEMENT:	
Isolation of infected patient from others in newborn nursery	
Occasional reports of treatment of cases, or of nursery contacts with human gamma globulin to help reduce severity of perinatal disease; no basis for general recommendation, however	141, 391, 392

Carditis

The following discussion pertains to carditis in children and adults. Infantile enteroviral carditis, as discussed in the previous section, is often associated with multisystem disease and a poor prognosis. Carditis is specifically associated with the coxsackie B viruses, although other viruses, notably the echoviruses, have been implicated in a few cases. Specific syndromes include myocarditis, pericarditis, or both. The incidence of enteroviral carditis is unknown. It appears to be a rare complication seen in community outbreaks of otherwise benign enteroviral disease. There is a strong tendency for enteroviral carditis, particularly that associated with the coxsackie B viruses, to occur in young adult men. The reason for this is obscure, although an association with intense anaerobic physical exertion is possible.

The clinical picture of myocarditis varies greatly from one individual to the next. There may be recognized antecedent respiratory or GI illness preceding major illness by 1 to 2 weeks. Some patients have no such prodrome. Patients typically present with fever, radiating or nonradiating precordial pain, arrhythmias, and signs and symptoms of congestive heart failure (CHF) including dyspnea, orthopnea, and tachypnea. The ECG is often abnormal, as indicated in the accompanying summary. Changes associated with myocardial ischemia or infarction may occasionally be seen. Illness may persist for weeks, although complete recovery is expected. Occasionally there is rapid progression to death by cardiac failure or infarction, but such outcomes are rare. Late deaths from residual cardiomyopathy may sometimes occur, and in neonatal carditis chronic cardiomyopathy may develop.[389]

The diagnosis is usually suspected on the basis of clinical presentation, physical examination, chest roentgenogram, and ECG. Postmortem diagnosis of cardiac tissue specimens has been made by in situ hybridization using cDNA probes. Epidemiologic clues include disease occurrence during the summer or fall, especially when enteroviruses are known to be prevalent in the community. Enteroviruses may be isolated from the stool early in the course of illness. Treatment must be individualized depending on the presence and extent of congestive heart failure, arrhythmias, ischemia, or other complications. Bed rest is important. Although steroids are often given on an empirical basis in the face of life-threatening disease, there is no evidence that they are of benefit.

Enterovirus infection may also result in acute benign pericarditis. A possible association with chronic relapsing pericarditis is incompletely defined. Many cases may be clinically silent. However, it is not unusual for pericarditis to be diagnosed during evaluation of associated pulmonary involvement including pleural effusion, pleurodynia and pleuritis, and other acute respiratory syndromes. Pericarditis may be associated with small pericardial effusions; large effusions associated with cardiac restriction are rare. The diagnosis is made on the basis of clinical presentation, physical examination, chest roentgenogram, and ECG. Bed rest is advised. Specific treatment is rarely indicated.

Carditis: Clinical and Epidemiological Summary

	References		References
FIRST DESCRIPTION: Coxsackievirus B heart disease in neonatal outbreaks in South Africa, Zimbabwe, Netherlands (1955); first case in adult (with associated pericarditis) reported by Fletcher and Brennan, Northern Ireland, 1957	412	SEX DISTRIBUTION: M/F ratio 1.5–2:1	
OCCURRENCE: Worldwide, generally occurring as sporadic cases during outbreaks of enteroviral disease (especially the coxsackievirus B group)	5	CLINICAL: *Signs/Symptoms* Common Myocarditis, pericarditis, or both (four syndromes: febrile influenzalike illness, pericarditis, myocarditis with progressive failure, myocarditis simulating myocardial infarction)	237, 413, 416–418
ASSOCIATED AGENTS: *Occurrence* Commonly associated Coxsackieviruses B1–5 (coxsackie B viruses are the most common viral etiology of myocarditis)	1, 4, 101, 226, 227, 413, 414	May be biphasic, with upper respiratory infection (URI) or gastrointestinal (GI) prodrome preceding major illness by 1–2 weeks in older children, adults	
Acute benign pericarditis (ABP): Coxsackieviruses B2–5		Presents with fever, precordial pain (with or without radiation to throat, usually relieved by sitting forward), congestive heart failure (tachycardia, dyspnea, orthopnea, cardiomegaly), arrhythmias (atrial, ventricular)	
Less commonly associated Coxsackieviruses A4, 14, 16; echoviruses 4, 6–9, 19, 20; polioviruses 1–3 (ECG changes in 12%–31% with poliomyelitis)		May be associated with respiratory symptoms, myalgias, headache, vomiting	
ABP: coxsackieviruses A1, 9; echoviruses 1, 9, 19		Neonates: generally well at birth, develop fulminant multisystem disease with cardiac failure (see preceding section)	
Etiologic Role Proven High-order association coxsackieviruses B1–5; echoviruses 9, 22; coxsackieviruses A4, 16		Asymptomatic focal myocarditis may be relatively common (up to 5% of routine autopsies at all ages; up to 50% of cases of enteroviral myocarditis may be subclinical)	
Moderate-order association echoviruses 1, 2', 4, 6, 14, 19, 25, 30; coxsackieviruses A1, 2, 5, 8, 9		ABP: abrupt onset of fever, tachycardia; may have pleural effusion	
ABP: coxsackieviruses B2–4		Less common Valvulitis, endocardial elastosis, vena caval obstruction	226, 236, 413, 419, 420
AGE DISTRIBUTION: *Usual Age Range* Except for neonatal myocarditis, mostly older children and adults (mean age 28 yr)	101, 111b, 250, 415	Ventricular fibrillation, cardiac arrest	
Clinical Differences by Age? Adults more likely to have pericardial involvement (pericarditis alone, or associated with myocarditis)		*Clinical Course* May last weeks; complete recovery generally expected (except neonates), with one report of 55% with chronic heart disease on follow-up	413, 417

(Continued)

Carditis *(cont.)*

	References			References

Complications

Common

Generally none; however, death common with neonatal disease — 101, 417

Uncommon

Early: pleural effusion, arrhythmias, congestive heart failure (CHF), hemopericardium — 1, 5, 226, 417, 421, 422

Late: residual cardiomegaly, decreased work capacity, chronic conduction defect, mitral/aortic insufficiency, congestive cardiomyopathy, constrictive pericarditis, arteriosclerosis

Death more common in older children and teenagers than in adults

Sudden death, especially due to arrhythmia

DIAGNOSIS:

Differential Diagnosis Myocarditis due to influenza, mumps, rubella, toxoplasmosis, cytomegalovirus (CMV), Epstein-Barr virus (EBV), meningococcus, streptococcus, pneumococcus, *Haemophilus influenzae*, diphtheria; uremia, pheochromocytoma, anaphylaxis, emetine HCl, accidental cobalt ingestion, mediastinal irradiation, heavy exertion without physical conditioning, pregnancy-puerperium, subarachnoid hemorrhage, pericarditis due to bacterial pathogens, tuberculosis, uremia, collagen-vascular disease, sarcoidosis, fungi, neoplasms, postinfarction (Dressler) syndrome — 226

Key to Clinical Recognition (1) Neonate with fulminant "septic" disease; (2) older patient with persistent tachycardia out of proportion to fever; weakness, fatigue; signs and symptoms — 237, 417

of CHF, abnormal ECG, especially if associated with myalgia and during local "enterovirus season"

Specimens for Viral Isolation (*isolation establishes etiologic role) stool; throat; *pericardial fluid, *myocardium, pericardium

LABORATORY FINDINGS:

ECG changes compatible with myocarditis (ST-T changes, QT changes, conduction defects such as partial or complete bundle-branch block [BBB], ectopic atrial/ventricular beats, atrial fibrillation and flutter, etc) — 112

Peripheral WBC may show left shift

Nonspecific: elevated erythrocyte sedimentation rate (ESR), myocardial enzymes may be elevated—aspartate aminotransferase (AST), lactic dehydrogenase (LDH), creatine phosphokinase (CPK) — 417

PATIENT MANAGEMENT:

Careful observation, including cardiac monitoring — 1, 76, 101, 236, 417

Treatment of CHF, including bed rest, fluid balance, careful use of digitalis, diuretics, oxygen

Treatment of arrhythmias, may require temporary or permanent pacemaker for heart block

Decreased physical exertion

Role of steroids controversial

Careful evaluation of recommendations for return to work or school

Enteroviral Enanthemas, Including Herpangina

Enteroviral enanthemas can be subdivided into two distinct syndromes—herpangina and lymphonodular pharyngitis. The latter syndrome has only been associated with coxsackievirus A10 and has been rarely observed since first described in the literature. Herpangina, on the other hand, is quite common, especially in association with coxsackie A viruses.

Herpangina is predominately a disease of childhood, especially children under 11 years old. Typical features include abrupt onset with fever, sore throat, and varying degrees of dysphagia, anorexia, and constitutional symptoms. However, mild and asymptomatic infections are probably more common than is appreciated. The illness is usually not as severe as florid herpetic gingivostomatitis, of consideration in the differential diagnosis.

Lesions develop as 2-mm red or burgundy-colored macules, typically on the soft palate and fauces. These rapidly become papular and vesiculate, resulting in the characteristic lesions of herpangina—small discrete white vesicles or shallow ulcerated vesicles with red bases. Lesions are confined to the posterior oral cavity, in contrast to primary herpetic gingivostomatitis and aphthous stomatitis, which are predominantly found in the anterior oral cavity. The disease is benign, and, other than analgesia, specific treatment is not required.

Lymphonodular pharyngitis is associated with discrete papules formed by lymphocytic infiltration of infected tissue. (These are not nodules, as the term erroneously suggests.) Lesions have firm white or yellow crowns that do not ulcerate or vesiculate, a factor distinguishing them from lesions of herpangina. They are somewhat larger than the lesions of herpangina, are surrounded by a red halo at the base, and appear simultaneously in the posterior pharynx. The condition is benign, self-limited, and does not require treatment. It has apparently been seen only rarely since it was initially reported in 1962.[423]

Occasionally infection with various enterovirus types results in an enanthema that appears clinically indistinct. These lesions are likewise benign and self-limited.

Herpangina and Other Enanthemas: Clinical and Epidemiological Summary

	References		References
FIRST DESCRIPTION: Zahorsky, 1924	8	**CLINICAL:**	
		Signs/Symptoms	
OCCURRENCE: Probably worldwide, occurs mostly during epidemics of coxsackievirus A infections		Common	
		Herpangina: abrupt onset with fever, sore throat, dysphagia, anorexia, vomiting, abdominal pain; mouth lesions—average 5 vesicles or shallow ulcers (both on erythematous bases) on anterior pillars, posterior pharynx, palate, uvula, tonsils, tongue	4, 5, 428
ASSOCIATED AGENTS:			
Occurrence			
Commonly associated			
Herpangina: Coxsackieviruses A2, 4, 5, 6, 8, 10, 16	1, 4, 424		
		Lymphonodular pharyngitis: similar to herpangina, but no vesicles; lesions are raised whitish-yellowish small solid pharyngeal papules on erythematous bases; lesions appear together and resolve without ulceration in 6–10 d	423
Lymphonodular pharyngitis: Coxsackievirus A10	423, 425		
Less commonly associated Herpangina: Coxsackieviruses A1, 3, 7, 9, 22; coxsackieviruses B1–5; echoviruses 3, 6, 9, 16, 17, 30	426, 427		
		Less common	
		Herpangina: petechiae leading to nodules, vesicles, and ulceration; headache; myalgias; genital, labial lesions; parotitis	
Gingivostomatitis: Coxsackieviruses A3, 5			
Miscellaneous: Coxsackieviruses A5, 9, 16: coxsackieviruses B2, 3, 5; echoviruses 6, 9, 16	1	*Clinical Course* Benign, self-limited, lasting 1–4 d (occasionally longer)	
		DIAGNOSIS:	
Etiologic Role Proven No isolates from non-parenteral sites, but accepted for coxsackieviruses A2, 4, 5, 6, 8, 10		*Differential Diagnosis* Herpangina, lymphonodular pharyngitis, herpetic stomatitis, aphthous ulcers (minor and major), aphthous ulcers (herpetiformis)	
AGE DISTRIBUTION:			
Usual Age Range Infants and young children, 3–10 yr old (median 4 yr)	427	*Key to Clinical Recognition* "Coxsackievirus A pharyngitis" during the summer or fall	
Clinical Differences by Age? Occurs mostly in children		*Specimens for Viral Isolation* (*isolation establishes etiologic role) *lesion; throat; stool	
SEX DISTRIBUTION: M/F ratio approximately 1:1		LABORATORY FINDINGS: Nonspecific	
		PATIENT MANAGEMENT: Supportive	

Enteroviral Exanthemas

The best known of the exanthematous enteroviral syndromes goes by the cumbersome name of hand-foot-and-mouth disease. It is classically associated with coxsackievirus A16, but also may be caused by coxsackievirus A5 and several other enteroviruses, including enterovirus 71.[429] Hand-foot-and-mouth disease is to be distinguished from foot-and-mouth disease, an affliction of cattle caused by an unrelated picornavirus.

Young children are at greatest risk, especially those 1 to 5 years old. Fever is often minimal, and constitutional symptoms are less pronounced than with other enterovirus syndromes. A prodromal phase is unusual. Multiple discrete red macular lesions of about 4 mm appear on the palms, soles, ventral surfaces of the fingers and toes, the lateral margins of the hands and feet, and the buttocks (Figure 17–8). During the early stages the palmar-plantar lesions may appear to represent mottling, but typically they become pap-

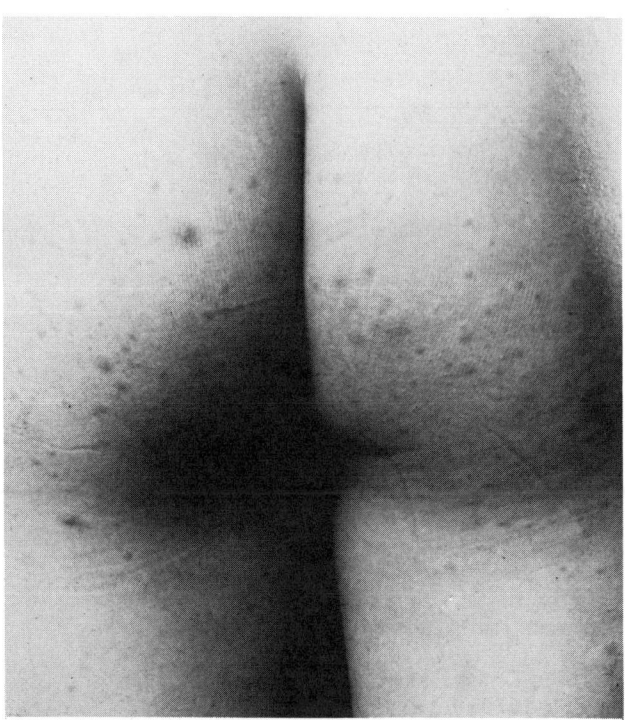

Figure 17–8. A young child with hand-foot-and-mouth disease associated with coxsackievirus A16. Lesions are often found on the buttocks; one such lesion, of the left upper medial buttock, is beginning to vesiculate.

ular. In some cases the lesions do not progress beyond this stage. In others they form vesicles, leaving white or gray flaccid lesions that contain infectious viruses and represent a possible source of contagion. The differential diagnosis includes varicella, but the latter can be ruled out in most cases on the basis of history (previous varicella or lack or recent exposure or time of year) and physical examination: the lesions of varicella are more central in distribution and are rarely seen in the same unusual distribution as those of hand-foot-and-mouth disease, tending to rupture and crust to a greater degree. When present, lesions on the buttocks virtually confirm the diagnosis of hand-foot-and-mouth disease. The enanthema associated with hand-foot-and-mouth disease is similar to that of herpangina (and, in fact, some of the same viruses may cause both herpangina and hand-foot-and-mouth disease), the major exception being that in hand-foot-and-mouth disease there is a greater tendency for oral lesions to be in the anterior oral cavity. The syndrome can be complete or incomplete, with manifestations on the hands, feet, or mouth only, or any combination of these.

Boston exanthema disease is the term applied to disease associated with echovirus 16 as recognized in outbreaks by several investigators.[9, 10] Echovirus 16 has circulated elsewhere, however, without causing epidemics of the apparently distinctive Boston exanthema disease. The disease is seen most commonly in children under 8 years, is preceded by fever and constitutional symptoms, and is characterized by a florid morbilliform or rubelliform rash appearing at the time of, or shortly following, defervescence. Ulcers with roughly the same distribution as those of herpangina may also be seen. It is possible that the spectrum of disease as-

sociated with echovirus 16 is not greatly different from that of many other echoviruses and this allegedly distinctive enteroviral disease is, to some extent, an historical artifact of early recognition of unusual cases in large outbreaks. The disease is self-limited, and there is no specific treatment.

Maculopapular exanthemas are associated with man, and probably most enteroviruses, in a variable percentage of cases. What factors predispose to development of a rash in one individual and absence of rash in another infected with the same virus is unknown, except that rashes seem to be more common in children than in adults, and are more frequently noted in light-skinned persons. Echoviruses are more likely to cause rash disease than other enteroviruses. Rash is uncommon with poliovirus infection. Among the echoviruses, echovirus 9 has been frequently implicated (Figure 17–9). Rash is seldom the sole clinical feature in symptomatic enterovirus infections, being more commonly associated with one or more of the other syndromes, including (otherwise) nonspecific febrile illnesses. The maculopapular enteroviral exanthemas usually appear after disease onset, may begin on the face or neck and spread downward, and at the peak of their existence appear as small (2–8 mm) discrete or grouped pink, pinkish-red, or salmon-colored macules or low papules that blanch on pressure and may appear to blush and fade at various times throughout their course. The papules are often surrounded by a halo of blanching. The rash is often neither distinctive nor impressive. However, it is more apt to resemble the rash of dengue than that of measles or rubella. Enteroviruses have been associated with a host of other rash types including generalized vesicular (particularly in association with coxsackievirus A9 infection) and, purportedly, zosteriform, urticarial, petechial, purpuric, and those resembling erythema multiforme.

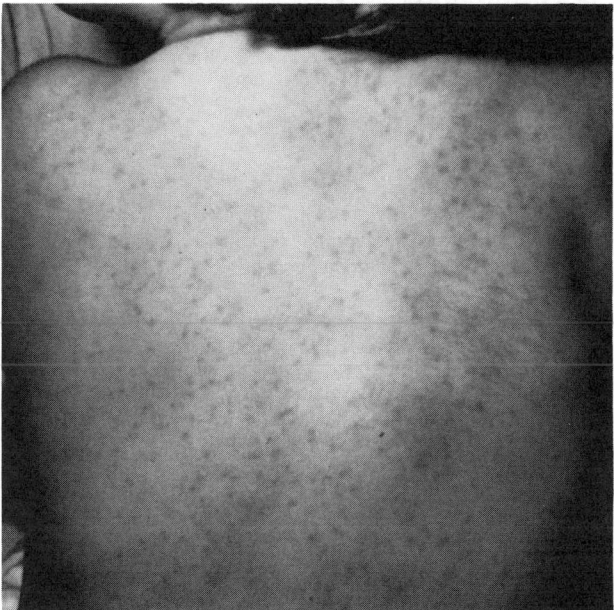

Figure 17–9. Echovirus type 9 infection in young child. Discrete papular lesions are scattered over the back in apparently random distribution. The lesions blanch upon pressure, indicating dermal involvement.

Hand-Foot-and-Mouth Disease: Clinical and Epidemiological Summary

	References		References
FIRST DESCRIPTION: Seddon, 1957 (endemic); Robinson et al, 1958 (epidemic); both associated with coxsackievirus A16	430–432	ulceration); located on palms, soles, fingers, toes, lateral margins hands or feet, buttocks	
OCCURRENCE: Probably worldwide, occurrence as small outbreaks, as in nursery schools (coxsackieviruses A16, enterovirus 71 [EV71]), or as sporadic cases	429	Associated with malaise (52%), anorexia (21%)	
		Less common Exanthema involving proximal limbs, knees	
ASSOCIATED AGENTS: *Occurrence* Commonly associated Coxsackievirus A16	4	Coalescence of lesions into bullae	
Less commonly associated Coxsackieviruses A4, 5, 7, 9 (variant), 10; coxsackieviruses 2, 5; EV71	4, 5, 429	Vesicles on vaginal mucosa (case report, coxsackievirus A7)	
Etiologic Role Proven Coxsackieviruses A5, 7, 16; EV71	429	Other constitutional findings including headache, abdominal pain; cough, conjunctival injection, coryza, diarrhea, nausea, vomiting, pleuritis, carditis, or pneumonia	
AGE DISTRIBUTION: *Usual Age Range* Young children, especially 1–5 yr old (may be older with enterovirus 71) uncommon < 1 yr.	5, 104	*Clinical Course* Benign, self-limited, lesions dry and scale in 1–2 wk	433
Clinical Differences by Age? Babies present with refusal to eat; older patients present with sore mouth, sore throat		*Complications* Common None	
SEX DISTRIBUTION: Approximately equal		Uncommon Neurologic complications (aseptic meningitis in 3.7% studied with hand-foot-and-mouth disease due to EV71; all with complications were < 5 yr old, representing 4.5% of this age group); findings included headache, stiff neck, seizure, pleocytosis; onset day 1–3 of illness	114
CLINICAL: *Signs/Symptoms* Common No prodrome	424, 430, 433	DIAGNOSIS: *Differential Diagnosis* Herpangina, herpetic stomatitis, aphthous stomatitis, erythema multiforme, infected eczematous pompholyx, varicella, disseminated vaccinia virus infection, monkeypox infection	433
Presents with fever (low grade in 25%–48%) and sore throat (69%); fever may precede eruption by 1–2 d; enanthema precedes exanthema		*Key to Clinical Recognition* Original triad = fever, stomatitis, vesicular eruption from macular exanthema, in child 1–5 yr old, especially during summer or fall	
Syndrome may be complete (hand, foot, and mouth involvement, 68%), or incomplete (hand and foot involvement, 11%; mouth involvement alone, 21%)		*Specimens for Viral Isolation* (*isolation establishes etiologic role) *vesicle fluid; mouth ulcers; stool; pharynx	
Enanthema (90%): 1–8 small red macules becoming vesicles and then ulcers (shallow, yellow-gray base, surrounded by an erythematous halo), on mucous membranes of lips, anterior tongue, gums, inner cheeks, soft palate, pharynx (not on outer lips or posterior pharynx)		LABORATORY FINDINGS: Peripheral WBC normal (may be relative increase in percentage mononuclear WBC, with atypical lymphocytes present)	
Exanthema (80%): 20–30 lesions appear over 1–2 d; nonpruitic; maculopapular eruption, some with vesicles (1–5 mm on erythematous base, flaccid with grayish center, no		PATIENT MANAGEMENT: Supportive; viscous xylocaine for severe mouth lesions	

Boston Exanthem Disease: Clinical and Epidemiological Summary

	References
FIRST DESCRIPTION: Neva, Boston (1951), Pittsburgh (1954); first description of specific enteroviral exanthema	9, 10
OCCURRENCE: Occurs (rarely) as outbreaks of rash disease	9, 111, 434
ASSOCIATED AGENTS:	
Occurrence	
Commonly associated Echovirus 16	
Etiologic Role Proven Echovirus 16	
AGE DISTRIBUTION:	
Usual Age Range Mostly children < 8 yr; mean age with rash is 40 mo	97
Clinical Differences by Age? Children have milder illness, except neonates who may appear "septic"; adults have more severe systemic illness	
SEX DISTRIBUTION: M/F ratio may be about equal	9
CLINICAL:	
Signs/Symptoms	
Common	
No prodrome	
Onset with fever (moderate to high), exanthema with or without enanthema	
Exanthema (children): nonpruritic, diffuse, morbilliform or rubelliform eruption on face, upper chest, arms, buttocks, legs, back; exanthema follows 2 h to 2 d after defervescence	

	References
Enanthema: tiny punched-out ulcers on soft palate or tonsillar pillars	
Adults: Abrupt onset with fever, chills, headache, myalgias, prostration, burning sensation in eyes, sore throat, abdominal pain, cramping; occasionally with exanthema or enanthema	
Less common	
Exanthema may involve palms, soles	
Clinical Course Children: benign, self-limited, 1–5 d; adults: 48–72 h	
Complications	
Common	
None	
Uncommon	
Neurologic complications reported in one series	434
DIAGNOSIS:	
Differential Diagnosis Herpangina, measles, rubella, arboviral infection (eg, dengue), roseola infantum	
Key to Clinical Recognition Well-looking child with fever preceding onset of diffuse morbilliform rash on face, upper chest, extremities	
Specimens for Viral Isolation Feces	
LABORATORY FINDINGS: Nonspecific	
PATIENT MANAGEMENT: Supportive	

Other Enteroviral Exanthemas: Clinical and Epidemiological Summary

	References
FIRST DESCRIPTION: Echovirus 9 exanthema first described by Crawford et al. in London, 1954	435
OCCURRENCE: Worldwide during outbreaks of enteroviral disease; besides outbreaks of hand-foot-and-mouth disease or Boston exanthema, outbreaks of rash disease were reported with coxsackievirus A4, echoviruses 2, 25	436, 437

	References
ASSOCIATED AGENTS:	
Occurrence	
Commonly associated Echovirus 9	
Less commonly associated Echoviruses 1–7, 11, 14, 16, 18, 19, 25; coxsackieviruses A2, 4, 5, 9, 16; coxsackieviruses B1 to 5	1, 97, 221, 401, 436, 438, 439
Etiologic Role Proven Echoviruses 9, 16; coxsackieviruses A9, 16	

(Continued)

Other Enteroviral Exanthemas *(cont.)*

	References		References
AGE DISTRIBUTION:		Urticarial lesions; coxsackieviruses A9, 16; B5; echovirus 11	1, 435, 436
Usual Age Range Echovirus rashes most common in young children; most children < 3 yr display rash	274		
		Petechiae: coxsackieviruses A9, B3; echoviruses 4, 9, 11	1, 425
Clinical Differences by Age? Not reported			
		Purpura: coxsackieviruses A9; B3; echovirus 4.	436
SEX DISTRIBUTION: Probably similar to distribution for enterovirus infections in general			
		Erythema multiforme-like echoviruses 6, 11; coxsackievirus B4	1
CLINICAL:			
Signs/Symptoms		*Clinical Course* Benign, self-limited	1
Common			
Echovirus 9: Especially in children 0–4 yr, associated with aseptic meningitis; nonpruritic eruption, macular and/or papular (1–5 mm, discrete, morbilliform), appears after onset of illness; on face, neck spreading to trunk, extremities, and occasionally palms, soles; trunk clears quickly; rash becomes blotchy, purplish on cheeks, lasting 3–5 d (range 1–10 d)	1, 74, 92, 97, 123, 425	*Complications*	
		Common	
		None	
		Uncommon	
		None	
		DIAGNOSIS:	
		Differential Diagnosis Measles, rubella, fifth disease, mononucleosis, meningococcemia, varicella, scarlet fever, herpangina, zoster	62
Coxsackievirus A9: Especially in children; may have prodrome of 1–3 d; clear vesicles, may be associated with pneumonia or aseptic meningitis; rash appears during fever· lesions— maculopapules, petechiae, urticaria on face, trunk and becoming generalized (on extremities distal > proximal and extensor > flexor surfaces)	163, 220, 423	*Key to Clinical Recognition* Generally cannot distinguish, except specific rash syndromes	1
		Specimens for Viral Isolation Feces	
		LABORATORY FINDINGS: None	
Febrile exanthemas: coxsackievirus A4, echoviruses 2, 25			
Less common			
Vesicular lesions: coxsackieviruses A4, 5, 9, 16; B3; echoviruses 4, 9, 11	1, 425, 440, 441		

Acute Hemorrhagic Conjunctivitis (AHC) and Other Conjunctivitis

AHC is one of the more unusual and recognizable of all enterovirus syndromes. Two distinct enterovirus serotypes have been recognized as etiologic agents for this disease, enterovirus type 70 (EV70) and an antigenic variant of coxsackievirus A24 (CA24v). EV70 apparently arose de novo in western Africa in the late 1960s and rapidly spread along the coasts of Africa, eastward to the Middle East, Asia, Japan, and Oceania.[442] The first recognized outbreak of AHC caused by CA24v occurred in 1970 in Singapore as part of the first wave of AHC in southeast Asia. After the pandemic of 1969–1971, sporadic epidemics were seen in many of the equatorial countries of Asia and Africa with either CA24v, EV70, or both involved during the period 1972 through 1980. The next pandemic due to EV70 began in 1981 and spread to the Western Hemisphere for the first time with outbreaks affecting most tropical countries in Central and South America with large coastal cities. There were outbreaks in southern Florida, but only a few sporadic cases in the rest of the United States which were associated with travel to epidemic areas. In 1986, CA24v reached the Western hemisphere for the first time as part of a series of epidemics which may have begun in Singapore and Taiwan in late 1985.[443, 444] The virus was then seen in May of 1986 in Taiwan and American Somoa and then reported later that year in several Caribbean countries.[445] Cases of AHC continued to be reported in several countries from Brazil through Mexico and Puerto Rico in 1987.[446]

AHC is a disease of some importance, especially in previously unaffected areas, because of the high susceptibility of the population, the potential economic impact,[447] including direct medical costs and days lost from work, the extreme contagion, the short incubation period, the rapidity of spread, and the presumed amenability to public health intervention, especially with school exclusion policies. Although most outbreaks of AHC have been attributed to EV70 and CA24v, occasionally adenovirus type 11 has been implicated in outbreaks. AHC almost always occurs as epidemics, in which attack rates may be high. All age groups are affected, although in a well-studied outbreak in Miami community transmission appeared to be accelerated by intraschool transmission.[448] Otherwise, the household is the population unit at greatest risk. Once a household index case is infected from a community source, rapid intrafamily transmission may ensue. Crowded urban neighborhoods of lower socioeconomic status are typically involved. Factors associated with transmission within families include crowding and unsanitary conditions, sharing towels and washcloths, and infrequent handwashing. Transmission is thought to be mediated via contact with infectious secretions on hands or fomites, and virus survival in the environment may be greatly increased by high relative humidity, even under extreme temperatures. Mechanical transmission by gnats from eye to eye is theoretically possible. Transmission within the physician's office may be mediated by improperly cleansed instruments (eg, tonometers) or sharing of ophthalmic solutions. Nosocomial cases have also been documented.

The incubation period is short, averaging about 24 hours, but often is as short as 12 hours. Onset is sudden, with rapid progression of irritation, foreign body sensation, burning, pain, redness, and swelling of the lids and periorbital soft tissues. If onset is unilateral, disease quickly becomes bilateral. Subconjunctival hemorrhage is almost universal for EV70 (greater than 95%), although in some cases close inspection is required to detect small hemorrhages. Frequently there is dramatic crimson subconjunctival hemorrhage. Extraophthalmic signs and symptoms are usually not seen. Disease severity peaks rapidly and then subsides, resolving within seven to ten days. Comparison of physical findings in recent epidemics suggests that CA24v infection may be associated with less severe conjunctival hemorrhage and, more frequently, respiratory symptoms.

Diagnosis during an AHC outbreak need be only clinical: the signs are so impressive that misdiagnosis is unlikely. Some smaller outbreaks have been associated with recovery of other viruses, including adenoviruses, particularly adenovirus type 11, but the meaning of this is uncertain. In the Miami outbreak investigated by CDC in 1981, there were a number of cases of secondary gonococcal and *Proteus* ophthalmitis resulting from home-remedy instillation of urine into affected eyes.[448] For sporadic cases, or when circumstances necessitate, viral culture can be attempted by inoculation of conjunctival cell scrapings. Tears are less desirable for culture, and stool is typically negative. Presumptive virologic diagnosis may be made on the basis of fluorescent antibody test of fixed conjunctival scrapings. However, diagnosis of AHC is beyond the scope of most viral diagnostic laboratories. The viruses grow poorly at times and may be identifiable only after blind passages. Serodiagnosis has recently been facilitated by the development of an ELISA for detection of IgM antibody to EV70 (described in "Serodiagnosis" section). Whenever AHC is suspected, it should be reported to health authorities who may then be able to assist in reference diagnosis.

The course of AHC is benign. Keratitis is rarely of clinical significance. Treatment with steroids is not indicated. Some EV70 outbreaks have been associated with cases of poliomyelitislike paralysis, either shortly after onset or much later (range: less than a week to 8 weeks after onset). The significance of these associations is uncertain. If EV70 is associated with paralysis, it must be a rare complication, by one estimate one case of paralysis per 10,000 to 15,000 total cases.[449]

No other enteroviruses have been causally associated with AHC. However, other enterovirus types have been occasionally associated with nonhemorrhagic conjunctivitis, including coxsackieviruses A9, 10, 16, and B5; and echoviruses 1, 4, 6, 7, 9, 16, and 20.[1, 450] Usually, enteroviral conjunctivitis occurs as a part of another illness syndrome more typically associated with the particular virus. Such cases are benign and of short duration.

Acute Hemorrhagic Conjunctivitis (AHC): Clinical and Epidemiological Summary

	References		References
FIRST DESCRIPTION: Pandemic in Africa and southeast Asia 1967–1973 associated with enterovirus 70 (EV70)	14	*Clinical Differences by Age?* More likely to be severe in adults; children may have milder illness	
OCCURRENCE: Worldwide, occurring as epidemics; introduced into Western Hemisphere 1981	448, 451, 452	SEX DISTRIBUTION: M/F ratio approximately 1:1	

ASSOCIATED AGENTS:
Occurrence
  Commonly associated EV70; coxsackievirus A24 variant
		CLINICAL:
		Signs/Symptoms
		  Common
		Prodrome: burning sensation in eyes, irritation, tearing
			4, 14, 15

Etiologic Role Proven EV70; coxsackievirus A24 variant		Sudden onset, with pain, congestion, redness, swelling; unilateral onset, rapidly spreads to other eye (bilateral in 66% of coxsackievirus A24 cases)	
AGE DISTRIBUTION: *Usual Age Range* Unclear	11		

(Continued)

Acute Hemorrhagic Conjunctivitis (AHC) *(cont.)*

	References
Subconjunctival hemorrhages, especially in upper bulbar conjunctiva (minimal involvement of palpebral conjunctiva)	
May be pinpoint, blotches, or frank hemorrhages	
Less common Corneal involvement rare	
Generally no fever, malaise, sore throat, or vision changes	
Asymptomatic infection rare, particularly in adults	
Clinical Course Benign; self-limited with benign (57%) to severe (43%) conjunctivitis; heals in 6–10 d (longer with coxsackievirus A24)	12, 15
Complications Common	
Steroid treatment may lead to corneal involvement Uncommon	15

	References
Neurologic complications reported associated with EV70 outbreaks; poliolike paralysis, with onset an average of 2 d after onset of AHC; mostly in patients ≥ 20 yr old; mean duration 2.4 wk	113
DIAGNOSIS: *Differential Diagnosis* Conjunctivitis due to bacterial or viral pathogens	
Key to Clinical Recognition Outbreak setting, with hemorrhagic conjunctivitis principal finding	
Specimens for Viral Isolation (*isolation establishes etiologic role) *conjunctival scrapings; *tears; throat; serologic testing for EV70 only; limited availability	
LABORATORY FINDINGS: None	
PATIENT MANAGEMENT: For contacts (especially medical personnel), good hygienic practices, especially handwashing	

Pleurodynia

Several synonymous terms for pleurodynia are in current use, including epidemic pleurodynia, epidemic myalgia, and Bornholm disease. The syndrome itself is impressive not only in its clinical features, but also for its tendency to occur in localized outbreaks. This latter tendency led pleurodynia to become one of the earliest described enterovirus syndromes. With the advent of viral diagnosis, it became clear that most outbreaks were associated with coxsackie B viruses. Cases are recognized mostly in school-age children and in adults, with the peak age being children 2 to 9 years old. The onset is acute, with fever, constitutional symptoms, and severe pleuritic chest pain, especially in adults. Children with pleuritic or diaphragmatic insult of any type often have pain referred to the abdomen. Differential diagnosis of the childhood acute abdomen should include pneumonia and pleurodynia. However, pain associated with inspiration is not generally characteristic of a purely abdominal process. In adults and most children pain is sharp, usually bilateral, and typically localized to the area of the lower lateral rib cage. The intercostal muscles are likely to be sore. Patients often spontaneously avoid even slight exertion to circumvent the pain associated with deep inspiration. Particularly unfortunate are those who feel the need to cough, a paroxysm of which can be excruciatingly painful. Patients may force periodic shallow coughs in an attempt to stave off a cough paroxysm. Older patients may have severe substernal pain which they may attribute to a "heart attack."

The typical case of pleurodynia lasts less than a week, although short relapses are common. Older boys and men have been reported to develop unilateral orchitis. It has not been established that involvement of the ovaries occurs. There is no specific treatment, and the prognosis is excellent.

Pleurodynia: Clinical and Epidemiological Summary

	References
FIRST DESCRIPTION: (1) Finsen, Iceland, 1856, 1863 (reported 1874); (2) Daae, Norway, 1874 (described summer epidemic of Bamble disease in Norway); (3) Dabney, USA, 1888; (4) Sylvest, Denmark, 1933 (described Bornholm disease after outbreak on island of Bornholm, 1930; also epidemic myalgia, devil's grip, etc)	6

	References
OCCURRENCE: Worldwide, occurs mostly as epidemics of pleurodynia alone or associated with aseptic meningitis outbreaks (reported from United States, Europe, South Africa)	41
ASSOCIATED AGENTS: *Occurrence*	

(Continued)

Pleurodynia *(cont.)*

	References
Commonly associated Coxsackieviruses B1–6	1, 135
Less commonly associated Echoviruses 1, 6, 9, 11, 19; coxsackieviruses A4, 6, 9, 10	1, 453
Etiologic Role Proven Coxsackieviruses B, echovirus 19	453, 454

AGE DISTRIBUTION:
Usual Age Range   Children, young adults, peak at 2–9 yr (< 15 yr: > 15 yr = 1.5:1)

References: 1, 6, 131, 135, 271

Clinical Differences by Age?   Adults more often with chest pain; children may have abdominal pain

SEX DISTRIBUTION: M/F ratio approximately 1:1

CLINICAL:
Signs/Symptoms
   Common
May have prodrome, with headache (34%–57%), malaise, anorexia, nausea, vomiting, dizziness

References: 4, 135, 455–458

May have abrupt onset with fever (moderate to high-grade), chest pain (severe, either side, or substernal, "stabbing" or "gripping," pleuritic), and/or abdominal pain (from diaphragmatic involvement, right more than left side, sometimes with radiation to lung apex, scapula, or umbilicus to groin muscles may be tender, swollen, firm on palpation

Pharyngitis (about 45%)

   Less common
Myalgias of other muscles of back, neck, limbs
Vomiting, photophobia, chills

References: 131, 455

Clinical Course
Illness lasts 1–7 d in 74%, 1–2 wk in 20%, > 2 wk in 6%; chest pain, mild to disabling, lasts 2–7 d; abdominal pain lasts about 4 d

References: 4, 131, 455

Complications
   Common
Recurrences/relapses in 25%–31% (after < 1 mo in 20%, > 1 mo in a further 8%, both early and late in 2%), occurs 2–3 d after illness or at intervals longer than 1 wk

References: 6, 131, 135, 365

Orchitis in 10%–40% of males, onset 8–39 d after onset of pleurodynia, almost always unilateral

   Uncommon
Aseptic meningitis (6%), pericarditis, pleuritis, pneumonia, bronchitis

References: 5, 250

DIAGNOSIS:
Differential Diagnosis   Pleurisy, acute abdomen (including appendicitis, especially in children), hepatitis A (preicteric phase)

References: 131, 457

Key to Clinical Recognition   Summer occurrence (especially during coxsackievirus B outbreak) of abrupt illness with fever, severe stabbing or constrictive pain in lower chest or upper abdomen

Specimens for Viral Isolation (*isolation establishes etiologic role)   *CSF (if associated enteroviral meningitis); stool

LABORATORY FINDINGS:
Peripheral WBC generally not elevated, may occasionally be depressed

References: 135

Chest roentgenogram normal

PATIENT MANAGEMENT:
Supportive

Respiratory Illness

Enteroviruses have been associated with a wide variety of signs and symptoms referable to the upper and lower respiratory tract. In addition to pleurodynia, enteroviruses may cause upper respiratory tract infections indistinguishable from those caused by rhinoviruses, coronaviruses, adenoviruses, and other viruses; pharyngitis; laryngitis; croup; bronchiolitis; pneumonitis; bronchitis; and pneumonia. Rarely are the syndromes distinct, and rarely is there any pathognomonic sign or symptom to implicate an enterovirus. Especially in children, tympanitis may develop in the course of disease and may, in conjunction with inflammation of nasopharyngopalatal and eustachian tube edema, predispose to bacterial otitis media. Respiratory tract disease caused by enteroviruses is quite common, but because it is often mild, it is less likely to come to the attention of the physician. Treatment is symptomatic. The prognosis is excellent. Cases of fatal enteroviral pneumonia are medical curiosities.

Respiratory Illnesses: Clinical and Epidemiological Summary

	References		References
OCCURRENCE: Generally occurs during enterovirus outbreak, associated with other clinical syndromes; may occur as predominant respiratory disease outbreak	459	Herpangina: "febrile pharyngitis"	
		Acute lymphonodular pharyngitis (coxsackievirus A10)	
ASSOCIATED AGENTS:			
Occurrence		Less common	
Commonly associated	1, 4, 67, 163,	Lower respiratory tract disease	5, 62, 466
Upper respiratory infection (URI): Coxsackieviruses A10, 21, 24; Coxsackievirus B2	234, 415, 460–465	Croup	
Less commonly associated		Vomiting, conjunctivitis, tympanitis, myringitis, cough, rash, chest/abdominal pain	
URI: Echoviruses 1, 3, 4, 6, 7, 9, 11, 19, 20, 22, 25; coxsackieviruses B1, 3, 4; polioviruses 1–3		*Clinical Course* Variable, depending on site and extent of involvement	
Lower respiratory infection: Coxsackieviruses A7, 9; echovirus 9; enterovirus 68; coxsackieviruses B1, 4		*Complications* Common None	
Croup: Coxsackieviruses B5, A9; echovirus 11		Uncommon	
Etiological Role Proven Neonatal disease: coxsackieviruses B4, 5; other: coxsackieviruses A9; B4; echoviruses 9, 20		Death (common in fulminant neonatal disease, also reported are rare cases of fatal pneumonia in older patients)	1, 4, 163
AGE DISTRIBUTION:		DIAGNOSIS:	
Usual Age Range Children and adults (respiratory system may be involved in fulminant neonatal disease, especially with coxsackieviruses B)	1	*Differential Diagnosis* Respiratory illnesses due to bacterial agents (eg, group A β-hemolytic streptococcus) or nonenteroviruses (eg, adenoviruses, parainfluenza viruses, respiratory syncytial virus, etc)	
Clinical Differences by Age? None		*Key to Clinical Recognition* Generally nonspecific; maybe suspected in outbreaks of mild respiratory disease and in outbreaks in closed populations (eg, military recruits)	
SEX DISTRIBUTION: M/F ratio 1.4:1	CDC, unpublished data, 1981		
CLINICAL:		*Specimens for Viral Isolation* Throat and mouth; nasopharynx; lung tissue; no epidemiologic association between stool positivity and disease etiology, although stool may be positive	
Signs/Symptoms Common			
Febrile or afebrile URI most common, especially with sore throat, coryza, headache	1, 5	LABORATORY FINDINGS: Nonspecific	
Most often associated with another enteroviral syndrome rather than pure respiratory disease		PATIENT MANAGEMENT: Supportive	

Nonspecific Febrile Illnesses

The term "nonspecific febrile illness" describes a significant proportion of symptomatic persons infected with a variety of enterovirus types. How "nonspecific" the syndrome may be is a question of interpretation, but the term is meant to be descriptive of illness in which there is no reason to suspect, on the basis of signs and symptoms, an enterovirus over any of a host of other infectious agents. It could be argued that a summer febrile illness accompanied by maculopapular rash is specific enough to warrant

suspicion of an enterovirus infection, although in practice the term nonspecific febrile illness is mostly applied to cases, including those suspected of being due to enteroviruses, that do not have some other organ-specific involvement. Nonspecific febrile illnesses associated with enteroviruses are particularly common in children, especially those less than 4 years old.[221, 467] The male-to-female ratio is approximately 1.4:1. Influenza-like illness with or without rash is typical, but there is much overlap with upper respiratory tract syndromes, lower respiratory tract syndromes, GI syndromes, lymphadenopathy syndromes, and others.[4, 467] A biphasic course is occasionally noted. Though it is likely that most enteroviruses cause nonspecific febrile illnesses, a relatively small number of enteroviruses have been associated with the syndrome of nonspecific febrile illness in the medical literature, (eg, coxsackieviruses A9 and 16 and B4; echoviruses 3', 4, 9, and 16; and the polioviruses),[5, 221, 468] an unfortunate misrepresentation partly due to the understandable failure of investigators to dignify such cases with a special name. Isolations can be obtained from throat, stool, or rectal swab specimens. The course is benign, and there is no specific treatment.

Postviral Fatigue Syndrome

Recently, attention has been given to a poorly defined syndrome consisting of symptoms of excessive muscle fatigue on exercise accompanied by myalgia and dysphasia, with no other organic cause. This syndrome has been variously referred to as "chronic fatigue syndrome," epidemic neuromyasthenia, and epidemic myalgic encephalomyelitis. One group of viruses that has been implicated in this syndrome is the coxsackie B viruses. Several reports have described both outbreaks[469] and sporadic cases[470–472] in Scotland in which a high percentage of the patients had elevated levels of antibodies to one of the coxsackie B viruses. In one prospective study,[473] 46% of cases and 25% of matched controls had significant antibody titers. In many of these cases, the antibody levels were still elevated 1 year later. A recent report directly suggests a chronic enterovirus could be isolated from five of 17 cases 1 year later.[474] In addition, circulating viral antigen was demonstrated in IgM complexes in nearly 50% of the cases. Further studies will be required to examine this possible association.

Gastrointestinal Disease

It is ironic that enteroviruses, named after the major site of replication (the GI tract), so rarely cause gastroenteritis. This nondistinctive syndrome may occur in the course of an enterovirus infection causing another clinical syndrome (eg, respiratory disease), or, less commonly, alone. Observed predominantly in young children, especially full–term or premature neonates,[475, 476] it is often hard to know whether vomiting or diarrhea is associated with infection per se, or secondary to other signs, symptoms, or treatments, including medication, altered diet, emotion, coughing, swallowing of secretions, etc. Even in cases where this distinction can be reasonably made, there is no consistent picture of enteroviral gastroenteritis: diarrhea may predominate in some children, nausea and vomiting in others, and both symptoms in still others. Abdominal pain, cramps, colic, constipation, anorexia, and signs and symptoms of respiratory and other enterovirus syndromes may also be seen.[5, 475] Cases of "pseudoappendicitis" have rarely been associated with various echoviruses, and the occasional isolation of enteroviruses from cases of necrotizing enterocolitis is of uncertain significance.[475, 477] Pediatricians should be especially aware that gastroenteritis seen in office practice is not likely to be due to enteroviruses. Nursery outbreaks are occasionally seen, however, and are commonly associated with echoviruses 1 and 18, as well as types 2, 6, 7, 11, 14, 19, 20, 22, and others.[1, 4, 59, 62, 102, 275, 478–483] A host of other viral and nonviral infectious agents are more likely to cause acute gastroenteritis. The differential diagnosis includes gastroenteritis associated with rotaviruses, Norwalk-like viruses,

Escherichia coli, Shigella, Salmonella, Campylobacter, Yersinia, Giardia, amoebae, etc. Fecal leukocytes are not prominent in gastroenteritis caused by viruses. Many viral pathogens may be isolated from or detected in stool or rectal swab specimens.

While there is no specific treatment, it is particularly important that adequate hydration is maintained in children with gastroenteritis. A clear liquid or bland diet may be of benefit for both upper and lower GI tract disease. Oral rehydration solution, as supported and distributed by WHO and the United Nations Children's Fund (UNICEF), should suffice to treat most cases of gastroenteritis. Frequent small feedings are desirable when vomiting is present, serving to maintain hydration and prevent vomiting induced by introduction of large boluses of food or liquid into the stomach. Most physicians do not recommend antidiarrheals that act on the autonomic nervous system. Bismuth subsalicylate may be beneficial and is nontoxic, but efficacy has not been proved for children or for adults with enterovirus-associated gastroenteritis. The outlook is excellent, with prompt resolution in several days being the rule. In developing countries, infantile gastroenteritis of any cause may be serious or fatal, especially when coupled with undernutrition, undesirable hydration practices, and forced starvation during illness.

Hepatitis

Excepting hepatitis A virus, which was provisionally (and probably erroneously) classified as enterovirus type 72, clinical hepatitis associated with enteroviruses is rare. Viral hepatitis is generally caused by hepatitis A or B viruses, hepatitis C virus, delta virus (hepatitis D), hepatitis E virus, other unidentified "non-A, non-B" hepatitis viruses, Epstein-Barr virus (EBV), or CMV infection. The contribution of the other enteroviruses to the overall incidence of hepatitis is not precisely known, but is presumed to be minor. Coxsackieviruses A4, 9, and 10, B2, B3, and 5; and echoviruses 3, 9, and 14 have all been implicated.[1, 484, 485] Presumably, other enteroviruses may also cause hepatic disease. Cases are often reported in neonates, where hepatitis may be a part of multisystem disease. Cases in older children and adults are usually benign, virtually never fulminant. Enterovirus hepatitis cases are diagnosed so uncommonly that description of the typical clinical picture is difficult. Signs and symptoms of enterovirus infection at other sites may be present. Icteric patients generally have elevated bilirubin and serum transaminase levels. Other symptoms suggestive of hepatitis in general are common, including anorexia, weight loss, nausea, abdominal pain, and lassitude. In addition to the different types of viral hepatitis noted above, the differential diagnosis includes leptospirosis, other infectious causes of hepatitis, and other physical, metabolic, and toxic causes of hepatic disease. Viruses can generally be isolated from stool or liver tissue. However, liver biopsy is not routinely indicated. In neonates icteric enteroviral hepatitis has a grave prognosis. In older children and adults, a prolonged but full convalescence is to be expected. Treatment is supportive and includes rest and adequate nutrition.

Diabetes Mellitus and Other Pancreatic Disease

Acute enteroviral pancreatitis is an uncommon disease of infants, children, and adults, associated principally with the coxsackie B viruses, especially B1, B2 and B4.[486–490] In neonates pancreatitis occurs in association with multisystem disease and may only be diagnosed at autopsy. Virus may be isolated from pancreatic tissue or stool. Differential diagnosis includes ethanol toxicity, mumps, trauma, gallstones, and a host of other possibilities.[491] Treatment is symptomatic and supportive. The course in adults is not as severe as typical pancreatitis due to other causes and may be milder than that seen in association with ethanol toxicity.

Viral etiologies have been postulated for juvenile-onset insulin-dependent diabetes mellitus (IDDM) since the nineteenth century, including mumps virus, rubella virus, and various herpesviruses. Intense speculation has centered on the possible role of the coxsackie B viruses. This topic, including most of the published studies, is covered in several reviews.[492–495] To date, the studies have neither proved nor disproved the association. Several lines of evidence have maintained interest in this possible association including secular and seasonal trends and geographic distribution in incidence of IDDM. Studies in murine models,[496] where infection of certain inbred strains of mice with another picornavirus, encephalomy-ocarditis virus,[496] or coxsackievirus B4[486] produces diabetes, contribute to the continued plausibility of coxsackie B virus-induced IDDM. In humans, serologic case-control studies and several individual case reports[486, 488, 497–505] support an association between coxsackie B virus infection and diabetes mellitus. For example, a study conducted in Sweden[506, 507] found that 16 (67%) of 24 patients less than 15 years old, newly diagnosed with IDDM, had IgM antibodies to one or more coxsackie B viruses, whereas none of the age-matched controls had IgM antibodies to coxsackie B viruses. Follow-up on the 16 positive patients revealed titers had declined and were below detection in most cases after 6 months, supporting the inference of recent infection.

In addition to specific associations with recent coxsackie B virus infection, the genetic susceptibility of the patient seems to be very important. In studies of patients in Austria,[508] 22 (96%) of 23 cases with coxsackie B virus-specific IgM had human leukocyte antigen (HLA) DR3, DR4, or both, compared with 76% with these HLA types in the viral IgM-negative patients. A study in Pittsburgh also investigated the association of HLA type, coxsackie B virus antibody, and diabetes.[509] In this study, HLA type was determined for 172 persons hospitalized for IDDM. The DR3 type was found more often in males and the DR4 types more often in females. In addition, cases with the DR4 type had a greater frequency of coxsackie B virus antibodies. From these recent studies, further support is provided for the association between coxsackie B infection and IDDM, and suggestive evidence for some HLA correlation with this disease. Proving a cause-and-effect relationship is difficult, in part because IDDM appears to have more than a single etiology. In any case, there is no evidence that IDDM associated with previous enterovirus infection requires different treatment or is associated with a different prognosis.

Disease of the Urinary Tract

Reports of acute or chronic glomerulonephritis, hemorrhagic or nonhemorrhagic cystitis, and asymptomatic renal disease in association with enteroviruses surface so rarely that it is difficult to ascertain the extent to which enterovirus infections may cause these syndromes, if at all.[510–514] Implicated enteroviruses include coxsackieviruses B1 to 5 and echovirus 9.[512–514] Cases are reported in children and adults. Virus is isolated from tissue, urine, or stool. The laboratory profile reflects the syndromes as associated with other etiologies, and management of patients is likewise guided by clinical experience with similar renal disease of known cause.

There is some evidence to implicate enteroviruses in the hemolytic-uremic syndrome, discussed later under Miscellaneous Syndromes.

Arthritis

Although arthralgias may occasionally occur during the course of enterovirus infections, frank arthritis is rare.[515–521] When it does occur in enterovirus infection, arthritis is typically seen in older children and adults, and may be mono- or polyarticular. Enteroviruses are not recognized as a cause of juvenile or adult rheumatoid arthritis, although in one recent report, the authors claim evidence of coxsackie B virus infection at the onset of juvenile rheumatoid arthritis in a 12-year-old girl.[517] Another group of investigators have reported an association between coxsackie B viruses and juvenile dermatomyositis.[522] The differential diagnosis in children includes juvenile rheumatoid arthritis, "toxic synovitis," bacterial arthritis, drug reaction, Perthes disease, trauma, rubella, leptospirosis, and others. In adults the differential diagnosis is even broader, and includes collagen-vascular diseases, rubella vaccination, Reiter syndrome, erythema infectiosum (human parvovirus B19 infection), and a variety of other infections and immunologic diseases. Virus may be isolated from stool or throat, rarely from synovial fluid.[519] The typical laboratory profile, including that of the synovial fluid, is not known. Treatment is symptomatic, including avoidance of trauma to, and weight bearing on, the affected joint, maintenance of full range of motion, and prescription of anti-inflammatory agents. Associated signs and symptoms may reflect enteroviral involvement of other sites, including the respiratory tract. Occasionally such involvement may precede arthritis by weeks, making the association more tenuous.

Miscellaneous Syndromes

A number of other disease syndromes associated with enteroviruses are either uncommon, or an etiologic link is only speculative.

Hemolytic-uremic syndrome, a serious and occasionally fatal condition of early childhood, results from renal microangiopathy associated with reduced glomerular filtration, microangiopathic hemolytic anemia, and thrombocytopenia. There is good evidence that the syndrome is of multifactorial etiology, including a variety of infectious agents. It is endemic in Argentina and South Africa, but appears to occur sporadically elsewhere. Hemolytic-uremic syndrome has been associated with several enteroviruses, including coxsackieviruses B2, 4, and 5, A4 and 9; and echovirus 22, by concomitant viral isolation or serology.[523–526] Viruses may be isolated from stool, urine, or renal tissue. Hemolytic-uremic syndrome requires comprehensive medical management. The outcome is generally favorable, but death may occur in about 5% of cases.

Orchitis complicating enterovirus infection has been mentioned above in association with pleurodynia (predominantly of coxsackievirus B etiology). Orchitis also has been associated rarely with other enteroviruses. It is usually unilateral and benign. Sterility secondary to enterovirus orchitis is not known. Oophoritis has not been recognized. There is no specific treatment.

Reye syndrome is a well-described complication of ingestion of aspirin during infection with influenza B, influenza A, or varicella viruses.[527] Enteroviruses have rarely been incriminated in Reye syndrome, and there is no convincing evidence that enteroviral infection can cause Reye syndrome.

The cause or causes of sudden infant death syndrome (SIDS) are obscure. In a number of instance, viruses, including enteroviruses, have been isolated from tissues of infants dying of SIDS, but it is difficult to prove an etiologic link in most cases, particularly in view of the absence of pathologic findings suggestive of serious infection. SIDS may be a result of the interaction of a number of factors, including maturational, physiologic, and infectious. The role of enteroviruses in SIDS is speculative.

Myopathy, myositis, and rhabdomyolysis may result from virus infections other than arbovirus infections, most notably with influenza B. Enteroviruses, however, have occasionally been associated with these syndromes. As noted above, the term "epidemic myalgia" is a misnomer, actually describing pleurodynia, and not the typical picture of viral myalgias which are often most prominent in the large muscle groups—for example, the quadriceps femoris. Little is known about enterovirus-associated myositis, as it is rarely recognized as a distinct entity. Rhabdomyolysis, which probably represents the severe end of the spectrum of myositis, is occasionally linked to an enterovirus. Crystalline arrays of enteroviruses may be seen in muscle biopsies of patients with myositis[528] and in patients dying of serious enterovirus infections associated with other clinical syndromes (see Fig 17–6). An association between enteroviruses and polymyositis or dermatomyositis appears to be real, although the incidence is not known. A recent study of patients with pediatric dermatomyositis found increased antibody levels against coxsackie B viruses[522] and, as noted below, enterovirus-associated polymyositis is seen frequently enough to have stimulated articles on possible treatment strategies.

Although lymphadenitis may occasionally occur in the course of an enteroviral illness, it is not commonly seen by itself. Reports of outbreaks of "glandular fever" possibly associated with enteroviruses are uncommon. Enteroviruses are not likely causes of chronic lymphadenopathy or of lymphadenopathy in the cervical triangles or elsewhere, if unassociated with other signs or symptoms.

Recently, an investigative group has drawn attention to an apparent epidemiologic association between deaths from amyotrophic lateral sclerosis and reports of poliomyelitis 40 years earlier.[528a] However, no biologic data to support this association have yet been presented.

Enterovirus Infection in the Immunocompromised Host

Persons with congenital or acquired immunodeficiency, and those receiving immunosuppressive chemotherapy, steroids, and extensive radiation are generally more susceptible to infection with a variety of microorganisms, and are also more susceptible to serious complications of infections they acquire. Enteroviruses are not prominent among the microorganisms that cause serious morbidity and mortality in immunocompromised persons, but their occasional implication in disease suggests that physicians caring

for such patients, particularly children, be aware of the possible manifestations. In childhood, serious enterovirus infection does not appear to be particularly common in the T cell immunodeficiency syndromes, including the DiGeorge or Nezelhof syndromes. Most reports of serious enterovirus disease have been in children with Burton X-linked agammaglobulinemia or, less frequently, severe combined immunodeficiency. Curiously, these infections may be persistent, including chronic enteritis, arthritis, and persistent CNS infection.[213, 529–533] In other cases, enterovirus illness is simply more severe than expected, and it has been presumed in the absence of population-based studies that such immunocompromised patients are thereby at greater risk. Dermatomyositis-like illness also has been associated with hereditary agammaglobulinemia.[525] Although echovirus infections have been implicated most frequently in serious infections of agammaglobulinemic children,[535, 536] coxsackievirus A and B infections have also been documented.[201, 536–538] In one instance, an infant with agammaglobulinemia was shown to chronically excrete both coxsackieviruses A4 and A15.[201] It is believed that immunodeficiency may be associated with paralysis during poliovirus infection; therefore, patients with a recognized immunodeficiency condition should be given inactivated rather than live oral polio vaccine. Inactivated polio vaccine is also recommended for all persons infected with HIV who require immunization.[539, 540]

LABORATORY

What Specimens to Collect

Establishing an association between an enterovirus and a particular disease in a patient requires laboratory confirmation of infection, usually by either isolation of the virus, or documentation of a specific serologic response in properly timed specimens (fourfold or greater rise or fall in antibody titer, or a single high titer of type-specific IgM antibody).

Whereas many clinical virology laboratories are able to attempt enterovirus isolation in cell culture, complete serologic evaluation can be performed only in a few reference or research laboratories that maintain stock viruses. Laboratories sometimes receive serum specimens with a request to "test for enteroviruses." But "blind" serodiagnosis is impractical: since few enteroviruses cross-react sufficiently, it would require 65 different tests to rule out NPEV infection, a feat that would be economically infeasible even if enough serum were available. Infections with NPEVs are not generally amenable to serologic diagnosis unless an isolation has been made, or available clinical or epidemiologic information can narrow the number of possible viruses. Nevertheless, if enteroviral disease is suspected and specific diagnosis is important, acute and convalescent phase serum specimens should be obtained in anticipation of viral isolation from the stool or elsewhere. The acute specimen should be collected as soon after onset of illness as possible. The convalescent specimen should be collected about 3 to 4 weeks after illness onset. If the "acute" specimen is obtained late, a "late convalescent" specimen (after several months) may be collected to look for a late titer fall.

Before collecting specimens, it is important to determine who will handle and test them. Such information will prevent collection of unnecessary specimens that cannot actually or practically be tested or that are costly and not likely to yield helpful information. In situations where the clinician or epidemiologist is not familiar with laboratory capabilities, contacting the laboratory ahead of time to discuss the situation may be of value in developing a plan to maximize the chances for, and precision of, diagnosis. Most large university medical centers have virology laboratories, and almost all of these have capabilities for virus isolation. However, very few can definitively identify a specific enterovirus type. The laboratory determination of presumptive enterovirus isolation based on characteristic cytopathic effect in tissue culture may be sufficient for a presumptive diagnosis. If it is not, or if there is some other reason for more specific diagnosis, the isolate is forwarded to a commercial, reference, or state health department laboratory, where it may in turn be forwarded to CDC (in the United States) or to other WHO reference laboratories (in other countries). Clinicians not affiliated with hospitals that have access to viral diagnostic laboratories may forward specimens directly to local, state, or regional health department laboratories. As can be appreciated, the path from specimen collection to final diagnosis may easily involve four or more agencies, for example, the clinician, local hospital laboratory, local reference diagnostic virology laboratory, and "tertiary" reference laboratory with capabilities for serotyping. However, the clinician's most important relationship is with the local viral diagnostic laboratory, which makes the isolation in most cases and which eventually (often after a period of weeks) returns the results.

Since enteroviruses replicate in the alimentary tract and pass eventually to specific target organs, there is a rational basis for deciding what specimen to submit for virus isolation in a patient with a particular syndrome. The stool (or rectal swab) is most important, but enteroviruses may also be isolated from upper and lower respiratory tract swabs and washings, CSF, blood, urine, conjuctival scrapings, and various organs and tissues. Successful isolation of an enterovirus is related to: (1) virus type and strain; (2) the virus titer within the specimen; (3) duration of viral shedding in realtion to the time after onset of infection or illness that the specimen is obtained; (4) patient age; (5) clinical syndrome; (6) the site from which the specimen is obtained; (7) transportation and storage conditions; and (8) the laboratory system used for viral isolation.

Although the isolation rate of coxsackievirus B5 is inversely related to host age, especially among asymptomatic cases,[164] it is not known whether the same phenomenon is true for enteroviruses in general. Most enteroviruses are excreted first in the oropharynx and shortly thereafter in the stool of both asymptomatic and symptomatic cases. The duration of viral shedding from the upper alimentary tract is from a few days to 1 to 2 weeks.[4, 102, 107, 223] Fecal excretion generally lasts longer, about 1 to 4 weeks, and occasionally longer.[5, 62, 84, 102, 107, 541–543] Polioviruses are shed for 5 weeks or more.[161] Echoviruses are shed for the shortest period of time, the duration of coxsackievirus excretion falling between these extremes.[80] Enterovirus 70 and coxsackievirus A24 variant, both of which cause AHC, are usually shed in the upper respiratory tract for no more than three to five days.

Alimentary tract specimens include throat specimens (swabs or washes), stool, and rectal swabs. Higher virus isolation rates are usually obtained from stool rather than rectal swab specimens, with viruses being isolated from swabs in as few as one third to one half of stool-positive patients.[544, 545] However, multiple rectal swabs (three) may increase the chance of virus isolation fourfold over that for a single rectal swab.[545] Isolation rates for almost all enteroviruses are higher from stool than from throat specimens.[82, 114, 546] However, throat specimens may be as good or better for cases of respiratory or rash illness associated with certain of the coxsackieviruses A and B and echoviruses.[67, 273, 547, 548] Throat specimens are most likely to be positive during the first few days of illness; fecal specimens may become positive after the first few days.[114, 542] Conjunctival scrapings are indicated in cases of enteroviral conjunctivitis; stool is characteristically virus-negative.

Although polioviruses are rarely isolated from the CSF, other enteroviruses associated with aseptic meningitis can be isolated with relative ease. Echoviruses are most frequently isolated from the CSF of meningitis patients, particularly those with echoviruses 9 (75%–87%) and 19 (35%–40%).[74, 92, 115, 128, 166, 549] Other echoviruses found in the CSF include echoviruses 2, 4 to 7, 11, 14 to 20, 23, 30, and 31.[1, 126, 361, 367, 401, 437, 543] CSF isolations of coxsackieviruses A9, B2 and EV71 have also been reported.[163, 320, 550] Chances for isolation are best when CSF specimens are obtained during the first few days of illness and handled as described below.

Some enteroviruses may also be isolated from the blood, for example, coxsackieviruses A4 and A6, echovirus 9, and others;[4, 204, 551] from skin lesions, for example, EV71, and from biopsy or necropsy tissues. Isolation from blood may be facilitated by obtaining a fasting sample in the morning.[528] Coxsackieviruses B 1 to 6 are rarely isolated from tissue specimens, except those from fatal neonatal cases.[160]

Laboratory Evaluation of Clinical Specimens
Virus Isolation and Identification

It is important to take steps to optimize chances for recovery of an enterovirus without overburdening the laboratory with useless specimens to process. Whenever possible, specimens should be obtained early in the illness; chances for successful enterovirus isolation decrease as illness progresses much beyond the first few days. However, virus in the stool may be detected for weeks in some cases, so attempts at isolation need not be abandoned if identification is important. Except for ACH, enterovirus isolation attempts should always include stool or rectal swab culture—the stool is by far the most likely site from which most enteroviruses can be isolated. In addition, the probability of establishing a cause–effect relationship may be increased by attempting isolation from an affected target organ—for example, from CSF in the case of aseptic meningitis.

The specimen should be obtained at the bedside, placed in viral transport medium, and taken directly to the virology laboratory on wet ice. Although enteroviruses are hardy, if rapid transport is not possible, the specimen should be frozen at −70°C or placed on dry ice or in liquid nitrogen for storage and transportation. (Although freezing at −20°C is acceptable for enteroviruses, it is not generally to be recommended when isolation of other viruses that do not survive at that temperature is considered.) Repeated freezing-thawing cycles of specimens should be avoided, as decline in virus titer is inevitable. The type of medium into which the specimen is inoculated will vary depending on the practices of the laboratory or institution. Many laboratories have special "viral

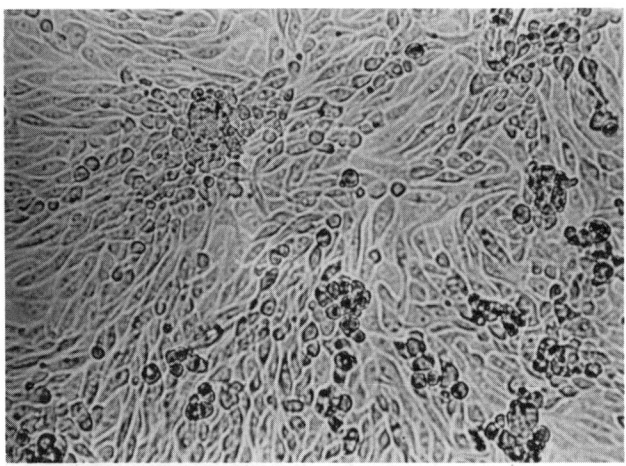

Figure 17–10. Cytopathic effect (CPE) in primary monkey kidney (PMK) cells infected with echovirus type 9. Note cellular changes apparent in numerous foci: cell rounding, change in refractility, and cell shrinking. The CPE seen above is graded 2+, indicating visible involvement of 25% to 50% of cells. Typically, after the appearance of such focal changes, destruction of the cell sheet rapidly progresses.

transport medium,'' such as tryptose phosphate broth or Hank's balanced salt solution buffered to a pH of about 7 and containing 0.25% to 0.50% bovine serum albumin or gelatin, and various antimicrobial agents to prevent bacterial growth. Such solutions provide a neutral, stable environment in which viruses may retain infectivity until they can be inoculated onto living cells. Typically, 1 to 2 mL of such medium is placed in a 5- to 10-cc glass screw-cap vial. Care must be taken to prevent contaminating the cap and the lips of the vial during the process. If such contamination does occur, the lip or cap can be gently ''flamed.'' A common source of error in obtaining rectal or other swabs occurs when the investigator either breaks off the shaft of the swab into the tube such that it cannot easily be retrieved later in the laboratory; or, in breaking off the shaft at the level of the tube lips, contaminates it with (often bare) fingers; or, less commonly, breaks the shaft at such a high point that the cap will not screw on properly and the medium subsequently leaks. A few minutes of practice in proper technique can be worth the effort. In the laboratory, elution of virus from the cotton swab is enhanced by alkalinization of the medium or fluid to pH 7.5. In some cases it may be desirable to obtain tissue culture medium beforehand and inoculate the specimen directly into it.

If a rectal swab is to be obtained it should first be moistened with medium, placed deeply into the rectum, and twirled. To ensure an adequate specimen, the swab should become discolored with fecal material. Proper technique also includes swirling the swab in the medium, sealing the cap, and labeling the tube with indelible ink. A 4- to 8-g stool specimen in an empty glass jar is usually the single best specimen. If isolation from the mouth and throat is desired, it may be helpful to have the patient gargle several times with medium or sterile saline over a period of two to three minutes and spit periodically into a small cup. Vesicles may be aspirated with a 26- or 27-gauge needle after skin preparation with ether or acetone, or ruptured and swabbed with a cotton swab, making sure to include the base of the lesion. In attempting to

isolate enteroviruses from the blood, it may be necessary to break up antigen-antibody complexes. Success with an acid-dissociation technique has been reported.[552]

Upon arrival at the laboratory, specimens are usually refrigerated at 4°C before inoculation. If long delays are unavoidable, they should be frozen, as mentioned above. CSF samples in particular must be frozen if they cannot be inoculated immediately. Stool specimens are generally prepared by emulsification to yield a 10% to 20% suspension in sterile saline, followed by low-speed centrifugation to remove debris, and decanting of the supernatant for inoculation. In the laboratory, specimens are generally inoculated into cell culture and, if available, suckling mice (mouse inoculation is discussed later). Primary cultures of monkey kidney cells (PMK) are an excellent ''broad spectrum'' cell type, supporting the growth of polioviruses; coxsackieviruses A7, 9, and 16; coxsackieviruses B; and echoviruses excepting type 21. They are generally available and often used in diagnostic virology laboratories. Most enteroviruses also replicate in human embryonic diploid cells. Many coxsackieviruses A may replicate in RD cells, which are continuous cells derived from human rhabdomyosarcoma. Coxsackieviruses B in particular replicate in continuous cell cultures such as HEp-2 and HeLa. The use of several different cell lines with different sensitivities to different enteroviruses increases the frequency of isolating virus.[544] The inoculated cells have usually been grown beforehand in glass or plastic tubes until a monolayer is formed, as described in Chapter 5. An inoculum of the specimen is then added to the monolayer. Any enteroviruses present may then infect the cells in the monolayer. Infection is usually detected within one to seven days by the appearance of characteristic CPE (usually graded 1+ to 4+), which features visible rounding, shrinking, nuclear pyknosis, refractility, and cell degeneration (Figs 17–10 and 17–11).

The earliest effects may be seen within 24 hours if the inoculum contains a large number of infectious particles; usually, however, changes are not identified for several days, and some agents either do not cause CPE at all, or do so only on subsequent passage.[6] In general, however, once focal CPE is detected, there is rapid spread of infection throughout the cell sheet with total destruction of the monolayer, sometimes in a matter of hours (Fig 17–12). The nature of the CPE in various cell cultures is so characteristic that a cautious presumptive diagnosis of enterovirus infection can often be made at initial detection of cytopathic changes. However, early changes (in the first 24 hours) may be confused with cell toxicity, associated with nonviral components of the inoculum. Under agar overlay, plaque formation may be visualized; when present, poliovirus plaques are most characteristic, with sharply defined, circular, clear-centered holes (Fig 17–13). Coxsackievirus B plaques may appear more slowly and do not have distinct edges. Coxsackievirus A plaques are variable in appearance. The titer roughly correlates with the rapidity with which CPE develops for those enteroviruses that readily cause CPE.

As mentioned above, presumptive diagnosis of an enterovirus infection can often be made on the basis of characteristic CPE alone, but conclusions about the infecting type or group cannot be made on this basis. Tissue cultures are usually held about a week, then passed blindly one time. Identification of the enterovirus type is a time-consuming and costly process not uniformly undertaken by diagnostic laboratories. Since there are 67 different known enteroviruses, it would be impractical to attempt neutralization using all possible reference antisera individually. Instead, an ingenious and efficient process for identification of isolates has been developed for use by reference and research laboratories. This process utilizes equine type–specific reference antiserum reagents mixed together into several "intersecting" pools (ie, pools containing antisera to individual enteroviruses in some of the pools, but not in others). After attempted neutralization of an isolated enterovirus is completed with all of these pools separately, an inference about the enterovirus type can be made by observing which pools result in neutralization and which do not, a pattern that is designed to be distinct for each specific enterovirus type. Usually, the field is narrowed to one enterovirus type, and final confirmation can be obtained by conducting one last neutralization test with that single type-specific equine antiserum.

If, for example, it is necessary to identify a virus presumed to be an enterovirus on the basis of CPE in PMK cells, the laboratory may go through the following process. A typical neutralization

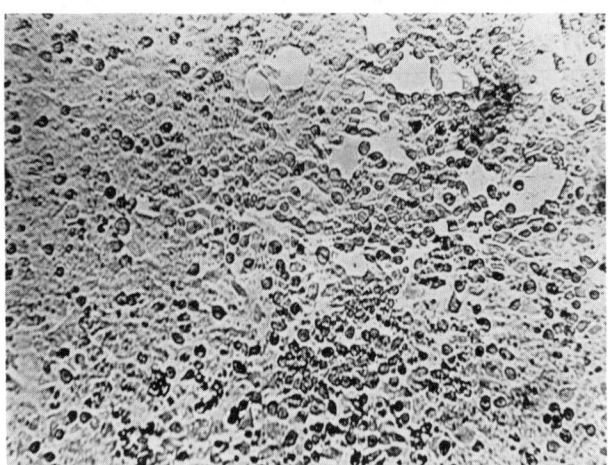

Figure 17–11. Poliovirus infection of HeLa cells.

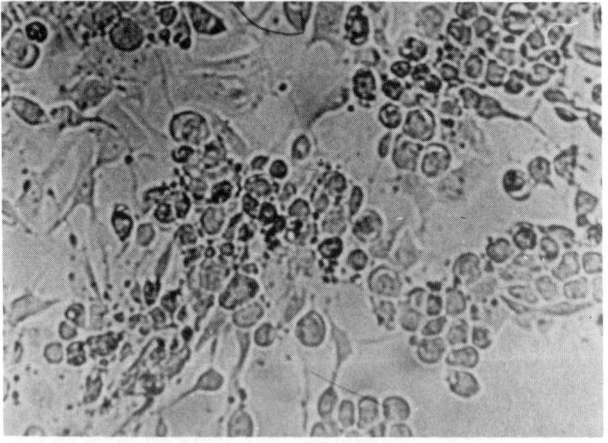

Figure 17–12. Primary monkey kidney cells infected with poliovirus. Cytopathic effect is graded 4+. Few normal-appearing cells can be identified, much of the cell sheet is destroyed, and those cells that remain are abnormally rounded and refractile. The line in the lower center of the photograph is artifactual.

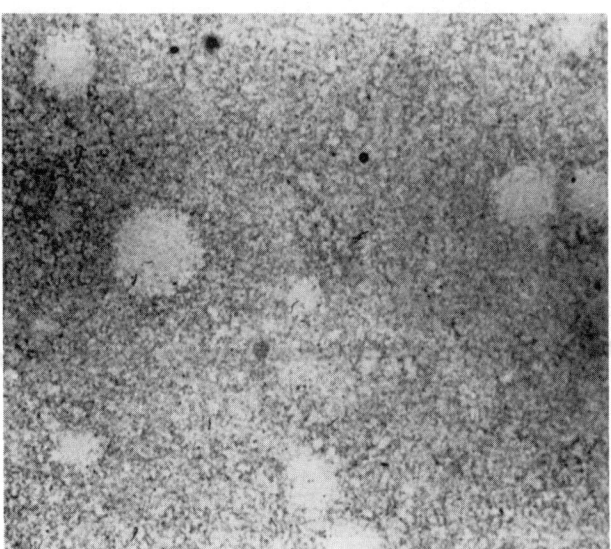

Figure 17–13. Poliovirus plaques as seen visually in a plaque assay. Plaques are round, roughly same-sized, clear-centered, and exhibiting distinct edges.

test consists of mixing approximately 100 $TCID_{50}$ (50% tissue culture dose) of the unknown virus with 20 units of an antiserum pool, incubating at 37°C for two hours, followed by inoculation of the virus–antiserum mixture onto a susceptible tissue culture system which is then observed for CPE over several days time. A separate virus-antiserum mixture is made for each of the available antiserum pools, and observation of which of the pools are associated with neutralization and which are not allows an inference about the infecting virus. The most widely used reagent antiserum can be obtained from WHO, and is prepared by inoculating horses successively with antigen over a 6-month period, and exsanguinating the horse 2 weeks after the booster dose. This results in approximatley 10 L of reagent antiserum of titer 1:1000 to 1:20,000, depending on the enterovirus type used for immunization. Type-specific antisera are then combined in intersecting pools in such a way that antibody to any one type is present in only a limited number of pools, for example, only two pools.[554, 555] In the Lim, Benyesh-Melnick or LBM pool scheme, antibody to 42 different enteroviruses sorted into eight pools (labeled A–H) are used (Table 17–5). If only pools A and B (Table 17–5) neutralize the unknown virus, it is presumptively identified as coxsackievirus A7; if only pools B, D, and F neutralize the isolate, echovirus 26 is implicated. Other pool schemes have been devised and used successfully, but are less widely used due to limited reagent availability. If the virus cannot be identified by use of the A to H pools, seven other pools (labeled J–P), representing 19 coxsackievirus A serotypes, can be used for mouse or tissue culture neutralization. But the process is not always problem-free. Viruses may escape neutralization because of aggregation, which is especially commonplace with echovirus types 4 and 30. Passage through small pore size filters or treatment with sodium deoxycholate or chloroform may be necessary. Failure of neutralization may also result from a mixed enterovirus infection, in which case the virologist may be forced to attempt to purify the mixture by terminal dilution or plaque purification. In major reference laboratories, "untypable" entero-

Table 17–5
Type Specific Antibodies Included in Each of Eight Intersecting "Lim, Benyesh-Melnick (LBM) Pools"*

Pool Designation	Enteroviruses Against Which Type-Specific Antibodies Are Represented in Pool
A	Coxsackieviruses A7, B1, Bf; echoviruses 1, 4, 5, 7, 15, 29 33
B	Coxsackieviruses A7, A9, B2; echoviruses 2, 3, 9, 21, 26; poliovirus 2
C	Coxsackieviruses B1, B3, B5; echoviruses 2, 6, 12, 24, 29, 30; poliovirus 1
D	Coxsackieviruses B2; echoviruses 6, 13, 14, 16, 25, 26, 32, 33; poliovirus 3
E	Coxsackieviruses B4, B5; echoviruses 5, 11, 13, 17, 18, 22, 20, 32; poliovirus 2
F	Coxsackieviruses B6; echoviruses 7, 14, 18, 19, 20, 26, 27, 29; poliovirus 1
G	Coxsackieviruses A9, B3; echoviruses 4, 5, 16, 17, 20, 23, 30, 31
H	Coxsackieviruses A16, B6; echoviruses 1, 3, 9, 12, 22, 23, 32; poliovirus 3

*Antibodies against 19 additional coxsackie A viruses in pools J to P are not shown. After Lim and Benyesh-Melnick.[554]

viruses are frequently encountered. They may represent mixed infections, aggregates of viruses, extreme antigenic drift or undiscovered types. In theory, it should be possible to identify or characterize all of these, but such laborious and time-consuming processes are rarely justifiable for routine clinical isolation. Fortunately for the clinician, it is seldom critical to identify the specific nonpolio enterovirus type. In any case, a high index of suspicion of an enterovirus, and even of the enterovirus group, can be developed by reflecting upon the clinical picture, the isolation systems susceptible and not susceptible to infection, and knowledge of what enteroviruses are prevalent in the community.

Even though most coxsackie A viruses have been successfully grown in various tissue culture systems, isolation from clinical specimens is sometimes unsuccessful, necessitating the inoculation of suckling mice. Inoculation of suckling mice and subsequent identification is a process analagous to that of cell culture inoculation. With coxsackievirus A infection, newborn mice develop flaccid paralysis and die within a week. The specific enterovirus type can be identified by serum pool neutralizations in other litters of suckling mice. As noted, coxsackievirus B infection proceeds more slowly and results in spastic paralysis. Echoviruses do not generally cause disease in mice (although echovirus type 9 can be an exception because some isolates do indeed produce disease in mice). Sometimes blind passage in mice is necessary because of initial low titer or, perhaps, adaptation to growth in mice.

Several recent technical advances have allowed the development of alternative procedures for detecting and characterizing enteroviruses. Nucleic acid probes have been developed for detecting enterovirus genomes. These probes have been made by synthesizing complementary DNA (cDNA) from coxsackieviral and polioviral RNA. Using conventional procedures, cDNA was made to representatives of all six serotypes of CB viruses.[556] The cDNA can be cloned into bacteria, amplified, and radiochemically labeled to provide a reagent for detecting enterovirus genomes by nucleic acid hybridization.[557] Partial genomic clones were made in this manner to several of the CB viruses[558, 559] and used to detect viral geomes in tissue culture,[560] reconstructed clinical specimens,[561] and tissues.[558, 559] This technique is more rapid than isolation and therefore may be clinically helpful; however, it is currently less sensitive than isolation and cannot be used to type enteroviruses.

As should be obvious from the above discussion, laboratory personnel working with enteroviruses, including those in diagnostic virology laboratories, should take appropriate safety precautions to prevent infection. Laboratory-acquired enterovirus infections are not uncommon, including, in rare instances, disabling and fatal infections. Work should be done in a biosafety level 2 laboratory. Gloves should be worn when handling specimens. Mouth-pipetting is always prohibited. Work is done in a class II biological safety cabinet. It is essential that all personnel be tested for poliovirus antibody, and if seronegative to one or more types, immunized (ideally with inactivated vaccine) and subsequently retested to ensure that antibody to all three types has developed.

Serodiagnosis

Serologic diagnosis of enterovirus infection is made by comparing titers in acute and convalescent phase ("paired") serum specimens. If an enterovirus isolation and identification has been made, the task is greatly simplified: serum pairs can be tested against the patient's own isolate. If not, it still may be possible to prove enterovirus infection if there is a high index of suspicion of a particular type. In that case, a reference strain maintained in the laboratory may be used in a neutralization test. In general, however, enterovirus serodiagnosis is more relevant to epidemiologic studies than to clinical problem solving. The most basic serologic test is that of neutralization of CPE in cell culture or of paralysis in suckling mice. Plaque reduction neutralizaiton in bottles, plastic dishes or large-well polystyrene plates is used in some laboratories, especially for echoviruses 4 and 30 which are less readily neutralized in tube culture. Usually either 90% or 50% plaque reduction is used as the end point indicative of virus neutralization. There are other serologic methods, all with particular strengths and weaknesses. None enjoy universal acceptance today. These tests include CF, passive hemagglutination, HI, immunofluorescence, and others. Unfortunately, the nature of many enteroviral illnesses is such that antibody may already be present at the time the original specimen is obtained, complicating interpretation of results. A fourfold or greater rise (or fall, in the case of late specimens) in type-specific antibody titer is considered diagnostic of infection.

Recently, ELISA tests have been developed for detecting coxsackie B virus-specific and EV70-specific IgM.[562–566] Though these tests may be relatively sensitive in detecting IgM, they are not purely serotype-specific,[567] since 10% to 70% of sera may exhibit cross-reactive responses, presumably due to infection with other enteroviruses.

Ideally, interpretation by the clinician of serologic testing for enteroviruses depends on consultation with the viral diagnostic laboratory. Although enterovirus neutralizing antibody is generally type-specific, low level cross-reactions may occur. For example, in the case of poliovirus infection, heterotypic and homotypic antibodies may be detected in the patient serum in response to infection with a single poliovirus type. An excellent review of the laboratory diagnosis of enterovirus infections was published.[527]

TREATMENT

There is no specific treatment for any enterovirus infection. Enteroviruses are not susceptible to antibiotics and have not been shown to respond to any viral chemotherapeutic agents in safe doses. No experimental drugs expected to be efficacious for enterovirus disease are awaiting licensure at present.

Nevertheless, the physician should not be unduly pessimistic about treatment; serious morbidity and mortality is the exception rather than the rule (except for neonatal disease), and even in some severe cases there is reason to hope that optimal supportive care may succeed until the acute infection runs its course. Depending on the illness and the age of the patient, such supportive care may include limitation of physical activity, proper nutrition, maintenance of fluid and electrolyte balance, respiratory support including mechanical ventilation, and administration of life-supporting drugs such as digitalis.

Even for minor illnesses, such as herpangina, the physician may do much, for example, alleviate pain by prescribing local or systemic analgesics. And for those rare cases that result in chronic disability, such as paralytic poliomyelitis, the physician will ideally coordinate the long-term rehabilitation, physical therapy, and orthotic treatment. Furthermore, children and adults with chronic disability, such as typically occurs with paralytic poliomyelitis, may need the emotional support of a concerned physician.

As is the case with most systemic viral infections, treatment of enterovirus infections is generally supportive and nonspecific. Since the vast majority of infections are mild and resolve within a matter of days, treatment aims are directed at assuring the patient, preventing exacerbation of disease (eg, recommending against heavy physical exertion during coxsackie B virus infection), or preventing or treating secondary complications (eg, bacterial conjunctivitis during EV70 infection). Some of these approaches are mentioned elsewhere in sections that deal with specific diseases.

In recent years, physicians have begun to explore the possible benefits of human immune globulin in treating enterovirus infections. The therapeutic strategies, types of preparation, routes of administration, and nature and severity of diseases treated have differed to such a degree, however, that it is not possible to make generalizations about the efficacy of such treatment. Early treatment attempts were made in patients with immunodeficiency diseases, some of whom had received immune globulin on a long-term basis.[568] In some cases, successful reversal of echoviral encephalitis has been achieved with intraventricular immune globulin in children with X-linked agammaglobulinemia,[569, 569a] but other physicians have been less successful with intrathecal or intravenous

(IV) immune globulin for the same or similar conditions.[570–572] A recently published international literature review of chronic enteroviral meningoencephalitis in agammaglobulinemic patients concluded that administration of intraventricular immune globulin resulted in marked improvement in about half of the cases reported,[573] though it is still not accepted that such therapy is of proven benefit. Other investigators have treated agammaglobulinemic patients with polymyositis by administering immune globulin with mixed results.[574] Since immunosuppressive agents, the standard treatment for polymyositis, are contraindicated in these severely ill patients, immunoglobulin may be the only therapeutic option.[574] The value of immunoglobulin in neonatal disease is currently under investigation. Some reports have discussed the use of IM immunoglobulin in contacts of infants with echovirus infections in neonatal wards.[158, 291, 292] Use of immunoglobulin was based on the rationale that serum antibody titers in neonates would be low, as has been shown for antibody to several agents. However, it is unclear whether single doses of immunoglobulin given IM have any effect on serum levels despite their virus-specific titers.[575] The possible value of administration of secretory IgA in decreasing the shedding of polioviruses or other enteroviruses in immunodeficient children is not known.[576]

Although there are currently no specific antiviral agents with which to treat enterovirus infections, a number of compounds have been or are now being evaluated. Both 2-(α-hydroxybenzyl)-benzimidazole (HBB) and arildone have been shown to be effective against a variety of enteroviruses in mouse prophylaxis and treatment trials,[577–579] but the effect is pronounced only on very young animals. Interestingly, the effect of HBB appears to be enhanced by both guanidine hydrochloride and virus-specific antiserum.[579, 580] Newer compounds with demonstrated in vivo activity against enteroviruses include phenoxypyridinecarbonitriles such as 6-(3,4-dichlorophenoxy)-3-(ethylthio)-2-pyridinecarbonitrile, *p*-benzoylphenoxypyridines such as [4-[(5-methylsulfonyl-2-pyridinyl)oxy]phenyl] phenyl methanone, and aralkylaminopyridines such as 2-(3,4-dichlorobenzylamino)-5-methylsulfonylpyridine, all active when tested against coxsackievirus A21, and disoxaril or WIN 51711, 5-[7-[4-(4,4-dihydro-2-oxazolyl)phenoxy]heptyl]-3-methylisoxazole, active against echovirus 9 in prevention and oral treatment trials.[575, 581–584] None of these compounds have been tested in humans to date, and no specific antiviral compounds active against human enteroviruses appear likely to be licensed in the near future.

PREVENTION

History of Poliovirus Vaccines

No discussion of enteroviruses is complete without consideration of the development and use of vaccines to prevent poliomyelitis, a public health triumph that ranks among the great accomplishments of medicine. Interested readers are referred to the classic description by Paul.[552] The history of poliovirus immunization began in 1910 after the discovery of Landsteiner that monkeys could be immunized by subcutaneous injection of emulsified simian spinal cord known to contain the (then uncharacterized) infectious agent. Although improved over the next 5 years, the technique was imperfect and, of course, impractical for human use. During roughly the same time period (1910–1914), animal experimentation with inactivated and partially inactivated vaccines was undertaken. Heat, aluminum hydroxide, phenol, and formalin inactivation all met with little success. Vaccine combined with immune serum was also unsuccessful.

The cause of poliovirus immunization was advanced little in the next 20 years. Then, in the summer of 1935, two scientists working independently and, in fact, competitively, startled the world by conducting human trials of poliovirus vaccines they had produced. John Kolmer of Temple University had developed the first attenuated poliovirus vaccine from viruses multiply passed in monkeys and then partially inactivated with sodium ricineolate. After trials in monkeys, and on himself, his two children, and 23 other persons, Kolmer conducted a vaccine trial of thousands of children.[585] At the same time Maurice Brodie of the New York City Health Laboratory (funded with ''Birthday Ball'' money) was developing a formalin-inactivated emulsion of spinal cord of infected monkeys for use as an intradermal vaccine. After trial in two small groups of monkeys, in human adults (most of whom were probably already immune), and in 12 children,[586] Brodie tested the vaccine on a group of several thousand children at the same time that the Kolmer studies were being conducted. What happened with these two vaccine trials has since been shrouded in mystery. It appears that the Kolmer (live virus) vaccine caused some paralytic and fatal cases of poliomyelitis. Results of the trials of the Brodie (inactivated virus) vaccine are obscure. It was speculated that the Brodie vaccine also had caused paralysis. In any case, there was an outcry in the public health community sufficient to cause suspension of vaccine testing. Brodie and Kolmer were discredited, and Brodie apparently took his own life shortly thereafter.

But 1935 was prophetic: it anticipated by nearly 20 years the fevered search for an effective vaccine, the scientific partisanship over attenuated versus inactivated vaccines, and the development of immunogenic and acceptably safe products.

Further setbacks on the road to prevention of poliomyelitis occurred in the summer of 1949 when, in England, it was observed that paralytic poliomyelitis was not only more apt to occur in children who had recently received routine inoculations against diphtheria, pertussis, and tetanus, but apt to occur in the limb of the inoculation site as well. A report from Australia corroborated these observations. This was disheartening news, as recent research had indicated that poliovirus viremia preceded CNS infection, arguing strongly for a role for pre- or postinfection prophylaxis with IM gamma globulin. Despite the controversy, field trials of gamma globulin were begun during epidemics in the United States in 1951. When given (presumably) before exposure, gamma globulin was shown to be protective.[587] Although mass administration of prophylactic gamma globulin was never feasible, these trials proved that small amounts of circulating antibody (such as might be reasonably expected to result from vaccination) could prevent poliomyelitis.

After a hiatus of nearly 15 years, scientists began in the late 1940s to reconsider the possibility of polio vaccinations. In 1946, the virologist (and subsequent Nobel laureate in 1951) Max Theiler reported to the NFIP (unpublished data)[552] the first success in immunizing monkeys with a live strain of poliovirus attenuated by successive passage in mice. Five years later, in 1951 Hilary Koprowski provided a long-awaited breakthrough by attenuating poliovirus in rats; he successfully vaccinated 20 humans, dem-

onstrating subsequent carriage of infectious viruses in the stool and proving that neutralizing serum antibody had been induced.[588] The next year, 1952, saw proof of poliovirus attenuation by passage in tissue culture in experiments by Enders, Weller, and Robbins.[27] That same year, Howard Howe reported successful immunization of human volunteers with a formalin-inactivated trivalent vaccine.[589] Suddenly, within the space of about a year, mass vaccination to prevent paralytic poliomyelitis became inevitable, and the race was on. The National Foundation on Infantile Paralysis (NFIP) took up the cause of vaccine development in the early 1950s, creating a committee on immunization. The obstacles were great. Surprisingly perhaps, considering the public hysteria, and the occurrence of nearly 40,000 recognized total and 20,000 paralytic poliomyelitis cases annually, there was no great outcry for vaccine production: memories of the 1935 vaccine fiasco still lingered; the Nuremberg trials had created a new horror of misuse of human experimentation; and there had been no truly dramatic breakthrough in vaccine production per se. But, in fact, research had come a long way in those years: tissue culture had been found to support replication of enteroviruses[27]; three distinct poliovirus serotypes had been delineated[590]; viremia had been shown to precede CNS invasion and subsequent paralysis; and research with other viruses and vaccines had lent a broader perspective from which to work.

Jonas Salk of the University of Pittsburgh came to poliovirus research in the early 1950s after having had extensive experience with a formalin-inactivated influenza vaccine tested by the US Army in the 1940s. It was not surprising that he favored an inactivated virus vaccine. Salk published his first results with inactivated poliovirus vaccine (IPV) in 1953, involving 161 volunteers. The next month the NFIP streamlined its operations by supplanting the committee on immunization with a smaller vaccine advisory committee with the avowed aim of supporting production of IPV, presumed to be safer, on theoretical grounds, than a live vaccine. Meanwhile, Salk vaccinated 5000 children with IPV. Excitement in the public health community mounted throughout the last half of 1953 as the NFIP geared up for the largest vaccine trial ever undertaken. In early 1954 Dr. Thomas Francis, Jr, chairman of the Department of Epidemiology of the University of Michigan School of Public Health, took over as director of the field trial, quickly assembling a vaccine evaluation center in Ann Arbor. Connaught Laboratories in Toronto propagated the virus, and different American manufacturers inactivated it. As the world watched, one of the most important public health experiments ever undertaken was conducted with the participation of 1.8 million American children in 1954 to 1955. Speculation was rampant, the drama was intense, and a media spectacle predominated until April 12, 1955, when the press assembled at the University of Michigan in Ann Arbor to hear Dr Francis formally announce the success of IPV (Figure 17–14).

Only days later, an apparent disaster of incalculable magnitude came to light. Cases of paralytic poliomyelitis were detected in 204 vaccinated children and vaccine contacts, largely in California and Idaho—the infamous ''Cutter incident.''[591–593] Confusion and doubt reigned during April, May, and June, as the US Communicable Disease Center investigated the cases, and speculation mounted that a repeat of the Kolmer-Brodie vaccine trials of 20 years earlier might be occurring. As summer approached and vaccination programs started up in Canada and Denmark, the tragedy

Figure 17–14. Press conference announcing the first successful poliovirus vaccine, the University of Michigan, Ann Arbor, April 12, 1955. From left to right: Dr. Thomas Francis, Jr., chairman of the Department of Epidemiology at the University of Michigan School of Public Health and principal investigator for the national vaccine trial; Dr. Jonas Salk, who led development of the IPV used in the trial; and Basil O'Connor, president of the National Foundation for Infantile Paralysis, which supported vaccine development, production, and testing.

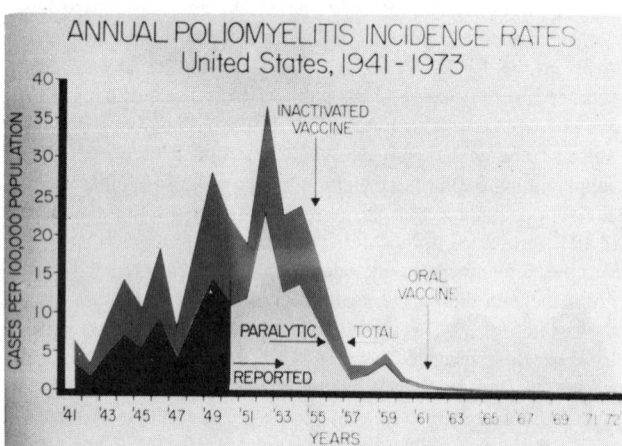

Figure 17–15. Graphic presentation of estimated annual poliomyelitis incidence rates in the United States over a 32-year period, 1941 to 1973. Note the dramatic drop in incidence temporally associated with the introduction of poliovirus vaccine, which was administered in mass nationwide campaigns beginning in 1955.

unfolded—incompletely inactivated lots from a single manufacturer were responsible. The United States went ahead and immunized millions of children during the summer of 1955. Canada, Denmark, France, Germany, and South Africa were not far behind. The effectiveness of IPV mass immunization was apparent from the outset, with dramatic decreases in polio incidence in the United States from 13.9 to 0.5 paralytic cases per 100,000 in the 6 years following release of the vaccine (Fig 17–15). Decreases in incidence of similar magnitude were demonstrated in Australia, the United Kingdom, Czechoslovakia, Denmark, and Sweden.

Despite documentation of this remarkable success, there were problems. The vaccine was of questionable immunogenicity, multiple booster doses were sometimes needed, and it was felt that IPV was impractical for the developing world (see below). Furthermore, in the United States, despite 5 years of the most intensive mass inoculation yet mounted, there were still by some estimates, 2545 cases of paralytic poliomyelitis reported in 1960.

Meanwhile, Koprowski and others at Lederle Laboratories had not given up on development of a live attenuated vaccine after the success of IPV was acknowledged. By 1953 both Albert Sabin and Joseph Melnick had extended the work of Koprowski to attenuate polioviruses by sequential tissue culture passage. Experiments with monkeys showed Sabin's attenuated virus to be safe and highly efficacious. In 1955, shortly after the first national IPV campaign was underway, Koprowski reported safety and efficacy for an oral vaccine given to 150 volunteers and followed for 5 years. Sabin also presented early results on a different oral vaccine. The cause of oral vaccine received a setback in 1957 when a field trial of Koprowski's vaccine in Belfast, Northern Ireland, resulted in carriage of strains that had apparently reverted to the wild type. But work continued, including a large field trial involving millions of persons in the Soviet Union. Momentum built up gradually until 1962 when the live attenuated poliovirus vaccines were licensed in the United States. The weight of public health evidence at that time resulted in adoption of vaccination policies based on live, trivalent oral poliovirus vaccine (OPV) in the United States, England, and numerous other countries. Despite early problems with paralysis in adults following attenuated poliovirus type 3 vaccination, the oral vaccine gained wide acceptance. Although occasional cases of poliomyelitis in vaccinees or their contacts are still detected, the live oral vaccine is used today by most of the world (Fig 17–16).

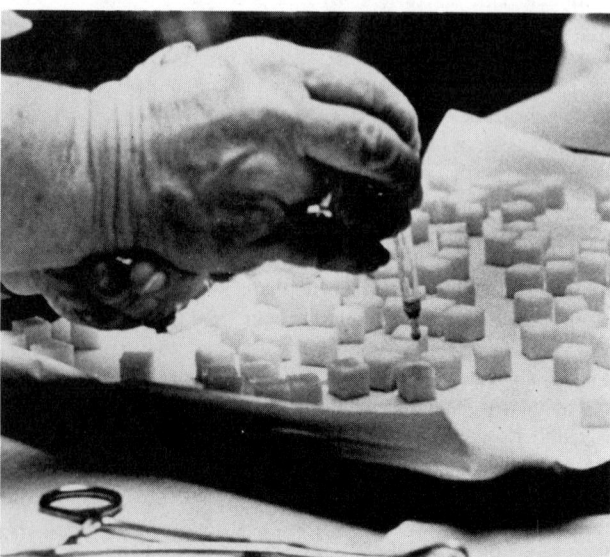

Figure 17–16. The "sugar cube" replaced injection of inactivated poliovirus vaccines in the United States in the early 1960s. The pieces of sucrose absorbed with live poliovirus vaccine became widely accepted by children and parents alike.

Current Poliovirus Vaccines and Recommendations for Immunization

Currently the three major poliovirus vaccines are oral live poliovirus, or Sabin vaccine (OPV); inactivated poliovirus, or Salk vaccine (IPV); and "conventional enhanced-potency" IPV produced in human diploid cells.[594] Table 17–6 summarizes the key characteristics of the two major classes of polio vaccine. For the purpose of discussion in this text, current (1988) vaccination recommendations of the ACIP and American Academy of Pediatrics (AAP) are presented. However, it is likely that revised recommendations, including recommendations for enhanced-potency IPV,[598] will be available by the time this review is in print. The reader should consult current recommendations of ACIP and other agencies for updated information.

OPV viruses replicate in the alimentary tract, and the resulting intestinal infection induced both a gut and systemic immune response. Grown in human diploid cells, or in monkey kidney cells, OPV viruses comprise the standard poliovirus vaccine used worldwide. The vaccine is recommended by the AAP, the US Public Health Service Immunization Practice Advisory Committee, and by WHO in its Expanded Programme of Immunizations (EPI), the goal of which was originally to immunize all children against six diseases (including poliovirus infections) by 1990. The AAP recommends OPV vaccination in primary series of three to four OPV doses, at 2, 4, and 18 months of age, and a booster at school entry (4–6 years of age),[595] to confer lifelong immunity. The AAP recommends an optional OPV dose at 6 months for children residing in areas of the United States where poliovirus importation is likely. Such an "extra" dose may be an important addition to the schedule in developing countries (see below), as may an optional booster dose at 10 years. In no case should sequential doses be given less than 6 weeks apart. If return for immunization seems unlikely, a child who presents for measles-mumps-rubella vaccination should also receive OPV at the same time. In developing countries with a high incidence of poliomyelitis, or in endemic areas with inadequate health care delivery, OPV immunization at birth is desirable, but the normal primary series should follow. For children whose first physician visit is delayed, the schedule is "shifted" so that vaccination begins at that visit, and at 2, 4, and 10 to 16 months thereafter, and again at school entry. Persons with unknown immunization status should be immunized unless there is proof of immunity (ie, poliovirus antibodies to all three serotypes). There is no need to delay OPV vaccination because of minor viral illness. Premature infants should begin their primary series at 2 months and continue on a normal schedule of OPV. Asplenic children and pregnant teenagers under 18 years of age should also receive OPV. However, OPV may be contraindicated in the following circumstances and consideration should be given to IPV vaccination: children with progressive neurologic disease (because of the possibility of aggravation of the underlying process); children who have already had poliomyelitis (because of the theoretical possibility that they are constitutionally predisposed to paralysis); persons with congenital or acquired immunodeficiency diseases and altered immune status as a result of disease or immunosuppressive therapy (eg, systemic steroids, cancer chemotherapy) or recipients of gamma globulin within the previous 3 months,[596] persons infected with HIV, and all persons over 18 years of age.[539, 540, 597]

Persons with AIDS should probably not receive OPV, and in persons with asymptomatic HIV infection consideration may also be given to IPV, although surveillance of HIV-infected infants who have received OPV has not revealed any serious sequelae.[597a] The ACIP recommends that American children with symptomatic and asymptomatic HIV infection, and their family contacts, all receive IPV.[597b] The World Health Organization, on the other hand, recommends OPV for all such children.[597b] General recommendations for vaccination of persons with HIV infections, including AIDS, have been published.[539, 540] Current practice in the United States dictates that children be given OPV without delay occasioned by concern for potential effects on the child's healthy contacts (parents, other household members, and babysitters). However, an acceptable alternative, endorsed by the AAP, is to obtain a poliovirus immunization history of all adult household contacts and administer OPV to those with partial completion of the OPV schedule, or administer IPV to those with partial completion of the IPV schedule, at the same time as administration of OPV to the index child. If the immunization status of adult household contacts is not known or if they have had no previous immunization, a decision can be made to give IPV to the susceptible adult initially and at 1 and 2 months thereafter,[595] giving the child OPV at the 2-month visit. Since it is important that there be no delay in immunizing the child, this strategy is best applied to situations in which the contact history is obtained at birth of the infant, when there is still time for immunization of contacts before the first scheduled OPV dose, at 2 months of age.

The cost of OPV in the United States has risen dramatically in recent years, to the point where it is now nearly as expensive as IPV (Table 17–6). Adverse reactions are extremely rare, leading most experts to consider the vaccine both effective and safe. However, adverse reactions that do occur are sometimes serious: vaccine recipients or their contacts may develop clinical poliomyelitis—including permanent paralysis—from the vaccine.[599–603] The early recognition of this problem in the United States[604] led to a change in national immunization policy, so that adults—who appeared to be at greater risk of adverse reactions—were no longer routinely included in immunization drives. The risk today is very small, but real: based on United States data, a conservative estimate suggests that two to three vaccine-associated cases occur for every million children immunized,[284] reflecting roughly one case in vaccinees per 2.7 million doses distributed, and one case in contacts of vaccinees per 5 million doses distributed. The estimated risk to vaccinees of the first OPV dose is 0.5 to 1.0 per million, dropping to 1.0 per 22 million for subsequent doses, due presumably to the protective effect of immunity.[600] The lower incidence for subsequent doses holds for recipients to a greater degree than for contacts.[600] International data suggest that the greatest OPV risks are associated with type 2 and, especially, type 3 vaccine viruses,[601] though the international risk may be lower, on the order of less than 0.3 cases among recipients and contacts combined per million doses administered.[601a] Two countries appeared to have had higher rates of paralysis than ten other countries using OPV, conceivably due to differences in case ascertainment.[601] During ten years of surveillance, two countries that used OPV and one that used IPV reported no cases of poliomyelitis, suggesting that both vaccines may be effective public health tools in poliomyelitis prevention. In recent years the majority of poliomyelitis cases in the United

States and probably in other developed countries that use OPV are due to the vaccine. It has become accepted practice to obtain formal informed consent before OPV vaccination. For those persons who decline OPV, vaccination with IPV should then be carried out. Recent Finnish reports have suggested that OPV may cause Guillain-Barré syndrome, but the evidence is far from complete.[604a, 604b] Similarly, it has been claimed that IPV administered in the early years of its production, and known to have been contaminated by SV40, may have caused later adverse effects, including tumors and malignancies in offspring of vaccinated mothers.[604c]

Beginning on March 21, 1988, the National Childhood Vaccine Injury Act required health care providers who administer OPV, IPV, and certain other vaccines to report a variety of side effects and complications of vaccination, and to maintain records in sufficient detail to trace vaccine lots and identify individuals actually administering the vaccines.[605] Information on the following complications is required: for OPV, paralysis (by immunocompetency status and ''community-case'' status); for IPV, information on anaphylaxis; for both IPV and OPV, events that would constitute contraindications to additional doses.[605] Reports should be made to local or state health departments. In June 1988, the Supreme Court ruled unanimously that victims of OPV-associated paralysis had the right to sue the federal government for damages. The test case *(Berkovitz v. United States)* involved a batch of commercially prepared OPV that had been licensed by the Food and Drug Administration, but which had subsequently caused paralysis in a 2-month-old child who received a single dose in 1979. Although the implications of the decision are not immediately clear, it is conceivable that both the licensing and production of vaccines and the formulation of immunization policy will be adversely affected by it.

IPV used in the United States is grown in monkey kidney cell culture. The new enhanced-potency IPV (N-IPV) is grown in human diploid cells. IPV is given by injection. Antigenic challenge induces circulating serum antibody and secretory antibody in upper respiratory secretions though perhaps not as frequently as OPV.[606] The degree to which gut immunity may be induced by IPV, especially when compared with OPV, is a subject of debate.[607] One recent study has even suggested that N-IPV-vaccinated American infants who received three doses had higher anti-viral titers in the serum than similar infants vaccinated with OPV.[595a] A field trial of N-IPV in Senegal also showed efficacy after only two doses based on lower than expected incidence rates in vaccinees.[595b] Although IPV is used on a smaller scale today, it is recognized as effective by WHO. In the United States, it is recommended for persons who refuse OPV, or for whom OPV is contraindicated.[598] Primary immunization with current IPV consists of four doses, the first three at 1- to 2-month intervals beginning at 2 months of age, and the fourth dose six to 12 months later.[595] A booster dose should be given at school entry and every five years until adulthood. The enhanced-potency IPV requires three doses, eight weeks apart for the first two doses, and 12 months later for the third, for primary immunization. Further testing is necessary to determine the need, if any, for subsequent booster doses. A primary series is considered to be complete after three doses of IPV and OPV in any combination (eg, two OPV doses followed by one IPV dose); however, if enhanced-potency IPV is given to a person with an incomplete series of conventional OPV, a total of four doses is required. All children should still receive boosters before school entry unless the last dose of the primary series was given on or after the fourth birthday. Recommendations for unvaccinated adults have recently been published.[595] IPV is preferred, and is generally given in a schedule similar to that for infants. Travelers, certain health care workers, laboratory workers, and members of certain religious or other groups at risk should consider adult vaccination.[595] The cost of conventional IPV is now in the same range as that of OPV, since the cost of the latter vaccine has, in recent years, risen dramatically due to fear of litigation, and to actual litigation. The cost of N-IPV, once large-scale production is mounted, is expected to decline. There are no known serious adverse reactions

Table 17–6
Summary of Current Poliovirus Vaccines

	Live Virus (Sabin)	Killed Virus (Salk)
Delivery	Oral	Injected
Efficacy	High	High
Mucosal immunity	Yes	Some
Duration of immunity	Long-term	Unknown
Thermolability	Labile	Stable
Usage	Countries not listed under killed virus vaccine	Netherlands, Sweden, Finland, selected Canadian provinces; to begin in France; specific situations in USA and elsewhere (see text)
Types of vaccine	Monovalent Trivalent	Only trivalent
No. of doses	Primary: 3 Boosters: 1–2	Conventional IPV: primary, 4; boosters, 3
		Enhanced-potency vaccine: primary, 3; boosters (?)
Retail Cost in 1988 US dollars	$8.07	$8.82
Side effects	Poliomyelitis in recipient or contact (rare)	None known

IPV = *inactivated poliovirus vaccine.*

associated with the IPV vaccines, except allergic and anaphylactic reactions to the antibiotics they contain in trace amounts (streptomycin and neomycin). Theoretical risks include the Guillain-Barré syndrome, a problem which surfaced in the United States in 1976 in association with the widespread use of a killed influenza vaccine. Tested in both industrialized and developing countries, the enhanced-potency IPV appears to be effective.[608-616]

Both OPV and IPV are effective in inducing immunity in individuals under optimal conditions, but OPV has been found in some developing countries to be distinctly less immunogenic, as measured by lower seroconversion rates.[278, 279, 616-623] To some extent, diminished seroconversion may reflect interference by breast feeding or infection with other enteroviruses, and by vaccine interserotype interference,[624] but it should also be considered that despite population-based data from outbreaks in Brazil, Senegal, and The Gambia, there is no certainty that failure of vaccination to elicit detectable neutralizing antibody is indicative of susceptibility. Nevertheless, as is the case in the developed countries, almost all countries of the developing world have chosen OPV for routine immunization, based on cost considerations and, in some cases, on the predication that despite incomplete induction of immunity with OPV, the degree of ''free vaccination'' of the community by the introduction of OPV circulation will compensate, especially when the alternative strategy (IPV vaccination) requires a more highly sophisticated health care delivery system. Both vaccines are safe, but OPV does carry the risk (albeit small) of vaccine-associated poliomyelitis, and OPV cannot be given to immunodeficient patients. (Unfortunately, a patient's immunodeficient status may first be recognized when poliomyelitis develops after administration of OPV.) OPV is considered the vaccine of choice for epidemic control regardless of whether or not it is also the mainstay of national vaccination policy. For the foreseeable future OPV will probably remain the vaccine of choice for most of the developed and developing world, with a complementary role for IPV in adults and immunocompromised persons, and perhaps in normal children in selected situations as well. A recent report of the Institute of Medicine to ACIP has suggested a mixed schedule of two doses of IPV and two of OPV once the combined DPT polio vaccine is licensed (expected in about 1990 in the United States). In selected developed countries with highly effective healthcare delivery systems, usually government-run, IPV may be an acceptable alternative for routine immunizations, though even then epidemics may be difficult to prevent.[80] Recently, a single author has resurrected the theory[625, 626, 626a] that some poliomyelitis epidemics may result from ''epidemics'' of injections (with a variety of medications and vaccines, conceivably including IPV). But despite the fact, noted above, that cases of ipsilateral provocation poliomyelitis occur, it is not yet accepted that epidemics can be explained in this way. In any case, it is not clear what impact such provocation poliomyelitis might have on prevention strategy. Would IPV or OPV be the safer choice? Would injectable IPV predispose to wild virus-associated poliomyelitis, or would OPV cause poliomyelitis in injected persons who received or were contacts of those who received OPV?

National poliovirus vaccination policy should be based on prevailing needs and conditions in each country. Vaccine strategies may be different for industrialized and developing countries[627-630] (Tables 17-7 and 17-8). Over the past 10 years, polio vaccine policy has come under increasing debate in the United States. Major public health policy-making organizations (eg, ACIP, AAP and the Institute of Medicine) have consistently recommended, however, that the United States continue a predominantly OPV-based prevention strategy. Most experts concur,[631-633] but an alternative viewpoint favoring return to IPV, especially the enhanced-potency IPV, persists.[634, 635] The debate centers mostly on the trade-off between a possible increase in wild virus-associated poliomyelitis cases under a (hypothetical) IPV policy, and the documented ten (or so) annual cases under the existing OPV policy, the majority (70%-80%) of which are vaccine-associated, and about half of those in contacts of recipients.[631, 632, 634] While it seems unlikely that the United States and other developed countries will switch to IPV policies in the near future, some health experts have suggested a third alternative policy based on both OPV and IPV.[636-639] Such a policy has actually been followed in Denmark, since 1968[638] with much success. In Denmark infants receive IPV at 5, 6, and 15 months of age, followed by OPV at 2, 3, and 4 years. A similar schedule was used successfully in the Gaza Strip,[640] and on the West Bank IPV has been given at $3\frac{1}{2}$ and 5 months, with OPV at 2, $3\frac{1}{2}$, 5, $6\frac{1}{2}$, and 12 months.[640b] A recent publication has reported Phase I trials of an IPV made from inactivated OPV, documenting inactivated titer boosts in persons who had been previously vaccinated with either OPV alone, or IPV followed by OPV.[640a] However, the possible role of such a vaccine in public health policy remains to be determined. Another alternative, practiced by some physicians but never developed into a governmental policy, is to simultaneously vaccinate all family members with OPV, to thereby prevent contact cases in the child and in those persons exposed to vaccinees who may (eventually) excrete mutated wild-type vaccine virus progeny. Obtaining vaccination histories of adult household contacts may be of limited value since the majority of adults in a recent survey were unable to recall having been vaccinated, and in many of those who did, vaccination could not be documented.[641] Recently some poorer countries with serious poliomyelitis problems and imperfect health care delivery have attempted to control poliovirus circulation by annual campaigns of short-term vaccination, including national vaccination days.[642, 643] Regional attempts to eliminate poliomyelitis in parts of Latin America are currently in progress, under the direction of the Pan American Health Organization. The elimination campaigns, which emphasize increased OPV vaccination and improved poliomyelitis surveillance, have been successful in reducing the incidence of poliomyelitis in the Americas as a whole with a 64% decline in confirmed cases between 1986 and 1988.[643a] A surprising majority of developing countries have had little experience with poliovirus vaccination on which to base decisions about national policy today. The reasons are not obscure, however. In many such areas there are infectious and sociocultural causes of childhood mortality that are of considerably greater importance, for example, gastroenteritis, neonatal tetanus, measles, meningitis, etc. In some such areas, the neonatal mortality rate may be over 10%, and as many as 25% to 50% of children may die before reaching their fifth birthday. In such an environment, poliomyelitis may be considered a relatively inconsequential disease, hence an understandable reluctance to spend precious public health monies that could be better spent on sanitation, oral rehydration, measles vaccination, and such other basic needs as building an accessible health-care

Table 17–7

Formulating Poliomyelitis Immunization Policy: Advantages and Disadvantages of Oral Poliovirus Vaccine (OPV) and Enhanced-Potency Inactivated Poliovirus Vaccine (N-IPV) in *Industrialized* Countries

OPV	N-IPV
Advantages	
1. Effective	1. Effective
2. Lifelong immunity	2. Uncertain duration of immunity
3. Induces gut immunity like that of natural infection	3. Can be incorporated into routine immunizations (with DPT)
4. May circulate in community	4. Good stability with transport and storage
5. Greater acceptability to vaccinees (oral)	5. Greater safety
6. Easily administered (untrained personnel)	6. Safe in immunodeficient patients
7. Inexpensive	
8. Repeated boosters not required	
9. Spreads to contacts (indirect immunization)	
Disadvantages	
1. Interval between doses longer (longer time required for primary immunization)	1. More expensive than OPV
2. Vaccine-associated poliomyelitis in vaccinees or contacts	2. Virulent (seed) virus potentially dangerous if not properly inactivated
3. Spread of vaccine to contacts without their consent	3. Injection less acceptable than oral administration
4. Unsafe for immunodeficient patients	4. Must achieve higher community immunization levels than with OPV
	5. Extent of gut immunity uncertain

DPT = diphtheria-pertussis-tetanus combined vaccine.

Table 17–8

Formulating Poliomyelitis Immunization Policy: Advantages and Disadvantages of Oral Poliovirus Vaccine (OPV) and Enhanced-Potency Inactivated Poliovirus Vaccine (N-IPV) in Developing Countries

OPV	N-IPV
Advantages	
1. Easily administered	1. More frequently elicits detectable serum antibody than OPV in some tropical areas
2. Induces gut immunity like that of natural infection	2. Safe: no serious adverse effects
3. Lifelong immunity	3. Can be incorporated into routine immunization schedule with DPT
4. Greater acceptability to vaccinees	4. Uncertain duration of immunity
5. Preferable for epidemic control	5. More stable for transport and storage
6. Inexpensive	
7. Spread to contacts in conducive environment	
Disadvantages	
1. Inconsistent immunogenicity	1. More expensive than OPV
2. Lower seroconversion rates	2. Injection may be less acceptable to vaccinees
3. Cold chain problems (can be stabilized with $MgCl_2$)	3. Must achieve higher community immunization levels than with OPV
4. Longer interval between doses (longer to fully immunize)	4. Requires more efficient health care delivery system
5. Vaccine-associated disease in vaccinees or contacts	5. Extent of gut immunity uncertain

DPT = diphtheria-pertussis-tetanus combined vaccine.

delivery system. Even so, an estimated quarter of a million cases of paralytic poliomyelitis occur annually in developing countries, and lameness surveys in these countries may suggest an alarmingly high prevalence of postpoliomyelitis paralysis in young children, with 30% or more of these children either unable to walk, or able to ambulate only with the help of sticks or crutches (see Fig 17–7.)[644]

However, the WHO Expanded Programme on Immunization (EPI) has mounted a worldwide attack on poliomyelitis (and five other childhood diseases) abetted by funds from developed nations that have largely eradicated the disease. While it is obvious that poliomyelitis (and five others) will not be "eradicated" worldwide by 1990, there is every reason to hope that the EPI will make the 1990s the most important decade since the 1950s in the continuing quest for poliomyelitis control. In May 1988 the World Health Assembly, supported by experts and agencies around the world, called upon WHO members to make the world free of new cases by the year 2000. By the time this chapter is in print, it may be that a campaign to eradicate poliovirus will have begun.

Immunization Against Other Enteroviral Diseases

The "need", if any, for vaccines against selected nonpolio enteroviruses has not yet been established, although some investigators have raised the issue.[100, 645] As early as 1968, Plotkin spoke for a definite need of research on enterovirus vaccines.[646] However, problems are many, including the large number of different virus types, the cyclical occurrence of many viruses in a population, and the possibility that new antigenic variants would develop and become established. Before specific research on such vaccines is undertaken, it is important to establish, in cost-benefit terms, a valid need for vaccine development. Other than poliovirus vaccines, there are no human enterovirus vaccines on the horizon.

Prevention of Nosocomial Transmission

Nosocomial transmission of enteroviruses can be prevented if the etiology is suspected and appropriate control and isolation techniques implemented.[647] The specifics of these techniques are discussed in the CDC's *Guideline for Isolation Precautions in Hospitals,* published by the US Department of Health and Human Services.[305] The nature of the control measure varies depending on the syndrome and, consequently, the likely mode of spread. Excretion precautions are indicated for the duration of hospitalization for aseptic meningitis, diarrhea, hand-foot-and-mouth disease, and wild-type poliovirus infection. (The *Guideline*[305] recommends seven days of enteric precautions for poliomyelitis and, presumably, other poliovirus infection.) Only staff with a history of poliovirus vaccination, or known immunity, should care for patients with wild-type poliovirus infection. Both excretion precautions and secretion precautions are advised for herpangina for the duration of hospitalization. Although not specifically mentioned in the *Guideline,* it is prudent to observe excretion precautions for all other cases of suspected or proven acute enterovirus infection, at least for the duration of illness and ideally for the duration of hospitalization or 2 months after illness onset, whichever comes first. Guidelines for prevention of nosocomial AHC have not been widely disseminated; however, in view of the ease with which fomite-mediated transmission occurs, a conservative approach to hospital inpatients would include observance of wound and skin precautions whenever feasible and, at a minimum, wearing of disposable gloves for treating outpatients and scrupulous cleaning of instruments, equipment, and other potential fomites with alcohol or other readily available disinfectants.

Dealing with Contacts of Poliomyelitis Patients

Because of the dread associated with poliomyelitis, there is predictably great concern on the part of family, friends, patients, and medical staff members exposed to cases. Furthermore, in the United States and most other countries, it is not always apparent whether an individual case is associated with vaccine virus, further confusing the picture. Standard history taking may give sufficient clues about the origin of poliovirus infection. In developed countries relevant questions would include those about immunization history, travel to polio endemic and epidemic areas, contact with travelers from other countries, contact with vaccinees, contact with other poliomyelitis and poliovirus infection cases, and underlying conditions or recent treatments (eg, immunodeficiency or receipt of chemotherapeutic agents). In the absence of information to the contrary, poliomyelitis should be assumed to result from infection with wild-type virus until proved otherwise. A careful investigation should be made on the spot to determine the possible sources of a case. Health officials must be contacted immediately and often prove to be of great assistance in sorting out the many problems associated with contacts. Since most persons are immune to poliovirus infection by virtue of vaccination or infections from vaccine recipients, or, in the case of older individuals, because of prior natural infection, and since in any case, as noted above, infection with wild-type polioviruses uncommonly leads to serious complications such as paralysis, the situation is not nearly as critical as it might first seem.

A reasonable procedure to follow is to (1) identify each person exposed, usually by history—turning to serology only when time and circumstances dictate (exposure is taken to mean physical contact of the kind that occurs among household members); (2) characterize each person exposed in terms of presumed susceptibility; (3) characterize each person exposed in terms of likelihood of complications should infection occur (eg, exposed immunodeficient patient contacts in hospital); and (4) inform each contact of the risk of contracting poliomyelitis, which is usually very small, and attempt to counsel and reassure exposed persons whenever possible. There is no need to vaccinate persons with history of completion of OPV or IPV series. When there is doubt, or when contacts have not been properly vaccinated, they should receive or complete an IPV series (most adults) or OPV series (most children) to protect against that and subsequent contacts, as described above under immunization recommendations for contacts of children receiving OPV.

In such situations there is usually a need for education, especially of concerned hospital staff. The clinician, virologist, and epidemiologist may all play a leading role in informing and educating staff, who may then help counsel other contacts. Finally, in situations where even a single case of poliomyelitis results from wild-type virus infection, public health officials may decide to administer OPV to all children and adults in the community where transmission is likely unless completion of immunization with OPV or IPV is known. OPV is used in mass vaccination during an outbreak or in response to a single community case, except for vaccination of compromised individuals (eg, persons with immunodeficiency syndrome, and others noted above) without known immunity.

ACKNOWLEDGMENTS

The authors thank Milford H. Hatch, ScD, former Chief, Enterovirus Branch, Division of Viral Diseases, Center for Infectious Disease, CDC; and Olen M. Kew, PhD, Molecular Virology Branch, Division of Viral Diseases, CDC, for their comments and help in preparing the manuscript; and Carole J. Diamond, Nancy J. Krause, Caprice A. Mahalla, Sandra Nakasone, and Ratna Soetjahja Morens for their help in editing and preparation.

REFERENCES

1. Kibrick S: Current status of coxsackie and ECHO viruses in human disease. *Prog Med Virol* 1964; 6:27–70.
2. Howe HA: Poliomyelitis, in Rivers TM (ed): *Viral and Rickettsial Infections of Man*. Philadelphia, Lippincott, 1952, pp 300–337.
3. Horstmann DM: Poliomyelitis: Severity and type of disease in different age groups. *Ann NY Acad Sci* 1955; 61:956–967.
4. Melnick JL: Enteroviruses, in Evans AS (ed): *Viral Infections of Humans, Epidemiology and Control*. New York, Plenum, 1978, pp 163–207.
5. Brown EH: Enterovirus infections. *Br Med J* 1972; 2:169–171.
6. Sylvest E: *Epidemic Myalgia: Bornholm Disease*. Copenhagen, Levin & Munksgaard/Humphrey Milford, 1934, pp 1–138.
7. Christian HA: Nearly ten decades of interest in idiopathic pericarditis. *Am Heart J* 1951; 42:645–651.
8. Zahorsky J: Herpangina. *Arch Pediatr* 1924; 41:181–184.
9. Neva FA: A second outbreak of Boston exanthem disease in Pittsburgh during 1954. *N Engl J Med* 1956; 254:838–843.
10. Neva FA, Feemster RF, Grobach IJ: Clinical and epidemiological features of an unusual epidemic exanthem. *JAMA* 1954; 155:544–548.
11. Arnow PM, Hierholzer JC, Higbee J, et al: Acute hemorrhagic conjunctivitis: A mixed virus outbreak among Vietnamese refugees on Guam. *Am J Epidemiol* 1977; 105:68–74.
12. Chang WK, Liu KC, Foo TC, et al: Acute hemorrhagic conjunctivitis in Hong Kong, 1971–1975. *Southeast Asian J Trop Med Public Health* 1977; 8:1–6.
13. Yin-Murphy M, Lim KH, Ho YM: A coxsackievirus type A-24 epidemic of acute conjunctivitis. *Southeast Asian J Trop Med Public Health* 1976; 7:1–5.
14. Kono R, Sasagawa A, Ishii K, et al: Pandemic of new type of conjunctivitis. *Lancet* 1972; 1:1191–1194.
15. Metselaar D, Awan AM, Ensering HL: Acute hemorrhagic conjunctivitis and enterovirus 70 in Kenya. *Trop Geogr Med* 1976; 28:131–136.
16. Klein AE: *Trial by Fury: The Polio Vaccine Controversy*. New York, Scribners, 1972.
17. Berg RH: *The Challenge of Polio: The Crusade Against Infantile Paralysis*. New York, Dial Press, 1946.
18. Boerhaave H: Praelectiones academicae de morbis nervorum quas ex auditorum manuscriptis collectas edi curavit Jacobus von Eems. Lugduni Batavorum, P. van der Eyk et C. de Pecker, 1761.
19. Underwood M: *A Treatise on the Disease of Children*, ed 2. Philadelphia, Dobson, 1793.
20. Badham J: Paralysis in childhood: Four remarkable cases of suddenly induced paralysis in the extremities, occurring in children, without any apparent cerebral or cerebro-spinal lesion.

London Med Gazette 1834; 15:215–218.
21. Heine J: Beobachtungen über Lähmungszustände der unteren Extremitäten und deren Behandlung. Stuttgart: FH Köhler, 1840.
22. Caverly CS: Notes of an epidemic of acute anterior poliomyelitis. *JAMA* 1896; 26:1–5.
23. Osler W: *The Principles and Practice of Medicine. Designed for the Use of Practitioners and Students of Medicine*. New York, Appleton, 1892.
24. Horstmann DM: Enterovirus infection of the central nervous system. The present and future of poliomyelitis. *Med Clin North Am* 1967; 61:681–693.
25. Lepow ML: Enteroviral meningitis: A reappraisal. *Pediatrics* 1978; 62:267–269.
26. Landsteiner K, Popper E: Uebertragung der Poliomyelitis acuta auf Affen. *Z Immunitätsforsch Exp Ther* 1909; 2:377–390.
27. Enders JF, Weller TH, Robbins FC: Cultivation of the Lansing strain of poliomyelitis virus in cultures of various human embryonic tissues. *Science* 1949; 109:85–87.
28. Dalldorf G: Coxsackie viruses. *Ann Rev Microbiol* 1955; 9:277–296.
29. Robbins FC, Enders JF, Weller TH, et al: Studies on the cultivation of poliomyelitis viruses in tissue culture. V. The direct isolation and serologic identification of the virus strains in tissue culture from patients with nonparalytic and paralytic poliomyelitis. *Am J Hyg* 1951; 54:286–293.
30. Dalldorf G, Sickles GM: An unidentified, filtrable agent isolated from the feces of children with paralysis. *Science* 1948; 108:61–63.
31. Dalldorf G: *Annual Report, Division of Laboratories and Research, New York State Department of Health*, 1950, p 5.
32. Dalldorf G: The coxsackie group of viruses. *Science* 1949; 110:594.
33. Melnick JL, Shaw EW, Curnen EC: A virus isolated from patients diagnosed as nonparalytic poliomyelitis or aseptic meningitis. *Proc Soc Exp Biol Med* 1949; 71:344–349.
34. Curnen EC, Shaw EW, Melnick JL: Disease resembling nonparalytic poliomyelitis associated with virus pathogenic for infant mice. *JAMA* 1949; 141:894–901.
35. Banker DD, Melnick JL: Isolation of coxsackie virus (c virus) from North Alaskan Eskimos. *Am J Hyg* 1951; 54:383–390.
36. Rhodes AJ, Clark EM, Knowles DS, et al: Studies on poliomyelitis in Ontario: Further observation on the association of coxsackie and poliomyelitis viruses. *Can J Public Health* 1950; 41:183–188.
37. Findlay GM, Howard EM: Coxsackie virus and Bornholm disease. *Br Med J* 1950; 1:1233–1236.
38. Lepine P, Thieffney S, Reinie L, et al: Présence en France d'infections humaines du groupe Coxsackie (virus C). Isolement du virus. *Ann Inst Pasteur* 1951; 80:200–203.
39. Schaeffer LF: Epidemic of Bornholm disease in North Amsterdam. *Ned Tijdschr Geneeskd* 1951; 95:2938–2948.
40. von Magnus H: Isolation of 3 virus strains of coxsackie group from patients with meningeal symptoms: Preliminary report. *Ugeskr Laeger* 1949; 111:1451–1453.
41. Rhodes AJ, Beale AJ: Aseptic meningitis: Evidence for the etiologic role of coxsackie B "orphan" viruses. *Ann NY Acad Sci* 1957; 67:212–222.
42. Melnick JL, Agren K: Poliomyelitis and coxsackie viruses isolated from normal infants in Egypt. *Proc Soc Exp Biol Med* 1952; 81:621–624.
43. Ramos-Alvarez M, Sabin AB: Characteristics of poliomyelitis and other enteric viruses recovered in tissue culture from healthy American children. *Proc Soc Exp Biol Med* 1954; 87:655–661.
44. Committee on the ECHO Viruses. Enteric cytopathogenic human orphan viruses. *Science* 1955; 122:1187–1188.
45. Hogle JM, Chow M, Filman DJ: Three-dimensional structure of poliovirus at 2.9 Å resolution. *Science* 1985; 229:1358–1365.
46. Pallansch MA, Kew OM, Semler BL, et al: Protein processing

map of poliovirus. *J Virol* 1984; 49:873–880.

47. Page GS, Mosser AG, Hogle JM, et al: Three-dimensional structure of poliovirus serotype 1 neutralizing determinants. *J Virol* 1988; 62:1781–1794.

48. Minor PD, Evans DM, Ferguson M, et al: Principal and subsidiary antigenic sites of VP1 involved in the neutralization of poliovirus type 3. *J Gen Virol* 1985; 66:1159–1165.

49. Toyoda H, Kohara M, Kataoka Y, et al: Complete nucleotide sequences of all three poliovirus serotype genomes. Implication for genetic relationship, gene function and antigenic determinants. *J Mol Biol* 1984; 174:561–585.

50. Iizuka N, Kuge S, Nomoto A: Complete nucleotide sequence of the genome of coxsackievirus B1. *Virology* 1987; 156:64–73.

51. Lindberg AM, Stalhandske PO, Pettersson U: Genome of coxsackievirus B3. *Virology* 1987; 156:50–63.

52. Jenkins O, Booth JD, Minor PD, et al: The complete nucleotide sequence of coxsackievirus B4 and its comparison to other members of the Picornaviridae. *J Gen Virol* 1987; 68:1835–1848.

53. Hughes PJ, Phillips A, Minor PD, et al: The sequence of the coxsackievirus A 21 polymerase gene indicates a remarkably close relationship to the polioviruses. Brief report. *Arch Virol* 1987; 94:141–147.

54. Young NA: Polioviruses, coxsackieviruses and echoviruses: Comparison of the genomes by RNA hybridization. *J Virol* 1973; 11:832–839.

55. Tracy S: A comparison of genomic homologies among the coxsackievirus B group: use of fragments of the cloned coxsackievirus B3 genome as probes. *J Gen Virol* 1984; 65:2167–2172.

56. Hyypiä T, Maaronen M, Auvinen P, et al: Nucleic acid sequence relationships between enterovirus serotypes. *Mol Cell Probes* 1987; 1:169–176.

57. Fenner F, McAuslan BR, Mims CA, et al: The structure and chemistry of the virion: A systematic survey, in Fenner F, McAuslan BR, Mims CA, et al (eds): *The Biology of Animal Viruses,* ed 2. New York, Academic Press, 1974, pp 72–154.

58. Rueckert RR: Picornaviral architecture, in Maramorosch K, Kurstak E (eds): *Comparative Virology.* Academic Press, New York, 1971, pp 255–306.

59. Wenner HA: The ECHO viruses. *Ann NY Acad Sci* 1962; 101:398–412.

60. Narang HK, Codd AA: Action of commonly used disinfectants against enteroviruses. *J Hosp Infect* 1983; 4:209–212.

61. McLean DM: Infection hazards in swimming pools. *Pediatrics* 1963; 31:811–818.

62. McAllister RM: Echovirus infections. *Pediatr Clin North Am* 1960; 7(14):927–945.

63. Dalldorf G: The coxsackie viruses. *Bull NY Acad Med* 1950; 26:329–335.

64. Mertens T, Pika U, Eggers HJ: Cross antigenicity among enteroviruses as revealed by immunoblot technique. *Virology* 1983; 129:431–442.

65. Abraham A: Isolation of two enteroviruses, possibly "prime" strains of coxsackie A type 17 virus. *Proc Soc Exp Biol Med* 1967; 125:195–200.

66. Schmidt NJ, Lennette EH, Ho HH: Observations on antigenic variants of echovirus type 11. *Proc Soc Exp Biol Med* 1966; 123:696–700.

67. Jackson GG, Muldoon RL: Viruses causing common respiratory infections in man. II. Enteroviruses and paramyxoviruses. *J Infect Dis* 1973; 128:387–408.

68. Rosen L, Kern J, Bell JA: An outbreak of infection with ECHO virus type 3 associated with a mild febrile illness. *Am J Hyg* 1964; 79:163–169.

69. Schmidt NJ, Lennette EH: Antigenic variance of coxsackievirus type A-24. *Am J Epidemiol* 1970; 91:99–109.

70. Subrahmanyan TP, Lesiak JM, Labzoffsky NA: A new intratypic variant of coxsackie B-6 virus. *Arch Virusforsch* 1973; 41:360–364.

71. Richter FA, Macpherson LW, Campbell JB, et al: Studies on intratypic variants of coxsackie B-1 virus. *Arch Virusforsch* 1972; 38:77–84.

72. Harris LF, Haynes RE, Cramblett HG, et al: Antigenic analysis of echoviruses 1 and 8. *J Infect Dis* 1973; 127:63–68.

73. Margalith M, Margalith E, Goldblum N: Genetic characteristics of echovirus type 9 strains: Selection and characterization of variants. *J Gen Virol* 1968; 3:77–85.

74. Sabin AB, Krumbiegel FR, Wigand R: ECHO type 9 virus disease. *Am J Dis Child* 1958; 96:197–219.

75. Abraham AA, Inverso K: Isolation and characterization of an echovirus, intratypic variant of echovirus 33. *Arch Virol* 1977; 53:39–44.

76. Kawamoto H: Antigenic analysis of acute hemorrhagic conjunctivitis viruses (enterovirus type 70). *Microbiol Immunol* 1979; 23:859–866.

77. Gust ID, Coulepis AG, Feinstone SM, et al: Taxonomic classification of hepatitis A virus. *Intervirology* 1983; 20:1–7.

78. Najarian R, Caput D, Gee W, et al: Primary structure and gene organization of human hepatitis A virus. *Proc Natl Acad Sci USA* 1985; 82:2627–2631.

79. Kim-Farley RJ, Lichfield P, Orenstein WA, et al: Outbreak of Poliomyelitis, Taiwan. *Lancet* 1984; 2:1322–1324.

80. Kinnunen E, Hovi T, Stenvik N: Outbreak of poliomyelitis in Finland in 1984: Description of 9 cases with persisting paralysis. *Scand J Infect Dis* 1986; 18:15–18.

81. Assaad F, Gispen R, Kleemola M, et al: Neurological diseases associated with viral and *Mycoplasma pneumoniae* infections. *Bull WHO* 1980; 58:297–311.

82. Cooney MK, Hall CE, Fox JP: The Seattle Virus Watch. III. Evaluation of isolation methods and summary of infections detected by virus isolation. *Am J Epidemiol* 1972; 96:286–305.

83. Spigland I, Fox JP, Elvedack LR, et al: The Virus Watch program: A continuing surveillance of virus infections in metropolitan New York families. II. Laboratory methods and preliminary report on infections revealed by virus isolation. *Am J Epidemiol* 1966; 83:413–435.

84. Kogon A, Spigland I, Frothingham TE, et al: The Virus Watch program: A continuing surveillance of viral infections in metropolitan New York families. VII. Observations on viral excretion, seroimmunity, intrafamilial spread and illness association in coxsackie and echovirus infections. *Am J Epidemiol* 1969; 89:51–61.

85. Centers for Disease Control: Poliomyelitis surveillance summary 1979, US Dept. of Health and Human Services, Atlanta, 1981.

86. John TJ, Patoria NK, Christopher S, et al: Epidemiology of enterovirus infections in children in Nagpur. *Indian J Med Res* 1978; 68:549–554.

87. Moore M: Enteroviral disease in the United States, 1970–1979. *J Infect Dis* 1982; 146:103–108.

88. Meyer HM, Johnson RT, Crawford IP, et al: Central nervous syndromes of "viral" etiology. A study of 713 cases. *Am J Med* 1960; 29:334–347.

89. Honig EI, Melnick JL, Isacson P, et al: Endemiological study of enteric virus infections, poliomyelitis, Coxsackie, and orphan (ECHO) viruses isolated from normal children in 2 socio-economic groups. *J Exp Med* 1956; 103:247–262.

90. Otatume S, Addy PA-K: Ecology of enteroviruses in tropics. I. Circulation of enteroviruses in healthy infants in tropical urban areas. *Jpn J Microbiol* 1975; 19:201–209.

91. Jenista JA, Powell KR, Menegus MA: Epidemiology of neonatal enterovirus infection. *J Pediatr* 1984; 104:685–690.

92. Rothenberg R, Murphy W, O'Brien CL, et al: Aseptic meningitis associated with ECHO virus, type 9: An outbreak. *South Med J* 1970; 63:280–285.

93. Gelfand HM, Fox JP, Leblanc DR: The enteric viral flora of a population of normal children in Southern Louisiana. *Am J Public Health* 1957; 47:421–431.

94. Gelfand HM, Holguin AH, Marchetti GE, et al: A continuing surveillance of enterovirus infection in healthy children in six

United States cities. I. Viruses isolated during 1960 and 1961. *Am J Hyg* 1963; 78:358–375.

95. Garber HJ, Glick TH, Joseph JM, et al: Aseptic meningitis epidemic involving ECHO 4 and coxsackie B-5 viruses. *Public Health Rep* 1970; 85:1–7.

96. Payne AM-M: Poliomyelitis as a world problem, in Fishbein M (ed): *Poliomyelitis Papers and Discussions Presented at the Third International Poliomyelitis Conference.* Philadelphia: JB Lippincott, 1955, pp 393–400.

97. Lerner AM, Klein JO, Cherry JD, et al: New viral exanthems. *N Engl J Med* 1963; 269:678–685.

98. Irvine DH, Irvine ABH, Gardner PS: Outbreak of ECHO virus type 30 in a general practice. *Br Med J* 1967; 4:774–776.

99. Eichenwald HF, McCracken GH Jr, Kindberg SJ: Virus infections of the newborn. *Prog Med Virol* 1967; 9:35–104.

100. Gear JHS, Measroch V: Coxsackievirus infections of the newborn. *Prog Med Virol* 1973; 15:42–62.

101. Woodruff JF: Viral myocarditis: A review. *Am J Pathol* 1980; 101:427–483.

102. Parrott RH: The clinical importance of group A coxsackie viruses. *Ann NY Acad Sci* 1957; 67:230–240.

103. MacKay-Scollay EM, Hobday JDG, Harnett GB, et al: Echovirus type 30 infection: Clinical and virological observations on an epidemic in western Australia. *Med J Aust* 1973; 2:417–421.

104. Public Health Laboratory Service: Hand, foot, and mouth disease. *Br Med J* 1976; 1:350.

105. Forbes JA: Some clinical aspects of meningoencephalitis. *Med J Aust* 1963; 1:568–572.

106. Ball AP: Disease due to echovirus type 19 in Birmingham, England, 1975: Relationship to "epidemic neuromyasthenia." *Postgrad Med J* 1978; 54:737–740.

107. Karzon DT, Eckert GL, Barron AL, et al: Aseptic meningitis epidemic due to Echo 4 virus. *Am J Dis Child* 1961; 101:102–114.

108. Gould KL, Osher A, Olda A, et al: An epidemic of aseptic meningitis due to echovirus type 9 in Oahu, Hawaii. *Am J Public Health* 1970; 60:2336–2344.

109. Jarvis WR, Tucker G: Echovirus type 7 in young children. *Am J Dis Child* 1981; 135:1009–1012.

110. Bell TM, Sims DG, Bacon CJ, et al: Epidemic of echovirus 19 in the northeast of England. *J Hyg (Camb)* 1976; 76:307–317.

111a. Nelson D, Hiemstra H, Minor T, et al: Non-polio enterovirus activity in Wisconsin based on a 20-year experience in a diagnostic virology laboratory. *Am J Epidemiol* 1979; 109:352–361.

111b. Ray CG, McCollough RH, Doto IL, et al: Echo 4 illness. Epidemiological, clinical and laboratory studies on an outbreak in a rural community. *Am J Epidemiol* 1966; 84:253–267.

112. Helin M, Savola J, Lapinleimu K: Cardiac manifestations during a coxsackie B5 epidemic. *Br Med J* 1968; 3:97–99.

113. Kono R, Miyamura K, Tajiri E, et al: Virological and serological studies of neurological complications of acute hemorrhagic conjunctivitis in Thailand. *J Infect Dis* 1977; 135:706–713.

114. Miwa C, Ohtani M, Watanabe H, et al: Epidemic of hand, foot and mouth disease in Gifu Prefecture in 1978. *Jpn J Med Sci Biol* 1980; 33:167–180.

115. Goldwater PN, Laws J: Echovirus 19 outbreak in Auckland 1975–1976. *NZ Med J* 1977; 86:319–322.

116. Virus disease surveillance. Echovirus type 24. *Weekly Epidemiol Rec* 1978; 46:334.

117. Virus diseases surveillance: Enteroviruses. *Weekly Epidemiol Rec* 1978; 50:367.

118. Dery P, Marks MI, Shapera R: Clinical manifestations of coxsackievirus infections in children. *Am J Dis Child* 1974; 128:464–468.

119. Khatib R, Chason JL, Silberberg BK, et al: Age-dependent pathogenicity of group B coxsackieivurses in Swiss-Webster mice: Infectivity for myocardium and pancreas. *J Infect Dis* 1980; 141:394–403.

120. Burch GE, Sun S-C, Chu K-C, et al: Interstitial and coxsackievirus B myocarditis in infants and children: A comparative histologic and immunofluroescent study of 50 autopsied hearts.

JAMA 1968; 203:1–8.

121. Kunin CM: Virus-tissue union and the pathogenesis of enterovirus infections. *J Immunol* 1962; 8:556–569.

122. Loria RM, Shadoff N, Kibrick S, et al: Maturation of intestinal defenses against peroral infection with group B coxsackievirus in mice. *Infect Immun* 1976; 13:1397–1401.

123. Landsman JB, Bell EJ: ECHO type 9 infection in 1960, a study in general practice. *Br Med J* 1962; 1:12–16.

124. Haynes RE, Cramblett HG, Kronfol HJ: Echovirus 9 meningoencephalitis in infants and children. *JAMA* 1969; 208:1657–1660.

125. Oren J, Schiff GM, Fodor AR, et al: Aseptic meningitis on an Indian reservation, an epidemic associated with ECHO 9 virus. *Am J Dis Child* 1961; 102:95–104.

126. Winkelstein W Jr, Karzon DT, Barron AL, et al: Epidemiologic observations on an outbreak of aseptic meningitis due to ECHO virus type 6. *Am J Public Health* 1957; 47:741–749.

127. Sharp JCM, Bell EJ: Echovirus type 4 infections in Scotland, 1971–1972. *Scand J Infect Dis* 1975; 7:239–242.

128. Bell EJ, Grist NR: Further studies of enterovirus infections in cardiac disease and pleurodynia. *Scand J Infect Dis* 1970; 2:1–6.

129. Smith WG: Coxsackie B myopericarditis in adults. *Am Heart J* 1970; 80:34–46.

130. Reference deleted in proof.

131. Warin JF, Davies JBM, Sanders FK, et al: Oxford epidemic on Bornholm disease, 1951. *Br Med J* 1953; 1:1345–1354.

132. Grist NR: Type A–7 coxsackie (type 4 poliomyelitis) virus infection in Scotland. *J Hyg (Camb)* 1962; 60:323–332.

133. Artenstein MS, Cadigan FC, Buescher EL: Clinical and epidemiological features of coxsackie group B virus infection. *Ann Intern Med* 1965; 63:597–603.

134. McLean DM, Coleman MA, Larke RPB: Viral infections of Toronto children during 1965: I. Enteroviral disease. *Can Med Assoc J* 1966; 94:839–843.

135. Chong AYH, Lee LH, Wong HB: Epidemic pleurodynia (Bornholm disease) outbreak in Singapore. A clinical and virological study. *Trop Geogr J* 1975; 27:151–159.

135a. Wong CY, Woodruff JJ, Woodruff JF: Generation of cytotoxic lymphocytes during coxsackievirus B-3 infection: III. Role of sex. *J. Immunol* 1977; 119:591–597.

136. Lehan PH, Chick EW, Doto IL, et al: An epidemic illness associated with a recently recognized enteric virus (Echo virus type 4), I. Epidemiologic and clinical features. *Am J Hyg* 1957; 66:63–75.

137. Kelen AE, Labzoffsky NA: Variations in the prevalence of enterovirus infections in Ontario, 1956–1965. *Can Med Assoc J* 1967; 97:797–801.

138. Kono R: Apollo 11 disease or acute hemorrhagic conjunctivitis: A pandemic of a new enterovirus infection of the eyes. *Am J Epidemiol* 1975; 101:383–390.

139. Horstmann DM, Emmons J, Gimpel L, et al: Enterovirus surveillance following a community-wide oral poliovirus vaccination program: A 7-year study. *Am J Epidemiol* 1973; 97:173–186.

140. Parrott RH, Huebner RJ, McCullough NB, et al: The hospital as a factor in assessing the occurrence of coxsackie viruses in various illness groups. I. Children from the outpatient department and various hospital wards. *Pediatrics* 1955; 15:255–263.

141. Schwartz RH, Tobin JOH: Coxsackie B-2 virus outbreak in a special care baby unit. *Comm Dis Rep* 1978; 35:59.

142. Lapinleimu K, Kaski U: An outbreak caused by coxsackievirus B-5 among newborn infants. *Scand J Infect Dis* 1972; 4:27–30.

143. Brightman VJ, Scott TFM, Westphal M, et al: An outbreak of coxsackie B-5 virus infection in a newborn nursery. *J Pediatr* 1966; 69:179–192.

144. German LJ, McCracken AW, Wilkie KMcD: Outbreak of febrile illness associated with ECHO virus type 5 in a maternity unit in Singapore. *Br Med J* 1968; 1:742–744.

145. Nagington J, Wreghitt TG, Gandy G, et al: Fatal echovirus 11 infections in outbreak in special-care baby unit. *Lancet* 1978; 2:725–728.

146. Hasegawa A: Virologic and serologic studies on an outbreak of echovirus type 11 infection in a hospital maternity unit. *Jpn J Med Sci Biol* 1975; 28:179–188.

147. Jones MJ, Kolb M, Votava HV, et al: Intrauterine echovirus type 11 infection. *Mayo Clin Proc* 1980; 55:509–512.

148. Cramblett HG, Haynes RE, Azimi PH, et al: Nosocomial infection with echovirus type 11 in handicapped and premature infants. *Pediatrics* 1973; 51:603–607.

149. Berkovich S, Kibrick S: Echo 11 outbreak in newborn infants and mothers. *Pediatrics* 1964; 33:534–540.

150. Faulkner RS, van Rooyen CE: Echovirus type 17 in the neonate. *Can Med Assoc J* 1973; 108:877–882.

151. World Health Organization: *WHO Yearly Report*, Geneva, World Health Organization, 1978, p 65.

152. Eichenwald HF, Ababio A, Arky AM, et al: Epidemic diarrhea in premature and older infants caused by echo virus type 18. *JAMA* 1958; 166:1563–1566.

153. Purdham DR, Purdham PA, Wood BSB, et al: Severe echo 19 virus infection in a neonatal unit. *Arch Dis Child* 1976; 51:634–636.

154. Berkovich S, Pangan J: Recoveries of virus from premature infants during outbreaks of respiratory disease: The relation of echo virus type 22 to disease of the upper and lower respiratory tract in the premature infant. *Bull NY Acad Med* 1968; 44:377–387.

155. McDonald LL, St Geme JW, Arnold BH: Nosocomial infection with echo virus type 31 in a neonatal intensive care unit. *Pediatrics* 1971; 47:995–999.

156. Reiss-Levy L, Baker A, Don N, et al: Two concurrent epidemics of enteroviral meningitis in an obstetric neonatal unit. *Aust NZ J Med* 1986; 16:365–372.

157. Modlin JF: Perinatal echovirus infection: Insights from a literature review of 61 cases of serious infection and 16 outbreaks in nurseries. *Rev Infect Dis* 1986; 8:918–926.

158. Nagington J, Walker J, Gandy G, et al: Use of normal immunoglobulin in an echovirus 11 outbreak in a special-care baby unit. *Lancet* 1983; 2:443–446.

159. Rabkin CS, Telzak EE, Ho M-S, et al: Outbreak of echovirus 11 infection in hospitalized neonates. *Pediatr Infect Dis J* 1988; 7:186–190.

160. Artenstein MS, Cadigan FC, Beuscher EL: Epidemic coxsackie virus infection with mixed clinical manifestations. *Ann Intern Med* 1964; 60:196–203.

161. Clemmer DI, Li F, Le Blanc DR, et al: An outbreak of subclinical infection with coxsackievirus B-3 in southern Louisiana. *Am J Epidemiol* 1966; 83:123–129.

162. Hall CE, Cooney MK, Fox JP: The Seattle Virus Watch program. I. Infection and illness experience of Virus Watch families during a community-wide epidemic of echovirus type 30 aseptic meningitis. *Am J Public Health* 1970; 60:1456–1465.

163. Lerner AM, Klein JO, Levin HS, et al: Infections due to coxsackie virus group A, type 9, in Boston, 1959, with special reference to exanthems and pneumonia. *N Engl J Med* 1960; 263:1265–1272.

164. Chin TDY, Lehan PH, Rubin H, et al: Epidemic infection with coxsackievirus, group B, type 5. II. Virus excretion and neutralizing antibody response. *Am J Hyg* 1958; 67:321–330.

165. Gelfand HM, LeBlanc DR, Fox JP, et al: Studies on the development of natural immunity to poliomyelitis in Louisiana. II. Description and analysis of episodes of infection observed in study group households. *Am J Hyg* 1957; 65:367–385.

166. Gould I, Clarke PD, Ball AP, et al: An outbreak of meningitis caused by echo virus type 19. *Practitioner* 1977; 218:371–375.

167. Lagercrants M, Hugo H, Sterner G, et al: Spread of echovirus type 18 infections within families. *Scand J Infect Dis* 1973; 5:249–252.

168. Hoskins TW, Davies JR, Smith AJ, et al: The spread of coxsackie B-1 infection. *Arch Dis Child* 1979; 54:291–294.

169. Centers for Disease Control: The 1979 Amish outbreak, in *Poliomyelitis Surveillance Survey*, 1979. Atlanta, Centers for Disease Control, 1981, pp 14–19.

170. Centers for Disease Control: Poliomyelitis—Pennsylvania, Maryland. *MMWR* 1979; 28:49–50.

171. Centers for Disease Control: Poliomyelitis—Netherlands. *MMWR* 1978; 27:222.

172. Townsend TR, Yolken RH, Bishop CA, et al: Outbreak of Coxsackie A1 gastroenteritis: A complication of bone-marrow transplantation. *Lancet* 1982; 1:820–823.

173. Feachem R, Garelick H, Slade J: Enteroviruses in the environment. *Trop Dis Bull* 1981; 78:185–230.

174. Keswick BH, Gerba CP, Goyal SM: Occurrence of enteroviruses in community swimming pools. *Am J Public Health* 1981; 71:1026–1030.

175. Gerba CP, Goyal SM, Labelle RL, et al: Failure of indicator bacteria to reflect the occurrence of enteroviruses in marine waters. *Am J Public Health* 1979; 69:1116–1119.

176. D'Alessio DJ, Minor TE, Allen CI, et al: A study of the proportion of swimmers among well controls and children with enterovirus-like illness shedding or not shedding an enterovirus. *Am J Epidemiol* 1981; 113:533–541.

177. Hawley HB, Morin DP, Geraghty ME, et al: Coxsackievirus B epidemic at a boys' summer camp: Isolation of virus from swimming water. *JAMA* 1973; 226:33–36.

178. Goyal SM, Gerba CP, Melnick JL: Human enteroviruses in oysters and their overlying waters. *Appl Environ Microbiol* 1979; 37:572–581.

179. Denis FA: Coxsackie group A in oysters and mussels. *Lancet* 1973; 1:1262.

180. Clark CS, Bjornson AB, Schiff GM, et al: Sewage worker's syndrome. *Lancet* 1977; 1:1009.

181. Moore BE, Sagik BP, Sorber CA, et al: Procedure for the recovery of airborne human enteric viruses during spray irrigation of treated waste water. *Appl Environ Microbiol* 1979; 38:688–693.

182. Favero MS: Sterilization, disinfection, and antisepsis in the hospital, in *Manual of Clinical Microbiology*, ed 3, Washington DC, American Society of Microbiology, 1980, pp 952–957.

183. Drulak M, Wallbank AM, Lebtag I, et al: The relative effectiveness of commonly used disinfectants in inactivation of coxsackievirus B-5. *J Hyg (Camb)* 1978; 81:389–397.

184. Glikmann G, Moynihan M, Petersen I, et al: Intratypic differentiation of poliovirus strains by enzyme-linked immunosorbent assay (ELISA): poliovirus type 1. *Dev Biol Stand* 1984; 55:199–208.

184a. Glikmann G, Pedersen M, Petersen I: Intratypic differentiation of poliovirus strains by enzyme-linked immunosorbent assay (ELISA): poliovirustype 2 and poliovirus type 3. *J. Virol Methods* 1987; 18:25–36.

185. Crainic R, Couillin P, Blondel B, et al: Natural variation of poliovirus neutralization epitopes. *Infect Immun* 1983; 41:1217–1225.

186. Ferguson M, Magrath DI, Minor TD, et al: WHO collaborative study on the use of monoclonal antibodies for the intratypic differentiation of poliovirus strains. *Bull WHO* 186; 64:239–246.

187. Minor PD, John A, Ferguson M, et al: Antigenic and molecular evolution of the vaccine strain of type 3 poliovirus during the period of excretion by a primary vaccinee. *J Gen Virol* 1986; 67:693–706.

188. Huovilainen A, Hovi T, Kinnunen L, et al: Evolution of poliovirus during an outbreak: sequential type 3 poliovirus isolates from several persons show shifts of neutralization determinants. *J Gen Virol* 1987; 68:1373–1378.

189. Guo R, Tang EH, Wang H, et al: Preliminary studies on antigenic variation of poliovirus using neutralizing monoclonal antibodies. *J Gen Virol* 1987; 68:989–994.

190. Magrath DI, Evans DMA, Ferguson M, et al: Antigenic and molecular properties of type 3 poliovirus responsible for an outbreak of poliomyelitis in a vaccinated population. *J Gen Virol* 1986; 67:899–905.

192. Prabhakar BS, Haspel MV, McClintock PR, et al: High frequency of antigenic variants among naturally occurring human Coxsackie B4 virus isolates identified by monoclonal antibodies. *Nature* 1982; 300:374–376.

193. Prabhakar BS, Menegus MA, Notkins AL: Detection of conserved and nonconserved epitopes on Coxsackievirus B4: frequency of antigenic change. *Virology* 1985; 146:302–306.

194. Reference deleted in proof.

195. Nottay BK, Kew OM, Hatch MH, et al: Molecular variation of type 1 vaccine-related and wild polioviruses during replication in humans. *Virology* 1981; 108:405–423.

196. Kew OM, Nottay BK, Hatch MH, et al.: Multiple genetic changes can occur in the oral poliovaccines upon replication in humans. *J Gen Virol* 1981; 56:337–347.

197. Kew OM, Nottay BK: Molecular epidemiology of polioviruses. *Rev Infect Dis* 1984; (suppl 2):S499–S504.

198. Kew OM, Nottay BK, Hatch MH, et al: Oligonucleotide fingerprint analysis of enterovirus 70 isolates from the 1980 to 1981 pandemic of acute hemorrhagic conjunctivitis: evidence for a close genetic relationship among Asian and American strains. *Infect Immun* 1983; 41:631–635.

199. Takeda N, Miyamura K, Ogino T, et al: Evolution of enterovirus type 70: oligonucleotide mapping analysis of RNA genome. *Virology* 1984; 134:375–388.

200. Miyamura K, Tanimura M, Takeda N, et al: Evolution of enterovirus 70 in nature: all isolates were recently derived from a common ancestor. *Arch Virol* 1986; 89:1–14.

201. O'Neill KM, Pallansch MA, Winkelstein JA, et al: Chronic group A coxsackie infections in agammaglobulinemia: Demonstration of genomic variation of serotypically identical isolates persistently excreted by the same patient. *J Infect Dis* 1986; 157:483–486.

202. Rico-Hesse R, Pallansch MA, Nottay BK, et al: Geographic distribution of wild poliovirus type 1 genotypes. *Virology* 1987; 160:311–322.

203. Charcot JM, Joffroy A: Cas de paralysie infantile spinale avec lésions des cornes antérieures de la substance grise de la moelle épiniere. *Arch Physiol Norm Pathol* 1870; 3:134.

203a. Couderc T, Christodoulu C, Kopecka H, et al: Molecular pathogenesis of neural lesions induced by poliovirus type 1. *J Gen Virol* 1989; 70:2907–2918.

204. Yoshioka L, Horstmann DM: Viremia in infection due to ECHO virus type 9. *N Engl J Med* 1960; 262:224–228.

205. Gelfand HM: The occurrence and nature of the coxsackie and ECHO viruses. *Prog Med Virol* 1961; 3:193–244.

206. Kibrick S, Loria RM: Enteric resistance and coxsackievirus B 1–3. *Am J Clin Nutr* 1977; 30:1871–1875.

207. Kräusslich HG, Nicklin MJH, Toyoda H, et al: Poliovirus proteinase 2A induces cleavage of eucaryotic initiation factor 4F polypeptide p220. *J Virol* 1987; 61:2711–2718.

208. Fradkin LG, Yoshinaga SK, Berk AJ, et al: Inhibition of host cell RNA polymerase III—mediated transcription by poliovirus: Inactivation of specific transcription factors. *Mol Cell Biol* 1987; 7:3880–3887.

209. Reference deleted in proof.

210. Rueckert RR: Picornaviridae and their replication, in Fields BN (ed): *Virology.* New York, Raven Press, 1990, pp 507–548.

211. Omata T, Kohara M, Kuge S, et al: Genetic analysis of the attenuation phenotype of poliovirus type 1. *J Virol* 1986; 58:348–358.

212. Almond JW, Westrop GD, Evans DM, et al: Studies on the attenuation of the Sabin type 3 oral polio vaccine. *J Virol Methods* 1987; 17:183–189.

213. Gnann JW, Hayes EC, Smith JZ, Wilfert CM: ECHOvirus 33 replication in human peripheral white blood cells. *J Med Virol* 1979; 3:291–299.

214. Ogra PL: Effect of tonsillectomy and adenoidectomy on nasopharyngeal antibody response to poliovirus. *N Engl J Med* 1971; 284:59–64.

215. Eley RC, Flake CG: Acute anterior poliomyelitis following tonsillectomy and adenoidectomy: With special reference to the bulbar form. *J Pediatr* 1938; 13:63–70.

216. Aycock WL: Tonsillectomy and poliomyelitis. I. Epidemiologic considerations. *Medicine* 1942; 21:65–94.

217. Lucchesi PF, LaBocretta AC: Relationship of tonsils and adenoids to the type of poliomyelitis: An analysis of four hundred and thirty-two cases. *Am J Dis Child* 1944; 68:1–4.

218. Fischer AE, Stillerman M, Marks HH: Relationship of tonsillectomy and of adenoidectomy to the incidence of poliomyelitis: With special reference to the bulbar form. *Am J Dis Child* 1941; 61:305–321.

219. Anderson GW, Rondeau JL: Absence of tonsils as a factor in the development of bulbar poliomyelitis. *JAMA* 1954; 155:1123–1130.

220. Allison AC: Immunity and immunopathology in virus infections. *Ann Inst Pasteur* 1972; 123:585–608.

221. Lerner AM, Wilson FM: Virus myocardiopathy. *Prog Med Virol* 1973; 15:63–91.

222. Buckland FE, Bynoe ML, Rosen L, et al: Inoculation of human volunteers with ECHO virus type 20. *Br Med J* 1961; 1:397–400.

223. Schiff GM: Coxsackievirus B epidemic at a boys' camp. *Am J Dis Child* 1979; 133:782–785.

224. Langford MP, Stanton GJ, Barber JC, et al: Early-appearing antiviral activity in human tears during a case of picornavirus epidemic conjunctivitis. *J Infect Dis* 1979; 139:653–658.

225. Berkovich S, Ressel M: Effect of sex on susceptibility of adult mice to coxsackie B-1 virus infections. *Arch Virusforsch* 1967; 22:246–251.

226. Lerner AM, Klein JL, Cherry JD, et al: New viral exanthems (concluded). *N Engl J Med* 1963; 269:736–740.

227. Whitehead JEM: Silent infections and the epidemiology of viral carditis. *Am Heart J* 1973; 85:711–713.

228. Woodruff JF, Woodruff JJ: Modification of severe coxsackievirus B-3 infection in marasmic mice by transfer of immune lymphoid cells. *Proc Natl Acad Sci USA* 1971; 68:2108–2111.

229. Jones VJ: Muscle pain induced by exercise in coxsackie pericarditis. *Br Med J* 1975; 3:100.

230. Woodruff JF: The influence of quantitated post-weaning undernutrition on coxsackievirus B-3 infection of adult mice. II. Alteration of host defense mechanisms. *J Infect Dis* 1970; 121:164–181.

231. Teodoru CV, Shwartzman G: Relation of certain endocrine disturbances to susceptibility of golden Syrian hamster to experimental poliomyelitis. *J Exp Med* 1954; 100:563–574.

232. Reyes MP, Lerner AM: Interferon and neutralizing antibody in sera of exercised mice with coxsackievirus B-3 myocarditis. *Proc Soc Exp Biol Med* 1976; 151:333–338.

233. Cherry JD, Jahn CL: Herpangina: The etiologic spectrum. *Pediatrics* 1965; 36:632–634.

234. Lerner AM: An experimental approach to virus myocarditis. *Prog Med Virol* 1965; 7:97–115.

235. Tilles JG, Elson SH, Shaka JA, et al: Effects of exercise on coxsackie A-9 myocarditis in adult mice. *Proc Soc Exp Biol Med* 1964; 117:777–782.

236. Abelmann WH: Virus and the heart. *Circulation* 1971; 44:950–956.

237. Lansdown ABG: Viral infections and diseases of the heart. *Prog Med Virol* 1978; 24:70–113.

238. Haahr S, Teisner B: The influence of different temperatures on mortality, virus multiplication and interferon production in adult mice infected with coxsackie B-1 virus. *Arch Virusforsch* 1973; 42:273–277.

239. Bendinelli M, Ruschi A, Campa M, et al: Depression of humoral and cell-mediated immune responses by coxsackieviruses in mice. *Experientia* 1975; 31:1227–1229.

240. Feigin RD, Middlecamp JN, Reed C: Circadian rhythmicity in susceptibility of mice to sublethal coxsackie B3 infection. *Nature (New Biol)* 1972; 240:57–58.

241. Loria RM, Kibrick S, Madge GE: Infection of hypercholesterolemic mice and coxsackievirus B. *J Infect Dis* 1976; 133:655–662.

242. Russell WR: The pre-paralytic stage and the effect of physical activity on the severity of paralysis. *Br Med J* 1947; 2:1023–1029.

243. Horstmann DM: Acute poliomyelitis—Relation of physical ac-

tivity at the time of onset to the course of the disease. *JAMA* 1950; 142:236–241.

244. Russell WR: Paralytic poliomyelitis—The early symptoms and the effect of physical activity on the course of the disease. *Br Med J* 1949; 1:465–471.

245. Horstmann DM: Clinical aspects of poliomyelitis. *Am J Med* 1949; 6:592–605.

246. Levinson SO, Milzer A, Lewin P: Effect of fatigue, chilling and mechanical trauma on resistance to experimental poliomyelitis. *Am J Hyg* 1945; 42:204–213.

247. Gatmaitan BG, Chason JL: Augmentation of the virulence of murine coxsackievirus B-3 myocardiopathy of exercise. *J Exp Med* 1970; 131:1121–1136.

248. Sutton GC, Harding HB, Truehart RP, et al: Coxsackie B-4 myocarditis in an adult: Successful isolation of virus from ventricular myocardium. *Aerospace Med* 1967; 38:66–69.

249. Dalldorf G, Gifford R: Susceptibility of gravid mice to coxsackie virus infection. *J Exp Med* 1954; 99:21–27.

250. Plager H, Beebe R, Miller J: Coxsackie B-5 pericarditis in pregnancy. *Arch Intern Med* 1962; 110:735–738.

251. Saliba GS, Franklin FL, Jackson GG: ECHO-11 as a respiratory virus: Quantitation of infection in man. *J Clin Invest* 1968; 47:1303–1313.

252. Kaneda Y, Hayes H, Uchida T, et al: Regional assignment of five genes on human chromosome 19. *Chromosome* 1987; 95:8–12.

253. Mapoles JE, Krah DL, Crowell RL: Purification of a HeLa cell receptor protein for group B coxsackieviruses. *J Virol* 1985; 55:560–566.

254. Hsu K-HL, Lonberg-Holm K, Alstein B, et al: A monoclonal antibody specific for the cellular receptor for the group B coxsackieviruses. *J Virol* 1988; 62:1647–1652.

255. Ogra PL, Karzon DT: Formation and function of poliovirus antibody in different tissues. *Prog Med Virol* 1971; 13:156–193.

256. Ogra PL, Koppola PR, MacGillivray MH, et al: Mechanisms of mucosal immunity to viral infections in IgA immunoglobulin-deficiency syndromes. *Proc Soc Exp Biol Med* 1974; 145:811–816.

257. Ogra PL, Karzon DT: Distribution of poliovirus antibody in serum, nasopharynx and alimentary tract following segmental immunization of lower alimentary tract with polio vaccine. *J Immunol* 1969; 102:1423–1430.

258. Ogra PL: Distribution of echovirus antibody in serum, nasopharynx, rectum, and spinal fluid after natural infection with echovirus type 6. *Infect Immun* 1970; 2:150–155.

259. Hanson LA, Carlsson B, Jalil F, et al: Different secretory IgA antibody responses after immunization with inactivated and live poliovirus vaccines. *Rev Infect Dis* 1984; 6(suppl 2):S356–S360.

260. Carlsson B, Zaman S, Mellander L, et al: Secretory and serum immunoglobulin class-specific antibodies to poliovirus after vaccination. *J Infect Dis* 1985; 152:1238–1244.

260a. Zhaori G, Sun M, Faden HS, et al: Nasopharyngeal secretory antibody response to poliovirus type 3 virion proteins exhibit different specificities after immunization with live or inactivated poliovirus vaccines. *J Infect Dis* 1989; 159:1018–1024.

261. El-Hagrassy MMO, Banatvala JE, Coltart DJ: Coxsackie-B-virus-specific IgM responses in patients with cardiac and other diseases. *Lancet* 1980; 2:1160–1162.

262. Bussell RH, Karzon DT, Barron AL, et al: Hemagglutination-inhibiting complement-fixing and neutralizing antibody responses in echo 6 infections, including studies on heterotypic responses. *J Immunol* 1962; 88:47–54.

263. Ogra PL, Ogra SS, Al-Nakeed S, et al: Local antibody response to experimental poliovirus infection in the central nervous system of rhesus monkeys. *Infect Immun* 1973; 8:931–937.

264. Bass JW, Halstead SB, Fischer GW, et al: Oral poliovaccine—effect of booster vaccination one to fourteen years after primary series. *JAMA* 1978; 239:2252–2255.

265. Aycock WL: Alterations in autareologic susceptibility to experimental poliomyelitis. *Proc Soc Exp Biol Med* 1936; 34:573–574.

266. Magee WE, Miller OV: Individual variability in antibody response of human volunteers to infection of the upper respiratory tract by coxsackie A-21 virus. *J Infect Dis* 1970; 122:127–138.

267. Lennette EH, Shinomoto TT, Schmidt NJ, et al: Observations on the neutralizing antibody response to group B coxsackieviruses in patients with central nervous system disease. *J Immunol* 1961; 86:257–266.

268. Moscovici C, Maisel J: Intestinal viruses of newborn and older prematures. *Am J Dis Child* 1961; 101:771–777.

269. Hammon WM, Coriell LL, Wehrle PF: Evaluation of Red Cross gammaglobulin as a prophylactic agent for poliomyelitis. 4. Final report of results based on clinical diagnosis. *JAMA* 1953; 151:1272–1285.

270. Opton EM, Nagaki D, Melnick JL: Poliomyelitis antibodies in human gammaglobulin. *J Immunol* 1955; 75:178–185.

271. Kilbourne ED: The coxsackie viruses and human disease. *Am J Med Sci* 1952; 224:93–102.

272. Gamble DR: Isolation of coxsackie viruses from normal children aged 0–5 years. *Br Med J* 1962; 1:16–18.

273. Cook I, Allan BC, Welham S: Coxsackieviruses in normal children. *Med J Aust* 1969; 2:789–792.

274. Adler JL, Mostow SR, Mellin H, et al: Epidemiologic investigation of hand, foot, and mouth disease: Infection caused by coxsackievirus A-16 in Baltimore, June through September, 1968. *Am J Dis Child* 1970; 120:309–313.

275. Sanford JP, Sulkin SE: The clinical spectrum of echo-virus infection. *N Engl J Med* 1959; 261:1113–1122.

276. Melnick JL, Kaplan AS, Zabin E, et al: An epidemic of paralytic poliomyelitis characterized by dual infections with poliomyelitis and coxsackie viruses. *J Exp Med* 1951; 94:471–492.

277. Levitt LP, Bond JO, Hall IE, et al: Meningococcal and ECHO-9 meningitis, report of an outbreak. *Neurology* 1970; 20:45–51.

278. John TJ, Christopher S: Oral polio vaccination of children in the tropics. III. Intercurrent enterovirus infections, vaccine virus take and antibody response. *Am J Epidemiol* 1975; 102:422–428.

279. Choudhury DS, Nossik NN, Bindu, et al: Poliomyelitis vaccination of infants: Preimmunization status and seroconversion. *Bull WHO* 1973; 48:195–198.

280. Swartz TA, Skalska P, Gerichter CG, et al: Non-polio virus interference with oral polio vaccine immunization: Possible influence of physical climate and socioeconomic status. *Adv Exp Med Biol* 1972; 31:237–240.

281. John TJ, Jayabal P: Oral polio vaccination of children in the tropics. I. The poor seroconversion rates and the absence of viral interference. *Am J Epidemiol* 1972; 96:263–269.

282. Horstmann DM: The clinical epidemiology of poliomyelitis. *Ann Intern Med* 1955; 43:533.

283. Abramson H, Greenberg M: Acute poliomyelitis in infants under one year of age: Epidemiological and clinical features, in Rogers FB (ed): *Studies in epidemiology: Selected Papers of Morris Greenberg M.D.* New York, GP Putnam Sons, 1965; 182–195.

284. Nathanson N, Martin JR: Epidemiology of poliomyelitis: Enigmas surrounding its appearance, epidemicity, and disappearance. *Am J Epidemiol* 1979; 110:672–692.

285. Sabin AB: Epidemiologic patterns of poliomyelitis in different parts of the world, in International Poliomyelitis Congress (ed): *Poliomyelitis: Papers and Discussions at the First International Poliomyelitis Conference.* Philadelphia, Lippincott, 1949, pp 3–33.

286. Medin O: Ueber eine Epidemie von spinaler Kinderlähmung. *Verhandl, X Int Med Kongr 1890.* 1891; 7:379.

287. Wickman I: Studien über *Poliomyelitis acuta; zugleich ein Beitrag zur Kenntnis der Myelitis acuta.* Berlin, Karger, 1905.

288. Peabody FW, Draper G, Dochez AR: *A Clinical Study of Acute*

Poliomyelitis. New York, Rockefeller Institute for Medical Research, monograph no. 4, 1912.

289. Erb W: Ueber acute Spinallähmung (Poliomyelitis anterior acuta) bei Erwachsener [etc]. *Arch Psychiatr Nervenkrank* 1875; 5:758.

290. Centers for Disease Control: Poliomyelitis—United States 1975–1984. *MMWR* 1986; 35:180–182.

291. Kim-Farley RJ, Schonberger LB, Nkowane BM, et al: Poliomyelitis in the USA: Virtual elimination of disease caused by wild virus. *Lancet* 1984; 2:1315–1317.

292. Peterson CR, Bryan JA, Kern J, et al: Poliomyelitis in an isolated population: Report of a type 1 epidemic in the Marshall Islands, 1963. *Am J Epidemiol* 1966; 82:273–296.

293. Sabin AB, Silva E: Residual paralytic poliomyelitis in a tropical region of Brazil, 1969–1977. Prevalence of surveys in different age groups as indicators of changing incidence. *Am J Epidemiol* 1983; 117:193–200.

294. Howe H: Poliomyelitis, in Rivers TM (ed): *Viral and Rickettsial Infections of Man,* ed 2. Philadelphia, Lippincott, 1952, pp 300–337.

295. Greenberg JM: An epidemic experience report on poliomyelitis. *J Am Hosp Assoc* 1951; 25:52–54.

296. Nitshke RA: Frequency of paralysis in various muscles during poliomyelitis. *Phys Ther Rev* 1950; 30:131–134.

297. Guyer B, Bison AAE, Gould J, et al: Injections and paralytic poliomyelitis in tropical Africa. *Bull WHO* 1980; 58:285–291.

298. Francis T: Symposium on controlled vaccine field trials: Poliomyelitis. *Am J Public Health* 1957; 47:283–287.

299. Ben-Efraim S, Long DA: The sensitising power of diphtheria prophylactics in relation to poliomyelitis. *Lancet* 1957; 2:1033–1035.

300. Neva FA: Poliomyelitis in a family with occurrence of localized paralysis after inoculation with combined diphtheria, pertussis, tetanus vaccine. *Pediatrics* 1956; 18:59–63.

301. McCloskey BP: The relation of prophylactic inoculations to the onset of poliomyelitis. *Lancet* 1950; 1:659–663.

302. Peach AM, Rhodes AJ: Further investigation into the association between immunizing injections and paralytic poliomyelitis. *Am J Public Health* 1954; 44:1185–1188.

303. Injections and paralytic poliomyelitis. *Weekly Epidemiol Rec* 1980; 38–39.

304. Moore M, Katona P, Kaplan JE, et al: Poliomyelitis in the United States, 1969–1981. *J Infect Dis* 1982; 146:558–563.

304a. Sutter RW, Brink EW, Cochi SL, et al: A new epidemiologic and laboratory classification system for paralytic poliomyelitis cases. *Am J Public Health* 1989; 79:495–498.

305. Centers For Disease Control: *Guideline for Isolation Precautions in Hospitals.* Springfield, Va, National Technical Information Service, 1983.

306. Dalakas MC, Sever JL, Madden DL, et al: Late postpoliomyelitis muscular atrophy: clinical, virologic, and immunologic studies. *Rev Infect Dis* 1984; 6(suppl 2):S562–S567.

307. Johnson RT: Late progression of poliomyelitis paralysis; discussion of pathogenesis. *Rev Infect Dis* 1984; 6(suppl 2):S568–S570.

308. Holman KG: Post polio syndrome. The battle with an old foe resumes. *Postgrad Med* 1986; 79:44–53.

309. Dalakas MC: New neuromuscular symptoms in patients with old poliomyelitis: a three-year follow-up study. *Eur Neurol* 1986; 25:381–387.

310. Dalakas MC, Elder G, Hallett M, et al: A long-term follow-up study of patients with post-poliomyelitis neuromuscular symptoms. *N Engl J Med* 1986; 314:959–963.

311. Halstead LS, Ross CD: New problems in old polio patients: Results of a survey of 539 polio survivors. *Orthopedics* 1985; 8:845–850.

312. Hayward M, Seaton D: Late sequelae of paralytic poliomyelitis: a clinical and electromyographic study. *J Neurol Neurosurg Psychiatry* 1979; 42:117–122.

313. Abom B, Laursen H, Egsgård H, et al: Late effects of polio-

myelitis or muscular function and morphology: A preliminary report. *Birth Defects* 1987; 23:223–227.

314. Shindarov LM, Chumakov MP, Voroshilova MK, et al: Epidemiological, clinical, and pathomorphological characteristics of epidemic poliomyelitis-like disease caused by enterovirus 71. *J Hyg Epidemiol Microbiol Immunol* 1979; 23:284–295.

315. Chonmaitree T, Menegus MA, Schervish-Swierkosz EM, et al: Enterovirus 71 infection: Report of an outbreak with two cases of paralysis and a review of the literature. *Pediatrics* 1981; 67:489–493.

316. Hayward JC, Gillespie SM, Kaplan K, et al: Outbreak of poliomyelitis-like paralysis associated with enterovirus 71. *Pediatr Infect Dis J* 1989; 8:611–616.

317. Melnick JL, Kaplan AS: Dual antibody response to coxsackie and poliomyelitis viruses in patients with paralytic poliomyelitis. *Proc Soc Exp Biol Med* 1950; 74:812–815.

318. Chumakov MP, Voroshilova MK, Zhevandrova VI, et al: Voprosy virusologii. *Probl Virol* 1956; 1:16–19.

319. Enterovirus 71 surveillance. *Weekly Epidemiol Rev* 1979; 54:81–82.

320. Chumakov M, Voroshilova M, Shindarov L, et al: Enterovirus 71 isolated from cases of epidemic poliomyelitis-like disease in Bulgaria. *Arch Virol* 1979; 60:329–340.

321. Jarcho LW, Fred HL, Castle CH: Encephalitis and poliomyelitis in the adult due to coxsackievirus group B, type 5. *N Engl J Med* 1963; 268:235–238.

322. Doherty RL, Whitehead RH, Allan BC, et al: Investigations of enteroviruses in the etiology of aseptic meningitis, poliomyelitis, encaphalitis and other syndromes in Queensland, 1958 to 1962. *Med J Aust* 1966; 2:535–543.

323. Magoffin RL, Lennette EH: Nonpolioviruses and paralytic disease. *Calif Med* 1962; 97:1–7.

324. Burry JN, Moore B, Mattner C: Hand, foot and mouth disease in south Australia. *Med J Aust* 1968; 2:587–589.

325. Stevenson J, Hambling MH: Paralysis in echovirus-3 infection. *Lancet* 1968; 1:525–526.

326. Williams H, MacArthur P, Bell EJ, et al: Paralysis in echovirus 3 infection. *Lancet* 1968; 1:425.

327. Kopel FB, Shore B, Hodes HL: Nonfatal bulbospinal paralysis due to ECHO 4 virus. *J Pediatr* 1965; 67:588–594.

328. Grist NR, Bell EJ: Enteroviral etiology of the paralytic poliomyelitis syndrome. Studies before and after vaccination. *Arch Environ Health* 1970; 21:382–387.

329. Gear J: Coxsackie viruses in southern Africa. *Yale J Biol Med* 1961–1962; 34:289–303.

330. Foley JF, Chin TDY, Gravelle CR: Paralytic disease due to infection with echo virus type 9; report of a case with residual paralysis. *N Engl J Med* 1959; 260:924–926.

331. Roden VJ, Cantor AG, O'Connor DM, et al: Acute hemiplegia of childhood associated with coxsackie A-9 viral infection. *J Pediatr* 1975; 86:56–58.

332. Magoffin RL, Lennette EH, Schmidt NJ: Association of coxsackie viruses with illness resembling mild paralytic poliomyelitis. *Pediatrics* 1961; 28:602–613.

333. Hammon W McD, Yohn DS, Ludwig EH, et al: A study of certain nonpoliomyelitis and poliomyelitis enterovirus infections: Clinical and serologic association. *JAMA* 1958; 167:727–735.

334. Menkes JH: Viral neurologic infections in children. *Hosp Pract* 1977; 12(Nov):101–109.

335. Combined Scottish Study: Poliomyelitis-like disease in 1960: Mumps and echo 9 virus infections. *Scott Med J* 1964; 9:141–151.

336. Morens DM, Zweighaft RM, Bryan JA: Nonpolio enterovirus disease in the United States, 1971–1975. *Int J Epidemiol* 1979; 8:49–54.

337. Sells CJ, Carpenter RL, Ray CG: Sequelae of central nervous system enterovirus infections. *N Engl J Med* 1975; 293:1–4.

338. Farmer K, MacArthur BA, Clay MM: A follow-up study of 15 cases of neonatal meningoencephalitis due to Coxsackie virus B5. *J Pediatr* 1975; 87:568–571.

339. Chamberlain RN, Christie PN, Holt KS, et al: A study of
school children who had identified virus infections of the central
nervous system during infancy. *Child Care Health Dev* 1983;
9:29–47.

340. Wilfert CM, Thompson RJ, Sunder TR, et al: Longitudinal assessment of children with enteroviral meningitis during the first
three months of life. *Pediatrics* 1981; 67:811–815.

341. Rantakallio P, Saukkonen A, Krause V, et al: Follow-up study
of 17 cases of neonatal coxsackie B5 meningitis and one with
suspected myocarditis. *Scand J Infect Dis* 1970; 2:25–28.

342. Overall JC, Glasgow LA: Virus infections of the fetus and newborn infant. *J Pediatr* 1970; 77:315–333.

343. Grist NR, Bell EJ: Coxsackieviruses and the heart *Am Heart J*
1969; 77:295–300.

344. Selzer G: Transplacental infection of the mouse fetus by
coxsackie viruses. *Isr J Med Sci* 1969; 5:125–127.

345. Bell EJ, Ross CAC, Grist NR: ECHO 9 infection in pregnant
women with suspected rubella. *J Clin Pathol* 1975; 28:267–
269.

346. Lansdown ABG: Coxsackievirus B-3 infection in pregnancy and
its influence on foetal heart development. *Br J Exp Pathol*
1977; 58:378–385.

347. Czeizel A: Coxsackievirus and congenital malformation. *JAMA*
1967; 201:156.

348. Ogilvie MM, Tearne CF: Spontaneous abortion after hand-foot-
and-mouth disease caused by coxsackie virus A-16. *Br Med J*
1980; 281:1527–1528.

349. Davies DP, Hughes CA, MacVicar J, et al: Echovirus-11 infection in a special-care baby unit. *Lancet* 1979; 1:96.

350. Brown GC, Karunas RS: Relationship of congenital anomalies
and maternal infection with selected enteroviruses. *Am J Epidemiol* 1972; 95:207–217.

351. Coid CR: Infection in pregnancy and impaired fetal growth.
Proc R Soc Med 1976; 69:365–366.

352. Coid CR, Ramsden DB: Retardation of foetal growth and
plasma protein development in foetuses from mice injected with
coxsackie B-3 virus. *Nature (New Biol)* 1973; 241:460–461.

353. Burton AE, Robinson ET, Harper WF, et al: Fetal damage after
accidental polio vaccination of an immune mother. *J R Coll
Gen Pract* 1984; 34:390–394.

354. Batcup G, Holt P, Hambling MH, et al: Placental and fetal pathology in coxsackie virus A9 infection: A case report. *Histo-
pathol* 1985; 9:1227–1235.

355. Brady WK, Purdon A: Intrauterine fetal demise associated with
enterovirus infection. *South Med J* 1986; 79:770–772.

356. Reyes MP, Zalenski D, Smith F, et al: Coxsackievirus-positive
cervices in women with febrile illnesses during the third trimester in pregnancy. *Am J Obstet Gynecol* 1986; 155:159–161.

357. Piraino FF, Sedmak G, Raab K: Echovirus 11 infection of newborns with mortality during the 1979 enterovirus season in Mil-
waukee, Wis. *Public Health Rep* 1982; 997:346–353.

358. Wallgren A: Une nouvelle maladie infectieuse du système ner-
veux central. *Acta Paediatr* 1925; 4:158–182.

359. Kelen AE, Lesiak JM, et al: Sporadic occurrence of echo virus
types 27 and 31 associated with aseptic meningitis in Ontario.
Can Med Assoc J 1964; 91:1266–1268.

360. Virus diseases surveillance: Enteroviruses. *Weekly Epidemiol
Rec* 1978; 50:367.

361. Habel K, Silverberg RJ, Shelokov A: Isolation of enteric viruses from cases of aseptic meningitis. *Ann NY Acad Sci* 1957;
67:223–229.

362. Wilfert CM, Lauer BA, Cohen M, et al: An epidemic of echovirus 18 meningitis. *J Infect Dis* 1975; 131:75–78.

363. Mendez-Cashion D, Sanchez-Longo LP, Valcarcel MI, et al:
Echo virus type 1 and aseptic meningitis. *J Pediatr* 1963;
61:432–436.

364. Kelen AE, Lesiak JM, Labzoffsky NA: Occurrence of echovirus
33 infections in Ontario. *Can Med Assoc J* 1968; 98:985–987.

365. Yeager AS, Bruhn FW, Clark J: Cerebrospinal fluid: Presence
of virus unaccompanied by pleocytosis. *J Pediatr* 1974;
85:578–579.

366. Bain HW, McLean DM, Walker SJ: Epidemic pleurodynia
(Bornholm disease) due to coxsackie B-5 virus. The inter-rela-
tionship of pleurodynia, benign pericarditis and aseptic meningitis. *Pediatrics* 1961; 27:889–903.

367. Miller DG, Gabrielson MO, Bart KJ, et al: An epidemic of
aseptic meningitis, primarily among infants, caused by echovirus 11-prime. *Pediatrics* 1968; 41:77–90.

368. Karte H, Wecker I: Echovirus-30-Epidemie. *Deutsch Med
Wochenschr* 1978; 103:1136–1138.

369. Haynes RE, Cramblett HG, Hilty MD, et al: ECHO virus type
3 infections in children: Clinical and laboratory studies. *J Pediatr* 1972; 80:589–595.

370. Duncan IBR: Aseptic meningitis associated with a previously
unrecognized virus. *Lancet* 1960; 2:470–471.

371. Nogen AG, Lepow ML: Enteroviral meningitis in very young
infants. *Pediatrics* 1967; 40:617–626.

372. Lepow ML, Coyne N, Thompson LB, et al: A clinical, epidemiologic and laboratory investigation of aseptic meningitis during the four-year period, 1955–1958. II. The clinical disease
and its sequelae. *N Engl J Med* 1962; 266:1188–1193.

373. Singer JI, Maur PR, Riley JP, et al: Management of central nervous system infections during an epidemic of enteroviral aseptic
meningitis. *J Pediatr* 1980; 96:559–563.

374. Adair CV, Gauld RL, Smadel JE: Aseptic meningitis, a disease
of diverse etiology: Clinical and etiological studies on 854
cases. *Ann Intern Med* 1953; 39:675–704.

375. Walker SH, Togo Y: Encephalitis due to group B, type 5
coxsackie virus. *Am J Dis Child* 1963; 105:209–212.

376. Kleinman H, Cooner MK, Nelson CB, et al: Aseptic meningitis
and paralytic disease due to newly recognized enterovirus.
JAMA 1964; 187:90–95.

377. Brown EH: Virus meningitis. *Postgrad Med J* 1967; 43:418–
421.

378. Chesney PJ, Quennec P, Clark C: Hypoglycorrhachia and
coxsackie B-3 meningal encephalitis. *Am J Clin Pathol* 1978;
70:947–948.

379. Madhavan HN, Chandrasekaran S, Srinivas S, et al: Encephalitis due to EHCO virus type 9. *Indian J Med Res* 1973; 61:51–
53.

380. Hagg E, Aström L, Steen L: Persistent hypothalamic-pituitary
insufficiency following acute meningoencephalitis: A report of
two cases. *Acta Med Scand* 1978; 203:231–235.

381. Urano T, Kawase T, Kodaira K, et al: Guillain-Barré syndrome
associated with ECHO virus type 7 infections. *Pediatrics* 1970;
45:294–295.

382. Chalub EG, DeVivo DC, Siegel BA, et al: Coxsackie A9 focal
encephalitis associated with acute infantile hemiplegia and po-
rencephaly. *Neurology* 1977; 27:574–579.

383a. Anonymous: Coxsackie virus infections, in *Annual Report for
1952.* South African Institute for Medical Research, Johannesburg, 1953, pp 38–39.

383b. Kibrick S, Benirschke K: Severe generalized disease (encepha-
lohepatomyocarditis) occurring in the newborn period and due
to infection with coxsackie virus, group B: Evidence of intrauterine infection with this agent. *Pediatrics* 1958; 22:857–875.

384. Reyes MP, Ostrea EM, Roskamp J, et al: Disseminiated neonatal echovirus 11 disease following antenatal maternal infection
with a virus-positive cervix and virus-negative gastrointestinal
tract. *J Med Virol* 1983; 12:155–159.

385. Schurmann W, Statz A, Mertens T, et al: Two cases of
Coxsackie B2 infection in neonates: Clinical, virological, and
epidemiological aspects. *Eur J Pediatr* 1983; 140:59–63.

386. Mostoufizadeh M, Lack EE, Gang DL, et al: Postmortem manifestations of echovirus 11 sepsis in five newborn infants. *Hum
Pathol* 1983; 14:818–823.

387. Speer ME, Yawn DH: Fatal hepatoadrenal necrosis in the neonate associated with echovirus types 11 and 12 presenting as a
surgical emergency. *J Pediatr Surg* 1984; 19:591–593.

388. Spector SA, Straube RC: Protean manifestations of perinatal enterovirus infections. *West J Med* 1983; 138:847–851.

389. Rozkovec A, Cambridge G, King M, et al: Natural history of

left ventricular function in neonatal coxsackie myocarditis. *Pediatr Cardiol* 1985; 6:151–156.

390. Jin H-Z, Shao X-M, Xia L-D, et al: Neonatal epidemic coxsackie B5 meningitis. *Chin Med J* 1987; 100:312–315.

391. Carolane DJ, Long AM, McKeever PA, et al: Prevention of spread of echovirus 6 in a special care baby unit. *Arch Dis Child* 1985; 60:674–676.

392. Isaacs D, Wilkinson A, Moxon ER, et al: Prevention of spread of echovirus 6 in a special care baby unit. *Arch Dis Child* 1985; 60:1205–1206.

393. Eichenwald HF, Kotsevalov O: Immunologic responses of premature and full-term infants to infection with certain viruses. *Pediatrics* 1960; 25:829–839.

394. Barton LL: Febrile neonatal illness associated with echovirus type 5 in the cerebrospinal fluid. *Clin Pediatr* 1977; 16:383–385.

395. Krous HF, Dietzman D, Ray CG: Fatal infections with echovirus types 6 and 11 in early infancy. *Am J Dis Child* 1973; 126:842–846.

396. Sanders DY, Cramblett HG: Viral infections in hospitalized neonates. *Am J Dis Child* 1968; 116:251–256.

397. Cheeseman SH, Hirsch MS, Keller EW, et al: Fetal neonatal pneumonia caused by echovirus type 9. *Am J Dis Child* 1977; 131:1169.

398. Nogen AG, Lepow ML: Enteroviral meningitis in very young infants. *Pediatrics* 1967; 40:617–626.

399. Phillip AGS, Larson EJ: Overwhelming neonatal infection with ECHO 19 virus. *J Pediatr* 1973; 82:391–397.

400. Wright HT, Landing BH, Lennette EH, et al: Fatal infection in an infant associated with coxsackie virus group A, type 16. *N Engl J Med* 1963; 268:1041–1044.

401. Medearis DN Jr, Kramer RA: Exanthem associated with echo virus type 18 viremia. *J Pediatr* 1959; 55:367–373.

402. Moossy J, Geer JC: Encephalomyelitis, myocarditis and adrenocortical necrosis in coxsackie B-3 virus infection. *Arch Pathol* 1960; 70:614–622.

403. Murphy AM, Simmul R: Coxsackie V-4 virus infections in New South Wales during 1962. *Med J Aust* 1964; 2:443–445.

404. Delaney TB, Fukunaga RH: Myocarditis in a newborn infant with encephalomeningitis due to coxsackie virus group B, type 5. *N Engl J Med* 1958; 259:234–236.

405. Morens DM: Enteroviral disease in early infancy. *J Pediatr* 1978; 92:374–377.

406. Lake AM, Lauer BA, Clark JC: Enterovirus infections in neonates. *J Pediatr* 1976; 89:787–791.

407. Rapmund G, Gauld JR, Rogers NG, et al: Neonatal myocarditis and meningoencephalitis due to coxsackie virus group B, type 4: Virologic study of a fatal case with simultaneous aseptic meningitis in the mother. *N Engl J Med* 1959; 260:819–821.

408. Plotkin SA: Perinatally acquired viral infections. *Curr Top Microbiol Immunol* 1977; 78:111–120.

409. Nathenson G, Spigland I, Eisenberg R: Benign neonatal arrhythmias and coxsackie B virus infection. *J Pediatr* 1975; 86:152–153.

410. Barson WJ, Craenen J, Hosier DM, et al: Survival following myocarditis and myocardial calcification associated with infection by coxsackie virus B-4. *Pediatrics*. 1981; 68(1):79–81.

411. Sanders DY, Cramblett HG: Viral infections in hospitalized neonates. *Am J Dis Child* 1968; 116:251–256.

412. Fletcher E, Brennan CF: Cardiac complications of coxsackie infection. *Lancet* 1957; 1:913–915.

413. Haynes RE, Azimi PH, Cramblett HG, et al: Clinically distinguishable syndromes caused by viruses. *Curr Prob Pediatr* 1975; 5:3–48.

414. Reken DV, Strauss A, Hernandez A, et al: Infectious pericarditis in children. *J Pediatr* 1974; 85:165–169.

415. Babb JM, Stoneman MER, Stern H: Myocarditis and croup caused by coxsackie virus type B-5. *Arch Dis Child* 1961; 36:551–556.

416. Abelmann WH: Current concepts: Myocarditis. *N Engl J Med* 1966; 275:832–834.

417. Bandt CM, Staley NA, Noren GR: Acute viral myocarditis: Clinical and histologic changes. *Minn Med* 1979; 62:234–237.

418. Abelmann WH: Viral myocarditis and its sequelae. *Ann Rev Med* 1873; 24:145–152.

419. Woods JD, Nimmo MJ, Mackay-Scollary EM: Acute transmural myocardial infarction associated with active coxsackie virus B infection. *Am Heart J* 1975; 89:283–287.

420. Chandy KG, John TJ, Mukandan P, et al: Coxsackie B antibodies in "rheumatic" valvular heart disease. *Lancet* 1979; 1:381.

421. Longson M, Cole FM, Davies D: Isolation of a coxsackievirus group B, type 5, from the heart of a fatal case of myocarditis in an adult. *J Clin Pathol* 1969; 22:654–658.

422. Rose HD: Recurrent illness following acute coxsackie B-4 myocarditis. *Am J Med* 1973; 54:544–548.

423. Steigman AJ, Lipton MM, Braspennickx H: Acute lymphonodular pharyngitis: A newly described condition due to coxsackie A virus. *J Pediatr* 1962; 61:331–336.

424. Forman ML, Cherry JD: Enanthems associated with uncommon viral syndromes. *Pediatrics* 1968; 41:873–882.

425. Horstmann DM: Viral exanthems and enanthems. *Pediatrics* 1968; 41:867–870.

426. Keuth U, Esser I, Wilhelmi J, et al: Die "Herpangina"—Epidemie 1967–68 (Echo 30-6-3): Bericht über klinische-beobachtete Fälle im Säuglings und Kindesalter. *Deutsch Med Wochenschr* 1969; 94:1959–1965.

427. Cole RM, Bell JA, Beeman EA, et al: Studies of coxsackie viruses: Observations on epidemiological aspects of group A viruses. *Am J Public Health* 1951; 41:1342–1358.

428. Moffet HL, Siegel AC, Doyle HK: Nonstreptococcal pharyngitis. *J Pediatr* 1968; 73:51–60.

429. Tagoya I, Takayama R, Hagiwara A: A large-scale epidemic of hand, foot and mouth disease associated with enterovirus 71 infection in Japan in 1978. *Jpn J Med Sci Biol* 1981; 34:191–196.

429a. Gilbert GL, Dickson KE, Waters M, et al: Outbreak of enterovirus infection in Victoria, Australia, with a high incidence of neurologic involvement. *Pediatr Infect Dis J* 1988; 7:484–488.

430. Alsop J, Flewett TH, Foster JR: "Hand-foot-and-mouth disease" in Birmingham in 1959. *Br Med J* 1960; 2:1708–1711.

431. Robinson CR, Doane FW, Rhodes AJ: Report of an outbreak of febrile illness with pharyngeal lesions and exanthem: Toronto, Summer, 1957–Isolation of group A coxsackie virus. *Can Med Assoc J* 1958; 79:615–621.

432. Magoffin RL, Jackson EW, Lennette EH: Vesicular stomatitis and exanthem: A syndrome associated with coxsackie virus, type 16. *JAMA* 1961; 175:441–445.

433. Higgins PG, Warin RP: Hand, foot, and mouth disease: A clinically recognizable virus infection seen mainly in children. *Clin Pediatr* 1967; 6:373–376.

434. Hall CB, Cherry JD, Hatch MH, et al: The return of Boston exanthem: Echovirus 16 infections in 1974. *Am J Dis Child* 1977; 131:323–326.

435. Crawford M, Macrae AD, O'Reilly JN: Unusual illness in young children associated with enteric virus. *Arch Dis Child* 1956; 31:182–188.

436. Moritsugu Y, Sawada K, Hinohara M, et al: An outbreak of type 25 echovirus infection with exanthem in an infant home near Tokyo. *Am J Epidemiol* 1968; 87:599–608.

437. Rendtorff RC, Walker LC, Hale BD, et al: An epidemic of ECHO virus 2 infection in an orphanage nursery. *Am J Hyg* 1964; 79:64–73.

438. Cherry JD, Lerner AM, Klein JO, et al: Echo 11 virus infections associated with exanthems. *Pediatrics* 1963; 32:509–516.

439. Guidotti MB: An outbreak of skin rash by echovirus 25 in an infant home. *J Infect* 1983; 6:67–70.

440. Lerner AM, Klein JO, Finland M: Infection with coxsackie virus group B, type 3, with vesicular eruption—Report of two cases. *N Engl J Med* 1960; 263:1305.

441. Deseda-Tous J, Byatt PH, Cherry JD: Vesicular lesions in adults due to echovirus 11 infections. *Arch Dermatol* 1977; 113:1705–1706.

442. Yin-Murphy M: Acute hemorrhagic conjunctivitis. *Prog Med Virol* 1984; 29:23–44.

443. Yin-Murphy M, Baharuddin-Ishak, Phoon MC, et al: A recent epidemic of coxsackie virus type A24 acute hemorrhagic conjunctivitis in Singapore. *Br J Ophthalmol* 1986; 70:869–873.

444. Chou M-Y, Malison MD: Outbreak of acute hemorrhagic conjunctivitis due to coxsackie A24 variant—Taiwan. *Am J Epidemiol* 1988; 127:795–800.

445. Centers for Disease Control: Acute hemorrhagic conjunctivitis caused by coxsackie A24 variant—Caribbean. *MMWR* 1987; 36:245–246.

446. Centers for Disease Control: Acute Hemorrhagic conjunctivitis caused by coxsackie A24 variant—Puerto Rico. *MMWR* 1988; 37:123–124, 129.

447. Srinivasa DK, D'Souza V: Economic aspects of an epidemic of hemorrhagic conjunctivitis in a rural community. *J Epidemiol Community Health* 1987; 4:79–81.

448. Patriarca PA, Onorato IM, Sklar VF, et al: Acute hemorrhagic conjunctivitis: Investigation of a large-scale community outbreak in Dade County, Florida. *JAMA* 1983; 249:1283–1289.

449. Hung TP, Kono R: Neurologic complications of acute hemorrhagic conjunctivitis (a polio-like syndrome in adults), in Vinken PJ, Bruyn GW, Klawans HL (eds): *Handbook of Clinical Neurology.* Amsterdam, North Holland, 1979, vol 38, pp 595–623.

450. Sandelin K, Tuomioja M, Erkkilä H: Echovirus type 7 isolated from conjunctival scrapings. *Scand J Infect Dis* 1977; 9:71–73.

451. Onorato IM, Morens DM, Schonberger LB, et al: Acute hemorrhagic conjunctivitis caused by enterovirus type 70: an epidemic in American Samoa. *Am J Trop Med Hyg* 1985; 34:984–991.

452. Reeves WC, Brenes MM, Quiroz E, et al: Acute hemorrhagic conjunctivitis epidemic in Colon, Republic of Panama. *Am J Epidemiol* 1986; 123:325–335.

453. Bell EJ, Grist NR: Echoviruses, carditis, and acute pleurodynia. *Lancet* 1970; 1:326–328.

454. Schmidt NJ, Magoffin RL, Lennette EH: Association of group B coxsackieviruses with cases of pericarditis, myocarditis, or pleurodynia by demonstration of immunoglobulin in antibody. *Infect Immun* 1973; 8:341–348.

455. Dowling HF, Lepper MH, Jackson EG: Important guides in the recognition of viral diseases of the respiratory and central nervous systems. *Med Clin North Am* 1960; 44:5–16.

456. Nichamin SJ: Clinical and epidemiologic aspects of epidemic pleurodynia. *JAMA* 1948; 129:600–605.

457. Jamieson WM, Prinsley DM: Bornholm disease in the tropics. *Br Med J* 1947; 2:47–50.

458. Disney ME, Howard EM, Wood BSB, et al: Bornholm disease in children. *Br Med J* 1953; 2:1351–1354.

459. Rozenshtein AM, Malakhova TS, Kosarikhina MA: On the problem concerning the role of EHCO viruses in respiratory illnesses. *Vopr Viruso* 1969; 14:249.

460. Bloom HH, Johnson KM, Mufson MA, et al: Acute respiratory disease associated with coxsackie A-21 virus infection. *JAMA* 1962; 179:120–125.

461. Schieble JH, Fox VL, Lennette EH: A probable new human picornavirus associated with respiratory diseases. *Am J Epidemiol* 1967; 85:297–310.

462. Oei KG, van der Veen J: Epidemiological study of coxsackie A-21 virus infections in military recruits. *Am J Epidemiol* 1967; 85:93–100.

463. Kepfer PD, Hable KA, Smith TF: Viral isolation rates during summer from children with acute upper respiratory tract disease and healthy children. *Am J Clin Pathol* 1974; 61:1–5.

464. Hable KA, O'Connell EJ, Herrmann EC: Group B coxsackieviruses as respiratory viruses. *Mayo Clin Proc* 1970; 45:170–176.

465. Schleissner LA, Portnoy B: Hepatitis and pneumonia associated with ECHO virus, type 9, infection in two adult siblings. *Ann Intern Med* 1968; 68:1315–1319.

466. Sanders DY, Powell RV, Smith A: Outbreak of coxsackie B-5 virus in a children's home. *South Med J* 1969; 62:474–476.

467. Yodfat Y, Nishmi M: Epidemiologic and clinical observations in six outbreaks of viral disease in a kibbutz, 1968–1971. *Am J Epidemiol* 1973; 97:415–423.

468. Melnick JL, Walton M, Myers IL: Isolation of a coxsackie virus during a summer outbreak of acute minor illness. *Public Health Rep* 1953; 68:1179–1183.

469. Behan PO, Behan WM, Bell EJ: The postviral fatigue syndrome—an analysis of the findings in 50 cases. *J Infect* 1985; 10:211–222.

470. Fegan KG, Behan PO, Bell EJ: Myalgic encephalomyelitis—report of an epidemic. *J R Coll Gen Pract* 1983; 33:335–337.

471. Calder BD, Warnock PJ: Coxsackie B infection in a Scottish general practice. *J R Coll Gen Pract* 1984; 34:15–19.

472. Keighley BD, Bell EJ: Sporadic myalgic encephalomyelitis in a rural practice. *J R Coll Gen Pract* 1983; 33:339–341.

473. Calder BD, Warnock PJ, McCartney RA, et al: Coxsackie B viruses and the post-viral syndrome: a prospective study in general practice. *J R Coll Gen Pract* 1987; 37:11–14.

474. Yousef GE, Bell EJ, Mann GJ, et al: Chronic enterovirus infection in patients with postviral fatigue syndrome. *Lancet* 1988; 1:146–150.

475. Liebman WM, St Geme JW: Enteroviral pseudoappendicitis. *Am J Dis Child* 1970; 120:77–78.

476. Ramos-Alvarez M: Cytopathogenic enteric viruses associated with undifferentiated diarrheal syndromes in early childhood. *Ann NY Acad Sci* 1957; 67:326–331.

477. Johnson FE, Crnic DM, Simmons MA, et al: Association of fatal coxsackie B-2 viral infection and necrotizing enterocolitis. *Arch Dis Child* 1977; 52:802–804.

478. Klein JO, Lerner AM, Finland M: Acute gastroenteritis associated with ECHO virus, type 11. *Am J Med Sci* 1960; 240:749–753.

479. Ramos-Alvarez M, Sabin AB: Enteropathogenic viruses and bacteria; role in summer diarrheal diseases of infancy and early childhood. *JAMA* 1958; 167:147–156.

480. Morens DM: Boston exanthem agent: Echovirus 16. *Am J Dis Child* 1977; 131:1306.

481. Hass R, Vivell O: *Virus und Rickettsien Infectionen des Menschen.* Munich, Lehmann, 1965.

482. Wenner HA: The ECHO viruses. *Ann NY Acad Sci* 1962–1963; 101:398–412.

483. Tobe T: Inapparent virus infections as a trigger of appendicitis. *Lancet* 1965; 1:1343–1346.

484. Schultz WW, Weiss E: Demonstration of specific antibodies to a coxsackie-like virus in patients of a hepatitis outbreak. *Am J Epidemiol* 1979; 110:124–131.

485. Hughes JR, Wilfert CM, Moore M, et al: Echovirus 14 infection associated with fatal neonatal hepatic necrosis. *Am J Dis Child* 1972; 123:61–67.

486. Yoon J-W, Austin M, Onodera T, et al: Virus-induced diabetes mellitus: Isolation of a virus from the pancreas of a child with diabetic ketoacidosis. *N Engl J Med* 1979; 300:1173–1179.

487. Imrie CW, Ferguson JC, Sommerville RG: Coxsackie and mumps virus infection in a prospective study of acute pancreatitis. *Gut* 1977; 18:53–56.

488. Ujevich MM, Jaffe R: Pancreatic islet cell damage: Its occurrence in neonatal coxsackievirus encephalomyocarditis. *Arch Pathol Lab Med* 1980; 104:438–441.

489. Ursing B: Acute pancreatitis in coxsackie B infection. *Br Med J* 1973; 3:524–525.

490. Capner P, Lendrum R, Jeffries DJ, et al: Viral antibody studies in pancreatic disease. *Gut* 1975; 16:866–870.

491. Morens DM, Hammer SL, Heicher DA: Idiopathic acute pancreatitis in children: Association with a clinical picture resembling Reye syndrome. *Am J Dis Child* 1974; 128:401–404.

492. Notkins AL, Yoon J-W, Onodera T, et al: Virus-induced diabetes mellitus. *Perspect Virol* 1981; 11:141–162.

493. Craighead JE: The role of viruses in the pathogenesis of pancreatic disease and diabetes mellitus. *Prog Med Virol* 1975; 19:161–214.

494. Banatvala JE: Insulin-dependent (juvenile-onset, type 1) diabetes mellitus coxsackie B viruses revisited. *Prog Med Virol* 1987; 34:33–54.

495. Barrett-Connor E: Is insulin-dependent diabetes mellitus caused by coxsackievirus B infection? A review of the epidemiologic evidence. *Rev Infect Dis* 1985; 7:207–215.

496. Jordan GW, Cohen SH: Encephalomyocarditis virus-induced diabetes mellitus in mice: model of viral pathogenesis. *Rev Infect Dis* 1987; 9:917–924.

497. Nihalani KD, Pethani RR, Menon PS, et al: Coxsackie B4 virus causing insulin-dependent diabetes mellitus, myopericarditis and encephalitis—a case report. *J Assoc Physicians India* 1982; 30:107–109.

498. Niklasson BS, Dobersen MJ, Peters CJ, et al: An outbreak of coxsackievirus B infection followed by one case of diabetes mellitus. *Scand J Infect Dis* 1985; 17:15–18.

499. Mirkovic RR, Varma SK, Yoon JW: Incidence of coxsackievirus B type 4 (CB4) infections concomitant with onset of insulin-dependent diabetes mellitus. *J Med Virol* 1984; 14:9–16.

500. Asplin CM, Cooney MK, Crossley JR, et al: Coxsackie B4 infection and islet cell antibodies three years before overt diabetes. *J Pediatr* 1982; 101:398–400.

501. Champsaur H: Diabetes and coxsackie virus B5 infection. *Lancet* 1980; 1:251.

502. Mertens T, Gruneklee D, Eggers HJ: Neutralizing antibodies against coxsackie B viruses in patients with recent onset of type 1 diabetes. *Eur J Pediatr* 1983; 140:293–294.

503. Alberti AM, Amato C, Candela A, et al: Serum antibodies against Coxsackie B1–6 viruses in type 1 diabetics, *Acta Diabetol Lat* 1985; 22:33–38.

504. King ML, Shaikh A, Bidwell D, et al: Coxsackie-B-virus-specific IgM responses in children with insulin-dependent (juvenile-onset; type I) diabetes mellitus. *Lancet* 1983; 1:1397–1399.

505. Banatvala JE, Bryant J, Schernthaner G, et al: Coxsackie B, mumps, rubella, and cytomegalovirus specific IgM responses in patients with juvenile-onset insulin-dependent diabetes mellitus in Britain, Austria, and Australia. *Lancet* 1985; 1:1409–1412.

506. Friman G, Fohlman J, Frisk G, et al: An incidence peak of juvenile diabetes. Relation to Coxsackie B virus immune response. *Acta Paediatr Scand* (suppl) 1985; 320:14–19.

507. Frisk G, Fohlman J, Kobbah M, et al: High frequency of Coxsackie-B-virus-specific IgM in children developing type I diabetes during a period of high diabetes morbidity. *J Med Virol* 1985; 17:219–227.

508. Schernthaner G, Banatvala JE, Scherbaum W, et al: Coxsackie-B-virus-specific IgM responses, complement-fixing islet-cell antibodies, HLA DR antigens, and C-peptide secretion in insulin-dependent diabetes mellitus. *Lancet* 1985; 2:630–632.

509. Eberhardt MS, Wagener DK, Orchard TJ, et al: HLA heterogeneity of insulin-dependent diabetes mellitus at diagnosis. The Pittsburgh IDDM study. *Diabetes* 1985; 34:1247–1252.

510. Burch G, Harb J, Hiramoto Y: Coxsackie B-4 viral infection of the human kidney. *J Urol* 1974; 112:714–722.

511. Burch GE, Colclough HL: Progressive coxsackieviral pancarditis and nephritis. *Ann Intern Med* 1969; 71:963–970.

512. Bayatpour M, Zbitnew A, Dempster G, et al: Role of coxsackievirus B-4 in the pathogenesis of acute glomerulonephritis. *Can Med Assoc J* 1973; 109:873–875.

513. Aronson MD, Phillips CA: Coxsackievirus B-5 infections in acute oliguric renal failure. *J Infect Dis* 1975; 132:303–306.

514. Yuceoglu AM, Berkovich S, Minkowitz S: Acute glomerulonephritis associated with ECHO virus type 9 infection. *J Pediatr* 1966; 69:603–609.

515. Rahal JJ, Millian SJ, Noriega ER: Coxsackievirus and adenovirus infection: Association with acute febrile and juvenile rheumatoid arthritis. *JAMA* 1976; 235:2496–2501.

516. Soboleva VD, Lozovskaya LS, Alexseyeva VB, et al: Coxsackie A-13 virus in the foci of rheumatism. *J Hyg Epidemiol Microbiol Immunol* 1978; 22:195–202.

517. Blotzer JW, Myers AR: Echovirus-associated polyarthritis. Report of a case with synovial fluid and synovial histologic characterization. *Arthritis Rheum* 1978; 21:978–981.

518. Hurst NP, Martynoga AG, Nuki G, et al: Coxsackie B infection and arthritis. *Br Med J* 1983; 286:605.

519. Kujala G, Newman JH: Isolation of echovirus type 11 from synovial fluid in acute monocytic arthritis. *Arthritis Rheum* 1985; 28:98–99.

520. Ackerson BK, Raghunathan R, Keller MA, et al: Echovirus 11 arthritis in a patient with X-linked agammaglobulinemia. *Pediatr Infect Dis* 1987; 6:485–488.

521. Heaton DC, Moller PW: Still's disease associated with coxsackie infection and haemophagocytic syndrome. *Ann Rheum Dis* 1985; 44:341–344.

522. Christensen ML, Pachman LM, Schneiderman R, et al: Prevalence of coxsackie B virus antibodies in patients with juvenile dermatomyositis. *Arthritis Rheum* 1986; 29:1365–1370.

523. Ray CG, Tucker VL, Harris DJ, et al: Enteroviruses associated with the hemolytic-uremic syndrome. *Pediatrics* 1970; 46:378–388.

524. Ray CG, Portman MS, Stamm SJ, et al: Hemolytic-uremic syndrome and myocarditis. *Am J Dis Child* 1971; 122:418–420.

525. Austin TW, Ray CG: Coxsackie virus group B infections and the hemolytic-uremic syndrome. *J Infect Dis* 1973; 127:698–701.

526. O'Regan S, Robitaille P, Mongeau J-G, et al: The hemolytic uremic syndrome associated with ECHO 22 infection. *Clin Pediatr* 1980; 19:125–127.

527. Committee on Infectious Diseases, American Academy of Pediatrics: Aspirin and Reye syndrome. *Pediatrics* 1982; 69:810–812.

528. Melnick JL, Wenner HA, Phillips CA: Enteroviruses, in Lennette EH, Schmidt NJ (eds): *Diagnostic Procedures for Viral, Rickettsial, and Chlamydial Infections.* ed 5. Washington DC, American Public Health Association, 1979, pp 471–534.

528a. Martyn CN, Barker DJP, Osmond C: Motoneuron disease and past poliomyelitis in England and Wales. *Lancet* 1988; 1:1319–1322.

529. Bodensteiner JB, Morris HH, Howell JT, et al: Chronic ECHO type 5 virus meningoencephalitis in X-linked hypogammaglobulinemia: Treatment with immune plasma. *Neurology* 1979; 29:815–819.

530. Wilfert CM, Buckley RH, Mohanakumar T, et al: Persistent and fatal central-nervous-system echovirus infections in patients with agammaglobulinemia. *N Engl J Med* 1977; 296:1485–1489.

531. Mease PJ, Ochs HD, Wedgwood RJ: Successful treatment of echovirus meningoencephalitis and myositis-fasciitis with intravenous immune globulin therapy in a patient with X-linked agammaglobulinemia. *N Engl J Med* 1981; 304:1278–1281.

532. Webster ADB, Tripp JH, Hayward AR, et al: Echovirus encephalitis and myositis in primary immunoglobulin deficiency. *Arch Dis Child* 1978; 53:33–37.

533. Junker AK, Dimmick JE: Progressive generalized edema in an 8-year-old boy with agammaglobulinemia. *J Pediatr* 1982; 101:147–153.

534. Bardelas JA, Winkelstein JA, Seto DSY, et al: Fatal ECHO 24 infection in a patient with hypogammaglobulinemia: Relationship to kermatomyositis-like syndrome. *J Pediatr* 1977; 90:396–399.

535. Lederman HM, Winkelstein JA: X-linked agammaglobulinemia: An analysis of 96 patients. *Medicine* 1985; 64:145–156.

536. McKinney RE, Kotz SL, Wilfert CM: Chronic enteroviral meningoencephalitis in agammaglobulinemic patients. *Rev Infect Dis* 1987; 9:334–356.

537. Cooper JB, Pratt WR, English BK, et al: Coxsackievirus B3 producing fatal meningoencephalitis in a patient with X-linked agammaglobulinemia. *Am J Dis Child* 1983; 137:82–83.

538. Gewurz A, Potempa R, Goetz C, et al: Coxsackie A-11 encephalitis (CAE) in a patient with common variable immunodeficiency (CVID): Response to intravenous and intraventricular

treatment with intravenous immune globulin (IVIG) *Ann Allergy* 1985; 55:272.

539. von Reyn CF, Clements CJ, Mann JM: Human immunodeficiency virus infection and routine childhood immunization. *Lancet* 1987; 2:669–672.

540. Centers for Disease Control: Immunization of children infected with human immunodeficiency virus—supplementary ACIP statement. *MMWR* 1988; 37:181–183.

541. Tosato G, Rocchi G, Archetti I: Epidemiological study of a "hand-foot-and-mouth disease" outbreak observed in Rome in the fall of 1973. *Zentralbl Bakteriol (Orig A)* 1975; 230:415–421.

542. Ager EA, Felsenstein WC, Alexander ER, et al: An epidemic of illness due to coxsackievirus group B, type 2. *JAMA* 1964; 187:97–102.

543. Plager H, Deibel R: Echo 30 virus infections: Outbreak in New York State. *NY State J Med* 1970; 70:391–393.

544. Chin TDY, Marine WM, Hall CE, et al: The influence of Salk vaccination on the epidemic pattern and the spread of the virus in the community. *Am J Hyg* 1961; 74:67–94.

545. Nolan JP, Wilmer BH, Melnick JL: Poliomyelitis: Its highly invasive nature and narrow stream of infection in a community of high socioeconomic level. *N Engl J Med* 1955; 61:943–955.

546. Kennett ML, Birch CJ, Lewis FA, et al: Enterovirus type 71 infection in Melbourne. *Bull WHO* 1974; 51:609–615.

547. Herrmann EC, Person DA, Smith TF: Experience in laboratory diagnosis of enterovirus infections in routine medical practice. *Mayo Clin Proc* 1972; 47:577–586.

548. Prince JT, St Geme JW Jr, Scherer WF: Echo-9 virus exanthema. *JAMA* 1958; 167:691–696.

549. Mirani M, Ogra PL, Barron AL: Epidemic of echovirus type 9 infection: Certain clinical and epidemiologic features. *NY State J Med* 1973; 73:403–406.

550. Hummeler K, Kirk D, Ostapiak M: Aseptic meningitis caused by coxsackievirus with isolation of virus from cerebrospinal fluid. *JAMA* 1954; 156:676–679.

551. Sarkar JK, Biswas ML, Chatterjee SN, et al: Coxsackie virus from blood of two cases of encephalitis. *Indian J Med Res* 1966; 54:905–909.

552. Paul JR: *A History of Poliomyelitis.* New Haven, Conn, Yale University Press, 1971.

553. Dagan R, Menegus MA: A combination of four cell types for rapid detection of enteroviruses in clinical specimens. *J Med Virol* 1986; 19:219–228.

554. Lim KA, Benyesh-Melnick M: Typing of viruses by combinations of antiserum pools. Application to typing of enteroviruses (coxsackie and ECHO). *J Immunol* 1960; 84:309–317.

555. Schmidt NJ, Guenther RW, Lennette EH: Typing of ECHO virus isolates by immune serum pools. The "Intersecting Serum Scheme." *J Immunol* 1961; 87:623–626.

556. Tracy S: Comparison of genomic homologies in the coxsackievirus B group by use of cDNA: RNA dot-blot hybridization. *J Clin Microbiol* 1985; 21:371–374.

557. Tracy S: A comparison of genomic homologies among the coxsackievirus B group: use of fragments of the cloned coxsackievirus B3 genome as probes. *J Gen Virol* 1984; 65:2167–2172.

558. Hallam NF, Eglin RP, Holland P, et al: Fatal coxsackie B meningoencephalitis diagnosed by serology and in-situ nucleic acid hybridization. *Lancet* 1986; 2:1213–1214.

559. Bowles NE, Richardson PJ, Olsen EGJ, et al: Detection of coxsackie-B-virus-specific RNA sequences in myocardial biopsy samples from patients with myocarditis and dilated cardiomyopathy. *Lancet* 1980; 1:1120–1122.

560. Hyypiä T, Stalhandske P, Vainiopää R, et al: Detection of enteroviruses by spot hybridization. *J Clin Microbiol* 1984; 19:436–438.

561. Rotbart HA, Levin MJ, Villarreal LP, et al: Factors affecting the detection of enteroviruses in cerebrospinal fluid with coxsackievirus B3 and poliovirus 1 cDNA probes. *J Clin Microbiol* 1985; 22:220–224.

562. Dörries R, Ter Meulen V: Specificity of IgM antibodies in acute human coxsackievirus B infections, analysed by indirect solid phase enzyme immunoassay and immunoblot technique. *J Gen Virol* 1983; 64:159–167.

563. Morgan-Capner P, McSorley C: Antibody capture radioimmunoassay (MACRIA) for coxsackievirus B4 and B5-specific IgM. *J Hyg* 1983; 90:333–349.

564. Chan D, Hammond GW: Comparison of seriodiagnosis of group B coxsackie virus infections by an immunoglobulin M capture enzyme immunoassay versus microneutralization. *J Clin Microbiol* 1985; 21:830–834.

565. McCartney RA, Banatvala JE, Bell EJ: Routine use of u-antibody-capture ELISA for the serological diagnosis of coxsackie B virus infections. *J Med Virol* 1986; 19:205–212.

566. Wulff H, Anderson LJ, Pallansch MA, et al: Diagnosis of enterovirus 70 infection by demonstration of IgM antibodies. *J Med Virol* 1987; 21:321–327.

567. Pattison JR: Tests for coxsackie B virus-specific IgM. *J Hyg* 1983; 90:327–332.

568. Buckley RH: Long term use of intravenous immune globulin in patients with primary immunodeficiency diseases: inadequacy of current dosage practices and approaches to the problem. *J Clin Immunol* 1982; 2(suppl):155–215.

569. Erlendsson K, Swartz T, Dwyer JM: Successful reversal of echovirus encephalitis in X-linked hypogammaglobulinemia by intraventricular administration of immunoglobulin. *N Engl J Med* 1985; 312:351–353.

569a. Dwyer JM, Erlendsson K: Intraventricular gamma-globulin for the management of enterovirus encephalitis. *Pediatr Infect Dis J* 1988; 7:530–533.

570. Johnson PR, Edwards KM, Wright PF: Failure of intraventricular gamma globulin to eradicate echovirus encephalitis in a patient with X-linked agammaglobulinemia. *N Engl J Med* 1985; 313:1546–1547.

571. Hadfield MG, Seidlin M, Houff SA, et al: Echovirus meningomyeloencephalitis with administration of intrathecal immunoglobulin. *J Neuropathol Exp Neurol* 1985; 44:520–529.

572. Bernatowska E, Madalinski K: Intravenous immunoglobulin therapy of progressive encephalitis in X-linked hypogammaglobulinemia. *Acta Paediatr Scand* 1987; 76:155–156.

573. McKinney RE, Katz SL, Wilfert CM: Chronic enteroviral meningoencephalitis in agammaglobulinemic patients. *Rev Infect Dis* 1987; 9:334–356.

574. Crennan JM, Van Scoy RE, McKenna CH, et al: Echovirus polymyositis in patients with hypogammaglobulinemia. Failure of high-dose intravenous gammaglobulin therapy and review of the literature. *Am J Med* 1986; 81:35–42.

575. Hammond GW, Lukes H, Wells B, et al: Maternal and neonatal neutralizing antibody titers to selected enteroviruses. *Pediatr Infect Dis J* 1985; 4:32–35.

576. Matsumoto S, Watanabe T, Chiba S, et al: Oral administration of secretory immunoglobulin A and its clinical significance. *Birth Defects* 1983; 19:229–237.

577. McKinlay MA, Miralles JV, Brisson CJ, et al: Prevention of human poliovirus-induced paralysis and death in mice by the novel antiviral agent arildone. *Antimicrob Agents Chemother* 1982; 22:1022–1025.

578. Eggers HJ, Roskopf U, Arnold G: Myocarditis in experimental poliomyelitis. A contribution to pathogenesis of disease. *Zentralbl Bakteriol Mikrobiol Hyg [A]* 1983; 255:164.

579. Eggers HJ: Benzimidazoles, in Came PE, Caliguiri LA (eds): *Chemotherapy of Viral Infection.* New York, Springer-Verlag. 1982, p 377–417.

580. Eggers HJ: Successful treatment of enterovirus infected mice by 2-(alpha-hydroxybenzyl)-benzimidazole and guanidine. *J Exp Med* 1976; 143:1367–1381.

581. Kenny MT, Dulworth JK, Torney HL: *In vitro* and *in vivo* antipicornavirus activity of some phenoxypyridinecarbonitriles. *Antimicrob Agents Chemother* 1985; 28:745–750.

582. Kenny MT, Dulworth JK, Torney HL: *In vitro* and *in vivo* antipicornavirus activity of some p-benzoylphenoxypyridines. *Antiviral Res* 1986; 6:355–367.

583. Kenny MT, Dulworth HK, Bargar TM, et al: Antipicornavirus activity of some diaryl methanes and aralkylaminopyridines. *Antiviral Res* 1987; 7:87–97.

584. McKinlay MA, Frank JA, Benziger DP, et al: Use of WIN 51711 to prevent echovirus type 9-induced paralysis in suckling mice. *J Infect Dis* 1986; 154:676–681.

585. Kolmer JA, Klugh GF, Rule AM: A successful method for vaccination against acute anterior poliomyelitis: Further report. *JAMA* 1935; 104:456–460.

586. Brodie M: Active immunization against poliomyelitis. *Am J Pub Health* 1935; 25:54–67.

587. Hammon W McD, Coriell LL, Wehrle PF, et al: Evaluation of Red Cross gamma globulin as a prophylactic agent for poliomyelitis. 4. Final report of results based on clinical diagnoses. *JAMA* 1953; 151:1272–1285.

588. Koprowski HH, Jervis GA, Norton TW: Immune responses in human volunteers upon oral administration of rodent-adapted strain of poliomyelitis virus. *Am J Hyg* 1952; 55:108–126.

589. Howe HA: Antibody response of chimpanzee and human beings to formalin-inactivated trivalent poliomyelitis vaccine. *Am J Hyg* 1952; 56:265–286.

590. Bodian D, Morgan IM, Howe HA: Differentiation of three types of poliomyelitis viruses. III. The grouping of 14 strains into three immunological types. *Am J Hyg* 1949; 49:234–245.

591. Nathanson N, Langmuir AD: The Cutter incident: Poliomyelitis following formaldehyde-inactivated poliovirus vaccination in the United States during the spring of 1955. I. Background. *Am J Hyg* 1963; 78:16–28.

592. Nathanson N, Langmuir AD: The Cutter incident: Poliomyelitis following formaldehyde-inactivated poliovirus vaccination in the United States during the spring of 1955. II. Relationship of poliomyelitis to Cutter vaccine. *Am J Hyg* 1963; 78:29–60.

593. Nathanson N, Langmuir AD: The Cutter incident: Poliomyelitis following formaldehyde-inactivated poliovirus vaccination in the United States during the spring of 1955. III. Comparison of the clinical character of vaccinated and contact cases occurring after use of high rate lots of Cutter vaccine. *Am J Hyg* 1963; 78:61–81.

594. von Seefried A, Chun JH, Grant JA, et al: Inactivated poliovirus vaccine and test development at Connaught Laboratories, Ltd. *Rev Infect Dis* 1984; 6 (suppl 2):S345–S349.

595. Committee on Infectious Diseases, American Academy of Pediatrics: *Report of the Committee on Infectious Diseases,* ed 20. Elk Grove, Ill, American Academy of Pediatrics, 1986.

595a. McBean AM, Thomas ML, Albrect P, et al: Serologic response to oral vaccine and enhanced-potency inactivated polio vaccines. *Am J Epidemiol* 1988; 128:615–628.

595b. Paralytic Poliomyelitis—Senegal, 1986–1987: Update on the N-IPV efficacy study. *MMWR* 1988; 37:257–259.

596. Stenvik N, Hovi L, Siimes MA, et al: Antipolio prophylaxis of immunocompromised children during a nationwide oral polio vaccine campaign. *Pediatr Infect Dis J* 1987; 6:1106–1110.

597. Immunization Practices Advisory Committee: Immunization of children infected with human T-lymphotrophic virus type III lymphadenopathy-associated virus. *MMWR* 1986; 35:595–598., 603–606.

597a. McLaughlin M, Thomas P, Onorato I, et al: Live virus vaccines in human immunodeficiency virus-infected children: A retrospective study. *Pediatrics* 1988; 82:229–233.

597b. Onorato IM, Markowitz E, Oxtoby MJ: Childhood immunization, vaccine-preventable diseases and infection with human immunodeficiency virus. *Pediatr Infect Dis J* 1988; 6:588–595.

598. Immunization Practices Advisory Committee: Poliomyelitis prevention: Enhanced-potency inactivated poliomyelitis vaccine—supplementary statement. *MMWR* 1987; 36:795–798.

599. Schonberger LB, McGowan JE, Gregg MB: Vaccine-associated poliomyelitis in the United States, 1961–1972. *Am J Epidemiol* 1976; 104:202–211.

600. Nkowane BM, Wassilak SGF, Orenstein WA, et al: Vaccine-associated paralytic poliomyelitis. United States: 1973 through 1984. *JAMA* 1987; 257:1335–1340.

601. Cockburn WC: The work of the WHO Consultative Group on poliomyelitis vaccines. *Bull WHO* 1988; 66:143–154.

601a. Esteves K: Safety of oral poliomyelitis vaccine: Results of a WHO inquiry. *Bull WHO* 1988; 66:739–746.

602. Bakeman DE, Elrington G, Kennedy P, et al: Vaccine related poliomyelitis in non-immunised relatives and household contacts. *Br Med J* 1987; 294:170–171.

603. Gaebler JW, Kleiman MB, French ML, et al: Neurologic complications in oral polio vaccine recipients. *J Pediatr* 1986; 108:878–881.

604. Gelfand HM: Oral vaccine: Associated paralytic poliomyelitis, 1962. *JAMA* 1963; 184:948–956.

604a. Hovi T, Cantell K, Huovilainen A, et al: Outbreak of paralytic poliomyelitis in Finland: Widespread circulation of antigenically altered poliovirus type 3 in a vaccinated population. *Lancet* 1986; 1:1427–1432.

604b. Uhari M, Rantala H, Niemelä M: Cluster of childhood Guillain-Barré cases after an oral poliovaccine campaign. *Lancet* 1989; 2:440–441.

604c. Rosa FW, Sever JL, Madden DL: Absence of antibody response to simian virus 40 after inoculation with killed-poliovirus vaccine of mothers of offspring with neurologic tumors. *N Engl J Med* 1988; 318:1469.

605. Centers for Disease Control: National Childhood Vaccine Injury Act: Requirements for permanent vaccination records and for reporting of selected events after vaccination. *MMWR* 1988; 37:197–200.

606. Smith DJ, Gahnberg L, Taubman MA, et al: Salivary antibody responses to oral and parenteral vaccines in children. *J Clin Immunol* 1986; 6:43–49.

607. Selvakumar R, John TJ: Intestinal immunity induced by inactivated poliovirus vaccine. *Vaccine* 1987; 5:141–144.

608. Salk J, Cohen H, Fillastre C, et al: Killed poliovirus antigen titration in humans. *Dev Biol Stand* 1978; 41:119–132.

609. Salk J, vanWezel AL, Stoeckel P, et al: Theoretical and practical considerations in the application of killed poliovirus vaccine for the control of paralytic poliomyelitis. *Dev Biol Stand* 1981; 47:181–198.

610. Fillastre C, Emmou C, Meyran M, et al: Clinical trial of concentrated inactivated polio vaccine in a simplified immunization program. *Dev Biol Stand* 1981; 47:207–213.

611. van Wezel AL, van Steenis G, Hannick CA, et al: New approach to the production of concentrated and purified inactivated polio and rabies tissue culture vaccines. *Dev Biol Stand* 1978; 41:159–168.

612. Salk J, Stoeckel P, van Wezel AL, et al: Antigen content of inactivated poliovirus vaccine for use in a one- or two-dose regimen. *Ann Clin Res* 1982; 14:204–212.

613. Simoes EA, Padmini B, Steinhoff MC, et al: Antibody response of infants to two doses of inactivated poliovirus vaccine of enhanced potency. *Am J Dis Child* 1985; 139:977–980.

614. McBean AM, Thomas ML, Johnson RH, et al: A comparison of the serologic responses to oral and injectible trivalent poliovirus vaccines. *Rev Infect Dis* 1984; 6 (suppl 2): S552–S555.

615. Robertson SE, Drucker JA, Fabre-Teste B, et al: Clinical efficacy of a new, enhanced potency, inactivated poliovirus vaccine. *Lancet* 1988; 1:897–899.

616. John TJ, Joseph A, Vijayarathnam P: A better system for polio vaccination in developing countries? *Br Med J* 1980; 281:542.

617. John TJ: Antibody response in infants in tropics to five doses of oral polio vaccine. *Br Med J* 1976; 1:812.

618. Cockburn WC: Poliomyelitis vaccination in tropical countries. *Adv Exp Med Biol* 1972; 31:223–236.

619. Pollak O, Power DJ, Bundred I, et al: Serum antibody levels after immunization with trivalent oral poliovirus vaccine. *S Afr Med J* 1980; 57:191–193.

620. John TJ, Devarajan LV, Balasubramanyan A: Immunization in India with trivalent and monovalent oral poliovirus vaccines of enhanced potency. *Bull WHO* 1976; 54:115–117.

621. Oduntan SO, Lucas AO, Wennen EM: The immunological response of Nigerian infants to attenuated and inactivated polio-

vaccines. *Ann Trop Med Parasitol* 1978; 72:111–115.

622. Domok I, Balayan MS, Fayinka OA, et al: Factors affecting the efficacy of live poliovirus vaccine in warm climates. *Bull WHO* 1974; 51:333–347.

623. Hardas UD, Pathak AA, Jahagirdar VL: Seroconversion after oral polio vaccine. *Indian J Pediatr* 1978; 45:310–311.

624. Patriarca PA, Palmeira G, Lima Filho J, et al: Randomized trial of alternative formulation of oral poliovaccine in Brazil. *Lancet* 1988; 1:429–432.

625. Wyatt HV: Provocation of poliomyelitis by multiple injections. *Trans R Soc Trop Med Hyg* 1985; 79:355–358.

626. Wyatt HV: Injections and poliomyelitis: What are the risks of vaccine associated paralysis? *Dev Biol Stand* 1986; 65:123–126.

626a. Wyatt HV: Poliomyelitis in developing countries: Lower limb paralysis and injections. *Trans R Soc Trop Med Hyg* 1989; 83:545–549.

627. Robbins FC, Nightingale EO: Selective primary health care: Strategies for control of disease in the developing world. IX. Poliomyelitis. *Rev Infect Dis* 1983; 5:957–968.

628. Schoub BD, Johnson S, McAnerney J, et al: Monovalent neonatal polio immunication—a strategy for the developing world. *J Infect Dis* 1988; 157:836–839.

629. Katz SL: Controversies in immunization. *Pediatr Infect Dis J* 1987; 6:607–613.

630. Amren DP, Mayer TR: National immunization policymaking: A controversial endeavor. *Postgrad Med* 1985; 77:93–100.

631. Hinman AR, Koplan JP, Orenstein WA, et al: Live or inactivated poliomyelitis vaccine: An analysis of benefits and risks. *Am J Public Health* 1988; 78:291–295.

632. Hinman AR, Koplan JP, Orenstein WA, et al: Decision analysis and polio immunization policy. *Am J Public Health* 1988; 78:301–303.

633. Sabin AB: Commentary: Is there a need for a change in poliomyelitis immunization policy? *Pediatr Infect Dis J* 1987; 6:887–889.

634. Salk D: Polio immunization policy in the United States: A new challenge for a new generation. *Am J Public Health* 1988; 78:296–300.

635. Salk J: Commentary: Poliomyelitis vaccination—choosing a wise policy. *Pediatr Infect Dis J* 1987; 6:889–893.

636. Mcbean AM, Modlin JF: Rationale for the sequential use of in-activated poliovirus vaccine and live attenuated poliovirus vaccine for routine poliomyelitis immunization in the United States. *Pediatr Infect Dis J* 1987; 6:881–887.

637. Melnick JL: Vaccination against poliomyelitis: Present possibilities and future prospects. *Am J Public Health* 1988; 78:304–305.

638. von Magnus H, Peterson I: Vaccination with inactivated poliovirus vaccine and oral polio vaccine in Denmark. *Rev Infect Dis* 1984; 6 (suppl 2):S471–S474.

639. Chamberlain R: Poliomyelitis vaccination. *Br Med J* 1987; 295:158–159.

640. Lasch EE, Abed Y, Marcus O, et al: Combined live and inactivated poliovirus vaccines to control poliomyelitis in a developing country—five years after. *Dev Biol Stand* 1986; 65:137–143.

640a. Murph JR, Grose C, McAndrew P, et al: Sabin inactivated trivalent poliovirus vaccine: first clinical trial and seroimmunity survey. *Pediatr Infect Dis J* 1988; 7:760–765.

640b. Tulchinsky T, Abed Y, Shaheen S, et al: A ten-year experience in control of poliomyelitis through a combination of live and killed vaccines in two developing areas. *Am J Public Health* 1989; 79:1648–1652.

641. Le CT: Parental knowledge of their own immunization to poliomyelitis. *JAMA* 1985; 254:608–609.

642. Sabin AB: Oral polio vaccine: History of its development and use and current challenge to eliminate poliomyelitis from the world. *J Infect Dis* 1985; 151:420–436.

643. Sabin AB: Strategy for rapid elimination and continuing control of poliomyelitis and other vaccine preventable diseases of children in developing countries. *Br Med J* 1986; 292:531–533.

643a. Progress toward eradicating poliomyelitis from the Americas. *MMWR* 1989; 38:532–535.

644. Maru M, Getahun A, Hoshna S: Prevalence of paralytic poliomyelitis in rural and urban populations in Ethiopia: Report of a house-to-house survey. *Am J Trop Med Hyg* 1988; 38:633–635.

645. Farquhar JW: Juvenile diabetes mellitus: Possibility of prevention. *Arch Dis Child* 1979; 54:569–580.

646. Plotkin SA: The future of vaccines against viral diseases. *Pediatr Clin North Am* 1968; 15:447–472.

647. Garner JS, Simmons BP: Guidelines for isolation precautions in hospitals. *Infect Control* 1983; 4:326–349.

Hepatitis A Virus

Gert Frösner

The term ''viral hepatitis'' is used in human virology to describe an inflammatory disease of the liver caused by an infection with either hepatitis A, B, C, D, or E virus. All these viruses belong to different taxonomic groups of viruses. There is a wide variation in the epidemiology and in the clinical characteristics of these infections. The only feature common to these agents is that after infection the liver is the main target organ and also the only known site of replication. Other viruses, such as cytomegalovirus or Epstein-Barr virus, may also cause hepatitis, but usually in combination with other symptoms.

Among the agents of viral hepatitis, the hepatitis A virus (HAV) is most prevalent, but it is clinically less important than the hepatitis B virus. HAV infection in childhood is usually mild, and it is always self-limited. However, in developed countries the number of more severe infections in adults is increasing, indicating the need for a vaccine against this disease.

HISTORY

Infectious jaundice is a disease described by Hippocrates. In previous centuries it was frequently epidemic during periods of war. Most of these cases can be assumed to have been hepatitis A infections. Large epidemics were noted during World Wars I and II and the Korean and Vietnamese conflicts. In Germany an estimated 5 to 10 million cases occurred during World War II among army personnel and civilians. Among the British troops in the Mediterranean area there were 4000 cases of jaundice in 1941 to 1942 and 12,000 in 1942 to 1943.

These epidemics stimulated extensive research on the epidemiology, clinical features, and pathology of hepatitis virus in Great Britain,[1] United States,[2, 3] Germany,[4] and West Africa.[5] At the request of the Ministry of Health, the Medical Research Council of Great Britain appointed a Jaundice Committee and a Jaundice Research Team in May 1943. Because of the failure to produce disease in laboratory animals, most of these studies had to be carried out in human volunteers. The results of these studies have been summarized[6] by MacCallum. One type of hepatitis, called ''serum hepatitis,'' had a long incubation period of 60 to 160 days and was parenterally transmitted by blood. This was clearly distinguished from so-called ''infectious hepatitis'' which manifested a shorter incubation period and was transmitted orally by infectious stool. By recommendation of the World Health Organization (WHO)[7] serum hepatitis was later renamed hepatitis B, and infectious hepatitis renamed hepatitis A.

The characteristics of hepatitis A that could be confirmed in later studies were: incubation period between 15 and 40 days, presence of virus in feces and blood, but not in nasopha-

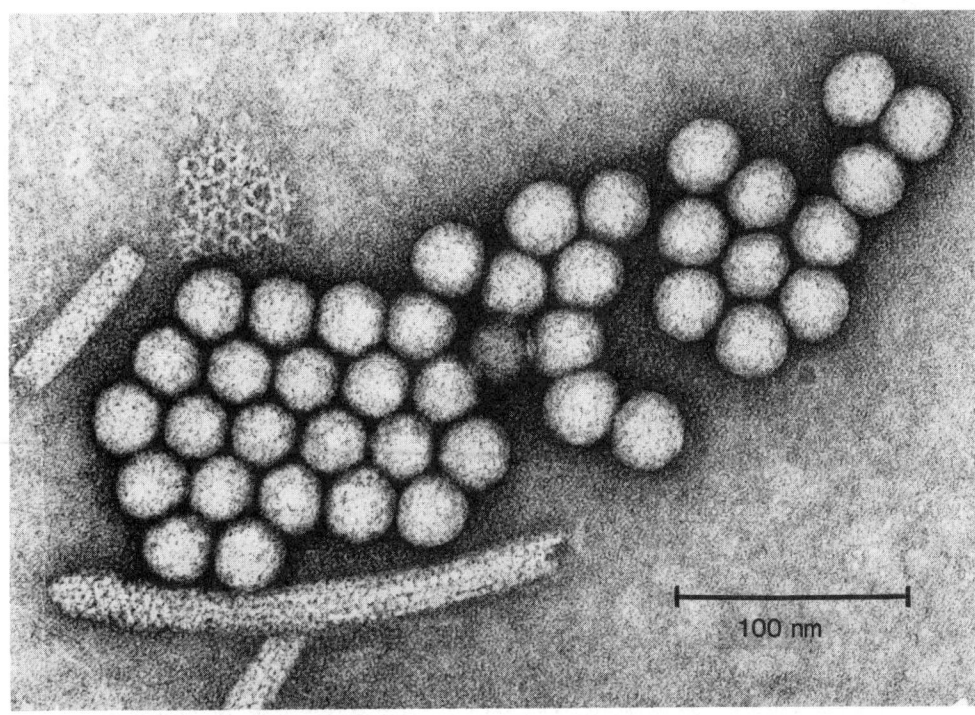

Figure 18–1. Hepatitis A particles detected in the stool of a patient with hepatitis A by electron microscopy. *(Electron photomicrograph courtesy of Prof. G. Siegl, Bern, Switzerland.)*

ryngeal washings; oral and parenteral mode of infection; homologous immunity after infection; protection by prophylactic administration of normal immune serum globulin; and resistance to heat (56°C for 30 min) and diethyl ether (10% vol/vol for 24 h at 4°C).

Further studies in the 1960s in an institution for mentally retarded children led to the isolation of the first internationally used reference strain (MS-1) of HAV.[8] At about the same time marmoset monkeys were found to be a suitable experimental animal for HAV infection (for review see Deinhardt[9]). However, HAV was not visualized until 1973, when Feinstone, Kapikian, and Purcell[10] detected by immune electron microscopy particles approximately 27 nm in diameter in acute phase stool specimens from two of four adult volunteers infected with the MS-1 strain. This led to the development of sensitive methods to determine hepatitis A antigen (HAAg) and anti-HAV. Extensive seroepidemiologic studies were performed in the late 1970s and culminated in the first International Workshop on Hepatitis A Virus Infection[11] held in November 1980 in Athens. Biochemical and biophysical properties of HAV were studied more closely and the virus was classified as a picornavirus.

In 1979 two groups independently succeeded in cultivating HAV in different cell culture systems.[12, 13] This made it possible to develop candidate vaccines (live attenuated and killed virus) against hepatitis A.

STRUCTURE AND BIOLOGY OF THE AGENT

HAV is a spherical, RNA-containing particle 27 to 28 nm in diameter without an envelope (Fig 18–1) having a sedimentation coefficient of 156 to 160S and a density of 1.33 to 1.34 g/mL in cesium chloride.[14–17] Table 18–1 lists these and other biologic and physical characteristics of HAV as summarized in the report of the International Workshop on Hepatitis A Virus Infection[11] and in a recent review.[18] The capsid has cubical symmetry and consists of 32 capsomers. In addition to the mature virion, dense particles (1.38–1.44 g/mL) and immature particles (1.32–1.33 g/mL) can be purified from fecal material of infected man and chimpanzee and from tissue culture-grown viral suspensions.

The mature virion contains 60 copies each of four structural polypeptides (VP$_{1-4}$); each has a molecular weight between 2500 and 33,200 daltons.[19] Immature particles additionally exhibit a precursor protein (VP$_0$ that is cleaved to VP$_2$ and VP$_4$ during maturation. Measurement of the relative susceptibility of the protein of the virion to iodination suggests that VP$_1$ and VP$_3$ are partially exposed on the surface, whereas VP$_2$ and VP$_4$ appear to be located inside the particle.[20] In contrast with other picornaviruses, there is a protein consisting of VP$_1$ and the 2A region of VP$_2$ in the mature particle.[21]

HAV possess a single-stranded linear RNA genome of 7478 nucleotides with a sedimentation coefficient of 32.5S under nondenaturing conditions. Like the genome of other picornaviruses, it can be functionally divided into a 5′-terminal untranslated region composed of 734 nucleotides, a single open reading frame of 6681 nucleotides, and a short untranslated segment of 63 nucleotides at the 3′ end.[19] The molecular weight of the genome was calculated to be 2.25×10^6 on the basis of sedimentation under nondenaturing conditions and 2.8×10^6 from the electrophoretic mobility of completely denatured molecules. From cloning experiments done in bacteria,[22] a positive polarity of the RNA can be deduced,

Table 18–1
Properties of Hepatitis A Virus

Virion
    Naked, spherical particles; capsid probably consisting of 32 capsomers arranged according to the symmetric requirements of a rhombic triacontahedron.

Diameter		27–28 nm	
Sedimentation coefficient		156–160S	
Density in CsCl (g/mL)	Dense particle 1.38–1.44	Mature virion 1.33–1.34	Immature particles*[†] 1.32–1.33

Proteins (daltons)[†]
VP_0	
VP_1	33,200
VP_2	24,800
VP_3	27,800
VP_4	2,500 (17 amino acids)

Nucleic acid
Type	RNA
Configuration	Single-stranded, linear
Sedimentation coefficient[‡]	32.5S
Mol wt (daltons)	$2.25 \times 16^{6\S} - 2.8 \times 10^{6\|}$
Number of nucleotides	8000–8100
Polyadenylic acid	40–80 nucleotides
Polarity	Positive
Translation strategy	Monocistronic

*Immature particles (empty viral capsids or defective particles) also contain a precursor protein VP_0 having the sequences of VP_2 and VP_4.

[†]In preliminary experiments the structural disposition of these polypeptides in the capsid was studied by measurement of their relative susceptibility to iodination. It was concluded that the VP_1 and VP_3 polypeptides are partially exposed. Other polypeptides, VP_2 and VP_4, appear to be located inside.

[‡]Under nondenaturing conditions.

[§]Calculated on the basis of sedimentation under nondenaturing conditions.

[‖]From electrophoretic mobility of completely denatured molecules.

(Reproduced with permission from International Workshop on Hepatitis A Virus Infection: Summary of discussion and statement of opinions on selected issues at an international workshop in Athens, 17–19 November 1980. Eur J Clin Microbiol 1983; 2:57–73; supplemented by further data from Siegl.[18])

and translation occurs as a monocistronic message. The RNA is polyadenylated at its 3′ end by 40 to 80 nucleotides. There exists a small protein, VP_g of 23 amino acids covalently linked to the 5′ terminus.

In comparison with the four established genera of the picornavirus family, the genome of HAV has a low GC content. Nucleotide sequence exhibits less homology with other picornaviruses than non-HAV picornaviruses show with one another. The closest amino acid homology is found for the RNA transcribing portions 2C and 3C (28% and 25%, respectively) of HAV and encephalomyocarditis virus.[19] Although the genome size and organization is similar to those of enteroviruses, the amino acid sequence of HAV proteins is distinct.

HAV genome has been cloned in *Escherichia coli,* resulting in expression of HAV-specific proteins.[23–26] Most of the described biochemical and physical properties, as well as the mode of transmission, are consistent with a classification of HAV as a member of the **Picornaviridae,** enterovirus 72. Like enteroviruses, HAV is stable at pH 3 and in organic solvents such as ether, chloroform, or Freon. However, a higher stability at elevated temperatures (see Table 18–2) distinguishes HAV from most known enteroviruses. Temperatures above 60°C are necessary to destroy infectivity within a short time. At room temperature or lower, the virus maintains its infectivity in the environment for several weeks, even in a dried form.

A less than 100-fold reduction in infectious HAV is found after 56 days at 25°C in ground water, coralla sand, cecil clay, and marine sediment, and isolation of virus usually is possible even after 86 days.[26] In these samples, HAV survives much longer than poliovirus.

Chlorine concentrations usually used for the treatment of drinking water (0.2–0.3 mg/L) are effective in killing the virus and purified HAV is inactivated by formalin treatment as applied in the preparation of a killed virus vaccine (1:4000, 37°C, 72 h). For the complete inactivation of unpurified HAV present in tissue culture supernatant, much higher formalin concentrations (1:100, 37°C, 72 h) are necessary, and this also completely destroys the antigenicity of HAAg. Peracetic acid is an effective disinfectant to inactivate HAV and is used in hospitals. Blood and blood products may be sterilized by a combined UV-β-propiolactone treatment in countries where this procedure is licensed.

Complete cross-reactivity with available immunological test methods has been obtained with isolates from different parts of the world.[11, 27] Antigenic properties seem to be highly conserved. The immunodominant neutralization site of HAV is conformationally determined.[28] Antibodies against HAV polypeptides do not neutralize the virus. Neutralization escape mutants have been mapped to exhibit mutations only in a few areas of the βB and βC loops of VP_3 and VP_1. VP_3 and VP_1 loops form a single functional site.

In contrast to the identical serology of HAV isolates from different parts of the world, there is some variation in nucleotide sequence.[21] Determination of nucleotide sequence can demonstrate epidemiological links between different hepatitis A outbreaks.

Complete sequencing of wild-type strain HM-175 (isolated in marmoset monkeys in Australia) and of tissue culture-adapted strain LA (isolated in Los Angeles) revealed 98.5% amino acid homology. As with polio types 1 and 2, the highest variation was seen in the N terminus of VP_1.[19]

The existence of only one immunologically distinct strain of HAV is supported by the observation that immune serum globulin prepared in one part of the world will render protection to persons in other areas. This implies that a vaccine prepared from one strain of HAV would be protective everywhere. However, because the neutralizing antigen is conformationally determined, production of a vaccine by genetic engineering is difficult. Classical approaches like live attenuated vaccine, or killed whole virus vaccine have to be followed.

HAV is the first human hepatitis virus to be propagated in tissue culture. Provost and Hilleman[12] used primary marmoset liver cells and fetal rhesus kidney cells (FRhK6) whereas Frösner et al[13] succeeded in propagation in an easier-to-handle continuously growing hepatoma cell line (PLC/PRF/5 cells). The described cultivation in human embryo fibroblasts[29] is of special interest for vaccine production. In addition, HAV has been adapted to grow in the frequently used Vero cells, in African green monkey kidney cells, and in several other cell lines. Wild-type HAV grows very slowly in tissue culture.

Specific growth characteristics of HAV that may be responsible for the many unsuccessful attempts are the lack of any visible cytopathic effect (CPE) and the late appearance of viral antigen (HAAg) in infected cells after primary inoculation of fecal specimens. HAAg usually can first be recognized more than 4 weeks after infection by indirect immunofluorescence in the cytoplasm of tissue culture cells or by solid phase radioimmunoassay (RIA) in cell extracts prepared by repeated freezing and thawing of cells. The greater part of the HAAg and of the complete HAV remains cell-associated even after prolonged incubation.

In primary isolation of HAV, expression of viral antigen as well as infectivity titer can be strongly increased by the addition of 80 µmol 5,6-dichlorobenzimidazole riboside to the culture medium.[30]

During further passages, the time of first appearance of antigen can decrease to 1 week (Fig 18–2) or even less. In parallel, the number of 50% tissue culture infectious doses ($TCID_{50}$) obtained from one 25-mL tissue culture flask increases from about 10^3 to 10^9 (Fig 18–3).[31] Using highly adapted strains, the inactivation of HAV by physical and chemical treatment can easily be studied by conventional virologic methods. Tissue culture adapted strains exhibit mutations in the 2B and 2C regions of the nonstructural P_2 protein. Additional mutations in the 5' non-coding region affect the rate of growth and host range of the virus.[32]

Splitting of infected tissue cultures every three to six weeks leads to a persistent HAV infection in which virtually all cells show strong HAAg-specific cytoplasmic fluorescence. Again, no morphologic cell alternation can be found, and HAV is mainly cell-associated.

Obviously, the virus is not able to shut off macromolecular

Table 18–2
Stability of Hepatitis A Virus

Exposure to	Treatment Conditions	Effect on Infectivity	Reference
Acid	pH 3, room temp	Stable	Provost et al,[222] Scheid et al[223]
Organic solvents	Ether, chloroform, Freon	Stable	Provost et al[222] Frösner, G., unpublished results
Temperature	−20°C or −70°C for 6 wk	No reduction in infectivity	Scheid et al[223]
	Room temp, 1 wk	No measurable reduction in Infectivity	Scheid et al[223]
	Room temp, 8 wk	Infectivity destroyed	McCaustland et al[226]
	25°C for 30 d (in dried feces)	Stable	McCaustland et al[226]
	56°C for 30 min	No reduction in infectivity	Ward et al[86]
	60°C for 4 h	Partial inactivation	Ward et al[86]
	60.6°C for 19 min	Partial inactivation	Peterson et al[225]
	85°C for 1 min	Complete inactivation	Scheid et al[223]
	98°C for 1 min	Complete inactivation	Krugman et al[226]
Chlorine	0.5–1.0 mg HOCl/L for 60 min	Partial inactivation	Peterson et al[227]
	1.5–2.5 mg HOCl/L for 30 min	Complete inactivation	Peterson et al[227]
Formalin	1:350, room temp, 60 min	Partial inactivation	Scheid et al[223]
	1:4000, 37°C, 72 h	Inactivation	Provost et al[222]
	About 1:1000 (0.055% formaldehyde) 37°C, 72 h	Nearly inactivated (tissue culture supernatant)	Billing et al[228]
	About 1:100 (0.35% formaldehyde), 72 h	Complete inactivation (tissue culture supernatant)	Billing et al[228]
Peracetic acid	1%, room temp, 1 h	Not inactivated (tissue culture extract)	Frösner, G., unpublished results
	2%, room temp, 4 h	Complete inactivation	Frösner, G., unpublished results
	1%, room temp, 1 h	Complete inactivation	Frösner, G., unpublished results
β-propiolactone	0.25%, 5°C, 1 h, pH 7.2	Complete inactivation	Frösner et al[229]
UV irradiation	2 mW/cm²/min	Complete inactivation	Frösner et al[229]

synthesis of the host cell. The parital block in viral replication responsible for establishment of chronic persistent infection could be sought at the level of penetration and uncoating[33] or at the level of processing viral precursor proteins.[34] Most probably defective interfering particles caused by limited replication of viral RNA are responsible for the low level of replication found in persistently infected cells.[35] Defective particles also appear after infection, with very low multiplicity of the virus, and therefore seem to always emerge in virus replication.

Recently, cytopathogenic strains of HAV have been selected from persistently infected cell lines.[36, 37] These will enable titration of infectivity by plaque assay.

Superinfection of HAV-infected cell cultures with polio-, coxsackie-, and echoviruses has not produced an interference phenomenon, and HAV does not agglutinate erythrocytes from mouse, rat, chicken, pigeon, rabbit, pig, marmoset or man.[11]

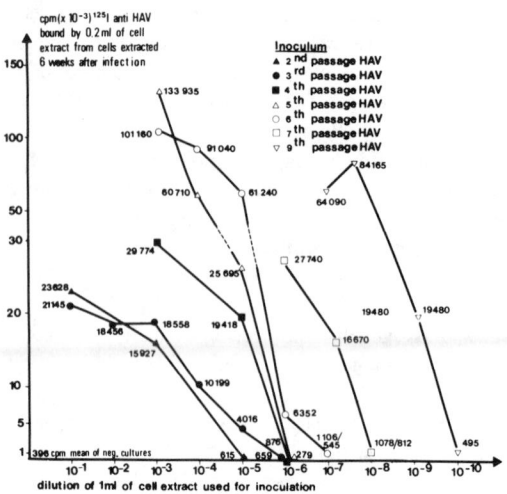

Figure 18–3. Infectivity titration of tissue culture cell extract 6 weeks after inoculation of hepatitis A virus (HAV) with different passage levels. With successive passage 50% tissue culture infectious dose per milliliter cell extract increases from 10^3 to 10^5 up to 10^9.

EPIDEMIOLOGY

Incidence and Prevalence in Different Geographic Areas

The incidence of HAV infections cannot be deduced from mortality data because death is extremely infrequent, especially in children. Morbidity data, which are not available from many developing and even some developed countries, are biased by several facts: only clinical but not the frequently occurring subclinical cases are registered; because of limited epidemiologic and laboratory services in most parts of the world, it is not possible to differentiate among hepatitis A, B, and hepatitis C, and cases of hepatitis are usually registered as a single nosologic entity; there is a considerable underreporting of clinical cases of hepatitis.[38, 39] Heightened awareness by physicians of viral hepatitis may increase the number of registered cases without a change in the true incidence of the disease. Nevertheless, data reported from children, where the vast majority of cases usually are of type A,[40] may give some indication of trends in the epidemiology of hepatitis A infection.

The most appropriate means to obtain information on the incidence of HAV infection in different geographic areas and epidemiologic settings is by a calculation from the prevalence of anti-HAV in the sera of appropriate population groups.[41] Three different patterns of anti-HAV prevalence have been described from different areas of the world (Fig 18–4).

1. In developing countries of Asia, Africa, and the Americas virtually all individuals become anti-HAV positive during childhood[42] and remain positive during adulthood[43, 44] (pattern Ia). A decline in the proportion of anti-HAV-positive individuals may be found in older age groups[45, 46] and this is probably due to a decrease in antibody concentration below the detection limit of the test systems used (pattern Ib). In these countries, where sanitary and hygienic conditions are relatively primitive, HAV infection is

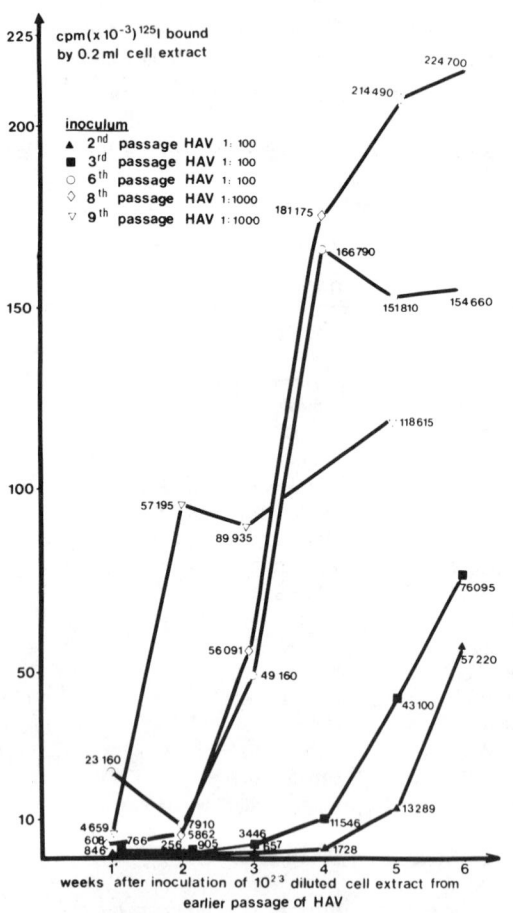

Figure 18–2. Hepatitis A antigen (HAAg) detected by radioimmunoassay in cell extracts of PLC/PRF 5 cells inoculated with hepatitis A virus (HAV) of different passage levels. The time of first appearance of HAAg is reduced from 4 weeks to 1 week with increasing numbers of tissue culture passages.

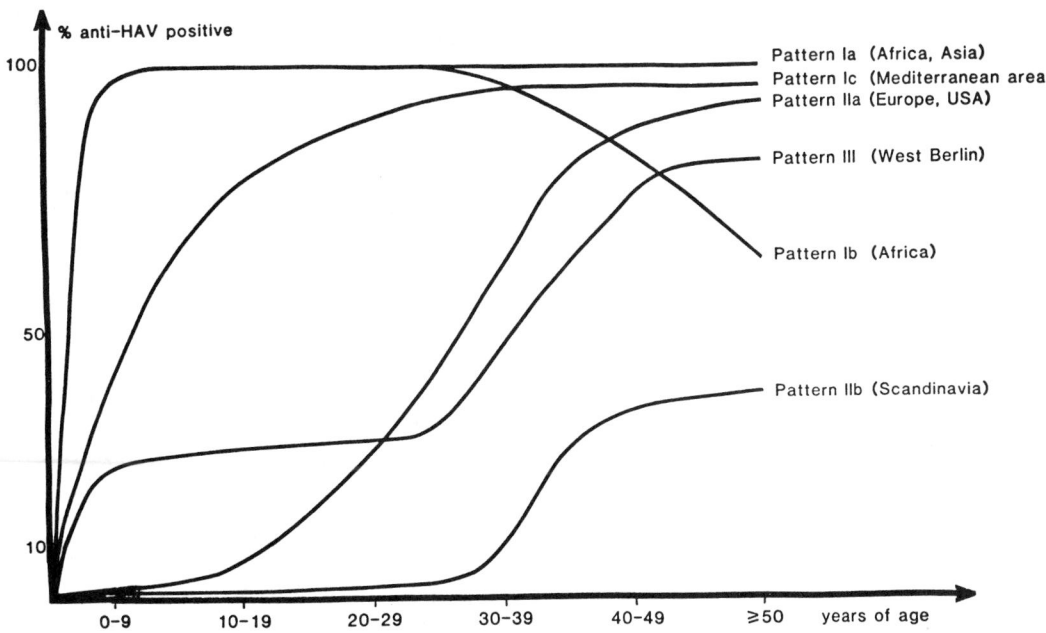

Figure 18–4. Different patterns of age–specific prevalence of anti–hepatitis A virus (anti–HAV) in different parts of the world.

highly endemic and usually acquired in early childhood. In endemic countries with a lower incidence in infection, the same saturation type of age-dependent prevalence curve is found. However, the increase of the proportion of anti-HAV-positive individuals is not as fast as in pattern Ia, reaching high levels only in adulthood[45, 47, 48] (pattern Ic).

2. In highly developed countries of Europe and in the United States a sigmoidal type of age-dependent prevalence curve is noted.[47, 49] The percentage of antibody-positive individuals is low during childhood, increases sharply during adolescence or early adulthood, and reaches a high (pattern IIa) or medium (pattern IIb) level during late adulthood. This pattern is caused by a cohort effect in countries where the incidence of HAV infection has decreased substantially during recent decades. The relatively high prevalence of anti-HAV in adults is due to a more universal exposure of these adults when they were children at a time when there was a higher incidence of infection. An extreme of this pattern is the complete or nearly complete disappearance of hepatitis A infection in younger individuals of isolated populations and a virtually universal exposure of adults during previous large-scale epidemics, as documented in Greenland[50] and in the South Pacific islands.[44] In the future the low incidence of HAV infection in these countries will lead to a mostly susceptible population which is endangered during travel to endemic areas.

3. A third type of antibody pattern may be found in populations in which hepatitis A is no longer an endemic disease but is introduced regularly from endemic areas and transmitted to certain groups of the population. This type III pattern, at present found in Germans living in West Berlin, is characterized by an increase to 25% anti-HAV-positive children aged 2 to 5 years, a stable prevalence of 25% to 30% up to 20 years of age, followed by an increase to 85% in those older than 50 years.[51] The relatively high prevalence of infection in German children may be due to close

contact with children of emigrant workers from Mediterranean countries in the kindergarten. The population of some districts of Berlin consists of 20% to 29% emigrant workers whose children usually acquire HAV infection during a visit in their home countries.

From the above data it is obvious that there is a wide variation in prevalence of anti-HAV in the adult population of different countries (for review see Dienstag.[52]) The lowest prevalence is found in Scandinavian countries (Sweden 13%, Norway 17%). In the United States (41%–44%), Japan (50%), Australia (62%) and some European countries (Germany 55%, Holland 52%, Poland 60%) 40% to 70% of the population are positive, whereas the majority of persons living in Mediterranean countries (Greece 82%, Israel 94%, Yugoslavia 97%), in Africa (Senegal 75%, Kenya 88%), and Asia (Sri Lanka 76%, Taiwan 88%, South Pacific islands 52%–95%) show serologic signs of past infection with HAV.

Recent evaluation of 3970 sera collected during the second National Health and Nutrition Examination Survey from 1976 to 1980 showed an overall anti-HAV prevalence of 42% in the United States population.[53] Anti-HAV prevalence was 13.2% in the age group 10 to 19 years, 20% in the age group 20 to 29 years, 34.9% in the age group 30 to 39 years, 51.7% in the age group 40 to 49 years, and 78.6% in the age group older than 49 years. The highest prevalence, 69.7%, was found in hispanics as compared to 48.4% in blacks, and 38.4% in whites. In the age group 20 to 24 years, the corresponding values were about 75%, 45%, and 15%.

Epidemiologic Trends and Seasonal Distribution

The most likely explanation for the occurrence of a sigmoidal type II age-dependent anti-HAV prevalence curve in highly developed countries is a decrease in the incidence of hepatitis A infection during the last decades. Accordingly, most of the anti-HAV-positive adults were infected during childhood when HAV infection was still a frequent disease.[54]

This hypothesis is supported by a downward trend in the number of registered clinical cases of hepatitis in 1- to 14-year-old children from the United States, Denmark, Czechoslovakia, and Puerto Rico.[55, 56] This hypothesis could be proved by investigating sera collected under the same conditions several years apart. Between 1965 and 1975 the prevalence of anti-HAV decreased in Germany from 51% to 11% in the age group of 20 to 29 years and from 88% to 46% in the group of 30 to 39 years.[57] Similar observations were made in Australia,[58] in Japan[59], and in northern Italy.[60] A mathematical analysis of the age-specific prevalence curves by a catalytic model[38] suggested that this decrease already started in the 1920s in Scandinavian countries, and after World War II in most other developed countries.

In the United States, nationwide epidemics occurred in 1961 (incidence 40.5/100,000 population) and 1971 (incidence 27.9/100,000), but did not recur in the 1980's.[61] A peak in cases was no longer seen in autumn and winter.[62] In contrast to earlier years, hepatitis cases were more frequently reported from urban than from rural areas.

In contrast to the United States, a seasonal distribution of hepatitis A cases with a peak in autumn and a low level of cases in early summer is still found in Germany.[62, 63] The autumn peak is much more pronounced in children than in adults. This difference may be explained by the fact that children usually travel to Mediterranean countries with still endemic hepatitis A infection during school holidays in summer, whereas adults are on business and vacation trips during the whole year. Actually, about two thirds of all German persons with hepatitis A had visited an endemic country within 8 weeks before onset of illness. Therefore, hepatitis A is probably no longer an endemic disease in Germany, and the virus cannot further sustain itself in the population without continuous reintroduction.

Endemic HAV may have disappeared from some island populations including Greenland.[50] In 1970, anti-HAV was detected in 38 of 41 persons (93%) born before an epidemic outbreak of hepatitis A in 1947 to 1948, but in only one of 29 persons (3%) born thereafter. During a further epidemic of hepatitis A between 1970 and 1974 following this survey, 4961 clinical cases were registered (11% of the total population of Greenland). Of these cases, 93% occurred in persons less than 25 years of age. Also, a high prevalence of anti-HAV in adults and the fact that there is no anti-HAV-positive person below 20 years of age on Ponape suggests that HAV disappeared from this South Pacific island in 1943 after a period of major virus activity.[44]

Age, Sex, Social, Economic, and Other Factors

In developing countries hepatitis A is a frequent infection in childhood, and most adults possess immunity against this disease. In highly industrialized countries with a decreasing incidence of hepatitis A, on the other hand, clinical cases now predominantly occur in the age group of 20 to 35 years because this age group

has a vanishing immunity and frequent exposure during travel in countries with endemic hepatitis A.[63, 64] In spite of the fact that in these countries hepatitis A is obviously no longer a frequent disease in children (only 1%–2% of German children exhibit anti-HAV up to 16 years of age[65]), it still contributes 80% of all clinical cases of viral hepatitis in this age group.[40]

Since 1983, incidence has gradually increased by 26% to 11.6/100,000 in 1988, and a projected annual rate for 1989 may be nearly 40% greater than the rate for 1988. Incidence is highest in western and mountain states.

In most studies performed in Europe[66, 67] and in the United States,[68] the prevalence of hepatitis A patients among all clinical cases of viral hepatitis in adults was found to be between 10% and 25%. In Germany a prevalence of 17%[69] and 14%[70] was reported in clinical studies. Surprisingly, 46% of cases registered separately since July 1980 by the German public health service as "hepatitis A," hepatitis B," and "nonidentified hepatitis" were hepatitis A.[51] This may be due to the fact that the disease is more severe in older individuals and therefore diagnosed and registered more frequently when it occurs in this group. This is in agreement with a rise in the incidence of viral hepatitis, despite improved socioeconomic conditions, in Israel.[71] At the same time peak, incidence shifted from the 1 to 4 year age group to the 5 to 9 year age group. There is no indication of a different incidence of hepatitis A in males or females, nor is there a difference in the prevalence of anti-HAV between the sexes.

Socioeconomic factors, however, are closely associated with the percentage of antibody-positive persons. Two American studies demonstrated a lower prevalence in persons of the upper socioeconomic class[72] and a higher prevalence among the ghetto poor[73] compared to the middle class. Similar results were found in a north Italian urban population.[76] A striking difference in the age-specific prevalence of antibody between black and white persons living in the same areas of South Africa may largely be due to socioeconomic factors. All black persons above 9 years of age, but less than 50% of white persons up to 39 years of age, exhibited anti-HAV. In comparison, no significant difference could be verified in six socioeconomically different population groups in Germany.[75]

Other factors favoring the transmission of hepatitis A are large-sized families, crowded living conditions, and poor hygienic and sanitary conditions.[76] In developed countries the decrease in incidence of hepatitis A infections during the last decades was associated with a considerable improvement of living conditions as measured by the percentage of families with an indoor toilet, by the quality of community water supply, and by the method of waste water disposal. A higher prevalence of anti-HAV was demonstrated in rural compared to urban areas of Greece, Switzerland, and Austria.[47, 77]

Seroepidemiologic studies have identified several population groups with increased risk of HAV infection. First of all, these are persons from low-incidence countries traveling to areas with highly endemic hepatitis A. Among German travelers, there seems to be a 39-fold excess in the yearly incidence of infections contracted in tropical countries (0.116 compared with 0.003 in Germany) and a 17-fold excess in subtropical countries (0.051).[70] Seroconversion to anti-HAV was found in 48% of 108 anti-HAV negative French volunteers working for 18 to 35 months in the field in West and central Africa.[78] A specialist unit of the British army that frequently travels to endemic areas displayed an increased level of anti-HAV.[79]

Homosexual men exhibited an increased prevalence of anti-HAV,[80] and in a prospective study the annual incidence of hepatitis A in susceptible homosexuals was as high as 22%.[81] A positive correlation was found between the prevalence of anti-HAV and the number of episodes of syphilis.

Drug addicts are not only exposed to hepatitis B and hepatitis C, but also to hepatitis A.[82] In Norway, prevalence of anti-HAV in drug addicts was 43% in 1983, versus about 5% in corresponding age groups of the general population and 1% in Norwegian (United Nations) soldiers sent to Lebanon.[83] Epidemics of hepatitis A were seen among drug addicts in 1975 and 1979, coinciding with epidemics in Malmö, Sweden.

More recently, several outbreaks of hepatitis A have been observed in the United States, too.[84] Between 1983 and 1988, the percentage of persons with hepatitis A reporting a history of intravenous drug use had risen from 4.2% to 12.6%.[61] HAV may be transmitted from person to person by sharing of needles, sexual contact, or generally poor sanitary and personal hygiene. Common-source outbreaks may be caused by injection or ingestion of contaminated drugs. Cultivation of fecal coliforms from marijuana suggests that drugs can become contaminated with fecal material at the cultivation site (eg, through use of human feces as fertilizer) or during transportation (eg, smuggling in condoms concealed in the rectum).

Institutionalized populations, including inmates of correction centers[85] or mentally retarded patients,[86] have shown a higher rate of anti-HAV than age-matched noninstitutionalized populations of the same area. In the latter group a positive correlation was demonstrated between the prevalence of anti-HAV and the duration of institutionalization, but not with age, sex, and cause of mental retardation. The unusually poor hygienic habits of these patients favor the fecal-oral route of HAV transmission. A high rate of hepatitis has also been reported from attendant personnel of such institutions.[87] On the other hand, large outbreaks involving up to 57% of the patients[88] suggest that hepatitis A is not endemic in all such institutions.

In the United States many outbreaks of hepatitis A have been registered, usually in adult contacts of children attending a day care center.[89] Transmission from these centers is associated with the presence of diapered children less than 1 year old, with large centers open more than 15 hours a day, and with centers operating for profit.[90]

Medical personnel not especially exposed to hepatitis A patients do not seem to be at a special risk of contracting hepatitis A. No increased prevalence of anti-HAV was detected in staff (and patients) of dialysis centers[91] and in nurses.[75]

PATHOGENESIS

Reservoir of Infection and Mode of Transmission

HAV is usually transmitted from human to human. However, various nonhuman primates may also be susceptible to infection. In addition to marmosets and chimpanzees, which are used as experimental animals,[92, 93] several other nonhuman primates have

been found to be anti-HAV-positive,[94] even when caught in the wild.[95, 96] The spread of HAV was registered within colonies of captive owl monkeys (*Aotus trivirgatus*)[97] as well as in Malaysian cynomologous monkeys (*Macaca fascicularis*).[98] Experimentally infected stump-tailed monkeys (*M. speciosa*) shed HAV[99] as do marmosets and chimpanzees. Since the report of Hillis[100] of an outbreak of infectious hepatitis among chimpanzee handlers, it is generally accepted that the disease can be transmitted from monkey to man.

The significance of these findings for transmission of HAV is probably low. Most likely, animals living in close proximity to man are infected by contaminated food or water. Even if this leads to subsequent transmissions within a colony, the virus is probably not able to maintain itself there because of the limited number of susceptible animals. Therefore infections in nonhuman primates do not contribute significantly to the number of HAV infections among humans and seem ecologically unimportant for the survival of the virus.

The usual source of infection is human feces. Testing of stool confirmed earlier human experiments showing its infectivity during the late incubation period and early acute phase of the disease.[1, 87] Excretion of 27-nm particles was visualized by electron microscopy in stool up to six days before the first elevation of transaminases and up to 13 days before the transaminase peak.[101–103] After the transaminase peak or after development of jaundice, particles were only seen occasionally.

Chronic excretion of HAV has not been found. Of 11 patients with transaminases persistently elevated for more than 14 weeks, shedding of HAV was exhibited only during the first days after onset of illness.[73] There is also epidemiologic evidence that chronic excretion does not exist or is a very rare event. The high clinical attack rates of 45% and 21% found during outbreaks in persons born after earlier epidemics in Alaska[104] and Greenland,[105] respectively, suggest that the virus has not been continuously present in these populations.

Transmission of hepatitis A could be achieved with blood, too,[1] and the MS-1 reference material used in many volunteer studies and animal experiments[8] was a serum pool collected during the late incubation period and the early acute phase from one patient. In tissue culture experiments, the infectivity of two of 21 sera collected during the first week of illness could be demonstrated even in the presence of high-titered anti-HAV.[106] Recently 22 (39% of 56 susceptible patients) in six different clinical centers developed hepatitis A after receiving lymphokine-activated killer cells that had been grown in a medium supplemented with pooled human serum.[107] However, transmission by blood seems to be a rare event. Only few cases of posttransfusion hepatitis have been reported.[108] Therefore the period of infectivity of blood seems to be short.[109]

Some nonconfirmed studies also suggested the infectivity of urine.[5, 110] After oral inoculation of a chimpanzee[111] and of owl monkeys[112] HAV could be isolated from throat swabs. However, there is no evidence for transmission of HAV by nasopharyngeal secretions or droplet infection in men.

HAV is usually transmitted from person to person by the fecal-oral route to family contact, neighbors, and contact persons in kindergartens, schools, prisons, and other closed institutions.[87, 88, 113–117] This is consistent with the observation that the highest virus concentrations are found in feces (up to 10^7 to 10^9

infectious doses per mL; in blood 10^3 to 10^5 infectious doses per mL, and in saliva 10^0 to 10^5 infectious doses per mL).[118]

More spectacular, but epidemiologically less important, are common-source outbreaks caused by contaminated food or beverage. These outbreaks may be caused by drinking water,[119, 120] milk,[121] fruit juice and fruit salad,[122, 123] cream,[124] glazed and iced pastries,[125] and cold meats.[126] Between 1983 and 1987, a total of 29 foodborne outbreaks involving 1,067 persons were registered in the United States.[127] Of these, 16 of the outbreaks were traced to a delicatessen, a cafeteria, or a restaurant. Contamination usually occurs via a person in the late incubation period of hepatitis A preparing or handling food. The vehicle of transmission can be recognized by a well-defined clustering of cases during a short time period in a limited geographic area. More difficult to trace are infections caused by contaminated frozen food, because of its widespread distribution and its longer use. Food stored at $-20°C$ may stay infectious for many years.

Consumption of raw or undercooked bivalve mollusks is also an important mode of transmission in certain parts of the world.[128–130] The largest epidemic of hepatitis A ever reported occurred during January to April 1988 in Shanghai.[131] After consumption of hairy clams, 310,746 persons suffered from clinical hepatitis A. The mean age of patients was 28 years. Males and females were equally affected. Because clams and oysters filter large quantities of water, they probably yield high concentrations of the virus in only minimally polluted water. Under optimal filtration conditions mussels (*Mytilus chilensis*) exhibit a more than 1000-fold concentration of HAV three hours after addition of virus to the water.[132] Due to its high stability, HAV may survive in shellfish for many months, especially in the winter season. Ingestion of shellfish collected from fecally contaminated lagoons can explain the continuous presence of HAV in small isolated populations of the South Pacific islands.

Incubation Period

The incubation period is defined as the time between infection and the onset of symptoms. In icteric cases the first appearance of dark urine is a good reference point. In anicteric or subclinical cases the first elevation of transaminases or the time of seroconversion to anti-HAV may serve to define the incubation period. In experimentally infected volunteers these two markers appeared directly before or together with the onset of symptoms.[133] Usually the incubation time is about 4 weeks with a variation between 14 and 40 days. In the Shanghai outbreak, mean incubation period was 21 days (12 to 36 days).[131] There is no difference in the incubation periods after parenteral or oral infection.[8] The first sign of infection is the shedding of HAAg in stool, which may be found up to ten days before illness.

Site of Viral Replication

From experimental infections in marmosets, chimpanzees, and human volunteers, preliminary conclusions of the replication of HAV can be drawn. HAV can first be detected by immune fluorescence in the liver of marmosets 1 to 2 weeks after infection. The granular staining of the cytoplasm of hepatocytes and of Kupffer cells is maximal after about 20 to 25 days.[134] HAV has been visualized by electron microscopy in the bile of diseased chim-

panzees.[135, 136] Shedding in stool starts later than the intrahepatic localization of the virus and is most pronounced in the late incubation period.[63, 117] Viremia has also been demonstrated in the late incubation period and shortly after onset of illness.[106, 109] However, HAV was not detected by immune fluorescence in the duodenum, jejunum, ileum, or transverse colon of seven marmosets intravenously inoculated and sacrificed at different times after infection.[137] HAAg was demonstrated in the germinal centers of spleen and abdominal lymph nodes as well as in the glomeruli of the kidney.

After oral inoculation of a chimpanzee, HAV was detected in tonsils, saliva, and throat swabs only after the virus had been isolated from serum.[111] After oral inoculation of owl monkeys, HAV was isolated from saliva only after the virus had been detected in stool and blood.[112] There is no evidence that HAV replicates in the pharynx before viremia.

These observations are consistent with the hypothesis that, in contrast to enteroviruses, there is no replication of HAV in the gut. Liver cells seem to be the only site of virus multiplication and HAV gains access to the stool via the biliary system and to the blood via sinusoids. The presence of HAV in lymphoid tissue and the kidney is probably not the result of an extrahepatic manifestation of the infection, but of an early humoral immune response leading to the elimination of HAV.

Host Response

Clinical Syndromes

The ratio of subclinical to clinical hepatitis A infection was sometimes estimated to be higher than 10:1. These figures are largely based on a high percentage of anti-HAV-positive persons who do not recall an earlier episode of hepatitis.[54, 86, 138] However, several prospective studies revealed a ratio of 2:1 or less in older children and adults.[11, 117] In two carefully investigated epidemics in China the proportions of inapparent, sub-clinical and overt infections were, respectively, 24% to 25%, 46% to 50%, and 20% to 25%.[139] It seems likely that in many persons with clinical illness the diagnosis of hepatitis is not even suspected except in an investigational setting.

Young children usually experience a mild, anicteric disease, whereas in adults the illness is generally more severe and more prolonged.[55, 140] The ratio of anicteric to icteric cases varies 12:1 to 1:3.5 in different epidemiologic investigations.[141] In the United States, icteric disease is found in less than 10% of children below 6 years of age, in about 40% to 50% of children between 6 and 14 years of age, and in about 70% to 80% of persons older than 14 years of age.[118]

In diseased patients the first symptoms are usually nonspecific. Typically, the illness starts abruptly with fever above 38°C, fatigue, headache, nausea, vomiting, and abdominal discomfort.[52] Less common are diarrhea, myalgia, coryza, and sore throat. Occasionally a rash has been seen in serologically diagnosed hepatitis A, but no serum sickness–like syndrome with arthritis and/or urticaria has been described as reported of up to 10% of patients with hepatitis B or some patients with hepatitis C. Suggestive for hepatitis A and very uncommon in hepatitis B and C are the sudden onset of symptoms and the development of high fever.

After this prodromal stage, usually lasting one to seven days, specific symptoms develop: darkening of the urine, followed closely by a lightening of the stool color, jaundice, and pruritis. Some of the patients may complain of pain in the right upper quadrant of the abdomen and have enlargement and tenderness of the liver, enlarged spleen, and lymphadenopathy.

An elevation of alanine aminotransferase (ALT) and aspartate aminotransferase (AST) in serum is already found in the prodromal stage. Typical for all types of viral hepatitis is a higher value of ALT than AST. The gamma glutamyltranspeptidase, which frequently increases to high levels in toxic hepatitis, is only moderately elevated in hepatitis A. Peak enzyme levels are usually reached within a week when serum bilirubin values start to rise and abnormally high levels of immunoglobulin M develop. This last biochemical abnormality is consistently found even in subclinical hepatitis A and is absent in most patients with other types of viral hepatitis.[142]

Jaundice may be evident from a few days to several months, and a positive correlation between duration of jaundice and age has been described.[143] In children, all biochemical indices of hepatitis usually return to normal within 2 to 3 weeks.[144] In young adults abnormal values are found for an average of 3 to 4 weeks.[145] In Italy, 7.4% of 225 patients with clinical hepatitis A exhibited a second peak of ALT elevation 3 to 8 weeks after the first elevation.[146] Because shellfish consumption was the only likely source of infection in 13 of these 18 patients (72%), this second peak may be caused by simultaneous infection with epidemic waterborne hepatitis E virus.

Hepatitis A infection may run a protracted course. Six of 32 diseased persons of the Holy Cross College football team outbreak still exhibited slightly elevated aminotransferase activity 143 days after exposure,[147] and 14 weeks after an outbreak in naval recruits, 11 of 130 persons still had abnormal enzyme activity. After 1 year complete normalization was registered in these persons.[148] There is no evidence that hepatitis A can become chronic. Follow-up studies of serologically confirmed cases revealed complete recovery in all but one case.[82, 149] The only exception was a drug addict with morphologically confirmed chronic persistent hepatitis who may also have been exposed to hepatitis C virus. The same prevalence of anti-HAV is found in hepatitis B surface antigen (HBsAg)-positive and HBsAg-negative chronic liver disease and in age-matched normal controls.[150–152] In addition, neither chronic excretion of HAV in stool, nor the presence of intrahepatic HAV could be demonstrated in patients with chronic hepatitis.[141]

A rare complication of clinical hepatitis A is the development of fulminant hepatitis leading to death within a few days in the majority of cases.[152–155] Fulminant hepatitis is heralded by a rapid and high increase in transaminases and a decrease in prothrombin time. Hepatic coma then develops. Jaundice, which is usually evident, may not be seen in patients with a very rapid course.

The case fatality rate was determined to be 0.3% during an epidemic outbreak in Greenland involving 4961 diseased persons.[50] In Denmark, lethality was calculated to be 0.8% according to the registered number of hepatitis cases, the number of deaths among those patients, and the percentage of hepatitis A among lethal infections.[141] Similar calculations using figures reported from the United States led to a case fatality rate of 0.1% to 0.5%, which is slightly lower than the rate estimated for hepatitis B or hepatitis C. In the Shanghai epidemic, only 40 HAV associated deaths were

registered in 310,746 clinical cases.[131] Of these, 25 deaths were due to fulminant hepatitis A, and 15 deaths occurred in persons with preexisting chronic active hepatitis B.

Fulminant and fatal hepatitis A may be favored by a simultaneous infection with another hepatitis agent, as has been reported for the simultaneous infection with hepatitis B and the hepatitis D virus[156] and for the simultaneous infection with hepatitis B and hepatitis C virus.[157] This concept is supported by a severe jaundiced hepatitis with marked liver damage in a chimpanzee having simultaneously acute hepatitis A and B infection.[158] On the other hand, acute hepatitis A infection in otherwise healthy chronic HBsAg carriers resulted in an anicteric-to-icteric ratio (1.7:1) similar to that in HBsAg-negative individuals (2.1:1), and there was no significant difference in the clinical course.[159]

Case fatality rate probably also increases with age, as does the severity of the disease. A marked increase in severity of hepatitis A in pregnant women as described in Asia and the Middle East has not been confirmed in the United States and in Europe and may be due to the poor nutritional state in developing countries.[160] The existence of antigenically different HAV strains[161] that may also have different pathogenicity for man has not been confirmed.

Immunologic Response and Immunity

Anti-HAV usually becomes positive in serum before the first rise in transaminases is registered.[133] It is virtually always detectable at onset of disease, and generally high titers are present when the patient seeks medical attention.[63] However, very occasionally symptoms of viral hepatitis A can precede production of specific antibody.[162] During the first days of illness, most and sometimes all of the detectable anti-HAV belongs to the immunoglobulin M (IgM) class (anti-HAV IgM).[163] In clinical cases a peak in anti-HAV IgM is reached about eight to 16 days after hospitalization, then the titer decreases gradually, becoming undetectable by currently used techniques between 3 and 6 months after onset of illness (Fig 18–5).[164]

Anti-HAV of the IgG class (anti-HAV IgG), which may not be detectable at onset of illness, slowly increases in titer during the next weeks and reaches a maximal titer after about 6 to 12 months. By immune adherence hemagglutination (IAHA), a method which mainly detects antibody of the IgG and not of the IgM class, a negative result for anti-HAV may be found up to 49 days after the first transaminase elevation[165] or up to 4 weeks after onset of illness.[166] Using a test system that does not differentiate between anti-HAV of the IgG and IgM classes, a transient decrease in total anti-HAV titer can be found about 1 month after onset of illness. In some of the patients secretory anti-HAV IgA can be demonstrated in stool for a few days after the appearance of dark urine.[167]

From the high prevalence of antibody in older individuals of developed countries with decreasing incidence of hepatitis A, it can be assumed that anti-HAV IgG usually persists for life. Persons infected during an epidemic outbreak still exhibited high antibody titers when tested 12 years later.[117] Only in highly endemic countries, with very early infection in childhood, may anti-HAV decline to nondectable levels in some of the older persons.

This antibody prevalence pattern also suggests that reinfection with a boosting of serum antibody titer is uncommon even in endemic areas. Obviously, after hepatitis A infection, immunity, as indicated by a positive result for anti-HAV, persists for life in most cases. Nevertheless, a rise in titer has been documented in some exposed anti-HAV-positive persons.[117, 168] Epidemiologic evidence suggests that persons with nondetectable anti-HAV levels on rare occasions may even have clinical reinfection.[11]

As postulated for hepatitis B infection, cellular or humoral immune mechanisms may play an important role in the pathogenesis of hepatitis A. HAV itself does not seem to be cytopathogenic. It replicates for months in tissue cultures without cell destruction,[31] and it is excreted in the stool of patients for 1 to 2 weeks before symptoms develop. Transaminase elevation and onset of symptoms usually develop shortly after anti-HAV becomes positive in serum. However, the lack of cell destruction in HAV-infected tissue culture cells after addition of anti-HAV (and complement) suggests that cellular immunity may be more important for the resolution of the disease than humoral immunity. Peripheral blood lymphocytes of HAV-infected individuals are capable of lysing HAV-infected tissue culture cells of human origin.[169] Recently, it has been shown that T lymphocytes cloned from biopsy material of patients with acute hepatitis A, will kill HAV-infected human skin fibroblasts.[170] This strongly supports the hypothesis that liver cell injury is mediated by HAV-specific CD8+ T lymphocytes.

This is consistent with the observation that portal and periportal mononuclear cell infiltrations appear in the liver later than intrahepatic localization and fecal excretion of HAV and at about the time of first transaminase elevation.

In contrast to a more diffuse distribution in hepatitis B, focal necrosis of hepatocytes occurs in hepatitis A mainly in the periphery of the lobule, sparing the central zone.[52] Liver histology of hepatitis A is also characterized by complete resolution of inflammatory activity within a few weeks without distortion of the lobule architecture and without signs of chronic hepatitis.

LABORATORY DIAGNOSIS OF INFECTION

Demonstration of Anti-HAV IgM

Demonstration of anti-HAV IgM in a single serum specimen drawn in the acute or convalescent stages is the fastest, most simple, and most reliable way to diagnose acute hepatitis A infection. This antibody is nearly always present at onset of illness and usually persists for 3 to 6 months (see Fig 18–5). The methods of choice are the radioimmune or enzyme immune assay using a solid phase coated with antihuman IgM.[164, 171–173] After incubation with patient serum, binding of anti-HAV IgM is shown by consecutive binding of HAAg and labeled anti-HAV to the solid phase during further incubation steps. The method is very sensitive, yielding titers up to 10^{-6} during the acute stage, but it may be biased by nonspecific binding of high-titered anti-HAV IgG to the solid phase.[63]

Separation of IgM and IgG by density gradient ultracentrifugation (or gel filtration) with consecutive testing of gradient fractions for anti-HAV activity is also a reliable but cumbersome and time-consuming method for the demonstration of anti-HAV IgM.[163] It may serve to measure the relative proportion of anti-HAV IgM and anti-HAV IgG at different times after infection.

Other methods, such as testing of serum for anti-HAV after absorption of IgG by staphylococcal protein A[174] or after the destruction of IgM antibody by mercaptoethanol,[175] as well as methods in which the solid phase was first coated with the patient's serum[176] or with HAAg,[177] are less reliable.

Anti-HAV Determination

The majority of anti-HAV tests do not discriminate anti-HAV as belonging to different immunoglobulin classes (ie, IgG, IgM,

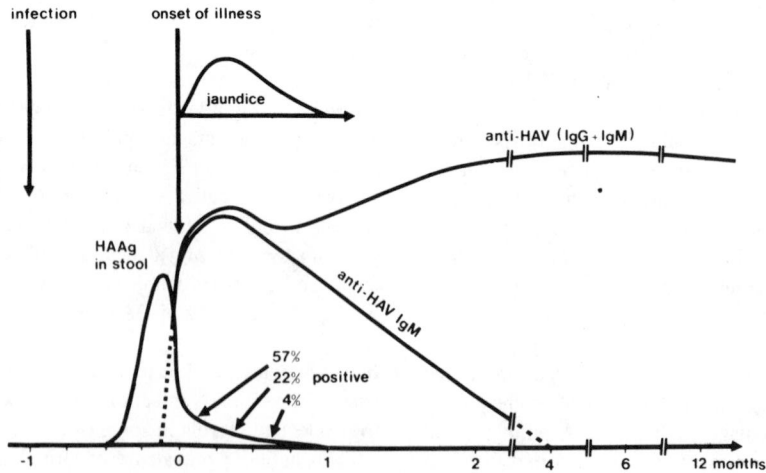

Figure 18–5. Model of the serology of clinical hepatitis A infection. The percentages of patients with HAAg in stool during the first, second, and third week after onset of illness are from an earlier study.[185] HAV = hepatitic A virus; HAAg = hepatitis A antigen.

IgA). Therefore a positive result is found in acute infection as well as in persons with past infection and immunity. Only a negative result in a diseased person will exclude hepatitis A etiology. A high titer of anti-HAV, which is usually present some days after onset of illness, is suggestive of acute infection. However, in up to 10% of the cases low titers can be found for up to 40 days after onset of illness.[63]

When using tests which do not differentiate antibody class, the only way to prove acute hepatitis A infection is the demonstration of a significant rise in titer in two consecutive sera. Because of the decrease of the anti-HAV IgM proportion, however, a fourfold increase in the total anti-HAV titer is registered in only a quarter of patients within the first month and in about two thirds within the second month.[63] According to these limitations, tests detecting total anti-HAV are used mainly to determine the immunity against hepatitis A and to investigate the prevalence of hepatitis A infection in epidemiologic studies. Large scale screening programs for immunity may be facilitated by reliable detection of anti-HAV IgG in saliva, by IgG capture radioimmunoassay.[178]

Total anti-HAV is usually detected by a competitive solid phase RIA or enzyme immunoassay in which anti-HAV of the patient serum competes with labeled anti-HAV for the binding to HAAg attached to the solid phase.[117, 133] Blocking tests having a sequential incubation with test serum and labeled antibody, or a later addition of the labeled antibody,[179, 180] may be somewhat more sensitive but also more cumbersome and may lead more often to nonspecific positive test results.

Another sensitive and economical method to demonstrate an increase in anti-HAV titer during acute illness and to determine the prevalence of anti-HAV in population groups is immune adherence hemagglutination.[165, 166, 181, 182] As this test mainly detects antibody of the IgG class, it may not become positive within the first 4 weeks after onset of illness. Another disadvantage of the test is its difficult standardization and the necessity to use purified HAAg. Another test no longer widely used because of its low sensitivity and the large amount of HAAg required is the complement-fixation assay.[183]

Immune electron microscopy has remained a basic reference technique for the detection of anti-HAV and HAAg because of its high specificity and sensitivity.[10, 184] However, it is cumbersome and requires great experience and expensive equipment.

Detection of HAAg in Stool

Demonstration of HAAg in stool enables the diagnosis of acute hepatitis A infection because the shedding of HAV occurs only during the late incubation period and in some patients also after onset of illness. In clinical cases of hepatitis A, HAAg is found by RIA in only about a half of the patients during the first week of illness, in about a quarter of the patients during the second week, and only occasionally during the third week.[185] A negative result will not exclude recent hepatitis A infection. HAV excretion in stool is the first marker of infection because it begins up to 2 weeks before seroconversion to anti-HAV, elevation of transaminases, or first symptoms of disease are recognized. Consequently, detection of HAV shedding identifies persons during the incubation period at a time when infection control measures to prevent the further spread of the infection are still effective.

In addition, HAAg determination in stool will give some indication of the infectivity of a patient and therefore of the time for which special hygienic precautions have to be maintained. There is a fair correlation between the presence of HAAg in stool and its infectivity as measured by isolation of HAV in tissue culture. During investigation of 29 stool samples from seven hepatitis A patients, infectivity could be demonstrated in all six HAAg-positive samples of two patients and in addition in six HAAg-negative samples of two further patients.[106]

The most convenient method to detect HAAg in stool is solid phase RIA[179, 186] or enzyme immunoassay.[187] These methods are at least as sensitive as immune electron microscopy.[188] In two patients with clinical hepatitis A, 27-nm particles disappeared from the stool at onset of jaundice,[189] whereas HAAg could be demonstrated for an additional five or ten days, respectively.[117]

Isolation of HAV in Tissue Culture

The successful propagation of HAV in tissue culture[12, 13] enabled the testing of specimens for infectivity. The method is more sensitive than the demonstration of HAAg, but rather time-consuming and therefore not practical for routine diagnosis. After primary inoculation of HAV in tissue culture, replication cannot be demonstrated for 4 to 6 weeks. Not only patient specimens (stool, blood, liver biopsy material) but also possibly contaminated food or waste water[190] can be investigated for the presence of the virus. Because of its high susceptibility and its easy handling, the PLC/PRF 5 hepatoma cell line is used widely in scientific studies evaluating the pathogenesis of HAV infection.

Detection of Viral RNA by Hybridization

Extracted viral RNA can be demonstrated in cell culture, serum, liver and feces by molecular hybridization with complementary DNA (cDNA) cloned HAV.[176] The method is more sensitive than immune electron microscopy or RIA for HAAg, but less sensitive than assay for HAV infectivity in tissue culture. As little at 10^3 $TCID_{50}$ of HAV, or approximately 0.1 pg of viral RNA, can be detected. In situ hybridization, with complementary single-stranded RNA, has been used for quantitative enumeration of HAV in infected cells.[192]

PREVENTION AND TREATMENT

Prophylaxis with Immune Serum Globulin

Effectiveness of normal immune serum globulin (ISG) in preventing hepatitis A infection was recognized in the 1940s and 1950s after its mass administration in summer camps, armed forces, orphanages, and institutions for the mentally retarded (for review see Maynard[193]). More recently, Krugman[194] demonstrated the neutralization of HAV (MS-1 strain) after mixing with ISG. Illness from hepatitis A is prevented effectively when ISG is given to contact persons of hepatitis A patients.[195]

However, infection is not always abolished but may only be reduced in severity to a subclinical level.[88, 194, 196] Epidemiologic studies suggest that ISG can prevent clinical disease even when given up to ten days after exposure.[197, 198] Therefore, ISG can be given not only prophylactically, but also to infected contacts of hepatitis A patients during the incubation period.

Recommendations for the application of ISG have been summarized by the Immunization Practices Advisory Committee[199] in the United States. In postexposure situations when infection spreads by personal contact, ISG should be given to all household and sexual contacts of cases. If spread of hepatitis A occurs in day care centers with diapered children, ISG should be given to staff, attendees, and to all members of households whose diapered children attend the nursery. In schools, widespread administration of ISG to children and teachers is only reasonable if epidemiologic evidence suggests a school- or classroom-centered outbreak. Also in institutions for custodial care (prisons and facilities for the mentally retarded), large-scale administration of ISG to residents and staff is only justified during an epidemic outbreak. Routine ISG administration is not recommended to hospital personnel or office and factory workers exposed during work to patients or fellow workers, respectively, with hepatitis A.

In common-source outbreaks caused by contaminated food or beverage, prophylaxis by ISG usually comes too late when the first clinical cases are registered. If a food handler is diagnosed as having hepatitis A, ISG should be given to other kitchen employees. Consumers may also receive ISG if the diseased food handler is directly involved in preparing or handling of food that is not supposed to be cooked before eating, the hygienic practices of the food handler are deficient, and the consumers can be identified and treated within 2 weeks.

Preexposure prophylaxis with ISG is recommended for persons living in low-incidence countries before traveling to highly endemic areas when they leave ordinary tourist routes. A high incidence of hepatitis has been reported for Peace Corps volunteers,[200] Catholic missionaries,[201] and persons working in community development projects or for commercial companies (for review, see Diesfeld[202]). Persons at risk for 2 to 3 months should receive a single dose of 0.02 mL/kg. For more prolonged exposure, the administration of 0.06 mL/kg should be repeated every 5 months. The former dose is also effective in postexposure prophylaxis.

Administration of ISG is only needed when the exposed person is not immune against hepatitis A. Therefore, especially when long-term exposure in endemic countries is anticipated, a single determination of anti-HAV may save considerable costs.

The decrease in prevalence of anti-HAV in developed countries raised concern whether ISG prepared from blood donors of these countries may still be protective in future. Investigation of 56 lots of ISG for intramuscular administration from six different manufacturers selling their products in the Federal Republic of Germany between 1975 and 1979 revealed high anti-HAV titers in virtually all preparations. For the lots of the various manufacturers, mean anti-HAV concentrations between 25.2 and 50.1 units/mL (according to the German national reference serum), with a standard variation betwen 16% and 32%, were measured.[65] No decline in concentration was found in 200 tested lots from six manufacturers that were released in the United States between 1967 and 1977.[11] Nevertheless, the situation may change soon. Therefore, declaration of the concentration present in each lot of ISG using available international reference preparations is needed. A minimal acceptable concentration should be defined. To reach this concentration in low–incidence countries, even the ISG preparations from selected anti–HAV–positive blood donors may become necessary.

Hepatitis A Vaccine Development

Hepatitis A has become a major public health problem in many developing countries as a result of improvement of hygienic conditions: the resulting higher mean age of infection leads to more severe illness in an increasing number of persons. Presence of only one single serotype of HAV and development of lifelong immunity after infection suggest that control of hepatitis A through routine vaccination of young children may be achievable in these countries. In areas of low endemicity, hepatitis A vaccine may be most useful for persons in high-risk settings (ie, persons who intend to travel to endemic regions or children entering institutions for the mentally retarded).

In 1978, Provost and Hilleman described the successful immunization of marmosets with a killed hepatitis A vaccine prepared from liver of a marmoset infected with the Costa Rica HAV isolate CR326[203] In 1986 the same group reported on an excellent immunogenicity in mice and marmosets of a formalin-inactivated vaccine produced from CR326-infected, continuous monkey kidney cells (LLC-MK2).[204] Three subcutaneous doses of 1 ng each induced anti-HAV in 50% of marmosets and three doses of 10 ng induced antibody in 100% of animals. All marmosets that developed detectable antibody were protected from infection after experimental challenge with virulent virus. Protection was also shown after immunization of owl monkeys with a formalin-inactivated vaccine produced from BS-C-1 cells infected with the Australian isolate HM175.[205]

Inactivation with β-propiolactone was used by Flehmig et al for preparation of a vaccine derived from diploid human embryonic kidney cells infected with the German isolate GBM.[206] After two 6-μg doses of the vaccine, a marked increase in anti-HAV titer was seen in three antibody-positive human volunteers.[207] Vaccination of 32 anti-HAV negative volunteers, with HAAg coupled to aluminium hydroxide, did produce anti-HAV titers substantially higher than after ISG administration, which can protect against clinical HAV infection.[208] However, anti-HAV titers found after natural infection were 10 to 100 times higher than after vaccination.

Several large scale evaluations of killed hepatitis A vaccine were presented to the 1990 International Symposium on Viral Hepatitis and Liver Disease, April 4 through 8, 1990 in Houston. Inactivated vaccines have been shown to be safe and immunogenic. Because an efficacy study is now under way, this type of vaccine probably will be licensed in the near future.

Development of live attenuated vaccine has been done in parallel with killed vaccine. Serial passage of CR326 (isolated from blood) and CR326F (isolated from feces) in FRhK6 cells and MRC5 cells,[209, 210] as well as passage of GBM in primary diploid human kidney cells and human fibroblasts,[211] resulted in HAV variants with attenuated virulence for marmosets and chimpanzees.

An HAV isolate from China (H2 strain), was attenuated by serial passage in newborn monkey kidney cells at 35°C and 32°C, and human lung diploid cells at 32°C.[212] Live virus vaccine was given subcutaneously to 12 volunteers without local or systemic reactions, and without liver enzyme elevation. All vaccinated subjects developed anti-HAV antibody at a mean time of 3 weeks after inoculation.

Prevention of Foodborne Hepatitis A

Food can be contaminated either before it reaches food service establishments, or the kitchen at home (i.e., shellfish harvested from polluted water), or during preparation (mostly by foodhandlers infected with HAV).

Surveillance of water beds where shellfish are harvested for evidence of fecal contamination seems to be effective in reducing transmission of HAV.[213] Keeping shellfish in depuration plants for some days before consumption probably can reduce the virus concentration in already contaminated mussels. Polyvinylpyrrolidone used in depuration plants has been shown to reduce infectivity titer of HAV.[214] Most important, the public has to be educated about the need to cook shellfish in order to make them safe for eating.

Contamination by foodhandlers can be reduced by training regarding proper hygiene and foodhandling practice.[215] Consistent maintenance of good handwashing is important because shedding of virus starts already in the incubation period, and HAV infection may even be asymptomatic. Administration of ISG to other employees after diagnosis of hepatitis A in a foodhandler can prevent further food contamination by secondary cases.

Treatment of Infection

As in other types of acute viral hepatitis, no specific treatment of HAV infection is known. Only in severe or fulminant hepatitis A may hospitalization and symptomatic treatment (infusion therapy in patients with nausea and vomiting, substitution of clotting factors, reduction of the bacterial flora of the gut) become necessary.

Management

Except in severe cases, there is no medical indication for the hospitalization of hepatitis A patients. Hospitalization and isolation does not seem to be justified for epidemiologic reasons either. The highest infectivity of patients is during the late incubation period and transmission to contact persons usually occurs in that time. After onset of illness, excretion of HAV decreases rapidly, and still-noninfected contacts can be protected efficiently by enforced hygienic measures and by the administration of ISG. Therefore hospitalization will not significantly influence the spread of the infection in the community.

Within the hospital no specific precautions seem to be necessary to avoid transmission to fellow patients and to medical personnel. In Greece no case of nosocomial hepatitis was detected among 21 susceptible patients with non-A hepatitis hospitalized in the same rooms and sharing the same toilets with hepatitis A patients.[216] The same medical personnel, not practicing specific precautions with urine and feces, took care of these patients. In Sweden a total of 1113 patients with hepatitis were cared for without isolation in a department of infectious diseases between 1948 and 1970.[217] Only five possibly hospital-acquired infections were seen, and all five occurred in 1948 to 1949, at a time when hepatitis A was epidemic in the general population.

In the United States a retrospective study involving several thousand patients hospitalized because of hepatitis (20%–25% with hepatitis A) over a period of 10 years gave no indication of hospital-acquired hepatitis A infection.[218] An increased risk for the transmission of hepatitis A within the hospital may be given by diapered children, fecally incontinent children, or children with diarrhea, especially if the diagnosis of hepatitis A is not suspected. An epidemic involving 11 of 55 staff members of a pediatric unit was traced to an 18-month-old child with fever and diarrhea.[219]

Considering all the available data, Favero et al[220] and Daschner et al[221] reached very similar conclusions:

1. Persons with hepatitis A do not have to be hospitalized but can be treated at home.

2. Isolation of adult patients within the hospital is not necessary under normal conditions when appropriate hygienic measures can be maintained. No private room or private toilet is necessary. However, washing of hands is mandatory.

3. Fecally incontinent patients, patients with diarrhea, and small children should be isolated.

4. The same precautions used for handling of feces from all other hospitalized patients are sufficient. This includes wearing of disposable gloves when handling bed pans or fecally contaminated instruments, dressings, and linen.

5. Gowns should be worn by persons with close contact to the patient or to fecal material.

6. The same daily cleaning procedures used in the rest of the hospital ward can be used for rooms housing hepatitis A patients. Cleaning personnel must be told about the potential hazard associated especially with feces of the patient and should wear gloves.

As long as the diagnosis of hepatitis A is not serologically confirmed, blood precautions, which are most important in the care of hepatitis B, hepatitis C, and human immunodeficiency virus (HIV)–infected patients, should also be maintained.

REFERENCES

1. MacCallum FO, McFarlan AM, Miles JAR, et al: Infective hepatitis. Studies in East Anglia during the period 1943–1947. Medical Research Council Special Report Series No. 273. London, His Majesty's Stationary Office, 1951.
2. Neefe JR, Gellis SS, Stokes J: Homologous serum hepatitis and infectious (epidemic) hepatitis: Studies in volunteers bearing on immunological and other characteristics of the etiological agents. *Am J Med* 1946; 1:3–22.
3. Havens WP Jr: Period of infectivity of patients with experimentally induced infectious hepatitis. *J Exp Med* 1946; 83:251–258.
4. Voegt H: Zur Aetiologie der Hepatitis epidemica. *Munch Med Wochenschr* 1942; 89:76–79.
5. Findlay GM, Willcox RR: Transmission of infective hepatitis by feces and urine. *Lancet* 1945; 1:212.
6. MacCallum FO: Early studies of viral hepatitis. *Br Med Bull* 1972; 28:105–108.
7. World Health Organization: Viral hepatitis. Report of a WHO scientific group. *WHO Tech Rep Ser* 1973; 512:1–52.
8. Krugman S, Giles JP, Hammond J: Infectious hepatitis: Evidence for two distinctive clinical, epidemiological and immunological types of infection. *JAMA* 1967; 200:365–373.
9. Deinhardt F: Hepatitis in primates. *Adv Virus Res* 1976; 20:113–157.
10. Feinstone SM, Kapikian AZ, Purcell RH: Hepatitis A: Detection by immune electron microscopy of a viruslike agent associated with acute illness. *Science* 1973; 182:1026–1028.
11. International Workshop on Hepatitis A Virus Infection: Summary of discussion and statement of opinions on selected issues at an international workshop in Athens, 17–19 November 1980. *Eur J Clin Microbiol* 1983; 2:57–73.
12. Provost PJ, Hilleman MR: Propagation of human hepatitis A virus in cell cultures in vitro. *Proc Soc Exp Biol Med* 1979; 160:213–221.
13. Frösner GG, Deinhardt F, Scheid R, et al: Propagation of human hepatitis A virus in a hepatoma cell line. *Infection* 1979; 7:303–306.

14. Siegl G, Frösner GG: Characterization and classification of virus particles associated with hepatitis A. I. Size, density and sedimentation. *J Virol* 1978; 26:40–47.

15. Siegl G, Frösner GG: Characterization and classification of virus particles associated with hepatitis A. II. Type and classification of nucleic acid. *J Virol* 1978; 26:48–53.

16. Coulepis AG, Locarnini SA, Ferris AA, et al: The polypeptides of hepatitis A virus. *Intervirology* 1978; 10:24–31.

17. Tratschin JD, Siegl G, Frösner GG, et al: Characterization and classification of virus particles associated with hepatitis A. III. Structural proteins. *J Virol* 1981; 38:151–156.

18. Siegl G: Virology of hepatitis A, in Zuckerman AJ (ed): *Viral Hepatitis and Liver Disease.* New York, Alan R Liss, 1988, pp 3–7.

19. Cohen JI, Ticehurst JR, Purcell RH, et al: Complete nucleotide sequence of wild-type hepatitis A virus: Comparison with different strains of hepatitis A virus and other picornaviruses. *J Virol* 1987; 61:50–59.

20. Gerlich WH, Frösner GG: Topology and immunoreactivity of capsid proteins in hepatitis A virus. *Med Microbiol Immunol* 1983; 172:101–106.

21. Siegl G: Replication of HAV and Protein Processing. 1990 International Symposium on Viral Hepatitis and Liver Disease, Houston, April 4–8, 1990.

22. Von der Helm K, Winnacker EL, Deinhardt F, et al: Cloning of hepatitis A virus genome. *J Virol Methods* 1981; 3:37–43.

23. Ostermayr R, von der Helm K, Seelmair S, et al: Expression of HAV VP1 antigen as recombinant protein in *Escherichia coli,* in Zuckerman AJ (ed): *Viral Hepatitis and Liver Disease.* New York, Alan R Liss, 1988, pp 59–61.

24. Ross BC, Anderson BN, Gust ID: Expression of the hepatitis A virus genome as β-galactosidase fusion protein in *Escherichia coli* in Zuckerman AJ (ed): *Viral Hepatitis and Liver Disease.* New York, Alan R Liss, 1988, pp 62–64.

25. Johnston JM, Harmon SA, Binn LN, et al: Antigenic and immunogenic properties of a hepatitis A virus capsid protein expressed in *Escherichia coli. J Infect Dis* 1988; 157:1203–1211.

26. Sobsey MD, Shields PA, Hauchman FS, et al: Survival and persistence of hepatitis A virus in environmental samples, in Zuckerman AJ (ed): *Viral Hepatitis and Liver Disease.* New York, Alan R Liss, 1988, pp 121–124.

27. Rakela J, Fay OH, Stevenson D, et al: Similarities of two hepatitis A virus strains. *Bull WHO* 1976; 54:561–564.

28. Lemon S: Immunobiology of Hepatitis A. 1990 International Symposium on Viral Hepatitis and Liver Disease, Houston, April 4–8, 1990.

29. Gauss-Müller V, Frösner GG, Deinhardt F: Propagation of hepatitis A virus in human embryo fibroblasts. *J Med Virol* 1981; 7:233–239.

30. Widell A, Hansson BG, Nordenfelt E, et al: Enhancement of hepatitis A virus propagation in tissue culture with 5,6,dichloro-1-β-D-ribofuranosylbenzimidazole (DRB), in Zuckerman AJ (ed): *Viral Hepatitis and Liver Disease.* New York, Alan R Liss, 1988, pp 16–18.

31. Frösner GG, Gauss-Müller V, Siegl G, et al: Adaption of human hepatitis A virus to growth in tissue culture and development of chronic persistent infection, in Szmuness W, Alter HJ, Maynard JE (eds): *Viral Hepatitis, 1981 International Symposium.* Philadelphia, Franklin Institute Press, 1982, pp 803–804.

32. Emerson S, McRill C, Purcell R: Effect of 5' mutations on the host range of hepatitis A virus in cell culture. 1990 International Symposium on Viral Hepatitis and Liver Disease, Houston, April 4–8, 1990.

33. Wheeler CM, Fields HA, Schable CA, et al: Adsorption, purification, and growth characteristics of hepatitis virus strain HAS-15 propagated in fetal rhesus monkey kidney cells. *J Clin Microbiol* 1986; 23:434–440.

34. Anderson DA, Locarnini SA, Ross BC, et al: Single-cycle growth kinetics of hepatitis A virus in BSC-1 cells, in Brinton WA, Rueckert RR (eds): *Positive Strand RNA Viruses.* New York, Alan R Liss, 1987, pp 497–507.

35. Garelick H, Mann GF, Harrison TJ, et al: Defective interfering particles in hepatitis A, in Zuckerman AJ (ed): *Viral Hepatitis and Liver Disease.* New York, Alan R Liss, 1988, pp 12–15.

36. Anderson DA: Cytopathology, plaque assay, and heat inactivation of hepatitis A virus strain HM175. *J Med Virol* 1987; 22:35–44.

37. Cromeans T, Sobsey MD, Fields HA: Development of a plaque assay for a cytopathic, rapidly replicating isolate of hepatitis A virus. *J Med Virol* 1987; 22:45–56.

38. Bryan JA, Gregg MB: Viral hepatitis in the United States: 1970–1973. An analysis of morbidity trends and the impact of HBsAg testing on surveillance and epidemiology. *Am J Med Sci* 1975; 270:271–282.

39. Frösner G, Englert H, Sugg U, et al: Zur Frage der Ermittlung eines Vergleichskollektivs mit "normaler" Häufigkeit von Anti-HBs. *Forschungserg Transfusionsmed Immunhaematol* 1976; 3:149–155.

40. Franzen C, Brodersen M, Frösner G, et al: Hepatitis type A, B and non A, non B in childhood. *Eur J Pediatr* 1979; 132:261–269.

41. Schenzle D, Dietz K, Frösner GG: Antibody against hepatitis A in seven European countries. II. Statistical analysis of cross-sectional surveys. *Am J Epidemiol* 1979; 110:70–76.

42. Barin F, Denis F, Chotard J, et al: Early asymptomatic hepatitis A in Senegalese children. *Lancet* 1980; 1:212–213.

43. Villarejos VM, Provost PJ, Ittensohn OL, et al: Seroepidemiologic investigations of human hepatitis caused by A, B, and a possible third agent. *Proc Soc Exp Biol Med* 1976; 152:524–528.

44. Wong DC, Rosen L, Purcell RH: Seroepidemiology of viral hepatitis in the South Pacific, in Vyas GN, Cohen SN, Schmid R (eds): *Viral Hepatitis.* Philadelphia, Franklin Institute Press, 1978, pp 733–734.

45. Szmuness W, Dienstag JL, Purcell RH, et al: The prevalence of antibody to hepatitis A antigen in various parts of the world. *Am J Epidemiol* 1977, 106:391–398.

46. Gust ID, Lehmann NI, Dimitrikakis MA: A seroepidemiologic study of infection with HAV and HBV in five Pacific islands. *Am J Epidemiol* 1979; 110:237–242.

47. Frösner GG, Papaevangelou G, Bütler R, et al: Antibodies against hepatitis A in different European countries. I. Comparison of prevalence data in different age groups. *Am J Epidemiol* 1979; 110:70–76.

48. Holland P, Golosova T, Szmuness W, et al: Viral hepatitis markers in Soviet and American blood donors. *Transfusion* 1980; 20:504–510.

49. Szmuness W, Dienstag JL, Purcell RH, et al: Distribution of antibody to hepatitis A antigen in urban adult populations. *N Engl J Med* 1976; 295:755–759.

50. Skinhøj P, Mikkelsen F, Hollinger FB: Hepatitis A in Greenland: Importance of specific antibody testing in epidemiologic surveillance. *Am J Epidemiol* 1977; 105:140–147.

51. Lange W, Masihi KN: Virushepatiden. Zur Epidemiologie der Hepatitis A in Berlin (West). *Bundesgesundheitsblatt* 1982; 25:265–272.

52. Dienstag JL: Hepatitis A virus: Identification, characterization and epidemiologic investigations, in Popper H, Schaffner F (eds): *Progress in Liver Disease,* New York, Grune & Stratton, 1979, vol 6, pp 343–370.

53. Shapiro CN, McQuillan GM, Robertson B, Hadler SC, Margolis HS: Seroepidemiology of hepatitis A infection in the United States. 1990 International Symposium on Viral Hepatitis and Liver Disease, Houston, April 4–8, 1990.

54. Frösner GG, Frösner H-R, Haas H, et al: Häufigkeit von Hepatitis A-Antikörpern in Bevölkerungsgruppen verschiedener europäischer Länder. *Schweiz Med Wochenschr* 1977; 107:129–133.

55. Mosley JW: The epidemiology of viral hepatitis: An overview. *Am J Med Sci* 1975; 270:253–270.

56. Raska H, Helcl J, Svandova E: Epidemiology of infectious hepatitis. *Am J Dis Child* 1972; 123:340–345.

57. Frösner G, Willers H, Müller R, et al: Decrease in incidence of hepatitis A infection in Germany. *Infection* 1978; 6:259–260.

58. Gust ID, Lehmann NI, Lucas CR: Relationship between preva-

lence of antibody to hepatitis A antigen and age: A cohort effect? *J Infect Dis* 1978; 138:425–426.

59. Ikematsu H, Kashiwagi S, Hayashi J, et al: A seroepidemiological study of hepatitis A virus infections: Statistical analysis of two independent cross-sectional surveys in Okinawa, Japan. *Am J Epidemiol* 1987; 126:50–54.

60. Zanetti AR, Ferroni P, Davies RE, et al: Decline in incidence of hepatitis A infection in Milan: A serologic study (abstract), in Szmuness W, Alter HJ, Maynard JE (eds): *Viral Hepatitis, 1981 International Symposium*. Philadelphia, Franklin Institute Press, 1982, p 736.

61. Shapiro CN, Shaw FE, Mandel EJ, et al: Epidemiology of hepatitis A infection in the United States. 1990 International Symposium on Viral Hepatitis and Liver Diseases, Houston, April 4–8, 1990.

62. Gregg MB: The changing epidemiology of viral hepatitis in the United States. *Am J Dis Child* 1972; 123:350–354.

63. Frösner GG, Deinhardt F, Roggendorf M, et al: Laboratory diagnosis of hepatitis A infection, in Bianchi L, Gerok W, Sickinger K, et al (eds): *Virus and the Liver*. Lancaster, England, MTP Press, 1980, pp 17–26.

64. Roggendorf M, Pantiz G, Scheid R, et al: Shift in hepatitis A epidemiology in Germany. Population distribution of hepatitis A virus antibodies of the immunoglobulin M class. *Infection* 1980; 8:262–266.

65. Frösner GG: Passive Immunisierung bei Hepatitis A, B und nicht-A, nicht-B, in Tittor W, Schwalbach G, Gehring D (eds): *Chronische Lebererkrankungen. Ursache, Entstehung, Verlauf*. Stuttgart, Georg Thieme, 1982, pp 108–113.

66. Norkrans G, Frösner G, Hermodsson S, et al: Clinical, epidemiological and prognostic aspects of hepatitis "non-A, non-B"—A comparison with hepatitis A and B. *Scand J Infect Dis* 1979; 11:259–264.

67. Caredda F, d'Arminio Monforte A, Rossi E, et al: Non-A, non-B hepatitis in Milan. *Lancet* 1981; 2:48.

68. Alter HJ, Gerety RJ, Smallwood LA, et al: Sporadic non-A, non-B hepatitis: Frequency and epidemiology in an urban US population. *J Infect Dis* 1982; 145:886–893.

69. Müller R, Willers H, Frösner GG, et al: The seroepidemiological pattern of acute viral hepatitis. An epidemiological study on viral hepatitis in the Hanover region. *Infection* 1978; 6:65–70.

70. Frösner GG, Roggendorf M, Frösner H-R, et al: Epidemiology of hepatitis A and B infection in Western European countries and in Germans traveling abroad, in Szmuness W, Alter HJ, Maynard JE (eds): *Viral Hepatitis, 1981 International Symposium*. Philadelphia, Franklin Institute Press, 1982, pp 157–168.

71. Green MS, Block C, Slater PE: Rise in the incidence of viral hepatitis in Israel despite improved socioeconomic conditions. *Rev Infect Dis* 1989; 11:464–469.

72. Maynard JE, Bradley DW, Hornbeck CL, et al: Preliminary serologic studies of antibody to hepatitis A virus in populations in the United States. *J Infect Dis* 1976; 134:528–530.

73. Dienstag JL, Szmuness W, Stevens CE, et al: Hepatitis A virus infection: New insights from seroepidemiologic studies. *J Infect Dis* 1978; 137:328–340.

74. Zanetti AR, Ferroni P: Prevalence of antibody to hepatitis A virus in healthy individuals of Milan. *Boll Ist Sieroter Milan* 1978; 57:523–527.

75. Frösner GG, Deinhardt F: Die Epidemiologie der Hepatitis A-Infektion. *Bundesgesundheitsblatt* 1978; 21:271–276.

76. Papaevangelou GJ, Gourgouli KP, Vissoulis HG: Epidemiologic characteristics of hepatitis A virus infections in Greece. *Am J Epidemiol* 1980; 112:482–486.

77. Horak W, Winter M, Renner F: Immunologische Marker der Hepatitis A und B bei Blutspendern im Raum Wien. *Z Gastroenterol* 1979; 17:28–31.

78. Larouze B, Gaudebout C, Mercier E, et al: Infection with hepatitis A and B virus in French volunteers working in tropical Africa. *Am J Epidemiol* 1987; 126:31–37.

79. Braithwaite MG, Sims MM, Bowler A: Immunity to hepatitis A in a British army battle group, in Zuckerman AJ (ed): *Viral Hepatitis and Liver Disease*. New York, Alan R Liss, 1988, pp 106–110.

80. Kryger P, Pedersen NS, Mathiesen L, et al: Increased risk of infection with hepatitis A and B virus in men with a history of syphilis: Relation to sexual contacts. *J Infec Dis* 1982; 145:23–26.

81. Corey L, Holmes KK: Sexual transmission of hepatitis A in homosexual men. *N Engl J Med* 1980; 302:435–438.

82. Norkrans G: Clinical, epidemiological and prognostic aspects of hepatitis A, B and "non-A, non-B." *Scand J Infect Dis Suppl* 1978; 17:1–44.

83. Holter E, Siebke J-C: Hepatitis A in young Norwegian drug addicts and prison inmates. *Infection* 1988; 16:91–94.

84. Centers for Disease Control: Hepatitis A among drug abusers. *MMWR* 1988; 37:297–305.

85. McFarlane ES, Embil JA: Antibody to hepatitis A virus in young inmates. *J Infect Dis* 1982; 146:442.

86. Szmuness W, Purcell RH, Dienstag JL, et al: Antibody to hepatitis A antigen in institutionalized mentally retarded patients. *JAMA* 1977; 237:1702–1705.

87. Ward R, Krugman S, Giles JP, et al: Infectious hepatitis. Studies of its natural history and prevention. *N Engl J Med* 1958; 258:407–416.

88. Matthew EB, Dietzman DE, Madden DL, et al: A major epidemic of infectious hepatitis in an institution for the mentally retarded. *Am J Epidemiol* 1973; 98:199–215.

89. Storch G, McFarland LM, Kelso K, et al: Viral hepatitis associated with day-care centers. *JAMA* 1979; 242:1514–1518.

90. Hadler SC, Erben JJ, Francis DP, et al: Risk factors for hepatitis A in day-care centers. *J Infect Dis* 1982; 145:255–261.

91. Szmuness W, Dienstag JL, Purcell RH, et al: Hepatitis type A and hemodialysis. *Ann Intern Med* 1977; 87:8–12.

92. Holmes AW, Wolfe L, Rosenblate H, et al: Hepatitis in marmosets: Induction of disease with coded specimens from a human volunteer study. *Science* 1969; 165:816–817.

93. Dienstag JL, Feinstone SM, Purcell RH, et al: Experimental infection of chimpanzees with hepatitis A virus. *J Infect Dis* 1975; 132:532–545.

94. Eichberg J, Kalter SS: Hepatitis A and B: Serologic survey of human and nonhuman primate sera. *Lab Anim Sci* 1980; 30:541–543.

95. Smith MS, Swanepoel PJ, Bootsma M: Hepatitis A in nonhuman primates in nature. *Lancet* 1980; 2:1241–1242.

96. Burke D, Heisey GB: Wild malaysian cynomolgus monkeys are exposed to heptitis A virus. *Am J Trop Med Hyg* 1984; 33:940–944.

97. LeDuc WJ, Escajadillo A, Lemon SM: Hepatitis A virus among captive Panamanian owl monkeys. *Lancet* 1981; 2:1427–1428.

98. Burke DS, Graham RR, Heisey GB: Hepatitis A virus in primates outside captivity. *Lancet* 1981; 2:928.

99. Mao JS, Go YY, Huang HY, et al: Susceptibility of monkeys to human hepatitis A virus. *J Infect Dis* 1981; 144:55–60.

100. Hillis WD: An outbreak of infectious hepatitis among chimpanzee handlers at a United States air force base. *Am J Hyg* 1961; 73:316–328.

101. Dienstag JL, Feinstone SM, Kapikian AZ, et al: Fecal shedding of hepatitis-A antigen. *Lancet* 1975; 1:765.

102. Dienstag JL: Immune electron microscopy and hepatitis A. *Lancet* 1975; 1:102.

103. Hopkins R, Scott TG: Hepatitis-A antigen in Edinburgh. *Lancet* 1976; 2:206.

104. Maynard JE: Infectious hepatitis at Fort Yukon, Alaska—Report of an outbreak 1960–1961. *Am J Public Health* 1963; 53:31–39.

105. Skinhøj P, McNair A, Andersen ST: Hepatitis and hepatitis B-antigen in Greenland. *Am J Epidemiol* 1974; 99:50–57.

106. Frösner GG: Züchtung des Hepatitis-A-Virus in Gewebekultur: Möglichkeit zur Virusproduktion für Impfstoffe und Testzwecke, zur Untersuchung von Patienten auf Infektiosität und zur Prüfung von Desifektionsmitteln. *Öff Gesundheitswes* 1982; 44:370–373.

107. Weisfuse IB, Graham DJ, Will M, et al: An outbreak of hepatitis A among cancer patients treated with interleukin-2 and lymphokine-activated killer cells. *J Infect Dis* 1990; 161:647–652.

108. Barbara JA, Howell DR, Briggs M: Post-transfusion hepatitis A. *Lancet* 1982; 1:738.

109. Krugman S, Ward R, Giles JP, et al: Infectious hepatitis: Detection of virus during the incubation period and in clinically inapparent infection. *N Engl J Med* 1959; 261:729–734.

110. Giles JP, Liebhaber H, Krugman S, et al: Early viremia and viruria in infectious hepatitis. *Virology* 1964; 24:107–113.

111. Cohen JI, Feinstone S, Purcell RH: Hepatitis A virus infection in a chimpanzee: Duration of viremia and detection of virus in saliva and throat swabs. *J Infect Dis* 1989; 160:887–890.

112. Asher L, Binn LN, Mensing T, et al: Pathogenesis of HAV in owl monkeys following oral inoculation. 1990 International Symposium on Viral Hepatitis and Liver Disease, Houston, April 4–8, 1990.

113. Capps RB, Bennett AM, Stokes J Jr: Epidemic infectious hepatitis in an infants' orphanage. I. Epidemiologic studies in student nurses. *Arch Intern Med* 1952; 89:6–23.

114. Clark W, Sacks D, Williams, H: Outbreak of infectious hepatitis on college campus. *Am J Trop Med Hyg* 1958; 7:268–279.

115. Bothwell PW, Martin D, Macara AW, et al: Infectious hepatitis in Bristol (1959–1962). *Br Med J* 1963; 2:1613–1617.

116. Williams SV, Huff JC, Bryan JA: Hepatitis A and facilities for preschool children. *J Infect Dis* 1975; 131:491–495.

117. Frösner GG, Overby LR, Flehmig B, et al: Seroepidemiological investigation of patients and family contacts in an epidemic of hepatitis A. *J Med Virol* 1977; 1:163–173.

118. Hadler SL: Global impact of HAV: Changing patterns. 1990 International Symposium on Viral Hepatitis and Liver Disease, Houston, April 4–8, 1990.

119. Peczenik A, Duttweiler DW, Moser RH: An apparently waterborne outbreak of infectious hepatitis. *Am J Public Health* 1956; 46:1008–1017.

120. Morse LJ, Bryan JA, Hurley JP, et al: The Holy Cross College football team hepatitis outbreak. *JAMA* 1972; 219:706–708.

121. Murphey WJ, Petrie LM, Work SD Jr: Outbreak of infectious hepatitis apparently milkborne. *Am J Public Health* 1946; 36:169–173.

122. Philip JR, Hamilton TP II, Albert TJ, et al: Infectious hepatitis outbreak with Mai Tai as the vehicle of transmission. *Am J Epidemiol* 1973; 97:50–59.

123. Hooper RR, Jules CW, Routenberg JA, et al: An outbreak of type A viral hepatitis at the naval training center, San Diego: Epidemiologic evaluation. *Am J Epidemiol* 1977; 105:148–155.

124. Chaudhuri AKR, Cassie G, Silver M: Outbreak of food-borne type A hepatitis in greater Glasgow. *Lancet* 1975; 2:223.

125. Schoenbaum SC, Baker O, Jezek Z: Common-source epidemic of hepatitis due to glazed and ice pastries. *Am J Epidemiol* 1976; 104:74–80.

126. Zachoval R, Frösner G, Deinhardt F, John I: Hepatitis A transmission by cold meats. *Lancet* 1981; 2:260.

127. Centers for Disease Control: Foodborne disease outbreaks, 5-year summary, 1983–1987. In CDC surveillance summaries, March 1990. *MMWR* 1990; 39(No.SS-1):15–57.

128. Dougherty W, Altman R: Viral hepatitis in New Jersey 1960–1961. *Am J Med* 1962; 32:704–716.

129. Stille W, Kunkel B, Nerger K: Austern-Hepatitis. *Dtsch Med Wochenschr* 1972; 97:145–147.

130. Dienstag JL, Gust ID, Lucas CR, et al: Mussel-associated viral hepatitis, type A: Serological confirmation. *Lancet* 1976b; 1:561.

131. Yao GB: Clinical spectrum and natural history of hepatitis A in an epidemic in Shanghai 1988. 1990 International Symposium on Viral Hepatitis and Liver Disease, Houston, April 4–8, 1990.

132. Enriquez R, Frösner GG, Hochstein-Mintzel V, et al: Concentration of hepatitis A virus in mussels from surrounding water, in *Abstracts IXth International Congress of Infectious and Parasitic Diseases, Munich, July 20–26, 1986.* Munich, Futuramed Verlag, 1986, p 195.

133. Decker RH, Overby LR, Ling C-M, et al: Serological studies of transmission of hepatitis A in humans. *J Infect Dis* 1979; 139:74–82.

134. Mathiesen LR, Feinstone SM, Purcell RH, et al: Detection of hepatitis A antigen by immunofluorescence. *Infect Immun* 1977; 18:524–530.

135. Schulman AN, Dienstag JL, Jackson DR, et al: Hepatitis A antigen particles in liver, bile and stool of chimpanzees. *J Infect Dis* 1976; 134:80–84.

136. Bradley DW, Hollinger FB, Hornbeck CL, et al: Isolation and characterization of hepatitis A virus. *Am J Clin Pathol* 1976; 65:876–889.

137. Mathiesen LR, Drucker J, Lorenz D, et al: Localization of hepatitis A antigen in marmosets during acute infection with hepatitis A virus. *J Infect Dis* 1978; 138:369–377.

138. Tabor E, Jones R, Gerety RJ, et al: Asymptomatic viral hepatitis types A and B in an adolescent population. *Pediatrics* 1979; 62:1026–1030.

139. Yang N-Y, Yu P-H, Mao Z-X, et al: Inapparent infection of hepatitis A virus. *Am J Epidemiol* 1988; 127:599–604.

140. Krugman S, Gocke DJ: Viral hepatitis in *Major Problems in International Medicine.* Philadelphia, Saunders, 1978, vol 15, p 38.

141. Mathiesen LR: The hepatitis A virus infection. *Liver* 1981; 1:81–109.

142. Norkrans G, Nilsson LA, Frösner G, et al: Serum immunoglobulin levels in hepatitis non-A, non-B: A comparison with hepatitis A and B. *Infection* 1980; 8:98–100.

143. Mathiesen LR, Skinhøj P, Hardt F, et al: Epidemiology and clinical characteristics of acute hepatitis type A, B, and non-A, non-B. *Scand J Gastroenterol* 1979; 14:849–856.

144. Krugman S, Ward R, Giles JP: The natural history of infectious hepatitis. *Am J Med* 1962; 32:717–728.

145. Routenberg JA, Dienstag JL, Harrison WO, et al: A food borne epidemic of hepatits-A virus (HAV) infection among navy recruits, abstract. *Gastroenterology* 1975; 69:859.

146. Caredda F, Antinori S, Re T, et al: Acute biphasic hepatitis A: Are different viruses involved? *Infection* 1986; 14:195–196.

147. Wacker WEC, Riordan JF, Snodgrass PJ, et al: The Holy Cross hepatitis outbreak: Clinical and biochemical abnormalities. *Arch Intern Med* 1972; 130:357–360.

148. Routenberg JA, Dienstag JL, Harrison WO, et al: Foodborne outbreak of hepatitis A: Clinical and laboratory features of acute and protracted illness. *Am J Med Sci* 1979; 278:123–137.

149. Thomssen R, Gerlich W, Böttcher U: Virusserologische Diagnostik der Hepatitis B, in Spiess H (ed): *Virusdiagnostik für Klinik und Praxis.* Marburg, Deutsches Grünes Kreuz, 1980, pp 117–150.

150. Gust ID, Lehmann NI, Lucas CR, et al: Studies on the epidemiology of hepatitis A in Melbourne, in Vyas GN, Cohen SN, Schmid R (eds): *Viral Hepatitis.* Philadelphia, Franklin Institute Press, 1978, pp 105–112.

151. Rakela J, Redeker AG, Edwards VM, et al: Hepatitis A virus infection in fulminant hepatitis and chronic active hepatitis. *Gastroenterology* 1978; 74:879–882.

152. Lindberg J, Frösner G, Hansson BG, et al: Serologic markers of hepatitis A and B in chronic active hepatitis. *Scand J Gastroenterol* 1978; 13:525–527.

153. Acute Hepatic Failure Study Group: Etiology of acute hepatic failure, abstract. *Gastroenterology* 1977; 73:1236.

154. Dienstag JL, Alaama A, Mosley JW, et al: Etiology of sporadic hepatitis B surface antigen—Negative hepatitis. *Ann Intern Med* 1977; 87:1–6.

155. Mathiesen LR, Skinhøj P, Nielsen JO, et al: Hepatitis type A, B, and non-A, non-B in fulminant hepatitis. *Gut* 1980; 21:72–77.

156. Smedile A, Farci P, Verme G, et al: Influence of delta infection on severity of hepatitis B. *Lancet* 1982; 2:945–947.

157. Marmion BP, Burell CJ, Tonkin RW, et al: Dialysis-associated hepatitis in Edinburgh, 1969–1978. *Rev Infect Dis* 1982; 4:619–637.

158. Drucker J, Tabor E, Gerety RJ, et al: Simultaneous acute infections with hepatitis A and hepatitis B viruses in a chimpanzee. *J Infect Dis* 1979; 139:338–342.

159. Hindman SH, Maynard JE, Bradley DW, et al: Simultaneous infection with type A and B hepatitis viruses. *Am J Epidemiol* 1977; 105:135–139.

160. Haemmerli UP: Jaundice during pregnancy. *Acta Med Scand* 1966; (suppl 444):23–30.

161. Stakhanova VM, Vyazov SO, Doroshenko NV, et al: Are there antigenic variants of hepatitis A virus? *Lancet* 1979; 2:631–632.

162. Zachoval R, Kroener M, Brommer M, et al: Serology and Interferon Production during the early phase of acute hepatitis A. *J Infect Dis* 1990; 161:353–354.

163. Frösner GG, Scheid R, Wolf H, et al: Immunoglobulin M anti-hepatitis A virus determination by reorienting gradient centrifugation for diagnosis of acute hepatitis A. *J Clin Microbiol* 1979; 9:476–478.

164. Roggendorf M, Frösner GG, Deinhardt F, et al: Comparison of solid phase test systems for demonstrating antibodies against hepatitis A virus (anti-HAV) of the IgM-class. *J Med Virol* 1980; 5:47–62.

165. Rakela J, Stevenson D, Edwards VM, et al: Antibodies to hepatitis A virus: Patterns by two procedures. *J Clin Microbiol* 1977; 5:110–111.

166. Krugman S, Friedman H, Lattimer C: Viral hepatitis, type A. Identification by specific complement fixation and immune adherence tests. *N Engl J Med* 1975; 292:1141–1143.

167. Locarnini SA, Coulepis AG, Kaldor J, et al: Coproantibodies in hepatitis A: Detection by enzyme-linked immunosorbent assay and immune electron microscopy. *J Clin Microbiol* 1980; 11:710–716.

168. Villarejos VM, Hu R, Visona KA: Persistence and reinfection with hepatitis A virus, in Zuckerman AJ (ed): *Viral Hepatitis and Liver Disease.* New York, Alan R Liss, 1988, pp 111–112.

169. Vallbracht A, Gabriel P, Maier K, et al: Cell-mediated cytotoxicity in hepatitis A virus infection. *Hepatology* 1986; 6:1308–1314.

170. Vallbracht A, Maier K, Stierhof Y-D, et al: Liver-derived Cytotoxic T cells in hepatitis A virus infection. *J Infect Dis* 1989; 160:209–217.

171. Duermeyer W, Wielaard F, van der Veen J: A new principle for the detection of specific IgM antibodies applied in an ELISA for hepatitis A. *J Med Virol* 1979; 4:25–32.

172. Møller AM, Mathiesen LR: Detection of immunoglobulin M antibodies to hepatitis A virus by enzyme-linked immunosorbent assay. *J Clin Microbiol* 1979; 10:628–632.

173. Flehmig B, Ranke M, Berthold H, et al: A solid-phase radioimmunoassay for detection of IgM antibodies to hepatitis A virus. *J Infect Dis* 1979; 140:169–175.

174. Bradley DW, Fields HA, McCaustland K, et al: Serodiagnosis of viral hepatitis A by a modified competitive binding radioimmunoassay for immunoglobulin M anti-hepatitis A virus. *J Clin Microbiol* 1979; 9:120–127.

175. Girardet C, Peitrequin R, Frei PC: Radioimmunoassay diagnosis of hepatitis A. *Lancet* 1979; 1:876–877.

176. Bradley DW, Maynard JE, Hindman SH, et al: Serodiagnosis of viral hepatitis A: Detection of acute-phase immunoglobulin M anti-hepatitis A virus by radioimmunoassay. *J Clin Microbiol* 1977; 5:521–530.

177. Locarnini SA, Coulepis AG, Stratton AM, et al: Solid-phase enzyme-linked immunosorbent assay for detection of hepatitis A-specific immunoglobulin M. *J Clin Microbiol* 1979; 9:459–465.

178. Parry JV, Farrington CP, Perry KR, et al: Rational programme for screening travellers for antibodies to hepatitis A virus. *Lancet* 1988; (1):1447–1449.

179. Purcell RH, Wong DC, Moritsugu Y, et al: A microtiter solid-phase radioimmunoassay for hepatitis A antigen and antibody. *J Immunol* 1976; 116:349–356.

180. Mathiesen LR, Feinstone SM, Wong DC, et al: Enzyme-linked immunosorbent assay for detection of hepatitis A antigen in stool and antibody to hepatitis A antigen in sera: Comparison with solid phase radioimmunoassay, immune electron microscopy, and immune adherence hemagglutination assay. *J Clin Microbiol* 1978; 7:184–193.

181. Miller WJ, Provost PJ, McAleer WJ, et al: Specific immune adherence assay for human hepatitis A antibody. Application to diagnostic and epidemiologic investigations. *Proc Soc Exp Biol Med* 1975; 149:254–261.

182. Gust DG, Dienstag JL, Purcell RH, et al: Non-B hepatitis in Melbourne: A serological study of hepatitis A virus infection. *Br Med J* 1977; 1:193–195.

183. Provost PJ, Ittensohn OL, Villarejos VM, et al: A specific complement-fixation test for human hepatitis A employing CR 326 virus antigen. Diagnosis and epidemiology. *Proc Soc Exp Biol Med* 1975; 148:962–969.

184. Dienstag JL, Alling DW, Purcell RH: Quantitation of antibody to hepatitis A antigen by immune electron microscopy. *Infect Immun* 1976; 13:1209–1213.

185. Frösner GG: Nachweis von Hepatitis-A-Antigen und -Antikörpern zur Diagnose der Hepatitis-A-Infektion. *Munch Med Wochenschr* 1977; 119:825–829.

186. Hollinger FB, Bradley DW, Maynard JE, et al: Detection of hepatitis A viral antigen by radioimmunoassay. *J Immunol* 1975; 115:1464–1466.

187. Locarnini SA, Garland SM, Lehmann NI, et al: Solid-phase enzyme-linked immunosorbent assay for detection of hepatitis A virus. *J Clin Microbiol* 1978; 8:277–282.

188. Hall WT, Bradley DW, Madden DL, et al: Comparison of sensitivy of radioimmunoassay and immune electron microscopy for detecting hepatitis A antigen in fecal extracts. *Proc Soc Exp Biol Med* 1977; 155:193–198.

189. Flehmig B, Frank H, Frösner GG, et al: Hepatitis A-virus particles in stool of patients from a natural outbreak in Germany. *Med Microbiol Immunol* 1977; 163:209–214.

190. Pana A, Diviza, M, de Filippis P, et al: Isolation of hepatitis A virus from polluted river water on FRP/3 cells. *Lancet* 1987; 2:1338.

191. Ticehurst JR, Feinstone SM, Chestnut T, et al: Detection of hepatitis A virus by extraction of viral RNA and molecular hybridization. *J Clin Microbiol* 1987; 25:1822–1829.

192. Jiang X, Estes MK, Metcalf TG: In situ hybridization for quantitative assay of infectious hepatitis A virus. *J Clin Microbiol* 1989; 27:874–879.

193. Maynard JE: Passive and active immunization in the control of viral hepatitis, in Szmuness W, Alter HJ, Maynard JE (eds): *Viral Hepatitis, 1981 International Symposium.* Philadelphia, Franklin Institute Press, 1982, pp 379–384.

194. Krugman S: Effect of human immune serum globulin on infectivity of hepatitis A virus. *J Infect Dis* 1976; 134:70–74.

195. Hall WT, Madden DL, Mundon FK, et al: Protective effect of immune serum globulin (ISG) against hepatitis A infection in a natural epidemic. *Am J Epidemiol* 1977; 106:72–75.

196. Krugman S, Ward R, Giles JP, et al: Infectious hepatitis: Studies on the effect of gamma globulin and on the incidence of inapparent infection. *JAMA* 1960; 174:823–830.

197. Ward R, Krugman S: Etiology, epidemiology and prevention of viral hepatitis. *Prog Med Virol* 1962; 4:87–118.

198. Mosley JW, Reisler DM, Brachott D, et al: Comparison of two lots immune serum globulin for prophylaxis of infectious hepatitis. *Am J Epidemiol* 1968; 87:539–550.

199. Immunization Practices Advisory Committee: Immune globulins for protection against viral hepatitis. *MMWR* 1981; 30:423–435.

200. Woodson RD, Clinton JJ: Hepatitis prophylaxis abroad. Effectiveness of immune serum globulin in protecting peace corps volunteers. *JAMA* 1969; 209:1053–1058.

201. Woodson RD, Cahill KH: Viral hepatitis abroad. Incidence in Catholic missionaries. *JAMA* 1972; 219:1191–1193.

202. Diesfeld HJ: Hepatitisinfektionen beim Aufenthalt in tropischen und subtropischen Entwicklungsländern und ihre Beurteilung durch die Unfallversicherungsträger. *Med Klin* 1974; 69:1634–1638.

203. Provost PJ, Hilleman MR: An inactivated hepatitis A virus vaccine prepared from infected marmoset liver. *Proc Soc Exp Biol Med* 1978; 159:201–203.

204. Provost PJ, Hughes JV, Miller WJ, et al: An inactivated hepatitis A viral vaccine of cell culture origin. *J Med Virol* 1986; 19:23–31.

205. Binn LN, Bancroft WH, Lemon SM, et al: Preparation of a prototype inactivated hepatitis A virus vaccine from infected cell cultures. *J Infect Dis* 1986; 153:749–756.

206. Flehmig B, Haage A, Pfister M: Immunogenicity of a hepatitis A virus vaccine. *J Med Virol* 1987; 22:7–16.

207. Flehmig B, Haage A, Heinricy U, et al: Studies with an inactivated hepatitis A vaccine, in Zuckerman AJ (ed): *Viral Hepatitis and Liver Disease.* New York, Alan R Liss, 1988, pp 100–105.

208. Flehmig B, Heinricy U, Pfister M: Immunogenicity of a killed hepatitis A vaccine in seronegative volunteers. *Lancet* 1989; (1): 1039–1041.

209. Provost PJ, Bishop RP, Gerety RJ, et al: New findings in live, attenuated hepatitis A vaccine development. *J Med Virol* 1986; 20:165–175.

210. Provost PJ, Emini EA, Lewis JA, et al: Progress toward the development of a hepatitis A vaccine, in Zuckerman AJ (ed): *Viral Hepatitis and Liver Disease.* New York, Alan R Liss, 1988, pp 83–86.

211. Flehmig B, Mauler RF, Noll G, et al: Progress in the development of an attenuated, live hepatitis A vaccine, in Zuckerman AJ (ed): *Viral Hepatitis and Liver Disease.* New York, Alan R Liss, 1988, pp 87–90.

212. Mao JS, Dong DX, Zhang HY, et al: Primary study of attenuated live hepatitis A vaccine (H2 strain) in Humans. *J Infect Dis* 1989; 159:621–624.

213. Mele A, Rastelli MG, Gill ON, et al: Recurrent epidemic hepatitis A associated with consumption of raw shellfish, probably controlled through public health measures. *Am J Epidemiol* 1989; 130:540–546.

214. Franco E, Divizia M, Leoni V, et al: Virucidal effect of commercially available disinfectants against hepatitis A virus. 1990 International Symposium on Viral Hepatitis and Liver Disease, Houston, April 4–8, 1990.

215. Centers for Disease Control: Foodborne hepatitis A — Alaska, Florida, North Carolina, Washington. *MMWR* 1990; 39:228–232.

216. Papaevangelou GJ, Roumeliotou-Karayannis AJ, Contoyannis PC: The risk of nosocomial hepatitis A and B virus infections from patients under care without isolation precaution. *J Med Virol* 1981; 7:143–148.

217. Belfrage S, Cederberg A: Need hepatitis patients be isolated? *Lancet* 1980; 1:704–705.

218. Mosley JW: Epidemiology of HAV infection, in Vyas GN, Cohen SN, Schmid R (eds): *Viral Hepatitis: A Contemporary Assessment of Epidemiology, Pathogenesis and Prevention.* Philadelphia, Franklin Institute Press, 1978, pp 85–104.

219. Centers for Disease Control: Outbreak of viral hepatitis in the staff of a pediatric ward—California. *MMWR* 1977; 26:77–78.

220. Favero MS, Maynard JE, Leger RT, et al: Guidelines for the care of patients hospitalized with viral hepatitis. *Ann Intern Med* 1979; 91:872–876.

221. Daschner F, Deinhardt F, Frösner G, et al: Hygienische Massnahmen zur Verhütung und Bekämpfung von Hepatitis A, Hepatitis B und der Nicht-A, Nicht-B Hepatitis auf Allgemein-, Infektions- und Dialysestationen. *Internist* 1981; 22:590–594.

222. Provost PJ, Wolanski BS, Miller WJ, et al: Biophysical and biochemical properties of CR 326 human hepatitis A virus. *Am J Med Sci* 1975; 270:87–91.

223. Scheid R, Deinhardt F, Frösner G, et al: Inactivation of hepatitis A and B viruses and risk of iatrogenic transmission, in Szmuness W, Alter HJ, Maynard JE (eds): *Viral Hepatitis, 1981 International Symposium.* Philadelphia, Franklin Institute Press, 1982, pp 627–628.

224. McCaustland KA, Bond WW, Bradley DW, et al: Survival of hepatitis A virus in feces after drying and storage for 1 month. *J Clin Microbiol* 1982; 16:957–958.

225. Peterson DA, Wolfe LG, Larkin EP, et al: Thermal treatment and infectivity of hepatitis A virus in human feces. *J Med Virol* 1978; 2:201–206.

226. Krugman S, Giles JP, Hammond J: Hepatitis virus: Effect of heat on the infectivity and antigenicity of the MS-1 and MS-2 strains. *J Infect Dis* 1970; 122:432–436.

227. Peterson DA, Hurley TR, Hoff JC, et al: Hepatitis A virus: Infectivity and chlorine treatment, in Szmuness W, Alter HJ, Maynard JE (eds): *Viral Hepatitis, 1981 International Symposium.* Philadelphia, Franklin Institute Press, 1982, pp 624–625.

228. Billing A, Flehmig B, Gerth H-J: Influence of formaldehyde on HAV-antigenicity and infectivity (abstract). *Zentralbl Bakteriol Mikrobiol Hyg (A)* 1982; 253:5.

229. Frösner G, Stephen W, Dichtelmüller H: Inactivation of hepatitis A virus added to pooled human plasma by β-propiolactone treatment and UV-irradiation. *Eur J Clin Microbiol* 1983; 2:355–356.

Rabies Virus

Patrick A. Robinson

Rabies has long held a special terror for man. The fearful symptoms experienced by both animals and humans who are stricken with the disease can only partially explain the awe in which rabies is held. Perhaps as important is its effect on the special relationship which exists between man and animals. Man's usual supremacy over animal and a pet's devotion to its master are transformed by rabies, and a loyal dog or a shy fox becomes aggressive, charging into the midst of man's previously serene and protected environment, inflicting disease-laden bites upon those he can reach. Thus, one can understand why rabies is considered one of the great horrors of the world.

Human rabies deaths still occur in small numbers in developed countries and in somewhat greater numbers in developing and underdeveloped nations. However, widespread public health con-cern regarding rabies is not without reason. It is an eminently preventable disease through vaccination and animal control. Potential exposures occur frequently, and each time many people are concerned with the need for rabies prevention. An estimated 600,000 to 2 million dog bites occur yearly in the United States,[1, 2] and the number of nondog exposures is unknown. Approximately 20,000 to 30,000 people receive treatment for rabies prevention following potential exposures each year in the United States.[1] Thus, rabies is not a disease of the past; it is very much part of modern medicine.

HISTORY

One of the earliest references to rabies is cited in the pre-Mosaic Eshnunni Code of Mesopotamia (before 2200 BC) which establishes a fine of 40 shekels to the owner of a mad dog that bites a man and causes his death,[3] perhaps a small price considering the consequences. Democritus provided a detailed description of animal rabies in about 400 BC and Aulus Cornaelius Celsus first contradicted Aristotle's assertion that humans were exempt from rabies. Writing in AD 100, Celsus was the first to recommend an efficacious treatment for rabies: excision and cauterization of the bite inflicted by a rabid animal.[3, 4] A lucid description of human disease was conveyed by Girolamo Fracastoro, a sixteenth-century Italian physician (Table 19–1).

Human cases and epidemics of animal rabies were recognized throughout Europe and in the Americas in the 1700s and 1800s. Animal control measures were used successfully to eliminate the disease from Scandinavia by 1826 and subsequently from Great Britain by 1903.[3] However, cases continued to occur frequently in Eastern and Western Hemispheres through the 1800s.[5, 6] The agent and definitive modes of prevention of rabies in exposed persons remained unknown into the late 1800s.

Although rabies had been recognized for centuries to be an illness transmitted by the bite of a rabid animal, and certain measures might diminish the likelihood of transmission, the tremendous strides in understanding the rabies pathogenesis and in developing measures which could provide the nearest certainty of

Table 19–1
Landmarks in the History of Rabies

Date	Event
BC	
2200	Eshnunna law establishes fine to owner of "mad dog"
400	Democritus' description of animal rabies
200	Aristotle's description of animal rabies; denies human susceptibility
AD	
100	Celsus recognizes human susceptibility; prescribes cautery of bites
1546	Fracastoro provides detailed description of human disease
1804	Zinke experimentally transmits disease with saliva
1826	Scandinavia made rabies-free by animal control measures
1882	Pasteur first transmits rabies experimentally by intracerebral inoculation
July 6, 1885	Joseph Meister is first human to receive (Pasteur) rabies vaccine
1903	Negri describes pathology; Negri bodies
1912	Babes publishes *Traité de la Rage*
1935	Mouse brain inoculation test for diagnosis
Early 1900s	Semple-type vaccine in use
1948	Duck embryo vaccine experimentally produced by Koprowski and Cox
1954	Efficacy of serum plus vaccine established
1973	Human diploid cell rabies vaccine (HDCV) experimentally introduced
1980	HDCV available for general use—United States

preventing disease were made by one of the greatest microbiologists to have lived—Louis Pasteur.[7, 8] Pasteur's interest in rabies may have stemmed from a childhood experience in Arbois. He may never have forgotten the terror a rabid wolf produced when it attacked several persons in his neighborhood. He witnessed the hot-iron cautery of one of the victims and was aware of the horrible death from hydrophobia of others. Pasteur's interest in dramatic problems may also have played a role in choosing to study rabies. He began his work in late 1880, but it was early in 1882 that he first experimentally transmitted rabies by inoculating spinal material of a rabid dog onto the brain of another. Two years later, Pasteur announced to the Academy of Sciences that he was able to stabilize a submicroscopic infectious agent by serial passages of the virus through brain, increasing its virulence for laboratory animals and shortening the incubation period. It was to this preparation that he first applied the term "fixed virus." Virus survival experiments by Roux suggested to Pasteur a technique of virus attenuation. Rabbits were injected with fixed virus, and after their death the spinal cord was removed and suspended in dry, sterile air. He inoculated this preparation into dogs and discovered that he could establish immunity by using progressively less attenuated preparations. He surmised that dogs bitten by rabid animals could be protected by vaccination, because of the long incubation period. Dog experiments bore this out, but Pasteur experienced grave hesitancy in applying these findings to humans.

Then on July 6, 1885, Joseph Meister, a 9-year-old boy, was brought to Pasteur by his mother. He had been bitten numerous times by a rabid dog, and the boy's physician assured Pasteur that the nature of the bites made rabies the likely outcome. The boy was injected 12 times with rabid spinal cord vaccine and suffered no ill effects. A second boy, a shepherd who saved some children from the attack of a rabid dog and was severely bitten, was treated in a similar manner and survived. The two dramatic successes brought many patients to the Pasteur Institute for treatment, but controversy soon followed. Claims that the vaccine induced rabies in some patients and that the vaccine was not effective continued for years. However, mounting experience at the institute underlined the success of Pasteur's vaccine. By October 1886, of 726 persons treated by inoculation, only ten had succumbed to the disease, and a mortality rate of only 0.29% had been recorded in 51,107 patients by 1935. These data may be overly optimistic, but the efficacy of vaccination to prevent rabies was well established.

Another major landmark in the history of rabies was the publication of *Traité de la rage* by Babes in 1912.[9] This was a compendium of the state of knowledge of rabies at the time and even today represents a complete collection of clinical information on rabies. The year 1903 brought the publication of Negri's pathologic descriptions of rabies, including the cytoplasmic inclusion bodies which now bear his name.[10] Investigations of Murphy and many others in the 1950s to 1970s added tremendously to our knowledge of the pathogenesis of rabies.

Vaccines were derived from the Pasteur vaccine during the 1900s: the Semple vaccine in the early 1900s, the mouse brain vaccine, and the duck embryo-derived vaccine in 1948.[11] The addition of passive immunization with rabies immune serum as a necessary adjuvant in the prevention of rabies was scientifically evaluated in 1954.[12] This set the stage for the combined use of rabies vaccine and rabies immune globulin as standard practice in postexposure prophylaxis. Finally, the combined efforts of a number of investigators resulted in a human rabies vaccine derived from fixed virus grown in human cell culture.[11] This vaccine superseded other vaccines because of its efficacy and its extremely low complication rate.

VIROLOGY

Rabiesvirus is a member of the **Rhabdoviridae** family (Greek *rhabdos,* rod), which includes pathogens for a wide variety of mammals, fish, birds, and plants.[13] The morphology of rabiesvirus and other **Rhabdoviridae** resembles myxovirus morphology to the extent that some investigators have argued for classifying them with the myxoviruses. *Lyssavirus* (Greek *lyssa,* rage) is the formal name for the rabiesvirus genus of the **Rhabdoviridae**. Rabiesvirus has a morphology similar to the other family members.[14–19] It is

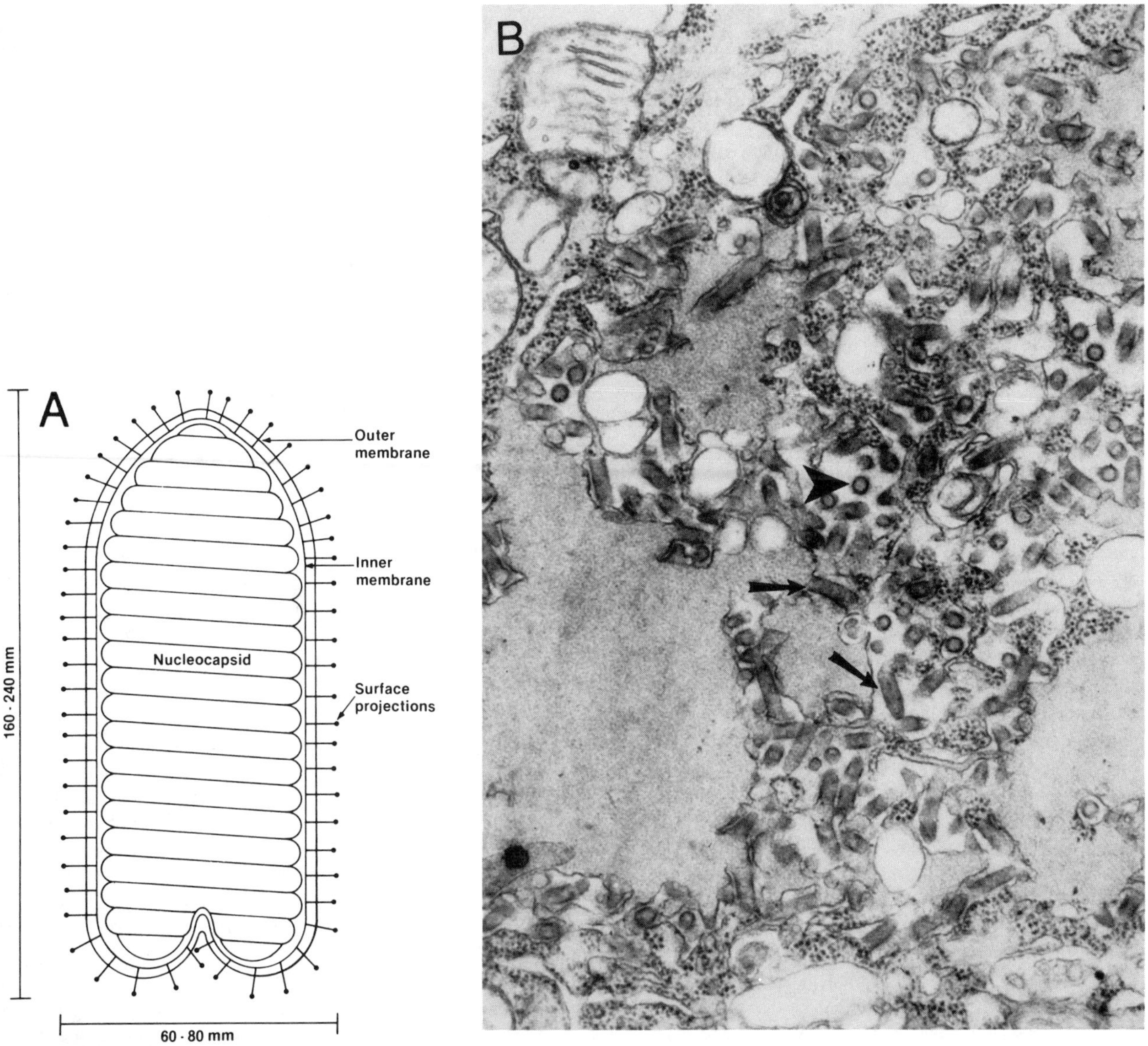

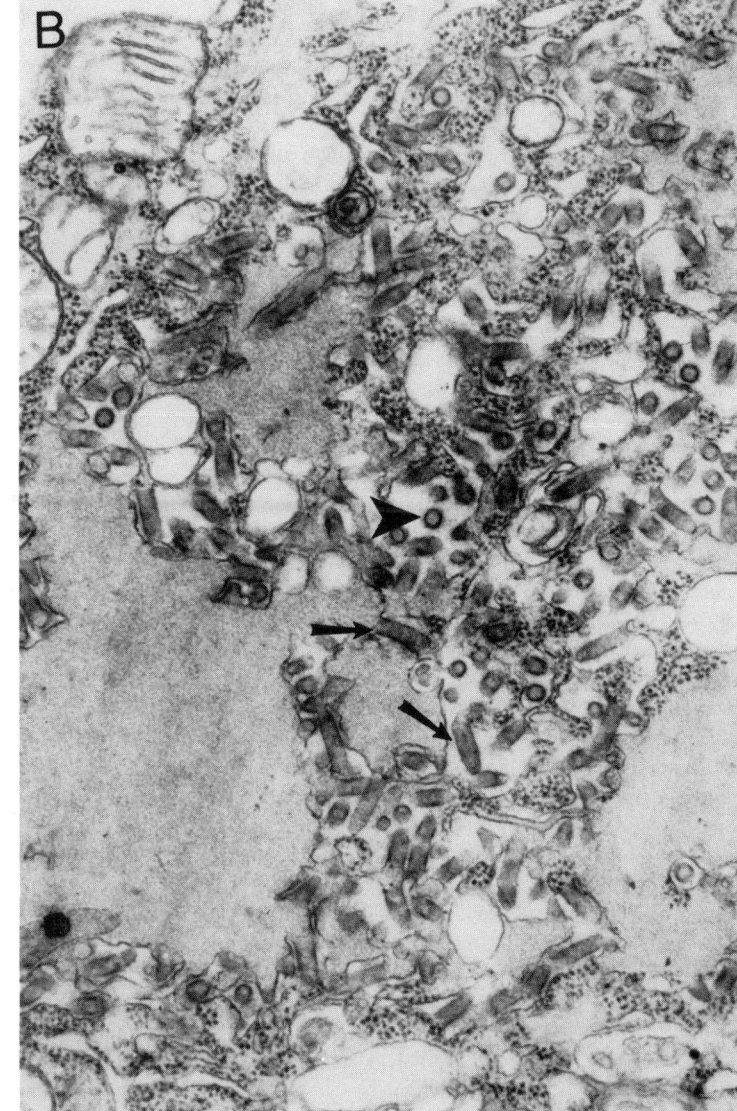

Figure 19–1. Rabies virus morphology and electron micrograph of rabies virus in brain tissue. Arrows denote longitudinal sections of virus.

a bullet-shaped cylinder, rounded at one end and flat at the other (Figure 19–1). A series of transverse striations can be identified within the virus. ***Rhabdoviridae*** are RNA-containing viruses, whose nucleoprotein is a tightly wound helix in the core of the virus. The rabiesvirus surface is studded with regularly spaced knoblike sur-face projections formed of an 80,000-dalton glycoprotein. These projections are structurally associated with the more internal of two membranes which envelope the virus. The projections are termed G protein, while the two nonglycosylated proteins of the membranes are termed M_1 (40,000 daltons) and M_2 (25,000 dal-

Table 19–2
Rabiesvirus Characteristics

Virus type
   Rhabdovirus
	Envelope
	   Bilayer membrane, lipid solvent–soluble, 6–7 nm
	   projections which contain G protein (glycoprotein) (mol
	   wt = 65,000–80,000), M_1 and M_2 proteins (mol wt =
	   21,000–25,000)

Morphology
   130–240 nm length, 65–80 nm width, bullet-shaped
	Transcription enzyme
	   RNA-dependent RNA transcriptase

Nucleic acid
   Single-stranded RNA, negative polarity, mol wt =
   4.6×10^6
	Preferred laboratory systems
	   Small mammals (esp mouse, hamsters, rabbit), birds
	   (less susceptible), embryonated eggs (esp duck,
	   chick), tissue culture (esp human diploid cell)

Nucleocapsid
   Helix, N protein, mol wt = 54,000–62,000,
   transcriptase
	Natural hosts
	   Mammals

The figure labels in A:
- Outer membrane
- Inner membrane
- Nucleocapsid
- Surface projections
- 160 · 240 mm
- 60 · 80 mm

tons) proteins. These projections hemagglutinate goose red blood cells and serve to attach the virion to host cells, properties which resemble those of the red blood cell agglutinins of *Orthomyxoviridae* (Table 19–2).

Single-stranded RNA makes up the unimolecular nucleocapsid.[13, 15] Also contained in the nucleocapsid is RNA-dependent RNA transcriptase, the enzyme on which the virus depends for duplication, and several structural proteins: L protein (190,000 daltons), N protein (69,000 daltons), and NS protein.

Virus infectivity is rapidly disrupted by the application of formalin, phenol, bichloride of mercury, and disinfectants. Drying, sunlight, and heat will destroy the virus infectivity, but protein or glycerol suspensions will allow the virus to be stored at -30 to $-60°C$, or to remain viable for long periods of time at 4°C.[3, 13, 20]

A number of laboratory host systems have proved satisfactory for the propagation of rabiesvirus. Virus replication and disease is easily elicited by intracerebral injections of virus-containing substances into mouse or rabbit brain. Other laboratory animals that have been satisfactorily used include hamsters, rats, and guinea pigs. Subcutaneous or intramuscular (IM) inoculations have been used but are less reliable than are intracerebral injections. Embryonated duck or chick eggs have been used for virus cultivation. These systems can provide large quantities of virus for vaccine. Tissue culture systems that have proved useful for virus cultivation include human diploid cell, chick embryo cell, or hamster kidney cell lines. Because only minimal cytopathic effect (CPE) is evident in infected cells,[21] immunofluorescence may be used to detect the presence of virus antigen.[22] WI-38 and MRC-5 are the two human diploid cell lines currently used for production of killed vaccine in the United States and Europe, respectively.

Wild-type or street rabiesvirus should be differentiated from "fixed" virus used for vaccination. Pasteur first produced fixed virus when he serially passed a wild virus in rabbit brain. This resulted in a virus that is partially attenuated to other animals, but which is still rapidly pathogenic for disease in the animal in which it was passed. The fixed virus is propagated with greater ease in tissue culture and animal systems than is the wild virus, but it maintains similar antigenicity and is suitable for vaccine. The fixed virus can be sufficiently attenuated for safe use as a live virus vaccine in animals.

Different strains of rabiesvirus appear to be immunologically similar. However, fixed viruses and wild-type viruses demonstrate pathogenic differences, and there is epidemiologic suggestion of functional differences among various wild virus strains. For example, some wild viruses appear to be better suited to propagation in one host than another.

Replication of rabiesvirus appears to be similar to vesicular stomatitis virus, another rhabdovirus that has been intensely studied.[14, 15] The method is similar to RNA production of the paramyxoviruses. The virion's transcriptase, an RNA-dependent RNA polymerase, transcribes messenger RNA (mRNA). Another polymerase (replicase) probably constructs a positive-strand RNA (40S) to serve as a template for virion RNA, and which has polarity oppostie that of the transcribed mRNA. The transcriptase begins forming the mRNA at a single promoter site, resulting in a complementary messenger (positive-strand) molecule derived from the negative viral RNA strand. This produces a long mRNA which acts as an intermediate for replication of new virion nucleoprotein. Virus replication takes place in the cytoplasm of the host cell,

where collections of the nucleocapsids are identifiable as inclusions termed Negri bodies.

The elapsed time for the virus multiplication cycle in cell cultures is similar to that of other viruses.[14–16] The initial cycle of multiplication follows an eclipse period of about six to eight hours. Multiplication is completed in 19 to 20 hours. Budding from cytoplasmic membranes occurs as the virions assemble and the virus forms its envelope from the host cell membrane. However, de novo viral envelope synthesis probably also occurs within or at the border of host cytoplasmic membrane, without budding.[14, 23, 24] Infection of cultured cells is not lethal to the cells, and an endosymbiotic infection transpires,[21] resulting in continued infection of the initial cells and subsequent virus shedding, a phenomenon also demonstrated by paramyxoviruses.

PATHOLOGY

The pathologic findings of human rabies are viral encephalitis and neuronal degeneration. Considerable variability in pathologic findings has been noted and can be ascribed to examination of the brain at various stages of infection, secondary complications of the disease such as hypoxia and cerebral edema, and perhaps some individual variation in host response to the infection. Gross changes of the brain include vascular congestion and edema.[25, 26] Frank evidence of meningitis is unusual and is generally limited to children.[27, 28]

The microscopic appearance of rabies encephalitis is similar to that of other viral encephalitides. Lymphocyte and plasma cell exudates with perivascular cuffing can involve most of the brain but primarily affect the paleoencaphalon. Polymorphonuclear cells may be present in the early stages of disease, as suggested by their presence in early spinal fluid specimens. However, acute inflammatory cells are virtually absent by the time the patient comes to autopsy. Perivascular cuffing is the most common finding, present in 94% of patients with an encephalitic picture. Neuronophagia (57%) and Babes nodules (42%) are frequently observed in encephalitis.[27] Babes nodules are focal collections of "embryonal cells" (activated microglial cells) which surround infected neurons. Once thought to be specific for rabies infection, Babes nodules are also encountered in other viral encephalitides and some toxic states. Encephalitis if found most frequently in the medulla (38.1%), pons (38.1%), and spinal cord (35.7%). The thalamus, cerebral cortex, and basal ganglia are involved in slightly more than 25% of cases, and the cerebellum, hippocampus, and peripheral ganglia occasionally manifest encephalitis. Degeneration of neurons is unimpressive.[27]

Negri bodies are cytoplasmic inclusions seen within the human and animal neurons affected with rabiesvirus. They are best demonstrated by special stains such as fuchsin-methylene blue or dinitrofluorobenzene. Encompassed by a halo, Negri bodies are generally round and exhibit a visible internal structure.[13, 17] Electron microscopy reveals that they are composed of clusters of assembling virion nucleocapsid.[14, 19] They are generally considered pathognomonic of rabies infection, but they are not always present. Approximately 20% of animal brains which harbor culturable rabiesvirus will not contain Negri bodies, and only 71% to 90% of human material if Negri body–positive.[27, 29] Negri bodies are seen most frequently in the cerebellum (59.5%) and the hippocampus (42.9%), but can be seen less frequently in the medulla, pontine

Table 19–3
Relationship of Brain Histopathology to Duration of Human Rabies

Average Total Duration	Number of Days of Illness Before Death
Encephalitis only	31
Congestion only	38.2
Encephalitis and equivocal inclusions	41.5
Negri bodies only	66.5
Mixed Negri bodies and encephalitis	72.7

Modified from DuPont JR, Earl KM: Human rabies encephalitis—A study of forty-nine fatal cases with a review of the literature. Neurology 1965; 15:1023–1034.

nuclei, spinal cord, cerebral cortex, mesencephalon, basal ganglia, thalamus, and peripheral ganglia. Although Negri bodies or encephalitis may be seen alone in rabies, the combination of the two is seen most frequently (56.3%). The anatomical distribution of Negri bodies and encephalitis roughly correlates with virus titer distribution in various sites of the brain. The highest titers are found in the basilar brain and thalamus.[30, 31] Lyssa bodies are seen more frequently than Negri bodies. These resemble Negri bodies but are smaller and homogeneous cytoplasmic inclusions without an obvious internal structure. Histopathologic findings appear to be related to the length of illness before autopsy (Table 19–3). Histologic evidence of encephalitis appears to precede the development of Negri bodies, which may be seen with encephalitis or in its absence.

Extraneuronal infections have been described in salivary glands, corneal epithelial cells, and cutaneous neural tissue.[32, 33] High concentrations of virus collect in salivary gland acini and bud from membranes of mucogenic cells, but the cytoplasmic architecture if often intact.[34] Immunofluorescence has demonstrated rabiesvirus antigen in nerve endings on the outer root sheath of hair follicles on the nape of the neck, lips, eyelids, and head.[33] Virus has been demonstrated within olfactory bulb neurons of bats[35] and in a person who acquired rabies by inhalation.[36] Myocarditis accompanying rabies has been described.[30, 37, 38]

PATHOGENESIS

Rabies infections are generally established by virus inoculation into peripheral tissues, ascent via afferent peripheral nerves, and ultimate involvement of brain neurons. The virus subsequently descends via peripheral nerves to other sites, including the salivary glands, resulting in virus excretion in the saliva; this may in turn infect another host and completes the cycle of infection (Figure 19–2).

Although the usual method of transmission is inoculation of infected saliva into subcutaneous tissue or muscle by an animal bite or by saliva inoculation onto broken skin, other modes of transmission have been recognized. Virus inhalation,[39–41] transplantation of corneal tissue containing virus,[42–44] and inoculation onto mucous membranes[35] can result in infection. Once virus is inoculated into striated muscle cells, it begins to replicate. Electron microscopy has demonstrated virus particles budding from plasma membranes and sarcoplasmic reticulum membranes of infected cells and amplifying of the number of virions locally. Striated muscle is probably the site of virus sequestration in long incubation infections. Virus particles accumulate at sensory stretch proprioceptor nerve fibers (neuromuscular spindles) within the muscles.

The spindles, and perhaps the neurotendinal spindles, afford a source of entry to peripheral sensory nerves. The virus moves rapidly across the cellular junction either by directly traversing the junction and invading the neuronal cells, or by inducing cell membrane fusion and entering the neurons without crossing the junction.[45–47] Extracellular virions appear to concentrate at the nerve junction acetylcholine receptors, a phenomenon which can be partially blocked by receptor binders.[48] The receptors may serve to bind rabiesvirus and may be one means whereby nerve cell uptake of virus is facilitated. Whether there is preferential use of peripheral sensory neurons over motor neurons by the virus for centripetal migration has not been entirely resolved. Nerve sectioning experiments have demonstrated centripetal transmission of the virus via both dorsal and ventral root neurons and each could play a role in central migration of the virus.[49] Virus infection at neuronal motor end plates also occurs. However, the sensory neurons appear to be the more important paths for centripetal migration. Viremia has been demonstrated in mouse and rabbit experimental models,[49] but there has been little other evidence of significant hematogenous or other nonneuronal modes of virus spread.

Virus moves from the periphery to the central nervous system by passive neuronal transit. Virions can occasionally be identified within axonal endoplasmic reticulum and at nodes of Ranvier, but the precise mechanism of transmission has not been delineated.[50] Once the infection reaches the level of the spinal cord, the viral genome can be demonstrated in dorsal root ganglia cell bodies, but it is not clear whether the resultant amplification infects adjacent neurons or whether it is crucial for propagation of infection. Once the virus has reached the spinal cord, its ascent to the brain may be rapid, occurring over hours in some animal models.[47, 49, 51, 52] These data are supported clinically by the rapidly ascending paralysis seen in some humans and animals. Schwann cell and glial cell infections have been demonstrated in the course of disease, but they do not play a significant role in infection pathogenesis.

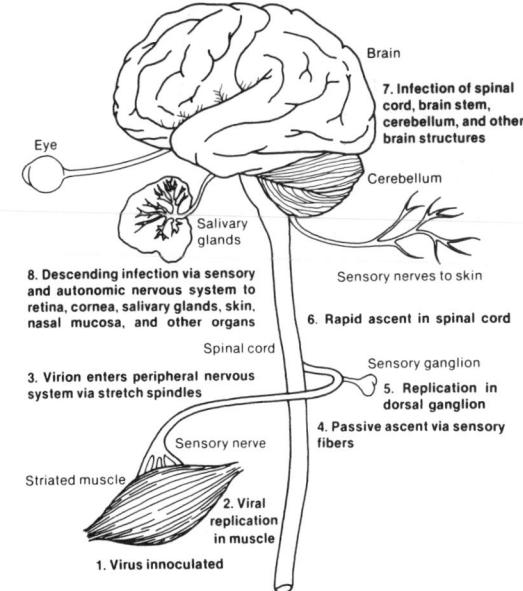

Figure 19–2. Schematic representation of pathogenesis of rabies virus infection. Numbered steps describe sequence of events of infection.

Once virus has reached the brain, widespread infection ensues[27, 30, 31] and nearly all neurons in many different regions may be infected. The heaviest infection appears to occur in the hippocampus, brain stem, ganglionic cells of pontine nuclei, and the Purkinje cells of the cerebellum.[30, 31, 52] Symptoms of rabies appear to be consistently related to the anatomical location of infection. Lesser infection in the neocortex may result in continued alertness through much of the early stages of disease, and aggressiveness and aberrant sexual behavior probably results from heavy infection of the limbic system. Respiratory myoclonus may be related to involvement of the inferior olivary nucleus and central brain stem tegmentum,[53] and periodic breathing may be due to midpontine or pontomedullary junction infection in the brain stem. In contrast, hydrophobia is probably just a conditioned response to the severe throat pain brought on by pharyngeal or laryngeal spasm.[53]

Once the brain has been infected, virus passes centrifugally along neuronal routes similar to its ascent. Head and neck skin sensory nerve endings frequently demonstrate virus antigen, which allows rapid antemortem diagnosis of rabies by immunofluorescent staining of frozen skin biopsies.[32] Salivary gland infection results from neuronal descent of virus to the parotid and other glands[34, 49] and saliva become virus-laden, providing potential for further transmission. The virus can descend other afferent neurons to involve retinal cells[45, 52] and corneal epithelium. The latter allows antemortem diagnosis of rabies to be made by immunofluorescent staining of corneal epithelial cells obtained by slide impressions.[32, 54]

Infection of olfactory end organs and of taste buds also results from centrifugal viral migration.[35, 46] Myocarditis has rarely occurred.[38, 53] Viral spread along the autonomic nervous system has been demonstrated in animals[52] and man[55] and may result in infection of other organs, but this is probably an unusual event.

One must wonder why the rabiesvirus is privileged to escape the effects of host defense mechanisms and result in fatal infection. Extensive experimentation regarding the cell-mediated immune system suggests that it may provide little or no protection in rabies infections. Suppression of lymphocytes with antilymphocyte serum appears not to change the outcome of disease and adoptive immunization with exogenous spleen cells fails to protect infected mice.[56] The T lymphocyte response may play a role in development of paralysis.[57] However, another study[58] noted T cell protection in mouse infection with attenuated virus. Some investigators have remarked on the paucity of inflammatory mononuclear infiltration in rabies-infected brain, which contrasts to the usual vigorous infiltration seen in most other viral CNS infections. However, any conclusions from these data should be drawn cautiously.[47]

Humoral immunity clearly provides protection against infection. Passively administered antibody prolongs mouse survival[59] and vaccination can protect animals[58, 60] and humans alike.[12, 61] However, antibody in naturally acquired infection without vaccination usually rises only after illness is well established. Serum neutralizing antibodies generally do not appear until the fifth day or later following onset of symptoms in human disease.[62] The small amounts of viral antigen early in the infection and its intracellular location may be the reason for delayed processing and response by the immune system. Once established intracellularly, rabiesvirus is protected from humoral and T lymphocyte-mediated responses to infection. Moreover, if immune-mediated cytolysis of rabies-infected cells occurred, it would result in death of neuronal cells, detrimental to the host.

Rabies infection induces the production of interferon.[63] Interferon inhibits infection in tissue culture[64] and the administration of exogenous interferon and of interferon inducers[65–67] has demonstrated interferon's ability to protect against rabies infection. However, the production of interferon in natural infection does not appear to be timely or sufficient to protect an unvaccinated individual. Thus, while the native immune system may be stimulated by rabiesvirus infection, without augmentation it is not capable of protecting against disease progression and death.

EPIDEMIOLOGY

Rabies is an archetypal example of a zoonotic infection—one in which the natural cycle of infection involves animals, and human disease results from exposure to infected animals and is not part of the mainstream of the cycle of infection. Thus, knowledge of animal rabies epidemiology is important in understanding human rabies epidemiology for three reasons: First, outbreaks of animal disease may threaten human populations. Second, control of rabies in animal populations must be based on the occurrence and behavior of rabies in various animals. Finally, animal rabies epidemiology profoundly influences choices regarding postexposure prophylaxis of persons with potential rabies exposure. Data pertaining to rabies epidemiology are generally derived from public health sources, including passive and active surveillance systems; physician, veterinarian, and laboratory reporting of cases; and epidemiologic investigations. These sources depend on the reliability of surveillance system reporting, animals submitted for testing, and the selection of problems for study by investigators. Although the problems of underreporting of rabies may be more marked in developing nations, data in developed countries depend on selection of animals for testing and completeness of case reporting; these factors may bias surveillance information. However, the data derived from these sources can usually provide information adequate to its purpose.

The incidence of human rabies has declined markedly in many parts of the world, including the United States (Figure 19–3). In the United States, 80 human cases were recorded in 1934, the highest in the last 60 years. The number of cases dropped off abruptly in the early and mid-1950s and now zero to two cases are recorded yearly.[68] Similar low rates of infection are seen in other developed nations, but developing nations may experience higher case rates.[69]

The incidence of rabies appears to be higher in males (70%–80% of cases) than females and the greatest number of cases is in persons aged less than 20 years.[62, 70] Greater outdoor activity and frequency with which children are bitten by dogs[2] may explain these findings. Persons with outdoor occupations and no recorded occupation (presumably transients who spend more time outdoors than nontransients) composed nearly half of one group with rabies, but laboratory technicians working with rabies also had risk of exposure.[62] Illness has its onset most frequently from May through September, which correlates with most frequent exposures occurring between April and August. This may be related to greater outdoor activity and less protective heavy clothing being worn,

Human rabies cases, United States,* by 5-year periods, 1940-1986

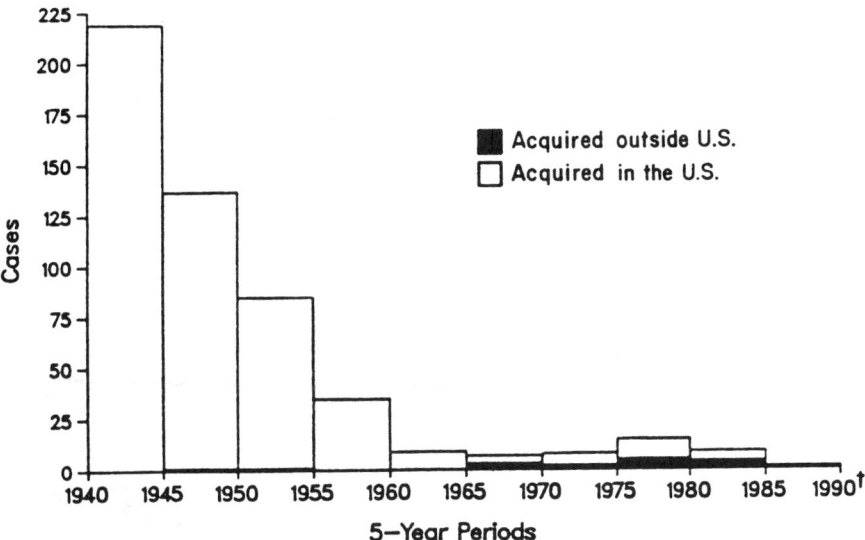

Figure 19–3. Human rabies cases, United States, by 5–year periods, 1940–1986. (Includes all cases diagnosed in the United States and cases diagnosed outside the United States in United States citizens; t = 2-year period only.) Surveillance statistics from Centers for Disease Control.[98]

but it also temporally correlates with increased canine rabies in March and April.[71]

The geographic distribution of human cases generally follows the distribution of animal cases throughout the world.[69] Within a single country there may be variation in the geographic distribution of human cases related to differences in animal disease.[70] Cases of imported rabies may occur in persons returning from endemic areas to relative rabies-free areas.[68, 72, 73] Rabies is a concern to the international traveler, and the probability of exposure varies strikingly from country to country.[74]

The medical history in human rabies patients usually includes exposure to animals that are most frequently infected. Infected domestic animals provide a relatively greater risk for human exposure than do infected wild animals.[75] Urban dog rabies is a particular problem because of the close association between dog and man, and therefore human cases as a result of dog exposure are often seen.[62, 69, 70] Unvaccinated, owned adult dogs appear to provide the greatest risk of rabies exposure.[71] As domestic animal rabies becomes controlled, a relative increase may be noted in human cases which result from wild animal exposures.[70, 76] Wild terrestrial mammals now account for the greatest number of non-canine human exposures in the United States. However, bat rabies is an important source of exposure in the Western Hemisphere.[62, 69, 70] Thirteen percent of recent United States cases had bat exposures noted.[62] Unusual exposures, such as laboratory accident,[39, 77] inhalation of aerosol,[78] or transplantation of infected corneal tissue[38–44] may result in human infection. More than 20% of recent United States cases had no identifiable source of exposure.[62]

The epidemiology of animal rabies is complex and dynamic. Variations in animal species that are infected can be seen within a country, as demonstrated by United States rabies surveillance (Figure 19–4), and throughout the world. Examples of worldwide

distribution of rabid animals are given in Table 19–4. Patterns of disease distribution change over years. A prime example is the spread of fox rabies from an endemic focus in northwestern Poland in a southwesterly direction to involve much of Western Europe over the last 40 years (Figure 19–5).[79–81] In the United States, raccoon rabies was only sporadically recognized before 1950, but became well entrenched in the 1950s and 1960s in Florida and Georgia[82] and appears to be moving northward to involve South Carolina.[83] Bat rabies is a recently recognized phenomenon in the United States,[84–86] although Central America has experienced vampire bat rabies for many years. Rabies in insectivore bats is now recognized in 48 of the 50 states,[68, 83, 87, 88] and may be the largest numerical and geographic rabies reservoir in the United States.[82] Changes in the relative importance of domestic animal rabies and wild animal rabies have been noted in the United States (Figure 19–6), and the absolute number of wild animals with rabies has increased sharply over the last several years. Certain countries of the world have either never experienced animal rabies or have been rendered rabies-free by control measures. These are listed in Table 19–4.[89] Rabies in wild animals tends to be limited to only several species in a particular geographic area. Some interspecies spread must occur, as is evidenced by domestic animal rabies and observations in bats,[82, 90] but it is probably infrequent. Limited crossing of species boundaries by rabies may be a result of infrequent interspecies contact, species-specific adaptation of virus strains, or a combination of both.

Rabies tends to be maintained within wild animal populations for many years, despite its high mortality.[91] In some species, such as bats and skunks, this may be a result of long asymptomatic periods. Asymptomatic infection may be associated with periodic virus shedding without rapid death of the infected animal, as recognized in bats.[92] Long incubation periods and changes of virus virulence may explain periodic epizootic outbreaks in foxes and skunks.

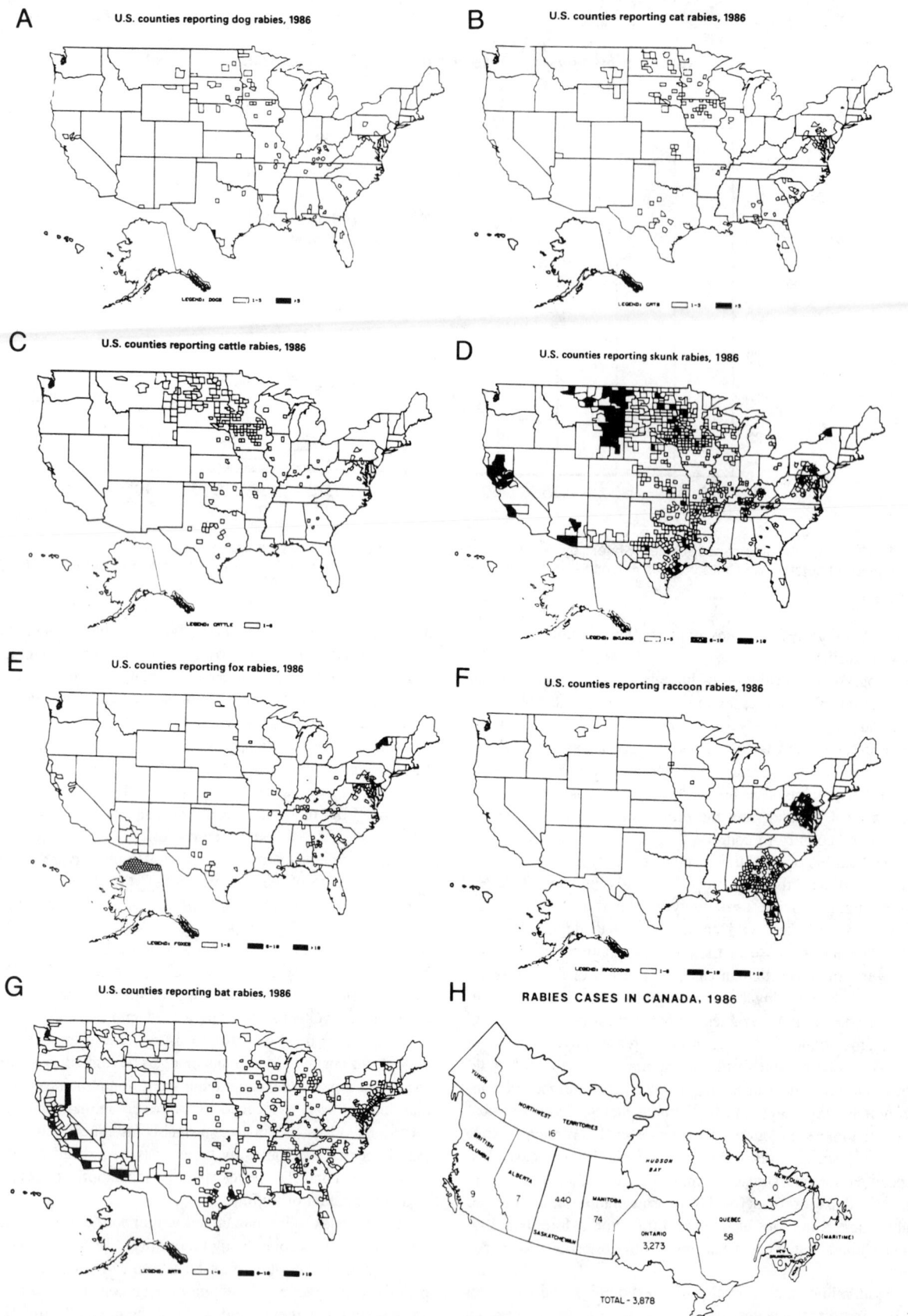

Figure 19–4. A–J Geographic distribution of animal rabies in the United States and Canada, 1979. Surveillance data from the Centers for Disease Control.[98]

I
Raccoon rabies cases by county, mid-Atlantic states, 1980-1986

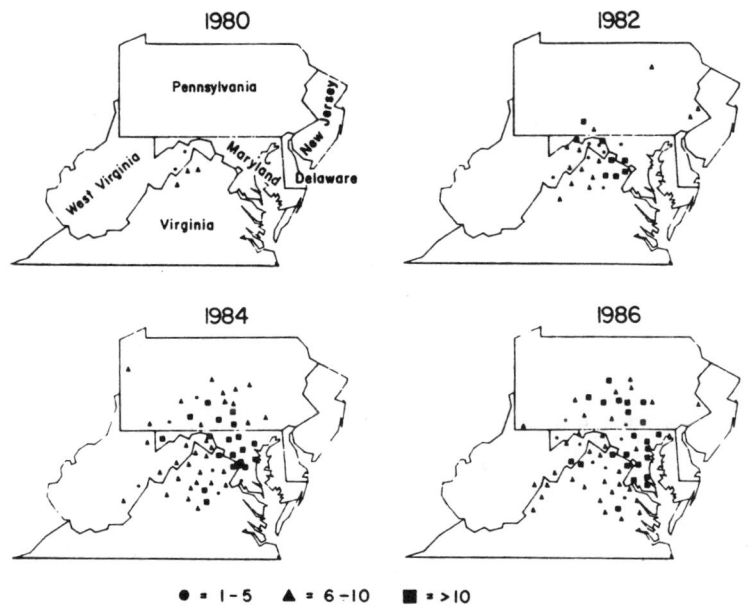

● = 1–5   ▲ = 6–10   ■ = >10

J
Raccoon rabies cases, mid-Atlantic states, 1978-1986

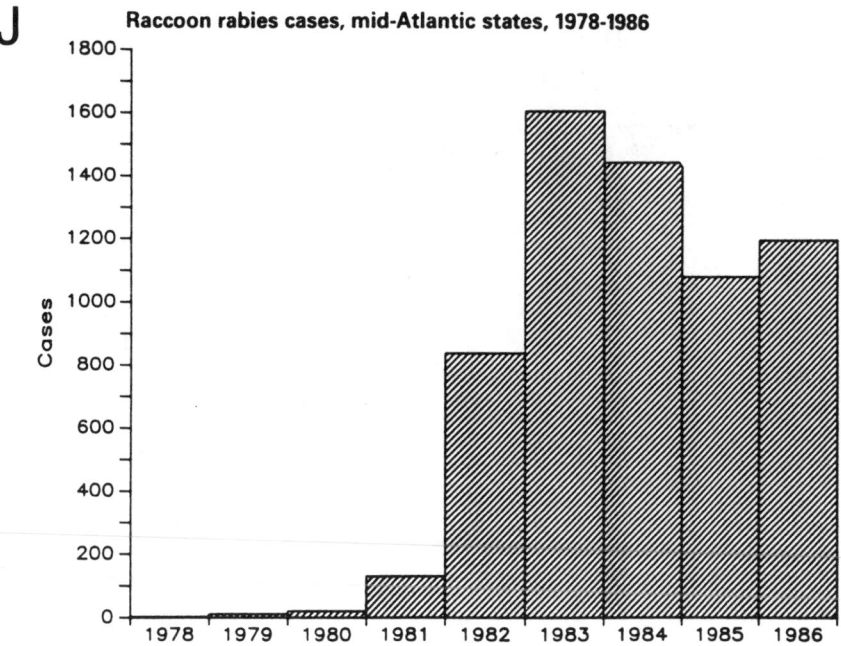

Raccoon rabies cases by county, mid-Atlantic states, 1980-1986

Table 19–4
Worldwide Distribution of Animal Rabies

A. Major animal reservoirs* (distribution often varies from country to country)	
Africa†	Cat, dog, farm animals,‡ jackal, mongoose; occasionally honey badger, wild cat, others
Asia†	Cat, dog, donkey, farm animals,‡ jackal, wolf; occasionally others
Australia, South Pacific islands	None
Central America, Caribbean islands	Bat (especially vampire), cat, dog, farm animals,‡ mongoose; occasionally coyote, monkey, rat, others
Europe	Badger, cat, dog, farm animals,‡ fox, marten, roe deer; occasionally chamois, deer, ferret, polecat, raccoon, squirrel, weasel, wildcat, others
North America	Bat (insectivore), cat, dog, farm animals,‡ fox, raccoon, skunk; occasionally coyote, deer, groundhog, opossum, weasel, wolf, others
South America	Bat (especially vampire), cat, dog, farm animals‡; occasionally alpaca, llama, mongoose, monkey, rat, others
B. Rabies-free countries[89]	
Americas	Anguilla, Antigua, Aruba, Bahamas, Barbados, Bermuda, Curaçao, Guadeloupe, Jamaica, Martinique, Montserrat, Nevis, St Kitts, St Lucia, St Martin, St Vincent, Virgin Islands
Europe	Faeroe Islands, Finland, Iceland, Sweden, United Kingdom
Asia	Japan, Taiwan
Oceania	American Samoa, Australia, Fiji, Guam, New Zealand, Saipan

*Data derived from various reports, surveillance, and surveys.
†Incomplete information from many parts of the continent.
‡Cattle are predominantly affected farm animals in most countries.

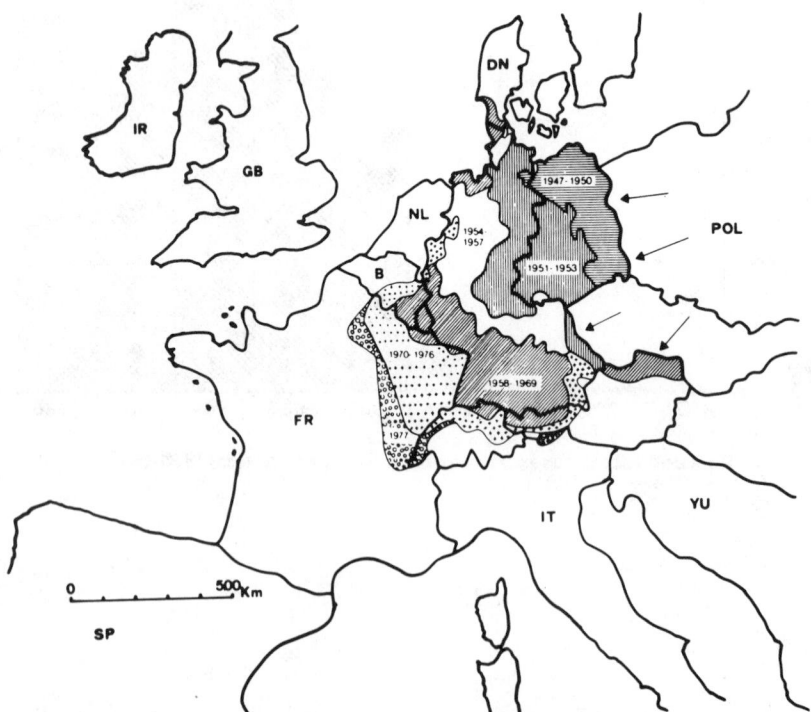

Figure 19–5. Spread of fox rabies in Europe 1947–1977. (B = Belgium; DN = Denmark; FR = France; GB = Great Britain; IR = Ireland; IT = Italy; NL = Netherlands; POL = Poland; SP = Spain; YU = Yugoslavia). (From Steck F, Wandelees A: The epidemiology of fox rabies in Europe. *Epidemiol Rev* 1980; 2:72. Reproduced with permission.)

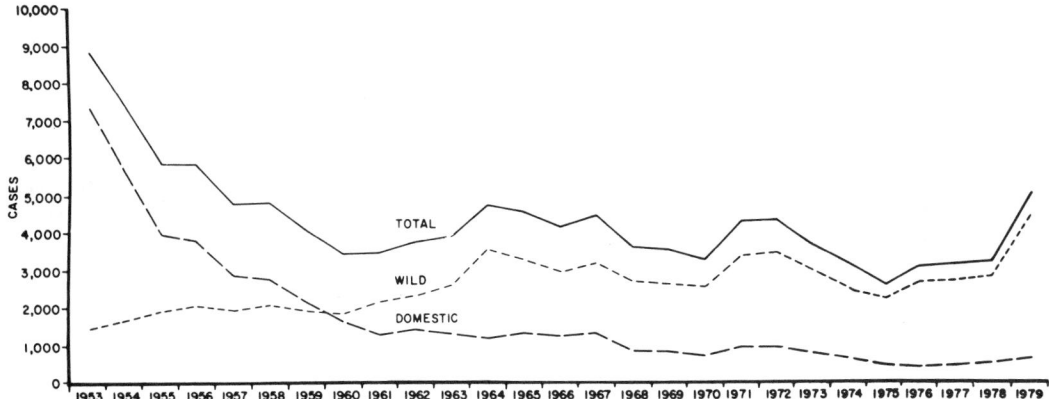

Figure 19–6. Annual number of cases of animal rabies in the United States. Surveillance data from the Centers for Disease Control.[88]

Both intraspecies and interspecies transmission may operate to perpetuate rabies in domestic animals. Vampire bat attacks result in bovine rabies in South and Central America,[72, 92] and ungulate rabies in North America probably is transmitted by smaller wild animals, such as skunks and raccoons. Although canine rabies can result from wild animal exposure, intraspecies transmission may be more important in epizootics.[75]

The occurrence of rabies in wild animals has changed in the northeastern United States since 1978. An epizootic of raccoon rabies has been moving north, to involve several states in the Middle Atlantic region, which had previously seen virtually no rabies in raccoons (see Figure 19–4, I and J). During the 1982–1983 period, the Centers for Disease Control (CDC) and Middle Atlantic state health departments reported increasing numbers of cases in raccoons. Animal positivity rates ranged as high as 70% in killed animals.[93, 93a] Raccoons found in the day, those exhibiting abnormal behavior, and those that interacted with domestic animals were more likely to be infected. Beck et al reported an increase of 617% in reported cases in Maryland from 1982 to 1984.[94] Although as much as 50% of postexposure prophylaxis given was to persons whose exposure risk was low or nonexistent,[93] there was a substantial increase in the human prophylaxis given as a direct result of the epizootic and raccoon exposure.[93, 94] Antigen characterization using monoclonal antibodies to viral nucleocapsid protein demonstrated that isolates from Middle Atlantic raccoons was similar to raccoon isolates from the southeastern United States.[95, 96] This finding and the rapidity of the epizootic spread suggests that the epizootic originated with transportation of infected raccoons from the southeastern United States, where raccoon rabies has been endemic.

Recent reviews of rabies epidemiology in the United States continue to show decline in canine rabies over the last 30 years and increases in wildlife rabies.[93, 97, 98] Rabies has been recognized in small but increasing numbers among wild rodents and lagomorphs.[99] Of 104 cases in rodents and lagomorphs reported to the CDC during the years 1971–1984, 80% of the cases were reported between 1980 and 1984. Woodchucks (*Marmota monax*) accounted for 64% of the cases, and were associated with the epizootic of raccoons. Recently, several cases of rabies have been reported in ferrets, an unusual source animal in the United States.[98]

In 1980–1983, an outbreak of rabies occurred for the first time

in 25 years among jackals in Zimbabwe. Additional animal cases involved domestic cattle and subsequent cases in dogs. Two human cases resulted from the outbreak.[100] In Hong Kong, five human cases occurred during a 4-year period as a direct result of a canine epizootic.[101] A study of rabies epidemiology in northern Nigeria indicated that owned, unvaccinated dogs over 1 year of age posed the most serious threat of human rabies exposure. Breeding season was the time of most canine rabies cases.[102]

Occasional cases of human rabies continue to occur in developed countries.[98, 103–107] Cases which result from foreign exposure constitute a significant proportion of these.[98, 108] Endemic cases resulting from exposure to local canines and wild animals are an ongoing problem in the developing world.[108–111] A recent survey by the World Health Organization (WHO) estimated the incidence of rabies and rabies exposure in developing countries.[108] The mean number of postexposure treatments was 866.8 per million population (range 2.7 to 4570.4) and of human cases of rabies was 3.7 per million (range 0.1 to 28.8).

RABIES IN ANIMALS

A discussion of animal rabies is important to aid in understanding human exposure risk.[112] Although rabies is generally considered to be an illness of large or medium-sized mammals, infection can be induced in a variety of animals. Carnivores, including canines, felines, skunks, raccoons, foxes, wolves, and mongooses; bats; and large domestic animals such as cattle, horses, sheep, and pigs, are animals most likely to be infected naturally. Laboratory rabies can be easily induced in rodents, in lagomorphs, and even in avians, but these animals are rarely infected in the wild. Pathology and pathophysiology of animal rabies are essentially identical to human rabies, and the clinical presentation is also similar. Either "furious" or "dumb" rabies may be manifest. Aggressive behavior, marked by attacks on animals and inanimate objects, agitation, confusion, and alteration in normal behavior patterns are seen in furious rabies. Animals may exhibit exaggerated response to sudden stimuli, irritability, restlessness, and nervousness. They have been known to eat foreign objects such as wood, stones, or straw, and they may emit unusual vocalizations. Paralytic rabies may be marked by hindquarter or generalized weakness. If pharyngeal or mastication muscles are involved, the animal

528   *P. A. Robinson*

may be unable to eat or drink and drooling of saliva may be observed. The appearance of choking may induce an animal owner to attempt to remove a nonexistent foreign body from the animal's throat, thereby resulting in a dangerous exposure.

Rabies has been found in hematophagous and nonhematophagous bats. Symptomatic bats exhibit aggressive behavior similar to other animals. Insectivorous species are probably always symptomatic with infection, but vampire and frugivorous bats may be asymptomatic carriers.[113] An outbreak of rabies in Trinidad suggested to the investigators that asymptomatic bats may have been the vector of the outbreak.[114] This and other data indicate that rabies may not invariably be a fatal disease.[115] Virus has been isolated from normal-appearing skunks[115] and weasels.[116] This may represent infection during the incubation period, however. Reports of animals recovering from clinical rabies have been recorded,[117] and excretion of the virus from otherwise asymptomatic animals has been recognized.[118–121] The significance of these findings is not entirely clear but suggests the possibility of spread by asymptomatic animals.

Although Pasteur had developed an effective canine vaccine by 1884,[7] it was not until after World War I that the first extensive animal vaccination program was implemented.[122] Large-scale vaccinations in Hungary virtually eliminated the disease, and vaccination programs reduce or eliminate canine rabies.[75, 123] Currently, inactivated and modified, live virus animal vaccines are available. The US Public Health Service publishes a compendium of vaccines marketed in the United States[124, 125] that have been thoroughly tested for safety and efficacy.[126] An updated compendium of animal rabies vaccination was published in 1986 and serves as an excellent guide to animal vaccination procedures.[125] Recommended use of these vaccines is limited to domestic dogs and cats, and certain vaccines may be used in cattle, horses, sheep, and goats. Many

of these vaccines have not been proved efficacious in wildlife or exotic animals, and modified live virus vaccines may induce vaccine-associated rabies in them.

Modified live virus vaccine strains are attenuated by repeated tissue or egg passages of virus. These fixed vaccines rarely cause disease in animals if used properly in the recommended species and accidental human exposure to the vaccine is felt to constitute no rabies hazard.[124] Occasional instances of vaccine-induced rabies in animals, including dogs and cats, have been recorded,[127] but current recommendations for vaccine use in animals have made such occurrences rare. The use of new monoclonal antibody virus identification techniques have confirmed the source of active infection as vaccine virus.[96, 128] Tests of rabiesvirus isolated from 11 dogs, two cats, and a fox clearly distinguished vaccine strains from wild strains isolated from man and domestic and wild animals.[128]

Enteric inoculation of attenuated rabiesvirus for wildlife rabies control is currently being investigated.[129–131] A sufficiently avirulent and stable vaccine strain must be developed to induce immunity via the enteric route without causing disease or allowing virus reversion to a virulent form. If an efficient system of vaccine delivery, such as concealing the vaccine in bait, can be devised, this may prove to be an efficient method of controlling wildlife rabies in some species.

CLINICAL PRESENTATION

Following exposure, human rabies evolves through five clinical phases: (1) incubation period, (2) prodrome, (3) acute neurologic phase, (4) coma, and (5) death or recovery (Figure 19–7). Recovery is rare and infected individuals will usually succumb in one of the later stages of disease. Some individuals have brought about their own death in the early stages of the disease rather than

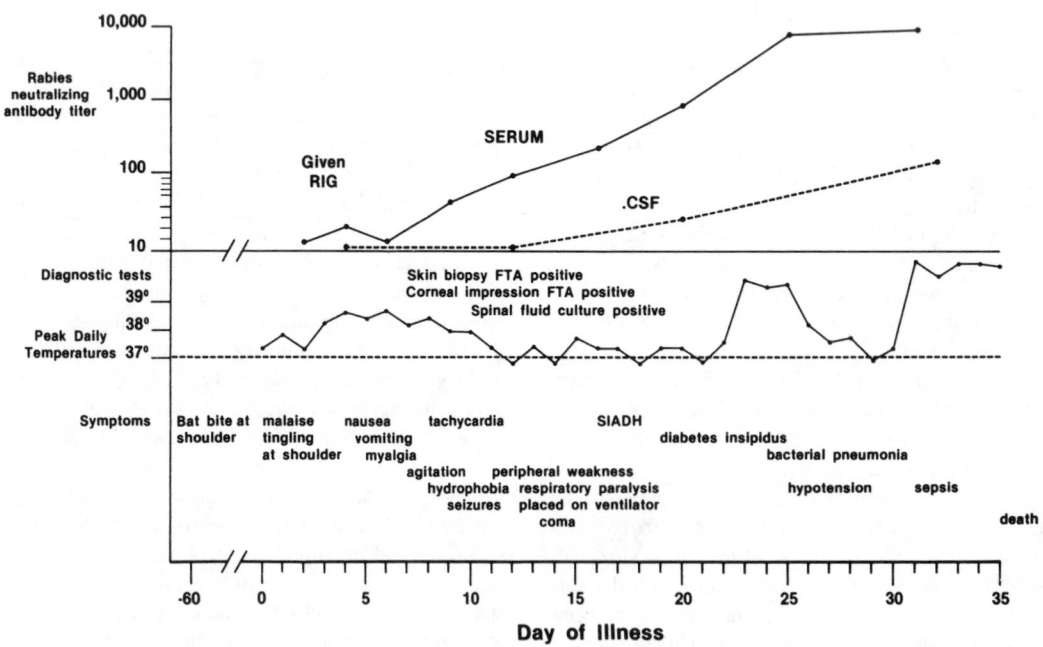

Figure 19–7. Typical course of illness in a patient with rabies. RIG = rabies immune globulin; FTA = direct fluorescent test for antibody; SIADH = syndrome of inappropriate antidiuretic hormone secretion.

to experience the horrors of rabies.[4] The development of rabies following exposure to a potentially rabid animal is not a certainty. It depends on the type of exposure, the animal involved, and pre- and postexposure treatment given. Some of these factors have been discussed in the pathophysiology and prevention sections.

The incubation period in human rabies is quite variable. It may be as short as nine days or as long as several years, but various studies generally report a mean incubation period of 30 to 78 days.[27, 37, 62, 70, 132] Although incubation periods longer than 90 days are not frequent, approximately 14% of cases exhibit extended incubations. Illness has been reported following a year or longer after exposure,[133] but reexposure may have resulted in miscalculation of some of the reported long incubations. Short incubation is generally seen in patients with more severe exposures[70] and in those with bite exposures to the face and head.[37, 132] Children tend to have shorter incubations than adults,[37, 40] perhaps related to the shorter distance between a peripheral bite site and the brain. A trend toward a shorter incubation period has also been noted in vaccine recipients with vaccine failure,[37, 70, 132] but this difference may not be significant.[62] The trend may represent a selective effect of vaccine treatment: postexposure vaccine recipients who would have long incubation times may be more likely to benefit from vaccine than those who would have short incubation times, and therefore the cases with short incubation are likely to become ill despite vaccine.

The patient is completely asymptomatic during incubation. Several authors have suggested that steroid therapy or acute stress may precipitate clinical disease, ending the incubation.[133a, 134] This phenomenon has been suggested to occur in wildlife, but its occurrence in man is speculative.

Onset of the prodrome marks the end of the incubation period. The earliest symptoms are generally nonspecific for the diagnosis of rabies and often suggest another illness (Table 19–5). Malaise, headache, gastrointestinal (GI) symptoms, upper respiratory symptoms, anorexia, and fatigue are the most frequent early symptoms.[27, 37, 62, 132, 135–137] Most patients are febrile during the prodrome; more than half of one series of patients had temperatures in excess of 101°F (38.3°C).[62] Chills may accompany the fever. Subtle mental changes are often seen in the early prodrome, and preliminary diagnoses may include psychiatric disorders or malingering. Nausea, vomiting, abdominal cramping, and diarrhea are the most common early GI symptoms. Frequent insomnia and nightmares have been described.[9, 37] Visual hallucinations to vision have been noted in persons receiving bites near the eye and olfactory hallucinations are described in those bitten on the nose.[9] Anxiety may heighten psychological symptoms, especially if a patient attributes his illness to rabies. Other nonspecific presenting symptoms include sore throat, photophobia, headache, dizziness. Neuralgia related to the site of the exposure is the only relatively specific prodromal symptom. Tingling, burning, pain, itching, or numbness may occur at the site of the bite. Three of four patients who acquired rabies by corneal transplant noted pain referable to the eye receiving the infected cornea.[42–44]

The two- to ten-day prodrome is followed by the acute neurologic phase, when neurologic findings specifically suggest rabies (see Table 19–5). This phase is generally two to seven days in duration and is marked by either a furious presentation, a dumb presentation, or a combination of the two. Signs of nervous system

Table 19–5
Clinical Findings of Human Rabies: Two Random Studies

| | Anderson[62] | DuPont[27] | |
	When Hospitalized	Presenting	Most Prominent
Fever	73%	18.6%	*
Dysphagia	58%[†]	4.7%[†]	50.0%[‡]
Altered mental state	55%	16.3%	63.3%
Pain, paresthesias referable to site of exposure	45%	46.5%	*
Excitement, agitation	45%	*	*
Paralysis, weakness	26%	9.3%	9.1%
Hydrophobia	21%	(see miscellaneous)	43.1%
Hypersalivation	16%	*	4.5%
Nausea, vomiting	*	18.6%	13.6%
Malaise	*	16.3%	*
Dyspnea	*	14.0%	9.1%
Headache	*	14.0%	2.3%
Convulsions, spasms	*	*	9.1%
Coma	*	*	4.5%
Miscellaneous (lethargy, dysuria, anorexia, hydrophobia, etc)	*	16.3%	*
≥ 1 neurologic finding in course of illness	89%	*	*
≥ 2 classic symptoms in course of illness	71%	*	*
No history of rabies exposure	16%		39%

*Not addressed.
†Excluding pharyngeal symptoms relating to hydrophobia.
‡Including pharyngeal symptoms relating to hydrophobia.

hyperactivity, disorientation, hallucinations, periods of excitement, and bizarre behavior are the hallmark of the furious form of rabies.[27, 37, 42, 62, 132, 137] Hydrophobia, the most characteristic finding of rabies, has been noted in 21% of United States cases and in 17% to 50% of other reported cases.[37, 62] Painful contractions of the larynx and pharynx often develop.[27] These spasms last about 5 to 15 seconds and often result in aspiration, coughing, sneezing, choking, or vomiting. With sufficient arousal, they may lead to focal or generalized convulsions. The patient quickly develops a conditioned aversion to swallowing and to water. Even the thought of water may be sufficient to trigger terror and spasms. Similar muscle spasms and terror may be brought about by a draft of air on the skin (aerophobia), by the patient's attempt to speak, by loud sounds, by touching the patient's skin, or by bright lights.[37] Focal or generalized seizures are frequently seen and have been reported to cause 28% of patient deaths in one series.[27]

Episodes of hyperexcitability may be marked by disorientation, agitation, and hallucination. The patient may exhibit bizarre behavior or may become aggressive, attempting to injure or bite persons caring for him. The patient's hyperexcitable state often alternates with periods of calm and insight into his disease. Muscle fasciculations at the site of exposure, hyperventilation, lacrimation, sweating, "gooseflesh," and dilation of the pupils are occasionally noted. Increased libido, priapism, and spontaneous ejaculation have also been rarely described.

Paralytic or dumb rabies represents another presentation of the acute neurologic phase of rabies. It may be the primary presentation or it may follow the furious phase. Between 15% and 60% of patients with human rabies will exhibit paralysis as the only manifestation of disease.[9, 37, 136] The paralysis may be a diffuse, symmetric process[132, 137]; it may be more pronounced in the region of the bite[37]; or in about 20% it may be a flaccid ascending paralysis of the Guillain-Barré-Landry type.[44, 62, 132, 138] Paralysis usually results in mechanical respiratory insufficiency from involvement of respiratory muscle innervation. Cranial nerve paralysis has also been noted.[135] Neurologic findings may wax and wane during the acute neurologic phase, and nuchal rigidity is present only in a minority of patients.

Unless a patient has succumbed earlier to complications, coma follows two to ten days after the onset of the acute neurologic phase (see Figure 19–7). During this phase, a variety of potentially fatal complications is most likely to cause death. The length of coma is quite variable and survival during this phase depends on aggressive supportive therapy. The overall duration of illness until death averages 18 days (range 3–133 days).[62] Intensive supportive care significantly affects the duration of illness; the average duration was 8.5 days for those not given intensive care and 27.5 days for those who received it. There appears to be no relationship between incubation period and duration of illness,[27] but patients with furious manifestation may have a longer survival than those with only paralysis.[37] Occasional prolonged survivals have been recorded,[139] but only three patients have had a well-documented recovery from rabies.[77, 136, 140] One patient began improving 24 days after onset of clinical illness. He had complete neurologic recovery at 6 months.[136] The other two had incomplete recovery with moderate to severe neurologic deficits.[77, 140]

Neurologic and pulmonary complications are the most important of a wide variety of problems that accompany rabies. Neurologic complications may result directly from infection of the neural tissue or as a consequence of cerebral edema. Focal and general seizures, hyperactivity, centrally mediated hyperventilation, and CNS depression from cerebral edema are among the most commonly encountered problems. Pulmonary complications may be a consequence of centrally mediated respiratory drive depression, respiratory muscle paralysis, or secondary infection. Hypo- and hyperventilation, apnea, pneumonia, and atelectasis are frequently encountered. Hypersalivation and increased production of respiratory tract secretions may lead to aspiration. Hypothalamic abnormalities may result in diabetes insipidus or a syndrome of inappropriate antidiuretic hormone secretion (SIADH), which can occur in alternating sequence in a single patient. Autonomic nervous system abnormalities may result in cardiac arrhythmias, hypo- and hypertension, paralytic ileus, and urinary bladder retention. Hyperthermia can be a consequence of sepsis or of hypothalamic abnormalites, and hypothermia may also result from hypothalamic dysfunction. Complications related to intensive therapy for severe illness also occur: anemia, GI bleeding, congestive heart failure, blood volume abnormalities, and complications of invasive monitoring, such as thrombosis or infection due to monitoring catheters.[132]

DIAGNOSIS

The diagnosis of animal and human rabies can be made by four methods: (1) histopathology, (2) virus cultivation, (3) serology, and (4) virus antigen detection. Although each of the first three methods has advantages, none provides a rapid definitive diagnosis. Methods of rapid rabies antigen detection, first developed in the mid-1950s,[29, 141] allow early and accurate antemortem diagnosis of rabies, important for prompt appropriate therapy.

Details of rabies histophathology have previously been discussed (see Pathology). Negri bodies, virtually pathognomonic of rabies, are present in only 71% of cases,[27] but electron microscopy may increase the diagnostic yield of histopathology. Histopathology requires brain tissue and is generally limited to postmortem diagnosis. It is more time-consuming than the rapid diagnostic tests.

The most definitive means of diagnosis is by virus cultivation from infected tissue. Tissue culture lines, such as WI-38, BHK-21, or CER,[21, 142] can be used. Since rabiesvirus induces minimal CPE, direct fluorescent antibody staining for presence of rabiesvirus increases the sensitivity and rapidity of the test.[22] Intracerebral inoculation of mice or other laboratory rodents is a more commonly used method of virus cultivation. Intracerebral injections of 20% suspensions of infected material are made, and mice are examined for signs of disease. Upon death or at 28 days after inoculation, they are sacrificed, and the brains are examined for virus by immunofluorescence.[143] Neural tissue, salivary gland, saliva, and spinal fluid are most likely to contain virus cultivatable by these methods.

Rabies infection or vaccination results in antibody production, which can be measured by the mouse infection neutralization test (MNT)[144] or the rapid fluorescent focus inhibition test (RFFIT).[145, 146] To perform the MNT, serial dilutions of serum or cerebrospinal fluid are incubated with a standard rabiesvirus. The virus-serum mixture is then injected into mice, and the highest serum titer resulting in a 50% infection dose (ID_{50}) is determined. Presence of neutralizing antibodies at a titer of 1:2 or greater indicates active or passive immunization, or infection. The RFFIT is an indirect fluorescent test: patient antibodies competitively interfere with fluorescein-labeled antirabies antibody applied to an impression slide of rabies-infected mouse brain, and therefore the antibodies inhibit fluorescence. A plaque-reduction method for determining titers can also be used. Titers from each of these methods are not equivalent and may not even be proportional.[11, 145] Clinical rabies and immunization are sometimes difficult to distinguish serologically, but the presence of spinal fluid antibodies and very high serum antibody titers each strongly suggest infection rather than immunization.

In recent years rapid virus antigen detection using fluorescein-labeled antibody has become widely used in virology.[147] Detection of rabiesvirus by direct immunofluorescence is accomplished by incubating potentially infected tissue with fluorescein-labeled antirabies antibody. The cells are examined by fluorescent microscopy for evidence of fluorescent intracytoplasmic inclusions, which indicate the presence of rabiesvirus.[144] Immunofluorescence is a rapid and reliable method for identifying rabiesvirus in fresh brain biopsy or autopsy material. It can also be modified for rapid antemortem diagnosis using other tissue. Glass slide impressions of corneal epithelial cells that contain virus can often be detected by direct immunofluorescence.[32, 54, 148] Glass slides are gently placed against the cornea to lift off epithelial cells. They are air-dried, incubated with fluorescein-conjugated antibody, and examined for inclusions. Antemortem diagnosis of rabies can be made by direct immunofluorescence of sensory nerves in skin from the nape of the neck.[33] Direct immunoflourescence has been extremely reliable in animal studies and in evaluation of human cases. However, rare false-positives have been occasionally noted, so diagnosis should be substantiated with appropriate virus cultures.

Several new studies have documented additional methods that hold promise for the diagnosis of rabies. An avidin-biotin peroxidase system of rabies antigen detection may be more sensitive in detecting tissue antigen in formalin-fixed specimens than the comparative immunofluorescence test.[149] Similar results were obtained using immunoperoxidase staining of brain impression smears.[150] Other authors have compared immunofluorescent and immunoperoxidase tests, finding similar results.[151, 152] The immunoperoxidase method was more convenient, however.

Another immunodiagnosis method uses antinucleocapsid antibody fixed to microtiter plates to detect rabiesvirus antigen in a suspension of tissue.[153] The detection reagent was peroxidase-labeled IgG antibody to nucleocapsid. Test sensitivity was similar to immunofluorescent methods. A tissue culture infection test used microtiter suspensions of mouse neuroblastoma cells that were inoculated with infected brain tissue.[154, 154b] Hamster polyclonal antirabies antibody detected infection by four days of incubation. This method was more economical and at least as sensitive as the mouse inoculation test.

Serodiagnosis using a dot immunobinding assay has been developed for detection of rabies antibodies.[155] When compared to the rapid fluorescence focus inhibition test, the results were identical for both human and canine serum. Mouse monoclonal antibody resulted in the ability of the test to detect rabiesvirus glycoprotein and core antigens.

Monoclonal antibody technology has proved to be a useful diagnostic and research tool in the areas of epidemiology and the study of rabiesvirus antigens. Large panels of monoclonal antibodies to nucleocapsid protein have been used to study the antigenic character of rabies isolates in the United States.[95, 96, 98] Virus strains of different geographic origin have been linked using similarity of their monoclonal antibody reaction. In addition, nucleocapsid- and glycoprotein-specific antibodies have been able to distinguish between vaccine (fixed) and wild virus strains.[96, 128]

TREATMENT

Although the outlook for recovery from rabies is dismal, three documented human survivors provide a glimmer of hope,[77, 136, 139] and physicians should continue to make therapeutic efforts. Three aspects of treatment of rabies are important: (1) prevention and treatment of complications, (2) immune-related antirabies therapy, and (3) prevenion of exposure of patient caretakers to the virus.

Complications that require respiratory support occur in virtually all rabies patients. Progressive hypoxia may ensue during the prodrome and during agitation, despite hyperventilation, and oxygen should be administered. In later stages, mechanical ventilation may be required to counteract the respiratory depression which results from ascending paralysis or brain stem disease. Careful maintenance of pulmonary toilet is necessary to prevent atelectasis and secondary pulmonary infections. Excessive oral secretions require careful respiratory tract suctioning to prevent pooling of secretions, which may contribute to aspiration pneumonia.

Hyperactive episodes early in the course of rabies may be diminished by minimizing the patient's external stimuli. A darkened, quiet room may lessen agitation and seizures, and phenothiazine tranquilizers can be useful. Focal and generalized seizures can be controlled by phenytoin. Mannitol can be used as an osmotic diuretic in patients manifesting cerebral edema. SIADH is best managed by fluid restriction, and diabetes insipidus should be treated with fluid therapy and pitressin.[132]

Cardiovascular complications may result from hypoxia or from autonomic nervous system dysfunction. Treatment of arrhythmias should include oxygen therapy and a trial of antiarrhythmic medications. Hypotension should be corrected with fluid administration and vasopressors, while congestive heart failure may respond to fluid restriction, digitalis, and diuretics. Monitoring of central venous, pulmonary artery, and wedge pressures should be carried out when fluid balance, congestive heart failure, and hypotension are difficult to manage. Cardiac arrest should be treated with standard resuscitation measures.[127, 132, 136]

Controversy still exists concerning the use of immunotherapy in patients with symptomatic rabies infection. Remarkably high neutralizing antibody titers are often present early in the course of clinical illness and frequently high titers are present by the time the diagnosis is made[135] (C. Helmick, unpublished results, 1981). Additional stimulation by vaccine after onset of disease is unlikely to afford any additional protective antibody titer. Rabies immune globulin (RIG) blunts antibody response in patients receiving duck embryo vaccine for postexposure prophylaxis[156, 157] and could theoretically blunt the patient's native antibody response to the wild virus infection. However, some authors have suggested using RIG in treatment of symptomatic patients because serum and CSF neutralizing antibody may be absent for the first ten days of some patients' illnesses.[158] Neither vaccine nor RIG has resulted in survival, and their use may cause some difficulty in interpretation of serology for early confirmation of diagnosis.

Tissue culture experiments have demonstrated the antirabies virus effects of human interferon.[64] If given early, interferon is protective in experimental animal rabies.[65–67, 159] Pharmacokinetics of human leukocyte interferon A in humans seem favorable for its use in therapy.[160] Administration of 1 to 20×10 units produced peak serum levels of 76 to 1196 units in five patients suspected of having rabies. Intraventricular administration of 0.5 to 5.0×10 units resulted in peak CSF levels of 4000 to 35,000 units. However, a small therapeutic trial produced disappointing results.[160] Intramuscular and intrathecal administration of about 10^6 to 10^7 units to five patients for 10 to 17 days did not prevent death. All of the patients had been symptomatic for 8 to 14 days before therapy was begun. Interferon appeared to limit the titers of neutralizing antibody produced, but no symptomatic side effects were observed. Conceivably, interferon could afford some benefit if given early, but the final answer regarding its usefulness awaits further investigation.

Animal rabies models have been used to explore the antirabies efficacy of a variety of other substances. Prevention of infection was provided in mice pretreated with some heteropolyanions, two of which prolonged survival in foxes. Some protection was afforded in a weanling mouse model by iododeoxyuridine, actinomycin D, 6-azacytidine, and azathioprine (Imuran), given intracerebrally or IM.[161, 162] Other compounds, including several nucleoside analogues (ribavirin, tiazofurin, pyrazofurin), amantadine, lipacids, phenols, didemnin-B, and procaine had no apparent effect. Attempts to modify the course in previously infected monkeys using a highly attenuated virus (RV 675) have proved unsuccessful.[163] Human application of other therapeutic agents has not yet been tried.

One final consideration is the prevention of rabies exposure among patient contacts. Despite the large number of human rabies contacts, there has never been a documented instance of human-to-human transmission of rabies, except by corneal transplantation. However, appropriate preventive measures should still be taken. Although the details of virus shedding in infected humans are not entirely known, it is clear that the virus can be detected in human saliva, spinal fluid, neural tissue, and corneas. There is little evidence for human viremia, and virus shedding in the stool is unlikely. However, foxes and bats have been shown to occasionally excrete the virus in urine.[164, 165] Care should be taken to avoid direct contact with neural tissue, CSF, nasopharyngeal secretions, and perhaps urine. The patient should be placed in isolation, and persons performing autopsies on a patient suspected of having rabies should take care to avoid inhalation of CSF and brain tissue aerosols created by power cutting tools. If patient contacts have had risk exposures, they should be treated with standard postexposure prophylaxis as soon as possible, and they may often require reassurance.

PREVENTION

Since rabies is almost invariably a fatal illness, emphasis has been rightly placed on preventing human infection. Three aspects of disease prevention should be recognized: (1) prevention of exposure by contact with animals, (2) prophylaxis of those individuals most likely to be exposed to the virus, and (3) prevention of the onset of infection in those who have been exposed to the virus.

Since rabies is a zoonosis, man becomes a casual host only by exposure to an infected animal. Human illness can be prevented by elimination of this exposure through control of rabies in wild, feral, and domestic animals. Currently, control of rabies in domestic animals is most feasible, and it is extremely important, since a rabies-free domestic animal population provides a buffer between rabies-infected wild animals and humans. Rabies outbreaks in domestic and feral animals have resulted in human rabies. Control of rabies in the domestic animal population has been demonstrated to prevent human exposures and cases of rabies.[75, 166] Enacting and enforcing rabies vaccination laws, capture of stray animals, and providing rabies vaccination through low-cost animal clinics will result in control of domestic animal rabies and diminished human risk. Wildlife rabies control still awaits practical methods.

Persons likely to be exposed to rabies should receive preexposure prophylaxis. Laboratory workers who handle potentially infected tissue and virus, veterinarians, animal control officers working in rabies-prevalent areas, and individuals who travel to areas where rabies is highly endemic ought to receive initial immunization followed by maintenance boosters with killed rabies vaccine.[167] Currently, the preferred vaccine is human diploid cell vaccine (HDCV), because of its demonstrated safety and efficacy.[168, 169] The recommended vaccination schedule is illustrated in Table 19–6. Persons with continuing risk of exposure should receive a booster dose every 2 years. Use of vaccines other than the HDCV should be monitored with antibody titers, to assure that the vaccine recipient has developed a protective antibody titer. Since 100% of HDCV recipients acquire protective antibody levels following preexposure vaccination,[170, 171] monitoring of titers is generally not necessary.

Rabies infection has been described in a US Peace Corps volunteer to Africa, who had received recommended pre-exposure prophylaxis. An investigation of other Peace Corps workers discovered inadequate antibody levels in some. Further study suggested that concomitant chloroquine administration may have diminished antibody response to the vaccine. Thus, chloroquine should not be given while the patient is receiving pre-exposure prophylaxis.

Postexposure prophylaxis is intended to prevent rabies in persons who have been exposed to the virus. Each exposure situation should be evaluated individually by a physician and three factors should be considered before instituting postexposure prophylaxis: (1) species of the biting animal, (2) circumstances of the bite incident, and (3) type of exposure. Careful review of each factor will help the physician to determine the potential risk of rabies exposure, to appropriately decide on administration of postexposure prophylaxis, and to minimize unnecessary prophylaxis. Public health officers can provide valuable assistance in making decisions. An algorithm has been developed to guide postexposure therapy (Figure 19–8). If data are available regarding the rabies status of the biting animal, further consideration of the species is not necessary. Lacking this information, the likelihood of rabies exposure can be judged according to the species that are most often infected

Table 19–6
Recommended Rabies Prophylaxis With Human Diploid Cell Strain Vaccine (HDCV) and Rabies Hyperimmune Globulin (RIG)

| | Postexposure | |
Preexposure	Demonstrated Previous Rabies Antibody Titer	No Previous Demonstrated Antibody Titer
1. RIG*		
None	None	20 IU/kg body weight†
2. HDCV*		
1 mL on days 0, 7, 21	1 mL on days 0, 3	1 mL on days 0, 3, 7, 14, 28
3. Booster*		
Every 2 yr while exposure continues	None, except as needed for continuing preexposure prophylaxis	None

*Intramuscular injection.
†Administer half of dose intramuscularly; half of dose should be infiltrated around bite.
Data from Centers for Disease Control. Supplementary statement on rabies vaccine and serologic testing. MMWR 1981; 30:355–356.

with rabies, locally. Wild carnivores (such as skunks, raccoons, foxes, coyotes, and bobcats), bats, canines, and cattle are animals commonly infected with rabies in the United States. In other parts of the world, wolves, mongooses, and other carnivores are infected. Small warm-blooded animals, such as rodents (ie, squirrels, hamsters, chipmunks, rats, and mice) and lagomorphs, rarely carry rabies and have not transmitted rabies to humans. Antirabies prophylaxis is virtually never indicated following a bite by one of the latter animal groups. However, a bite by one of the former groups of wild animals would require postexposure prophylaxis, unless the animal has been demonstrated nonrabid by laboratory testing. Knowledge of the regional epidemiology of rabies is also important in deciding whether a biting animal may have been infected. In countries (see Table 19–4) or in regions that are rabies-free, postexposure prophylaxis is not needed. The likelihood of dog or cat rabies infection may vary from region to region, and the need for prophylaxis following a bite would depend on the local rabies epidemiology. If rabies vaccination can be documented in a dog or cat, the likelihood that the animal is infected is extremely low and prophylaxis is not necessary.

The circumstances of a biting incident may provide additional rabies exposure information. An unprovoked attack by a domestic animal should be regarded with suspicion. A bite provoked by teasing, feeding, or handling an apparently healthy strange domestic animal, or by trespassing on an animal's territory is less likely to indicate rabies. Abnormal behavior, paralysis, or other rabies-associated symptoms (see Rabies in Animals) in a domestic animal may indicate active rabies. Interpretation of wild animal behavior for rabies is unreliable, and the animal should be sacrificed as the circumstances warrant for brain examination.

Bites, any penetration of the skin by teeth, allow direct entry of the rabiesvirus into tissues. Nonbite exposures, such as contaminiation of open wounds, or abrasions of mucous membranes with saliva or brain tissue from a rabid animal can transmit the disease as well. Contact that does not include such exposure, such as petting, does not constitute a risk and prophylaxis is not required.

Documentation of rabies in an animal should be obtained as promptly as possible. Depending on the local rabies epidemiology,

appropriate wild animals and stray or unwanted domestic animals that show any signs of rabies should be humanely sacrificed. The animal's head should be removed and shipped under refrigeration for examination by a qualified laboratory. An improperly preserved brain may render testing useless[172] and result in unnecessary rabies prophylaxis for the patient. A healthy domestic dog or cat may be confined and observed for ten days. If illness suggesting rabies ensues, a veterinarian should evaluate the animal and it should be humanely killed and the brain examined. If brain tissue contains no evidence of infection, there will be no virus in the animal's saliva and prophylaxis is not needed.

Preventive therapy should be instituted as soon as possible following an exposure. The bite should be washed thoroughly with soap and debrided as necessary. Animal studies have clearly demonstrated the protective effect of washing rabies-infected wounds with 20% soap solution or various concentrations of benzalkonium chloride (BZC), which decreases rabies mortality by 35% to 90%.[173–176] Reduction in mortality is greater with mechanical scrubbing than with only irrigation of the wound, and mortality is similar with the use of commercially available concentrations of BZC and soap. Prompt and thorough scrubbing of wounds with soap is recommended.[177] Tetanus toxoid and antibiotic therapy should be administered, as situations warrant.

RIG and rabies vaccine should be given promptly, when indicated. Every effort to obtain pertinent exposure risk information should be made before beginning therapy, but needless delay may increase the likelihood of vaccine failure. Occasionally RIG and vaccine therapy must be started pending determination of exposure risk and may later be discontinued if therapy is unnecessary. Although a number of apparent vaccine failures have been noted with the duck embryo, mouse brain, and HDC vaccines, nearly all of these failures may have resulted from delayed administration of vaccine, serum, or less than adequate postexposure therapy as judged by current recommendations.[178, 179] Steroid administration may potentially result in vaccine failure.[133, 134]

A prospective study of postexposure prophylaxis among 21 states revealed that 88% of the courses given were appropriate, if a state health department was involved. However, when the potential exposure resulted from domestic animals, rodents, and la-

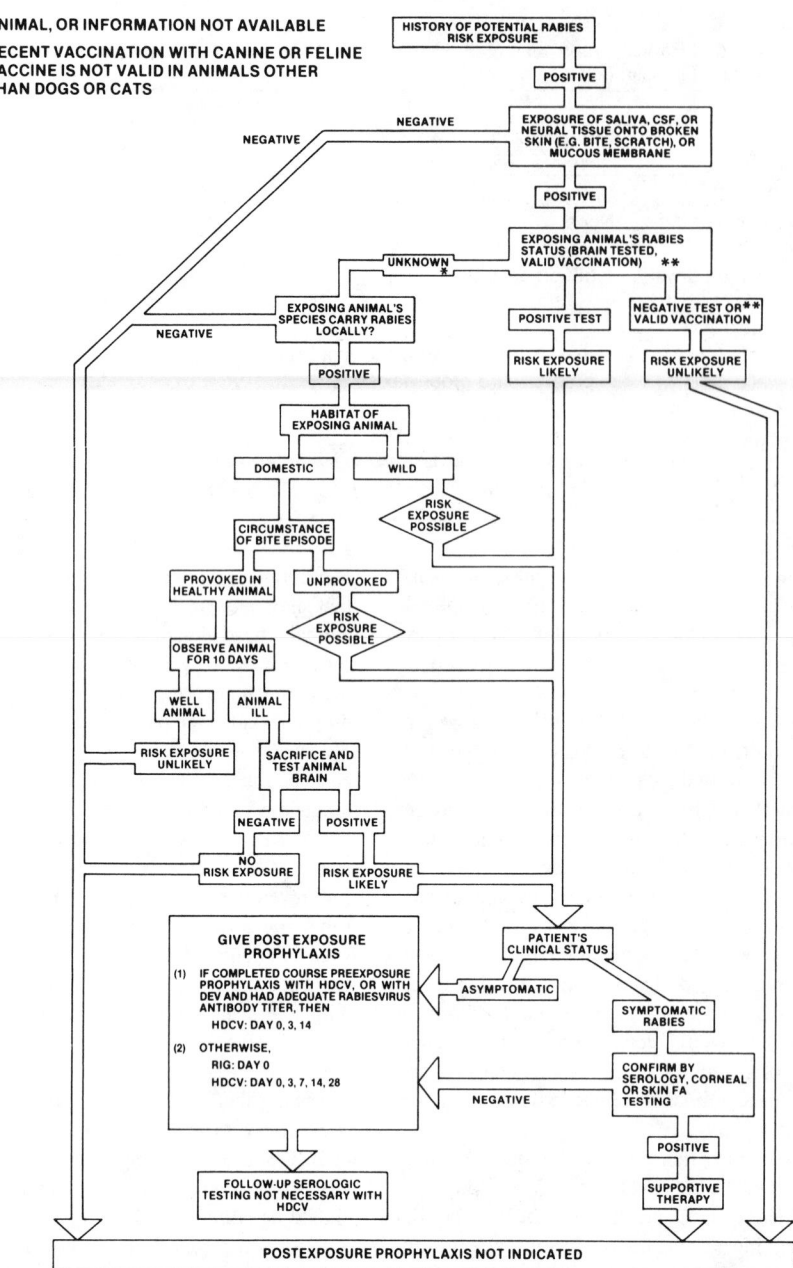

Figure 19–8. Decision algorithm for rabies postexposure prophylaxis. HDCV = human diploid cell vaccine; DEV = duck embryo vaccine; RIG = rabies immune globulin; FA = direct fluorescent antibody test.

gomorphs, postexposure prophylaxis was utilized out of proportion to the role which these animals play in rabies exposures.[180]

Table 19–6 indicates appropriate treatment regimens for postexposure prophylaxis. Half the RIG should be infiltrated into the site of exposure to neutralize local virus. If a patient has already complete primary immunization, such as preexposure prophylaxis or a previous course or postexposure therapy, or if he has received more than seven days of his current postexposure course, he should not be given RIG, which may delay his native antibody response. Serum neutralizing antibody generated by vaccination appears to have a direct relationship to protection against rabies in several animal models,[122] and probably represents the protective antibody in man.

The glycoprotein-containing spikes that project from the viral envelope appear to be the sole antigen responsible for induction of neutralizing antibodies.[181] When subvirion components were used to inoculate mice or rabbits, the purified envelope glycoprotein resulted in neutralizing titers 3.5 to 80 times higher than "core particles" or nucleocapsid material. Core particles, a mixture of envelope proteins, and whole virus induced titers proportional to the amount of "contaminating" glycoprotein each contained. Purified glycoprotein had a neutralzing antibody-binding activity value that was 8 times higher than core particles, suggesting neutralizing antibodies had a high degree of specificity for envelope glycoproteins. Nucleocapsid and core particles administered to mice provided virtually no protection against rabiesvirus infection. Whole virion inoculation was more protective than either glycoprotein or envelope preparations, probably due to interferon induction. These data suggest the protection of whole virus or subunit vaccines depends on the presence of envelope glycoprotein. Finally, liposomally anchored spike glycoprotein (immunosomes) induced both strong humoral and cellular immune responses. Pre- and postexposure potency testing demonstrated a high level of protection.[181a]

Semple-Type Vaccine

The Semple vaccine is derived from virus-inoculated rabbit brain. A neural tissue suspension was prepared and inactivated by formalin phenol.[182] Vaccine modification included use of goat, sheep, or monkey brain and inactivation with formalin. Antibody production following immunization is satisfactory, but allergic encephalomyelitis from the exposure to brain tissue can be a significant problem.[183, 184] This appears to be related to myelin basic protein contained in the vacine.[184a] A recent epidemiologic study has defined a minimum rate of 4.6 cases of neurologic complications per 1000 vaccinees.[185] Encephalitis or myelitis occurred in 22 of 31 identified cases (68.8%). The case-fatality proportion was 3.13%. Semple-type vaccines are employed in some developing countries.[11]

Suckling Mouse Brain (SMB)

Mouse brain-derived vaccine is used principally in Central and South America for rabies vaccination.[186, 187] The vaccine is prepared by intracerebral inoculation of virus into suckling mice. The animals are killed, and brain suspension is treated with ultraviolet light and phenol to inactivate the virus.[187–189]

Mouse brain vaccine is very immunogenic, resulting in high antibody titers in about 93% of recipients.[186, 187] Unfortunately, it carries with it a considerable risk of allergic encephalomyelitis and other neurologic diseases, a consequence of the brain antigen contained in the vaccine.[188–190] It has been supplanted by duck embryo vaccine (DEV) in many countries, but SMB remains important in South America. Although SMB causes more serious side effects than DEV, it results in a higher rate of seroconversion.

Duck Embryo Vaccine (DEV)

Once the sole human rabies vaccine in the United States, DEV is no longer marketed in the United States.[191] The vaccine virus is grown in embryonated duck eggs and is inactivated with β-propriolactone.[192–194] It is lyophilized in single-dose vials for reconstitution to a 1-mL volume. Adverse reactions to DEV are considerable. One hundred percent of persons receiving postexposure prophylaxis have local reactions, 33% have constitutional symptoms such as fever, malaise, myalgia, generalized adenopathy, and 0.9% have anaphylaxis. Rare reports of transverse myelitis, cranial or peripheral neuropathy, thrombocytopenic purpura, and fatal or nonfatal encephalopathy are noted.[195]

Human Diploid Cell Vaccine (HDVC)

HDVC was introduced in 1978. It is a killed cirus human vaccine. Rabiesvirus is grown on WI-38 (United States) or MRC-5 (Europe) cells and is inactivated by tri-*n*-butyl phosphate (WI-38 strain) or β-propiolactone (MRC-5 strain). The vaccine is lyo-

phylized and should be stored at 4°C until used.[167] Since the discontinuance of distribution of DEV in 1981, it is currently the only vaccine available in the United States, and it is widely available worldwide. Only five (USPHS recommendation) or six (WHO recommendation) IM injections are required. Studies demonstrate remarkably good immunogenicity in both preexposure and postexposure prophylaxis.[61] In two large studies from Canada and the United States, 100% of persons receiving postexposure IM treatment attained protective titers.[170, 196] Several studies show good immunogenicity using intradermal administration.[197, 198] Antibody duration is shorter, but major side effects are less than with IM administration.[199] Serious adverse reactions to HDCV are extremely rare. Of 2500 patients receiving HDCV, 0.16% had systemic allergic reactions and 0.16% reported fever and severe headache. Occasional reports of diarrhea, chills, and headache were noted and minor local reactions were present in less than one fourth of the patients.[200] No cases of postvaccination encephalopathy occurred. Similar experience has been noted in Europe.[198, 201, 202] One rabies death has been reported in a person who did not receive prescribed therapy.[177] However, a small number of cases of human rabies has occurred despite apparently adequate administration and timing of human diploid cell vaccine and human rabies immune globulin.[203, 204] Although the reasons for these failures are not clear, it was speculated to result from intragluteal administration of vaccine, a practice that has been shown to result in lower hepatitis B antibodies when that vaccine is given intragluteally rather than in the deltoid muscle.[205] Passive immunization using antirabies serum (ARS) or RIG in conjunction with vaccination has clearly reduced human rabies mortality.[206] Several studies have helped to elucidate the ideal combination of DEV and human RIG, and of HDCV and RIG.[156–158, 196]

Recent studies continue to support the efficacy of human diploid cell virus strain (HDCV) in preventing rabies in patients with significant exposure.[111] Intradermal postexposure vaccination has been used with success by some physicians. Incomplete courses of vaccination may result in significant risk of clinical rabies.

Another tissue culture-source vaccine has been recently licensed in the United States.[207] It is an inactivated vaccine derived from a diploid fetal rhesus lung cell-adapted Kissling strain and concentrated by adsorption to aluminum phosphate.[208] Preexposure, simulated postexposure, and booster testing has indicated that adequate neutralizing antibody levels are achieved in more than 99% of vaccine recipients.[209–211] The timing of vaccination for each of these circumstances should be the same as for HDCV.[207, 212] Local reactions to primary vaccination with the adsorbed vaccine are similar to HDCV and occur in about 85% to 90% of recipients. About 10% experience mild systemic reactions. The systemic allergic reactions seen with HDCV have occurred with much less frequency in patients given the adsorbed vaccine.

Another inactivated vaccine is widely used in the People's Republic of China. It is derived from virus grown in primary hamster kidney cell tissue culture.[213] Cost of the vaccine is less than other diploid cell vaccines. The vaccine has been reported to have high potency, and neutralizing antibody production was similar to HDCV. Two episodes of high-risk exposure support the vaccine's efficacy. Fifty-eight persons were bitten by two rabid wolves. All who received appropriate vaccination were protected, while 12 who did not died from subsequent rabies.

Antirabies Serum (ARS)

Horse serum hyperimmunized by vaccination is concentrated and refined to produce equine antirabies serum. The neutralizing antibody content is standardized to 1000 IU/5-mL vial. Although effective, 40% of adults who receive ARS will experience serum sickness.

Rabies Immune Globulin (RIG)

Human rabies immune globulin is prepared by cold ethanol fractionation of plasma to obtain a concentrated gamma globulin fraction from hyperimmunized human donors. One hundred fifty international units of neutralizing antibody are contained in each milliliter. Rare adverse reactions to RIG make it preferable to ARS.

Although the production of monoclonal antibodies to rabies virus in tissue culture hybridomas is in the very early experimental stage, these antibodies may ultimately replace equine and human antirabies globulin for passive immunization. Continuous tissue culture cell lines are produced by merging mouse myeloma cells and spleen cells from mice that have been immunized with rabies vaccine. The derived cells are cloned and cell lines which produce the desired antibodies are continuously cultivated. Highly specific antibodies can be harvested cheaply and in large quantities. Monoclonal antibodies react more specifically than polyclonal antibodies produced in hyperimmunized animals and humans and may neutralize virus more effectively.[4]

THE FUTURE

There are several areas that promise advances in understanding, control, and therapy of rabies. Work is progressing in the area of wildlife rabies control: surveillance to help us to better understand its behavior in animals and vaccine development to provide a safe, effective wildlife vaccine and the means to deliver it. Further investigation ought to elucidate the occurrence and importance of prolonged survival and possible recovery from rabies in animals. Endonuclease reduction fingerprinting and monoclonal antibodies will help to better characterize virus strains and track their occurrence. Monoclonal antibodies may also provide highly effective passive immunotherapy of human disease. The usefulness of interferon and antiviral therapy needs further investigation. Finally, genetic engineering has already resulted in encoded *Escherichia coli* which can synthesize viral envelope glycoprotein, a potential source for inexpensive subunit vaccine production.[214]

REFERENCES

1. Hildreth EA: Prevention of rabies or the decline of Sirius. *Ann Intern Med* 1963; 88:883–896.
2. Parrish HM, Clark FB, Brobst D, et al: Epidemiology of dog bites. *Public Health Rep* 1967; 82:1009–1018.
3. Tierkel ES: Rabies. *Adv Vet Sci* 1959; 5:183–226.
4. Kaplan MM, Koprowski H: Rabies. *Sci Am* 1980; 242:120–134.
5. Walton HH: Case of hydrophobia. *Lancet* 1844; 2:214–215.
6. Merriman WJ: Hydrophobia and its prevention. *Lancet* 1844; 2:164–166.
7. Dubos RJ: *Louis Pasteur—Freelance of Science.* Boston, Little, Brown, 1950.
8. Vallery-Radott: *Louis Pasteur—A Great Life in Brief.* Joseph A (trans-ed). New York, Knopf, 1958.
9. Babes V: *Traité de la rage.* Paris, Bailliere, 1912.
10. Negri A: *Zeit Hyg Infectionskr* 1903; 44:519–540.
11. Plotkin SA: Rabies vaccine prepared in human cell cultures; progress and perspective. *Rev Infect Dis* 1980; 2:433–448.
12. Baltazard M, Ghodssi M: Prevention of human rabies—treatment of persons bitten by rabid wolves in Iran. *Bull WHO* 1954; 10:797–803.
13. Ginsberg HS: Rhabdoviruses, in Davis DD, Dulbecco R, Eisen HM, et al (eds): *Microbiology* Hagerstown, Md, Harper & Row, 1980, pp 1167–1175.
14. Matsumoto S: Rabies virus. *Adv Virus Res* 1970; 16:257–301.
15. Howatson AF: Vesicular stomatitis and related virus. *Adv Virus Res* 1970; 16:196–256.
16. Wagner RR: Reproduction of rhabdoviruses. *Comp Virol* 1975; 4:1–93.
17. Ditchfield WJB: Rabies, in Rhodes AJ, Van Rooyden (eds): *Textbook of Virology.* Baltimore, Williams & Wilkins, 1968.
18. Almeida JD, Howatson AF, Pinteric L, et al: Electron microscope observations on rabiesvirus by negative staining. *Virology* 1962; 18:147–151.
19. Matsumoto S: Electron microscope studies of rabiesvirus in mouse brain. *Cell Biol* 1963; 19:565–591.
20. Sikes RK, Larghi OP, Simpson CF, et al: Physical and chemical properties of rabies virus. International Symposium on Rabies, Talloires, France, 1965; *Symp Ser Immunobiol Stand* 1966; 1:55–64.
21. Fernandes MV, Wiktor TJ, Koprowski H: Endosymbiotic relationship between animal viruses and host cells. A study of rabiesvirus in tissue culture. *Exp Med* 1964; 120:1099–1116.
22. Rudd RJ, Trimarchi VC, Abelseth MK: Tissue culture technique for routine isolation of street strain rabies virus. *J Clin Microbiol* 1980; 12:590–593.
23. Davies MC, Englert ME, Sharpless GR, et al: The electron microscopy of rabies virus in cultures of chicken embryo tissue. *Virology* 1963; 21:642–651.
24. Atanasiu P, Lepine P, Dragonas P: Étude cinétique du virus rabique en culture de tissus a l'aide des anticorps fluorescents et des coupes ultrafines. *Ann Inst Pasteur* 1963; 105:813–824.
25. Rickettsial, chlamydial, and viral diseases, in Anderson WAD, Kissane JM (eds): *Pathology,* ed 7, St Louis, Mosby, 1977.
26. The nervous system, in Robbins SL, Cotran RS (eds): *Pathologic Basis of Disease.* Philadelphia, Saunders, 1979.
27. Dupont JR, Earle KM: Human rabies encephalitis—A study of forty-nine fatal cases with a review of the literature. *Neurology* 1965; 15:1023–1034.
28. Lowenberg K: Rabies in man. *Arch Neurol Psychiatry* 1928; 19:638–646.
29. Goldwasser RA, Kissling RE: Fluorescent antibody staining of street and fixed rabies virus antigens. *Proc Soc Exp Biol Med* 1958; 98:219–233.
30. Leach CN, Johnson HN: Human rabies, with special reference to virus distribution and titer. *Am J Trop Med* 1940; 20:335–340.
31. Robinson PA, Shaddock J, et al: Quantitation of rabies virus isolation in a patient. In preparation.
32. Kock FJ, Sagartz JW, Davidson DE, et al: Diagnosis of human rabies by the corneal test. *Am J Clin Pathol* 1975; 63:509–515.
33. Smith WB, Blenden DC, Fuk TH, et al: Diagnosis of rabies by immunofluorescent staining of frozen sections of skin. *J Am Vet Med Assoc* 1972; 161:1495–1501.
34. Dierkes RE, Murphy FA, Harrison AK: Extraneural rabiesvirus infection. Virus development in fox salivary gland. *Am J Pathol* 1969; 54:251–273.
35. Constantine DG, Emmons RW, Woodie JD: Rabiesvirus in nasal mucosa of naturally infected bats. *Science* 1972; 175:1255–1256.
36. Conomy JP, Leibovitz A, McCombs W, et al: Airborne rabies encephalitis: Demonstration of rabies virus in the human central

nervous system. *Neurology* 1977; 27:67–69.
37. Warrell DA: The clinical picture of rabies in man. *Trans R Soc Trop Med Hyg* 1976; 70:188–195.
38. Ross E, Armentrout SA: Myocarditis associated with rabies—Report of a case. *N Engl J Med* 1962; 266:1087–1089.
39. Winkler WG, Fashinell TR, Leffingwell L, et al: Airborne rabies transmission in a laboratory worker. *JAMA* 1973; 226:1219–1221.
40. Constantine DG: Rabies transmission by nonbite route. *Public Health Rep* 1962; 77:287–289.
41. Winkler EG: Airborne rabies virus isolation. *Bull Wildlife Dis Assoc* 1968; 4:37–40.
42. Centers for Disease Control: Human-to-human transmission of rabies via corneal transplant—Thailand. *MMWR* 1981; 30:472–474.
43. Centers for Disease Conrol: Human-to-human transmission of rabies via a corneal transplant—France. *MMWR* 1980; 29:25–26.
44. Houff SA, Burton RC, Wilson RW, et al: Human-to-human transmission of rabies virus by corneal transplant. *N Engl J Med* 1979; 300:603–604.
45. Murphy FA, Bauer SP: Early street rabiesvirus infection in striated muscle and later progression to the central nervous system. *Intervirology* 1974; 3:256–268.
46. Murphy FA, Bauer SP, Harrison AK, et al: Comparative pathogenesis of rabies and rabies-like viruses: Viral infection in transit from inoculation site to the central nervous system. *Lab Invest* 1973; 28:361–376.
47. Murphy FA: Rabies pathogenesis—Brief review. *Arch Virol* 1977; 54:279–297.
48. Lentz TL, Burrage TG, Smith AC, et al: Is the acetylcholine receptor a rabies virus receptor? *Science* 1982; 215:182–184.
49. Dean DJ, Evans WM, McClure RC: Pathogenesis of rabies. *Bull WHO* 1963; 29:803–811.
50. Jenson AB, Rabin ER, Bentick DC, et al: Rabiesvirus neuronitis. *J Virol* 1969; 3:265–269.
51. Baer GM, Shanthaveerappa TR, Bourne GH: Studies on the pathogenesis of fixed rabies virus in rats. *Bull WHO* 1965; 33:119–125.
52. Murphy FA, Harrison AK, Winn WC, et al: Comparative pathogenesis of rabies and rabies-like viruses. Infection of the central nervous system and centrifugal spread of virus to peripheral tissues. *Lab Invest* 1973; 29:1–16.
53. Warrell DA, Davison NM, Pope HM, et al: Pathophysiologic studies in human rabies *Am J Med* 1976; 60:180–190.
54. Larghi OP, Gonzalez E, Held L, et al: Evaluation of the corneal test as a laboratory method for rabies diagnosis. *Appl Microbiol* 1973; 25:187–189.
55. Duenas A, Bekey MA, Escobar J, et al: Isolation of rabies virus outside the human central nervous system. *J Infect Dis* 1973; 127:702–704.
56. Turner GS: Humoral and cellular immune responses of mice to rabies and smallpox vaccines. *Nature* 1973; 241:90–92.
57. Smith JS: Mouse mode for abortive rabies infection of the central nervous system. *Infect Immun* 1981; 31:247–308.
58. Iwasaki Y, Gerhard W, Clark HF: Role of host immune response in the development of either encephalitic or paralytic disease after experimental rabies infection in mice. *Infect Immun* 1977; 18:220–225.
59. Baer GM, Cleary WF: A model in mice for the pathogenesis and treatment rabies. *J Infect Dis* 1972; 125:520–527.
60. Turner GS: Immunoglobulin (IgG) and (IgM) antibody responses to rabies vaccine. *J Gen Virol* 1978; 40:595–604.
61. Bhamanyar M, Fayaz A, Nour-Salehi S, et al: Successful protection of humans exposed to rabies infection—postexposure treatment with the new human diploid cell rabies vaccine and antirabies serum. *JAMA* 1976; 236:2751–2754.
62. Anderson LJ, Nicholson KG, Tauxe RV, Winkler WG: Human rabies in the United States 1960–1979. Epidemiology, diagnosis and prevention. *Ann Intern Med,* 1984; 100:728–735.
63. Stewart WE, Sulkin SE: Interferon production in hamsters experimentally infected with rabiesvirus. *Proc Soc Exp Biol Med* 1966; 123:650–654.
64. Wiktor TJ, Koprowski H: Cyclic appearance of viral inhibitor in tissue cultures chronically infected with rabies virus. *Bacteriol Proc* 1967; 166.
65. Postic B, Fenje P: Effect of administered interferon on rabies in rabbits. *Appl Microbiol* 1971; 22:428–434.
66. Wiktor TJ, Postic B, Ho M, et al: Role of interferon induction in the protective activity of rabies vaccines. *J Infect Dis* 1972; 126:408–418.
67. Baer GM: Antiviral action of interferon in animal systems: Effect of interferon on rabies infection of animals. *Tex Rep Biol Med* 1977; 35:461–471.
68. Centers for Disease Control: Annual summary, 1980. *MMWR* 1981; 29:12–17.
69. Turner GS: A review of the world epidemiology of rabies. *Trans R Soc Trop Med Hyg* 1976; 70:175–178.
70. Held JR, Tierkel ES, Steele JH: Rabies in man and animals in the United States. 1946–1965. *Public Health Rep* 1967; 82:1009–1018.
71. Kappus KD: Canine rabies in the United States, 1971–1973: Study of reported cases with reference to vaccination history. *Am J Epidemiol* 1976; 103:242–249.
72. Centers for Disease Control: Rabies surveillance, July–September 1976. March, 1977.
73. Centers for Disease Control: Rabies surveillance, Annual summary 1976. October, 1977.
74. Bjorvath B, Gundersen SG: Rabies exposure among Norwegian missionaries working abroad. *Scand J Infect Dis* 1980; 12:257–264.
75. Robinson PA: Human rabies epidemic as a result of a canine epizootic. In preparation.
76. Baker EF: Rabies in Europe and a comparison of US and European rabies data. *Public Health Rep* 1978; 93:186–188.
77. Centers for Disease Control: Rabies in a laboratory worker—New York. *MMWR* 1977; 26:183–184.
78. Irons JV, Eads RB, Grimes JE, et al: The public health importance of bats. *Tex Rep Biol Med* 1957; 15:292–298.
79. Steck F, Wandeler A: The epidemiology of fox rabies in Europe. *Epidemiol Rev* 1980; 2:71–96.
80. Anderson RM, Jackson HC, May RM, et al: Population dynamics of fox rabies in Europe. *Nature* 1981; 289:765–771.
81. Lloyd HG: Wildlife rabies in Europe and the British situation. *Trans R Soc Trop Med Hyg* 1976; 70:179–187.
82. Winkler WG: Rabies in the United States, 1951–1970. *J Infect Dis* 1972; 125:674–675.
83. Centers for Disease Control: Rabies—United States, 1977. *MMWR* 1978; 27:499–500.
84. Sulkin SE, Greve MJ: Human rabies caused by bat bite. *Tex J Med* 1954; 50:620–621.
85. Vetners HD, Hoffert WR, Scatterday JE, et al: Rabies in bats in Florida. *Am J Public Health* 1954; 44:182–185.
86. Witte EJ: Bat rabies in Pennsylvania. *Am J Public Health* 1954; 44:186–187.
87. Centers for Disease Control: Rabies—Continental Europe, United States, 1979. *MMWR* 1980; 29:454–455.
88. Centers for Disease Control: Rabies—United States, 1980. *MMWR* 1981; 30:147.
89. Centers for Disease Control: Health information for international travel, 1981. *MMWR* 1981; 30:80.
90. Bell GP: A possible case of interspecific transmission of rabies in insectivorous bats. *J Mammal* 1980; 61:528–530.
91. Chapman RC: Rabies: Decimation of wolf pack in arctic Alaska. *Science* 1978; 201:365–367.
92. Steele JH: The epidemiology and control of rabies. *Scand J Infect Dis* 1973; 5:299–312.
93. Hurst EW, Pawan JL: An outbreak of rabies in Trinidad without history of bite and with symptoms of acute ascending myelitis. *Lancet* 1931; 2:622–628.

93a. Jenkins SR, Winkler WG: Descriptive epidemiology from an epizootic of raccoon rabies in the Middle Atlantic States, 1982–1983. *Am J Epidemiol* 1987; 126:429–437.

94. Beck AM, Felser SR, Glickman LT: An epizootic of rabies in Maryland. *Am J Public Health* 1987; 77:42–44.

95. Smith JS, Sumner JW, Rouillat LF, et al: Antigenic characteristics of isolates associated with a new epizootic of raccoon rabies in the United States. *J Infect Dis* 1984; 149:769–774.

96. Rollin PE, Sureau P: Monoclonal antibodies as a tool for rabies epidemiological studies. *Dev Biol Stand* 1984; 57:193–197.

97. Pacer RE, Fishbein DB, Baer GM, et al: Rabies in the United States and Canada, 1983. *MMWR* (CDC Surveillance Summary) 1985; 34:11SS–27SS.

98. Centers for Disease Control: Rabies surveillance 1986. *MMWR* 1987; 36(suppl 3):1S–27S.

99. Fishbein DB, Belotto AJ, Pacer RE, et al: Rabies in rodents and lagomorphs in the United States, 1971–1984: Increased cases in the woodchuck (*Marmota monax*) in mid-Atlantic states. *J Wildlife Dis* 1986; 22:151–155.

100. Kennedy DJ: An outbreak of rabies in north-western Zimbabwe 1980 to 1983. *Vet Rec* 1988; 122:129–133.

101. Wong TW, Chan PK, Fung KP: Human rabies cases in Hong Kong: a case review. *Ann Acad Med* Singapore 1987; 16:663–665.

102. Ezeokoli ED, Umoh JU: Epidemiology of rabies in northern Nigeria. *Trans R Soc Trop Med Hyg* 1987; 81:268–272.

103. Centers for Disease Control: Human rabies—California, 1987. *MMWR* 1988; 37:305–308.

104. Webster WA, Casey GA, Charlton KM, et al: A case of human rabies in western Canada. *Can J Public Health* 1987; 78:412–413.

105. Centers for Disease Control: Human rabies diagnosed 2 months postmortem—Texas. *MMWR* 1985; 34:700–707.

106. Centers for Disease Control: Imported human rabies—Australia, 1987. *MMWR* 1988; 37:351–353.

107. Centers for Disease Control: Human rabies—Pennsylvania. *MMWR* 1984; 33:633–635.

108. Bogel K, Motschwiller E: Incidence of rabies and postexposure prophylaxis in developing countries. *Bull WHO* 1986; 64:883–887.

109. Narayan KG, Konar M: Hydrophobia cases and post-exposure anti-rabic vaccines in Ranchi, Bihar (1979–84). *Int J Zoonoses* 1986; 13:63–69.

110. Lakhanpal U, Sharma RC: An epidemiological study of 177 cases of human rabies. *Int J Epidemiol* 1985; 14:614–617.

111. Monson MH: Practical management of rabies and the 1982 outbreak in Zorzor District, Liberia. *Trop Doct* 1985; 15:50–54.

112. Baer GM (ed): *The Natural History of Rabies.* New York, Academic Press, 1975.

113. Afshar A, Bahmanyar M: Nonfatal rabies virus in infection. *The Veterinary Bulletin* (Commonwealth Bureau of Animal Health) 1978, vol 48.

114. Baer GM: Rabies in nonhematophagous bats, in Baer GM (ed): *The Natural History of Rabies.* New York, Academic Press, 1975.

115. Webster LT: Epidemiologic and immunologic experiments on rabies. *N Engl J Med* 1937; 217:687–690.

116. Johnson HM: In National Symposium Proceedings—National Communicable Disease Center. Atlanta, Centers for Disease Control, May 1966, pp 25–30.

117. Fekadu M, Baer GM: Recovery from clinical rabies of 2 dogs inoculated with a rabiesvirus strain from Ethiopia. *Am J Vet Res* 1980; 41:1632–1634.

118. Fekadu M, Shaddock JH, Baer GM: Intermittent excretion of rabies virus in the saliva of a dog two and six months after it had recovered from experimental rabies. *Am J Trop Med Hyg* 1981; 30:1113–1115.

119. Andral L, Serie C: Étude expérimentals sur la rage in Ethiopia. *Ann Inst Pasteur* 1951; 93:475–488.

120. Fekadu M: Atypical rabies in dogs in Ethiopia. *Ethiop Med J* 1972; 10:79–86.

121. Bell JF: Latency and abortive rabies, in Baer GM (ed): *The Natural History of Rabies.* New York, Academic Press, 1975.

122. Crick J: The vaccination of man and other animals against rabies. *Postgrad Med J* 1973; 49:551–564.

123. Frederickson LE, Willet JC, Smith JE, et al: Mass immunization of dogs against rabies—Its influence on a rabies epizootic. *Am J Public Health* 1953; 43:399–404.

124. Centers for Disease Control: Compendium of animal rabies vaccines, 1990. *MMWR* 1990; 39:1–8.

125. The National Association of State Public Health Veterinarians: Compendium of animal rabies vaccines, 1986. *MMWR* 1986; 34:770–781.

126. Sikes RK, Peacock GV, Acha T, et al: Rabies vaccines: Duration-of-immunity study in dogs. *J Am Vet Med Assoc* 1971; 159:1491–1499.

127. Centers for Disease Control: Follow-up on suspected vaccine-induced rabies in cats. *MMWR* 1980; 29:86–87.

128. Whetstone CA, Bunn TO, Emmons RW, et al: Use of monoclonal antibodies to confirm vaccine-induced rabies in ten dogs, two cats, and one fox. *J Am Vet Assoc* 1984; 185:285–288.

129. Nicholson KG, Bauer SP: Enteric inoculation with ERA rabies virus: Evaluation of the candidate wildlife vaccine in laboratory rodents. *Arch Virol* 1981; 67:51–56.

130. Winkler WG, Shaddock J, Williams LW: A liver rabies vaccine: Evaluation of its infectivity in three species of rodent. *Am J Epidemiol* 1976; 104:294–298.

131. Winkler WG, Baer GM: Rabies immunization of red foxes (*Vulpes fulva*) with vaccine in sausage baits. *Am J Epidemiol* 1976; 103:408–415.

132. Hattwick MAW: Human rabies. *Public Health Rev* 1974; 3:229–274.

133. Hattwick MAW, Gregg MB: The disease in man, in Baer GM (ed): *The Natural History of Rabies.* New York, Academic Press, 1975.

133a. Nikolitsch M: Second observation on the method of infection by neutrotropic viruses (reviewed by Spooner ETC). *Trop Dis Bull* 1953; 50:1133–1134.

134. Soave OA: Reactivation of rabies virus in a guinea pig with adrenocorticotropic hormone. *J Infect Dis* 1962; 110:129–131.

135. Bhatt DR, Hattwick MAW, Gerdsen R, et al: Human rabies—Diagnosis complications, and management. *Am J Dis Child* 1974; 127:862–869.

136. Hattwick MAW, Weis TT, Stechschulte CJ, et al: Recovery from rabies—A case report. *Ann Intern Med* 1972; 76:931–942.

137. Baraff LJ, Hafkin B, Wehrle TF, et al: Human rabies. *West J Med* 1978; 128:159–164.

138. Pawan JL: Paralysis as a clinical manifestation in human rabies. *Ann Trop Med Parasitol* 1939; 33:21–29.

139. Emmons RW, Leonard LL, DeGenaro F, et al: A case of human rabies with prolonged survival. *Intervirology* 1973; 1:60–72.

140. Barboza JJ, Porras C, Fuenzalida E, et al: Recovery in a presumptive human rabies case, Mendoza, Argentina. *Vigilancia Epidemiologica* (Rabies Surveillance for the Americas) 1972; 4:90–91.

141. Goldwasser RA, Kissling RE, Carski RT, et al: Fluorescent antibody staining of rabies virus antigens in the salivary glands of rabid animals. *Bull WHO* 1959; 20:579–588.

142. Smith AL, Tignor CH, Emmons RW, et al: Isolation of field rabies virus strains in CER and murine neuroblastoma cell cultures. *Intervirology* 1978; 9:359–361.

143. Koprowski H: Mouse inoculation test, in Atonasiu P (ed): *Laboratory Technique in Rabies,* ed 2. Geneva, World Health Organization, 1966.

144. Rabies procedures, in Ballow H, Forrester FT, Lyerla HC, et al (eds): *Laboratory Diagnosis of Viral Disease.* Atlanta, US Public Health Service—Centers for Disease Control, 1977.

145. Grandien M: Evaluation of tests for rabies antibody and analysis of serum responses after administration of three different types of rabies vaccine. *J Clin Microbiol* 1977; 5:263–267.

146. Louie RE, Dobkin MB, Meyer P, et al: Measurement of rabies

antibody comparison of the mouse neutralization tests (MNT) and the rapid fluorescent focus inhibition test (RFFIT). *J Biol Stand* 1975; 3:365–373.

147. II. Immunofluorescence and human viral disease, in Kurstak E, Morisset R (eds): *Viral Immunodiagnosis.* New York, Academic Press, 1974.

148. Cifuentes E, Calderon E, Bijlenga G: Rabies in a child diagnosed by a new intra-vitam method—The cornea test. *J Trop Med Hyg* 1971; 74:23–25.

149. Fekadu M, Greer PW, Chandler FW, et al: Use of the avidin-biotin peroxidase system to detect rabies antigen in formalin-fixed paraffin-embedded tissues. *J Virol Methods* 1988; 19:91–96.

150. Anjaria JM, Jhala CI: Immunoperoxidase reaction in diagnosis of rabies. *Int J Zoonoses* 1985; 12:267–275.

151. Palmer DG, Ossent P, Suter MM, et al: Demonstration of rabies viral antigen in paraffin tissue sections: comparison of the immunofluorescence technique with the unlabelled antibody enzyme method. *Am J Vet Res* 1985; 46:283–286.

152. Kotwal S, Naraya KG: Direct immunoperoxidase test in the diagnosis of rabies—an alternative to fluorescent antibody test. *Int J Zoonoses* 1985; 12:80–85.

153. Perrin P, Rollin PE, Sureau P: A rapid rabies enzyme immunodiagnosis (RREID): a useful and simple technique for the routine diagnosis of rabies. *J Biol Stand* 1986; 14:217–222.

154. Centers for Disease Control: Imported human rabies—Australia, 1987. *MMWR* 1988; 37:351–353.

154a. B. Rudd RJ, Trimarchi CV: Development and evaluation of an in vitro virus isolation procedure as a replacement for the mouse inoculation test in rabies diagnosis. *J Clin Microbiol* 1989; 27:2522–2528.

155. Heberling RL, Kalter SS, Smith JS, et al: Serodiagnosis of rabies by dot immunobinding assay. *J Clin Microbiol* 1987; 25:1262–1264.

156. Corey L, Hattwick MAW, Baer GM, et al: Serum neutralizing antibody after rabies postexposure prophylaxis. *Ann Intern Med* 1976; 85:170–176.

157. Hattwick MAW, Rubin RH, Music S, et al: Postexposure rabies prophylaxis with human rabies immune globulin. *JAMA* 1974; 227:407–410.

158. Hattwick MAW, Corey L, Creech WB: Clinical use of human globulin immune to rabies virus. *J Infect Dis* 1976; 133(suppl):A266–A272.

159. Wiktor TJ, Koprowski H, Mitchell JR, et al: Role of interferon in prophylaxis of rabies after exposure. *J Infect Dis* 1976; 133(suppl):A260–A265.

160. Merigan TC, Baer GM, Winkler WG, et al: Human leukocyte interferon administration to patients with symptomatic and suspected rabies. *Ann Neurol* 1984; 16:82–87.

161. Bussereau F, Picard M, Blancou J, et al: Treatment of rabies in mice and foxes with antiviral compounds. *Acta Virol (Praha)* 1988; 32:33–49.

162. Sodja I: Experimental chemotherapy of rabies. *Acta Virol (Praha)* 1986; 30:63–68.

163. Warrell MJ, Ward GS, Elwell MR, et al: An attempt to treat rabies encephalitis in monkeys with intrathecal live rabies virus RV 675. *Arch Virol* 1987; 96:271–273.

164. Girard KF, Hitchcock HB, Edsall G, et al: Rabies in bats in Southern New England. *N Engl J Med* 1965; 272:75–80.

165. Debbi JG, Trimarchi CV: Rabies in fox urine. *Wildlife Dis* 1970; 6:500–506.

166. Glosser JW, Hutchinson LR, Rich AB, et al: Rabies in El Paso, Texas, before and after institution of a new rabies control program. *J Am Vet Med Assoc* 1970; 157:820–825.

167. Centers for Disease Control: Rabies prevention. *MMWR* 1980; 29:265–280.

168. Anderson LJ, Baer GM, Smith JS, et al: Rapid antibody response to human diploid rabies vaccine. *Am J Epidemiol* 1981; 113:270–275.

169. Hafkin B, Hattwick MAW, Smith JS, et al: A comparison of a WI-38 and duck embryo vaccine for preexposure rabies prophylaxis. *Am J Epidemiol* 1978; 107:439–443.

170. Centers for Disease Control: Use of human diploid cell vaccine for postexposure rabies treatment—Canada. *MMWR* 1981; 30:266–267.

171. Centers for Disease Control: Supplementary statement on rabies. Vaccine and serologic testing. *MMWR* 1981; 30:535–536.

172. Lewis VJ, Thacker WL: Limitations of deteriorated tissue for rabies diagnosis. *Health Lab Sci* 1974; 11:8–12.

173. Shaughnessy HJ, Zichis J: Prevention of experimental rabies—Treatment of wounds contaminated by rabies virus with fuming nitric acid soap solution, sulfanilamide or tincture of iodine. *JAMA* 1943; 123:528–534.

174. Shaughnessy HJ, Zichis J: Treatment of wounds inflicted by rabid animals. *Bull WHO* 1954; 10:805–813.

175. Kaplan MM, Cohen D, Koprowski H, et al: Studies on the local treatment of wounds for the prevention of rabies. *Bull WHO* 1962; 26:765–775.

176. Dean DJ, Baer GM, Thompson WR: Studies on the local treatment of rabies-infected wounds. *Bull WHO* 1963; 28:477–486.

177. Anderson LJ, Winkler WG: Aqueous quaternary ammonium compounds and rabies treatment. *J Infect Dis* 1979; 139:494–495.

178. Anderson JA, Daly FT, Kidd JC: Human rabies after antiserum and vaccine postexposure treatment—Case report and review. *Ann Intern Med* 1966; 1297–1302.

179. Centers for Disease Control: Human rabies—Rwanda. *MMWR* 1982; 144:135.

180. Helmick CG: The epidemiology of human rabies postexposure prophylaxis, 1980–1981. *JAMA* 1983; 250:1990–1996.

181. Wiktor TJ, Gyorgy E, Schlumberger HD, et al: Antigenic properties of rabies virus components. *J Immunol* 1973; 110:269–276.

181a. Sureau P, Perrin P: The use of immunosome technology for vaccines against rabies and other viral diseases. *Eur J Epidemiol* 1989; 5:275–278.

182. Semple D: The preparation of a safe and efficient antirabic vaccine, in *Scientific Memoranda of the Medical and Sanitation Department of India* 1911, p 44.

183. Greenberg M, Chidress J: Vaccination against rabies with duck-embryo and Semple vaccines. *JAMA* 1960; 173:333–337.

184. Pait CF, Pearson HE: Rabies vaccine encephalomyelitis in relation to incidence of animal rabies in Los Angeles. *Am J Public Health* 1940; 39:875–877.

184a. Javier RS, Kunishita T, Koike F, et al: Semple rabies vaccine: Presence of myelin basic protein and proteolipid protein and its activity in experimental allergic encephalomyelitis. *J Neurol Sci* 1989; 93:221–230.

185. Swaddiwudhipong W, Prayoonwiwat N, Kunasol P, et al: A high incidence of neurologic complications following Semple anti-rabies vaccine. *Southeast Asian J Trop Med Public Health* 1987; 18:526–531.

186. Fuenzalida E: Human preexposure rabies immunization with suckling mouse brain vaccine. *Bull WHO* 1972; 46:561–563.

187. Fuenzalida E, Palacios R, Borgono JM: Antirabies antibody response in man to vaccine made from infected suckling-mouse brains. *Bull WHO* 1964; 30:431–436.

188. Toro G, Vergara I, Roman G: Neuroparalytic accidents of antirabies vaccination with suckling mouse brain vaccine—Clinical and pathologic study of 21 cases. *Arch Neurol* 1977; 34:694–700.

189. Held JR, Adaros HL: Neurologic disease in man following administration of suckling mouse brain antirabies vaccine. *Bull WHO* 1972; 42–6:321–327.

190. Kissling RE, Reese DR: Anti-rabies vaccine of tissue culture origin. *J Immunol* 1963; 91:362–368.

191. Centers for Disease Control: Discontinuation of duck embryo rabies vaccine. *MMWR* 1981; 30:407–408.

192. Peck FB, Powell HM, Culbertson CG: Duck-embryo rabies vaccine—Study of fixed virus vaccine grown in embryonated duck

eggs and killed with beta-propriolactone. *JAMA* 1956; 162:1373–1376.

193. Powell HM, Culbertson CG: Cultivation of fixed rabies virus in embryonated duck eggs. *Public Health Rep* 1950; 65:400–401.

194. Powell HM, Culbertson CG: Recent advances in preparation of antirabies vaccines containing inactivated virus. *Bull WHO* 1954; 10:815–822.

195. Rubin RH, Hattwick MAW, Jones S, et al: Adverse reactions to duck embryo rabies vaccine—Range and incidence. *Ann Intern Med* 1973; 78:643–649.

196. Anderson LJ, Sikes RK, Langkop CW, et al: Postexposure trial of a human diploid cell strain rabies vaccine. *J Infect Dis* 1980; 142:133–138.

197. Turner GS, Aoki FY, Nicholson KG, et al: Human diploid cell strain rabies vaccine—Rapid prophylactic immunization of volunteers with small doses. *Lancet* 1976; 1:1379–1381.

198. Aoki FY, Tyrrell DAJ, Hill LE, et al: Immunogenicity and acceptability of the human diploid cell rabies vaccine in volunteers. *Lancet* 1975; 1:660–662.

199. Nicholson KG, Turner GS, Aoki FY: Immunization with a human diploid cell strain of rabies virus vaccine: Two year results. *J Infect Dis* 1978; 137:783–788.

200. Centers for Disease Control: Adverse reactions to human diploid cell rabies vaccine. *MMWR* 1980; 29:609–610.

201. Costy-Berger F: Vaccination antirabique préventive par du vaccine préparé sur cellules diploides humaines. *Dev Biol Stand* 1971; 40:101–104.

202. Kuwert EK, Marcus I, Hoker PG: Neutralizing and complement-fixing antibody responses in pre- and postexposure vaccines to a rabies vaccine prepared in human diploid cells. *J Biol Stand* 1976; 4:249–262.

203. Centers for Disease Control: Human rabies despite treatment with rabies immune globulin and human diploid cell rabies vaccine—Thailand. *MMWR* 1987; 36:759–765.

204. Shill M, Baynes RD, Miller SD: Fatal rabies encephalitis despite appropriate post-exposure prophylaxis. *N Engl J Med* 1987; 316:1257–1258.

205. Shaw FE, Guess HA, Coleman PJ, et al: The effect of the anatomic injection site and other host factors on the immunogenicity of hepatitis B vaccine, in *Program and Abstracts of the 26th Interscience Conference on Antimicrobial Agents and Chemotherapy* Washington, DC, American Society for Microbiology, 1986, p155, Abstr. No. 321.

206. Habel K, Koprowski H: Laboratory data supporting the clinical trial of antirabies serum in persons bitten by a rabid wolf. *Bull WHO* 1955; 13:773–779.

207. Centers for Disease Control: Rabies vaccine, adsorbed: a new rabies vaccine for use in humans. *MMWR* 1988; 37:217–218.

208. Burgoyne GH, Kajiya KD, Brown DW, et al: Rhesus diploid rabies vaccine (adsorbed), a new rabies vaccine using FRhL-2 cells. *J Infect Dis* 1985; 152:204–210.

209. Berlin BS, Mitchell JR, Burgoyne GH, et al: Rhesus diploid rabies vaccine (adsorbed), a new rabies vaccine: results of initial clinical studies of preexposure vaccination. *JAMA* 1982; 247:1726–1728.

210. Berlin BS, Mitchell JR, Burgoyne GH, et al: Rhesus diploid rabies vaccine (adsorbed), a new rabies vaccine: II. Results of clinical studies simulating prophylactic therapy for rabies exposure. *JAMA* 1983; 249:2663–2665.

211. Berlin BS, Goswick C: Rapidity of booster response to rabies vaccine produced in cell culture, letter. *J Infect Dis* 1984; 150:785.

212. Centers for Disease Control: Rabies prevention—United States, 1984. *MMWR* 1984; 33:393–402.

213. Fang-Tao L, Shu-Beng C, Guan-Fu W, et al: Study of the protective effect of the primary hamster kidney cell rabies vaccine. *J Infect Dis* 1986; 154:1047–1048.

214. Yelverton E, Norton S, Obijeski JF, et al: Rabies virus glycoprotein analogs: Biosynthesis in *Escherichia coli. Science* 1983; 219:614–620.

Arenaviruses

C. J. Peters*

The four established human pathogens in the arenavirus taxon cause chronic viremic infections in their natural rodent hosts with relatively little effect on the animal's longevity or health. When these viruses spread to man, transient infection results in a spectrum of disease with consequences ranging from mild symptoms to lethal hemorrhagic fever. The host immune response to the virus is critical in precipitating tissue injury and overt disease in rodent models, but the pathogenesis and pathophysiology of human disease, particularly viral hemorrhagic fever, are poorly understood. The probability of human infection is determined by the intimacy of contact with infected rodents, while the prevalence of rodent infection is a result of complex interactions among infection, population density, fecundity, and ecological variables.

HISTORY

Lymphocytic choriomeningitis virus (LCMV) is the prototype member of the family *Arenaviridae*. It was isolated initially by Armstrong and Lillie[1] while studying a fatal case of suspected St Louis encephalitis. Independently, Rivers and Scott[2] made isolations from aseptic meningitis cases and Traub[3] from chronically infected animals in a mouse colony. The significance of these observations for the ecology of human disease became apparent when the occurrence of infected mice in nature was linked to human disease.[4] Several investigators, following the work of Traub,[5] have established the immunobiology of LCMV as a fertile and fascinating area in the study of viral pathogenesis, ecology, and immunology.[6–10] These results have had important influences on theories of immunologic tolerance,[11] development of the concept of virus-induced immune complex disease,[12] and understanding of the role of the major histocompatibility complex in cell-cell recognition.[13]

Definition of the arenavirus taxon awaited the elucidation of the natural history, serologic relations, and ultrastructural morphology of newly discovered members[14] (see Chapter 1, Figure

The views of the author do not purport to reflect the positions of the Department of the Army or the Department of Defense.

Table 20–1
Known Arenaviruses

Virus	Natural Host*	Geographic Distribution	Isolated by	Naturally Occurring Human Disease	Human Laboratory Infections
Old World					
1. Lymphocytic chorio-meningitis (LCM)	*Mus musculus* (house mouse)	Americas, Europe	Armstrong & Lillie, 1934[1]	Undifferentiated febrile illness, aseptic meningitis; rarely serious	Common, usually mild, but 2 fatal
2. Lassa (multimammate rat)	*Mastomys natalensis*	West Africa	Buckley & Casals, 1970[23]	Lassa fever; mild to severe and fatal disease	Common, often severe
3. Ippy	*Arvicanthus*	Central African Republic	Digoutte, 1970[24] Swanepoel et al, 1985[25]	Unknown	None
4. Mopeia	*Mastomys natalensis*	Mozambique, Zimbabwe	Wulff et al, 1977[26] Johnson et al, 1981[27]	Unknown	None; little experience
5. Mobala	*Praomys*	Central African Republic	Gonzalez et al, 1983[28]	Unknown	None, little experience
New World					
6. Junin	*Calomys musculinus*	Argentina	Parodi et al, 1958[15] Pirosky et al, 1959[16]	Argentine hemorrhagic fever (AHF)	Common, often severe
7. Machupo	*C callosus*	Bolivia	Johnson et al, 1965[18]	Bolivian hemorrhagic fever (BHF)	Common, often severe
8. Tacaribe	*Artibeus* bats	Trinidad, West Indies	Downs et al, 1963[29]	None detected	One suspected; moderately symptomatic
9. Amapari	*Oryzomys gaeldi Neacomys guianae*	Brazil	Pinheiro et al, 1966[30]	None detected	None detected
10. Parana	*O buccinatus*	Paraguay United States	Webb et al, 1970[31]	None detected	None detected
11. Tamiami	*Sigmodon hispidus* (cotton rat)	United States (Florida)	Calisher et al, 1970[32]	Antibodies detected[33]	None detected
12. Pichinde	*O albigularis*	Colombia	Trapido & Sanmartin, 1971[34]	None detected	Common, asymptomatic or virtually so
13. Latino	*C callosus*	Bolivia	Webb et al, 1973[35]	None detected	None detected
14. Flexal	*O* spp	Brazil	Pinheiro et al, 1977[36]	None detected	One recognized; moderately severe

*The natural host is well established for viruses 1, 2, 6, 7, 11, 12, 13. For others a few or even single isolates implicate the species listed. Quaranfil, Johnston Atoll, and Araguari viruses isolated from ticks have now been found to bud from mammalian cells with typical ribosomal inclusions. The significance of this for their taxonomy awaits biochemical and genetic studies (H. G. Zeller, C. H. Calisher, and C. P. Cropp, unpublished observations, 1988).

1–2). Junin virus isolated from Argentine hemorrhagic fever patients (AHF)[15, 16] was found to be related serologically to Tacaribe virus, a previously unclassified *Artibeus* bat isolate from Trinidad.[17] Later both viruses were found to be serologically linked to the Bolivian hemorrhagic fever (BHF) agent, Machupo virus.[18] The chronic persistent infection that Machupo virus induces in its natural host and other early data led Johnson[19] to speculate on the possible relationship of these viruses to LCMV, subsequently established by ultrastructural[20, 21] and serologic[22] studies. The family *Arenaviridae*[14] (Table 20–1) now contains more than a dozen recognized viruses including the recently established human pathogen, Lassa fever.[23] The differentiation of individual viruses has been based in large part on their geographic origin, natural host, and serologic reactions, particularly results of neutralization tests.[37] All known rodent hosts for *Arenaviridae* from the New World, referred to as the Tacaribe virus complex, belong to the family *Cricetidae*.[38] Although related by indirect immunofluorescence assay (IFA) and complement-fixing (CF) antibody tests, sensitive plaque neutralization tests readily distinguish these viruses. Old World viruses, Lassa and its relatives from African *Muridae* and LCMV from Palearctic *Mus* (family *Muridae,* also), are difficult to neutralize although they can be distinguished by specialized cross-neutralization tests.[39]

The recognition of viruses causing severe human illness in Argentina, Bolivia, and West Africa as reported in 1958, 1965, and 1970 has led to speculation concerning the possibility that novel virulent agents may have recently evolved. There is no definitive answer to this question, but it seems likely that the viruses concerned have existed for many years in rodent populations and their recent recognition is a consequence of human intrusion into and/or alteration of the rodents' ecological sphere combined with improved communications. In each instance clinically diagnosed cases were known to have occurred several years before virus isolation.[40, 41] Furthermore, these diseases all have cyclic fluctuations in prevalence and occur in relatively isolated areas.

STRUCTURE AND REPLICATION

Arenaviruses form round-to-pleomorphic particles averaging 110 to 130 nm in diameter, but ranging from 50 to 300 nm (reviewed in Murphy and Whitfield[42]). Typical virions have a unit membrane resembling a condensed plasma membrane with 10-nm surface projections. Individual particles usually contain 20- to 25-nm electron-dense structures resembling ribosomes[43] which may be connected by fine filaments.[44] These particles in LCM and Pichinde viruses have been shown to be identical to host cell ribosomes by biochemical analysis[45, 46] and in the case of Pichinde virus by oligonucleotide fingerprint analysis.[46] In spite of this provocative mechanism, which might allow the host cell to influence viral properties, the number of ribosomes varies with passage history of the viruses, and their origin or plentitude has never been correlated with viral properties. Indeed, the ribosomes presumably are not even necessary for infection since mutant cells with temperature-sensitive (*ts*) ribosomes infected at permissive temperatures produce Pichinde progeny which behave normally when assayed at nonpermissive temperatures.[47] Aggregations of ribosomes occur in the cytoplasm of infected cells, at times in relation to viral antigen[43] or fine filaments.[42] They may form close-packed cytoplasmic arrays.

Viral maturation occurs by budding at the cytoplasmic membrane. Cell surface and cytoplasmic viral antigen is detected both in the region of budding and elsewhere.[43, 48] Host proteins are presumably incorporated into the virion envelope in this process since antisera to uninfected host cells can neutralize purified LCMV in the presence of complement.[49]

Three major virion structural proteins are usually found: G1 (50,000–72,000 daltons), G2 (34,000–41,000 daltons), and N (63,000–72,000 daltons),[46, 50–55] but Gard et al[56] demonstrated a single 42,000- to 44,000-dalton glycoprotein in the case of Tamiami and Tacaribe virions. Pichinde virions contain RNA-dependent polymerase activity.[57, 58] Additional virion protein species have been detected but their origins and functions are unknown.[56, 59, 60] Available data from LCM and Pichinde viruses suggest that G1 and G2 are expressed on virion and cell surfaces[50, 61] and may serve as virus neutralization targets.[60] The N protein in intact cells or virions is not accessible to antibody or proteolytic enzymes, but it (as well as G1 and G2) can be readily detected by fluorescent antibody staining of acetone-fixed cells. Mild detergent treatment of virions liberates denser N-containing nucleocapsid structures which can be isolated free of glycoproteins and which contain viral RNA. Nucleocapsids isolated under appropriate conditions appear to be about 10 nm in diameter and up to 450 nm in length. Two size classes (640 and 1300 nm) of closed circular nucleocapsids have also been reported. Smaller 3- to 4-nm-diameter beaded strands can also be resolved.[44, 50, 51, 56, 59, 62, 63]

LCMV- or Pinchinde virus-infected cells contain immunoprecipitable G1, G2, and N, as well as an additional glycoprotein with an apparent molecular weight of 74,000 to 79,000 daltons designated GPC.[50, 64] In the case of Pichinde virus, pulse-chase experiments implicated GPC as a precursor of G1 and G2; in the presence of tunicamycin, GPC has a molecular weight of 42,000 daltons. Several nonglycosylated species related to N by peptide mapping as well as a 200,000-dalton protein designated L are also described.[64]

Analysis of RNA extracted from purified virions usually shows four major species with distinctive T1 oligonucleotide fingerprints: virus-specific L (31S, mol wt 3×10^6) and S (22S, mol wt 1.6×10^6), as well as ribosomal 28S and 18S RNAs in varying proportions.[44, 57, 63, 65] Temperature-sensitive Pichinde mutants fall into two complementation groups,[66] presumably corresponding to the two RNA segments identified. When paired strains of Pichinde or LCMV were tested in dual infections, it was possible to demonstrate limited reassortment of the L and S RNA segments in progeny viruses and use these viruses to analyze determinants of plaque size, virulence, and coding assignments.[67, 68] In the case of Pichinde virus, the L segment correlated with plaque size and in the case of LCM the presence of the S segment correlated with the virulence of the reassortant virus analyzed. Other studies using reciprocal LCMV reassortants have found guinea pig virulence to segregate with the L segment, however.[69] Available evidence suggests that the L RNA segment (with sufficient information for about 280,000-dalton polypeptides) codes for the 200,000-dalton L protein, which is possibly the polymerase. The S RNA segment (about 130,000-dalton polypeptide capacity) codes for N and GPC.[64, 70, 71]

Now that all or part of the S RNA segments of Pichinde,[72] LCM,[73] Lassa,[74, 75] Tacaribe,[76] and Junin[77] viruses have been molecularly cloned and sequenced, a clearer pattern of replicative strategies is available.[72, 78] The 3′ half of S codes for the N in the viral complementary sequence and is separated by an intergenic region with hairpin structure from the 5′ region that codes for GPC in a viral sense sequence. This unusual ambisense coding provides a ready mechanism for independent regulation of GPC and N gene expression and also requires that viral RNA be replicated before the GPC gene can be translated. There is considerable homology in predicted amino acid sequences in different members of the family.[79] Two LCMV strains had about 95% homology, but LCMV has about 60% homology to Lassa virus. Even compared to a New World virus such as Pichinde, the Old World Lassa virus and LCM are 45% to 50% homologous. Tacaribe, another New World virus, is somewhat more closely related to Pichinde[76] and, in a partial sequence of N, shares 76% of amino acid sequence with Junin.[77] Indeed, it may be possible to identify useful sequences spanning all arenaviruses.[80]

One of the remarkable features of arenavirus infection in cell culture is the lack of obvious cytopathic effect (CPE). Cellular protein synthesis is not globally diminished after acute infection as is seen with some other virus families. Even if visible cell damage occurs, the culture almost always will recover and develop a persistently infected carrier state.[55, 81–89] In general, acute viral infection involves the majority of the cells in culture and high virus titers (10^6–10^8 plaque-forming units [PFU]/mL) are present in both cells and supernatant fluids. Soon, however, virus titers fall and cell surface antigens disappear, although intracellular antigen expression, predominantly N, persists.[84, 90] Prolonged cultivation over succeeding weeks usually results in a cyclic pattern of virus production which often terminates in a culture that yields little or no infectious virus in spite of intracellular antigen expression. Although growth rate and cellular appearance are usually normal, subtle functional defects may be present.[87] Carrier cultures are refractory to superinfection with the same or other arenaviruses (but not unrelated viruses). There is little evidence of a role for interferon activity or *ts* mutants in the development of these cultures. Supernatant fluids typically contain interfering activity when transferred to fresh cultures and the activity has the properties of defective-interfering (DI) virus. Cloning chronically infected cultures has yielded a proportion of viral antigen-negative, virus-susceptible progeny cells.[83, 86] Thus, the analysis of these cultures suggests an in vitro paradigm for in vivo regulation of arenavirus infectivity.

Defective-interfering particles have been implicated in regulation of infection in arenavirus carrier cultures and can modulate acute infections in vitro. The biologic activity of DI particles has been assayed principally by yield reduction from standard virus infection and protection of susceptible cells from lytic infection.[55, 90–93] DI virions purified from cell culture in general appear to have a normal protein composition but small RNA species.[84, 90, 94–97] In spite of the extensive literature on arenavirus interference and putative DI particles, the role of DI virus is still not definitively established; for example, a recent careful study of Pichinde virus regulation in acutely infected cell cultures detected no evidence of RNA deletions. These authors[98] and others[99] have speculated that an intracellular polypeptide related to N could be responsible for regulating virion production.

EPIDEMIOLOGY

All currently known arenaviruses pathogenic for man are rodent viruses. Thus, their epidemiology is governed by factors which affect spread of the viruses in rodent populations and that bring man in proximity to infected rodents. The chronically infected rodent sheds virus in oropharyngeal secretions, urine, and feces. Since the viruses are stable and infectious as aerosols, this may be the major route of infection. However, contaminated foodstuffs, or other fomites are alternate modes which cannot be excluded. Classically, a single rodent has been regarded as the important host for each arenavirus, but several species may experience chronic infections.

Arenavirus infection has a complicated impact on the population cycles which ecological and other variables impose on wild rodents. For example, in the case of Machupo virus and its reservoir *Calomys callosus*, laboratory studies have shown that newborn animals almost always become chronically viremic after infection. On the other hand, only a proportion of adults (about one half in a laboratory colony) will develop chronic viremia, depending primarily on their genetic constitution. The remainder clear their viremia and develop neutralizing antibody over the subsequent 1 to 3 months, although there may be persistent virus shedding in urine and oropharyngeal secretions. Persistently viremic animals do not appear to be ill but suffer a mild hemolytic anemia, are somewhat smaller than control animals, and have a slightly decreased longevity. Most importantly, chronically viremic females are virtually sterile due to fetal infection and death. Females with neutralizing antibody are fertile and protect their offspring from infection with milk-borne antibody.

One means of producing chronically viremic *Calomys* appears to be insemination of an uninfected female by a viremic male. This appears to be a highly efficient mechanism of horizontal transmission between adult animals and also results in a fertile pregnancy with offspring vertically infected by milk-borne virus.

Thus, when high-density *C callosus* populations with genes favoring chronic viremia occur, virus spread would be favored. However, as the proportion of infected females increases, fertility would be reduced in the chronically viremic animals and vertical transmission blocked in antibody-positive mothers. This progression would lead to an overall curtailment of reproduction, a decrease in virus circulation, and gradual change in the genetic composition of the population.[35, 100] These and related considerations for other arenaviruses have never been integrated into a quantitative theory of rodent-virus dynamics.

LCMV, the first arenavirus isolated, established the pattern of rodent-human clustering of cases.[4] Armstrong[101] then isolated LCM from 21% of house mice trapped in Washington, DC, homes and showed clustering of infection in certain homes. This was felt to explain the high prevalence of antibodies (11%) reported from the country as a whole, the higher prevalence of antibodies in the lower socioeconomic groups, and winter predominance of recognized human disease. Most cases have continued to be identified through laboratory surveillance of neurotropic virus diseases. For example, samples from 1194 hospitalized patients with suspected viral central nervous system disease were studied between 1941 and 1958[102, 103] and LCMV was found to be responsible for about 10% of the cases. LCM was most prevalent in winter months although cases were noted throughout the year. The decline in reported human LCM in recent years may be due in different degrees to urbanization and improved hygiene limiting human contact with mice, changes in LCMV infection dynamics in populations of *Mus musculus,* and/or decreased diagnostic awareness.

In the early 1970s, a fascinating chain of epidemiologic events overshadowed the classic sporadic murine-associated LCMV epidemiology. Although hamster tumors had been sources of human infections in the past,[104] more than 180 hamster-associated cases were identified throughout the United States in 1973 and 1974.[105] Virus-infected tumors from a research institute were presumed to be the origin of the epidemic. Numerous cases occurred in laboratories that received these tumors, thereby introducing LCMV into their laboratory animals. Many other cases were associated with pet hamsters ultimately traced to a hamster breeding colony maintained by one of the employees of the tumor supplier.

In Germany, hospitalized diagnosed cases and antibodies in the general population are rare. However, in defined rural foci human antibody prevalence reaches 9% and infected *M musculus* can be identified. Furthermore, in 1970 an urban epidemic of pet hamster–associated disease was reported.[106]

On a worldwide basis, the extent of LCMV involvement is unknown, but has been well documented in Europe (England, France, Germany, Belgium, Holland, Portugal, Hungary, Bulgaria, Czechoslovakia, and Russia, but not Scandinavia[8]) and the Americas. A recent 10-year compilation of 60,000 cases of diagnosed viral neurologic disease submitted from 49 countries to the World Health Organization (WHO) contained only 210 cases of LCM.[107] However, 70% came from Hungary, probably more indicative of interest and diagnostic capability[108] than any plethora of disease. An interesting situation occurs in Argentina where both Junin and LCMV occur in the same geographic area and agricultural workers are at risk for both arenavirus infections.[109]

In the case of Lassa virus, *Mastomys natalensis* appears to be the natural reservoir.[110, 111] These rodents sustain chronic viremia and virus shedding without histologic lesions.[112] Considerable work remains to be done on the ecology and determinants of infection of this widespread and heterogeneous rodent species. Occasional isolates from other murid rodents[111] are probably of little practical significance. Nevertheless, Lassa virus can cause widely varying patterns of infection in genetically defined strains of *Mus musculus*[55] (Table 20–2), and the possibility of alternate reservoirs in certain circumstances exists. Lassa fever is a West African disease, although related viruses (possibly not pathogenic for man; see below) have been isolated in Mozambique,[26] Zimbabwe,[27] and the Central African Republic.[24, 25, 28] Extensive clinical disease and high seroprevalence are well documented in areas of Nigeria, Sierra Leone, and Liberia. Other countries with serologic evidence of Lassa fever virus include Guinea, Ivory Coast, Ghana, Gambia, Senegal, Upper Volta, and Mali.[40, 113–118] The actual number of illnesses (thousands or tens of thousands or more per annum) and the impact of the disease on human health in West Africa remain to be determined but must be considerable. Since disease manifestations may be nonspecific, only surveys utilizing specific virologic tools will reveal how many Lassa fever cases are hidden under "clinical" diagnoses of typhoid, malaria, pharyngitis, etc.

Considerable information on the natural history of endemic Lassa fever has been derived from an ongoing study of an area of high virus activity in the diamond mining area of Sierra Leone. From 1977 to 1979, two hospitals registered 3849 medical admissions; 12% were proved to have Lassa fever and 2% died from Lassa fever. These fatalities represented 30% of all medical deaths. Diseases occurred year round with some increase during the dry season.[119] Seroprevalence in villages of eastern Sierra Leone ranged from 8% to 52%.[119] In four village-based longitudinal studies seronegative persons acquired Lassa virus antibodies at a rate of 5% to 20% per year. Of the 48 seroconverters, nine were ill and three were hospitalized with Lassa fever. Indeed, seroconversion to Lassa virus was found in 7% of all febrile episodes studied.[120] Thus, regionally Lassa virus infection is extraordinarily common and is often a cause of mild disease in villages, as well as serious disease in hospitals. The interpretation of case-to-infection ratios is, however, complicated by the additional findings of (1) reinfection of seropositives, diagnosed by antibody titer increases, and (2) loss of Lassa virus immunofluorescent (IF) antibodies by seropositive subjects at about the same rate that seronegatives acquire antibody, 6% per year. Thus, there is no way to know what proportion of humans seronegative by IFA may have previously experienced Lassa virus infection or what effect this might have on clinical expression of disease. Certainly expatriate missionaries in Africa with serologic evidence of previous Lassa virus exposure

(CF antibodies) usually recall a serious disease episode compatible with full-blown Lassa fever,[113] suggesting that their genetic or immunologic background adversely affects their clinical response to Lassa virus.

While there is no doubt that chronically infected *Mastomys natalensis* is the major reservoir of Lassa virus in nature and an important source of human infection, there was no relation between the degree of community infestation with *Mastomys* and the proportion of virally infected rodents.[120] Indeed, in case-control studies of Lassa fever patient contacts, there was no correlation of virus transmission with *Mastomys* density or infection in individual houses.[121] There was, however, considerable additional virus transmission within houses, whether acquired from rodents or man. Eleven percent of residents became infected, and in one household of 20, seven persons were ill including three hospitalized with confirmed Lassa fever (two fatalities).

When Junin virus was first identified in Argentina in 1958 the endemic region encompassed 16,000 km² but subsequently has spread to include an area exceeding 100,000 km² with more than 1 million inhabitants. This region in the humid pampas of Argentina is rich farmland, and lies in the most populous regions of the country, within 200 km of the capital. Infection involves predominantly adult males and is acquired in rural areas primarily in the fall (March–June) when agricultural products, particularly corn, are harvested. High densities of field-dwelling chronically infected *Calomys musculinus* contaminate the environment with excreta and, when caught in mechanical harvesters, with blood. Junin virus has been isolated from other wild-caught rodents, including *C laucha* and *Akodon azarae*, but field data and results of experimental infections support the role of *C musculinus* as the major reservoir and vector of AHF. Most years, several hundred AHF cases occur.[122, 123]

Bolivian hemorrhagic fever (BHF) has been confined to the sparsely populated remote agricultural savannah of northeastern Bolivia. The endemic area is about 28,000 km² with a population in 1975 of about 50,000. Sporadic cases of clinically diagnosed hemorrhagic fever were reported from the region for several years and seemed to follow the male-predominant agricultural risk pattern of AHF. However, in 1962 to 1964 a series of devastating epidemics in towns and settlements caused more than 1000 human cases and led to the isolation of Machupo virus and the elucidation of the mechanism of transmission. Readily available food supplies in houses (perhaps aggravated by flooding of cultivated savannah and absence of competing rodents) led to the invasion of houses by chronically infected *C callosus*. Human cases correlated with the presence of infected rodents in households and showed the

Table 20–2
Role of Mouse Genotype in Outcome of Lassa Virus Infection*

Mouse Strain	Adults	2–4 Days Old	
	Survivors/Inoculated	Survivors/Inoculated	Viremic on Day 35
C₅₇Bl/6N	5/6	18/18	0
CBA/CAHN	0/6	16/19	+
NFS/N	0/6	11/14	+
C₃H/HeN	0/6	3/10	0

*Mice were infected intracranially with 10²·⁷ PFU Josiah strain Lassa fever virus on day 0. On day 35 the mice infected as sucklings were exsanguinated and tested for viremia with the results indicated; all had immunofluorescent antibodies. (P. B. Jahrling and C. J. Peters, unpublished data, 1980).

Table 20–3
Clinical Diagnoses of Patients Proved to Have Lymphocytic Choriomeningitis Virus
Infection During Hamster-Associated Outbreaks

	Baum et al[137]*	Ackerman et al[138]†	Vanzee et al[139]	Deibel et al[140]	Total (%)
Total	10	46	47	47	150
Healthy		2	32	1	35(23)
"Flulike"	10	16	13	34	73(48)
Aseptic meningitis		23	2	8	33(22)
Encephalitis		4		4	8(5)
Myelitis		1			1(1)

*Laboratory outbreak, Bethesda, Md.
†Community-acquired infections over a $2^1/_2$-year period in Germany.

expected family clustering as well as infection rates relatively independent of age and sex. Control of *C callosus* in and around houses has eliminated epidemic disease and reported cases are currently numbered in the tens or fewer annually.[41, 124]

The discussion of the epidemiology of these diseases so far has exclusively considered the role of rodent contact. Few who are familiar with the story of the initial presentation of Lassa fever will forget the explosive human-to-human chain of lethal disease which led to the isolation of the virus or the two serious laboratory infections (one fatal) which ensued.[125,126] Subsequent lethal nosocomial outbreaks[40] did little to dispel the image of Lassa fever as a highly transmissable, severe disease. For example, in a Jos, Nigeria, hospital a single Lassa fever case apparently infected 18 persons on a hospital ward and more than half died.[127] There were four tertiary cases in one family and a physician died after an autopsy accident. Further analysis of these and other episodes has brought several facts into focus: (1) the index case has usually had severe disease with hemorrhage or pulmonary involvement; (2) although several secondary cases might occur, the actual attack rates among those exposed were low; (3) few or no isolation precautions were practiced; (4) affected persons were usually intimately exposed to fomites and droplets, or occasionally circumstances suggested the possibility of aerosol spread (as when the Jos outbreak was studied); (5) tertiary spread was not common. Thus when nosocomial outbreaks do occur they are not as formidable as they first appeared.

Now it is also known that many Lassa fever cases are treated in West African hospitals without secondary infections and that hospital personnel have antibody prevalence similar to or only modestly above that of the general population.[117, 128–130] This leads to the conclusion that most patients with Lassa fever do not disseminate virus and raises the question as to why the minority do and how then do we deal with Lassa fever patients. Current recommendations for barrier nursing precautions with surgical masks[131] are quite reasonable and should serve to counteract the initial atmosphere of hysteria that so hampered care of these patients. However, one must not lose sight of the aerosol infectivity of Lassa virus[132] and other arenaviruses and the quite different standards of care generally operative in West Africa, regardless of anecdotal case reports.[133]

The South American hemorrhagic fevers have rarely been associated with person-to-person or nosocomial spread.[122, 134] However, BHF[135] and AHF (J.I. Maiztegui, unpublished observations, 1978) have both been responsible for isolated well-documented

episodes. In light of current knowledge of the worldwide incidence of the severe arenaviral diseases, it may well be that dissemination of the unusual case to family and medical attendants occurs with similar frequency in all three diseases.

An exception to the low risk of person-to-person transmission may be the infection of spouses. The occurrence of such secondary cases in a small fraction of AHF patients could be recognized because of the rural male predominance of primary infection. In 23 such episodes, the secondary case became ill 1 to 3 weeks after her spouse returned from the hospital, suggesting that transmission was due to virus excretion in convalescence (J.I. Maiztegui, unpublished observations, 1984). Two well-documented BHF cases[136] (K.M. Johnson, unpublished observation, 1964) and several Lassa fever anecdotes suggest infection of spouses may occur in these diseases as well.

LYMPHOCYTIC CHORIOMENINGITIS (LCM)

Clinical Syndromes

A proper understanding of the spectrum of human response to LCMV has been hampered by case-finding methods attuned to neurologic disease surveillance. Furthermore, many clinical and autopsy studies in the older literature are not adequately documented and are further confused by LCMV contamination of laboratory animals. Recent reports of hamster-associated outbreaks (Table 20–3) give some idea of the occurrence of other clinical forms of the disease. For example, in an outbreak in a university hospital, a serologic survey of 165 potentially exposed personnel was conducted.[139, 141] Thirty-two subjects were seropositive with no history of clinical disease or lost work time attributable to LCMV infection. Only two persons were diagnosed as having aseptic meningitis and an additional 13 had an influenzal syndrome without clear-cut CNS involvement. Nevertheless, headache, photophobia, listlessness, apathy, memory defects, confusion, and subtle mental difficulties in early convalescence were common in these patients.

In spite of some uncertainties, a "typical" LCM case may be said to begin with fever, myalgia, retroorbital headache, lassitude, weakness, and anorexia.[137–140, 142–144] This phase may last up to 1 week with a remission of a few days, and then a second or even a third wave of fever may occur. Associated symptoms which are prominent in some patients include chills, sore throat, retrosternal pain, dysesthesias, cough, vomiting, and photophobia. Testicular and parotid pain, which may develop into frank orchitis and parotitis, are a definite feature of human LCMV. Arthralgias are common in fully developed disease or in convalescence, and a few patients develop frank arthritis, typically of the metacarpophalangeal and proximal interphalangeal joints. Rash has rarely been reported.[144] Physical examination during the early phase of the illness usually shows only an apathetic febrile patient, perhaps with facial flushing and pharyngeal injection or lymphadenopathy. Recrudescence of fever is typically associated with worsening of symptoms, including increasingly severe headache which often heralds the onset of frank neurologic involvement. In experimental human infections[145] half the patients were reported to have neurologic involvement; in reported hamster-associated cases, about one third (see Table 20–3).

Most neurologic disease takes the form of typical aseptic meningitis. However, in Baird and Rivers's[146] collection of 23 cases, there was one patient with transient facial paralysis and three patients with bladder symptoms and sensorimotor loss in the lower extremities. In a series of 79 patients hospitalized with LCMV infection,[102] the average duration of fever was six days and 39 patients (49%) had nuchal rigidity as their only abnormal neurologic finding. Five patients had abnormal tendon reflexes. Two patients had muscle weakness and recovered; one patient presented with bulbar paralysis and another with ascending paralysis and both died. Eighteen of the 79 were drowsy and two semicomatose; only the two fatal cases were comatose. In two patients Parkinson's disease was diagnosed one-half to 2 years later. In another series of hospitalized patients[103] LCMV was shown to be responsible for 38 cases of aseptic meningitis and 20 cases of meningoencephalitis or encephalitis; all recovered completely except one with encephalitis who survived with residual neurologic damage. A variety of unusual neurologic cases have been reported,[8, 147] but these are largely anecdotal and usually lacking in virologic documentation. Thus, human LCM is temporarily debilitating but rarely fatal, and even when neurologic involvement occurs, mild disease and complete recovery are the usual course. Encephalitis, ascending paralysis, and probably other syndromes do occur and occasionally may be fatal or leave permanent residua.

Another pattern of human LCM has been described.[148] One patient, apparently infected during a monkey necropsy, died after a severe febrile illness. Subsequently one of his autopsy attendants developed fever, necrotizing pharyngitis, and died with a hemorrhagic diathesis. LCMV was isolated from postmortem tissues of both, but the abbreviated clinical descriptions and postmorten findings are more suggestive of an arenavirus hemorrhagic fever than of commonly recognized LCMV syndromes.

LCMV may also be pathogenic for the fetus. One woman infected during pregnancy aborted 1 month later.[144] Two others infected during the second half of pregnancy[149] delivered infected babies with hydrocephalus, chorioretinitis, and mental retardation. A similar syndrome was reproduced in an LCMV-infected pregnant baboon,[150] further supporting the etiologic role of virus infection. In addition, Russian workers have reported a high prevalence of LCMV fluorescent antibodies in children with hydrocephalus.[151] A single case report also describes transplacental or perinatal infection of a child born to a mother recovering from LCMV aseptic meningitis. LCMV was isolated from the infant's CSF but the cause of his death at 12 days of age was not clear.[152]

Routine laboratory studies are often helpful in the diagnosis of LCM. Patients tested early usually have leukopenia (occasionally even less than 1000/µL) and may also experience thrombocytopenia (as low as 38,000/µL). Later, particularly after the onset of neurologic disease, these parameters are normal. Modest elevations of aspartate aminotransferase (AST) and lactic dehydrogenase (LDH) have been reported, and a single patient tested had an elevated serum creatine phosphokinase (CPK).[139] In the setting of neurologic disease, CSF findings are usually those of aseptic meningitis: cell counts in the hundreds, protein slightly elevated, and usually normal glucose although hypoglycorrhachia is not uncommon.[102, 142, 144]

Differential Diagnosis

Epidemiologic clues include exposure to mice, recent acquisition of a pet hamster, and winter seasonality. Any syndrome associated with arthritis, orchitis, or parotitis should raise suspicions. Any undiagnosed febrile neurologic disease should be examined virologically for LCMV infection, particularly aseptic meningitis, encephalitis, myelitis, or ascending paralysis. A febrile patient with dramatic leukopenia and thrombocytopenia, perhaps associated with modest abnormalities of serum enzymes, should also bring LCMV to mind. In cases of aseptic meningitis, a definite prodromal influenzal phase suggests LCMV.[102, 146, 153] At least two authors have noted the potential for LCMV to resemble infectious mononucleosis with[142] or without[140] meningeal involvement.

Treatment

There is no specific therapy. Steroids have been administered with apparent success to a case of arthritis 2 weeks after onset of disease. Most patients with neurologic disease are no longer viremic but often have virus in CSF; use of corticosteroids in these patients might diminish inflammatory damage or alternately might suppress protective immunity. Since immunosuppressed cancer patients with LCMV infection develop unchecked viral replication[154] and fatal LCM cases have had virus in brain tissue,[102, 155] immunosuppressive drugs should be used only with careful consideration.

Pathology

Postmorten results have been published from a number of putative cases of human LCM, but only a few are clearly documented virologically.[8] The best-studied of these died after a 13-day course of severe encephalitis.[155] There were prominent meningeal perivascular mononuclear infiltrates that were also apparent in the Virchow-Robin spaces of the cortex, mesencephalon, medulla, pons, and to a lesser extent the ventricular ependyma. Focal mononuclear inflammatory lesions were present in the pons. There was evidence of neuronal damage in the cortex, pons, medulla, basal ganglia, and cerebellar Purkinje cells as well as vacuolar changes in the subcortical white matter of the cerebrum, pons, and cerebellum. Viral antigen was detected by immunofluorescence in the meninges and in an estimated 15% of the cells, primarily neurons, in the parietal and temporal lobes.

Two autopsies have been reported[148] from atypical LCM cases dying with a hemorrhagic fever-like syndrome. Patchy areas of bronchopneumonia were the only abnormalities noted in one case. The other patient demonstrated diffuse hemorrhages, necrotizing pharyngitis, an interstitial and exudative pneumonitis, and scattered perivascular cuffs.

LASSA FEVER

Clinical Syndromes

The clinical picture of severe Lassa fever has been the subject of several reports.[119, 125, 126, 156–163] Observations of nosocomial spread in Africa suggest that cases may occur as early as five to seven days or possibly as late as 3 weeks after exposure but that the usual incubation is probably around ten to 14 days as with AHF and BHF.[125, 127, 160] Patients typically experience the insidious onset of progressive fever, malaise, and myalgia. These symptoms are commonly joined by weakness, nausea, vomiting, diarrhea, chest pain, abdominal pain, headache, sore throat, cough (sometimes productive), dizziness, or tinnitus. Dysuria or palpitations are occasionally noted. The frequency of symptoms drawn from four series of well-documented cases is indicated in Table 20-4.

At the time of hospitalization patients are usually toxic and mildly hypotensive. Relative bradycardia may occur. Additional physical findings are often scarce but lymphadenopathy, conjunctival inflammation, subconjunctival hemorrhages, muscle tenderness, abdominal tenderness, and coated tongue may be noted. Oral lesions have been observed in about half the cases (45%–83%; see Table 20–4) and are usually described as pharyngeal, tonsillar, or palatal erythema often accompanied by raised whitish plaques (several millimeters in diameter up to a confluent membrane) with erythematous borders. Typically pharyngeal signs occur early and may only last a day or so; they may occur in patients without pharyngeal symptoms or may not be present in patients with sore throat. Occasionally, vesicular or ulcerative pharyngeal lesions have been noted. Increased capillary permeability may be evidenced by facial and neck swelling. Patchy rales and wheezes are common, particularly at the lung bases. Pleural effusions and friction rub often occur. A macular rash which may desquamate in convalescence has been occasionally noted, particularly in white patients.

Neurologic signs and symptoms are much less prominent than in the South American hemorrhagic fevers but do occur in some patients (eg, case 3 in Frame et al[125]). Disturbances of consciousness, coma, and convulsions are often found in severely ill patients and indicate a poor prognosis; virus may be isolated from the CSF in these cases.[164] Petechiae are not commonly seen. Frank bleeding tendencies (oozing from puncture sites and mucous membranes, melena, metrorrhagia) may develop during the evolution of the illness, particularly in severely ill patients.[162]

Clinical laboratory studies are not usually a diagnostic help. A mild leukopenia is present in many patients, but in others the white count is normal or slightly elevated, particularly in the later stages of the disease. The differential may be normal or show a left shift with relative neutrophilia. Platelet counts are usually normal but occasionally are modestly decreased (50,000–100,000 μL). In severe Lassa fever associated with hemorrhagic phenomena, these platelets do not aggregate well in response to adenosine diphosphate, collagen, or arachidonate due to the presence of a circulating

inhibitor.[165] The few clotting studies reported show mild-to-moderate abnormalities of clotting time or prothrombin time. Fibrin split products are not reported to be present, even when clinical bleeding diathesis is evident. Similarly, the bleeding time is usually normal. Urea and creatinine are usually normal in Lassa fever, although severely ill patients may be mildly azotemic, particularly if diarrhea or vomiting have been severe. A few patients may have hyperamylasemia but most will demonstrate elevations of serum AST, LDH, and CPK. Marked elevations of serum enzymes are associated with a poor prognosis. Albuminuria, cylindruria, microscopic hematuria, and pyuria are frequent but not uniform findings.

Chest radiographs in two severely ill patients have shown lower lobe infiltrates consistent with edema or viral pneumonitis,[125, 158] but six other patients with pulmonary abnormalities on physical examination had normal x-ray examinations.[157] The ECG is usually normal, although ST segment and T wave abnormalities consistent with myocarditis have been described.[125, 126, 157, 166]

Illness may last 1 to 4 weeks but typically recovery begins by 2 to 3 weeks or death ensues. Poor prognostic signs include sustained high fever, bleeding diathesis, severe hypotension or shock, coma, convulsions, or marked enzyme abnormalities. Symptoms

Table 20–4
Clinical Features of Lassa Fever*

	N† (%)	Range‡
Symptoms		
Sore throat	86 (70)	60–100
Cough	86 (69)	50–78
Vomiting	86 (58)	36–100
Headache	86 (57)	45–100
Abdominal pain	86 (57)	45–65
Myalgia	86 (55)	22–73
Diarrhea	86 (41)	36–60
Chest pain	86 (38)	22–62
Dizziness	86 (31)	13–45
Tinnitus	44 (16)	4–40
Deafness	86 (15)	9–30
Signs		
Hypotension	21 (67)	60–73
Pharyngitis	53 (53)	45–83
Shock	63 (38)	9–45
Rales, wheezes	86 (36)	17–64
Facial or cervical swelling	86 (33)	26–70
Bleeding	44 (32)	9–40
Lymphadenopathy	86 (31)	14–91
Conjunctivitis	86 (28)	17–70
Petechiae	34 (9)	9,9§
Laboratory tests		
WBC < 4000/μL	33 (36)	26,60§
Albuminuria ≥ 2+	24 (54)	25,60§
Outcome		
Fatal	86 (27)	9–52

*Four series of ten (Mertens et al[160]), 11 (Monath et al[159]), 23 (White[158]), and 42 (Knobloch et al[157]) hospitalized Lassa fever patients from West Africa. All were virologically confirmed except seven of White's patients.
†Number of patients explicitly evaluated for the clinical feature.
‡Range of percent having the feature in the different series.
§Only two series reported.

Table 20–5
Comparison of Findings in Lassa Fever Compared to Other Febrile Patients Hospitalized in West Africa*

	306 Lassa Cases (%) (Sensitivity)	339 Controls (%) (1-Specificity)	Positive Predictive Value
Bleeding	17	6	0.74
Edema	24	9	0.70
Exudative pharyngitis	43	17	0.69
Conjunctivitis	39	16	0.69
Pharyngitis	70	40	0.61
Proteinuria	58	32	0.61
Diarrhea	52	29	0.61
Abdominal tenderness	45	26	0.61

*From the data of McCormick et al.[119] All had a positive predictive value greater than 0.60 and were associated with virologically confirmed Lassa fever, P < .0001.

parallel the fever, which terminates by lysis. In the later stages of illness, frequently as recovery begins, patients may experience pericarditis or deafness. Pericarditis is usually manifest only by a friction rub and is virtually confined to males. Sensorineural deafness is of sudden onset, may be bilateral, and is often permanent. It occurs late in the course of disease and is a common and useful diagnostic finding.[162] About one fifth of Lassa fever patients may have significant and lasting disability from this complication.[167] Occasionally a biphasic illness occurs. Several weeks are required before survivors are fully restored to health and no longer complain of weakness and dizziness. Orthostatic hypotension and/or hair loss may also occur.

It can be seen that there is considerable variation in the frequency of findings among series (Table 20–5), and that many of the findings are also common in patients with a variety of febrile illnesses. In spite of this, experienced clinicians with a high index of suspicion in areas of active disease have had their clinical diagnoses of severe Lassa fever cases virologically confirmed in 70% to 89% of patients tested.[129, 156] It is also clear that diagnosis in an individual patient, in a setting where Lassa fever is less common or in milder or atypical cases, cannot be attained clinically but requires specific virologic testing. In an attempt to aid the busy clinician in West Africa, findings in a large consecutive series of Lassa fever patients and in simultaneously hospitalized febrile controls have been compared.[119] Although the eight clinical variables in Table 20–5 were statistically associated with confirmed Lassa fever, their positive predictive value was only 0.61 to 0.74. Multivariate analysis identified combinations such as pharyngitis, retrosternal pain, and proteinuria which reached a positive predictive value of 0.81. Vomiting, sore throat, tachypnea, bleeding, and axillary temperatures over 39°C were identified as poor prognostic indicators in the same study. The clearest predictors of outcome are serum viremia and AST.[164] A viremia greater than 3.0 $TCID_{50}$ (50% tissue culture infectious doses) per milliliter carried a mortality of 54% (vs 14% for lower values) and an AST greater than 150 IU/mL implied a 67% mortality (vs 17% for lower values).

The following case report (adapted from White[158]) vividly illustrates several features of severe Lassa fever:

Ten days before the onset of disease a 46-year-old physician sustained a cut while performing an autopsy on a patient later found to have died from Lassa fever. The disease began with generalized myalgia and chills. On day 4 her myalgia and malaise became more severe and her temperature was 101 to 102°F (38.3–38.8°C). The next day her WBC count was 3000 with 54% neutrophils and the hemoglobin was 12.4. Because of vomiting and a temperature of 103.8°F (39.9°C) she was hospitalized on day 7. There was fever and slight pharyngeal injection but no other important physical findings. The WBC count was 2950 with 45% neutrophils. Urinalysis on days 6 and 8 of illness were normal. Oral tetracycline and aspirin were prescribed. She felt worse on day 8 and developed flushed skin, patchy tonsillar erythema, and a subconjunctival hemorrhage. On day 9 she was subjectively improved but the subconjunctival hemorrhages had spread, pharyngeal injection was increased, and white plaques were visible, including a sublingual lesion. Tender cervical and submandibular adenopathy was found. The next day she was somnolent and the pharyngeal plaques had enlarged. She received intravenous (IV) fluids. By day 11 the pharyngeal lesions had begun to recede but she was depressed and complained of epigastric and interscapular discomfort. On day 12 she still complained of epigastric discomfort. The pharynx continued to improve but fullness of the submandibular region (somewhat tender) and conjunctival edema were noted. The lungs were normal on physical examination but respirations were labored at 28 per minute and lower lobe infiltrates were present on the chest x-ray. IV fluids were supplemented with hydrocortisone.

On the morning of day 13 she was hypothermic. Conjunctival edema and respirations seemed improved but rales were heard at the right lung base. She experienced a small hemoptysis. By the afternoon her conjunctival edema was worse and she had hemorrhaged into the swelling. She was bleeding from injection sites and a recently placed cutdown incision. IV fluids and 150 mL Lassa convalescent plasma were infused. Several hours later (4 AM, day 14) she developed dyspnea and moist rales, but cardiomegaly or gallop rhythm were not mentioned. Furosemide (20 mg) was given intramuscularly (IM). She vomited dark bloody material and was noted to have multiple petechiae over her elbows. Digitalis, furosemide, penicillin, and vitamin K were given parenterally. By 11 AM the rales were less pronounced and her urinary output for the preceding 11 hours was 99 mL. Oxygen, hydrochlorthiazide, ammonium chloride, and IV furosemide were administered with an additional 80 mL convalescent plasma. At 4 PM on day 14 her blood pressure dropped to 80/60 and by 5:30 PM was not obtainable. The pulse was weak and thready and the patient was oliguric. BUN was 27 mg/dL; bilirubin 1.5 mg/dL; WBC count 11,200/μL with 17% stabs and 56% neutrophils; hemoglobin 16 g/dL; bleeding time four minutes; coagulation time 21 minutes; albuminuria 3 +, and many granular casts in the urinary sediment.

Over the next 24 hours during treatment with mannitol, hydrocortisone, pressors, sodium bicarbonate, and vitamin K, she became progressively obtunded. Laboratory studies showed BUN 35 mg/dL; WBC count 37,000/μL with 92% mature and immature neutrophils; and a hemoglobin of 19.8 g/dL. ECG was normal. Respiration became intermittent and ceased on the 15th day of illness. No autopsy was performed, but sera obtained on days 9 and 14 contained, respectively, 2.1 and 3.1 $\log_{10}$ PFU/mL Lassa fever virus.[158]

This clinical progression is typical of severe human Lassa fever with early nonspecific symptoms giving way to obvious multisystem involvement. Pulmonary edema, subconjunctival edema, and the "submandibular fullness" are clinical expressions of increased capillary permeability. Mild hemoptysis, a small hematemesis, petechiae over pressure points, and oozing from punctures demonstrate the rather undistinguished bleeding manifestations of Lassa fever which nevertheless identify the patient with severe and potentially fatal disease. Finally the abrupt onset of relentless shock led to death.

Lassa antibodies in persons with no history of disease and milder cases of Lassa fever unrelated to explosive hospital outbreaks were reported soon after isolation of the virus.[129, 158] The observed case fatality rate fell accordingly and currently is about 15% of hospitalized cases. The clinical syndrome associated with community infections has not been studied, but is less specific than that of the hospitalized patients discussed above, and interpretations may be complicated by a background of immunity, even in seronegatives.[120]

Lassa fever is a particular problem in pregnant women. Shedding of viremic blood at the time of delivery is an obvious hazard. There are several reports of increased mortality and stillbirth in infected pregnant women.[157, 159, 160] In a prospective study the mortality of third-trimester Lassa fever was 30% compared to 7% during the first 6 months of pregnancy. Viremia was higher in pregnant than nonpregnant women and in fatal versus nonfatal third-trimester cases. Spontaneous or induced uterine evacuation was associated with a better prognosis.[169] In this study, only two (8%) of 25 fetuses in the first two trimesters of gestation survived; 65% of third-trimester infants were livebirths, but only 25% of third-trimester fetuses survived. Furthermore, Lassa virus has been isolated from milk and there is a strong suggestion that mothers with Lassa fever infect their newborn infants with serious consequences.[156, 157, 159, 160, 170]

Lassa fever is also a common disease in West African children.[170, 171] Clinical presentation was not too dissimilar from adult Lassa fever, although cough or vomiting were often the major complaints. In some cases convulsions and neurologic signs dominated a presentation with poor prognosis. A number of young children have been described with a characteristic "swollen baby syndrome"; anasarca, abdominal distention, and bleeding.[170]

Differential Diagnosis

A history of travel to Africa, particularly West Africa, and exposure to sick persons or a rural itinerary should alert the clinician. If the fever, malaise, and myalgia which might be associated with any infectious process are accompanied by evidence of pharyngitis, GI, and/or pulmonary involvement, serious attention must be paid to the possibility of Lassa fever. A great many common infectious diseases, including numerous viruses, common rickettsiae, bacillary dysentery, and streptococcal pharyngitis, could present a similiar picture. Two diseases common in tropical regions will be major differential diagnostic problems: typhoid and malaria. Many African patients with Lassa fever will, of course, have a positive malaria smear as well. Other treatable infections that must be considered are rickettsioses, relapsing fever, leptospirosis, amebic liver abscess, meningococcemia, and septic conditions associated with shock and disseminated intravascular coagulation (DIC). Extensive pharyngeal involvement in Lassa fever has occasionally mimicked the membrane of diphtheria. Several African (Congo-Crimean, Rift Valley, Marburg, Ebola, yellow fever), South American (Bolivian, Argentine, yellow fever), or Asian (Korean, dengue) hemorrhagic fevers may closely resemble Lassa fever clinically. Acute collagen-vascular disease or thrombotic thrombocytopenia purpura could resemble Lassa or the South American hemorrhagic fever. Diagnosis may be further handicapped since blood and body fluids are potentially infectious, limiting the clinical laboratory data safely obtainable.

Treatment

These patients have suffered extensive capillary damage as evidenced by their edema, effusions, and hemorrhages. Any decision to move or evacuate patients suspected of having arenavirus hemorrhagic fever should be weighed against the potential to aggravate this damage. In Africa, most patients will be treated with antimalarials and, if diarrhea is present, will usually receive an antibiotic such as tetracyline or chloramphenicol. Dehydration, particularly in patients with vomiting and diarrhea, will require IV fluids but care should be taken not to overhydrate. Secondary bacterial infections should be assiduously sought and treated. Intramuscular injections should be avoided and aspirin not used. Small doses of soluble vitamin K will assure adequate body stores. Two cases have developed sufficient evidence of upper airway obstruction to require tracheostomy.[163, 172] Viral replication in the pancreas may occur in the absence of lesions; however, markedly elevated serum amylase has been reported in a few patients.[173] Until more is known, it would seem reasonable to use clinical judgment and reserve therapy for pancreatitis for the unusual case with hyperamylasemia and suggestive abdominal findings. Viral replication in the adrenal cortex has been found in every arenavirus infection where it has been sought, but neither significant histologic lesions nor biochemical evidence of adrenal insufficiency have occurred. Corticosteroids, dextran, heparin, and prophylactic antibiotics have no established role and should be avoided.

Little is known about the pathophysiology of shock in these patients, but increased vascular permeability complicates therapy. If possible a central venous (or ideally a Swan-Ganz) catheter should be in place. If the hematocrit is rising or very high, judicious administration of colloid is indicated, realizing the possibility of inducing pulmonary edema. Administration of fast-acting digitalis preparations is reasonable and, considering the poor prognosis in shock, there may be some rationale for the use of high-dose steroids (eg, 30 mg/kg methylprednisolone).[174]

Ribavirin is a nontoxic, nonimmunosuppressive nucleoside analogue with broad spectrum antiviral activity against several experimental arenaviral diseases[175] including Lassa fever.[39, 176] This drug is effective in Lassa fever[177, 178] and should be given IV in an initial dose of 30 mg/kg followed by 15 mg/kg every six hours for four days and 7 to 8 mg/kg every eight hours for six days. Oral drug (2 g initially and 250 mg qid) is also effective, although probably less so. The drug is embryotoxic in some experimental animals and, until more experience is available, it is relatively contraindicated in pregnant women. Relatively little experience is available in children also. A reversible arrest of erythropoiesis combined with mild hemolysis is predictable. (See Chapter 6, Antiviral Drug Therapy, and Chapter 26, Filoviruses and Management of Viral Hemorrhagic Fevers.) Mild hyperbilirubinemia and a modest anemia commonly occur, but transfusions are usually not required.

The studies that established ribavirin efficacy in human Lassa fever.[178] showed a two- to threefold decrease in mortality of high-risk Lassa fever patients (Table 20–6). Lesser reductions in mortality were evident in subsets of patients with a better prognosis. Initiation of therapy in the first six days of illness was more effective, but later treatment was also beneficial. The plasma used in those studies was obtained early in convalescence and tested for IF but not neutralizing antibodies, so the lack of efficacy is predictable based on nonhuman primate studies.[39]

Other potentially effective antiviral compounds have been identified,[179, 180] but none have undergone sufficient preclinical testing to justify their use in man. One is particularly promising, a ribavirin derivative which retains its antiviral activity but has much less hematopoietic toxicity.[181]

The administration of convalescent plasma, so useful in Junin infections, has produced seemingly dramatic results in anecdotal case reports[126, 159, 163] but has not been effective in larger series.[156, 178] The rationale for this has become apparent from studies of in vitro neutralization of Lassa virus. IF[167] or enzyme-linked immunosorbent assay (ELISA) (Figure 20–1) antibodies appear soon after infection but there is no correlation with control of viremia or clinical improvement. Neutralizing capacity develops late, is complement-dependent, and is quickly lost with dilution (Figure 20–2 and Table 20–7). The ability of serum to transfer protection in experimental infections correlates with the development of a minimum log neutralization index (LNI) of 2.0 if 6 mL/kg are given on days 0, 3, and 6.[39, 182] Most convalescent human sera have an LNI of 2.0 or less, particularly if collected within 3 to 6 months of infection.[183] Thus previous attempts to treat human Lassa fever with 1 to 2 units of plasma selected on the basis of IFA would not be expected to be effective. Production of IV IgG with Lassa plasma selected by LNI should provide a definitive test of the utility of antibody in therapy.[39] Specific antibody could be particularly useful in treatment of Lassa fever in childhood or pregnancy where ribavirin has not been proved safe and efficacious. Furthermore, plasma containing neutralizing antibodies has enhanced ribavirin therapy of nonhuman primates[184] (Figure 20–3) and might further reduce mortality in man.

Following an incident with a high probability of infection with Lassa virus, postexposure prophylaxis against Lassa fever may be desirable. There is no established safe and effective prophylaxis for Lassa fever. In our laboratory we have employed 2 units of convalescent Lassa plasma with an LNI of 2.0 to 3.0 and/or oral ribavirin for 14 to 21 days (15 mg/kg/d in three or four divided doses). This dosage of ribavirin should be effective and is usually well tolerated, but hematocrit levels should be monitored while drug is administered.[185, 186] Current Centers for Disease Control (CDC) recommendations are 500 mg oral ribavirin 4 times a day for seven days.[131] During and after the administration of drug, temperature and clinical status should be followed. In some arenavirus animal models, cessation of ribavirin prophylaxis leads to emergence of clinical disease,[175] or CNS involvement emerges in the face of continuing treatment.[187]

Table 20–6
Ribavirin Therapy of High-Risk Lassa Fever Patients

Study	Antiviral Therapy	AST ≥150 IU/L		Viremia ≥3.6 TCID$_{50}$/mL	
		N	% Fatal	N	% Fatal
1*	None	60	55	46	76
2†	Plasma (IF-positive, LNI unknown)	28	50§	21	52§
2	Oral ribavirin	14	14‖	10	30‖
3‡	IV ribavirin	63	19¶	31	32¶

AST = aspartate aminotransferase; TCID$_{50}$ = 50% tissue culture infective dose; IF = immunofluorescence; LNI = log neutralization index.
*Control group studied with supportive therapy only
†Randomized study with convalescent Lassa plasma (no neutralization test performed) compared to 2 g ribavirin PO stat followed by 1 g per day PO in divided eight-hourly doses.
‡All patients received IV ribavirin: 2 g initially, 1 g every six hours for four days and 0.5 g every eight hours for six days. Some patients received 1 unit convalescent plasma but there was no significant difference in mortality.
§No significant difference compared to study 1.
‖P < .01 compared to study 1.
¶P ≤ .0001 compared to study 1.
Data from McCormick et al.[178]

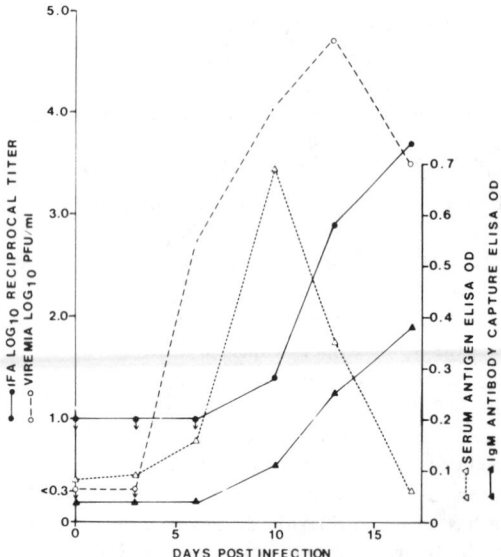

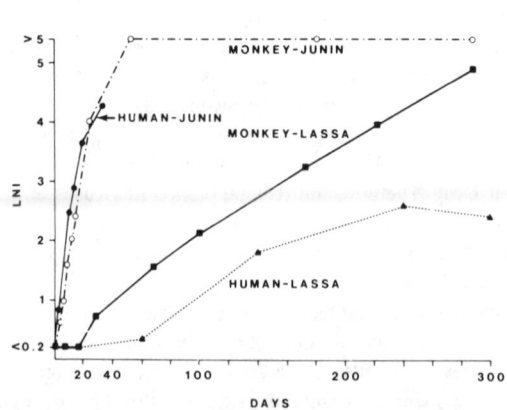

Figure 20–1. Evolution of viremia, antigenemia, and antibody response to Lassa virus in fatally infected rhesus monkeys.[297] Antigen was determined by a capture enzyme-linked immunosorbent assay (ELISA) using hyperimmune guinea pig and monkey sera. Immunofluorescent antibody test (IFA) utilized acetone-fixed infected cells as a target and a conjugate against monkey Ig. The IgM antibody test was modeled after systems in which anti-IgM bound to plastic plates traps serum IgM and the antiviral antibody is detected by adding sequentially viral antigen, IgG antivirus, and labeled anti-IgG. The simultaneous occurrence of circulating virus and IF antibody resembles the situation in human Lassa fever. Note that antigen clearance in the macaque had begun by day 13 when viral titers were still increasing. Infectious virus could not be precipitated by protein A but could be rendered noninfectious by treatment with anti-IgM. The appearance of IFA during a time of increasing viremia emphasizes the limited utility of that test in selecting plasma for potential use in immunotherapy.[39]

Figure 20–2. Evolution of neutralizing antibodies after arenavirus infection. *(P. B. Jahrling and J. I. Maiztegiu, unpublished data, 1988).* In this test tenfold virus dilutions are incubated in a mixture of 10% fresh normal monkey serum and 10% immune serum at 37°C for one hour.[39] Residual virus is measured and the $\log_{10}$ of the reduction in viral titer or the log neutralization index (LNI) calculated. Note the relatively rapid development of neutralizing antibodies after Junin infection as compared to Lassa fever. Even in the South American hemorrhagic fevers, however, neutralizing antibodies are not usually clearly demonstrable until 2 to 4 weeks after the onset of disease. This difference in the *in vitro* neutralization of these two viruses may explain the clearly demonstrable therapeutic efficacy of immune plasma in Argentine hemorrhagic fever and the much less convincing situation prevailing in Lassa fever.

Table 20–7

Neutralizing Antibodies to Lassa and Junin Viruses*

Virus	Serum Dilution Titer		Log Neutralization Index		Immunofluorescent Antibodies
	Without C	With C	Without C	With C	
Junin	10,300	7200	≥4.8	≥4.8	2560
Lassa 1	40	140	3.1	≥5.2	1280
Lassa 2	10	100	0.6	2.9	2560

Convalescent rhesus monkey sera were heated at 56°C for 30 minutes to destroy complement (C) activity and were tested in the presence of 10% heated or fresh normal monkey serum. Neutralization was calculated by probit analysis as the highest dilution of serum resulting in an 80% reduction of approximately 100 PFU (serum dilution titers) or as the reduction of PFU added to a 1:10 serum dilution (log neutralization index [LNI]; see legend, Figure 20-2 for details). These results with macaque sera are typical of human, guinea pig, and other monkey sera. Complement has little effect on Junin neutralization, but is important with Lassa virus. Lassa virus serum dilution neutralization titers are low, even when there is a substantial LNI. Protein A or anti-immunoglobulin treatment enhances the neutralization of Lassa virus at higher serum dilutions. It is not known whether these peculiar properties are due to Lassa virus itself or whether they relate to the quantity, avidity, or other properties of the antiviral immunoglobulin (P. B. Jahrling, unpublished observations, 1982).

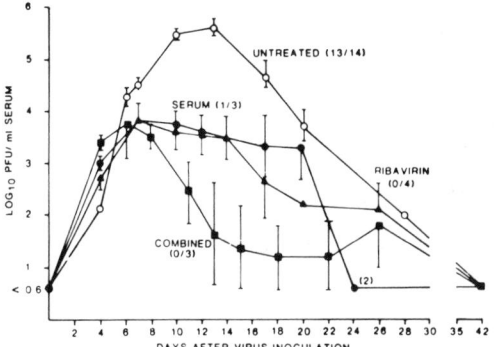

Figure 20–3. Effect of immune serum, ribavirin, or combined treatment on experimental lassa fever in *Maccaca fasciculatus* (Cynomologus monkey).[184] Monkeys were inoculated with 10⁶ PFU Lassa virus on day 0 and therapy initiated on day 4. Control animals were first noted to be clinically ill on days 6 to 7 and began to die on day 10 with a final mortality of 13/14. Ribavirin alone (75 mg/kg initially followed by 30 mg/kg/d) diminished viremia and all four treated monkeys survived. Serum treatment (1 ml/kg of serum with a log neutralization index of 5.1 on days 4, 7, 10) had a similar effect on viremia and one of three monkeys died on day 25. Combined therapy had a more marked effect on viremia and all three monkeys lived. Ribavirin or serum alone were progressively less effective in other experiments when therapy was initiated on days 7 or 10, but with combined therapy none of the monkeys died.

Pathology

Only ten fairly extensive autopsies and several other limited histologic examinations of fatal human Lassa fever have been reported.[125, 172, 173, 188] Gross findings were unimpressive: edema, effusions, petechiae, and occasionally hemorrhages. All cases examined have had some degree of liver necrosis, ranging from scattered single cells through multiple foci to extensive cell death bridging lobules. Necrotic cells were eosinophilic and formed Councilman-like bodies. Kupffer cell hyperplasia and phagocytosis of necrotic hepatocytes was noted. Ballooning necrosis, reticulin collapse, zonal predilection, or extensive cellular infiltrates were not seen.

In the spleen, necrosis and/or depletion of the malpighian corpuscles was regularly seen and this was usually accompanied by deposition of an amorphous eosinophilic material. Occasional small foci of tubular necrosis have been described and several cases have had congestion, edema, or cellular infiltrates of the lungs. There were minimal and inconstant lesions of the lymph nodes, adrenal cortex, heart, and skeletal muscle. No lesions were demonstrated in the CNS of the four cases examined. Vasculitis, fibrin thrombi, or notable cellular infiltrates have not been described. None of the lesions observed, including the hepatitis, were severe enough to attribute as a direct cause of death.

ARGENTINE HEMORRHAGIC FEVER (AHF)

Clinical Syndromes

During the seasonal epidemics in rural Argentina, several large series of cases have been reported, making AHF the best studied of all the human arenavirus diseases. Although subclinical cases may occur,[189] most infections are sufficiently severe to be recognized as AHF by the alert clinician. The incubation period is

typically about seven to 14 days.[190] Initial symptoms were noted within two days of inoculation of a large dose of virus into a human volunteer.[16] The gradual onset of asthenia, anorexia, myalgia, and fever over a period of several days gives way to further constitutional, GI, neurologic, and cardiovascular symptoms and signs.[16, 122, 191, 192] Back pain, epigastric pain, headache, retroorbital pain, photophobia, dizziness, constipation, meteorism, and occasionally cough and mild diarrhea may occur. On initial examination after two to six days of illness, the patient is typically febrile, acutely ill, and mildly hypotensive. Vascular phenomena such as flushing of the chest, neck, and face; conjunctival injection; congestion of the vessels bordering the gums; bleeding from the gums spontaneously or after mild trauma; and orthostatic hypotension are usually present. Although sore throat is not a prominent symptom, an enanthem is almost invariably present: petechiae and/or tiny vesicles spread over an erythematous palate and fauces. Most patients will have cutaneous petechiae, particularly in the axillary region.

Neurologic signs are almost universal during AHF if carefully sought.[147] Most patients will be irritable, lethargic, and hyporeflexic early in the course of the disease. They later develop palmomental reflex (62%), abnormalities of gait or station (49%), tremors of the upper extremities (38%), abnormal finger-to-nose tests (26%), snout reflex (24%), tongue tremor (17%), dysdiadochokinesis (14%), and other neurologic abnormalities.[193] Cutaneous hypersensitivity, dizziness, and postural hypotension are commonly seen and may also be reflections of nervous system involvement.

During the second week of disease many patients will begin to improve but the more severely ill will develop complications along one or more of the following pathways: (1) Extensive petechial hemorrhages, bleeding from all mucous membranes, and oozing from puncture wounds or cutdown sites occur. The gingival hemorrhages, melena, hematemesis, metrorrhagia, and epistaxis seem to represent extensive capillary damage and thrombocytopenia but do not usually result in life-threatening blood loss. (2) Hypotension develops and deepens into shock, generally associated with bleeding. (3) Florid signs of CNS involvement terminate in delerium, coma, and convulsions. These patients carry a poor prognosis and account for the approximately 15% mortality from AHF. Most patients destined to survive are improving by the third week of illness and experience a protracted convalescence. Temporary hair loss and nail furrows are common. Weakness, fatigue, and poorly documented mental difficulties may last weeks before full recovery. The occurrence of a late neurologic syndrome has been increasingly recognized (see below).

Simple clinical laboratory studies are quite helpful. Leukopenia, thrombocytopenia, albuminuria, and cylindruria are the rule and are usually present early in the disease. The white count may fall to 1000 to 2000/μL with a proportional decrease in both neutrophils and lymphocytes. Platelet counts typically descend to 25,000 to 100,000/μL, although the occasional patient will have normal values or may reach a nadir as low as 10,000/μL.[191, 194] Routine clotting studies are usually normal or only modestly deranged except in occasional severe cases where findings suggesting DIC occur.[194–197] AST, CPK, and LDH elevations are common but mild.[197] Hyperbilirubinemia or hyperamylasemia are rare. Serum urea or creatinine are normal or, in the severely ill patient, in-

Table 20–8
Immune Plasma Therapy of Argentine Hemorrhagic Fever (AHF)*

Therapy	Cases	Survived	Died (%)	Late Neurologic Disease†
Immune plasma	91	90	1(1.1%)	10
Normal plasma	97	81	16(16.5%)	0

*Virologically proven cases of AHF in the first eight days of illness received 2 units (500 mL) plasma in a double blind study. Immune plasma reduced mortality from 16.5% to 1.1% (P < .01). Data from Maiztegui et al.[206]

†Two to three weeks after discharge ten patients returned to hospital with transient and mild cerebellar signs. All ten were from the 90 immune plasma recipients (P < .01).

creased in proportion to dehydration and shock. Extremely high alpha interferon levels are found during the acute phase and are responsible for many of the clinical manifestations of AHF (see Pathogenesis below). Cerebrospinal fluid is normal in the acute illness, even in the face of severe neurologic involvement. Chest radiographs are unremarkable in the absence of secondary infection. The ECG often has mild ST and T wave changes.[198]

Differential Diagnosis

Residents of, or travelers returning from, the affected region of Argentina must be suspect if they were in rural areas. When patients present for medical care within the endemic zone, the usual problem is to distinguish early AHF from other febrile diseases. In a controlled study, many of the common symptoms and signs (such as the enathem) were not helpful in these circumstances.[199] However, 71% of 115 virologically proven patients had a constellation of asthenia, dizziness, conjunctival injection, and cutaneous petechiae, while only one (4%) of 28 negative patients met these criteria. Simple laboratory tests were also helpful since 85% of the AHF patients had fewer than 120,000 platelets per microliter of blood in addition to casts in the urine, as compared to only 10% of controls.

Although AHF and Lassa fever rarely would be a differential diagnostic problem on epidemiologic grounds, it is useful to compare current clinical concepts of the two diseases: Lassa fever has more prominent pharyngitis and pharyngeal exudative lesions, diarrhea, pulmonary involvement (chest pain, cough, rales, wheezes), and vascular permeability changes. Deafness and pericarditis are occasional features of Lassa but not of AHF. Hemorrhagic phenomena are much more obvious in AHF, as is neurologic involvement; both occur in severe Lassa fever but neither is seen in the frequency reported for AHF.

Treatment[200–202]

As with other hemorrhagic fevers, early hospitalization with avoidance of trauma is an unproven but probably highly desirable measure. The ECG and morphologic evidence of cardiac involvement[198, 203] plus the early hematocrit elevation[191] suggest that both cardiac compromise and increased vascular permeability may be present. Clinical impressions of the long-term value of norepinephrine therapy of shock are negative, but extensive experience with other pressors or with vasodilators has not been reported. Colloid may be useful when administered with caution. Although corticosteroids are often administered there is no evidence that they are effective and, indeed, they may be harmful.[204] Therapy of convulsions and other neurologic manifestations is similarly unsatisfactory; diphenhydramine (Benadryl) has been used to control agitation and opiates may be useful for the intense myalgias and hyperesthesias. Secondary bacterial infections such as pneumonia occur in about one fifth of AHF patients and should be vigorously treated when encountered.[205] Abscesses following IM injections are particularly troublesome, presumably because of leukopenia and secondary hemorrhage at the site.

Convalescent plasma therapy is generally agreed to be useful and has been employed since 1958.[201] Only recently, however, has a controlled double blind study documented validity.[206] Two units of plasma were administered to patients within eight days of onset of illness. Viremia disappeared,[207] duration of illness decreased, and mortality was only 1% compared to the 16% observed in randomized controls receiving normal plasma (Table 20–8). Patients not enrolled in the study that did not receive plasma or were treated with plasma nine days or more after onset had a mortality of 14% to 17%. Subsequently it has been possible to refine the dose of plasma by standardizing on "therapeutic units/kg," which are defined as Σ (volume of each unit $\times$ titer of each unit)/(body weight).[208] In a prospective study, only one of 123 (0.8%) patients receiving the currently recommended dose of at least 3000 therapeutic units/kg died.[209] The administration of passive antibody suppresses the subsequent humoral immune response[210] which, of course, makes recruitment of sufficient donors and exposure to bloodborne diseases a more difficult problem in the AHF endemic area. The development of neutralizing murine monoclonal antibodies effective in treating experimental AHF[211] suggests that human monoclonal antibodies might provide a long-term solution.

A fascinating offshoot of the initial convalescent plasma study was the observation that 11% of patients treated with convalescent plasma developed a late neurologic syndrome which was not observed in the survivors who had received normal plasma[206] (see Table 20–8). Patients returned 4 to 6 weeks after the onset of AHF with fever, headache, ataxia, and tremor, which cleared spontaneously after a few days. A total of 40 cases of the late neurologic syndrome after plasma therapy have now been compiled in the same center; most have been mild and transient but one death has been recorded.[209] There was no virus present in serum or CSF of patients studied. Neutralizing antibodies were uniformly present in sera and were detected more often in the CSF of patients with the late neurologic syndrome than in control AHF cases. Serum neutralizing antibodies appeared later but reached higher peak titers in patients with post-plasma neurologic disease, additional evidence for participation of Junin virus or the antiviral response in its pathogenesis.[209] Extensive studies have failed to relate the syndrome to individual donors, titer of antibodies infused, duration of illness before therapy, interferon response, or other variables.

A recent report has suggested that 2′-5′ oligoadenylate synthetase content of peripheral blood mononuclear cells is unusually high in patients returning with late neurologic signs.[212]

Melcon and Herskovits[213] have described 21 patients with late neurologic manifestations. Ten to thirty percent of the patients treated in the town of Junin have some form of delayed CNS disease. Their patients presented a varied picture of (in decreasing frequency) cerebellar involvement, hypotonic-hyporeflexic syndrome, cranial nerve palsies, dysarthria, frontal lobe signs, vertigo, meningeal involvement, pyramidal lesions, and extrapyramidal findings. Two patients died, and seven had mild signs of neurologic dysfunction 2 months or more later. CSF could be normal or express a mild pleocytosis and hyperproteinemia.

Delayed-onset neurologic disease is not unique to plasma therapy. Early reports of AHF identified a small proportion of recovered patients that presented a transient period of neurologic symptoms resembling the late neurologic sequelae noted in immune plasma–treated patients.[191, 200, 214, 215] The increased frequency of CNS disturbances seen in convalescence today is probably attributable to plasma therapy. Acute infections with both Junin and Machupo virus are associated with extensive neurologic signs and symptoms as well as the classic manifestations of hemorrhagic fever. Immune plasma may protect against the lethal effects of systemic disease, but those patients rescued from a fatal outcome may have CNS involvement, which is responsible for the late neurologic syndrome. Late viral encephalitis has been described in Junin virus–infected guinea pigs treated with antibody.[216] In BHF-infected monkeys, an analogous experimental system, prophylactic administration of large doses of human immunoglobulin, actually predisposes to the development of late nervous system disease.[217, 218]

The antiviral drug ribavirin is effective in treating the hemorrhagic phase of Junin infection in guinea pigs[187] and macaques.[39] Initial studies in AHF patients arriving too late for beneficial convalescent plasma therapy used the same IV regimen successful in Lassa fever.[219] The drug was well tolerated and viremia was decreased. The usual reversible erythropoietic suppression of ribavirin may have been exacerbated in the presence of Junin viral bone marrow involvement since one of six patients required packed cell transfusions. Ongoing studies may eventually lead to ribavirin replacing antibody as the treatment of choice in AHF.

Pathology

Complete autopsies from a number of patients have been reported,[16, 220–222] but the findings vary somewhat between series. The picture that emerges is one with unimpressive macroscopic findings except for congestion and the petechial, ecchymotic, and other hemorrhagic manifestations. Capillary congestion, diapedesis of erythrocytes, microscopic hemorrhages, and endothelial edema are seen in many organs. Fibrin thrombi are found but are uncommon. Marrow hypocellularity and necrosis are common but variable in extent. As with Lassa fever, there is focal hepatic necrosis with Councilman-like bodies. Interstitial pneumonitis, pulmonary hemorrhages, and a picture suggesting necrotizing bronchopneumonia or septic emboli are often found in the lung. The CNS commonly reveals meningeal edema, vascular congestion, and capillary hemorrhages. Perivascular cuffing, endothelial lesions, parenchymal necrosis, and glial activation all occur but they are inconsistent and not extensive. Other lesions include splenic congestion and hyperplasia, mild myocarditis, and renal tubular damage.

BOLIVIAN HEMORRHAGIC FEVER (BHF)

Studies of BHF patients during the San Joaquin epidemic[41, 223] (Mackenzie, Johnson, Garron, and Valverde, unpublished observations, 1968) indicate a remarkable similarity to AHF. The incubation period of naturally acquired disease is about nine to 15 days, although in one patient symptoms followed a cut sustained during an autopsy by only four to six days.[134–136] Detailed observations[136, 224] (Mackenzie, Johnson, Garron, and Valverde, unpublished observations, 1968) emphasized the florid bleeding diathesis (70% of patients had petechiae, bleeding gums, occult or gross blood in stool and vomitus), the neurologic involvement (half the patients), as well as the poor prognosis (estimated 15% mortality) associated with gross hemorrhage, clinical shock, and/or severe CNS manifestations. As in AHF, leukopenia, thrombocytopenia, and proteinuria are useful clinical laboratory parameters for diagnosis. Maximal proteinuria and hematocrit values are found between days 5 and 10 of illness, suggesting that vascular permeability may be most severely deranged during that period. A later outbreak outside the endemic area was clinically similar but associated with the occurrence of jaundice for unexplained reasons.[135] The differential diagnosis and therapy resemble those for AHF.

Pathologic findings in eight cases[225] resembled those in AHF. Subsequent necropsies from an atypical outbreak[135] were similar except for the high prevalence of secondary bacterial infection noted. Child and Ruiz[226] compared the acidophilic bodies in the liver of BHF, other hemorrhagic fevers, and nonviral conditions by histochemical and electron microscopic techniques and concluded that these classic Councilman-like bodies represented one of the limited repertoire of hepatic responses to several types of injury.

CLINICAL ASPECTS OF OTHER HUMAN ARENAVIRUS INFECTIONS

Limited surveys in the original area of isolation of other arenaviruses have disclosed serologic evidence of human infection only for Tamiami virus (see Table 20–1). Our only other information on their human pathogenicity comes from observations on laboratory workers. Junin, Machupo, and Lassa fever viruses, in addition to their natural disease potential, have all caused severe and fatal laboratory infections.[125, 172, 189] LCMV has been used in numerous laboratories and caused a number of infections, but the only severe disease occurred in a brief chain of transmission from monkey to man to man with two fatal hemorrhagic fever-like cases.[148] Flexal virus[36] has undergone limited laboratory study but has caused a severe constitutional illness, presumably after aerosol infection, and should be treated with caution (Pinheiro, unpublished observations, 1980).

Tacaribe, Amapari, Parana, Tamiami, and Latino viruses have been used in limited biochemical and animal studies with no overt human disease and no reports of seroconversion. Intensive work with Pichinde virus, particularly concentrates for biochemical determinations, has led to asymptomatic human infections (presumably by the aerosol route).[227] Furthermore, Junin, Machupo, Lassa, and LCM viruses are usually pathogenic for macaques and these viruses are not (G.A. Eddy, unpublished observations, 1977).

The recently isolated African viruses from Mozambique, Zimbabwe, and the Central African Republic (see Tables 20–1 and 20–8) have not been associated with human disease, but the level of surveillance is too low to engender confidence. Their similarity to Lassa fever virus dictates caution; however, they are all avirulent for macaques and guinea pigs.[39]

PATHOGENESIS

Experimental Arenavirus Diseases

Arenavirus infection per se need not elicit a pathologic response in the host animal, and this is usually true for the chronically infected natural reservoir (reviewed by Murphy and Walker[228]). For example, neonatal mice become lifelong carriers after LCMV inoculation, a situation initially proposed as a paradigm for immune tolerance. It is now clear that these animals produce antibodies to all three major virion polypeptides and this leads to persistent circulation of infectious virus-antibody complexes and, in genetically susceptible mouse strains, to the induction of chronic disease via deposition of soluble immune complexes in vessel walls and glomeruli (see review by Buchmeier et al[12]). In other situations arenaviruses themselves do not cause acute disease, but the immune response to viral antigens does. In the classic model of the adult laboratory mouse inoculated intracranially with LCMV, disease ensues if, and only if, there is a vigorous T cell response to LCMV antigens. Similar considerations apply when any of several arenaviruses are inoculated intracranially into laboratory rodents; disease induction is related to the extent of virus spread and the vigor of the cellular immune response.[12, 229, 230] These observations have fostered the concept that arenavirus disease is largely caused by the host's specific immune response to the virus. This is a likely explanation for human CNS disease from LCMV. However, the mechanisms of disease induction in human arenavirus hemorrhagic fevers and in realistic guinea pig and nonhuman primate models have remained puzzling. Histopathology, measurement of immune complexes, and experimental immunosuppression have not directly implicated any of these pathways of tissue damage (reviewed in Peters et al[39]).

Although arenavirus-cell interactions are relatively noncytopathic, there are exceptions, and this classic mechanism of cell injury may apply in some cell-virus combinations. For example, MDCK cell cultures are destroyed by LCMV infection. This is probably related to a failure by this cell line to generate DI viruses.[93] Even more subtle interactions have been described: LCMV-infected neuroblastoma cell lines are normal by ordinary criteria of growth and macromolecular synthesis, but closer examination reveals a decrease in their content of specialized neurotransmitter enzymes.[87] Similarly, normal murine macrophages lose their ability to proliferate in response to growth factors after Pichinde virus infection,[231] and Vero cells undergo alterations of cation-dependent adenosine triphosphatase (ATPase) activity.[232] Thus arenavirus infection may lead to loss of cellular functions important to the host

in the absence of cytopathologic changes demonstrable by conventional techniques.[233]

One of the major difficulties in studying pathogenesis of arenaviral hemorrhagic fevers is the lack of morphologic correlates of disturbed function.[39, 234] Physiologic studies of Lassa fever and its less hazardous analogues have been invaluable in dealing with this problem. In the Pichinde-infected guinea pig, a variety of phenomena have become apparent, including marked catabolism with body wasting accompanied by increased vascular permeability and shock.[235] There is severe cardiac dysfunction and elevated levels of sulfidopeptide leukotrienes. This cardiac decompensation is not due to direct viral involvement but can be partially reversed by leukotriene antagonists.[39, 236, 237] Lipid physiologic mediators were also implicated in a study of Lassa virus–infected monkeys.[238] Platelets continued to circulate in infected monkeys but lost their in vitro aggregation response. There was also evidence for a loss of prostacyclin production by postmortem aortic endothelium. This, of course, suggests a mechanism for endothelial dysfunction that could have important implications for hemorrhagic fever pathogenesis.

The widespread macrophage involvement which occurs in arenavirus infections might also be linked to induction of disease if infection modulates their ability to affect complement metabolism,[239] leukotriene production,[240] and prostaglandin regulation.[241] Mouse macrophages infected with LCMV in vitro undergo a period when they spontaneously activate the alternative complement pathway and are lysed in the presence of normal guinea pig serum.[242] This provides another potential mechanism for macrophage destruction and release of active proteases and mediators of vascular damage, permeability, or chemotaxis. Macrophages, like other cells, presumably express G1 and G2 on their surfaces providing targets for specific immunologic destruction by antibody and complement, antibody and Fc-bearing killer cells, or cytotoxic T cells releasing their repertoire of physiologically active molecules.

Just as the potential mechanisms leading to clinical disease are varied, so are those for control of the infection and termination of viremia. Since arenaviruses are not usually cytocidal in vitro, virus output from infected cells in vivo presumably is curtailed by one or more of the following mechanisms:

1. LCMV DI particles are known to be synthesized in vivo[92] and to be capable of modulating neurologic disease in certain circumstances.[243] Their ability to limit synthesis of infectious virus and decrease cell surface antigen expression in LCMV-infected mouse macrophages is impressive.[242] DI virus production has never been measured in human infections or in a hemorrhagic fever model, but may be involved in controlling viral replication.

2. Eradication of infected cells by cytotoxic T lymphocytes would eliminate virus production, and considerable evidence supports the importance of this mechanism of virus clearance in the mouse infected IV with LCMV (reviewed in Zinkernagel and Doherty[13]). In realistic guinea pig models of Lassa fever, protection can be transferred with spleen cells but not serum taken early in convalescence,[39] supporting the importance of cellular mechanisms in recovery. Spleen cell cytotoxicity thought to be due to antibody-dependent killing by non-T lymphocytes occurs in LCMV-infected hamsters[244] and arenavirus-infected guinea pigs,[245] but has never

been clearly linked to outcome of infection. In the Junin guinea pig model, not only must antibody be present, but spleen cells must be activated for cytolysis to occur.[245] Other potential mechanisms of cell killing (antibody and complement or spontaneous alternative complement pathway activation) may also be operative.

3. Macrophages are activated and natural killer (NK) cells induced during experimental arenavirus infections. Since macrophages are a major target for arenavirus infection and may be involved in the disease-producing mechanisms, their potential role is complex; definitive experimental data are not available to resolve the importance of their participation in recovery. NK cells do not seem to be of major importance, particularly in the LCMV-infected mouse.[246]

4. The humoral immune response probably plays a very significant role in recovery from Junin virus infections. Immunofluorescent antibodies appear as patients with AHF begin to improve[247] and are closely accompanied by neutralizing antibodies (see Figure 20–2). Convalescent sera are efficient in the therapy of Junin infections of man[206] (see Table 20–8) or guinea pig[216] and, indeed, monoclonal neutralizing antibodies are known to be sufficient therapy in guinea pigs.[211] The role of sera containing neutralizing antibodies in recovery from Lassa (and probably LCM) viral infections is quite different. Virus-specific antibodies are detectable by IFA or ELISA during the first few days of illness in man[164, 248] or monkeys[39, 176] (see Figure 20–1). Neither experimental animal nor human sera taken early in convalescence neutralize virus in vitro. Later, neutralizing antibodies appear (see Figure 20–2), the sera are curative in passive infusion experiments (see Figure 20–3), and presumably these antibodies afford some measure of protection against disease to the donor reexposed to virus.

5. Interferon appears to play a negligible or perhaps even a deleterious role (see below). Arenavirus replication is not very sensitive to alpha or beta interferons[249] in vitro and Lassa virus is no exception.[234] Prophylaxis with an interferon inducer (polyriboinosinic-polyribocytidylic acid complexed with poly-L-lysine and carboxymethylcellulose) did not not clinically benefit Machupo virus–infected rhesus monkeys and their serum virus titers were identical to or higher than those of control monkeys.[249] Indeed, in the mouse intracranially infected with LCMV, a virulent virus preparation induced larger quantities of interferon than a "docile" strain. Administration of interferon inducers converted the docile strain to virulence.[250] It has been proposed that arenaviruses may replicate in NK cells[251] and thus interferon theoretically could expand the cell substrate for viral replication in lymphoid tissues. Gamma interferon, however, may have a very important role, either as a lymphokine or because of its antiviral activity.[252]

Experimental arenavirus infections provide numerous examples of the importance of host-virus genetic interactions as well.[39] For example, in the LCMV-hamster system it is possible to select virulent (WE) or avirulent (Armstrong) virus strains.[253] Even using the virulent WE virus strain some inbred hamsters are genetically resistant (MHA, PD4) or susceptible (LSH, CB) to lethal infection. Similar factors are presumably at work in human hemorrhagic fevers. In the case of Junin virus, there is considerable virulence heterogeneity among different serologically identical human isolates when tested experimentally in guinea pigs.[254] When some of these Junin strains were inoculated into rhesus macaques, the re-

sulting disease pattern varied from florid hemorrhagic disease to a predominately encephalitic form with mild bleeding, and the clinical pattern in macaques resembled that seen in the patient from whom the virus was isolated.[255] There was an indication of an important host genetic factor in AHF patients when HLA typing was performed.[256] The prevalence of the B7 gene product was 12% to 15% in the general population or in patients with mild-to-moderate disease; nine of 23 (39%) severe cases carried this allele. Lassa viral strains also show considerable heterogeneity in virulence when tested in guinea pigs, and this virulence correlates with the severity of the human case yielding the isolate.[257]

Lymphocytic Choriomeningitis (LCM)

The prominent biphasic illness which often occurs in human LCM suggests that the second phase, which is associated with meningeal involvement, might be immunologically induced. Finding serum antibody with virus and lymphoid cells in spinal fluid further supports the analogy to murine disease induced by intracranial inoculation of LCMV. Disease in the mouse is precipitated by a T lymphocyte-mediated immune attack on virus-infected meninges and can be prevented by ablating this response.[12] When immunosuppressed terminal cancer patients were inoculated with LCMV as an experimental therapeutic measure,[154] serum virus titers reached 10^4 to $10^{6.5}$ infectious units per milliliter and continued at those levels for several days; overt CNS disease never developed, even though virus was present in high titer in brain tissue from one patient at necropsy.

Lassa Fever

Observations in humans[164, 173] and macaques[39, 176, 258] have yielded similar results, and the experimental results have important implications for the interpretation of the necessarily more limited human data. In nonhuman primates, several sites of replication were identified in the liver, lung, adrenal gland, pancreatic acinar cells, spleen (principally red pulp), kidney (tubular foci), and lymph node (mainly scattered cells resembling macrophages).[176, 258] Pathologic changes were virtually confined to focal liver necrosis resembling that described in man, and to interstitial pneumonitis, more extensive than found in human necropsies. As in the human studies, neither the hepatic lesions nor other histopathologic findings accounted for the demise of the animals in spite of extensive viral involvement as judged by viral titers and fluorescent antibody staining. Perhaps these infected cells are functionally deficient because of generalized or specific metabolic consequences of infection[233] or because of damage inflicted by host factors. Vasculitis, although not reported in human necropsies, has been seen in rhesus and squirrel monkeys, and in the immunologic context of arenavirus disease leads one to suspect that similar lesions may lead to compromise of function in at least some humans.

A significant lesion detectable clinically and pathologically in both monkeys and man is increased vascular permeability. For example, in the case report cited above, several manifestations of tissue edema occurred during the first 2 weeks of illness before the patient developed a final paroxysm in which vascular collapse was accompanied by severe hemoconcentration (hemoglobin 19.8 g/dL) and leukocytosis (WBC count 37,000/μL). Although there is no direct evidence for the mechanisms, one might speculate that activation of the complement pathway could be important to produce phlogistic fragments such as C3a and C5a in tissues or in the circulation. There is evidence for participation of these mediators in the adult respiratory distress syndrome,[259] and one is struck by the presence of clinical pulmonary findings in humans and interstitial pneumonitis in animals with Lassa fever. Furthermore, circulating C5a induces leukopenia and the C3e fragment leukocytosis, two findings occurring at times with Lassa fever.

Although there are data from Lassa-infected macaques consistent with a prostacyclin-related endothelial defect,[241] and an interesting case report on the use of a prostacyclin analogue in a Lassa patient,[133] the platelet defect in man seems to be due to a plasma inhibitor of platelet function.[165] This 43-kilodalton (kd) substance may be important in the apparent failure of platelet function observed in the face of modest decreases in the numbers of circulating platelets.

South American Hemorrhagic Fevers

Our understanding of the pathogenesis of these diseases in humans is enhanced by studies of rhesus monkeys infected with Junin[255] or Machupo virus and guinea pigs inoculated with Junin virus. The BHF monkey model (Figure 20–4) resembles the human disease; inoculated monkeys die 2 to 3 weeks later with multiple bleeding sites and similar pathologic lesions resembling those in man.[260, 261] When acutely infected monkeys were decomplemented with cobra venom factor or immunosuppressed with cyclophosphamide, the disease was not ameliorated. This suggests that the hemorrhagic phase may not require complement activation or an immunopathologic mechanism for its expression.[262] Detailed studies of clotting and physiologic parameters in this same model have been reported.[263] At the onset of viremia, platelet counts fell, the activated partial thromboplastin time began to increase, and serum

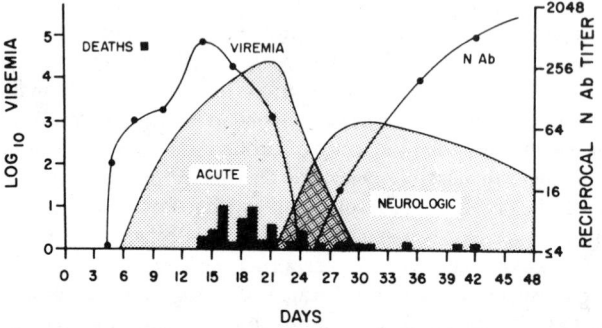

Figure 20–4. Experimental Bolivian hemorrhagic fever in the rhesus monkey.[217, 218, 260–263] Macaques were inoculated with 1000 PFU Machupo virus on day 0. Viremia is higher and antibodies appear somewhat sooner than reported for humans. The early viremic phase is accompanied by a florid hemorrhagic diathesis and clinicopathologic findings resembling those of the human disease. The CNS signs observed in animals dying after the second week of infection may have their counterpart either in the acute neurologic involvement seen in man or in the late neurologic syndrome following immune plasma therapy of Argentine hemorrhagic fever (see Table 20–8). Contrast to the earlier appearance of immunofluorescent antibody and much later evolution of neutralizing antibodies seen in Lassa fever (see Figures 20–1 and 20–2).

albumin fell. Blood pressure began to decline and later serum fibrin split products rose modestly to 10 μg/mL while fibrinogen increased. This pattern does not suggest DIC but rather is consistent with the histologically observed action of Machupo virus on bone marrow, modest viral liver damage, and another process (perhaps the presence of active enzymes in plasma) which may increase vascular permeability and alter clotting factors.

Numerous studies of guinea pigs infected with the prototype XJ strain of Junin virus have demonstrated similarities to human disease: thrombocytopenia, leukopenia, bone marrow necrosis, hemorrhagic phenomena, immunosuppression, and death without any single definitive fatal histopathologic lesion.[264] Interestingly, these animals develop abnormal serum phosphatase and protease activity[265] which may be responsible for the observed abnormalities of complement[266] and coagulation.[267] Since bone marrow necrosis and leukopenia occur, these enzymes may be derived from neutrophils, such as the complement-cleaving chymotryptic enzymes studied by Venge and Olsson[268] or those released in human progranulocytic leukemias associated with coagulopathies.[269] Alternately, the extensive involvement of macrophages may stimulate them to secrete some of their repertoire of enzymatic mediators. Immunosuppression with cyclophosphamide or cyclosporin A does not protect the guinea pigs from Junin infection and, indeed, converts infection with attenuated strains to a lethal outcome.[204]

Detailed studies are also available from human AHF cases. Viral antigens and a peculiar viruslike particle were observed in hepatocytes, kidney tubules, and other organs[220, 270] and corresponded to the distribution of ultrastructural and light microscopic pathologic lesions. The correlation was particularly striking in the kidney where the lack of glomerular disease has been a regular finding in both pathologic and functional studies. Tubular involvement has been demonstrated in fatal cases by immunohistochemical criteria; transient functional changes attributable to tubular lesions may be seen in nonfatal cases.[271, 272] Interestingly enough, detailed studies of lymphoid organs revealed the macrophage to be the major cell with detectable viral antigen or viruslike particles. Both macrophages and lymphocytes often appeared necrotic or damaged and there was depletion of the B cell areas.[273] Neither histologic studies, immunohistochemical techniques, nor detailed measurements of clotting and complement cascades have implicated infiltrating cytotoxic cells, immune complexes, classic or alternative pathway complement activation, or DIC[220, 274, 275] as major pathogenetic mechanisms. These findings together suggest that either viral cytopathologic or some direct humoral mechanism is responsible for cellular injury.

The necrosis of lymphocytes in lymphoid tissue may involve soluble mediators secreted from infected or injured macrophages. These mediators may be enzymes important in producing the abnormalities of coagulation and complement factors found in serum. The occurrence of normal or elevated serum levels of antigenically active C4, factor VIII, and other enzymes with decreased functional activity is consistent with this hypothesis.[274–276] AHF patients have the highest interferon response reported in any viral disease, often ranging from 1000 to 16,000 IU/mL.[277] Antiviral activity is neutralized by antibodies to alpha interferon, is acid-stable, and correlates with 2′–5′ oligoadenylate synthetase levels in peripheral blood mononuclear cells from patients.[212] Very high interferon levels have a bad prognosis,[278] although there is no correlation between viremia levels and interferon[277] or between viremia levels and prognosis (J.I. Maiztegui, personal communication, 1980). Serum interferon disappears brusquely after patients are treated with neutralizing antibodies and suppressed mitogen responses are normalized within 72 hours.[209] The prolonged elevations in alpha interferon are probably responsible for the fever, myalgia, and malaise, and may also contribute to the acute neurologic symptoms, immunosuppression, and hematologic abnormalities.

The relatively long course of disease and the delayed neutralizing antibody response have led to speculation about the role of viral immunosuppression in the pathogenesis of arenavirus hemorrhagic fever. Junin virus–infected guinea pigs are deficient in primary and secondary humoral antibody responses to an indifferent antigen and cannot express established delayed hypersensitivity.[279] This is perhaps not surprising since there is extensive lymphoid necrosis and depletion. In vitro phagocytosis by peritoneal macrophages and in vivo clearance of bacteria was normal in these animals,[280] an unexpected finding since the macrophage is so often involved in this and other arenavirus infections. Infection of guinea pigs with less virulent Junin strains which produce only minor lymphoid lesions is not immunosuppressive.[281] Humans suffering from Argentine HF undergo a reduction in both circulating T and B lymphocytes to 30% to 40% of normal levels. There was a decrease in the T4/T8 ratio from a normal of 2.3 to 0.7. When attempts were made to demonstrate macrophage migration inhibition with patients' peripheral blood mononuclear cells, their locomotion was found to be spontaneously inhibited, even in control cultures.[282, 283]

Thus, the South American hemorrhagic fevers seem to be multisystem diseases in which bone marrow, macrophage, and other target cell infection leads to extensive vascular damage and permeability increase, probably produced in part by secondary mediators. The extensive hemorrhage reflects vascular lesions compounded by thrombocytopenia. It seems likely that there is myocardial impairment also.[203] The pathogenesis of the CNS dysfunction is poorly understood; increasing experimental evidence suggests that Junin and Machupo viruses are both neuroinvasive and neurovirulent, although there is no direct evidence for viral encephalitis in man.[39]

LABORATORY DIAGNOSIS

The human pathogenic arenaviruses are all infectious by aerosol, a particular problem when handling infected animals. Anecdotal evidence from endemic areas suggests that samples from infected humans and cell culture material could be handled with only modest risks provided laminar flow biosafety cabinets and proper waste disposal were available.[130, 189] In the United States, current recommendations are that Junin, Machupo, and Lassa fever viruses be manipulated at the P4 containment level and LCMV isolates at the P3 level.[284]

Detailed procedures for laboratory diagnosis of arenaviruses have recently been published.[285, 286] Inactivated antigens suitable for serosurveys or work with convalescent sera can be prepared by treatment with β-propriolactone, psoralens in conjunction with long-wave ultraviolet light, gamma radiation, or a combination of these methods.[285, 287, 288] These reagents have been successfully used in CF, IF, and ELISA tests.

Virus Isolation

The best general method for arenavirus isolation currently is the inoculation of Vero or similarly susceptible cell cultures followed by IF or other immunologically specific staining of infected cells at intervals. This is a rapid and sensitive method for Machupo,[135] Lassa,[289] and Junin[290] viruses and probably would function well for LCMV also. Viremia in Junin virus infection is relatively low in titer and most easily detected between three and eight days of illness, but positive results have been obtained as late as day 12.[291] Cocultivation of peripheral blood mononuclear cells increases the frequency of virus isolation.[292] Suckling mice, guinea pigs, and Vero cells have all been used successfully, usually with clotted or heparinized whole blood. Virus may occasionally be obtained from throat wash fluids but rarely from urine. Machupo virus was difficult to isolate from blood during the original San Joaquin epidemic[18] and suckling hamsters were found to be far superior to suckling mice. In a later atypical BHF outbreak in Cochabamba, Bolivia, viremias appeared to be higher and more readily detectable.[135] Lassa patients usually have viremia when they initially present to hospital and this may persist up to 19 days after onset of disease. Throat wash and urine are often positive, although titers are low.[164]

In the presence of neurologic signs, CSF may also yield virus. Virus has persisted in urine 1 to 2 months after the onset of illness.[293] Isolation in cell culture is clearly the method of choice and infected cells have been detected by IF or reversed passive hemagglutination tests of cell lysates.[294] LCMV is present in blood, particularly during the first wave of illness. Isolation from CSF is often successful in patients with neurologic disease and occasional isolates have been obtained from pharyngeal secretions. The intracranially inoculated weanling mouse has been the most widely used host for isolation of LCMV. The addition of endotoxin challenge[295] probably enhances its utility for isolations from persistently infected animal colonies.

Once an arenavirus is isolated, the IF test permits presumptive classification if the identifying reagents have been tested against prototype strains expected in a given laboratory (Table 20–9). Monoclonal antibodies reacting to a conserved region of the arenaviral genome could be useful reagents for presumptive diagnosis or detection of new family members.[80] For Tacaribe complex viruses (Junin and Machupo), neutralization with standard antisera is definitive. Although the neutralization test is less sensitive and the taxonomy is less well developed, the Old World viruses certainly should have additional serologic study in clinically or geographically unusual cases (see Tables 20–9 and 20–10). Monoclonal antibodies may eventually contribute to the identification and classification of these viruses, but the number of strains examined so far is too limited to allow conclusions.[61, 301]

Rapid Diagnosis

Niklasson and coworkers demonstrated that ELISA technology can detect antigen in β-propriolactone or cobalt 60–inactivated sera from Lassa–virus–infected monkeys, and that appearance of IgM antibodies preceded the disappearance of antigenemia[302] (see Figure 20–1). This same pattern was found in humans infected in Sierra Leone.[248] In an extensive study from Liberia, using virus

Table 20–9
Typical Serologic Results With Convalescent Human Sera After Arenavirus Infections*

Virus Infection	IFA Titer vs				Log Neutralization Index vs		Serum Dilution Neutralization Titer vs		ELISA IgG		
	LCM	Lassa	Junin	Machupo	LCM	Lassa	Junin	Machupo	LCM	Lassa	Junin
LCM 1	20	<10	<10	<10	2.3	<0.3	<10	<10	400	<100	<100
LCM 2	160	20	<10	<10	<0.3	<0.3	<10	<10	3200	200	<100
LCM 3	320	20	<10	<10	3.1	<0.3	<10	<10	1600	100	<100
Lassa 1	<10	80	<10	<10	0.4	2.2	<10	<10	<100	400	<100
Lassa 2	40	320	<10	<10	1.3	3.5	<10	<10	100	1600	<100
Lassa 3	10	160	<10	<10	1.5	<4.5	<10	<10	<100	400	<100
Junin 1	<10	<10	640	10	<0.3	<0.3	640	<10	<100	<100	1600
Junin 2	<10	<10	20	<10	<0.3	<0.3	160	<10	<100	<100	200
Junin 3	<10	<10	320	40	<0.3	<0.3	320	<10	<100	<100	400
Machupo 1	<10	<10	<10	20	<0.3	<0.3	<10	80	<100	<100	<100
Machupo 2	<10	<10	40	640	<0.3	<0.3	20	640	<100	<100	<100
Machupo 3	<10	<10	<10	10	<0.3	<0.3	20	80	<100	<100	<100

IFA = immunofluorescent antibody; LCM = lymphocytic choriomeningitis (virus); ELISA = enzyme-linked immunosorbent assay.
Note the cross-reactivity by IFA.[22, 109, 296, 297] The infecting agent can usually be identified if all potential antigens are included. The serum dilution neutralization test[298] readily distinguishes Junin and Machupo viruses. The homologous serum dilution neutralization titers are much lower for LCM and Lassa viruses and this has led to the extensive use of IFA[289, 296, 299, 300] in most diagnostic work and of an alternate virus dilution neutralization test (see Figure 20-2 and Table 20-7) to assess protective capacity in immunotherapy of Lassa fever (P.B. Jahrling, K. McKee, G. A. Eddy, J. I. Maiztegui, T. G. Ksiazek, C. J. Peters, unpublished data, 1988).

isolation and IFA as comparative tests, it was possible to diagnose virtually all Lassa virus infections with a combination of antigen and IgM ELISA tests that can be performed within six hours of sample receipt (J. Yalley-Ogunro and P.B. Jahrling, unpublished observations, 1987). If β-propriolactone[303] or other methods are used to inactivate clinical samples, this approach makes safe and rapid Lassa fever diagnosis feasible in many international crossroads.

The IgG antibody ELISA for Junin virus has provided a sensitive diagnostic test using paired sera, but detection of IgM antibodies has been less successful.[304] In Argentina the IgG ELISA may also be useful in field surveys and selection of plasma for therapy.[305] Antigen detection has been possible in acutely infected

AHF patients. Promising initial results are under clinical evaluation (T.G. Ksiazek and J.L. Maiztegui, unpublished observations, 1988).

Earlier reports of the utility of fluorescent antibody detection of Lassa virus–infected cells in conjunctival scrapings have not been borne out, but a similar approach to detect Junin virus–infected cells in the urinary sediment of AHF patients has been proposed.[306]

Serologic Diagnosis

IF antibodies to Junin virus have been useful in diagnosis.[307] In recent studies they have been detected as early as 12 to 17 days

Table 20–10
Serologic Relations of Old World Arenaviruses*

Virus	Specificity of Antiserum		Log₁₀ Neutralization Index of Antiserum Against Virus Strain				
	Strain	Region	JOS	MAC	AN 20410	3080	ARM
Lassa	JOS	Sierra Leone	*4.7*	3.8	3.2	2.2	1.2
Lassa	MAC	Liberia	2.6	*4.1*	1.9	0.5	1.5
Mopeia	AN 20410	Mozambique	0.3	0.3	*2.4*	0.6	0.3
Mobala	3080	Central Africa	0.3	0.3	0.3	*2.8*	0.3
Lymphocytic choriomeningitis	ARM	United States	0.3	0.3	0.3	0.3	*3.1*

Guinea pigs surviving virus infection were exsanguinated 90 days later and their log₁₀ neutralization index determined as described in Figure 20-2. Similar results were obtained with monkey, human, and other guinea pig sera. These results demonstrate the relatedness of these viruses as well as significant geographic variations. Differences between these and other West African Lassa virus strains are modest but reproducible and may bear on the therapeutic use of convalescent plasma. For example, Sierra Leone serum in vitro neutralizes 100 times more homologous virus than virus from nearby Liberia, and is reflected in passive protection of monkeys.[182] Interestingly, cross-protection can occur in the absence of strong cross-neutralization by humoral antibody since prior lymphocytic choriomeningitis virus infection protects against subsequent Lassa challenge.[39]

after the onset of disease.[274] BHF patients reportedly developed detectable IF antibodies somewhat later (between days 17 to 30 of disease evolution), but the use of transmitted rather than epil-lumination may have adversely affected the sensitivity of the test.[296] Serum dilution–plaque reduction neutralization test antibodies to Machupo virus appear by 3 to 4 weeks after onset of illness and follow a similar time course except they persist at higher titers.[298]

Lassa virus IF antibodies can be detected earlier (7–10 d) than those to the South American hemorrhagic fever viruses and, in further contrast, are often present simultaneously with circulating viral infectivity.[164, 289] IgM fluorescent antibodies are present during the acute phase of illness and may persist 1 to 2 months, which allows additional specificity in diagnosis using a single serum sample.[308] Neutralization tests with human sera are not positive until 2 to 5 months after infection and even then titers are low (see Figure 20–2, Tables 20–7 and 20–9).

LCMV serology resembles that of Lassa virus. The IFA test is a useful routine procedure for diagnosis.[299, 300] The test is usually positive within the first week of illness and may be accompanied by viremia. IgM antibodies can be detected in most sera during the first 3 to 5 weeks of illness and CSF IgM antibodies may also be useful in diagnosis.[108] Several methods have been used for detection of neutralizing antibodies to LCMV[300, 309–333] and all have a theme similar to Lassa fever: neutralizing antibodies appear late, tend to be lost rapidly on serum dilution even though substantial virus dilution (LNI) titers may occur, require complement, and may be irretrievably diminished after heating serum.

Thus, in summary, the IFA test[296] is thought to be primarily directed toward the nucleocapsid protein and is currently the most practical single method for measuring the humoral immune response during human arenavirus infection. It should soon be replaced by sensitive, objective ELISA tests for IgG and IgM antibodies. Since these viruses cross-react by IFA[22, 296, 297, 314] it is not surprising that persons infected with, for instance, Machupo virus may even show some response to a distantly related virus such as LCM,[296] or that when two arenaviruses such as Junin and LCMV are simultaneously active in the same geographic area, interpretation becomes difficult.[109] This emphasizes the need to test unknown clinical sera against all pertinent arenavirus antigens if IFA is used. The neutralization test is considerably more specific and, where practical, should be used to confirm cases, particularly if unusual features are present (see Table 20–10). Neutralization tests for Junin and Machupo viruses are also more sensitive for detection of past infections.

Other serologic tests have been applied to diagnosis. Antibodies detected in the CF and agar gel diffusion tests react primarily with the nucleocapsid protein[315–318] and have little role in modern diagnosis. Radioimmunoassay (RIA) or ELISA tests have been used to detect human antibodies to LCMV[319] and will be increasingly applicable to other arenaviruses.[303, 304, 305, 320] Since the nucleocapsid protein is the antigen thought to be responsible for cross-reactivity,[61, 321] future tests directed toward detecting glycoprotein-reactive antibodies may enhance specificity.

VACCINES

Several attempts to produce experimental formalin-inactivated vaccines, attenuated homologous arenavirus strains, or to utilize heterologous arenavirus protection have met with limited success.[39, 322–324] The inability to obtain large quantities of arenaviruses from suitable cell substrates has limited the development of inactivated vaccines. This practical problem coupled with the prominent role of cellular immunity in arenavirus diseases and the unusual neutralizing antibody response following human LCM or Lassa fever has directed interest toward live attenuated vaccines.

The prototype strain of Junin virus (XJ) was passed in mice and cell culture and later cloned in cell lines to produce a mouse brain suspension (XJ clone 3) relatively attenuated for guinea pigs. Because of the number of serious infections in Argentine laboratories, XJ clone 3 was given to several laboratory workers as an experimental vaccine.[325] These trials were eventually extended to more than 600 persons,[323] without serious consequences. Only about 5% developed a temperature above 38°C and one fourth reported constitutional symptoms. About 80% had moderate leukopenia, thrombocytopenia, or both. Neutralizing antibodies were detectable in 92% of recipients tested 1 to 3 months after vaccination and about three fourths were still positive 5 years later. Long-term follow-up 10 years after vaccination uncovered no obvious adverse affects.[326] XJ clone 3 also protects rhesus monkeys from virulent Machupo virus challenge (G.A. Eddy, unpublished data, 1980). Thus, although reactogenic, XJ clone 3 would possibly be acceptable for use in agricultural workers in the endemic zone and at-risk laboratory personnel. Unfortunately, the passage history and method of preparation of the vaccine do not meet modern standards for human application.

It has, however, been possible to return to early XJ mouse passages, retrieve the virus in cell cultures suitable for vaccine production, and develop additional candidate clones for human vaccine use. One of these clones (Candid #1) has been shown to be free of adventitious agents, significantly more attenuated and less neurovirulent than XJ clone 3 for mice and guinea pigs, attenuated and nonneurovirulent for nonhuman primates, and immunogenic for guinea pigs and primates.[327] Latent Candid #1 infection was not detected in a series of cocultivation experiments with spleen, lymph node, peripheral blood lymphocytes, and brain from guinea pigs and macaques. Antibody responses to Candid #1 were, in general, good, and vaccinated animals resisted challenge with virulent strains of Junin virus, as measured by absence of clinical signs or weight loss, undetectable viremia, and failure to excrete virus in saliva. Interestingly, a few macaques failed to develop a detectable postvaccination antibody response, but responded anamnestically to challenge and were protected against disease. Although vaccine-induced antibodies do not neutralize Machupo virus, macaques are also protected against challenge with this agent.[39]

Candid #1 has now been tested in more than 150 human volunteers under close observation and has shown virtually no clinical reactogenicity. There is no detectable virus in serum, throat wash, or semen. Occasional isolates of vaccine virus have been obtained by cocultivation of peripheral blood mononuclear cells. The antibody response is best detected by the plaque reduction neutralization test with added guinea pig complement, or by ELISA, and does not appear until 3 to 6 weeks postvaccination. Titers decline after 3 to 6 months, but are detectable for more than 1 year in most vaccinees. Virtually all vaccinees tested develop evidence of cellular immunity with lymphocyte stimulation indices of 4 to 14 persisting at least 1 year. These numbers represent one to 25 Junin antigen-reactive lymphocytes per 10^5 peripheral blood mononuclear cells.[328, 329] A double blind placebo controlled trial in 6,000 subjects is under way to define the efficacy of the vaccine in the endemic area of Argentina (K.T. McKee, C. J. Peters, and J.I. Maiztegui, unpublished observations, 1989).

In spite of the considerable potential importance of a Lassa vaccine for West Africa, there are no short-term prospects for development of a successful immunogen. The finding of reinfection in humans in the field[120] and the poorly understood immunology of the Old World arenaviruses[39] complicate the issue.

One of the Lassa-like viruses isolated in Mozambique is attenuated for rhesus monkeys and protects against virulent Lassa virus challenge.[330] Additional studies have demonstrated that infection with this virus is also benign for cynomologous monkeys, guinea pigs, and even baby guinea pigs, but continues to confer cross-protection to Lassa virus in these circumstances. Virus can, however, be rescued from macaque spleens by cocultivation at intervals from 6 months to 2 years postinfection.[39] If field studies could establish whether human infections occur with this virus and, if so, their clinical manifestations, it might provide a beginning for a human candidate vaccine. Additional formidable questions related to safety, latency, and the mechanisms of cross-protection would, of course, have to be answered.

An alternate approach might utilize vectors that bear Lassa viral genes, thus avoiding questions of residual pathogenicity and latency inherent in the use of arenaviral immunogens. Infection with vaccinia virus bearing a Lassa GPC gene has resulted in protection of guinea pigs[331] and macaques[332] from mortality, although clinical disease and limited viremia did occur. The Lassa N gene vectored by vaccinia has also been reported to provide protection from lethal challenge,[333] and results of combined GPC and N protection experiments may be better still.

PREVENTION OF INFECTION

In the absence of effective vaccines, the basis of prevention lies in control of human contact with infected rodent populations. For example, in Bolivia, simple trapping of *Calomys callosus* in towns and settlements prevents human BHF.[124] Unfortunately, changes in Argentine agricultural practices (crops and their relation to rodent populations, mechanization of cultivation) are unlikely to impact on human exposure. The disruption of traditional habits in West Africa by diamond mining may well have contributed to the presence of attractive food supplies for *Mastomys natalensis* in houses. Although trapping programs have yielded equivocal results, rodent control may still be capable of decreasing human Lassa virus infection.[130] Urbanization and improved hygienic standards may be responsible for the decline in reported LCM in the Washington, DC, area in the United States. Certainly a case of LCM in the developed world would call for an investigation of rodents in the household of the index case.

What about distant spread and consequent introduction of the arenaviral hemorrhagic fevers? Earlier in this chapter it was argued that the patient who disseminates infection to numerous contacts represents an exception and not the rule. Furthermore, the specificity of a given arenavirus for its reservoir, while not absolute (see Tables 20–1 and 20–2), will probably suffice to prevent the establishment of indigenous cycles in other rodent populations. It is probably sufficient to maintain a high index of suspicion for the imported patient, provide specialized laboratory back-up, and utilize conventional isolation procedures until a diagnosis is established. Medical care goals should be to (1) prevent needless dissemination of potentially infective laboratory samples, (2) decontaminate infective material from seriously ill patients, and (3) render high-quality medical care both to the arenavirus-infected patient and to the uninfected patient who comes under suspicion (see Chapter 26 for details).

Finally, a word about the recovered patient. These persons may have persistent viral infection for several weeks and excrete virus in urine, semen, or milk.[334] They require definitive virologic testing before they return to unrestricted activity. After full convalescence, their participation in plasmapheresis programs could be of value in generating therapeutic tools for future cases.

ACKNOWLEDGMENTS

I would like to thank my colleagues who have read and discussed this chapter with me and particularly those who have allowed me to quote extensively from their unpublished data.

BIBLIOGRAPHIC EPILOGUE

The interested reader will find detailed reviews of arenaviruses in the proceedings of symposia held in Hamburg (1972),[9] Atlanta (1975),[10] Buenos Aires (1977),[335] and Hamburg (1985).[336] Comprehensive reviews and a monograph have also been recently published.[337–340]

REFERENCES

1. Armstrong C, Lillie RD: Experimental lymphocytic choriomeningitis of monkeys and mice produced by a virus encountered in studies of the 1933 St Louis encephalitis epidemic. *Public Health Rep* 1934; 49:1019–1027.
2. Rivers TM, Scott TF McN: Meningitis in man caused by a filterable virus. *Science* 1935; 81:439–440.
3. Traub E: A filterable virus recovered from white mice. *Science* 1935; 81:298–299.
4. Armstrong C, Sweet LK: Lymphocytic choriomeningitis. *Public Health Rep* 1939; 54:673–684.
5. Traub E: The epidemiology of lymphocytic choriomeningitis in white mice. *J Exp Med* 1936; 64:183–200.
6. Rowe WP: *Studies on Pathogenesis and Immunity in Lymphocytic Choriomeningitis Infection of the Mouse.* Bethesda, Md, Naval Medical Research Institute, National Naval Medical Center. Research Report No. 12 1954, pp 167–220.
7. Hotchin J: The biology of lymphocytic choriomeningitis infection: virus-induced immune disease. *Cold Spring Harbor Symp Quant Biol* 1962; 27:479–499.
8. Lehmann-Grube F: *Lymphocytic Choriomeningitis Virus.* New York, Springer-Verlag, 1971.
9. Lehmann-Grube F: Lymphocytic choriomeningitis virus and other arenaviruses. Berlin, Springer-Verlag, 1973.
10. International Symposium on Arenaviral Infections of Public Health Importance. Atlanta, Georgia, July 14–16, 1975. *Bull WHO* 1975; 52:381–766.
11. Burnet FM, Fenner F: *The Production of Antibodies,* ed 2. London, Macmillan, 1953.
12. Buchmeier MJ, Welsh RM, Dutko FJ, et al: The virology and immunobiology of lymphocytic choriomeningitis virus infection, in Dixon FJ, and Kunkel HG (eds): *Advances of Immunology.* New York, Academic Press, 1980, vol 30, pp 275–331.

13. Zinkernagel RM, Doherty PC: MHC-restricted cytotoxic T cells: studies on the biological role of polymorphic major transplantion antigens determining T-cell restriction-specificity, function, and responsiveness, in Kunkel HG, and Dixon FJ (eds): *Advances of Immunology.* New York, Academic Press, 1979, vol 27, pp 51–177.

14. Pfau CJ, Bergold GH, Casals J, et al: Arenaviruses. *Intervirology* 1974; 4:207–213.

15. Parodi AS, Greenway DJ, Rugiero HR: Sobre la etiologia del brote epidemico de Junin.*Dia Medico* 1958; 30:2300–2301.

16. Pirosky I, Zuccarini J, Molinelli EA, et al: *Virosis hemorragica del noroeste bonaerense.* Buenos Aires, Instituto Nacional de Microbiologia, 1959.

17. Mettler NE, Casals J, Shope RE: Study of the antigenic relationships between Junin virus, the etiological agent of Argentinian hemorrhagic fever, and other arthropod-borne viruses. *Am J Trop Med Hyg* 1963; 12:647–652.

18. Johnson KM, Wiebenga NJ, Mackenzie RB, et al: Virus isolations from human cases of hemorrhagic fever in Bolivia. *Proc Soc Exp Biol Med* 1965; 118:113–118.

19. Johnson KM: Epidemiology of Machupo virus infection. III. Significance of virological observations in man and animals. *Am J Trop Med Hyg* 1965; 14:816–818.

20. Dalton AJ, Rowe WP, Smith GH, et al: Morphological and cytochemical studies on lymphocytic choriomeningitis virus. *J Virol* 1968; 2:1465–1478.

21. Murphy FA, Webb PA, Johnson KM, et al: Morphological comparison of Machupo with lymphocytic choriomeningtis virus: Basis for a new taxonomic group. *J Virol* 1969; 4:535–541.

22. Rowe WP, Pugh WE, Webb PA, et al: Serological relationship of the Tacaribe complex of viruses to lymphocytic choriomeningitis virus. *J Virol* 1970; 5:289–292.

23. Buckley SM, Casals J: Lassa fever, a new virus disease of man from West Africa. III. Isolation and characterization of the virus. *Am J Trop Med Hyg* 1970; 19:680–691.

24. Digoutte JP: Arbovirus research, in *Annual Report of Institute Pasteur.* Bangui, Central African Republic, 1970.

25. Swanepoel R, Leman PA, Shepherd AJ, et al: Identification of Ippy as a Lassa-fever related virus. *Lancet* 1985; 1:639.

26. Wulff H, McIntosh BM, Hamner DB, et al: Isolation of an arenavirus closely related to Lassa virus from *Mastomys natalensis* in south-east Africa. *Bull WHO* 1977; 55:441–444.

27. Johnson KM, Taylor P, Elliott LH, et al: Recovery of a Lassa-related arenavirus in Zimbabwe. *Am J Trop Med Hyg* 1981; 30:1291–1293.

28. Gonzalez JP, McCormick JB, Saluzzo JF, et al: An arenavirus isolated from wild-caught rodents (*Praomys* species) in the Central African Republic. *Intervirology* 1983; 19:105–112.

29. Downs WG, Anderson CR, Spence L, et al: Tacaribe virus, a new agent isolated from artibeus bats and mosquitoes in Trinidad, West Indies. *Am J Trop Med Hyg* 1963; 12:640–646.

30. Pinheiro FP, Shope RE, Paes de Andrade AH, et al: Amapari, a new virus of the Tacaribe group from rodents and mites of Amapa Territory, Brazil. *Proc Soc Exp Biol Med* 1966; 122:531–535.

31. Webb PA, Johnson KM, Hibbs JB, et al: Parana, a new Tacaribe complex virus from Paraguay. *Arch Gesamte Virusforsch* 1970; 32:379–388.

32. Calisher CH, Tzianabos T, Lord RD, et al: Tamiami virus, a new member of the Tacaribe group. *Am J Trop Med Hyg* 1970; 19:520–526.

33. Karabatsos, N: *International Catalogue of Arboviruses Including Certain Other Viruses of Vertebrates,* ed 3. San Antonio, American Society of Tropical Medicine and Hygiene, 1985.

34. Trapido H, Sanmartin C: Pichinde virus: A new virus of the Tacaribe Group from Colombia. *Am J Trop Med Hyg* 1971; 20:631–641.

35. Webb PA, Johnson KM, Peters CJ, et al: Behavior of Machupo and Latino viruses in *Calomys callosus* from two geographic areas of Boliva, in Lehmann-Grube F (ed): *Lymphocytic Chorio-*

36. Pinheiro FP, Woodall JP, Da Rosa APAT, et al: Studies of arenaviruses in Brazil. *Medicina (B Aires)* 1977; 37(suppl):175–181.

37. Johnson KM, Webb PA, Justines G: Biology of Tacaribe-complex viruses, in Lehmann-Grube F (ed): *Lymphocytic Choriomeningitis Virus and Other Arenaviruses.* Berlin, Springer-Verlag, 1973, pp 241–258.

38. Arata AA, Gratz NG: The structure of rodent faunas associated with arenaviral infections. *Bull WHO* 1975; 52:621–627.

39. Peters CJ, Jahrling PB, Liu CT, et al: Experimental studies of arenaviral hemorrhagic fevers, in Oldstone MB (ed): *Current Topics in Microbiology and Immunology.* Heidelberg, Springer-Verlag, 1987, vol 134; *Arenaviruses: Biology and Immunotherapy.* pp 5–68.

40. Monath TP: Lassa fever: review of epidemiology and epizootiology. *Bull WHO* 1975; 52:577–592.

41. Johnson KM, Halstead SB, Cohen SN: Hemorrhagic fevers of Southeast Asia and South America: A comparative appraisal. *Prog Med Virol* 1967; 9:105–158.

42. Murphy FA, Whitfield SG: Morphology and morphogenesis of arenaviruses. *Bull WHO* 1975; 52:409–419.

43. Abelson HT, Smith GH, Hoffman HA, et al: Use of enzyme-labeled antibody for electron microscope localization of lymphocytic choriomeningitis virus antigens in infected cell cultures. *J Natl Cancer Inst* 1969; 42:497–515.

44. Pedersen IR: LCM virus: Its purification and its chemical and physical properties, in Lehmann-Grube F (ed): *Lymphocytic Choriomeningitis Virus and Other Arenaviruses.* Berlin, Springer-Verlag, 1973, pp 13–23.

45. Farber FE, Rawls WE: Isolation of ribosome-like structures from Pichinde virus. *J Gen Virol* 1975; 26:21–31.

46. Vezza AC, Gard GP, Compans RW, et al: Structural components of the arenavirus Pichinde. *J Virol* 1977; 23:776–786.

47. Leung W-C, Rawls WE: Virion-associated ribosomes are not required for the replication of Pichinde virus. *Virology* 1977; 81:174–176.

48. Manweiler KI, Lehmann-Grube F: Electron microscopy of LCM virus-infected L cells, in Lehmann-Grube F (ed): *Lymphocytic Choriomeningitis Virus and Other Arenaviruses.* Berlin, Springer-Verlag, 1973, pp 37–48.

49. Welsh RM Jr: Host cell modification of lymphocytic choriomeningitis virus and Newcastle disease virus altering viral inactivation by human complement. *J Immunol* 1977; 118:348–354.

50. Buchmeier MJ, Elder JH, Oldstone MB: Protein structure of lymphocytic choriomeningitis virus: Identification of the virus structural and cell associated polypeptides. *Virology* 1978; 89:133–145.

51. Ramos BA, Courtney RJ, Rawls WE: Structural proteins of Pichinde virus. *J Virol* 1972; 10:661–667.

52. Gangemi JD, Rosato RR, Connell EV, et al: Structural polypeptides of Machupo virus. *J Gen Virol* 1978; 41:183–188.

53. Kiley MP, Tomori O, Regnery RL, et al: Characterization of the arenaviruses Lassa and Mozambique. Bishop DHL, Compans RW (eds): *The Replication of Negative Strand Viruses.* New York, Elsevier/North Holland, 1981, pp 1–9.

54. Martinez Segovia ZM, De Mitri MI: Junin virus structural proteins. *J Virol* 1977; 21:579–583.

55. Lukashevich IS: Human pathogens of the Arenaviridae family. *Soc Med Rev Virol* 1987; 2:133–186.

56. Gard GP, Vezza AC, Bishop DHL, et al: Structural proteins of Tacaribe and Tamiami virions. *Virology* 1977; 83:84–95.

57. Carter MF, Biswal N, Rawls WE: Characterization of nucleic acid of Pichinde virus. *J Virol* 1973; 11:61–68.

58. Leung WC, Leung MF, Rawls WE: Distinctive RNA transcriptase, polyadenylic acid polymerase, and polyuridylic acid polymerase activities associated with Pichinde virus. *J Virol* 1979; 30:98–107.

59. Young PR, Chanas AC, Howard CR: Analysis of the structure and function of Pichinde virus polypeptides, in Bishop DHL,

564   *C. J. Peters*

Compans RW (eds): *The Replication of Negative Strand Viruses.* New York, Elsevier/North Holland, 1981, pp 15–22.

60. Buchmeier MJ, Parekh BS: Protein structure and expression among arenaviruses, in Oldstone MBA (ed): *Current Topics in Microbiology and Immunology.* vol 133: Heidelberg, Springer-Verlag, 1987, *Arenaviruses, Genes, Proteins, and Expression.* pp 41–58.

61. Buchmeier MJ, Lewicki HA, Tomori O, et al: Monoclonal antibodies to lymphocytic choriomeningitis and Pichinde viruses: Generation, characterization, and cross-reactivity with other arenaviruses. *Virology* 1981; 113:73–85.

62. Palmer EL, Obijeski JF, Webb PA, et al: The circular segmented nucleocapsid of an arenavirus-Tacaribe virus. *J Gen Virol* 1977; 36:541–545.

63. Vezza AC, Clewley JP, Gard GP, et al: Virion RNA species of the arenaviruses Pichinde, Tacaribe, and Tamiami. *J Virol* 1978; 26:485–497.

64. Harnish DG, Leung WC, Rawls WE: Characterization of polypeptides immunoprecipitable from Pichinde virus-infected BHK-21 cells. *J Virol* 1981; 38:840–848.

65. Anon MC, Grau O, Segovia ZM, et al: RNA composition of Junin virus. *J Virol* 1976; 18:833–838.

66. Vezza AC, Bishop DHL: Recombination between temperature-sensitive mutants of the arenavirus Pichinde. *J Virol* 1977; 24:712–715.

67. Vezza AC, Cash P, Jahrling P, et al: Arenavirus recombination: The formation of recombinants between prototype Pichinde and Pichinde Munchique viruses and evidence that arenavirus S RNA codes for N polypeptide. *Virology* 1980; 106:250–260.

68. Kirk WE, Cash P, Peters CJ, et al: Formation and characterization of an intertypic lymphocytic choriomeningitis recombinant virus. *J Gen Virol* 1980; 51:213–218.

69. Riviere Y: Mapping arenavirus genes causing virulence, in Oldstone MBA (ed): *Current Topics in Microbiology and Immunology.* vol 133: Heidelberg, Springer-Verlag, 1978, *Arenaviruses, Genes, Proteins, and Expression.* pp 59–66.

70. Compans RW, Boersma DP, Cash P, et al: Molecular and genetic studies of Tacaribe, Pichinde, and lymphocytic choriomeningitis viruses, in Bishop DHL, Compans RW (eds): *The Replication of Negative Strand Viruses.* New York, Elsevier/North Holland, 1981, pp 31–42.

71. Leung WC, Harnish D, Ramsingh A, et al: Gene mapping in Pichinde virus, in Bishop DHL, Compans RW (eds): *The Replication of Negative Strand Viruses.* New York, Elsevier/North Holland, 1981, pp 51–57.

72. Auperin DD, Romanowski V, Galinski M, et al: Sequencing studies of Pinchinde arenavirus S RNA indicate a novel coding strategy, an ambisense viral S RNA. *J Virol* 1984; 52:897–904.

73. Romanowski V, Matsuura Y, Bishop DHL: Complement sequence of the S RNA of lymphocytic choriomeningitis virus (WE strain) compared to that of Pichinde arenavirus. *Virus Res* 1985; 3:101–114.

74. Clegg JCS, Oram JD: Molecular cloning of Lassa virus RNA: nucleotide sequence and expression of the nucleocapsid protein gene. *Virology* 1985; 114:363–372.

75. Auperin DD, Sasso DR, McCormick JB: Nucleotide sequence of the glycoprotein gene and intergenic region of Lassa virus S genome RNA. *Virology* 1986; 154:155–167.

76. Franze-Fernandez MT, Zetina C, Iapalucci S, et al: Molecular structure and early events in the replication of Tacaribe arenavirus S RNA. *Virus Res* 1987; 7:309–324.

77. Baro NI, Ghiringhelli PD, Rosas MF, et al: Clonado molecular del genoma del virus Junin, in *Libro de resumenes, Segundo Congreso Argentino de Virologia,* Cordoba, Sociedad Argentina de Virologia, 1986.

78. Bishop DHL, Auperin DD: Arenavirus gene structure and organization, in Oldstone MGA (ed): *Current Topics in Microbiology and Immunology,* vol 133: Heidelberg, Springer-Verlag, 1987, *Arenaviruses, Genes, Proteins, and Expression.* pp 5–18.

79. Southern PJ, Bishop DHL: Sequence comparison among arenaviruses, in Oldstone MGA (ed): *Current Topics in Microbiology*

and Immunology. vol 133: Heidelberg, Springer-Verlag, 1987, *Arenaviruses, Genes, Proteins, and Expression.* pp 19–40.

80. Weber EL, Buchmeier MJ: Find mapping of a peptide sequence containing an antigenic site conserved among arenaviruses. *Virology* 1988; 164:30–38.

81. Lehmann-Grube F, Slenczka W, Tees R: A persistent and inapparent infection of L cells with the virus of lymphocytic choriomeningitis. *J Gen Virol* 1969; 5:63–81.

82. Staneck LD, Trowbridge RS, Welsh RM, et al: Arenaviruses: Cellular response to long-term in vitro infection with Parana and lymphocytic choriomeningitis viruses. *Infect Immun* 1972; 6:444–450.

83. Stanwick TL, Kirk BE: Analysis of baby hamster kidney cells persistently infected with lymphocytic choriomeningitis virus. *J Gen Virol* 1976; 32:361–367.

84. Gimenz HB, Compans RW: Defective interfering Tacaribe virus and persistently infected cells. *Virology* 1980; 107:229–239.

85. Boxaca MC: Establishment and characteristics of a cell subline persistently infected with Junin virus. *Medicina (B Aires)* 1970; 30:50–61.

86. Hotchin J, Kinch W, Benson L, et al: Role of substrains in persistent lymphocytic choriomeningitis virus infection. *Bull WHO* 1975; 52:457–463.

87. Oldstone MBA, Holmstoen J, Welsh RM Jr: Alterations of acetylcholine emzymes in neuroblastoma cells persistently infected with lymphocytic choriomeningitis virus. *J Cell Physiol* 1977; 91:459–472.

88. Lukashevich IS, Maryankova RF, Fidarov FM: Acute and persistent infection of Vero cells with Lassa virus. *Vopr Virusol* 1981; 4:452–456.

89. Coto CE, Vidal M delC, D'Aiutolo AC, et al: Selection of spontaneous ts mutants of Junin and Tacaribe viruses in persistent infections, in Bishop DHL, Compans RW (eds): *The Replication of Negative Strand Viruses.* Elsevier/North Holland, 1981, pp 59–64.

90. Welsh RM Jr, Buchmeier MJ: Protein analysis of defective interfering lymphocytic choriomeningitis virus and persistently infected cells. *Virology* 1979; 96:503–515.

91. Welsh RM, Pfau CJ: Determinants of lymphocytic choriomeningitis interference. *J Gen Virol* 1972; 14:177–187.

92. Popescu M, Lehmann-Grube F: Defective interfering particles in mice infected with lymphocytic choriomeningitis virus. *Virology* 1977; 77:78–83.

93. Jacobson S, Dutko FJ, Pfau CJ: Determinants of spontaneous recovery and persistence in MDCK cells infected with lymphocytic choriomeningitis virus. *J Gen Virol* 1979; 44:113–121.

94. Dutko FJ, Wright EA, Pfau CJ: The RNAs of defective interfering Pichinde virus. *J Gen Virol* 1976; 31:417–427.

95. Welsh RM, Burner PA, Holland JJ, et al: A comparison of biochemical and biological properties of standard and defective lymphocytic choriomeningitis virus. *Bull WHO* 1975; 52:403–408.

96. Dutko FJ, Hefland J, Pfau CJ: The RNAs of standard and defective interfering Parana virus, in *Abstracts of the Annual Meeting of the American Society for Microbiology.* 1978, p 250.

97. Peralta LM, Bruns M, Lehmann-Grube F: Biochemical composition of lymphocytic choriomeningitis virus interfering particles. *J Gen Virol* 1981; 55:475–479.

98. Dimock K, Harnish DG, Sisson G, et al: Synthesis of virus-specific polypeptides and genomic RNA during the replicative cycle of Pichinde virus. *J Virol* 1982; 43:273–283.

99. Young PR, Lee SR, Howard CR: Regulation of Pichinde virus replication in Vero and BHK-21 cells. *Med Microbiol Immunol* 1986; 175:63–66.

100. Webb PA, Justines G, Johnson KM: Infection of wild and laboratory animals with Machupo and Latino viruses. *Bull WHO* 1975; 52:493–499.

101. Armstrong C: Studies on choriomeningitis and poliomyelitis. *Bull NY Acad Med* 1941; 17:295–318.

102. Adair CV, Gauld RL, Smadel JE: Aseptic meningitis, a disease of diverse etiology: Clinical and etiologic studies on 854 cases. *Ann Intern Med* 1953; 39:675–704.

103. Meyer HM Jr, Johnson RT, Crawford IP, et al: Central nervous system syndromes of "viral" etiology. *Am J Med* 1960; 29:334–347.

104. Biggar RJ, Deibel R, Woodall JP: Implications, monitoring, and control of accidental transmission of lymphocytic choriomeningitis virus within hamster tumor cell lines. *Cancer Res* 1976; 36:537–553.

105. Gregg MB: Recent outbreaks of lymphocytic choriomeningitis in the United States of America. *Bull WHO* 1975; 52:549–553.

106. Ackerman R: Epidemiologic aspects of lymphocytic choriomeningitis in man, in Lehmann-Grube F (ed): *Lymphocytic Choriomeningitis Virus and Other Arenaviruses.* Berlin, Springer-Verlag, 1973, pp 233–237.

107. Assaad F, Gispen R, Kleemola M, et al: Neurological diseases associated with viral and *Mycoplasma pneumoniae* infections. *Bull WHO* 1980; 58:297–311.

108. Simon M: Lymphocytic choriomeningitis infections in Hungary between 1973 and 1977. *Orv Hetil* 1978; 119:1535–1541.

109. Barrera-Oro JG, Grela ME, Zannoli VH, et al: Antibodies against Junin and LCM virus in presumptive cases of Argentine hemorrhagic fever. *Medicina (B Aires)* 1977; 37:69–77.

110. Monath TP, Newhouse VF, Kemp GE, et al: Lassa virus isolation from *Mastomys natalensis* rodents during an epidemic in Sierra Leone. *Science* 1974; 185:263–265.

111. Wulff H, Fabiyi A, Monath TP: Recent isolations of Lassa virus from Nigerian rodents. *Bull WHO* 1975; 52:609–613.

112. Walker DH, Wulff H, Lange JV, et al: Comparative pathology of Lassa virus infection in monkeys, guinea-pigs, and *Mastomys natalensis. Bull WHO* 1975; 52:523–534.

113. Frame JD: Surveillance of Lassa fever in missionaries stationed in West Africa. *Bull WHO* 1975; 52:593–598.

114. McCormick JB, Johnson KM: Lassa fever: Historical review and contemporary investigation, in Pattyn SR (ed): *Ebola Virus Haemorrhagic Fever.* New York, Elsevier/North Holland, 1978, pp 279–286.

115. Tomori O, Fabiyi A, Sorungbe A, et al: Viral hemorrhagic fever antibodies in Nigerian populations. *Am J Trop Med Hyg* 1988; 38:407–410.

116. Frame JD, Jahrling PB, Yalley-Ogunro JE, et al: Endemic Lassa fever in Liberia. II. Serological and virological findings in hospital patients. *Trans R Soc Trop Med Hyg* 1984; 78:656–660.

117. Frame JD, Yalley-Ogunro JE, Hanson AP: Endemic Lassa fever in Liberia. V. Distribution of Lassa virus activity in Liberia: hospital staff surveys. *Trans R Soc Trop Med Hyg* 1984; 78:761–763.

118. Yalley-Ogunro JE, Frame JD, Hanson AP: Endemic Lassa fever in Liberia. VI. Village serological surveys for evidence of Lassa virus activity in Lofa County, Liberia. *Trans R Soc Trop Med Hyg* 1984; 78:764–770.

119. McCormick JB, King IJ, Webb PA, et al: A case-control study of the clinical diagnosis and course of Lassa fever. *J Infect Dis* 1987; 155:445–455.

120. McCormick JB, Webb PA, Krebs JW, et al: A prospective study of the epidemiology and ecology of Lassa fever. *J Infect Dis* 1987; 155:437–444.

121. Keenlyside RA, McCormick JB, Webb PA, et al: Case-control study of *Mastomys natalensis* and humans in Lassa virus–infected households in Sierra Leone. *Am J Trop Med Hyg* 1983; 32:829–837.

122. Maiztegui JI: Clinical and epidemiological patterns of Argentine haemorrhagic fever. *Bull WHO* 1975; 52:567–575.

123. Sabattini MS, de Rios LEG, Diaz G, et al: Natural and experimental infection of rodents with Junin virus. *Medicina (B Aires)* 1977; 37:149–161.

124. Mercado R: Rodent control programmes in areas affected by Bolivian haemorrhagic fever. *Bull WHO* 1975; 52:691–696.

125. Frame JD, Baldwin JM Jr, Gocke DJ, et al: Lassa fever, a new virus disease of man from West Africa. I. Clinical description and pathological findings. *Am J Trop Med Hyg* 1970; 19:670–679.

126. Leifer E, Gocke DJ, Bourne H: Lassa fever, a new virus disease of man from West Africa. II. Report of a laboratory-acquired infection treated with plasma from a person recently recovered from the disease. *Am J Trop Med Hyg* 1970; 19:677–679.

127. Carey DE, Kemp GE, White HA, et al: Lassa fever epidemiological aspects of the 1970 epidemic, Jos, Nigeria. *Trans R Soc Trop Med Hyg* 1972; 66:402–408.

128. Frame JD, Casals J, Dennis EA: Lassa virus antibodies in hospital personnel in western Liberia. *Trans R Soc Trop Med Hyg* 1979; 73:219–224.

129. Fraser DW, Campbell C, Monath TP, et al: Lassa fever in the eastern province of Sierra Leone, 1970–1972. *Am J Trop Med Hyg* 1974; 23:1131–1139.

130. Helmick CG, Scribner CL, Webb PA, et al: No evidence for increased risk of Lassa fever infection in hospital staff. *Lancet* 1982; 2:1202–1205.

131. Management of patients with suspected viral hemorrhagic fever. *MMWR* 1988; 27(suppl).

132. Stephenson EH, Larson EW, Dominik JW: Effect of environmental factors on aerosol-induced Lassa virus infection. *J Med Virol* 1984; 14:295–303.

133. Fisher-Hoch SP, Craven RB, Forthall DN, et al: Safe intensive-care management of a severe case of Lassa fever with simple barrier nursing techniques. *Lancet* 1985; 2:1227–1229.

134. Mackenzie RB: Epidemiology of Machupo virus infection. I. Pattern of human infection, San Joaquin, Bolivia, 1962–1964. *Am J Trop Med Hyg* 1965; 14:808–813.

135. Peters CJ, Kuehne RW, Mercado RR, et al: Hemorrhagic fever in Cochabamba, Bolivia, 1971. *Am J Epidemiol* 1974; 99:425–433.

136. Douglas RG Jr, Weibenga NH, Couch RB: Bolivian hemorrhagic fever probably transmitted by personal contact. *Am J Epidemiol* 1965; 82:85–91.

137. Baum SG, Lewis AM Jr, Rowe WP, et al: Epidemic nonmeningitic lymphocytic-choriomeningitis-virus infection. An outbreak in a population of laboratory personnel. *N Engl J Med* 1966; 274:934–936.

138. Ackermann R, Stille W, Blumenthal W, et al: Syrian hamster as a vector of lymphocytic choriomeningitis. *Dtsch Med Wochenschr* 1972; 97:1725–1731.

139. Vanzee BE, Douglas RG Jr, Betts RF, et al: Lymphocytic choriomeningitis in University Hospital personnel. Clinical features. *Am J Med* 1975; 58:803–809.

140. Deibel R, Woodall JP, Decher WJ, et al: Lymphocytic choriomeningitis virus in man. Serologic evidence of association with pet hamsters. *JAMA* 1975; 232:501–504.

141. Hinman AR, Fraser DW, Douglas RG, et al: Outbreak of lymphocytic choriomeningitis virus infections in medical center personnel. *Am J Epidemiol* 1975; 101:103–110.

142. Farmer TW, Janeway CA: Infections with the virus of lymphocytic choriomeningitis. *Medicine* 1942; 21:1–64.

143. Lewis JM, Utz JP: Orchitis, parotitis and meningoencephalitis due to lymphocytic-choriomeningitis virus. *N Engl J Med* 1961; 265:776–780.

144. Biggar RJ, Woodall JP, Walter PD: Lymphocytic choriomeningitis outbreak associated with pet hamsters. Fifty-seven cases from New York State. *JAMA* 1975; 232:494–500.

145. Lepine P: Experimental infection of man with lymphocytic choriomeningitis, abstract, in Third International Congress of Microbiology. Section III, New York, 1939, pp 96–97.

146. Baird RD, Rivers TM: Relation of lymphocytic choriomeningitis to acute aseptic meningitis (Wallgren). *Am J Public Health* 1938; 28:47–53.

147. Oldstone MBA, Peters CJ: Arenavirus infections of the nervous system, in Vinken PJ, Bruyn GW (eds): *Infections of the Nervous System.* New York, Elsevier/North Holland, 1978 vol 34, pp 193–207.

148. Smadel JE, Green RH, Paltauf RM, et al: Lymphocytic choriomeningitis: Two human fatalities following an unusual febrile illness. *Proc Soc Exp Biol Med* 1942; 49:683–686.

149. Ackermann R, Karver G, Twiss R, et al: Prenatal infection with

the virus of lymphocytic choriomeningitis: report of two cases. *Dtsch Med Wochenschr* 1974; 99:629–632.

150. Ackermann R, Kalter SS, Heberling RL, et al: Fetal infection of the baboon *(Papio cynocephalus)* with lymphocytic choriomeningitis virus. *Arch Virol* 1979; 60:311–323.

151. Sheinbergas MM: Antibody to lymphocytic choriomeningitis virus in children with congenital hydrocephalus. *Acta Virol* 1975; 19:165–166.

152. Komrower GM, Williams BL, Stones PB: Lymphocytic choriomeningitis in the newborn. Probable transplacental infection. *Lancet* 1955; 1:697–698.

153. Duncan PR, Thomas AE, Tobin JO'H: Lymphocytic choriomeningitis: Review of ten cases. *Lancet* 1951; 1:956–959.

154. Horton J, Hotchin JE, Olson KB, et al: The effects of MP virus infection in lymphoma. *Cancer Res* 1971; 31:1066–1068.

155. Warkel RL, Rinaldi CF, Bancroft WH, et al: Fatal acute meningoencephalitis due to lymphocytic choriomeningitis virus. *Neurology* 1973; 23:198–203.

156. Keane E, Gilles HM: Lassa fever in Panguma Hospital, Sierra Leone, 1973–6. *Br Med J* 1977; 1(6073):1399–1402.

157. Knobloch J, McCormick JB, Webb PA, et al: Clinical observations in 42 patients with Lassa fever. *Tropenmed Parasitol* 1980; 31:389–398.

158. White HA: Lassa fever. A study of 23 hospital cases. *Trans R Soc Trop Med Hyg* 1972; 66:390–398.

159. Monath TP, Maher M, Casals J, et al: Lassa fever in the Eastern Province of Sierra Leone, 1970–1972. II. Clinical observations and virological studies on selected hospital cases. *Am J Trop Med Hyg* 1974; 23:1140–1149.

160. Mertens PE, Patton R, Baum JJ, et al: Clinical presentation of Lassa fever cases during the hospital epidemic at Zorzor, Liberia, March-April 1972. *Am J Trop Med Hyg* 1973; 22:780–784.

161. Monson MH, Frame JD, Jahrling PB, et al: Endemic Lassa fever in Liberia. I. Clinical and epidemiological aspects of Curran Lutheran Hospital, Zorzor, Liberia. *Trans R Soc Trop Med Hyg* 1984; 78:549–553.

162. Frame JD: Clinical features of Lassa fever in Liberia. *Rev Infect Dis* in press, 1989.

163. Bowen GS, Tomori O, Wulff H, et al: Lassa fever in Onitsha, East Central State, Nigeria, in 1974. *Bull WHO* 1975; 52:599–604.

164. Johnson KM, McCormick JB, Webb PA, et al: Clinical virology of Lassa fever in hospitalized patients. *J Infect Dis* 1987; 155:456–464.

165. Cummins D, Fisher-Hoch S, Bennett D, et al: Detection of a plasma inhibitor of platelet function in patients with severe Lassa fever. Presented at 36th Annual Meeting of the American Society of Tropical Medicine and Hygiene, Los Angeles, 1987.

166. Woodruff AW, Monath TP, Mahmoud AAF, et al: Lassa fever in Britain: An imported case. *Br Med J* 1973; 3:616–617.

167. Fisher-Hoch SP, Cummins D, Bennett D, et al: Deafness due to Lassa fever. Presented at 36th Annual Meeting of the American Society of Tropical Medicine and Hygiene, Los Angeles, 1987.

168. Henderson BE, Gary GW Jr, Kissing RE, et al: Lassa fever. Virological and serological studies. *Trans R Soc Trop Med Hyg* 1972; 66:409–416.

169. Price ME, Fisher-Hoch SP, Craven RB, et al: A prospective study of maternal and fetel outcome in acute Lassa virus infection during pregnancy. *Br Med J* in press, 1988.

170. Monson MH, Cole AK, Frame JD: Pediatric Lassa fever: A review of 33 Liberian cases. *Am J Trop Med Hyg* 1987; 36:408–415.

171. Webb PA, McCormick JB, King IJ, et al: Lassa fever in children in Sierra Leone, West Africa. *Trans R Soc Trop Med Hyg* 1986; 80:577–582.

172. Winn WC Jr, Walker DH: The pathology of human Lassa fever. *Bull WHO* 1975; 52:535–545.

173. Walker DH, McCormick JB, Johnson KM, et al: Pathologic and virologic study of fatal Lassa fever in man. *Am J Pathol* 1982; 107:349–356.

174. Sheagren JN: Septic shock and corticosteroids. *N Engl J Med* 1981; 305:456–458.

175. Stephen EL, Jones DE, Peters CJ, et al: Ribavirin treatment of toga-, arena- and bunyavirus infections in subhuman primates and other laboratory animal species, in Smith RA, Kirkpatrick W (eds): *Ribavirin: A Broad Spectrum Antiviral Agent.* New York, Academic Press, 1980, pp 169–183.

176. Jahrling PB, Hesse RA, Eddy GA, et al: Lassa virus infection of Rhesus monkeys: Pathogenesis and treatment with ribavirin. *J Infect Dis* 1980; 141:580–589.

177. McCormick JB, Webb PA, Johnson KM: Lassa immune plasma and ribavirin in the therapy of acute Lassa fever, in Smith RA, Kirkpatick W (eds): *Ribavirin: A Broad Spectrum Antiviral Agent.* New York, Academic Press, 1980, p 213.

178. McCormick JB, King IJ, Webb PA, et al: Lassa fever. *N Engl J Med* 1986; 314:20–26.

179. Canonico PG, Jahrling PB, Pannier WL: Antiviral efficacy of pyrazofurin against selected RNA viruses. *Antiviral Res* 1982; 2:331–337.

180. Canonico PG: Antivirals for high hazard viruses, in de Clercq E, Walker T (eds): *Antiviral Drug Development.* New York, Plenum, 1988, pp 55–72.

181. Pifat DY, Sidwell RW, Canonico PG: Toxicity evaluation if 1-β-D-ribofuranosyl-1,2,4-triazole-3-carboxamidine hydrochloride (AVS 206) in rhesus monkeys: comparison with ribavirin. Presented at Second International Conference on Antiviral Research, Williamsburg, Va, 1988.

182. Jahrling PB, Peters CJ: Passive antibody therapy of Lassa fever in cynomolgus monkeys: importance of neutralizing antibody and Lassa virus strain. *Infect Immun* 1984; 44:528–533.

183. Jahrling PB, Frame JD, Rhoderick JB, et al: Endemic Lassa fever in Liberia. V. Selection of optimally effective plasma for treatment by passive immunization. *Trans R Soc Trop Med Hyg* 1985; 79:380–384.

184. Jahrling PB, Peters CJ, Stephen EL: Enhanced treatment of Lassa fever by immune plasma combined with ribavirin in cynomolgus monkeys. *J Infect Dis* 1984; 149:420–427.

185. Shulman NR: Assessment of hematologic effects of ribavirin in humans, in Smith R (ed): *Clinical Applications of Ribavirin.* New York, Academic Press, 1988, pp 79–92.

186. Roberts RB, Laskin OL, Laurence J, et al: Ribavirin pharmacodynamics in high-risk patients for acquired immunodeficiency syndrome. *Clin Pharmacol Ther* 1988; 42:365–373.

187. Kenyon RH, Canonico PG, Green DE, et al: Effect of ribavirin and tributylribavirin on Argentine hemorrhagic fever (Junin virus) in guinea pigs. *Antimicrob Agents Chemother* 1986; 29:521–523.

188. Edington GM, White HA: The pathology of Lassa fever. *Trans R Soc Trop Med Hyg* 1972; 66:381–389.

189. Weissenbacher MC, Sabattini MS, Maiztegui JI, et al: Inapparent infections with Junin virus among laboratory workers. *J Infect Dis* 1978; 137:309–313.

190. Ruggiero HR, Parodi AS, Ruggiero HG, et al: Fiebre hemorragica argentina. I. Periodo de incubacion e invasion. *Rev Assoc Med Argentina* 1964; 78:221–226.

191. Molteni HD, Guarinos HC, Petrillo CO, et al: Estudio clinico estadistico sobre 338 pacientes afectados por la fiebre hemorragica epidemica del noroeste de la provincia de Buenos Aires. *Semana Med* 1961; 118:838–855.

192. Rugiero HR, Ruggiero H, Cambaceres GG, et al: Fiebre hemorragica argentina. I. Estudio clinico descriptivo. *Rev Asoc Med Argentina* 1964; 78:281–294.

193. Biquard C, Figini HA, Monteverde DA, et al: Estudio neurologico de 120 casos de fiebre hemorragica argentina. *Prensa Med Argentina* 1969; 56:605–614.

194. Schwarz ER, Mando OG, Maiztegui JI, et al: Alteraciones de la coagulacion en la fiebre hemorragica Argentina. *Medicina (B Aires)* 1972; 32:247–259.

195. Agrest A, Avalos JCS, Slepoy MAyA: Fiebre hemorragica argentina y coagulopatia por consumo. *Medicina (B Aires)* 1969; 29:194–201.

196. Molinas FC, de Bracco ME, Maiztegui JI: Coagulation studies in Argentine hemorrhagic fever. *J Infect Dis* 1981; 143:1–6.

197. Mando OG: Hepatic and enzymatic alterations in Argentine hemorrhagic fever. *Medicina (B Aires)* 1977; 37:190–192.

198. Ruggiero H, Rugiero HR, Cintora FA, et al: Fiebre hemorragica argentina. III. Aparato cardiovascular. *Rev Asoc Med Argentina* 1964; 78:360–371.

199. Schwarz ER, Mando OG, Maiztegui JI, et al: Initial signs and symptoms of significance in the diagnosis of Argentine hemorrhagic fever. *Medicina (B Aires)* 1970; 30:8–14.

200. Pintos IFM, Guarinos HC, Czeplowodski LA, et al: Neustra experiencia en el tratamiento del "Mal de Los Rastrojos." *Semana Med* 1961; 118:856–863.

201. Ruggiero HA, Magnoni C, Cintora FA, et al: Tratamiento de la fiebre hemorragica argentina con plasma de convaleciente. *Prensa Med Argentina* 1972; 59:1569–1578.

202. Sabattini MS, Maiztegui JI: Fiebre hemorragica argentina. *Medicina (B Aires)* 1970; 30:111–128.

203. Milei J, Bolomo NJ, McAllister H: Lesiones miocardicas en las fiebres hemorragicas virales. *Medicina (B Aires)* 1979; 39:799–800.

204. Kenyon RH, Green DE, Peters CJ: Effect of immunosuppression on experimental Argentine hemorrhagic fever in guinea pigs. *J Virol* 1985; 53:75–80.

205. Bustos OJ, de Damilano AJ, Fernandez NJ, et al: Infecciones bacterianas en enfermos con fiebre hemorragica argentina (FHA). Presented at V Jornadas Nacionales de Enfermedades Transmisibles, La Plata, Argentina, Oct 1975.

206. Maiztegui JI, Fernandez NJ, de Damilano AJ: Efficacy of immune plasma in treatment of Argentine hemorrhagic fever and association between treatment and a late neurological syndrome. *Lancet* 1979; 2:1216–1217.

207. Montardit AI, Fernandez NJ, de De Sensi MRF, et al: Neutralizacion de la viremia en enfermos de fiebre hemorragica Argentina tratados con plasma immune (abstract). *Medicina (B Aires)* 1979; 39:799.

208. Enria DA, Fernandez NJ, Briggiler AM, et al: Importance of neutralising antibodies in treatment of Argentine haemorrhagic fever with immune plasma. *Lancet* 1984; 2:255.

209. Enria D, Franco SG, Ambrosio A, et al: Current status of the treatment of Argentine hemorrhagic fever. *Med Microbiol Immunol* 1986; 175:173–176.

210. Enria D, Briggiler A, Franco SG, et al: Efecto del tratamiento con plasma immune sobre el titulo de anticuerpos neutralizantes en convalescientes de FHA, in *Libro de resumenes, Segundo Congreso Argentino de Virologia*. Cordoba, Sociedad Argentina de Virologia, 1986.

211. Pifat DY, Kenyon RH, Sanchez A, et al: Identification of protective epitopes on Junin virus using monoclonal antibodies, in *Libro de resumenes, Segundo Congreso Argentino de Virologia, Sociedad Argentina de Virologia* 1985.

212. Ferbus D, Saavedra MC, Levis S, et al: Relation of endogenous interferon and high levels of 2'–5' oligoadenylate synthetase in leukocytes from patients with Argentine hemorrhagic fever. *J Infect Dis* 1988; 157:1061–1064.

213. Melcon MO, Herskovits E: Complicaciones neurologicas tardias de la fiebre hemorragica argentina. *Medicina (B Aires)* 1981; 41:137–145.

214. Rugiero HR, Cintora A, Libonatti E, et al: Formas nerviosas de la fiebre hemorragica epidemica. *Prensa Med Argentina* 1960; 47:1845–1849.

215. Rugiero HR, Cintora A, Magnoni C, et al: Fiebre hemorragica epidemica. Diagnostico precoz. *Prensa Med Argentina* 1959; 46:980–984.

216. Kenyon RH, Green DE, Eddy GA, et al: Treatment of Junin virus–infected guinea pigs with immune serum: development of late neurological disease. *J Med Virol* 1986; 20:207–218.

217. Eddy GA, Wagner FS, Scott SK, et al: Protection of monkeys against Machupo virus by the passive administration of Bolivian haemorrhagic fever immunoglobulin (human origin). *Bull WHO* 1975; 52:723–727.

218. McLeod CG Jr, Stookey JL, Eddy GA, et al: Pathology of chronic Bolivian hemorrhagic fever in the rhesus monkey. *Am J Pathol* 1976; 84:211–214.

219. Enria DA, Briggiler AM, Levis S, et al: Preliminary report. Tolerance and antiviral effect of ribavirin in patients with Argentine hemorrhagic fever. *Antiviral Res* 1987; 7:353–359.

220. Maiztegui JI, Laguens RP, Cossio PM, et al: Ultrastructural and immunohistochemical studies in five cases of Argentine hemorrhagic fever. *J Infect Dis* 1975; 132:35–43.

221. Polak M, Jufe R: Anatomia patologica del "Mal de los rastrojos." *Semana Med* 1961; 118:864–878.

222. Elsner B, Schwarz E, Mando OC, et al: Pathology of 12 fatal cases of Argentine hemorrhagic fever. *Am J Trop Med Hyg* 1973; 22:229–236.

223. Mackenzie RB, Beye HK, Valverde L, et al: Epidemic hemorrhagic fever in Bolivia. I. A preliminary report of the epidemiologic and clinical findings in a new epidemic area in South America. *Am J Trop Med Hyg* 1964; 13:620–625.

224. Stinebaugh BJ, Schloeder FX, Johnson KM, et al: Bolivian hemorrhagic fever. A report of four cases. *Am J Med* 1966; 40:217–230.

225. Child PL, Mackenzie RB, Valverde LR, et al: Bolivian hemorrhagic fever. A pathologic description. *Arch Pathol* 1967; 83:434–445.

226. Child PL, Ruiz A: Acidophilic bodies. Their chemical and physical nature in patients with Bolivian hemorrhagic fever. *Arch Pathol* 1968; 85:45–50.

227. Buchmeier M, Adam E, Rawls WE: Serological evidence of infection by Pichinde virus among laboratory workers. *Infect Immun* 1974; 9:821–823.

228. Murphy FA, Walker DH: Arenaviruses: Persistent infection and viral survival in reservoir hosts, in Kurstak E, Maramorosch K (eds): *Viruses and Environment*. New York, Academic Press, 1978, pp 155–180.

229. Nathanson N, Monjan AA, Panitch HS, et al: Virus-induced cell-mediated immunopathological disease, in Notkins AL (ed): *Viral Immunology and Immunopathology*. New York, Academic Press, 1975.

230. Weissenbacher MC, Calello MA, Quintans CJ, et al: Junin virus infection in genetically athymic mice. *Intervirology* 1983; 19:1–5.

231. Friedlander AM, Jahrling PE: Inhibition of macrophage DNA synthesis by viral infection, in *Abstracts of the Annual Meeting of the American Society for Microbiology*. 1981, p 56.

232. Rey O, Rossi JPFC, Lopez R, et al: Tacaribe virus infection may induce inhibition of the activity of the host cell Ca^{2+} and Na^+/K^+ pumps. *J Gen Virol* 1988; 69:951–954.

233. Oldstone MBA: Immunopathology of persistent viral infections. *Hosp Pract* 1982; 12:61–72.

234. Peters CJ, Liu CT, Anderson GW Jr, et al: Pathogenesis of viral hemorrhagic fevers: Rift Valley fever and Lassa fever contrasted. *Rev Infect Dis* in press, 1989.

235. Liu CT, Griffin MJ, Jahrling PB, et al: Physiological responses of strain 13 guinea pigs to Pichinde virus infection. *Fed Proc* 1982; 41:1133.

236. Liu CT, Jahrling PB, Peters CJ: Evidence for the involvement of sulfidopeptide leukotrienes in the pathogenesis of Pichinde virus infection in strain 13 guinea pigs. *Prostaglandins Leukotrienes Med* 1986; 24:120–138.

237. Liu CT, Peters CJ: Improvement of cardiovascular functions with a sulfidopeptide leukotriene antagonist (FPL-55712) in a guinea pig model of viral hemorrhagic fever. *Pharmacologist* 1987; 29:196.

238. Fisher-Hoch SP, Mitchell SW, Sasso DR: Physiological and immunological disturbances associated with shock in a primate model of Lassa fever. *J Infect Dis* 1987; 155:465–474.

239. Allison AC: Mechanisms by which activated macrophages inhibit lymphocyte responses. *Immunol Rev* 1978; 40:3–27.

240. Scott WA, Rouzer CA, Cohn ZA: Leukotriene C release by macrophages. *Fed Proc* 1983; 42:129–133.

241. Kuehl FA Jr, Egan RW: Prostaglandins arachidonic acid, and inflammation. *Science* 1980; 210:978–985.

242. Welsh RM, Oldstone MBA: Inhibition of immunologic injury of cultured cells infected with lymphocytic choriomeningitis virus: Role of defective interfering virus in regulating viral antigenic expression. *J Exp Med* 1977; 145:1449–1468.

243. Welsh RM, Lampert PW, Oldstone MBA: Prevention of virus-induced cerebellar disease by defective-interfering lymphocytic choriomeningitis virus. *J Infect Dis* 1977; 136:391–399.

244. Nelles MJ, Streilein JW: Immune response to acute virus infection in the Syrian hamster. *Immunogenetics* 1980; 10:185–199.

245. Kenyon RH, Peters CJ: Cytolysis of Junin infected target cells by immune guinea pig spleen cells. *Microbiol Pathogenesis* 1986; 1:453–464.

246. Welsh RM: Regulation and role of large granular lymphocytes in arenavirus infections, in Oldstone MBA (ed): *Current Topics in Microbiology and Immunology,* Heidelberg, Springer-Verlag, 1987, vol 134; *Arenaviruses, Biology and Immunotherapy.* pp 185–210.

247. Cossio PM, Rabinovich A, Maiztegui JI, et al: Immunofluorescent anti-Junin virus antibodies in Argentine hemorrhagic fever. *Intervirology* 1979; 12:26–31.

248. Jahrling PB, Niklasson BS, McCormick JB: Early diagnosis of human Lassa fever by ELISA detection of antigen and antibody. *Lancet* 1985; 1:250.

249. Stephen EL, Scott SK, Eddy GA, et al: Effect of interferon on togavirus and arenavirus infections of animals. *Tex Rep Biol Med* 1977; 35:449–453.

250. Jacobson S, Friedman RM, Pfau CJ: Interferon induction by lymphocytic choriomeningitis viruses correlates with maximum virulence. *J Gen Virol* 1981; 57:275–283.

251. Gee SR, Chan MA, Clark DA, et al: Role of natural killer cells in Pichinde virus infection of Syrian hamsters. *Infect Immun* 1981; 31:919–928.

252. Saavedra M, Levis S, Tiano E, et al: Sensibilidad del virus Junin a los interferones. Presented at 32nd Annual de la Sociedad Argentina de Investigacion Clinica, Sociedad Argentina de Immunologia, Buenos Aires, Nov 1987.

253. Genovesi EF, Johnson AJ, Peters CJ: Susceptibility and resistance to inbred strains of Syrian golden hamsters *(Mesocricetus auratus)* to wasting disease caused by lymphocytic choriomeningitis virus: pathogenesis of lethal and non-lethal infections. *J Gen Virol* 1988; 69:2209–2220.

254. Kenyon RH, McKee KT Jr, Maiztegui JI, et al: Heterogeneity of Junin virus strains. *Med Microbiol Immunol* 1986; 175:169–172.

255. McKee KT, Mahlandt BG, Maiztegui JI, et al: Virus-specific factors in experimental Argentine hemorrhagic fever in rhesus macaques. *J Med Virol* 1987; 22:99–111.

256. Saavedra M, Feuillade MR, Levis F, et al: Antigenos de histocompatibilidad en la fiebre hemorragica Argentina (FHA). Presented at 32nd Annual de la Sociedad Argentina de Investigacion Clinica, Buenos Aires, Nov 1985.

257. Jahrling PB, Frame JD, Smith SB, et al: Endemic Lassa fever in Liberia. III. Characterization of Lassa virus isolates. *Trans R Soc Trop Med Hyg* 1985; 79:374–379.

258. Callis RT, Jahrling PB, DePaoli A: Pathology of Lassa virus infection in the rhesus monkey. *Am J Trop Med Hyg* 1982; 31:1038–1045.

259. Henson PM, Larsen GL, Webster RO, et al: Pulmonary microvascular alterations and injury induced by complement fragments: synergistic effect of complement activation, neutrophil sequestration, and prostaglandins. *Ann NY Acad Sci* 1982; 384:287–300.

260. Kastello MD, Eddy GA, Kuehne RW: A rhesus monkey model for the study of Bolivian hemorrhagic fever. *J Infect Dis* 1976; 133:57–62.

261. Terrell TG, Stookey JL, Eddy GA, et al: Pathology of Bolivian hemorrhagic fever in the rhesus monkey. *Am J Pathol* 1973; 73:477–494.

262. Eddy GA, Scott SK, Wagner PF, et al: Pathogenesis of Machupo virus infection in primates. *Bull WHO* 1975; 52:517–521.

263. Scott SK, Hickman RL, Lang CM, et al: Studies of the coagulation system and blood pressure during experimental Bolivian hemorrhagic fever in rhesus monkeys. *Am J Trop Med Hyg* 1978; 27:1232–1239.

264. Carballal G: El modelo cobayo en la fiebre hemorrhagica argentina experimental. *Cienc Invest* 1977; 33:225–234.

265. Kierszenbaum F, Budzko DB, Parodi AS: Alterations in the enzymtic activity of plasma of guinea pigs infected with Junin virus. *Arch Ges Virusforsch* 1970; 30:217–223.

266. Rimoldi MT, de Bracco MMdeE: In vitro inactivation of complement by a serum factor present in Junin-virus infected guineapigs. *Immunology* 1980; 39:159–164.

267. Molinas FC, Paz RA, Rimoldi MT, et al: Studies of blood coagulation and pathology in experimental infection of guinea pigs with Junin virus. *J Infect Dis* 1978; 137:740–746.

268. Venge P, Olsson I: Cationic proteins of human granulocytes. VI. Effects on the complement system and mediation of chemotactic activity. *J Immunol* 1975; 115:1505–1508.

269. Egbring R, Schmidt W, Fuchs G, et al: Demonstration of granulocytic proteases in plasma of patients with acute leukemia and septicemia with coagulation defects. *Blood* 1977; 49:219–231.

270. Laguens RP, Maiztegui JI, Cossio PM, et al: Ultrastructural and immunohistochemical studies in 8 fatal cases of Argentine hemorrhagic fever. *Medicina (B Aires)* 1977; 37:205–209.

271. Davalos M, Etchegoyen FP, Otero RE, et al: Evaluation of renal function in patients with Argentine hemorrhagic fever. *Medicina (B Aires)* 1977; 37:182–185.

272. Cossio P, Laguens R, Arana R, et al: Ultrastructural and immunohistochemical study of the human kidney in Argentine haemorrhagic fever. *Virchows Arch (Pathol Anat)* 1975; 368:1–9.

273. Gonzalez PH, Cossio PM, Arana R, et al: Lymphatic tissue in Argentine hemorrhagic fever. *Arch Pathol Lab Med* 1980; 104:250–254.

274. de Bracco MME, Rimoldi MT, Cossio PM, et al: Argentine hemorrhagic fever. Alterations of the complement system and anti-Junin-virus humoral response. *N Engl J Med* 1978; 299:216–221.

275. Molinas FC, de Bracco MME, Maiztegui JI: Studies of hemostasis and the complement system in Argentine hemorrhagic fever. *Rev Infect Dis* in press, 1989.

276. Molinas FE, Maiztegui JI: Factor VIII:C and factor VIII R:Ag in Argentine hemorrhagic fever. *Thromb Haemost* 1981; 46:525–527.

277. Levis SC, Saavedra MC, Ceccoli C, et al: Endogenous interferon in Argentine hemorrhagic fever. *J Infect Dis* 1984; 149:428–433.

278. Levis SC, Saavedra MC, Ceccoli C, et al: Correlation between endogenous interferon and the clinical evolution of patients with Argentine hemorrhagic fever. *J Interferon Res* 1985; 5:383–389.

279. Frigerio J: Immunologic aspects of guinea pigs infected with Junin virus. *Medicina (B Aires)* 1977; 37:96–100.

280. Nejamkis DMR, Nota NR, Bisso GM, et al: Estudios immunologicos en la fiebre hemorragica argentina experimental. II. Comportamiento de las celulas fagocitarias en animales infectados con la cepa prototipo XJ. *Medicina (B Aires)* 1971; 31:166–169.

281. Galassi NV, Blejer JL, Barrios H, et al: New attenuation marker for Junin virus based on immunologic responses of guinea pigs. *J Infect Dis* 1982; 145:331–336.

282. Arana RM, Ritacco GV, de la Vega MT, et al: Immunological studies in Argentine hemorrhagic fever. *Medicine (B Aires)* 1977; 37:186–189.

283. Vallejos DA, Ambrosio AM, Gamboa G, et al: Alteraciones de las subpoblaciones linfocitarias en la fiebre hemorragica Argentina (FHA). Presented at 32nd Annual de la Sociedad Argentina de Investigacion Clinica, Buenos Aires, Nov 1985.

284. The Subcommittee on Arbovirus Laboratory Safety of the American Committee on Arthropod-Borne Viruses: Laboratory safety for arboviruses and certain other viruses of vertebrates. *Am J Trop Med Hyg* 1980; 29:1359–1381.

285. Jahrling PB, Peters CJ: Arenaviruses, in Lennette EH (ed): *Laboratory Diagnosis of Viral Infections.* New York, Marcel Dekker, 1985, pp 172–189.

286. Jahrling PB: Arenaviruses and filoviruses, in Emmons RW, Schmidt NJ (eds): *Diagnostic Procedures for Viral, Rickettsial, and Chlamydial Infections.* Washington, DC, American Public Health Association, 1988, chap 25, 753–777.

287. Elliott LH, McCormick JB, and Johnson KM: Inactivation of Lassa, Marburg, and Ebola viruses by gamma irradiation. *J Clin Microbiol* 1982; 16:704–708.

288. Van der Groen G, Elliott LH: Use of betapropiolactone inactivated Ebola, Marburg and Lassa intracellular antigens in immunofluorescent antibody assay. *Ann Soc Belg Med Trop* 1982; 62:49–54.
289. Wulff H, Lange JV: Indirect immunofluorescence for the diagnosis of Lassa fever infection. *Bull WHO* 1975; 52:429–436.
290. Lascano EF, Berria MI, Candurra NA: Diagnosis of Junin virus in cell cultures by immunoperoxidase staining. *Arch Virol* 1981; 70:79–82.
291. Boxaca MC, de Guerrero LB, Parodi AS, et al: Viremia en enfermos de fiebre hemorragica argentina. *Rev Asoc Med Argentina* 1965; 79:230–238.
292. Ambrosio AM, Enria DA, Maiztegui JI: Junin virus isolation from lympho-mononuclear cells of patients with Argentine hemorrhagic fever. *Intervirology* 1986; 25:97–102.
293. Monath TP, Casals J: Diagnosis of Lassa fever and the isolation and management of patients. *Bull WHO* 1975; 52:707–715.
294. Goldwasser RA, Elliott LH, Johnson KM: Preparation and use of erythrocyte-globulin conjugates to Lassa virus in reversed passive hemagglutination and inhibition. *J Clin Micribiol* 1980; 11:593–599.
295. Hotchin J, Sikora E: Laboratory diagnosis of lymphocytic choriomeningitis. *Bull WHO* 1975; 52:555–559.
296. Peters CJ, Webb PA, Johnson KM: Measurement of antibodies to Machupo virus by the indirect fluorescent technique. *Proc Soc Exp Biol Med* 1973; 142:526–531.
297. Wulff H, Lange JV, Webb PA: Interrelationships among arenaviruses measured by indirect immunofluorescence. *Intervirology* 1978; 9:344–350.
298. Webb PA, Johnson KM, MacKenzie RB: The measurement of specific antibodies in Bolivian hemorrhagic fever by neutralization of virus plaques. *Proc Soc Exp Biol Med* 1969; 130:1013–1019.
299. Cohen SM, Triandaphilli IA, Barlow JL, et al: Immunofluorescent detection of antibody to lymphocytic choriomeningitis virus in man. *J Immunol* 1966; 96:777–784.
300. Lewis VJ, Walter PD, Thacker W, et al: Comparison of three tests for the serological diagnosis of lymphocytic choriomeningitis virus infection. *J Clin Microbiol* 1975; 2:193–197.
301. Buchmeier MJ, Lewicki HA, Tomori O, et al: Monoclonal antibodies to lymphocytic choriomeningitis virus react with pathogenic arenaviruses. *Nature* 1980; 288:486–487.
302. Niklasson BS, Jahrling PB, Peters CJ: Detection of Lassa fever antigens and Lassa-specific immunoglobulins G and M by enzyme-linked immunosorbent assay. *J Clin Microbiol* 1984; 20:239–244.
303. Lloyd G, Bowen ETW, Slade JHR: Physical and chemical methods of inactivating Lassa virus. *Lancet* 1982; 1:1046–1048.
304. Meegan J, LeDuc J, Franco G, et al: Rapid diagnostic methods to detect Junin virus infection. Presented at 35th Annual Meeting of the American Society of Tropical Medicine and Hygiene, Denver, Colo, Dec 8–11, 1986.
305. Franco SG, Ambrosio A, Feuillade M: Anticuerpos contra el virus Junin en convalescientes de FHA: correlation de los titulos en-pruebas de Elisa y neutralizacion. in *Libro de resumenes,* Segundo Congreso Argentino de Virologia, Sociedad Argentina de Virologia, Cordoba, Argentina, 1986.
306. Ruggiero HA, Milani HL, Magnoni C, et al: Argentine hemorrhagic fever: Early diagnosis by immunofluorescence. *Arch Virol* 1981; 70:165–168.
307. Grela ME, Garcia CA, Zannoli VH, et al: Serologia de la fiebre hemorragica argentina. II. Comparacion de la prueba indirecta de anticuerpos fluorescentes con la de fijacion de complemento. *Acta Bioquimi Clin Latino* 1975; 9:141–146.
308. Wulff H, Johnson KM: Immunoglobulin in M and G responses measured by immunofluorescence in patients with Lassa or Marburg virus infections. *Bull WHO* 1979; 57:631–635.
309. Scheid W, Ackermann R, Jochheim K-A, et al: Die neutralisierenden Serumantikörper des Menschen nach Infektionen mit dem Virus der lymphozytären Choriomeningitis und das Verhalten von Normalseren im Neutralisationsversuch. *Arch Gesamte Virusforsch* 1960; 9:295–309.
310. Hotchin J, Benson L, Sikora E: The detection of neutralizing antibody to lymphocytic choriomeningitis virus in mice. *J Immunol* 1969; 102:1128–1135.
311. Hotchin J, Kinch W: Microplaque reduction: New assay for neutralizing antibody to lymphocytic choriomeningitis virus. *J Infect Dis* 1975; 131:186–188.
312. Lehmann-Grube F, Ambrassat J: A new method to detect lymphocytic choriomeningitis virus-specific antibody in human sera. *J Gen Virol* 1977; 37:85–92.
313. Lehmann-Grube F: An improved method for determining neutralizing antibody against lymphocytic choriomeningitis virus in human sera. *J Gen Virol* 1978; 41:377–383.
314. Casals J: Serological reactions with arenaviruses. *Medicina (B Aires)* 1977; 37:59–68.
315. Chastel C: Antigenic relationships in arenaviruses II. Results obtained by means of agar gel diffusion. *Ann Inst Pasteur* 1972; 122:1205–1217.
316. Gschwender HH, Lehmann-Grube F: Antigenic properties of the LCM virus: virion and complement-fixing antigen, in Lehmann-Grube F (ed): *Lymphocytic Choriomeningitis Virus and Other Arenaviruses.* Berlin, Springer-Verlag, 1973, pp 25–35.
317. Buchmeier MJ, Gee SR, Rawls WE: Antigens of Pichinde virus. I. Relationship of soluble antigens derived from infected BHK-21 cells to the structural components of the virion. *J Virol* 1977; 22:175–186.
318. Rezapkin GV, Bashkirtsev VN, Tkachenko EA, et al: Investigation of the biochemical nature of complement-fixing antigen of arenaviruses. *Vopr Virusol* 1980; 2:228–232.
319. Blechschmidt M, Gerlich W, Thomssen R: Radioimmunoassay for LCM virus antigens and anti-LCM virus antibodies and its application in an epidemiologic survey of people exposed to Syrian hamsters. *Med Microbiol Immunol* 1977; 163:67–76.
320. Rezapkin GV, Tkachenko EA, Ivanov AP, et al: Detection of arenavirus antigens and antibody by solid phase radioimmunoassay. *Vopr Virusol* 1981; 4:459–462.
321. Buchmeier MJ, Oldstone MBA: Identity of the viral protein responsible for serologic cross reactivity among the Tacaribe complex arenaviruses, in Mahy BWJ, Barry RD (eds): *Negative Strand Viruses and the Host Cell.* New York, Academic Press, 1978, pp 91–97.
322. Johnson KM: Status of arenavirus vaccines and their application. *Bull WHO* 1975; 52:729–735.
323. Frigerio MJ: Prevencion de la fiebre hemorrhagic Argentina. *Cienc Invest* 1977; 33:265–274.
324. Hotchin J, Carballal G, Sikora E, et al: Experimental vaccination against lymphocytic choriomeningitis. *Medicina (B Aires)* 1977; 37:232–236.
325. Rugiero HR, Astarloa L, Gonzalez Cambaceres F, et al: Immunizacion contra la fiebre hemorragica argentina con una cepa atenuada de virus Junin. *Medicina (B Aires)* 1969; 29:81–92.
326. Ruggiero HA, Magnoni C, de Guerrero LB, et al: Argentine hemorrhagic fever immunization. *J Med Virol* 1981; 7:227–232.
327. Barrera Oro JG, Eddy GA: Characteristics of candidate live attenuated Junin virus vaccine. Presented at the Fourth International Conference on Comparative Virology. Banff, Alberta, Canada, Oct 17–22, 1982.
328. Barrera Oro JG, Kenyon R, Meegan J, et al: The immune response to Candid #1 (C#1): a live attenuated Junin virus vaccine against Argentine hemorrhagic fever (AHF). Presented at 36th Annual Meeting of the American Society of Tropical Medicine and Hygiene, Los Angeles, Nov 29–Dec 3, 1987.
329. Kenyon RH, Barrero Oro J, MacDonald C, et al: Lymphocyte transformation assays for Junin virus (Argentine hemorrhagic fever). Presented at Second International Conference on the Impact of Viral Diseases on the Development of Latin American Countries and the Caribbean Region, Mar del Plata, Argentina, 1988.
330. Kiley MP, Lange JV, Johnson KM: Protection of rhesus monkeys from Lassa virus by immunisation with closely related arenavirus. *Lancet* 1979; 2:738.
331. Auperin DD, Esposito JJ, Lange JV, et al: Construction of a recombinant vaccinia virus expressing the Lassa virus glycoprotein

gene and protection of guinea pigs from a lethal Lassa virus infection. *Virus Res* 1988; 9:233–248.

332. McCormick JB, Fisher-Hoch S, Auperin D, et al: Protection of rhesus monkeys from a lethal Lassa virus infection by vaccination with a vaccinia–Lassa virus glycoprotein construct, in *Abstracts, Resumes*. VII International Congress of Virology, Edmonton, Alberta, Canada, 1987, p 66.

333. Clegg JCS, Lloyd G: Vaccinia recombinant expressing Lassa virus internal nucleocapsid protein protects guinea pigs against Lassa fever. *Lancet* 1987; 2:186–188.

334. Maiztegui JI, Voeffrey JR, Fernandez NJ, et al: Aislamiento de virus Junin a partir de leche materna. *Medicina (B Aires)* 1973; 33:659.

335. Agrest A, Alva-Correa JJ, Barcat JA, et al (eds): Fiebres hemorragicas producidas por arenavirus. *Medicina (B Aires)* 1977; 37:1–259.

336. Lehmann-Grube F (ed): Arenaviruses. *Med Microbiol Immnunol* 1986; 175:61–215.

337. Oldstone MBA (ed): *Current Topics in Microbiology and Immunology*. Heidelberg, Springer-Verlag, 1987, vol 133: *Arenaviruses: Genes, Proteins, and Expression*.

338. Oldstone MBA (ed): *Current Topics in Microbiology and Immunology*. Heidelberg, Springer-Verlag, 1987, vol 134: *Arenaviruses: Biology and Immunotherapy*.

339. Howard CR: Perspectives in Medical Virology, in Zuckerman AJ (ed): *Arenaviruses*. New York, Elsevier, 1986, pp 1–247.

340. Bishop DHL (ed): *The Arenaviridae. The Viruses*. New York, Plenum, in preparation.

21

Bunyaviridae: Bunyaviruses, Phleboviruses, and Related Viruses

C. J. Peters
James W. LeDuc*

HISTORY

EPIDEMIOLOGIC CONSIDERATIONS

HUMAN HEALTH IMPACT

REPLICATION, STRUCTURE, AND GENETICS

***BUNYAVIRUS* GENUS**

BUNYAMWERA GROUP
BWAMBA GROUP
GROUP C
CALIFORNIA GROUP
GUAMA GROUP
SIMBU GROUP
OTHER MEMBERS OF THE *BUNYAVIRUS* GENUS

***PHLEBOVIRUS* GENUS**

NAPLES AND SICILIAN SANDFLY FEVER VIRUSES
TOSCANA VIRUS
NEW WORLD PHLEBOVIRUSES
RIFT VALLEY FEVER

***UUKUVIRUS* GENUS**

***NAIROVIRUS* GENUS**

CRIMEAN-CONGO HEMORRHAGIC FEVER
NAIROBI SHEEP DISEASE GROUP
OTHER MEMBERS OF THE *NAIROVIRUS* GENUS

***BUNYAVIRIDAE*, GENUS UNKNOWN**

BHANJA VIRUS
TATAGUINE VIRUS

**PATHOGENESIS AND IMMUNOLOGY OF
BUNYAVIRIDAE INFECTIONS**

VIROLOGIC DIAGNOSIS

VIRUS ISOLATION
SEROLOGY
RAPID METHODS

PREVENTION

The ***Bunyaviridae*** family comprises more than 200 named viruses accepted by or proposed to the International Committee on Taxonomy of Viruses,[1, 2] including several major human pathogens (Table 21–1). Membership is usually based on antigenic interrelatedness or morphologic similarity (Tables 21–2 to 21–6). The serologic relations are usually reflected in similarities in the natural history of the viruses as well. The family is divided into five genera which differ significantly in their structure, chemistry, and biology: *Bunyavirus, Phlebovirus, Uukuvirus, Nairovirus,* and *Hantavirus.* The hantaviruses, rodent-borne causes of hemorrhagic fever with renal syndrome, are sufficiently distinct in their epidemiology and clinical presentation to warrant coverage in a separate chapter (see Chapter 22). The remaining genera are discussed below.

Bunyavirid viruses have been isolated from sick humans and domestic animals, or obtained during ecological investigations from arthropods and wild vertebrates. The preponderance of isolates originates from the ecologically complex tropical areas of Africa and Latin America where a rich flora exists and where many of these studies were performed. Nevertheless, the family is well represented in temperate climates where some members are also important human pathogens (La Crosse viral encephalitis; sandfly fever; Crimean-Congo hemorrhagic fever), and in arctic habitats as well (eg, Northway, snowshoe hare, Inkoo, and Uukuniemi viruses).

Known members of the family ***Bunyaviridae*** probably represent only a fraction of the distinguishable viruses that exist in nature. Attempts to isolate "new" viruses from vertebrate hosts or arthropods continue to be successful, particularly if the work is conducted outside the major areas of previous virologic endeavors, and many so-called new viruses have ultimately been found to be ***Bunyaviridae.*** For example, in a recent ecological study of Rocio virus encephalitis in southern Brazil, ten isolates

The views of the authors do not purport to reflect the positions of the Department of the Army or the Department of Defense.

Table 21–1
Some Important Members of the Family *Bunyaviridae*

	Disease	Area	Importance
Bunyavirus			
La Crosse	Encephalitis	North America	The major cause of endemic arboviral encephalitis in United States, about 100 reported cases annually
Tahyna	Fever, myalgia, aseptic meningitis	Europe, Asia, Africa	Locally important cause of disease; infection widespread and emerging as an important disease complex
Phlebovirus			
Sandfly fever (Sicilian and Naples)	Fever, myalgia	Circum-Mediterranean Europe, North Africa, Asia	Endemic and epidemic over large regions
Toscana	Aseptic meningitis	Italy, Portugal, possibly other Mediterranean countries	Important cause of aseptic meningitis in Tuscany; emerging elsewhere
Rift Valley fever	Fever, myalgia; hemorrhagic fever; retinitis; encephalitis	Sub-Saharan Africa	Endemic; periodic epidemics; potential for distant spread
Nairovirus			
Crimean-Congo hemorrhagic fever	Fever, myalgia; hemorrhagic fever	Eastern Europe, Africa, Asia	Broad geographic distribution; local epidemics dictated by ecological conditions; nosocomial spread
Hantavirus			
Hantaan and relatives	Hemorrhagic fever with renal syndrome	Europe, Asia, perhaps worldwide	Broad geographic distribution; severe disease (See Chap 22)

of the flavivirus Rocio were made, but 19 *Bunyavirus* isolates were also obtained, including four previously undescribed viruses.[3] Most of the original surveys utilized intracranially inoculated suckling mice for virus isolation, but it is now clear that several naturally occurring arboviruses require mammalian[4] or insect cell culture for propagation. Had these alternative isolation systems also been used, additional viruses may have been recovered from the same material. Finally, many currently ungrouped arboviruses have properties which suggest that they are, indeed, members of the *Bunyaviridae*.[5] The challenge to medical research at this time, however, is not only the discovery of new family members, but perhaps more importantly a better understanding of the evolution, natural history, biomedical significance, and control of the agents already identified.

HISTORY

The story of the *Bunyaviridae* family is linked to that of arbovirology, the study of arthropod-borne viruses. Many of the originally described insect-transmitted pathogens were segregated into two antigenically cross-reacting groups by hemagglutination-inhibition (HI) tests in the classic work of Clarke and Casals.[11] These collections of serologically related viruses, first known as groups A and B, later became the *Alphavirus* and *Flavivirus* genera of the family *Togaviridae*, and today are recognized as distinct families, the *Togaviridae* (including genus *Alphavirus*) and the *Flaviviridae* (including genus *Flavivirus*). The embryonic assembly assigned to "group C" never achieved separate taxonomic status. Serologic work spearheaded by Casals[12] soon established

that the multitude of viruses isolated by field programs in the tropics and elsewhere could each be placed in one or another of several closely related serologic groups including the group C, Bunyamwera, Simbu, and California serogroups. Furthermore, these groups could at times be linked one to another through low-level but reproducible serologic cross-reactions between individual members, leading to the proposal of the "Bunyamwera supergroup" as a title for these agents. Accumulating evidence of biochemical similarities among Bunyamwera supergroup viruses, as well as other unclassified viruses, was crystalized by the extensive morphologic and morphogenetic observations of Murphy, Harrison, and Whitfield[13] into the concept of a new taxon, the family *Bunyaviridae*.[1] Continued integration of new virus groups into the family and delineation of five distinct genera has followed with work from several laboratories, most notably the biochemical investigations from Bishop and colleagues and continued serologic work from Shope, Calisher, and coworkers.[14, 15]

While immunology and molecular biology have brought these viruses together into a rational taxonomic unit, field investigations in the areas of entomology, ecology, epidemiology, and clinical medicine have attempted to understand the natural history and biomedical significance of the family *Bunyaviridae*.

EPIDEMIOLOGIC CONSIDERATIONS

Viruses from the *Bunyaviridae* family (with the exception of hantaviruses) are thought to be transmitted in nature by arthropods: most frequently mosquitoes, but alternately, phlebotomine sandflies, biting midges of the genus *Culicoides*, or ticks (Table 21–

Table 21–2
Serologic Classification of Viruses of Family **Bunyaviridae**, Genus *Bunyavirus**

GROUP Complex *Virus* Subtype	GROUP Complex *Virus* Subtype	GROUP Complex *Virus* Subtype	GROUP Complex *Virus* Subtype
ANOPHELES A GROUP	**GROUP C**	**GAMBOA GROUP**	ZEGLA
ANOPHELES A	CARAPARU	GAMBOA	*Zegla*
Anopheles A	*Caraparu*	*Gamboa*	Pahayokee
Las Maloyas	Caraparu	Pueblo Viejo	
Lukuni	Ossa	ALAJUELA	**SIMBU GROUP**
Trombetas	*Bruconha*	*Alajuela*	SIMBU
TACAIUMA	*Vinces*	San Juan	*Simbu*
Tacaiuma	Apeu		AKABANE
	MADRID	**GUAMA GROUP**	*Akabane*
ANOPHELES B GROUP	*Madrid*	GUAMA	Yaba-7
ANOPHELES B	MARITUBA	*Guama*	MANZANILLA
Anopheles B	*Marituba*	Ananindeua	*Manzanilla*
Boraceia	Murutucu	Mahogany Hammock	Ingwavuma
	Restan	Moju	Inini
BUNYAMWERA GROUP	*Nepuyo*	BERTIOGA	Mermet
BUNYAMWERA	Nepuyo	*Bertioga*	*Buttonwillow*
Bunyamwera	Gumbo Limbo	Cananeia	Nola
Batai (Calovo)	ORIBOCA	Guaratuba	Oropouche
Birao	*Oriboca*	Itimirim	Facey's Paddock
Bozo	Itaqui	Mirim	Utinga
Cache Valley		BIMITI	Utive
Maguari	**CALIFORNIA GROUP**	*Bimiti*	Sabo
Playas	CALIFORNIA ENCEPHALITIS	CATU	Tinaroo
Xingu	*California encephalitis*	*Catu*	SATHUPERI
Ft Sherman	Inkoo	TIMBOTEUA	*Sathuperi*
Germiston	La Cross (snowshoe hare)	*Timboteua*	Souglas
Ilesha	San Angelo		SHAMONDA
Lokern	Tahyna (Lumbo)	**KOONGOL GROUP**	*Shamonda*
Mboke	MELAO	KOONGOL	Sango
Ngari	*Melao*	*Koongol*	Peaton
Northway	Jamestown Canyon	Wongal	SHUNI
Santa Rosa	(Jerry Slough, South River)		*Shuni*
Shokwe	Keystone	**MINATITLAN GROUP**	Aino
Tensaw	Serra do Navio	MINATITLAN	THIMIRI
KAIRI	TRIVITTATUS	*Minaititlan*	*Thimiri*
Kairi	*Trivittatus*	Palestina	
MAIN DRAIN	GUAROA		**TETE GROUP**
WYEOMYIA	*Guaroa*	**OLIFANTSVLEI GROUP**	TETE
Wyeomyia		OLIFANTSVLEI	*Tete*
Anhembi		*Olifantsvlei*	Bahig
Iaco	**CAPIM GROUP**	BOTAMBI	Matruh
Macaua	CAPIM	*Botambi*	Tsuruse
Sororoca	*Capim*	Dabakala	*Batama*
Taiassui	GUAJARA	Oubi	
Tucunduba	*Guajara*		**TURLOCK GROUP**
	BUSH BUSH	**PATOIS GROUP**	TURLOCK
BWAMBA GROUP	*Bush Bush*	PATOIS	*Turlock*
BWAMBA	Benfica	*Patois*	Umbre
Bwamba	*Juan Diaz*	Babahoyo	Lednice
Pongola	ACARA	Shark River	M'POKO
	Acara	Abras	*M'Poko*
	Moriche		Yaba-1
	BENEVIDES		
	Benevides		**NO GROUP ASSIGNED**
			Kaeng Khoi

*This table indicates the majority of the accepted or proposed members of the Bunyavirus genus. It is based on the 1982 International Committee on Taxonomy of Virus recommendations[2] with modifications using the serologic classification published by Calisher and Karabatsos.[15] An attempt was made to classify the virus serologically using neutralization, hemagglutination-inhibition, and complement-fixation tests: "Subtype" refers to viruses which can be distinguished only with difficulty. Each named virus can be easily distinguished. "Complex" refers to assemblies of viruses which are significantly cross-reactive. "Group" encompasses complexes which are distantly related by serologic reactivity.

Table 21–3
Viruses of the Family *Bunyaviridae,* Genus *Phlebovirus*[2, 79, 185, 186, 228]

Virus	Region	Source of Isolates
Alenquer	Brazil	Man
Ambe	Brazil	*Lutzomyia*
Anhanga	Brazil	Sloth
Belterra	Brazil	Rodent
Bujaru	Brazil	Rodent
Candiru	Brazil	Man
Icoaraci	Brazil	*Lutzomyia,* mosquito, rodent
Itaituba	Brazil	Opossum
Itaporanga	Brazil	Mosquito, bird
Joa	Brazil	*Lutzomyia*
Munguba	Brazil	*Lutzomyia*
Oriximina	Brazil	*Lutzomyia*
Pacui	Brazil	*Lutzomyia,* rodent
Turuna	Brazil	*Lutzomyia*
Urucuri	Brazil	Rodent
Arboledas	Colombia	*Lutzomyia*
Armero	Colombia	*Lutzomyia*
Buenaventura	Colombia	*Lutzomyia*
Durania	Colombia	*Lutzomyia*
Leticia	Colombia	*Lutzomyia*
Mariquita	Colombia	*Lutzomyia*
Ixcanal	Guatemala	*Lutzomyia*
Aguacate	Panama	*Lutzomyia*
Cacao	Panama	*Lutzomyia*
Caimito	Panama	*Lutzomyia*
Chagres	Panama	*Lutzomyia,* man
Chilibre	Panama	*Lutzomyia*
Frijoles	Panama	*Lutzomyia*
Nique	Panama	*Lutzomyia*
Punta Toro	Panama	*Lutzomyia,* man
Rio Grande	United States (Texas)	Rodent
Corfou	Greece	*Phlebotomus*
Arbia	Italy	*Phlebotomus*
Toscana	Italy	*Phlebotomus*
Naples	Europe, Africa, Asia	*Phlebotomus,* man
Sicilian	Europe, Africa, Asia	*Phlebotomus,* man
Karimabad	Africa, Asia	*Phlebotomus*
Arumowot	Africa	Mosquito, small mammal
Gabek Forest	Africa	Rodent
Gordil	Africa	Rodent
Odrenisrou	Africa	Mosquitoes
Rift Valley fever	Africa	Mosquitoes, *Culicoides,* domestic animals, man
Saint Floris	Africa	Rodent
Salehabad	Asia	*Phlebotomus*
Tehran	Iran	*Phlebotomus*

All New World sandfly isolates are from different species of the genus Lutzomyia. Old World sandfly isolates are often from different species of the genus Phlebotomus. Naples, Sicilian, and Karimabad viruses are primarily from P papatasii but Toscana is associated with P perniciosus. Although most viruses were isolated from sandflies, a few are known only from mammals. Repeated isolations of Arumowot, Icoaraci, Itaporanga, and Rift Valley fever viruses from mosquitoes, and their vigorous growth in mosquitoes after intrathoracic inoculation suggests mosquitoes rather than sandflies are their natural vectors.
Data from Intervirology,[2] International Catalogue of Arboviruses Including Certain Other Viruses of Vertebrates,[79] Tesh,[185] and Tesh et al,[186, 228].

Table 21–4
Viruses of the Family *Bunyaviridae,* Genus *Uukuvirus**

Uukuniemi
  (Oceanside)
Grand Arbaud
Manawa
Murre*
Ponteves
Precarious Point
Zaliv Terpeniya

*See footnote, Table 21-2.

Table 21–5
Viruses of the Family *Bunyaviridae,* Genus *Nairovirus**

GROUP
  COMPLEX
    Virus

CRIMEAN-CONGO HEMORRHAGIC FEVER GROUP
  CRIMEAN-CONGO HEMORRHAGIC FEVER
    Crimean-Congo hemorrhagic fever
    Hazara
    Khasan

DERA GHAZI KHAN GROUP
  DERA GHAZI KHAN
    Dera Ghazi Khan
    Abu Hammad
    Abu Mina
    Kao Shuan
    Panthum Thani
    Pretoria

HUGHES GROUP
  HUGHES
    Hughes
    Farallon
    Fraser Point
    Punta Salinas
    Raza
    Sapphire II
    Soldado
    Zirqa

NAIROBI SHEEP DISEASE GROUP
  NAIROBI SHEEP DISEASE
    Nairobi sheep disease (Ganjam)
    Dugbe

QALYUB GROUP
  QALYUB
    Qalyub
    Bandia
    Omo

SAKHALIN GROUP
  SAKHALIN
    Sakhalin
    Kachemak Bay
    Clo Mor
    Avalon (Paramushir)
    Taggert

*See footnote, Table 21-2.

Table 21-6
Other Possible Members of the Family *Bunyaviridae*

GROUP	GROUP
COMPLEX	COMPLEX
Virus	*Virus*
Subtype	Subtype
BAKU	**RESISTENCIA**
BAKU	RESISTENCIA
Baku	*Resistencia*
Ketapang	*Barranqueras*
	Antequera
BHANJA	
BHANJA	**YOGUE**
Bhanja	YOGUE
Forecariah	*Yogue*
Kismayo	*Kasokero*
KAISODI	**UPOLU**
KAISODI	UPOLU
Kaisodi	*Upolu*
Silverwater	*Arkansas Bay*
Lanjan	
	GROUP UNDETERMINED
MAPPUTTA	*Banqui*
MAPPUTTA	*Belmont*
Mapputta	*Bobaya*
Maprik	*Caddo Canyons*
GanGan	*Enseada*
Trubanaman	*Issyk-Kul (Keterah)*
	Kowanyama
MATARIYA	*Leanyer*
MATARIYA	*Lone Star*
Matariya	*Pacora*
Burg el Arab	*Razdan*
Garba	*Sunday Canyon*
	Tamdy
NYANDO	*Tataguine*
NYANDO	*Wanowrie*
Nyando	*Witwatersrand*

See footnote, Table 21–2.

7). The serologic and biochemical similarities of these viruses are reflected in similar patters of arthropod-host relationships. Most of the *Bunyavirus* agents are strongly associated with mosquitoes with two known exceptions: some members of the Simbu group are thought to be transmitted by culicine mosquitoes but many are transmitted by *Culicoides* midges, or possibly both (see Oropouche virus below); and within the Tete group, Bahig virus has been isolated from, and is transovarially transmitted by, *Hyalomma marginatum* ticks. The majority of phleboviruses are strongly associated with sandflies, but several have been isolated from mosquitoes and laboratory evidence suggests they may, indeed, be mosquito-associated viruses.[6] The little available evidence for the *Uukuvirus* genus indicates they are all tick viruses. Similarly, arthropod isolations of nairoviruses are virtually all from ticks, and the medically important members from ixodid ticks.

Definitive understanding of the maintenance cycle of any of these viruses is a complex process requiring elucidation of the ecology of the virus, arthropod, and vertebrate host. This has not yet been achieved for any member of the family *Bunyaviridae*, although information regarding some members of the California group is nearing that point. Many bunyavirids are known only from an isolation from arthropods or vertebrates so there may be surprises when additional information becomes available. In early studies it was felt that vertebrates, usually mammals or birds, provided a source of infection for the vector, resulting in a sylvatic cycle in which arthropod and vertebrate infections alternated in the maintenance of the virus. Quantitative studies sought to explain viral maintenance in terms of population dynamics, habitat, and feeding habits of the arthropod vector, and population dynamics, habitat, and prevalence of immunity in the vertebrate amplifier. Critical host-virus variables in this situation would include the level of viremia in an infected vertebrate, the threshold of infection for the arthropod, and the ability of the infected mosquito to transmit virus to the next vertebrate in the chain (see group C and epidemic Rift Valley fever virus for examples). It was generally assumed that in an evolutionarily stable system the vertebrate host would not be significantly harmed by the virus infection and would continue to reproduce and provide new amplifiers. By the same token, the virus would not adversely affect its arthropod host.

More recently, transovarial transmission in the vector has been shown to play an ancillary or even dominant role in virus maintenance in some systems. This mechanism was well known for a number of tick-transmitted pathogens, but was first suspected for viruses vectored by Diptera when *Phlebovirus* isolates were obtained from male sandflies. (Male sandflies and mosquitoes do not take a blood meal and therefore cannot be infected from a viremic host.) Later work with the California group of bunyaviruses (see below) has established that this is a major mechanism of virus maintenance and not merely an occasional event which allowed the virus to survive the winter. Transovarial transmission is now known or suspected in several systems: California group—*Aedes* mosquitoes; Gamboa group—*Aedeomyia* mosquitoes; Bahig (Tete group)—ixodid ticks; Nairobi sheep disease virus—ixodid ticks; Crimean-Congo hemorrhagic fever virus—ixodid ticks; Rift Valley Fever virus—*Aedes* mosquitoes; and several phleboviruses—sandflies. Further studies of this phenomenon will undoubtedly show it to be more general and more important than now appreciated.

Such complex, integrated cycles imply prolonged coevolution of the virus with its vertebrate and invertebrate hosts. This has led to stable and often focal geographic distributions of different family members. Even the epidemics associated with Crimean-Congo hemorrhagic fever virus in the Soviet Union are thought to have represented increased human contact with infected vectors rather than introduction of a new virus. There are exceptions, or apparent exceptions. For example, Rift Valley fever virus extended north of its usual sub-Saharan range in 1977–1979 and caused a major Egyptian epidemic, but this was based on epizootic transmission by mechanisms differing from its natural cycle which is operative south of the Sahara desert (see below). Likewise, it has been suggested that Ganjam virus may have migrated from India (see Nairobi Sheep Disease Group below) in the last several centuries. Certainly sandfly fever has caused major epidemics in previously uninvolved regions such as occurred in Serbia in 1948.[7]

Man is not known to be a natural amplifier or reservoir for any of these viruses, with the probable exception of amplifying sandfly fever or Oropouche viruses during epidemics. He becomes infected when he enters the ecological niche of the vector, so the epidemiology of human infection is determined by the prevalence of infected vectors and their habits.

Table 21–7
Suspected Arthropod Vectors of the Virus Family *Bunyaviridae*

		Vectors		
Class	Order	Family	Genus	Viruses
Insecta	Diptera (flying insects with 2 wings)	Culicidae (mosquitoes)	*Culex* *Aedes* several others	Most bunyaviruses except some of the Simbu and Tete group viruses; several phleboviruses
		Psychodidae (sandflies)	*Phlebotomus*	Old World phleboviruses
			Lutzomyia	New World phleboviruses
		Ceratopogonidae (biting midges or gnats)	*Culicoides*	Several bunyaviruses of the Simbu group
Arachnida (ticks, mites, spiders)	Acarina (ticks)	Argasidae (soft ticks)		Some uukuviruses; nairoviruses of the Hughes, Qalyub, and most of the Dera Ghazi Khan groups
		Ixodidae (hard ticks)		Some uukuviruses; nairoviruses of Crimean-Congo hemorrhagic fever, Nairobi sheep disease, and Sakhalin groups; the *Bunyavirus* Bahig of the Tete group

*C, California, Capim, mosquito-borne Simbu, and Turlock groups of the Bunyavirus and mosquito-borne agents of the Phlebovirus genus are associated with culicine mosquitoes. Other groups within **Bunyaviridae** have been isolated from both culicine and anopheline mosquitoes although it is not clear whether these are the actual vectors in many cases. Some groups of tick-borne **Bunyaviridae** are solely associated with argasid or ixodid ticks, but several groups are known from both. Vector status, of course, is another matter.*

HUMAN HEALTH IMPACT

Many of *Bunyaviridae* members are securely established as important agents of human disease by repeated seroconversion or isolation from sick patients (eg, Bunyamwera, Ilesha, Calavo, La Crosse, Jamestown Canyon, Tahyna, Guaroa, Bwamba, C group, Oropouche, Rift Valley fever, sandfly fever [Naples or Sicilian], Toscana, Crimean-Congo hemorrhagic fever, Dugbe, Bhanja, and

Tataguine viruses). Unfortunately, the pathogenic potential of most members of the family is unknown and must be inferred from fragmentary observations of a handful of patients which yields no real knowledge of the frequency of different clinical manifestations following human infection. Thus, even when sufficient serologic data are available to estimate human exposure to a virus, it is usually impossible to determine its total health impact. In geographic regions where many of these viruses are found, neither

Table 21–8
Studies of Febrile Patients in Africa

Family	Genus	Virus	Nigeria, 1964–1970[78] Isolation	Central African Republic, 1966–1979[8] Total	Isolation	Serology[†]
Total patients (% positive)			12,613 (1.3)	1074 (3.4)		518 (7.3)
Bunyaviridae	*Bunyavirus*	Bunyamwera	4	0	0	0
		Ilesha	0	10	8	2
		Bwamba	8	18	4	16
		Shuni (simbu)	1	0	0	
	Phlebovirus	Rift Valley Fever	0	5*	4	1
	Nairovirus	Dugbe	3	3	3	0
		CCHF	0	1*	1	0
	Unassigned	Tataguine	9	10	7	2
Togaviridae	Alphavirus		59	16	5	11
Flaviviridae	Flavivirus		76	8*	2	6
Reoviridae	Orbivirus		5	0	0	
Other			5	2	2	
Total			170	73	36	38

CCHF = Crimean-Congo hemorrhagic fever.
*One laboratory infection included in each group
†Virus isolation was serologically confirmed in 20 of 26 patients tested; exceptions were Dugbe (2/2), Tataguine (2/4), Ilesha (1/8), Alphavirus (1/3).

reliable clinical nor serologic data are available, so that some of these viruses may be more important than currently appreciated. As an example, studies of febrile patients were performed in the Central African Republic (Table 21–8).[8] The isolation rate from 1074 patients furnishing acute serum and CSF samples was only 3.4%, and only 7.3% of 518 paired sera gave diagnostic reactions when tested against all available arbovirus strains; however, Bunyaviridae were responsible for 48 (66%) of those 73 infections identified. Most patients remained undiagnosed and their disease may have been due to unidentified viruses within this family or to infections with unrelated agents, perhaps common respiratory or enteric pathogens. Even in temperate zones of the developed world arboviral disease is probably greatly underdiagnosed. Only 177 cases of arboviral encephalitis were diagnosed in the United States in 1979, but most of the 1192 undiagnosed encephalitis cases followed similar seasonal trends with peak summertime occurrence.[9]

Most recognized bunyavirid virus infections are undifferentiated febrile diseases (Tables 21–9 and 21–10). A generalized maculopapular rash is not uncommon (*fièvres rouges congolaises*) and its frequency is probably underestimated in dark-skinned patients.[10] Hemorrhagic fever, central nervous system involvement, or retinal vasculitis may also be seen.

This discussion is limited to those *Bunyaviridae* which are thought to be human pathogens or which represent an interesting facet of the biology of the family. It should be borne in mind that several viruses of the family are also major veterinary pathogens (eg, Rift Valley fever, Akabane and Nairobi sheep disease viruses).

REPLICATION, STRUCTURE, AND GENETICS

The structure,[13, 16] biochemistry,[14, 17, 18] and genetics[19] of the *Bunyaviridae* family have been reviewed in detail. These viruses are lipid-enveloped spherical structures typically 90 to 120 nm in diameter, and are fringed by 5- to 10-nm surface projections. They

Table 21–9
Acute Undifferentiated Febrile Illness Caused by *Bunyaviridae*

Fever	Abrupt onset and usually accompanied by chills
Myalgia	Often worst in lumbar region
Headache	Perhaps with photophobia
Malaise	Asthenia, prostration common
Anorexia	Nausea common, occasional vomiting; diarrhea or constipation may occur; GI symptoms rarely dominate
Arthralgia	Common, but not frank arthritis
Respiratory	Not usually prominent but some cases may have sore throat, cough, or even pulmonary infiltrates
Physical examination	Conjunctival injection common; mild adenopathy; some abdominal tenderness
Clinical laboratory	WBC normal, decreased, or moderately elevated
Course	Typical duration 2–4 d, perhaps up to a week; second wave of fever may occur; convalescence may require several days but no residua

Table 21–10
Distinctive Clinical Features of Some *Bunyaviridae* Infections

Cutaneous rash	Described in some Bunyamwera group, Bwamba, Oropouche, Dugbe, and Tataguine but not group C, Rift Valley fever, or other *Phlebovirus* infections; typically maculopapular, most notable on the trunk, nonpruritic, 36–72 h duration, and appearing after the onset of illness
Bleeding	Epistaxis or occasionally petechiae may occur but frank hemorrhagic phenomena seen only with Rift Valley or Crimean-Congo hemorrhagic fever
Aseptic meningitis	Bwamba, Dugbe, and Oropouche infections
Encephalitis or other neurologic disease	California group, Rift Valley fever, Bhanja
Retinal vasculitis	Rift Valley fever

mature by budding into cisternae in the region of the Golgi apparatus (Figure 21–1) and particles accumulate there before transport to the periphery of the cell and release by exocytosis or plasma membrane rupture. Paracrystalline arrays have been described in

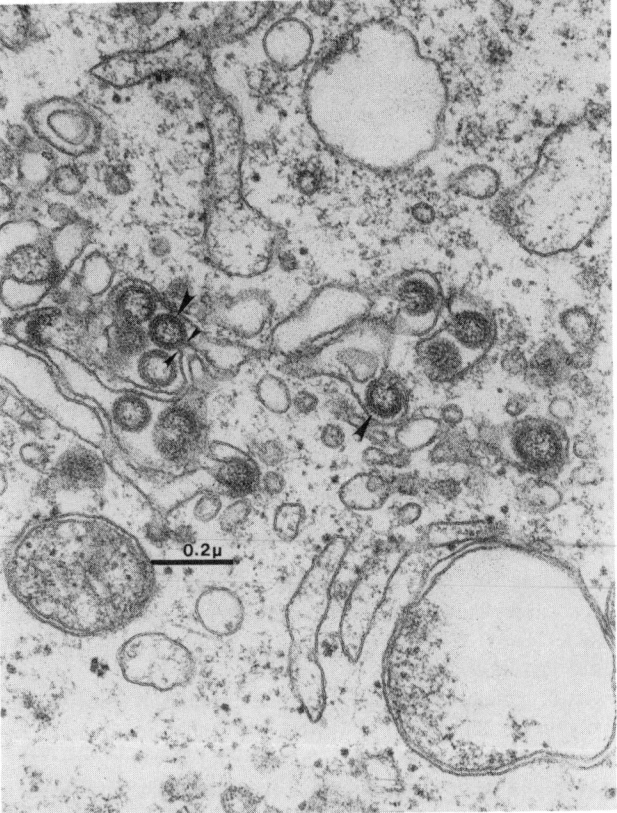

Figure 21–1. Morphogenesis of a *Phlebovirus*. Punta Toro virus is seen budding into smooth membrane vesicles near the nucleus of a Vero cell (*large arrows*). The viral envelope is continuous with the vesicle membrane (*small arrows*). (Adapted from Smith JF, Pifat DY: Morphogenesis of sandfly fever virus (Bunyaviridae family). *Virology* 1982; 121:61–81.)

Table 21–11
Biochemical Properties of Four Genera of *Bunyaviridae*

Genus	Molecular Weight of Virion Proteins (X 10³)			Molecular Weight of RNA Species (X 10⁶)			3' Terminus Sequence
	G1	G2	N	L	M	S	
Bunyavirus	108–120	21–41	19–25	2.7–3.1	1.8–2.3	0.3–0.5	UCAUCACAUGA
Phlebovirus	55–70	50–60	20–30	2.6–2.8	1.8–2.2	0.7–0.8	UGUGUUUCG
Uukuvirus	70–75	65–70	20–25	2.0–2.5	1.0–1.3	0.4–0.6	UGUGUUUCU
Nairovirus	72–84	30–40	48–54	4.1–4.9	1.5–1.9	0.6–0.7	AGAGAUUCUUU

Crimean-Congo hemorrhagic fever virus-infected cells[20, 21] and unusual knoblike surface structures found on purified Qalyub, but not other *Nairovirus* virions.[22] Thorough ultrastructural studies of Uukuniemi virus[23] have suggested the existence of surface units with icosahedral symmetry, although this degree of order has not yet been reported in other *Bunyaviridae.*

The virions contain two surface glycoproteins termed G1 and G2, and a nucleocapsid protein, N, of characteristic molecular weight for each genus (Table 21–11). At times a large (approximately 200,000-dalton) protein is found which may represent the polymerase activity occasionally detected in purified virus preparations. Infected cells have yielded these proteins, as well as smaller peptides presumed to be nonstructural virus-coded proteins. In some cases, the virion surface glycoproteins do not appear to be expressed on the cell surface in appreciable quantities, for example, Vero cells infected with Punta Toro virus[16] (Figure 21–2). Certain virus strains mature by budding from the plasma membrane of selected cells. This occurs, for example, when Rift Valley fever virus infects primary rat hepatocytes, and cell surface antigen is found in this case.[24]

The G1 and/or G2 proteins probably serve as hemagglutinin and as neutralizing antibody targets,[14,25–28] although their differential roles and antigenic epitopes are incompletely known. An interesting observation on La Crosse virus has a potentially important molecular corollary. La Crosse virus obtained directly from suckling mouse brain homogenates is difficult to neutralize in vitro. If cell culture–derived virus is treated with low concentrations of proteolytic enzymes, neutralization epitopes are selectively cleaved from G1 and the residual infectious virus also resists antibody neutralization. Presumably mouse brain preparations reach the same end through action of tissue enzymes.[29, 30]

The *Bunyaviridae* genome is composed of three RNA species designated large (L), medium (M), and small (S), with characteristic sizes and terminal nucleotide sequences for each genus (see Table 21–11).[18, 31–33] Individual nucleocapsids containing L, M, or S can be isolated and exist as circular structures complexed with N protein. The L RNA segment presumably codes for the polymerase molecule. The M RNA segment of bunyaviruses and phleboviruses codes in the negative sense for the two glycoproteins and a nonstructural protein, NS_m. There are major differences in replication strategies for the S RNA of bunyaviruses and phleboviruses. The *Bunyavirus* S is typical of negative-stranded viruses and codes for the N protein and a nonstructural protein NS_s derived from overlapping reading frames both coding in the viral complementary sense. *Phlebovirus* S (ambisense) specifies the N protein via a viral complementary messenger RNA (mRNA) derived from the 3' end and a nonstructural protein via a viral sense mRNA from the 5' end.[17, 18]

There are some nucleotide sequence data available to make direct comparisons of predicted amino acid sequences.[34–38] Proteins of the closely related La Crosse and snowshoe hare viruses of the California group have more than 90% homology while Germiston (Bunyamwera group) and Aino (Simbu group) only share 44% to 48% with one another or with the California group viruses. Similar patterns with somewhat more distant relationships were also evident when NS_s *Bunyavirus* proteins were compared. When M gene products of bunyaviruses of the same group were compared, snowshoe hare versus La Crosse (both California group) had 89% sharing and Germiston versus Bunyamwera (both Bunyamwera group), 61%. Across groups, homology fell to 40% to 45%. Some regions showed greater similarities, and overall features of protein structure were related. Comparisons of the predicted amino acid sequences of the glycoproteins of two phleboviruses, Rift Valley fever and Punta Toro, also showed 35% and 49% homology.[39]

Although there is a secure biochemical and genetic basis for separating genera within *Bunyaviridae,* the taxomony within each genus is based primarily on serologic differences. A *virus* is defined by being readily distinguishable from known viruses using

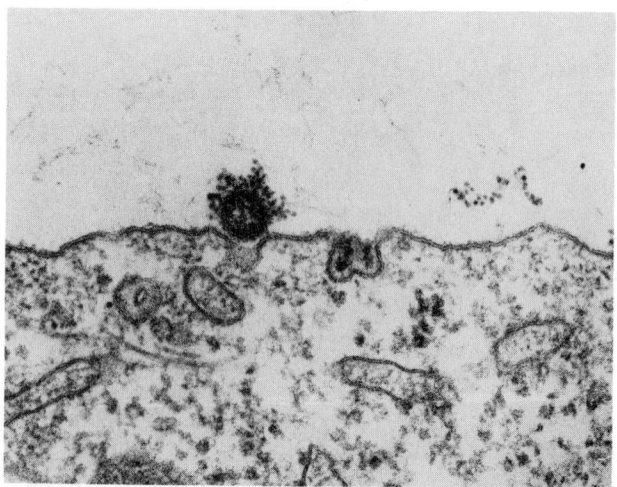

Figure 21–2. Viral antigen expression by Punta Toro virus–infected Vero cells. Ferritin-tagged antibodies intensely label virus being exocytosed but cell membrane only occasionally binds ferritin. (Adapted from Smith JF, Pifat DY: Morphogenesis of sandfly fever virus (Bunyaviridae family). *Virology* 1982; 121:61–81.)

conventional neutralization (N), hemagglutination-inhibition (HI), and complement-fixation (CF) tests. If a new isolate can be separated from a named virus only with difficulty it is called a *subtype* or *variety*. Viruses that show modest degrees of cross-reactivity are placed in a *complex* and an ensemble of cross-reactive viruses constitute a *group*. In most cases the terms virus and group convey reliable and useful information.

Further evidence for the significance of the serologic classification of members of *Bunyavirus* into groups comes from studies of recombination. The segmented genome of these viruses establishes a basis for the potential interchange of genetic information if cells are coinfected with two or more viruses. Reassortment possibilities have been explored in viruses of the California group[14, 19] using temperature-sensitive (*ts*) mutants, and for Bunyamwera group viruses.[25] Rescue of *ts* mutants reveals high-frequency reassortment of genome segments between related viruses, but certain potential combinations either do not occur or cannot be detected. High-frequency recombination has not been demonstrated between different *Bunyavirus* groups. Heterologous phleboviruses have not yielded reassortants, although gene segment mixing between two different strains of the same virus readily occurs. Apparently genetic restraints exist on the interchange of RNA segments and they are specific for the virus and RNA gene cluster involved.

Since many *Bunyaviridae* overlap in their geographic range, the potential exists for segment interchange in either their vertebrate or arthropod host to accelerate genetic recombination. This could occur if a vertebrate host were simultaneously infected with two different viruses, an uncommon event which would also require a vector to feed on the viremic host to rescue the putative viral recombinant or sustain a double infection. Most mammals infected with arboviruses have only a few days' viremia followed by lifelong immunity; however, in sloths and bats, virus may circulate for several days or weeks. Sloths are behaviorally unique as well, since they bridge the gap between the arboreal habitat where they routinely feed and sleep, and the forest floor, to which they descend to defecate (see Group C, below).

Because of the chronic infection which develops in arthropod vectors, attention has been focused on their role in RNA virus gene mixing. In an informative series of experiments,[40–43] simultaneous infection of *Aedes triseriatus* mosquitoes with heterologous California group viruses resulted in emergence of reassortants detectable either by direct assay of homogenized arthropods or by testing tissues of mice infected after mosquito bite. If two to three days passed after infection with La Crosse virus, the mosquitoes became refractory to mixed infection with other California group viruses, including other *ts* mutants of La Crosse. Interestingly, superinfection with Guaroa (a *Bunyavirus* of the Bunyamwera group) or unrelated viruses proceeded normally. Thus, in the California group, the chronically infected vector species would not be relevant to generation of "new" viruses. Arthropods may, however, be interrupted while taking a blood meal and subsequently choose a second host to feed to repletion. It must be a rare event for each host to be viremic with genetically compatible viruses which can both infect the vector.

Regardless of the quantitative or theoretical barriers to free genome segment interchange under experimental conditions, there are serologic data from the C, Gamboa, and Patois groups of the *Bunyavirus* genus that suggest this mechanism may be evolutionarily important. Neutralization, HI, and CF tests are commonly used for taxonomy and diagnosis of various viruses of these three groups. Within the *Bunyaviridae* family, neutralizing and HI antibodies are believed to react with surface glycoproteins coded by the M RNA segment. The CF test largely measures antibodies for the N protein (S RNA segment) because of its predominance in the infected mouse tissue homogenates generally used as an antigen source for this test. Comparison of viruses within each of these three groups by neutralization tests yields a particular pattern of interrelatedness, yet when the same viruses are examined by CF tests, a different pattern of relatedness is detected. For example, Shark River and Pahayokee are both Patois group viruses isolated in the Florida Everglades. They are virtually indistinguishable by CF, but distinct by N and HI tests.[44] Their L and S RNA segments cannot be distinguished by sensitive oligonucleotide analysis of T-1 ribonuclease digests, but their M segments are clearly unrelated.[45] Similar data are reviewed below for group C (Table 21–12) and Gamboa viruses. They also share several other properties: (1) numerous "serotypes" circulate in a well-defined and limited ecological setting, (2) their presumptive mosquito vectors belong to the same subgenus, (3) the vertebrate hosts of each group are limited and rapidly renewed, and (4) all are tropical or temperate zone American viruses.

In addition to these viruses, which have rather plausible evidence of recent segment interchange, there are examples within the family which present the same kinds of serologic contradictions. For example, within the genus *Phlebovirus,* N and CF tests each suggest different evolutionary relationships among viruses (Table 21–13). These and other such observations explain why attempts to develop comprehensive, rigid classification schemes are of limited use.

Segment interchange can also be used to generate new viruses potentially useful in the study of viral gene function, vector interactions, or disease potential. For example, among California group reassortant viruses the M RNA segment was a major determinant of invasion of the CNS of experimentally infected mice.[46] In experimental infection of the *Ae triseriatus* mosquito, the M segment also played a dominant role in determining the ease of infecting the mosquito gut cells, the ability of the virus to establish a disseminated infection in the mosquito, and its rate of transmission to susceptible hosts during subsequent blood feeding.[47] Thus the M RNA segment, which codes for the virion surface glycoproteins, appears to bear a major gene cluster responsible for the outcome of infection of both mosquitoes and the vertebrate host. This does not mean other gene products are unimportant. There are lesser but significant contributions to mouse virulence from RNA segments other than M, and mutations within L or M can result in marked attentuation.[48, 49] Furthermore, some combinations of L, M, and S have not been identified, which may suggest a requirement for specific segment interactions in order to produce viable, detectable viruses.

BUNYAVIRUS GENUS

Bunyamwera Group

These mosquito-borne viruses are found on every continent except Australia and occur under a wide variety of different ecological conditions. In some areas they commonly infect man. Their

Table 21–12
Serologic Relationships of the Prototype Group C Bunyaviruses

	Antigen	Reciprocal Antibody Titer Using Indicated Antisera*					
		ORI	MUR	MTB	Apeu	CAR	ITQ
CF[†]	Oriboca	*16*	64	0	4	0	4
antigen	Murutucu	16	*32*	0	0	0	0
	Marituba	4	16	*8*	8	0	0
	Apeu	0	16	8	*16*	0	0
	Caraparu	0	0	0	0	*64*	64
	Itaqui	4	0	0	0	64	*64*
HI[‡]	Oriboca	*320*	0	0	0	0	0
antigen	Murutucu	0	*160*	40	0	10	0
	Marituba	0	40	*640*	0	40	0
	Apeu	0	20	0	*2560*	320	0
	Caraparu	0	20	20	320	*1280*	0
	Itaqui	10	10	0	0	10	*320*
MPN[§]	Oriboca	*4.3*	0	0	0	0	1.4
virus	Murutucu	0	*3.0*	2.2	0	0	0
	Marituba	0	0	*4.2*	0	0	0
	Apeu	0	0	0	*3.0*	1.8	0
	Caraparu	0	0	0	2.4	*4.3*	0
	Itaqui	1.7	0	0	0	1.3	*2.7*

CF = complement fixation; HI = hemagglutination inhibition; MPN = mouse protection neutralization.
**Note that ORI-MUR, MTB-APEU, and CAR-ITQ are virtually indistinguishable by CF tests whereas when HI and MPN
are used viruses tend to pair MUR-MTB, APEU-CAR, ITQ-ORI. The patterns are consistent and more striking when
multiple sera and isolates are tested.*
[†]*Reciprocal CF titer, 0 = less than 4.*[84]
[‡]*Reciprocal HI titer, 0 = less than 10.*[84]
[§]*Log neutralization index, MPN 0 = less than 1.0.*[85]

serologic classification and speculations concerning their evolution have recently been reviewed.[14, 15, 50] In the Americas, Northway virus is able to survive in the sparsely populated arctic north. Cache Valley and Tensaw viruses are found in the temperate zone of the United States, where some human populations have antibody rates as high as 16% to 21%. The only human disease associated with these infections was a single case of encephalitis attributed to Tensaw virus.[51] Several viruses are known from Mexico (Tlacotalpan virus) or tropical Central and South America (Maguari, Guaroa, Kairi, Wyeomyia viruses) and antibodies reactive with the viruses are often present in resident human populations, although serology can be ambiguous.[52] Ft Sherman virus[53] (a subtype of Cache Valley) and Wyeomyia[54] virus have been isolated from patients with mild febrile illness in Panama. Increasing evidence suggests that Cache Valley (and its close serologic relatives such as Maguari) frequently infect domestic animals and on rare occasions cause disease in horses and sheep.[55]

Guaroa virus exemplifies the difficulty in interpreting the fragmentary data on human disease available for members of the family ***Bunyaviridae***. The initial isolates were made in a Colombian village in the wake of an epidemic of febrile disease, but five of six isolates came from apparently well, afebrile subjects.[56] Its potential for epidemic transmission is supported by studies in western Panama where Guaroa antibodies were found only in older residents, suggesting phasic activity (Gorgas Memorial Laboratory, unpublished observations, 1980). Guaroa virus antibody rates reported from tropical Colombia and Brazil ranged between 44% and 77%.[57] This virus has also been prominent in virus isolations from fever cases among Brazilian forest workers (Table 21–14). In one case

Guaroa was obtained from the liver biopsy of a patient presenting with clinical encephalitis.[58] The virus has also been isolated from *Anopheles* mosquitoes.[59]

The prototype member of the group, Bunyamwera virus, is clearly an important human pathogen. Human antibodies reactive with Bunyamwera virus have been detected in every serosurvey undertaken in sub-Saharan Africa, indicating widespread infection. Virus isolations have been obtained from febrile humans in Uganda, Nigeria, and South Africa. Rash, visual disturbances, and vertigo have occurred in some cases[59] and severe encephalitis developed in a tumor patient experimentally infected with Bunyamwera virus.[60] Aside from man, all isolates are from *Aedes* mosquitoes, implicating them as presumptive vectors. Antibodies are found in domestic animals, rodents, bats, and nonhuman primates. Rodents, bats, and primates also develop viremia after experimental inoculation, suggesting a potential role as a vertebrate reservoir or amplifier of Bunyamwera virus. Antibody studies indicate increased virus activity in the vicinity of rivers and swamps.[57]

Ilesha and Germiston viruses are also causes of febrile disease in Africa. Ilesha virus has been isolated from humans in Nigeria, Uganda, Cameroon, and the Central African Republic.[8, 59] Ten cases reported from the Central African Republic were all brief, undifferentiated febrile illnesses, eight of which were associated with generalized rash. Germiston virus has produced two laboratory infections, one of which was associated with mental symptoms which may have represented mild encephalitis.[61] Human antibodies to Germiston virus have been reported from South Africa, Uganda, Ethiopia, and Botswana.[59] It has been isolated from *Culex* mosquitoes in South Africa[61] and Uganda.[62] Rodents may

Table 21–13
Some Serologic Relations Within the *Phlebovirus* Genus

Antigen		SFN	TOS	TEH	SFS	PT	RVF	BTA	ICO	ITP
					Antibodies					
CF	Naples	256	256	256	0	0	—	0	0	0
	Toscana	64	256	256	0	0	—	16	0	0
	Tehran	64	128	256	0	0	—	0	0	0
	Sicilian	0	0	0	256	0	—	0	0	0
	Punta Toro	0	0	0	0	256	—	0	0	0
	Rift Valley fever	0	0	0	0	0	128	512	64	0
	Belterra	0	0	0	0	32	0	2560	512	0
	Icoaraci	0	8	0	0	0	0	512	1280	0
	Itaporanga	0	0	0	0	0	—	8	0	256
N	Naples	320	10	0	0	0	0	—	0	0
	Toscana	20	5120	0	0	0	0	—	0	0
	Tehran	0	0	80	0	0	0	—	0	0
	Sicilian	0	0	0	5120	0	0	—	0	0
	Punta Toro	0	0	0	0	10240	0	—	320	0
	Rift Valley fever	0	0	0	0	40	5120	640	0	0
	Belterra	0	—	—	—	—	0	320	0	—
	Icoaraci	0	0	0	0	0	0	0	1280	10
	Itaporanga	0	0	0	0	0	0	—	0	160
HI	Naples	1280	—	—	0	—	—	—	10	0
	Sicilian	0	—	—	80	—	—	—	160	—
	Rift Valley fever	40	80	20	0	160	2560	1280	320	80
	Icoaraci	80	—	—	0	—	—	—	640	—
FA	Naples	1024	—	—	0	0	0	—	0	0
	Sicilian	0	—	—	256	0	16	—	0	0
	Rift Valley fever	16	—	—	0	64	2048	—	32	8
ELISA	Rift Valley fever	200	100	50	50	400	25600	6400	3200	400

The neutralization (N) test is usually specific with occasional low-level cross-reactions. Several viruses cross extensively by complement fixation (CF), but this is also specific in most cases. Hemagglutination inhibition (HI), fluorescent antibody (FA), and enzyme-linked immunosorbent assay (ELISA) with inactivated mouse liver antigen are broadly cross-reactive.

As with other **Bunyaviridae** these cross-reactions follow no strict geographic pattern and may be "one-way."

Typical data from Travassos da Rosa et al,[197] Tesh and Modi,[224] and Tesh et al,[228] and unpublished results J. Meegan, R. Shope, C.J. Peters.

Table 21–14
Arthropod-Borne Virus Isolations From Febrile Patients in the Americas

	N	Percent Positive	Bunyaviridae				Phlebovirus	Togaviridae Alphavirus	Flaviviridae Flavivirus	Other
			Bunyavirus							
			Bunyamwera (Guaroa)	C group	Guama and Catu	Simbu (Oropouche)	Candiru			
Trinidad[92] 1954–1963	3380	0.9	0	1	0	1	0	5*	25†	0
Brazil[87] 1954–1965	1300	5	5	22	12	15‡	1	15*	24	0
Surinam[314] 1966	—	—	0	5	0	0	0	3	0	0
Panama[90] 1973	58	7	0	1	0	0	0	2	0	1

*Includes small outbreaks of Mayaro.
†Includes 14 epidemic yellow fever isolates.
‡Includes Oropouche epidemic isolates.

well be a reservoir or amplifier host since it has been isolated from them in Uganda[62] and Kenya,[63] and since experimentally infected rodents develop high viremias.[64, 65]

Batai (isolated from *Culex* mosquitoes in Malaysia), Chittoor (from *Anopheles* mosquitoes in India), and Calovo (*Anopheles* mosquitoes in Czechoslovakia) viruses are closely related serologically and all infect humans as determined by antibody studies.[57] Batai antibody prevalence rates in the Malaysian territory of Sarawak were consistent with a 0.5% to 1.0% yearly infection rate and two of 216 febrile patients tested seroconverted. Calovo infection was studied in the temperate moist lowlands near Bratislava, Czechoslovakia, where 17 (8%) of 204 febrile patients and none of 119 controls had significant antibody rises.[66] Seroconversions occurred predominantly during the summer. The clinical presentation[67] was that of a grippelike disease with fever, malaise, myalgia, and anorexia as the dominant symptoms. Pulmonary findings (including dyspnea, cough, or x-ray evidence of infiltrates), tonsillitis, or abdominal pain were described in over half the cases studied. The leukocyte count and erythrocyte sedimentation rate were normal early and elevated later in the course of disease.

In summary, the Bunyamwera group of viruses is a widely distributed, complicated, biomedically important group of viruses for which no truly effective control or prophylaxis exists. Human infection is acquired by mosquito bite and may be virtually asymptomatic or present an undifferentiated febrile illness, at times with exanthem. There is a suggestion that these viruses have neurotropic potential in humans and some observations suggest pulmonary or pharyngeal involvement may at times be prominent complaints. Several observations suggest that periods of increased transmission occur, but widespread epidemics have never been documented.

Bwamba Group

Bwamba virus was first isolated from nine road construction workers with acute febrile illness in Bwamba County, Uganda.[68] Subsequent studies showed that Bwamba viral antibodies were common in East African communities, where their prevalence rates varied but could exceed 70%, with high rates often found in children as well as adults. Antibodies were also detected in local monkeys, particularly arboreal species.[69] Bwamba viral antibodies are also prevalent in human sera from other areas of Africa (Nigeria,[70] Angola,[71] Botswana,[72] Congo,[73] Guinea,[74] Central African Republic,[75] Kenya,[76] South Africa[77]). Studies of febrile patients in Nigeria suggest that Bwamba is an important human pathogen there; it was responsible for 8 (5%) of 170 virus isolations from acute phase sera.[78] In a series from the Central African Republic, it was the most frequently diagnosed arboviral infection of man, providing 18 (25%) of the 73 cases with an etiologic diagnosis. Virtually all cases were typical brief prostrating illnesses with maculopapular rash, but half were associated with meningeal signs[8] (see Table 21–10).

Viruses identified as Bwamba or its close serologic relative Pongola have been isolated from several species of *Aedes*, *Anopheles*, and *Mansonia* mosquitoes in Africa.[79–82] Virtually nothing is known of the maintenance and natural history of these viruses.

The interpretation of entomologic and serologic data is complicated by inadequate understanding of the virologic and serologic relations of Bwamba and Pongola viruses. These viruses are difficult to classify by N and CF tests, yet are readily separable by agar gel precipitin tests.[83] Most human isolates are Bwamba-like, while most mosquito origin viruses are Pongola-like. One report suggests that a virus isolated from human serum and precipitating with Bwamba antibodies could be passed in mosquitoes to produce a strain nonreactive with Bwamba, but reacting with Pongola antiserum.[81]

Group C

The 11 named viruses of this group all originate from Central and South America, except for Gumbo Limbo virus from the Florida Everglades. Six of the viruses can be formed into closely related pairs on the basis of cross-CF tests: Caraparu and Itaqui, Apeu and Marituba, Murutucu and Oriboca. In contrast, cross-N and HI tests classify these same viruses into three different pairs: Caraparu and Apeu, Marituba and Murutucu, Oriboca and Itaqui[84, 85] (see Table 21–12). Since surface glycoproteins of *Bunyaviruses*, which are responsible for neutralization and hemagglutination, are coded for by the M RNA segment, and the nucleocapsid protein, which is the major viral antigen in the suckling mouse brain preparations used in the CF test, is coded for by the S RNA segment, these serologic findings have led to speculation that the viruses may have evolved by RNA segment reassortment with perhaps three archetypic parental species. Indeed, when 200 Brazilian group C virus isolates were tested, one (H5546) was found which did not fit the prototype patterns and may have represented a recent reassortant between Caraparu and Oriboca or Murutucu.[14, 84]

Studies conducted in the Amazon forests near Belem, Brazil, show how some group C viruses coexist in the same geographic region with each utilizing a unique ecological niche.[86] For example, Caraparu and Apeu viruses cross-neutralize, but circulate independently in the same area because Caraparu virus is transmitted among small rodents on the forest floor by *Culex* mosquitoes, while Apeu virus is most abundant in the forest canopy, maintained in a cycle of arboreal mammals and a different species of *Culex* mosquito. A similar situation appears to exist with Murutucu and Marituba viruses, with Marituba occupying the arboreal niche. Utilization of different mosquito vectors, as in the case of Oriboca virus and *Cx portesi* versus Itaqui virus and *Cx vomerifer* also permits antigenically similar viruses to coexist.

No large-scale outbreaks of group C viral disease have been reported, but antibody surveys in humans, sentinel animal studies, and mosquito isolations in areas of moist neotropical forest consistently show evidence for transmission of these viruses (Brazil,[87–89] Panama,[90] Peru,[91] Trinidad,[92] Guatemala,[93] Honduras[94]). They are also usually implicated as a cause of disease when nonimmunes enter these regions (see Table 21–14). As an example, 37 (7%) of 500 Dutch soldiers serving in Suriname for a year developed antibodies to Caraparu, Restan, and/or Oriboca group C arboviruses.[95]

Clinical disease from these agents is a benign self-limited febrile infection of one to seven days duration. Myalgia, photophobia, chills, and prostration are typical.[87, 90, 93, 96–98] Normal or modestly decreased leukocyte counts have been reported. A case report of laboratory infection with Apeu virus presumably acquired by aerosol is the only detailed description of group C disease in the literature:

A 35-year-old man presented for medical evaluation because of illness beginning with malaise, fever, and chilly sensations. His major complaint was a dull, steady headache but he also had eye soreness (without photophobia), mild nasal congestion, and post-nasal discharge as well as pharyngeal erythema. His temperature rose to 40.8°C that night. During the evening of day 2 he improved and was afebrile on day 3. However, on day 4 his fever returned (39.4°C) and he complained of severe headache and weakness. Once again findings on physical examination were normal except for tachycardia (118) and tachypnea (22). Numerous laboratory tests, x-rays, and an ECG were normal except for a leukocyte count of 4300 with 56% polymorphonuclear and 20% band neutrophils. By the evening of the fifth day of illness the patient was afebrile and was discharged totally asymptomatic a few days later. Apeu virus was isolated from the patient's serum on day 1. No antibodies were detected on day 5, but by day 15 hemagglutination inhibition, complement fixation, and neutralization tests were positive against Apeu virus.[99]

Prevention is solely on the basis of avoiding infected mosquitoes. The mosquito species which transmit these viruses are crepuscular or nocturnal feeders. Their sensitivity to low humidity restricts them to moist tropical regions, usually out of direct sunlight. However, in the environment where these mosquitoes are abundant and the viruses circulate, the risk of infection may be great. For example, in a tropical Brazilian forest, sentinel monkeys placed in the canopy were infected with a group C virus on an average of once per 127 days of exposure, while 12.5% of sentinel mouse litters were infected after a 24-hour exposure on the forest floor.[87]

California Group

California group viruses are found in tropic (Melao, Serra do Navio viruses), temperate (La Crosse, Keystone, and other viruses), and arctic (Inkoo, snowshoe hare viruses) regions where they are closely associated with their mosquito vectors, generally of the genus *Aedes*.[100] Small mammals are the usual vertebrate host of these viruses. Persistence in temperate and arctic zones requires an overwintering mechanism to support the viruses when their mosquito vectors are dormant and their vertebrate host inactive. Transovarial transmission of the virus from infected adult mosquitoes to their progeny, which overwinter in the egg stage, serves this role. Even though these viruses are all very closely related antigenically, each has evolved a unique virus-vector relationship with a single species of vector mosquito. The ecological niche occupied by the vector mosquito species, including the vertebrate hosts it preferentially seeks, and the overwintering habitat it utilizes, also defines the ecological boundaries of the specific virus.

La Crosse Virus

La Crosse virus was first isolated from the brain of a child that died of encephalitis in La Crosse, Wisconsin.[101] Since its original description, it has come to be recognized as a significant cause of arboviral encephalitis (Table 21–15) and except for years of epidemic St Louis encephalitis, it is probably the most prevalent mosquito-borne disease recognized in the United States.[102]

Epidemiology[103, 104].—Because of cross-reactivity in serologic tests, encephalitis due to California group viruses has usually been reported under the rubric "California encephalitis." More specific testing as well as virus isolation studies lead to the inference that

Table 21–15

Reported Cases of Encephalitis Due to California Group Viruses by State, United States, 1963–1985

State	No. of Cases (%)	Subtypes of La Crosse Virus*
Ohio	574 (33.8)	A,C
Wisconsin	394 (23.2)	A,B
Minnesota	257 (15.1)	A,B
Illinois	133 (7.8)	B
Indiana	93 (5.4)	A
Iowa	90 (5.3)	
New York	40 (2.4)	C
North Carolina	28 (1.6)	C
Michigan	14 (0.8)	
West Virginia	13 (0.8)	
Louisiana	12 (0.7)	
Missouri	12 (0.7)	
Georgia	10 (0.6)	C
Arkansas	5 (0.3)	
Pennsylvania	5 (0.3)	
Kentucky	4 (0.2)	
Tennessee	4 (0.2)	
New Jersey	3 (0.2)	
South Carolina	2 (0.1)	
Utah	2 (0.1)	
Maryland	1 (0.1)	
Mississippi	1 (0.1)	
Oklahoma	1 (0.1)	
Total	1699	

*Subtypes of La Crosse virus isolates circulating in some states determined by T-1 oligonucleotide fingerprints.[113]
Data from Kappus et al,[103] LeDuc[102] and T. P. Monath, Centers for Disease Control, Ft Collins, Colo, personal communication, 1987.

La Crosse virus infection is responsible for most California encephalitis, particularly in the Middle West. Several states contiguous with or east of the Mississippi River (see Table 21–15) furnish the majority of reported cases.[102] The disease tends to be focal even within states where encephalitis is common,[105] presumably a reflection of pockets of mosquito vectors with efficient transovarial virus transmission. This focality has also been reported in studies of mosquito infection in nature.[106] Cases occur in warm months (usually July, August, September) and there is little year-to-year variation in secular distribution of cases or in patterns of antibody titers.[102, 107] Cases are clearly underdiagnosed, particularly outside the recognized Ohio-Wisconsin-Minnesota focus.[105, 108, 109] Patterns of disease are best understood in relation to mosquito exposure. Antibodies are found most frequently in forest workers[110] and rural or suburban residents.[111] Disease is usually reported in children living near or playing in forested areas supporting breeding of the vector mosquito (rural, suburban, or recreational pattern).

Analysis of oligonucleotide fingerprints of the La Crosse genome has provided provocative data.[112, 113] This technique is estimated to be capable of detecting nucleotide substitutions composing as little as 1% of the genome[114] and is an exquisitely sensitive way to detect differences among bunyaviruses. For example, snowshoe hare virus has extensive nucleotide sequence homology with La Crosse virus[115] and serologically is classified as merely a "variety" (see Table 21–2) of La Crosse, but fingerprints of their T-1 ribonuclease digests bear virtually no resemblance and they are maintained in clearly distinct epidemiologic cycles. It has been possible to divide the La Crosse isolates examined to date into three groups which appear to have geographic significance (see Table 21–15). This has allowed speculation on the evolution of different isolates within the groups and has provided evidence suggesting reassortment between overlapping types in nature. Yet, within a given focus, striking genome conservation was seen. For example, virus obtained from a mosquito trapped in the yard of an encephalitis case 5 years after her death had only minor fingerprint differences as compared to the brain isolate from the fatal case. The S RNA segment was also found to be more constant than the L and M segments, a finding that may now be explained by the constraints of overlapping reading frames. Monoclonal antibodies may also add to the ability to discriminate geographic variants.[116]

The mosquito *Aedes triseriatus* has been implicated as the principal vector of the virus to man; however, until the work of Watts and colleagues,[117] the means by which the virus survived the harsh Wisconsin winters was a mystery. They established that infected adult female *Ae triseriatus* could transmit the infection to their ova. Infected mosquito eggs are then deposited near the waterline of tree holes or other containers where they remain dormant over the winter. The following spring, eggs hatch with the coming of warm weather and the accumulation of sufficient water in the habitats where the aquatic larval stages develop. In late spring or early summer, the first adult *Ae triseriatus* emerge, mate, and begin to seek a blood meal. Since a portion of the emerging adults are already infected from the previous generation through transovarial transmission, they are able to introduce the virus into the vertebrate-mediated portion of the cycle at their initial blood meal. At this time also, a large proportion of the new generation of mammalian host (chipmunks and squirrels) are susceptible to La Crosse virus infection. When fed upon by an infected vector, they become viremic and may thereby serve as a source of virus to infect other feeding mosquitoes, thus amplifying the prevalence of virus within the vector population.

A second method of virus amplification among the vector population is through venereal transmission of the virus from transovarially infected males to their uninfected female partners during mating.[118] Since male mosquitoes do not feed on blood, this represents their only direct contribution to the maintenance of the virus in nature. Through this system of vertical transmission from the infected female to her progeny and horizontal transmission mediated through viremic vertebrate hosts and venereal transmission between mosquitoes, the virus is able to persist year after year. Variations of this basic cycle appear to be characteristic of most California group bunyaviruses. The relative quantitative importance of these mechanisms is currently in dispute, but the transovarial route can be highly efficient in genetically matched virus-mosquito combinations.[119, 120, 121]

Humans are infected when they enter the woodland forests or inadvertently create suitable vector breeding sites by discarding containers such as old tires which may collect water. Since *Ae triseriatus* is a daytime feeder, the potential for exposure to infected vectors during work or play in the woods may be great.

Disease Syndromes.—Most reported cases have been diagnosed by serologic tests which do not distinguish different viruses of the California group and have been referred to simply as California encephalitis. In fact, analysis with the appropriate serologic tools (see below) confirms that the great majority of so-called California encephalitis patients from the pediatric age group are infected with La Crosse virus.

In spite of the high California group antibody prevalence in some areas, relatively little clinical disease has been reported. The obvious childhood distribution of encephalitis in concert with the antibody acquisition curve suggests that adults are resistant to the neurologic involvement that might bring these patients into the hands of a clinical virologist. The limited prospective data from La Crosse virus endemic areas bearing on this concept include (a) a study of 232 adult forest workers in Wisconsin; four seroconverted to California group viruses without clinical disease[110]; (b) a seroepidemiologic survey in Minnesota that yielded an estimate of one encephalitis case per 26 childhood La Crosse infections.[103] In this same study, 23 febrile children brought to their physician and diagnosed as having a "viral syndrome" were studied and one La Crosse virus infection was documented. (c) Surveillance of hospitalizations on a Cherokee Indian reservation in North Carolina yielded an estimate of 2.3 hospitalized children with California group seroconversion per 1000 at risk each year. Seven patients had frank encephalitis, three aseptic meningitis, and two presented fever, headache, and predominating respiratory symptoms.[122] (d) In suburban areas near La Crosse, Wisconsin, two La Crosse seroconversions occurred among 132 persons followed over 5 years and one was associated with encephalitis.[123] (e) A prospective study in Iowa detected four La Crosse virus seroconversions in 182 school children (2.2%) and one recalled a "cold."[124] Thus, clinical patterns of La Crosse virus infection are age-dependent and likely result in a spectrum of disease ranging from inapparent or mild febrile illness as the predominant presentation in adults through aseptic meningitis, and reaching severe or fatal encephalitis more frequently seen among the pediatric population.

Disease descriptions from early studies of hospitalized California encephalitis patients[110, 125, 126] have been borne out by larger series.[127–130] The estimated incubation period is three to seven days based on histories of intensive mosquito exposure.[129] Onset is relatively sudden and the early course is virtually always accompanied by fever, headache, and lethargy with nausea and vomiting noted in most patients. Diarrhea, abdominal pain, rash, and arthralgia are rare. Milder cases develop meningeal signs, disorientation, and usually recover within a week. More severe cases with greater disturbance of consciousness often develop seizures within the first one to two days of illness, even presenting initially with life-threatening convulsions. Up to one third of cases will develop coma and the hospital course may last 2 weeks or more. In the four major reported series, 86 (52%) of 166 California encephalitis patients had seizures and about one fourth were focal. Many patients had additional seizure activity and a few required vigorous therapy for status epilepticus. About one fifth of patients had hemiparesis (often in association with focal seizures) and two had definite papilledema. Tremor, aphasia, chorea, Babinski signs, and other pathologic reflexes were noted. The blood leukocyte count may be normal but was typically elevated, reaching levels of 20,000 to 30,000 in an appreciable number of cases; the differential usually showed a left shift, particularly if there was a leukocytosis.

The CSF cell count was virtually always abnormal initially and, in the few instances where it was normal, was elevated when repeated 24 to 72 hours later. Values were typically 30 to 500 but ranged from 10 to 1300 per microliter. More than half the cases had a mononuclear predominance but polymorphonuclears were often 25% to 90% of the total. Spinal fluid was rarely bloody, although up to 620 erythrocytes per microliter were noted. CSF protein was usually normal or in the minority of patients increased modestly (< 25 mg/dL). Glucose was normal in all cases. Nineteen of these hospitalized patients underwent technetium 99m brain scan because of focal neurologic findings and five had frontal or parietal accumulations of isotope. Electroencephalograms showed generalized slow-wave activity in most patients but some had localized changes and/or epileptiform discharges. By the time of discharge, mild neurologic signs were still present and patients were often described as being irritable, distractable, and emotionally labile for a few weeks after discharge. Evidence of residua is remarkably slight; from 166 reported cases only two died and two suffered lasting hemiparesis (one having undergone brain biopsy). Careful long-term follow-up studies have failed to demonstrate objective evidence for any important long-term effects on academic or social functioning of children recovered from California encephalitis.[131–134] "Soft" neurologic signs and borderline abnormalities in some children with more severe acute disease deserve further attention, but the overall prognosis is excellent, particularly compared to other viral encephalitides. The exception to this generalization lies in the area of recurrent seizure activity. Patients with seizures during the acute illness have about one chance in five of suffering recurrent convulsions.[130, 133, 135] These usually are manifest within the first year but there may be an increased risk for several years.

Pathologic examination of the two reported fatal cases of La Crosse encephalitis showed cerebral edema, perivascular cuffing of capillaries and venules, as well as glial nodules in the brain. These were not qualitatively different from those found in other viral encephalitides but their distribution in cortical gray matter of frontal, parietal, and temporal lobes, basal nuclei, midbrain, and pons with sparing of other regions may be distinctive.[136] The single available brain biopsy showed congestion, margination of polymorphonuclear leukocytes, focal neuronal necrosis, and endothelial cell swelling.[129]

Virologic Diagnosis.—Repeated attempts to isolate virus from throat swab, blood, CSF, and stool have failed. In fatal cases, La Crosse virus has been isolated from brain, but with some difficulty. The single biopsy tested failed to yield virus.[129]

While not yet widely used, measurement of IgM-specific antibody appears to hold the greatest promise as a diagnostic tool sufficiently rapid to yield clinically relevant results.[137, 138] Among 18 individuals sampled on the reported day of onset of illness, 94% had IgM antibody by enzyme immunoassay, 50% had neutralizing antibody, 33% had hemagglutinating antibody, and 11% had IgG antibody by enzyme immunoassay.[139] The plaque reduction neutralization test is the single most valuable established diagnostic tool.[111, 129, 140, 141] It is often positive by three to five days

after onset of illness and virtually always so by a week. Peak titers occur by 1 to 3 weeks and antibodies probably are lifelong. The test is technically simple if cell cultures are available and its selectivity among related viruses is as good or usually better than other available tests. HI antibodies develop with a similar chronology in most patients but do not persist as long. CF antibodies appear later, usually being detectable within 2 to 3 weeks of illness. After reaching a maximum at 4 to 6 weeks they disappear by 1 year. In one series of 92 diagnosed La Crosse encephalitis patients,[141] all patients had neutralizing antibodies and 85% seroconverted by that test, often within a week of collection of the first sample. La Crosse viral antigen can also be detected in mosquito pools by enzyme-linked immunosorbent assay (ELISA), enhancing surveillance for infected arthropods.[142]

Therapy and Prevention.—Treatment is symptomatic and supportive. Convulsions may require vigorous therapy, particularly if status epilepticus develops. Vomiting and fever often lead to dehydration; most clinicians advise keeping patients somewhat "dry" because of the potential role of cerebral edema. The favorable prognosis of California encephalitis should be borne in mind and potentially dangerous therapeutic maneuvers reserved for the deteriorating patient in whom intracranial pressure monitoring and vigorous therapy of cerebral edema may be indicated. Anticonvulsants are often given in convalescence in hopes of aborting seizure recurrence. No vaccine is available for La Crosse virus, and control relies on use of repellants, spraying insecticides to control adult mosquitoes, or eliminating larval breeding habitats.[143] The last is an especially difficult task because tree hole breeding sites are widely distributed throughout the woodlands and are not readily accessible. Removal of steel-belted tires is a particular problem because of their ubiquity and the ecological constraints on their destruction. Infected mosquitoes have been found breeding in these tires in the yards of La Crosse encephalitis patients, and there is a suggestion that such tires may be a significant risk factor for developing disease.[109] Some success at reducing disease in the La Crosse, Wisconsin, area has been claimed[144] by using a multifaceted approach which included public education, removal of discarded tires and other artificial breeding sites, and an active program to find and fill tree holes.

Tahyna Virus.—Tahyna virus has been studied most extensively in an endemic focus of infection in southern Moravia, Czechoslovakia, at a flatland forest near the junction of two rivers.[145] There annual flooding creates breeding sites for mosquitoes and lush vegetation provides high relative humidity, ideal for adult mosquito survival. Virus transmission begins each spring with the emergence of *Ae vexans* mosquitoes, some of which have been vertically infected. A second possible source of overwintered virus is the mosquito *Culiseta annulata,* which is also believed to transmit the virus transovarially, but this species overwinters as larvae rather than in the egg stage.[146] Once introduced into the vertebrate-mediated horizontal amplification cycle, several different mosquito species are apparently able to become infected and transmit the virus. Vertebrate hosts which develop sufficient viremia to potentially infect feeding mosquitoes include hedgehogs, hares, and rabbits, and perhaps some species of domestic mammals. Hedgehogs may in fact play a dual role in the maintenance of Tahyna virus, both as an amplifier host during the summer cycle and as an overwintering host. In a series of experiments with hibernating hedgehogs, it was shown that under certain conditions hedgehogs remained viremic throughout the winter and for several days following awakening the following spring.[147, 148]

Human infection in this region is common and rural residents often have antibodies reacting with Tahnya virus.[145] The spectrum of disease ranges from a mild febrile illness[149] to aseptic meningitis. In an area of high virus transmission, Tahnya virus was implicated as the cause of 10% to 20% of hospitalized febrile illness both in adults and children.[150] Most such cases[151, 152] are mild undifferentiated febrile illnesses, but pharyngitis, pulmonary involvement (cough, chest pain, x-ray evidence of an infiltrate), or gastrointestinal (GI) symptoms (nausea, vomiting, abdominal pain) are common and may dominate the clinical picture. CNS involvement is apparently confined to aseptic meningitis and serious illness has not been reported from Tahnya virus infection. Leukocytosis and elevated sedimentation rate are usually present. Virus isolation from blood is occasionally possible early in the disease but most cases are diagnosed by rising N or HI antibody titers. The only practical preventive measure is avoidance of mosquito vectors.

Virus isolations and/or antibodies in man extend the known range of Tahnya activity to Yugoslavia, Germany, Austria, France and Italy.[153–156] Tahnya-like viruses are known from several regions of the USSR as well, and some strains may be responsible for CNS disease in these and related ecosystems.[157, 158] A virus originally designated Lumbo, but serologically indistinguishable from Tahnya virus, was also isolated in Mozambique.[159] In addition, antibodies have been reported from Sri Lanka,[160] and southern China.[161] It seems likely that closer serologic and genetic analysis will split these agents into several viruses or subtypes. Nevertheless, these data show the broad geographic distribution and disease potential of California group viruses.

Other California Viruses.—In North America three other members of the California group are known to cause encephalitis: California encephalitis, snowshoe hare,[162, 163] and Jamestown Canyon[164–166] viruses. The most significant of these appears to be Jamestown Canyon virus. The first indication that infection with this virus resulted in overt disease came from a report of mild febrile illness among young men working in a forest camp in northern Wisconsin. This was followed by the recognition of human encephalitis due to the virus, and in the 1980s reports of several cases in New York, Wisconsin, Ohio, and Ontario. In contrast to the childhood predilection of La Crosse virus CNS involvement, patients with aseptic meningitis or encephalitis due to Jamestown Canyon virus are usually adults. The only suggestive clinical finding in reported cases has been a frequent history of preceding respiratory tract symptoms. The significant human antibody prevalence in these states, Michigan,[167] and elsewhere, suggests that Jamestown Canyon viral encephalitis should be more widely sought. Until the extent of this problem is better understood and until better diagnostic modalities are available, a Jamestown Canyon HI test should be included in diagnostic batteries for adults with possible arboviral encephalitis.[168]

Snowshoe hare virus has been implicated as a cause of febrile CNS disease in children and adults, and in one case was associated with Reye syndrome.[163]

Guama Group

Guama group viruses are found exclusively in the humid forest environment of the New World tropics. They are vectored primarily by mosquitoes of the *Culex (Melanoconion)* subgenus and utilize small forest rodents and nonhuman primates as their principle vertebrate hosts. Most isolations have been from the tropical forests of Brazil, Trinidad, Surinam, French Guyana, or Panama.[79] Mahogany hammock virus is the only North American representative of the group, and it was isolated in the Everglades National Park of southern Florida.[169]

Two viruses of the group, Guama and Catu, are known to cause mild human disease characterized by fever, headache, myalgia, arthralgia, and leukopenia.[79, 170] No deaths or sequelae have been recorded. Although these viruses are often isolated from mosquitoes or rodents during ecological studies, only isolated human cases have been recognized among persons who enter the tropical forest environment (see Table 21–14).

Simbu Group

Simbu group viruses have been recovered from temperate and tropical zones around the world. Tiny biting midges (family Ceratopogonidae, genus *Culicoides*) are important vectors, although isolates have also been made from mosquitoes. Simbu group viruses have been isolated from both mammalian and avian hosts and a number are known to infect domestic animals. The most important of these is the *Culicoides*-transmitted Akabane virus, which is an important cause of abortion, stillbirth, and congenital malformation among domestic animals in many areas of the world, including Japan, Israel, and Australia.[171, 172] Cattle, sheep, and goats are frequently infected and outbreaks of Akabane virus may result in considerable economic loss. The virus is also widely distributed in Africa but has not been identified as a fetal pathogen there, either because of virus strain differences or natural infection of animals before breeding age.[173, 174]

Oropouche virus, first isolated from a febrile patient in Trinidad, has caused at least eight major epidemics in northern Brazil within the past 20 years. More than 165,000 persons have been infected in remote population centers of Para and eastern Amazonas states with attack rates as high as 40% of the local residents.[175] The disease in man is characterized by sudden onset of fever (to 40°C), severe headache, generalized myalgia and arthralgia, chills, and occasionally nausea and vomiting. Rash sometimes accompanies the illness, as does meningitis or meningismus. Clinical illness usually lasts from two to five days, although myalgia may persist for an additional three to five days. Many patients are virtually incapacitated, but no fatalities or sequelae have yet been attributed to the disease. A proportion of patients, particularly those who resume strenuous physical activities early, report the recurrence of one or more disease manifestations from one to ten days after initial recovery. Virus has, however, never been isolated from patients during a relapse. The incubation period in man infected by arthropod vectors is four to eight days. Suspected aerosol infection among laboratory workers has also been reported and the incubation period for such cases was three to four days.[176] Virtually all patients are viremic during the first two days of illness. Virus in diminishing titer was detected in 72%, 44%, and 23% of patients examined on the third, fourth, and fifth days of illness, respectively. About 10% of patients develop a viremia of sufficient titer required to infect feeding vectors.

Oropouche virus probably occurs in nature in two distinct cycles: a sylvatic cycle and an urban cycle. The sylvatic cycle is responsible for maintenance of the virus in nature, with primates, sloths, and perhaps birds suspected as potential vertebrate hosts, and with the arthropod vector still unknown. In the urban cycle, man appears to be the most significant vertebrate host, and the biting midge, *Culicoides paraensis,* has been shown to be the vector.[177] Although virus isolates have been made from *Culex quinquefasciatus,* its vectorial efficiency appears to be low.[178] Epidemics occur where large populations of *C paraensis* are present and the human population is susceptible. Virus is introduced either through travel of incubating or viremic humans, or directly from the sylvatic cycle. The urban vector lives in close association with man, is a diurnal feeder, is highly anthropophilic, and breeds in discarded organic material from tropical agricultural crops such as cacao husks and banana tree stalks. When these wastes are abundant, enormous populations of *C paraensis* may result. While the threshold of infection for the midge is relatively high, the sheer numbers of these insects assure continued transmission. Destruction of breeding sites might limit transmission, particularly since the midges are generally weak fliers.

Much less is known about the ecology or biomedical significance of other Simbu group viruses. Shuni virus has been isolated from a febrile human in Nigeria, as well as from local cattle, sheep, and *Culicoides* spp.[78, 79] Simbu virus antibodies have been detected in humans in Botswana[72] and South Africa.[77] A few humans in Trinidad were found with antibodies to Manzanilla virus.[92]

Other Members of the *Bunyavirus* Genus

There is serologic evidence suggesting that viruses from several other groups may infect man. For example, Koongol (Koongol group) antibodies were reported from Australia,[179] M'poko (Turlock group) from the Central African Republic, Boraceia (*Anopheles* B group) from Brazil,[180] and Sukuni and Tacaiuma (*Anopheles* A group) from Trinidad and Brazil.[79] Tacaiuma virus has also been isolated from a febrile human. Kaeng Khoi virus[181] has been isolated from bats as well as bedbugs (*Stricticimex* and *Cimex* species) collected within caves in Thailand. Antibodies were detected in other bats in the caves and in guano harvesters.

Several other viruses of the *Bunyavirus* genus possessing interesting ecological facets are known. For example, the Gamboa group[182] is linked by serologic tests that suggest the possibility of prior RNA segment reassortment in nature as an evolutionary mechanism (compare C and Patois groups). They are apparently maintained in Latin American ecosystems by a cycle which involves transovarial infection of *Aedeomyia squamipennis* mosquitoes and infection of birds. Members of the Patois group have been detected in North and Central America and humans noted to have antibodies; ecological investigations suggest rodents and *Culex (Melanoconion)* mosquitoes might be their major ecological focus.[44, 79, 93] Viruses of the Tete group have been isolated from birds in many areas of the world suggesting that migratory fowl may be important in disseminating these viruses.[183] Two members are known from ticks,[79] and one, Bahig virus, is transovarially transmitted, suggesting an intimate ecological relationship to one

of its potential ixodid tick hosts, *Hyalomma marginatum.*[184] This is the only member of the *Bunyaviridae* family outside the *Uukuvirus* and *Nairovirus* genera closely associated with ticks.

PHLEBOVIRUS GENUS

There are 45 named members (see Tables 21–3 and 21–6) of the *Phlebovirus* genus and probably many more awaiting isolation and description.[185, 186] They exist in diverse ecological settings and are particularly prevalent in tropical forest areas. For example, a 3-year study of Panamanian sandflies yielded 111 *Phlebovirus* isolates of seven different virus types, including five "new" viruses.[4] Most phleboviruses are strongly associated with sandflies, and this vector relationship is reflected in the fact that these viruses usually do not replicate in mosquitoes, even after direct intrathoracic inoculation, although they will grow in inoculated sandflies.[6] There is evidence for transovarial transmission of many phleboviruses, either by isolation of the virus from male sandflies or direct demonstration of virus in laboratory-reared progeny of infected females.[187]

Sicilian and Naples viruses are the best known and most widely distributed phleboviruses.[188] They are thought to be the cause of most clinically described sandfly fever in the Mediterranean basin, southwest Asia,[189] India,[190] and perhaps even China.[191] The wide geographic dispersion of these two viruses and certain similarities of their epidemiology to that of leishmaniasis are a consequence of the wide geographic range and specific habits of their vector, the sandfly *Phlebotomus papatasi.* Other phleboviruses have been isolated from *Phlebotomus* sandflies and three infect man. Karimabad and Salehabad viruses occur in the Middle East,[188] but little is known about their clinical disease potential, while Toscana virus occurs in Italy[192] (Table 21–16) and is emerging as an important local pathogen (see below).

Another large group of sandfly-associated phleboviruses comes from the New World and patterns of human infection reflect the contrasting ecology of the various vector species.[4, 185, 193–196] A few of these viruses have been isolated only from vertebrates, so their arthropod vector is completely unknown. Icoaraci virus has been isolated from both sandflies and mosquitoes and Itaporanga virus only from mosquitoes; this may represent a chance occurrence or mosquitoes may be involved in transmission of these two Brazilian viruses.

Five phleboviruses are known from sub-Saharan Africa. Gordil (Central African Republic), Saint Floris (Central African Republic), and Gabek Forest (Ethiopia, Nigeria) viruses have been isolated only from rodents. Arumowat (Sudan, Nigeria, Central African Republic, Kenya) virus has been isolated from rodents and mosquitoes. Interestingly, Arumowat and Itaporanga grow to higher titer than most phleboviruses when inoculated into mosquitoes.[6] Finally, Rift Valley fever virus (see below) appears to be a mosquito-associated agent.

Naples and Sicilian Sandfly Fever Viruses

Sandfly fever (pappataci fever, phlebotomus fever) has been recognized as an important febrile illness among invading armies in the Mediterranean basin since the Napoleonic Wars and remained so during World Wars I and II.[189] An Austrian military

Table 21–16
Phleboviruses Infecting Man*

	Country†	Infections of Man		References
		Isolation‡	Serology§	
New World				
Alenquer	Brazil	1	1/227 PRN	197
Bujaru	Brazil	0	13/53 HI	88
Cacao	Panama	0	13/177 PRN	4
Candiru	Brazil	1	1/253 HI	88
Chagres	Panama	5	7/129 PRN	193,194,196
			155/4608 HI	
			172/4427 PRN	
			(0.4%–17%)	
Itaporanga	Brazil (Trinidad, French Guinea)	0	27/82 PRN	88,79
			8/538 PRN	
Punta Toro	Panama	2	40/180 PRN	79,4,196
			(6%–40%)	
			46/303 PRN	
			(15%) PRN	
			289/2556 PRN	
			(0%–34%)	
Old World				
Arumowot	Egypt, Somalia, Sudan, Nigeria (Central African Republic, Kenya, South Africa, Zimbabwe)	0	80/521 PRN (1%–73%)	6,79
			33/72 HI	
Gabek Forest	Nigeria, Sudan, Egypt Morocco	0	127/679 PRN (3%–28%)	188
Gordil	Sudan, Somalia (Central African Republic)	0	2/105 PRN (1%–4%)	188
Karimabad	Egypt, Iran, USSR	0	538/2785 PRN (1%–62%)	188
Rift Valley fever	Sub-Saharan Africa, Egypt	Many	See text	See text
Saint Floris	Egypt, Sudan, Somalia, (Central African Republic)	0	14/193 PRN (2%–13%)	188
Salehabad	Pakistan (Iran)	0	12/338 HI (2%–6%)	79
Sandfly fever Naples	Circum-Mediterranean, USSR, Southwest Asia, India	Several	970/5244 PRN (2%–62%)	188
Sandfly fever Sicilian	Circum-Mediterranean, USSR, Southwest Asia, India	Several	720/536 PRN (1%–59%)	188
Toscana	Italy	Several	58/237 PRN	192

Note that while plaque reduction neutralization (PRN) or mouse protection neutralization (MPN) tests are rather specific, hemagglutination-inhibition (HI) tests are broadly reactive and should be interpreted with reservations.

*Relatively little is known about the disease potential of most of the agents listed in Table 21–3. Usually a serosurvey of persons residing in the area where the virus was isolated was performed; if no antibodies were found, no additional human studies were performed.

†Countries where human infection is known; additional countries where virus is known to be present are shown in parenthesis.

‡Number of human infections proven by virus isolation. Illness resembles classic sandfly fever in all cases except Rift Valley fever where retinal vasculitis, encephalitis, and hemorrhagic fever also occur. Note small number of cases actually observed for most viruses except Rift, Naples, and Sicilian. Incidence of subclinical disease unknown even for agents such as Karimabad, where there is extensive serologic evidence of infection.

§Number positive/number tested. Figures in parenthesis refer to percentage positive in different subsamples. See text for details of Rift Valley fever, Punta Toro, and Chagres. Extensive serosurveys of several Old World viruses were performed by Tesh et al,[188] and should be consulted for details.

commission[198] first demonstrated that the cause of sandfly fever was a filterable agent found in patients' blood and that the disease could be transmitted through the bite of the sandfly, *Phlebotomus papatasi*. (The genus name *Phlebovirus* is in recognition of the role of *Phlebotomus* sandflies as vectors of classic sandfly fever.) Sabin[199] first demonstrated that sandfly fever in the Middle East could be caused by either of two distinct viruses, named Sicilian sandfly fever and Naples sandfly fever viruses after their sites of original isolation.

Disease Syndromes

The clinical syndrome which results from infection with either virus is similar and is characterized by sudden onset; fever lasting about two to four days and ranging from 38 to 40°C; severe frontal headache; pain in the eyes, back, and joints; photophobia; anorexia; and general malaise. Nausea, vomiting, abdominal discomfort, diarrhea, mild sore throat, epistaxis, drowsiness, dizziness, and a biphasic fever are occasionally seen. Conjunctival injection and prominent facial flushing are common but rash or meningeal signs are rare.[189, 199-202] The disease is self-limiting with complete recovery; no deaths have been recorded among thousands of clinically diagnosed naturally occurring human sandfly fever infections. Clinical attack rates as high as three fourths have been noted in virgin-soil epidemics[7] and most experimental infections with Sicilian or Naples virus strains result in clinical disease.[199] Several observations have suggested that the disease in children is milder and may be subclinical.[7, 203-205] However, about 0.7% of febrile children attending an Egyptian clinic yielded serum isolates of Sicilian or Naples virus[204]; true age-specific attack rates for both infection and disease are lacking. In areas where sandfly fever is endemic, most of the population is thought to be infected during childhood. In contrast, when nonimmune adults enter an endemic area, classic sandfly fever usually results. While this concept is undoubtedly true in large measure, neutralizing antibody rates rarely exceed 40% to 60% in adults, even in endemic areas.[188, 204, 205] Because of the prolonged persistence of these antibodies in man, it seems unlikely that this represents antibody decay and these persons may be protected from infection in some other fashion, perhaps by natural resistance, induced immunity without detectable humoral antibody, or the focality of infected sandflies.

Experimental infections of human volunteers with Naples or Sicilian virus have demonstrated that a single infection with either virus confers solid immunity to the homologous virus for at least 2 years; individuals subsequently challenged with the heterologous virus became infected and suffered typical sandfly fever.[189] Neutralizing antibody to Sicilian virus persists over 30 years and thus a single infection with sandfly fever probably confers lifelong immunity to the homologous virus.[206] Multiple attacks presumably reflect inaccurate clinical diagnosis or infection with other *Phlebovirus* types.

Epidemiology

The epidemiology of Sicilian and Naples sandfly fever viruses in the Old World is closely associated with the habits of the vector, *P papatasi*. This species is found throughout the Mediterranean region and extends as far east as India and Transcaucasia. It occurs in an extraordinary variety of habitats, including both rural areas as well as the heart of large cities. The breeding places are in moist soil; in dark, humid, sheltered locations such as beneath stones; in deep cracks in soil, or in animal burrows. Mediterranean *P papatasi* overwinter in the larval stage and begin to emerge in April. Most sandfly fever is seen during the warmer months when the flies are abundant, and little occurs after October or November when the adults have disappeared. In different studies, 0.015% to 0.5% of captured phlebotomines were infected with Sicilian virus.[79, 207-209] Their flight range is very short, usually about 100 m or so, although marked flies, presumably carried on the wind, have been recaptured up to 1500 m away in the desert. Their hopping pattern of locomotion makes residual spraying of walls and breeding sites particularly effective in preventing infection in buildings.[189] Although *P papatasi* bite inside cool dark buildings in daytime,[210] they are primarily nocturnal feeders. Thus, considerable protection can be obtained by liberal use of repellants at dusk and fine-mesh netting over beds; however, the small size of the flies allows them to penetrate ordinary mosquito nets and screens.[189] Transovarial transmission of sandfly fever viruses has been documented in this species[187, 211] and may, coupled with their limited flight range, result in a highly focal distribution of infection. Overall attack rates were 3% to 10% in troops in the Middle East and Sicily during World War II, but some units had over half their members afflicted; there were even differences within a single building.[189]

The relative contributions of oral infection and transovarial virus transmission to maintenance of infected sandflies in nature is not well understood. Laboratory studies with different *Phlebovirus*-sandfly combinations have shown the flies to be relatively refractory to oral infection; once infected by intrathoracic inoculation they develop disseminated infections and often transmit the virus transovarially to their progeny, but the prevalence of infection in newly hatched flies varies from 1.5% to 50% depending on the virus-host combination.[185] In the case of Sicilian and Naples viruses, transovarial infection of *P papatasi* occurs but the actual rate has never been measured and is possibly low.[199] No natural vertebrate reservoir has been incriminated, although antibodies have been detected in gerbils[205, 212] and *P papatasi* are often found in gerbil burrows.[213] Viremic humans can also infect *P papatasi*[199]; in one study, nine of 69 arthropods feeding on man became infected and one of the three sandflies living to refeed on laboratory animals transmitted the virus.[214]

It seems likely that transovarial transmission of the viruses plays a particularly important role in their maintenance in remote desert regions.[211, 213] This factor also complicates control programs, requiring particular attention to emergence of overwintering infected flies and to residual foci of human disease.[215]

As a consequence of residual insecticide use in malaria control programs and improvements in environmental sanitation after World War II, *P papatasi* has been greatly reduced in numbers in Greece[206] and Italy[192] and antibodies to Naples and Sicilian viruses are rarely found in persons born since 1950. In spite of successful malaria eradication, significant populations of *P papatasi* are still found along the Adriatic littoral of Yugoslavia and sandfly fever virus transmission continues.[216, 217] This region was presumably the origin of the virus that caused the major epidemics from 1946 to 1950 extending north and east to previously uninvolved areas of Yugoslavia, involving Belgrade, and reaching into Hungary. In northern Serbia attack rates of 75% were estimated in a population

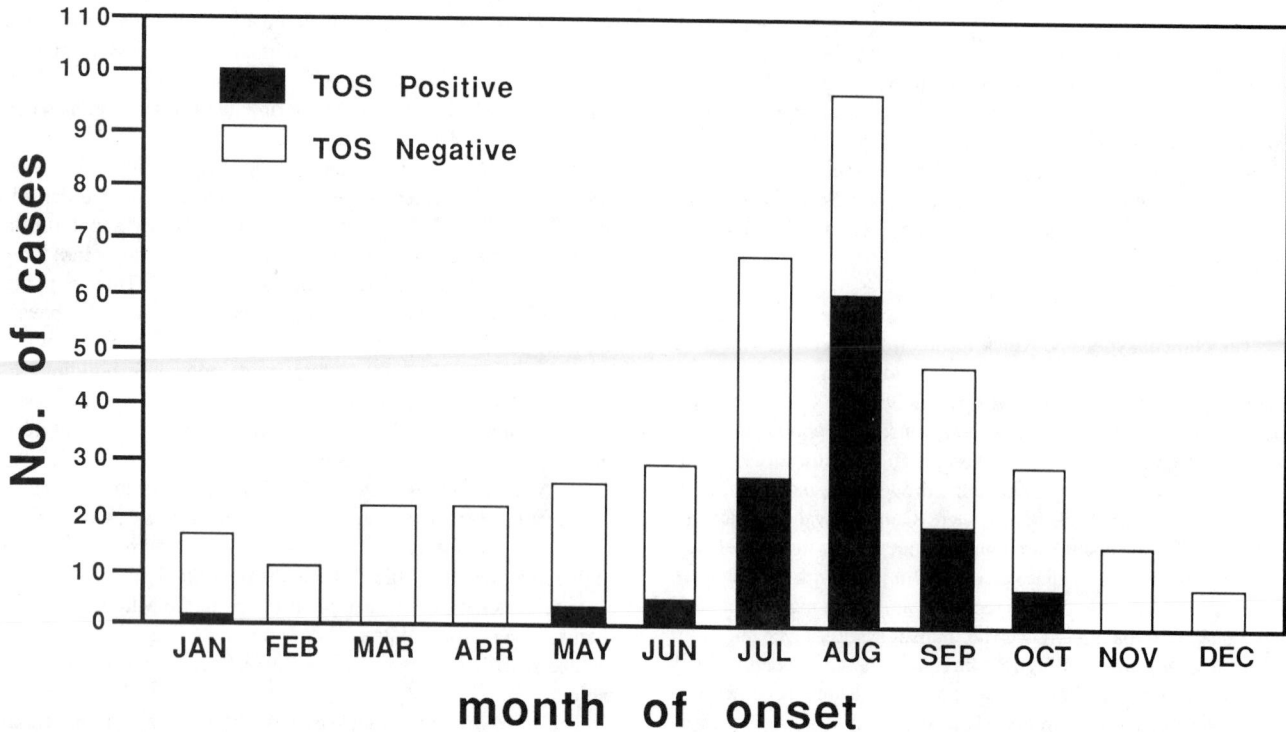

Figure 21–3. Number of cases of CNS disease of unknown origin hospitalized in several towns of central Italy (1977–1986) and tested for Toscana (TOS) virus infection. The diagnosis of recent virus infection was obtained by means of seroconversion (by hemagglutination inhibition and plaque reduction neutralization) and/or presence of IgM (indirect fluoroescent antibody and capture–enzyme-linked immunosorbent assay) (P. Verani, unpublished observations, 1987).

of 1.2 million.[7] Another major sandfly fever epidemic occurred in southern Italy following a series of earthquakes at the turn of the century. Rubble and waste water provided breeding sites for an explosion of phlebotomines which transmitted epidemic sandfly fever in areas where the virus was introduced, thought to be largely by travel of infected persons.[218] Reappearance of *P papatasi* populations has been noted in Italy and Israel and may signal the possibility of recurrent epidemics.

Diagnosis is suspected from the characteristic "three-day fever" and is readily achieved by virus isolation, IgM-capture ELISA in early convalescence, or serology on paired sera. An antigen-detection ELISA developed for Sicilian virus has been successful in a small group of patients.[219]

Only symptomatic therapy is available. Oral administration of 1200 mg/day of ribavirin to volunteers inoculated with Sicilian sandfly fever virus successfully prevented symptomatic disease and viremia.[219] If lower doses should also prove effective in prophylaxis, travelers and those exposed during an epidemic can be protected. Avoidance of sandfly bites can be achieved by liberal use of repellants containing DEET.

Toscana Virus

Toscana virus was first isolated in 1971 from *Phlebotomus perniciosus* sandflies collected in central Italy (region of Tuscany) in the provinces of Florence and Grosseto.[192] Subsequent investigatons found high neutralizing antibody prevalence rates (25%) against Toscana virus among residents of the province of Florence,

and several patients with a clinical diagnosis of aseptic meningitis presented with serologic responses suggestive of recent infection.[220] More recently, investigations of patients suffering from acute CNS disease of suspected viral etiology in several towns in the endemic area of central Italy found that a large proportion of cases seen during the summer months could be attributed to infection with Toscana virus and that cases occurred every summer (Figure 21–3; P. Verani, unpublished observations, 1987). Most patients were adults with rural or suburban exposure. Clinical findings were those of viral meningitis.[220] In some instances, Toscana virus was isolated from the CSF of acutely ill patients,[220, 221] but most diagnoses are virologically confirmed by finding IgM fluorescent antibodies or a fourfold rise in HI, plaque reduction neutralization (PRN), or CF tests.[220]

Toscana virus isolations are most frequently made from *P perniciosus* sandflies, including from males.[222] This species is most abundant in central Italy during July, and most virus isolations have been made from sandflies captured at that time. In field studies undertaken between 1980 and 1985 near Florence and Siena, about 0.2% of sandflies were infected with Toscana virus and isolates were made every year.[222] Oral infection of *P perniciosus* is possible and transovarial transmission occurs.[223] Toscana virus has been maintained by vertical transmission in colonized sandflies for 13 generations over a 23-month period, but each successive generation had a lower percentage of infected arthropods than the previous one.[224] This suggests the need for a vertebrate amplifying host, but none has been identified as yet.[222, 225]

P perniciosus in Tuscany inhabits the moist floor of hardwood forests interlaced with small rivers. The species is also found in France, Spain, and Portugal to the west, as well as Yugoslavia and Greece to the east.[225] Recent isolation of Toscana virus from an aseptic meningitis patient infected in Portugal[221] suggests that the virus may be a more widespread pathogen than is currently appreciated.

New World Phleboviruses

These viruses differ in their epidemiology from the Naples, Sicilian, and Toscana agents in that most have been found in the ecologically complex tropical regions where several different species of sandfly vectors are suspected. Large-scale outbreaks of sandfly fever similar to those recorded in the Mediterranean region have not been observed in the New World tropics. Rather, isolated single cases are the rule, generally among persons exposed in the forests either occupationally or for recreation (see Table 21–16). Chagres,[160] Punta Toro,[79] Candiru,[88] and Alenquer[197] viruses were all originally isolated from febrile patients who suffered illness similar to classic sandfly fever described above, but the total number of patients observed is small and the clinical spectrum of disease is not well established.

A serologic survey of rural Panama, where both Chagres and Punta Toro viruses were first isolated, found antibody to Punta Toro virus in all areas sampled, with the exception of the coastal islands, in prevalence rates ranging from 2% to 34%. Antibody to Chagres virus was restricted to eastern and central Panama residents and prevalence rates were generally lower than those to Punta Toro virus, ranging from less than 1% to 17%. Highest antibody prevalence rates to both viruses were found in the heavily forested Darien province. The incidence of infections with these viruses among susceptible military personnel in the forests of Panama was about one per 100 man-years of exposure for Punta Toro virus and about one-half that rate for Chagres virus.[196]

New World sandfly vectors are restricted to the humid forest habitat, frequently around the base of large buttress trees. They breed in the moist leaf litter on the forest floor and feed on forest-dwelling vertebrates. The species most frequently associated with Chagres and Punta Toro viruses are *Lutzomyia trapidoi* and *L ylephilator;* however, several other species have been the source of virus isolations.[4] Transovarial transmission has been demonstrated for New World phleboviruses.[4, 185, 187] Primates, rodents, sloths, and porcupines have antibody to Punta Toro virus and perhaps serve as vertebrate amplifying hosts. Although about 1000 sera from various species of mammals have been examined for antibody to Chagres virus, only a few primates and porcupines were found to be positive (J.W. LeDuc, unpublished observations, 1981).

The only phlebovirus known to occur in the United States is Rio Grande virus, isolated from wood rats *(Neatoma micropus)* near Brownsville, Texas. Human infections have not been identified. The agent is probably transmitted between wood rats by the sandfly *Lutzomyia anthophora,* which often shares their burrows. Transovarial transmission in *L anthophora* has been demonstrated.[226, 227]

Rift Valley Fever Virus

This virus differs from other known phleboviruses in its path-ogenicity for domestic animals, ability to cause serious and fatal infections of man, aerosol infectivity, and wide laboratory host range including vertebrates, insects, and cell cultures.[229] It was originally isolated in the Rift Valley in Kenya during an epizootic of fatal hepatic necrosis and abortion in sheep.[230] Since that time it has repeatedly infected herds of sheep, cattle, and goats in which it produces 10% to 30% mortality and may abort virtually every pregnant animal infected. The impact of epizootic disease on both large and small domestic animal raisers in the Rift Valley and southern Africa is substantial.[230–235] These savage epizootics have greatest impact on large herds of sheep and cattle; native ungulates[236–238] seem to be more resistant to the lethal effects of virus infection. Rift Valley fever virus has probably been distributed over the entire sub-Saharan African continent for centuries.[239] The discovery that Zinga virus, an established human pathogen in West Africa is in reality Rift Valley fever virus has solidified this view.[240]

Indeed, a recent (1987) major outbreak of Rift Valley fever occurred in the Senegal river basin, the first such outbreak recognized in West Africa. This episode probably resulted in 25,000 or more human infections and at least 49 reported deaths.[241–243] Rift Valley fever virus had been known for some time to exist in several areas within the region, but evidence of transmission was scanty and antibody rates in man and animals were low.[238, 244, 245] The inciting event may well have been a major irrigation project on the Senegal river and related ecological changes.[246] Without the presence of concerned physicians in Rosso, Mauritania, this outbreak might never have come to medical attention, and without competent laboratory investigation it would have been clinically diagnosed as yellow fever. Thus, this episode may only be the first *recognized* Rift Valley fever epidemic in West Africa. It also points out the potential future impact of Rift Valley fever on African water control projects. The epidemic was reported in a recently published symposium.[246a, 246b]

The extension of Rift Valley fever virus into Egypt in 1977[235, 247, 248] radically changed then-existing concepts of the world health significance of Rift Valley fever virus. The factors leading to this unprecedented event have never been elucidated,[239, 249, 250] but it seems likely that this epidemic was the first of its kind, at least for many decades.[251] Once established in the irrigated Nile valley, the virus resulted in extensive human and animal disease in 1977–1979, but never spread beyond Egypt.[239, 252] More than 600 human deaths were officially reported and estimates range much higher; several hundred thousand human infections probably occurred. The subsequent disappearance of virus activity has not been convincingly explained, although animal vaccination, aerial spraying, climate, and other factors have all been invoked. This question is of more than theoretical importance since Egypt stands at risk of a recurrence and since other areas such as the Tigris-Euphrates river basin or circum-Mediterranean regions represent potential extension zones for the disease.[253, 254] Control of disease in those areas or in areas of the United States or Europe with large livestock populations and high vector density could be difficult or impossible.[239] It should be noted that uncomplicated Rift Valley fever[255] and Rift Valley fever retinitis[256, 257] have both been identified in travelers returning from Africa to North America or Europe, and that many species of North American mosquitoes have been shown to be capable of transmitting Rift Valley fever virus.[258]

Epidemiology

The epidemiology of Rift Valley fever virus can be discussed under three topics:

1. Its maintenance in forest and other regions in the absence of epizootic disease. Rift Valley fever virus has been isolated from several genera of mosquitoes (including *Aedes, Eretmapodites,* and *Mansonia*[259-262]) in the absence of epizootic or epidemic human disease and it is usually assumed that the virus is mosquito-transmitted in that setting. However, it does multiply in and can be transmitted by intrathoracically inoculated sandflies[263] as well as by *Culicoides variipennis.*[264] There are also isolates from African species of *Culicoides,*[265] further confusing vector assignment, and mechanical transmission has been demonstrated for several species of hematophagus insects.[266] Attempts to implicate rodents, primates, birds, game animals, and reptiles as vertebrate hosts have been largely unsuccessful.[232, 234, 236, 267-269] In the Central African Republic, it was isolated from mosquitoes that commonly feed on buffalo, and antibodies have been found in buffalo there.[261] In Kenya, antibodies were not present in local buffalo, and buffalo developed only modest viremia after experimental inoculation.[237]

The recent finding in Kenya that *Aedes* mosquitoes emerging from flooded depressions called "damboes" are already infected with virus provides strong evidence for transovarial transmission of Rift Valley fever virus in nature.[270] The lack of an obligatory vertebrate maintenance host would explain the negative results from previous studies. Furthermore, damboes or similar geologic structures are often found in Rift Valley fever virus endemic areas and related *Aedes* mosquitoes may also breed in other floodwater habitats, providing the basis for multiple foci of Rift Valley fever virus throughout sub-Saharan Africa.

2. Epizootics occur at variable intervals but generally follow unusually high rainfall.[234, 269, 271] Furthermore, disease occurs more or less simultaneously throughout the affected areas.[234, 269, 272] Virus isolates have been made from several species of *Aedes, Culex,* and *Anopheles* mosquitoes during African epizootics, but none of the implicated species were particularly efficient vectors when tested in the laboratory.[262, 273, 274] All required high virus titers ($>10^{5.0}$/mL) in the ingested blood meal to become infected and even then were not efficient transmitters of virus.[262] Isolates have also been made from *Culicoides* during epizootics,[273] but their significance remains to be determined.

If confirmed, transovarial transmission of Rift Valley fever virus[270] could explain several features of the epidemiology. Periods of high rainfall would flood depressions where dormant eggs of certain floodwater *Aedes* spp would be triggered into development. The adult mosquitoes would emerge soon afterward, already infected, and would then infect domestic livestock or other amplifiers. Susceptible sheep and cattle generate extremely high viremias and these massive virus concentrations can infect even inefficient mosquito vectors which would sustain the epizootic. Large rainfall would thus be necessary to hatch a critical mass of transovarially infected floodwater *Aedes* spp and to generate high densities of other mosquitoes to perpetuate the epizootic. This hypothesis is now under test with simultaneous field observations, ecological survey via satellite, and mathematical modeling of critical measurements to develop predictive parameters for epizootic disease in Kenya.[275]

3. Direct aerosol transmission. Rift Valley fever virus is highly infectious by aerosol, and human infections have been well documented in the research laboratory,[276, 277] when domestic animals undergo necropsy,[278, 279] and at slaughter.[247, 280] Although vector transmission, particularly mosquitoes, is essential in propagating epizootic disease, the relative roles in aerosol transmission and perhaps other mechanisms such as fomites in different epidemics cannot be easily assessed. Many South African cases that occurred during epizootics recalled prior contact with animal carcasses[281]; however, mosquito transmission was felt to be a more important factor in the Egyptian epidemic where man and his domestic animals lived in closer proximity, human population density was higher, and a different vector was involved.[247, 249]

In the wake of the 1974–1975 South African epidemic, human antibody rates on infected farms ranged from 7% to 45%. Overall prevalence was 14.5% with prevalence significantly greater in adults (16%) than in children (11%), and in males (17%) than in females (12%), presumably reflecting the greater risk for men employed on the farms. This is less than rates in Egyptian serosurveys which were typically 15% to 30% in affected areas, but were as high as two thirds in some regions.[249, 282] This contrasts to rates reported from areas without epizootic disease which rarely reach 10% to 15%.[71, 244, 261, 283, 284]

Disease Syndromes

Most Rift Valley fever infections of man are symptomatic, but present as acute, undifferentiated febrile illnesses (see Table 21–9). A small proportion, perhaps 1%, will develop hemorrhagic fever, encephalitis, or retinal vasculitis (see Table 21–10).

Uncomplicated illness[8, 221, 230, 238, 276, 277, 284, 285] follows a two- to six-day incubation period and is ushered in by the abrupt onset of fever, chills, and malaise. Incapacitating prostration, myalgia, and fever typically resolve after two to three days, but may last a week. Physical findings are confined to conjunctival and pharyngeal injection. Epistaxis may occur and a "saddleback" fever curve is not uncommon. Transient leukopenia is common early, but in the few cases studied, liver enzymes and coagulation tests were normal. Diagnosis rests on the clinical and epidemiologic setting or specific virologic tests. If other cases with some of the more characteristic complications are occurring (eg, hemorrhagic fever, encephalitis, or retinal vasculitis; see below), if abortion and deaths are occurring in domestic livestock, or if the patient has a history of high-risk exposure (abattoir worker, veterinarian, virologist, farmer present at necropsy of cow, sheep, or goat) Rift Valley fever should be suspected.

Virologic diagnosis is relatively easy. Viremia occurs through the acute phase and may exceed 10^6 to 10^8/mL.[235, 276] Rift Valley fever virus is readily isolated in virtually any system employed; AP61 mosquito cells, intracranially inoculated suckling mice, or intraperitoneally inoculated adult hamsters probably are the most sensitive, but Vero cells or intraperitoneally inoculated adult mice have also been used. The resulting isolate can then be definitively identified by serologic testing. If paired sera are available, serologic diagnosis is efficient. In a known endemic area virtually any serologic technique gives presumptive confirmation. HI, IFA, or ELISA with infected mouse liver antigens are cross-reactive.[197, 228, 229, 286, 287] CF is relatively specific although antisera to some of the Brazilian phleboviruses, particularly Belterra, will react with Rift Valley fever antigen (see Table 21–13).[197] The neutralization test is probably the most specific; convalescent titers generally exceed 1:640 and often reach 1:2560. Most convalescent sera also react specifically in agar gel precipitin test. Single sera may yield a presumptive serologic diagnosis using IgM-capture ELISA.

Detection of Rift Valley fever virus antigen or nucleic acid can be used as an alternative to viral isolation. Antigen-capture ELISA has been effective in detecting infection of mosquitoes as well as mammals[288] (see Figure 21–3). Among 130 hospitalized cases of virus isolation–confirmed Rift Valley fever in a recent outbreak in Mauritania, 30% were also positive by Rift Valley fever antigen detection. Rift Valley fever–specific nucleic acid was also detected by hybridization in 15% of the patients from whom virus was isolated.[246a, 246b] While less sensitive than virus isolation, antigen detection and nucleic acid hybridization offer much greater speed (three hours for antigen detection) while retaining viral specificity,[288] clearly useful properties in detecting and evaluating the spread of an outbreak of Rift Valley fever. The central role of domestic livestock in propagating epidemics is reflected in their utility as sentinels to detect virus activity.

Antigen also remains detectable for a short period after infectivity has disappeared (Figure 21–4). This residual antigenemia is probably the result of circulating materials, such as the nucleocapsid, which are not bound by virus-neutralizing antibodies. The belated clearance of viral antigen may be responsible for the second fever hump and must be considered in relation to the occurrence of late retinal vasculitis and encephalitis.

Although Rift Valley fever had been regarded as an essentially nonfatal disease, increased awareness of the threat of viral hemorrhagic fevers in South Africa led to the discovery in 1975 that some humans infected with the virus develop fatal hemorrhagic fever rather than the temporarily incapacitating illness previously recorded.[281, 289] This has been confirmed from Zimbabwe,[290] Angola,[291] Zambia,[291] Central Africa,[292] Mauritania,[241] and Egypt.[248, 293–295] Hemorrhagic disease begins as classic Rift Valley fever but in the first few days of illness the patients develop petechial, mucous membrane, and GI bleeding. They become jaundiced and die in shock. Disseminated vascular damage and hepatic failure probably both contribute to the patient's demise. Hemorrhagic fever accounted for most of the 0.5% mortality rate estimated for the Mauritanian outbreak.[242] In that episode, several patients were identified with overwhelming clinical signs of vascular damage but little evidence of liver disease, whereas the largest number of deaths occurred in patients with both hemorrhage and icteric liver involvement. The most prominent autopsy finding is extensive liver necrosis, sometimes with a midzonal predominance. Virus can usually be recovered from the blood; postmortem liver samples may yield diagnostic antigen, electron microscopically visualized particles, or virus isolation.

Encephalitis has also been recently added to the clinical spectrum of human disease.[152, 241, 248, 281, 294, 296] Typically, these patients have recovered from the acute febrile illness three days to 2 weeks previously, but then present with headache, meningismus, confusion, and often a recrudescence of fever. Reported cases have suffered a severe course with hallucinations, vertigo, stupor, coma, focal motor signs, or decerebration often leaving residua or terminating in death.

Spinal fluid usually shows a lymphocytic pleocytosis in the hundreds of cells, modest elevation of protein, and normal glucose. These patients are not viremic when seen with neurologic involvement. Rift Valley fever encephalitis can be suspected by the presence of higher serum antibody levels than are usually seen in convalescence or by the presence of virus-specific serum IgM antibodies. Definitive diagnosis requires demonstrating increasing antibody titers in serum, or occasionally CSF.[296, 297] Virus-specific IgM is present in CSF and can be detected at times by IFA or more reliably by an IgM-capture enzyme immunoassay.[297]

Ocular complications, like encephalitis, are late manifestations of Rift Valley fever.[298–300] Typically an otherwise asymptomatic patient presents up to 3 weeks after acute Rift Valley fever with

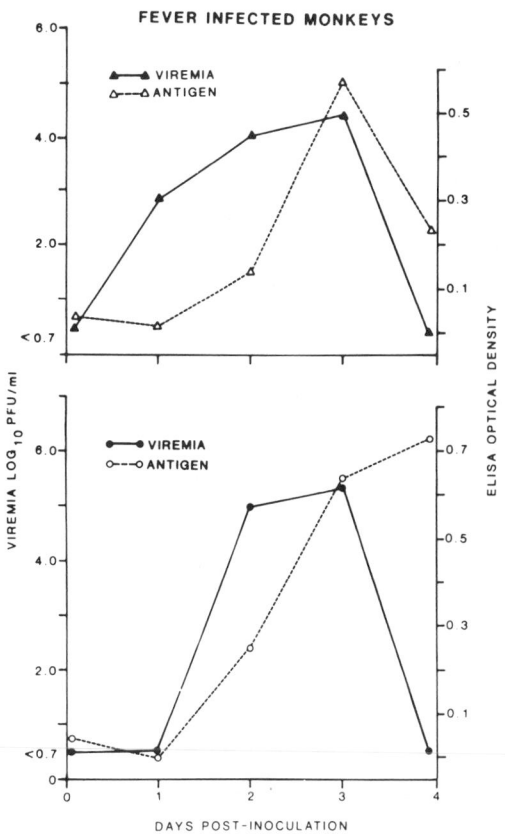

Figure 21–4. Rift Valley fever virus and antigen in the serum of experimentally infected rhesus monkeys. Viremia begins on day 1 or 2 after subcutaneous inoculation of the ZH501 strain of virus. Peak titer occurs on day 3 and virus is no longer detectable on day 4. Serum neutralizing antibodies are found by day 6. The ratio of antigen to infectivity varies throughout the infection. In the first monkey (*top, triangles*) clearance of antigenemia has begun between days 3 and 4, but viremia has decreased 1000-fold. In the other (*bottom, circles*) antigenemia is still increasing on day 4. Late immune clearance of antigen is a possible explanation for the biphasic fever curve sometimes seen in human Rift Valley fever. Circulating antigen may be nucleocapsid. (Drawn from Niklasson B, Grandien M, Peters CJ, et al: Detection of Rift Valley fever virus antigen by enzyme-linked immunosorbent assay. *J Clin Microbiol* 1983; 17:1026–1031.)

the brisk onset of decreased visual acuity. Examination reveals retinal hemorrhages, exudates, and macular edema to be the cause. Fluorescein angiography suggests retinal vasculitis is the basic lesion with both increased permeability and vascular blockage. Vision returns days to weeks later as the edema and exudates resolve, but perhaps half the patients will experience some degree of permanent loss of sight. Uveitis has also been reported. There are no virologic studies of ocular fluids and since the patients suffer none of the fatal complications of Rift Valley fever, there are no histopathologic data either. Virologic diagnosis depends on evidence of a recent Rift Valley fever immune response (rising titers, serum IgM present).

Therapy and Prevention

Uncomplicated Rift Valley fever is best managed by symptomatic treatment and observation. Retinal vasculitis and late encephalitis have both been treated with steroids without any clear benefit. Immunosuppression should be employed with caution until more is known about the pathogenesis of these conditions. In experimental rodent models, late encephalitis is due to active viral replication in the brain so that blunting the immune response could be harmful. The hemorrhagic fever syndrome is associated with disseminated intravascular coagulation (DIC) in nonhuman primate models,[301] but heparinization on this basis in the face of liver disease is ill-advised. In experimental models (including nonhuman primates), ribavirin, interferon or its inducers, and passive antibody are highly effective in prophylaxis and therapy of Rift Valley fever, but human efficacy data are not available.[302–305] The prophylactic efficacy of ribavirin in the related Sicilian sandfly fever infection of man[219] suggests that the antiviral drug deserves a trial in prevention of severe complications of Rift Valley fever. (See Chapter 26 for general management of hemorrhagic fevers.)

A formalin-inactivated monkey cell culture vaccine has been developed,[306, 307] and experience to date is favorable. Several thousand people have received the original vaccine or a somewhat improved product with minimal side effects and good serologic response.[308–311] One milliliter administered subcutaneously on days 0, 7, and 28 results in a neutralizing antibody response by day 42 in virtually all recipients. Annual booster injections are needed to maintain antibody levels. This vaccine appears to offer good protection for laboratory workers and available evidence suggests it would be efficacious in natural circumstances. Unfortunately, the vaccine is expensive to produce and available in limited supply so that widespread use in Africa is not feasible. Those with high-risk occupations, such as veterinary or microbiologic workers, should be considered for vaccination.

The highest risk for transmission to man occurs during epizootics in sheep and cattle. It is believed that both the economic impact on domestic animal production and transmission to man can be minimized by vaccination of livestock.[239, 254] Live attenuated and inactivated vaccines have been employed for this purpose, and while largely successful, they have significant limitations.[239] Recently, intensive mutagenesis has been employed to derive an attenuated Rift Valley fever virus strain which shows considerable promise for human and livestock use.[312] This virus, in addition to being attenuated for rodents and newborn lambs, is of low neurovirulence for rhesus monkeys and nonabortagenic and protective for pregnant ewes and pregnant cattle.[313]

UUKUVIRUS GENUS

Members of this genus (see Table 21–4) are primarily known from ticks, although they have been isolated from birds, rodents, and cattle.[79] They have never been associated with human disease, although human sera from Czechoslovakia,[315] Hungary,[79] and Norway[316] contain antibodies to Uukuniemi virus. *Ixodes ricinus,* the reservoir of Uukuniemi virus, is a widely distributed tick in Europe and Asia which feeds on man and many other vertebrates. It also accompanies migrating birds and hosts at least five other viruses. Thus, the ecology of Uukuniemi virus is undoubtedly complex and probably will not be resolved unless it proves to be of greater biomedical significance than is now recognized.[317, 318]

NAIROVIRUS GENUS

All known members of the *Nairovirus* genus (see Table 21–5) are thought to be tick-transmitted and have often been shown to be vertically transmitted. Their epidemiology is incompletely understood and is often linked to the interesting and complex life cycles of their tick hosts.

Crimean-Congo Hemorrhagic Fever

In the wake of World War II an epidemic of more than 200 cases of severe hemorrhagic fever was described from the Crimean peninsula. Clinically similar diseases were subsequently recognized from other areas of European Russia, Bulgaria, Romania, and reported under the rubric "Central Asian hemorrhagic fever" in the Uzbek, Tadzhik, Turkmen, and Kazakh Soviet Socialist Republics.[319] Five thousand miles away and a decade later, Dr Courtois in the Belgian Congo isolated a virus subsequently named "Congo virus."[320] When the etiologic agent of Crimean hemorrhagic fever was finally isolated in tractable form in suckling mice, it was found to be serologically closely related to Congo virus[321] and to the various Russian strains.[322] Subsequently, considerable effort has failed to distinguish the serologic or biologic behavior of various Crimean-Congo hemorrhagic fever virus isolates.[21, 323–325] This serologic unity is particularly surprising since this single virus is now thought to be widely distributed over sub-Saharan Africa into eastern Europe, across the Middle East, and possibly in the Indian subcontinent as well.[318, 326, 327]

Epidemiology

The basic patterns of Crimean-Congo hemorrhagic fever virus epidemiology revolve around ecological relations between vertebrates and ticks, principally ixodid ticks of the genus *Hyalomma.* The virus is clearly capable of persisting in its tick vector as it passes through the stages of its life cycle from larva to nymph to adult (transstadial survival). Furthermore, adult females of several of the 25 species and subspecies of ticks known to harbor the virus can transmit it transovarially to their progeny. Infection of certain vertebrate hosts, including hares, hedgehogs, and domestic animals, results in viremia sufficient to infect some species of ticks. Unfortunately, there are insufficient quantitative studies to assess the roles of vertical virus transmission in the tick, vertebrate amplification of tick infection, tick-vertebrate interactions, and tick biology in maintaining populations of infected ticks that are capable of biting man. Virus circulation in nature proceeds independent of man. We will discuss only two important examples, in part summarized from the synthesis of Hoogstraal.[318]

A brief consideration of the biology of one of the major tick vectors in Bulgaria and European Russia, *Hyalomma marginatum marginatum,* will give some idea as to the complexity of potential life cycles. This subspecies is distributed in southern Europe from Spain eastward to the Caspian Sea, but related *H marginatum* subspecies with somewhat differing taxonomic characteristics are widely known in Africa, Asia, and Europe. Crimean-Congo hemorrhagic fever virus has been isolated numerous times from this tick and has been shown to persist in the tick and to be transmitted both transstadially and transovarially. *H marginatum marginatum* attaches itself to birds or small mammals such as hares or hedgehogs and develops through both larval and nymphal stages on a single host. The adult tick, however, prefers to feed on domestic animals or man. Hares infected in the laboratory undergo substantial viremia and can infect this tick species. Hares often are antibody-positive when trapped in endemic areas. Thus, immature ticks can and do infect hares naturally and this event results in some unquantified amplification of infection among immature ticks. Calves and lambs also become viremic after experimental infection and in known enzootic foci are found to have antibodies. Thus, further virus amplification may occur when adult ticks feed on domestic ungulates. Alternately, if man is attacked by an infected *H marginatum marginatum,* Crimean-Congo hemorrhagic fever may result. In contrast, rooks and other groundfeeding birds that are alternate hosts for immatures have never been found to have viremia or antibody, either after experimental inoculation or in nature. They are, however, important in providing a blood meal for further tick development and are thought to play an important role in disseminating virus-infected ticks both locally and during migation over long distances. European ticks such as *H marginatum marginatum* have been repeatedly taken from birds arriving in Cyprus and Egypt. Indeed, the virus has been isolated from *Hyalomma impeltatum* ticks borne by migrating birds in Ethiopia.[328] The *H marginatum marginatum* role in epidemic Crimean-Congo hemorrhagic fever appears secure because of these virologic and ecological observations as well as the close parallel between increased populations of this tick and the various epidemics in Bulgaria and European Russia. For example, the 1944–1945 Crimean epidemic was associated with dense populations of hares and large numbers of *H marginatum marginatum,* which were readily attacking humans.

The major vector of the virus in the south central Soviet Union (Tadzhik, Uzbek, Turkmen, and Kazak Soviet Socialist Republics) is thought to be *Hyalomma anatolicum anatolicum.* This subspecies is known from India west across Pakistan, southern Soviet Union, and southeastern Europe with African representation as far south as the equator. This widely distributed and common tick utilizes two hosts, parasitizing primarily domestic ungulates, but also biting man. Thus, in contrast to *H marginatum marginatum,* patterns of virus amplification in eastern USSR are independent of populations of hares, but depend on availability and movements of animals such as goats, sheep, cows, and camels. Similarly, migratory birds would not be expected to play a role in dissemination, since this species rarely feeds on birds. Transovarial transmission of the virus has not been definitively studied with this species.

Geographic distribution of the virus is extensive. Virologically documented, naturally acquired human disease is known from the Soviet Union,[322] Bulgaria,[329] Yugoslavia,[330] Pakistan,[331] Iraq,[332] Dubai,[333] Tanzania,[334] Zaire,[334, 335] Uganda,[335] Mauritania,[336] Burkina Faso,[337] and South Africa.[334, 338, 339] It is becoming increasingly apparent that Crimean-Congo hemorrhagic fever is a significant human pathogen in South Africa, with 15 cases and four deaths diagnosed in 1987.[340] The virus has also been isolated from ticks in several additional African countries (Madagascar, Senegal, Nigeria, Central African Republic, Kenya, and Ethiopia) usually with evidence of antibodies in domestic animal or human populations.[79, 318, 326, 341, 342, 343] Recently the virus was obtained from ticks in Greece and convincing serologic evidence of human infection presented.[344] Antibodies alone have been reported from Hungary,[345] Portugal,[346] Turkey,[327] Egypt,[347] India,[348] Afghanistan,[327] and Iran.[349]

In the Soviet Union and Bulgaria the disease has a strong spring-summer prevalence which correlates with the activity and density of suspected tick vectors. Humans, hares, and domestic animals all show antibody acquisition or disease during this season. Persons whose occupations bring them into contact with domestic animals and their ticks (such as milkmaids, sheep shearers, or slaughterhouse personnel) are at maximum risk, although in the rural setting housewives and schoolchildren sustain illness as well. Tick bite or crushing ticks removed from cattle or humans is a usual antecedent of illness. A cluster of disease observed following slaughter of a sick cow suggests that at times infected animals may be a direct source of contagion,[350] and a similar observation has been reported from South Africa.[351] The probability of infection appears to be quantitatively related to the frequency of tick attachment and the probability of tick infection[352] so that these parameters afford a focus for control measures.

In the Middle East sporadic cases are recognized usually among shepherds or those living in close relationship to sheep.[331–333] One patient lived near a cattle market, which is particularly significant in light of the circulation of tick-borne viruses in trade animals (see epidemiology of Nairobi sheep disease and Dugbe below).

Medical personnel are at some risk of secondary infection and it comes as no surprise that parenteral or heavy contact exposure to blood is dangerous.[353] However, one of the most striking aspects of Crimean-Congo hemorrhagic fever epidemiology is the case that disseminates widely to family or to hospital personnel (Figure 21–5). These incidents have been reported from the Soviet Union,[354] Yugoslavia,[330] the Middle East,[331, 333] and South Africa[334, 335] and follow a similar pattern. A severely infected patient presents to the hospital with florid hemorrhage. Medical staff attend with no precautions and may not even suspect the diagnosis, but may be involved in surgery or resuscitation of the patient. Then, three to seven days later, medical personnel and close family members begin to develop severe hemorrhagic fever, usually with a high mortality rate. There may also be tertiary cases in their family members.

Disease Syndromes

The clinical picture of Crimean-Congo hemorrhagic fever infection in the Soviet Union has been described in detail.[319, 354–358] The incubation period is typically three to six days in nosocomially acquired cases, whereas the estimated period based on recall of

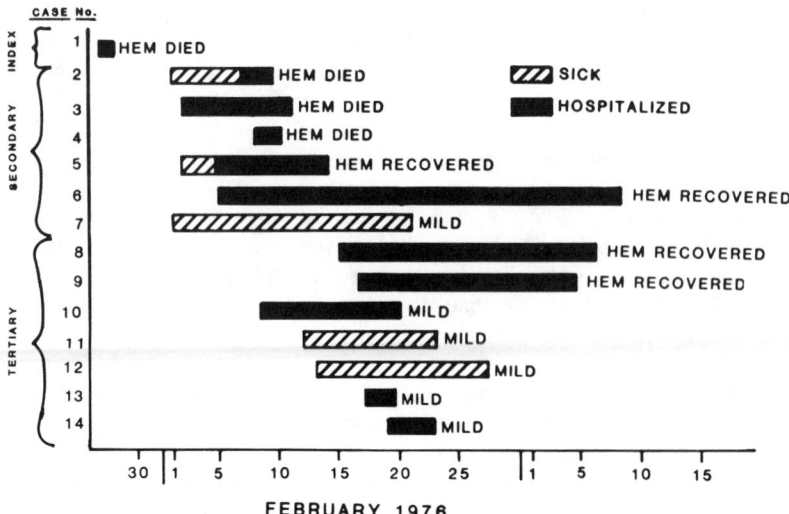

Figure 21–5. Nosocomial spread of Crimean-Congo hemorrhagic fever.[331] The index case, a shepherd, entered a Rawalpindi, Pakistan, hospital and underwent laparotomy for a presumed bleeding peptic ulcer. Six secondary cases occurred, including the admitting physician and two surgeons; five were hemorrhagic and three were fatal. Five tertiary cases were identified among hospital staff and two among family contacts. These cases tended to be milder and only two were hemorrhagic. This is typical of the devastating pattern seen with the rare hemorrhagic fever patient who forms a focus for nosocomial dissemination. (Adapted from Burney MI, Ghafoor A, Saleem M, et al: Nosocomial outbreaks of viral hemorrhagic fever caused by Crimean hemorrhagic fever–Congo virus in Pakistan, January 1976. *Am J Trop Hyg* 1980; 29:941–947.)

tick contact is three to 12 days. An abrupt onset is seen in virtually all cases with fever, myalgia, weakness, headache, and nausea often accompanied by vomiting, epigastric pain, drowsiness, and chills. During this initial phase lasting two to three days the pulse is normal in spite of the continuous 38 to 40°C temperature. There is hyperemia, most notable on the face, mucous membranes, and upper part of the body, often accompanied by mild hypotension. In one third to two thirds of patients there is a temporary remission of the fever for several hours before entering the second phase of the disease. This period, which is associated with the full development of hemorrhagic manifestations, usually lasts three to four days but may extend for eight to ten days. Thirst is severe, as are headache and myalgia (particularly lumbar pain). Epigastric pain, tenderness to abdominal palpation, and continued vomiting are frequent and usually accompanied by constipation or occasionally diarrhea. Most cases will be apathetic or obtunded, with halting speech; dizziness and mild meningeal signs are common. More severe cases will be delirious or comatose, but focal neurologic findings are rare.

Hemorrhage is found during this stage in most diagnosed cases; mild cases may have no bleeding manifestations and occasionally neurologic disease may dominate the presentation. Petechiae are distributed over the chest, abdomen, or inframammary area and epistaxis is also common. Spreading cutaneous ecchymoses, profuse bleeding from puncture sites, menometrorrhagia, hematemesis, melena, hematuria, and other more severe hemorrhagic manifestations signal the gravely affected patients, as does marked neurologic involvement. Bradycardia may be more intense in the second phase of illness, or tachycardia may supervene, particularly in some cases with severe hemorrhage or secondary infections. Declining blood pressure may lead to shock and death in circulatory collapse. The cardiovascular decompensation may be partially due

to blood loss; however, evidence of changes in vascular permeability and clinical evidence of myocardial depression suggest other factors are of major importance.

Additional clinical findings include (1) hepatomegaly (2–4 cm) and occasionally splenomegaly in severe cases; (2) mild tachypnea and scattered rales, as a part of the disease process or related to aspiration of bloody sputum or secondary infection; (3) a nonhemorrhagic rash may occasionally appear on the face or trunk and enanthems have been mentioned.

Survivors finally pass into a phase of recovery. Fever terminates by lysis, hemorrhages (except perhaps epistaxis) cease, the GI tract rapidly normalizes, and vascular phenomena (hyperemia, bradycardia, lability of the pulse, hypotension) resolve over a week or two. Patients may experience transient hair loss and in the absence of any specific findings they often complain of persistent fatigue, dizziness, and other symptoms for several weeks. Signs and symptoms suggestive of residual peripheral neuropathy may be noted.[359]

Clinical laboratory data are quite helpful in the diagnosis. Leukopenia is usually present from the beginning and often reaches a nadir below 2000 before normalizing with defervescence. Initial differential counts may show a normal percentage of neutrophils with a marked left shift, but later the neutropenia is even more marked than the lymphopenia. Occasional patients present with an early polymorphonuclear leukocytosis and this seems to be a bad prognostic sign.[360] Thrombocytopenia is usually present early and reaches a nadir of 30,000 to 60,000 per microliter during the period of severest disease. The hemoglobin and erythrocyte count are initially normal or somewhat elevated, but then begin to fall, reaching values less than half-normal in severe cases with extensive hemorrhage. Convalescence is accompanied by a marked reticulocytosis and relatively rapid normalization of the erythron. Serum albumin can be increased, but usually falls. Serum transaminases are modestly elevated, but jaundice occurs in less than 10% of cases.[361] Proteinuria and mild microscopic hematuria are the rule and leukocytes or hyaline casts are also common urinary findings. Azotemia and urine flow reflect the circulatory disturbance and increases of blood urea are not usually severe.

No systematic surveys of the coagulation system are available. Prothrombin time, activated partial thromboplastin time (APTT), fibrinogen, and fibrin split products had often been reported as abnormal,[331–333, 338, 362] but clear documentation of DIC as an important disease mechanism was lacking until the accumulated data from 15 fatal and 35 nonfatal cases were reported from South Africa.[360] Prothrombin time, APTT, thrombin time, fibrinogen, and fibrinogen degradation products are all markedly abnormal early in the course of severe Crimean-Congo hemorrhagic fever. Indeed, during the first five days of disease, occurrence of thrombocytopenia ($\leq$20,000/mL), prolonged APTT ($\geq$60 s), hypofibrinogenemia ($\leq$110mg/dL), or modest elevations of asparatate transferase (AST) ($\geq$200U/L) each predicted a 90% mortality.

The diverse mortality rates reported in the Soviet Union (9% to 40%) may reflect true geographic variation or differences in case ascertainment.[318, 319, 354] Nosocomial outbreaks seem to be more lethal than sporadic tick-borne disease. It does seem clear, though, that mild undiagnosed human infections occur; this rate has been estimated to be five infections per hemorrhagic fever case in the Rostov region of the Soviet Union.[352]

Human Crimean-Congo hemorrhagic fever cases reported from the Middle East have evidenced the full-blown hemorrhagic fever syndrome (Dubai,[333] Pakistan,[331] Iraq[332]), often with extensive nosocomial secondary and even tertiary spread. Serologic evidence of infection, although not entirely definitive, occurs in many people in the region with no history suggestive of disease.[349, 363, 364] Clinical and laboratory findings in general resembled those reported from the Soviet Union, except for the high prevalence of severe liver involvement, accompanied by clotting derangements, in one series.[332]

Several human infections in Africa have resembled the typical Bunyaviridae-induced fever[318, 335] (see Table 21–9), but these were found largely as the result of outpatient surveys of patients with undifferentiated febrile illness. In contrast, the recognized human infections in South Africa often presented with florid hemorrhagic fever and a mortality of 30% (15/50).[273, 334, 338, 340] Mild and severe cases were observed in a cattle-associated[351] and a nosocomial[355] outbreak; about 1.5% of healthy farmers were found to be seropositive, although none of 98 veterinarians tested had antibodies.[365]

Seven laboratory infections[8, 318, 335] from Africa failed to conform to the hemorrhagic fever syndrome. One of these patients appeared to be recovering from a febrile illness but three days later developed abdominal pain and hemetamesis. When he died the next day, autopsy showed only multiple gastric ulcers with none of the stigmata of Crimean-Congo hemorrhagic fever. Although there are no available series of Soviet laboratory infections, severe and even fatal cases have occurred.[353, 366]

Differential Diagnosis

Severe disease resembles other viral hemorrhagic fevers. Crimean-Congo hemorrhagic fever may have more flagrant hemorrhagic manifestations on the average, and performance of laparotomy for intractable GI bleeding is an occasional and potentially lethal mistake for the surprised surgeon. In the Soviet Union, sandfly fevers and influenza are often mentioned in the differential diagnosis of the early stages of disease; mycotoxicoses, leptospirosis, Omsk hemorrhagic fever, and hemorrhagic fever with renal syndrome are considerations with full-blown disease. In Africa tick typhus is a particularly important consideration.

Pathology

Lesions in fatal cases are not pathognomonic.[319, 322, 367–370] Congestion, edema, focal hemorrhage, and focal necrosis are present in virtually all organs examined and usually with little inflammatory cell reaction unless secondary infection occurs. As with most viral hemorrhagic fevers, focal hepatic necrosis and the formation of Councilman bodies are common, but severe liver destruction sufficient to suggest hepatic insufficiency is unusual.[360, 361] The presence of myocardial necrosis and damage to the conduction system is particularly relevant to patient management. Focal necroses and hemorrhages in the brain were often accompanied by cerebral edema, leading even to brainstem herniation.[367, 369] Individual neuronal necrosis is also seen. Foci of tubular necrosis are described in the kidney. Lymphoid depletion also occurs. Fluorescent antigen tracing[368] showed viral antigen to be most prominent in foci of hepatic necrosis and scattered macrophagelike cells in many organs. Lesser involvement of brain and kidney were reported and endothelial involvement was minimal. If these results are substantiated, it would suggest that vascular lesions may be triggered indirectly through viral effects on macrophages.

Virologic Diagnosis

Virus isolation is readily achieved from blood and the most widely used system is the intracranially inoculated suckling mouse. Mice typically die in four to eight days with paralytic disease and the etiology may be confirmed by CF or fluorescent antibody testing of brains. Virus titers tended to be highest during the first three days of illness and declined subsequently. Isolations were obtained from 85% of samples taken in the first week of disease but virus was present in four of ten samples taken between days 8 and 12. The virus is relatively labile; however, in the Rostov epidemic isolates were obtained from plasma, heparinized blood, or clotted blood stored at 4°C for up to a week.

Results from the Pakistani outbreak suggested that cell cultures may also be useful; four of the five early sera tested resulted in mild cytopathic effect (CPE) and viral antigen detectable by fluorescence when inoculated into Vero cells.[331] Virus inoculation attempts on specimens from 26 acutely ill patients seen in South Africa employed both suckling mouse intracerebral inoculation and inoculation onto monolayers of CER and/or Vero E6 cells, and yielded 20 isolations from suckling mouse inoculations, but only 11 isolations from cell culture, indicating that suckling mouse inoculation is probably the most sensitive isolation system available. Although cell cultures were less sensitive, they produced diagnostic results much more rapidly (mean time 7.7 days for suckling mice vs 3.3 days for cell cultures).[371] Several cell cultures[323, 325, 372–374] have been found susceptible and develop intracellular antigen and modest (10^4–10^7 TCID$_{50}$[50% tissue culture infectious dose]/mL) infectivity titers: primary hamster kidney, BHK 21, pig embryo kidney, primary green monkey kidney,

CV-1, LLC-MK2, SW-13, and CER cells. Serial passage in CV-1 cells resulted in a substrain capable of causing CPE and producing plaques under agar. Plaques under agar occur with some virus strains using LLC-MK2, Vero, and primary green monkey kidney cells. SW-13 cells are the only cell line that regularly produces plaques under agar with several virus strains and seems uniquely suited for neutralization tests.[374]

Sensitive antigen-detection ELISAs have been developed[375–377] and in one series detected infection in nine of 11 fatal and nine of 17 nonfatal cases.[377] The ability to identify by patients with the highest risk of dissemination and in the greatest need of treatment should be valuable. Antigen-capture ELISA has also been successful in detection of infected ticks,[376] which has obvious application for evaluating risks to persons finding attached ticks or for ecological studies.

Sera from convalescent human cases contain antibodies detectable in agar gel precipitin and CF tests by one to 15 days after onset of illness. After 6 months the percentage reacting and titers begin to decline and after a year only about half will be positive. Antibodies persist longer in severe cases than in mild ones.[378, 379] It has been difficult to prepare a hemagglutinin, but in expert hands the HI test has also been useful.[324, 327, 349] The neutralization test has been plagued by nonspecific serum inhibitors of viral infectivity, both when performed in mice and with plaque techniques in cell culture.[325, 327, 380] Acetone-ether extraction of sera has apparently remedied that problem[324] and development of sensitive PRN tests using SW-13 cells[374] should lead to wider application in diagnosis, therapy, and seroepidemiology. If suckling mice are used as the indicator system for infectivity in a constant-serum, varying-virus test, titers tend to be relatively low, less than 10^3.[320, 324, 378, 381, 382] Serum dilution tests with mice, fluorescent foci, or plaques as indicators also have given low titers, on the order of 1:8 to 1:16.[325, 380, 382] Somewhat higher titers[373, 383] reported more recently are still low compared to other viral diseases and require more experience to evaluate.

Indirect immunofluorescence has also been used to determine antibody response[331, 333, 385] and was applied and found to be useful in diagnosis of acute cases in the Middle East.[331] The reverse passive hemagglutination test has been adapted with apparent success[386] as was the indirect hemagglutination test.[387]

As the variety of available tests suggests, none are entirely satisfactory. Routine diagnosis of cases is probably best accomplished with IFA or ELISA. IgM detection, as well as rising IgG titers, has been useful. Because of cross-reactions among nairoviruses, serosurveys are most plausible when multiple tests yield concordant results.[349, 388, 389]

Therapy and Prevention

The occurrence of viremia throughout the course of illness[329] and the improvement that follows appearance of serum antibodies[383] suggest that passive administration of virus-specific IgG would be effective therapy. Hyperimmune horse serum[381, 390] and 60 to 200 mL convalescent human plasma[329, 391] have failed to alter the clinical course of Soviet cases. The reported experience of a recent South African outbreak is instructive.[355, 362, 392, 393] These patients received 1 to 2 units of convalescent plasma known to have neutralizing antibody titers. Transient subjective improvement was noted after infusion on several occasions, but there is no clear

relationship to objective indices of cure nor to cessation of viremia. Interpretation was further compounded by administration of 18 × 10^6 units of interferon every second day for a week. Failure to suppress viremia and induce passive neutralizing antibody titers may reflect the relatively low and transient serum neutralization response (see above) that develops in convalescent donors.[383] The situation may resemble that seen in Lassa fever, in which poor neutralizing antibody levels require careful selection of convalescent plasma and administration of at least 10 mL/kg to show experimental efficacy.[384] In any case, prompt administration of convalescent plasma with the best neutralizing capacity available in volumes of at least 500 mL is a reasonable therapeutic approach in Crimean-Congo hemorrhagic fever.

Preclinical testing of ribavirin in mice and cell culture[394, 395] has shown the virus to be relatively sensitive in cell culture and infected mice. The administration of IV ribavirin to patients or oral prophylaxis of high-risk contacts is a reasonable avenue of therapy that merits systematic evaluation (see Chapter 26). The virus is also sensitive to the antiviral effects of interferon in vitro; although nothing is known of serum interferon levels in Crimean-Congo hemorrhagic fever patients, they presumably already have made an interferon response.

Supportive care of the hematologic abnormalities is particularly important. Blood loss may require transfusions and in fatal cases 30 to 40 units have been administered.[392] Aggressive replacement of coagulation factors and platelets has been advocated[392] and is a reasonable approach. If clear-cut laboratory evidence of DIC is present, heparin therapy should be considered. Patients should be adequately replaced with lost fluid and electrolytes but should not be overexpanded. Russian workers have advocated corticosteroids, anabolic hormones, rutin, ascorbic acid, calcium gluconate, and ε-aminocaproic acid in severe cases, but there are no controlled studies as to the value of these measures.[391] As with other hemorrhagic fevers, secondary infections are common and should be sought and aggressively treated. Pneumonia may be heralded by tachypnea, tachycardia, increasing fever, and even leukocytosis. Peritonitis, parotitis, epididymitis, and sepsis have also been described.[319, 369]

An experimental vaccine has been prepared by formalin inactivation of protamine-precipitated suckling mouse brain.[396–399] The vaccine was administered to approximately 3000 humans without serious adverse reactions. Most recipients developed CF and agar gel precipitin antibodies after three doses. Unfortunately, neutralizing antibody titers have been very low. There are no published data on efficacy. In Bulgaria an intravenous IgG prepared from hyperimmunized donors is thought to be highly effective.[399a]

Exposure to Crimean-Congo hemorrhagic fever can be minimized by several means. The danger from infected ticks cannot be overemphasized; isolation rates from *Hyalomma* ticks may approach 1%[334, 336, 341] and history of tick exposure is very common. Permethrin-impregnated clothing is highly effective in repelling and even killing all stages of ticks. Repellants such as DEET, while highly effective against mosquitos and sandflies, are less useful against ticks. Trousers tucked into boots and other dress measures may also be helpful. In infested regions, visual inspection for ticks on the body should be carried out frequently. If found they should be removed by gentle traction with blunt forceps or gloved hand.[400] Crushing the tick will contaminate the skin with infected materials and may create droplets (mucous membrane exposure) or small-particle aerosols (pulmonary infection). Other measures include acaracides applied to domestic animals, brush clearing, and intensive application of acaracides to frequently traveled paths.

Nairobi Sheep Disease Group

This virus, distributed over much of Africa, is maintained in nature by ixodid ticks. It is a major veterinary pathogen and produces a lethal gastroenteritis in affected sheep of all ages. Nairobi sheep disease virus and closely related or identical Ganjam virus have been isolated from sick humans in Uganda[87] and India,[401] and an appreciable antibody prevalence demonstrated. Nevertheless, doubts about the specificity of serologic tests for the virus prevent any definite conclusions about the direct impact of the virus on human health.[402]

The epizootiology in Kenya[403–408] is of interest for comparison with other tick-borne viruses. The tick *Rhipicephalus appendiculatus* was the sole vector implicated in endemic transmission of Nairobi sheep disease virus and about 1 in 500 to 1500 were infected. Surveys of wild game and rodents yielded no evidence of infection. Virtually all sheep raised within the geographic distribution of this tick had antibodies to the virus, yet there was no reported disease from these regions. In contrast, animals from other areas traversing these regions often developed clinical illness. This suggests that lambs born within endemic regions were protected from disease by maternal antibody, but nevertheless were asymptomatically infected. This type of phenomenon probably accounts for the high isolation rates of tick-borne viruses such as Dugbe, Bhanja, Crimean-Congo hemorrhagic fever, and Thogoto viruses from blood[409] and ticks[341, 410] taken from livestock being driven to market in Nigeria and Central Africa. In the laboratory *R appendiculatus* could be infected from viremic sheep and transmit virus to susceptible sheep. Furthermore, under certain conditions the ticks remained virus-infected throughout their development from larvae to nymphs to adults (even when fed on immune hosts) and could then pass the virus transovarially.

Additional quantitative studies are needed to define the frequency of these events and to evaluate whether infected lambs protected by passive antibody can in turn infect new ticks or whether the virus is exclusively maintained in the tick population by vertical transmission. *R appendiculatus* could maintain their infectivity for more than 2 years in the laboratory, providing additional evidence for their importance in maintaining natural endemicity of Nairobi sheep disease virus. Furthermore, the focal nature of the disease may well be accounted for by the relation between the virus and *R appendiculatus* ticks. For example, an outbreak in Kenya occurred outside the usual endemic area. Several tick species were excluded as vectors because of their feeding habits or the failure to transmit virus in the laboratory. The tick *Amblyomma variegatum* was implicated as a vector in these episodes, but it was not an efficient vector in the laboratory. More importantly, it did not transmit the virus transovarially, providing an explanation for the failure of the virus to establish itself in this new region but rather to be confined to the distribution of *R appendiculatus*.

Ganjam virus was isolated in India from ticks and from man[79] and shown to be closely related or identical to Nairobi sheep disease

virus.[411] This, plus the lack of demonstrated involvement of African wildlife in Nairobi sheep disease maintenance,[412] led to the suggestion that the virus may have been brought to tropical Africa over busy trade routes from India when sheep and goats were initially imported hundreds of years ago.[411]

Dugbe virus of the Nairobi sheep disease group appears to be widely distributed in tropical Africa and may be of some importance in causing human disease. Seven isolates, including one from a laboratory infection, have been made from febrile humans in the Central African Republic[8] and Nigeria.[78] One patient had a mild meningitis, and virus was obtained from CSF. A serosurvey in Nigeria failed to detect convincing evidence of human infection[413]; however, the serologic response in convalescent sera from proven cases has not been impressive.[8, 78]

The virus has been frequently isolated from ticks on market cattle (eg, 45 isolates from 10,085 [0.45%] *A varigatum* in Senegal) and was obtained from about 10% of cattle blood samples at Dugbe abattoir, Ibadan, Nigeria. A single isolate has been made from a Nigerian giant rat, *Cricetomys gambiensus*.

Other Members of the *Nairovirus* Genus

None of the other nairoviruses (see Table 21–5) have been associated with disease in man and only Bandia virus (Qalyub group) is implicated in human infection. Bandia virus was isolated from ticks and rodents in Senegal and 4.3% of humans resident in the area had CF antibodies to the virus.[87] Two of the groups are closely associated with birds, particularly sea birds: Hughes virus from argasid or soft ticks and Sakhalin virus from ixodid or hard ticks, but little is known of their natural history.[414]

BUNYAVIRIDAE, GENUS UNKNOWN

The viruses discussed in this section are thought to be *Bunyaviridae* based on morphologic or serologic evidence, but cannot be reliably classified into any of the five recognized genera, usually for lack of biochemical data rather than any indication of unique characteristics (see Table 21–6). The basis for attribution to the family is weakest in this group; for example, Thogoto virus was classified in this family in the first edition of this book and is now known to be an orthomyxovirus.

Nyando virus has been isolated from a febrile human in Central Africa[415] and there is serologic evidence of human infection in Uganda and Kenya.[76] Kasokero virus is an interesting isolate made from fruit-eating bats in Uganda; four laboratory infections, one rather serious, occurred under circumstances suggesting aerosol spread.[416] Wanowrie virus, a tick-borne agent originally isolated in Egypt, caused a fatal systemic illness with hemorrhage in Sri Lanka.[417] Antibodies to several others have been detected in human sera: Bakau (Bakau group, Malaysia[79]) Ketapang (Bakau group, Malaysia[79]) Trubanaman (Maputta group, Australia[179]); Witwatersrand (ungrouped, South Africa[79]); and Lone Star (ungrouped; United States[418]).

Bhanja Virus

Bhanja, a tick-borne virus, was originally isolated in India[419] but probably ranges across Russia into eastern and southern Europe. It has been isolated in West (Nigeria, Cameroon, Senegal),

Central (Central African Republic), and East (Somalia) Africa.[87] Antibody studies and virus isolation have associated Bhanja with domestic animals[341, 409, 410, 420–422] and with small mammals,[423] but its life cycle is far from understood.[424] Bhanja may be disseminated through its wide geographic range by migratory birds, although they do not appear to participate in its amplification by producing a viremia sufficient to infect ticks.[425] In humans, low-titered antibodies to Bhanja have been detected in Italy[421] and the Central African Republic,[342] and there is convincing serologic evidence for foci of infection in Yugoslavia.[153] Two mild (presumably aerosol) laboratory infections have been reported.[426, 427] One case of naturally acquired meningoencephalitis was detected during serologic screening of suspected tick-borne encephalitis cases in Yugoslavia.[428]

Tataguine Virus

Tataguine virus was isolated from mosquitoes in Senegal and subsequently 20 (57%) of 35 human residents of the area were found to have antibody to the virus.[429] Although little is known about its ecology, it appears to be an important human pathogen in Africa. Ten infections were identified in the Central African Republic, all associated with a mild febrile illness and generalized rash.[8] Tataguine virus was the most frequently isolated *Bunyaviridae* in a Nigerian study[78] (see Table 21–8), where it was also associated with an acute undifferentiated febrile syndrome.

PATHOGENESIS AND IMMUNOLOGY OF *BUNYAVIRIDAE* INFECTIONS

Most infections are thought to be initiated by the bite of an infected arthropod and thus virus is either inoculated subcutaneously during probing or into a capillary during feeding. The aerosol infections with Rift Valley fever virus, Crimean-Congo hemorrhagic fever virus, or occasional laboratory infections with others of the family do not result in pneumonic disease, but rather a typical sytemic disease course. Viremia is usually brief and corresponds to the duration of acute illness. Although small quantities of virus may be isolated from lymphoid organs in convalescence, true persistence has not been a recognized feature of *Bunyaviridae* infections of vertebrates. Cell-mediated immunity has never been adequately addressed, but in general the antibody response closely follows cessation of viremia and is thought to be responsible for recovery.

Some data on the pathogenesis of Rift Valley fever and Crimean-Congo hemorrhagic fever infection of humans were discussed in the appropriate sections above. Several animal models of *Bunyaviridae* infections may also help understand the human diseases. In general these experimental systems tend to identify cell-virus (particularly macrophage-virus) interactions and interferon as important determinants of natural resistance and implicate the antibody response as critical in recovery.

Although human infection with California group viruses such as La Crosse virus is a common occurrence, encephalitis is relatively rare and even then is usually a childhood phenomenon. California virus infection in mice[430] also shows a marked age-dependence. Mice under 2 weeks of age inoculated subcutaneously experience a generalized infection of muscle, fat, and endothelial cells in association with viremia. Brain vascular structures contain fluorescent antigen which is subsequently detected in adjacent neurons and spreads throughout the CNS leading to death from encephalitis. Adult mice inoculated by a peripheral route have little or no evidence of viral replication, but if virus is introduced directly into the CNS, virus proliferates in neurons and encephalitis develops. Thus, in this model, age-related resistance develops because peripheral structures, particularly vascular endothelium, do not replicate virus to high titer. La Crosse virus has been shown to replicate in embryonic human skin and muscle explants, but age-dependence has never been studied. The related Tahyna virus is not associated with human encephalitis, and also grows to much lower titer in these explants.[330, 431]

Studies of *Phlebovirus*-infected rodents have detected important host genetic influences in several systems including Rift Valley fever virus with *Rattus norvegicus* or gerbils[432] and Punta Toro virus with *Mus musculus*.[433] In the Rift Valley fever virus–infected rat, host genotype determines whether mild infection, fulminant liver necrosis, or necrotizing encephalitis is the outcome.[434] These disease patterns appear to resemble those seen in human infection, whatever the respective mechanisms. Resistance to fulminant infection in the rat is determined by a single dominant gene whose presence results in a millionfold increase in resistance. This gene appears to influence an early step in the virus-host interaction, since virus titers in resistant animals are significantly lower than those in susceptible rats as early as 16 hours postinfection.[435] The gene is expressed in cultured peritoneal macrophages and is responsible for a marked increase in the sensitivity of these cells to the antiviral action of interferon.

When resistant rats are immunosuppressed with cyclophosphamide, early postinfection events are unaltered, but viral replication proceeds and they eventually die. Since unmanipulated resistant animals have detectable serum neutralizing antibody the day after viremia disappears, the humoral immune response is a candidate for the mechanism of recovery. Furthermore, injection of quantities of convalescent serum that mimicked the antibody titers observed after infection protected immunosuppressed rats, further supporting a dominant role for serum antibody in protection and recovery from Rift Valley fever infections.[435] Studies in Rift Valley fever-infected macaques have shown similar patterns.[303–305] Viremia is brusque and rapidly terminated coincidental with the appearance of serum neutralizing antibody. Small quantities of passive antiserum (0.025 mL/kg) protect against viremia. Pretreatment with interferon (5×10^3–5×10^4 µm/kg) suppresses viremia and liver damage. About 20% of the macaques develop lethal hemorrhagic fever and these animals have a significantly delayed serum interferon response. In two of three fatally infected animals, subsequent interferon levels were also abnormally low.

Virtually no attention has been paid to cellular immunity in the family *Bunyaviridae*. The inconstant expression of cell surface antigen[24] in *Phlebovirus* infections suggests that cytolytic T cells may have very specific and perhaps limited roles to play, although they have been detected in Bunyamwera[436] and Rift Valley fever[437] infections of mice.

The pathogenesis of *Bunyaviridae* infections of invertebrate vectors must also be considered. Dissection and organ virus titration, immunohistochemistry, and electron microscopy can be used to trace viral replication after ingestion or intrathoracic inoculation of infective suspensions. No specific arthropod immune responses are known; however, phagocytic cells are present and mosquito cells in vitro produce a viral inhibitor active against viruses of the family **Togaviridae.** In vitro interactions of **Bunyaviridae** with mosquito[432, 438, 439] and sandfly cells appear to be largely noncytopathic, which is in keeping with their general lack of adverse effects on the chronically infected arthropod. In the case of Bunyamwera virus, these chronically infected cells express large quantities of S but only traces of L or M RNA.[440]

An infective blood meal enters the midgut of the mosquito, but the virus must reach the salivary glands before the arthropod becomes infective and the gonads before vertical transmission can occur. For example, in *Aedes triseriatus* mosquitoes, La Crosse virus infects midgut cells by day 7 postingestion and then spreads to other organs, probably via the hemolymph. The role of the M RNA segment in this process was discussed above under Replication, Structure, and Genetics. Salivary gland antigen is detectable by 14 days, coincident with the onset of ability to transmit virus.[441] In transovarially infected *Ae triseriatus*, La Crosse antigen was widely distributed in larval and pupal organs throughout the process of metamorphosis with no apparent interference with arthropod development. Salivary glands, ovaries, and testes were involved at the time of hatching.[443] Detailed studies of ovarian infection in a related California group laboratory model (San Angelo virus in *Ae albopictus*[443]) suggested that the ova themselves are not involved at the time adults emerge. Surrounding ovarian cells, however, contained antigen. After blood meal ingestion and subsequent ovarian development, extensive infection of follicles and ova occurred. Interestingly, only about one half of the follicles in some ovaries were antigen-positive, which is in accord with variations in rates of transovarial transmission in this virus-host combination.

Similar studies have been performed with colonized Egyptian *Culex pipiens* mosquitoes and Rift Valley fever virus. Under genetic influence some mosquitoes develop midgut infections which disseminate to the salivary glands to permit transmission.[444] The critical event may well be infection of the intussusucepted foregut at the juncture with the midgut.[445] Subsequent virus growth in fat bodies, salivary glands, and nervous tissue occurs.[446]

VIROLOGIC DIAGNOSIS

Virus Isolation

It is, perhaps, no surprise that a taxon originally united by serology would yield ambiguous serologic results in the diagnostic arena. For this reason the mainstay of diagnosis remains virus isolation from serum or, occasionally, CSF. Since most members of the family were originally isolated by intracranial inoculation of suckling mice, it follows that this is widely regarded as the host system of choice. However, there are few systematic comparisons of isolation systems from clinical samples, so it is difficult to judge the validity of this opinion. For example, suckling mouse inoculation proved more sensitive than cell culture in isolating Crimean-Congo hemorrhagic fever virus from acutely ill patients, but the longer time required made the results of lesser value in terms of patient management.[371] Indeed, use of Vero cell cultures during ecological studies of Panamanian phleboviruses allowed isolation

of new viruses that were not pathogenic for suckling mice.[4] The prototype *Phlebovirus*, the sandfly Sicilian virus, was only adapted to suckling mice with difficulty.[199] Thus, a reasonable addition to suckling mice would be sensitive cell culture systems. Vero, LLC-MK2, BHK-21, HeLa, SW-13, mosquito cells, and others have been used.[79, 242, 447–451] During a recent Rift Valley fever epidemic, AP61 mosquito cells were found to be more sensitive than suckling mice for isolation of virus from clinical samples.[242] Cytopathic effect is common, but Crimean-Congo hemorrhagic fever and Naples sandfly fever[452] viruses are notable exceptions, as are most insect cell infections. Immunologic antigen detection in infected cells would be a valuable adjunct. Inoculation of living mosquitoes was no more sensitive than suckling mice in detecting laboratory strains of Guaroa, Bunyamwera, and Germiston viruses.[453] Several of the viruses are capable of killing adult mice or hamsters and this can be of differential diagnostic value.

Once a virus is isolated, it is usually placed within one of the serogroups using antisera derived by sequential immunization of mice with several members of the group. Subsequently, exhaustive serologic testing by conventional means using antisera to individual viruses is necessary to establish identity with a known member of the group or to identify so-called new viruses and place them in their taxonomic pew. The problem is magnified by the possibility of segment interchange in viral evolution. One approach was presented when the identity between classic Rift Valley fever virus strains and West African isolates previously designated as Zinga virus was established.[240] In addition to applying conventional serologic tests, specific monoclonal antibodies demonstrated that the two known gene products of the M RNA segment (G1 and G2) and the major protein coded by the S RNA segment (N) were indistinguishable from those of Rift Valley fever virus. Thus, diagnostic systems using nucleic acid or monoclonal antibody probes to identify important contributions of genetic information from each of the three RNA segments and possibly the presence of specific genes related to virulence may eventually be developed.

Serology

In most cases **Bunyaviridae** react in HI, N, CF, IFA, and ELISA antibody tests. There is reasonable evidence to associate the hemagglutinin and the neutralizing target(s) with one or both of the virion surface glycoproteins. Neutralization has usually been quantitated by the ability of a constant volume of serum to block infectivity of decimal dilutions of virus for intracranially inoculated suckling mice (MPN test). The neutralization of a fixed number of virus plaques in cell culture by serial dilutions of sera (PRN test) is replacing the MPN. CF tests usually employ sucrose acetone extracts of infected suckling mouse organs[11] in which the nucleocapsid protein is thought to be the major antigenic component.

With most of the viruses there is little experience in testing human sera taken at intervals after proven virus infection to define the magnitude of reactivity, duration of response, and cross-reactivity with other viruses, a particular problem in interpreting serosurveys. The available human data supplemented with analysis of immunized or hyperimmunized laboratory animals suggest the following generalizations: (1) Neutralizing antibodies for bunyaviruses and phleboviruses have been found to persist for years, probably for a lifetime. Reported neutralizing antibody responses

Table 21–17
Human Serologic Response to Germiston Virus Infection*

Days of Illness	Case 1						Case 2					
	Germiston			Bunyamwera			Germiston			Bunyamwera		
	HI	CF	MPN	HI	CF	MPN	HI	CF	MPN	HI	CF	MPN
0	0†	0†	0†	0	0	0	0	0	0	0	0	3.5
7	—	—	—	—	—	—	40	8	1.8	40	16	4.0
22–24	160	8	2.4	0	0	0	1280	8	5.1	2560	32	4.8
210	80	0	3.2	0	0	0	—	—	—	—	—	—

HI = hemagglutination inhibition; CF = complement fixation; MPN = mouse protection neutralization.
Adapted from Kokernot et al.[61] Both patients had Germiston infections proven by virus isolation from acute phase sera. Case 2 was infected with Bunyamwera 3 years before laboratory infection with Germiston virus. Note that case 1 had a monotypic antibody response to the infecting virus. Case 2 had broadly reactive antibody with Bunyamwera titers similar to or higher than Germiston antibody titers.
†Titer less than 10 (HI), 8 (CF), or 1.7 (MPN).

following *Nairovirus* infection are less impressive in magnitude and of shorter duration. Neutralizing antibodies have the greatest specificity, in general, but when hypothesized reassortant viruses are concerned this may not be true. (2) HI antibodies to bunyaviruses are fairly long-lasting and may be broadly reactive or relatively specific in different virus groups. *Phlebovirus* HI antibodies also persist for years but they are often cross-reactive. (3) CF antibodies within the *Bunyavirus* and *Nairovirus* genera are fairly group-specific and within the group may display virus selectivity. *Phlebovirus* CF responses tend to be virus-specific, with a few notable exceptions.

The problem arising from cross-reactivity within the family can sometimes be overcome by testing sera against a battery of viruses known to be active locally. However, even then, multiple infections with related agents may be misleading. The "original antigenic sin" phenomenon first described for influenza virus also applies to humans infected with Bunyamwera group viruses[61] (Table 21–17), deer infected with California group viruses,[454] and perhaps other situations.

The need for more reliable serologic tests for diagnosis and epidemiologic assessment of disease impact is acute. Simple radioisotope or enzyme immunoassay procedures using solid phase adsorption of infected cell lysates or purified virions may be useful in certain situations but are unlikely to resolve these problems since potentially all virion antigens would be available in a sensitive detection system. Testing with purified virion polypeptides and hyperimmune mouse sera demonstrated extensive cross-reactivity, although there was discrimination.[455] This may be overcome in the future by using specific virion proteins selectively trapped by monoclonal antibodies or other approaches.

The serology of the California group viruses in North America, Rift Valley fever, and other phleboviruses (see Table 21–13), and Crimean-Congo hemorrhagic fever[388, 389] viruses are discussed above. References to human infections, serologic cross-reactions, or to reviews[1, 2, 12, 14, 15, 79, 185, 389, 456] should be consulted for details of other virus groups.

Rapid Methods

Rapid diagnostic systems are replacing conventional techniques for several of the most important diseases. IgM-capture ELISA now is the method of choice for La Crosse encephalitis, Rift Valley fever retinitis or encephalitis, and hantavirus infections. It is also exceedingly useful for early convalescent diagnosis of Rift Valley fever, Sicilian or Naples sandfly fever, and Crimean-Congo hemorrhagic fever. Antigen can be detected by ELISA in acute sera from patients with Rift Valley fever, Sicilian sandfly fever, or Crimean-Congo hemorrhagic fever with sufficient frequency to make the tests useful clinical adjuncts. La Crosse, Rift Valley fever, and Crimean-Congo hemorrhagic fever viruses can also be found by ELISA in their natural arthropod vectors with high efficiency. Nucleic acid hybridization has been successfully adapted to acute human Rift Valley fever sera and other samples, indicating another area of development for diagnostic procedures.

PREVENTION

Most human infections with **Bunyaviridae** result when man enters the ecologic zone where these esentially zoonotic infections are being transmitted, and is bitten by an infected vector. Under certain circumstances epidemics also occur. Ecological control is usually impractical and prophylactic vaccines have not usually been developed because of the inadequate technical base, multiple regionally distinctive viruses, and insufficient economic motivation. There are exceptions. Two of the diverse array of viral diseases in this group stand out as significant global problems: Rift Valley fever and Crimean-Congo hemorrhagic fever. Rift Valley fever virus is distributed throughout sub-Saharan Africa, has demonstrated its potential for extension to receptive zones, causes extensive and occasionally grave human disease, and has serious economic impact on domestic livestock. Although they have significant limitations, successful animal vaccines exist, can control the economic impact of epidemics, and can limit spread to man.[239, 254] Useful investigational human vaccines have been developed[308, 311] and are indicated for protection of high-risk persons.

Crimean-Congo hemorrhagic fever virus is poorly understood but appears to be widely distributed in Europe, Asia, and Africa. It has caused sporadic cases and epidemics of hemorrhagic fever as well as lethal nosocomial transmission. Vaccines, therapy with the antiviral drug ribavirin, or convalescent plasma are under study, but measures to prevent tick bite are the only proven prophylactic maneuvers available.

At times the particular habits of the vector can be exploited to protect humans (see above in discussions of sandfly fever, Oropouche, La Crosse, and group C viruses). Repellants are effective if applied in sufficient concentration and frequency.

It should be borne in mind that nonfatal laboratory infections have been reported with several ***Bunyaviridae*** (Bunyamwera, Germiston, Apeu, group C, Oropouche, Keystone, Catu, Punta Toro, Dugbe, Nairobi sheep disease, Kasokero viruses), often in a setting suggesting aerosol transmission. Varying degrees of microbiologic containment are recommended for working with members of the group.[457] Rift Valley fever virus is highly infectious by aerosol, has caused numerous laboratory infections, and is a potential threat to the livestock industry; it should be manipulated by vaccinated personnel with stringent precautions to prevent escape into the environment. Crimean-Congo hemorrhagic fever virus has been studied in several laboratories with minimal containment, but laboratory workers have sustained infections,[8, 335] including fatalities.[353] Most Crimean-Congo hemorrhagic fever virus strains are now manipulated in BL-4 containment or under BL-3 conditions with particular care.

BIBLIOGRAPHIC EPILOGUE

This numerous and diverse family of viruses poses interesting and important problems in the fields of general virology, evolution, ecology, and biomedical science, but attempts to understand the biology of individual viruses or the entire taxon are hampered by the difficulty of access to the literature. Anyone interested in a particular virus should initially consult the *International Catalog of Arboviruses Including Certain Other Viruses of Vertebrates*.[79] Informal communications published through the auspices of the Centers for Disease Control, Ft Collins, Colorado, communicate results of recent work in the arbovirus field.[458] In addition to the summary of the Rockefeller Foundation work focused on tropical settings,[456] there are several available symposia pertinent to arctic and temperate zones.[459–461] Useful symposia or reviews exist for the California group,[462] Rift Valley fever,[232, 238, 246a, 246b, 463, 464] and Crimean-Congo hemorrhagic fever.[318, 319, 326, 327, 465] Several series of investigations cited above for each virus were actually carried out on a regional basis and could be cross-indexed by area rather than by virus. Australia,[171, 179]; the Americas: Canada,[162, 163] the United States,[44, 164, 169, 418] Brazil,[3, 58, 86–89, 175, 180, 197, 466] Panama,[4, 53, 54, 90, 97, 182, 196, 466] Suriname,[95, 96, 314, 468] Trinidad,[92, 96, 140] and other Latin America countries[93, 94, 182, 186]; Africa[75]: Egypt,[207, 209, 282, 347, 469] Angola,[71] Botswana,[72] Central African Republic,[8, 261, 341, 342] Kenya,[63, 76, 81, 173, 236, 283, 406, 407, 470] Nigeria,[78, 80, 265, 284, 409, 410, 423] South Africa,[61, 77, 82, 262, 269, 334, 471, 472] and Uganda[62, 64, 69, 259, 260, 320, 416]; Europe[393]: Czechoslovakia,[66, 145, 315] France,[156] Greece,[206, 344] Italy,[155, 183, 192, 421] Norway,[316] Portugal,[346] S Union,[157, 158, 212, 319] and Yugoslavia[7, 153, 217, 330, 422, 428]; Asia: India,[190, 208, 348, 401, 419] Iran,[205, 207, 349] Sri Lanka,[160, 417] and others.[161, 191, 181, 188, 204, 211, 311]

REFERENCES

1. Bishop DHL, Calisher CH, Casals J, et al: Bunyaviridae, in Melnick JL (ed): *Intervirology*. Basel, Karger, 1980, vol 14, pp 125–143.
2. Classification and nomenclature of viruses, in Melnick JL (ed): *Intervirology. Fourth Report of the International Committee on Taxonomy of Viruses*, Basel, Karger, 1982, vol 17, pp 115–118.
3. Calisher CH, Coimbra TLM, Lopes O DeS, et al: Identification of New Guama and group C serogroup Bunyaviruses and an ungrouped virus from Southern Brazil. *Am J Trop Med Hyg* 1983; 32:424–431.
4. Tesh RB, Chaniotis BN, Peralta PH, et al: Ecology of viruses isolated from Panamanian phlebotomine sandflies. *Am J Trop Med Hyg* 1974; 23:258–269.
5. El Mekki AA, Nieuwenhuysen P, van der Groen G, et al: Characterization of some ungrouped viruses. *Trans R Soc Trop Med Hyg* 1981; 75:799–806.
6. Tesh RB: Multiplication of phlebotomus fever group arboviruses in mosquitoes after intrathoracic inoculation. *J Med Entomol* 1975; 12:1–4.
7. Guelmino DJ, Jevtic M: An epidemiological and hematological study of sandfly fever in Serbia. *Acta Trop* 1955; 12:179–182.
8. Georges AJ, Saluzzo JF, Gonzalez JP, et al: Arboviruses from Central African Republic: Incidence, diagnosis in human pathology. *Med Trop* 1980; 40:561–568.
9. Centers for Disease Control: Annual Summary 1980: reported morbidity and mortality in the United States. *MMWR* 1981; 29.
10. Chambon L, Bres P, Chippaux Cl, et al: Rôle des arbovirus dans l'étiologie des fièvres exanthématiques en Afrique Centrale. *Med Afrique Noire* 1969; 2:185–188.
11. Clarke DH, Casals J: Techniques for hemagglutination and hemagglutination-inhibition with arthropod-borne viruses. *Am J Trop Med Hyg* 1958; 7:561–573.
12. Casals J: New developments in the classification of arthropod-borne animal viruses. *Ann Microbiol* 1963; 11:13.
13. Murphy FA, Harrison AK, Whitfield SC: Bunyaviridae: Morphologic and morphogenetic similarities of Bunyamwera serologic supergroup viruses and several other arthropod-borne viruses. *Intervirology* 1973; 1:297–316.
14. Bishop DHL, Shope RE: Bunyaviridae, in Fraenkel-Conrat H, and Wagner RR (eds): *Comprehensive Virology*. New York, Plenum, 1979, vol 14, pp 1–156.
15. Calisher CH, Karabatsos N: Arbovirus serogroups: Definition and geographic distribution, in Monath TP (ed): *Epidemiology of Arthropod-borne Viral Diseases*. Boca Raton, Fla, CRC Press, 1988, vol l, pp 19–57.
16. Smith JF, Pifat DY: Morphogenesis of sandfly fever viruses (Bunyaviridae family). *Virology* 1982; 121:61–81.
17. Bishop DHL: Ambisense RNA genomes of arenaviruses and phleboviruses, in Maramorosch K, Murphy FA, Shatkin AJ (eds): *Advances in Virus Research*. New York, Academic Press, 1986, vol 31, pp 1–51.
18. Bishop DHL: The infection and coding strategies of arenaviruses, phleboviruses and nairoviruses. *Rev Infect Dis* 1989; 11:S722–S729 .
19. Bishop DHL: Genetic potential of bunyaviruses, in Arber W, Falkow S, Henle W, et al (eds): *Current Topics in Microbiology and Immunology*. Berlin, Springer-Verlag, 1979, pp 1–33.
20. Korolev MB, Donets MA, Rubin SG, et al: Morphology and morphogenesis of Crimean hemorrhagic fever virus. *Arch Virol* 1976; 50:169–172.
21. Donets MA, Chumakov MP, Korolev MB, et al: Physicochemical characteristics, morphology and morphogenesis of virions of the causative agent of Crimean hemorrhagic fever. *Intervirology* 1977; 8:294–308.
22. Clerx JPM, Bishop DHL: Qalyub virus, a member of the newly proposed *Nairovirus* genus (Bunyaviridae). *Virology* 1981; 108:361–372.
23. von Bonsdorff C-H, Pettersson R: Surface structure of Uukuniemi virus. *J Virol* 1975; 16:1296–1307.
24. Anderson GW Jr, Smith JF: Immunoelectron microscopy of Rift Valley fever viral morphogenesis in primary rat hepatocytes. *Virology* 1987; 161:91–100.
25. Iroegbu CU, Pringle CR: Genetics of the Bunyamwera complex, in Bishop DHL, Compans RW (eds): *The Replication of Negative Strand Viruses. Developments in Cell Biology*. New York, Elsevier/North Holland, 1981, vol 7, pp 159–172.
26. Dalrymple JM, Peters CJ, Smith JF, et al: Antigenic components of Punta Toro virus, in Bishop DHL, Compans RW (eds): *The Replication of Negative Strand Viruses. Developments in Cell Biology*. New York, Elsevier/North Holland, 1981, vol 7, pp 167–172.
27. Gonzalez-Scarano F, Shope RE, Calisher CH, et al: Characterization of monoclonal antibodies against the G1 and N proteins of La Crosse and Tahyna, two California serogroup bunyaviruses. *Virology* 1982; 120:42–53.
28. Smith JF, Lanciotti RS, Ennis WH: Antigenic analysis of protective epitopes on Rift Valley fever virus surface glycoproteins.

Presented at the 1985 Annual Meeting of the American Society for Virology, University of New Mexico, Albuquerque, July 21–25, 1985.

29. Kingsford L, Hill DW: The effects of proteolytic enzymes on structure and function of La Crosse G1 and G2 glycoproteins, in Bishop DHL, Compans RW (eds): *The Replication of Negative Strand Viruses. Developments in Cell Biology.* New York, Elsevier/North Holland, 1981, vol 7, pp 111–116.

30. Kingsford L, Ishizawa LD, Hill DW: Biological activities of monoclonal antibodies reactive with antigenic sites mapped on the G1 glycoprotein of La Crosse virus. *Virology* 1983; 129:443–455.

31. Clerx-van Haaster CM, Clerx JPM, Ushijima H, et al: The 3′ terminal RNA sequences of bunyaviruses and nairoviruses (Bunyaviridae): Evidence of end sequence generic differences within the virus family. *J Gen Virol* 1982; 61:289–292.

32. Parker MD, Hewlett MJ: The 3′-terminal sequences of Uukuniemi and Inkoo virus RNA genome segments, in Bishop DHL, Compans RW (eds): *The Replication of Negative Strand Viruses. Developments in Cell Biology.* New York, Elsevier/North Holland, 1981, vol 7, pp 125–133.

33. Clerx-van Haaster CM, Akashi H, Auperin DD, et al: Nucleotide sequence analyses and predicted coding of bunyavirus genome RNA species. *J Virol* 1982; 41:119–128.

34. Akashi H, Gay M, Ihara T, Bishop DHL: Localized conserved regions of the S RNA gene products of bunyaviruses are revealed by sequence analyses of the Simbu serogroup Aino virus. *Virus Res* 1984; 1:51–63.

35. Gerbaud S, Vialat P, Pardigon N, et al: The S segment of the Germiston virus RNA genome can code for three proteins. *Virus Res* 1987; 8:1–13.

36. Pardigon N, Vialat P, Gerbaud S, et al: Nucleotide sequence of the M segment of Germiston virus: comparison of the M gene product of several bunyaviruses. *Virus Res* 1988; 11:73–85.

37. Eshita Y, Bishop DHL: The complete sequence of the M RNA of snowshoe hare bunyavirus reveals the presence of internal hydrophobic domains in the viral glycoprotein. *Virology* 1984; 137:227–240.

38. Lees JF, Pringle CR, Elliott RM: Nucleotide sequence of the Bunyamwera virus M RNA segment: conservation of structural features in the bunyavirus glycoprotein gene product. *Virology* 1986; 148:1–14.

39. Ihara T, Smith J, Dalrymple JM, et al: Complete sequences of the glycoproteins and M RNA of Punta Toro phlebovirus compared to those of Rift Valley fever virus. *Virology* 1985; 144:246–259.

40. Beaty BJ, Rozhon EF, Gensemer P, et al: Formation of reassortant bunyaviruses in dually infected mosquitoes. *Virology* 1981; 111:662–665.

41. Beaty BJ, Bishop DHL, Gay M, et al: Interference between bunyaviruses in *Aedes triseriatus* mosquitoes. *Virology* 1983; 127:83–90.

42. Sundin DR, Beaty BJ: Interference to oral superinfection of *Aedes triseriatus* infected with La Crosse virus. *Am J Trop Med Hyg* 1988; 38:428–432.

43. Beaty BJ, Sundin DR, Chandler LJ, et al: Evolution of bunyaviruses by genome reassortment in dually infected mosquitoes *(Aedes triseriatus). Science* 1985; 230:548–550.

44. Fields BN, Henderson BE, Coleman PH, et al: Pahayokee and Shark River, two new arboviruses related to Patois and Zegla from the Florida Everglades. *Am J Epidemiol* 1969; 89:222–226.

45. Ushijima H, Clerx-Van Haaster CM, Bishop DHL: Analyses of Patois group bunyaviruses: Evidence for naturally occurring recombinant bunyaviruses and existence of immune precipitable and nonprecipitable nonvirion proteins induced in bunyavirus-infected cells. *Virology* 1981; 110:318–332.

46. Shope RE, Rozhon EJ, Bishop DHL: Role of the middle-sized bunyavirus RNA segment in mouse virulence. *Virology* 1981; 114:273–276.

47. Beaty BJ, Fuller F, Bishop DHL: Bunyavirus gene structure—

function relationships and potential for RNA segment reassortment in the vector: La Crosse and snowshoe hare reassortant viruses in mosquitoes, in Calisher CH, Thompson WH (eds): *California Serogroup Viruses,* New York, Alan R Liss, 1983, vol 123, pp 119–128.

48. Rozhon EJ, Gensemer P, Shope RE, et al: Attenuation of virulence of a bunyavirus involving an L RNA defect and isolation of LAC/SSH/LAC and LAC/SSH/SSH reassortants. *Virology* 1981; 111:125–138.

49. Janssen RJ, Nathanson N, Endres MJ: Virulence of La Crosse virus is under polygenic control. *J Virol* 1986; 59:1–7.

50. Hunt AR, Calisher CH: Relationships of Bunyamwera group viruses by neutralization. *Am J Trop Med Hyg* 1979; 28:740–749.

51. McGowan Jr JE, Bryan JA, Gregg MB: Surveillance of arboviral encephalitis in the United States, 1955–1971. *Am J Epidemiol* 1973; 79:199–207.

52. Calisher CH, Lazuick JS, Lieb S, et al: Human infection with Tensaw virus in south Florida: evidence that Tensaw virus subtypes stimulate the production of antibodies reactive with closely related Bunyamwera serogroup viruses. *Am J Trop Med Hyg* 1988; 39:117–122.

53. Mangiafico JA, Sanchez JL, Figueiredo LT, et al: Isolation of a newly recognized Bunyamwera serogroup virus from a human in Panama. *Am J Trop Med Hyg* 1988; 39:593–596.

54. Srihongse S, Johnson CM: Wyeomyia subgroup of arbovirus: isolation from man. *Science* 1965; 149:863–864.

55. McConnell S, Livingston C Jr, Calisher CH, et al: Isolations of Cache Valley virus in Texas, 1981. *Vet Microbiol* 1987; 13:11–18.

56. Groot H, Oya A, Bernal C, et al: Guaroa virus, a new agent isolated in Colombia, South America. *Am J Trop Med* 1959; 8:604–609.

57. Sanmartin C: Ecology of the arboviruses of the Bunyamwera group, in Bárdoš V et al (eds): *Arboviruses of the California Complex and the Bunyamwera Group.* Bratislava, Czechoslovakia, Slovak Academy of Sciences, 1969, pp 167–189.

58. Causey OR, Shope RE, Rodrigues A: Isolamento do virus guaroa do figado por biopsia percutanea de um caso humano com paralisia. *Rev Serv Espec Saude Publica* 1962; 12:55–59.

59. Woodall JP: Human infections with arboviruses of the Bunyamwera group, in Bárdoš et al (eds): *Arboviruses of the California Complex and the Bunyamwera Group.* Bratislava, Czechoslovakia, Slovak Academy of Sciences, 1969, pp 317–332.

60. Southam CM, Moore AE: West Nile, Ilheus, and Bunyamwera virus infections in man. *Am J Trop Med Hyg* 1951; 31:724–741.

61. Kokernot RH, Smithburn KC, Paterson HE, et al: Isolation of Germiston virus, a hitherto unknown agent, from culicine mosquitoes, and a report of infection in two laboratory workers. *Am J Trop Med Hyg* 1960; 9:62–69.

62. Henderson BE, McCrae AWR, Kirya BG, et al: Arbovirus epizootics involving man, mosquitoes and vertebrates at Lunyo, Uganda 1968. *Ann Trop Med Parasitol* 1972; 66:343–355.

63. Johnson BK, Chanas AC, Shockley P, et al: Arbovirus isolations from, and serological studies on, wild and domestic vertebrates from Kano Plain, Kenya. *Trans R Soc Trop Med Hyg* 1977; 71:512–517.

64. Monath TPC, Henderson BE, Kirya GB: Characterization of viruses (Witwatersrand and Germiston) isolated from mosquitoes and rodents collected near Lunyo Forest, Uganda, in 1968. *Arch Gesamte Virusforsch* 1972; 38:125–132.

65. McIntosh BM: Susceptibility of some African wild rodents to infection with various arthropod-borne viruses. *Trans R Soc Trop Med Hyg* 1961; 55:63–68.

66. Bardos V, Sluka F, Cupkova E: Serological study on the medical importance of Calovo virus, in Bárdoš V et al (eds): *Arboviruses of the California Complex and the Bunyamwera Group.* Bratislava, Czechoslovakia, Slovak Academy of Sciences, 1969, pp 333–335.

67. Sluka F: The clinical picture of the Calovo virus infection, in

Bárdoš V et al (eds): *Arboviruses of the California Complex and the Bunyamwera Group.* Bratislava, Czechoslovakia, Slovak Academy of Sciences, 1969, pp 337–339.

68. Smithburn KC, Mahaffy AF, Paul JH: Bwamba fever and its causative virus. *Am J Trop Med* 1941; 21:75–90.

69. Dick GWA: Epidemiological notes of some viruses isolated in Uganda, in *Ordinary Meeting of the Royal Society of Tropical Medicine and Hygiene,* London, Dec 11, 1952, p 13.

70. MacNamara FN, Horn DW, Porterfield JS: Yellow fever and other arthropod-borne viruses. *Trans R Soc Trop Med Hyg* 1959; 53:202–212.

71. Kokernot RH, Casaca VMR, Weinbren MP, et al: Survey for antibodies against arthropod-borne viruses in the sera of indigenous residents of Angola. *Trans R Soc Trop Med Hyg* 1965; 59:563–570.

72. Kokernot RH, Szlamp EL, Levitt J, et al: Survey for antibodies against arthropod-borne viruses in the sera of indigenous residents of the Caprivi Strip and Bechuanaland Protectorate. *Trans R Soc Trop Med Hyg* 1965; 59:553–562.

73. Pellissier A, Rousselot R: Enquête sérologique sur l'incidence des virus neurotropes chez quelque singes de l'afrique équitoriale française. *Bull Soc Pathol Exot Filiales* 1954; 47:228–231.

74. Pinto MR: Survey for antibodies to arboviruses in the sera of children in Portuguese Guinea. *Bull Org Mond Sante/Bull WHO* 1967; 37:101–108.

75. Bres P: Recent data from serological surveys on the prevalence of arbovirus infections in Africa, with special reference to yellow fever. *Bull Org Mond Sante/Bull WHO* 1970; 43:223–267.

76. Bowen ETW, Simpson DIH, Platt GS, et al: Large scale irrigation and arbovirus epidemiology, Kano Plain, Kenya II. Preliminary serological survey. *Trans R Soc Trop Med Hyg* 1973; 67:702–709.

77. Smithburn KC, Kokernot RH, Heymann CS, et al: Neutralizing antibodies for certain viruses in the sera of human beings residing in Northern Natal. *S Afr Med J* 1959; 33:555–561.

78. Moore DL, Causey OR, Carey DE, et al: Arthropod-borne viral infections of man in Nigeria, 1964–1970. *Ann Trop Med Parasitol* 1975; 69:49–64.

79. Karabatsos N (ed): *International Catalogue of Arboviruses Including Certain Other Viruses of Vertebrates, ed 3.* San Antonio, American Society of Tropical Medicine and Hygiene, 1985.

80. Lee VH, Monath TP, Tomori O, et al: Arbovirus studies in Nupeko Forest, a possible natural focus of yellow fever virus in Nigeria. *Trans R Soc Trop Med Hyg* 1974; 68:39–43.

81. Johnson BK, Chanas AC, Squires EF, et al: The isolation of a Bwamba virus variant from man in western Kenya. *J Med Virol* 1978; 2:15–20.

82. Kokernot RH, Smithburn KC, Weinbren MP, et al: Studies on arthropod-borne viruses of Tongaland. VI. Isolation of Pongola virus from *Aedes (Banksinella) circumluteolus* Theo. *S Afr J Med Sci* 1957; 22:81–92.

83. Tomori O, Fabiyi A: Differentiation of Bwamba and Pongola viruses by agar-gel diffusion and immunoelectrophoretic techniques. *Am J Trop Med Hyg* 1976; 25:489–493.

84. Shope RE, Causey OR: Further studies on the serological relationships of Group C arthropod-borne viruses and the application of these relationships to rapid identification of types. *Am J Trop Med Hyg* 1962; 11:283–290.

85. Karabatsos N, Henderson JR: Cross-neutralization studies with Group C arboviruses. *Acta Virol* 1969; 13:544–548.

86. Woodall JP: Transmission of group C arboviruses (Bunyaviridae), in Kurstak E (ed): *Arctic and Tropical Arboviruses.* New York, Academic Press, 1979, pp 123–138.

87. Causey OR, Causey CE, Maroja OM, et al: The isolation of arthropod-borne viruses, including members of two hitherto undescribed serological groups, in the Amazon region of Brazil. *Am J Trop Med Hyg* 1961; 10:227–249.

88. Woodall JP: Virus research in Amazonia. *Atlas Simposio Biota Amazonica* 1967; 6:31–63.

89. Pinheiro FP, Bensabath G, Andrade AHP, et al: Infectious diseases along Brazil's Trans-Amazon highway: surveillance and research. *Bull PAHO* 1974; 8:111–122.

90. Srihongse S, Stacy HG, Gauld JR: A survey to assess potential human disease hazards along proposed sea level canal routes in Panama and Colombia. IV. Arbovirus surveillance in man. *Milit Med* 1973; 138:422–426.

91. Scherer WF, Madalengoitia J, Menesis O, et al: Study of VE virus and isolation of SLE, EE, Group C, and Guama group arboviruses in the Amazon region of Peru, 1975. *Bull PAHO* 1979; 13:272–284.

92. Spence L, Jonkers AH, Grant LS: Arboviruses in the Caribbean Islands. *Prog Med Virol* 1968; 10:415–586.

93. Schere WF, Dickerman RW, Ordonez JV, et al: Ecologic studies of Venezuelan encephalitis virus and isolations of Nepuyo and Patois viruses during 1968–1973 at a marsh habitat near the epicenter of the 1969 outbreak in Guatemala. *Am J Trop Med Hyg* 1976; 25:151–162.

94. Calisher CH, Chappell WA, Maness KSC, et al: Isolations of Nepuyo virus strains from Honduras, 1967. *Am J Trop Med Hyg* 1971; 20:331–337.

95. Jonkers AH, Spence L, Karbatt J: Arbovirus infections in Dutch military personnel stationed in Surinam: Further studies. *Trop Geogr Med* 1968; 20:251–256.

96. Jonkers AH, Metselaar D, de Andrade AHP, et al: Restan virus, a new group C arbovirus from Trinidad and Surinam. *Am J Trop Med Hyg* 1967; 16:74–78.

97. de Rodaniche E, de Andrade AP, Galindo P: Isolation of two antigenically distinct arthropod-borne viruses of group C in Panama. *Am J Trop Med Hyg* 1964; 13:839–843.

98. Shope RE, Causey CE, Causey OR: Itaqui virus, a new member of arthropod-borne group C. *Am J Trop Med Hyg* 1961; 10:264–265.

99. Gibbs CJ, Bruckner EA, Schenker S: A case of Apeu virus infection. *Am J Trop Med Hyg* 1964; 13:108–113.

100. LeDuc JW: The ecology of California group viruses. *J Med Entomol* 1979; 16:1–17.

101. Thompson WH, Kalfayan B, Anslow RO: Isolation of California encephalitis group virus from a fatal human illness. *Am J Epidemiol* 1965; 81:245–253.

102. LeDuc JW: Epidemiology and ecology of California serogroup viruses. *Am J Trop Med Hyg* 1987; 37:60S–68S.

103. Kappus KD, Monath TP, Kaminski RM, et al: Reported encephalitis associated with California serogroup virus infections in the United States, 1963–1981, in Calisher CH, Thompson WH (eds): *California Serogroup Viruses.* New York, Alan R Liss, 1983, vol 123, pp 31–41.

104. Calisher CH: Taxonomy, classification, and geographic distribution of California serogroup bunyaviruses, in Calisher CH, Thompson WH (eds): *California Serogroup Viruses.* New York, Alan R Liss, 1983, vol 123, pp 1–16.

105. Berry RL, Parsons MA, Restifo RA, et al: California serogroup virus infections in Ohio: an 18-year retrospective summary, in Calisher CH and Thompson WH (eds): *California Serogroup Viruses.* New York, Alan R Liss, 1983, vol 123, pp 215–223.

106. Gauld LW, Hanson RP, Thompson WH, et al: Observations on a natural cycle of La Crosse virus (California group) in southwestern Wisconsin. *Am J Trop Med Hyg* 1974; 23:983–992.

107. Grimstad PR, Barrett CL, Humphrey RL, et al: Serological evidence for widespread infection with La Crosse and St Louis encephalitis viruses in Indiana human populations. *Am J Epidemiol* 1984;119:913–930.

108. Hurwitz ES, Schell W, Nelson D, et al: Surveillance for California encephalitis group virus illness in Wisconsin and Minnesota, 1978. *Am J Trop Med Hyg* 1983; 32:595–601.

109. Baron RC, Hoffman RD, Powers JM, et al: Arboviral infections of the central nervous system—United States, 1987. *MMWR* 1988; 37:506–516.

110. Thompson WH, Evans AS: California encephalitis virus studies in Wisconsin. *Am J Epidemiol* 1965;81:230–244.

111. Monath TPC, Nuckolls JG, Berall J, et al: Studies on California

encephalitis in Minnesota. *Am J Epidemiol* 1970; 92:40–50.

112. El Said LH, Vorndam V, Gentsch JR, et al: A comparison of La Crosse virus isolates obtained from different ecological niches and an analysis of the structural components of California encephalitis serogroup viruses and other bunyaviruses. *Am J Trop Med Hyg* 1979; 28:364–386.

113. Klimas RA, Thompson WH, Calisher CH, et al: Genotypic varieties of La Crosse virus isolated from different geographic regions of the continental United States and evidence for a naturally occurring intertypic recombinant La Crosse virus. *Am J Epidemiol* 1981; 114:112–131.

114. Aaronson RP, Young JF, Palese P: Oligonucleotide mapping: evaluation of its sensitivity by computer-simulation. *Nucleic Acids Res* 1982; 10:237–246.

115. Bishop DHL, Clerx JPM, Clerx-van Haaster CM, et al: Molecular and genetic properties of members of the Bunyaviridae, in Bishop DHL, Compans RW (eds): *The Replication of Negative Strand Viruses.* New York, Elsevier/North Holland, 1981, pp 135–145.

116. Grady LJ, Sanders ML, Campbell WP: The sequence of the mRNA of an isolate of La Crosse virus. *J Gen Virol* 1987; 68:3057–3071.

117. Watts DM, Thompson WH, Yuill TM, et al: Overwintering of La Crosse virus in *Aedes triseriatus. Am J Trop Med Hyg* 1974; 23:694–700.

118. Thompson WH, Beaty BJ: Venereal transmission of La Crosse virus from male to female *Aedes triseriatus. Am J Trop Med Hyg* 1978; 27:187–196.

119. Fine PEM, LeDuc JW: Towards a quantitative understanding of the epidemiology of Keystone virus in the eastern United States. *Am J Trop Med Hyg* 1978; 27:322–338.

120. DeFoliart GR: *Aedes triseriatus:* vector biology in relationship to the persistence of La Crosse virus in endemic foci, in Calisher, CH, Thompson WH (eds): *California Serogroup Viruses.* New York, Alan R Liss, 1983, vol 123, pp 89–104.

121. Turell MJ, Hardy JL, Reeves WC: Stabilizated infection of California encephalitis virus in *Aedes dorsalis,* and its implications for viral maintenance in nature. *Am J Trop Med Hyg* 1982; 31:1252–1259.

122. Kappus KD, Calisher CH, Baron RC. et al: La Crosse virus infection and disease in western North Carolina. *Am J Trop Med Hyg* 1982; 31:556–560.

123. Thompson WH, Gundersen CB: La Crosse encephalitis: occurrence of disease and control in a suburban area, in Calisher CH, Thompson WH (eds): *California Serogroup Viruses.* New York, Alan R Liss,, 1983, vol 123, pp 225–236.

124. Rowley WA, Wong YW, Dorsey DC, et al: California serogroup viruses in Iowa, in Calisher CH, Thompson WH (eds): *California Serogroup Viruses.* New York, Alan R Liss, 1983, vol 123, pp 237–246.

125. Young DJ: California encephalitis virus. *Ann Intern Med* 1966; 65:419–428.

126. Cramblett HG, Stegmiller H, Spencer C: California encephalitis virus infections in children. *JAMA* 1966; 198:128–132.

127. Chun RWM, Thompson WH, Grabow JD, et al: California arbovirus encephalitis in children. *Neurology* 1968; 18:369–375.

128. Hilty MD, Haynes RE, Azimi PH, et al: California encephalitis in children. *Am J Dis Child* 1972; 124:530–533.

129. Balfour JHH, Siem RA, Bauer H, et al: California arbovirus (La Crosse) infections I. Clinical and laboratory findings in 66 children with meningoencephalitis. *Pediatrics* 1973; 52:680–691.

130. Gundersen CB, Brown KL: Clinical aspects of La Crosse encephalitis: preliminary report, in Calisher CH, Thompson WH (eds): *California Serogroup Viruses.* New York, Alan R Liss, 1983, vol 123, pp 169–177.

131. Matthews CG, Chun RWM, Grabow JD, et al: Psychological sequelae in children following California arbovirus encephalitis. *Neurology* 1968; 18:1023–1030.

132. Sabatino DA, Cramblett HG: Behavioral sequelae of California encephalitis virus infection in children. *Dev Med Child Neurol* 1968; 10:331–337.

133. Grabow JD, Matthews CG, Chun RWM, et al: The electroencephalogram and clinical sequelae of California arbovirus encephalitis. *Neurology* 1969; 19:394–404.

134. Rie HE, Hilty MD, Cramblett HG: Intelligence and coordination following California encephalitis. *Am J Dis Child* 1973; 125:824–827.

135. Deering, WM: Neurologic aspects and treatment of La Crosse encephalitis, in Calisher CH, Thompson WH (eds): *California Serogroup Viruses.* New York, Alan R. Liss, 1983, vol 123, pp 187–191.

136. Kalfayan B: Pathology of La Crosse virus infection in humans, in Calisher CH, Thompson WH (eds): *California Serogroup Viruses.* New York, Alan R Liss, 1983, vol 123, pp 179–186.

137. Jamnback TL, Beaty BJ, Hildreth SW, et al: Capture immunoglobulin M system for rapid diagnosis of La Crosse (California encephalitis) virus infections. *J Clin Microbiol* 1982; 16:577–580.

138. Beaty BJ, Jamnback TL, Hildreth SW, et al: Rapid diagnosis of La Crosse virus infections: evaluation of serologic and antigen detection techniques for the clinically relevant diagnosis of La Crosse encephalitis, in Calisher CH, Thompson WH (eds): *California Serogroup Viruses.* New York, Alan R Liss, 1983, vol 123, pp 293–302.

139. Calisher CH, Pretzman CI, Meth DJ, et al: Serodiagnosis of La Crosse virus infection in humans by detection of immunoglobulin M class antibodies. *J Clin Microbiol* 1986; 23:667–671.

140. Lindsey HS, Calisher CH, Mathews JH: Serum dilution neutralization test for California group virus identification and serology. *J Clin Microbiol* 1976; 4:503–510.

141. Calisher CH, Bailey RE: Serodiagnosis of La Crosse virus infections in humans. *J Clin Microbiol* 1981; 13:344–350.

142. Hildreth SW, Beaty BJ, Meegan JM, et al: Detection of La Crosse arbovirus antigen in mosquito pools: application of chromogenic and fluorogenic enzyme immunoassay systems. *J Clin Microbiol* 1982; 15:879–884.

143. Francey DB: Mosquito control for prevention of California (La Crosse) encephalitis, in Calisher CH, Thompson WH (eds): *California Serogroup Viruses.* New York, Alan R Liss, 1983, vol 123, pp 365–375.

144. Parry JE: Control of *Aedes triseriatus* in La Crosse,Wisconsin, in Calisher CH, Thompson WH (eds): *California Serogroup Viruses.* New York, Alan R Liss, 1983, vol 123, pp355–363.

145. Rosicky B, Malkova D (eds): *Tahyna Virus: Natural Focus in Southern Moravia.* Prague, Academia Praha, 1980.

146. Bardos V, Ryba J, Hubalek Z: Isolation of Tahyna virus from field collected *Culiseta annulata* (Schrk.) larvae. *Acta Virol* 1975; 9:446.

147. Simkova A: Tahyna virus in hedgehogs. *Acta Virol* 1964; 8:285.

148. Malkova D, Hodkova Z, Chaturvedi R: Overwintering of the virus Tahyna in hedgehogs kept under natural conditions. *Folia Parasitol* 1969; 16:245–254.

149. Bardos V, Medek M, Kania V, et al: Isolation of Tahyna virus from the blood of sick children. *Acta Virol* 1975; 19:447.

150. Bardos V, Cupkova E, Sefcovicova L: Serological study on the medical importance of Tahyna virus, in Bárdoš V et al (eds): *Arboviruses of the California Complex and the Bunyamwera Group.* Bratislava, Czechoslovakia, Slovak Academy of Sciences, 1969, pp 301–308.

151. Likar M, Casals J: Isolation from man in Slovenia of a virus belonging to the California complex of arthropod-borne viruses. *Nature* 1963; 197:1131.

152. Mayerova A, Hruzik J, Mayer V: Tahyna virus neutralizing antibody levels in cases of acute febrile illness, in Bardos V, (ed): *Arboviruses of the California Complex and the Bunyamwera Group.* Bratislava, Czechoslovakia, Slovak Academy of Sciences, 1969, pp 305–308.

153. Vesenjak-Hirjan J: Arboviruses in Yugoslavia, in Vesenjak-Hirjan J, Porterfield JS, Arslanagic E (eds): *Arboviruses in the Mediterranean Countries. Zentralbl Bakteriol Mikrobiol Hyg* 1980; (suppl 9):165–177.

154. Pilaski J, Mackenstein H: Isolation of Tahyna virus from mosquitoes in 2 different European natural foci. *Zentralbl Bakteriol Mikrobiol Hyg (B)* 1985; 180:394–420.

155. Verani P: Arboviruses in Italy, in Vesenjale-Hirjan J, Porterfield JS, Arslanic E (eds): *Arboviruses in the Mediterranean Countries. Zentralbl Bakteriol Mikrobiol Hyg* 1980; (Suppl 9):123–128.

156. Rodhain F, Hannoun C: Present status of arboviruses in France, in Vesenjak-Hirjan J, Porterfield JS, Arslanigic E (eds):*Arboviruses in the Mediterranean Countries. Zentralbl Bakteriol Mikrobiol Hyg* 1980; (suppl 9):111–116.

157. Lvov SC, Pogorelyi IA, Skvortsova TM, et al: Isolation of the Tahyna bunyavirus in the Arctic. *Vopr Virusol* 1985; 30:736–740.

158. Lvov SD, Gromashevskii VL, Bogoiavlenskii GV, et al: Isolation of Zaliv-Terpeniia, Uukumiemi and Tahyna-like viruses from mosquitoes collected in the tundra, forest tundra and northern taiga of the Kola and Taimyr peninsulas and in the central taiga of Karelia. *Med Parazitol (Mosk)* 1987; 6:40–43.

159. Kokernot RH, McIntosh BM, Worth CB, et al: Isolation of viruses from mosquitoes collected at Lumbo, Mozambique. *Am J Trop Med Hyg* 1962; 11:678–682.

160. Peiris JSM, Perera LP, Arunagiri CK, et al: A survey of arboviruses in Sri Lanka. Presented at Third International Symposium on Ecology of Arboviruses, Smolence, Czechoslovakia, Sept 7–11 1987.

161. Gu H-X, Artsob H: The possible presence of Tahyna (Bunaviridae, California serogroup) virus in the People's Republic of China. *Trans R Soc Trop Med Hyg* 1987; 81:693.

162. Artsob H: Distribution of California serogroup viruses and virus infections in Canada, in Calisher CH, Thompson WH (eds): *California Serogroup Viruses.* New York, Alan R Liss, 1983, vol 123, pp 277–290.

163. Mahdy MS, McLaughlin B, Paul NR, et al: Surveillance of arboviruses in Ontario in 1983—increased detection of seropositive cases to the California group viruses (CGV). *Can Dis Weekly Rep* 1984; 10:168–171.

164. Sudia WD, Newhouse VF, Calisher CH, et al: California group arboviruses: Isolations from mosquitoes in North America. *Mosquito News* 1971; 31:576–600.

165. Deibel R, Srihongse S, Grayson MA, et al: Jamestown Canyon virus: the etiologic agent of an emerging human disease, in Calisher CH, Thompson WH (eds): *California Serogroup Viruses.* New York, Alan R Liss, 1983, vol 123, pp 313–325.

166. Grimstad PR, Shabino CL, Calisher CH, et al: A case of encephalitis in a human associated with a serologic rise to Jamestown Canyon virus. *Am J Trop Med Hyg* 1988; 31:1238–1244.

167. Grimstad PR, Calisher CH, Harroff RN, et al: Jamestown Canyon virus (California serogroup) is the etiologic agent of widespread infection in Michigan humans. *Am J Trop Med Hyg* 1986; 35:376–386.

168. Grimstad PR, Artsob H, Karabatsos N, et al: Production and use of a hemagglutinin for detecting antibody to Jamestown Canyon virus. *J Clin Microbiol* 1987; 25:1557–1559.

169. Coleman PH, Ryder S, Work TH: Mahogany hammock virus, a new Guama group arbovirus from the Florida Everglades. *Am J Epidemiol* 1969; 89:217–221.

170. Tikasingh ES, Ardoin P, Williams MC: First isolation of Catu virus from a human in Trinidad. *Trop Geogr Med* 1974; 26:414–416.

171. Inaba Y, Kurogi H, Omori T: Akabane disease: Epizootic abortion, premature birth, stillbirth, and congenital arthrogryposis-hydranencephaly in cattle, sheep, and goats caused by Akabane virus, letter. *Aust Vet J* 1975; 51:584–585.

172. Parsonson IM, Della-Porta AJ, Snowden WA, et al: Congenital abnormalities in foetal lambs after inoculation of pregnant ewes with Akabane virus, letter. *Aust Vet J* 1975; 51:585–586

173. Davies FG, Jessett DM: A study of the host range and distribution of antibody to Akabana virus (genus *Bunyavirus,* family *Bunyaviridae*) in Kenya. *J Hyg Camb* 1985; 95:191–196.

174. Al-Busaidy S, Hamblin C, Taylor WP: Neutralising antibodies to Akabane virus in free-living wild animals in Africa. *Trop Anim Health Prod* 1987; 19:197–202.

175. LeDuc JW, Hoch AL, Pinheiro FP, et al: Epidemic Oropouche virus disease in Northern Brazil. *Bull PAHO* 1981; 15:97–103.

176. Pinheiro FP, Travassos da Rosa APA, Travassos da Rosa JFS, et al: Oropouche virus I. A review of clinical epidemiological, and ecological findings. *Am J Trop Med Hyg* 1981; 30:149–160.

177. Pinheiro FP, Travassos da Rosa APA, Gomes MLC, et al: Transmission of Oropouche virus from man to hamster by the midge *Culicoides paraensis. Science* 1982; 215:1251–1253.

178. Hoch AL, Pinheiro FP, Roberts DR, et al: Laboratory transmission of Oropouche virus by *Culex quinquefasciatus* Say. *Bull PAHO* 1987; 21:55–61.

179. Doherty RL, Whitehead RH, Wetters EJ, et al: A survey of antibody to 10 arboviruses (Koongol group, Mapputta group and ungrouped) isolated in Queensland. *Trans R Soc Trop Med Hyg* 1970; 64:748–753.

180. Lopes ODeS, Sacchetta LDeA: Epidemiology of Boraceia virus in a forested area in Sao Paulo, Brazil. *Am J Epidemiol* 1974; 100:410–413.

181. Williams JE, Imlarp S, Top Jr FH, et al: Kaeng Khoi virus from naturally infected bedbugs (Cimicidae) and immature free-tailed bats. *Bull WHO* 1976; 53:365–369.

182. Calisher CH, Lazuick JS, Justines G, et al: Viruses isolated from *Aedeomyia squamipennis* mosquitoes collected in Panama, Ecuador, and Argentina: establishment of the Gamboa serogroup. *Am J Trop Med Hyg* 1981; 30:219–223.

183. Balducci M, Verani P, Lopes MC, et al: Isolation in Italy of Bahig and Matruh viruses (Tete group) from migratory birds. *Ann Inst Pasteur (Paris) Microbiol* 1973; 124B:231–237.

184. Converse JD, Hoogstraal H, Moussa MI, et al: Bahig virus (Tete group) in naturally- and transovarially- infected *Hyalomma marginatum* ticks from Egypt and Italy. *Arch Ges Virusforsch* 1974; 46:29–35.

185. Tesh RB: The genus *Phlebovirus* and its vectors. *Ann Rev Entomol* 1988; 33:169–181.

186. Tesh RB, Boshell SJ, Young DG, et al: Characterization of five new phleboviruses recently isolated from sand flies in Tropical America. *Am J Trop Med Hyg* 1989; 40:529–533.

187. Tesh RB, Chaniotis BN: Transovarial transmission of viruses by phlebotomine sandflies. *Ann NY Acad Sci* 1975; 266:125–134.

188. Tesh RB, Saidi S, Gajdamovic SJA, et al: Serological studies on the epidemiology of sandfly fever in the Old World. *Bull WHO* 1976; 54:663–664.

189. Hertig M, Sabin AB: Sandfly fever (pappataci, phlebotomus, three-day fever) I. History of incidence, prevention, and control, in Coates JB, Hoff EC, Hoff PM (eds): *Preventive Medicine in World War II.* Washington, DC, Office of the Surgeon General, 1964, pp 109–174.

190. Sinton JA: Notes on some Indian species of the genus *Phlebotomus.* Part XI. The role of insects of the genus *Phlebotomus* as carriers of disease, with special reference to India. *Indian J Med Res* 1925; 12:701–729.

191. Bolt RA: Sandflies *(Phlebotomus)* in China and their relation to disease. *China Med J* 1915; 29:78–86.

192. Verani P, Lopes MC, Nicoletti L, et al: Studies on *Phlebotomus*-transmitted viruses in Italy: I. Isolation and characterization of a sandfly fever Naples-like virus, in Vesenjak-Hirjan J, Porterfield JS, Arslanagic E (eds) *Arboviruses in the Mediterranean Countries. Zentralbl Bakteriol Mikrobiol Hyg* 1980 (suppl 9):195–201.

193. Srihongse S, Johnson CM: Human infections with Chagres virus in Panama. *Am J Trop Med Hyg* 1974; 23:690–693.

194. Peralta PH, Shelokov A, Brody JA: Chagres virus: a new human isolate from Panama. *Am J Trop Med Hyg* 1965; 14:146–151.

195. Aitken THG, Woodall JP, De Andrade AGP, et al: Pacui virus, phlebotomine flies, and small mammals in Brazil: an epidemio-

logical study. *Am J Trop Med Hyg* 1975; 24:358–368.

196. LeDuc JW, Cuevas M, Garcia M: The incidence and prevalence of phlebotomus fever group viruses in Panama, in Pinheiro FP (ed): *International Symposium on Tropical Arboviruses and Hemorrhagic Fevers.* Rio de Janeiro, Brazil Academy of Science, 1982; pp 385–390.

197. Travassos da Rosa APA, Tesh RB, Pinheiro FP, et al: Characterization of eight new phlebotomus fever serogroup arboviruses (Bunyaviridae: *Phlebovirus*) from the Amazon region of Brazil. *Am J Trop Med Hyg* 1983; 32:1164–1171.

198. Doerr R, Franz K, Taussing S: Pappataci Fieber, ein endemisches drei-Tage-Fieber im adriatischen Küstengebiete Oesterreich Ungarns. Leipzig, Deuticke, 1909.

199. Sabin AB: Experimental studies on phlebotomus (pappataci, sandfly) fever during World War II. *Arch Gesamte Virusforsch* 1951; 4:367–410.

200. Sabin AB, Philip CB, Paul JR: Phlebotomus (pappataci or sandfly) fever. *JAMA* 1944; 125:603–606, 693–699.

201. Fleming J, Bignall JR, Blades AN: Sand-fly fever. Review of 664 cases. *Lancet* 1947; 1:443–445.

202. Bartelloni PJ, Tesh RB: Clinical and serologic responses of volunteers infected with phlebotomus fever virus (Sicilian type). *Am J Trop Med Hyg* 1976; 25:456–462.

203. Peschle B: Osservazioni cliniche su un epidemia di febbre da pappataci. *Pediatria* 1936; 44:41–51.

204. Taylor RM: Phlebotomus (sandfly) fever in the Middle East, in *Proceedings of the Sixth International Congress on Tropical Medicine and Malaria.* 1959, vol 5, pp 149–158.

205. Saidi S, Tesh R, Javadian E, et al: Studies on the epidemiology of sandfly fever in Iran. II. The prevalence of human and animal infection with five phlebotomus fever virus serotypes in Isfahan Province. *Am J Trop Med Hyg* 1977; 26:288–293.

206. Tesh RB, Papaevangelou G: Effect of insecticide spraying for malaria control on the incidence of sandfly fever in Athens, Greece. *Am J Trop Med Hyg* 1977; 26:163–166.

207. Tesh R, Saidi S, Javadian E, et al: Studies on the epidemiology of sandfly fever in Iran. I. Virus isolates obtained from *Phlebotomus. Am J Trop Med Hyg* 1977; 26:282–287.

208. Goverdhan MK, Dhanda V, Modi PN, et al: Isolation of phlebotomus (sandfly) fever virus from sandflies and humans during the same season in Aurangabad Districk, Maharashtra State, India. *Indian J Med Res* 1976; 64:57–63.

209. Schmidt JR, Schmidt ML, Said MI: Phlebotomus fever in Egypt. Isolation of phlebotomus fever viruses from *Phlebotomus papatasi. Am J Trop Med Hyg* 1971; 20:483–490.

210. Javadian E, Tesh R, Saidi S, et al: Studies on the epidemiology of sandfly fever in Iran. III. Host-feeding patterns of *Phlebotomus papatasi* in an endemic area of the disease. *Am J Trop Med Hyg* 1977; 26:294–298.

211. Barnett HC, Suyemoto W: Field studies on sandfly fever and kala-azar in Pakistan, in Iran, and in Baltistan (Little Tibet) Kashmir. *Trans NY Acad Sci Ser II* 1961; 23:609–617.

212. Gaydamouich SYa, Obukhova VR, Sveshnikova NA, et al: Natural foci of viruses, *Phlebotomus papatasi,* in the U.S.S.R. based on serological surveys of the human population. *Vopr Virusol* 1978; 23:556–560.

213. Patrishcheva PA: Bloodsucking insects and ticks in Kara-Kum and their medical importance in the development of deserts. *Zool Zh* March-April 1954; No. 2, 241–267.

214. Watts DM, MacDonald C, Bailey CL, et al: Experimental infection of *Phlebotomus papatasi* with sandfly fever Sicilian virus. *Am J Trop Med Hyg* 1988; 39:611–616.

215. Korolev PA, Markov TL, Tikhomirova NI: Experience in the liquidation of an endemic focus of pappatachi fever (Russian). *M Parazitol (Mosk)* 1954; 4:344–347.

216. Gligic A, Miscevic Z, Tesh RB, et al: First isolation of Naples sandfly fever virus in Yugoslavia. *Mikrobiologija* 1982; 19:167–175.

217. Borcic B, Punda V: Sandfly fever epidemiology in Croatia. *Acata Med Iugosl* 1987; 41:89–97.

218. Gabbi U: On how the "three-day fever" appeared and spread in eastern Sicily and southern Calabria. *Pathologica* 1915; 7:51–55.

219. MacDonald C, McKee K Jr, Huggins J, et al: Ribavirin (RB) prophylaxis of sandfly fever–Sicilian (SFS) infection in human volunteers. Presented at the 86th Annual Meeting of the American Society for Microbiology, Washington, DC, March 23–28, 1986.

220. Paci P, Balducci M, Verani P, et al: Toscana virus, a new *Phlebotomus*-transmitted virus isolated in Italy. Studies on its ecology and evaluation of its possible role in the etiology of cases of human CNS infections, in *Proceedings of the International Congress for Infectious Diseases, Vienna, Austria, August 24–27, 1983,* pp 35–39.

221. Ehrnst A, Peters CJ, Niklasson B, et al: Neurovirulent Toscana virus (a sandfly fever virus) in Swedish man after visit to Portugal. *Lancet* 1985; 1:1212–1213.

222. Verani P, Ciufolini MG, Caciolli S, et al: Ecology of viruses isolated from sand flies in Italy and characterizations of a new *Phlebovirus* (Arbia virus). *Am J Trop Med Hyg* 1988; 38:433–439.

223. Ciufolini MG, Maroli M, Verani P: Growth of two phleboviruses after experimental infection of their suspected sand fly vector, *Phlebotomus perniciosus* (Diptera: Psychodidae). *Am J Trop Med Hyg* 1985; 34:174–179.

224. Tesh RB, Modi GB: Maintenance of Toscana virus in *Phlebotomus perniciosus* by vertical transmission. *Am J Trop Med Hyg* 1987; 36:189–193.

225. Balducci M, Fausto AM, Verani P, et al: Phlebotomus-transmitted viruses in Europe. Comparative studies on their biology, ecology, epidemiology and pathogenicity, in *Proceedings of the International Congress for Infectious Diseases, Cairo, Egypt, April 20–24, 1985,* pp 101–104.

226. McLean RG, Szmyd DM, Calisher CH: Experimental studies of Rio Grande virus in rodent hosts. *Am J Trop Med Hyg* 1982; 31:569–573.

227. Endris RG, Tesh RB, Young DG: Transovarial transmission of Rio Grande virus (Bunyaviridae: *Phlebovirus*) by the sand fly *Lutzomyia anthophora. Am J Trop Med Hyg* 1983; 32:862–864.

228. Tesh RB, Peters CJ, Meegan JM: *Studies on the antigenic relationship among phleboviruses. Am J Trop Med Hyg* 1982; 31:149–155.

229. Shope RE, Meegan JM, Peters CJ, et al: Immunologic status of Rift Valley fever virus. *Contrib Epidemiol Biostatistics* 1981; 3:42–52.

230. Daubney R, Hudson JR, Garnham PC: Enzootic hepatitis or Rift Valley fever. An undescribed virus disease of sheep, cattle and man from East Africa. *East Afr Med J* 1933; 10:2–19.

231. Weiss KE: Rift Valley fever—A review. *Bull Epizootic Dis Afr* 1957; 5:431–458.

232. Easterday BC: Rift Valley fever. *Adv Vet Sci* 1965; 10:65–127.

233. Erasmus BJ, Coetzer JAW: The symptomatology and pathology of Rift Valley fever in domestic animals. *Contrib Epidemiol Biostatistics* 1981; 3:77–82.

234. Swanepoel R: Observations on Rift Valley fever in Zimbabwe. *Contrib Epidemiol Biostatistics* 1981; 3:83–91.

235. Meegan JM: The Rift Valley fever epizootic in Egypt 1977–78. I. Description of the epizootic and virological studies. *Trans R Soc Trop Med Hyg* 1979; 73:618–623.

236. Davies FG: Observations on the epidemiology of Rift Valley fever in Kenya. *J Hyg Camb* 1975; 75:219–230.

237. Davies FG, Karstad L: Experimental infection of the African buffalo with the virus of Rift Valley fever. *Trop Anim Health Prod* 1981; 13:185–188.

238. Peters CJ, Meegan JM: Rift Valley fever, in Steele JH (ed): *CRC Handbook Series in Zoonoses.* Boca Raton, Fla, CRC Press, 1981, vol 1, pp 403–420.

239. Lupton HW, Peters CJ, Eddy GA: Rift Valley fever: Global spread or global control? in *Proceedings of the 86th Annual Meeting of the United States Animal Health Association,* Nashville, 1982, pp 261–275.

240. Meegan JM, Digoutte JP, Peters, CJ, et al: Monoclonal antibodies to identify Zinga virus as Rift Valley fever. *Lancet* 1983; 1:641.
241. WHO Collaborating Centre for Arbovirus Reference and Research, Pasteur Institute, Dakar, Senegal: Rift Valley fever. *Weekly Epidemiol Rec* 1988; 8:52–53.
242. Digoutte JP, Jouan A, Le Guenno B, et al: Rift Valley fever epidemic in Mauritania, in *Abstracts of the Annual Meeting of the American Journal of Tropical Medicine and Hygiene,* Los Angeles, Calif, November 1988.
243. Peters CJ: Rift Valley fever update—West Africa. *Foreign Anim Dis Rep*; 1988; 16:7–11.
244. Saluzzo JF, Chartier C, Bada R, et al: La fievre de la vallee du Rift en Afrique de l'Ouest. *Rev Elev Med Vet Pays Trop* 1987; 40:215–223.
245. Tomori O, Fabiyi A, Sorungbe A, et al: Viral hemorrhagic fever antibodies in Nigerian populations. *Am J Trop Med Hyg* 1988; 38:407–410.
246. Walsh J: Rift Valley fever rears its head. *Science* 1988; 240:1397–1399.
246a. Rift Valley fever outbreak in 1987 (Part 1). *Res Virol* 1989; 140:27–77.
246b. Rift Valley fever outbreak in 1987 (Part 2). *Res Virol* 1989; 140:129–186.
247. Hoogstraal H, Meegan JM, Khalil GM, et al: The Rift Valley fever epizootic in Egypt 1977–78. 2. Ecological and entomological studies. *Trans R Soc Trop Med Hyg* 1979; 73:624–629.
248. Laughlin LW, Meegan JM, Strausbaugh LJ, et al: Epidemic Rift Valley fever in Egypt: observations of the spectrum of human illness. *Trans R Soc Trop Med Hyg* 1979; 73:630–633.
249. Meegan JM: Rift Valley fever in Egypt: an overview of the epizootics in 1977 and 1978. *Contrib Epidemiol Biostatistics* 1981; 3:100–113.
250. Sellers RF, Pedgley DE, Tucker MR: Rift Valley fever, Egypt 1977: disease spread by windborne insect vectors? *Vet Rec* 1982; 110:73–77.
251. Shimshony A: RVF outbreak echoes biblical plague. *Vet Rec* 1979; 104:511.
252. Kark JD, Aynor Y, Mordechai B, et al: A serological survey of Rift Valley fever antibodies in the northern Sinai. *Trans R Soc Trop Med Hyg* 1982; 76:427–430.
253. Shope RE, Peters CJ, Davies FG: The spread of Rift Valley fever and approaches to its control. *Bull WHO* 1982; 60:299–304.
254. *Rift Valley Fever: An Emerging Human and Animal Problem.* Geneva, WHO Offset Publications, 1982, pp 1–63.
255. Woodruff AW, Bowen ET, Platt GS: Viral infections in travellers from tropical Africa. *Br Med J* 1978; 1:956–958.
256. Canada Diseases Weekly Report: *Potential Importation of Dangerous Exotic Arbovirus Diseases. A Case Report of Rift Valley Fever with Retinopathy. Health and Welfare,* Canada. 1979, vol 5, pp 189–192.
257. Deutman AF, Klomp HJ: Rift Valley fever retinitis. *Am J Ophthalmol* 1981; 92:38–42.
258. Gargan TP II, Clark GC, Dohm DF, et al: Vector potential of selected North American mosquito species for Rift Valley fever virus. *Am J Trop Med Hyg* 1988; 38:440–446.
259. Smithburn KC, Haddow AJ, Gillett JD: Rift Valley fever. Isolation of the virus from wild mosquitoes. *Br J Exp Pathol* 1948; 29:107–121.
260. Weinbren MP, Williams MC, Haddow AJ: A variant of Rift Valley fever virus. *S Afr Med J* 1957; 31:951–957.
261. Digoutte J-P, Cordellier R, Robin Y, et al: Le virus Zinga (Ar B 1976), nouveau prototype d'arbovirus isolé en République Centrafricaine. *Ann Microbiol* 1974; 125:107–118.
262. McIntosh BM, Jupp PG, Dos Santos I, et al: Vector studies on Rift Valley fever virus in South Africa. *S Afr Med J* 1980; 58:127–132.
263. Hoch AL, Turell MJ, Bailey CL: Replication of Rift Valley fever virus in the sand fly *Lutzomyia longipalpis. Am J Trop Med Hyg* 1984; 33:295–299.
264. Jennings M, Platt GS, Bowen ET: The susceptibility of *Culicoides variipennis* Coq. (Diptera: Ceratopogonidae) to laboratory infection with Rift Valley fever virus. *Trans R Soc Trop Med Hyg* 1982; 76:587–589.
265. Lee VH: Isolation of viruses from field populations of *Culicoides* (Diptera: Ceratopogonidae) in Nigeria. *J Med Entomol* 1979; 16:76–79.
266. Hoch AL, Gargan II TP, Bailey CL: Mechanical transmission of Rift Valley fever virus by hematophagous diptera. *Am J Trop Med Hyg* 1985; 34:188–193.
267. Swanepoel R, Blackburn NK, Efstratiou S, et al: Studies on Rift Valley fever in some African murids (Rodentia: Muridae). *J Hyg Camb* 1978; 80:183–196.
268. Davies FG, Addy PAK: Rift Valley fever. A survey for antibody to the virus in bird species commonly found in situations considered to be enzootic. *Trans R Soc Trop Med Hyg* 1979; 73:584–585.
269. McIntosh BM, Jupp PG: Epidemiological aspects of Rift Valley fever in South Africa with reference to vectors. *Contrib Epidemiol Biostatistics* 1981; 3:92–99.
270. Linthicum KJ, Davies FG, Kairo A, et al: Rift Valley fever virus (family *Bunyaviridae* genus *Phlebovirus*). Isolations from Diptera collected during an interepizootic period in Kenya. *J Hyg Camb* 1985; 95:197–209.
271. Davies FG, Linthicum KJ, James AD: Rainfall and epizootic Rift Valley fever. *Bull WHO* 1985; 63:941–943.
272. Scott GR, Weddell W, Reid D: Preliminary findings on the prevalence of Rift Valley fever in Kenya cattle. *Bull Epizootic Dis Afr* 1956; 4:17–25.
273. Davies FG, Highton RB: Possible vectors of Rift Valley fever in Kenya. *Trans R Soc Trop Med Hyg* 1980; 74:815–816.
274. Meegan JM, Khalil GM, Hoogstraal H, et al: Experimental transmission and field isolation studies implicating *Culex pipiens* as a vector of Rift Valley fever virus in Egypt. *Am J Trop Med Hyg* 1980; 29:1405–1410.
275. Linthicum KJ, Bailey CL, Davies FG, et al: Detection of Rift Valley fever viral activity in Kenya by satellite remote sensing imagery. *Science* 1987; 235:1656–1659.
276. Smithburn KC, Mahaffy AF, Haddow AJ, et al: Rift Valley fever. Accidental infections among laboratory workers. *J Immunol* 1949; 62:213–227.
277. Francis T Jr, Magill TP: Rift Valley fever. A report of three cases of laboratory infection and the experimental transmission of the disease to ferrets. *J Exp Med* 1935; 62:433–448.
278. Mundel B, Gear J: Rift Valley fever. I. The occurrence of human cases in Johannesburg. *S Afr Med J* 1951; 25:797–800.
279. Gear J, de Meillon B, Measroch V, et al: Rift Valley fever in South Africa. 2. The occurrence of human cases in the Orange Free State, the North-western Cape Province, the Western and Southern Transvaal. *S Afr Med J* 1951; 25:908–912.
280. Chambers PG, Swanepoel R: Rift Valley fever in abattoir workers. *Cent Afr J Med* 1980; 26:122–126.
281. McIntosh BM, Russell D, Dos Santos I, et al: Rift Valley fever in humans in South Africa. *S Afr Med J* 1980; 58:803–806.
282. Imam IZE, EL-Karamany R, Omar F, et al: Rift Valley fever in Egypt. *J Egypt Public Health Assoc* 1981; 56:356–383.
283. Johnson BK, Ocheng D, Gitau LG, et al: Viral haemorrhagic fever surveillance in Kenya, 1980–1981, in Tukei PM, Njogu AR (eds): *Current Medical Research in Eastern Africa. Proceedings of the Third Annual Medical Scientific Conference, Nairobi, Kenya.* 1982, pp 97–101.
284. Tomori O: Rift Valley fever virus infection in man in Nigeria. *J Med Virol* 1980; 5:343–350.
285. Digoutte JP, Jacobi JC, Robin Y, et al: Infection à virus Zinga chez l'homme. *Bull Soc Pathol Exot Filiales* 1974; 67:451–457.
286. Niklasson B, Peters CJ, Grandien M, et al: Detection of human immunoglobulins G and M antibodies to Rift Valley fever virus by enzyme-linked immunosorbent assay. *J Clin Microbiol* 1984; 19:225–229.
287. Meegan JM, Yedloutschnig RJ, Peleg BA, et al: Enzyme-linked

immunosorbent assay for detection of antibodies to Rift Valley fever virus in ovine and bovine sera. *Am J Vet Res* 1987; 48:1138–1141.

288. Niklasson B, Grandien M, Peters CJ, et al: Detection of Rift Valley fever virus antigen by enzyme-linked immunosorbent assay. *J Clin Microbiol* 1983; 17:1026–1031.

289. Van Velken DJJ, Meyer JD, Oliver J, et al: Rift Valley fever affecting humans in South Africa. A clinicopathological study. *S Afr Med J* 1977; 51:867–871.

290. Swanepoel R, Manning B, Watt JA: Fatal Rift Valley fever of man in Rhodesia. *Cent Afr J Med* 1979; 25:1–8.

291. Gear JHS: Rift Valley fever, in Gear JHS (ed): *CRC Handbook of Viral and Rickettsial Hemorrhagic Fevers.* Boca Raton, Fla, CRC Press, 1988, p 101.

292. Gonzalez JP, Bouquety JC, Lesbordes JL, et al: Rift Valley fever virus and haemorrhagic fever in the Central African Republic. *Ann Inst Pasteur Virol* 1987; 138:385–390.

293. Abdel-Wahab KS, El Baz LM, El Tayeb EM, et al: Rift Valley fever virus infections in Egypt: pathological and virological findings in man. *Trans R Soc Trop Med Hyg* 1978; 72:392–396.

294. Boctor WM: The clinical picture of Rift Valley fever in Egypt. *Egypt Public Health Assoc* 1979; 53:177–180.

295. Imam IZE, Darwish MA, El-Karamany R: An epidemic of Rift Valley fever in Egypt 1. Diagnosis of Rift Valley fever in man. *Bull WHO* 1979; 57:437–439.

296. Maar SA, Swanepoel R, Gelfand M: Rift Valley fever encephalitis a description of a case. *Cent Afr J Med* 1979; 25:8–11.

297. Meegan JM, Watten RH, Laughlin LW: Clinical experience with Rift Valley fever in humans during the 1977 Egyptian epizootic. *Contrib Epidemiol Biostatistics* 1981; 3:114–123.

298. Schrire L: Macular changes in Rift Valley fever. *S Afr Med J* 1951; 25:926–930.

299. Cohen C, Luntz MH: Rift Valley fever and rickettsial retinitis including fluorescein angiography. *Klin Microbiol Augenhelik* 1976; 169:685–699.

300. Siam AL, Meegan JM, Gharbawi KF: Rift Valley fever ocular manifestations: Observations during the 1977 epidemic in Egypt. *Br J Ophthalmol* 1980; 64:366–374.

301. Cosgriff TM, Morrill JC, Jennings GB, et al: The hemostatic derangement produced by Rift Valley fever virus in rhesus monkeys. *Rev Infect Dis* 1989; 11:S807–S814.

302. Peters CJ, Reynolds JA, Slone TW, et al: Prophylaxis of Rift Valley fever with antiviral drugs, immune serum, an interferon inducer, and a macrophage activator. *Antiviral Res* 1986; 6:285–297.

303. Peters CJ, Jones D, Trotter R, et al: Experimental Rift Valley fever in rhesus macaques. *Arch Virol* 1988; 99:31–44.

304. Morrill J, Jennings G, Cosgriff T, et al: Prevention of Rift Valley fever in Rhesus monkeys with interferon-2. *Rev Infect Dis* 1989; 11:S815–S825.

305. Morrill JC, Jennings GB, Johnson AJ, et al: Pathogenesis of Rift Valley fever in rhesus monkeys: role of interferon response. *Arch Virol* 1990; 110:195–212.

306. Randall R, Gibbs CJ, Aulisio CG, et al: The development of a formalin-killed Rift Valley fever vaccine for use in man. *J Immunol* 1962; 89:660–671.

307. Randall R, Binn LN, Harrison VR: Immunization against Rift Valley fever virus. *J Immunol* 1964; 93:293–299.

308. Eddy GA, Peters CJ, Meadors G, et al: Rift Valley fever vaccine for humans. *Contrib Epidemiol Biostatistics* 1981; 3:124–141.

309. Niklasson B: Rift Valley fever virus vaccine trial: study of side-effects in humans. *Scand J Infect Dis* 1982; 14:105–109.

310. Kark JD, Aynor Y, Peters CJ: A Rift Valley fever vaccine trial. I. Side effects and serologic response over a six-month follow-up. *Am J Epidemiol* 1982; 116:808–820.

311. Meadors GF III, Gibbs PH, Peters CJ: Evaluation of a new Rift Valley fever vaccine: safety and immunogenicity trials. *Vaccine* 1986; 4:179–184.

312. Caplen H, Peters CJ, Bishop DHL: Mutagen-directed attenuation of Rift Valley fever virus as a method for vaccine development. *J Gen Virol* 1985; 66:2271–2277.

313. Morrill JC, Jennings GB, Caplen H, et al: Pathogenicity and immunogenicity of a mutagen-attenuated Rift Valley fever virus immunogen in pregnant ewes. *Am J Vet Res* 1987; 48:1042–1047.

314. Metselaar D: Isolation of arboviruses of Group A and Group C in Surinam. *Trop Geogr Med* 1966; 18:137–142.

315. Sekeyova M, Gresikova M, Stupalova S: Serological study on distribution of Uukuniemi virus in man. *Folia Parasitol* 1970; 17:341–343.

316. Traavik T: Arboviruses in Norway, in Kurstak E (ed): *Arctic and Tropical Arboviruses.* New York, Academic Press, 1979, pp 67–82.

317. Hoogstraal H: Viruses and ticks from migrating birds, in Verhandlungen Internationales Arbeitskolloquium über Naturherde von Infektionskrankheiten in Zentraleuropa. 1976, pp 27–50.

318. Hoogstraal H: The epidemiology of tick-borne Crimean-Congo hemorrhagic fever in Asia, Europe, and Africa. *J Med Entomol* 1979; 15:307–417, [Reprinted as Tick-borne Crimean-Congo hemorrhagic fever, in Steele JH (ed): *CRC Handbook Series in Zoonoses: Viral Zoonoses.* Boca Raton, Fla, CRC Press, 1981, vol 1, pp 267–402.]

319. Smorodintsev AA, Kazbintsev LI, Chudakov VG: *Virus Hemorrhagic Fevers.* Israel Program for Scientific Translations. Jerusalem, S Sivan Press, 1964.

320. Woodall JP, Williams MC, Simpson DIH: Congo virus: A hitherto undescribed virus occurring in Africa. Part 2—Identification Studies. *East Afr Med J* 1967; 44:93–98.

321. Casals J: Antigenic similarity between the virus causing Crimean hemorrhagic fever and Congo virus. *Proc Soc Exp Biol Med* 1969; 131:233–236.

322. Chumakov MP, Smirnova SE, Tkachenko EA: Relationship between strains of Crimean haemorrhagic fever and Congo viruses. *Acta Virol* 1970; 14:82–85.

323. Smirnova SE: A comparative study of the Crimean hemorrhagic fever–Congo group viruses. *Arch Virol* 1979; 62:137–143.

324. Casals J, Tignor GH: Neutralization and hemagglutination-inhibition tests with Crimean hemorrhagic fever–Congo virus. *Proc Soc Exp Biol Med* 1974; 145:960–966.

325. Tignor GH, Smith AL, Casals J, et al: Close relationship of Crimean hemorrhagic fever–Congo (CHF-C) virus strains by neutralizing antibody assays. *Am J Trop Med Hyg* 1980; 29:676–685.

326. Watts DM, Ksiazek TG, Linthicum KJ, et al: Crimean-Congo hemorrhagic fever, in Monath TP (ed): *The Arboviruses: Epidemiology and Ecology.* Boca Raton, Fla, CRC Press, vol 2, 1988.

327. Casals J: Crimean-Congo hemorrhagic fever, in Pattyn SR (ed): *Ebola Virus Haemorrhagic Fever.* New York, Elsevier/North Holland, 1978, pp 301–318.

328. Wood OL, Lee VH, Ash JS et al: Crimean-Congo hemorrhagic fever, Thogoto, Dugbe, and Jos viruses isolated from ixodid ticks in Ethiopia. *Am J Trop Med Hyg* 1978; 27:600–604.

329. Butenko AM, Chumakov MP, Smirnova SE, et al: Isolation of CHF virus from patient blood and autopsy material (1968–1969 investigation data) in Rostov and Astrakhan Oblast, and Bulgaria, in Eldridge BF (ed): *Miscellaneous Publications of the Entomological Society of America.* Baltimore, Geo W King, 1974, vol 9, pp 128–134.

330. Stamatovic L, Panev D, Gerovski V, et al: An epidemic of hemorrhagic fever. *Vojnosanit Pregl* 1971; 28:237–241.

331. Burney MI, Ghafoor A, Saleen M, et al: Nosocomial outbreak of viral hemorrhagic fever caused by Crimean hemorrhagic fever–Congo virus in Pakistan, January 1976. *Am J Trop Med Hyg* 1980; 29:941–947.

332. Al-Tikriti SK, Al-Ani F, Jurji FJ, et al: Congo/Crimean haemorrhagic fever in Iraq. *Bull WHO* 1981; 59:85–90.

333. Suleiman MNEH, Muscat-Baron JM, Harries JR, et al: Congo/

Crimean haemorrhagic fever in Dubai. *Lancet* 1980; 2:939–941.

334. Swanepoel R, Shepherd AJ, Leman PA, et al: Epidemiologic and clinical features of Crimean-Congo hemorrhagic fever in Southern Africa. *Am J Trop Med Hyg* 1987; 36:120–132.

335. Simpson DIH, Knight EM, Courtois GH, et al: Congo virus: A hitherto undescribed virus occurring in Africa. Part 1—Human Isolations—Clinical Notes. *East Afr Med J* 1967; 44:87–92.

336. Saluzzo JF, Aubry P, McCormick J, et al: Haemorrhagic fever caused by Crimean Congo haemorrhagic fever virus in Mauritania. *Trans R Soc Trop Med Hyg* 1985; 79:268.

337. Saluzzo JF, Digoutte JP, Cornet M et al: Isolation of Crimean-Congo haemorrhagic fever and Rift Valley fever viruses in Upper Volta. *Lancet* 1984; 1:1179.

338. Gear JHS, Thomson PD, Hopp M, et al: Congo-Crimean haemorrhagic fever in South Africa. Report of a fatal case in the Transvaal. *S Afr Med J* 1982; 62:576–580.

339. Swanepoel R, Struthers JK, Shepherd AJ, et al: Crimean-Congo hemorrhagic fever in South Africa. *Am J Trop Med Hyg* 1983; 32:1407–1415.

340. Schoub BD: Director's report—1987, in *South Africa National Institute for Virology Annual Report*. 1988, pp 3–4.

341. Sureau P, Cornet JP, Germain M, et al: A survey on tick borne arboviruses in Central African Republic (1973–1974). Isolation of Dugbe, CHF/Congo, Jos and Bhanja viruses. *Bull Soc Pathol Exot Filiales* ;1976; 69:28–33.

342. Saluzzo JF, Gonzalez JP, Herve JP, et al: Serological survey for the prevalence of certain arboviruses in the human population of the southeast area of Central African Republic. *Bull Soc Pathol Exot Filiales* 1981; 74:490–499.

343. Mathiot CC, Fontenille D, Digoutte JP, et al: First isolation of Congo-Crimean haemorrhagic fever virus in Madagascar. *Ann Inst Pasteur Virol* 1988; 139:239–241.

344. Antoniadis A, Casals J: Serological evidence of human infection with Congo-Crimean hemorrhagic fever virus in Greece. *Am J Trop Med Hyg* 1982; 31:1066–1067.

345. Horvath LB: Precipitating antibodies to Crimean haemorrhagic fever virus in human sera collected in Hungary. *Acta Microbiol Acad Sci Hung* 1976; 23:331–335.

346. Filipe AR, Calisher CH, Lazuick J: Antibodies to Congo-Crimean haemorrhagic fever, Dhori, Thogoto and Bhanja viruses in southern Portugal. *Acta Virol* 1985; 29:324–328.

347. Darwish MA, Imam IZE, Omar FM, et al: Results of a preliminary seroepidemiological survey for Crimean/Congo hemorrhagic fever virus in Egypt. *Acta Virol* 1978; 22:77.

348. Shanmugam J, Smirnova SE, Chumakov MP: Presence of antibody to arboviruses of the Crimean haemorrhagic fever–Congo (CHF-Congo) group in human beings and domestic animals in India. *Indian J Med Res* 1976; 64:;1403–1413.

349. Saidi S, Casals J, Faghih MA: Crimean hemorrhagic fever–Congo (CHF-C) virus antibodies in man, and in domestic and small mammals, in Iran. *Am J Trop Med Hyg* 1975; 24:353–357.

350. Chumakov MP, Vafakulov BKH, Zavodova TI, et al: Cases of transmission of Crimean hemorrhagic fever virus in Uzbekistan by contacts with blood of a sick cow and a human patient as well as by tick bites (Russian). *Trans Inst Polio Virus Entsef* 1974; 22:29–34.

351. Swanepoel R, Shepherd AJ, Leman PA, et al: A common-source outbreak of Crimean-Congo haemorrhagic fever on a dairy farm. *S Afr Med J* 1985; 68:635–637.

352. Goldfarb LG, Chumakov MP, Myskin AA, et al: An epidemiological model of Crimean hemorrhagic fever. *Am J Trop Med Hyg* 1980; 29:260–264.

353. Badalov ME, Lazarev VN, Koimchidi EK, et al: Contribution to the problem of CHF infections in hospitals and laboratories, in Eldridge BE (ed): *Miscellaneous Publications of the Entomological Society of America*. Baltimore, Geo W King, 1974, vol 9, pp 160–161.

354. Leshchinskaya BV, Chumakov MP: Comparative study of Crimean hemorrhagic fever in different endemic foci of similar diseases in central Asia, in Chumakov MP (ed): *Endemicheskie virusnye infektsii (Gemorragicheskaya likhoradka s pochechnym sindromon, Krymskaya gemorragicheskaya likhoradka, Omskaya gemorrhagiceheskaya likhoradka, Arstrakhanskiy virus iz kleshcha Hyalomma pl. plumbeum)*. 1965, vol 7, pp 315–323.

355. Van Eeden PJ, Joubert JR, Van De Wal BW: A nosocomial outbreak of Crimean-Congo hemorrhagic fever at Tygerberg Hospital. Part I. Clinical features. *S Afr Med J* ;1985; 68:711–717.

356. Lazarev VN, Reunova NM, Manukyan NS, et al: Certain clinical laboratory features of Crimean hemorrhagic fever in Rostov Oblast, in Eldridge BF (ed): *Miscellaneous Publications of the Entomological Society of America*. Baltimore, Geo W King, 1974, vol 9, pp 170–172.

357. Leshchinskaya EV: Clinical features of hemorrhagic fever of Crimean type in Astrakhan Oblast, in *Tick-Borne Encephalitis, Kemerovo Tick-Borne Fever, Hemorrhagic Fevers, and Other Arbovirus Infections*. Moscow, 1964, pp 266–268.

358. Leshchinskaya EV: Differential diagnosis of hemorrhagic fever of the Crimean type, in *Tick-Borne Encephalitis, Kemerovo Tick-Borne Fever, Hemorrhagic Fevers, and Other Arbovirus Infections*. Moscow, 1964, pp 268–270.

359. Leshchinskaya EV, Egorova PS: Data from observations of post-hospitalized patients recovered from Crimean type hemorrhagic fever, in *Tick-Borne Encephalitis, Kemerovo Tick-Borne Fever, Hemorrhagic Fevers, and Other Arbovirus Infections*. Moscow, 1964, p 270.

360. Swanepoel R, Gill DE, Shepherd AJ, et al: The clinical pathology of Crimean-Congo hemorrhagic fever. *Rev Infect Dis* 1989; 11:S794–S800.

361. Lazarev VN, Rychnev VE: Condition of the liver in Crimean hemorrhagic fever. *Klin Med (Mosk)* 1974; 52:100–102.

362. Joubert JR, King JB, Rossouw DJ, et al: A nosocomial outbreak of Crimean-Congo haemorrhagic fever at Tygerberg Hospital. Part III. Clinical pathology and pathogenesis. *S Afr Med J* 1985; 68:722–728.

363. Tantawi HH, Shony MO, Al-Tikriti SK: Antibodies to Crimean-Congo haemorrhagic fever virus in domestic animals in Iraq: A seroepidemiological survey. *Int J Zoonoses* 1981; 8:115–120.

364. Al-Tikriti SK, Hassan FK, Moslih IM, et al: Congo/Crimean haemorrhagic fever in Iraq: a seroepidemiological survey *J Trop Med Hyg* 1981; 84:117–120.

365. Swanepoel R, Shepherd AJ, Leman PA, et al: Investigations following initial recognition of Crimean-Congo haemorrhagic fever in South Africa and the diagnosis of 2 further cases. *S Afr Med J* 1985; 68:638–641.

366. Karimov SK, Kiryushchenko TV, Reformatskaya AF, et al: Case of laboratory infection by Crimean hemorrhagic fever virus (Russian). *Zh Mikrobiol Epidemiol Immunobiol* 1975; 136–137.

367. Radev M, Bakardzhiev T: Comparative clinico-anatomical study of Crimean hemorrhagic fever (Russian). *Probl Zarazn Parazn Bol* 1975; 3:135–143.

368. Karmyshev VYA, Leshchinskaya EV, Butenko AM, et al: Results of laboratory and clinical-morphological investigations of Crimean hemorrhagic fever. *Arkh Patol* 1973; 2:17–22.

369. Gusarev AF: Pathomorphological characteristics of CHF in Rostov Oblast, in Eldridge BF (ed): *Miscellaneous Publications of the Entomological Society of America*. Baltimore, Geo W King, 1974, vol 9, pp 174–176.

370. Baskerville A, Satti A, Murphy F, et al: Congo-Crimean haemorrhagic fever in Dubai: histopathological studies. *J Clin Pathol* 1981; 34:871–874.

371. Shepherd AJ, Swanepoel R, Leman PA, et al: Comparison of methods for isolation and titration of Crimean-Congo hemorrhagic fever virus. *J Clin Microbiol* 1986; 24:654–656.

372. Benda R, Plaisner V, Hronovsky V: Experiences with the adaptation of Crimean hemorrhagic fever virus to the CV-1 monkey cell line. *Acta Virol* 1975; 19:340–348.

373. Tantawi HH, Shony MO: Laboratory characteristics of the

"Yarmouk" strain of Crimean-Congo haemorrhagic fever virus. *Int J Zoonoses* 1981; 8:121–126.

374. Watts DM, Hasty SE, Nash D, et al: Development and evaluation of a plaque assay and plaque reduction neutralization test for Crimean-Congo hemorrhagic fever virus. Presented at the 36th Annual Meeting of the American Society of Tropical Medicine and Hygiene, Los Angeles, 1987.

375. Donets MA, Rezapkin GV, Ivanov AP, et al: Immunosorbent assays for diagnosis of Crimean-Congo hemorrhagic fever (CCHF). *Am J Trop Med Hyg* 1982; 31:156–162.

376. Saluzzo JF, LeGuenno B: Rapid diagnosis of human Crimean-Congo hemorrhagic fever and detection of the virus in naturally infected ticks. *J Clin Microbiol* 1987; 25:922–924.

377. Shepherd AJ, Swanepoel R, Gill DE: Evaluation of enzyme-linked immunosorbent assay and reversed passive hemagglutination for detection of Crimean-Congo hemorrhagic fever virus. *J Clin Microbiol* 1988; 26:347–353.

378. Obradovic M, Gligic A: Specific antibodies in the sera of patients formerly affected by Crimean-Congo hemorrhagic fever, in Vesenjak-Hirjan J, Porterfield JS, Arslanagic E (eds): *Arboviruses in the Mediterranean Countries. Zentralbl Bakteriol Mikrobiol Hyg,* 1980, pp 203–208.

379. Karinskaya GA, Chumakov MP, Butenko AM, et al: Certain data on serological investigation of patients recovered from CHF in Rostov Oblast, in Eldridge BF (ed): *Miscellaneous Publications of the Entomological Society of America.* Baltimore, Geo W King, 1974, vol 9, pp 142–144.

380. Buckley SM: Cross plaque neutralization tests with cloned Crimean hemorrhagic fever-Congo (CHF-C) and Hazara viruses. *Proc Soc Exp Biol Med* 1974; 146:594–600.

381. Blagoveshchenskaya NM, Butenko AM, Vishnivetskaya LK, et al: Dynamics of antibodies to Crimean hemorrhagic fever virus in hyperimmunized horses, in Eldridge BF (ed): *Miscellaneous Publications of the Entomological Society of America.* Baltimore, Geo W King, 1974, vol 9, pp 144–147.

382. Zavodova TI, Butenko AM, Tkachenko EA, et al: Properties of the neutralization test in Crimean hemorrhagic fever, in Chumakov MP (ed): *Viral Hemorrhagic Fevers.* Trudy Inst Polio Virus Entsef Akad Med Nauk SSSR 1971, vol 19, 61–65.

383. Shepherd AJ, Swanepoel R, Leman PA: Antibody response in Crimean-Congo hemorrhagic fever. *Rev Infect Dis* 1989; 11:S801–S806.

384. Peters CJ, Jahrling PB, Liu CT, et al: Experimental studies of arenaviral hemorrhagic fevers. *Curr Top Microbiol Immunol* 1987; 134:5–68.

385. Zgurskaya GN, Chumakov MP: Titration by indirect immunofluorescence of antibody to Crimean hemorrhagic fever virus in a drop of cell suspension from infected cell cultures. *Vopr Virusol* 1977; 5:606–608.

386. Swanepoel R, Struthers JK, McGillivray GM: Reversed passive hemagglutination and inhibition with Rift Valley fever and Crimean-Congo hemorrhagic fever viruses. *Am J Trop Med Hyg* 1983; 32:610–617.

387. Gaidamovich SYa, Klisenko GA, Shanoyan NK, et al: The indirect hemagglutination test with CHF-Congo Group viruses. *Vopr Virusol* 1974; 19:705–708.

388. Casals J, Tignor GH: A new set of antigenic relationships that includes Crimean-Congo hemorrhagic fever, Nairobi sheep disease and other arboviruses: the Nairovirus supergroup, in Pinheiro FDP (ed): *International Symposium on Tropical Arboviruses and Hemorrhagic Fevers.* Rio de Janeiro, April 14–18, 1980, pp 271–281.

389. Casals J, Tignor GH: The *Nairovirus* genus: serological relationships. *Intervirology* 1980; 14:144–147.

390. Milyutin VN, Blagoveshchenskaya NM, Bliznichenko AG, et al: Hyperimmune gamma-globulin for prophylaxis and treatment of Crimean hemorrhagic fever, in Eldridge BF (ed): *Miscellaneous Publications of the Entomological Society of America.* Baltimore, Geo W King, 1974, vol 9, pp 183–185.

391. Leshchinskaya EV, Martynenko IN: Certain questions of CHF therapy, in Eldridge BF (ed): *Miscellaneous Publications of the*

Entomological Society of America. Baltimore, Geo W King, 1974, vol 9, pp 168–170.

392. Van Eeden PJ, Van Eeden SF, Joubert JR, et al: A nosocomial outbreak of Crimean-Congo haemorrhagic fever at Tygerberg Hospital. Part II. Management of patients. *S Afr Med J* 1985; 68:718–721.

393. Shepherd AJ, Swanepoel R, Shepherd SP, et al: A nosocomial outbreak of Crimean-Congo haemorrhagic fever at Tygerberg Hospital. Part V. Virological and serological observations. *S Afr Med J* 1985; 68:733–736.

394. Watts DM, Ussery MA, Peters CJ: Effects of ribavirin on the replication of Crimean-Congo hemorrhagic fever. Presented at the Annual Meeting of the American Society for Virology, Chapel Hill, NC, May 31–June 4, 1987.

395. Berezina LK, Leont'eva NA, Kondrashina NG, et al: Influence of ribavirin on the reproduction of bunyaviruses in cell culture and in experiments on white mice. *Vopr Virusol* 1983; 5:627–629.

396. Tkachenko EA, Butenko AM, Butenko SA, et al: Characteristics of prophylactic vaccine against CHF, in Eldridge BF (ed): *Miscellaneous Publications of the Entomological Society of America.* Baltimore, Geo W King, 1974, vol 9, p 178.

397. Badalov ME, Tkachenko EA, Butenko AM, et al: Prophylactic vaccination against CHF. Report 1. Epidemiological analysis and preliminary data on observations of reactions in Rostov Oblast, in Eldridge BF (ed): *Miscellaneous Publications of the Entomological Society of America.* Baltimore, Geo W King, 1974, vol 9, pp 179–182.

398. Tkachenko EA, Butenko AM, Badalov ME, et al: Investigation of immunogenic activity of killed brain vaccine against Crimean hemorrhagic fever, in Chumakov MP (ed): *Viral Hemorrhagic Fevers.* Trudy Inst Polio Virus Entsef Akad Med Nauk SSSR 1971, vol 19, pp 119–129.

399. Vasilenko S, Levy S, Radev M, et al: Investigations on the effectivity of killed vaccine against Crimean hemorrhagic fever (CHF). *Probl Zaraz Parazitol Bol* 1975; 3:181–189.

399a. Vassilenko SM, Vassilev TR, Bozadjiev LG, et al: Specific intravenous immunoglobulin for Crimean-Congo haemorrhagic fever. *Lancet* 1990; 335:791–792.

400. Needham GR: Evaluation of five popular methods for tick removal. *Pediatrics* 1985; 75:997–1002.

401. Dandawate CN, Work TH, Webb JKG, et al: Isolation of Ganjam virus from a human case of febrile illness: a report of a laboratory infection and serological survey of human sera from three different states of India. *Indian J Med Res* 1969; 57:975–982.

402. Davies FG: Nairobi sheep disease, in Monath TP (ed): *The Arboviruses: Epidemiology and Ecology.* Boca Raton, Fla, CRC Press, 1988; vol 3, pp 191–203.

403. Montgomery E: On a tick-borne gastro-enteritis of sheep and goats occurring in British East Africa. *J Comp Pathol* 1917; 30:28–57.

404. Daubney R, Hudson JR: Nairobi sheep disease: Natural and experimental transmission by ticks other than *Rhipicephalus appendiculatus. Parasitology* 1934; 26:496–509.

405. Lewis EA: Nairobi sheep disease: The survival of the virus in the tick *Rhipicephalus appendiculatus. Parasitology* 1946; 37:55–59.

406. Davies FG: A survey of Nairobi sheep disease antibody in sheep and goats, wild ruminants and rodents within Kenya. *J Hyg Camb* 1978; 81:251–258.

407. Davies FG: Nairobi sheep disease in Kenya. The isolation of virus from sheep and goats, ticks and possible maintenance hosts. *J Hyg Camb* 1978; 81:259–265.

408. Davies FG, Mwakima F: Qualitative studies of the transmission of Nairobi sheep disease virus by *Rhipicephalus appendiculatus* (Ixodoidea, Ixodidae). *J Comp Pathol* 1982; 92:15–20.

409. Kemp GE, Causey OR, Causey CE: Virus isolations from trade cattle, sheep, goats, and swine at Ibadan, Nigeria, 1964–68. *Bull Epizootic Dis Afr* 1971; 19:131–135.

410. Williams RW, Causey OR, Kemp GE: Ixodid ticks from do-

mestic livestock in Ibadan, Nigeria as carriers of viral agents. *J Med Entomol* 1972; 9:443–445.

411. Davies FG, Casals J, Jesset DM, et al: The serological relationships of Nairobi sheep disease virus. *J Comp Pathol* 1978; 88:519–523.

412. Davies FG: The possible role of wildlife as maintenance hosts for some African insect-borne virus diseases, in Karstad L, Nestel B, Graham M (eds): *Wildlife Disease Research and Economic Development.* Ottawa, International Development Research Centre, 1981, pp 24–27.

413. David-West TS, Cooke AR, David-West AS: A serological survey of Dugbe virus antibodies in Nigerians. *Trans R Soc Trop Med Hyg* 1975; 69:358.

414. Clifford CM: Tick-borne viruses of seabirds, in Kurstak E (ed): *Arctic and Tropical Arboviruses.* New York, Academic Press, 1979, pp 83–100.

415. Digoutte JP, Gagnard VJM, Bres P, et al: Infection à virus Nyando chez l'homme. *Bull Soc Pathol Exot Filiales* 1972; 65:751–758.

416. Kalunda M, Mukwaya LG, Mukuye A, et al: Kasokero virus: a new human pathogen from bats *(Rousettus aegyptiacus)* in Uganda. *Am J Trop Med Hyg* 1986; 35:387–392.

417. Pavri KM, Anandarajah M, Hermon YE, et al: Isolation of Wanowrie virus from brain of a fatal human case from Sri Lanka. *Indian J Med Res* 1976; 64:557–561.

418. Kascask RJ, Shope RE, Donnenfeld H, et al: Antibody response to arboviruses. *Arch Neurol* 1978; 35:440–442.

419. Shah KV, Work TH: Bhanja virus: a new arbovirus from ticks *Haemaphysalis intermedia* Warburton and Nuttall, 1909, in Orissa, India. *Indian J Med Res* 1969; 57:793–798.

420. Johnson BK, Chanas AC, Squires EJ, et al: Arbovirus isolations from ixodid ticks infesting livestock, Kano Plain, Kenya. *Trans R Soc Trop Med Hyg* 1980; 74:732–737.

421. Verani P, Balducci M, Lopes MC: Isolation of Bhanja virus in Italy and serologic evidence of its distribution in man and animals of different Italian regions. *Folia Parasitol* 1970; 17:367–374.

422. Vesenjak-Hirjan J, Galinovic-Weisglass M, Urlic V, et al: Occurrence of arboviruses in the Middle and the South Adriatic (Yugoslavia), in Vesenjak-Hirjan J, Porterfield JS, Arslanagic E (eds): *Arboviruses in the Mediterranean Countries, Zentralbl Bakteriol Mikrobiol* 1980 (suppl 9):303–310.

423. Kemp GE, Causey OR, Setzer HW, et al: Isolation of viruses from wild mammals in West Africa, 1966–1970. *J Wild Dis* 1974; 10:279–293.

424. Hubalek Z: Geographic distribution of Bhanja virus. *Folia Parasitol* 1987; 34:77–86.

425. Hubalek Z, Cerny V, Rodl P: Possible role of birds and ticks in the dissemination of Bhanja virus. *Folia Parasitol* 1982; 29:85–95.

426. Calisher CH, Goodpasture HC: Human infection with Bhanja virus. *Am J Trop Med Hyg* 1975; 24:1040–1042.

427. Punda V, Beus J, Calisher CH, et al: Laboratory infections with Bhanja virus, in Vesenjak-Hiran J, Porterfield JS, Arslanagic E (eds): *Arboviruses in the Mediterranean Countries.* Stuttgart, Gustav Fischer Verlag, 1980, pp 273–275.

428. Vesenjak-Hiran J, Calisher CH, Beus I, et al: First natural clinical human Bhanja virus infection, in Vesenjak-Hiran J, Porterfield JS, Arslanagic E (eds): *Arboviruses in the Mediterranean Countries.* Stuttgart, Gustav Fischer Verlag, 1980, pp 297–301.

429. Bres P, Williams MC, Chambon L: Isolation of a new arbovirus prototype, the "Tataguine" strain (IPD/A 252) in Senegal. *Ann Inst Pasteur* 1966; 111:585–591.

430. Johnson KP, Johnson RT: California encephalitis. II. Studies of experimental infection in the mouse. *J Neuropathol Exp Neurol* 1968; 27:390–400.

431. Schwanzerova I: Tahyna virus in tissue explants of experimentally infected suckling mice. *Acta Virol* 1976; 20:73–75.

432. Peters CJ, Anderson GW Jr: Pathogenesis of Rift Valley fever. *Contrib Epidemiol Biostatistics* 1981; 3:21–41.

433. Pifat DY, Smith JF: Punta Toro virus infection of C57BL/6J mice: a model for phlebovirus-induced disease. *Microbiol Pathol* 1987; 3:409–422.

434. Peters CJ, Slone TW: Inbred rat strains mimic the disparate human response to Rift Valley fever virus infection. *J Med Virol* 1982; 10:45–54.

435. Anderson GW Jr, Slone TW Jr, Peters CJ: Pathogenesis of Rift Valley fever virus (RVFV) in inbred rats. *Microbiol Pathol* 1987; 2:283–293.

436. Mullbacher A, Marshall ID, Ferris P: Classification of Barmah Forest virus as an alphavirus using cytotoxic T Cell assays. *J Gen Virol* 1986; 67:295–299.

437. Balady MA: Primary CTL response in mice immunized with vaccinia viral vectors expressing Rift Valley fever viral glycoproteins. Presented at the Seventh International Congress of Virology, Edmonton, Alberta, Canada, Aug 9–15, 1987.

438. Newton SE, Short NJ, Dalgarno L: Bunyamwera virus replication in cultured *Aedes albopictus* (mosquito) cells: establishment of a persistent viral infection. *J Virol* 1981; 38:1015–1024.

439. Lyons MJ, Heyduk J: Aspects of the developmental morphology of California encephalitis virus in cultured vertebrate and arthropod cells and in mouse brain. *Virology* 1973; 54:37–52.

440. Elliott RM, Wilkie ML: Persistent infection of *Aedes albopictus* C6/36 cells by Bunyamwera virus. *Virology* 1986; 150:21–32.

441. Beaty BJ, Thompson WH: Tropisms of La Crosse virus in *Aedes triseriatus* (Diptera: Culicidae) following infective blood meals. *J Med Entomol* 1978; 14:499–503.

442. Beaty BJ, Thompson WH: Delineation of La Crosse virus in developmental stages of transovarially infected *Aedes triseriatus.* *Am J Trop Med Hyg* 1976; 25:505–512.

443. Tesh RB, Cornet M: The location of San Angelo virus in developing ovaries of transovarially infected *Aedes albopictus* mosquitoes as revealed by fluorescent antibody technique. *Am J Trop Med Hyg* 1981; 30:212–218.

444. Turell MJ, Gargan TP II, Bailey CL: Replication and dissemination of Rift Valley fever virus in *Culex pipiens. Am J Trop Med Hyg* 1984; 33:176–181.

445. Romoser WS, Faran ME, Bailey CL: Newly recognized route of arbovirus dissemination from the mosquito (Diptera: Culicidae) midgut. *J Med Entomol* 1987; 24:431–432.

446. Faran ME, Romoser WS, Routier RG, et al: Use of the avidin-biotin-peroxidase complex immunocytochemical procedure for detection of Rift Valley fever virus in paraffin sections of mosquitoes. *Am J Trop Med Hyg* 1986; 35:1061–1067.

447. Karabatsos N, Buckley SM: Susceptibility of the baby-hamster Kidney-cell line (BHK-21) to infection with arboviruses. *Am J Trop Med Hyg* 1967; 16:99–105.

448. Stim TB: Arbovirus plaquing in two Simian kidney cell lines. *J Gen Virol* 1969; 5:329–338.

449. Bergold GH, Mazzali R: Plaque formation by arboviruses. *J Gen Virol* 1968; 2:273–284.

450. Leake CJ, Varma MGR, Pudney M: Cytopathic effect and plaque formation by arboviruses in a continuous cell line (XTC-2) from the toad *Xenopus laevis. J Gen Virol* 1977; 35:335–339.

451. David-West TS: Tissue culture studies of common Nigerian arboviruses: propagation in different tissue culture systems. *West Afr Med J* 1972; 21:3–9.

452. Salim AR: A carrier state in hamster-embryo cells with the Naples strain of phlebotomus fever virus. *Arch Ges Virusforsch* 1968; 23:89–95.

453. Hayes CG, Corristan EC: A comparison of suckling mouse and mosquito susceptibility to infection by the Bunyamwera group arboviruses. *Mosquito News* 1972; 32:172–176.

454. Watts DM, Tammariello RF, Dalrymple JM, et al: Experimental infection of vertebrates of the Pocomoke Cypress Swamp, Maryland with Keystone and Jamestown Canyon viruses. *Am J Trop Med Hyg* 1979; 28:344–350.

455. Klimas RA, Ushijima H, Clerx-van Haaster CM, et al: Radioimmune assays and molecular studies that place *Anopheles* B

and Turlock serogroup viruses in the *Bunyavirus* genus (Bunyaviridae). *Am J Trop Med Hyg* 1981; 30:876–887.

456. Theiler M, Downs WG: *The Arthropod-Borne Viruses of Vertebrates. An Account of The Rockefeller Foundation Virus Program 1951–1970.* Yale University Press, New Haven, 1973.

457. Subcommittee on Arboviruses Laboratory Safety of the American Committee on Arthropod-borne Viruses: Laboratory Safety for arboviruses and certain other viruses of vertebrates. *Am J Trop Med Hyg* 1980; 29:1359–1381.

458. Calisher CH (ed): *Arthropod-borne Virus Information Exchange.* Fort Collins, Colo, Division of Vector-Borne Viral Diseases, Centers for Disease Control, 1990.

459. Kurstak E: Considerations on arbovirus infections in northern regions, in Kurstak E (ed): *Arctic and Tropical Arboviruses.* New York, Academic Press, 1979, pp 1–6.

460. Bárdoš V et al: *Arboviruses of the California Complex and the Bunyamwera Group.* Bratislava, Czechoslovakia, Slovak Academy of Sciences, 1969.

461. Vesenjak-Hirjan J, Porterfield JS, Arslanagic E (eds): *Arboviruses in the Mediterranean Countries. Zentralbl Bakteriol Mikrobia Hyg* (suppl 9): 1980.

462. Calisher CH, Thompson WH: *California Serogroup Viruses.* New York, Alan R Liss, 1983, vol 123.

463. El-Kholy S (ed): *J Egypt Public Health Assoc* 53:1979.

464. Swartz TA, Klingberg MA, Goldblum N: Rift Valley fever *Contrib to Epidemiol Biostatistics.* 3:1981.

465. Eldridge BF (ed): *Miscellaneous Publications of the Entomological Society of America.* Baltimore, Geo W King, 1974, vol 9.

466. Dixon KE, Llewellyn CH, Travassos da Rosa APA, et al: A multidisciplinary program of infectious disease surveillance along the Transamazon highway in Brazil: epidemiology of arbovirus infections. *Bull PAHO* 1981; 15:11–25.

467. Peralta PH, Shelokov A: Isolation and characterization of arboviruses from Almirante, Republic of Panama. *Am J Trop Med Hyg* 1966; 15:369–378.

468. Karbaat J, Jonkers AH, Spence L: Arbovirus infections in Dutch military personnel stations in Surinam. A preliminary study. *Trop Geogr Med* 1964; 4:370–376.

469. Darwish M, Hoogstraal H: Arboviruses infecting humans and lower animals in Egypt: a review of thirty years of research, in El-Kholy S (ed): *J Egypt Public Health Assoc* 1981; 56:1–112.

470. Johnson BK, Shockley P, Chanas AC, et al: Arbovirus isolations from mosquitoes: Kano Plain, Kenya. *Trans R Soc Trop Med Hyg* 1977; 71:518–521.

471. McIntosh BM, Dickinson DB, Serafini ET, et al: Antibodies against certain arbor viruses in sera from human beings and domestic animals from the South African highveld. *S Afr J Med Sci* 1962; 27:87–94.

472. McIntosh BM, Serafini ET, Dickinson DB, et al: Antibodies against certain arbor viruses in sera from human beings resident in the coastal areas of Southern Natal and Eastern Cape provinces of South Africa. *S Afr J Med Sci* 1962; 27:77–86.

22

Hantaviruses

Kelly T. McKee, Jr.
James W. LeDuc
C. J. Peters*

HISTORY

ETIOLOGIC AGENT

EPIDEMIOLOGY

CLINICAL DISEASE

NEPHROPATHIA EPIDEMICA
SEVERE HFRS CAUSED BY HANTAAN VIRUS (EPIDEMIC
    HEMORRHAGIC FEVER, KOREAN HEMORRHAGIC FEVER)
MILD HFRS CAUSED BY SEOUL VIRUS
SEVERE HFRS OF THE BALKAN REGION CAUSED BY
    POROGIA VIRUS

PATHOLOGY AND PATHOGENESIS

DIAGNOSIS

THERAPY AND PREVENTION

Hantaan is the name accorded the prototype member of a group of recently identified viruses which cause febrile diseases accompanied by hematologic and renal abnormalities. These disorders were first brought to the attention of Western physicians in the early 1950s during the Korean conflict, although Soviet, Chinese, and Japanese scientists had been familiar with them for decades previously. Widely recognized across northern Asia, these syndromes are characterized by hemorrhagic phenomena, severe renal failure, and appreciable mortality. In 1953, Gajdusek noted parallels between clinically severe disorders indigenous to the Far East, and a milder Scandinavian illness, nephropathia epidemica (NE).[1] On the basis of clinical and epidemiologic similarities, he proposed a common etiology. Subsequent work has validated this hypothesis by revealing antigenic similarities among agents responsible for febrile nephropathies across northern Europe, the Balkans, Asia, and the Orient.

The views of the authors do not purport to reflect the positions of the Department of the Army or the Department of Defense.

Prior to the 1960s, the broad geographic distribution of these disorders was reflected in an exhaustive list of syndromes identified by place of origin or predominant clinical feature (eg, Songo fever, Korean hemorrhagic fever, hemorrhagic nephrosonephritis, epidemic hemorrhagic fever, etc). Recently, the nomenclature has been unified with the designation "hemorrhagic fever with renal syndrome" (HFRS).[2, 3]

Epidemiologic investigations suggest that Hantaan and related agents are viruses which cause chronic infections of small mammals. It has been possible to show that these viruses are widely distributed among predominantly rodent species in nature. The identification of infection with Hantaan-like viruses among rodents in North and South America, Africa, and Australia has underscored their widespread distribution, and it appears that the human disease potential of these agents, although incompletely understood, may be considerable.

Morphologic and biochemical analyses have related Hantaan and its relatives to the virus family *Bunyaviridae*. However, molecular biologic as well as epidemiologic data indicate that these agents are distinct from other known genera within this large virus family. Consequently, a fifth genus within the *Bunyaviridae* family, *Hantavirus,* has been created to accommodate these widely distributed and important pathogens[4] (see Chapter 21).

HISTORY

Infectious febrile diseases with hemorrhagic and renal manifestations have been recognized across the Eurasian land mass for more than 50 years. There are, in fact, suggestions that HFRS was observed in China as early as 960 A.D.[5] In recent history, the disease was first noted by Soviet workers in 1913,[6] with sporadic outbreaks recorded in the Far Eastern USSR during the 1920s and 1930s. Between 1932 and 1935, annual outbreaks of this "new" disease were noted in the Amur River Valley region by Soviet scientists, while simultaneous observations of similar illness among troops stationed in nearby Manchuria were being made by

Table 22–1
Currently Registered* Strains of Hantaviruses

Virus	Predominant Rodent/Host	Geographic Distribution	Clinical Syndrome
Hantaan	*Apodemus agrarius*	Far East, northern Asia, USSR	Far Eastern (severe) HFRS
Seoul	*Rattus rattus* *R norvegicus*	Probably worldwide	"Mild" HFRS
Puumala	*Clethrionomys glareolus*	Europe, Scandinavia, western USSR, Balkans	Nephropathia epidemica
Prospect Hill	*Microtus pennsylvanicus*	United States	None described
Porogia†	*Apodemus flavicollis*	Balkans	Balkan (severe) HFRS

*International Catalogue of Arboviruses Including Certain Other Viruses of Vertebrates.[116]
†Not yet officially registered.

Table 22–2
Comparison of Serologic Cross-Reactivity Among Pathogenic Hantaviruses, by Immunofluorescent Antibody and Plaque Reduction Neutralization Tests

Virus	Antisera							
	Immunofluorescent Antibody				Plaque Reduction Neutralization			
	HTN	SEO	POR	PUU	HTN	SEO	POR	PUU
Hantaan	*640*	640	640	160	*1024*	256	128	<8
Seoul	160	*2560*	40	160	64	*1024*	16	<8
Porogia	320	160	*640*	320	512	8	*256*	8
Puumala	160	160	160	*640*	<8	<16	<8	*128*

Data from J. LeDuc and C. Rossi, unpublished observations, 1988.

the Japanese.[7] Presumptive evidence for both an infectious and viral etiology of HFRS was obtained independently by investigators from both the USSR and Japan in the early 1940s.[8] The Far Eastern form of the disease was reproduced in human volunteers (and possibly monkeys) by parenteral inoculation of filtered serum and urine from patients prior to their fifth day of disease and by administration of bacteria-free filtrates of tissues from field mice (*Apodemus agrarius*) and their mites collected in HFRS endemic areas. Serial human passage was made, and protection from rechallenge established. Extensive efforts to identify an experimental animal model for the disease failed, however.

During the Korean conflict, over 3000 cases were diagnosed among United Nations forces. A monumental investigative effort was mounted by military scientists to further define the etiology as well as the clinical, pathogenetic, and preventive aspects of infection.[8, 9] In spite of these efforts, attempts to reproducibly identify a causative agent were stymied until 1976, when Lee and Lee used human convalescent HFRS sera to demonstrate antigen in the lungs of *A agrarius* trapped along the banks of the Hantaan river near the border between North and South Korea.[10] Two years later, Hantaan virus, as it was subsequently named, was serially transmitted in *A agrarius*.[11] Growth in cell culture was achieved when the 76-118 *Apodemus* lung strain was propagated in A-549 (human type II alveolar epithelium) cells by French et al.[12]

At about the same time that initial efforts to characterize HFRS in the Far East were under way, a clinical complex characterized by fever, abdominal and back pain, and renal findings was described independently in Sweden by Zetterholm[13] and Myhrman.[14] During World War II, more than 1000 similar cases were reported

during an epidemic among Finnish and German troops stationed in Lapland.[15–17] The name "nephropathia epidemica" was proposed for this affliction in 1945.[18]

As with Hantaan virus in the Far East, attempts to identify the NE agent were frustrated until recently, when lung sections from infected bank voles (*Clethrionomys glareolus*) trapped in NE endemic areas demonstrated specific immunofluorescence when reacted with sera from convalescent NE patients.[19] This finding was corroborated in the USSR using both *C glareolus* and *C rutilus* (red-backed vole).[20] Isolation of the NE agent (Puumala virus) in E-6 Vero cell culture was then accomplished,[21, 22] allowing for comparative study with Hantaan virus.

Subsequent studies identified serologically related viruses in wild and laboratory rodents from Asia, Europe, the Americas, and elsewhere. Human hantavirus isolates have been obtained from patients infected in Korea, China, the Soviet Union, and Greece. Serologic findings indicate that additional viruses and host species are yet to be described. Extensive study of the relationship among hantaviruses, their mammalian hosts, and the environment, as well as their pathogenic potential for man, is under intensive investigation worldwide.

ETIOLOGIC AGENT

At present, the *Hantavirus* genus contains at least five antigenically distinct viruses as determined by cross-neutralization testing and confirmed by monoclonal antibody analysis (Tables 22-1 and 22-2).[23] Antigenic variants, either subtypes of already defined viruses or additional serotypes, are recognized as well.[23]

Among the currently recognized strains, Hantaan virus, prototype of the genus and the most extensively studied, is associated with *Apodemus* field mice in Asia, and has been implicated in epidemic hemorrhagic fever in China and Korean hemorrhagic fever in Korea.[23] Puumala virus, recovered from *C glareolus* in Scandinavia, is associated with NE.[21, 22] Seoul virus originally was isolated from rats in Seoul, Korea, and is responsible for HFRS acquired in urban areas of the Far East and perhaps elsewhere,[23-25] as well as laboratory rat–associated outbreaks worldwide.[26-28] Prospect Hill virus, recovered from field-dwelling *Microtus* rodents in the United States, has not yet been associated with human disease.[29] Recently, another hantavirus, Porogia virus, was isolated in Greece from a seriously ill patient and shown to be antigenically distinct.[30] This agent probably will represent a fifth antigenic type. Two additional and as yet incompletely characterized viruses have been isolated from rodents captured in Yugoslavia which are thought to be associated with human disease: Fojnica virus, isolated from *A flavicollis* mice, and Vranica virus, isolated from *C glareolus*.[31] Fojnica virus is closely related to both Porogia virus and prototype Hantaan virus, although preliminary analysis suggests that all may be distinct. In contrast, Vranica virus may represent a regional isolate of Puumala virus.

Several isolations of hantaviruses from a variety of mammals, including cats,[32, 33] shrews,[34] rabbits,[35] and bandicoots,[36] have been made. Little is known about these other hantaviruses. Comparative neutralization testing in progress with many of these exotic strains should help to establish whether these are additional isolates of recognized hantaviruses associated with a novel vertebrate host, or are new hantaviruses.

Direct isolation of hantaviruses in cell culture is painstaking and difficult, but has been accomplished from both human and small mammal specimens. Once adapted, the viruses grow well in several mammalian cell lines, the most useful of which are A-549 (ATCC No. CCL 185) and the E-6 clone of Vero (ATCC No. CRL 1586). In these cell lines, the viruses typically produce noncytolytic, persistent infections detectable by immunofluorescence and other antigen-visualization techniques. Viral antigen is restricted to the cytoplasm and appears in a pattern of small, discrete granules.

Plaque assays using both E-6 Vero and A-549 cells have been developed[37] and plaque reduction neutralization (PRN) testing of sera has been accomplished. Serum accessory factors appear to increase the sensitivity of the PRN test.

Although initial reports attributed orbivirus or reoviruslike morphology to Hantaan virus,[38, 39] confusion resulting from discrepancies with known physical properties of the agent[40] prompted further investigation. These conflicts were resolved by the discovery of reovirus contamination among many Hantaan pools (K. Johnson, J. Dalrymple, personal communication, 1982) and the demonstration of coexistence of the two viruses in earlier preparations.[37] Substantiating preliminary observations by French et al[41] and White et al,[42] subsequent morphologic and physiochemical studies revealed that Hantaan is an enveloped RNA virus with properties similar to viruses of the family ***Bunyaviridae***.[37, 42-44] Hantaan particles generally appear spherical to oval in shape, although virion polymorphism occurs (Figure 22-1).[45] The average diameter of virus particles is 80 to 115 nm. Virions often contain electron-dense granules, and possess surface projections.[41, 42, 45]

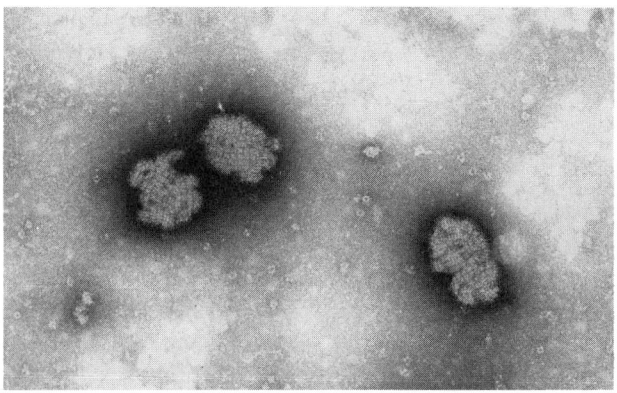

Figure 22–1. Hantaan virus, strain 76-118 (original magnification, × 105,000). (Photo courtesy of Dr John White, USAMRIID.)

The virus envelope contains lipid, and it is sensitive to 70% ethanol, deoxycholate, ether, and chloroform.[40] Infectivity is stable at pH 7.0 to 9.0, but the virus is inactivated at pH 5.0. While no significant drop in titer occurs overnight at 4°C, infectivity is rapidly lost at 37°C. Nearly 90% of infectious particles are lost by heating at 56°C for 30 minutes. Virus suspensions can be stored at −60°C in balanced salt solution with 1% bovine albumin for over 5 years.[40]

Biochemical characteristics of hantaviruses support the morphologic similarities to ***Bunyaviridae***, while properties unique to hantavirus isolates establish their existence as a separate genus within this family.[4] Intact virus particles sediment to a density of 1.15 to 1.19 g/mL in sucrose,[37] and 1.20 to 1.21 g/mL in cesium chloride.[46] Following virion disruption with nonionic detergents, three distinct ribonuclease-sensitive nucleocapsids similar in size to those of other ***Bunyaviridae***[47] can be resolved. In common with other ***Bunyaviridae*** members, three major structural proteins are found: a nucleocapsid protein (N) and two envelope glycoproteins (G1 and G2).[46, 48-51] Electrophoretic profiles of these proteins are different from those of other ***Bunyaviridae*** genera, however.[51] In comparison with other family members, hantavirus nucleocapsids are large (48,000–55,000). Molecular masses of G1 and G2 vary by isolate (68,000 and 54,000 for prototype Hantaan).[51] A large polypeptide (200,000 molecular mass), thought to represent the viral RNA polymerase, has been identified as well.[50, 51] G1 and G2 appear to be glycosylated, with the carbohydrate moieties mostly of the asparagine-linked, high-mannose type.[50-53] No nonstructural proteins have yet been found in hantaviruses.

Three RNA segments—large (L), medium (M), and small (S)—with molecular weights of 2.5, 1.3, and 0.5 × 10⁶ daltons, respectively, can be distinguished, each of which is complexed with N protein to form three nucleocapsids.[46] Most virion RNA is of negative polarity, although some message-sense RNA can be detected within nucleocapsids.[51] Assessment of the hantavirus coding strategy indicates that G1 and G2 arise from a single, continuous open reading frame in the M RNA segment which must be cotranslationally or posttranslationally processed to yield the mature glycoproteins.[51, 54] The N protein is the sole gene product of the S segment, and has been cloned, sequenced, and expressed.[51, 55] The L segment, on the other hand, has not been well characterized. Consistent with the ***Bunyaviridae***,[56-58] a consensus 3′ terminal sequence on each RNA segment has been defined for all hantaviruses thus far examined that is distinct from other genera within the virus family.[4]

Serologic cross-reactivity among hantaviruses is extensive.[59–69] However, serologic testing designed to detect antigenic similarities between Hantaan and other virus groups reveals no cross-reactions with Ebola, Marburg, several arenaviruses, and most known *Bunyaviridae*[38] (K.M. Johnson, personal communication, 1983).

Breeding and laboratory colonization of the rodent reservoir for Hantaan virus, *A agrarius coreae,* has been notoriously difficult[70] However, Hantaan virus has been adapted to laboratory rats[70] and suckling mice.[71–74] Similarly, Puumala virus has been studied in captive *C glareolus* as well as *Meriones unguiculatus* (Mongolian gerbils).[75–77] Such readily available models provide workable substrates for studies of viral pathogenesis, with the caveat that disease observed in these rodents bears no resemblance clinically or pathologically to human HFRS.

EPIDEMIOLOGY

Clinical forms of HFRS have been recognized in Korea, China, Japan, USSR, Sweden, Finland, Norway, Denmark, Belgium, France, Germany, Scotland, Hungary, Czechoslovakia, Romania, Bulgaria, Yugoslavia, Greece, and the Central African Republic.[78–84] Cases have been serologically confirmed in all but a few of the Balkan nations. Furthermore, positive serum specimens have been obtained from India, Iran, Gabon, Nigeria, Argentina, Bolivia, Alaska, Canada, and the continental United States[78, 85–87] (J.W. LeDuc, H.W. Lee, J. Maiztegui, personal communication, 1988). Coupling these serologic findings with a growing appreciation for a broad host range leads to the inescapable conclusion that HFRS is, in all likelihood, a worldwide rodent-borne zoonosis.

Small mammals, especially field mice, voles, and rats, maintain hantaviruses in nature and are thus central to the epidemiology of the human diseases which result from hantavirus infections (Figure 22–2).[88] Hantaviruses cause chronic, apparently asymptomatic infections of their rodent hosts, and are in many respects more similar to viruses of the family *Arenaviridae* (see Chapter 20) than to viruses of the family *Bunyaviridae*, where they are presently assigned. As with *Arenaviridae,* each of the known hantaviruses is predominantly associated with one or a limited small number of rodent species (see Table 22-1). Knowledge of the biology, ecology, and population dynamics of these small mammal species

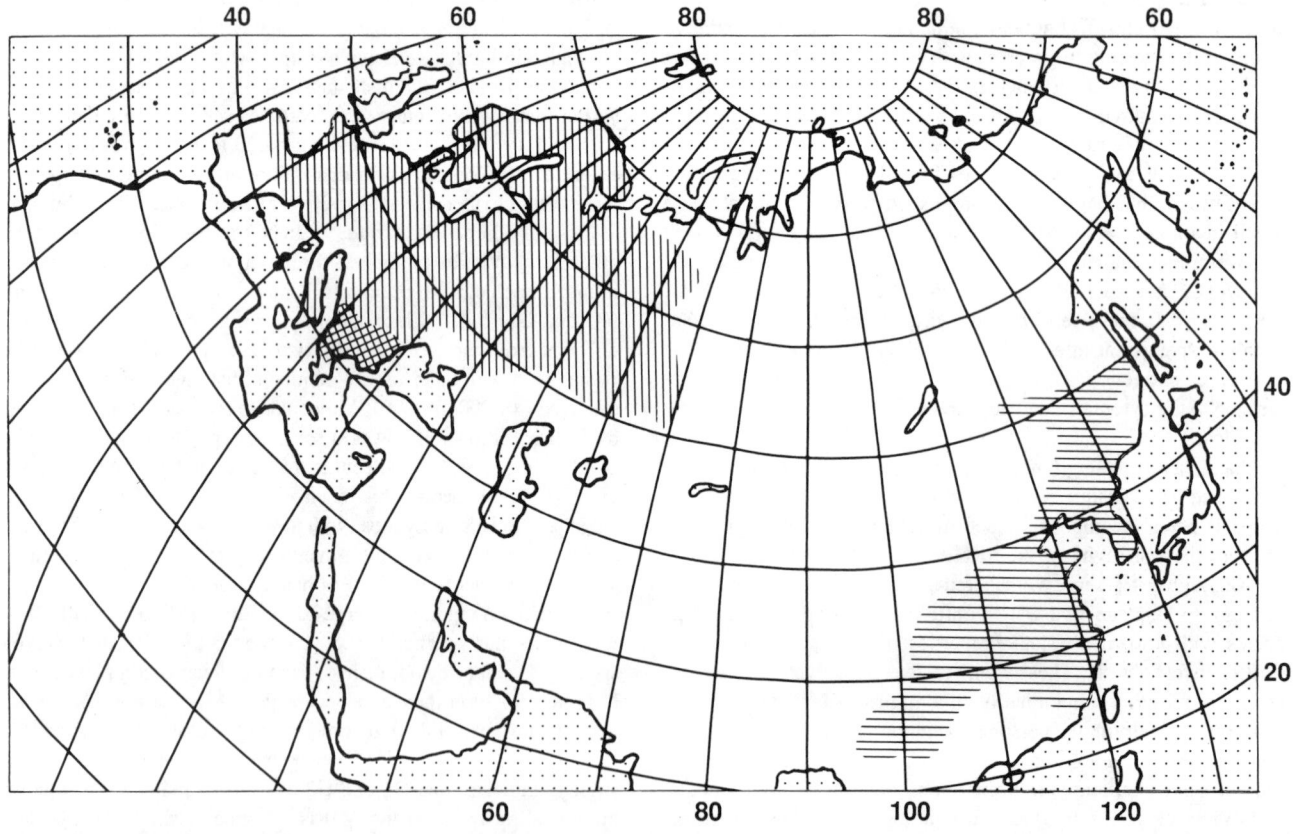

Figure 22–2. Predominant geographic distribution of rodent hosts for pathogenic hantaviruses. As noted in the text, host ranges correspond to the distribution of human hemorrhagic fever with renal syndrome (HFRS). Horizontal bars: *Apodemus agrarius,* principal reservoir for Hantaan virus (severe HFRS); vertical bars: *Clethrionomys glareolus,* principal reservoir for Puumala virus (nephropathia epidemica). *Apodemus flavicollis* is widely distributed in Western Europe; the crosshatched area represents regions where this species is thought to harbor Porogia and related viruses (Balkan HFRS). *Rattus* spp. are virtually ubiquitous, explaining in part the emergence of HFRS as a global disease problem.

which serve as reservoirs of infectious hantaviruses is key to an understanding of the epidemiology of hantavirus infections in humans. When susceptible rodents become infected, a viremia of several days duration occurs, during which virus is disseminated throughout the host's body.[89-91] Following viremia, hantavirus antigen is detectable in lungs, kidneys, and perhaps other organs, and may persist for the life of the animal. An immune response also follows viremia, and antibodies (both IgM and IgG isotypes) measurable by several serologic techniques are produced and persist, in the case of IgG, probably for the life of the host. In spite of the presence of serum neutralizing antibodies, some or all infected small mammals are able to shed infectious virus in their urine, feces, and/or saliva. Duration of shedding varies and the dynamics of this process remain obscure. Nonetheless, it is this shed virus that is thought to be the source of human infection.

Intercage transmission of Hantaan virus among *Apodemus* mice housed in cages 1 to 4 m apart has been demonstrated, and virus has been recovered from feces, urine, and saliva of infected rodents.[90] Intracage transmission of Puumala virus between bank voles together with infectious excretory products have been demonstrated as well.[77, 91] Recently, laboratory studies have found median infectious doses of 0.5, 0.7, and 0.3 plaque-forming units (PFU) for Wistar rats after aerosol exposure to Hantaan, Seoul, and Puumala viruses, respectively.[92] By comparison, the median infectious doses for these same viruses were 20- to 200-fold less when administered to rats by intramuscular (IM) inoculation.

The demonstrated presence of infectious virus in saliva of infected rodents and the marked sensitivity of these animals to hantaviruses following inoculation suggests that biting may be an important mode of transmission among rodents. The prospective seroepidemiologic studies of Childs and colleagues[93, 94] are especially instructive in this regard. Their studies in Baltimore found hantavirus infections to be very common among populations of city-dwelling rats, with overall antibody prevalence rates of nearly 50%. The mean incidence of seroconversion to the local strain of Seoul-like virus was 12 in 100 rats per month. Rats that seroconverted were generally sexually mature, and seroconversions occurred throughout the year. Those rats which seroconverted remained positive for the duration of the study, suggesting that antibody persisted for life. Young rats when first captured were either seronegative or had low-titered antibody which was interpreted as being passively acquired maternal antibody. As rats matured, especially as they became sexually active, seroconversions were detected, with antibody prevalence rates among adult rats reaching 65% to 85%. When the frequency and severity of wounding was measured among these free-living rats, a strong association was found between the presence of severe wounds and acquisition of antibody.[95] Taken together, these studies indicate that the grooming and biting behaviors associated with rodent aging and sexual maturation are an important mechanism for transmitting and maintaining hantaviruses among their reservoir hosts.

Data are accumulating to indicate that vertical transmission of hantaviruses from infected rodents to their offspring probably does not occur, at least in utero.[90, 91] Barrier breeding and foster rearing on noninfected female rats has proved effective in eliminating hantavirus contamination from infected rat colonies.[96]

The role of ectoparasites in transmission of hantaviruses remains controversial. Recent reports from China (summarized in Tsai[97]) indicate that gamasoid mites may play a role in maintaining hantaviruses in nature. The significance of this observation for human infection must still be determined. In early investigations, Soviet and Japanese scientists postulated transmission of the HFRS agent to man by means of rodent ectoparasites. Reports of disease transmission following inoculation of *Laeleps* mite suspensions[98] were not confirmed, however.[40] While a role for arthropod vectors cannot be definitely excluded, it is clear that ectoparasites are not required for transmission either among rodents or to humans.

Airborne spread appears to be the principal mechanism by which hantaviruses are transmitted from infected animals to man.[97] Investigations during the Korean conflict strongly suggested that exposure to small rodents and/or their ectoparasites was associated with subsequent human hantavirus infection. However, the most telling observations are those from laboratory outbreaks, where some exposures have been quite limited and many confounding variables such as the presence of ectoparasites have been absent. Outbreaks of HFRS have occurred in laboratories in the USSR,[99] Korea,[27] Japan,[26, 100] Belgium,[28] France,[80] and the United Kingdom.[101] While some have followed the introduction of field-caught rodents, as in the case of Moscow in 1961,[99] many others have involved laboratory-reared rats known to be ectoparasite-free. Visits of no more than a few minutes by persons to laboratories where infected rodents were housed have resulted in hantavirus infection, supporting the conclusion that aerosolization is an important mode of transmission for these agents. Incidental reports of human infection following rodent bites suggest that direct inoculation is an effective but less common mode of transmission of hantaviruses.[80, 100]

There is no indication that person-to-person spread of hantaviruses occurs. Epidemiologic studies during the Korean conflict found little to support such transmission, and while most patients seen today in Korea or China are restricted to special wards, barrier nursing is not practiced and there is no transmission to attending staff (J. LeDuc, unpublished observations, 1987).

Puumala Virus

Nephropathia epidemica is the western Eurasian HFRS variant caused by Puumala virus, a hantavirus which is antigenically more distantly related to prototype Hantaan virus than either Seoul or Porogia viruses.[4, 19] Puumala virus is maintained in nature principally by chronic infections of the bank vole, *C glareolus,* although hantavirus antigen has been found in several other species of small rodent. Puumala virus and NE have traditionally been associated with Scandinavia, especially Sweden and Finland, where they have been extensively studied.[79, 102] More recently, HFRS due to Puumala or a closely related virus has been recognized in several other European countries: France, Belgium, Federal Republic of Germany, and Great Britain (Scotland).[80-82, 103]

While bank voles are common throughout much of Europe, the Soviet Union west of the Ural Mountains, and Scandinavia, they reach their greatest population densities and undergo greatest population fluctuations near the northern limits of their distribution.[102, 104] These areas, from roughly the 60th parallel north to the Arctic Circle, are the regions where most cases of NE occur.[105, 106] Within this area, highly endemic foci have been identified, especially the region around 64N latitude in Sweden.[102, 105, 106] The disease is clearly associated with rural exposure, and is an illness primarily of adults, with males aged 20 to 40 years predominating.[79, 102, 105–107] The ratio of men to women infected is about 2:1 overall, but exceeds 3:1 in some age groups.[105, 106] Cases in children are uncommon.

Most human disease in Scandinavia is seen in late fall and early winter, with peak incidence rates from November to January; however, many cases also are diagnosed during the late summer, following the traditional summer vacations.[105, 106] Cases during the colder months are generally attributed to exposure to voles invading houses and barns with the onset of winter,[79, 102] while summertime cases are frequently associated with occupying summer cabins or cleaning out barns or other outbuildings where rodents may have nested.

Annual incidence rates of NE are tied to the cyclic population fluctuations of *C glareolus*. Bank vole population densities vary on roughly 4-year cycles, and peak populations may be 1000-fold greater than those immediately after a crash (L. Hansson, personal communication, 1986). As might be expected, human NE incidence rates correspond closely to these changes in vole abundance. In Sweden, crude incidence rates for the entire country over a 4-year period corresponding to one complete vole population cycle were estimated to be 1.3 cases per 100,000 population, but reached as high as 9.7 per 100,000 in endemic counties.[106] Annual incidence rates for a single year during which peak vole populations were recorded exceeded 20 per 100,000 in endemic counties.[105] Antibody prevalence rates increase with age and duration of residence, and may exceed 10% in endemic counties of Sweden.[105] Comparisons of incidence and prevalence rates suggested that 14 to 20 infections might occur for each hospitalized NE case.[108]

Diagnosis of HFRS cases in Europe is increasing with a greater awareness of the disease by physicians and increased availability for serologic confirmation of the diagnosis by some medical research facilities. Few large serosurveys of human populations have been attempted, but one recent study in Belgium found 1.35% of 19,890 sera possessed antihantavirus antibodies.[109] HFRS cases of variable clinical severity have been recorded in France, Belgium, Scotland, Germany, and Yugoslavia.[80–82, 84, 103] Unfortunately, it has not been possible in most instances to establish with certainty which hantavirus was responsible for a given infection, since serologic confirmation is usually provided by immunofluorescent antibody assays which are broadly cross-reactive among all hantaviruses (see Table 22-2). However, one recent attempt to clarify this situation using comparative PRN studies of patients infected in Slovenia, western Yugoslavia, clearly established that many individuals had been infected with a Puumala-like virus (T. Avsic-Zupanc and J.W. LeDuc, unpublished observations, 1988). Surveys of small mammals have indicated that *C glareolus* is the species most commonly positive for either hantavirus antigen or antibody in European areas exclusive of the Balkan region, indicating that most HFRS diagnosed in Europe may be due to Puumala virus infection.

Hantaan Virus

Epidemic hemorrhagic fever (EHF) of China, Korean hemorrhagic fever (KHF) of Korea, hemorrhagic nephrosonephritis, and Far Eastern HFRS (severe form) are synonyms for the clinical disease resulting from infection with Hantaan virus. While isolations of Hantaan or closely related viruses have been recorded from several species of rodent, it is apparent that *A agrarius* is the principal host of this virus. This species is discontinuously distributed across Asia to Europe,[104] and most rodent Hantaan virus infections have been found in Asian populations of *A agrarius* which are found from about 95E to 140E longitude and 25N to 55N latitude. Geographic distribution of human disease due to Hantaan virus infection closely parallels this distribution of *A agrarius*.

Human infection with Hantaan virus is seasonal and affects primarily adults in rural areas who are exposed to infected *A agrarius* as part of their occupational or recreational activities, or as a consequence of their living conditions (eg, farmers, forest workers, soldiers stationed in the field). Those aged 20 to 50 years represent the majority of cases, and cases in children less than 10 years old are uncommon.[40, 110] Male cases predominate, although females often are infected. Most human disease is seen during the late fall and early winter months, with peak incidence rates in November and December in the Far East.[5, 110, 111] A second, smaller peak of disease has been reported to occur in the spring in China and Korea, but this disease appears to be clinically less severe than that seen in the fall and early winter, is associated with *Rattus norvegicus* house rats, and probably represents infection with Seoul virus rather than Hantaan virus (see below).[111]

Man becomes infected with Hantaan virus as a consequence of his intrusion into the ecological niche occupied by reservoir rodents. During the Korean conflict, for example, larger numbers of cases appeared among front-line troops than in rear guard areas.[112] There are suggestions that Hantaan virus infections are not evenly distributed among rodent populations, even within hyperendemic areas (H.W. Lee, K. McKee, unpublished observations, 1987). A practical consequence of this phenomenon is the regular observation of small foci of human disease in the midst of larger, generally unaffected, populations.[79, 110, 113]

Soviet scientists have observed the largest HFRS case numbers during years when small rodents are very prevalent.[110] The late fall, early winter seasonality is due in part to the biologic characteristics of *A agrarius*, which are reproductively active during this time and have a greater prevalence of Hantaan virus infection.[5, 40, 114] Gravid *Apodemus* spp excrete more urine than nongravid mice, so that more infectious virus is introduced into the environment at this time. Farmers spend more time in their fields harvesting crops during the fall months. Environmental conditions are driest at that time, increasing the potential for airborne transmission. As cold weather sets in and crops are stored in or near houses, field mice are likely to invade human habitats, further increasing the risk for exposure.[5]

Historically, KHF was an important pathogen among military troops during the Korean conflict,[8, 9] but its importance did not cease with the signing of the armistice. In addition to cases that occur in Korean forces, several US soldiers every year are infected while on duty in Korea, and fatal infections are not uncommon.[23] As recently as 1986, an outbreak of KHF occurred among US Marines while participating in field exercises in an endemic region of South Korea.[113, 113a] Fourteen cases were identified and two fatalities recorded. Cases clustered in certain parts of the Marines' campsite, but no factors could be identified which would suggest that particular activities might have placed individuals at greater risk of infection.

Incidence and prevalence rates for Hantaan virus infection in the Far East are rough estimates at best. Between 500 and 1000 cases allegedly occur annually in the Soviet Union,[79] but this is almost certainly a gross underestimate. Approximately 300 to 900 persons are thought to be infected each year in Korea, and antibody prevalence rates of about 5% exist in the recognized endemic areas.[40] Chinese reports place the incidence of all HFRS cases as approaching 100,000 cases per year, including disease due to both Hantaan and Seoul-like virus infections.[111, 115] Regardless of the actual rates, it is clear that this disease is a significant public health problem in the affected areas.

Seoul Virus

Early serologic investigations utilized immunofluorescent antibody (IFA) tests to survey rodent populations for the presence of "Hantaan-like" viruses. Since this test is broadly cross-reactive among all hantaviruses, initial reports indicated that "Hantaan" or Hantaan-like viruses were present in domestic rat populations.[24] Subsequent isolations and characterization of viruses from *R norvegicus* and *R rattus* demonstrated that the virus harbored by rats, while antigenically similar, was clearly distinct from Hantaan virus.[116] This new virus was named Seoul virus, after the Korean city where the first virus isolate was obtained.

Outbreaks of HFRS in Osaka City, Japan,[117, 118] metropolitan Seoul,[119] and urban China[120, 121] among individuals having no contact with the usual endemic foci of Hantaan virus infection led to the discovery that house rats function as reservoirs in these areas.[24, 25, 120] Unlike the rural distribution of Hantaan virus and its resulting human disease, most human infections with Seoul virus have occurred among urban populations, where exposure to rats may be common. In China, epidemics of this generally milder form of HFRS have increased since 1981 in urban districts of the provinces of Henan, Shanxi, Jiangsu, and Shandong, and sporadic cases have occurred in other provinces as well.[115] When comparing populations infected with Seoul-like viruses to those infected with prototype Hantaan virus, there is a marked difference in seasonality, with most cases occurring in the spring and early summer months rather than late fall or early winter.[111]

The recognition of Hantaan-like viruses in domestic rats, especially those found in major Asian seaports, led several years ago to speculation that hantaviruses may have been distributed worldwide through international shipping. As a result, domestic rat populations were sampled at several ports in the United States, and infected rats were indeed identified in areas where food and harborage were abundant and little or no rodent control efforts were in place.[122–125] However, subsequent studies demonstrated that domestic rats infected with hantaviruses were present in many other parts of the world as well, including locations distant from any port facilities.[93, 126, 127] It became apparent that the Hantaan-like viruses of domestic rats were not a new introduction, but rather were likely to have been associated with these rodent species for many, many years.

Many of the rats obtained for study in Baltimore were captured in close proximity to human dwellings.[93, 94] The existence of hantavirus-infected rats coexisting with humans in a major urban center raises an obvious question: Why has associated human disease not been identified? Attempts to address this question currently are under investigation (J. Childs, personal communication, 1988),

and while overt HFRS *disease* has yet to be identified, human *infection* has, in fact, been documented.[128] Four residents of Baltimore, three of whom were known to be lifelong residents, were found to possess antibodies to hantaviruses, with highest titers to the local Seoul-like virus isolate.[128] Nearly 20 people now have been found to possess neutralizing antibody to the local rat hantavirus isolate (J. Childs, G. Gurri-Glass, and J. LeDuc, unpublished observations, 1988), indicating that human infection is not an isolated event. Studies to identify associated human disease in Baltimore are in progress, but at present no cases have been found.

Seoul-like viruses are not restricted to free-living rats. Otherwise normal laboratory rats used in physiology, immunology, and other research areas also have been found infected with hantaviruses. Infections first were reported in Japan, but additional investigations among laboratory rats in Korea, Belgium, France, and England were associated with outbreaks of HFRS among animal handlers, investigators, and others.[26–28, 100, 101] Cases were limited to persons either directly or indirectly exposed to laboratory rats, but included some individuals who visited infected animal rooms for only a matter of minutes.

Recently, a strain of hantavirus was isolated from rat immunocytomas used and stored at a research facility where an outbreak of HFRS had occurred.[129] Both transplantation to rats and storage at $-79°C$ for 8 to 10 years had not eliminated the virus from the immunocytomas. Concern that rat-origin cell line or rat-mouse hybridomas might be infected with hantaviruses led to the examination of all such cell lines and hybridomas held by the American Type Culture Collection. Fortunately they were found free of adventitious hantaviruses[130]; however, the risk of importation of rats or rat-origin cells contaminated with hantaviruses continues to be of concern and these biologicals warrant special screening procedures before being made available for general use.

Porogia Virus

A severe clinical variant of HFRS occurs in the Balkan nations, with the greatest number of cases currently recorded from Yugoslavia, Albania, Greece, and Bulgaria. While a prototype Greek isolate, Porogia virus, is thought to cause at least some of the human infections recorded,[30] assignment of a specific etiologic agent as the cause of this regional syndrome is clouded by the presence of other hantaviruses in the area and evidence suggesting that still others might exist (see above).

The yellow-necked mouse, *Apodemus flavicollis*, is widely distributed throughout the region where Balkan HFRS cases have been recorded. Serologic analysis of small mammals captured in the endemic area suggest that this species is likely to be the principal maintenance host for the virus which causes that disease.[84, 131] Like other forms of HFRS, disease in the Balkans is seen primarily among adults, especially woodcutters, foresters, shepherds, military personnel, and others whose occupations require them occasionally to work and sleep outdoors.[132] Unlike either NE or the Far Eastern forms of HFRS, most cases of HFRS in the Balkan region occur during the warmer months of the year—late spring, summer, and into early fall—when workers are likely to be involved in outdoor activities.[132] Most clusters of cases are thought to have originated around campsites, and frequently a positive history of rodent sightings in the camp, especially around stored food, can be elicited from patients. While *A flavicollis* readily

Table 22–3
Comparative Clinical Features of Recognized Hemorrhagic Fever With Renal Syndrome (HFRS)

	Nephropathia Epidemica	Far Eastern HFRS	"Mild" (Rat-borne) HFRS	Balkan HFRS
Overall severity	1+–2+	2+–4+	1+–2+	2+–4+
Multiphasic	Occasionally	Yes	Blurred	Yes
Renal abnormalities	1+–2+	4+	1+–2+	4+
Hepatic abnormalities	0	0–1+	1+–3+	0–1+
Hemorrhagic phenomena	0–1+	1+–4+	1+–2+	1+–4+
Mortality	<1%	5%–15%	1%	5%–35%

Scale = 0–4+; assignments are based on reported findings relative to other clinical types.

enters campsites in search of food, it apparently does not enter permanent man-made structures as predictably as the rodent hosts for either Hantaan or Puumala viruses; consequently, the late fall–early winter seasonality associated with field rodents invading barns and houses and typical of the diseases caused by these viruses is not seen in the Balkan region.

The incidence of Balkan HFRS is modest, with a few hundred cases reported in most years.[84, 132, 133, 133a] However, rates are influenced by the abundance of reservoir rodent populations, which fluctuate considerably. Population explosions of small rodents, as occurred during 1986 in this area, are clearly associated with outbreaks of this disease.[133a] Human antibody prevalence rates have not been recorded for all endemic areas, but in Greece, where *C glareolus* is very uncommon and Puumala or related hantaviruses are thought to be absent, antibody prevalence rates ranged from 0% to 14%, with an overall rate of 4%; seropositives resided in 15 of 22 counties examined.[132] Most counties in which seropositives were detected were in the northern and western portions of Greece, adjacent to the borders of Albania and Yugoslavia.

Prospect Hill Virus

Aside from the original isolation of Prospect Hill virus from a meadow vole, *Microtus pennsylvanicus,* captured in Frederick, Maryland, the only other recovery of this virus recently was made from *Microtus* captured in Wisconsin (K. Burek, C. Rossi, and J. LeDuc, unpublished observations, 1988). Nevertheless, antibodies specific for Prospect Hill virus have been recorded in other microtine and cricetid rodents,[134] and antibodies to the virus have been documented among mammalogists.[135] Human disease has not been associated with this virus, however.

CLINICAL DISEASE

A spectrum of clinical severity ranging from asymptomatic infection to fulminant hemorrhagic fever and death is observed in HFRS (Table 22-3). In general, milder, more benign illness is recognized at the western end of the Eurasian distribution, and is linked etiologically with Puumala virus. In contrast, serious and frequently fatal outcomes are more characteristic of Far Eastern disease associated with Hantaan virus. A generally milder, though potentially fatal, clinical variant caused by Seoul virus is recognized in the Far East as well. In the Balkan nations, a severe form of HFRS caused by Porogia virus recently has been described.[30, 132, 136, 137] There is considerable clinical as well as regional overlap, however, and geographic origin of disease does not necessarily ensure a predictable pattern of illness. Moreover, there is emerging evidence that clinical patterns as well as severity may vary by infecting strain even within a given geographic region (eg, Hantaan vs Seoul virus infections in Korea).[23] Separate discussions of the various clinical forms described to date are presented for descriptive as well as comparative purposes.

Nephropathia Epidemica

Nephropathia epidemica, caused by Puumala virus, is a generally benign febrile disorder in which renal signs predominate. The incubation period is poorly defined, but appears to be about 1 month; a range from three days to 6 weeks is reported. Onset of illness is abrupt, with little or no prodrome. Fever is the initial sign in over 94% of patients, rising within a few hours to its peak of 38 to 40°C, and persisting for two to nine days.[79, 138, 139] Headache and malaise appear within two days, and continue for the duration of the febrile phase. Presenting symptoms simulate influenza, although coryza and other respiratory symptoms are rare. Between the third and fourth days, fever, nausea, vomiting, back pain, abdominal pain, and occasional joint pain herald the second, or renal, phase of illness. Severe abdominal pain appears in over half the patients and is generally diffuse. It may localize to the right lower quadrant, however, and often mimics an acute surgical condition. Loin pain is described by some authors as being especially characteristic. Backache, typically in the costovertebral angles or lumbar area, occurs in 66% to 80% of cases.[79, 138] These clinical signs are accompanied by proteinuria (nearly 100%), azotemia (more than 70%), and oliguria (more than 50%). Proteinuria, which may be quite heavy, increases rapidly to peak 1 week into the illness, then decreases in severity over the next three to six days. A rise in serum creatinine and BUN to moderate levels in most cases (2–10 mg/dL, and 50–200 mg/dL, respectively) follows a similar course, but some elevation may persist for several weeks. Oliguria is of only a few days' duration and is followed regularly by polyuria of 3 to 4 L daily for seven to ten days. Hyposthenuria is a universal finding, beginning by the second week of illness and persisting for up to several months. Cylindruria, pyuria, and microscopic hematuria are observed in most patients; gross hematuria is seen in 3% to 7% of confirmed cases.[138, 140]

An increase in arterial blood pressure typically does not occur. Hypotension, usually mild, appears in about 40% of patients during the first week or so.

During the second phase of illness, patients often appear severely ill. Somnolence, restlessness, confusion, and meningismus are seen in up to one fifth of cases. While CSF examination is usually normal, elevated protein values occasionally are seen.[138] Transient myopia or blurred vision, present in 6% to 12% of patients, is regarded as nearly pathognomonic for NE when present in an otherwise compatible clinical setting, and is probably due to interstitial edema of the lens and ciliary body.[79, 138, 139]

Interstitial nephritis and hemorrhage are characteristic histologic features of the renal lesion. Clinical renal failure is uncommon, however, with dialysis an unusual requirement (1% or less).[138, 139] Hepatomegaly without jaundice or splenomegaly is sometimes observed, and tender cervical lymphadenopathy is reported in 15%. Facial flushing and an indistinct maculopapular rash of the neck and trunk are occasionally seen. Hemorrhagic phenomena such as epistaxis, palatal or oropharyngeal petechiae, and gastrointestinal (GI) bleeding occur in up to 5% to 10% of individuals.[79, 138, 139] Mild leukocytosis and thrombocytopenia are observed during the renal phase of the illness. An elevated sedimentation rate is a common finding.

With the onset of polyuria, clinical improvement occurs. Two weeks following onset of fever, most patients are subjectively well. Rapid normalization of urinary sediment is accompanied by a decrease in BUN and creatinine. Lassitude and backache may recur for several weeks; hyposthenuria may persist even longer. Clinical recovery is usually complete.[140]

Mortality with NE is low (consistently less than 1%). Causes of death in the few reported cases are unclear. While asymptomatic infection initially was thought to be unusual, the relatively high prevalence (2%–8%) of antibodies against Puumala virus in endemic areas in comparison to the number of reported cases indicates a subclinical-clinical ratio of 14:1 to 20:1.[105, 141] Individual cases vary greatly in severity, with geography perhaps playing a role. In 76 Finnish patients studied by Lahdevirta,[79] 23 (30%) were regarded as mild, 46 (60%) as moderate, and seven (9%) as severe. A review of 355 serologically confirmed Swedish NE cases revealed 5% with moderate to severe hemorrhage, and 1% requiring dialysis.[138] The disease in children under 15 years of age appears to be milder.

Severe HFRS Caused by Hantaan Virus (Epidemic Hemorrhagic Fever, Korean Hemorrhagic Fever)

The severe Far Eastern forms of HFRS generally are similar in the eastern USSR,[110] rural China,[142] and Korea.[40] Those individuals who develop severe disease progress through a series of clinical stages (Table 22–4). These arbitrarily designated phases—febrile, hypotensive, oliguric, diuretic, and convalescent—are not distinct, and often overlap.[40, 144] Many patients with milder disease may not, however, exhibit the five characteristic phases during the course of illness.[23, 110, 142]

Table 22–4
Clinical and Laboratory Characteristics of Severe HFRS Caused by Hantaan Virus*

Phase	Duration	Predominant Sign and Symptoms	Laboratory Findings
Febrile	3–7 d	Fever, malaise, headache, myalgia, back pain, abdominal pain, nausea, vomiting, facial flush, petechiae (face, neck, trunk), conjunctival hemorrhage	WBC: normal or elevated Platelets: decreasing Hematocrit: rising Urine: proteinuria 1 + →3 +

Hypotensive	2 h–3 d	Nausea, vomiting, tachycardia, hypotension, shock, visual blurring, hemorrhagic signs, ± oliguria (late)	WBC: ↑ with left shift
			Platelets: ↓ ↓
			Bleeding time: ↑, prothrombin time maybe prolonged
			Hematocrit: ↑ ↑
			Urine:
			  Proteinuria 4 +
			  Hematuria 1 +
			  Hyposthenuria
			BUN and creatinine: ↑ ↑

Oliguric	3–7 d	Oliguria ± anuria, BP may rise, nausea and vomiting may persist, one third with severe hemorrhage (epistaxis, cutaneous, gastrointestinal, genitourinary, CNS)	WBC: normalizes
			Platelets: normalize
			Hematocrit: normalizes, then ↓
			Urine:
			  Proteinuria 4 +
			  Hematuria 1 + →4 +
			BUN and creatinine: ↑ ↑
			NA+ ↓, K+ ↑, Ca²+ ↓

Diuretic	Days to weeks	Polyuria: r + (3–6 L daily)	BUN and creatinine: normalize electrolytes: possibly abnormal (diuresis) Urine: normalizes
Convalescent	Weeks to months	Strength and function regained slowly	Anemia and hyposthenuria: may persist for months

*Phases as seen in Korean hemorrhagic fever. All phases may not be present in a given patient (see text).
Used by permission from McKee KT Jr, et al: Hemorrhagic fever with renal syndrome—a clinical perspective. Milit Med 1985; 150:640–647.

Febrile Phase

Prodromal symptoms are rare. Disease is usually initiated with the abrupt onset of chills, high fever (39–40 + °C), malaise, myalgia, myasthenia, headache, eye pain, dizziness, and anorexia. Within one to three days, large extravasations of plasma into the peritoneum and retroperitoneal space result in severe back and abdominal pain, often accompanied by excruciating tenderness over the kidneys. Vascular dysregulation leads to a characteristic flushing of the face, neck, and chest, together with conjunctival, palatal, and pharyngeal injection. Nausea and vomiting begin and are often aggravated by an excessive thrist.

This phase lasts for three to seven days, and toward the end petechiae appear on the face, neck, axillae, chest, and soft palate. Conjunctival hemorrhage occurs. The white blood count is normal or slightly elevated, while platelet numbers decrease, and the hematocrit rises. Albumin appears early in the urine, increasing rapidly in quantity to result in massive proteinuria by the end of the febrile phase.

Clinical features are said to correlate with prognosis and disease severity, particularly degree of facial flushing, fever, conjunctival hemorrhage, duration of fever, and number of petechiae.[145]

Hypotensive Phase

Coincident with defervescence, hypotension develops abruptly, lasting from several hours to three days. Systemic symptoms increase in severity, particularly nausea, vomiting, and retching. Persistence of fever at this point is an ominous prognostic sign. The classic picture of shock quickly develops, with tachycardia and hypotension; warm, moist skin soon becomes cold and clammy, and mental changes are seen. Visual blurring is common. A third of all deaths occur at this stage, apparently as a result of relative hypovolemia. The pathophysiologic mechanisms responsible for these changes are not well understood, but reduced circulating blood volume due to plasma leakage and loss of arteriolar tone are major contributing features.[146] The hematocrit rises rapidly to levels as high as 70%, and there is evidence of erythrocyte trapping in dilated capillaries. Capillary hemorrhages are prominent, and more widespread bleeding phenomena begin to appear.

Laboratory findings include leukocytosis, usually with a marked left shift or leukemoid reaction, thrombocytopenia to levels below 100,000 per milliliter, increased hematocrit, and, in severely ill patients, prolonged bleeding time. Massive proteinuria persists, and mild hematuria and hyposthenuria appear. Progressive oliguria develops, and azotemia begins.

Oliguric Phase

The vascular derangements characterizing the initial stages of disease begin to normalize during the second week of illness. Blood pressure returns to its baseline level, and many patients experience a transient (usually mild) hypertension, presumably as a result of relative hypervolemia. At the same time, the previously narrowed pulse pressure widens, heart rate decreases, and hematocrit returns to normal.

While oliguria may have occurred earlier in patients with shock, most patients experience a reduction in urinary output at this stage. BUN and creatinine rise to peak levels, and metabolic expressions of renal failure appear. Hyponatremia, hyperkalemia, and hypo-

calcemia are common, but, curiously, metabolic acidosis at this stage is unusual.

In the most severely ill individuals, nausea and vomiting persist. Pulmonary edema and central nervous system symptoms are common findings, related presumably to relative hypervolemia and previous vascular damage.

Facial flushing and petechiae, persistent from earlier in the disease course, begin to disappear. In spite of the fact that platelet counts are returning to normal, more serious bleeding, probably a consequence of uremia, supervenes. A third of patients will show hemorrhagic manifestations of varying degree, including epistaxis, dermal purpura, and conjunctival, GI, urinary tract, and CNS bleeding.

Nearly 50% of deaths occur in this phase. Renographic studies with ^{131}I-hippurate typically show a nonfunctioning or obstructive pattern.[147] The degree of oliguria appears to be relatively proportional to severity of disease, as does the presence of a nonfunctioning-type (as opposed to obstructive) renogram; the occurrence of anuria is ominous. Pulmonary infection and/or edema, electrolyte disturbances, late shock, and CNS hemorrhage are precipitating events in a fatal outcome.

The oliguric phase generally lasts three to seven days. Toward the end, correction of the bleeding diathesis and return of renal function are seen.

Diuretic Phase

With the onset of diuresis, clinical recovery is usually initiated. The volume of urine excreted is dependent upon severity of disease, but urinary outputs of 3 to 6 L daily are the rule. Azotemia and proteinuria rapidly disappear. Patients with mild or moderate disease begin subjective improvement. Over a period of days to weeks, strength and an appetite for food are regained. On the other hand, severely ill patients, particularly those dehydrated as a result of antecedent clinical difficulties, are at extreme risk at this point. Negative fluid balances may result in shock, while persistent metabolic derangements, together with secondary infection, hazard survival.

Convalescent Phase

Complete clinical recovery often requires 3 or more months. Anemia and hyposthenuria may persist for months to years, respectively, but other abnormalities return to their premorbid norms. Aside from those patients who sustained CNS hemorrhages, complete recovery is the usual course.

Mortality in severe HFRS in the Far East has decreased from the 10% to 15% seen during the Korean War to 5% or less, due primarily to a more physiologic approach to patient management and supportive care and to the introduction of renal dialysis. In Korea,[23, 40] one third of patients will develop only a mild form of illness. About 50% to 60% will become moderately ill, while 20% will exhibit signs of severe clinical disease. One assessment of predictors of mortality in HFRS among Chinese patients suggested that admission serum total protein less than 5 mg/dL and AST (aspartate aminotransferase) greater than 90 U/L were independent predictors of mortality.[148] Total patient numbers in this study were relatively small, however (mortality = 9/95, or 9%), and these findings will require validation with larger population sizes.

Children under 10 years of age rarely contract HFRS, although vertical transmission with subsequent intrauterine fetal death has been documented.[23] The incidence of asymptomatic infection is unknown. However, among 2078 US Marines participating in a military training exercise in Korea during November 1986, the only seropositives detected were clinically ill.[113] Parenthetically, certain areas in Korea are reported to have relatively high antibody prevalances, with little or no recognized disease (H. W. Lee, personal communication, 1982).

Infections with the Hantaan-like viruses apparently confer life-long immunity, as reinfection has not been reported.

Mild HFRS Caused by Seoul Virus

Patients infected with Seoul virus appear generally to suffer a milder clinical form of HFRS than that seen following Hantaan virus infection.[23] The clinical syndrome is similar in Korea and China, as well as in laboratory rat–associated outbreaks outside the Far East.[26-28] Principal disease manifestations include fever, generalized toxicity, mild hemorrhagic phenomena, and less severe renal failure. The five distinct clinical phases characteristic of Hantaan virus infection often are blurred, and the clinical course usually is shorter. Although fatalities have been documented following Seoul virus infection, death occurs less commonly than in Hantaan-associated HRFS (perhaps 1% or less). In contrast to HFRS caused by Hantaan virus, abdominal pain, hepatomegaly, and hepatic dysfunction may dominate the clinical picture.[23] Recent reports from Hong Kong and Malaysia[23, 149, 150] serve to emphasize the predominantly hepatic, rather than renal, clinicopathologic abnormalities that may be seen in patients with this form of disease.

Currently, only sporadic cases of HFRS due to Seoul virus have been reported outside the Far East. The abundance of domestic rats in urban centers worldwide, coupled with the fact that many rat populations are known to harbor hantaviruses, suggests that this disease will gain further recognition as our appreciation and diagnostic capabilities improve. However, until this disease is commonly included by physicians in the differential diagnosis of acute febrile disorders, HFRS caused by Seoul virus or other, as yet unidentified, hantaviruses probably will remain under-diagnosed.

Severe HFRS of the Balkan Region Caused by Porogia Virus

HFRS in humans contracting disease from *A flavicollis* in the Balkan nations is not yet as extensively studied as that in Scandinavia or the Far East. Clinical illness appears often to be severe. In a study of 27 Greek HFRS patients, ten required dialysis and six developed hemorrhagic manifestations. Mortality was 15%.[137] Similarly, a mortality rate of 35% (7/20 cases) has been reported in one outbreak in Bulgaria.[133] Like severe HFRS in the Far East, the clinical picture can be divided into five distinct phases (febrile, hypotensive, oliguric, diuretic, and convalescent), each of which mimics to a large degree that described for Hantaan virus–associated disease (see above).

As with NE and typical Far Eastern HFRS, a prodrome has not been observed with this geographic variant. The abrupt onset of high fever (> 39°C) is accompanied by malaise, myalgias, chills, headache, abdominal pain, and back pain. Impairment of consciousness (from confusion to coma) is common. Flushing of the face and neck, conjunctival injection, and hypotension are seen in over 50% of patients, while arthralgias, diarrhea, and cough are less frequent. Most patients in Greece present during the hypotensive phase (4–7 days postonset).[137] At this time, thrombocytopenia and elevations of serum creatinine are present. Hemoconcentration is evident, and hematocrit values greater than 55% and hypoproteinemia are common. Leukocytosis to variable degree appears in about half the patients.

With entry into the oliguric phase (9–12 days postonset), nausea and vomiting become pronounced. Serum creatinine values peak, and hematuria (gross or microscopic) is present. Pulmonary edema (15%) and hemorrhagic phenomena (22%) complicate management. Bleeding is manifested as cutaneous petechiae, as well as nasal, renal, and GI hemorrhage. Evidence for disseminated intravascular coagulation (DIC) has been found in those individuals with severe hemorrhage in whom it has been sought. Three of four deaths in the Greek series occurred during the oliguric phase, in patients with concurrent coagulation abnormalities.[137]

Passage from the oliguric to the diuretic phase signals the onset of clinical recovery, as renal and other organ dysfunction return gradually to normal. A 1- to 2-week period of diuresis (2–4 L/d) is followed by a typically prolonged convalescence.

PATHOLOGY AND PATHOGENESIS

Typical pathologic features of HFRS have been described in Korea, Japan, China, the Soviet Far East, the western USSR, and Scandinavia.[79, 110, 151-153] While European findings are usually much milder, it is apparent that the observed clinical and pathologic lesions represent a spectrum of host responses to similar disease mechanisms.

The underlying pathologic abnormality is vascular damage, apparently at the endothelial cell level. Capillaries and small blood vessels are dilated and extravasate plasma and cellular elements into surrounding tissues.[154] The genesis of these vascular lesions is unknown. Circumstantial evidence from murine hantavirus models[71, 74] implicate both direct (ie, viral invasion) and indirect (ie, immunopathologic) mechanisms. Early clinical signs such as flushing, dizziness, and petechial hemorrhage probably are at least partially attributable to these vascular changes. In NE, where pathologic study has been confined for the most part to serial examination of renal biopsies, nodular thickenings of arteriolar walls and glomerular basement membranes, interstitial edema, and interstitial medullary hemorrhage are characteristic of acute phase changes.[79, 140, 155-157] In virtually all cases of Far Eastern HFRS, widespread capillary damage evidenced by engorgement, dilatation, diapedesis of erythrocytes, and rupture in present. Severe vascular abnormalities are most apparent in those individuals who die during the hypotensive and early oliguric phases. In almost all patients who die within the first week, large retroperitoneal plasma accumulations are observed, and many patients exhibit ascites, pleural effusions, and other extravascular fluid accumulations. Dependent edema, such as that seen with cardiac failure, is not usually present.

The pathologic changes observed in HFRS involve multiple systems, and all stem from underlying damage to the vascular bed. A distinctive triad consisting of hemorrhagic necrosis of the renal medulla, anterior pituitary, and cardiac right atrium is regularly observed in fatal Far Eastern HFRS. The peculiar distribution of the triad lesions is poorly understood, but infarctions resulting from volume shifts, pressure necrosis, anoxemia, and vascular damage are probable mechanisms. Other organs and tissues are prominently affected, as well. Pulmonary congestion and hemorrhage, together with cellular infiltrates, are frequently seen. Additional pathologic changes that have been observed include cellular degeneration and necrosis in the liver, splenic engorgement, adrenal necrosis, scattered CNS hemorrhages, and mild perivascular mononuclear cell infiltrates of the brain and other organs. The most dramatic and characteristic lesions, however, involve the kidney. Gross examination reveals swelling and congestion, with a pale or normal-appearing cortex. In contrast, the medulla is markedly abnormal with changes ranging from moderate congestion and bleeding to massive swelling and hemorrhagic necrosis. Microscopically, capillary and arteriolar congestion, red blood cell extravasation, and inflammatory (principally mononuclear cell) infiltrates are seen. The microdissection studies of Oliver and MacDowell suggest that the renal lesions result from the coincidence of an atonic vascular bed and a unique anatomical arrangement of vascular and tubular elements, particularly in the critical subcortical zone.[158] Extrusion of plasma and, later, cellular material causes tubular separation and compression, leading eventually to anoxia, tubulorrhexis, and necrosis. Tubular dilatation and degeneration are readily apparent, and tubules frequently contain fibrous material similar to that observed in expelled urine.

Sequential renal computed tomographic (CT) examination of patients with HFRS in Korea to evaluate contrast medium kinetics have provided radiographic correlates of the hemodynamic pathologic findings.[159] Prolonged enhancement of the renal profile, together with contrast washout, were typical findings, and were relatively proportional to degree of oliguria. Failure of renal tubular function was felt to be the cause of the enhancement phenomenon. A more rapid washout, often resulting in a "cartwheel" appearance of the kidney, was observed in patients with less severe oliguria, reflecting patchy recovery of perfusion, leading to improved tubular function.

The absence of clear evidence for virus cytopathologic changes in fatal cases of HFRS and the coincidence of the humoral immune response with disease onset has led to speculation regarding an immunopathologic basis for this disease. Indeed, there is now considerable evidence for activation of the interrelated complement, coagulation, and kinin cascades during the early stages of illness.

Pronounced depression of circulating C3 levels disproportionate to C4 led Korean investigators to suggest that alternative complement pathway activation was occurring in HFRS.[160] However, circulating immune complexes have been demonstrated in the serum of Scandinavian NE,[161] as well as Korean,[162] Soviet,[163] and Chinese[164, 165] HFRS patients, particularly early in the course of illness. Furthermore, patchy granular deposits of IgG and IgM, together with C3, have been identified along glomerular basement membranes, mesangium, and tubular basement membranes in patients with NE.[166, 167] These findings, together with the demonstration that C3 depression is proportional to elevated values in immune complex tests,[162] the temporal correlation between complexes and decreased C3,[168] and definitive evidence for C1 acti-

vation in the serum of patients with HFRS[164] speak strongly for classic pathway complement activation. Elevations of C3a, C4a, C5a, and other C3 fragments have been noted during the early stages of HFRS by Chinese and Korean investigators as well.[168–170]

Thrombocytopenia, defects in platelet function, and shortened platelet survival are found early in patients with Far Eastern HFRS,[168, 169] and have been associated with immune complex deposition on platelet surfaces.[169] Bleeding times are prolonged, as are prothrombin time and activated partial thromboplastin time. Specific coagulation factors (II, V, VIII, IX, and X) are depressed, while fibrinogen concentrations are decreased and fibrin degradation products are increased. Evidence of DIC is virtually univeral in severely affected patients by day 4 of disease, but decreases in frequency as disease progresses.[169] Plasminogen, alpha-2 antiplasmin, and antithrombin III levels also are diminished.[160] Depressed serum C3 levels are found predominantly in patients with DIC.[170]

Studies of the kallikrein, kinin, and renin systems also indicate extensive activation.[169, 171–174] Involvement of these pathways provides a mechanism (through bradykinin, for example) for the flushing and other vascular permeability phenomena observed clinically in HFRS. Moreover, the demonstration that elevations in plasma renin activity occur in many patients during the oliguric phase simultaneous with expanded blood volume and increased peripheral vascular resistance[175] provides a possible target in the form of renin-angiotensin inhibitors to treat hypertension during this phase. It is clear, however, that the complex intrarenal effects of these mediators[176] coupled with the potential for interaction between noxious and physiologic stimuli at the glomerular[176] and medullary[177] levels dictate a need to proceed cautiously with renin-angiotensin inhibitors or other (eg, prostaglandin inhibitors[178]) potential drug studies.

Thus, classic and alternative pathway activation of the complement cascade, perhaps most importantly through immune complex formation, is an important early event in HFRS pathogenesis. Biologically active components formed during complement activation are capable of inducing vascular alterations which in turn could provide a trigger for the observed activation of the kinin, clotting, and fibrinolytic systems. The pathophysiologic events observed early in HFRS might result from unbridled activation of these interconnected pathways and their metabolic consequences.

DIAGNOSIS

Given the global distribution of hantaviruses, the diagnosis of HFRS probably should be considered in any patient with fever and renal dysfunction or abdominal pain, regardless of location. Certainly, these diseases should rank high in the differential diagnosis of disorders affecting persons living or traveling in known HFRS endemic areas. Specific diseases with which HFRS can be readily confused on clinical grounds include leptospirosis, rickettsioses, and poststreptococcal syndromes. A high index of suspicion and recognition of characteristic clinical features, together with an appropriate exposure history, should stimulate appropriate investigative studies. With the emerging vista of widespread rodent infection with these agents, however, broader criteria to initiate specific diagnostic studies will be necessary to fully appreciate the nature of this disease worldwide.

Repeated attempts to isolate virus from serum or urine specimens obtained from patients with HFRS have met with only limited success. Isolation and subsequent identification procedures are time-consuming and therefore of little value in the management of the acutely ill patient. More rapid diagnostic assays to identify hantavirus antigen in human clinical specimens have been similarly frustrated. Attempts to capture Hantaan virus antigen from acute sera obtained from patients on the day of hospitalization in central China by enzyme immunoassay were generally unsuccessful. Viral antigen was inconsistently detected, and when present, was found in low titer, making interpretation of results difficult (J. M. Meegan and J. W. LeDuc, unpublished observations, 1987).

Demonstration of specific antihantaviral antibodies is the method of choice for laboratory confirmation of HFRS. The indirect immunofluorescent antibody (IFA) assay has been widely applied and accepted as an efficient diagnostic tool for this purpose. Given the availability of appropriate reagents and equipment, IFA results may be available within a few hours. Antibody is usually measurable by IFA within 1 week postonset of illness, often (but not always) coincident with clinical diagnosis. Attempts to measure specific IgM antibodies using this technique, however, have yielded inconsistent results, perhaps due to variation in the quality of reagents available. Also, the IFA suffers from high rates of false-positive reactions, especially when low titers of antibody (<1:64) are found. The IFA test is broadly cross-reactive among the hantaviruses (see Table 22–2), reacting with antibodies to all recognized viruses in the genus. IFA antibodies appear to persist for many years, and perhaps for life, making diagnosis based on single acute sera difficult.

Recently, hantavirus-specific IgM-capture enzyme immunoassays have been developed which may overcome some of the deficiencies of the IFA test. During a double blind, placebo-controlled efficacy trial of the antiviral drug ribavirin in China, IgM-class antibodies specific to Hantaan virus were detected in high titer (>1:1000) in virtually all of more than 200 hospitalized HFRS patients at the time of admission (J. M. Meegan and J. W. LeDuc, unpublished observations, 1987). Titers rose rapidly during the first 1 to 2 weeks of illness, reached a plateau, then began to decline at 1 to 3 months following disease onset. Similar results have been obtained by Soviet scientists examining sera from patients infected in the Far Eastern part of the Soviet Union,[179] and by Swedish investigators using Puumala virus and testing sera from NE patients.[180] The IgM-capture enzyme immunoassay requires approximately four hours for completion and could clearly provide results in sufficient time to influence clinical management. With the indication that ribavirin may be of value in treatment of HFRS (see below), prompt laboratory confirmation of the diagnosis will be critical, and the IgM-capture assay may provide that capability. While preparation and inactivation of hantaviral antigen for use in the enzyme immunoassay currently limits its application, the recent success of Schmaljohn and colleagues in expressing nucleocapsid protein products of the S segment of Hantaan virus in a baculovirus system, and application of these products in serologic tests, suggest that these limitations may be overcome shortly.[55]

Identification of which hantavirus is responsible for infection is difficult to establish by serologic analysis alone. Antibodies to Hantaan, Seoul, Puumala, and Porogia viruses all cross to high titer in the IFA (see Table 22–2) and enzyme immunoassay tests.

The PRN test is the most specific test available, and may yield tenfold or greater differences in titer between the infecting virus and heterologous hantaviruses (see Table 22–2). This test, however, utilizes live virus, requires sophisticated cell culture and biocontainment facilities, and up to 17 days may elapse before results can be read. These limitations severely restrict its utility for the routine diagnostic laboratory.

Serologic surveys to detect the presence of hantavirus antibodies in human and animal populations generally are conducted using IFA or enzyme immunoassay techniques. With an increasing appreciation for the global distribution of these agents it is becoming even more important to confirm results obtained by this broadly reactive and sometimes nonspecific test. Neutralization testing provides the most specific confirmation currently available but, for practical reasons as noted above, is not widely utilized. Alternatively, a western blot test recently has been developed which correlates well with the presence of hantavirus neutralizing antibody, but cannot distinguish among virus strains (J. E. Childs, unpublished observations, 1988). This test may be quite useful for confirming results obtained by IFA or enzyme immunoassay, and should find wide utility for serosurvey specimens.

THERAPY AND PREVENTION

Management of infected patients is often complex, phase-specific, and must be highly individualized. Close observation and supportive care remain the cornerstones of therapy. Hospitalization and avoidance of trauma are important early measures to avoid exacerbating existing vascular injury. Transport of patients should be minimized. Bed rest is essential, particularly early in disease. Sedation and narcotic analgesia may be needed for restlessness and pain associated with plasma extravasation. Attention to fluid balance and volume status must be given prime consideration, with caution not to allow fluid overload in the initial stages of illness, while maintaining adequate input to cover losses during the later (polyuric) periods. Control of hypotension should involve intravascular volume expanders such as human serum albumin rather than dextrose, saline, or electrolyte solutions. Administration of pressor agents may be helpful in severe cases.

Modern clinical imaging techniques should be useful in improving patient management. An appreciation for the extent and severity of hemodynamic changes both during and following HFRS may be gained through nephrography[147] or CT.[159] Recent studies have suggested, for example, that pituitary involvement may be more frequent (and certainly more severe) than previously appreciated.[181]

Electrolyte and acid-base status must be scrupulously monitored. Hyperkalemia in particular is not uncommon and is an occasional cause of death. Dialysis technology has improved survival through management of acute renal failure in some areas, and peritoneal or hemodialysis should be considered if available for use. Secondary infection is a significant threat to recovery, but antibiotics must be administered with attention to salt content. The use of heparin for control of hemorrhage potentially due to DIC[169, 182] has been advocated by some, but this therapy is unproven in controlled trials. Attempts to modify the course of disease through use of immunosuppressant therapy have been made by Chinese investigators,[142] but results are contradictory.

The presence of virus neutralizing antibody in convalescent plasma suggests its possible utility in prophylaxis. Individuals receiving 250 to 500 mL of convalescent plasma following parenteral exposure to virus in laboratory accidents have not become ill (K. T. McKee, C. J. Peters, and J. Dalrymple, personal communication, 1984). However, theoretical considerations such as the risk of immune complex formation and the small window of time after disease onset before appearance of antibody in natural HFRS should be addressed prior to considering passive antibody therapy. In short, there is neither an empirical nor theoretical rationale to support therapy of HFRS with immune plasma.

Specific antiviral therapy has been a highly desirable but elusive goal in HFRS. Recently, however, studies were completed that indicate that ribavirin is effective in treating at least some individuals with the disease. Based upon evidence of specific antiviral activity in a newborn mouse model,[183] human clinical studies with ribavirin were initiated in China and Korea in 1985.[184] These double-blind, placebo-controlled trials involved multiple study sites in areas selected for significant disease activity. Despite such difficulties as ensuring uniformity of clinical status at the time of protocol entry, analyses pointed to a clear reduction in mortality with ribavirin among patients treated early in the disease course. In addition, many objective disease parameters, both clinical and biochemical, were positively affected.

Preventive measures should focus on avoidance of potentially infected rodents and use of rodenticides in endemic areas. Laboratory work with these agents should be conducted under BL-3 or higher-level containment conditions. The high risk associated with exposure to infected rodents, particularly under laboratory conditions, is well established. Measures such as gowns, gloves, and respirators should be employed to prevent aerosol and fomite exposure when performing animal experiments. There currently is no vaccine of proven benefit available for hantavirus prophylaxis, although human clinical trials with inactivated mouse and rat brain preparations are underway.[185]

REFERENCES

1. Gajdusek DC: Acute infectious hemorrhagic fevers and mycotoxicoses in the Union of Soviet Socialist Republics. Medical Science Publication No. 2, Army Medical Service Graduate School, Walter Reed Army Medical Center, Washington, DC, 1953.
2. World Health Organization: Report of the Working Group on Hemorrhagic Fever with Renal Syndrome, Tokyo, Feb 22–24, 1982.
3. World Health Organization: Haemorrhagic fever with renal syndrome. Memorandum from a WHO meeting. *Bull WHO* 1983; 61:269–275.
4. Schmaljohn CS, Hasty SE, Dalrymple JM, et al: Antigenic and genetic properties of viruses linked to hemorrhagic fever with renal syndrome. *Science* 1985; 227:1041–1044.
5. Lee HW: Epidemiologic features of Korean hemorrhagic fever and research activities on this disease in the Republic of Korea. Read before WHO Working Group on Hemorrhagic Fevers with Renal Syndrome, Tokyo, Feb 22–24, 1982.
6. Casals J, Henderson BE, Hoogstraal, H, et al: A Review of Soviet viral hemorrhagic fevers, 1969. *J Infect Dis* 1970; 122:437–453.
7. Gajdusek DC: Hemorrhagic fevers in Asia: A problem in medical ecology. *Geogr Rev* 1956; 46:20–42.
8. Gajdusek DC: Virus hemorrhagic fevers. Special reference to hemorrhagic fever with renal syndrome (epidemic hemorrhagic fever). *J Pediatr* 1962; 60:841–857.
9. Earle DP: Symposium on epidemic hemorrhagic fever. *Am J Med* 1954; 16:617–709.
10. Lee HW, Lee PW: Korean hemorrhagic fever. I. Demonstration of causative antigen and antibodies. *Korean J Intern Med* 1976; 19:371–383.
11. Lee HW, Lee PW, Johnson KM: Isolation of the etiologic agent of Korean hemorrhagic fever. *J Infect Dis* 1978; 137:298–308.
12. French GR, Foulke RS, Brand OA, et al: Korean hemorrhagic fever: Propagation of the etiologic agent in a cell line of human origin. *Science* 1981; 211:1046–1048.
13. Zetterholm SG: Akuta nefriter simulerande akuta bukfall. *Svenska Lakartidningen* 1934; 31:425–429.
14. Myhrman G: En njursjukdom med egenartad symptombild. *Nord Med Tidskr* 1934; 7:793–794.
15. Stuhlfauth K: Bericht über ein neues Schlammfieberähnliches Krankheitsbild bei deutschen Truppen in Lappland. *Dtsch Med Wochenschr* 1943; 69:439–443,474–477.
16. Hortling H: Leptospirosista muistuttava epidemica Lapissa. *Sotilaslaak Aikak* 1944; 19:8–14.
17. Hortling H: En epidemi av falteber (?) in finska Lappland. *Nord Med* 1946; 30:1001–1004.
18. Myhrmann G: En ny infektionssjukdom i Nordsverige och Nord finland. *Nord Med* 1945; 28:2571–2572.
19. Brummer-Korvenkontio M, Vaheri A, Hovi T, et al: Nephropathia epidemica: Detection of antigen in bank voles and serologic diagnosis of human infection. *J Infect Dis* 1980; 141:131–134.
20. Chumakov MP, Gavrilovskaya IN, Boko MA, et al: Detection of hemorrhagic fever with renal syndrome (HFR) virus in the lungs of bank voles *Clethrenomys glareolus* and redbacked voles *Clethreonomys rutilus* trapped in HFRS foci in the European part of USSR and serodiagnosis of this infection in man. *Arch Virol* 1981; 69:295–300.
21. Niklasson B, LeDuc, JW: Isolation of the nephropathia epidemica agent in Sweden. *Lancet* 1984; 1:1012–1013.
22. Yanagihara R, Goldgaber D, Lee PW, et al: Propagation of nephropathia epidemica virus in cell culture. *Lancet* 1984; 1:1013.
23. Lee HW: Hemorrhagic fever with renal syndrome in Korea. *Rev Infect Dis* 1989; in press.
24. Lee HW, Baek LJ, Johnson KM: Isolation of Hantaan virus, the etiologic agent of Korean hemorrhagic fever, from wild urban rats. *J Infect Dis* 1982; 146:638–644.
25. Morita C, Sugiyama K, Matsurra Y, et al: Detection of antibody against hemorrhagic fever with renal syndrome (HFRS) in sera of house rats captured in port areas of Japan. *Jpn J Med Sci Biol* 1983; 36:55–57.
26. Umenai T, Lee HW, Lee PW, et al: Korean haemorrhagic fever in staff in an animal laboratory. *Lancet* 1979; 1:1314–1316.
27. Lee HW, Johnson KM: Laboratory-acquired infections with Hantaan virus, the etiologic agent of Korean hemorrhagic fever. *J Infect Dis* 1982; 146:645–651.
28. Desmyter J, LeDuc JW, Johnson KM, et al: Laboratory rat associated outbreak of haemorrhagic fever with renal syndrome due to Hantaan-like virus in Belgium. *Lancet* 1983; 2:1445–1448.
29. Lee PW, Amyx HL, Yanagihara R, et al: Partial characterization of Prospect Hill virus isolated from meadow voles in the United States. *J Infect Dis* 1985; 152:826–829.
30. Antoniadis A, Grekas D, Rossi CA, et al: Isolation of a Hantavirus from a severely ill patient with hemorrhagic fever with renal syndrome in Greece. *J Infect Dis* 1987; 156:1010–1013.
31. Gligic A, Frusic M, Obradovic M, et al: Hemorrhagic fever with renal syndrome in Yugoslavia: Antigenic characterization of Hantaviruses isolated from *Apodemus flavicollis* and *Clethrionomys glareolus*. *Am J Trop Med Hyg* 1989; 41:109–115.
32. Luo ZZ: Isolation of epidemic hemorrhagic fever virus from a cat. *Chin J Microbiol Immunol* 1985; 5:79–81.
33. Xu ZY, Tang YW, Kan LY, et al: Cats—source of protection or infection? A case-control study of hemorrhagic fever with renal syndrome. *Am J Epidemiol* 1987; 126:942–948.

34. Tang YW, Xu ZY, Zhu ZH, et al: Isolation of haemorrhagic fever with renal syndrome virus from *Suncus murinus*, an insectivore. *Lancet* 1985; 2:513–514.

35. Zhu ZY: Isolation of epidemic hemorrhagic fever virus from rabbit. *J Public Health Dis Control* 1984; 3:25–27.

36. Elwell MR, Ward GS, Tingpalapong M, et al: Serologic evidence of Hantaan-like virus in rodents and man in Thailand. *Southeast Asian J Trop Med Public Health* 1985; 16:349–354.

37. McCormick JB, Palmer EL, Sasso DR, et al: Morphological identification of the agent of Korean haemorrhagic fever (Hantaan virus) as a member of the Bunyaviridae. *Lancet* 1982; 1:765–768.

38. Lee HW: Korean hemorrhagic fever, in Pattyn SR (ed): *Ebola Virus Hemorrhagic Fever*. New York, Elsevier, North-Holland, 1978, pp 331–343.

39. Lee HW, Cho HJ: Electron microscope appearance of Hantaan virus the causative agent of Korean Haemorrhagic fever. *Lancet* 1981; 1:1070–1072.

40. Lee HW: Korean hemorrhagic fever. *Prog Med Virol* 1982; 28:96–113.

41. French GR, Brand OA, Foulke RS, et al: Search for a subhuman primate model for Korean hemorrhagic fever. Presented at the American Society for Tropical Medicine and Hygiene, Tuscon, Nov 1979.

42. White JD, Shirey FC, French GR, et al: Hantaan virus, aetiological agent of Korean haemorrhagic fever, has Bunyaviridae-like morphology. *Lancet* 1982; 1:768–771.

43. Hung T, Xia S-M, Zhao TX, et al: Morphological evidence for identifying the viruses of hemorrhagic fever with renal syndrome as candidate members of the Bunyaviridae family. *Arch Virol* 1983; 78:137–144.

44. Hung T, Xia S-M, Song G, et al: Viruses of classical and mild forms of haemorrhagic fever with renal syndrome isolated in China have similar bunyavirus-like morphology. *Lancet* 1983; 1:589–591.

45. Hung T, Choi Z, Zhao T, et al: Morphology and morphogenesis of viruses of hemorrhagic fever with renal syndrome (HFRS). I. Some peculiar aspects of the morphogenesis of various strains of HFRS virus. *Intervirology* 1985; 23:97–108.

46. Schmaljohn CS, Hasty SE, Harrison SA, et al: Characterization of Hantaan virions; prototype virus of hemorrhagic fever with renal syndrome. *J Infect Dis* 1983; 148:1005–1012.

47. Bishop DHL, Shope RE: Bunyaviridae, in Fraenkel-Corat H, Wagner RR (eds): *Comprehensive Virology*. New York, Plenum, 1979, vol 14, pp 1–156.

48. Schmaljohn CS, Dalrymple JM: Analysis of Hantaan virus RNA: Evidence for a new genus of Bunyaviridae. *Virology* 1983; 131:482–491.

49. Schmaljohn CS, Dalrymple JM: in Compans RW, Bishop DHL (eds): *Segmented Stored Viruses*. Orlando, Fla, Academic Press, 1984, pp 117–124.

50. Elliot LH, Kiley MP, McCormick JB: Hantaan virus identification of virion proteins. *J Gen Virol* 1984; 69:1285–1293.

51. Schmaljohn C: Hantaan virus, in Davae G (ed): *Virus Diseases in Laboratory and Captive Animals*. Boston, Martinus Nijhoff, 1988, pp 535–554.

52. Yaminishi K, Dantas JR, Jr, Takahashi M, et al: Antigenic differences between two viruses, isolated in Japan and Korea, that cause hemorrhagic fever with renal syndrome. *J Virol* 1984; 52:231–237.

53. Schmaljohn CS, Hasty SE, Rasmussen L, et al: Hantaan virus replication: effects of monensin, tunicamycin and endoglycosidases on the structural glycoproteins. *J Gen Virol* 1986; 67:707–717.

54. Schmaljohn CS, Schmaljohn AL, Dalrymple JM: Hantaan virus M RNA: coding strategy, nucleotide sequences, and gene order. *Virology* 1987; 157:31–39.

55. Schmaljohn CS, Sugiyama K, Schmaljohn AL, et al: Baculovirus expression of the small genome segment of Hantaan virus and potential use of the expressed nucleocapsid protein as a di-

56. Parker MD, Hewlett MJ: The 3'-terminal sequences of Uukuniemi and Inkoo RNA genome segments, in Bishop DH, Compans R (eds): *Replication of Negative Strand Viruses*. New York, Elsevier/North Holland, 1981, pp 125–133.

57. Obijeski JF, McCauley J, Skehel JJ: Nucleotide sequences at the termini of La Crosse virus RNAs. *Nucleic Acids Res* 1980; 8:2431–2438.

58. Clerx-Van Haaster CM, Clerx JPM, Ushimjimi H, et al: The 3' terminal RNA sequences of Bunyaviruses and Nairoviruses (Bunyaviridae): Evidence of end sequence generic differences within the virus family. *J Gen Virol* 1982; 61:289–292.

59. Svedmyr A, Lee HW, Berglund A, et al: Epidemic nephropathy in Scandinavia is related to Korean haemorrhagic fever. *Lancet* 1979; 1:100.

60. Svedmyr A, Lee PW, Gajdusek DC, et al: Antigenic differentiation of the viruses causing Korean haemorrhagic fever and epidemic (endemic) nephropathy of Scandinavia. *Lancet* 1980; 2:315–316.

61. Lee HW, Antoniadis A: Serologic evidence for Korean haemorrhagic fever in Greece. *Lancet* 1981; 1:832.

62. Lee HW, Lee PW, Lahdevirta J, et al: Aetiological relation between Korean haemorrhagic fever and nephropathia epidemica. *Lancet* 1979; 1:186–187.

63. Lee HW, Lee PW, Tamura M, et al: Etiologic relation between Korean hemorrhagic fever and epidemic hemorrhagic fever in Japan. *Biken J* 1979; 22:41–45.

64. Lee PW, Gajdusek DC, Gibbs CJ, et al: Aetiological relation between Korean haemorrhagic fever and haemorrhagic fever with renal syndrome in People's Republic of China. *Lancet* 1980; 1:819–820.

65. Lee PW, Gibbes CJ Jr, Gajdusek DC, et al: Identification of epidemic haemorrhagic fever with renal syndrome in China with Korean haemorrhagic fever. *Lancet* 1980; 1:1025–1026.

66. Tkachenko EA, Donets MA, Rezapkin GV, et al: Serotypes of HFRS (haemorrhagic fever with renal syndrome) virus in East European and Far Eastern USSR. *Lancet* 1982; 1:863.

67. Friman G, French GR, Hambraeus L, et al: Scandinavian epidemic nephropathy and Korean haemorrhagic fever. *Lancet* 1980; 2:100.

68. Friman G, French GR, Hambraeus L, et al: Serum antibodies reactant with Korean hemorrhagic fever agent in Scandinavian epidemic (endemic) nephropathy (nephropathia epidemica) demonstrated by immunofluorescence utilizing an in vitro antigen source. *Scand J Infect Dis* 1981; 13:89–93.

69. Lahdevirta J, Enger E, Hunderi OH, et al: Hantaan virus is related to haemorrhagic fever with renal syndrome in Norway. *Lancet* 1982; 2:606.

70. Lee PW, Amyx HL, Gibbs CJ Jr, et al: Propagation of Korean hemorrhagic fever virus in laboratory rats. *Infect Immun* 1981; 31:334–338.

71. Tsai TF, Bauer S, McCormick JB, et al: Intracerebral inoculation of suckling mice with Hantaan virus. *Lancet* 1982; 2:503–504.

72. Kurata T, Tsai TF, Bauer SP, et al: Immunofluorescence studies of disseminated Hantaan virus infection of suckling mice. *Infect Immun* 1983; 41:391–398.

73. Kim GR, McKee KT Jr: Pathogenesis of Hantaan virus infection in suckling mice: clinical, virologic, and serologic observations. *Am J Trop Med Hyg* 1985; 34:388–395.

74. McKee KT Jr, Kim GR, Green DE, et al: Hantaan virus infection in suckling mice. Virologic and pathologic correlates. *J Med Virol* 1985; 17:107–117.

75. Yanagihara R, Svedmyr A, Amyx HL, et al: Isolation and propagation of nephropathia epidemica virus in bank voles. *Scand J Infect Dis* 1984; 16:225–228.

76. Yanagihara R, Goldgaber D, Gajdusek DC: Propagation of nephropathia epidemica virus in Mongolian gerbils. *J Virol* 1985; 53:973–975.

77. Yanagihara R, Amyx HC, Gajdusek DC: Experimental infection

with Puumala virus, the etiologic agent of nephropathia epidemica in bank voles *(Clethrionomys glareolus)*. *J Virol* 1985; 55:34–38.

78. Gajdusek DC: Rodent-borne viral nephropathy (hemorrhagic fever with renal syndrome; nephropathia epidemica). Read before WHO Working Group on Haemorrhagic Fevers with Renal Syndrome, Tokyo, Feb 22–24, 1982.

79. Lahdevirta J: Nephropathia epidemica in Finland. A clinical, histological, and epidemiological study. *Ann Clin Res* 1971; 3(suppl 8):1–154.

80. Dournon E, Moriniere B, Matheron S, et al: HFRS after a wild rodent bite in Haute-Savoie and risk of exposure to Hantaan-like virus in a Paris laboratory. *Lancet* 1984; 1:676–677.

81. Zeier M, Andrassy K, Walkherr R, et al: Acute kidney failure caused by Hantaan virus. Case report from the West Germany. *Dtsch Med Wochenschr* 1986; 111:207–210.

82. Walker E, Boyd AJ, Kudesia G, et al: A Scottish case of nephropathy due to Hantaan virus infection. *J Infect* 1985; 11:57–58.

83. Coulaud X, Chouaib E, Georges AJ, et al: First human case of haemorrhagic fever with renal syndrome in the Central African Republic. *Trans R Soc Trop Med Hyg* 1987; 81:686.

84. Gligic A, Obradovic M, Stojanovic R, et al: Hemorrhagic fever with renal syndrome in Yugoslavia: Detection of hantaviral antigen and antibody in wild rodents and serological diagnosis of human disease. *Scand J Infect Dis* 1988; 20:261–266.

85. Lee HW, Seong IW, Baek LJ, et al: Positive serological evidence that Hantaan virus, the etiologic agent of hemorrhagic fever with renal syndrome, is endemic in Canada. *Can J Microbiol* 1984; 30:1137–1140.

86. Tomori O, Morikawa S, Matsuura Y, et al: Antibody to Japanese strain of haemorrhagic fever with renal syndrome (HFRS) virus in Nigerian sera. *Trans R Soc Trop Med Hyg* 1986; 80:1008–1009.

87. LeDuc JW: Hemorrhagic fever with renal syndrome in the Americas. Abstracts, Second International Conference on the Impact of Viral Diseases on the Development of Latin American Countries and the Caribbean Region, Mar del Plata, Argentina, March 20–25, 1988, p 95.

88. LeDuc JW: Epidemiology of Hantaan and related viruses. *Lab Anim Sci* 1987; 37:413–418.

89. Lee HW, French GR, Lee PW, et al: Observations on natural and laboratory infection of rodents with the etiologic agent of Korean hemorrhagic fever. *Am J Trop Med Hyg* 1981; 30:477–482.

90. Lee HW, Lee PW, Baek LJ, et al: Intraspecific transmission of Hantaan virus, etiologic agent of Korean hemorrhagic fever, in the rodent *Apodemus agrarius*. *Am J Trop Med Hyg* 1981; 30:1106–1112.

91. Bogdanova SB, Gavrilovskaya IN, Boyko VA, et al: Persistent infection caused by hemorrhagic fever with renal syndrome in red mice *(Clethrionomys glareolus)*, natural hosts of the virus. *Mikrobiol Zh* 1987; 49:99–106.

92. Nuzum EO, Rossi CA, Stephenson EH, et al: Aerosol transmission of Hantaan and related viruses to laboratory rats. *Am J Trop Med Hyg* 1988; 38:636–640.

93. Childs JE, Korch GW, Glass GE, et al: Epizootiology of *Hantavirus* infections in Baltimore: Isolation of a virus from Norway rats, and characteristics of infected rat populations. *Am J Epidemiol* 1987; 126:55–68.

94. Childs JE, Glass GE, Korch GW, et al: Prospective seroepidemiology of hantaviruses and population dynamics of small mammal communities of Baltimore, Maryland. *Am J Trop Med Hyg* 1987; 37:648–662.

95. Glass GE, Childs JE, Korch GW, et al: Association of intraspecific wounding with hantaviral infection in wild rats *(Rattus norvegicus)*. *Epidemiol Infect* 1988; 101:459–472.

96. van der Groen G, Beelaert G, Hoofd G, et al: Eradication of a hantavirus infection among laboratory rats by application of cesarian section and foster mother technique. Abstracts, 29th International Colloquium, Hantaviruses, Antwerp, Belgium, Dec 10–11, 1987.

97. Tsai TF: Hemorrhagic fever with renal syndrome: Mode of transmission to humans. *Lab Anim Sci* 1987; 37:428–430.

98. Kasahara S, Kitano M, Kikuchi H, et al: Ryukosei shekketsu netsu no byogentai no kettei. *Nihon Byori Gakkai Zasshi* 1944:34:1–2,3–5.

99. Kulagin SM, Fedorova NI, Ketiladze ES: Laboratory outbreak of hemorrhagic fever with renal syndrome (clinico-epidemiological characteristics) (Russian). *J Microb Epidemiol Immunol* 1962; 33:121–126.

100. Kawamata J, Yamanouchi T, Dohmae K, et al: Control of laboratory acquired hemorrhagic fever with renal syndrome (HFRS) in Japan. *Lab Anim Sci* 1987; 37:431–436.

101. Lloyd G, Bowen ETW, Jones N, et al: HFRS outbreak associated with laboratory rats in UK. *Lancet* 1984; 1:1175–1176.

102. Nystrom K: *Incidence and Prevalence of Endemic Benign (Epidemic) Nephropathy in AC County, Sweden in Relation to Population Density and Prevalence of Small Rodents*. Umea University Medical Dissertations, New Series, No. 30, Umea, Sweden, Umea University, 1977.

103. Clement J, van der Groen G: Acute hantavirus nephropathy in Belgium: Preliminary results of a sero-epidemiological study, in Amerio A, Coratelli P, Campese VM, Massry SG (eds): *Acute Renal Failure*. New York, Plenum, 1987, pp 251–263.

104. Corbet GB: *The Mammals of the Palaeartic Region: A Taxonomic Review*. Ithaca, NY, British Museum (Natural History), Cornell University Press, 1978, pp 1–314.

105. Niklasson B, LeDuc JW: Epidemiology of nephropathia epidemica in Sweden. *J Infect Dis* 1987; 155:269–276.

106. Settergren B, Juto P, Wadell G, et al: Incidence and geographic distribution of serologically verified cases of nephropathia epidemica in Sweden. *Am J Epidemiol* 1988; 127:801–807.

107. Ornstein K, Soderhjelm L: Nephropathia epidemica. *Med Welt* 1965; 17:898–901.

108. Niklasson B, LeDuc J, Nystrom K, et al: Nephropathia epidemica: Incidence of clinical cases and antibody prevalence in an endemic area of Sweden. *Epidemiol Infect* 1987; 99:559–562.

109. Clement J, Lefevre A, Verhagen R, et al: Hantavirus nephropathy (HVN) in Belgium. Abstracts, 25th Congress of the European Dialysis and Transplant Association–European Renal Association, Madrid, Sept 5–8, 1988.

110. Smorodintsev AA, Chudakov VG, Churilov AV: *Haemorrhagic Nephrosonephritis*, Mathews C (trans). London, Programm Press, 1959.

111. Chen HX, Qui FX, Dong BJ, et al: Epidemiological studies on hemorrhagic fever with renal syndrome in China. *J Infect Dis* 1986; 154:394–398.

112. Paul JR, McClure WW: Epidemic hemorrhagic fever attack rates among United Nations Troops during the Korean War. *Am J Hyg* 1958; 68:126–139.

113. Pon E, Merrell B, Thomas R, et al: Korean hemorrhagic fever. *MMWR* 1988; 37:87–96.

113a. Pon E, McKee KT Jr, Diniega BM, et al: Hemorrhagic fever with renal syndrome among U.S. Marines in Korea. *Am J Trop Med Hyg* 1990; 42:612–619.

114. Lee HW, Baek LJ, Doo CD: The study on breeding season of *Apodemus agrarius*, the natural host of Korean hemorrhagic fever. *Korean J Virol* 1981; 11:1–5.

115. Song G, Hang C, Liao H, et al: Antigenic differences between viral strains causing classical and mild types of epidemic hemorrhagic fever with renal syndrome in China. *J Infect Dis* 1984; 150:889–894.

116. Karabatsos N: *International Catalogue of Arboviruses Including Certain Other Viruses of Vertebrates*. San Antonio, Texas, American Society of Tropical Medicine and Hygiene, 1985, pp 927–928.

117. Tamura M: Occurrence of epidemic hemorrhagic fever in Osaka City; first cases found in Japan with characteristic feature of marked proteinuria. *Biken J* 1964; 7:79–94.

118. Tamura T, Yatsukuru T, Okano K: Clinical features of epidemic hemorrhagic fever. *Kansen, Ensho, Men-eki* 1979; 9:280–289.

119. Lee HW, Bark DH, Baek LJ, et al: Korean hemorrhagic fever patients in urban areas of Seoul. *Korean J Virol* 1980; 10:1–6.

120. Hang CS, Song G, Qui XZ, et al: Etiological study of outbreaks of a mild type of hemorrhagic fever. *Chin J Epidemiol* 1982; 3:204–205.

121. Sung G, Hang CS, Qui XZ, et al: Etiologic studies of epidemic hemorrhagic fever (hemorrhagic fever with renal syndrome). *J Infect Dis* 1983; 147:654–659.

122. Tsai TF, Bauer SP, Sasso DR, et al: Preliminary evidence that Hantaan or a closely related virus is enzootic in domestic rodents. *N Engl J Med* 1982; 307:623–624.

123. LeDuc JW, Smith GA, Bagley LR, et al: Preliminary evidence that Hantaan or a closely related virus is enzootic in domestic rodents. *N Engl J Med* 1982; 307:624.

124. LeDuc JW, Smith GA, Johnson KM: Hantaan-like viruses from domestic rats captured in the United States. *Am J Trop Med Hyg* 1984; 33:992–998.

125. Tsai TF, Bauer SP, Sasso DR, et al: Serological and virological evidence of a Hantaan virus–related enzootic in the United States. *J Infect Dis* 1985; 152:126–136.

126. LeDuc JW, Smith GA, Pinheiro FP, et al: Isolation of a Hantaan-related virus from Brazilian rats and serologic evidence of its widespread distribution in South America. *Am J Trop Med Hyg* 1985; 34:810–815.

127. LeDuc JW, Smith GA, Childs JE, et al: Global survey of antibody to Hantaan related viruses among peridomestic rodents. *Bull WHO* 1986; 64:139–144.

128. Childs JE, Glass GE, Korch GW, et al: Evidence of human infection with a rat-associated *Hantavirus* in Baltimore, Maryland. *Am J Epidemiol* 1988; 127:875–878.

129. Lloyd G, Jones N: Infection of laboratory workers with hantavirus acquired from immunocytomas propagated in laboratory rats. *J Infect* 1986; 12:117–125.

130. LeDuc JW, Smith GA, Macy M, et al: Certified cell lines of rat origin appear free of infection with *Hantavirus*. *J Infect Dis* 1985; 152:1082–1083.

131. LeDuc JW, Antoniadis A, Siampoulus K: Epidemiological investigations following an outbreak of hemorrhagic fever with renal syndrome in Greece. *Am J Trop Med Hyg* 1986; 35:654–659.

132. Antoniadis A, LeDuc JW, Daniel-Alexiou A: Clinical and epidemiological aspects of hemorrhagic fever with renal syndrome (HFRS) in Greece. *Eur J Epidemiol* 1987; 3:295–301.

133. Vassilenko S, Shindarov L, Katzarov G: On the problem of the ethimological virus diagnosis of haemorrhagic fever with renal syndrome (HFRS) (sic). Abstracts, Third International Symposium on Ecology of Arboviruses, Smolenice, Czechoslovakia, Sept 7–11, 1987, p 77.

133a. Gligic A, Obradovic M, Stojanovic R, et al: Epidemic hemorrhagic fever with renal syndrome in Yugoslavia, 1986. *Am J Trop Med Hyg* 1989; 41:102–108.

134. Yanagihara R, Daum CA, Lee PW, et al: Serological survey of Prospect Hill virus infection in indigenous wild rodents in the USA. *Trans R Soc Trop Med Hyg* 1987; 81:42–45.

135. Yanagihara R, Gajdusek DC, Gibbs CJ Jr, et al: Prospect Hill virus: serological evidence for infection in mammalogist. *N Engl J Med* 1984; 310:1325–1326.

136. Antoniadis A, Pyrpasopoulos M, Sion M, et al: Two cases of hemorrhagic fever with renal syndrome in northern Greece. *J Infect Dis* 1984; 149:1011–1013.

137. Antoniadis A, LeDuc JW, Acritidis N, et al: Hemorrhagic fever with renal syndrome in Greece: Clinical and laboratory characteristics of the disease. *Rev Infect Dis* 1989; 11:S891–S896..

138. Settergren B, Juto P, Trollfors B, et al: Hemorrhagic complications and other clinical findings in nephropathia epidemica in Sweden: a study of 355 serologically verified cases. *J Infect Dis* 1988; 157:380–382.

139. Lahdevirta J, Savola J, Brummer-Korvenkontio M, et al: Clinical and serological diagnosis of nephropathia epidemica, the milder type of a hemorrhagic fever with renal syndrome. *J Infect* 1984; 9:230–238.

140. Lahdevirta J, Collan Y, Jokinen EJ, et al: Renal sequelae to nephropathia epidemica. *Acta Pathol Microbiol Scand (A)* 1978; 86:265–271.

141. Lahdevirta J: The minor problem of hemostatic impairment in nephropathia epidemica, the mild Scandinavian form of hemorrhagic fever with renal syndrome. *Rev Infect Dis* 1989; 11:S860–S863..

142. Cohen MS: Epidemic hemorrhagic fever revisited. *Rev Infect Dis* 1982; 4:992–997.

143. McKee KT Jr, MacDonald C, LeDuc JW, et al: Hemorrhagic fever with renal syndrome—a clinical perspective. *Milit Med* 1985; 150:640–647.

144. Sheedy JA, Froeb HF, Batson HA, et al: The clinical course of epidemic hemorrhagic fever. *Am J Med* 1954; 16:619–628.

145. Lee HW, Lee MC, Cho KS: Management of Korean haemorrhagic fever. *Med Prog Technol* 1980 (Sept); 15–21.

146. Earle DP: Analysis of sequential physiologic derangements in epidemic hemorrhagic fever. *Am J Med* 1954; 16:690–709.

147. Choi TK, Lee JS, Koh CS, et al: A study of renogram in Korean hemorrhagic fever. *Korean J Nucl Med* 1974; 8:13–24.

148. Cosgriff TM, Guang MY, Huggins JW, et al: Early predictors of fatal outcome in haemorrhagic fever with renal syndrome. *Trans R Soc Trop Med Hyg* 1989, in press.

149. Chan YC, Wan TW, Yap EH, et al: Haemorrhagic fever with renal syndrome involving the liver. *Med J Aust* 1987; 147:248–249.

150. Wah LT, Mangalam S, Lee HW: Hemorrhagic fever with renal syndrome: report of a case in Malaysia. *J Infect Dis* 1987; 156:1035–1036.

151. Hullinghorst RL, Steer A: Pathology of epidemic hemorrhagic fever. *Ann Intern Med* 1953; 38:77–101.

152. Kessler WH: Gross anatomic features found in 27 autopsies of epidemic hemorrhagic fever. *Ann Intern Med* 1953; 38:73–76.

153. Lukes RJ: The pathology of thirty-nine cases of epidemic hemorrhagic fever. *Am J Med* 1954; 16:639–650.

154. Giles RB, Langdon EA: Blood volume in epidemic hemorrhagic fever. *Am J Med* 1954; 16:654–661.

155. Kuhlback B, Fortelius P, Tallgren LG: Renal histopathology in a case of nephropathia epidemica Myhrman. A study of successive biopsies. *Acta Pathol Microbiol Scand* 1964; 60:323–333.

156. Collan Y, Lahdevirta J, Jokinen EJ: Electron microscopy of nephropathia epidemica. Renal tubular basement membrane. *Am J Pathol* 1978; 92:167–172.

157. Collan Y, Lahdevirta J, Jokinen EJ: Electron microscopy of nephropathia epidemica. Glomerular changes. *Virchows Arch Pathol Anat* 1978; 377:129–144.

158. Oliver J, MacDowell M: The renal lesion in epidemic hemorrhagic fever. *J Clin Invest* 1957; 36:99–223.

159. Lim TH, Lee JS, Choi BI, et al: An explanation of renal hemodynamics in acute renal failure based on sequential CT in patients with Korean hemorrhagic fever. *J Comput Assist Tomogr* 1987; 11:474–479.

160. Lee M, Lee JS, Kim BK: Disseminated intravascular coagulation in Korean hemorrhagic fever, in Abe T and Yamanaka M (eds): *Disseminated Intravascular Coagulation.* Tokyo, University of Tokyo Press, 1983, pp 181–198.

161. Penttinen K, Lahdevirta J, Kekomaki R, et al: Circulating immune complexes, immunoconglutinins and rheumatoid factors in nephropathia epidemica. *J Infect Dis* 1981; 143:15–21.

162. Park JS, Kim S, Lee JS, et al: Circulating immune complexes in Korean hemorrhagic fever. Hemorrhagic fever with renal syndrome. *Seoul J Med* 1986; 26:143–155.

163. Gavrilovskaya IN, Podgorodnichenko VK, Apekina NS, et al: Determination of specific immune complexes and dynamics of their circulation in patients suffering from hemorrhagic fever with a renal syndrome. *Mikrobiol Zh* 1987; 49:71–76.

164. Yan D, Gu X, Wang D, et al; Studies on immunopathogenesis in epidemic hemorrhagic fever. Sequential observations on activation of the first complement component in sera from patients with epidemic hemorrhagic fever. *J Immunol* 1981; 127:1064–1067.

165. Dai ZY, Xu ZY, Wang JR, et al: Epidemiological and clinical studies of epidemic hemorrhagic fever. *Chin Med J* 1981; 94:143–148.

166. Jokinen EJ, Collan Y, Lahdevirta J: Renal immune complexes in epidemic nephropathy. *Lancet* 1977; 1:1012–1013.

167. Jokinen EJ, Lahdevirta J, Collan Y: Nephropathia epidemica; immunohistochemical study of pathogenesis. *Clin Nephrol* 1978; 9:1–5.

168. Jia-rui W, Pei-zhen Y, Qian W, et al: The role of tissue immune complex, complement activation and its immunopathologic injury in the pathogenesis of the epidemic hemorrhagic fever. *Chin Med J* 1986; 99:21–26.

169. Lee M, Kim B-K, Kim S, et al: Coagulopathy in hemorrhagic fever with renal syndrome (Korean hemorrhagic fever). *Rev Infect Dis* 1989; 11:S877–S883.

170. Tong M: Measurement of C-3 in human sera and its preliminary use in epidemic hemorrhagic fever. *Chin J Epidemiol* 1979; 3:247.

171. Sirotin BZ, Zayev AP, Bystrovskiy VF: Arterial hypertonia, central and renal hemodynamics and renin activity in the plasma of patients with hemorrhagic fever with renal syndrome. *Klin Med (Mosk)* 1978; 56:68–73.

172. Obukhova GG: Components of the kinen system and inhibitors of proteinases from blood serum in hemorrhagic fever with renal syndrome. *Vopr Med Khim* 1980; 26:118–120.

173. Sirotin VZ, Obukhova GG, Mogila TV: Kallikrein-kinin, coagulation and fibrinolytic blood systems in patients suffering from hemorrhagic fever with renal syndrome. *Ter Arkh* 1981; 53:84–87.

174. Kim S, Cho BY, Lee JS, et al: A study on plasma renin activity in Korean hemorrhagic fever. *Korean J Nucl Med* 1976; 10:35–46.

175. Han JY, Lee JS, Koh CS, et al: Hemodynamics in Korean hemorrhagic fever. *Korean J Nucl Med* 1974; 8:1–11.

176. Badr KF, Ichikawa I: Prerenal failure: a deleterious shift from renal compensation to decompensation. *N Engl J Med* 1988; 319:623–630.

177. Heyman SN, Brezis M, Reubinoff CA, et al: Acute renal failure with selective medullary injury in the rat. *J Clin Invest* 1988; 82:401–412.

178. Dunn MJ: Clinical effects of prostaglandins in renal disease. *Hosp Pract* 1984; 19(March):99–113.

179. Ivanov AP, Tkachenko EA, Petrov VA, et al: Enzyme immunoassay for the detection of virus specific IgG and IgM antibody in patients with haemorrhagic fever with renal syndrome. *Arch Virol* 1988; 100:1–7.

180. Niklasson B, Kjelsson T: Detection of nephropathia epidemica (Puumala virus)–specific immunoglobulin M by enzyme-linked immunosorbent assay. *J Clin Microbiol* 1988; 26:1519–1523.

181. Lim TH, Chang KH, Han MC, et al: Pituitary atrophy in Korean (epidemic) hemorrhagic fever: CT correlation with pituitary function and visual field. *J Am Soc Neuroradiol* 1986; 7:633–637.

182. Dennis LH, Conrad ME: Accelerated intravascular coagulation in a patient with Korean hemorrhagic fever. *Arch Intern Med* 1968; 121:449–452.

183. Huggins JW, Kim GR, Brand OM, et al: Ribavirin therapy for Hantaan virus infection in suckling mice. *J Infect Dis* 1986; 153:489–497.

184. Huggins JW, Hsiang CM, Cosgriff TM, et al: Intravenous ribavirin therapy of hemorrhagic fever with renal syndrome (HFRS), abstract, *Antiviral Res* 1988; 9:123.

185. Lee HW, An CN: Development of vaccine against hemorrhagic fever with renal syndrome. *J Korean Soc Virol* 1988; 143–148.

23

Flaviviruses

Robert B. Craven

The viruses of the family *Flaviviridae* are important arthropod-borne viruses (arboviruses) in both human and veterinary medicine. They are transmitted by mosquitoes and ticks and usually are maintained in a transmission cycle in nature. The isolation of yellow fever virus launched an era of important research on flaviviruses and the vectors which transmit them.

Flaviviruses produce a broad spectrum of clinical responses in humans ranging from asymptomatic infection to fulminant fatal encephalitis or hemorrhagic fever. These viruses are widely distributed throughout the world with the exception of the polar regions, although a specific flavivirus may be geographically restricted to a continent or a subdivision of it. Because of the widespread distribution of potential vectors, some flaviviruses such as yellow fever and dengue virus cause widespread public health concerns. Since some flaviviral illnesses occur in epidemics, physicians and laboratory workers who are aware of confirmed cases should report them immediately to public health authorities, even if the presumed origin of the disease is another country. The control of epidemics of flaviviral disease can be enormously complex and expensive and requires time and planning. If epidemic activity is suspected or evident, the choices for managing the situation may vary from the mass immunization campaigns which have been conducted for yellow fever to measures designed to reduce exposure to infected vectors such as public education and possibly the use of insecticides on a large scale.

Nearly 60 flaviviruses are known to exist; however, many are not presently recognized as human pathogens. When using commonly available serologic tests, distinguishing between flaviviruses can be difficult, especially in areas of hyperendemic transmission, where patients may have been infected by antigenically related viruses from the family. The serologic response to infection with a second related flavivirus, as measured by the commonly used hemagglutination-inhibition (HI) or complement-fixation (CF) tests, may demonstrate cross-reacting antibodies to other members of the family such that one is unable to define with certainty the true infecting agent. This problem can often be circumvented by the use of the plaque reduction neutralization (PRN) test, which is much more costly and time-consuming. Monoclonal antibody tests may also be useful in resolving this laboratory dilemma.

STRUCTURE AND BIOLOGY OF FLAVIVIRUSES

Chemically, the flaviviruses are composed of protein, carbohydrate, phospholipid, and RNA. The structural proteins of flaviviruses studied thus far show that all of them contain an envelope glycoprotein ranging in size from 51 to 59×10^3 daltons, a nucleoprotein of 13.5×10^3 daltons, and a small membrane protein of 7.7 to 8.7 $\times$ 10^3 daltons. The envelope protein is the largest structural protein and is the major antigen of the virions.

The flaviviral virion has a sedimentation rate of 108S in sucrose. Rate zonal centrifugation of flaviviruses yields three separate antigens: an infectious virion composed of three structural proteins, a noninfectious doughnut-shaped particle which hemagglutinates, and a "soluble complement-fixing antigen".

Flaviviruses are single-stranded, enveloped RNA viruses ranging in size from 40 to 50 nm. Nucleocapsid symmetry is unknown. The RNA weight is 4.2 to 4.4 $\times$ 10^6 daltons. The 5' end is type 1 and the 3' end contains no poly A. Genes for the structural proteins are located at the 5' end. Flaviviruses do not produce subgenomic messenger RNA (mRNA) and thus have the largest mRNA completely translated in eukaryotic cells.

In addition, flaviviruses do not appear to produce polyproteins in infected cells. In cell-free systems, the translation of the flavivirus genome produces structural proteins. Their nucleocapsids have not been visualized or isolated. Maturation occurs within the cisternae of infected cells, but the mechanism of morphogenesis is not known. The RNA of flaviviruses is infective. They are stable at pH 7 to 9, but are relatively inactivated at 50°C. They are also sensitive to lipid solvents, ionic and nonionic detergents, and trypsin.

Flaviviruses may be isolated in a number of vertebrate and invertebrate systems as well as numerous tissue culture cell lines. Serologic diagnosis can be by CF, HI, neutralization (N), immunoprecipitation, and solid phase binding assays.

Diseases of man produced by this family range from asymptomatic infection to undifferentiated febrile illnesses, febrile rashes, hemorrhagic fevers, and encephalitis.

The flavivirus family is divided into seven subgroups of viruses based on their reactions by serum dilution tests. The antigenic properties of the flaviviruses depend on glycoproteins of 51,000 to 59,000 molecular weight which are on the surface of the virions. This surface glycoprotein is the reactive structure in both the HI and N tests. As measured by the HI test, three antigenic determinants are found for flaviviruses: (1) type-specific determinants unique for each virus, (2) complex-reactive determinants shared by closely related viruses, and (3) group-reactive determinants shared by all serologically related flaviviruses. The envelope glycoprotein contains mostly type-specific antigen determinants and lesser amounts of complex- and group-reactive determinants. The nucleocapsid proteins analyzed to date show only group-reactive determinants. Nonstructural flavivirus antigens also have been detected in infected tissues and cells. One of these is the soluble CF antigen described earlier. The biologic role of these antigens is not known. While antigenic similarities do exist between flaviviruses as measured by the HI and CF tests, differences can be demonstrated not only between related viruses, but also between strains of the same virus. West Nile, Japanese encephalitis, St Louis encephalitis, tick-borne encephalitis, and dengue viruses vary in biologic properties and antigenic reactivity. For example, marked variations occur in the virulence in man of St Louis encephalitis (SLE) viral strains which correlate with virulence on peripheral inoculation into weanling mice. Oligonucleotide mapping of the RNA of SLE virions also shows subsets of genomic types that correlate with virulence and geographic origin of the strains.

FLAVIVIRUSES PRODUCING ENCEPHALITIS

The flavivirus family contains many viral agents which produce encephalitis. Table 23–1 shows the flaviviruses which produce encephalitis, their vectors, and geographic location. Flaviviral encephalitides are either mosquito-borne, tick-borne, or have an unknown vector. For a discussion of the general syndrome of encephalitis and its differential diagnosis, see Chapter 24, Togaviruses.

MOSQUITO-BORNE FLAVIVIRUSES

St Louis Encephalitis

St Louis encephalitis (SLE) occurs in endemic and epidemic form throughout the Americas and is the most important arboviral disease of North America. SLE is closely related antigenically to Japanese encephalitis in Japan and other areas of Asia and to Murray Valley encephalitis in Australia. The isolation of the virus in North America and the subsequent elucidation of the mode of its transmission to man have given great impetus to the study of arboviruses in the Americas.

History.—SLE virus was first isolated in 1933 by Muckenfuss, Armstrong, and McCordock, who injected rhesus monkeys intracerebrally with infected human brain tissue collected post mortem.[2] During the same period, workers from the Rockefeller Institute for Medical Research demonstrated several isolates obtained after intracerebral inoculation of white mice.[3] The discovery that mice were susceptible was an important one since it led to the development of a mouse neutralization test with which human sera could be tested for antibodies to SLE virus.

Various theories of the mechanism of transmission were considered, but it was a Public Health Service medical epidemiologist, Leslie Lumsden, who was the first to suggest that the disease was transmitted by mosquitoes breeding in sewage-contaminated sluggish or standing water.[4] Lumsden's conclusions, in the form of an internal report, were largely ignored at the time, but a similar conclusion was reached epidemiologically by other workers and published in 1938.[5] Due to technical problems, SLE virus was not isolated from mosquitoes until Hammon and coworkers successfully isolated the virus from wild _Culex tarsalis_ and _Cx pipiens_ mosquitoes in California in the early 1940s.[6] Experimental transmission to doves, pigeons, and baby mice by _Cx pipiens_ by Reeves et al finally confirmed Lumsden's theory of mosquito transmission.[7] Further studies during the 1950s and 1960s showed _Cx quinquefasciatus,_ closely related to _Cx pipiens,_ to be an important transmitter of SLE virus; transovarial transmission of SLE virus was shown not to be a mechanism of overwintering of the virus; and birds identified as being of major importance to the natural transmission cycle were house sparrows, pigeons, and blue jays.[8]

Structure and Biology of the Agent.—SLE virus demonstrates structural and biologic characteristics in common with other flaviviruses as described earlier in this section. It is inactivated by lipid solvents, enzymes, chemicals, ultraviolet irradiation, soft x-rays, and temperatures greater than or equal to 56°C for 30 minutes. The virus can be grown in a wide variety of continuous and primary cell lines. Of the continuous cell lines, it will grow in tissues of

Table 23–1
Vectors, Natural Hosts, and Geographic Localization of Flaviviruses Causing Encephalitis

Vector	Virus	Known or Possible Vectors	Natural Hosts	Geographic Location
Mosquito-borne	St Louis encephalitis	*Culex tarsalis, Cx pipiens pipiens, Cx pipiens quinquefasciatus*	Birds	Americas, Caribbean
	Japanese encephalitis	*Cx tritaeniorhynchus, Cx gelidus*	Birds, pigs	Northern and southeast Asia, India
	Murray Valley encephalitis	*Cx vishnui, Cx annuliorostris, Cx bitaeniorhynchus, Aedes normanensis*	Birds	Australia, N. Guinea
	West Nile	*Cx univittatus, Cx antennatus, Cx modestus, Cx vishnui*	Birds	Africa, Asia, Europe
	Ilheus	*Psorophora, Aedes, Culex, Haemagogus, Sabethes* spp	Birds (humans?)	Central and South America
Tick-borne	Russian spring-summer encephalitis	*Ixodes persulcatus, Ix ricinus*	Rodents, birds	USSR
	Central European encephalitis	*Ix ricinus*	Rodents, birds, goats	Western and central Europe, western USSR
	Louping ill	*Ix ricinus*	Rodents, sheep, (?birds)	Great Britain
	Powassan	*Ix cookei, Ix marxi, Ix spinipalpus*	Squirrels, chipmunks	United States, Canada, USSR
No known vector	Rio Bravo	Unknown	Bats	Americas
	Rocio	Unknown	Birds (?humans)	Brazil
	Negishi	?tick	Unknown	Japan

both vertebrate and invertebrate origin. In some cell lines, cytopathic effect (CPE) is not produced. Antigenically, SLE virus is related most closely to Japanese encephalitis, Murray Valley encephalitis, West Nile virus, and Kunjin virus, but also to Ilheus and possibly Rocio virus.

Epidemiology.—From 1955 to 1988, over 5000 cases of SLE have been reported to the Centers for Disease Control (CDC), with cases being reported every year. Reported cases are only a fraction of those that actually occur so these reported cases are an underestimation of the true number of cases that occurred during those years. The number of reported cases ranges from a low of five in 1973 to a high of 1815 in 1975. Larger outbreaks and epidemics caused by *Cx pipiens* mosquitoes tend to occur at roughly 10-year intervals. The 1975 epidemic was the greatest ever recorded in the United States and occurred at a time when a great deal of knowledge about the prevention and containment of SLE epidemics was available but, unfortunately, not widely employed.

The epidemiology of SLE varies from east to west due to ecologically different zones of disease transmission and to different vector mosquitoes occupying those zones as well as populations affected. In the eastern United States, SLE is transmitted by the peridomestic *Cx pipiens-quinquefasciatus* complex (by *Cx nigripalpus* in Florida), whereas in the West the vector is *Cx tarsalis*, which occupies a more rural niche, including irrigated agricultural land and areas of standing water from spring flooding or snowmelt runoff. The eastern vector prefers to deposit its eggs in pol-

luted waters in urban and suburban environments, especially where areas of poor sewage sanitation exist.

A definite seasonal distribution for SLE occurs in North America, with the majority of cases reported during late summer and early fall and with peak transmission in August and September. SLE outbreaks tend to begin somewhat earlier in the West than in the East and frequently follow outbreaks of western equine encephalitis (WEE). This later onset of SLE epidemics is attributed to the virus's longer extrinsic incubation period in the *Cx tarsalis* vector and its longer intrinsic incubation in infected avian hosts. Both phenomena may be related, in part, to the lower viremia produced in avians by SLE virus compared to WEE virus. Also, maximum SLE transmission is favored by high ambient temperatures which tend to occur later in the summer months and shorten the extrinsic incubation period.

Human cases of SLE have been reported from all of the contiguous 48 states of the United States, with the exception of the northeastern states of Connecticut, Maine, Massachusetts, New Hampshire, and Rhode Island, and the southern state of South Carolina. In North America, the north-to-south axis for distribution of human SLE cases stretches from Mexico to Canada. The occurrence of human cases in Canada suggests that, under conditions appropriate for introduction of SLE virus, the northeastern states, which have been apparently spared in the past, might also have human SLE cases.

Areas of the Caribbean and Central and South America where human cases have been reported in the past include Argentina, Brazil, Panama, and Trinidad. Other countries in this area where

SLE virus has been isolated from birds and arthropods are Ecuador, French Guiana, Guatemala, and Jamaica.[9]

Some rather marked epidemiologic differences exist between SLE as seen in western and eastern regions of the continental United States. Whether in the East or West, SLE tends to produce focal outbreaks, with the result that morbidity rates are higher in rural or small community areas than in large urban areas, although for different reasons. *Cx tarsalis,* the western vector, is more likely to be found in rural areas or suburban areas. In the East, although a greater absolute number of SLE cases come from large urban areas, morbidity rates (cases per 100,000 population) are usually higher also in rural areas and small communities. One explanation for this difference in the East is that morbidity rates for urban areas may be calculated using the total urban population rather than the focal population involved in the outbreak. The former calculation tends to dilute the morbidity rate while the latter produces morbidity rates more closely approaching those seen in rural or small community areas. The reader should note, however, that real ecological (eg, sewage sanitation practices) and other differences may be responsible for higher rates in the less densely populated areas.

For most SLE epidemics, and particularly those in the East, age-specific incidence, mortality rates, and case fatality rates increase sharply after 60 years of age. On occasion in the West, morbidity and mortality rates have been higher in young children. A plausible explanation for this is that SLE has been present in endemic form longer in the West and that endemic transmission occurs at a higher level than in the East. This has the effect of producing increased numbers of immune individuals in an age cohort with increasing age and of leaving the largest susceptible population among the younger age groups in the event of an epidemic.[10]

In the East, SLE epidemics have had either a strong trend toward an increase or a statistically significant increase in morbidity rates for females, particularly in those over age 40. The reasons for this are not clear. Conversely, in western epidemics males usually have higher morbidity rates than females. In this instance, the difference is probably a vocational one in that men in agricultural jobs are more likely to be exposed to the preferred habitat of the vector.[10]

Several studies of SLE epidemics have noted increased morbidity rates in blacks, but many of these studies have not controlled sufficiently for such confounding variables as socioeconomic status, geographic location, and cultural practices. Some examples of these variables are high unemployment rates that may encourage more time spent in a high-risk peridomestic habitat and which affect the ability to afford screens or air conditioning. Geographic variables include residence near stagnant water rich in organics or residence in districts with mosquito-control programs. Examples of cultural variables include preferences for socializing either indoors or outdoors and the degree to which premises and neighborhood environmental sanitation are maintained. Two studies in 1975 in Greenville, Mississippi, and Memphis, Tennessee, which attempted to control for geographic location and socioeconomic factors, suggest, however, that morbidity rates are higher in blacks than whites in the south.[11]

Pathogenesis.—The overwintering mechanism for SLE virus is still under study. Three possibilities are overwintering or transovarial transmission in the *Cx pipiens* complex mosquitoes and recrudescent viremia on awakening in infected, hibernating bats.[12–14] By whatever method, the virus is introduced into the natural bird-mosquito-bird cycle (especially nestling and juvenile birds). The birds then develop viremias lasting two to four days and act as amplifying hosts by infecting more of the *Culex* spp vectors. Once the vector consumes an infected blood meal, a variable period of time (extrinsic incubation period) must pass before the virus infects the salivary glands of the mosquito and makes it a vector for life. The length of the extrinsic incubation period is affected by the titer of virus in the blood meal and the ambient temperature. After the bite of an infected mosquito, the incubation period in humans varies from five to 21 days.

Host Response.—The clinical expressions of SLE range from inapparent infections to fulminant encephalitis and death. The ratio of inapparent to apparent infections ranges from 16:1 to 425:1. An inverse correlation exists between age and the number of inapparent infections so that many children, but much fewer elderly adults, have inapparent infections.

Patients who are symptomatic will usually present with, or progress to, one of three clinical syndromes—febrile headache, aseptic meningitis, or encephalitis. The syndrome of febrile headache presents as an acute febrile illness with headache frequently accompanied by nausea and vomiting. No signs of meningeal irritation or localized neurologic abnormalities occur with this grippelike presentation. Cerebrospinal fluid (CSF) pleocytosis may be found in these patients. The aseptic meningitis presentation is one of an acute febrile illness associated with signs of meningeal irritation—a stiff neck. Kernig's and Brudzinski's signs may or may not be positive. CSF pleocytosis is present. The syndrome of encephalitis includes also such presentations as meningoencephalitis and encephalomyelitis. It is characterized by alterations of consciousness and/or localizing neurologic abnormalities. Alterations of consciousness which may be observed include lethargy, stupor, coma, confusion, disorientation, or delirium. Signs of central neurologic abnormalities which may be seen are cranial nerve palsies, dysarthria, paralysis, paresis, rigidity, tremor, or abnormal reflexes. Convulsions occur in only 10% or less of patients with SLE and, when present, have been associated with a poor prognosis.

The more severe clinical presentations, aseptic meningitis and encephalitis, vary in frequency with age. Aseptic meningitis occurs less frequently with increasing age, and frank encephalitis becomes more frequent with increasing age. SLE, in contrast to western and eastern equine encephalitis, almost never produces severe neurologic involvement in children under 1 year of age.

The onset of encephalitis symptoms in SLE cases is either abrupt or after a prodrome of headache, malaise, myalgias and arthralgias, fever of moderate degree with chills, lassitude, abdominal pain, nausea and vomiting, sore throat, and occasionally conjunctivitis and photophobia. Early descriptions of SLE noted the frequent occurrence of urinary tract symptoms: dysuria, frequency, urgency, or acute retention. The degree to which these symptoms are related to SLE as opposed to urinary tract pathologic changes, which may be incidentally present in the older age group affected by SLE, has been questioned.[15, 16]

From 18 published reports of neurologic symptoms and signs in patients with SLE, Brinker and Monath and colleagues have compiled the median incidence of their signs and symptoms. From 70% to 80% of patients complain of headache and have nuchal rigidity and altered level of consciousness. Nearly 50% will have tremor, pathologic reflexes, and/or confusion. Twenty to thirty percent of patients will have multiple cranial nerve abnormalities, hypoactive deep tendon reflexes, positive Babinski signs, and/or myalgia. Eleven to twenty percent of them will have coma, seventh cranial nerve lesions, lower motor neuron lesions, hyperactive deep tendon reflexes, and/or myoclonus; and 10% or less will have convulsions, paresis, photophobia, nystagmus, and/or ataxia.[15, 17]

Immunologic Response.—Most patients infected with SLE virus will develop HI, CF, and N antibodies. HI and N antibodies appear rapidly, often within three to five days after illness onset. CF antibody is slower to appear (10–14 days), and some persons apparently never develop CF antibody or only have CF antibody for a short time. Infection by SLE virus probably confers lifelong immunity.

Pathology.—The gross appearance of the brain of an SLE victim is unremarkable, except for varying degrees of leptomeningeal and parenchymal congestion. Microscopic examination shows small lymphocytes infiltrating the meninges and parenchyma. Perivascular cuffing with lymphocytes is prominent. Cellular nodules composed of monocytes, lymphocytes, and microglial cells are seen in the parenchymal gray matter. The most severely involved regions of gray matter are the substantia nigra of the midbrain and thalamic nuclei.[18, 19]

Laboratory Findings and Diagnosis.—Examination of peripheral blood reveals a moderate neutrophilic leukocytosis with the majority of patients having white blood counts between 5000 and 15,000 cells per microliter. Platelet counts and coagulation studies are usually normal. Urinalysis may reveal pyuria, proteinuria, or microscopic hematuria. Elevation of BUN is seen in less than a third of patients. One study has reported detection of SLE viral antigen associated with cellular material in urinary sediment.[20]

Lumbar puncture will demonstrate elevated opening pressure in 30% of patients. The CSF abnormalities include pleocytosis, generally in the range of five to 100 cells per microliter to as many as 500/μL. Rarely the cell count can exceed 500. In approximately 20% of SLE patients, for whom a lumbar puncture is performed early in their illness, polymorphonuclear cells will predominate in the cell count, thus leading to possible confusion with a pyogenic infection. A repeat lumbar puncture will usually reveal a transition to lymphocytic predominance. CSF glucose is usually normal, but moderate elevation of protein occurs in a majority of patients.

Blood chemistry abnormalities that may be seen in addition to elevated BUN are elevated serum creatinine phosphokinase (CPK) (75% of patients) and elevated aspartate aminotransferase (AST) (25%).[15]

Diagnosis of SLE by attempts to isolate the virus from blood or CSF have been disappointing. However, six instances of recovery of SLE virus from acute blood have been reported.[21] The virus can be isolated from postmortem brain tissue with much greater success and occasional isolates have been reported from liver, spleen, kidney, and lung.[3, 22, 23] Tissue for virus isolation should be collected under sterile conditions and promptly frozen on dry ice or in an ultra-low-temperature freezer at −60°C. If neither of these is available, the specimen should be placed in a 50% solution of glycerine and stored at −20°C to 4°C. Tissue for virus isolation must not be placed in preservatives or disinfectants, as these will inactivate the virus; refreezing of the specimen is also detrimental to virus survival. Tissue should be shipped to a laboratory on dry ice.

Serologic diagnosis can be performed by HI, CF, N or IgM-capture enzyme immunoassay.[24] The last-named procedure is preferred since it measures the primary antibody response and thus differentiates recent from past infection. Sera should be obtained as soon after onset as possible and 1 to 2 weeks after onset. As noted earlier, CF antibody may be slow in developing, and collection of a serum sample later in the convalescence may be necessary to show a diagnostic fourfold rise in antibody titer. If, for some reason, an early serum sample is not obtained, then one taken later in illness and another obtained 4 to 6 weeks after illness may be collected with the hope of demonstrating a diagnostic fourfold drop in antibody titer. Sera collected and processed aseptically can be shipped at ambient temperature if shipping does not exceed two to three days. Otherwise, they should be shipped on wet ice, cold packs, or dry ice.

Prevention and Treatment.—No vaccine for SLE is available, and it is doubtful that sufficient commercial interest to develop a vaccine will come about in the foreseeable future.

Individuals may undertake several measures to prevent bites of the vector mosquitoes. (See Dengue for a discussion of individual measures.) The means to prevent or lessen the impact of SLE outbreaks are available and have been successfully employed. An ongoing commitment by government agencies to fund such a program is, however, crucial. The fundamental basis for prevention is a surveillance program which monitors the activity of SLE virus in nature. This is accomplished by monitoring the development of antibody to SLE virus in nesting or juvenile birds and/or sentinel chicken flocks. A further useful surveillance technique is the trapping of mosquitoes, combined with attempts to isolate SLE virus from pools of the trapped vectors.[25–27]

These two approaches indicate the presence of SLE virus in the natural transmission cycle. The trapping of mosquitoes, when done in a systematic fashion, also provides an estimate of the size of the vector population. When rates of serologic positivity to SLE virus in young birds or sentinel chickens rises to 4% or greater in a given survey area, a definite risk of human cases exists. The infection rate in mosquitoes associated with risk of human transmission has not been established for SLE. When serologic results in avians indicate a risk to the human population, the public should be alerted to avoid mosquito bites, and a program of insecticide application to reduce the adult and larval populations of mosquitoes should be undertaken by public health authorities.[25]

No specific therapy for SLE is presently available, and treatment is supportive. Complications that can occur during SLE include pneumonia, pulmonary embolism, aspiration of vomitus, central nervous system–related respiratory failure, and gastrointestinal (GI) hemorrhage. Vigilance for these complications can prevent deaths from SLE.

Diagnosis and Management.—The differential diagnosis of

SLE from other causes of encephalitis is discussed under Togaviruses Producing Encephalitis. Neurologic sequelae are rare in children, but 30% to 50% of adults will suffer from a disorder called "convalescent fatigue syndrome." This syndrome consists of weakness, fatigue, tremulousness, irritability, sleeplessness, depression, memory loss, difficulty in concentrating, and headaches. By three years, 80% of patients with this syndrome will have regained normal health. Therapy for this syndrome is also symptomatic.

Japanese Encephalitis

Japanese encephalitis (JE) is a public health problem of major concern in Asia, southeast Asia, and the Indian subcontinent. Prior to 1967, thousands of cases with several hundred deaths were reported each year. In endemic areas where vector control and vaccination have been undertaken, the incidence of this disease has dropped dramatically.

History.—JE was first described in Japan in 1871. In the particularly severe epidemic of 1924, several investigators demonstrated that a filterable agent was present in the postmortem brain tissue of patients, and this agent was pathogenic for rabbits. In 1935 the virus was isolated. The association of major epidemics with increased populations of culicine mosquitoes was noted by Japanese epidemiologists in the 1930s; subsequently, isolation of JE virus from *Cx tritaeniorhynchus* mosquitoes was accomplished.

The first major epidemic documented in Korea occurred in 1949 when 5548 cases were recorded.[28] Subsequently, cases averaged 2000 per year until the latter half of the 1960s when fewer than 200 cases per year were reported.[29] The most recent major outbreak was noted in 1982 with nearly 3000 cases. Other countries that have experienced epidemic JE include China (1940 and 1966), the USSR (1965), northern Thailand (late 1960s), northern Vietnam, northern Burma, Bangladesh, India (1954 and 1978), Nepal (1968), Indonesia, Malaysia, Phillippines, and Java (Indonesia).[30–54]

Structure and Biology of the Agent.—The structure and replication of JE virus are similar to other flaviviruses as discussed above. It is a member of an antigenically related subgroup of flaviviruses including the following other agents pathogenic for man: St Louis encephalitis, Murray Valley encephalitis, West Nile, Rocio, and Ilheus viruses. Considerable amino acid homology in the genome sequences has been shown among JE, yellow fever and dengue viruses.[55, 56] Geographic and temporal strain differences have been shown for JE viruses. While these differences are useful epidemiologically, their clinical significance, if any, is not presently known.

The virus replicates well after intracerebral inoculation into one- to four-day-old Swiss mice, baby hamsters, monkeys, horses, or pigs. Tissue cultures in which JE virus will replicate include chick embryo, hamster kidney, Vero, BHK-21, HeLa, LLC MK-2, and others.[26]

Epidemiology.—Precise figures on incidence and prevalence of JE in recent years are not available for most countries; clearly, the incidence has decreased in Japan, Korea, and Taiwan. Two patterns of disease occurrence are observed. In temperate climate zones, explosive outbreaks are associated with the larger vector population increases that occur in the warmer months. In subtropical and tropical countries, which are warm year round, cases occur in more sporadic fashion throughout the year but tend to increase in the late rainy season and early dry season.

An example of a severe epidemic year in the past is 1958 when Korea reported 5700 cases with 1322 deaths (23% mortality), Japan reported 1800 cases and 519 deaths (29% mortality), and Taiwan reported 142 cases and 52 deaths (37% mortality).[57] An analysis of morbidity and mortality data from Japan for the period 1924 to 1961 revealed the incidence of JE to vary from 0.1 to 10.4 hospitalizations per 100,000 populations. The case fatality rate for cases in the same period varied from 24% to 92%.[58] Because these data are based on hospitalized patients, they underestimate the total incidence of infection and disease and overestimate case fatality rates.

JE virus produces a high inapparent-to-apparent-infection ratio, variously estimated between 25 to 500 infections to one overt case of encephalitis.[59–61] However, when encephalitis does occur, mortality rates in the range of 20% to 50% are reported, and rates of permanent neurologic sequelae are high.[62] The endemic geographic distribution of JE is in Japan, the eastern USSR, Korea, China, Indochina, Indonesia, and India.

No differences in infection rates by sex have been reported; however, overt clinical illness occurs more frequently in males. Young children, especially those between 5 and 9 years of age, and persons over 65 years of age experience higher case fatality rates.[63] Occupational and residential factors also play an important role in the risk of exposure to JE virus. The principal amplification cycle involves pigs, so that proximity to pigs or rice paddies by vocation or area of residence increases the risk of developing JE.

JE virus has been isolated from numerous mosquito species in nature, including *Cx mansonia, aedes* and *auropheles*. The majority of isolates has been obtained from *Cx tritaeniorhynchus* and this is considered the principal vector in most areas. Other species are important in other local areas. *Cx tritaeniorhynchus* breeds in rice paddies, marshes, ponds, and other still collections of water.

The transmission cycle for JE virus in nature involves *Culex* and *Aedes* spp mosquitoes and domestic animals, birds, bats, and reptiles. The classic vector for JE virus is *Cx tritaeniorhynchus*, and this species is the major one responsible for transmission in Japan, China, and Korea. Other *Culex* spp important as vectors are *Cx annulus* (Taiwan), *Cx gelidus* and *fuscocephalus* (Thailand and Malaysia), *Cx vishnui* and *pseudovishnui* (India), and *Cx annulirostris* (Guam).[64] *Cx tritaeniorhynchus* feeds during the night and is most active during the first hour after sunset. *Aedes* spp feed on birds and possibly pigs, which are potentially viremic and occasionally serve as a source of infection for humans. Horses are also infected.

Several potential mechanisms exist for overwintering of JE virus. Transovarial transmission of JE virus in *Cx tritaeniorhynchus* has been demonstrated experimentally, and survival of the virus through winter may occur in this manner.[65] Other mechanisms that have been shown to exist are overwinter survival in protected locations of adult vectors and prolonged viremias in reptiles and bats during hibernation.[66, 67]

JE virus produces abortions in pregnant sows, but asymptomatic illness occurs in nongravid pigs.[68] Equines are susceptible to JE virus and develop encephalitis with a case fatality rate of 50%.[69]

Because of their markedly greater numbers, pigs play a more important role as amplifying hosts than horses. Slaughtering of pigs for food removes many animals immune to JE virus and leaves a generally susceptible population of young pigs to serve as amplifying hosts. Birds also play a role in the amplification cycle as nestlings are fed upon by vector mosquitoes.

Pathogenesis.—Man is not a preferred host for *Culex* spp mosquitoes and transmission of JE virus by infected vectors does not usually occur until mosquito populations are large. Once the virus has been transmitted to man, a period of replication outside the nervous system presumably occurs, and this leads to the development of viremia. The method of invasion of the CNS is unknown, but pathologic studies show the major areas of involvement to be the cerebral cortex, cerebellum, and spinal cord. The incubation period for JE varies from four days to two weeks.

Abortions during the first trimester of pregnancy have been reported in women with laboratory–documented JE virus infections.[70] Similarly, placental tissue from the first trimester supports JE virus replication whereas tissue from the third trimester does not.[71]

The clinical manifestations of JE vary from asymptomatic infection to a fulminant course leading to death in as few as ten days after onset of illness. The vast majority of infections are asymptomatic. The reason why some persons develop encephalitis while most do not is presently unknown. Some patients with JE will show only an undifferentiated febrile illness or will have mild respiratory tract complaints. The onset of illness in patients who develop encephalitis is with headache and GI and respiratory tract symptoms. GI complaints include poor appetite, nausea, vomiting, and abdominal pain. Episodes of psychosis also occur.[72]

Illness progresses with onset of high fever and alterations of sensorium including confusion, somnolence, or delirium, and may result in coma. Grand mal tonic-clonic seizures occur rarely in adults but are seen in up to 20% or more of children. Hyperactive deep tendon reflexes frequently are seen followed by hypoactive reflexes and positive Babinski signs. A few patients develop tremor and rigidity resembling Parkinson's disease. Facial motor weakness causing masklike facies is common. Upper motor neuron paralysis and paresis are often seen. Nonneurologic manifestations that may occur are bradycardia relative to the degree of fever present, diarrhea, and oliguria.

After two to four days of sustained fever, the temperature gradually diminishes, and a variable period of convalescence begins. A lengthy convalescence is the rule with persisting weakness, lethargy, tremors, difficulty with coordination, marked emotional instability, personality changes, and impaired mentation. Next in frequency of occurrence is paralysis of upper or lower motor neuron type. Infrequently, aphasia, cerebellar disorders, decerebrate rigidity, or organic psychoses occur. Pneumonia, bed sores, marked weight loss, and urinary tract infections are among the commonly seen complications.[73–75]

Laboratory findings include pleocytosis of CSF, initially polymorphonuclear, but changing to lymphocytic after a few days. Modest elevations of CSF proteins are frequently present. Albuminuria is common.

Pathology.—The brain and meninges show edema, conges-tion, and focal hemorrhages on gross examination. Microscopic abnormalities include degeneration and necrosis of neurons with neuronophagia in the cerebral cortex, cerebellum, and spinal cord. Destruction of Purkinje cells in the cerebellum is marked. Perivascular cuffing and inflammatory infiltrates into surrounding neural tissue are seen also. Focal hemorrhages may occur in both lungs and kidneys. Interstitial pneumonitis may be observed. In hepatocytes, hyaline changes in the cytoplasm have been noted.[76, 77]

Diagnosis of JE is made serologically in most cases since the yield of virus from CSF and peripheral blood is very low. Virus may be recovered from the brain of patients who die early after onset of symptoms. The virus can be isolated by intracerebral inoculation of infected brain tissue into suckling mice or by inoculation into one of several tissue culture cell lines (Vero, LLC MK-2, chick embryo cells, or primary monkey kidney cells). The isolated virus is then identified by CF or N testing using appropriate antisera.

Serologic diagnosis of JE can be made using paired sera by either HI, CF, or N. Antibodies detected by the HI and N tests appear from 1 to 2 weeks after illness onset. CF antibodies appear after 2 or more weeks. In flavivirus hyperendemic areas (see discussion of flavivirus cross-reactivity under Dengue) more specific tests such as CF, N, or the JE-specific IgM test may be required for precise diagnosis.[26, 78] A diagnostic IgM antibody test for JE which utilizes absorption of IgG antibodies with *Staphylococcus aureus* appears to be simple, rapid, and inexpensive; but the test has problems with specificity in areas hyperendemic for flaviviruses.[79]

Prevention.—During the early 1960s an ultracentrifuged, protamine-precipitated, formalin-inactivated, suckling mouse brain vaccine was developed at the Research Foundation for Microbial Diseases (BIKEN) at Osaka University, Osaka, Japan. This vaccine has been used extensively throughout Asia and has been credited with markedly reducing the incidence of JE where it has been used. Studies of the efficacy of the vaccine produced reductions of infections ranging from 56% to 90%.[80, 81]

Persons working, living, or traveling for periods of more than 30 days in endemic areas, and those present for shorter periods in epidemic areas, are candidates for immunization. Vaccine is administered subcutaneously in three doses at least a week apart, followed by a booster dose in one year. Adults and children three years or older receive 1 mL of vaccine each dose. Children under three years old should receive 0.5 mL subcutaneously on the same schedule.

The BIKEN vaccine is not licensed for use in the United States and is not presently available, although it has been evaluated by the CDC as an investigational new drug. Connaught Laboratories may receive a limited license for distribution of this vaccine during 1990. The vaccine does not produce effective protection until about a month after the primary inoculation series; therefore, short-term travelers to endemic or epidemic areas who receive vaccine in those areas would not be protected. These individuals should use measures to prevent mosquito bites (see below). Persons planning prolonged stays in these areas should contact their embassy or consular offices for safe local sources of vaccine.

A published account of adverse reactions (headache, malaise, and local erythema, pain and swelling) notes an occurrence rate of less than 1%.[81] Although the BIKEN vaccine is mouse brain-derived and poses at least a theoretical risk of producing allergic encephalitis, no postvaccination demyelinating encephalitis has been reported. The rate for any other CNS reaction is reported to be approximately one in one million vaccinations. Unpublished data from the CDC showed low rates of local and systemic reactogenicity, but the sample size was inadequate to draw conclusions about the possibility of low-frequency events such as allergic encephalitis.

Live attenuated vaccines for pigs are also available, and, when administered to young pigs after they lose maternal antibody to JE, the vaccines are effective in preventing amplification of JE virus in them. The removal of pigs from urban areas of high human population density will reduce substantially amplification and transmission of JE virus. Improved techniques of rice cultivation and the appropriate use of insecticides are useful methods to reduce the vector population. Individual protective measures are also of great importance. The major vector mosquitoes are most active during the hour after sunset. Remaining in screened areas during this time reduces the risk of being bitten. Additional precautions to prevent bites are wearing shirts with long sleeves, wearing long pants, and applying mosquito repellents to exposed skin areas.

Treatment.—No specific therapy for JE is currently available. Attention to treating the complications of JE is particularly important and can be lifesaving. The fever induced by JE is often sufficiently high to threaten life. Hypothermia to reduce body temperature to 30°C has been recommended to reduce the neurologic consequences of the hyperpyrexia. Care must be exercised during hypothermia to maintain fluid and electrolyte balance, since severe dehydration can occur. Shivering should be controlled by slow intravenous (IV) administration of chlorpromazine at a dosage of 0.25 to 0.5 mg/kg.[82]

Increased intracranial pressure can be life-threatening, producing respiratory and/or cardiac arrest due to brainstem herniation. These complications should be anticipated, and equipment and drugs for cardiopulmonary resuscitation should be readily available. Standard methods for the reduction of cerebral edema, such as steroids or the IV administration of hyperosmotic solutions of mannitol or urea to effect osmotic diuresis, may be required. Hypothermia also has been claimed to be useful in reducing intracranial pressure.[82] Convulsions occur frequently and can be controlled by diazepam or phenobarbital. Convulsions may be a problem during convalescence and may require regular administration of other anticonvulsants such as phenytoin sodium, possibly for months. Patients should be observed closely for aspiration which can lead to asphyxiation. Pulmonary toilet must be maintained to prevent pneumonia; if pneumonia develops, the etiologic agent should be determined and aggressive antibiotic therapy instituted.[83, 84]

Diagnosis and Management.—Other arboviral encephalitides that may be confused with JE are tick-borne encephalitis and the rarely reported encephalitis due to Negishi virus. For a more comprehensive discussion of nonarboviral agents which produce the syndrome of encephalitis, see Chapter 24.

Murray Valley Encephalitis

Murray Valley encephalitis (MVE) virus is a flavivirus closely related antigenically to Japanese encephalitis and St Louis encephalitis viruses. In many respects, MVE resembles Japanese encephalitis clinically. This virus is found only in Australia and New Guinea, where periodically it is an important cause of epidemic encephalitis.

History.—Originally called Australian X disease, MVE was first recognized in 1917 to 1918 in an epidemic in southeastern Australia. The suspected etiologic agent was obtained by inoculation of postmortem brain tissue intracerebrally into rhesus monkeys but was not successfully propagated. During a 1951 epidemic, the virus was again isolated from postmortem material and successfully maintained.[85, 86] Since 1917 to 1918, epidemics have recurred in rural areas of southeastern Australia in 1922, 1925, 1951, 1956, 1971, 1974, and 1978.[87–89]

Structure and Biology of the Agent.—The structure of MVE virus is typical of flaviviruses as described above. The virus is highly pathogenic for chick embryos and hamsters. Suckling mice are susceptible by any route of inoculation. Adult mice and rhesus monkeys develop encephalitis after intracerebral but not subcutaneous injections. Unlike Japanese encephalitis virus, MVE does not produce clinical illness in equines nor does it produce abortion in pregnant sows. Many domestic and wild avians will develop viremias of varying amount if infected with MVE virus.[90, 91]

Epidemiology.—Like most arboviral infections, it is difficult to calculate incidence and prevalence for MVE because of the sporadic temporal occurrence and the focal areas of intense transmission.[92] In the eight epidemics that occurred in Australia between 1917 and 1974, 330 cases were reported from varying locations. Like Japanese encephalitis, MVE virus produces a very high inapparent-to-apparent-infection ratio estimated to be 500 or 1000 infections to one clinically apparent case.[93] Mortality during epidemics has ranged from 60% in early epidemics to as low as 20% more recently, probably due to the availability now of more intensive care technology and facilities.

MVE virus in Australia is geographically distributed in an endemic, enzootic focus in the north while epidemics occur in more southern areas in the Murray-Darling River drainage basin.[87] The northern tropical areas support a continuing enzootic transmission cycle, while the drier southern areas can support transmission best under climatic conditions of increased rainfall. Seroconversions occur regularly in humans in the north during both the wet and dry seasons, lending further support to the endemicity of MVE virus there.

In earlier epidemics of MVE, the age group with the highest attack rate was young children, but the trend in more recent epidemics has been for increasing involvement of older age groups.[89] A changing trend also has been noted with respect to risk by sex. Recent epidemics have produced more nearly equal attack rates, whereas, in the past, males were more affected.[94]

Transmission of MVE is by the bites of infected *Cx annulirostris* mosquitoes. The enzootic cycle in the north involves this vector and several species of wild birds.[95–97] While *Cx annulirostris* is usually a rural breeding mosquito, it will readily deposit eggs in peridomestic pooled water containing waste material. This characteristic also serves to make it an effective vector during outbreaks in urban areas.[97]

The movement of MVE virus from its endemic zone in the wetter north to the more populous dry zone in the south appears to be related to abnormally high spring rainfalls which allow a more southward extension of the vector-host complex. As with Japanese encephalitis, antibodies to MVE virus has been found in pigs in Australia. A serologic study of 617 feral pigs after the MVE epidemic of 1974 demonstrated antibodies in 58% of the pigs. Whether or not pigs play an important part in the virus amplification cycle for MVE is not presently known.[98]

Pathogenesis.—Clinically, MVE begins with a prodrome of fever, headache, photophobia, myalgia, nausea, and vomiting. The progression over the next few days closely resembles the clinical course of Japanese encephalitis. Early signs of CNS involvement include drowsiness, difficulties in mentation, disorientation, behavior and speech disturbances, and ataxia. Localized or grand mal convulsions can occur. Patients who do not become comatose have a relatively benign outcome but will display a variety of marked speech disturbances, tremors, incontinence, and stiffened limbs and neck. Patients with more severe disease will become comatose and frequently develop respiratory paralysis necessitating mechanically assisted respiration. Fatalities occur due to superimposed infection or massive brain destruction which is accompanied by decerebrate rigidity.[99, 100]

Laboratory Diagnosis.—Patients with MVE will develop HI, CF, and N antibodies. HI antibodies appear early and in low titer but disappear rapidly during convalescence. CF antibodies appear more slowly and may be useful if a drop in HI convalescent titer is suspected. The immunoglobulin N test has shown promise as a more rapid diagnostic test.[101] Isolation of MVE virus has only been successful utilizing postmortem nervous tissue. The pathologic findings of MVE are similar to those of other arboviral encephalitides and cannot be distinguished from them histopathologically.

Prevention and Treatment.—No vaccines are available to prevent MVE. No effective antiviral agents have yet been found to treat MVE. The management of MVE cases is the same as outlined for Japanese encephalitis.

Diagnosis.—In Australia and New Guinea, the differential diagnosis of MVE would include exclusion of treatable causes of encephalitis as detailed in the introduction to arboviral encephalitis in Chapter 24. The enteroviruses and herpes encephalitis should also be considered, particularly since the latter is treatable.

The clinician outside of Australia should be able to differentiate between other possible agents on the basis of geographic exposure: Japanese encephalitis (Japan, China, Korea, southeast Asia, and the Indian subcontinent) and West Nile (Africa, the Mediteranean basin, and central Asia).

Ilheus Virus Encephalitis

Ilheus virus (ILH) is a flavivirus which was first isolated from

a mixed pool of *Aedes* spp and *Psorophora* spp mosquitoes from Ilheus, Brazil, in 1944 by workers from the Rockefeller Foundation. The virus has subsequently been detected in several other areas of South and Central America: Belém, Trinidad, Colombia, Guatemala, Panama, and Honduras. The major vector is *Psorophora ferox*, which breeds in ground pools of water at the lowland edge of rain forests. ILH virus also has been isolated from several bird species, suggesting a natural cycle between birds and mosquitoes. Primates also have been demonstrated to have neutralizing antibodies to ILH virus, and, on one occasion, virus was isolated from a sentinel monkey caged near Belém[102]

Antibody prevalence studies in South America show a high prevalence of ILH infection in populations residing near rain forests and a larger percentage of males infected than females, possibily due to forest-related occupations of the males. The percentage of persons with antibody increases as their ages increase, indicating continuing long-term endemic exposure in affected areas.[103]

Clinically, ILH usually produces a febrile illness in which patients complain of joint and muscle pains. Occasionally, the virus invades the CNS, usually producing mild symptoms from which patients recover without neurologic sequelae. The small number of identified human cases in areas with high prevalence of antibodies suggests ILH virus may produce a high ratio of inapparent to apparent infections and/or many cases of mild, nonspecific febrile illness.[104]

The treatment of Ilheus infection is symptomatic and is directed at reducing fever with an antipyretic. Analgesics may be required for body pains. Care should be taken to assure adequate hydration and electrolyte balance.

No vaccine for ILH is presently available. Measures to avoid mosquito bites, such as wearing clothing of adequate length and mosquito repellents, can reduce the risk of infection.

The presentation of ILH infection in the area where the virus occurs is so nonspecific that it could be confused with a plethora of infections due to other agents such as dengue, St Louis encephalitis, yellow fever, and influenza viruses. ILH virus can be isolated from peripheral blood in the acute stages of the illness in some cases. ILH virus can be grown in BHK-21, Vero, or LLC MK-2 cells. Serologic tests that will detect antibodies to ILH virus include HI, CF, and PRN tests.

TICK-BORNE ENCEPHALITIS VIRUSES

Tick-borne encephalitis (TBE) viruses occur in western and eastern Europe and the Soviet Union. These viruses have been the subject of debate for some years as to whether their degree of antigenic relatedness is sufficient to include them all as minor variants of the same virus or to group them as separate viruses on the basis of their antigenic and biologic differences. A result of the latter approach is a group of synonyms for TBE: Central European tick-borne encephalitis, Far Eastern or Russian spring-summer encephalitis, diphasic milk fever, and others. This group of viruses also is closely related antigenically to louping ill virus. For this discussion, TBE is considered as a spectrum of disease produced by two closely related viruses.[105, 106]

History.—TBE was first described in the Far Eastern region of the Soviet Union in 1934. TBE virus was isolated 3 years later, and the tick vector was demonstrated soon afterward. The early outbreaks that were recognized were clinically quite severe, although milder forms of the disease were subsequently described in the Soviet Union. Soviet workers also noted that the disease could be transmitted by unpasteurized goat's milk. The disease was first recognized outside the Soviet Union in Czechoslovakia in 1948 and 1949. In 1951, the first milk-borne outbreak occurred in Czechoslovakia, involving over 600 persons.[107]

Structure and Biology of TBE Viruses.—The structure of TBE viruses is typical of flaviviruses as described above. Cytopathic effect (CPE) or plaque production can be shown for a number of continuous or primary tissue culture cell lines. A very wide range of animals have been shown to be susceptible to infection with TBE virus by different routes. Laboratory mice are susceptible by intracerebral or peripheral inoculation and by the alimentary route. Newborn guinea pigs and white rats succumb to infection. Hamsters are susceptible at all ages. Goats, cows, and sheep develop viremia after peripheral inoculation experimentally and after tick bite, and shed the virus in their milk. A number of wild rodents as well as hedgehogs and bats develop viremias. Some hibernating animals may maintain viremias during a sustained period of their dormancy and thus may provide a mechanism for overwintering of the virus.[107–113]

Epidemiology.—The epidemiology of TBE is greatly influenced by whether the disease is tick-borne or milk-borne. Cases which are tick-borne tend to be sporadic in occurrence and affect adult males in agricultural or forestry occupations in greater numbers, especially in the Soviet Union. However, where newly developed settlements intrude into the natural cycle of TBE virus, both sexes and all age groups can be involved. In central Europe, where hiking, camping, and other outdoor pursuits bring people into contact with the vector, illness may be more correlated with recreational activities. Milk-borne outbreaks tend to involve whole families and especially children.[107]

Because the vector ticks are only active during the warmer months, the incidence of disease is highest during the spring through early fall period. TBE occurs and is of varying importance in Austria, Bulgaria, Denmark, Finland, East and West Germany, Hungary, Poland, Sweden, and Yugoslavia, in addition to Czechoslovakia and the Soviet Union.[107, 108]

Pathogenesis.—TBE is transmitted by two main tick vectors, *Ixodes persulcatus* and *Ix ricinus*. The cycle in nature probably involves principally the vector ticks and small rodents, although a number of wild vertebrates may participate. In the vector ticks, the virus has been shown experimentally to be transmitted transovarially and transstadially as well as during hibernation in both ticks and vertebrates. Thus a number of mechanisms are available to allow for survival of the virus through the winter months.[114–117]

Milk-borne transmission of TBE virus is due to the shedding of the virus in the milk of viremic cattle, goats, and sheep and to the stability of the virus in milk and other dairy products. Inactivation of the virus by pasteurization requires a relatively high temperature of 65°C for 30 minutes.[107]

The clinical presentations of TBE vary from asymptomatic infection to fulminant encephalitis and rapid death. Central European encephalitis has been classically described as a more benign

form of the disease, while Russian spring-summer encephalitis (RSSE) has been more severe. However, severe cases do occur in central Europe and milder forms of RSSE are described. When case fatality (C-F) ratios for the two areas are compared, it is apparent that there is greater virulence of the Russian strain where C-F rates of 20% to 29% have been reported compared to 0% to 5% in central Europe. Central European TBE also is described frequently as being biphasic in nature with an influenzalike prodrome which resolves either altogether or is followed by a short period of subjective improvement after which the rapid onset of encephalitic symptoms is noted.[107, 108, 115]

The incubation period for TBE is eight to 14 days after exposure. The illness onset is then sudden with fever, severe headache, photophobia, nuchal rigidity, nausea, and vomiting. The more severe cases may develop central paralysis or have involvement of the brainstem or spinal cord leading to bulbospinal or spinal paralyses.

Delirium, coma, and generalized seizures are also features of more severe disease. Patients who have brainstem involvement or demonstrate ascending paralysis or hemiparesis have a poor prognosis. Residual paralyses involving particularly the upper limb and shoulder girdle muscles are common, especially with RSSE, but also have been described for central European cases. Convalescence is prolonged to as many as several months in some cases with persistent tremors and psychic and emotional lability.[118]

Persons infected with TBE virus will develop N, CF, and HI antibodies.

Laboratory Diagnosis.—The laboratory findings in TBE include early leukopenia sometimes followed by leukocytosis and an increased sedimentation rate. The CSF typically has normal glucose, elevated protein, and a mononuclear pleocytosis.

Definitive diagnosis depends on virus isolation or serologic tests. The viremia of TBE is apparently over when overt clinical manifestations are seen, so the virus is not isolated from the blood or CSF of acutely ill patients. Virus can be isolated readily from the postmortem brain tissue of patients who succumb early in their illness.[107]

HI, CF, and N serologic tests all show rapid rises in antibody titers with the appearance of CF titers occasionally being more variable so that serologic specimens will have to be obtained relatively early in the course of the illness to demonstrate a fourfold or greater rise in titer.[107]

Prevention and Treatment.—The first formalin-inactivated vaccine for TBE was produced in the Soviet Union in 1939. The vaccine currently used in the Soviet Union is a formalin-inactivated preparation in chick embryo cell cultures. In the Soviet Union, the vaccine is recommended for persons living in areas endemic for TBE and for laboratory workers with possible exposure to the virus.[107, 108, 119] A vaccine produced in Vienna (Austria) is available in Western Europe.

Other preventive measures against TBE include avoiding unpasteurized dairy products and tick bites. When in tick-infested areas, long shirts and long pants should be worn with shirt cuffs tightly buttoned and pant cuffs tucked into boot tops or clamped with rubber bands or string. Skin and scalp should be inspected carefully for ticks at least once a day.

The treatment of TBE is symptomatic and supportive. For severe cases, the therapeutic measures outlined for Japanese encephalitis are appropriate for TBE.

Powassan Encephalitis

Powassan encephalitis is a rare form of encephalitis which occurs clinically in North America along the United States–Canadian border. The virus was first isolated from postmortem brain tissue of a 5-year-old child from Ontario, Canada in 1958.[120] Powassan virus is widely distributed in nature throughout a wide range of the North American continent, but fortunately in areas of low human population density. This flavivirus is a member of the Russian spring-summer encephalitis group.[121] The structure and biology of Powassan virus is typical of other flavivirus, as described above.

Epidemiology.—Less than two dozen human cases of Powassan encephalitis have been reported; these have been clustered geographically in upstate New York in the United States and in nearby Ontario, Canada. These cases have clustered temporally during the warmer months when the hard tick vectors are active. The majority of cases reported have been children under the age of 15 years. The severity of disease has been greatest in the younger age groups. The low numbers of human cases reported to date are due to several factors: geographic distribution of the virus in areas of low human population density, failure to obtain appropriate diagnostic tests, and misdiagnoses since antibodies to Powassan virus have been found in serologic surveys of humans.[121–124]

Pathogenesis.—Powassan virus in nature has been isolated from *Ix marxi, Ix cookei,* and *Dermacentor andersoni* ticks, all of which are known to feed on humans. The natural cycle with ixodid ticks involves squirrels, porcupines, and groundhogs. Man is an accidental host when bitten by an infected tick. Infected ticks may be brought into the home by domestic dogs and cats.[122, 125]

The incubation period is usually 1 or more weeks after a tick bite and begins with fever, headache, and progressive neurologic symptoms. Altered sensorium may proceed to coma. Abnormal reflexes and paralysis frequently occur. Spasticity can persist for weeks after the initial illness.

Laboratory Diagnosis.—Laboratory findings in the CSF are normal glucose, elevated protein, and an initially polymorphonuclear pleocytosis which shifts to lymphocytic cells later in the illness. Diagnosis of Powassan encephalitis is best made by serologic tests: HI, CF, or N. Neutralizing antibodies appear rapidly, whereas detection of antibodies by HI or CF may be delayed in appearance for a few weeks. Powassan virus may be isolated from fresh postmortem brain tissue in fatal cases, provided the tissue is not placed in formalin and is maintained frozen until processed for virus isolation.

Prevention and Treatment.—No vaccine for Powassan encephalitis is available. The only preventive measures are those which avoid tick bites. Tick-infected areas should be avoided; when in potentially tick-infested areas, clothing, skin, and scalp should be inspected frequently for ticks. Repellents may also be useful.

Treatment of Powassan encephalitis is symptomatic and sup-portive. Physical therapy should be started early, particularly with patients who have prolonged spastic symptoms.

The differential diagnosis of Powassan encephalitis in the geographic region to which it is presently restricted includes, among the arboviral agents, eastern equine, St Louis, and California encephalitis. For a discussion of other etiologies of the syndrome of encephalitis, see Chapter 24.

Louping III[126–130]

Louping ill is primarily a disease of sheep in England, Ireland, and Scotland due to a tick-borne flavivirus transmitted in nature by infected *Ix ricinus* ticks. Cattle, pigs, deer, and some small mammals and ground-dwelling birds are also infected. It is a relatively rare disease of humans caused by contact with the infected tissues of sheep (butchers and veterinarians), laboratory accidents, or the bite of an infected tick.

The disease produced in humans is reminiscent of the milder forms of tick-borne encephalitis. The clinical course begins with fever, lymphadenopathy, and an influenzalike illness which may terminate at that stage or proceed to a usually mild meningoencephalitis, from which most patients recover without neurologic sequelae. Papilledema and tremor are sometimes seen with the encephalitis phase when it occurs. Infected individuals will develop HI, CF, and N antibodies which may be detected by serologic tests for a laboratory diagnosis. The CSF in louping ill encephalitis will demonstrate normal glucose, elevated protein, and pleocytosis, usually lymphocytic.

A veterinary vaccine for sheep is available which could reduce human risk by reducing the possibilities of exposure. Experimental, formalin-inactivated vaccines have been produced and are used for persons working with sheep or in laboratories.

The treatment for louping ill in man is symptomatic and supportive.

OTHER FLAVIVIRUSES PRODUCING ENCEPHALITIS

Rocio Virus

Rocio virus was first isolated in 1975 by Oscar Lopes from postmortem brain tissue from ten patients in an encephalitis epidemic in São Paulo, Brazil. The disease has not recurred in epidemic form since 1977, but it appears to have the potential for recurrence and introduction into other areas of South America and into the North American continent.[131] The reasons for the recent disappearance of this disease are not clear but may be related to geographic constraints on the suspected vector. The structure and biology of Rocio virus are typical of flaviviruses as described above.

Epidemiology.—The first outbreak of encephalitis due to Rocio virus began in March 1975 and ended in June. A total of 465 cases with 61 deaths were reported. The overall attack rate was 15 per 1000 population. The case fatality rate was 13%, and the mortality rate was two per 1000 population. The attack rate was higher in males than females, and the age group most affected was persons from 15 to 30 years of age. Family studies indicated that no person-to-person transmission occurred; the disease was probably vector-borne.[132]

A vector study by Lopes et al in 1975 yielded an isolate of Rocio virus from the mosquito species, *Psorophora ferox*.[133] Subsequent work by Mitchell and Forattini has suggested that the more likely vector was *Aedes scapularis*, which was present in abundant numbers during the epidemic.[134] Other isolates of Rocio virus have been obtained from sentinel mice exposed in the epidemic area and from a rufous collared sparrow captured in the wild.[131] Mitchell et al have demonstrated that two prevalent North American mosquito species, *Cx tarsalis* and *Cx pipiens pipiens*, can be readily infected with Rocio virus, and these species may transmit the virus.[135] These data suggest that if Rocio virus were introduced into North America, there is a potential for epidemic transmission. The natural transmission cycle in Brazil is most likely between the vector mosquito and wild birds. Monath et al experimentally infected North American house sparrows *(Passer domesticus)* with Rocio virus. Although these birds are important in the transmission cycle for the related St Louis encephalitis flavivirus in North America, in these transmission studies the sparrows did not attain high levels of viremia and were not judged to be an important potential amplifying host.[136] Rocio encephalitis epidemics thus far have been seasonal with a peak incidence in late summer and early fall.[137]

Pathogenesis.—The incubation period for Rocio encephalitis is thought to be 12 days. The illness is characterized by fever, headache, vomiting, disturbances of consciousness, and occasionally signs of meningitis. Other clinical signs include aerophobia, hypertension, sighing respirations, purposeless masticatory movements, and falling. Electroencephalograms during sleep have showed a generalized decrease of cortical activity that suggests widespread cerebral involvement.[138]

Peripheral blood cell counts in one study showed decreased numbers of red cells and decreased hemoglobin and hematocrit levels in half the patients. CSF fluid examination revealed 200 to 3500 cells (mononuclear in type in 75% of patients). CSF protein was usually elevated while chloride and glucose were normal.[137]

Patients who recover from Rocio encephalitis develop HI, CF, and N antibodies.

Laboratory Diagnosis.—Isolation of Rocio virus from blood and CSF is difficult. Isolation of the virus can be made from postmortem brain tissue only if the patient died within five days of illness onset.[131] In one case, virus was demonstrated by immunofluorescence test in thalamic neurons obtained from a postmortem brain specimen.[139]

Serologic testing can be performed by HI, CF, or N tests. Blood specimens should be collected during the acute illness and two to four weeks after onset and submitted to a laboratory capable of performing arboviral serologic testing. A more sensitive immunoglobulin M antibody capture-enzyme linked immunosorbent assay (MAC-ELISA) test has been described.[140]

The pathologic lesions in the brain due to Rocio virus are typical of acute viral encephalitis; however, some neuroanatomical distinctions based on seven cases have been reported.[141] The virus seems to produce its most severe damage to the nuclei of neurons in the thalamus, hypothalamus, and dentate nucleus.

Prevention and Treatment.—Although the vector involved with the Brazilian outbreaks was not conclusively proved, standard mosquito control strategies such as adulticiding and larviciding should be useful to reduce mosquito populations and thereby the risk of transmission of Rocio virus. Personal protective measures include wearing protective clothing and using repellents on exposed skin areas. No vaccine for the prevention of Rocio encephalitis is currently available.

No specific therapy for Rocio virus has been developed to date; supportive treatment, including intensive care when necessary, has been shown to decrease the death rate.[132] Maintenance of pulmonary toilet and adequate oxygenation are important. Intravenous fluid therapy to maintain fluid and electrolyte balance may be required.

After treatable nonviral causes of infection have been excluded, the other agents which must be considered as possible etiologic agents include eastern equine encephalitis, Venezuelan equine encephalitis, western equine encephalitis, and St Louis encephalitis.

Negishi and Rio Bravo Viruses

Negishi and Rio Bravo viruses are flaviviruses with modes of transmission that have not yet been elucidated. Negishi virus has been isolated from the postmorten brain specimens of two patients who succumbed with encephalitis in Tokyo in the summer of 1948. A laboratory infection with Negishi virus producing fever but not encephalitis occurred in 1950. Negishi virus has been shown to be most closely related serologically to the Russian spring-summer encephalitis virus family.[142] This family of viruses is tick-borne, and Negishi virus may be tick-borne also.

Rio Bravo virus was first isolated from the salivary glands of Mexican free-tailed bats *(Tadarida mexicana)* and has been shown to be antigenically related to the Japanese encephalitis, West Nile, St Louis encephalitis, and Murray Valley group of viruses. Although antibodies to this agent have been found during a serosurvey of humans in Trinidad, the relationship of these antibodies to prior illnesses is not presently clear.[143, 144] In laboratory accidents with Rio Bravo virus, febrile illnesses with encephalitis or aseptic meningitis have occurred. Since the mode of transmission of Rio Bravo virus in nature is unknown, no prevention strategies are available now. Treatment of both Negishi and Rio Bravo encephalitis is nonspecific and supportive.

FLAVIVIRUSES PRODUCING SYSTEMIC FEBRILE ILLNESSES

West Nile Fever

West Nile virus was first isolated in 1937 from the blood of a febrile patient in Uganda. West Nile fever is a denguelike illness that occurs in both epidemic and endemic forms in Africa, Asia, and the Mediterranean countries. Early descriptions of the disease were from outbreaks which occurred in Egypt and Israel. A major epidemic of West Nile fever occurred in South Africa in 1974.[145–148]

Structure and Biology of the Agent.—The structure and biology of West Nile virus is typical of flaviviruses as described above. The virus is a member of the St Louis encephalitis complex. It is pathogenic for hamsters and adult and suckling mice by peripheral inoculation. Mice of all ages succumb to intracerebral inoculation. The virus grows readily in a number of tissue culture cell lines in which it produces plaques and CPE. Viremia in humans persists for four to five days after illness onset.[146]

Epidemiology.—West Nile fever occurs in both endemic and epidemic transmission patterns. Areas of high endemic transmission include Egypt and southern Iran and most of the adult population in these areas will have antibodies against the virus since they have been infected in childhood. In areas where transmission is more sporadic and occurs in epidemics of varying magnitude, all age groups are likely to be involved. West Nile fever occasionally occurs in southern Europe and Australia, but is more prevalent in Africa and Asia. Outbreaks tend to occur most often during the summer months.[147, 149, 150]

Age at the time of infection is important in determining the clinical manifestations that will be seen. Children usually have a mild undifferentiated febrile illness which rapidly resolves. Because of the mild nature of West Nile fever in childhood, the disease is often not recognized clinically in areas of high endemic transmission where most infections occur in young children. Adults infected with West Nile virus usually have a denguelike illness. In the elderly, West Nile fever can present as encephalitis that is sometimes fatal.[151, 152]

Pathogenesis.—West Nile fever is transmitted by the bites of *Culex* spp mosquitoes, most often by *Cx univittatus, Cx fatigans,* and *Cx theileri.* The enzootic transmission cycle for West Nile virus is between culicine mosquitoes and birds. Experimental peripheral inoculation studies with West Nile virus have demonstrated that almost all birds tested to date develop viremia after this type of exposure. Cattle, horses, and sheep can be infected with West Nile virus and encephalomyelitis may be produced in some horses. Humans are incidentally infected when bitten by a culicine mosquito that has become infected in the enzootic cycle.[147, 148, 153]

The incubation period is three to six days, after which there is sudden onset of fever, severe headache, photophobia, myalgia, arthralgia, flushed facies, lymphadenopathy, and a pink maculopapular rash often surrounded by a pale halo and generally confined to truncal areas. The fever may be diphasic and the clinical illness is usually a benign one that resolves within two to five days. Occasionally GI symptoms of anorexia, nausea, vomiting, and diarrhea occur. Patients frequently complain of sore throat but other manifestations of upper respiratory infection are usually absent. When meningoencephalitis occurs in elderly patients in areas where West Nile virus is known to exist, it should be considered as a possible etiologic agent. Leukopenia is a frequent laboratory finding.[145, 147, 150]

Laboratory Diagnosis.—Patients infected with West Nile virus will develop HI, CF, and N antibodies. Any of these three serologic tests may be used for diagnosis. If the patient has had a previous infection with another flavivirus, the serum may contain broadly reacting antibodies which make a specific diagnosis difficult. In these instances, a neutralization test is frequently useful in distinguishing between possible flaviviral infections.[153]

West Nile virus can be isolated from the blood in tissue culture, particularly if a blood sample is taken in the first 24 to 48 hours of illness. If the blood specimen for virus isolation is not to be inoculated into tissue culture soon after collection, it must be frozen and shipped frozen to an appropriate laboratory.[154]

Prevention and Treatment.—No vaccine for West Nile fever is available, and there is no specific therapy. Treatment is symptomatic and supportive. Since person-to-person spread of West Nile fever is not known to occur, isolation of patients with this illness is not required. Care should be exercised in handling blood or needles.

Among the arboviruses it is very difficult to distinguish clinically between West Nile fever, dengue fever, and chikungunya. In the absence of rash, a number of togaviruses and bunyaviruses must also be considered in the differential diagnosis. Rubella, measles, and other viral diseases producing exanthems must be excluded when rash is present. Treatable bacterial causes of rash such as rickettsiae, leptospires, and meningococci should be ruled out.

Wesselsbron Fever[155–157]

Wesselsbron virus is a flavivirus primarily infecting sheep and causing abortion. It was first isolated from a dead lamb in 1955 and, in the same year, from a febrile patient and mosquitoes in Natal. It grows readily in a number of tissue cultures, but especially well in primary cultures of lamb kidney. Suckling mice develop encephalitis after intracerebral inoculation.

Virus isolation or serologic surveys show the virus to be present widely on the African continent and in Thailand. It is transmitted to man by the bites of infected *Aedes* and *Culex* mosquitoes. In South Africa the presumed vectors are *Ae caballus, Ae circumluteolus,* and *Cx zombaensis.* In Thailand, *Cx quinquefasciatus* has been demonstrated experimentally to be an efficient vector. Man can also be infected by exposure to the tissues of animals infected with Wesselsbron virus.

Clinically, Wesselsbron fever is a denguelike illness that has an incubation period of two to four days, after which there is acute onset of fever, arthralgias, myalgia, fever, orbital pain, headache and, in many cases, a macular rash. In severely ill patients, signs of CNS involvement such as impaired mentation, delirium, and visual blurring may occur.

Wesselsbron fever can be diagnosed by virus isolation from the blood of acutely ill patients or by serologic testing using HI, CF, or N tests.

Treatment of Wesselsbron fever is symptomatic and supportive. No human vaccine is available. Avoidance of mosquito bites and precautions in handling sick animals are the only effective preventive measures.

FLAVIVIRUSES PRODUCING HEMORRHAGIC FEVER

Yellow Fever

Yellow fever, once a scourge of the port cities of North America and Europe, remains an important endemic and epidemic disease of tropical and subtropical Africa and South America. While the arthropod vector *Aedes aegypti* is no longer present in Europe, it is still present in the Southeast Atlantic and Gulf states of the United States, thus presenting the potential for reintroduction of yellow fever into those areas. The unraveling of the mystery of this disease and the mode of its transmission was an important milestone in the progress of medical science in that yellow fever was the first recognized disease of viral etiology and the first identified arthropod-borne disease.

History.—Yellow fever was first recognized as a disease in the seventeenth century in North America. It is thought to have originated in one of the two areas where it is now present in endemic form—Africa and South America. Considerable traffic by sailing ships occurred between both these areas and the United States mainland. Incredible epidemics producing marked mortality were a regular occurrence in the West Indies, Central America, and the southern United States. The sailing ships have been incriminated as a source of introduction of yellow fever in northeastern port cities from Boston to Baltimore by the presence on board of vector mosquitoes which bred in the freshwater containers.

While the names of Walter Reed and William Gorgas are closely associated with yellow fever as pioneers in the cause and control of the disease, the first to propose that it was transmitted by mosquitoes was Dr Carlos Finlay of Havana, Cuba. It was Reed and his fellow members of the Yellow Fever Commission whose experimental work confirmed Finlay's theory and formed the basis for a control program by mosquito eradication which was administered by Gorgas and was successful in ridding Cuba of yellow fever (YF).

The next era of importance to the understanding of YF was presided over by the Yellow Fever commissions of the Rockefeller Foundation. The first commission was formed in 1916 and a YF eradication program was begun in Guayaquil, Ecuador, in 1918. The program was successful and requests for assistance in vector eradication came from many other countries of South and Central America. In 1920 the Foundation began studies on YF in Africa which eventually led to the isolation of YF virus and the discovery of "jungle YF." The Asibi strain of virus, originally isolated from a patient in Ghana, was adapted first to mouse embryo tissue and then to chick embryo tissue, and in 1937 Theiler and Smith announced the development from this strain of the live attenuated 17-D vaccine for human immunization. This early, quite successful work with YF focused the attention of the Rockefeller Foundation on the then unexplored field of arbovirology and, beginning in 1950, launched more than two fruitful decades of research on arboviruses, their ecology, and the diseases they produce in man and animals.[158, 159]

In spite of progress in all these areas, YF has remained an important public health problem in Africa and South America into the 1980s. We have lacked a coordinated approach to studying the clinical management of severe YF cases. Rapid, reliable, and simple diagnostic tests were needed. The molecular structure and biology of YF virus required study. And, although a very effective vaccine is available, its proper use in highly affected areas depends absolutely on refrigeration, which is often not available in those areas.[160]

Fortunately, we have noted progress in all these issues.[161] An expert group convened by the Pan American Health Organization recommended a number of therapeutic approaches to severe YF cases and a mobile force to study them.[162] Promising rapid diagnostic techniques have been described and are currently being evaluated for sensitivity and specificity.[163–165] Rice et al have elucidated the genomic sequence of YF 17-D virus.[166] The importance of their work to YF pathogenesis, to rapid diagnosis, and to subunit and recombinant vaccine development has been reviewed.[167] A thermostable YF vaccine has been developed and is being evaluated for efficacy and safety.[168]

Structure and Biology.—The YF 17-D RNA genome has 10,862 nucleotides. Its open reading frame is 10,233 nucleotides in length and encodes all three structural proteins and up to 12 nonstructural proteins. The C, M, and E structural polypeptides occur at the 5' terminus. The envelope (E) glycoprotein contains all antigenic structures with biologic functions. The nonstructural protein gene segments lie adjacent to the E segment.[166]

The virus is inactivated by ether and bile salts and is quite heat-labile, being inactivated after incubation at 60°C for 10 minutes. Suckling and adult mice are killed by intracerebral inoculation of YF virus, and rhesus monkeys are sensitive to peripheral inoculation, developing severe, frequently fatal hepatitis.[169]

Epidemiology.—YF is a quarantinable disease of international public health significance which should be reported to the World Health Organization (WHO) by countries recognizing sporadic cases or epidemics within their borders. In actual practice, many areas subject to YF outbreaks have isolated populations at risk, poor communications, rudimentary health care delivery, and limited laboratory facilities. As a result, the number of cases of YF reported to WHO is only a small fraction of the actual number of cases that occur each year, and epidemics are frequently approaching or are already at their peak when recognized, thus precluding timely intervention measures.[170] Depending on population density, preexisting immunity level, and vector abundance, epidemics of YF can produce thousands of cases.[171, 172]

YF occurs in two major forms: urban YF and jungle or sylvatic YF. Jungle YF is the natural reservoir for the disease in a cycle involving nonhuman primates and forest or canopy mosquitoes. Prior to the recognition of this reservoir, early workers in YF thought that eradication of the known urban vector, *Ae aegypti*, would remove YF as a health problem, and some of their early successes (such as in the Panama Canal Zone and South America) supported that hypothesis.[158] Given the present technology of mosquito control, it is not feasible to interrupt the jungle cycle, although much can be done to reduce populations of the urban vector. The cornerstone of control of YF today is the use of the very effective vaccine (see below).

The temporal distribution of urban YF cases depends on the occurrence of rainfall (rainy vs dry season) and ambient temperatures. The rainfall is critical since *Ae aegypti* mosquitoes lay their eggs in peridomestic water-filled containers and refuse and thus require adequate rainfall in order to increase their population to the critical levels which can support epidemic transmission. Similarly, warmer temperatures lead to increased activity of adult mosquitoes; this effect in endemic YF zones, where temperatures rarely get cool during periods of maximum adult vector activity, is probably less important than the effect of warmer temperatures in shortening the period of larval development and thus increasing the rate of emergence of adults.

The potential geographic distribution of urban YF is in any areas where infestation with *Ae aegypti* occurs, including Africa, South America, Central America, the Caribbean, and the Southeast and Gulf Coast cities of the United States mainland. Although the urban vector is present in Asia and southeast Asia, YF has never become established there. The majority of reported human YF cases (1980 to 1988) come from Africa (Angola, Cameroon, Gambia, Ghana, Nigeria, Sudan, and Zaire) and South America (Bolivia, Brazil, Colombia, Ecuador, Peru, and Venezuela).[173] Both of these continents have enzootic and epizootic jungle YF transmitted in a monkey-mosquito-monkey cycle. South American primates are more prone to mortality once infected with YF than are the Old World primates of Africa, and the finding of dead monkeys in South America is a useful clue in detecting and following the progress of jungle epizootics.

The intrusion of jungle YF into urban areas varies somewhat between Africa and South America and within different ecological zones within the two countries. Most jungle transmission in South America is by *Haemagogus spp.* mosquitoes, while the situation is entomologically more complex in Africa. The high forested areas of the northern half of Africa sustain a dispersed primate population and low enzootic transmission rates mainly by the vector *Ae africanus*. In the savannahs and riverine forest areas of West and East Africa, the primate density and proximity to human population create so-called zones of emergence for YF. Within these zones in East Africa *Ae simpsoni* plays an important role in introducing YF virus into the urban *Ae aegypti* cycle.[158] In West Africa, the initial transmission to man by sylvatic vectors appears to be by *Ae furcifer taylori* group and possibly by *Ae luteocephalus, Ae metallicus,* and *Ae vittatus* as well.[172]

Given a universally susceptible human population in an urban YF outbreak, no differences in infection rates due to age or sex will be seen. Transmission patterns of this sort might be seen if YF were introduced into susceptible portions of the United States mainland (assuming low levels of YF immunization). In the endemic zones, however, a number of factors, including social, cultural, economic, and historical ones, can act to modify the distribution of cases within a population. If the population exposed to YF in an outbreak has had periodic exposures in the past, disease will be primarily detected in the younger susceptible population rather than the previously infected (and therefore immune) older population. An example of this occurred in Senegal in 1965, when a decision was made to stop the routine immunization of children against YF.[174] In the ensuing outbreak, attack rates were highest in the young unimmunized group. In South America, sporadic cases of YF related to forest exposure occur more frequently in males who enter there to cut trees. As mentioned elsewhere (see Dengue below), other social, cultural, and economic factors may be of importance in *Ae aegypti*–transmitted disease. Severity of clinical illness may be less in children and in African blacks. In the latter group this may be due to cross-protecting antibodies from prior antigenically related flavivirus infections.

Pathogenesis.—Once a yellow fever–susceptible urban or jungle vector consumes an infected blood meal, an extrinsic incubation period follows during which YF virus migrates out of the mosquito's gut finally reaching the salivary glands, after which time the mosquito will remain infectious for the remainder of its lifetime. Transovarial transmission of YF by *Ae aegypti* and other mosquitoes that carry YF virus provides a mechanism for continuing the cycle in either urban or jungle situations by producing offspring that are infectious when they emerge as adults.[175]

Once the virus is inoculated into human skin, local replication occurs with dissemination to regional lymph nodes and eventually viremia. During the period of hematogenous dissemination, YF virus tends to localize in lymphoid tissues such as lymph nodes, spleen, and liver but also in heart, kidneys, and foregut. The incubation period varies from three to six days in humans.

Clinical Symptoms.—The usual onset of YF is abrupt with chills, fever, and headache. Many patients can recall the time of onset quite clearly. These symptoms will soon be followed by generalized myalgias (often including severe back pain) and GI complaints of nausea and vomiting. Physical findings at this stage include facial flushing, redness of the tip and sides of the tongue, and conjunctival injection. Some patients will have virtually asymptomatic infection or an undifferentiated febrile illness alone or accompanied by some of the manifestations described above. After a period of three to four days of illness, moderately ill patients will begin to improve and usually recover in less than a week. More severely ill patients with a classic yellow fever course will defervesce and have a remission of symptoms for a short period of time followed by the return of fever, bradycardia relative to the degree of fever (Faget's sign), jaundice, and hemorrhagic manifestations of varying severity. Jaundice in blacks can be very difficult to discern and in Africa the use of palm oil in the diet can cause yellowish discoloration of sclerae, making even the evaluation of scleral icterus questionable.[169] Bleeding manifestations vary from petechial lesions of the mucous membranes to epistaxis, bleeding gums, upper GI hemorrhage, melena, or vaginal bleeding. Swallowed blood from epistaxis or gum bleeding and/or bleeding from the stomach or duodenum may produce the "black vomit" of YF, classically described but not a pathognomonic sign.

Varying from one epidemic to another, a small percentage to as many as 50% of patients with overt symptoms of YF will develop fatal disease characterized by severe hemorrhagic manifestations, oliguria, and hypotension. Frank renal failure is rare. Terminal events can include profuse black vomit, coma, or delirium. In some fulminant cases, there is rapid progression of severe symptoms without an intervening afebrile period. Other clinical presentations (meningoencephalitis in the absence of other findings) have been described.[176]

Immunologic Response.—YF virus contains both hemagglutin and CF antigens, and the infected host will produce detectable antibody to both these antigens. YF virus shares antigens with other flaviviruses and, in flavivirus hyperendemic areas, serologic distinction between different viruses using common serologic tests may be difficult or impossible. The infected host also produces neutralizing antibodies, and these may be detected more specifically. Natural infection with YF virus appears to confer lifetime immunity and recent studies of persistence of antibody in United

States armed forces immunized with 17-D vaccine revealed neutralizing antibody to be present up to 35 years after immunization.[177] It was observed in the past that immunization with 17-D YF vaccine did not produce CF antibodies in vaccinees. This difference in serologic response between persons naturally infected with YF and those vaccinated with 17-D vaccine was thought to be useful in certain epidemic situations to distinguish these two groups. Monath et al, however, observed that a population in West Africa residing in a flavivirus hyperendemic area, who were previously infected with a heterologous flavivirus, did in fact develop YF CF antibody when immunized with 17-D vaccine.[178]

Pathology.—YF is a viscerotropic virus which causes its major pathologic manifestations in liver, kidney, heart, and GI tract, although petechial hemorrhages may be present in oral mucous membranes and skin. Gross examination reveals varying degrees of icterus, hemorrhage in various organs, blood in the GI tract, and often a flabby, pale heart.

Histopathologic examination of the liver reveals the lesions of midzonal necrosis of lobules, coagulation necrosis (producing hyaline deposits which are acidophilic and called Councilman bodies), fatty degeneration, and a striking lack of inflammatory cells. Pathologic changes in the kidneys mainly involve the proximal tubules which show cloudy swelling and fatty degeneration of cells and lumina filled with debris and casts, again without inflammatory cells. The heart reveals petechial hemorrhages of the pericardium and degeneration of myocardial fibers.

Laboratory Findings and Diagnosis.—A comprehensive laboratory profile of YF in humans has been very slow in developing due to the usual occurrence of outbreaks in geographically isolated areas without access to modern laboratory facilities. Some information has begun to accumulate, however, and data on hemostasis in experimentally infected rhesus monkeys are also of interest.[179] Severely ill patients have leukopenia and albuminuria, elevated bilirubin and BUN, and prolonged prothrombin times.

Studies with experimentally infected rhesus monkeys have shown multiple coagulation abnormalities: prolonged one-stage prothrombin time and partial thromboplastin time and significant depression of factors II, V, VII, VIII, X, and XI. Terminally, the monkeys developed a mild thrombocytopenia, hypofibrinogenemia, and increased fibrin degradation products, suggesting the development of disseminated intravascular coagulation (DIC). In these monkeys, however, hepatic necrosis appeared to be a more significant factor in mortality than DIC, although this finding may not be applicable in humans whose hepatic lesions are not so dramatic.

YF can be diagnosed serologically or by virus isolation. Serologic diagnosis can be made by HI, CF, or PRN tests, the latter being especially useful when cross-reacting flavivirus antibodies are a consideration (for a fuller discussion of flavivirus cross-reactivity see Dengue).[180] An IFA test has also been described.[163] Blood for serologic testing should be obtained as soon after illness onset as possible and again in 2 to 3 weeks. The blood should be spun down and the sera reserved under refrigeration until shipped for testing. If the specimens were collected and manipulated under sterile conditions, they may be shipped at ambient temperatures if the shipping period does not exceed two to three days. If longer shipping is required or bacterial contamination is a concern, sera should be shipped frozen on wet or dry ice. Specimens should always be accompanied by appropriate clinical and epidemiologic information to facilitate diagnosis (see Dengue).

If virus isolation from blood is to be attempted, the blood (or serum) specimen must be obtained within the first four days after illness and stored in liquid nitrogen or at $-60°C$ in a special freezer if it cannot be processed within a few days. Otherwise it can be kept at $4°C$. Freezing, thawing, and refreezing is detrimental to YF and other flaviviruses' survival and should be avoided when possible. Specimens for virus isolation should be shipped on dry ice in a well-insulated container. Again, comprehensive clinical and epidemiologic information should accompany the specimen.

Techniques for YF virus isolation include intracerebral inoculation of acute phase blood or serum into one- to four-day-old Swiss mice or inoculation of one of the following cell cultures: Vero, LLC MK-2, BHK, or the arthropod cell cultures, C6/36 (Igarashi clone of *Ae albopictus*), and *Ae pseudoscutellaris* cells. Identification of the isolate can be done by HI, CF, or PRN. The YF virus can also be detected in serum by antigen–capture enzyme immunoassay.[164]

Prevention and Treatment.—The successes of Reed, Gorgas and, subsequently, workers from the Rockefeller Foundation in controlling urban yellow fever by reduction of the *Ae aegypti* population underscore the importance of vector control to the prevention of YF. (For a discussion of the methods and strategies for *Ae aegypti* control, see Dengue.) The major prevention strategy at present is immunization with YF vaccine.

The first vaccine against yellow fever was developed by Wilbur Sawyer, who combined a less virulent mouse-adapted strain of YF virus as a 10% suspension in fresh, sterile human YF immune sera. It was first tested in humans in 1931 and was successful in preventing YF in Rockefeller Foundation workers. Prior to the use of this vaccine, numerous laboratory infections, some fatal, had occurred.[181]

The current most widely used vaccine, 17-D, was developed from the Asibi strain which was first adapted to grow in embryonic mouse tissue, then in whole chick embryo tissue, and finally in chick embryo tissue from which brain and spinal cord had been removed. This procedure yielded a markedly attenuated live virus vaccine that Theiler and Smith tested safely in monkeys both subcutaneously and by intracerebral inoculation.[182] Human trials were conducted first in New York and finally large-scale studies were completed during 1937 and 1938 in Brazil.[183]

The French also developed a vaccine during this period, utilizing virus grown in mouse brain. This French neurotropic vaccine can be administered by scarification with a bifurcated needle, is more stable than the 17-D vaccine, but it has been associated with an increased risk of allergic encephalitis, particularly in children. The 17-D vaccine must be kept frozen until immediately before use, must be administered by needle and syringe or jet injection gun, and protected from inactivation by direct light.

Residents and travelers above the age of 9 months in endemic YF zones should be immunized. Below age 9 months an increased risk of vaccine–associated encephalitis occurs. Travelers should be immunized at least 2 weeks prior to departure to allow sufficient time for development of adequate antibody levels. In endemic YF countries, which have or are establishing childhood immunization programs, routine YF vaccination should be included. The official recommendation currently is that a booster immunization should be administered every 10 years, although this may change in view of recent data on the long persistence of YF antibody after immunization with 17-D vaccine.[184]

The contraindications to the use of 17-D YF vaccine are pregnancy, altered immune states, and hypersensitivity to eggs. Although no evidence currently exists which shows 17-D vaccine to damage the fetus, it is a live virus vaccine and thus poses at least a theoretical risk. However, if a pregnant woman must travel in an area of high risk of YF, she should be immunized since the risk of morbidity from YF would be greater than the small risk of YF vaccine to the mother and the theoretical risk to the fetus. Because YF vaccine infection might be potentiated in persons with altered immunity due either to disease (leukemia, lymphoma, generalized malignancy) or to immunosuppressive therapy (steroids, alkylating drugs, antimetabolites, or radiation), 17-D vaccine should not be administered to them. Adverse reactions are generally mild and occur in 5% to 10% of vaccinees. Headache, myalgia, and low-grade fever are the most frequently reported symptoms.

The availability of a new thermostable 17-D vaccine is a major achievement for YF control in areas of Africa and South America, where the lack of refrigeration has presented formidable problems to mass immunization programs in the past. Studies reported to date indicate that the thermostable 17-D vaccine is comparable in immunogenicity and reactogenicity to its thermolabile counterpart.[168]

No specific antiviral therapy for YF exists. Unfortunately, epidemics of YF usually occur in geographically remote and medically underserved areas. Thus, providing and evaluating intensive medical management of severe YF cases has not been possible.[160, 162] A recent panel of the Pan-American Health Organization has proposed a systematic therapeutic approach for trials and evaluation. Additionally, this panel recommended the organization of a suitably equipped mobile medical force to deal with the problem of epidemics in remote areas.[162]

Useful laboratory indicators of potentially fatal YF cases are levels of serum bilirubin, aspartate aminotransferase (AST), and alanine aminotransferase (ALT). In severe YF, bilirubin levels are elevated as early as the third day of illness and peak by the eighth day. Bilirubin levels peak later and decline rapidly in nonfatal cases. AST and ALT levels are two to three times higher in fatal cases than in nonfatal icteric cases.

Extrahepatic manifestations of liver injury in YF involve multiple organ systems and include hemorrhage, hypoglycemia, hypotension, metabolic acidosis, renal failure, and encephalopathy. The management of these clinical emergencies requires standard medical intensive care techniques that are described in detail in the expert panel recommendations.[162]

Algorithms for Diagnosis and Management.—The differential diagnosis of severe YF includes typhoid fever, leptospirosis, tick-borne relapsing fever, typhus, Q fever, falciparum malaria, severe viral hepatitis, Rift Valley fever, Crimean-Congo hemorrhagic fever, Lassa fever, Marburg fever, Ebola fever, and Bolivian hemorrhagic fever.

When YF is first suspected, every attempt should be made to confirm the diagnosis by use of the classic and rapid diagnostic tests described above and by virus isolation, where possible. When isolation of YF virus is attempted in mosquito cell lines, sera should first be treated with dithiothreitol to dissociate virus-IgM antibody complexes which will not normally infect these cell lines.[162] If the patient dies, permission for an autopsy should be sought and, failing that, a limited autopsy to obtain liver tissue should be performed. However, because of the high complication rate, liver biopsy should not be performed during an acute YF illness. Personnel performing autopsies should be immunized against YF when possible and should undertake them with appropriate measures to protect against the diagnostic possibilities listed above.

Public health officials should be notified to prevent introduction of virus into a nonendemic area and to begin investigation into the probable source of the infection. Once an epidemic area is identified, major public health measures such as vector eradication and mass immunization campaigns must be instituted to contain or prevent an epidemic.

Dengue

Dengue, a mosquito-borne flaviviral infection of humans, is endemic and epidemic in tropical and subtropical areas of the world. The large number of cases occurring each year and the possibility for dengue viruses to produce potentially fatal disease (dengue hemorrhagic fever and shock syndrome) place the dengue viruses among the most important of the arboviral infections of humans. The incursion of dengue across the border of Texas from Mexico in 1980 has made the possibility of dengue outbreaks or epidemics in the United States a matter of continuing public health concern.[185] Since 1977, hundred of cases of dengue imported into North America from the Caribbean have been documented; these reported cases represent only a fraction of the total cases imported each year.

History.—Outbreaks of denguelike illness have been recorded since the late part of the eighteenth century from tropical and subtropical regions of the world, principally from southeast Asia and the Caribbean and Gulf-Atlantic region of Central and North America. The first clinical description of dengue is attributed to Benjamin Rush from an outbreak that occurred in the summer and autumn of 1780 in Philadelphia.[186]

A noteworthy aspect of Dr Rush's report was the degree to which his clinical description of dengue coincides with modern descriptions of the disease. Carey has observed that many other descriptions of "dengue" outbreaks during the eighteenth and nineteenth centuries were more likely descriptions of outbreaks of the alphaviral disease chikungunya, which produces more pronounced and prolonged arthritic symptoms.[187] A curiosity of past descriptions of dengue epidemics in the Caribbean and Gulf-Atlantic areas during the 1880s, as summarized by Ehrenkranz et al, was the frequency of spontaneous abortion and stillbirths reported in association with dengue epidemics, complications which have not been prominently noted with dengue in modern times.[188, 189] Whether this represents a mistaken attribution of the infecting agent, an altered virulence of the virus, a different host susceptibility pattern, or the result of treatments in vogue at that time (such as purging) is not clear.

Our modern understanding of the transmission of dengue began in 1906 with the suggestion by Bancroft that it was transmitted by *Ae aegypti* mosquitoes; this was subsequently proved in 1919 by Cleland and coworkers.[190] In 1907, dengue was shown to be due to a filterable agent, which could be transmitted experimentally by inoculating blood from an acutely ill patient into a volunteer.[190] In 1960, Hammon et al reported the isolation of dengue virus from ill patients in the Philippines and subsequently from patients in Bangkok.[191]

In southeast Asia, Hammon and his coworkers studied the two more serious manifestations of dengue, dengue hemorrhagic fever (DHF) and dengue shock syndrome (DSS).[192] Severe hemorrhagic symptoms and deaths were earlier noted to be occurring only in children in this area.[193] Previous outbreaks of this nature had been reported from Durban, South Africa, in 1927, and Athens in 1928, but the earliest report consistent with these diagnoses is felt to be from Queensland, Australia, in 1898.[194] Since the 1950s, DHF and DSS have continued to occur in southeast Asia, and studies there have suggested a possible pathophysiologic mechanism for these severe forms of dengue. In spite of the documentation of several dengue pandemics in the Caribbean, remarkably few cases of DHF or DSS had been reported until 1981, when a dengue epidemic in Cuba produced many cases of DHF and DSS and 158 deaths, mostly in children.[195–199]

Structure and Biology of the Agent.—Four serologically distinguishable types of dengue can be recognized (DEN-1–4). They are RNA viruses of particle size 45 to 55 nm. The virion surface structure is controversial but has been described in one study as being made up of doughnut-shaped rings 7 nm in diameter with a 2- to 3-nm central hole; the rings cover the surface without apparent symmetry. Each virion contains a unit membrane envelope layer and an internal core particle (nucleocapsid). In electron microscopic studies, core particle structure does not appear to be composed of regularly arrayed subunits, and there is disagreement as to the exact nature of core organization.[200]

The process by which dengue and other flaviviruses acquire their membrane envelope is thought to be host cell–derived. But, whether it is by a mechanism of budding from the host cell membrane or otherwise is not established. In common with other flaviviruses, dengue viruses contain a nonsegmented, single-stranded, infectious 42S RNA and three virion structural polypeptides. As with other flaviviruses examined, the structural polypeptides of dengue are a nucleocapsid protein, a large envelope glycoprotein, and a small nonglycosylated envelope protein. Molecular weights of the large envelope glycoproteins vary from 51,000 for dengue serotype 4 to 59,000 for dengue serotype 2.[201] Dengue 2 virions have sedimentation rates which vary, depending on the cells in which they were propagated, from 175S when grown in mouse brain to 200S in cell culture. Similarly, the method of virus propagation affects density measurements of dengue 2 virus as measured by equilibrium centrifugation in cesium chloride (1.22–1.24 g/cm³).[201]

Dengue virus stability is greatest at pH 8, and the virus is inactivated at acid pH. Other chemical inactivation of the virus occurs on exposure to lipid solvents, trypsin, chymotrypsin, papain, and pancreatic lipase. Photoinactivation of the virus occurs after exposing it to UV light or neutral red and visible light. Dengue virus is generally stable when subjected to rate zonal centrifugation through sucrose and to equilibrium centrifugation in deuterium oxide-sucrose, but it is unstable on equilibrium centrifugation in CsCl.[201]

Within a given dengue serotype, strain variations have been shown to occur by N test, oligonucleotide fingerprinting, RNA–DNA hybridization probes, and antigen signature analysis by radioimmunoassay with monoclonal antibodies.[202–209] The latter two techniques are quite rapid and allow elegant molecular epidemiologic studies of the origin and movements of various strains of dengue viruses. While the ability to detect the arrival of a new strain is a useful surveillance tool, it has not yet identified those biochemical markers which predict either the epidemic or virulence potential of dengue viruses.

Epidemiology.—Hundreds of thousands of cases of dengue occur every year in epidemic or endemic form around the world. The attack rates during epidemics in focal areas of high transmission can reach over 50%, and it has been estimated that during the 1978 epidemic of DEN-1 in Puerto Rico, almost 13% of the entire island's population was infected.[210] Endemic transmission levels are particularly sensitive to the number of susceptible persons in the populations and the size of the infected vector population.

In the Americas, major outbreaks of dengue serotypes 1, 2, or 4 occurred in Brazil, Colombia, Mexico, and Puerto Rico in 1986 and in El Salvador in 1987.[211] The first outbreak in East Africa was reported in 1982 in Kenya and subsequently in 1983 from Somalia.[212] A widespread epidemic due to strains 1 and 2 occurred in Delhi, India, in 1982.[213] Endemic and focal epidemic dengue activity continued to occur in southeast Asia during the 1980s.

Temporal factors of importance to dengue transmission are seasonal changes involving rainfall and daily temperatures. *Ae aegypti* mosquitoes deposit their eggs in peridomestic, water-holding containers such as old tires, buckets, flowerpots, pet watering bowls, tin cans, etc. Periods of increased rainfall, which keep these containers filled with water, result in greater mosquito populations. Higher temperatures also favor the size of mosquito populations and, combined with high rainfall, account for the density of the vector in subtropical and tropical areas of the world. Although the Gulf and Southeast Atlantic coasts of the United States are infested with the vector mosquito, the populations of *Ae aegypti* diminish remarkably during the winter months; thus, the probability of dengue outbreaks during those months in the United States is quite low. Dengue is a prevalent public health problem in southeast Asia, the Caribbean, Central America, northern South America, and Africa.

The age distribution of persons with clinically apparent dengue varies geographically. In the hyperendemic area of southeast Asia, most cases appear in young children since the majority of the older population has been infected with multiple serotypes before reaching adulthood. In contrast, observations in Puerto Rico suggest that in the Caribbean older children and adults are more often reported by physicians as having dengue.[214] There are no reported differences in susceptibility to dengue infection between the sexes, but data from Puerto Rico suggest that females may be more likely to seek medical attention and, when they do visit a physician, have significantly different clinical complaints. Also, after age 3 years more girls than boys are hospitalized for DHF and for DSS in southeast Asia.[215] Other clinical complaints also vary according to age group.[214]

Cultural and socioeconomic factors have an impact on dengue epidemiology. Halstead has noted that poorly nourished children are less likely to have DHF or DSS as a complication of dengue.[216] Transmission is affected by attitudes toward keeping water-holding debris or containers on premises. Water storage practices (when plumbing is not available) and the custom of maintaining flowerpots at grave sites, providing a habitat for *Ae aegypti* larvae, also affect vector density. Recent work suggests that crowded, disadvantaged neighborhoods are more prone to dengue outbreaks. More economically advantaged areas with screened windows and doors or air conditioning tend to have lower attack rates (Donald Eliason, Division of Vector-Borne Viral Diseases, Fort Collins, Colorado, personal communication, June, 1983).

Unlike most arboviruses, which are maintained in nature by an arthropod vector and a vertebrate host and only infect man incidentally, survival of dengue virus appears, under most circumstances, to depend on a man-mosquito-man cycle. Dengue virus and antibody have been detected in sera from wild primates in southeast Asia and Africa, but the importance of "jungle dengue" is probably not great since the virus can persist endemically in many areas which have no nonhuman primate populations.[217-224] Enzootic dengue may be epidemiologically more important in Africa than in Asia; recent evidence has been obtained for a forest cycle involving monkeys and wild *Aedes* spp mosquitoes in West Africa.

Pathogenesis.—The vector mosquito becomes infected by feeding on a viremic host. After the infected blood meal is taken, a variable interval of time passes until the virus becomes established in the salivary glands of the mosquito, from where infectious virions will be transmitted while feeding on a susceptible human host. The length of this extrinsic incubation period in the mosquito has been shown to be profoundly affected by the temperature to which the mosquito is exposed after consuming an infective blood meal. Watts et al have shown experimentally that *Ae aegypti* fed on a viremic monkey will not transmit virus if kept at 26°C or less after feeding. As they were kept at successively higher temperatures to 32°C, increasing precentages of them became able to transmit virus.[225] This study provides a plausible explanation for the observed increase in dengue transmission rates during the warmer months in Thailand and elsewhere. Transovarial transmission of dengue virus to the offspring of infected *Ae aegypti* mosquitoes has not been documented; thus, in areas where no nonhuman primates exist, either some presently unknown cycle in nature must exist or else the virus is able to persist in a man-mosquito-man cycle.

The intrinsic incubation period in the human host ranges from two to seven days. The mode of dissemination of the virus from the site of introduction, whether hematogenously or via the lymphatics, is unknown. Once disseminated, however, the virus shows a marked tropism in man for organs of the reticuloendothelial system: bone marrow, spleen, lymph nodes, and liver, although other organs are also involved (heart, lungs, GI tract).

Host Response and Clinical Findings.—As noted above, clinical signs and symptoms of classic or uncomplicated dengue fever vary depending on such factors as age, sex, and whether the infection is a first exposure or a reinfection. The incidence of reported dengue from Puerto Rico's surveillance system reveals lower-than-expected numbers of cases in children, particularly those below 5 years of age, in every major epidemic since 1976. The clinical presentation of dengue in young children is varied. The disease may be manifested as an undifferentiated febrile illness, an acute respiratory illness, or as a GI illness—atypical presentations which may not be recognized by clinicians as dengue.[226] Older children and adults infected with dengue for the first time will display more classic symptoms: sudden onset of fever (occasionally diphasic), severe muscle aches, bone and joint pains, chills, frontal headache or retroorbital pain, altered taste sensations (frequently a metallic taste), lymphadenopathy, and a skin rash which appears one to three days after onset of fever. The rash may be maculopapular, petechial, or purpuric and is often preceded by flushing of the skin. Other hemorrhagic manifestations of varying severity may be seen: epistaxis, gingival bleeding, ecchymoses, GI bleeding, vaginal bleeding, and hematuria. Severe cases of bleeding should not be diagnosed as DHF or DSS unless they meet the criteria described in Table 23–2.

In two major series of laboratory-confirmed dengue cases stud-

Table 23–2
Criteria for Clinical Diagnosis of Dengue Hemorrhagic Fever (DHF) and Dengue Shock Syndrome (DSS)*

Clinical
  Fever — acute onset, high, continuous, and lasting 2–7 d.
  Hemorrhagic manifestations including at least a positive tourniquet test† and any of the following: petechiae, purpura, ecchymosis; epistaxis, gum bleeding; hematemesis and/or melena
  Enlargement of liver (observed at some stage of illness in 90%–96% of Thai children and in 60% of adults)
  Shock—manifested by rapid and weak pulse with narrowing of pulse pressure (≤20 mmHg) or hypotension, with the presence of cold, clammy skin and restlessness
Laboratory
  Thrombocytopenia (≤100,000 μL)‡
  Hemoconcentration: Hct increased by 20% or more

*Criteria have been selected for the clinical diagnosis of DHF, and in 90% of cases, dengue infection has been confirmed by etiologic diagnosis in the laboratory. Their use will avoid an overdiagnosis of the disease.
†Standard method using a blood pressure cuff is recommended. In DHF patients, the test usually gives a definitely positive result, that is, more than 20 petechiae per inch. The test may be negative or mildly positive during the phase of profound shock. It usually becomes positive and even strongly positive if looked for when recovery from shock has occurred.
‡Direct count using phase contrast microscope (normal 200,000–500,000/μL). In practice, for outpatients a qualitative count from peripheral blood smear is acceptable. In normal persons, 4 to 10 platelets per oil field (an average of ten oil field readings is recommended) indicates an adequate platelet level. An average of, or below, 2 to 3 per oil field is considerably low (approximately < 100,000).

Table 23–3
Grading the Severity of Dengue Hemorrhagic Fever (DHF)*

Grade I	Fever accompanied by nonspecific constitutional symptoms; the only hemorrhagic manifestation is a positive tourniquet test
Grade II	The additional manifestation to those of grade I is spontaneous bleeding—skin and/or other hemorrhages
Grade III	Circulatory failure manifested by rapid and weak pulse, narrowing of pulse pressure (≤20 mmHg), or hypotension, with the presence of cold clammy skin and restlessness
Grade IV	Profound shock with undetectable blood pressure and pulse

*The presence of thrombocytopenia with concurrent hemoconcentration will differentiate grade I and II DHF from classic dengue fever. Grading the severity of the disease has been found clinically and epidemiologically useful in DHF epidemics in children in southeast Asia and the western Pacific region. However, it may not be applicable to dengue in adults.

ied in Puerto Rico (1358 cases in 1977 and 2500 cases in 1978), nausea and vomiting were seen in over 60% of cases, most frequently in children and the elderly. Diarrhea was reported in 27% or more of patients in these two series. Cough was also a prominent symptom, occurring in 43% to 57% of the patients. From samples in both studies, a dual infection with influenza was excluded as a cause of the cough. These studies further showed statistically significant differences in the frequency of reported symptoms and signs that depended on sex and whether the illness was due to first exposure to dengue virus (primary dengue) or to reinfection with a different serotype (secondary dengue). Rash is more frequent in primary dengue, and joint pains are more common in secondary dengue, especially in females. Females also complained more frequently of skin rash and nausea and vomiting.[210, 227] Hepatomegaly, present in over 90% of southeast Asia children with DHF, is rarely described in the Caribbean, probably because of the low incidence of DHF in this region.

DHF and DSS are usually seen in children. DHF usually occurs in two stages. The first stage is milder, resembling classic dengue with abrupt onset of fever, general malaise, and headache often accompanied by anorexia and vomiting. A cough is frequently present. After two to five days the patient's condition rapidly worsens as the manifestations of shock begin to appear: restlessness; irritability; cold, clammy extremities; circumoral cyanosis; and narrowed pulse pressure (≤20 mmHg) or frank hypotension. The trunk remains warm and facial flushing is frequently present. Petechiae are found on the face and extremities. Other hemorrhagic manifestations include ecchymoses and bleeding from the gums and from sites of venipuncture. Up to 10% of patients will develop severe ecchymoses or GI bleeding. Over 90% of children with dengue in southeast Asia will have a palpable nontender enlarged liver. The WHO Expert Committee on dengue has developed guidelines for the diagnosis of DHF and DSS and a scheme for grading the severity is outlined in Tables 23–2 and 23–3. The important features of DHF are a positive tourniquet test, hemorrhagic manifestations, thrombocytopenia, and hemoconcentration. If circulatory failure occurs, manifested as either frank hypotension or narrowed pulse pressure, then a diagnosis of DSS can be made. DHF and DSS are seen frequently in children in southeast Asia, but until 1981 were only rarely observed in the Caribbean.[199]

Dengue in the Caribbean may exhibit severe hemorrhagic manifestations occasionally accompanied by hypotension. Thrombocytopenia, often striking, is common to these cases, but, instead of hemoconcentration, these patients have quite low to low-normal hematocrits. This syndrome, as observed in Puerto Rico, most often occurs in young adults but is occasionally seen in children and older adults as well (author, unpublished data, 1981).[189, 195, 210]

Immunologic Response.—The immunologic response to dengue infection depends on the individual's past flavivirus exposure(s). As measured by HI and CF tests and to a lesser degree the N test, the flavivirus group shares cross-reacting antigen(s). A person with no previous exposure to flaviviruses who is infected with dengue (or another flavivirus) will develop a primary (monotypic or homotypic) serologic response to the infecting serotype such that antibody is produced only against that serotype or in greater amount against the infecting serotype than heterologous types.

Reinfection with another dengue serotype (or other flaviviruses) usually produces a secondary (heterotypic) serologic response characterized by very high titers to all four dengue serotypes (and other flaviviruses), so that serologic identification of the infecting agent is quite difficult if not impossible to discern by HI or CF testing. Examples of situations where multiple flavivirus exposures may be encountered are individuals who have been immunized against yellow fever and are infected subsequently by dengue. In 1979, an epidemic of dengue occurred in areas of Texas where many persons had antibody to SLE. Those persons subsequently developed secondary serologic responses to both dengue and SLE.

In situations such as these, where the patient may have been infected with two or more group B arboviruses, an assay for IgM antibody will be specific for the most recently infecting virus. IgM antibody will not differentiate among different serotypes of dengue when sequential dengue infections occur, but it is useful in distinguishing among infections due to different group B arboviruses.

In addition to the difficulties these secondary responses introduce into the precise diagnosis of the infecting dengue serotype when using conventional serologic tests (HI and CF), Halstead et al[226] noted a strong epidemiologic association between the secondary-type serologic response, resulting from sequential dengue infection, and the development of DHF and DSS in southeast Asian children. Named at that time the "two-infection" hypothesis, it has since been modified and is now called the "antibody-dependent infection enhancement" theory, and is described below.[215, 216]

Once infected with a given serotype of dengue, there is no evidence that homotypic reinfection occurs. After a first infection with one dengue serotype, cross-immunity to other serotypes may persist for a few months, but after 6 months reinfection with a different serotype can occur. Epidemiologic studies conducted by Halstead suggest that infection with a third serotype rarely produces a clinical illness.[216]

Pathophysiology.—Early studies of dengue in southeast Asia understandably focused on DHF and DSS, the most dramatic manifestations of dengue.[228] Since that time, little has been done to elucidate the pathophysiology of uncomplicated infection, since most of these patients are seen as outpatients or do not seek medical attention. The studies that have been done suggest that bone marrow suppression occurs, and this may explain the leukopenia and thrombocytopenia which are so frequently seen. Minor bleeding episodes and petechiae may be the direct result of thrombocytopenia, but other parameters of the clotting mechanism need to be studied.[229]

The 1980 WHO clinical classification scheme for dengue[230, 231] (see Table 23–3) emphasizes that dengue with hemorrhagic manifestations must be differentiated from DHF.[226] While the WHO recommendations do not classify dengue with hemorrhagic manifestation as a separate diagnostic category, observations in the Caribbean and elsewhere suggest that patients in this category may merit consideration as a separate group (author, unpublished data, January 1980). This particular clinical presentation in Puerto Rico occurs more often in adults, is most severe when patients have a secondary serologic response, and is associated with severe thrombocytopenia ($<70,000/\mu L$) and a low hematocrit as opposed to hemoconcentration. Pathophysiologic mechanisms remain to be elucidated.

The two theories proposed for the pathogenesis of DHF and DSS have been a matter of controversy for several years: virus virulence[194, 195, 232] or an immunopathologic mechanism.[216, 233–237] Over recent years, evidence tends to support the latter. The immunopathologic theory, as proposed by Halstead, was originally based on the two-infection hypothesis, which was derived from the observation that DHF and DSS occurred most often in patients with a secondary (reinfection) serologic response.[226] However, the observation that DHF and DSS occurred in infants with a primary serologic response cast some doubt on this theory until it was demonstrated in the laboratory and epidemiologically that preexisting maternal antibody in these infants, often detectable only at extremely low levels, provided a similar immunopathologic insult to that of the reinfected older child with naturally acquired first-infection antibody.[226]

The principal features of the antibody-dependent theory are the presence of nonneutralizing antibody to dengue, whether maternally derived or endogenous, which combines with a heterologous infecting dengue virus. Virus-antibody complexes are more capable of infecting permissive mononuclear phagocytes than uncomplexed dengue virus. Cellular infection under these conditions, can be increased 100-fold or greater.[238] This effect can also be observed in the presence of cross-reactive (heterologous) antibodies from a closely related flavivirus such as yellow fever virus, but not in the presence of Japanese Encephalitis virus.[239, 240]

When the mononuclear phagocyte containing the virus-antibody complexes is attacked by an effector lymphocyte, vascular permeability leading to the leakage of intravascular fluids into tissues and subsequent hemoconcentration can be produced by any of three possible pathways: (1) dengue virus–antibody complexes can activate complement by the classic pathway; (2) the escape of lysosomal enzymes from the mononuclear phagocyte can activate the alternative pathway for complement; and (3) vasoactive lymphokines can escape from the mononuclear phagocyte or the effector lymphocyte and directly produce increased vascular permeability without resort to complement activation. DIC could also be initiated by the release of thromboplastin from the mononuclear phagocyte. While none of these mechanisms have been established at present, they do represent a comprehensive pathophysiologic theory which can be tested.[216]

Pathology.—In fatal dengue the pathologic findings at autopsy are remarkably benign, aside from the occasional case where gross hemorrhage from the GI tract is observed. Usually, modest focal hemorrhages or petechial lesions are seen in the gut, liver, adrenals, heart, lung, and brain. The liver may appear large and fatty. Microscopic findings are not diagnostic. Councilman-like bodies may be seen in liver sinusoids. The possible sequence leading to death in untreated cases is hypovolemic shock producing metabolic acidosis and hyperkalemia, complicated by DIC.[237]

Laboratory Findings and Diagnosis.—In uncomplicated dengue, the usual laboratory findings are leukopenia, mild to moderate thrombocytopenia, normal hematocrit, and modest elevations of AST. Patients with DHF or DSS typically have leukopenia early in illness followed by a normal leukocyte count or leukocytosis, hemoconcentration (Hct $>20\%$ of normal) and thrombocytopenia ($<100,000/\mu L$). Total serum protein and albumin are typically reduced. Coagulation abnormalities include increased bleeding time, silicone clotting time, and prothrombin time, and reduced factors II, V, VII, and X, as well as fibrinogen. Blood chemistry abnormalities include hyponatremia, serum bicarbonate less than 15 mmol/L, and elevated AST, ALT, and BUN.[230]

Laboratory diagnosis of dengue can be performed serologically or by virus isolation. Commonly used serologic tests include HI, CF, or PRN tests. As noted above, the high degree of cross-reactivity between flaviviruses can make the interpretation of serologic results quite difficult. Sera should be collected during the acute phase and at 2 weeks after illness onset. Specimens should be accompanied by clinical information, date of illness onset, dates of collection of sera, geographic location of exposure prior to illness onset, and history of prior flavivirus illness or exposure (including yellow fever immunization).[241]

A new serologic test—the hemadsorption immunosorbent immunoglobulin M technique—has been described as specific, simple, inexpensive, and highly reproducible. It detects infection early and can be diagnostically significant from a single serum specimen.[242]

Virus isolation and identification can be accomplished in a number of ways. The earliest technique for isolation of dengue virus was by intracerebral inoculation of sera from acutely ill patients into suckling mice. A more sensitive technique is the intrathoracic inoculation of infected human sera into *Ae aegypti, Ae albopictus,* or one of several species of *Toxorhynchites* mosquitoes.[243–252] Successful isolations also have been obtained by intracerebral inoculation of *Toxorhynchites* spp. Head squash preparations are made from inoculated mosquitoes after 1 week and, if negative, again after 2 weeks and stained with FA to dengue virus. If positive fluorescence is observed, specific dengue serotypes can be identified by CF or N tests.

Cell cultures used for isolation of dengue viruses include LLC MK-2 and several mosquito-derived cell lines from *Ae albopictus* (C6/36 Igarashi strain), *Ae pseudoscutellaris,* and *Toxorhynchites* spp. Cell cultures can be screened for the presence of virus by direct or indirect FA and the virus identified subsequently by CF, N, or an indirect fluorescent monoclonal antibody technique.[246, 247, 249, 251, 252]

Prevention.—No vaccine for dengue is commercially available. Experimental vaccines are being studied at present by the United States Army. One such vaccine against DEN-2 virus was shown to have certain shortcomings in both immunogenicity and reactogenicity.[253]

To prevent dengue, travelers to endemic areas should avoid mosquito bites by staying in screened hotel rooms or using mosquito netting around the bed. Long-sleeved shirts and long pants are useful in preventing bites. Exposed skin should be protected by using insect repellent.

The prevention of dengue for persons living in an endemic area usually requires the cooperative efforts of citizens and health authorities. Citizens must remove all containers or potential containers from their premises to prevent egg deposition in them and subsequent increases in the population of *Ae aegypti* adults. Commercially available insecticides should be used in houses to kill adult mosquitoes. In the event of hyperendemic or epidemic transmission, health authorities may have to intervene with a large-scale adulticiding and larviciding campaign. However, because the vector mosquitoes are peridomestic in their habitat, public education about dengue prevention should stress the importance of premises management by individual citizens for the ultimate reduction and control of the vector.

Treatment.—Therapy for uncomplicated dengue is nonspecific and aimed at symptomatic relief. Generally, antipyretics, analgesics, and attention to adequate hydration are the major points of concern. Acetaminophen is the antipyretic of choice since thrombocytopenia may be present, and bleeding symptoms may be exacerbated by aspirin, which decreases platelet adhesiveness. In most cases, adequate hydration can be maintained by oral intake; for those cases with nausea and vomiting or diarrhea, or when ambient temperatures are high, IV fluid replacement and careful monitoring and correction of electrolyte balance will be required.

In a series of 61 patients ill during 1980 to 1981 in Puerto Rico with more severe hemorrhagic manifestations, but who did not meet the criteria for DHF or DSS, 14 (23%) developed GI bleeding and three (5%) developed shock and required whole blood or packed red cell replacement (author, unpublished data, December 1979). All 14 patients had a moderately low to low hematocrit on admission, and none demonstrated hemoconcentration. When GI bleeding is detected, vital signs should be frequently monitored and care taken to maintain intravascular volume.

The major problem to be corrected in the management of DHF and DSS is the leakage of plasma into the extravascular space—leading to hemoconcentration, hypovolemia, hypotension, and, if uncorrected, tissue anoxia, metabolic acidosis, DIC, and death. Nearly 80% of patients with DSS have abnormal coagulation studies consistent with DIC: thrombocytopenia, increased fibrinogen degradation products, and prolonged partial thromboplastin time or decreased fibrinogen. When shock is not promptly reversed, DIC may be an important factor in GI bleeding. Adequate rapid fluid replacement can reverse DSS and prevent DIC.[231]

Only one third of DHF cases usually progress to DSS, so that with adequate family education many patients with DHF can be managed as outpatients, provided that their platelet counts and hematocrits are monitored daily from the first day of illness in an outpatient facility and that family members are instructed to return with the patient immediately if any of the following signs of hy-

potension develop: (1) restlessness or lethargy, (2) cold extremities and circumoral cyanosis, and (3) rapid, feeble pulse.

Outpatients should be encouraged to take ample electrolyte and glucose oral rehydration solution such as is used in the treatment of mild diarrheal disease (sodium chloride 3.5 g, sodium bicarbonate 2.5 g, potassium chloride 1.5 g, and glucose 20.0 g dissolved in 1 L of potable water). Salicylates should not be administered to patients with DHF or DSS.[231]

Patients manifesting any signs of shock such as listed above, or a narrowed pulse pressure (20 mmHg or less), frank hypotension, sudden rise in hematocrit (often preceded by development of marked thrombocytopenia), or an elevated hematocrit that does not decline with administration of IV fluids, should be admitted as medical emergencies. Plasma loss must be replaced immediately with lactated Ringer's or isotonic saline solution. If shock is not reversed, plasma or plasma expander (dextran) should be administered. Blood must be obtained for grouping and matching in the event of hemorrhage. If dextran is used, blood for grouping and matching must be obtained before its administration since some dextran preparations interfere with grouping and matching tests.[231]

Once vital signs have improved, continued IV volume replacement (5% glucose in half-normal saline) should be maintained for a period of 24 to 48 hours, during which time continued plasma leakage may occur. Hematocrit determinations should be made at frequent intervals to monitor the course of therapy. When adequate urine flow returns, and when the hematocrit has dropped to 40% and vital signs are stable, IV fluid therapy should be discontinued, generally within 48 hours after shock has terminated. Most patients will then begin to reabsorb extravasated plasma, leading to a further drop in hematocrit, which, in the absence of shock, should not be interpreted as bleeding.[230]

Other measures to be undertaken in the management of DSS are monitoring of electrolytes and blood gases to detect and correct hyponatremia and acidosis. Restless, agitated patients may require sedation, and a nonhepatotoxic compound such as chloral hydrate or paraldehyde is recommended. All patients in shock should also be treated with oxygen. Significant bleeding, usually from the GI tract and usually occurring during the shock phase, may require treatment with fresh whole blood, fresh frozen plasma, or platelet concentrates. Prothrombin time and partial thromboplastin time should be monitored during the shock phase to detect incipient DIC and its possible severity. Aggressive fluid replacement and correction of acidosis in most cases will prevent the development of DIC.[230]

Diagnosis and Management.—A careful history about possible geographic regions of exposure is essential to an accurate clinical diagnosis of probable dengue versus diseases of other etiologies which may mimic dengue in the early or even later stages of illness (Tables 23–4 and 23–5). Important treatment conditions to exclude are malaria and scrub typhus. Other diseases that may be confused with uncomplicated dengue fever are anicteric leptospirosis, chikungunya, yellow fever, influenza, Rift Valley fever, o'nyong-nyong, West Nile, and Ross River virus infection (see Table 23–4). Influenza and chikungunya may be particularly difficult to distinguish from dengue fever. However, laboratory findings of leukopenia and thrombocytopenia are useful in excluding influenza, although both findings can occur also in chikungunya.

Table 23–4
Endemic Location of Diseases Requiring Differentiation From Dengue Fever

Diseases Resembling Dengue Fever	Endemic Geographic Area							
	Africa	Caribbean	Central America	Europe	Middle East	South America	Southeast Asia	South Pacific
Bacterial	Typhus	Leptospirosis	Leptospirosis	Leptospirosis			Typhus Leptospirosis	
Protozoan	Malaria	Malaria	Malaria		Malaria	Malaria	Malaria	Malaria
Viral	Chikungunya	Influenza	Chikungunya	West Nile fever	West Nile fever	Mayaro fever	Chikungunya	Ross River fever
	O'nyong-nyong		Yellow fever	Influenza	Influenza	Influenza	West Nile fever	Influenza
	Rift Valley Fever		Influenza		Rift Valley fever		Influenza	
	Yellow fever							
	Influenza							
	West Nile fever							
	Wesselsbron fever							

In the differential diagnosis of DHF and DSS, a number of viruses (most of which are rare in North America and Western Europe) must also be considered: yellow fever, Lassa fever, Marburg, Ebola, Machupo, Junin, and Rift Valley fever, Omsk hemorrhagic fever, Kyasanur forest disease, Korean hemorrhagic fever, and Crimean–Congo hemorrhagic fever. Most of these agents have relatively specific geographic localizations, some of which do not overlap with dengue, and thus they may be excluded with reasonable certainty on the basis of geographic exposure history (see Table 23–5). The type of arthropod or other vector exposure may be useful information also: yellow fever and Rift Valley fever are mosquito-borne; Omsk hemorrhagic fever, Kyasanur Forest disease, and Crimean–Congo hemorrhagic fever are tick-borne; and Lassa, Machupo, Junin, and Korean hemorrhagic fevers are rodent-associated. If Lassa, Marburg, or Ebola infections are suspected, local health authorities must be alerted immediately because of the virulence of these viruses and the potential for person-to-person transmission. All laboratory tests involving tissues (including blood tests), secretions, or excretions from these patients must be performed in a maximum containment (P-4) laboratory. Patients must be maintained in maximum isolation (see Chapters 20 and 21).

Therapeutic and management decisions for dengue cases will almost always have to be made prior to the establishment of a definitive laboratory diagnosis. A plan for management is as follows:

Uncomplicated dengue fever
1. Maintain adequate oral hydration.
2. Antipyretics* (acetaminophen).
3. Analgesics as needed.

Dengue fever with hemorrhage (severe GI and/or vaginal bleeding)
1. Hospitalization with frequent vital sign checks.
2. Monitor hematocrit, platelet count, and electrolytes.
3. IV fluids.
4. Whole blood, packed cell (possibly platelet) replacement.
5. Antipyretic,* analgesic.

Dengue hemorrhagic fever (grades I and II)
1. Frequently managed as outpatients with adequate responsible family support.

Table 23–5
Endemic Location of Febrile Hemorrhagic Diseases Requiring Differentiation From Dengue Hemorrhagic Fever (DHF) and Dengue Shock Syndrome (DSS)

Diseases Resembling DHF or DSS	Endemic Geographic Area					
	Africa	Eurasia	Mysore State, India	Scandinavia	South America	Southeast Asia
Viral	Yellow fever	Omsk HF	Kyasanur Forest Disease	Korean HF	Yellow fever	Korean HF
	Lassa fever	Korean HF			Machupo fever	
	Marburg fever	Crimean-Congo HF			Junin fever	
	Ebola fever					
	Rift Valley fever					
	Crimean-Congo HF					

HF = hemorrhagic fever.

*Salicylates should not be used as an antipyretic or analgesic.

2. Outpatient monitoring of hematocrit, platelet count, hydration, and electrolytes.
3. Oral electrolyte solutions and/or outpatient administration of IV electrolyte solutions.
4. Antipyretic,* analgesic.

Dengue shock syndrome (DHF grades III and IV)
1. Hospitalize as medical emergency.
2. Continuous monitoring of vital signs, hematocrit, platelets, electrolytes, blood gases, clotting ability (in severe shock, central venous pressure); type and cross-match, in case blood replacement is needed.
3. Immediate replacement of plasma loss.
4. Maintain circulating volume by continued replacement of further plasma loss.
5. Correction of acidosis and electrolyte abnormalities.
6. Sedation, oxygen.
7. Whole blood or platelet replacement.

Kyasanur Forest Disease

Kyasanur Forest disease virus is a tick-borne flavivirus related to the tick-borne encephalitis complex and geographically restricted to Karnataka State in India. It was first noted as a disease in 1957 when deaths in wild primates and humans were noted to be occurring there. The first isolation of the virus occurred that same year.[254]

The structure of the virus is typical of flaviviruses as described earlier. It is lethal to mice of any age and suckling hamsters by the intracerebral or peripheral routes of inoculation. Young chicks develop viremias.[255]

Annually, 400 to 500 cases occur. The highest recorded incidence was in 1983 when 1,555 cases and 150 deaths were reported.

Kyasanur Forest disease occurs in the dry season of the year in persons having forest contact. The major vector tick is thought to be *Haemaphysalis spinigera*, which is involved in a natural transmission cycle involving small vertebrates. Because the virus is lethal for monkeys, they are not felt to be part of the normal natural transmission cycle. The case fatality rate is estimated at 5%.[254–256]

The clinical syndrome of Kyasanur Forest disease shares some aspects of mild tick-borne encephalitis and Omsk hemorrhagic fever. There is sudden onset of fever, headache, and severe muscle pains. GI disturbances include hemorrhage, and pulmonary involvement is indicated by a persistent cough and abnormal roentgenogram of the chest. Bradycardia, relative hypotension, and pronounced dehydration are commonly seen. Many patients will have a biphasic course with the symptoms described, followed by an afebrile period of 1 to 2 weeks and then onset of meningoencephalitic symptoms, usually mild.[257] No sequelae occur but convalescence is prolonged. Laboratory findings include leukopenia, thrombocytopenia, and a decreased hematocrit. In cases with meningoencephalitis, the CSF contains normal glucose with elevated protein and cells. Laboratory diagnosis can be made by virus isolation or the usual serologic tests (HI, CF, or N tests).

Prevention of Kyasanur Forest disease is by avoidance of tick bites in the high-risk area. Treatment is nonspecific and symptomatic. Fluid replacement should be given to dehydrated patients, and significant blood loss should be replaced also.

Omsk Hemorrhagic Fever

Omsk hemorrhagic fever virus is a flavivirus antigenically related to the tick-borne encephalitis complex. The disease was first noted in the Omsk oblast of the Soviet Union during large outbreaks in the 1940s. The disease is confined in its geographic distribution to the Soviet Union and possibly Rumania.[258–260]

The structure and biology of Omsk hemorrhagic fever virus is typical of flaviviruses as described in the introduction. The virus is pathogenic for laboratory mice by any route of inoculation and is also lethal for field mice and muskrats. The virus grows fairly well in embryonated eggs.[261]

Omsk hemorrhagic fever has a spring-summer-fall temporal distribution of occurrence dependent on the seasonal activity of the vector ticks, *Dermacentor reticulatus* and *D marginatus*. The cycle in nature is presumably between *Ixodes* ticks and wild muskrat hosts. Laboratory-acquired infections, presumably by the aerosol route, have been common. The case fatality rates are low, ranging from 0.5% to 3%.[261]

Omsk hemorrhagic fever has an incubation period of three to seven days, after which there is onset of headache and frequently a biphasic fever. This is followed by a variety of hemorrhagic manifestations: epistaxis, GI and uterine bleeding, and hemorrhages of the palate. Bronchopneumonia occurs frequently. Skin rash is infrequently seen. Leukopenia is common. Infection with Omsk hemorrhagic fever virus produces neutralizing, HI, and CF antibodies which are useful for diagnostic serologic tests. The virus can be isolated from peripheral blood during the acute febrile stage.[261]

A vaccine for Omsk hemorrhagic fever is available in the Soviet Union and is reported to be very effective. Measures to avoid tick bites should also be undertaken for prevention.[261]

Treatment is nonspecific and supportive. It is aimed at controlling hemorrhages and replacing blood loss in severe cases. The disease does not produce permanent sequelae.

REFERENCES

1. Westaway EG, Beinton MA, Gaidamovich SYA, et al: Flaviviridae. *Intervirology* 1985;24:183–192.
2. Muckenfuss RS, Armstrong C, McCordock HA; Encephalitis: Studies on experimental transmission. *Public Health Rep* 1933; 48:1341–1343.
3. Webster LT, Fite GL: A virus encountered in the study of material from cases of encephalitis in the St Louis and Kansas City epidemic of 1933. *Science* 1933; 78:463–465.
4. Lumsden LL: St Louis encephalitis in 1933. Observations on epidemiological features. *Public Health Rep* 1958; 73:340–353.
5. Casey AE, Brown GO: Epidemiology of St Louis encephalitis. *Science* 1938; 88:450–451.
6. Hammon W McD, Reeves WC, Brookman B, et al: Isolation of viruses of western equine and St Louis encephalitis from *Culex tarsalis* mosquitoes. *Science* 1941; 94:328–330.
7. Reeves WC, Hammon W McD, Izumi EM: Experimental transmission of St Louis encephalitis virus by *Culex pipiens* Linnaeus. *Proc Soc Exp Biol Med* 1942; 50:125–128.
8. Hammon W McD, Reeves WC, Sather GE: Western equine and St Louis encephalitis viruses in the blood of experimentally infected wild birds and epidemiological implications of findings. *J Immunol* 1951;67:354–367.

---

*Salicylates should not be used an an antipyretic or analgesic.

9. Spence L: St Louis Encephalitis in tropical America, in Monath TP (ed): St Louis Encephalitis. Washington DC, American Public Health Association 1980, pp 451–472.

10. Monath TP: Epidemiology, in Monath TP (ed): St Louis Encephalitis. Washington DC, American Public Health Association, 1980, pp 239–312.

11. Levy JS, Carver H, Moseley IK, et al: Epidemiologic features of the St Louis encephalitis epidemic in Memphis, Tennessee, 1975. *South Med J* 1978; 71:633–640.

12. Bailey CL, Eldridge BF, Hayes DE, et al: Isolation of St Louis encephalitis virus from overwintering *Culex pipiens* mosquitoes. *Science* 1978; 199:1346–1349.

13. Francy DB, Rush WA, Montoya M, et al: Transovarial transmission of St Louis encephalitis virus by *Culex pipiens* complex mosquitoes. *Am J Trop Med Hyg* 1981; 30:699–705.

14. Allen R, Taylor SK, Sulkin SE: Studies of arthropod-borne virus infections in Chiroptera. VIII. Evidence of natural St Louis encephalitis virus infection in bats. *Am J Trop Med Hyg* 1970; 19:851–859.

15. Brinker KR, Monath TP: The acute disease, in Monath TP (ed): *St Louis Encephalitis*. Washington DC, American Public Health Association, 1980, pp 505–554.

16. Quick DT, Thompson JM, Bond JO: The 1962 epidemic of St Louis encephalitis in Florida. IV. Clinical feature of cases in the Tampa Bay area. *Am J Epidemiol* 1965; 81:415–427.

17. Brinker KR, Paulson G, Monath TP, et al: St Louis encephalitis in Ohio, September 1975, clinical and EEG studies in 16 cases. *Arch Intern Med* 1979; 139:561–566.

18. Brown GO, Haymaker W, Smith JE: Sequelae of the arthropod-borne encephalitides. IV. St Louis encephalitis. *Neurology* 1958; 8:883–887.

19. Shinner JJ: St Louis virus encephalomyelitis. *Arch Pathol* 1963; 75:309–322.

20. Luby JP, Murphy FK, Gilliam JN, et al: Antigenuria in St Louis encephalitis. *Am J Trop Med Hyg* 1980; 29:265–268.

21. Luby JP: St Louis encephalitis. *Epidemiol Rev* 1979; 1:55–73.

22. Luby JP, Stewart WE, Sulkin SE, et al: Interferon in human infections with St Louis encephalitis virus. *Am J Intern Med* 1969; 71:703–707.

23. Coleman PH, Lewis AL, Schneider NJ, et al: Isolation of St Louis encephalitis virus from postmortem tissues of human cases in the 1962 Florida epidemic. *Am J Epidemiol* 1968; 87:530–538.

24. Monath TP, Nystrom RR, Bailey RE, et al: Immunoglobulin M antibody capture enzyme-linked immunosorbent assay for diagnosis of St Louis encephalitis. *J Clin Microbiol* 1984; 20:784–790.

25. Bowen GS, Francy DB: Surveillance, in Monath TP (ed): *St Louis Encephalitis*. Washington DC, American Public Health Association, 1980, pp 473–499.

26. Shope RE: Arboviruses, in Lennette EH, Spaulding E, Truant JP (eds): *Manual of Clinical Microbiology*. Washington DC, American Society for Microbiology, 1974, pp 740–745.

27. Broom AK, Charlick J, Richards SJ, et al: An enzyme-linked immunosorbent assay for detection of flavivirus antibodies in chicken sera. *J Virol Methods* 1987; 15:1–9.

28. Pond WL, Smadel JE: Neurotropic viral diseases in the Far East during the Korean war. *Med Sci Publ Army Med Serv Grad Sch* 1954; 4:219–224.

29. Umenai T, Krzysko R, Bektimirov TA, et al: Japanese encephalitis: current worldwide status. *Bull WHO* 1985; 63:625–631.

30. Chu FT, Wu JP, Teng CH: Acute encephalitis in children: clinical and serologic study of ten epidemic cases. *Chin Med J* 1940; 58:68–75.

31. Grayston JT, Wang SP, Yen CH: Encephalitis on Taiwan. *Am J Trop Med Hyg* 1962; 11:126–130.

32. Mackenzie JS: *Viral Diseases in Southeast Asia and the Western Pacific: Proceedings of an International Seminar*. Sydney, Australia, Academic Press, 1982.

33. Olson JG, Ksiazek TG, Gubler DJ, et al: A survey for arboviral antibodies in sera of humans and animals in Lombok, Republic of Indonesia. *Ann Trop Med Parasitol* 1983; 77:131–138.

34. Olson JG, Ksiazek TG, Lee VH, et al: Isolation of Japanese encephalitis virus from *Anopheles annularis* and *Anopheles vagus* in Lombok, Indonesia. *Trans R Soc Trop Med Hyg* 1985; 79:845–851.

35. O'Rourke TF, Hayes CG, SanLuis AM, et al: Epidemiology of Japanese encephalitis in the Philippines, in St George TS, Kay BH, Blok J (eds): *Proceedings of the Fourth Australian Symposium on Arboviruses*. Brisbane, Australia, Queensland Institute of Medical Research, 1986.

36. Peterson PY, Ley HL Jr, Wisseman CL JR, et al: Japanese encephalitis in Malaya. I. Isolation of virus and serologic evidence of human equine infections. *Am J Hyg* 1952; 56:320–329.

37. Trosper JH, Ksiazek TG, Cross JH, et al: Isolation of Japanese encephalitis virus from the Republic of the Philippines. *Trans R Soc Trop Med Hyg* 1980; 74:292–298.

38. Van Peenan PFP, Irsiani R, Sulianti-Saroso J, et al: First isolation of Japanese encephalitis from Java. *Milit Med* 1974; 139:821–826.

39. Smith CEG, Simpson DIH, Peto S, et al: Arbovirus infections in Sarawak: serologic studies in man. *Trans R Soc Trop Med Hyg* 1974; 68:96–100.

40. Ksiazek TG, Trosper JH, Cross JH, et al: Additional isolations of Japanese encephalitis from the Philippines. *Southeast Asian J Trop Med Public Health* 1980; 11:507–511.

41. Burke DS, Tingpalapong M, Ward GS, et al: Intense transmission of Japanese encephalitis virus to pigs in a region free of epidemic encephalitis. *Southeast Asian J Trop Med Public Health* 1985; 16:199–206.

42. Yamada T, Rojanasuphot S, Takagi M: Studies on the epidemic of Japanese encephalitis in the northern region of Thailand in 1969 and 1970. *Biken J* 1971; 14:267–275.

43. Grossman RA, Gould DJ, Smith TJ, et al: Study of Japanese encephalitis virus in Chiangmai Valley, Thailand. I. Introduction and study design. *Am J Epidemiol* 1973; 98:111–120.

44. Grossman RA, Edelman R, Chiewanich P, et al: Study of Japanese encephalitis virus in Chiangmai Valley, Thailand. II. Human clinical infections. *Am J Epidemiol* 1973; 98:121–127.

45. Netler R: Enquête serologique sur l' encephalitis Japonaise B au Viet Nam. I. Recherches chez l'homme. *Bull Soc Pathol Exot Filiales* 1956; 49:883–889.

46. Ketel WB, Ognibene AJ: Japanese B encephalitis in Vietnam. *Am J Med Sci* 1971; 261:271–279.

47. Khan AQ, Khan AM, Dewan ZU, et al: An outbreak of Japanese encephalitis in Bangladesh. *Bangladesh Med J* 1980; 8:71–79.

48. Ming CK, Swe T, Thaung U, et al: Recent outbreaks of Japanese encephalitis in Burma. *Southeast Asian J Trop Med Public Health* 1977; 8:113–121.

49. Swe T, Thein S, Myint MS: Pilot sero-epidemiological survey on Japanese encephalitis in northwestern Burma. *Biken J* 1979; 22:125–128.

50. Carey DE, Myers RM, Reuben R: Japanese encephalitis in South India. A summary of recent knowledge. *J Indian Med Assoc* 1969; 52:10–17.

51. Mathur A, Chaturvedi UC, Tandon HO, et al: Japanese encephalitis epidemic in Uttar Pradesh India during 1978. *Indian J Med Res* 1982; 75:161–170.

52. Rodrigues RM: Epidemiology of Japanese encephalitis in India, in *National Conference on Japanese Encephalitis 1982*. Indian Council of Medical Research, 1984, vol 1, pp 4–18.

53. Khatri IB, Joshi DD, Pradhan TMS, et al: Status of viral encephalitis (Japanese encephalitis) in Nepal. *J Nepal Med Assoc* 1983; 21:97–101.

54. Henderson A, Leake CJ, Burke DS: Japanese encephalitis in Nepal. *Lancet* 1983; 2:1359–1364.

55. Takegami T, Washizu M, Yasui K: Nucleotide sequence of the 3' end of Japanese encephalitis genomic RNA. *Virology* 1986; 152:483–486.

56. McAda PC, Mason TL, Schmaljohn CS, et al: Synthesis and cloning of cDNA from the Japanese encephalitis virus genome, in Dalrymple JM (ed): *International Workshop on the Molecular Bi-*

ology of Flaviviruses. Fort Detrick, Md, US Army Medical Research Institute of Infectious Diseases, 1984, pp 8–17.

57. US Dept of Health, Education and Welfare: Japanese encephalitis in Asia. *MMWR* 1958; 7:2.

58. Matsuda S: An epidemiologic study of Japanese B encephalitis with special reference to the effectiveness of the vaccination. *Bull Inst Public Health* 1962; 11:173–190.

59. Southam CM: Serological studies of encephalitis in Japan. II. Inapparent infections by Japanese B encephalitis. *J Infect Dis* 1956; 99:163–169.

60. Benenson MW, Top FJ Jr, Gresso W, et al: The virulence to man of Japanese encephalitis virus in Thailand. *Am J Trop Med Hyg* 1975; 24:974–980.

61. Halstead SB, Russ SB: Subclinical Japanese encephalitis. II. Antibody responses of Americans to single exposure to JE virus. *Am J Hyg* 1962; 75:190–201.

62. Kono R, Kim KH: Comparative epidemiological features of Japanese encephalitis in the Republic of Korea, China (Taiwan) and Japan. *Bull WHO* 1969; 40:263–277.

63. Okuno T, Tsing PT, Hsu ST, et al: Japanese encephalitis surveillance in China (Province of Taiwan) during 1968–1971. II. Age-specific incidence in connection with Japanese vaccination program. *Jpn J Med Sci Biol* 1975; 28:255–267.

64. Monath TP, Trent DW: Togaviral diseases of domestic animals, in Kurstak E, Kurstak C (eds): *Comparative Diagnosis of Viral Diseases.* Academic Press, 1981, vol 4, pp 331–440.

65. Rosen L, Tesh RB, Lieu JC, et al: Transovarial transmission of Japanese encephalitis by mosquitoes. *Science* 1978; 199:909–911.

66. Shortridge KF, Oya A, Kobayashi M, et al: Arbovirus infections in reptiles. *Southeast Asian J Trop Med Public Health* 1975; 6:161–169.

67. Sulkin SE, Sims R, Allen R: Studies of arthropodborne virus infections in Chiroptera. II. Experiments with Japanese B and St Louis encephalitis viruses in the gravid bat. Evidence of transplacental transmission. *Am J Trop Med Hyg* 1964; 13:475–481.

68. Scherer WB, Moyer JT, Izumi T: Immunologic studies of Japanese encephalitis virus in Japan. V. Maternal antibodies, antibody responses and viremia following infection of swine. *J Immunol* 1959; 83:620–626.

69. Matsuda S: An epidemiologic study of Japanese B encephalitis with special reference to the effectiveness of the vaccination. *Bull Inst Public Health* 1962; 11:173–190.

70. Mathur A, Tandon HO, Mathur KR, et al: Japanese encephalitis virus infection during pregnancy. *Indian J Med Res* 1985; 81:9–12.

71. Bhonde RR, Wagh UV: Susceptibility of human placenta to Japanese encephalitis virus in vitro. *Indian J Med Res* 1985; 82:371–373.

72. Halstead SB, Grosz CR: Subclinical Japanese encephalitis. I. Infection of Americans with limited residence in Korea. *Am J Hyg* 1962; 75:190–201.

73. Dickerson RB, Newton JR, Hansen JE: Diagnosis and immediate prognosis of Japanese B encephalitis. *Am J Med* 1952; 12:277–288.

74. Lincoln AF, Sivertson SE: Acute phase of Japanese B encephalitis. Two hundred and one cases in American soldiers, Korea. *JAMA* 1950; 150:268–273.

75. Edgren DC, Polladino VS, Arnold A: Japanese B and mumps encephalitis. A clinicopathologic report of simultaneous outbreaks on the island of Guam. *Am J Trop Med Hyg* 1958; 7:471–480.

76. Zimmerman HM: The pathology of Japanese B encephalitis. *Am J Pathol* 1946; 22:965–991.

77. Wolf A: The pathology of some viral encephalitides, in Kidd JG (ed): *The Pathogenesis and Pathology of Viral Diseases.* New York, Columbia University Press, 1975, pp 154–195.

78. Banerjee K, Deshmane SL: Cross-reactivity of antigens specified by Japanese encephalitis and West Nile viruses. *Indian J Med Res* 1987; 85:339–346.

79. George S, Reddy MV, Yergolkar PN, et al: Absorption of IgG with *Staphylococcus aureus* in a diagnostic test for IgM antibod-

80. Hsu TC, Hsu ST: Supplementary report. Effectiveness of Japanese encephalitis vaccine: Study in the second year following immunization, in Hammon W McD, Kitaoka M, Downs WG (eds): *Immunization for Japanese Encephalitis.* Baltimore, Williams & Williams, 1971, pp 266–267.

81. Oya A: Japanese encephalitis vaccine, in Fukumi M (ed): *The Vaccination.* Tokyo, International Medical Foundation of Japan, 1975, pp 114–138.

82. Anonymous: Artificial hibernation in treatment of epidemic encephalitis type B. *Chin Med J* 1959; 78:419–423.

83. Hiraki K, Demiya Y, Kageyama H, et al: The therapeutic effects of ACTH on Japanese B encephalitis. *Acta Med Okayama* 1958; 12:51–56.

84. *Seminar on Japanese Encephalitis and Other Arbovirus Infections, Tokyo.* Manila, WHO Regional Office. Geneva, World Health Organization, 1962, pp 2–11, 14–18.

85. French EL: Murray Valley encephalitis: Isolation and characterization of the aetiological agent. *Med J Aust* 1952; 1:100–103.

86. Miles JAR, Fowler MC, Haves DW: Isolation of a virus from encephalitis in South Australia: A preliminary report. *Med J Aust* 1951; 1:799–800.

87. Anderson SG: Murray Valley encephalitis and Australian X disease. *J Hyg Camb* 1954; 52:447–468.

88. Doherty RL, Carley JG, Cremer MR, et al: Murray Valley encephalitis in eastern Australia, 1971. *Med J Aust* 1972; 2:1170–1173.

89. Doherty RL, Carley JG, Filippich C, et al: Murray Valley encephalitis in Australia, 1974: Antibody response in cases and community. *Aust NZ J Med* 1976; 6:446–453.

90. Miles JAR: Infection of birds with Murray Valley encephalitis (X disease). *Aust J Exp Biol Med Sci* 1954; 32:69–78.

91. McLean DM: The behaviour of Murray Valley encephalitis virus in young chickens. *Aust J Exp Biol Med Sci* 1953; 31:491–503.

92. Doherty RL: Arboviruses and their diseases: Australia, in Feigin RD, Cherry JD (eds): *Textbook of Pediatric Infectious Diseases.* Philadelphia, Saunders, 1981, pp 1156–1158.

93. Anderson SG: Murray Valley encephalitis: Epidemiological aspects. *Med J Aust* 1952; 1:97–103.

94. *The Queensland Institute of Medical Research Twenty-ninth Annual Report.* Queensland, Australia, 1974, p 8.

95. Doherty RL, Carley JG, Kay BH, et al: Murray Valley encephalitis virus infection in mosquitoes and domestic fowls in Queensland 1974. *Aust J Exp Biol Med Sci* 1976; 54:237–243.

96. Doherty RL, Carley JG, Mackerras MJ, et al: Studies of arthropod-borne viruses in Queensland. III. Isolation and characterization of virus strains from wild-caught mosquitoes in North Queensland. *Aust J Exp Biol Med Sci* 1963; 41:17–39.

97. Standfast HA, Barrow GJ: Studies of the epidemiology of arthropod-borne virus infections at Mitchell River Mission, Cape York Peninsula, North Queensland. I. Mosquito collections, 1963–1966. *Trans R Soc Trop Med Hyg* 1968; 62:418–429.

98. Gard GP, Giles JR, Dwyer-Gray RJ, et al: Serological evidence of inter-epidemic infection of feral pigs in New South Wales with Murray Valley encephalitis virus. *Aust J Exp Biol Med Sci* 1976; 54:297–302.

99. Bennett N McK: Murray Valley encephalitis, 1974: Clinical features. *Med J Aust* 1976; 2:446–450.

100. Robertson EG, McLorinan H: Murray Valley encephalitis: Clinical aspects. *Med J Aust* 1952; 1:103–107.

101. Wiemers MA, Stallman ND: Immunoglobulin M in Murray Valley encephalitis. *Pathology* 1975; 7:187–191.

102. Theiler M, Downs WG: Group B viruses, in *The Arthropod-Borne Viruses of Vertebrates.* New Haven, Conn, Yale University Press, 1973, pp 153–154.

103. Causey OR, Theiler M: Virus antibody survey on residents of the Amazon Valley in Brazil. *Am J Trop Med Hyg* 1958; 6:36–46.

104. Spence L, Anderson CR, Downs WG: Isolation of Ilheus virus from human beings in Trinidad, West Indies. *Trans R Soc Trop Med Hyg* 1962; 56:504–509.

105. Clarke DH: Antigenic relationships among viruses of the tick-borne encephalitis complex as studied by antibody absorption and agar gel precipitin techniques, in Libikova H (ed): *Biology of Viruses of the Tick-Borne Encephalitis Complex*. New York, Academic Press, 1962, pp 67–75.

106. Clarke DH: Further studies on antigenic relationships among the viruses of the group B tick-borne complex. *Bull WHO* 1964; 31:45–56.

107. Clarke DH, Casals J: Arboviruses: Group B, in Horsfall FL, Tamer I (eds): *Viral and Rickettsial Infections of Man*. Philadelphia, Lippincott, 1965, pp 606–658.

108. Smorodinstev AA: Tick-borne spring-summer encephalitis. *Prog Med Virol* 1958; 1:210–247.

109. Gresikova M: Recovery of the tick-borne encephalitis virus in the milk of subcutaneously infected sheep. *Acta Virol* 1958; 2:113–119.

110. Gresikova M: Excretion of the tick-borne encephalitis virus in the milk of subcutaneously infected cows. *Acta Virol* 1958; 2:188–192.

111. Kozuch O, Nosek J, Ernede E, et al: Persistence of tick-borne encephalitis virus in hibernating hedgehogs and dormice. *Acta Virol* 1963; 7:430–433.

112. Nosek J, Gresikova M, Rehacek J: Persistence of tick-borne encephalitis virus in hibernating bats. *Acta Virol* 1961; 5:211–218.

113. Van Tongeren HAE: Central European encephalitis—Epidemiology and vectors, in *Proceedings of Sixth International Congress of Tropical Medicine and Malaria, Lisbon, Portugal, Sept 5–13, 1958*. International Congress of Tropical Medicine and Malaria, 1959, vol 5, pp 174–179.

114. Kuznetsova RI, Sukhomlinova OI, Churilova AA: The character of the biphasic meningoencephalitis in the Leningrad Oblast. *J Microbiol Epidemiol Immunol* 1960; 31:262–268.

115. Silber LA, Soloviev VV: Far Eastern tick-borne spring-summer (spring) encephalitis. *Annu Rev Soviet Med* (suppl), 1946.

116. Pretzmann G, Loew J, Radda A: Untersuchungen in einem Naturherd der Frühsommer-Meningoencephalitis (FSME) in Niederösterreich. *Zentralbl Bakteriol Mikrobiol Hyg* 1963; 190:299–312.

117. Feoktistov AZ: Tick-borne encephalitis virus circulation in nature. *Med Parasitol Dis* 1963; 32:35–39.

118. Galant IB: Certain features of the course of contemporary Far Eastern tick-borne encephalitis. *Probl Virol* 1959; 4:66–68.

119. Blaskovic D, Nosek J: The ecological approach to the study of tick-borne encephalitis. *Prog Med Virol* 1972; 14:275–320.

120. McLean DM, Donohue WL: Powassan virus: Isolation of virus from a fatal case of encephalitis. *Can Med Assoc J* 1959; 80:708.

121. Casals J: Antigenic relationship between Powassan and Russian spring-summer encephalitis viruses. *Can Med Assoc J* 1960; 82:355.

122. Deibel R, Glanagan TD, Smith V: Central nervous system infections in New York State: Etiologic and epidemiologic observations, 1974. *NY State J Med* 1975; 75:2337.

123. Whitney E: Serologic evidence of group A and B arthropod-borne virus activity in New York State. *Am J Trop Med Hyg* 1963; 12:417–424.

124. Thomas LA, Kennedy RC, Eklund CM: Isolation of a virus closely related to Powassan virus from *Dermacentor andersoni* collected along North Cache La Poudre River, Colorado. *Proc Soc Exp Biol Med* 1960; 104:355–359.

125. McLean DM, Smith PA, Livingstone SE: Powassan virus: Vernal spread during 1965. *Can Med Assoc J* 1966; 94:532–536.

126. Webb HE, Connolly JH, Kane FF, et al: Laboratory infections with louping ill with associated encephalitis. *Lancet* 1968; 2:255–258.

127. Williams H, Thorburn H: Serum antibodies to louping ill virus. *Scott Med J* 1962; 7:353–355.

128. Edward DG: Immunization against louping ill. Immunization of man. *Br J Exp Pathol* 1948; 29:372–378.

129. Lawson JH, Mauderson WG, Hurst EW: Louping-ill meningoencephalitis. A further case and a serological survey. *Lancet* 1949; 2:696–699.

130. Likar M, Dane DS: An illness resembling acute poliomyelitis caused by a virus of the Russian spring-summer encephalitis/louping ill group in Northern Ireland. *Lancet* 1958; 1:456–468.

131. De Souza Lopes O, Coimbra TLM, De Abreu Sachetta L, et al: Emergence of a new arbovirus disease in Brazil: I. Isolation and characterization of the etiologic agent, Rocio virus. *Am J Epidemiol* 1978; 107:444–449.

132. De Souza Lopes O, De Abreu Sachetta L, Coimbra TLM, et al: Emergence of a new arbovirus disease in Brazil: II. Epidemiologic studies on 1975 epidemic. *Am J Epidemiol* 1978; 108:394–401.

133. De Souza Lopes O, De Abreu Sachetta L, Francy DB, et al: Emergence of a new arbovirus disease in Brazil. III. Isolation of Rocio virus from *Psorophora ferox* (Humboldt, 1819). *Am J Epidemiol* 1981; 113:122–125.

134. Mitchell CJ, Forattini OP: Experimental transmission of Rocio encephalitis virus by *Aedes scapularis* from the epidemic zone in Brazil. *J Med Entomol* 1984; 21:34–37.

135. Mitchell CJ, Monath TP, Cropp CB: Experimental transmission of Rocio virus by mosquitoes. *Am J Trop Med Hyg* 1981; 30:465–472.

136. Monath TP, Kemp GE, Cropp CB, et al: Experimental infection of house sparrows *(Passer domesticus)* with Rocio virus. *Am J Trop Med Hyg* 1978; 27:1251–1254.

137. Iversson LB: Epidemio de encefalite por arbovirus na região sul do Estado de São Paulo, Brazil, em 1975 e 1976. Aspectos da distribuicão cronológica e geográfica dos casos. *Rev Saude Publica* 1977; 11:375–388.

138. Tiriba AC, Miziara AM, Lorenco R, et al: Encefalite humana primária epidêmica por arbovirus observada no litoral sul do Estado de São Paulo; Estudo clinico efetuado en hospital de emergência. *Rev Asoc Med Bras* 1976; 22:415–420.

139. Rosenberg S: Neuropathology of S Paulo south coast epidemic encephalitis (Rocio flavivirus). *J Neurol Sci* 1980; 45:1–2.

140. Monath TP, Nystrom RR, Bailey RE, et al: Immunoglobulin M antibody capture enzyme-linked immunosorbent assay for diagnosis of St Louis encephalitis. *J Clin Microbiol* 1984; 20:784–791.

141. Rosenberg S: Neuropathological study of a new viral encephalitis: The encephalitis of São Paulo southcoast. (Preliminary report.) *Rev Inst Med Trop São Paulo* 1977; 19:280–282.

142. Okuno T, Oya A, Ito T: The identification of Negishi virus. A presumably new member of Russian spring-summer encephalitis virus family isolated in Japan. *Jpn J Med Sci Biol* 1961; 14:51–59.

143. Sulkin SE, Wallis C, Allen R: Relationship of bat salivary gland virus to St Louis encephalitis group of viruses. *Proc Soc Exp Biol Med* 1956; 93:79–81.

144. Price JL: Isolation of Rio Bravo and a hitherto undescribed agent, Tamana bat virus, from insectivorous bats in Trinidad with serological evidence of infection in bats and man. *Am J Trop Med Hyg* 1975; 27:153–161.

145. Smithburn KC, Hughes TP, Bushe AW, et al: A neurotropic virus isolated from the blood of a native of Uganda. *Am J Trop Med Hyg* 1940; 20:471–492.

146. Bankopf H, Levine S, Nelson R: Isolation of West Nile virus in Israel. *J Infect Dis* 1953; 93:207–218.

147. Taylor RM, Work TH, Hurlbut HS, et al: A study of ecology of West Nile virus in Egypt. *Am J Trop Med Hyg* 1956; 5:579–620.

148. McIntosh BM, Jupp PG, Dos Santos I, et al: Epidemics of West Nile and Sindbis viruses in South Africa with *Culex univittatus* Theobold as vector. *S Afr J Sci* 1976; 72:295.

149. Saidi S, Tesh R, Javadian E, et al: The prevalence of human infection with West Nile virus in Iran. *Iranian J Public Health* 1976; 5:8–13.

150. Goldblum N, Sterk VV, Paderski B: West Nile fever. The clinical features of the disease and the isolation of West Nile virus from the blood of nine human cases. *Am J Hyg* 1954; 59:89–103.

151. Clarke DH, Casals J: Arboviruses, Group B, in Horsfall FL, Tamm I (eds): *Viral and Rickettsial Infections of Man*. Philadelphia, Lippincott, 1965, pp 606–658.

152. Spigland I, Jasinska-Klingberg W, Hofshi E, et al: Clinical and laboratory observations in an outbreak of West Nile fever in Israel. *Harefuah* 1958; 54:275–281 [English summary].

153. Goldblum N: West Nile fever in the Middle East, in *Proceedings of the Sixth International Congress on Tropical Medicine and Malaria, Lisbon, Portugal, Sept 5–13, 1958*. International Congress of Tropical Medicine and Malaria, 1959, vol 5, pp 112–125.

154. Goldblum N, Sterk VV, Jasinska-Klingberg W: The natural history of West Nile fever. II. Virological findings and the development of homologous and heterologous antibodies in West Nile infection in man. *Am J Hyg* 1957; 66:363–380.

155. Smithburn KC, Kokernot RH, Weinbren MP, et al: Isolation of Wesselbron virus from a naturally infected human being and from *Aedes* (Banksinella) *circumluteolus* Theo. *S Afr Med J* 1957; 22:113–120.

156. Weiss KE, Haig DA, Alexander RAL: Wesselbron virus—a virus previously not described associated with abortion in domestic animals. *Onderstepoort J Vet Res* 1956; 27:183–195.

157. *International Catalogue of Arboviruses*, ed 2. US Dept of Health, Education and Welfare, Public Health Service publication No. (CDC) 75-8301. Government Printing Office, 1975.

158. Strode GK (ed): *Yellow Fever*. New York, McGraw-Hill, 1951.

159. Theiler M, Downs WG (eds): *The Arthropod-Borne Viruses of Vertebrates*. New Haven, Conn, Yale University Press, 1973.

160. Monath TP: Yellow fever: a medically neglected disease. Report on a seminar. *Rev Infect Dis* 1987; 9:165–175.

161. Bres PL: A century of progress in combating yellow fever. *Bull WHO* 1986; 64:775–786.

162. Present status of yellow fever: memorandum from a PAHO meeting. *Bull WHO* 1986; 64:511–524.

163. Monath TP, Schlesinger JJ, Brandriss MW, et al: Yellow fever monoclonal antibodies: type-specific and cross-reactive determinants identified by immunofluorescence. *Am J Trop Med Hyg* 1984; 33:695–698.

164. Monath TP, Hill LJ, Brown NV, et al: Sensitive and specific monoclonal immunoassay for detecting yellow fever virus in laboratory and clinical specimens. *J Clin Microbiol* 1986; 23:129–134.

165. Monath TP, Nystrom RR: Detection of yellow fever virus in serum by enzyme immunoassay. *Am J Trop Med Hyg* 1984; 33:151–157.

166. Rice CM, et al: Nucleotide sequence of yellow fever virus: implications for *Flavivirus* gene expression and evolution. *Science* 1985; 229:726–733.

167. Monath TP: Glad tidings from yellow fever research. *Science* 1985; 229:734–735.

168. Roche JC, Jouan A, Brisou B, et al: Comparative clinical study of a new 17-D thermostable yellow fever vaccine. *Vaccine* 1986; 4:163–165.

169. Clarke DH, Casals J: Arboviruses, group B, in Horsfall FL, Tamm I (eds): *Viral and Rickettsial Infections of Man*, ed 4. Philadelphia, Lippincott, 1965, pp 608–615.

170. Monath TP, Wilson DC, Lee VH: The 1970 yellow fever epidemic in Okwoga District, Benue Plateau State, Nigeria I. Epidemiological observations. *Bull WHO* 1973; 49:113–121.

171. Monath TP, Craven RB, Adjukiewicz AA, et al: Yellow fever in the Gambia, 1978–1979: Epidemiologic aspects with observations on the occurrence of Orungo virus infections. *Am J Trop Med Hyg* 1980; 29:912–928.

172. Germain M, Francy DB, Monath TP, et al: Yellow fever in the Gambia, 1978–1979: Entomological aspects and epidemiological correlations. *Am J Trop Med Hyg* 1980; 29:929–940.

173. World Health Organization: Yellow fever in 1979. *Weekly Epidemiol Rec* 1980; 46:355–360.

174. Cambon L, Wone I, Brès P, et al: Une épidémie de fièvre jaune au Senegal en 1965, L' épidémie humaine. *Bull WHO* 1967; 36:113–150.

175. Aitken THG, Tesh RB, Beaty BJ, et al: Transovarial transmission of yellow fever virus by mosquitoes (*Aedes aegypti*). *Am J Trop Med Hyg* 1979; 25:119–121.

176. Berdonneau R, Série C, Panthier R, et al: Sur l' épidémie de fièvre jaune de l' année 1959 en Ethiopie (Frontière soudano-éthiopienne). *Bull Soc Pathol Exot Filiales* 1961; 54:276–283.

177. Poland JP, Calisher CH, Monath TP, et al: Persistence of neutralizing antibody to yellow fever virus 30 to 35 years following immunization with 17-D yellow fever vaccine: A study of World War II veterans in 1975–1976. *Bull WHO* 1981; 59:895–900.

178. Monath TP, Craven RB, Muth DJ, et al: Limitations of the complement-fixation test for distinguishing naturally acquired from vaccine-induced yellow fever infection in flavivirus-hyperendemic areas. *Am J Trop Med Hyg* 1980; 29:624–634.

179. Dennis LH, Reisberg BE, Crosbie J, et al: The original hemorrhagic fever—Yellow fever. *Br J Haematol* 1969; 17:455–462.

180. Monath TP: Togaviruses, bunyaviruses, and Colorado tick fever, in Rose NR, Friedman H (eds): *Manual of Clinical Immuniology*. Washington DC, American Society for Microbiology, 1976, pp 456–461.

181. Sawyer W, Kitchen SF, Lloyd W: Vaccination of humans against yellow fever with immune serum and virus fixed for mice. *Proc Soc Exp Biol Med* 1931; 29:62–64.

182. Theiler M, Smith HH: Use of yellow fever virus modified by in vitro cultivation for human immunization. *J Exp Med* 1937; 65:787–800.

183. Smith MG, Penna HA, Paoliello A: Yellow fever vaccination with cultured virus (17-D) without immune serum. *Am J Trop Med Hyg* 1938; 18:437–468.

184. *Health Information for International Travel—1988*. US Public Health Service, Atlanta, Centers for Disease Control.

185. Centers for Disease Control: Dengue in Texas. *MMWR* 1980; 29:451.

186. Rush B: An account of the bilious remitting fever as it appeared in Philadelphia in the summer and autumn of the year 1780, in *Medical Inquiries and Observations*. Philadelphia, 1789, pp 89–100.

187. Carey DE: Chikungunya and dengue: A case of mistaken identity? *J Hist Med Allied Sci* 1971; 26:243–262.

188. Ehrenkranz NJ, Ventura AK, Cuadado RR, et al: Pandemic dengue in Caribbean countries and the Southern United States—Past, present and potential problems. *N Engl J Med* 1971; 285:1460–1469.

189. *1979 Annual Report, San Juan Laboratories*. San Juan, Puerto Rico, Centers for Disease Control.

190. Clarke DH, Casals J: Arboviruses, Group B, in Horsfall FL, Tamm I (eds): *Viral and Rickettsial Diseases of Man*, ed 4. Philadelphia, Lippincott, 1965, pp 606–658.

191. Hammon W McD, Rudnick A, Sather GE: Viruses associated with epidemic hemorrhagic fevers of the Philippines and Thailand. *Science* 1960; 131:1102–1103.

192. Hammon W McD, Rudnick A, Sather G, et al: New hemorrhagic fevers of children in the Philippines and Thailand. *Trans Assoc Am Physicians* 1960; 73:140–155.

193. Quintos FN, Lin L, Juliano L, et al: Hemorrhagic fever observed among children in the Philippines. *Philippine J Pediatr* 1954; 3:1–9.

194. Hare FE: *Austr Med Gaz* 1898:17:98–107, quoted in Schlesinger RW (ed): *The Togaviruses*, ed 1. New York, Academic Press, 1980, p 110.

195. Lopez-Correa RH, Cline BL, Ramirez-Ronda C, et al: Dengue fever with hemorrhagic manifestations. A report of three cases from Puerto Rico. *Am J Trop Med Hyg* 1978; 27:1216–1224.

196. Ramirez-Ronda CH, Maldonado NM, Rabell V, et al: Dengue hemorrhagic shock in the western hemisphere. *Trop Geogr Med* 1979; 31:127–131.

197. Van Der Sar A: An outbreak of dengue hemorrhagic fever on Curaçao. *Trop Geogr Med* 1973; 25:119–129.

198. Fraser HS, Wilson WA, Thomas EJ, et al: Dengue shock syndrome in Jamaica. *Br Med J* 1978; 27:893–894.

199. Anonymous: Program for dengue elimination and *Aedes aegypti* eradication in Cuba. *Bull Pan Am Health Organ* 1982; 3:7–10.

200. Murphy FA: Togavirus morphology and morphogenesis, in Schlesinger RW (ed): *The Togaviruses*, ed 2. New York, Academic Press, 1980, pp 241–316.

201. Russell PK, Brandt WE, Dalrymple JM: Chemical and Antigenic structure of Flaviviruses, in Schlesinger RW (ed): *The Togaviruses*, ed 1. New York, Academic Press, 1980, pp 503–530.

202. Russell PK, McCown JM: Comparison of dengue-2 and dengue-3 virus strains by neutralization tests and identification of a subtype of dengue-3. *Am J Trop Med Hyg* 1972; 21:97–99.

203. Henchal EA, Repik PM, McCown JM, et al: Identification of an antigenic and genetic variant of dengue 4 virus from the Caribbean. *Am J Trop Med Hyg* 1986; 35:393–400.

204. Gubler DJ, Rosen L: Quantitative aspects of replication of dengue viruses in *Aedes albopictus* (Diptera:Culicidae) after oral and parenteral infection. *J Med Entomol* 1977; 13:469–474.

205. Vezza AC, Rosen L, Repik P, et al: Characterization of the viral RNA species of prototype dengue viruses. *Am J Trop Med Hyg* 1980; 29:643–652.

206. Trent DW, Grant JA, Rosen L, et al: Genetic variation among dengue 2 viruses of different geographic origin. *Virology* 1983; 128:271–284.

207. Repik PM, Dalrymple JM, Brandt WE, et al: RNA finger-printing as a method for distinguishing dengue 1 virus strains. *Am J Trop Med Hyg* 1983; 32:577–589.

208. Kerschner JH, Vorndam AV, Monath TP, et al: Genetic and epidemiologic studies of dengue type 2 viruses by hibridization using synthetic deoxyoligonucleotides as probes. *J Gen Virol* 1986; 67:2645–2661.

209. Monath TP, Wands JR, Hill LJ, et al: Geographic classification of dengue-2 virus strains by antigen signature analysis. *Virology* 1986; 154:313–324.

210. *1978 Annual Report, San Juan Laboratories*. San Juan, Puerto Rico, Centers for Disease Control.

211. Anonymous: Dengue in the Americas—1986. *Weekly Epidemiol Rec* 1988; 31:233–240.

212. Saleh AS, Hassan A, Scott RM, et al: Dengue in north-east Africa, letter. *Lancet* 1985; 2:211–212.

213. Rao CV, Bagchi SK, Pinto BD, et al: The 1982 epidemic of dengue fever in Delhi. *Indian J Med Res* 1985; 82:271–275.

214. *1980 Annual Report, San Juan Laboratories*. San Juan, Puerto Rico, Centers for Disease Control.

215. Halstead SB, Nimmannitya S, Cohen SN: Observations related to the pathogenesis of dengue hemorrhagic fever. VI. Hypotheses and Discussion. *Yale J Biol Med* 1970; 42:311–328.

216. Halstead SB: Immunological Parameters of togavirus disease syndromes, in Schlesinger RW (ed): *The Togaviruses*, ed 1. New York, Academic Press, 1980, pp 107–174.

217. Rudnick A: Studies of the ecology of dengue in Malaysia: A preliminary report. *J Med Entomol* 1965; 2:203–208.

218. Fagbami AH, Monath TP, Fabiyi A: Dengue virus infections in Nigeria: A survey for antibodies in monkeys and humans. *Trans R Soc Trop Med Hyg* 1977; 71:60–65.

219. Rudnick A: The ecology of the dengue virus complex in Peninsular Malaysia, in Pang T, Pathmanathan R (eds): *Proceedings of the International Conference on Dengue/DHF*. Kuala Lumpur, University of Malaysia Press, 1984, p 7.

220. Cordellier R, Bouchité B, Roche JC, et al: Circulation silvatique du virus Dengue 2 en 1980, dans less savannes sub-soudaniennes du Côte d'Ivoire, *Cah ORSTOM ser Entomol Med Parasitol* 1983; 21:165–172.

221. Roche JC, Cordellier R, Hervy JP, et al: Isolement de 96 souches de virus dengue 2 a partir de moustiques capturés en Côte d'Ivoire et Haute-Volta. *Ann Virol* 1983; 134E:233–238.

222. Monath TP, Lee VH, Wilson DC, et al: Arbovirus studies in Nupeko Forest, A possible natural focus of yellow fever virus in Nigeria. I. Description of the area and serological survey of humans and other vertebrate hosts. *Trans R Soc Trop Med Hyg* 1974; 68:30–38.

223. Rudnick A: Ecology of dengue virus. *Asian J Infect Dis* 1978; 2:156–163.

224. Gubler DJ, Novak RJ, Vergne E, et al: *Aedes (Gymnometopal) mediovittatus* (Diptera:Culicidae), a potential maintenance vector of dengue viruses in Puerto Rico. *J Med Entomol* 1985; 22:469–474.

225. Watts DM, Burke DS, Harrison BA, et al: Effect of temperature on the vector efficiency of *Aedes aegypti* for dengue-2 virus. *Am J Trop Med Hyg* 1987; 36:143–152.

226. Halstead SB, Nimmannitya S, Margiotta MR: Dengue and chikungunya virus infection in man in Thailand. II. Observations on disease in outpatients. *Am J Trop Med Hyg* 1969; 18:972–983.

227. Lopez-Correa RH, Moore CG, Sather CE, et al: The 1977 dengue epidemic in Puerto Rico: Epidemiologic and clinical observations, in *Dengue in the Caribbean*. Washington, DC, Pan American Health Organization scientific publication No. 375, 1979, pp 60–67.

228. Sabin AB: Research on dengue during World War II. *Am J Trop Med Hyg* 1952; 1:30–50.

229. Nelson ER, Bierman HR: Dengue fever—A thrombocytopenia disease? *JAMA* 1964; 190:99–103.

230. World Health Organization: *Dengue Hemorrhagic Fever. Diagnosis, Treatment and Control*. Geneva, World Health Organization, 1986.

231. Kuberski T, Rosen L, Reed D, et al: Clinical and laboratory observations on patients with primary and secondary dengue type 1 infections with hemorrhagic manifestations in Fiji. *Am J Trop Med Hyg* 1977; 26:775–783.

232. Rosen L: "The Emperor's New Clothes" revisited or reflections on the pathogenesis of dengue hemorrhagic fever. *Am J Trop Med Hyg* 1977; 26:337–343.

233. Halstead SB: Etiologies of the experimental dengue of Siler and Simmons. *Am J Trop Med Hyg* 1974; 23:974–982.

234. Halstead SB, Udomsakdi S, Singharaj P, et al: Dengue and chikungunya infection in man in Thailand, 1962–1964. III. Clinical, epidemiologic and virologic observations on disease in nonindigenous white persons. *Am J Trop Med Hyg* 1969; 18:984–996.

235. Halstead SB: Different dengue syndromes—The perspective from a pathogenic point of view. *Asian J Infect Dis* 1978; 2:59–65.

236. Halstead SB: Dengue hemorrhagic fever—A public health problem and a field for research. *Bull WHO* 1980; 58:1–21.

237. Cohen SN, Halstead SB: Shock associated with the dengue infection. I. The clinical and physiological manifestations of dengue hemorrhagic fever in Thailand, 1964. *J Pediatr* 1966; 68:448–456.

238. Halstead SB, Venkateshan CN, Gentry MK, et al: Heterogeneity of infection enhancement of dengue 2 strains by monoclonal antibodies. *J Immunol* 1984; 132:1529–1532.

239. Eckels KH, Kliks SC, Dubois DR, et al: The association of enhancing antibodies with seroconversion in humans receiving a dengue-2 live-virus vaccine. *J Immunol* 1985; 135:4201–4203.

240. Putyatana R, Yoksan S, Chayayodhin T, et al: Absence of dengue 2 infection enhancement in human sera containing Japanese encephalitis antibodies. *Am J Trop Med Hyg* 1984; 33:288–294.

241. *Dengue Laboratory Diagnostic Procedures*. Washington DC, Pan American Health Organization, 1984.

242. Gunasegaran K, Lim TW, Ahmed A, et al: Hemadsorption immunosorbent technique for the detection of dengue immunoglobulin M antibody. *J Clin Microbiol* 1986; 23:170–174.

243. Kuberski TT, Rosen L: A simple technique for detection of dengue antigen in mosquitoes by immunofluorescence. *Am J Trop Med Hyg* 1977; 26:533–537.

244. Kuberski TT, Rosen L: Identification of dengue viruses using complement-fixing antigen in mosquitoes by immunofluorescence. *Am J Trop Med Hyg* 1977; 26:538–543.

245. Rosen L, Gubler D: The use of mosquitoes to detect and propagate dengue viruses. *Am J Trop Med Hyg* 1974; 23:1153–1160.

246. Race M, Williams MC, Agostini CFM: Dengue in the Caribbean: Virus isolation in a mosquito *(Aedes pseudoscutellaris)* cell line. *Trans R Soc Trop Med Hyg* 1979; 73:18–22.

247. Tesh RB: A method for the isolation and identification of dengue viruses, using mosquito cell cultures. *Am J Trop Med Hyg* 1979; 28:1053–1059.

248. Russell PK, Nisalak A: Dengue virus identification by the plaque-

reduction neutralization test. *J Immunol* 1967; 99:291–296.

249. Kuno G: A continuous cell line of a nonhematophagus mosquito. *Toxorhynchites ambionensis. In Vitro* 1980; 16:915–917.

250. Igarashi A: Isolation of a Singh's *Aedes albopictus* cell clone sensitive to dengue and chikungunya viruses. *J Gen Virol* 1978; 40:531–544.

251. Rosen L: The use of *Toxorhynchites* mosquitoes to detect and propagate dengue and other arboviruses. *Am J Trop Med Hyg* 1981; 30:177–183.

252. Gubler DJ, Kuno G, Sather GE, et al: Mosquito cell cultures and specific monoclonal antibodies in surveillance for dengue viruses. *Am J Trop Med Hyg* 1984; 33:158–165.

253. Bancroft WH, Scott RM, Eckels KH, et al: Dengue virus type 2 vaccine: reactogenicity and immunogenicity in soldiers. *J Infect Dis* 1984; 149:1005–1010.

254. Work TH: Russian spring-summer virus in India. Kyasanur Forest disease. *Prog Med Virol* 1958; 1:248–279.

255. Clarke DH, Casals J: Arboviruses, Group B, in Horsfall FL, Tamm I (eds): *Viral and Rickettsial Infections of Man.* Philadelphia, Lippincott, 1965, pp 606–658.

256. Anderson CR: Recent advances in arthropod-borne virus research in India. *Bull Natl Inst Sci India* 1963; 24:205–216.

257. Webb HE, Rao RL: Kyasanur Forest disease: A general clinical study in which some cases with neurological complications were observed. *Trans R Soc Trop Med Hyg* 1961; 55:284–298.

258. Gadjusek DC: Acute infectious hemorrhagic fevers and mycotoxicoses in the Union of Soviet Socialist Republics. *Med Sci Publ Army Med Serv Grad School* 1953; 2:19–25.

259. Chumakov MP: Tick-borne hemorrhagic diseases in the USSR, in *Proceedings of the Sixth International Congress on Tropical Medicine and Malaria, Lisbon, Portugal, Sept 5–13, 1958.* International Congress of Tropical Medicine and Malaria, 1959, vol 5, pp 165–173.

260. Chumakov MP: Studies of virus hemorrhagic fevers. *J Hyg Epidemiol Microbiol Immunol* 1959; 7:125–135.

261. Clarke DH, Casals J: Arboviruses, Group B, in Horsfall FL, Tamm I (eds): *Viral and Rickettsial Infections of Man.* Philadelphia, Lippincott, 1965, pp 606–658.

Togaviruses

Robert B. Craven

The *Togaviridae* family contains four genera: *Alphavirus, Rubivirus, Pestivirus,* and *Arterivirus.*[1,2] The only member of the *Rubivirus* genus is rubella virus (see Chapter 25). The genus *Pestivirus* contains three viruses of veterinary importance—bovine diarrhea virus, hog cholera virus, and border disease virus. The *Arterivirus* genus also contains a single member—equine arteritis virus. For this chapter, only the *Alphavirus* genus is discussed.

The *Alphavirus* genus has 25 members of which 11 are recognized as pathogenic for man in varying degrees and modes of expression. The disease spectrum produced by alphaviruses ranges from asymptomatic infection to undifferentiated febrile illness, fever with rash or arthralgia or both, or encephalitis. All alphaviruses are mosquito-borne and are geographically distributed mostly in the New World. None have yet been isolated in the polar regions.

No licensed vaccines exist for prevention of illnesses caused by the alphaviruses. The control of epidemics is aimed at reducing the numbers of vector mosquitoes. Some experimental vaccines for alphaviral encephalitis are being evaluated in individuals at high risk such as laboratory workers. These will be discussed with the appropriate viruses.

STRUCTURE AND BIOLOGY OF ALPHAVIRUSES

Alphavirus is a genus of the family *Togaviridae*.[1] Prior to 1984, the *Togaviridae* also included the genus *Flavivirus*. Because of several fundamental differences from the *Togaviridae* family the flaviviruses were elevated to family status as the *Flaviviridae* by the International Committee on Taxonomy of Viruses.

The alphavirus virions are 60 to 65 nm in diameter with a core particle size of 35 to 39 nm. The nucleocapsids are icosahedral. The RNA of alphaviruses is infectious and varies in size from 4.2 to 4.4×10^6 daltons. The 5' end of the genome is type 0 cap structure. The 3' end contains poly (A). The glycosylated lipid envelope is double-layered measuring 50 to 59 kilodaltons (kd). The core structural protein is 30 to 34 kd. Alphaviruses specify a 26S subgenomic messenger RNA (mRNA) that represents the 3' one third of the genome. Structural proteins are translated from this area. In cell-free systems alphavirus translation of the genome produces nonstructural proteins. Nucleocapsids of alphaviruses are visible and can be isolated. Maturation occurs at the host plasma membrane and morphogenesis occurs by budding. Penetration of host cells occurs by endocytosis. Because of their lipid membrane layer, alphaviruses are inactivated by ether and detergents, and are also labile to heat and acids.

Depending on the type of analysis performed, the sedimentation coefficient of the RNA ranges from 42S to 49S. The RNA codes for both structural and nonstructural viral proteins.

On the basis of neutralization tests and molecular virology, alphaviruses have been subdivided into six antigenic groups. The prototype viruses for these subgroups are Venezuelan equine encephalitis virus, western equine encephalitis virus, Semliki Forest virus, eastern equine encephalitis virus, Ndumu virus, and Middleburg virus. The latter three viruses are the sole known representatives of their subgroups and are not closely related antigenically either to one another or to any other known alphaviruses.

Alphaviruses differ from one another in the size of the plaques they form in cell culture, in the host cell origin of tissue cultures in which they will grow, in their virulence in different hosts, and in their stability to heat. An example of variation in virulence is

Table 24-1
Vectors, Natural Hosts, and Geographic Localization of Togaviruses Causing Encephalitis

Group	Virus	Known or Possible Vectors	Natural Hosts	Geographic Location
Alphaviruses	EEE	*Culiseta melanura,* *Aedes* spp, *Coquillettidia* sp	Birds	Eastern United States, Central and South America, Caribbean
Mosquito-borne	WEE	*Culex tarsalis, Culex* spp	Birds	United States, Canada
	VEE	*Aedes* spp, *Psorophora* spp	Rodents, equines	Central and South America
	Everglades	*Culex* spp	Rodents	Florida

EEE = eastern equine encephalitis; WEE = western equine encephalitis; VEE = Venezuelan equine encephalitis.

apparent for Venezuelan equine encephalitis (VEE) virus which has subtypes that are either virulent or avirulent for man and equines. VEE viruses may be divided into four subtypes (I–IV). Subtype I is further composed of four antigenically distinguishable variants: IAB, IC, ID, and IE. Disease in equines and humans is produced only by variants IAB and IC. Cell culture systems in which alphaviruses will replicate are listed for the individual viruses in the sections where they are described. A discussion of the importance among the alphaviruses of the E2 glycoprotein may be found in the section on VEE virus.

ALPHAVIRUSES PRODUCING ENCEPHALITIS

The *Alphavirus* genus contains four agents which produce encephalitis. These viruses, their usual vectors, and their geographic localizations are shown in Table 24–1. Alphavirus encephalitides are all mosquito-borne and restricted in their distribution to the New World. These agents are eastern, western, and Venezuelan equine encephalitis viruses (EEE, WEE, and VEE) as well as Everglades virus which is closely related to VEE virus.

The Encephalitis Syndrome

The general syndrome of encephalitis, depending on the virus producing it, consists of varying combinations of the following signs and symptoms: fever; headache; confusion; stupor, or coma; aphasia or mutism; convulsions; hemiparesis with asymmetric deep tendon reflexes and positive Babinski signs; ataxia, myoclonus, and involuntary movements; and cranial nerve dysfunctions producing facial weakness, nystagmus, and ocular palsies. In some instances disturbances of the autonomic nervous system are also observed. Togaviruses which cause encephalitis vary widely in both the degree of neurologic sequelae and the case fatality rates they produce. The severity of disease, again depending on the particular infecting virus, can vary from asymptomatic infection to death.

Surveillance of Alphavirus Encephalitis

Togavirus encephalitis viruses are maintained in nature by cycles between birds and mosquitoes, rodents and mosquitoes, or equines and mosquitoes. Man is almost always an incidental host. In the United States, the mosquito-bird-mosquito transmission cycles for EEE and WEE have been extensively studied and factors influ-

encing the probability of human infections have been identified. As a result, it is now possible to construct surveillance programs which monitor the course of the disease in nature and allow interdictive vector control which can prevent human disease. The techniques employed include monitoring the size of vector mosquito populations, testing pools of mosquitoes for presence of encephalitis virus, equine surveillance, and serologic studies of fledgling birds or sentinel chicken flocks. In spite of the availability of this technology, encephalitis due to these viruses continues to occur endemically and epidemically, mainly because either state or local governments are reluctant to provide the continuous funding that such a surveillance and prevention program requires.

When a mosquito-borne encephalitis case is suspected, public health officials should be alerted immediately. Intervention in an epidemic is only possible by the use of insecticides to reduce the vector population and public education about prevention of mosquito bites. Intensified human case surveillance must be instituted. Insecticide and the equipment to deliver it must be obtained and funds for these secured from local or state govenment sources. This process requires time, during which more human cases or a severe epidemic can occur. It is of crucial importance that every effort be made to secure a diagnosis by virus isolation from blood (or brain tissue at autopsy if the case is fatal) and/or by serologic testing.

Differential Diagnosis of Viral Encephalitis

Before a diagnosis of viral meningoencephalitis of any etiology is made, care must be taken to rule out specifically treatable causes of the meningoencephalitis syndrome. (Herpes simplex encephalitis is a treatable viral encephalitis. Refer to Chapter 34.) Infectious conditions which can be treated and which may mimic viral encephalitis include partially treated bacterial meningitis, brain abscess, subdural empyema, embolic encephalitis associated with bacterial endocarditis, tuberculous meningitis, fungal meningitis, and cerebral malaria. Other treatable infections which infrequently may produce the meningoencephalitis syndrome include plague, typhoid fever, diphtheria, rickettsial infections, botulism, and toxoplasmosis. Noninfectious conditions to be excluded are cerebrovascular, neoplastic, and granulomatous disease as well as toxic encephalopathies and disease of unknown etiology (Behçet disease, Guillain-Barré syndrome, multiple sclerosis, Reye syndrome, and systemic lupus erythematosus).

Nontogaviral agents which can produce meningoencephalitis are flaviviruses (see Chapter 23), lymphocytic choriomeningitis, echo-, coxsackie-, polio-, herpes-, and rabies viruses. Other viruses less commonly producing the meningoencephalitis syndrome are mumps, influenza, adenoviruses, Colorado tick fever, respiratory syncytial viruses, hepatitis, and the hemorrhagic fever viruses (Lassa, Marburg, Crimean–Congo, Ebola, Junin, Machupo, Hantaan). Differentiating between this plethora of diagnostic possibilities depends heavily on an accurate history from relatives or acquaintances, a thorough physical examination, and appropriate diagnostic laboratory tests. Many of the diseases listed are restricted to defined geographic areas and may be considered or rejected on the basis of where the patient has been prior to illness onset. The history of arthropod contact and type, or the lack thereof, is of obvious usefulness. The season of the year and the knowledge of illness in horses or similar illnesses in other humans in the community are also important differentiating points. Physical findings such as rash or jaundice suggest certain diseases and help to eliminate others. Examination and culturing of cerebrospinal fluid is mandatory and helpful in differentiating infectious from noninfectious etiologies and bacterial from viral infections. Ultimately, however, it may be necessary to institute antibiotic therapy for possible treatment of infecting organisms and to await definitive laboratory diagnostic tests.

Eastern Equine Encephalitis

History.—EEE virus was first isolated from a postmortem brain tissue specimen from a horse in 1933 during an epizootic of equine encephalitis.[3, 4] In 1938, EEE virus was demonstrated to be the etiologic agent in a human epidemic of encephalitis.[5] Focal epidemics have occurred sporadically in New Jersey and Massachusetts, and occasional cases have been diagnosed in the Southeast (Georgia, Florida, and Louisiana), often occurring with concurrent cases in equines. Pigeons, quail, and pheasants also are susceptible to EEE virus infection, and mortality rates among them can be high. This is particularly true in penned pheasants and other exotic avians where pecking or preening exposes the birds to EEE virus persistently maintained in quill follicles.[6]

Epidemiology.—In the United States EEE is maintained in a natural transmission cycle between *Culiseta melanura* mosquitoes and birds in swampy and forested areas. Migrating birds have been implicated as carriers, transporting the virus either north or south during their long flights.[7] However, two points militate against the importance of migratory birds as an overwintering mechanism. EEE virus carried by birds migrating north from South America are local strains of virus from that continent. Secondly, native birds produce EEE virus isolates prior to the arrival of birds migrating northward.[8]

Cs melanura mosquitoes usually do not feed on humans, and it is necessary for the virus to become established in *Aedes* spp mosquitoes before human and equine cases occur. Climatic factors (higher temperatures and plentiful rainfall),[9] which favor abundant *Aedes* spp populations, increase the risk of transmission to humans. Since they do not develop sufficient viremias to infect mosquitoes, horses play no part in amplifying transmission of EEE virus.

In those areas which have endemic EEE, areas of transmission tend to be recurrent in focal sites bordering freshwater, swampy areas. EEE is a disease of the summer months, and the major epidemics of the past have occurred in New Jersey and Massachusetts, where the virus can be isolated from its natural transmission cycle virtually every summer. Major equine epizootics occurred in Michigan during 1980 and 1981.

Fortunately, considering the high human mortality associated with EEE virus encephalitis (50%), it is a disease of relatively low frequency in the United States. From 1982 to 1987, 35 human cases were reported to the Centers for Disease Control (CDC) from northeastern and Gulf coastal states. The largest single outbreak during that period occurred in 1983 when 14 cases were reported.[10–12] The presence of equine cases should, however, alert the public health and medical communities to the increased likelihood of a human outbreak. In the past, most states of the eastern seaboard of the United States have had epizootic or epidemic EEE or both. The virus is also present around the Great Lakes area extending into Canada and is present on the Gulf coast. Documented disease or infection in humans has been reported from Brazil, the Dominican Republic, Guatemala, Honduras, Jamaica, Mexico, and Trinidad.[13–15] The transmission cycles of EEE are not entirely understood in the Caribbean and South America. Some evidence suggests a forest cycle between *Culex taeniopus* and wild birds.

Aside from a lower age-specific mortality, young children suffer a greater likelihood of acquiring encephalitis and, if infected, of developing long-term or permanent neurologic sequelae. The inapparent-to-apparent ratio of cases ranges from a high of 29:1 in middle-aged adults to a low of 8:1 in children under 4 years. Fatality rates are highest in the elderly.[16] Familial clusters in man and premises-related clusters in equines have been reported.[16, 17]

Pathogenesis.—Except for two states, the exact vector responsible for transmission to man has not been fully elucidated. In New Jersey, this vector is *Aedes solicitans* and in the recent Michigan outbreak, the prominent vector species was *Coquillettidia perturbans*.[18] It is presumed that when an adequate natural reservoir of infected birds are fed upon by the less fastidiously host-oriented *Aedes* spp mosquitoes, these mosquitoes then transmit the disease to horses and man. Once infected with EEE virus, humans appear to undergo a period of initial replication in visceral sites followed first by viremia and probably CNS invasion by the hematogenous route via CNS vessels damaged during this process. Animal studies, however, suggest the importance of the olfactory bulbs in this process.[19, 20] The incubation period in humans varies from five to 15 days.

Clinical Syndromes.—EEE is clinically the most severe encephalitis in North America. Onset of illness is usually rapid with high fever, vomiting, stiff neck, and drowsiness. Coma can occur by the second day. Children commonly manifest edema, either generalized, facial, or periorbital. Paralyses are common during the acute phase, and EEE seems to produce a greater disturbance in autonomic functions than other togaviral encephalitides. The major autonomic disturbance of concern is impaired respiratory function which can produce life-threatening hypoxia. Excessive salivation, which can cause airway obstruction in comatose patients, may also be a problem. Case fatality rates vary from 50%

to 75% of patients. Up to 30% of patients surviving the acute infection will have neurologic sequelae, often of a severe nature, requiring permanent institutional care. Sequelae frequently seen are minimal brain dysfunction to severe intellectual impairment, personality disorders, seizures, spastic paralysis, or specific cranial nerve dysfunction. Inapparent infections and milder clinical forms have been described.[21, 22]

Immunologic Response.—Persons who survive EEE will develop complement-fixing (CF), neutralizing (N), and hemagglutination-inhibition (HI) antibodies. CF antibodies only persist for up to 2 years, while the latter persist for at least several years.

Pathology.—On gross examination, the brain and spinal cord are edematous, as are the viscera. Multiple punctate hemorrhages are seen on the brain surface. Microscopic changes in neuronal tissue range from slight alterations of nucleus and cytoplasm to areas of total cellular destruction in which are found focal collections of polymorphonuclear cells. Vascular lesions are prominent. Perivascular cuffing, inflammation of vessel walls, and multiple thromboses of vessels are seen. The brainstem and surrounding area are most severely affected, but cortical areas of the frontal and occipital lobes also demonstrate significant lesions.[21, 23]

Laboratory Findings and Diagnosis.—The major hematologic findings are early leukopenia followed by leukocytosis. Lumbar puncture often demonstrates elevated cerebrospinal fluid (CSF) pressure, and analysis of CSF usually shows lymphocytic pleocytosis, sometimes with thousands of cells (especially in young children).[22]

Diagnosis of EEE for those who survive is usually by serologic testing of blood samples collected acutely and 2 to 5 weeks after illness onset by one or more of the following serologic tests: CF, HI, or plaque reduction neutralization (PRN). Other serologic techniques of growing importance are the EEE-specific IgM indirect immunofluorescence (IFA) test and the EEE IgM–capture enzyme-linked immunosorbent assay (ELISA).

Virus isolation from blood during the acute illness is rarely successful, since the viremic period is over at the point of illness onset. Virus isolation is often successful from brain tissue collected post mortem. The specimen should be collected aseptically, frozen, and transported on dry ice to the diagnostic laboratory. Specimens for virus isolation must not be placed in formalin, since this will inactivate the virus. Virus isolation can be performed by intracerebral inoculation of suckling mice or inoculation of a number of tissue culture lines such as primary duck embryo, Vero, and LLC MK-2. EEE virus in brain biopsies can be identified by immunofluorescent techniques.

Prevention.—The key preventive measure for EEE and all arbovirus encephalitis is the avoidance of mosquito bites. In the case of EEE, forested and swampy areas should be avoided during the mid- and late summer months in endemic areas. Skin should be protected by clothing of adequate length. Numerous commercially available mosquito repellents are useful when applied on exposed skin. Windows and doors of dwellings should be screened. When sleeping in unscreened areas, mosquito netting should be used.

An effective inactivated vaccine is available for horses in which fatality rates can reach 90% in unvaccinated animals. Immunization of horses against EEE is not a useful public health measure to protect humans as it is with Venezuelan equine encephalitis since, with natural infection, horses do not develop sufficient viremias to serve as an amplifying host.

An experimental inactivated human vaccine prepared from embryonated eggs has been developed by the Walter Reed Army Institute of Research and is distributed by the US Public Health Service Centers for Disease Control in limited quantities for persons at high risk, such as laboratory workers with potential exposure to EEE virus. Data on efficacy and adverse reaction to this vaccine are currently being collected.

Treatment of Infection.—No specific antiviral therapy for EEE is available, and therapeutic efforts are aimed at management of symptoms: reduction of fever, maintenance of adequate hydration and electrolyte balance, assurance of adequate respiratory function (including intubation and mechanical ventilatory assistance if required), anticonvulsant medication, osmotic diuretics to decrease intracranial pressure, and physical therapy. Person-to-person transmission does not occur, and no isolation procedures are required. Patients with neurologic sequelae should be evaluated for an appropriate rehabilitation program. Some cases with severe impairment may require institutional care.

Western Equine Encephalitis

History.—Although WEE produces high mortality in horses, it appears to be less virulent for adult humans in its distribution in the Americas, producing lower case fatality rates and a lower incidence of neurologic sequelae than it does in equines. In 1930, the virus was first isolated from the brains of horses with fatal encephalitis in San Joaquin Valley of California.[24] This was the first virus and first arbovirus isolated in the United States. In 1938, Howitt obtained the first human WEE virus isolate from a child who had succumbed to the disease.[25] The isolation of WEE in 1930 led to increased research activities which identified the etiologic agents of the remaining major arboviruses producing encephalitis in the Americas: EEE, St Louis encephalitis (SLE), VEE, and California encephalitis.

Structure and Biology of the Agent.—The structure and biology of WEE virus is outlined above in the discussion on alphaviruses in general.

Epidemiology.—WEE virus is endemic in the western United States and generally only occurs sporadically east of the Mississippi River. Highlands J (HJ) virus, a member of the antigenically related WEE subgroup, has been isolated frequently in the eastern United States and may have been erroneously identified in the past as WEE virus. Although horses and man are rarely infected with HJ virus, it is still unknown whether this fact is due to differences between HJ and WEE viruses or to the narrow ecological zone in the eastern United States occupied by *Culiseta melanura,* the vector of HJ virus there.[26–28] Major epidemics with hundreds of human cases, usually preceded by equine epizootics, have occurred in California, the Dakotas, Utah, and the Midwestern United States and southern Canadian plains. In recent years the incidence of human cases decreased until 1987. From 1982 to 1987, a total of 67 human cases of WEE were reported to the CDC by Western states. During that period, the largest outbreak of human WEE cases (41) since the 1975 outbreak (133) was reported in 1987. Cases from the 1987 outbreak were reported from five states: Colorado, Montana, Nebraska, North Dakota, and Texas.[10–12]

WEE is mosquito-borne, and the height of vector activity and peak disease transmission usually occur during the early summer months of June and July, peaking in either July or August and ending in September. For WEE, the case-infection ratio is estimated to vary from a low of 1:1150 in adults to a high of 1:58 in children 4 years old or less.[29] Although the risk of fatal outcome for WEE is low in infants, the risk of infection is highest in this group as is the greater likelihood of serious sequelae.[30] Infection with WEE virus three to ten days prior to parturition has been reported to produce encephalitis in newborns, but no teratogenic effects of WEE virus infection have been reported.[31] The total case-fatality rate is 3% to 9% depending on geographic location and reporting area. Age-specific mortality has been consistently higher in the elderly. Attack rates are higher in males, in those with rural residence, and in farmers.[29]

Pathogenesis.—Transmission in nature occurs principally between *Culex tarsalis* and *Culiseta melanura* mosquitoes and wild passerine birds. These mosquitoes deposit their eggs in irrigated fields, flood plains, and swampy areas and also utilize these areas as habitat. Man is an incidental host for WEE, and no human-to-human or human-vector-human transmission is known to occur. The extrinsic incubation period (time from an infected blood meal until able to transmit virus) for *Cx tarsalis* is relatively short compared to other neurotropic togaviruses, and this allows rapid amplification of virus transmission, possibly accounting for the early summer appearance of WEE.

In a number of animal studies, peripheral inoculation of WEE virus leads first to virus replication in extraneural sites. In some animal models, CNS invasion through the olfactory bulbs has been suggested. The pathologic presentation in man, however, demonstrates no predilection for frontal lobe lesions and a degree of vascular pathology which suggests hematogenous dissemination.[19–20]

Clinical Syndromes.—The incubation period for WEE is five to ten days, and the clinical symptoms observed depend on the age of the patient. A large number of asymptomatic infections or undifferentiated febrile illness occur and these may not be recognized as due to WEE infection. Illness onset usually begins with headache, followed rapidly by fever, which can be life-threateningly high. Various manifestations of altered sensorium can progress to coma. Most infants will suffer convulsions. Cases which continue to worsen develop pathologic reflexes or may lose normal reflexes in a changing pattern. Alternating spastic or flaccid paralysis commonly occurs in severe cases. Most adults, even with a severe clinical course, will recover completely if death does not occur. Children under 1 year of age frequently suffer permanent sequelae ranging from minimal brain dysfunction to epilepsy or severe psychomotor disorders.

By the time of onset of clinical symptoms, most patients will have N antibodies present, while HI and CF antibodies require longer to develop. Natural infection presumably confers long-term immunity.

Pathology.—On gross examination, the brain usually is edematous. Histologic examination reveals focal necrosis in the midbrain, basal nuclei, and cerebellum. Perivascular cuffing is prominent, and more severe cases have hemorrhagic lesions in the pons, medulla, and basal ganglia.[34]

Laboratory Diagnosis.—WEE virus can be isolated frequently from postmortem brain tissue and occasionally from CSF or blood taken in the first two days of illness by isolation in suckling mice or a variety of tissue cultures. Specimens for virus isolation which cannot be processed quickly should be frozen and shipped frozen to an appropriate laboratory. Detailed clinical and epidemiologic information should accompany the specimen. Serologic tests which can aid in diagnosis are the CF and HI tests. As noted above, N antibodies are present early in the disease, and their presence is good presumptive evidence of WEE until a diagnosis can be established by virus isolation or a fourfold rise in antibody by HI or CF testing from sera collected acutely and 2 to 3 weeks after onset. N and HI antibodies persist much longer than CF antibodies, and thus, in some situations the latter may be useful in classifying antibody of recent origin.[32, 33]

Two recently developed tests appear to be rapid and sensitive: the IgM-specific IFA and the IgM-capture ELISA tests. Both tests rely on detection of WEE-specific IgM antibodies. Direct immunofluorescent detection of WEE virus in brain biopsy tissue may be available in the future.

Examination of CSF will reveal a pleocytosis, ranging from 10 to 400 cells, which is acutely polymorphonuclear in cell type but soon becomes predominantly lymphocytic as the illness progresses. CSF protein is elevated and glucose remains normal.

Prevention and Treatment.—Prevention of human WEE depends on surveillance by public health agencies to detect the presence of virus in mosquitoes and birds. When virus is present, public warnings can be issued and mosquito control programs instituted. The observation of encephalitis cases in equines may also be of use, since these cases may precede those in humans by weeks. Reliance on the predictive value of equine cases should be tempered by the extent to which those cases are confirmed in a laboratory, by vaccination rates in resident equines, and by the local committment to reporting equine cases.[35] An effective vaccine for horses is available, but, like the vaccine for EEE, it is not a useful public health tool in human epidemics, since horses with WEE have quite low viremias and are not important as amplifying hosts. A human vaccine has been produced by Walter Reed Army Institute for Research but is available only in limited quantity and is reserved for persons at high risk, such as laboratory workers. The human vaccine is not useful as an intervention measure in epidemics either, since the achievement of adequate antibody levels requires three injections spaced over a period of several weeks. Data are currently being gathered on the safety and efficacy of this vaccine.

No specific therapy exists for WEE, and treatment is aimed at management of specific symptoms. The occasional high fever produced by this virus is a special problem among the arboviruses producing encephalitis, and hypothermia should be considered to prevent neurologic damage or even death on the basis of the fever alone. If hypothermia is employed, special attention must be paid to assuring adequate hydration. Seizures may be controlled by phenobarbital or diazepam. Patients should be monitored for adequate respiratory function, and adequate pulmonary toilet is of particular importance. In the event of permanent neurologic deficits, patients should be evaluated and begun on a program to achieve maximum rehabilitation.

Uncontrolled trials of therapy combining barbiturates, steroids, and hyperventilation have yielded favorable results, but require further investigation.[36, 37] Five antiviral compounds have been shown to have in vitro activity against WEE virus as well as other alphaviruses and flaviviruses: amantadine, rimantidine, chloroquine, selenazofurin, and tiazofurin. None of these drugs has undergone appropriate clinical testing in humans and none is licensed for this use.[38]

Venezuelan Equine Encephalitis and Everglades Encephalitis

VEE, called *peste loca* in South America, is an important disease problem there and occasionally is detected in North America, where it occurred in an epidemic in 1971 in Texas. There are four subtypes of VEE virus, and subtype II, which is related but distinct, is Everglades (EVE) virus, which is restricted in its geographic distribution to the state of Florida in the United States. Only five human cases of EVE encephalitis have been described in the literature, but serosurveys reveal an antibody prevalence as high as 27% in residents of south Florida. Subtypes of VEE virus that produce epidemic disease in humans are designated IA, IB, and IC. Strains other than these are most often enzootic, but occasionally produce disease in man ranging from undifferentiated febrile illness to fatal encephalitis.

History.—The earliest documented epizootic of VEE was in 1938, when the virus was isolated from the brains of dead horses.[39] The first documented epidemic involving humans occurred in Colombia in 1952.[40] Subsequently, large epidemics preceded by epizootics in horses occurred in Panama, Venezuela, Guatemala, Honduras, Mexico, and Texas.[41] During the 1971 epidemic in Texas, 19 nonfatal human cases of VEE were reported along with several thousand horse deaths. In the United States, no human cases of VEE have been reported to the CDC since 1971.[10–12] However, the geographic proximity of VEE virus activity in Central and northern South America poses a continuing potential threat.

Structure and Biology of the Agent.—The alphavirus E2 glycoprotein has long been recognized as that part of the virus particle which elicits N antibody in the infected host. Much recent work using monoclonal antibodies to define more precisely this function of the E2 glycoprotein has focused on VEE virus. The VEE virus E2 glycoprotein antigenic structure has eight epitopes named E2[a–h]. One of these epitopes, E2[c], strongly elicits production of neutralizing monoclonal antibodies. Very small concentrations of these anti E2[c] monoclonal antibodies (5 ng/mL) were capable of producing 100% virus neutralization in PRN tests. While other epitopes were demonstrated that would produce neutralization of the virus, it was necessary that they were in spatial proximity to

E2[c] for neutralization to occur. In vitro studies of anti-E2[c] monoclonal antibody demonstrated that when it was administered prior to challenge with VEE virus, it protected 3-week-old mice. Anti-E1 monoclonal antibodies were also tested, but anti-E2[c] monoclonal antibodies were found to be from ten- to 100-fold more protective.[42–44]

Epidemiology.—Epidemics of VEE affecting 20,000 to 30,000 people have been documented in Venezuela and Ecuador. Four percent of the Venezuelan cases demonstrated major neurologic involvement and, of those, 16% died. Outbreaks of lesser magnitude are more common.[41] VEE viruses that produce illness in humans are present in the tropical areas of the Americas, but are most prevalent in South America.

Given a susceptible population, attack rates generally do not vary as a result of age or sex. Where populations have been previously infected, younger, nonimmune members may show higher attack rates. Also, probably because of occupational or recreational pursuits which may cause greater exposure to vector habitats, attack rates can be higher in males. Attack rates are also higher in rural areas because of the greater likelihood of suitable vector habitat.

The strains of VEE virus pathogenic for man and horses, in contrast to other alphaviral encephalitides, are mainly amplified in horses, producing equine cases prior to the beginning of human disease. Also, in contrast, birds do not seem to play an important reservoir role in nature. The reservoir in nature for the epizootic and epidemic strains of VEE virus (IA, IB, IC) remains unknown. The enzootic, less pathogenic strains are maintained in a mosquito-rodent-mosquito cycle. Transovarial transmission of VEE viruses in mosquitoes has not been demonstrated. EVE virus is maintained in a similar cycle. The mosquitoes which transmit VEE virus are *Culex* spp and *Aedes aegypti*.

Seasonal periods of peak transmission of VEE coincide with peak rainfall, during which vector mosquitoes will be present in greatest abundance. Ecological zones where particularly intense transmission can occur are coastal areas of the tropics where distinct dry and rainy seasons occur.

Pathogenesis.—Transmission of VEE and EVE viruses is by the bites of infected *Culex* spp mosquitoes, primarily, but for VEE also, by *Aedes* spp and *Psorophora* spp. Numerous other species transmit the enzootic VEE strains in nature. Since the more important amplification of pathogenic VEE strains occurs in horses, equine epizootics usually precede human cases. Humans are incidentally infected by the non-*Aedes* spp vector mosquitoes since they are not a preferred host. Once a human is infected, an incubation period of two to five days ensues. The method of penetration of the CNS by VEE virus is unknown.

Clinical Syndromes.—Very few people infected with VEE virus will have inapparent infection, but, fortunately, only a small percentage of those infected develop neurologic involvement. Many patients will have an undifferentiated febrile illness, but more typically, exhibit an influenza-like illness. Symptoms are sudden in onset with fevers, chills, myalgias, generalized malaise, headache, nausea, and vomiting. Lumbosacral pain is a frequent complaint, and occasionally patients will also complain of sore throat and diarrhea. Physical findings include flushed facies, congestion of the sclerae and conjunctivae, erythematous pharynx, and muscle tenderness. Lymphadenopathy occurs only rarely. Some patients with mild CNS involvement will show lethargy, somnolence, or even mild confusion but do not develop seizures or other localizing signs.[40]

VEE infection rarely progresses to encephalitis in adults and is most common in children under 15 years of age. Case fatality rates are highest in children 5 years of age and under (35%) and decrease to less than 10% for older children and young adults. The findings in VEE vary little from the general description of encephalitis given in the introduction, except that visual field defects and involuntary movements are unusual. Patients who survive VEE may have permanent neurologic sequelae, but this outcome is less likely with VEE than encephalitis associated with other togaviruses (eg, EEE).

Patients infected with VEE who survive will develop HI, CF, and N antibodies and long-term, if not lifetime, immunity will result.

Pathology.—Insufficient pathologic descriptions are available to generalize about the lesions produced in the human CNS by VEE infection.

Laboratory Findings and Diagnosis.—Blood studies in the first three days of illness frequently reveal leukopenia. Elevation of aspartate aminotransferase may occur. CSF pleocytosis, in the range of 500 cells or less, is seen. Polymorphonuclear cells may predominate early, but there is rapid progression to lymphocytic pleocytosis.

Specific diagnosis of VEE can be accomplished by virus isolation and/or serologic testing. Curiously, VEE virus is present in the nasopharynx of patients during the first one to three days of illness and may be isolated from nasopharyngeal washings or swabs. During the same viremic period, VEE virus can be isolated from peripheral blood. Specimens for virus isolation should be frozen and shipped to an appropriate laboratory on dry ice. The virus can be grown in suckling mice and a variety of cell lines. Specimens for serologic testing should be obtained acutely and at 2 to 3 weeks after onset. Serologic specimens obtained aseptically may be kept refrigerated at 4°C and may be shipped at ambient temperatures to the laboratory if the shipping period does not exceed two to three days. If contamination of the specimens is a possibility or if a longer shipping period is anticipated, the specimens should be frozen and then shipped with sufficient quantities of wet or dry ice to preserve them.

Prevention and Treatment.—No licensed vaccine for human use against VEE is available. A very effective vaccine for horses is available, and its appropriate use can prevent outbreaks of VEE since equines are the major amplifying species for VEE virus. Other strategies which may be employed are the wide-scale use of adulticiding and larviciding chemicals to control the vectors, and individual measures to prevent mosquito bites (see Dengue, Chapter 23).

An investigational live attenuated VEE vaccine for human use has been produced by the Walter Reed Army Institute for Research. This vaccine has been limited in its distribution to laboratory and other personnel at high risk of aerosol exposures to the virus. Its efficacy, safety, and reactogenicity are currently being evaluated.

Most cases of nonencephalitic VEE respond to bed rest, antipyretics, and analgesics. Most severe cases will require careful management of fluid and electrolyte balance and the treatment of specific symptoms such as seizures. Heroic measures such as mechanically assisted respiration may be needed in severe cases of encephalitis. No specific therapy for VEE is currently available. Mildly ill patients will recover in a week or less. Patients with encephalitis will have a prolonged recovery of a month or more, marked by weakness, headache, and other symptoms.

Diagnosis and Management.—(See the general discussion on togavirus encephalitis for differential diagnosis, and the section on treatment above.) Even though VEE virus is present in the nasopharynx of patients, no evidence exists which suggests that person-to-person transmission occurs as a result. Therefore, it is not necessary to isolate patients with VEE.

ALPHAVIRUSES PRODUCING FEVER, POLYARTHRITIS, AND RASH

Chikungunya Virus

Chikungunya virus derives its name from a Swahili word meaning "that which bends up," and is a characterization of the arthritic symptoms produced by the infection. The disease clinically resembles dengue in many aspects; indeed, outbreaks during the nineteenth century attributed to dengue virus may in fact have been due to chikungunya virus.[45, 46]

History.—The earliest clinical description consistent with chikungunya is attributed to Dr David Bylon in Jakarta in 1799. During the nineteenth century several epidemics involving Africa, Arabia, India, and Asia were described. Also, during the century it is likely that chikungunya virus was introduced into the Caribbean as a result of the slave trade and eventually involved the East Coast port cities of North America. It is thought that chikungunya virus probably originated in Africa and that the pandemic of the nineteenth century spread throughout much of the world by trading ships. By the 1960s an endemic focus of chikungunya appeared to have been established in southeast Asia, particularly in Cambodia, South Vietnam, and Thailand.[46-50]

Structure and Biology of the Agent.—Chikungunya virus is a member of the *Alphavirus* genus of the family *Togaviridae,* and its general structure and biology are typical of alphaviruses as described in the introduction. Serologically, the virus is related to o'nyong-nyong virus but cross-reacts only weakly to Semliki Forest and Mayaro viruses from the same subgroup as o'nyong-nyong.

Intracerebral inoculation of chikungunya virus is lethal to suckling mice and a number of other newborn species. Most other adult domestic animals and several species of birds can be infected but are relatively resistant to clinical illness. A number of primate species, including chimpanzees, baboons, monkeys, and red-tailed monkeys, have been found with antibodies to chikungunya virus. The importance of these animals to the enzootic transmission cycle is not precisely known, but an epizootic cycle involving several mosquito species and primates is suspected.

Chikungunya virus produces cytopathic effect (CPE) or plaques in a number of tissue culture cell lines as well as certain mosquito continuous cell lines.[51, 52]

Epidemiology.—Outbreaks of chikungunya are usually explosive and appear to be a function of the numbers of infected vector mosquitoes and of the susceptible human population. In a susceptible population within a given outbreak, the incidence of disease can be quite high. It frequently becomes so high so quickly that a mosquito-human-mosquito cycle based on mechanical transmission of the virus by the mosquitoes has been proposed.[53-55]

Because of transmission by mosquito vectors, the temporal occurrence of chikungunya outbreaks may be expected to be sensitive to the amount of rainfall such that transmission would be enhanced during the rainy season and depressed during the dry season. The geographic distribution of chikungunya outbreaks in modern times has been in sub-Saharan Africa, India, and southeast Asia. The potential geographic spread, however, includes any areas of the world where the major vector is known to exist assuming appropriate climatologic conditions for the vector to be active.

The principal vector for chikungunya virus is ordinarily the peridomestic-breeding mosquito, *Aedes aegypti*. In situations where the vector is distributed principally in the domestic environment, attack rates may be higher for females and small children who usually have greater periods of exposure there. As described for dengue, which is also transmitted by *Ae aegypti* mosquitoes, a number of sociologic and other factors may determine the degree of exposure to the vector and hence the probability of contracting chikungunya.

Pathogenesis.—Mechanical transmission of chikungunya virus during human outbreaks is suggested by several observations. Biologic transmission of virus by mosquitoes requires a period of time from ingestion of a viremic blood meal to infection and viral multiplication in the vector's salivary glands. This extrinsic incubation period is relatively long for chikungunya virus in *Ae aegypti* mosquitoes; if the virus were transmitted, one would expect the distribution of cases over time to approximate a normal distribution curve, rather than the explosion of cases which is seen. The viremias that occur in humans can be 10^8 infectious doses per milliliter of blood, levels that should be adequate for mechanical transmission. Finally, mechanical transmission by *Ae aegypti* has been demonstrated to occur experimentally using mice. In nature, chikungunya virus has been isolated from a number of other *Aedes* spp as well as *Mansonia*, *Culex*, and *Anopheles* spp.[53-55]

The incubation period for chikungunya varies from one to six days. The disease then has a strikingly abrupt onset, such that adult patients can frequently recall the exact time of onset. The initial symptom is sudden intense pain in one or more joints that forces immediate cessation of activity. The arthralgia is followed soon after by myalgia, flushed face, marked conjunctival injection, and fever. The arthritic manifestations are less common in children and infants. The early episode may be accompanied by nausea and vomiting. The fever is frequently biphasic with the first phase lasting from one to six days followed by an afebrile period lasting one to three days and then recurrent fever.

In the second phase, patients have headache, severe pharyngitis, and cervical lymphadenopathy. From the third to the sixth day after illness onset in older children and adults, a maculopapular rash appears on the trunk and extensor surfaces of extremities. The arthritic symptoms in older children and adults may include

redness and swelling of affected joints and, in some cases, nodular swelling usually associated with the rheumatoid arthritis. These symptoms can persist for 6 months to a year, although the shorter duration is more usual.

Children with chikungunya may experience febrile convulsions, and infants may suffer residual neurologic deficits after febrile convulsions. Minor bleeding manifestations have been reported in children hospitalized with chikungunya and include a positive tourniquet test, scattered petechiae, maculopapular rash, and epistaxis. Severe hemorrhagic manifestations have been reported from India but are rare in southeast Asia and Africa.[45, 56-60]

Patients with chikungunya develop HI, CF, and N antibodies. HI and N antibodies appear about 2 weeks after illness onset, and CF antibodies require longer.

Laboratory Diagnosis.—Chikungunya can be serologically diagnosed by HI, N, or CF tests when the sera (acute and convalescent) are collected at appropriate intervals. A fourfold rise in antibody titers between an acute and convalescent specimen is diagnostic.

O'nyong-nyong Virus

O'nyong-nyong (ONN) is an alphavirus that was first isolated during a major epidemic which began in Uganda in 1959 and rapidly spread through a larger areas of East Africa. Small outbreaks of the disease were still occurring by 1962. ONN is the first arthropod-borne viral disease for which anopheline species of mosquitoes were proposed as vectors. The odd name for this disease was the term given it by the Acholi tribe meaning "joint-breaker."[61, 62]

Structure and Biology.—The structure of ONN virus is typical of alphaviruses as described earlier in this chapter. It is antigenically closely related to chikungunya and Semliki Forest viruses. It will kill suckling mice by various routes of inoculation. It grows well in HeLa, Vero, and BHK-21 cell lines.[63]

Epidemiology.—ONN now appears to be occurring in sporadic fashion. From 1959 to 1962, it is estimated that 2 million persons in East Africa were infected with the virus. In some locales attack rates reached 70%. All age groups were affected and transmission occurred throughout the year, with peak activity from May through September. The mosquito species felt to be the most likely vector was *Anopheles funestus*, although isolates of ONN virus were also obtained from *An gambiae*, which is also an avid human biter.[62, 64, 65] The currently known geographic distribution of ONN includes Central African Republic, Kenya, Malawi, Mozambique, Senegal, Tanzania, and Uganda.

Clinical Syndromes.—The incubation period for ONN is thought to be eight or more days. Fever was absent in approximately one third of patients and, if present, persisted for five days. The illness was characterized by sudden onset of myalgia, arthralgia, orbital pain, and rash. In some patients a prodrome of chills and epistaxis was noted. The rash was described as beginning on the face and moving toward the trunk and extremities over a four- to seven-day period. Rash occurred in over 60% of cases. Generalized lymphadenopathy with especially prominent posterior cervical nodes was also a prominent feature. General malaise and joint pains caused a protracted illness in some patients. No deaths or permanent joint damage were noted.

Laboratory Diagnosis.—ONN can be diagnosed by isolation of virus from peripheral blood or serologically by HI, CF, or N tests. In areas where both chikungunya and ONN viruses are present, N tests may be required to distinguish between the two viruses.

Prevention and Treatment.—No vaccine for ONN is available. No specific antiviral drugs are available, and treatment is symptomatic.

Sindbis Virus

Sindbis virus is a member of the *Alphavirus* genus that was first isolated from *Culex univattatus* mosquitoes in the Nile delta of Egypt in 1952.[66] Clinical cases have since been detected in man in Africa,[67, 68] Australia,[69] Asia,[70] and the Middle East[70]; antibodies to Sindbis virus have been detected from the sera of Europeans. Whether clinical illness due to Sindbis virus occurs in Europe is not known.[67] Sindbis virus is maintained in nature in a mosquito-bird-mosquito cycle involving *Cx univittatus*, *Cx annulirostris*, and *Cx tritaeniorhynchus* mosquitoes and a number of wild bird species.[71] Most cases of Sindbis fever are related to mosquito exposure in rural areas.

The incubation period for Sindbis fever is three to six days. The onset typically is abrupt with fever, malaise, joint pains, and headache. A papular rash appears next, followed by small vesicular lesions on the soft palate and larger vesicular lesions on hands and feet. Sindbis virus can be isolated from these vesicular lesions. The majority of patients with Sindbis fever will recover in a week, but some patients will have arthritis involving the small joints that may persist for weeks. Uncommon clinical manifestations include encephalitis and transient myocarditis. The disease is usually milder in children.

Most cases are self-limited and can be managed by the use of antipyretics and analgesics. Painful oral lesions may prevent adequate fluid intake and intravenous (IV) fluids may be required to ensure adequate hydration.

Sindbis fever may be diagnosed by isolation and identification of the virus from blood in the first few days of illness and from vesicle fluid. The usual serologic tests employed are HI, CF, and PRN.

No vaccine for Sindbis virus is available, and the only practical preventive measures are the avoidance of mosquito bites (see Dengue, Chapter 23). The differential diagnosis of Sindbis fever includes chikungunya, West Nile, o'nyong-nyong, dengue, Tataguine, Bunyamwera, Ilheus, Zika, and Bangui fever.

Mayaro Virus

Mayaro (MAY) virus is an alphavirus most closely related to Semliki Forest virus from Africa. It was first isolated from febrile patients in Trinidad in 1954.[72] Since then it has been isolated in Bolivia,[73] Brazil,[74] Colombia, and Surinam.[75] MAY virus is indistinguishable from a virus named Uruma which was isolated from a serious outbreak of febrile illness among Okinawan agricultural settlers in the Bolivian rain forest in 1954 and 1955, but

it is doubtful that the deaths or all the disease was caused by Uruma.[73]

Structure and Biology.—The structure of MAY virus is typical of alphaviruses in general. The Brazilian and Trinidad strains are both lethal for suckling mice either intracerebrally or intraperitoneally. Adult mice are not susceptible. CPE or plaques are produced by MAY virus in the following cell cultures: baby hamster kidney (BHK), chick embryo, and Vero.

Epidemiology.—No precise data are available on the incidence or prevalence of MAY, but cases probably occur frequently in persons who are exposed to forested areas of Central America and northern South America. The epidemics that have occurred have involved large numbers of susceptible persons moving into an endemic forested area for occupational pursuits.[73, 74] Males have been infected more often than females, again most likely due to occupational exposures in the forest.

Pathogenesis.—Transmission to man is primarily due to *Haemogogus* mosquitoes but possibly also *Culex* spp, *Mansonia*, and *Psorophora*, from which the virus has also been isolated. Vertebrate hosts for MAY virus include nonhuman primates and rodents, and this may be the natural enzootic transmission cycle by which man is incidentally infected.

The incubation period for MAY is seven to 12 days. The clinical course is characterized by high fever, myalgia, arthralgia, severe headache, and epigastric pain. Other symptoms and findings which occur with less frequency are nausea, diarrhea, photophobia, conjunctival injection, swelling of small joints, and jaundice.

Laboratory Diagnosis.—MAY virus may be readily isolated from the blood of patients during the early stage of illness. Otherwise the disease can be diagnosed by standard serologic testing methods.

Prevention and Treatment.—No vaccine is currently available for human use. An inactivated MAY vaccine derived from human diploid cell culture has been produced but not tested in humans.[76] Measures to avoid mosquito bites are the only effective preventive measures at present.

MAY infection produces a self-limited disease of two to six days duration which resolves without apparent sequelae. Symptomatic therapy to control fever and pain is indicated, and some few severely affected patients may require hospitalization.

Ross River Virus

Epidemic polyarthritis is caused by the alphavirus, Ross River virus (RRV), which was first described in Australia in 1927 when an epidemic of febrile illness with rash and polyarthralgia occurred. In recent years sporadic epidemics have occurred elsewhere in the South Pacific, but eastern Australia continues to be the most important known endemic focus. RRV was first isolated in 1963 and proposed as the etiologic agent of epidemic polyarthritis. Recent outbreaks in Australia occurred in 1971, 1974, 1975, 1976 and 1979–1980.[77–81] The 1979–1980 epidemic also affected the western Pacific island nations of Fiji, Western Samoa, Cook Islands, Tonga, and the territory of New Caledonia. In Fiji alone, over 500,000 people are said to have been infected.[80]

Structure and Biology of the Agent.—The structure of RRV is typical of alphaviruses, as described above. It is related to the Semliki Forest virus subgroup, especially to Getah and Bebaru viruses. An antigenically distinct Ross River virus strain has been characterized from a limited area of New South Wales, but apparently produces an illness identical to the more common strain.[63, 82, 83]

Epidemiology.—The early occurrence of epidemic polyarthritis was one of major epidemics occurring at long intervals. Recently, however, the occurrence of the disease in Australia is seen to vary by geographic areas. In eastern Australia, the disease is regularly seen annually in the months from December to June as it probably is also in New South Wales and Victoria. While epidemics have occurred in the western and southern parts of the country, there is no evidence for annual endemic transmission. The disease is more frequently seen in females, and patients from 15 to 60 years old.[80, 81, 84]

Pathogenesis and Clinical Syndromes.—RRV is transmitted to man by the bites of infected *Aedes vigilax, Culex annulirostris,* and in southern Australia probably by *Ae camptorhynchus.*[80] It may be maintained in nature in a mosquito-marsupial cycle that probably includes kangaroos and wallabies.[80] Most RRV infections (60%) are asymptomatic.[80]

The clinical manifestations are usually relatively benign with arthralgias, swelling of joints (especially the small joints of the hands and feet), and a rash that involves both trunk and extremities. The rash is usually maculopapular, but occasionally is vesicular. Some patients have either rash without joint involvement or joint involvement without rash, or mild fever without either rash or joint involvement. Also described are pharyngitis, paresthesias of the palms and soles, lymphadenopathy and, rarely, petechiae. The majority of patients are fully recovered within 2 weeks. Some patients, however, will have continued joint symptoms that may persist for as long as a year.[84–86]

Patients with epidemic polyarthritis will develop HI, CF, and N antibodies. HI antibodies appear very quickly while CF antibodies do not occur until after the second week or later.

Laboratory Diagnosis.—Although RRV has been isolated from humans, isolation may be difficult, and serologic diagnosis is most frequently used. Curiously, no isolations of RRV were reported from Australia until 1985. Aaskov et al, who obtained the first human isolates there, attributed the difficulty to the relative inefficiency of suckling mice and Vero cells as primary isolation media when compared to C6/36 cells. They also reported that the likelihood of RRV isolation was greater from blood specimens collected in the first 48 hours of illness.[87]

The rapid appearance of HI antibody makes it possible to have a diagnosis within the first week of illness. Convalescent sera obtained more than a week after onset should be tested for CF antibodies to demonstrate a diagnostic rise in titer.[87]

Prevention and Treatment.—Epidemic polyarthritis is a benign disease in most patients, and no vaccine is available. Treatment is symptomatic and most patients recover quickly. Salicylates and steroids have been advocated for prolonged symptoms, but controlled studies of their efficacy have not been performed.

The only effective preventive therapy is to avoid mosquito bites, as described in the section on dengue.

Included in the differential diagnosis of epidemic polyarthritis are rheumatic fever, rheumatoid arthritis, rubella, and dengue.

Ockelbo Virus

Ockelbo fever in Sweden, Karelian fever in the western USSR, and Pogosta disease in Finland were all described in the early 1980s.[88–94] Although these agents have never been isolated from humans, they have been isolated from *Culiseta* spp and *Aedes* spp mosquitoes during epidemic periods of these diseases. All three agents produce a syndrome of acute febrile onset followed by polyarthralgias and rash.

The clinical similarity of the disease produced by these agents, their serologic relatedness to Sindbis virus, and their geographic proximity in northeastern Europe suggested that they were possibly the same virus. A recent collaborative study between workers from the Soviet Union and the United States demonstrated that, in fact, Karelian fever virus and Ockelbo virus are virtually the same, differing from each other by only one oligonucleotide.[95]

The structure and biology of Ockelbo virus is typical of alphaviruses. Therapy is symptomatic. The geographic localization of Ockelbo virus should differentiate it diagnostically from other viral causes of polyarthritis such as Ross River virus from Australia or o'nyong-nyong from Africa. Treatable bacterial causes such as meningococci and streptocci should be excluded.

REFERENCES

1. Schlesinger S, Schlesinger MJ (eds): *The Togaviridae and Flaviviridae.* New York, Plenum, 1986.
2. Monath TP, Trent DW: Togaviral disease of domestic animals, in Kurstak E, Kurstak C (eds): *Comparative Diagnosis of Viral Diseases.* New York, Academic Press, 1981, vol 4, pp 335–355, 356–357.
3. Giltner LT, Shrahan MS: The 1933 outbreak of infectious equine encephalomyelitis in the eastern states. *N Am Vet* 1973; 14:25–27.
4. TenBroeck C, Merrill MH: A serological difference between eastern and western equine encephalomyelitis virus. *Proc Soc Exp Biol Med* 1933; 31:217–220.
5. Fothergill LD, Dingle JH, Faber S, et al: Human encephalitis caused by the virus of the eastern variety of equine encephalomyelitis. *N Engl J Med* 1938; 219:411–417.
6. Wallis RC: Recent advances in research on the eastern encephalitis virus. *Yale J Biol Med* 1965; 37:413–421.
7. Calisher CH, Maness, KSC, Lord RC, et al: Identification of two South American strains of eastern equine encephalomyelitis virus from migrant birds captured on the Mississippi Delta. *Am J Epidemiol* 1971; 94:172–178.
8. Wallis RC, Main AJ Jr: *Eastern Equine Encephalitis in Connecticut—Progress and Problems. Memoirs.* Hartford, Conn, Connecticut Entomological Society, 1974, pp 117–144.
9. Chamberlain RW, Sikes RK, Nelson DB, et al: Studies on the North American arthropod-borne encephalitides, VI. Quantitative determinations of virus-vector relationships. *Am J Hyg* 1954; 60:278–285.
10. Centers for Disease Control: Arboviral infections of the central nervous system—United States, 1985. *MMWR* 1986; 35:341–344.
11. Centers for Disease Control: Arboviral infections of the central nervous system—United States, 1986. *MMWR* 1987; 36:450–455.
12. Centers for Disease Control: Arboviral infections of the central nervous system—United States, 1987. *MMWR* 1989; in press.
13. Belle EA, Grant LS, Thorburn MJ: An outbreak of eastern equine encephalomyelitis in Jamaica. II. Laboratory diagnosis and pa-

thology of eastern equine encephalomyelitis in Jamaica. *Am J Trop Med Hyg* 1964; 13:335–341.

14. Eklund CM, Bell JF, Brennan JM: Antibody survey following an outbreak of human and equine disease in the Dominican Republic, caused by the eastern strain of equine encephalomyelitis virus. *Am J Trop Med Hyg* 1951; 31:312–328.

15. Tikasingh ES, Ardoin P, Everard COR, et al: Eastern equine encephalitis in Trinidad, epidemiological investigations following two human cases of South American strain in Santa Cruz. *Trop Geogr Med* 1973; 25:355–361.

16. Goldfield M, Welsh JN, Taylor BF: The 1959 outbreak of eastern encephalitis in New Jersey. 5. The inapparent infection: disease ratio. *Am J Epidemiol* 1968; 87:32–38.

17. Hauser GH: Human equine encephalomyelitis, eastern type, in Louisiana. *New Orleans Med Surg J* 1948; 100:551–558.

18. Francy DB: Eastern equine encephalomyelitis (EEE) and consideration of some alternatives for dealing with EEE as a public health problem, in Engemann JG (ed): *Eastern Equine Encephalomyelitis (EEE) and Public Health in Southwestern Michigan.* Kalamazoo, Science for Citizens Center of Southwestern Michigan, Western Michigan University, 1982, 15–18.

19. Griffin DE: Alphavirus pathogenesis and immunity, in Schlesinger S, Schlesinger MJ (eds): *The Togaviridae and Flaviviridae.* New York, Plenum, 1986, pp 209–249.

20. Monath TP, Cropp CB, Harrison AK: Mode of entry of a neurotropic arbovirus into the central nervous system. Reinvestigation of an old controversy. *Lab Invest* 1983; 48:399–410.

21. Farber S, Hill A, Connerly ML, et al: Encephalitis in infants and children caused by the virus of the eastern variety of equine encephalitis. *JAMA* 1940; 114:1725–1731.

22. Feemster RF: Equine encephalitis in Massachusetts. *N Engl J Med* 1957; 257:701–704, 728, 732–733.

23. Haymsher W: Mosquito-borne encephalitides, in *Encephalitides.* New York, Elsevier, 1961, pp 38–56.

24. Meyer KF, Haring CM, Howitt B: The etiology of encephalomyelitis in horses in the San Joaquin Valley, 1930. *Science* 1931; 74:227–228.

25. Howitt BF: Recovery of the virus of equine encephalomyelitis from the brain of a child. *Science* 1938; 88:455–456.

26. Henderson JR, Karabatsos N, Bourke ATC, et al: A survey for arthropod-borne viruses in south-central Florida. *Am J Trop Med Hyg* 1962; 11:800–810.

27. Karabatsos N, Bourke ATC, Henderson JR: Antigenic variation among strains of western equine encephalomyelitis virus. *Am J Trop Med Hyg* 1963; 12:408–412.

28. Calisher CH, Monath TP, Muth DJ, et al: Characterization of Fort Morgan virus, an alphavirus of the western equine encephalitis virus complex in an unusual ecosystem. *Am J Trop Med Hyg* 1980; 29:1428–1440.

29. Reeves WC and Hammon W McD: Epidemiology of the arthropod-borne viral encephalitides in Kern County, California, 1943–1952. Berkeley, University of California Press, 1962, pp 1–257.

30. McGowan JE, Bryan JA, Gregg MB: Surveillance of arboviral encephalitis in the United States, 1955–1971. *Am J Epidemiol* 1973; 97:199–207.

31. Copps SC, Giddings LE: Transplacental transmission of western equine encephalitis. *Pediatrics* 1959; 24:31–33.

32. Froeschle JE, Reeves WC: Serologic epidemiology of western equine and St Louis encephalitis virus infection in California. II. Analysis of inapparent infections in residents of an endemic area. *Am J Epidemiol* 1965; 81:44–51.

33. Stallones RA, Reeves WC, Lennette EH: Serologic epidemiology of western equine and St Louis encephalitis virus infection in California. I. Persistence of complement-fixing antibody following clinical illness. *Am J Hyg* 1964; 79:16–28.

34. Finley KH, Longshore WA, Palmer RJ, et al: Western equine and St Louis encephalitis. Preliminary report of a clinical follow-up study in California. *Neurology* 1955; 5:223–235.

35. Potter ME, Currier RW III, Pearson JE, et al: Western equine encephalomyelitis in horses in the northern Red River Valley. *J Am Vet Med Assoc* 1975; 170:1936–1939.

36. Andreasson S, Larsson LE, Bergstrom T, et al: Severe acute encephalitis—improved outcome after barbiturate treatment? *Scand J Infect Dis* 1984; 16:25–27.

37. Rockoff MA, Marshall LF, Shapiro HM: High-dose barbiturate therapy in humans: A clinical review of 60 patients. *Ann Neurol* 1979; 6:194–199.

38. Huggins JW, Robins RK, Canonico PG: Synergistic antiviral effects of ribavirin and the C-nucleoside analogs tiazofurin and selenazofurin against togaviruses, bunyaviruses, and arenaviruses. *Antimicrob Agents Chemother* 1984; 26:476–480.

39. Beck CE, Wyckoff RWG: Venezuelan equine encephalomyelitis. *Science* 1938; 88:530–531.

40. Sanmartin-Barberi C, Groot H, Osborno-Mesa E: Human epidemic in Colombia caused the Venezuelan equine encephalomyelitis virus. *Am J Trop Med Hyg* 1954; 3:283–293.

41. Groot H: The health and economic impact of Venezuelan equine encephalitis, in *Venezuelan Encephalitis, Proceedings of the Workshop-Symposium on Venezuelan Encephalitis Virus.* Washington, DC, Pan American Health Organization, 1972, p 244.

42. Roehrig JT: The use of monoclonal antibodies in studies of the structural proteins of togaviruses and flaviviruses, in Schlesinger S, Schlesinger MJ, (eds): *The Togaviridae and Flaviviridae.* New York, Plenum, 1986, pp 251–278.

43. Trent DW, Clewley JP, France JK, et al: Immunochemical and oligonucleotide fingerprint analysis of Venezuelan equine encephalomyelitis complex viruses. *J Gen Virol* 1979; 43:365–381.

44. Kinney RM, Trent DW, France JK: Comparative immunological and biochemical analyses of viruses in the Venezuelan equine encephalitis complex. *J Gen Virol* 1983; 64:135–147.

45. Robinson MC: An epidemic of virus disease in Southern Province, Tanganyika Territory, in 1952–1953. I. Clinical features. *Trans R Soc Trop Med Hyg* 1955; 49:28–32.

46. Carey DE: Chikungunya and dengue: A case of mistaken identity? *J Hist Med Allied Sci* 1971; 26:243–262.

47. Bylon D: *Korte Aatekening, Wegens eene Aegemeene Ziekte, Doorgans Genaamd de Knokkel-Koorts. Verhandelungen van het Bataviaasch Genootochop der Konsten in Wetenschappen.* 1980, vol 2, pp 17–30.

48. Chastel C: Human infections in Cambodia with chikungunya or a closely allied virus. III. Epidemiology. *Bull Soc Pathol Exot Filiales* 1964; 57:65–82.

49. Vu-Qui D, Nguyen-thi KT, Ly QB: Antibodies to chikungunya virus in Vietnamese children in Saigon. *Bull Soc Pathol Exot Filiales* 1967; 60:353–359.

50. Halstead SB, Scanlon JE, Umpaivit P, et al: Dengue and chikungunya virus infection in man in Thailand, 1962–1964. IV. Epidemiologic studies in the Bangkok metropolitan area. *Am J Trop Med Hyg* 1969; 18:987–1021.

51. Berge TO (ed): *International Catalogue of Arboviruses, including Certain Other Viruses of Vertebrates,* ed 2. US Dept of Health, Education, and Welfare publication No. (CDC) 75–8301, 1975.

52. McIntosh BM: Antibody against chikungunya virus in wild primates in Southern Africa. *S Afr J Med Sci* 1970; 35:65–74.

53. Ross RW: The Newala epidemic. III. The virus: Isolation, pathogenic properties and relationship to the epidemic. *J Hyg* 1956; 54:177–191.

54. Rao TR, Devi PS, Singh KRP: Experimental studies on the mechanical transmission by *Aedes aegypti. Mosquito News* 1968; 28:406–408.

55. Halstead SB: Chikungunya, in Feigin RD, Cherry JD (eds): *Textbook of Pediatric Infectious Disease.* Philadelphia, Saunders, 1981, pp 1149–1156.

56. Halstead SB, Nimmannitya S, Margiotta MR: Dengue and chikungunya virus infection in man in Thailand, 1962–1964. II. Observations on disease in outpatients. *Am J Trop Med Hyg* 1969; 18:972–983.

57. Nimmannitya S, Halstead SB, Cohen SN, et al: Dengue and chikungunya virus infection in man in Thailand, 1962–1964. I. Observations on hospitalized patients with hemorrhagic fever. *Am J Trop Med Hyg* 1969; 18:954–971.

58. Jadhav M, Namboodripad M, Carman RH, et al: Chikungunya

disease in infants and children in Vellore: A report on clinical and haemotological features of virologically proved cases. *Indian J Med Res* 1965; 53:764–776.

59. Thiruvengadam KV, Kalyanasundaram V, Rajgopal J: Clinical and pathologic studies on chikungunya fever in Madras City. *Indian J Med Res* 1965; 53:720–728.

60. Sarkar JK, Chatterjee SN, Chakrevarti SK, et al: Chikungunya virus infection with hemorrhagic manifestations. *Indian J Med Res* 1965; 53:921–925.

61. Haddow AJ, Davies CW, Walker AJ: O'nyong-nyong fever: An epidemic virus disease in East Africa. I. Introduction. *Trans R Soc Trop Med Hyg* 1960; 54:517–522.

62. Corbet PS, Williams MC, Gillett JD: O'nyong-nyong fever: An epidemic virus disease in East Africa IV. Vector studies at epidemic sites. *Trans R Soc Trop Med Hyg* 1961; 55:463–480.

63. Karabatsos N (ed): *International Catalogue of Arboviruses Including Certain Other Viruses of Vertebrates*, ed 3. San Antonio, Tex, American Society of Tropical Medicine and Hygiene, 1985.

64. *Annual Report*. East African Virus Research Institute, Entebbee, Uganda. July 1961-June 1962, pp 31–32.

65. Shore H: O'nyong-nyong fever: An epidemic viral disease in East Africa. III. Some clinical and epidemiological observations in the Northern Province of Uganda. *Trans R Soc Trop Med Hyg* 1961; 55:361–373.

66. Taylor RM, Hurlbut HS, Work TH, et al: Sindbis virus: A newly recognized arthropod-transmitted virus. *Am J Trop Med Hyg* 1955; 4:844–862.

67. *Annual Report of the East African Virus Research Institute*, July 1962–June 1963, p 9.

68. McIntosh BM, McGillivray GM, Dickinson DB, et al: Illness caused by Sindbis and West Nile viruses in South Africa. *S Afr Med J* 1964; 38:291–294.

69. Doherty RL, Bodey AS, Caren JS: Sindbis virus infection in Australia. *Med J Aust* 1969; 2:1016–1017.

70. *Catalogue of Arthropod-Borne Viruses of the World*. US Dept of Health, Education and Welfare publication No (CDC) 75–8301, 1975.

71. McIntosh BM, McGillivray GM, Dickinson DB, et al: Ecological studies on Sinbis and West Nile viruses in South Africa. IV. Infection in a wild avian population. *S Afr Med J* 1968; 33:105–112.

72. Anderson CR, Downs WG, Wattley GH, et al: Mayaro virus: A new human disease agent II. Isolation from blood of patients in Trinidad, BWI. *Am J Trop Med Hyg* 1957; 6:1012–1016.

73. Schmidt JR, Gadjusek DC, Schaeffer M, et al: Epidemic jungle fever among Okinawan colonists in the Bolivian rain forest. II. Isolation and characterization of Uruma virus, a newly recognized human pathogen. *Am J Trop Med Hyg* 1959; 8:479–487.

74. Causey PR, Maroja DM: Mayaro virus: A new human disease agent. III. Investigation of an epidemic of acute febrile illness on the River Guama in Para, Brazil, and isolation of Mayaro virus as causative agent. *Am J Trop Med Hyg* 1957; 6:1017–1023.

75. Theiler M, Downs WG: in *The Arthropod-Borne Viruses of Vertebrates*. New Haven, Conn, Yale University Press, 1973, pp 364–367.

76. Robinson DM, McManns AT, Cole FE Jr, et al: Inactivated Mayaro vaccine produced in human diploid cell culture. *Milit Med* 1976; 141:163–166.

77. Nimmo JR: An unusual epidemic. *Med J Aust* 1928; 1:549–550.

78. Doherty RL, Waitehead RH, Gorman BM, et al: The isolation of a third group A arbovirus in Australia, with preliminary observations on its relationship to epidemic polyarthritis. *Aust J Sci* 1963; 26:183–184.

79. Doherty RL: Arthropod-borne viruses in Australia, 1973–1976. *Aust J Exp Biol Med Sci* 1977; 55:103–130.

80. Cook IF (ed): Ross River virus. *Commun Dis Intell* 1988; 88:21–24.

81. Seglenieks Z, Moore BW: Epidemic polyarthritis in South Australia: Report of an outbreak in 1971. *Med J Aust* 1974; 2:552–556.

82. Symons MH: Biochemistry of Ross River virus. *Rep Queensland Inst Med Res* 1976; 31:26.

83. Woodroffe G, Marshall ID, Taylor WP: Antigenically distinct strains of Ross River virus from North Queensland and coastal New South Wales. *Aust J Exp Biol Med Sci* 1977; 55:79–87.

84. Doherty RL, Barrett EJ, Gorman BM, et al: Epidemic polyarthritis in eastern Australia 1959–1970. *Med J Aust* 1971; 1:5–8.

85. Anderson SG, French EL: An epidemic exanthem associated with polyarthritis in the Murray Valley, 1956. *Med J Aust* 1957; 2:113–117.

86. Doherty RL, Gorman BM, Whitehead RH, et al: Studies of epidemic polyarthritis: The significance of three group A arboviruses isolated from mosquitoes in Queensland. *Aust Ann Med* 1964; 13:322–327.

87. Aaskov JG, Ross PV, Harper JJ, et al: Isolation of Ross River virus from epidemic polyarthritis patients in Australia. *Aust J Exp Biol Med Sci* 1985; 63:587–597.

88. Lvov DK, Skvortsova TM, Kondrashina NG, et al: Etiology of Karelian fever, a new arbovirus infection. *Vopr Virusol* 1982; 6:690–692.

89. Skogh M, Espmark A: Ockelbo disease: Epidemic arthritis-exanthema syndrome in Sweden caused by Sindbis virus-like agent. *Lancet* 1982; 1:795–796.

90. Brummer-Korvenkontio M, Kuusisto P: Has western Finland been spared the ''Pogosta''? *Suomen Laakarilehti* 1981; 32:2606–2607.

91. Espmark A, Niklasson B: Ockelbo disease in Sweden: epidemiological, clinical, and virological data from the 1982 outbreak. *Am J Trop Med Hyg* 1984; 33:1203–1211.

92. Calisher CH, Meurman O, Brummer-Korvenkontio M, et al: Sensitive enzyme immunoassay for detecting immunoglobulin M antibodies to Sindbis virus and further evidence that Pogosta disease is caused by a western equine encephalitis complex virus. *J Clin Microbiol* 1985; 22:566–571.

93. Niklasson B, Espmark A, LeDuc JW, et al: Association of a Sindbis-like virus with Ockelbo disease in Sweden. *Am J Trop Med Hyg* 1984; 33:1212–1217.

94. Lvov DK, Berezina LK, Yakovlev BI, et al: Isolation of Karelian fever agent from *Aedes communis* mosquitoes. *Lancet* 1984; 2:399–400.

95. Lvov DK, Vladimertseva EA, Butenko AM, et al: Identity of Karelian fever and Ockelbo viruses determined by serum dilution-plaque reduction neutralization tests and oligonucleotide mapping. *Am J Trop Med Hyg* 1988; 39:607–610.

Rubella Virus

Catherine L. Lamprecht

Rubella (German measles) is a mild viral infection characterized by low-grade fever, lymphadenopathy, and exanthematous rash, most commonly observed among school-age children and susceptible young adults. Despite minimal morbidity and mortality, rubella infection during early pregnancy is often associated with severe physical defects in the developing fetus. In the aftermath of the worldwide rubella epidemic of 1964 to 1965, increased efforts were made to develop an effective vaccine. In 1969, the introduction of rubella vaccine and its rapid acceptance as a routine immunization for young children heralded a new epidemiologic era in which the incidence of rubella and congenital rubella decreased dramatically. Current controversies concerning rubella control involve diagnosis and management of suspected rubella during pregnancy, identification and immunization of susceptible adults, duration of immunity induced by vaccines, and management of rubella outbreaks.

HISTORICAL ASPECTS

Rubella was recognized as a specific entity in the early 1800s by German physicians who called it *Rötheln*.[1,2] Prior to that time, the disease had been confused with other exanthematous illnesses, notably measles and scarlet fever. Because of continued interest by German physicians into the nineteenth century, the disease also became known as "German measles." In 1866, the more euphonious name, "rubella," was proposed by the Scottish physician Henry Veale, who described 30 cases in the *Edinburgh Medical Journal*.[1-3]

By the early twentieth century, the symptomatology and clinical characteristics of rubella had been well described, although joint manifestations had received little attention.[1-3] The belief that rubella was a mild illness with no real importance was shattered in 1941 when Sir Norman Gregg, an Australian ophthalmologist, published his findings of congenital cataracts and heart defects in infants of mothers who had had rubella early in pregnancy.[4] Despite initial skepticism, confirmatory reports of congenital malformations following maternal rubella soon appeared from all parts of the world.[5-9] By 1947, a comprehensive summary of 30 papers included 521 cases of fetal deformities caused by rubella.[2]

The viral etiology of rubella had been suggested as early as 1938 by experimental transmission of disease to monkeys and humans via filtered throat washings.[3] Isolation of rubella virus in tissue culture was not accomplished until 1962 when two groups of investigators simultaneously reported their findings. Weller and Neva[10] from the Harvard School of Public Health used the subtle cytopathic effect (CPE) produced in human amnion cell cultures to identify the virus. Parkman, Buescher, and Artenstein[11] at the Walter Reed Army Institute of Research used the interference technique in which rubella-infected African green monkey kidney (GMK) cells are resistant to secondary infection and the CPE produced by another virus.

Just 2 years later, the worldwide epidemic of rubella peaked in the United States.[13, 14] Approximately 12 million cases of rubella occurred, resulting in an estimated 30,000 stillbirths and 20,000 deformed infants.[15] At a rubella symposium in May 1965,[12] the classic description of congenital rubella syndrome (CRS) was expanded to include thrombocytopenia, petechiae, pneumonitis, bone lesions, and encephalopathy in addition to the previously recognized cataracts, heart disease, deafness, and mental retardation.

These events spurred development of an effective vaccine and in 1969, just 7 years after isolation of the virus, three live attenuated rubella vaccines were licensed.[13] Rapid acceptance of routine rubella immunization of prepubertal children has resulted in the administration of over 123 million doses of vaccine and a 98% decrease in rubella activity in the United States.[16, 17] Currently, sporadic outbreaks of rubella are reported in hospitals,[18, 19] schools,[14, 20] offices,[21-24] and military camps.[25] Adults who missed both routine immunization as children and natural rubella infection remain susceptible to disease. Continued efforts to immunize both young children and susceptible adults will be needed to further decrease the incidence of rubella and congenital rubella.

THE VIRUS

Taxonomy

Rubella virus is a moderately large, spherical, RNA-containing virus. Currently, it is the only member of the *Rubivirus* genus in the *Togaviridae* family.[26] While there are physical and biologic similarities to the other members of the *Togaviradae* family (alphavirus, flavivirus, pestivirus), rubella has no invertebrate host and is serologically unrelated to other togaviruses. Rubella has only one major antigenic type, and man is its only known natural host.[27]

Morphology

Electron microscopic studies (Figure 25–1) have shown that the rubella virion is approximately 60 to 80 nm in diameter.[27-33] The electron-dense core is 30 nm in diameter. It contains a single strand of infectious RNA with a molecular weight of 3×10^6 daltons[27]; this is sufficient genetic information to code for 20 virus-specific proteins containing 150 amino acid residues each.[27, 33] The RNA genome, enclosed within a capsid, is surrounded by a lipid bilayer envelope which is essential to infectivity.[28, 29] Small spicules 5 to 6 nm in length can be seen projecting from the outer envelope; these contain hemagglutinin.[28, 29]

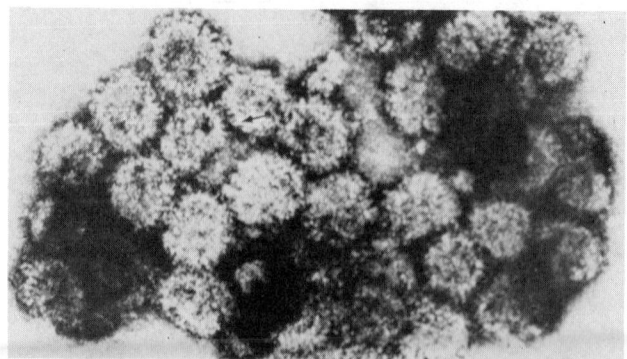

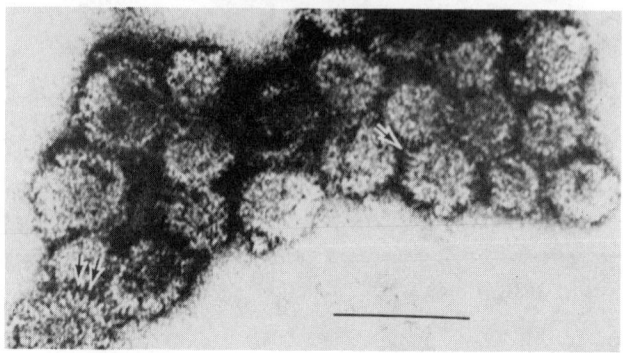

Figure 25–1. Rubella Virus. Particles associated with infectivity and hemagglutination; *arrows* point to surface spicules seen on some particles. Bar = 100 nm. (From Smith KO, Hobbins TE: Physical characteristics of rubella virus. *J Immunol* 1969; 102:1016–1023. Used by permission.)

Biologic Characteristics

Rubella virus is heat-liable. It is completely inactivated after 30 minutes at 56°C.[30-35] The virus is also unstable at room temperatures, exhibiting marked loss of infectivity after 24 hours at 37°C and 25°C.[30, 35-37] At 4°C, loss of infectivity is less rapid, with some virus surviving up to 1 week.[30, 36, 37] Similar instability is noted at normal refrigeration temperatures (−10 to −20°C),[30] but the virus can be maintained indefinitely at −60°C.[30] The addition of protein (1% serum or albumin) will stabilize the virus through several freeze-thaw cycles.

Infectivity of rubella virus is readily inactivated by ultraviolet irradiation, by pH extremes of less than 6.8 or more than 8.1, and by a variety of lipid-solubilizing agents: ether, chloroform, acetone, formalin, β-propiolactone, and liquid ethylene oxide.[30-37] Growth of rubella in tissue culture is inhibited by amantadine.[37]

Laboratory Hosts

Experimental rubella infections have been produced in primates and a variety of small laboratory animals.[3, 30, 34, 37] Despite viral replication and excretion in these experimental hosts, none developed a clinical illness or congenitally transmitted infection.

Growth in Tissue Culture

Rubella virus will grow in a variety of tissue culture cell types of both human and animal origin. Cultures of primary cells, cell strains, and cell lines are all susceptible.[30-32, 35] In most systems, adsorption of virus occurs within 90 minutes of inoculation. This is followed by a 12-hour eclipse period before cell-associated virus can be detected.[37] Extracellular virus appears shortly thereafter and both increase in titer similarly.[35-37] Peak viral production occurs 48 to 72 hours after inoculation.[36] Chronic infection and viral production without visible effect on cell morphology is typical of growth of rubella in most cell systems.[32, 35] The greatest viral yield is usually obtained from BHK-21 cells.[37]

Electron microscopic studies show that rubella virus replicates in the cell cytoplasm. The virion matures by budding into cytoplasmic vesicles or from the marginal plasma membrane, thus acquiring its outer envelope.[28, 31]

Growth of rubella virus in tissue culture can be detected either by CPE or by interference with the growth of another virus. Significant CPE is produced in only a few tissue culture cell types, notably RK-13 rabbit kidney, Vero, and human amnion cells.[10, 31, 32, 35] However, the CPE is not always clear, and additional passage of virus is frequently needed for accuracy. Therefore, for primary isolation of rubella from clinical specimens, the interference technique using GMK cells and an enterovirus is commonly used.[11, 31, 32, 34, 35] Specimens are inoculated onto primary GMK monolayers; after ten days, the cultures are challenged with a known inoculum of either echovirus type 11 or coxsackievirus A9. If rubella is present, the GMK cells will appear normal and will be resistant to growth and CPE of the enterovirus. The etiology of the rubella interference phenomenon is unknown. Interferon production by rubella-infected cells or another type of intracellular block have been postulated.[37]

Absolute identification of rubella requires specific neutralization of interference with rubella antiserum.[31, 32] Rubella may also be identified in tissue culture by measurement of specific viral antigens or by immunofluorescent staining techniques.[31-33, 37]

Viral Proteins and Antigens

Various structural proteins of the rubella virion have been isolated from virus grown in tissue culture. Complete characterization of the biology and function of these polypeptides has not yet been accomplished because of difficulties in growing virus stocks to high titer and in obtaining purified preparations.[3, 30-33, 38] Yet, a number of investigators[38-41] have identified three virus-specific polypeptides: E1, a glycopeptide with a molecular weight of 63,000; E2, a glycopeptide with a molecular weight of 47,000 to 54,000; and C, a nonglycosylated polypeptide with a molecular weight of 38,000. It is thought that E1 and E2 are components of the viral envelope and its spike proteins; E1 appears to be involved in hemagglutination. Polypeptide C is located inside the virion and is associated with the viral genome, forming the icosahedral capsid.

The three polypeptides are probably formed by proteolytic cleavage from a precursor molecule translated from a 24S subgenomic messenger RNA (mRNA), about one third of the total 40S genome.[39]

Rubella-infected tissue culture cells produce specific viral antigens as well as infectious virus which can be neutralized by specific antiserum. Viral antigens can be identified by hemagglutination, complement fixation, precipitation in agarose gel, platelet aggregation, and immunofluorescence.[3, 30-37, 42, 43]

Hemagglutinin (HA)

The hemagglutinating antigen is closely associated with the infectious viral core, and many of the treatments that destroy infectivity also inactivate HA.[32, 44, 45] The hemagglutinin is active at 4°C and 25°C, but not at 37°C.[44] Erythrocytes from the day-old chick, goose, and pigeon are agglutinated; red blood cells from the adult chicken, sheep, and human are not agglutinated. The inhibition of hemagglutination by serum antibodies to rubella forms the basis for the most commonly used serologic test, the hemagglutination-inhibition (HI) test.[30, 42, 44]

Complement-Fixing (CF) Antigens

Two distinct cell-associated CF antigens have been identified from rubella virus cultures.[30, 36, 43, 46-48] The large-particle antigen is sedimentable with ultracentrifugation and is associated with the infectious virus.[46, 48] This antigen is produced early in the infectious process and is destroyed by ether.[47, 48] The smaller, soluble CF antigen will pass through a 10-mμ filter and is not sedimented by ultracentrifugation.[43, 47, 48]

Precipitating Antigens

Two small-particle soluble antigens have been detected by immunodiffusion.[48, 49] Designated theta and iota, they are incompletely characterized but appear to be structural virion proteins.[47, 50, 51] Interestingly, anti-theta and anti-iota antibodies are produced regularly after natural rubella infection, but only rarely after immunization with some vaccines, and may be related to immunity from reinfection.[51, 52]

Serologic Testing

Measurement of serum antibodies to rubella virus can be performed for diagnosis of a rash illness or for assessment of immunity status. In either case, a number of serologic tests are available to measure antibodies to different viral antigens. The more common methods include enzyme-linked immunosorbent assay (ELISA), latex agglutination (LA), hemagglutination inhibition (HI), complement fixation (CF), passive hemagglutination (PHA), and fluorescence immunoassay (FIA). Commercially prepared kits for rubella antibody testing frequently make use of these methods.[53] Less common techniques used in some research laboratories include neutralization, radioimmunodiffusion, precipitation, and platelet aggregation.[31, 32]

Rubella neutralizing antibodies are considered to be protective and are most closely correlated with immunity.[30, 32, 54, 55] The methodology involves neutralization of the interference phenomenon and is quite cumbersome, costly, and slow. Development and persistence of neutralizing antibody is closely parallel to HI, ELISA, FIA, and LA antibodies, which are technically easier tests.[31, 32, 53]

Measurement of CF antibodies is not difficult, but is rarely performed. CF antibodies appear about a week later than HI antibody, wane over the years, and eventually become undetectable. Thus, CF tests are unreliable in assessing rubella immunity from past infection.[54, 55]

Until recently, the HI test was the most commonly used serologic test for rubella antibody.[31, 32, 44, 53-55] It is highly specific and reproducible when test conditions are carefully controlled.[55, 56] Nonspecific inhibitors found in the β-lipoprotein fraction of most sera must be removed with kaolin or heparin-manganous chloride treatment before testing. Unfortunately, this pretreatment can also remove some of the antibody, producing false-negative results, and incomplete removal of β-lipoproteins can lead to false-positive results.[31, 32, 55] In general, when rubella antibodies are absent at the lowest dilution tested after pretreating the serum (usually 1:8 or 1:10), the patient should be assumed to be susceptible to infection. After infection, rubella HI antibodies appear quickly and probably persist for life. Thus, the HI test is highly sensitive for both serodiagnosis and assessment of immunity from previous infection or vaccination.[53–55]

Newer methods, including ELISA, LA, PHA, and FIA are technically easier to perform and are all good alternatives to HI for rubella immune status testing.[53–60] Antibody titers obtained by ELISA testing are related to, but severalfold higher than, HI antibody titers.[57–60] Sera which have low or equivocal levels of HI antibody are frequently positive by more sensitive ELISA methods.[57] However, the specificity and protective efficacy of such low levels of rubella antibody have not been verified.[53, 56] Either ELISA or FIA can be used for immune screening or for confirming the diagnosis of recent rubella infection; LA and PHA are used only for determination of rubella immunity.

Measurement of IgM-specific rubella antibody can be performed for diagnosis of primary rubella infection. Rubella-IgM antibodies can be detected by ELISA or FIA methods, for which commercial kits are available.

EPIDEMIOLOGY

Morbidity Data

Rubella and congenital rubella became nationally reportable diseases in the United States in 1966.[14, 20, 61] Prior to that year, information on the incidence of rubella came from several states which had maintained rubella surveillance for many years through mandatory reporting.[14, 61] However, official statistics give an incomplete picture of the incidence of rubella, as underreporting is common. This occurs for several reasons.[62–64] Rubella is usually a mild or asymptomatic infection, and many cases are not seen by physicians. In addition, the clinical features of rubella are not highly specific, and sporadic cases are frequently misdiagnosed. Finally, failure to report even diagnosed cases is common for many diseases, especially mild illnesses like rubella. It is estimated that at most one of five or ten clinical cases is reported; and for each overt case of rubella, there is at least one subclinical infection which is equally important epidemiologically. It is likely that the proportion of cases that have gone unreported has not varied markedly from one time to another. Therefore, the data on reported cases are probably useful to show patterns and secular trends of the disease.

Incidence and Epidemic Behavior

The incidence of rubella from 1928 to 1983 in ten selected areas of the United States is shown in Figure 25–2.[17] Periods of increased incidence tend to occur at 6- to 9-year intervals, with major epidemics at intervals of 10 to 30 years.[14, 61–64] After the extensive rubella epidemic in 1964, when nearly 500,000 cases were reported throughout the country, a subsequent outbreak was predicted to occur between 1970 and 1973.[64]

However, the characteristic epidemic cycle of rubella in the United States was interrupted by the introduction of live attenuated rubella vaccine in 1969.[14, 61] Since then, there have been no large nationwide outbreaks of rubella, although endemic disease and localized epidemics of rubella continue to occur, especially among unimmunized older children and young adults. In 1970, 56,552 cases of rubella were reported; this decreased to approximately 10,000 to 20,000 cases annually between 1974 and 1978.[14] A record low number of 251 rubella cases was reported in 1988.[65]

The epidemiologic pattern of extensive outbreaks of rubella after long intervals of decreased incidence has not been fully explained. In the United States, ongoing endemic rubella plus regularly occurring epidemics have succeeded in immunizing 80% to 85% of the population.[14, 61, 62] But rubella virus is still able to circulate and cause disease among the remaining susceptibles in a highly immune population.[66, 67] Individual host factors may be involved, as some people appear more likely to spread disease than others.[68] However, the factors involved in the development of a major worldwide rubella epidemic as occurred in 1962 to 1965 are still unknown. Neither antigenic shifts nor changes in virulence have been detected among different viral isolates.

Temporal Pattern

Rubella occurs in late winter and early spring months in temperate climates. The number of reported cases begins to rise in January, and peaks during March, April, and May.[14, 65] However, sporadic cases are reported in all months of the year in urban areas. This seasonal pattern occurs in years of high as well as low incidence.[64]

Age

Before 1969, rubella was primarily a disease of young, school-age children.[14, 62–64] Significant numbers of cases also were reported among adolescents, reflecting the lower communicability of rubella as compared to measles or chickenpox.[14] Table 25–1 compares age-specific incidence rates from three areas for several representative time periods when rubella was not epidemic in the United States.[14] In 1966 to 1968, immediately prior to availability of rubella vaccine, children aged 5 to 9 years had the highest attack rate—101.3 cases per 100,000 population. Fully 77% of cases occurred in children less than 14 years of age. By contrast, in 1975 to 1977 the 15- to 19-year-olds had the highest incidence of rubella, and 76% of cases occurred in people over 15 years of age. Soon thereafter, increased efforts were made to effectively vaccinate susceptible adolescents and adults. Immunization requirements for school entry were enforced and many colleges and hospitals began requiring proof of rubella immunity. As a result, by 1981–1983, there were decreased cases of reported rubella in all age groups, and people over 15 years of age accounted for 37% of cases.[16]

Antibody prevalence surveys conducted prior to 1969 have shown a similar age-specific rubella attack rate. A 1968 study of 1143 sera from Tampa, Florida, found that the incidence of seropositivity was 35% among 5- to 9-year-old children, 59% among 10- to 14-year-olds, and 65% in those between 15 and 19.[64] Other studies have also shown the rapid acquisition of rubella antibody during the school-age years.[69] Among adults over 20 years of age, 80% to 85% possessed rubella antibody.[61–64, 69, 70] Currently, serologic studies have shown little change in rubella immunity among

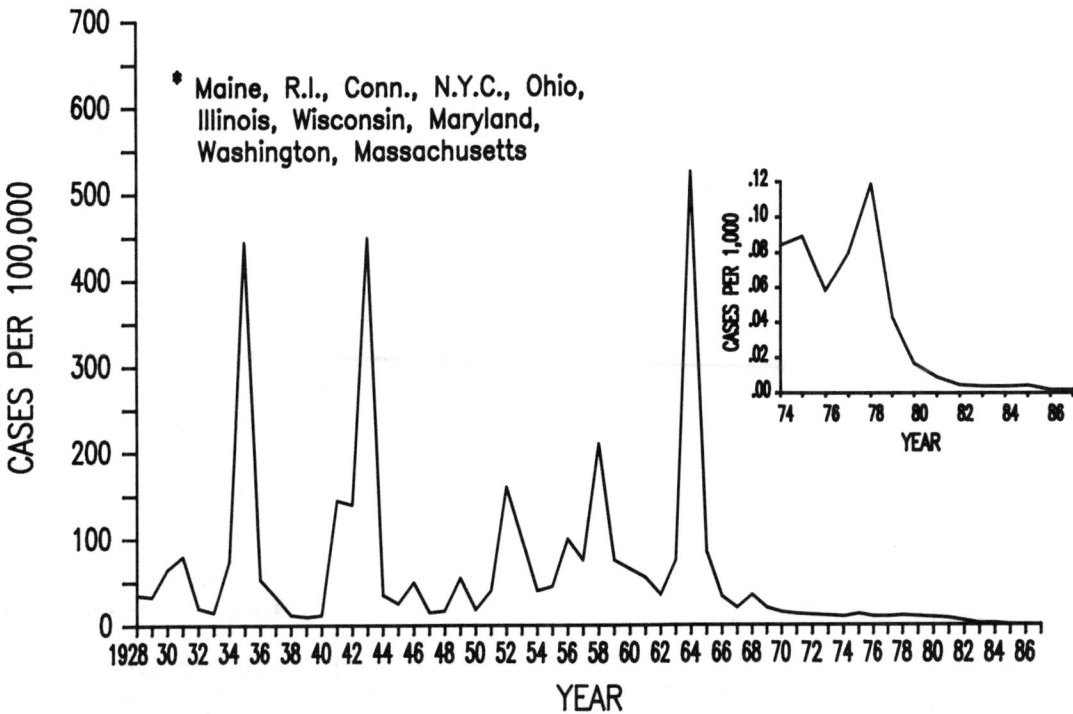

Figure 25–2. Rubella incidence in 10 selected areas (Maine, Rhode Island, Connecticut, New York City, Ohio, Illinois, Wisconsin, Maryland, and Massachusetts) of the United States, 1928–1987. (Data from Centers for Disease Control.[16])

adult women; approximately, 15% to 20% still remain susceptible to rubella.[14, 71]

Geographic Distribution

Rubella has a worldwide distribution, but there is a marked variation in the incidence of the disease from country to country.[72] The epidemiologic pattern of endemic disease with sporadic epidemics has been recognized in Canada, Great Britain, Australia, and most European countries. Serologic surveys in these countries indicate that usually at least 80% of adult women are immune to rubella.[72]

By contrast, some island populations have a low endemic incidence of rubella, and fewer women of childbearing age have rubella antibodies.[62, 72–75] In Hawaii, for example, Halstead et al found susceptibility rates of 25% to 50% among adolescents and adults from different islands.[73] Another study showed more than 50% of pregnant Hawaiian women to be susceptible to rubella.[74] A 1967 World Health Organization survey on the Caribbean islands of Jamaica and Trinidad found rubella antibodies in 52% and 47% of young adults, respectively.[72]

Taiwan has a completely different situation. Although it is a densely populated, cosmopolitan island, rubella is not endemic

Table 25–1

Age Distribution and Incidence of Reported Rubella Cases—Massachusetts, New York City, and Illinois, 1966–1968, 1975–1977, and 1981–1983*

Age Group (yr)	1966–1968		1975–1977		1981–1983	
	Number (%)	Rate	Number (%)	Rate	Number (%)	Rate
<5	1294(21.6)	63.3	160(9.8)	9.8	41(26.6)	2.5
5–9	2304(38.5)	101.3	233(14.2)	11.6	37(24.0)	2.2
10–14	1020(17.0)	44.0	229(13.9)	11.2	18(11.6)	0.9
15–19	759(12.7)	35.7	634(38.7)	27.4	14(9.1)	0.6
≥20	601(10.2)	3.7	384(23.4)	2.3	44(28.6)	0.3
Total	5987(100.0)	24.3	1640(100.0)	6.7	154(99.9)	0.6

*Reported rubella cases per 100,000 population; cases of unknown age are excluded.
The average annual figures are shown over the 3-year period.
Data from Centers for Disease Control.[17]

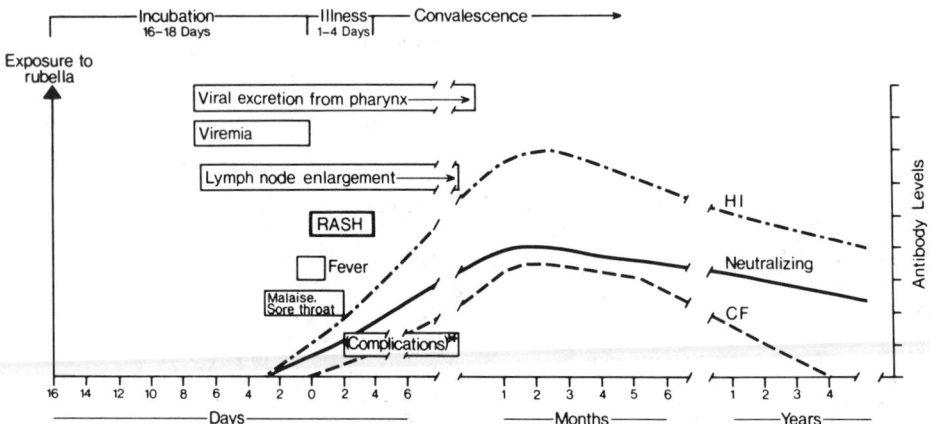

Figure 25–3. Pathophysiologic events in postnatally acquired rubella virus infection. (*Possible complications include arthralgia and/or arthritis, thrombocytopenic purpura, and encephalitis.) HI = hemagglutination inhibition; CF = complement fixation.

there.[62, 77] Instead, large epidemics occur at 10- to 13-year intervals and infect 80% to 90% of the school children. Few cases occur among adults, as over 95% possess rubella antibody.[77] Although the epidemiology of rubella is clearly different among various island populations, there are no explanations for these differences.

POSTNATALLY ACQUIRED RUBELLA

Rubella acquired after birth is usually a mild, self-limited illness; most children would continue their normal activities but for the rash. Among adults, a somewhat more severe disease may occur and necessitate time off from work.[78] The exanthematous rash is the most frequent and distinctive clinical feature of rubella, and often signals the onset of disease in children. However, in some cases, rash may be so faint as to be overlooked; in other cases, rubella infection occurs without rash and is completely inapparent.[78, 79] About 50% of rubella infections have been found to be inapparent in most studies.[78, 80] The ratio of subclinical to clinical infections probably varies somewhat with factors such as size of viral inoculum, host factors, and the sensitivity of the virologic and serologic procedures used for the detection of inapparent infections.[78]

Transmission

The virus is present in the oropharynx of infected individuals and is probably transmitted via respiratory secretions.[78, 81] Because the fragile virus is inactivated by heat or drying, close personal contact is necessary for transmission. Under experimental conditions, a single brief contact with an infected child produced rubella in 20% of susceptible children, while prolonged daily contact resulted in disease in 90% to 100% of susceptibles.[78] This parallels the high attack rates noted among families and closed groups, as in institutions and the military.

Pathogenesis

Following exposure and inoculation of virus into the nasopharynx, primary replication begins in respiratory epithelial cells and possibly in local lymphoid tissue. Viral production remains undetectable for several days until prolonged viremia results in widespread viral dissemination (Figure 25–3). Rubella virus has been variably isolated from many body sites, including serum,[78, 81] lymphocytes,[82] urine,[81] nasopharynx,[78, 83] stool,[78] conjunctivae, synovial fluid, uterine cervix, and lymph nodes. High titers of virus are regularly isolated from pharyngeal swabs obtained within two days of onset of rash.[78, 81] Prolonged respiratory shedding, beginning 1 week before the rash and lasting as long as 21 days afterward, is common (see Figure 25–3). Viremia usually ends with appearance of the rash and development of neutralizing antibody.[78] The incubation period from exposure to the first signs of illness is usually 16 to 18 days, with a range of 14 to 21 days.

Clinical Manifestations

Although rubella is a systemic infection, there are usually minimal constitutional symptoms.[84] Children typically experience lymphadenopathy and low-grade fever with the appearance of the rash. Adolescents and adults may report a mild prodrome of headache, malaise, and anorexia before the onset of rash. Complaints of sore throat, cough, coryza, eye pain, and conjunctivitis occasionally accompany more severe cases.[81, 82, 85]

Rash

The exanthematous rash is variable in appearance. Pale-pink to red macules, maculopapules, a faint pink eruption, or erythematous blush have all been described.[78, 81–84] Pruritis is occasionally reported. The rash is usually noted first on the face and neck; it spreads rapidly to the trunk, and reaches the extremities after one to two days.[79] The individual macules may be discrete at the onset, coalescing later into a confluent blush. The total duration of the rash is usually one to four days (see Figure 25–3).[78]

The etiology of the rash is unclear. Heggie[86] was able to isolate rubella virus from explant cultures of skin biopsy specimens of macules as well as uninvolved skin. One patient who excreted rubella from the nasopharynx but never developed a rash with his infection also had virus isolated from a skin biopsy specimen. Furthermore, detection of serum antibody and termination of viremia frequently coincide with appearance of the rash and suggest an antigen-antibody complex-mediated vasculitis.

The rash of rubella is not particularly distinctive in appearance and may appear similar to a heat rash, roseola, erythema infectiosum, or an enteroviral rash. However, it is somewhat more easily distinguished from the darker, purple-red lesions of rubeola and the confluent, papular rash of scarlet fever.

Lymphadenopathy

Lymph node enlargement is a frequent manifestation of rubella infection. It has been observed in 80% of young children with experimentally induced rubella[78] and in 50% to 100% of adolescents infected during rubella outbreaks.[85, 87, 88] Lymphadenopathy may be present even in the absence of rash.[78–80] Nodal enlargement often begins as long as a week before the rash (see Figure 25–3), but swelling and/or tenderness are most prominent with the appearance of the exanthem.[89] Posterior auricular, suboccipital, and cervical lymph nodes are most prominently involved.[78, 80, 81] In some cases, generalized lymphadenopathy and/or splenomegaly is noted.[80] The extent and duration of lymph node involvement is quite variable. Tenderness, if present, usually subsides rapidly, but swelling may persist for several weeks.[79]

Fever

Low-grade fever may be seen in about half of the children with rubella. It occurs most commonly with the onset of rash and subsides within 24 hours.[79] Temperatures are usually in the range of 99 to 101.5°F (37.2–38.5°C), but higher fevers to 104°F (40°C), are occasionally reported.[80] Among adolescents and adults, mild fever may be more common; elevated temperatures may be noted during the prodromal period and last for up to a week.[81]

Blood Profile

The complete blood count (CBC) of individuals with acquired rubella is variable and nonspecific. Mild leukopenia may be noted for four to five days after the rash appears.[79, 81] Transiently decreased platelet counts without purpura have been noted in a few cases when sequential platelet counts have been performed.

Complications

With most cases of rubella, recovery is rapid and uneventful. However, arthralgias and/or arthritis, thrombocytopenic purpura, and encephalitis are complications occasionally seen during convalescence from acute rubella. Rare cases of hemolytic anemia[90] and myocarditis[91, 92] have been reported.

Joint Involvement

The incidence of joint pain in rubella varies among different studies.[75, 87, 88, 93] Usually, adolescents and adults have more complaints of arthritis or arthralgia than children, and women are more frequently affected than men.[75, 87, 88] In some studies, nearly half of older individuals with rubella reported pain and/or stiffness of the joints[75, 76] Most frequently affected are the proximal interphalangeal and metacarpophalangeal joints.[94, 95] Involvement of wrists, elbows, knees, and ankles is also common.

Acute polyarthritis involving the same joints occurs primarily in postpubertal women.[78, 83, 84] Joint pain and swelling appear coincident with or a few days after appearance of the rash. Several women with tenosynovitis and carpal tunnel syndrome have been reported.[96, 97] Objective findings range from mild to severe pain

along with erythema, warmth, and tenderness; effusions may be noted in the larger joints. Synovial fluid from affected joints is highly viscous, with an increased protein level and mild to moderate pleocytosis;[96] rubella virus has occasionally been isolated from such fluid.[97] Aspirin produces little objective or subjective relief. Fortunately, most rubella-associated acute polyarthritis is benign and self-limited. The majority of joint symptoms resolve within a few days to weeks and leave no residual joint deformity. However, some adults have experienced prolonged or recurrent arthropathy lasting over 18 months postinfection.[76]

The etiology of arthritis in acquired rubella is unclear. Viral invasion of the joint space or an antigen-antibody-mediated immune response have been postulated but not proved. The arthritis of rubella may resemble the early stages of rheumatoid arthritis; the distribution of joint involvement is similar, and latex fixation tests are occasionally positive.[94, 95] Also, rubella virus has been isolated from lymphoreticular cells in seven of 19 children with either juvenile rheumatoid arthritis or seronegative spondyloarthritis, many of whom had received HPV$_{77}$DE$_5$ rubella vaccine in the remote past.[98] While rubella virus may be an etiologic agent in some cases of chronic joint disease, further investigations are needed.

Thrombocytopenic Purpura

Decreased platelet counts (<150,000/μL) without purpura may be a frequent occurrence in acquired rubella but severe thrombocytopenia with hemorrhagic symptoms is quite rare.[78, 99, 100] In most cases, epistaxis, gingival bleeding, and spontaneous bruising are noticed several days after appearance of the rubella rash.[99–101] Occasionally, acute idiopathic thrombocytopenic purpura is the only sign of rubella, occurring after clinically inapparent infection.[101–103] Platelet counts range between 20,000 and 50,000 per microliter, but may be as low as 4000 per microliter. Although hemorrhagic symptoms are often severe, splenectomy is not indicated,[99, 101] and treatment is mainly supportive. Spontaneous and complete recovery typically occurs within a few weeks to months.[99, 100]

The mechanism for the production of thrombocytopenia is unknown. Direct viral invasion of the marrow may result in decreased platelet production.[99–101] Alternatively, shortened life span of platelets, mediated by antiplatelet antibodies, may be triggered by the acute infection.[101]

Encephalitis

The incidence of encephalitis or meningoencephalitis following acquired rubella is estimated to be between 1 in 4000 and 1 in 6000 cases.[104–106] However, since rubella without rash is quite common, some cases of acute viral encephalitis of unknown etiology may be due to rubella virus. Pathogenesis of rubella-induced neurologic complications is unclear. It is possible that actual viral invasion of brain tissue occurs or that the encephalopathy is a response to unknown factors secondary to the presence of virus elsewhere.[104–106]

Characteristically, abrupt onset of headache, lethargy, irritability, and stiff neck is noted one to six days after the appearance of the rubella exanthem.[104–107] Rarely, neurologic changes may precede the rash. Fever, convulsions, and changes in level of consciousness may follow, but the disease is quite variable.[104–106] Cerebrospinal fluid findings include mild pleocytosis (10–300 cells/μL, usually lymphocytes), normal or slightly elevated glucose level, and increased protein (18–75 mg/100 mL).[104–106] Electroencephalography (EEG) reveals generalized dysrhythmia and slowing.[104, 107] Good supportive therapy with control of seizures, fever, and increased intracranial pressure is essential.[104–106] Steroid therapy may be indicated in severe cases.

Whether a mild or severe clinical course occurs, the duration of encephalitis is usually brief. A few fatal cases have been reported, but complete recovery with no permanent sequelae is more common.[104–108] A long-term follow-up study of seven survivors of rubella encephalitis showed only minor neurologic and EEG abnormalities; no defects in social adjustment or intellectual functioning were found.[109]

Immunologic Responses

Acquired rubella infection results in rapid development of serum antibody (see Figure 25–3). Within a few days after appearance of the rash, antirubella antibody is detectable by a variety of methods: neutralization, HI, ELISA, LA, or FIA tests. These antibodies are quite similar in pattern of development and persistence.[31, 32, 44, 53–55, 110, 111] The HI test has been considered the reference standard.[53]

Serum specimens obtained prior to rubella infection have no HI antibody (titer <1:8). Low levels of HI antibody may be detected on the first day of illness. HI titers rise rapidly and reach maximum levels within 2 to 4 weeks.[55] Although there is considerable variation among individuals in peak levels of antibody, HI titers usually remain high for several months, then decrease gradually over a year's time and persist for life.[31, 32, 54, 55, 110, 111] HI titers obtained 10 to 20 years after rubella infection are about eightfold lower than peak HI titers shortly after infection.[54] Rossier et al[112] found significant levels of rubella HI antibody among cloistered nuns who had had no intercurrent rubella infection for 10 to 53 years. Development of serum neutralizing and immunofluorescent antibodies (IFA) generally parallels the HI antibody response, but titers are four- to 16-fold lower than HI titers.[54, 55] CF antibodies develop more slowly, appearing 1 to 2 weeks after onset of illness; maximal titers are found 1 to 2 months later.[54, 55] CF antibodies decline gradually to undetectable levels 4 to 5 years after infection.[54]

Rubella antibodies may also be measured by ELISA.[57–60] Using this method, antirubella antibodies develop early after infection, rise rapidly, and persist at high titers.[58–60] There is excellent correlation between ELISA and HI antibodies, although titers tend to be two- to 16-fold higher by ELISA.[58] Furthermore, the greater sensitivity of ELISA allows early detection of low levels of antibody and acute rises in titer.

Acquired rubella infection is characterized by an initial response in IgM-specific antibody followed by a rise in IgG antibody.[113–115] In general, IgM antibody increases rapidly for 2 weeks and then gradually disappears 6 to 8 weeks after acute illness. Local IgA nasal antibodies are also produced in response to rubella virus infection.[115]

Cell-mediated immunity (CMI) to rubella virus regularly develops after infection. In vitro lymphocyte cultures from individuals who have previously had rubella demonstrate rubella-specific responses by interferon production, blast transformation, and migration inhibition factor production.[112, 115, 117] CMI responses are lifelong.

CONGENITAL RUBELLA

Sir Normal Gregg's initial report in 1941[4] described congenital cataracts, heart defects, and low birth weight among 78 infants born after maternal rubella during early pregnancy. Subsequent studies confirmed these findings and added deafness and mental retardation to the definition of congenital rubella syndrome (CRS).[2, 3, 5–9] After the extensive epidemic in 1964, study of hundreds of infants with CRS led to an understanding of an "expanded congenital rubella syndrome." Newly recognized defects were principally signs of ongoing, chronic viral infection—thrombocytopenia, purpura, hepatosplenomegaly, pneumonitis, bone lesions, and encephalitis.[13]

Incidence

The incidence of rubella during pregnancy and of CRS is difficult to determine. In a study of 30,000 pregnancies during the nonepidemic years 1959 to 1964, the Collaborative Perinatal Research Study found four to eight cases of clinical rubella per 10,000 women.[118] By contrast, 6000 pregnancies were under surveillance as rubella became epidemic in early 1964; the incidence of rubella during pregnancy increased to 200 cases per 10,000 women.[119] Obviously, the risk of infection with rubella virus during pregnancy is related both to individual susceptibility as well as to the risk of viral contact.

Since 1966, CRS has been a nationally reportable disease.[14] Cases reported to the Centers for Disease Control (CDC) are reviewed for diagnostic accuracy and then collected in the National Congenital Rubella Syndrome Registry (NCRSR) established in 1969. Based on clinical and laboratory information, reported cases are classified into six clinical categories: CRS Confirmed, CRS Compatible, Congenital Rubella Infection Only, Stillbirths, and not CRS. Children diagnosed later in infancy are included in the registry by date of birth.

Since this is a passive reporting system, the number of cases submitted may reflect interest in the disease, and underreporting is probably common. For example, after a recent rubella outbreak in Chicago, 17 infants with CRS were reported to public health authorities, but 14 other infants with CRS were later identified using active surveillance methods, including multiple physician contacts, hospital record searches, and review of laboratory results.[120]

The major decrease in incidence of CRS occurred between 1969 and 1971 (Table 25–2). During the 1970s, there were approximately 30 to 40 cases of CRS reported each year. The outbreak of rubella in Chicago in 1978[120] was responsible for over half of the 57 infants with CRS reported in 1979. Further decreases in the incidence of CRS occurred between 1980 and 1985, when only two cases were reported. However, 12 children with CRS were born in 1986, eight in New York City after a widespread rubella outbreak there.[24]

Pathogenesis

Transmission of rubella virus to the fetus occurs by hematogenous spread during maternal viremia.[121-123] Both clinically apparent illness and subclinical primary infections are accompanied by viremia and may result in fetal infection.[121, 123] Approximately half of the mothers of infants with CRS report a rash illness during pregnancy.[120, 121] Rubella virus has also been isolated from the maternal genital tract, but ascending infection of the fetus via this route has not been proved.

Infection of the placenta occurs during the period of maternal viremia and usually persists for some time.[123-126] Rubella virus has been recovered from placenta and fetal tissues after therapeutic abortion several weeks after maternal infection. Kay et al[126] were able to isolate virus from the products of conception 18 weeks after maternal rubella.

The ongoing placental infection is a continuous source of viral spread to the fetus. Histologic studies of rubella-infected placentas have shown scattered inflammatory foci in chorionic tissues. The most frequent lesions involve necrosis and fragmentation of endothelial cells of villous capillaries.[123, 127] Small emboli of infected cells may break off and disseminate virus widely throughout fetal tissues.

The pathogenesis of rubella-induced fetal damage is not clearly understood. It is postulated that cell death, changes in rate of cell growth, or both produce congenital malformations of developing organs. In vitro studies have shown that cells infected with rubella virus have decreased mitotic activity;[122, 123] this could account for the generally smaller size of infants with CRS. Alternatively, direct viral damage to fetal blood vessels could disrupt blood supply to developing structures, indirectly resulting in structural defects. Clearly, though, the time of fetal infection is crucial to subsequent teratologic events.

Fetal Effects

The clinical manifestations of rubella infection in utero are varied and unpredictable. Spontaneous abortion, stillbirth, livebirth of a mildly or severely affected infant, and normal-appearing infants are all part of the spectrum of congenital rubella.

Table 25–2
Number of cases of Congenital Rubella Reported to the National Congenital Rubella Syndrome Registry (NCRSR)—United States, 1969–1988

Year of Birth	Cases*	Year of Birth	Cases*
1969	62	1979	57
1970	67	1980	14
1971	44	1981	10
1972	32	1982	12
1973	30	1983	7
1974	22	1984	2
1975	32	1985	2
1976	22	1986	12
1977	29	1987	3
1978	30	1988	1

*Confirmed and compatible cases only. Data are provisional because of delayed reporting.
Data from Centers for Disease Control[65]

The risk of anatomical defects after maternal rubella is greatest during the first trimester of pregnancy, when most fetal organ differentiation and development take place. Viral infection at that time is highly likely to result in faulty organogenesis and multiple, severe congenital malformations. In a review of eight prospective studies published between 1953 and 1961, Sallomi[128] estimated the risk of major congenital anomalies to be 61% when rubella occurred during weeks 1 to 4 of gestation, 26% in weeks 5 to 8, and 8% in weeks 9 to 12. Sheridan[129] found a similar risk of defects among 160 children born after rubella infections in the first trimester of pregnancy; 26%, 42%, and 34% were abnormal after maternal infection during the first, second, or third month of pregnancy, respectively. Among a group of 218 infants born after first-trimester maternal rubella, Peckham[130] found that 58% had major defects detected by age 6 to 8 years.

Infection later in pregnancy is less likely to cause severe congenital defects.[119, 128, 129, 131, 132] Single-organ abnormalities or more subtle defects that are not readily apparent at birth are more common. Sheridan[129] found the risk of abnormality to be 20% after rubella infection during the fourth month of gestation; only two of 13 abnormalities were classified as severe. Hardy et al[131] followed 22 children born after second-trimester rubella. Evaluation at age 3 to 4 years showed that 15 children were abnormal, and ten of them had problems with hearing loss and speech.

Recently, Munro et al[133] reviewed the records of 422 children with CRS. Among 106 children born after laboratory-proven maternal rubella, all infants whose mothers were infected before 7 weeks' gestation had defects, while all infants born to women infected after the 17th week were normal. However, among 316 children whose mothers had rubella which was not laboratory-confirmed, defects followed infection reported between 2 and 33 weeks of gestation. These differences underscore the importance of laboratory confirmation of possible rubella during pregnancy.

Clinical Findings

Rubella virus produces widespread fetal infection and virtually any organ system can be affected. Defects may be single or multiple, transient, progressive, or permanent. The frequency of some of the major manifestations of congenital rubella is shown in Table 25–3.

Differences in methods of patient selection and length of follow-up may account for some of the differences among the five studies. Overall, low birth weight was reported in approximately 50% of newborns; 22% to 50% had thrombocytopenic purpura. Eye defects occurred in 50% to 90%, heart disease in 37% to 86%, and hearing loss in 57% to 76% of infants. Varying degrees of psychomotor retardation were found in 24% to 40%.

In general, types of congenital defects are related to gestational age at the time of maternal rubella.[129, 132, 133, 136] Ueda et al[136] correlated physical defects in 55 infants with gestational age at the time of maternal rash; cataracts followed infection on gestational days 26 to 57, heart disease on days 25 to 93, and deafness on days 16 to 131.

Mortality

The mortality rate of infants with CRS is high in the first year of life, ranging from 10% to 14% (see Table 25–3). Severely

Table 25–3
Incidence of Major Congenital Malformations After First-Trimester Rubella in Five Studies

Study	Cooper et al (1969)[132]	Plotkin et al (1967)[134]	Forrest and Menser (1970)[135]	Horstman et al (1965)[124]	Lamprecht et al (1981)[120]
Number	376	92	41	36	31
Age at study	0–4 yr	6–12 mo	School-Age	0–1 yr	0–1 yr
	(%)	(%)	(%)	(%)	(%)
Ocular defects	71	53	90	50	81
Cardiac defects	48	57	37	86	74
Hearing loss	67	51	76	—	68*
Birth weight <2500 g	NS	47	41	50	61
Failure to thrive	NS	28	32	NS	NS
Thrombocytopenic purpura	22	NS	NS	50	33
Retardation	40	42	24	NS	NS
Mortality in first year	16	NS	NS	14	10

NS = not studied.
* 16 of 31 patients tested.

affected infants with low birth weight and multiple defects have the highest mortality.[119, 122, 124, 130, 134, 138, 139, 141, 142]

Growth Retardation

One of the most frequently recognized manifestations of congenital rubella at birth is decreased body weight. At least 50% of affected infants weigh less than 2500 g despite normal gestational age. Low birth weight is usually seen in association with other anatomical defects of CRS and rarely occurs as an isolated finding. Postnatal growth failure may follow feeding problems and poor weight gain is often noted within the first month of life. Severe failure to thrive occurs among the most severely affected infants. Other children have a normal postnatal growth pattern but remain proportionately small. Among adolescents and young adults with CRS, the degree of growth failure is closely correlated with the magnitude of cognitive defects.[140]

Cardiovascular Defects[122, 124, 130–136, 138, 139, 142, 143]

Most cardiac malformations associated with congenital rubella are of the acyanotic type. Many are not detected at birth, but become evident when a heart murmur is noted later in infancy. Patent ductus arteriosus (PDA) is the most common cardiac lesion. Surgical ligation of the ductus may be necessary when severe congestive heart failure is found. PDA can occur alone or in combination with other cardiac defects.

Pulmonary artery lesions are the second most common cardiovascular defect. Diffuse hypoplasia and stenosis of the main pulmonary artery or its peripheral branches frequently occurs with a PDA. In a study of 37 infants with CRS, Hastreiter et al[144] found pulmonary artery lesions and PDA in 28 infants, isolated pulmonary lesions in six, and multiple, complex cardiac lesions in three.

Septal defects, coarctation of the aorta, and aortic stenosis are less frequent malformations after in utero rubella infection. Myocarditis manifested by electrocardiographic abnormalities has been reported in a few infants.[142] Histologic study of two infants who died showed extensive myocardial necrosis in the absence of an inflammatory response.

Ocular Defects[122, 124, 130–136, 138, 139, 141, 142, 145, 146]

Cataracts, either unilateral or bilateral, are the most common ocular consequences of congenital rubella. The pearly white cataracts typically have a dense central opacity surrounded by a rim of more normal capsule and cortex. In most cases, cataracts are noted at birth, but occasionally they develop later in the first few months of life. Microphthalmia and microcornea are often associated with cataracts and are more obvious when the lesions are unilateral. Early surgical removal of cataracts is necessary to preserve vision. However, the combination of cataract plus microphthalmia typically portends poor visual acuity.

Congenital glaucoma is less common and occurs in about 5% of infants with CRS. Corneal clouding, a benign condition reflecting corneal edema, is occasionally noted in the newborn period. This is a transient finding, but must be differentiated from glaucoma. A characteristic pigmentary retinopathy, consisting of "salt and pepper" lesions is a frequent finding. These areas of focal degeneration and absent pigmentation do not interfere with vision. The retinopathy may be progressive during childhood and of diagnostic significance in older children.

Hearing Deficits[120, 122, 129–136, 147, 148]

Sensorineural deafness may occur after maternal rubella during the first or second trimester. Hearing loss may be the only manifestation of congenital rubella, especially when infection occurs after the third month of gestation. Epidemiologic studies of children with idiopathic, isolated congenital perceptive deafness indicate that many cases are in fact due to congenital rubella.[148] Hearing deficits are usually bilateral and of similar severity in both ears. Unilateral defects are rare and may remain unnoticed until speech defects occur. Hearing loss may be progressive. Frequent reassessment of auditory function is important, as some children who appear to have normal hearing on early testing develop significant hearing deficits later in childhood.

Neurologic Findings[122, 130–135, 139, 142, 149–153]

Central nervous system (CNS) involvement is a frequent manifestation of CRS. Desmond et al[149] found neurologic abnormalities in 81 of 100 infants with CRS between birth and 18 months. In the newborn infant, a pattern of hypotonia, lethargy, and a large, full anterior fontanel is common. Irritability, hypertonic postures, and seizures may be seen in older infants.

Cerebrospinal fluid (CSF) examination in affected infants is usually characterized by increased protein and lymphocytic pleocytosis. Chronic meningoencephalitis is indicated by the persistence of rubella virus and abnormal findings in CSF. Desmond et al[149] were able to isolate rubella virus from 25 of 99 CSF specimens from infants up to 3 months of age. Nine patients had positive CSF virus isolates throughout the first year of life, and one patient had rubella in CSF cultures until 18 months after birth.

The frequency of microcephaly and psychomotor retardation in infants with CRS is high. Impairment may be mild, but more severe problems are found among children who also have neurosensory defects. Psychiatric and behavior disorders, including autism, have been noted among older children.

Other Manifestations

Many other manifestations of in utero rubella infection were recognized after the 1964 epidemic as part of the expanded congenital rubella syndrome. Most of these are related to the active, ongoing viral infection in the infant (Table 25–4). These findings tend to occur in combination among the most severely affected newborns with the highest mortality. Although many of these lesions are transiently apparent, they may have major effects on the infant.

Thrombocytopenia is a common finding in the neonate with CRS.[122, 124, 131, 132, ,138, 142] A petechial or purpuric skin rash often accompanies the thrombocytopenia and has led to the term "blueberry muffin" baby. The small red-purple macules are usually scattered most prominently over the face and thorax; palms and soles may also be affected. The petechial or purpuric rash is often present on the first day of life, but may appear a few days later. Platelet counts are occasionally as low as 10,000 per microliter,

Table 25–4
Major Manifestations of Congenital Rubella Infection

Class triad: Cataracts
      Heart defects (patent ductus arteriosus, pulmonary artery stenosis)
      Deafness

Growth retardation (prenatal, postnatal)
Other ocular defects (microphthalmia, glaucoma, cloudy cornea)
Psychomotor retardation
Behavior and psychiatric disorders

Neonatal findings
  Thrombocytopenia (petechiae, purpura)
  Hepatosplenomegaly
  Hyperbilirubinemia
  Hepatitis
  Pneumonitis
  Myocarditis
  Hemolytic anemia
  Bony lucencies
  Encephalitis
  Immunologic defects

but are more frequently between 30,000 and 100,000. Hemorrhagic complications are rare despite widespread purpura and thrombocytopenia. The period of recovery is variable, but purpuric lesions generally fade within the first week and the platelet count returns to normal several weeks later. Prolonged thrombocytopenia has been reported.[124]

Enlargement of the liver and/or spleen is common and may be quite prominent.[124, 131, 132, 138, 139, 141, 142] Severe hyperbilirubinemia and jaundice may begin within the first day of life. Hepatitis, with or without hepatomegaly, is characterized by elevated levels of direct-reacting bilirubin and transaminases. Hepatitis is usually self-limited in infants who survive the neonatal period, but exchange transfusions may be needed to relieve severe hyperbilirubinemia. Occasionally, prolonged obstructive jaundice and chronic hepatitis mimic the clinical picture of biliary atresia.

Interstitial pneumonitis is occasionally found in neonates with CRS.[122, 142] It may be quite severe and mimic congestive heart failure. Rubella virus has been isolated from lung tissue of infants who died with pneumonitis.[142]

Hemolytic anemia is a rare manifestation of CRS.[122, 132, 138, 142] It is characterized by normoblastemia, reticulocytosis, and abnormal red cell morphology in peripheral blood. The anemia is usually well compensated and transfusions are not required. The hemolytic process usually clears within the first few months of life. A single infant with CRS, Coombs-positive hemolytic anemia, bone marrow depression, and death at age 9 months from congestive heart failure has been reported from Japan.[143]

Characteristic osseous lesions in the long bones are detectable roentgenographically.[122, 124, 132, 138, 139, 141] The most striking feature is the alternating linear densities and lucent streaks in the metaphysis, giving a "celery stalk" appearance. Nonspecific metaphyseal changes may be found in the distal femur and proximal tibia. Periosteal reaction does not develop. Resolution of bone lesions is variable, but usually occurs within 6 to 8 weeks.

Minor Malformations[132, 135]

Other physical defects have been described in children with CRS. Skeletal defects, dental abnormalities, unusual dermatoglyphic patterns, and genitourinary problems have been reported. Because these anomalies also occur sporadically in uninfected infants, the relationship to congenital rubella infection is unclear.

Delayed Manifestations

Long-term follow-up of children with CRS has shown that some defects associated with the disease may appear in later life (Table 25–5). Undoubtedly, some of these delayed manifestations are related to subtle defects that are not detected earlier. Others may be due to chronic persistence of rubella virus in various tissues which ultimately causes recognizable damage.

Diabetes mellitus is the most frequently reported delayed manifestation of CRS. Forrest et al[154] performed glucose tolerance tests on 44 young adults with CRS and found overt or latent diabetes mellitus in 9 (20%) of those tested. Menser et al[155] reported another eight cases of insulin-dependent diabetes mellitus patients with congenital rubella. These and other case reports[156–160] indicate that almost all the affected children had deafness, and many had other stigma of CRS as well, suggesting rubella infection between the fourth and 16th week of prenatal life. Diabetes was subsequently

Table 25–5
Delayed Manifestations of Congenital
Rubella Infection

Endocrinopathies
 Diabetes mellitus
 Thyroid dysfunction
 Growth hormone deficiency

Ocular complications
 Glaucoma
 Keratic precipitates
 Keratoconus and corneal hydrops
 Absorption of cataractous lens

Progressive rubella panencephalitis

Deafness

diagnosed when the children were 18 months to 33 years old, with most cases recognized during adolescence or young adulthood.

The pathogenesis of diabetes may be a result of either direct viral invasion of the pancreas or virus-induced immunologic reaction in the islet cells.[155, 160] Rubella virus has been isolated from pancreatic tissues of fetuses[161] and infants[138, 162] who died of CRS; pancreatitis has been found at autopsy of another affected infant.[163] While it is possible that rubella virus persists in the congenitally infected pancreas, there are no reports of viral isolation from or detection of viral antigens in pancreatic tissue from diabetic patients with CRS.[160] Autoimmune phenomena or genetic susceptibility[160, 163–165] are also thought to be related to islet cell dysfunction.

Thyroid dysfunction has been reported in a number of older infants and children, most of whom had other malformations typical of CRS. Hyperthyroidism,[159, 166] hypothyroidism,[167, 168] and lymphocytic thyroiditis[169] have been reported in children aged 3 to 12 years. Clark et al found that 5% of 201 adolescents with CRS had thyroid dysfunction as measured by thyroid-stimulating hormone elevated (TSH) levels, although none had signs or symptoms of thyroid disease.[164] The presence of rubella virus in thyroid tissue has been documented in two cases,[166, 169] but autoimmune mechanisms may also play a role in thyroid disease.[165, 166]

Growth hormone (GH) deficiency has been reported in two patients with CRS.[170] One child with severe GH deficiency was diagnosed at 3 years of age; the second child had normal growth velocity until age 12 years when partial GH deficiency was found. Both patients responded to GH replacement.

Ocular complications that are separate and distinct from those found in the neonatal period have been described by Boger et al.[171–173] Late-onset glaucoma and keratic precipitates in eyes with no other signs of inflammation were diagnosed in 13 and 5 children, respectively, between 3 and 22 years of age; all the affected eyes had previously had cataracts which were either surgically removed or spontaneously absorbed. Four other patients had keratoconus and corneal hydrops, possibly due to chronic traumatizing mannerisms associated with severe psychomotor retardation.

Progressive rubella panencephalitis (PRP), a chronic, slowly progressive neurologic degeneration reminiscent of rubeola-related subacute sclerosing panencephalitis,[174–178] is a rare complication of CRS. There are only 12 known cases, seven of which have

been described in detail; five children had classic stigmata of CRS and two children had postnatally acquired rubella. Patients developed symptoms of PRP in the second decade of life. Subtle learning difficulties and ataxia appeared first, followed by seizures, spasticity, and deterioration of mental and motor functions. The disease is ultimately fatal. PRP is probably due to chronic infection of the brain with rubella virus, as affected patients have elevated levels of rubella antibody in serum and CSF, and rubella virus has been isolated from brain tissue of one child at biopsy.[176]

Delayed onset and progressive deafness are well-recognized sequelae of congenital rubella infection.[129, 153, 160] Clearly, all children exposed to rubella virus in utero require prolonged medical follow-up for these and other late-onset manifestations of CRS.

Virus Isolation[122, 124, 132, 133, 138, 139, 141, 142, 145, 146, 149, 179–185]

Rubella virus has been frequently recovered from fetal tissues after therapeutic abortion and from neonates with CRS. During the first month of life, virus may be recovered readily from pharyngeal secretions, urine, and CSF; conjunctivae, feces, peripheral blood, and bone marrow may also harbor virus. In fatal cases, rubella virus has been isolated from most of the major organs, providing further evidence of a widely disseminated infection.[124, 138, 180]

Prolonged virus excretion from the nasopharynx and/or urine of infants with CRS is common. In some infants, viruria has persisted longer than pharyngeal excretion[180, 181]; the reverse has been found among other infants.[179, 180] Cooper et al[132] were able to isolate rubella virus from throat swabs of 84% of neonates, 62% of 1- to 4-month-old infants, 33% of 5- to 8-month-olds, 11% of 9- to 12-month-olds, and 3% of those 13 to 20 months old. Michaels[181] isolated rubella from throat swab or urine of three of 16 2-year-old children. In another study, none of 20 older children (3–15 years old) were found to have rubella in pharyngeal secretions.[182]

By contrast, the CSF and lens may continue to harbor rubella virus after pharyngeal and urinary excretion have ceased. Desmond et al[149] recovered rubella from the CSF of one child for 18 months. In two children virus has been isolated from cataractous lens tissue obtained at surgery performed at ages 31 months[132] and 3 years.[184]

In general, a higher incidence of virus shedding is found among the more severely affected infants. However, rubella virus may also be isolated from normal-appearing infants whose mothers were exposed to or had clinical rubella during pregnancy.[124, 141, 179, 183] Horstmann et al[124] found 20% of such infants to be virus-positive at birth. Phillips et al[179] isolated rubella virus from five of seven normal infants only during the first 3 months of life.

Relatively high titers of virus ($10^{1.0}$ to $10^{3.0}$ TCID$_{50}$ [50% tissue culture infectious dose]/mL of throat swab specimen or urine) are excreted from the pharynx and urine of infected neonates, making them highly contagious.[124, 138, 181, 182, 185] Schiff and Dine[185] found a rubella attack rate of 75% among susceptible student nurses caring for newborns with CRS. Outbreaks of rubella have been reported among nurses, other health workers, physicians, and family members exposed to congenitally infected infants.

Immune Response[130, 131, 134, 139, 179–182, 186–189]

Immunogenesis begins early in fetal life, and serologic responses to rubella virus also begin before birth. Rubella neutralizing antibody has been detected in sera from 11- to 16-week-old fetuses after therapeutic abortion because of maternal rubella; this is usually IgG antibody and probably of maternal origin.[186] Later in gestation, fetal IgM antibody is produced in response to the persistent infection. Increased levels of serum IgM can be detected in most neonates and infants with CRS during the first 6 to 7 months of age.[180–182, 186–189]

Rubella-specific antibody at the time of birth includes actively acquired IgM antibody and passively acquired maternal IgG antibody. Since maternal IgG is present in large amounts, serologic testing commonly shows similar levels of rubella HI or neutralizing antibody in mother and infant. As maternal IgG wanes over the first 3 to 6 months of life, persistence of the infant's own actively acquired rubella antibody becomes obvious. Thus, for diagnostic purposes, persistence of rubella antibody beyond the expected life span of maternal IgG antibody would be indicative of congenital infection.

Detection of rubella-specific antibody in the IgM fraction of serum from a young infant suggests de novo antibody synthesis and in utero infection. Persistence of rubella IgM antibody for the first 6 months of life is a unique feature of congenital rubella.[188] By the end of the first year, rubella IgG antibody predominates.[180, 182, 186] Follow-up studies indicate that rubella HI antibodies decline gradually over time; a small percentage of children with CRS are seronegative when tested at 5 years of age.[120, 190, 191]

Persistent virus excretion despite the presence of high levels of specific serum antibody is an immunologic paradox. The phenomenon of immune tolerance or a teratologic effect of rubella on the immature immune system have been postulated to explain this paradox. Histologic evaluation of lymphoid tissue from neonates with CRS has shown precocious development of germinal centers in lymph nodes and spleen.[192] Quantitative immunoglobulin studies have shown a variable dysgammaglobulinemia in some infants; a pattern of increased IgM, decreased or normal IgG, and low or absent IgA is most common.[181, 189, 192–195] Qualitative immunoglobulin studies have indicated a failure to respond to isohemagglutinins, toxoids, and live virus vaccines in some infants during the time of virus shedding.[181, 194–196] Cell-mediated immune (CMI) responses have frequently been abnormal by skin testing or in vitro lymphocyte transformation studies.[194, 197, 198] Buimovici-Klein et al[198] found impairment of CMI to be most severe among children infected with rubella during the first 2 months of pregnancy.

RUBELLA VACCINE

Vaccine Development

Soon after rubella virus was isolated in 1962, efforts were under way to characterize the virus, evaluate immunologic responses to it, and eventually develop an effective vaccine. Early studies using killed virus vaccines were disappointing; inactivation of virus resulted in loss of antigenicity. Investigators turned their attention to development of a live virus vaccine which would be attenuated, immunogenic, and noncommunicable.

In 1966, Meyer, Parkman, and Panos[199] reported their initial evaluation of a rubella virus passed 77 times in primary GMK cells and thus referred to as "high-passage virus-77" or HPV₇₇. Another five passes in duck embryo tissue culture produced the

HPV₇₇DE₅ strain.[200] Similarly, 12 additional passes in dog kidney cell cultures produced the HPV₇₇DK₁₂ strain.[200]

A third attenuated rubella virus, the Cendehill strain, was isolated in GMK cells and passed 57 times in primary rabbit kidney cells.[201] The safety and immunogenicity of these live rubella strains had been proved by 1969, and licensure followed in that year.

A fourth live rubella vaccine was licensed in 1978, and is currently the only available rubella vaccine strain in the United States. The RA 27/3 strain developed by Plotkin and coworkers[202] was isolated and passed 25 times in WI-38 human diploid fibroblasts. The RA 27/3 virus is unusual in that it has retained the ability to cause infection when administered intranasally.

Adverse Reactions[202–214]

Various reactions to live rubella virus vaccine have been reported in approximately 10% to 15% of recipients. As with naturally acquired rubella, the incidence and severity of such reactions tend to be related to age and sex. Among young children, vaccination is rarely associated with any symptoms. Occasionally, signs of mild rubella—low-grade fever, lymphadenopathy, and rash—are reported ten to 20 days after immunization.[202, 203, 205–210]

More severe reactions are occasionally reported among adult vaccinees. Joint involvement with transient arthritis and/or arthralgia is of particular concern, especially among adult women.[203–212] Severity ranges from morning stiffness to overt arthritis with joint effusions. Fingers, hands, wrists, and knees are most frequently involved. Usually, joint complaints are of brief duration, lasting less than a week, and do not cause limitation of activities. Recurrent joint pain and swelling over a period of months has been reported rarely[76] Ogra and Herd[213] were able to isolate rubella vaccine virus from joint aspirates of three children with arthritis for 3 to 4 months after immunization with HPV₇₇DK₁₂.

All rubella vaccines have been associated with joint manifestations; HPV₇₇DK₁₂ has been most frequently implicated, followed by HPV₇₇DE₅, Cendehill, and RA 27/3.[204, 208–210, 212] Because of the frequency of joint involvement, the HPV₇₇DK₁₂ vaccine was withdrawn from distribution in 1973.

Clinical manifestations of peripheral neuropathy occur infrequently after rubella immunization.[204, 214] Cooper et al[204] reported transient paresthesias in ten adults and four children after HPV₇₇DK₁₂ vaccine; carpal tunnel syndrome occurred in one adult. Kilroy et al[214] described 32 cases of two pain syndromes after HPV₇₇ vaccine. Pain and paresthesias of the wrist and hands (the arm syndrome) occurred in nine children, and 18 children experienced knee pain accompanied by a crouching gait ("catcher's crouch" syndrome); five children had a mixed pattern. Abnormal nerve conduction tests were observed in six of nine children tested. These reactions usually occurred 1 to 2 months after vaccination, were transient, and resulted in complete recovery.

Virus Shedding and Communicability[199–202, 209, 210, 215–217]

Rubella vaccine virus can often be recovered from pharyngeal secretions at some time between seven and 28 days after immunization. Virus shedding is brief and often intermittent. Only small amounts of virus are excreted after immunization—approximately 100-fold less than during natural infection.[199–215]

Serologic studies have documented the lack of spread of rubella vaccine virus to susceptible contacts. Seronegative persons exposed to vaccinees in institutional settings,[199, 200, 209] families,[200, 210, 216, 217] and schools[217] have remained seronegative. Thus there is no contraindication to immunizing susceptible children living with a pregnant woman.

Immunologic Response[199–203, 205–211, 218–229]

Rubella antibody develops in approximately 95% of seronegative vaccinees regardless of type of vaccine administered. However, important quantitative and qualitative differences exist among antibody responses to different rubella vaccines and naturally acquired rubella.

Circulating Antibody Responses

Rubella HI titers produced in response to HPV_{77} or Cendehill vaccine are four- to eightfold lower than after natural rubella infection.[200, 209, 218] Significantly higher HI titers been found after RA 27/3 than after other vaccines.[210, 211, 219] Similarly, delayed acquisition of neutralizing antibody and generally low titers are found after $HPV_{77}DE_5$ or Cendehill vaccination, while the RA 27/3 vaccine induces neutralizing antibody responses more comparable to natural rubella.[219–221] CF antibodies develop infrequently among HPV_{77} or Cendehill vaccines[200, 209, 219]; after RA 27/3 vaccine, CF antibody appears regularly and in greater amounts.[219]

Antibodies to both theta and iota precipitating antigens appear after natural rubella infection and after immunization with RA 27/3 vaccine.[219, 222] By contrast, HPV_{77} or Cendehill vaccine stimulates moderate levels of anti-theta antibody but no anti-iota.

Secretory Antibody Response[218, 221]

Nasopharyngeal IgA-HI and neutralizing antibody occur regularly after natural rubella infection. Secretory IgA antibodies are not produced after HPV_{77} or Cendehill immunization. Following administration of RA 27/3 vaccine, nasal rubella-specific IgA antibody develops in approximately half of subjects immunized parenterally and in nearly all of those given intranasal vaccine.

Persistence of Antibody

Durability of vaccine-induced immunity, as measured by rubella HI titers, has been evaluated in several long-term serologic studies of vaccinated populations.[210, 211, 213, 223–231] In general, the lower levels of HI antibody induced by live attenuated rubella virus tend to decline gradually within the first 6 months to 2 years after immunization and then remain stable. By 10 years after HPV_{77} or Cendehill vaccination, 0% to 8.5% of recipients who initially seroconverted were found to have no rubella HI antibody.[223–226] Horstmann[226] found that vaccinees having low HI titers (1:8–1:16) by two months after immunization were more likely to be without detectable HI antibody 9 years later than vaccinees with a brisk antibody response.

A considerably higher rate of loss of vaccine-induced HI antibody was reported by Balfour and Amren[227]; 36% of children given $HPV_{77}DE_5$ vaccine in a private pediatric clinic were seronegative at a mean of 4.7 years after immunization. However, early postvaccination titers were not obtained, and it is impossible to determine whether primary failure of seroconversion or rapid decline of HI antibodies occurred.

Amoung recipients of RA 27/3 vaccine, HI antibodies have persisted for periods of 2 to 12 years.[210, 211, 221, 228–234] HI titers have remained stable or decreased minimally over the years, usually remaining at protective levels in 90% to 95% of recipients.[232–234] Only a few RA 27/3 recipients have undetectable HI antibody after initial seroconversion.

It must be noted that many HI antibody-negative vaccinees have been shown to be immune using more sensitive assays, such as ELISA or LA, by measurement of neutralizing antibody, or by assessment of CMI.[57, 225, 234] Reimmunization of HI antibody–negative vaccinees has resulted in an accelerated, anamnestic immune response with little or no rubella-specific IgM.[235, 236] However, intranasal challenge with a nonattenuated rubella virus has produced viremia and a primary immunologic response in some HI-negative RA 27/3 vaccinees.[234]

Reinfection of Vaccinees

Reinfection of seropositive individuals by rubella virus is usually asymptomatic and detectable only by a fourfold or greater rise in rubella HI antibody titer. Among naturally immune persons exposed to wild virus during an epidemic, the incidence of reinfection ranges from 1.5% to 4.2%.[237–239] Among HPV_{77} or Cendehill vaccine recipients, subclinical reinfections have been demonstrated in 4.4% to 80%.[237, 238, 240–246] One study of RA 27/3 vaccinees has shown a reinfection rate of only 3.5% after exposure to natural rubella.[245] Similarly, experimental challenge studies with unattenuated virus or intranasal RA 27/3 vaccine have shown that reinfection occurs less frequently among recipients of RA 27/3 vaccine (7%–11%) than among $HPV_{77}DE_5$ (24%–47%) or Cendehill (50%–63%) vaccinees.[228, 246–249] Resistance to reinfection has been correlated with higher HI antibody titers,[237, 238, 243–245, 249] neutralizing antibody,[219, 248] anti-iota precipitins,[228, 237] and rubella-specific nasopharyngeal IgA antibody.[218, 249]

Rubella virus has occasionally been isolated from pharyngeal secretions of reinfected vaccine recipients.[228, 237, 238, 240, 241, 250] In these cases, low titers of virus are excreted for brief periods of time, reducing the risk of transmission. Viremia is thought to be very rare during natural rubella reinfection.[238, 240, 250]

Several cases of rubella reinfection during pregnancy have been reported.[251–261] Importantly, none of the women had been previously vaccinated. Five women[251, 253–255, 260, 261] experienced clinically apparent rubella with fever, rash, and lymphadenopathy during pregnancy; rubella-specific IgM was demonstrated in two. These cases probably represent primary rubella, with nonspecific serum inhibitors accounting for preinfection HI activity, as documented in one case.[254]

Additionally, there have been at least six reported cases of inapparent rubella reinfection in pregnant women with naturally acquired immunity.[252, 256–258] Four women had increases in rubella-specific IgG antibody only and gave birth to normal appearing infants who had no measurable rubella IgM.[257, 258] Two mothers delivered malformed infants with either rubella IgM or a positive nasopharyngeal rubella virus isolate at birth.[252, 256] Both women had rubella HI and CF antibody before the affected pregnancy; one had no measurable rubella neutralizing antibody. There is a single case report[259] of an infant with CRS, born to a woman who was immunized with Cendehill vaccine 7 years previously; she had rubella HI titers of 1:32 three years before and again during her pregnancy when she was in contact with children with rubelliform rashes.

Nonetheless, the paucity of documented cases of congenital rubella after maternal reinfection indicates that the risk to the fetus is probably quite low in these circumstances.[14, 219]

Immunization During Pregnancy[263–274]

Although early studies indicated the lack of viremia after immunization, the potential teratogenicity of rubella vaccine virus for the developing fetus was recognized before 1969. Thus it was recommended that vaccine not be given during pregnancy and, furthermore, that pregnancy be avoided for 2 to 3 months after immunization. Despite these warnings, a number of women have received rubella vaccine either shortly before or after conception. A registry of such cases is maintained by the CDC.[263]

Rubella vaccine virus is capable of infecting the placenta and, to a lesser degree, the fetus.[262–271] Among women known to be seronegative at the time of vaccination, rubella virus has been isolated from specimens obtained at therapeutic abortion in 21% to 37% of cases.[262, 264, 265] Vaheri et al[264] evaluated fetal and placental specimens separately; rubella virus was isolated from six of 24 placentas but only one fetus. None of 11 specimens from seropositive women yielded virus.

Fetal infection with rubella vaccine virus has been documented in several reports. Nonspecific inflammatory changes have been recognized in products of conception obtained after rubella immunization.[267, 269–271] Fleet et al[271] isolated virus from the eye of one aborted fetus and also found histologic changes typical of congenital rubella in the other eye. Hayden and coworkers[272] found rubella IgM antibodies in four infants born after RA 27/3 immunization. Despite these findings, all infants born after inadvertent rubella vaccination during gestation have been free of congenital defects.[262, 266, 268, 270–274] Rubella virus has not been isolated from such infants and, except for the four cases previously mentioned, serologic studies have been negative.[262, 268, 271, 273]

Investigators from the CDC have attempted to make probability estimates of the risk of CRS based on follow-up studies of infants whose mothers inadvertently received rubella vaccine in the first trimester of pregnancy. Between January 1979 and December 1988, 683 pregnant women who received RA 27/3 rubella vaccine were reported to the CDC.[263] None of the 562 subsequent infants had defects compatible with CRS, including 212 infants born to rubella-susceptible women. Thus, the risk for occurrence of CRS after vaccination could theoretically be as high as 1.7%, based on the 95% confidence limits of the binomial distribution of a zero observed rate in this group of 212 infants. Clearly, the risk of CRS after inadvertent immunization is quite low. Under most circumstances, rubella vaccination of a pregnant woman should not be an indication for termination of pregnancy.[263]

Immunization Programs

The primary objective of rubella immunization is to prevent infection in pregnant women and subsequent congenital rubella. In 1969, extensive evaluation of the epidemiology of rubella and experience with various experimental vaccines led to two different proposals for effective vaccine use[13]: (1) routine immunization of prepubertal children, to decrease circulation of virus and reduce the risk of exposure in the community; and (2) routine immunization of adolescent girls to provide individual protection during future pregnancies. The United States adopted the first approach, while Great Britain, Canada, and many European countries adopted the second.

United States Policy[275, 276]

Rubella immunization policy in the United States is based on recommendations of the Public Health Service Advisory Committee on Immunization Practices and the Committee on Infectious Diseases of the American Academy of Pediatrics. Both groups recommend routine vaccination of boys and girls between 12 months of age and puberty and selective immunization of susceptible adult women.

Primary emphasis was placed on vaccination of prepubertal children to prevent the rubella epidemic that was predicted to occur between 1970 and 1973. This was successfully accomplished by the rapid acceptance and widespread administration of rubella vaccine as part of the routine childhood immunization schedule. As a result, the incidence of rubella and congenital rubella has declined over the past 18 years to record low levels (see Figure 25–2).

Several studies have indicated that increasing the level of "herd immunity" to rubella will not completely halt the circulation of wild virus in the community. In Casper, Wyoming, a rubella outbreak occurred in a community in which 83% of elementary school children and 52% of preschool children were vaccinated.[67] Lehane et al[277] showed that rubella spread easily to susceptible Marines despite immunity rates of 87% to 97%. Recent outbreaks of rubella among unimmunized adolescents and adults have shown that endemic rubella is still a problem in the United States, and that further control of the disease will depend on vaccination of older individuals.[18–25]

Secondary emphasis has been placed on selective immunization of seronegative adult women primarily because of concerns about potential risks of inadvertent vaccination during pregnancy. Even when nonpregnancy can be assured, as during the immediate postpartum period, immunization of susceptibles has been a failure.[120, 278, 279] As a result, recent serologic studies show no significant change in the prevalence of rubella immunity among women of childbearing age.[71, 120] Recognizing that further control of rubella will require individual protection, revised recommendations for use of rubella vaccine focus on more effective delivery of vaccine to women of childbearing age.[280]

Several strategies have been proposed to identify and immunize groups of susceptible adults. The military has already instituted a program for rubella screening and vaccination of seronegative recruits.[281, 282] Colleges and universities should require proof of rubella immunity before admission. Routine premarital rubella screening may be effective if there is careful follow-up and vaccination of seronegatives.[283] Women found to be susceptible during prenatal testing should be immunized in the immediate postpartum period—before hospital discharge. Breast feeding is not a contraindication to vaccination, although virus may be excreted in breast milk and infants may be infected.[284, 285]

Hospital and other health-care workers are at increased risk of acquiring rubella from patients with congenital or acquired rubella and of spreading it to other patients or fellow employees who

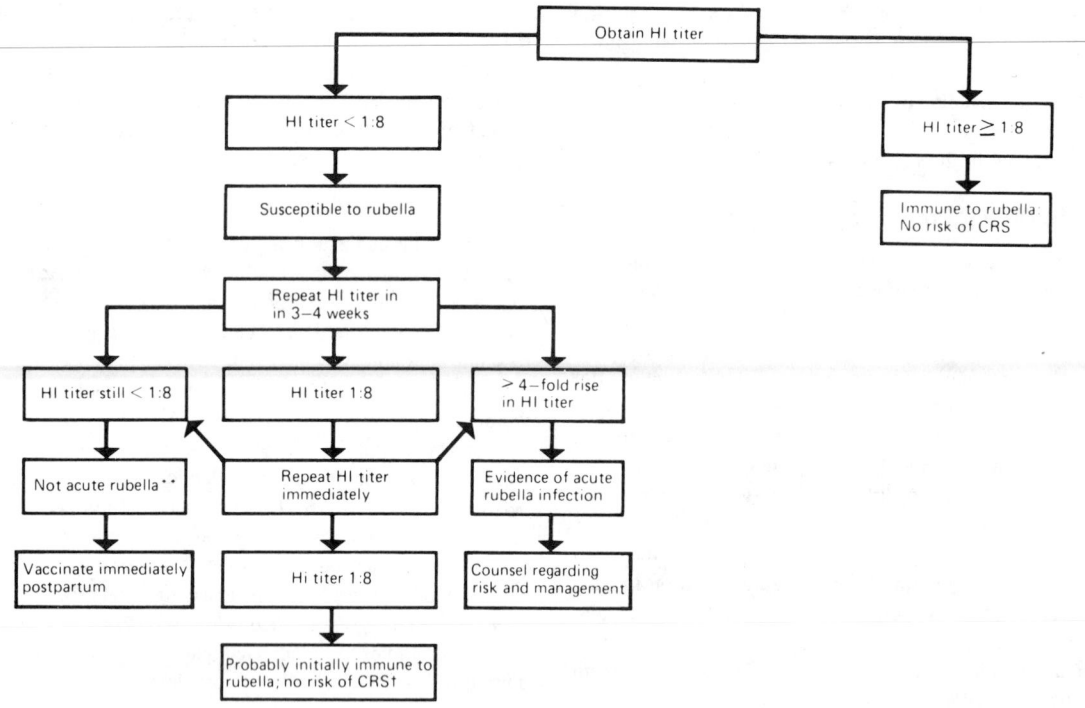

*An HI titer of < 1:8 is used to indicate susceptibility. The actual susceptibility cut-off level may vary in different laboratories (e g < 1 10)

**The patient should be followed closely during the first trimester for rash illness or exposure to rubella. Another HI titer at the end of the first trimester is advisable especially if rubella is present in the community.

†Over 99% of acute rubella infections will result in development and maintenance of HI titers > 1 32 for at least 6 months after onset. Original HI titer < 1:8 is suspect.

Figure 25–4. Management of the pregnant patient seen within one week after exposure to rash illness. HI = hemagglutination inhibition; CRS = congenital rubella syndrome. (From Mann JM, et al: Assessing risks of rubella infection during pregnancy. A standardized approach. *JAMA* 1981; 245:1647–1652. Used by permission.)

might be pregnant.[18, 19] Because of this high risk, programs to encourage or require rubella screening and/or immunization of health care workers are important. Unfortunately, some of these programs have experienced poor compliance with immunization, especially among physicians.[286–290]

United Kingdom Policy

Because of concerns about the duration of vaccine-induced immunity and possible teratogenic effects of vaccine, Great Britain and a number of European countries chose to focus immunization efforts on young adolescent females between 11 and 14 years of age. This would provide individual protection against rubella infection during pregnancy, but would allow rubella virus to continue to circulate among young children in the community. It was recognized that this approach would probably not affect the incidence of rubella and congenital rubella until the mid-1980s.[291, 292]

Although reporting of rubella cases is not mandatory in the United Kingdom, available data suggest that the number of cases of rubella and congenital rubella were relatively stable during the 1970s.[291] Outbreaks of rubella occurred in 1978–1979 and in 1982–1983, resulting in an increased number of therapeutic abortions and infants with congenital rubella.[291, 293]

Studies of serologic status among adult women indicate a higher incidence of seropositivity since the introduction of rubella vaccine. Hambling[294] found that 14.3% of women of childbearing age were seronegative in 1971, while only 8.6% of women tested in 1974 were seronegative. Clarke et al[295] tested 10,000 serum samples from blood donors and university students between 1976 and 1978. There were fewer seronegatives (4%–7%) among women born in 1956 and after (ie, among age groups offered rubella vaccine in school) than among women born before 1954 (11%–20%). More recent serologic surveys have continued to show a steady increase in the proportion of immune adult women, as compared to adult men.[293] Thus, the rubella immunization policy is having an impact on the immunologic status of adult females.

Thus, ongoing evaluation of the effects of vaccination programs in the United States and Britain suggest problems with each of the two strategies. Knox[296] has developed mathematical and computer-simulation models to predict the effectiveness of alternative rubella vaccination policies. He found that immunization of preschool boys and girls would provide rapid reductions in the incidence of rubella and congenital rubella. However, long-term reductions would depend on maintaining immunization rates of above 70% and on assuring long-lasting immunity after vaccination. A combined system of immunization aimed at young children and adolescent girls could overcome these problems.

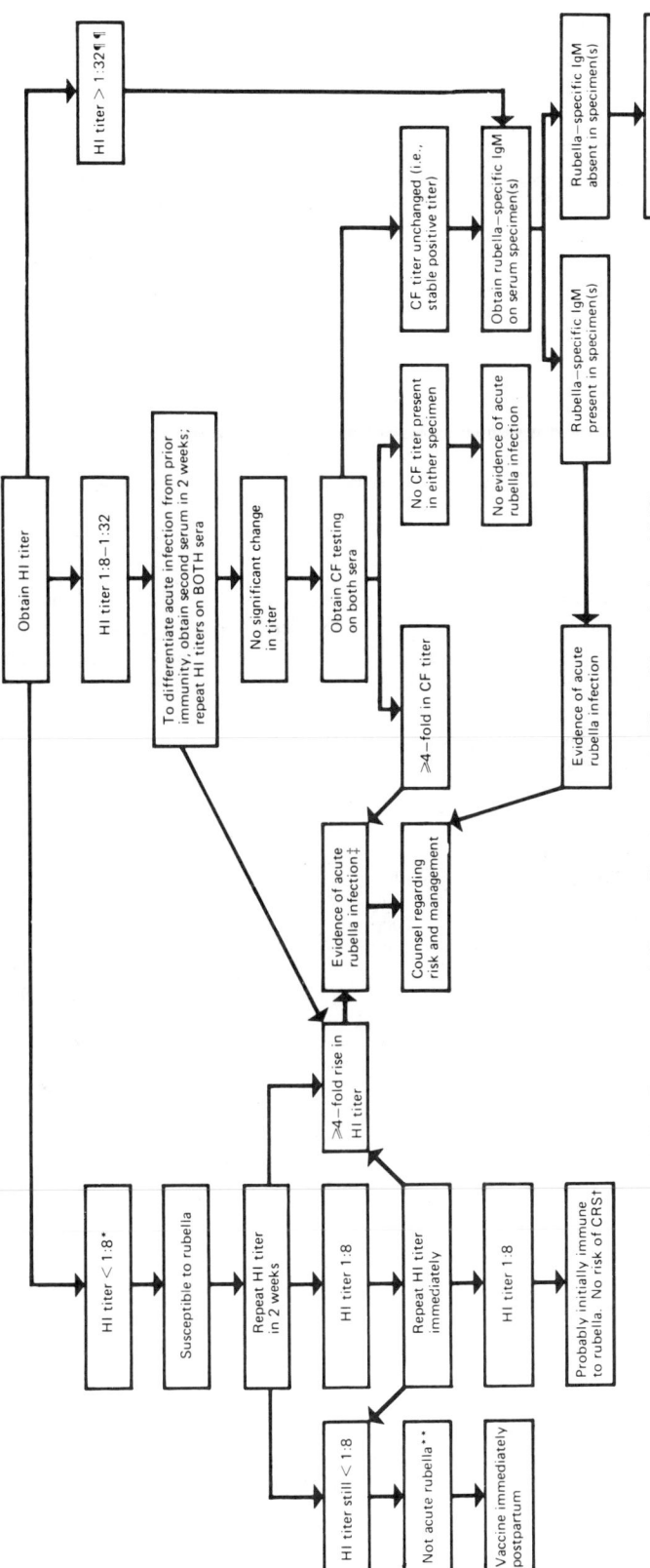

Figure 25–5.

Management of the pregnant patient seen one to five weeks after exposure, or within three weeks of a rash illness. HI = hemagglutination inhibition; CF = complement fixation; CRS = congenital rubella syndrome. (From Mann JM, et al: Assessing risks of rubella infection during pregnancy. A standardized approach. *JAMA* 1981; 245:1647–1652. Used by permission.)

*An acute titer of < 1:8 is used to indicate susceptibility. The actual susceptibility cut-off level may vary in different laboratories (e.g. < 1:10)

** The patient should be followed closely during the first trimester for rash illness or exposure to rubella. Another HI titer at the end of the first trimester is advisable especially if rubella is present in the community.

† Over 99% of acute rubella infections will develop and maintain HI titers > 1:32 for at least 6 months after onset. Original HI titer < 1:8 is suspect

‡ In the absence of rash illness, if reinfection is a major consideration, a properly timed IgM antibody assay may help to differentiate primary from secondary infection

¶ Absence of rubella–specific IgM may not exclude recent rubella infection

¶¶ The physician may elect to proceed as with a titer of 1:8–1:32

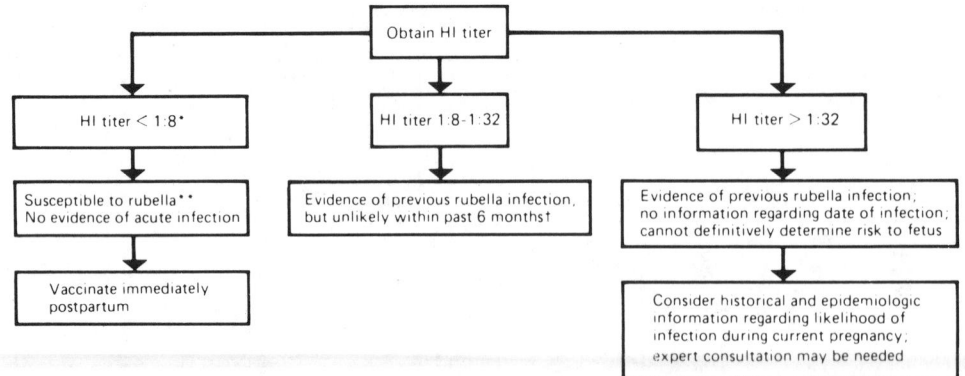

*An HI titer of < 1:8 is used to indicate susceptibility. The actual susceptibility cut-off level may vary in different laboratories (e.g., < 1:10)
**The patient should be followed closely during the first trimester of rash illness or exposure to rubella. Another HI titer at the end of the first trimester is advisable, especially if rubella is present in the community.
†Over 99% of acute rubella infections will result in development and maintenance of HI titers of > 1:32 for at least 6 months after onset.

Figure 25–6. Management of the pregnant patient seen more than five weeks after exposure to a rash illness, or more than three weeks after a rash illness, or with unknown exposure and no rash illness. HI = hemagglutination inhibition. (From Mann JM, et al: Assessing risks of rubella infection during pregnancy. A standardized approach. *JAMA* 1981; 245:1647–1652. Used by permission.)

MANAGEMENT OF RUBELLA EXPOSURE OR RUBELLA DURING PREGNANCY

Although the incidence of rubella has decreased significantly in the United States, the physician is often confronted with the problem of managing a pregnant women with or exposed to a rash illness. Because the clinical diagnosis of rubella is unreliable and inapparent infections are common, evaluation relies heavily on interpretation of serologic studies. Rubella virus has been isolated from amniotic fluid in several cases of first-trimester infection[297] and from chorionic villus sampling in one case.[298] This approach is time-consuming and unreliable, since a negative culture does not prove that the fetus is not infected. Similarly, detection of rubella-specific IgM in fetal blood obtained by cordocentesis between 21 and 33 weeks of gestation has diagnosed rubella infection in a few patients.[299]

Maternal rubella serology is frequently performed during the first prenatal visit. If rubella antibody is detected and there has been no exposure or rash illness during or 2 months prior to the current pregnancy, immunity can be assured.[120, 300] Exposure to rubella in such a woman would pose no risk to the fetus.

If no antibody is detected, susceptibility to rubella and the need for postpartum immunization should be discussed. If a subsequent exposure to rash illness occurs, repeat rubella serology should be performed after 3 or 4 weeks to determine if seroconversion has occurred. The use of gamma globulin as preventive therapy is controversial and probably of no benefit; it is recommended only when a pregnant woman exposed to rubella would not consider termination of pregnancy under any circumstances.[235]

A more difficult situation results when the rubella-immune status of a pregnant woman is unknown. Patients with a rubellalike illness should have serum for rubella serology drawn immediately and again 2 to 3 weeks later; demonstration of seroconversion, a rise in rubella titer, or the presence of rubella-specific IgM would indicate acute infection. Assessment of a pregnant woman who was recently exposed to a rash illness or had a rash illness is more complex. Mann et al[300] have developed algorithms to aid in the management and counseling of such patients (Figures 25–4, 25–5, 25–6). However, even using the algorithms, precise diagnosis of acute rubella may not be possible when there has been a long delay between exposure or illness and serologic evaluation.

REFERENCES

1. Forbes JA: Rubella: Historical aspects. *Am J Dis Child* 1969; 118:5–11.
2. Wesselhoeft C: Rubella (German measles). *N Engl J Med* 1947; 236:943–950, 978–988.
3. Alford CA: Rubella, in Remington JS, Klein JO (eds): *Infectious Diseases of the Fetus and Newborn Infant.* Philadelphia, Saunders, 1976.
4. Gregg NM: Congenital cataract following German measles in the mother. *Trans Ophthalmol Soc Aust* 1941; 3:35–46.
5. Gregg NM, Beavis WR, Heseltine M, et al: The occurrence of congenital defects in children following maternal rubella during pregnancy. *Med J Aust* 1945; 2:122–126.
6. Erickson CA: Rubella early in pregnancy causing congenital malformation of eyes and heart. *J Pediatr* 1944; 25:281–283.
7. Reese AB: Congenital cataract and other anomalies following German measles in the mother. *Am J Ophthalmol* 1944; 27:483–487.
8. Hughes I: Congenital defects following rubella in pregnancy. *Proc R Soc Med* 1945; 39:17–18.
9. Martin SM: Congenital defects and rubella. *Br Med J* 1945; 1:855.
10. Weller TH, Neva FA: Propagation in tissue culture of cytopathic agents from patients with rubella-like illness. *Proc Soc Exp Biol Med* 1962; 111:215–225.
11. Parkman PD, Buescher RL, Artenstein MS: Recovery of rubella virus from Army recruits. *Proc Soc Exp Biol Med* 1962; 111:225–230.
12. Krugman S (ed): Rubella Symposium. *Am J Dis Child* 1965; 110:345–476.
13. Krugman S (ed): International Conference on Rubella Immunization. *Am J Dis Child* 1969; 118:2–410.
14. Center for Disease Control: Rubella surveillance. January 1976–December 1978. Issued May 1980.
15. Center for Disease Control: Rubella surveillance. Report No. 1, 1969.
16. Centers for Disease Control: Elimination of rubella and congenital rubella syndrome—United States. *MMWR* 1984; 34:65–66.

17. Centers for Disease Control: CDC surveillance summaries, 1984. Rubella and congenital rubella surveillance, 1983. *MMWR* 1984; 33:1SS–10SS.
18. Polk BF, White JA, DeGirolami PC, et al: An outbreak of rubella among hospital personnel. *N Engl J Med* 1980; 303:541–545.
19. Center for Disease Control: Nosocomial rubella infection—North Dakota, Alabama, Ohio. *MMWR* 1980; 29:629–631.
20. Center for Disease Control: Rubella surveillance. July 1973–December 1975. Issued August, 1976.
21. Center for Disease Control: Rubella outbreak in an office building—New Jersey. *MMWR* 1980; 29:517–518.
22. Centers for Disease Control: Rubella outbreak among office workers—New York City. *MMWR* 1983; 32:349–352.
23. Centers for Disease Control: Rubella outbreak among office workers—New York City. *MMWR* 1985; 34:455–459.
24. Centers for Disease Control: Rubella and congenital rubella syndrome—New York City. *MMWR* 1986; 35:770–779.
25. Center for Disease Control: Measles and rubella at a military recruit training center—Illinois. *MMWR* 1979; 28:147–148.
26. Fenner F: Classification and nomenclature of viruses. *Intervirology* 1976; 7:1–115.
27. Sedwick WD, Sokol F: Nucleic acid of rubella virus and its replication in hamster kidney cells. *J Virol* 1970; 5:478–489.
28. Holmes IH, Work MC, Warburton MF: Is rubella an arbovirus? II. Ultrastructural morphology and development. *Virology* 1969; 37:15–25.
29. Smith KO, Hobbins TE: Physical characteristics of rubella virus. *J Immunol* 1969; 102:1016–1023.
30. Parkman PD, Hopps HE, Meyer HM: Rubella virus. Isolation, characterization and laboratory diagnosis. *Am J Dis Child* 1969; 118:68–77.
31. Herrman KL: Rubella virus, in Lennette EH, Ballows A, Hausler WJ, et al (eds): *Manual of Clinical Microbiology*, ed 3. Washington DC, American Society for Microbiology, 1980, pp 862–868.
32. Plotkin SA: Rubella virus, in Lennette EH, Schmidt NJ (eds): *Diagnostic Procedures for Viral and Rickettsial Infections*, ed 4. New York, American Public Health Association, 1969, pp 364–413.
33. Horstmann DM: Rubella: The challenge of its control. *J Infect Dis* 1971; 123:640–654.
34. Sever JL, Schiff GM, Traub RG: Rubella virus. *JAMA* 1962; 182:663–671.
35. Parkman PD, Bueschler EL, Artenstein MS, et al: Studies of rubella. I. Properties of the virus. *J Immunol* 1964; 93:595–607.
36. Fabiyi A, Sever JL, Ratner N, et al: Rubella virus: Growth characteristics and stability of infectious virus and complement-fixing antigen. *Proc Soc Exp Biol Med* 1966; 122:392–396.
37. McCarthy K, Taylor-Robinson CH: Rubella. *Br Med Bull* 1967; 23:185–191.
38. Vaheri A, Hovi T: Structural proteins and subunits of rubella virus. *J Virol* 1972; 9:10–16.
39. Waxham MN, Wolinsky JS: A model of structural organization of rubella virions. *Rev Infect Dis* 1985; 7(suppl 1):S133–S139.
40. Pettersson RF, Oker-Blom C, Kalkkinen N, et al: Molecular and antigenic characteristics and synthesis of rubella virus structural proteins. *Rev Infect Dis* 1985; 7(suppl 1):S140–S149.
41. Dorsett PH, Miller DC, Green KY: Structure and function of the rubella virus proteins. *Rev Infect Dis* 1985; 7(suppl 1):S150–S156.
42. Furakawa T, Plotkin SA, Sedwick WD, et al: Studies on hemagglutination by rubella virus. *Proc Soc Exp Biol Med* 1967; 126:745–750.
43. Schmidt NJ, Lennette EH: Antigens of rubella virus. *Am J Dis Child* 1969; 118:89–93.
44. Stewart GL, Parkman PD, Hopps HE: Rubella virus hemagglutination-inhibition test. *N Engl J Med* 1967; 276:554–557.
45. Halonen PE, Ryan JM, Stewart JA: Rubella hemagglutinin prepared with alkaline extraction of virus grown in suspension culture of BHK-21 cells. *Proc Soc Exp Biol Med* 1967; 125:162–167.
46. Schmidt NJ, Lennette EH, Gee PS: Demonstration of rubella complement-fixing antigens of two distinct particle sizes by gel filtration on Sephadex G-200. *Proc Soc Exp Biol Med* 1966; 123:758–762.
47. Schell K, Wong KT: Stability and storage of complement-fixing antigen. *Nature* 1966; 212:321–322.
48. Schmidt NJ, Styk B: Immunodiffusion reactions with rubella antigens. *J Immunol* 1969; 101:210–216.
49. LeBouvier GL: Precipitinogens of rubella-virus infected cells. *Proc Soc Exp Biol Med* 1969; 130:51–54.
50. Salmi AA: Characterization of a structural antigen of rubella virus reacting by gel precipitation. *Acta Pathol Microbiol Scand Section B*, 1972; 80:534–544.
51. LeBouvier GL, Plotkin SA: Precipitin responses to rubella vaccine RA 27/3. *J Infect Dis* 1971; 123:220–223.
52. Cappel R, Schluederberg A, Horstmann DM: Large-scale production of rubella precipitinogens and their use in the diagnostic laboratory. *J Clin Microbiol* 1975; 1:201–205.
53. Herrman KL: Available rubella serologic tests. *Rev Infect Dis* 1985; 7(suppl 1):S108–S112.
54. Sever JL, Fuccillo DA, Getnick GL, et al: Rubella antibody determinations. *Pediatrics* 1967; 40:789–797.
55. Lennette EH, Schmidt NJ, Magoffin RL: The hemagglutination inhibition test for rubella: A comparison of its sensitivity to that of neutralization, complement-fixation, and fluorescent antibody tests for diagnosis of infection and determination of immunity status. *J Immunol* 1966; 99:785–793.
56. Skendzel LP, Edson DC: Latex agglutination test for rubella antibodies: Report based on data from the College of American Pathologists surveys, 1983 to 1985. *J Clin Microbiol* 1986; 24:333–335.
57. Buimovici-Klein E, O'Beirne AJ, Millian SJ, et al: Low level rubella antibody detected by ELISA and specific lymphocyte transformation. *Arch Virol* 1980; 66:321–327.
58. Forghani B, Schmidt NJ: Antigen requirements, sensitivity, and specificity of enzyme immunoassays for measles and rubella viral antibodies. *J Clin Microbiol* 1979; 9:657–664.
59. Vejtorp M, Fanoe E, Leerhoy J: Diagnosis of postnatal rubella by the enzyme-linked immunosorbent assay for rubella IgM and IgG antibodies. *Acta Pathol Microbiol Scand Section B*, 1979; 87:155–160.
60. Gravell M, Dorsett PH, Gutenson O, et al: Detection of antibody to rubella virus by enzyme-linked immunosorbent assay. *J Infect Dis* 1977; 136(suppl):S300–S303.
61. Preblud SR, Serdula MK, Frank JA, et al: Current status of rubella in the United States, 1969–1979. *J Infect Dis* 1980; 142:776–779.
62. Horstmann DM: Rubella, in Evans SA (ed): *Viral Infections of Humans: Epidemiology and Control.* New York, Plenum, 1976, pp 409–427.
63. Horstmann DM: Problems in measles and rubella. *DM* 1978; 24:3–52.
64. Witte JJ, Karchmer AW, Case G, et al: Epidemiology of rubella. *Am J Dis Child* 1969; 118:107–111.
65. Centers for Disease Control: Rubella and congenital rubella—United States, 1985–1988. *MMWR* 1989; 38:173–185.
66. Guyer B, Giandelia JW, Bisno AL, et al: The Memphis State University rubella outbreak. An example of changing rubella epidemiology. *JAMA* 1974; 227:1298–1300.
67. Klock LE, Rachelefsky GS: Failure of herd immunity during an epidemic. *N Engl J Med* 1973; 288:69–72.
68. Hattis RP, Halstead SB, Herrman KL, et al: Rubella in an immunized island population. *JAMA* 1973; 223:1019–1021.
69. Sever JL, Schiff GM, Bell JA, et al: Rubella: Frequency of antibody among children and adults. *Pediatrics* 1965; 25:996–998.
70. Sever JL, Schiff GM, Huebner RJ: Frequency of rubella antibody among pregnant women and other human and animal populations. *Obstet Gynecol* 1964; 23:153–159.
71. Bart KJ, Orenstein W, Preblud SR, et al: Universal immunization to interrupt rubella. *Rev Infect Dis* 1985; 7(suppl 1):S177–S184.

72. Cockburn WC: World aspects of the epidemiology of rubella. *Am J Dis Child* 1969; 118:112–122.
73. Halstead SB, Diwan AR, Oda AI: Susceptibility to rubella among adolescents and adults in Hawaii. *JAMA* 1969; 210:1881–1883.
74. Sever JL, Fabiyi A, McCallin PF, et al: Rubella antibody among pregnant women in Hawaii. *Am J Obstet Gynecol* 1965; 92:1006–1008.
75. Judelsohn RG, Wyll SA: Rubella in Bermuda. Termination of an epidemic by mass vaccination. *JAMA* 1973; 123:401–406.
76. Tingle AJ, Allen M, Petty RE, et al: Rubella-associated arthritis. I. Comparative study of joint manifestations associated with natural rubella infection and RA 27/3 rubella immunization. *Ann Rheum Dis* 1986; 45:110–114.
77. Gale JL, Detels R, Kim KS, et al: Epidemiology of rubella on Taiwan. *Am J Dis Child* 1969; 118:143–145.
78. Green RH, Balsamo MR, Giles JP, et al: Studies of the natural history and prevention of rubella. *Am J Dis Child* 1965; 110:348–365.
79. Krugman S, Ward R, Jacobs KG, et al: Studies on rubella immunization. I. Demonstration of rubella without rash. *JAMA* 1953; 151:285–288.
80. Brody JA, Sever JL, McAlister R, et al: Rubella epidemic on St. Paul island in the Pribilofs, 1963: I. Epidemiologic, clinical, and serologic findings. *JAMA* 1965; 191:619–623.
81. Schiff GM, Sever JL, Huebner RJ: Experimental rubella. Clinical and laboratory findings. *Arch Intern Med* 1965; 116:537–543.
82. Chantler JK, Tingle AJ: Isolation of rubella virus from human lymphocytes after acute natural infection. *J Infect Dis* 1982; 145:673–677.
83. Phillips CA, Behbehani AM, Johnson LW, et al: Isolation of rubella virus. An epidemic characterized by rash and arthritis. *JAMA* 1965; 191:615–618.
84. Cooper LZ, Krugman S: Clinical manifestations of postnatal and congenital rubella. *Arch Ophthalmol* 1967; 77:434–439.
85. Finklea JF, Sandifer SH, Moore GT: Epidemic rubella at the Citadel. *Am J Epidemiol* 1968; 87:367–372.
86. Heggie AD: Pathogenesis of the rubella exanthem: Distribution of rubella virus in skin during rubella with and without rash. *J Infect Dis* 1978; 137:74–77.
87. Gross PA, Portnoy B, Mathies AW, et al: A rubella outbreak among adolescent boys. *Am J Dis Child* 1970; 119:326–331.
88. Landrigan PH, Stoffels MA, Anderson E, et al: Epidemic rubella in adolescent boys. Clinical features and results of vaccination. *JAMA* 1974; 227:1283–1287.
89. Anderson SG: Experimental rubella in human volunteers. *J Immunol* 1949; 62:29–40.
90. Ueda K, Singhaki Y, Sato T, et al: Hemolytic anemia following postnatally acquired rubella during the 1975–1977 rubella epidemic in Japan. *Clin Pediatr* 1985; 24:155–157.
91. Fujimoto T, Katoh C, Hayakawa H, et al: Two cases of rubella infection with cardiac involvement. *Jpn Heart J* 1979; 20:227–235.
92. Kriseman T: Rubella myocarditis in a 9–year–old patient. *Clin Pediatr* 1984; 23:240–241.
93. Simpson R: Rubella and polyarthritis. *Br Med J* 1940; 1:830–831.
94. Johnson RE, Hall AP: Rubella arthritis. Report of cases studied by latex tests. *N Engl J Med* 1958; 258:743–745.
95. Kantor TG, Tanner M: Rubella arthritis and rheumatoid arthritis. *Arthritis Rheum* 1962; 5:378–383.
96. Chambers RJ, Bywaters EG: Rubella synovitis. *Ann Rheum Dis* 1968; 22:263–268.
97. Yanez JE, Thompson GR, Mikkelsen WM, et al: Rubella arthritis. *Ann Intern Med* 1966; 64:772–777.
98. Chantler JK, Tingle AJ, Petty RE: Persistent rubella virus infection associated with chronic arthritis in children. *N Engl J Med* 1985; 313:1117–1123.
99. Ginsberg HS, Wilson JM: Acute thrombocytopenic purpura complicating rubella. *Am J Med* 1947; 3:652–656.
100. Wallace SJ: Thrombocytopenic purpura after rubella. *Lancet* 1963; 1:139–141.
101. Morse EE, Zinkham WH, Jackson DP: Thrombocytopenic purpura following rubella infection in children and adults. *Arch Intern Med* 1966; 117:573–579.
102. Ozsoylu S, Kanra G, Savas G: Thrombocytopenic purpura related to rubella infection. *Pediatrics* 1978; 62:567–569.
103. Volpato S, Vigi V, Gaburro D: Thrombocytopenic purpura as the only manifestations of rubella. *Lancet* 1969; 2:1249.
104. Walker JM, Nahmias AJ: Neurologic sequelae of rubella infection. *Clin Pediatr* 1966; 5:699–702.
105. Sherman FE, Michaels RH, Kenny FM: Acute encephalopathy (encephalitis) complicating rubella. *JAMA* 1965; 192:675–681.
106. Bell WE, McCormick WF: Rubella, in *Neurologic Infections in Children*. Philadelphia, Saunders, pp 446–467, 1981.
107. Pampiglione G, Young SE, Ramsey AM: Neurological and electroencephalographic problems of the rubella epidemic of 1962. *Br Med J* 1963; 2:1300–1302.
108. Mitchell W, Pampiglione G: Neurological and mental complications of rubella. *Lancet* 1954; 2:1250–1253.
109. Kenny FM, Michaels RH, Davis KS: Rubella encephalopathy. Later psychometric, neurologic, and encephalographic evaluation of seven survivors. *Am J Dis Child* 1965; 110:374–380.
110. Ziring PR, Florman AL, Cooper LZ: The diagnosis of rubella. *Pediatr Clin North Am* 1971; 18:87–97.
111. Iwakata S, Rhodes AJ, Labzoffsky NA: Laboratory diagnosis of rubella virus infections. *Can Med Assoc J* 1973; 108:894–904.
112. Rossi E, Phipps PH, Weber JM, et al: Persistence of humoral and cell-mediated immunity to rubella virus in cloistered nuns and school teachers. *J Infect Dis* 1981; 144:137–141.
113. Baublis JV, Brown GC: Specific response of the immunoglobulins to rubella infection. *Proc Soc Exp Biol Med* 1968; 128:206–210.
114. Best JM, Banatvala JE, Watson D: Serum IgM and IgG response in postnatally acquired rubella. *Lancet* 1969; 2:65–68.
115. Ogra PL, Kerr-Grant D, Umana G, et al: Antibody response in serum and nasopharynx after naturally acquired and vaccine-induced infection with rubella virus. *N Engl J Med* 1971; 285:1333–1339.
116. Morag A, Morag B, Bernstein JM, et al: In vitro correlates of cell-mediated immunity in human tonsils after natural or induced rubella virus infection. *J Infect Dis* 1975; 131:409–416.
117. Buimovici-Klein E, Weiss K, Cooper LZ: Interferon production in lymphocyte cultures after rubella infection in humans. *J Infect Dis* 1977; 135:380–385.
118. White LR, Sever JL, Alepa FP: Maternal and congenital rubella before 1964: Frequency, clinical features and search for isoimmune phenomena. *J Pediatr* 1969; 74:198–207.
119. Sever JL, Nelson KB, Gilkeson MR: Rubella epidemic 1964: Effect on 6,000 pregnancies. *Am J Dis Child* 1965; 110:395–407.
120. Lamprecht C, Schauf V, Warren D, et al: An outbreak of rubella in Chicago. *JAMA* 1981; 247:1129–1133.
121. Avery GB, Monif GG, Sever JL, et al: Rubella syndrome after inapparent maternal illness. *Am J Dis Child* 1965; 110:444–446.
122. Rudolph AJ, Desmond MM: Clinical manifestations of the congenital rubella syndrome. *Int Ophthalmol Clin* 1972; 12:3–19.
123. Dudgeon JA: Congenital rubella. Pathogenesis and immunology. *Am J Dis Child* 1969; 118:35–44.
124. Horstmann DM, Banatvala JE, Riordan JT, et al: Maternal rubella and the rubella syndrome in infants. Epidemiologic, clinical and virologic observations. *Am J Dis Child* 1965; 110:408–415.
125. Alford CA, Neva FA, Weller TH: Virologic and serologic studies on human products of conception after maternal rubella. *N Engl J Med* 1964; 271:1275–1281.
126. Kay HE, Peppercorn ME, Porterfield JS, et al: Congenital rubella infection of human embryo. *Br Med J* 1964; 2:166–167.
127. Driscoll SG: Histopathology of gestational rubella. *Am J Dis Child* 1969; 118:49–53.
128. Sallomi SJ: Rubella in pregnancy. A review of prospective studies from the literature. *Obstet Gynecol* 1966; 27:252–256.
129. Sheridan MD: Final report of a prospective study of children whose mothers had rubella in early pregnancy. *Br Med J* 1964; 2:536–539.

130. Peckham CS: Clinical and laboratory study of children exposed in utero to maternal rubella. *Arch Dis Child* 1972; 47:571–577.

131. Hardy JB, McCracken GH, Gilkeson MR, et al: Adverse fetal outcome following maternal rubella after the first trimester of pregnancy. *JAMA* 1969; 207:2414–2420.

132. Cooper LZ, Ziring PR, Ockerse AB, et al: Rubella: Clinical manifestations and management. *Am J Dis Child* 1969; 118:18–29.

133. Munro ND, Sheppard S, Smithells RW, et al: Temporal relations between maternal rubella and congenital defects. *Lancet* 1987; 1:201–204.

134. Plotkin SA, Cochran W, Lindquist JM, et al: Congenital rubella syndrome in late infancy. *JAMA* 1967; 200:435–441.

135. Forrest JM, Menser MA: Congenital rubella in school children and adolescents. *Arch Dis Child* 1970; 45:63–69.

136. Ueda K, Nishida Y, Oshima K, et al: Congenital rubella syndrome: Correlation of gestational age at time of maternal rubella with type of defect. *J Pediatr* 1979; 94:763–765.

137. Ueda K, Hisanaga S, Nishida Y, et al: Low birth weight and congenital rubella syndrome. Effect of gestational age at time of maternal rubella infection. *Clin Pediatr* 1981; 20:730–733.

138. Cooper LZ, Green RH, Krugman S, et al: Neonatal thrombocytopenic purpura and other manifestations of rubella contracted in utero. *Am J Dis Child* 1965; 110:416–427.

139. Rudolph AJ, Yow MD, Phillips CA, et al: Transplacental rubella infection in newly born infants. *JAMA* 1965; 191:843–845.

140. Chiribaga-Klein S, Oberfield SE, Casullo AM, et al: Growth in congenital rubella syndrome and correlation with clinical manifestations. *J Pediatr* 1989; 115:251–255.

141. Rudolph AJ, Singleton EB, Rosenberg HS: Osseous manifestations of the congenital rubella syndrome. *Am J Dis Child* 1965; 110:428–433.

142. Korones SB, Ainger LE, Monif GR, et al: Congenital rubella syndrome: Study of 22 infants. Myocardial damage and other new clinical aspects. *Am J Dis Child* 1965; 110:434–440.

143. Miyazaki S, Ohtsuka M, Ueda K, et al: Coombs positive hemolytic anemia in congenital rubella. *J Pediatr* 1979; 94:759–760.

144. Hastreiter AR, Joorabchi B, Pujatti G, et al: Cardiovascular lesions associated with congenital rubella. *J Pediatr* 1967; 71:59–65.

145. Dudgeon JA: Congenital cataracts: Virological aspects. *Proc R Soc Med* 1969; 62:693–694.

146. Wolff SM: The ocular manifestations of congenital rubella. *Trans Am Ophthalmol Soc* 1972; 70:577–614.

147. Peckham CS, Martin JA, Marshall WC, et al: Congenital rubella deafness: A preventable disease. *Lancet* 1979; 1:258–261.

148. Gumpel SM, Hayes K, Dudgeon JA: Congenital perceptive deafness: Role of intrauterine rubella. *Br Med J* 1971; 2:300–304.

149. Desmond MM, Wilson GS, Melnick JL, et al: Congenital rubella encephalitis. Course and early sequelae. *J Pediatr* 1967; 71:311–331.

150. Desmond MM, Montgomery JR, Melnick JL, et al: Congenital rubella encephalitis. Effect on growth and early development. *Am J Dis Child* 1969; 118:30–31.

151. Hardy JB: Clinical and developmental aspects of congenital rubella. *Arch Otolaryngol* 1973; 98: 230–236.

152. Chess S, Fernandez P, Korn S: Behavioral consequences of congenital rubella. *J Pediatr* 1978; 93:699–703.

153. Desmond MM, Fisher ES, Vorderman AL, et al: The longitudinal course of congenital rubella encephalitis in nonretarded children. *J Pediatr* 1978; 93:584–591.

154. Forrest JM, Menser MA, Burgess JA: High frequency of diabetes mellitus in young adults with congenital rubella. *Lancet* 1971; 2:332–334.

155. Menser MA, Forrest JM, Bransby RD: Rubella infection and diabetes mellitus. *Lancet* 1978; 1:57–60.

156. Forrest JM, Menser MA, Harley JD: Diabetes mellitus and congenital rubella. *Pediatrics* 1969; 44:445–446.

157. Johnson GM, Tudor RB: Diabetes mellitus and congenital rubella infection. *Am J Dis Child* 1970; 120:453–455.

158. Plotkin SA, Kaye R: Diabetes mellitus and congenital rubella. *Pediatrics* 1970; 46:650–651.

159. Floret D, Rosenberg D, Hage GN, et al: Hyperthyroidism, diabetes mellitus and the congenital rubella syndrome. *Acta Paediatr Scand* 1980; 69:259–261.

160. Sever JL, South MA, Shaver KA: Delayed manifestations of congenital rubella. *Rev Infect Dis* 1985; 7(suppl 1): S164–S169.

161. DePrins F, Van Assche FA, Desmyter J, et al: Congenital rubella and diabetes mellitus, letter. *Lancet* 1978; 1:439–440.

162. Monif GR, Avery GB, Korones SB, et al: Postmortem isolation of rubella virus from three children with rubella-syndrome defects. *Lancet* 1965; 1:723–724.

163. Bunnell CE, Monif GR: Interstitial pancreatitis in the congenital rubella syndrome. *J Pediatr* 1972; 80:465–466.

164. Clarke WL, Shaver KA, Bright GM, et al: Autoimmunity in congenital rubella. *J Pediatr* 1984; 104:370–373.

165. Ginsberg-Fellner F, Witt ME, Fedun B, et al: Diabetes mellitus and autoimmunity in patients with the congenital rubella syndrome. *Rev Infect Dis* 1985; 7(suppl 1):S170–S176.

166. Ziring PR, Fedun BA, Cooper LZ: Thyrotoxicosis in congenital rubella, letter. *J Pediatr* 1975; 87:1002.

167. Neiberg PI, Gardner LI: Thyroiditis and congenital rubella syndrome, letter. *J Pediatr* 1976; 89:156.

168. Comas AP: Congenital rubella and acquired hypothyroidism secondary to Hashimoto thyroiditis, letter. *J Pediatr* 1976; 88:1065–1066.

169. Ziring PR, Gallo G, Finegold M, et al: Chronic lymphocytic thyroiditis: Identification of rubella virus antigen in the thyroid of a child with congenital rubella. *J Pediatr* 1977; 90:419–420.

170. Preece MA, Kearney PJ, Marshall WC: Growth hormone deficiency in congenital rubella. *Lancet* 1977; 2:842–844.

171. Boger WP: Late ocular complications in congenital rubella syndrome. *Ophthalmology* 1980; 87:1244–1252.

172. Boger WP, Petersen RA, Robb RM: Keratoconus and acute hydrops in mentally retarded patients with congenital rubella syndrome. *Am J Ophthalmol* 1981; 91:231–233.

173. Boger WP, Petersen RA, Robb RM: Spontaneous absorption of the lens in congenital rubella syndrome. *Arch Ophthalmol* 1981; 99:433–434.

174. Townsend JJ, Baringer JR, Wolinsky JS, et al: Progressive rubella panencephalitis. Late onset after congenital rubella. *N Engl J Med* 1975; 292:990–993.

175. Weil ML, Itabashi HH, Cremer NE, et al: Chronic progressive panencephalitis due to rubella virus simulating subacute sclerosing panencephalitis. *N Engl J Med* 1975; 292:994–998.

176. Cremer NE, Oshiro LS, Weil ML, et al: Isolation of rubella virus in chronic progressive panencephalitis. *J Gen Virol* 1975; 29:143–153.

177. Waxham MN, Wolinsky JS: Rubella virus and its effect on the central nervous system. *Neurologic Clinics* 1984; 2:367–385.

178. Wolinsky JS, Berg BO, Maitland CJ: Progressive rubella panencephalitis. *Arch Neurol* 1976; 33:722–723.

179. Phillips CA, Rawls WE, Melnick JE, et al: Viral studies of a congenital rubella epidemic. *Health Lab Sci* 1966; 3:118–123.

180. Bellanti JA, Artenstein MS, Olson LC, et al: Congenital rubella. Clinicopathologic, virologic, and immunologic studies. *Am J Dis Child* 1965; 110:464–472.

181. Michaels RH: Immunologic aspects of congenital rubella. *Pediatrics* 1969; 43:339–350.

182. Cooper LZ, Krugman S: Diagnosis and management: Congenital rubella. *Pediatrics* 1966; 37:335–338.

183. Schiff GM, Sutherland JM, Light IJ, et al: Studies on congenital rubella. Preliminary results on the frequency and significance of presence of rubella virus in the newborn and the effect of gammaglobulin in preventing congenital rubella. *Am J Dis Child* 1965; 110:441–443.

184. Menser MA, Harley JD, Hertzberg R, et al: Persistence of virus in lens for three years after prenatal rubella. *Lancet* 1967; 2:387–388.

185. Schiff GM, Dine MS: Transmission of rubella from newborns. A controlled study among young adult women and report of an unusual case. *Am J Dis Child* 1965; 110:447–451.

186. Alford CA: Studies on antibody in congenital rubella infections.

I. Physicochemical and immunologic investigations of rubella neutralizing antibody. *Am J Dis Child* 1965; 110:455–463.

187. McCracken GH, Hardy JB, Chen TC, et al: Serum immunoglobulin levels in newborn infants. II. Survey of cord and follow-up sera from 123 infants with congenital rubella. *J Pediatr* 1969; 74:383–392.

188. Cradock-Watson JE, Ridehalgh MK, Chantler S: Specific immunoglobulins in infants with the congenital rubella syndrome. *J Hyg Camb* 1976; 76:109–123.

189. Hayes K, Dudgeon JA, Soothill JF: Humoral immunity in congenital rubella. *Clin Exp Immunol* 1967; 2:653–667.

190. Cooper LZ, Florman AL, Ziring PR, et al: Loss of rubella hemagglutination-inhibition antibody in congenital rubella. Failure of seronegative children with congenital rubella to respond to HPV-77 vaccine. *Am J Dis Child* 1971; 122:397–403.

191. Hardy JB, Sever JL, Gilkeson MR: Declining antibody titers in children with congenital rubella. *J Pediatr* 1969; 75:213–220.

192. Singer DB, South MA, Montgomery JE, et al: Congenital rubella syndrome. Lymphoid tissue and immunologic status. *Am J Dis Child* 1969; 118:54–61.

193. Claman HN, Suvatte V, Githens JH, et al: Histiocytic reaction in dysgammaglobulinemia and congenital rubella. *Pediatrics* 1970; 46:89–96.

194. Stern LM, Forbes IJ: Dysgammaglobulinemia and temporary immune paresis in a case of congenital rubella. *Aust Pediatr J* 1975; 11:38–41.

195. Plotkin SA, Klaus RM, Whitely JP: Hypogammaglobulinemia in an infant with congenital rubella syndrome; failure of amantadine to stop virus excretion. *J Pediatr* 1966; 69:1085–1090.

196. Michaels RH: Suppression of antibody response in congenital rubella. *J Pediatr* 1972; 80:583–588.

197. Olson GB, South MA, Good RA: Phytohemagglutinin unresponsiveness of lymphocytes from babies with congenital rubella. *Nature* 1967; 214:695–696.

198. Buimovici-Klein E, Lang PB, Ziring PR, et al: Impaired cell-mediated immune response in patients with congenital rubella: Correlation with gestational age at time of infection. *Pediatrics* 1979; 64:620–626.

199. Meyer HM, Parkman PD, Panos TC: Attenuated rubella virus. II. Production of an experimental live-virus vaccine and clinical trials. *N Engl J Med* 1966; 275:575–580.

200. Meyer HM, Parkman PD, Hobbins TE, et al: Attenuated rubella viruses. Laboratory and clinical characteristics. *Am J Dis Child* 1969; 118:155–165.

201. Prinzie A, Huygelin C, Gold J, et al: Experimental live attenuated rubella virus vaccine. Clinical evaluation of Cendehill strain. *Am J Dis Child* 1969; 118:172–177.

202. Plotkin SA, Farquhar JD, Katz M, et al: Attenuation of RA 27/3 rubella virus in WI-38 human diploid cells. *Am J Dis Child* 1969; 118:178–185.

203. Weibel RE, Stokes J, Buynak EB, et al: Live rubella vaccines in adults and children. *Am J Dis Child* 1969; 118:226–229.

204. Cooper LZ, Ziring PR, Weiss HJ, et al: Transient arthritis after rubella vaccination. *Am J Dis Child* 1969; 118:218–225.

205. Weibel RE, Stokes J, Buynak EB, et al: Influence of age on clinical response to HPV-77 duck rubella vaccine. *JAMA* 1972; 222:805–807.

206. Halstead SB, Char DF, Diwan AR: Evaluation of three rubella vaccines in adult women. *JAMA* 1970; 211:991–995.

207. Horstmann DM, Liebhaber H, Kohorn EI: Postpartum vaccination of rubella-susceptible women. *Lancet* 1970; 2:1003–1006.

208. Fox JP, Rainey HS, Hall CE, et al: Rubella vaccine in postpubertal women. Experience in Washington state. *JAMA* 1976; 236:837–843.

209. Dudgeon JA, Marshall WC, Peckham CS: Rubella vaccine trials in adults and children. Comparison of three attenuated vaccines. *Am J Dis Child* 1969; 118:237–242.

210. Weibel RE, Villarejos VM, Klein EB, et al: Clinical and laboratory studies of live attenuated RA 27/3 and HPV 77-DE rubella virus vaccines. *Proc Soc Exp Biol Med* 1980; 165:44–49.

211. Black FL, Lamm SH, Emmons JE, et al: Reactions to rubella vaccine and persistence of antibody in virgin-soil populations after vaccination and wild-virus-induced immunization. *J Infect Dis* 1976; 133:393–398.

212. Monto AS, Cavallaro JJ, Whale EH: Frequency of arthralgia in women receiving one of three rubella vaccines. *Arch Intern Med* 1970; 126:635–639.

213. Ogra PL, Herd JK: Arthritis associated with induced rubella infection. *J Immunol* 1971; 107:810–813.

214. Kilroy AW, Schaffner W, Fleet WF: Two syndromes following rubella immunization. *JAMA* 1970; 214:2287–2292.

215. Cherry JD, Bobinski JE, Comerci GD: A clinical trial with live attenuated rubella virus vaccine (Cendehill 51 strain). *J Pediatr* 1969; 75:79–86.

216. Halstead SB, Diwan AR: Failure to transmit rubella virus vaccine. A close-contact study in adults. *JAMA* 1971; 215:634–636.

217. Scott HD, Byrne EB: Exposure of susceptible pregnant women to rubella vaccinees. Serologic findings during the Rhode Island immunization campaign. *JAMA* 1971; 215:609–612.

218. Ogra PL, Kerr-Grant D, Umana G, et al: Antibody response in serum and nasopharynx after naturally acquired and vaccine-induced infection with rubella virus. *N Engl J Med* 1971; 285:1333–1339.

219. Plotkin SA, Farquhar JD, Ogra PL: Immunologic properties of RA 27/3 rubella virus vaccine. A comparison with strains presently licensed in the United States. *JAMA* 1973; 225:585–590.

220. Grillner L: Neutralizing antibodies after rubella vaccination of newly delivered women: A comparison of three vaccines. *Scand J Infect Dis* 1975; 7:169–172.

221. Schlueder berg A, Horstmann DM, Andiman WA, et al: Neutralizing and hemagglutination-inhibition antibodies to rubella virus as indicators of protective immunity in vaccinees and naturally immune individuals. *J Infect Dis* 1978; 138:877–883.

222. LeBouvier GL, Plotkin SA: Precipitin responses to rubella vaccine RA 27/3. *J Infect Dis* 1971; 123:220–222.

223. Weibel RE, Buynak EB, McLean AA, et al: Persistence of antibody in human subjects for 7 to 10 years following administration of combined live attenuated measles, mumps, and rubella virus vaccines. *Proc Soc Exp Biol Med* 1980; 165:260–263.

224. Herrmann KL, Halstead SB, Wiebanga NH: Rubella antibody persistence after immunization. *JAMA* 1982; 247:193–196.

225. Weibel RE, Buynak EB, McLean AA, et al: Persistence of antibody after administration of monovalent and combined live attenuated measles, mumps, and rubella vaccines. *Pediatrics* 1978; 61:5–11.

226. Horstmann DM: Controlling rubella: Problems and perspectives. *Ann Intern Med* 1975; 83:412–417.

227. Balfour HH, Amren DP: Rubella, measles and mumps antibodies following vaccination of children. A potential rubella problem. *Am J Dis Child* 1978; 132:573–577.

228. Liebhaber H, Ingalls TH, LeBouvier GL, et al: Vaccination with RA 27/3 rubella vaccine. Persistence of immunity and resistance to challenge after two years. *Am J Dis Child* 1972; 123:133–136.

229. Balfour HH, Groth KE, Edelman CK: RA 27/3 rubella vaccine. A four-year follow-up. *Am J Dis Child* 1980; 134:350–353.

230. Black FL, Lamm SH, Emmons JE, et al: Durability of antibody titers induced by RA 27/3 rubella virus vaccine. *J Infect Dis* 1978; 137:322–323.

231. Hillary IB, Griffith AH: Persistence of antibody 10 years after vaccination with Wistar RA 27/3 strain live attenuated rubella vaccine. *Br Med J* 1980; 2:1580–1581.

232. Horstmann DM, Schlueder berg A, Emmons JE, et al: Persistence of vaccine-induced immune responses to rubella: Comparison with natural infection. *Rev Infect Dis* 1985; 7(suppl 1):S80–S85.

233. Banatvala JE, Best JM, O'Shea S, et al: Persistence of rubella antibodies after vaccination: Detection after experimental challenge. *Rev Infect Dis* 1985; 7(suppl 1):S86–S90.

234. Schiff GM, Young BC, Stefanovic GM, et al: Challenge with rubella virus after loss of detectable vaccine-induced antibody. *Rev Infect Dis* 1985; 7(suppl 1):S157–S163.

235. Balfour HH, Groth KE, Edelman CK, et al: Rubella viraemia and antibody responses after rubella vaccination and reimmunization. *Lancet* 1981; 1:1078–1080.

236. Butler AB, Scott RMcN, Schydlower M, et al: The immunoglobulin response to reimmunization with rubella vaccine. *J Pediatr* 1981; 99:531–534.

237. Horstmann DM, Liebhaber H, LeBouvier GL, et al: Rubella: Reinfection of vaccinated and naturally immune persons exposed in an epidemic. *N Engl J Med* 1970; 283:771–778.

238. Davis WJ, Larson HE, Simsarian JP, et al: A study of rubella immunity and resistance to infection. *JAMA* 1971; 215:600–608.

239. Evans AS, Niederman JC, Sawyer RN, et al: Prospective studies of a group of Yale University freshmen. II. Occurrence of acute respiratory infections and rubella. *J Infect Dis* 1971; 123:271–278.

240. Wilkins J, Leedom JM, Portnoy B, et al: Reinfection with rubella virus despite live vaccine induced immunity. *Am J Dis Child* 1969; 118:275–294.

241. Detels R, Grayston JT, Kim KS, et al: Prevention of clinical and subclinical rubella infection. *Am J Dis Child* 1969; 118:295–300.

242. Vesikari T: Antibody response in rubella reinfection. *Scand J Infect Dis* 1972; 4:11–16.

243. Chang TW, DesRosiers S, Weinstein L: Clinical and serologic studies of an outbreak of rubella in a vaccinated population. *N Engl J Med* 1970; 283:246–248.

244. Abrutyn E, Herrmann KL, Karchmer AW, et al: Rubella vaccine comparative study. Nine-month followup and serologic response to natural challenge. *Am J Dis Child* 1970; 120:129–133.

245. Farquhar JD: Follow-up on rubella vaccinations and experience with subclinical reinfection. *J Pediatr* 1972; 81:460–465.

246. Plotkin SA, Farquhar JD: Immunity to rubella: Comparison between naturally and artificially induced resistance. *Postgrad Med J* 1972; 48:47–54.

247. Grillner L: Immunity to intranasal challenge with rubella virus two years after vaccination: Comparison of three vaccines. *J Infect Dis* 1976; 133:637–641.

248. Fogel A, Gerichter CB, Barnes B, et al: Response to experimental challenge in persons immunized with different rubella vaccines. *J Pediatr* 1978; 92:26–29.

249. Harcourt GC, Best JM, Banatvala JE: Rubella-specific serum and nasopharyngeal antibodies in volunteers with naturally acquired and vaccine-induced immunity after intranasal challenge. *J Infect Dis* 1980; 142:145–155.

250. Schiff GM, Donath R, Roth T: Experimental rubella studies. I. Clinical and laboratory features of infection caused by the Brown strain rubella virus. II. Artificial challenge studies of adult rubella vaccinees. *Am J Dis Child* 1969; 118:269–274.

251. Strannegard Ö, Holm SE, Hermodsson S, et al: Case of apparent reinfection with rubella. *Lancet* 1970; 1:240–241.

252. Eilard T, Strannegard Ö: Rubella reinfection in pregnancy followed by transmission to the fetus. *J Infect Dis* 1974; 129:594–596.

253. Haukenes G, Haram KO: Clinical rubella after reinfection. *N Engl J Med* 1972; 287:1204.

254. Haukenes G, Haram KO, Solberg CO: Clinical rubella after reinfection: False-positive reaction of specific HI antibody. *N Engl J Med* 1973; 289:429.

255. Northrop RL, Gardner WM, Geittmann WF: Rubella reinfection during early pregnancy. A case report. *Obstet Gynecol* 1972; 39:524–526.

256. Partridge JW, Flewett TH, Whitehead JEM: Congenital rubella affecting an infant whose mother had rubella antibodies before conception. *Br Med J* 1981; 282:187–188.

257. Biano S, Cochran W, Herrmann KL, et al: Rubella reinfection during pregnancy. A case of mistaken diagnosis of congenital rubella. *Am J Dis Child* 1975; 129:1353–1356.

258. Boué A, Nicholas A, Montagnon B: Reinfection with rubella in pregnant women. *Lancet* 1971; 1:1251–1253.

259. Saule H, Enders G, Zeller J, et al: Congenital rubella after previous immunity of the mother. *Eur J Pediatr* 1988; 147:195–196.

260. Levine JB, Berkowitz CD, St Geme JW: Rubella virus reinfection during pregnancy leading to late-onset congenital rubella syndrome. *J Pediatr* 1982; 100:589–591.

261. Levine JB, Berkowitz DC, St. Geme JW: Rubella virus reinfection during pregnancy leading to late-onset congenital rubella syndrome. *J Pediatr* 1982; 100:589–591.

262. Modlin JF, Herrmann K, Brandling-Bennett AD, et al: Risk of congenital abnormality after inadvertent rubella vaccination of pregnant women. *N Engl J Med* 1976; 294:972–974.

263. Centers for Disease Control: Rubella vaccination during pregnancy—United States, 1971–1988. *MMWR* 1989; 38:289–293.

264. Vaheri A, Vesikari T, Oker-Blom N, et al: Isolation of attenuated rubella-vaccine virus from human products of conception and uterine cervix. *N Engl J Med* 1972; 286:1071–1074.

265. Bolognese RJ, Corson SL, Fuccillo DA, et al: Evaluation of possible transplacental infection with rubella vaccination during pregnancy. *Am J Obstet Gynecol* 1973; 117:939–941.

266. Bolognese RJ, Corson SL: Rubella vaccination. A critical review. *Obstet Gynecol* 1973; 42:851–855.

267. Phillips CA, Maeck JV, Rogers WA, et al: Intrauterine rubella infection following immunization with rubella vaccine. *JAMA* 1970; 213:624–625.

268. Wyll SA, Herrmann KL: Inadvertent rubella vaccination of pregnant women. Fetal risk in 215 cases. *JAMA* 1971; 225:1472–1476.

269. Larson HE, Parkman PD, Davis WJ, et al: Inadvertent rubella virus vaccination during pregnancy. *N Engl J Med* 1971; 870–873.

270. Ebbin AJ, Wilson MG, Chandor SB, et al: Inadvertent rubella immunization in pregnancy. *Am J Obstet Gynecol* 1973; 117:505–512.

271. Fleet WF, Benz EW, Karzon DT, et al: Fetal consequences of maternal rubella immunization. *JAMA* 1974; 227:621–627.

272. Hayden GF, Herrmann KL, Buimovici-Klein E, et al: Subclinical congenital rubella infection associated with maternal rubella vaccination in early pregnancy. *J Pediatr* 1980; 96:869–872.

273. Bernstein DI, Ogra PL: Fetomaternal aspects of immunization with RA 27/3 live attenuated rubella virus vaccine during pregnancy. *J Pediatr* 1980; 97:467–470.

274. Preblud SR, Stetler HC, Frank JA, et al: Fetal risk associated with rubella vaccine. *JAMA* 1981; 246:1413–1417.

275. Centers for Disease Control: Prelicensing statement on rubella virus vaccine. Recommendation of the Public Health Service Advisory Committee on Immunization Practices. *MMWR* 1969; 18:124–125.

276. American Academy of Pediatrics: *Report of the Committee on Infectious Diseases,* ed 21. Evanston, Ill, American Academy of Pediatrics, 1988, pp 362–370.

277. Lehane DE, Newberg NR, Beam WE: Evaluation of rubella herd immunity during an epidemic. *JAMA* 1970; 213:2236–2239.

278. Cheldelin LV, Francis DP, Tilson H: Postpartum rubella vaccination. A survey of private physicians in Oregon. *JAMA* 1973; 225:158–159.

279. Povar GJ, Maloney M, Watson WN, et al: Rubella screening and follow-up immunization in Vermont. *Am J Public Health* 1979; 69:285–286.

280. Centers for Disease Control: Recommendation of the Immunization Practices Advisory Committee (ACIP): Rubella prevention. *MMWR* 1981; 30:37–47.

281. Crawford GE, Gremillion DH: Epidemic measles and rubella in Air Force recruits: Impact of immunization. *J Infect Dis* 1981; 144:403–410.

282. Vaeth SJ: A rubella vaccination program for women entering the US Army. *Public Health Rep* 1979; 94:564–567.

283. Lieberman E, Faich GA, Simon PR, et al: Premarital screening in Rhode Island. *JAMA* 1981; 245:1333–1335.

284. Klein EB, Byrne T, Cooper LZ: Neonatal rubella in a breast-fed infant after postpartum maternal infection. *J Pediatr* 1980; 97:774–775.

285. Landes RD, Bass JW, Millunchick EW, et al: Neonatal rubella following postpartum maternal immunization. *J Pediatr* 1980; 97:465–467.

286. Haley RW, Emori G: The employee health service and infection

control in US hospitals, 1976–1977. I. Screening procedures. *JAMA* 1981; 246:844–847.

287. Orenstein WA, Heseltine PN, LeGagnoux SJ, et al: Rubella vaccine and susceptible hospital employees. Poor physician participation. *JAMA* 1981; 245:711–713.

288. Lewy RM: Occupational health programs for house staff physicians. Preemployment medical examination. *JAMA* 1981; 246:1432–1434.

289. Wakefield M, Alexander WJ: Rubella immunization of susceptible medical students. *JAMA* 1981; 246:1900–1901.

290. Weiss KE, Falvo CE, Buimovici-Klein E, et al: Evaluation of an employee health service as a setting for a rubella screening and immunization program. *Am J Public Health* 1979; 69:281–283.

291. Preblud SR, Serdula MK, Frank JA, et al: Rubella vaccination in the United States: A ten-year review. *Epidemiol Rev* 1981; 2:171–194.

292. Rubella: Who needs a blood test, editorial. *Lancet* 1979; 1:1329–1331.

293. Tobin JO'H, Sheppard S, Smithells RW, et al: Rubella in the United Kingdom, 1970–1973. *Rev Infect Dis* 1985; 7(suppl 1):S47–S52.

294. Hambling MH: Effect of a vaccination programme on the distribution of rubella antibodies in women of childbearing age. *Lancet* 1975; 1:1130–1133.

295. Clarke M, Boustred J, Schild GC, et al: Effect of rubella vaccination on serologic status of young adults in the United Kingdom. *Lancet* 1979; 1:1224–1226.

296. Knox EG: Strategy for rubella vaccination. *Int J Epidemiol* 1980; 9:13–23.

297. Levin MJ, Oxman MN, Moore MG, et al: Diagnosis of congenital rubella in utero. *N Engl J Med* 1974; 290:1187–1188.

298. Terry GM, Ho-Terry L, Warren RC, et al: First trimester diagnosis of congenital rubella: A laboratory investigation. *Br Med J* 1986; 292:930–933.

299. Grose C, Itani O, Weiner CP: Prenatal diagnosis of fetal infection: Advances from amniocentesis to cordocentesis—congenital toxoplasmosis, rubella, cytomegalovirus, varicella virus, parvovirus and human immunodeficiency virus. *Pediatr Infect Dis J* 1989; 8:459–468.

300. Mann JM, Preblud SR, Hoffman RE, et al: Assessing risks of rubella infection during pregnancy. A standardized approach. *JAMA* 1981; 245:1647–1652.

Filoviruses and Management of Viral Hemorrhagic Fevers*

C. J. Peters
Eugene D. Johnson
Kelly T. McKee, Jr.

FILOVIRUSES: MARBURG VIRUS DISEASE AND EBOLA VIRAL HEMORRHAGIC FEVER

History

In 1967 a unique and lethal viral hemorrhagic fever (VHF) appeared simultaneously in workers from laboratories in Marburg and Frankfurt, West Germany, and Belgrade, Yugoslavia.[1] This infection was traced to contact with the blood and tissues of a group of African green or vervet monkeys imported from Uganda. The etiologic agent, subsequently designated Marburg (MBG) virus, was a large, pleomorphic, filamentous virus which could not be readily classified. Though a small outbreak of MGB virus disease occurred in South Africa during 1975, the biomedical community largely forgot MBG virus until the fall of 1976, when two epidemics of severe hemorrhagic fever with a 60% to 90% mortality were reported from northern Zaire and southern Sudan.[2] Epidemiologic and virologic investigations established that the epidemics were caused by two distinct virus strains morphologically similar to MBG virus. Named after the Ebola river, which separates Sudan and Zaire, the agents are referred to here as Ebola-Zaire and Ebola-Sudan, or EBO-Z and EBO-S. Although exhaustive epidemiologic studies of the original outbreaks as well as subsequent sporadic cases have failed to elucidate the natural history of these viruses, biochemical studies have revealed that these agents belong to a novel taxonomic family, now named *Filoviridae*.[3]

The usual pattern seen with large outbreaks begins with a focus that disseminates infection to a nucleus of patients—for example, a virus laboratory processing infected African monkey tissues or a cluster of nosocomial infections disseminated through unsterilized syringes. Secondary and subsequent generations of disease occur as close family members or medical personnel are infected, usually by extensive contact with the hemorrhagic fever patient. The epidemic terminates since the initial focus is transient, and the spread of the infection in families or close contacts is inefficient. Observations of epidemics and sporadic cases suggest that the major route of interhuman transmission of these viruses requires

* The views of the authors do not purport to reflect the positions of the Department of the Army or the Department of Defense.

Table 26-1
Proteins of Filoviruses

Protein Designation	Molecular Weight × 10⁻³		Proposed Protein Function
	EBO	MBG	
L	180	180	Transcriptase
GP	125	140	Glycoprotein, bromelain-sensitive in purified virions
NP	104	98	Phosphorylated nucleocapsid protein released by detergent treatment
VP40	40	40	Membrane protein (rhabdovirus M protein analogue)
VP35	35	35	Transcriptase modifier
VP30	30	30	Phosphorylated nucleocapsid protein associated with the nucleocapsid under low-salt conditions
VP24	24	24	Membrane protein?

EBO = Ebola virus; MBG = Marburg virus.
Data from Kiley et al,[12, 14] Buchmeier et al,[13] Elliott et al.[15]

direct contact with infective blood or body fluids, although droplet and aerosol infections may occur.

Clinically, Marburg virus disease and Ebola hemorrhagic fever are the most severe of the VHFs. Diarrhea, abdominal pain, extreme prostration, and cachexia are more impressive in comparison with the other VHFs, and suggestive evidence of disseminated intravascular regulation (DIC) is present. In reported epidemics, the ratio of disease to infection is high and mortality substantial. However, a clear understanding of the significance of these agents in human disease will require further investigation, particularly the development of comprehensive surveillance studies using suitable diagnostic tests. Ten percent to fifty percent of human sera from diverse African environments react in the widely used indirect fluorescent antibody or IFA test. If these serologic reactions represent infections with classical filoviruses, MBG and EBO viruses pose significant health threats in sub-Saharan Africa.

Replication, Structure, and Genetics

The morphology of MBG and EBO viruses is unique.[4-11] Viral nucleocapsids take form as cytoplasmic tubular structures, which appear to emerge from inclusion bodies and bud through the cell membrane. The resulting particles range from 130 nm up to 8000 to 14,000 nm in length, but are more uniform in diameter (80 nm). Although coenvelopment of multiple nucleocapsids during budding results in the formation of bizarre structures of widely varying lengths, as well as branching, circular, or shapes like the number 6, infectivity of purified preparations is associated with rodlike particles 790 nm (MBG) and 970 nm (EBO) in length. There is a central 20- to 30-nm axis surrounded by a helically wound 40- to 50-nm capsid which has a 3- to 5-nm interval between cross-striations. These nucleocapsids are invested with an envelope bearing 7- to 10-nm surface projections. The sequence of the virus-cell interaction in vivo in MBG-infected monkey hepatocytes[4] and in vitro in EBO-infected Vero cells[7] is similar. Early after infection, masses of nucleocapsids and other structures form inclusions in the cytoplasm. These nucleocapsids then are the focus for budding

of virions from apparently healthy cells. Later, vigorous virus production continues but evidence of intracellular edema appears, eventually terminating in destruction of organelles and cell lysis.

Biochemical analysis of the protein species from purified MBG or EBO virions show seven peptides (Table 26-1).[12-15] The virion RNA is single-stranded, with a molecular weight of 4×10^6 daltons. The failure of isolated RNA to bind to oligo-dT, or to infect cells, indicates that EBO is a negative-stranded virus.[16] The MBG and EBO viruses share 3′ RNA sequences, which in turn differ from those of rhabdoviruses.[17] Six polyadenylated positive-stranded messages have been detected in infected cells.[18]

In spite of their unusual morphologic properties and separate taxonomic status, these viruses resemble ordinary enveloped RNA viruses in their sensitivity to lipid solvents and inactivating agents such as formalin, ultraviolet light, hypochlorite, β-propriolactone, gamma radiation, and detergents or disinfectants containing phenol or quaternary ammonium compounds.[19-23] They are stable at room temperature for several days, and infectivity gradually declines over subsequent weeks. Inactivation at higher temperatures is much more rapid, but residual virus remains after heating at 56°C for 30 minutes. However, 60°C for 60 minutes inactivated $10^{5.5}$ guinea pig intraperitoneal LD_{50} (median lethal dose) of MBG in each of three experiments.[19]

The three viruses in the family each have differing properties (Table 26-2). MBG is clearly a distinct virus since its virion peptides have slightly different molecular weights than those of EBO virus,[3, 13, 14] the tryptic peptides of GP, NP, VP40, and VP24 are unrelated to those of EBO strains, and it is serologically quite unique. EBO-Z and EBO-S were originally regarded as two strains of the same virus because of their serologic cross-reactivity and their simultaneous appearance in two epidemics, albeit 850 km apart. Tryptic peptide and oligonucleotide fingerprints of EBO-Z isolates separated in time and space are similar to each other, as are EBO-S isolates from different years. However, substantial differences in these parameters between the two strains suggest that these viruses may differ more than was initially appreciated.[13, 24] Their serologic cross-reactivity is based solely on antibody-binding assays which, in other virus families, have generally been broadly reactive. Cross-neutralization tests have been inconclusive because of technical difficulties, although preliminary cross-challenge studies indicate a protective antigenic homology between the two Ebola viruses (E.D. Johnson, unpublished observations, 1988).

Epidemiology

Definitive evidence for the presence of these agents lies in the isolation of virus from clinical specimens. By these strict criteria, MBG and EBO viruses occupy nonoverlapping regions of sub-Saharan Africa. MBG virus has been identified in restricted regions of eastern and southern Africa: (1) The initial European epidemic followed exposure to monkeys captured and held in Uganda only 80 km from Mt Elgon on the Kenya-Uganda border,[1] and two additional index cases occurred in Kenya after travel in that country, including the Mt Elgon region[38] (E.D. Johnson, D. Silverstein, R. Zimmerman, B.K. Johnson, unpublished observations, 1988). (2) A single episode followed an index infection acquired in Zimbabwe or South Africa.[39, 40] Ebola virus has been isolated from fatal hemorrhagic fever cases in two northern regions of Zaire[35, 41] and a single site in southern Sudan.[36, 37]

However, the results of serologic surveys using the fluorescent antibody technique suggest MBG and EBO viruses have been active in Senegal, Nigeria, Ivory Coast, Liberia, Gabon, Cameroon, Central African Republic, Zaire, Sudan, Uganda, Kenya, and Zimbabwe.[42–50] A seroconversion to EBO with clinically compatible disease was reported from Kenya[51] and apparently asymptomatic seroconversions to EBO have been reported during field studies in Cameroon[45] and Central African Republic (E.D. Johnson, J.P. Gonzalez, C.J. Peters, A.J. Georges, unpublished observations, 1988). Though these results indicate a broad distribution of virus activity, there are several unresolved anomalies: (1) Highest antibody prevalence does not correlate with areas of reported disease. This discrepancy cannot be explained satisfactorily by the known inadequacy of surveillance for viral hemorrhagic fevers in the regions involved.[35, 41, 49] (2) Serologic evidence of virus infections is not limited to distinct ecological zones. EBO and, to a lesser extent, MBG virus antibodies occur in the moist tropical rain forest of central Africa and in seasonally dry grasslands of central and east Africa. (3) Positive IFA results are found under circumstances where filovirus activity seems unlikely[48] (Ho Wang Lee, E.D. Johnson, C. J. Peters, unpublished observations). Recent findings of extensive antibody positivity among monkeys from Africa, Asia, and elsewhere may lead to resolution of these apparent inconsistencies (see section on Recent Developments).

Recognized disease has occurred in sporadic cases, case clusters, or epidemics. Nosocomial, laboratory, or person-to-person spread often have been implicated in continuing transmission, but ultimately the reported seven well-established episodes of filovirus disease have been traced to a single index case. To the frustration of scientists in the field, the source of contagion to the index case has never been found nor has a natural source for these agents been identified in spite of attempts to detect antibodies in or isolate virus from presumed zoonotic reservoirs[35–40, 49, 52] (E.D. Johnson, J.P. Gonzales, A.J. Georges, unpublished observations, 1988). The original 1967 outbreak of MBG disease was traced to an incoming shipment of vervet monkeys, but careful testing of sera from primates trapped near their geographic origin in Uganda did not reveal antibodies to MBG virus.[52] Other surveys have identified a low prevalence of MBG antibodies in Kenyan vervets,[53] but the swiftly fatal infections induced by MBG in these and other primates argue against their role as a major reservoir. It was initially hoped that the finding of EBO-Z antibodies in guinea pigs in a small town in Zaire, which had experienced an Ebola HF case, might open a new approach to this enigmatic problem.[54] However, two subsequent studies failed to demonstrate household clustering of human or gunea pig antibodies or additional evidence to establish the guinea pig as a sentinel or disseminator of EBO-Z infection[55] (C.L. Scribner, E.D. Johnson, J. LeDuc, J.B. McCormick, unpublished observations, 1980).

In spite of an incomplete natural history for these viruses, useful information can be culled from the described outbreaks. In the 1967 MBG virus incident,[34] all 25 monkey-related cases were directly associated with contact with blood, organs, or cell cultures. Indeed, 20 of 29 persons with blood contact and four of 13 working with cell cultures fell ill. The five or six reported secondary cases occurred in medical personnel or spouses; four monkey handlers

Table 26–2
Comparison of Filoviruses

	Marburg (MBG)	Ebola, Zaire Strain (EBO-Z)	Ebola, Sudan Strain (EBO-S)
Morphology	Pleomorphic[5, 6]	Resembles MBG[7]	Increased prevalence of bizarre forms and empty virions[8]
Tryptic peptides of GP, NP, VP40, VP24	Unrelated to EBO-Z and EBO-S[14]	GP and VP40 have some similarities to EBO-S but only two apparently homologous oligopeptides[13]	See EBO-Z[13]
T-1 oligonucleotide fingerprints of RNA	Unrelated to EBO-Z and EBO-S	Some relation to EBO-S but at least 60 oligonucleotide differences[24]	See EBO-Z[24]
Serology	Slight if any cross with EBO-Z or EBO-S[25, 26]	Two- to ten-fold differences between EBO strains usually demonstrated[25, 27]	See EBO-Z[25, 27]
Isolation in Vero cells	Readily, CPE inconstant[28, 29]	Readily, CPE common[30, 31]	Difficult, CPE not observed[31]
Pathogenic for macaques	Occasional survivors	100% lethal[11]	Occasional survivors[11]
Pathogenic for suckling mice	No (replicates)[28, 32]	Yes[31]	No[31]
Adaptation to guinea pig lethality	Complete[33]	Complete[11]	More difficult[11]
Case fatality rate in epidemics	6/31 (19%) droplets, fomites, contact[34]	85/85 (100%) injection, 133/149 (90%) droplets, fomites or contact[35]	151/284 (53%)[36] 22/33 (67%)[37]

CPE = cytopathic effect.

and the many other intimate and casual medical or household contacts of the primary cases remained disease-free.

The first EBO-Z outbreak (1976), which lasted about 2 months and involved 318 persons with 280 deaths, was traced to the introduction of virus into a hospital setting where unsterilized needles and syringes were used to administer medicines to other patients.[35] A history of injection was elicited in 85 patients, an injection plus contact with another case in 43, and only contact with another case in 149. Most contact cases could be traced ultimately to a primary case receiving an injection in the hospital, and the epidemic waned with the closing of the hospital. Secondary attack rates within families ranged from 3% to 17% and were highest for first-degree relatives with intimate contact with sick patients. Up to five successive generations of human-to-human transmission occurred.

In the 1976 Sudanese epidemic[36] a similar pattern prevailed: about one third of cases were hospital-associated, although fewer data were obtained on parenteral exposure; secondary attack rates were about 12%; and close contact, such as nursing the patient, greatly increased the likelihood of infection. Sporadic MBG[38, 40, 56] and EBO-Z[41, 51] cases confirm the low rate of transmission in the absence of very close contact.

Virus may persist in sequestered sites such as the eye and the male genital tract for weeks,[56–58] but a true carrier state has not been described. The presence of virus in seminal fluid may be epidemiologically relevant.

Intensive retrospective investigation has been possible with only three index cases[38, 40] (E.D. Johnson and colleagues, unpublished observations, 1987) and has not elucidated the source of infection. The two MBG cases occurring in 1980 and 1987 had traveled in rural Kenya before their illness. Interestingly, both had visited the caves atop Mt Elgon within ten to 12 days of their fatal illnesses. There was no history of insect bites or animal exposure, which raises the speculation of aerosol transmission. Both MBG and EBO viruses are infectious by the aerosol route. Uninoculated monkeys housed in cages adjacent to virus-inoculated animals often develop typical fatal filovirus infections within 14 to 18 days, i.e., two seven- to nine-day incubation periods (E.D. Johnson, unpublished observations, 1984). Rhesus macaques and baboons (*Papio hamadryas*) exposed to as little as 100 plaque-forming units (PFU) of aerosolized EBO or MBG viruses also develop uniformly fatal hemorrhagic fevers (E.D. Johnson, J.D. White, R.W. Trotter, T.M. Cosgriff, unpublished observations, 1988).

Clinical Syndrome

Infection with all three agents presents a similar picture, although reported signs and symptoms vary in their frequency. Onset is sudden and marked by fever, chills, headache, myalgia, and anorexia. During the first days of disease abdominal pain, sore throat, nausea, vomiting, cough, and arthralgia are also common. Although constipation may occur in some cases, most patients will experience diarrhea, which is initially clear or mucoid and in severe cases becomes profuse, tarry, and/or bloody. Examination reveals an acutely ill, dehydrated, apathetic, often disoriented patient. Pharyngeal and conjunctival injection are usually present, sometimes accompanied by exudative or ulcerative lesions of the oropharynx. Basilar rales, abdominal tenderness, jaundice, and edema

are also described. Enlargement of spleen, liver, or lymph nodes is not a feature in EBO, but mild lymphadenopathy is common in MBG. At least half the patients will develop a nonpruritic maculopapular centripetal rash by day 5 to 7 of illness. This rash, which may involve the scrotum or labia majora, will be associated with varying degrees of erythema and subsequently desquamate. Hemorrhagic phenomena develop during the height of illness; although frequent, their occurrence and extent are of prognostic value. Gastrointestinal (GI) bleeding is most often recognized, but petechiae and hemorrhages from puncture wounds and mucous membranes are common. Changes in mentation, paresthesias, and nuchal rigidity often occur and emphasize neurologic involvement, which is also a poor prognostic sign.

In nonfatal cases fever lasts approximately five to nine days; fatal cases are usually signaled by clinical events early in their course and death commonly occurs on days 6 to 16 in association with intractable shock. Mortality is high (see Table 26–2): None of the 85 EBO-Z cases thought to be infected by contaminated needles survived and only 10% of contact cases recovered. Mortality in two EBO-S outbreaks was one half to two thirds. MBG cases have carried a lower mortality but have had better supportive care. Orchitis may occur during the acute phase or in recovery. Convalescence is prolonged with recuperation from wasting requiring weeks. Some patients have experienced myelitis, recurrent hepatitis, psychosis, or uveitis after recovery. Pregnant women may be at increased risk of abortion. Children of infected mothers frequently died during the Zaire EBO outbreak.

Laboratory studies usually show a leukopenia even in the earliest stages of illness. There is a left shift, and atypical lymphocytes may be seen. As the disease progresses, white blood counts may reach a nadir of 1000/μL and subsequently rise to elevated levels, particularly with secondary bacterial infection. Thrombocytopenia of 50,000 to 100,000/μL typically occurs with the fully developed VHF syndrome. Prothrombin and partial thromboplastin times are prolonged, and fibrin split products are present, although plasma fibrinogen levels may be modestly decreased, normal, or even elevated. Hypoproteinemia is common, and serum transaminase levels are usually markedly elevated, ranging from the hundreds to thousands of units per milliliter. Serum bilirubin elevations and frank jaundice occur in a minority of patients. Creatine phosphokinase measured in a few cases was normal. Hyperamylasemia in some patients has been associated with signs and symptoms consistent with pancreatitis. Proteinuria is common.

Diagnosis

In a tropical setting, the identification of isolated MBG-EBO disease may be difficult. The differential diagnosis resembles that for other hemorrhagic fevers. Rural travel, injections in a local hospital, and contact with sick persons are useful historical features in returning African travelers. Contact with monkeys (occupational and/or during travel) should be considered highly suspicious; the role of bats, spiders and ticks in filovirus ecology has also been the subject of conjecture. Prostration, lethargy, and wasting seem to be more severe than typically observed with most other VHF; diarrhea may also dominate the clinical picture. The rash is characteristic and a useful discriminator.

Virologic diagnosis is readily achieved by isolation from serum

Table 26-3
Pathogenesis of Filovirus Infections in Laboratory Primates*

Pathogenesis Disease Parameters	Ebola Virus	Marburg Virus
Mortality	16/16	12/13
Overt hemorrhage[†]	Absent	Present
Clinical chemistries		
AST, ALT	Elevated	Elevated
CPK	Elevated	Elevated
CK-MB	Elevated	Elevated
Hematology		
Thrombocytopenia	Mild, inconstant	Mild, inconstant
Neutrophilia	Marked	Marked
Coagulation abnormalities		
Prothrombin time	Prolonged	Prolonged
Partial thromboplastin time	Prolonged	Prolonged
Coagulation factors	Suppressed	Suppressed
Fibrinogen levels[†]	Stable	Suppressed
Circulating fibrin degradation products[†]	Low	High
Histopathology		
Tissue hemorrhage[†]	Absent	Severe
Fibrin clots	Liver, spleen, kidneys	Liver, spleen, kidneys

AST = aspartate aminotransferase; ALT = alanine aminotransferase; CPK = creatine phosphokinase; CK-MB = creatine kinase isoenzyme MB.
*Rhesus macaques or baboons infected parenterally or by aerosol (reference 59 and E. D. Johnson, N. Jaax, et al, unpublished observations, 1986).
[†]Disease parameters in which significant differences occurred during Ebola and Marburg virus infections.

during the febrile phase. In the case of EBO-Z and MBG, characteristic virions have been visualized from ultracentrifuged serum or from supernatants of recently infected Vero cells.[7, 58, 59] Virions can be identified by thin-section electron microscopy of antigens or fluorescent antibody (FA) staining of infected cell cultures. Vero cells are the most widely used laboratory system for isolation of these viruses, although others such as MA104, CV-7, and SW-13 cells are sensitive substrates as well. The laboratory results of the 1979 EBO-S and the 1987 MBG virus disease incidents suggest that multiple procedures should be used simultaneously to isolate filovirus from clinical specimens. EBO-S, in particular, may be relatively difficult to isolate requiring clinical material to be blind-passaged in multiple laboratory host systems such as Vero cells, SW-13 cells (diploid human adrenal carcinoma cells), or guinea pigs. Guinea pigs usually respond to primary infections by developing fevers within ten days, but additional passages are required to produce uniformly fatal disease. In 1987, MBG virus was easily isolated in SW-13 cells, but grew inconsistently in Vero cell cultures (E.D. Johnson, M. Kiley, B.K. Johnson, unpublished observations, 1987).

Occasional isolates have been made from acute urine or sputum samples, as well as convalescent semen. Virions also have been demonstrated by electron microscopy in formalin-fixed liver or kidney tissues.[35, 59, 60]

Several techniques have proven particularly useful in monitoring disease in monkeys and should have applicability in man.[3a] Antigen detection ELISA is positive in serum or fresh tissues often at dilutions exceeding 1:256. This provides a rapid, sensitive technique, particularly in light of the 2 to 3 weeks often required to cultivate the virus in cell culture. Fatal monkey infections could frequently be diagnosed by FA or immunoperoxidase staining of touch preparations of spleen or liver. Direct electron microscopic visualization of viral particles in monkey liver is also particularly useful.[60a] Retrospective diagnosis is readily achieved by immunohistochemical detection of antigen in routine formalin-fixed tissue blocks, including tissues prepared more than 7 years before testing.

Antibodies detectable by IFA have been useful in diagnosis.[35, 36, 61] Virus-specific IgM antibodies appear as viremia fades and are useful in diagnosis as well.[61] Epidemiologic surveys which have followed filovirus seropositives for at least 3 years suggest that IFA antibody is relatively short-lived and that high titers (≥ 1024) may reflect recent antigenic stimulation (E.D. Johnson, J.P. Gonzalez, C.J. Peters, A.J. Georges, unpublished observations, 1987). The complement-fixation (CF) test used for MBG diagnosis was of limited utility.[52] In vitro tests have not reliably detected virus-neutralizing antibodies in convalescent sera.

The high prevalence of filovirus IFA reactivity (particularly to EBO virus) found in some regions is difficult to interpret in light of the rare and lethal nature of filovirus disease. Newer alternative tests (antibody ELISA and Western blot) to resolve this apparent discrepancy have not been validated with double blind testing and field application. It seems very possible that less pathogenic but serologically cross-reactive filoviruses may exist in nature and account for these results.

Pathology and Pathogenesis[4, 62–69]

In fatal cases, generalized hemorrhage is found macroscopically and microscopically in most organ systems. Focal necrosis is also widespread but not extensive and is not usually accompanied by significant inflammation. The liver, while universally involved with Councilman-like bodies present, is not the site of massive potentially fatal necrosis. Renal tubular necrosis, perhaps an agonal event, is also common. A diffuse encephalitis with formation of glial nodules typical of many viral processes is present. Generalized lymphoid necrosis is characteristic. Diffuse intravascular fibrin thrombi have been observed in several studies. The few clotting studies available suggest that DIC occurs. MBG and EBO viral antigens can be readily detected in formalin-fixed tissue specimens using antivirus monoclonal antibodies and peroxidase-labeled avidin-biotin antimouse immunoglobulin complexes. Antigen is localized in the liver, kidney, spleen, and adrenal glands. Virus particles are also observed in these areas by electron microscopy (W.C. Hall, R.W. Trotter, J.D. White, E.D. Johnson, unpublished observations, 1988).

Pathogenesis of fatal filovirus infections in man and nonhuman primates is similar.[4, 9, 33, 65–67, 69] (Table 26–3). Clinical and biochemical observations support the anatomical findings of extensive liver involvement (but not hepatic failure), renal damage, changes in vascular permeability, and activation of the clotting cascade. DIC is suspected of being a major mechanism in filovirus hemorrhagic fever, although its mode of induction and overall significance are not established. Furthermore, there are interesting differences in the picture seen in MBG- and EBO-infected monkeys (see Table 26–3). In both situations there is obvious activation of the clotting cascade; however, only MBG-infected monkeys have gross and microscopic evidence of a hemorrhagic diathesis, which is accompanied by evidence of extensive fibrinolysis. Disease activity correlates with the viremic phase in EBO hemorrhagic fever, suggesting that virus replication is responsible for the process. In MBG virus infections, viremias may precede the onset of clinical disease by 24 to 48 hours. Because passive protection and in vitro neutralization have not been readily demonstrated with convalescent plasma, one may speculate that other mechanisms mediate recovery.

Therapy

There is no proven virus-specific treatment. A laboratory worker[58] treated with 3×10^6 units of leukocyte interferon every 12 hours and 800 mL convalescent plasma survived EBO-Z infection. However, EBO-Z is not particularly sensitive to interferon in vitro,[25] and neither interferon nor plasma have yielded impressive results in experimental monkey infections[70] (E.D. Johnson, J.B. Moe, and H.W. Lupton, unpublished observations, 1983). In the absence of any alternative therapy, and considering evidence for at least marginal effects of interferon in primates and hyperimmune serum in guinea pigs, similar treatment would seem reasonable when feasible in future recognized human infections.

Heparin therapy directed toward the DIC of MBG infection was instituted early in the course of two secondary cases and both survived.[56] However, when initiated late during a fulminating MBG virus infection, heparin therapy was incapable of altering the fatal disease process (D. Silverstein, R. Zimmermen, E.D. Johnson, unpublished observations, 1987). If laboratory facilities to monitor anticoagulation and therapy for bleeding are available, this course should be considered. The initial MBG cases were treated with fresh blood, fibrinogen, clotting factor concentrates, ε-aminocaproic acid, and platelet transfusions; clinical impressions were that this course was beneficial and mortality was 23%.[57]

Supportive therapy should be directed toward maintenance of effective blood volume using colloid such as human serum albumin or fresh frozen plasma, but avoiding volume overload. Electrolyte balance should be maintained, particularly with the potassium loss from diarrhea and vomiting. Occasional patients have developed profound renal failure requiring dialysis. Secondary bacterial infections should be sought on clinical grounds or suspected on the basis of leukocytosis, and vigorously treated.

Prevention and Control

Our ignorance of the biology of these agents precludes any meaningful suggestions as to primary prevention. A major factor in African nosocomial epidemics has been reuse of unsterilized needles and syringes. Plastic materials do not withstand even modest heat treatment, but for economic reasons are often employed with multiple patients, facilitating hospital and community spread of filoviruses as well as other agents.

Once cases are identified, person-to-person spread must be prevented. Though these agents are infectious by the aerosol route, intimate contact with blood and body secretions has preceded secondary cases seen to date. Ordinary sterilization techniques and barrier nursing will suffice to prevent continued transmission. Although undoubtedly desirable, it is difficult to be sure how important these measures may have been in terminating the African outbreaks, since the epidemics were already declining when they were instituted.

The need for a vaccine remains to be established and largely depends on unraveling the biomedical significance of the seropositivity reported in some regions of Africa. Although the failure to develop an efficient neutralizing antibody response in convalescent sera suggests that nonreplicating immunogens would be difficult to develop, an experimental inactivated vaccine provided some protection to guinea pigs.[71]

Recent Developments

Major readjustments in our concept of filoviruses are occurring following events that began in November 1989.[3a, 71a, 71b] Multiple introductions of Ebola virus into the United States have occurred in facilities responsible for the quarantine of cynomolgus monkeys imported from the Philippines. Although epidemiologic and laboratory investigations are still incomplete, it appears that most introductions have originated in a single export facility with active virus transmission. Once Ebola monkey deaths begin, cohorts of quarantined monkeys held in this country have often continued to have problems with disease spread presumably via droplet and/or small particle aerosols. In a facility in Reston, Va., with extensive monkey infection, four of five regular employees were also infected.[71c] One sustained a cut during a necropsy, but the other three had no defined exposure that could be implicated as the source, suggesting fomites, droplets, and/or aerosols as possible modes of transmission to man. Fortunately, the Ebola strain circulating among the Reston monkeys was apparently of less virulence for man than the previously recognized Sudan and Zaire isolates, since none of the four had any significant clinical disease. There was no evidence of acute infection of humans having lesser contact with infected monkeys. Occasional serological positives have been found among those working with nonhuman primates, but the interpretation awaits results from control populations. Although the Ebola isolate from Reston was pathogenic for macaques, other viruses (including simian hemorrhagic fever virus) were known to be circulating among the monkeys and may have modified the epidemic.

The virus isolated from the infected monkeys was initially identified with polyclonal Ebola antisera in the IFA test, and indeed reacts with most Ebola monoclonal antibodies.[3a] It has a protein profile resembling Ebola rather than Marburg, and preliminary data indicate modest nucleotide sequence homology to Ebola virus (A. Sanchez, unpublished data, 1990).

The fact that this virus originated in Asia and exhibits a number of biological properties that differ from those of the Sudan and Zaire Ebola strains only serves to point out the inadequacy of our current filovirus taxonomic tools. As noted (see Table 26–2), the Sudan and Zaire viruses also differ from one another to a considerable degree; it seems likely that continuing genetic and antigenic analysis will result in "Ebola virus" being further separated into multiple species.

Seroepidemiologic studies indicate that infection with Ebola-like agents may be widespread in southeast Asian cynomolgus macaques and is not a new occurrence. Suggestive serologic data are also accumulating for infection of African monkeys as well as other Asian species. It is not certain whether monkeys are merely serving as indicators of virus activity or whether they may be involved as amplifying hosts or perhaps even true reservoirs. Whatever their role, the appearance of active Ebola virus infection in imported animals has had significant impact on the importation and use of these animals for vaccine production and biomedical research.[71b]

MANAGEMENT OF VIRAL HEMORRHAGIC FEVERS

Diagnosis

The concept of a syndrome of ''viral hemorrhagic fever'' originated with Soviet physicians[72] and has proved to be useful in clinical medicine. With increasing knowledge of the existence of VHF and increasing potential for air travel to bring patients from the isolated areas where VHFs frequently occur, the differential diagnosis and management of these exotic maladies will become more important. There are several viral infections that are regularly associated with the VHF syndrome (Table 26–4) and they are discussed in depth in this chapter and elsewhere in this volume.

Patients with VHF eventually develop evidence of vascular instability, damage, and abnormal permeability. However, on initial presentation they may only report fever, myalgia, malaise, and dizziness. Physical findings may be confined to flushing over the face and upper trunk and conjunctival injection. The diagnosis should be entertained more seriously in the presence of periorbital edema, axillary or other petechiae, severe prostration, hypotension, mental confusion, or prominent back, pharyngeal, chest, or abdominal pain. In some virus infections leukopenia is a valuable sign, but in others leukocytosis is more common. Thrombocytopenia, elevated liver or muscle enzymes, proteinuria, and mild abnormalities of the activated partial thromboplastin time (APTT) are also common, but inconsistent, early laboratory findings.

As the disease progresses, overt bleeding usually appears, particularly in severe cases or in virus infections associated with marked thrombocytopenia. Hemorrhage usually reflects the severity and extent of vascular involvement rather than being life-threatening in its actual volume. Involvement of the central nervous, GI, and pulmonary systems is often present and reflects

Table 26–4
Viral Hemorrhagic Fevers (VHFs) of Man

Virus Family	Disease	Transmission to Man in Nature	Distinctive Clinical and Pathologic and Features	Aerosol Infectivity of Virus	Nosocomial Transmission	Specific Therapy
Arenaviridae	Lassa fever	Rodent	Hemorrhage not common except in severe cases; deafness, pericarditis may occur in recovery phase	Yes	Rare. Fomite or droplet? Aerosol?	Ribavirin. Virus-specific IgG?
	Argentine and Bolivian HF	Rodent	Prominent petechial and other hemorrhages as well as neurologic involvement	Yes	Rare. Fomite or droplet? Aerosol?	Immune plasma. Ribavirin?
Bunyaviridae *Phlebovirus* genus	Rift Valley fever	Mosquito, aerosol	Only occasional case hemorrhagic; icterus and anuria common in HF cases	Yes	Not reported	Ribavirin, immune plasma, or interferon of potential use
Nairovirus genus	Crimean-Congo HF	Tick	Copious hemorrhage and florid ecchymoses may dominate picture more frequently than other HF	Yes	Occasional. Fomite or droplet? Aerosol?	Immune plasma? Ribavirin?
Hantavirus genus	HFRS	Rodent	Unique sequence of events with fever, shock, hemorrhage, renal failure, and then diuresis	Yes	No; not viremic	Ribavirin
Filoviridae	Marburg, Ebola HF	Unknown	Severe prostration with marked wasting; maculopapular rash common; high mortality; findings of DIC common	Yes	Yes; probably fomite or droplet	Immune plasma and interferon possibly useful
Flaviviridae Mosquito-borne flavivirus	Yellow fever	Mosquito	Black vomit; midzonal liver necrosis; terminal hepatorenal syndrome?	Yes	No	None
	Dengue HF	Mosquito	Prominent vascular permeability component. Immune enhancement important in many cases	No	No	None
Tick-borne flavivirus	Omsk HF, Kyasanur Forest disease	Tick	Pulmonary involvement; biphasic with later CNS disease	Yes	Not reported	None

HF = hemorrhagic fever; HFRS = hemorrhagic fever with renal syndrome; DIC = disseminated intravascular coagulation.

Table 26–5
Rapid Laboratory Diagnosis of Viral Hemorrhagic Fevers

	ELISA Antigen Detection	ELISA IgM Capture	Remarks
Lassa fever	+	+	One or both tests positive in virtually all acutely ill patients
Argentine hemor-rhagic fever	+	+	Under evaluation; appears useful in patients
Rift Valley fever	+	+	Antigen test successful but sensitivity in man modest; IgM appears early in convalescence
Crimean-Congo hemorrhagic fe-ver	+	+	Antigen test useful in acute disease, particularly severe cases; IgM appears early in convalescence
Hemorrhagic fever with renal syn-drome	0	+	IgM present in virtually all acute sera. Antigenemia not detectable in man.
Marburg, Ebola	–	–	Not reported. Monkeys have readily detectable antigenemia.
Yellow fever	+	+	Antigenemia followed by IgM response
Dengue	+	+	Cannot differentiate types; under evaluation in primary and secondary dengue hemorrhagic fever
Kyasanur Forest disease, Omsk hemorrhagic fe-ver	–	–	Not reported

ELISA = enzyme-linked immunosorbent assay.

fundamental similarities in syndromes of differing pathogenesis.[73] Only in hemorrhagic fever with renal syndrome (HFRS) is oliguria a prominent intrinsic feature of the disease process; decreased urine output in the other VHFs is usually proportional to hypotension and shock or occurs terminally.

The differential diagnosis includes common viral diseases uncommonly associated with hemorrhage (measles, varicella, cytomegalovirus), rickettsial infections, serious bacterial diseases (particularly leptospirosis, relapsing fever, meningococcemia, typhoid, shigellosis, plague), parasitic infections (malaria, trypanosomiasis), and other conditions such as heat stroke, intoxications, thrombotic thrombocytopenia purpura, or acute collagen vascular disease.[72, 74]

Definitive diagnosis depends on the virus laboratory. Rapid techniques as well as conventional approaches have been developed for most of the VHFs (Table 26–5). The biohazard inherent in handling these agents has led to use of inactivated reagents for serology,[20–23] but more recently it has been possible to produce diagnostic antigens in baculovirus systems (see Chapter 22).

Epidemiology

Viral hemorrhagic fever should be suspected in travelers returning from the geographic regions where they are known to occur. With the exception of dengue and, historically, yellow fever, all are rural diseases. Recently rats have been incriminated as urban vectors of HFRS. A history of exposure to the natural vector or reservoir should increase awareness of the danger of infection, although rodent or mosquito exposure is frequently not noted. Increased vector or reservoir populations are often associated with a concomitant increase in VHF transmission, as well. Rift Valley fever and Crimean-Congo hemorrhagic fever (CCHF)

also are transmitted in nature by aerosols from slaughter or autopsy of infected domestic animals.

Introductions of exotic diseases into new ecosystems are often concerns with these agents. Historically this has occurred in the United States only with yellow fever and dengue through the adaptability of their urban *Aedes aegypti* vector; temporary control of this mosquito terminated virus circulation. Recolonization by *Ae aegypti* and the recent introduction of *Ae albopictus* to the United States reestablishes the possibility of transmission. Yellow fever may well represent a threat to large urban areas of Africa, southeast Asia, India, and South America. Rift Valley fever virus, as evidenced by the recent Egyptian epizootic,[75] may also be exported to receptive areas with large mosquito and livestock populations. It seems unlikely, but not impossible, that the other agents might establish themselves in a completely new habitat. Because of their zoonotic nature, the possibility of extensive human-to-human spread is less plausible.

Patient Containment

Infection of close personal contacts or medical personnel does, however, occur. Nosocomial transmission may occur through a variety of mechanisms. There are vivid descriptions in the literature of *Ae aegypti* mosquitoes breeding in water containers placed under bed legs to prevent crawling insects from gaining access to yellow fever patients. Today we are more concerned with transmission via fomites, droplets, or small-particle aerosols. Physical contact (fomites) or larger airborne droplets can bring infectious material into contact with unbroken skin, epidermis bearing unnoticed scratches or cuts, or mucosal surfaces of the eyes, oropharynx, and upper respiratory tract.

Small-particle aerosols have much less capability to contaminate skin or mucous membranes, but have the potential to remain in suspension in the air for long periods and to deposit in the respiratory bronchioles and alveoli with high efficiency. The practical consequence of determining the mode of transmission is that mask, gown, and gloves provide excellent protection against fomites, some protection from droplets, but are of no help in preventing small-particle aerosol infection. The latter requires an efficient respirator. As noted in Table 26–4, most of the viruses are thought to be aerosol-infectious, based on analysis of laboratory infections, formal studies of aerosol chambers, or inference from nosocomial episodes. In spite of this, only Lassa fever, CCHF, and the *Filoviridae* infections have been associated with multiple instances of person-to-person spread, and even with these diseases the mechanisms are not certain. Dissemination is not an invariable feature of VHFs and, indeed, with the arenaviruses and CCHF, it is an uncommon occurrence. When spread does occur, it is self-limited and secondary attack rates are low. Barrier nursing has generally been implemented, and subsequent cycles of transmission involve still fewer persons. Such simple isolation procedures are reasonable and should be employed, but even though they are often credited with preventing or terminating these episodes, there is little evidence as to their adequacy in the modern hospital setting.

Once the physician suspects a VHF, a paradoxical problem emerges. With the exception of HFRS and dengue hemorrhagic fever, blood and other samples may be presumed to contain dangerous concentrations of virus so that ordinary laboratory studies to assist in the differential diagnosis place clinical laboratory personnel at some risk. The tragedy of missing a treatable disease such as malaria, typhoid fever, or a rickettsiosis must be balanced against potential danger to laboratory personnel. Many laboratory tests can be performed on samples inactivated by acid treatment, gamma radiation, or disinfectants.[20–23] Rapid definitive microbiologic diagnosis may soon be available for Lassa fever, Argentine hemorrhagic fever, Rift Valley fever, CCHF, HFRS, yellow fever, Ebola and dengue, since enzyme-linked immunosorbent assays (ELISA) have been developed and are under evaluation (see Table 26–5).

Once a presumptive diagnosis of a potentially transmissible VHF is made, decisions about therapy for the patient and prophylaxis of the staff must be taken. There is no licensed therapy for any of these conditions, although convalescent plasma and the investigational antiviral drug ribavirin may be of therapeutic benefit in several VHFs (see Table 26–4).[74] These experimental modalities and timely advice on their utility are available only from specialized centers.

Care of patients infected with these diseases can be accomplished with several technological means to protect the medical team from infection. One system envelops the patient and his transport stretcher or sickbed in a flexible plastic film isolator. A slight negative pressure is maintained by blowers which exhaust through filters to remove hazardous organisms. In the polar approach, medical personnel are contained within a plastic suit maintained under positive pressure by filtered compressed air.[76–80] The relative merits of these and other systems are being argued and tested. Three conclusions appear inescapable: (1) These approaches to high-level protection against fomites, droplets, and aerosols is accomplished only with clumsy systems which hamper patient care and increase the probability of parenteral exposure.

(2) Such systems are expensive to establish and require trained crews to operate safely, as well as clinical laboratory and virologic laboratory support. (3) The average physician must deal with the suspected VHF patient before specialized help is available and must coordinate implementation of such aid.

Typically, the physician initially encounters a patient with a suggestive travel history and a suspicious clinical presentation. At this point he should isolate the patient in a private room with the usual barrier nursing precautions. Access to the patient should be limited to the minimal number of personnel necessary and they should be selected for their reliability and professional competence. Everything leaving the patient's room should be controlled by the responsible physician: excreta should be chemically sterilized; linen, dishes, clothing, needles, syringes, etc, exited in sealed bags to autoclave; and laboratory samples controlled. If feasible, room air should be exhausted outside the building away from crowded areas, and access to the room should be via an untrafficked area or anteroom. Maximum precautions should surround needles, syringes, glassware, and other potential sources of parenteral exposure.

Once the situation is stabilized under the best attainable conditions in a given situation, the attending physician must evaluate the picture and utilize continued observation, additional clinical laboratory testing, consultation, and/or transport to specialized facilities in order to serve both the patient's and the community's best interests.

Empirical chemotherapy for falciparum malaria may be justified. Rickettsial disease should also be excluded; an African patient with suspected VHF and a rash would justify empiric therapy for tick typhus. As the situation evolves, medical staff protection may be improved through education, provision of impermeable gowns, use of face shields or safety glasses to protect against conjunctival droplet infection, or use of full-face respirators to prevent small-particle aerosol exposure. Recommendations for these circumstances have been published.[7, 79–84]

In addition, flexible plastic hoods with a battery-powered blower to provide filtered air are now available and have proven quite acceptable to hospital staff. Furthermore, minimal additional training is required for their effective use (McKee, Hill, and Peters, unpublished observations, 1990). These hoods provide excellent mucous membrane and aerosol protection, as well as forming a contiguous barrier when used with impermeable gowns or jumpsuits. The high level of protection afforded and the ease of use also make this system applicable in the clinical laboratory or in field environments. It is also helpful to designate an anteroom as a grey area where protective clothing is decontaminated and/or removed and all material exiting the patient's contaminated room can be subjected to definitive surface disinfection.

Aerosol

The need for aerosol protection in the patient care setting is not firmly established. Most of the viruses causing VHF have been found to be aerosol-infectious and have caused numerous laboratory infections as well as intercage transmission in experimental animals. Episodes compatible with aerosol transmission in hospitalized patients have been reported with the South American hemorrhagic fevers, Lassa fever, and CCHF. Certainly Ebola transmission has occurred in families, and clinical laboratory workers have been infected with yellow fever,[85] although these were probably due to fomite or droplet spread. The risk from HFRS and dengue, of course, is negligible. The role of aerosols in transmission of many diseases (including rubeola, rubella, and varicella) is well established but often overlooked.[86] There is evidence to suggest that there is considerable variation among hosts in their propensity to disseminate virus. This was seen particularly clearly in smallpox. More seriously ill patients shed more virus and were more likely to give rise to secondary spread. These infections were probably disseminated largely by droplets, and household contacts were at greatest risk; but on occasion devastating airborne epidemics did occur.[87] Even localized zoster has rarely given rise to aerosol epidemics.[88] The authors of this chapter believe that, whenever practical, precautions should be taken to protect the staff and other patients from the risk of aerosol dissemination. This would be particularly important in severely ill patients, patients with cough, and during procedures such as tracheostomy or insertion of arterial lines.

When the presumptive diagnosis of VHF is established, there will inevitably be concern over possible spread to contacts and medical personnel. This chapter and the discussions of specific diseases in this book should make it clear that on rare and unpredictable occasions dissemination to multiple contacts, possibly by aerosol, may occur, but that in general these diseases are transmitted only inefficiently and then to close personal or medical contacts. Initial heroic surveillance measures[89] have been tempered as experience grows.[84, 90, 91]

Therapy
Supportive

Rapid nontraumatic hospitalization to prevent unnecessary damage to the fragile vascular bed is of critical importance. Transportation should be undertaken only for clear indications. Mild sedation of restless or combative patients serves a similar purpose, and opiates may be particularly useful in easing myalgias, as well.

Replacement of fluid and electrolyte losses should be cautious because of increased vascular permeability and the ease with which pulmonary edema develops. Volume expansion in the face of hypotension should be undertaken with colloid such as human serum albumin.

The mechanism of bleeding is complex. Vascular damage may not be due to direct viral invasion, but rather to the effects of soluble mediators or DIC.[73, 92, 93] DIC is suspected as a contributory mechanism in CCHF, HFRS, and filovirus disease; it is clearly not a regular feature of the arenavirus hemorrhagic fevers. Heparin therapy could reasonably be undertaken early in situations where adequate laboratory control indicates a significant consumptive coagulopathy. ϵ-aminocaproic acid should be avoided.

Vigorous replacement of clotting factors should be pursued in bleeding patients, regardless of the cause. The role of platelets is complex. Several VHFs have marked thrombocytopenia and tend to have florid hemorrhage. Failure of platelet function in the presence of modestly reduced numbers was first described in dengue hemorrhagic fever and HFRS patients and later reported in Lassa fever patients,[94-96] as well as animal models.[67, 92, 97] This defect certainly must modulate the hemorrhagic state, particularly in patients with only a moderate decrease in the number of thrombo-

cytes. Neither the mechanisms nor the specificity for VHF of this platelet abnormality are known. Later in their course, patients with HFRS will also develop abnormal platelet responses as oliguria leads to uremia. Platelet transfusions may be indicated.

The diffuse nature of the vascular process may lead to a requirement for support of several organ systems. Myocardial lesions are routinely seen at autopsy[98] and clinically suspected ante mortem. Pulmonary insufficiency may develop and in some cases (particularly yellow fever) the hepatorenal syndrome occurs.

Secondary infections are common and should be sought and treated. Immunosuppressive drugs, including steroids, are generally contraindicated. With the exception of HFRS, the fatal VHFs are usually associated with an ineffective immune response, which should not be further compromised. High-dose steroids may or may not be useful for patients with intractable shock.

Antiviral

Although work on antiviral drugs and immunomodulators may alter the equation,[99] the specific antiviral therapeutic measures of potential use today are interferon, antibody, and ribavirin. To a great extent, the utility of these approaches can be predicted from knowledge of disease pathogenesis[73, 93] and in vitro properties of viruses (Table 26–6).

Ribavirin is a relatively nontoxic, nonimmunosuppressive nucleoside analogue with broad spectrum antiviral activity,[100] including action against several hemorrhagic fever viruses.[101–107] Intravenous (IV) ribavirin has now been shown to be efficacious in treatment of Lassa fever[108] and HFRS[109] in man. In Argentine hemorrhagic fever, the drug is well tolerated[110] and produces improvement in virologic parameters (D.A.M. Enria, J.I. Maiztegui, K.T. McKee, unpublished observations, 1988); trials are under way to see if drug therapy can replace the established effective treatment with antibody. In all these studies a loading dose of 30 mg/kg was given followed by 15 mg/kg every six hours for four days and then 7.5 mg/kg every eight hours for six days. Studies are underway to evaluate lower doses in Lassa fever. The major toxicity identified is a reversible suppression of erythropoiesis and a mild hemolysis which may result in a dose-related anemia and mild hyperbilirubinemia.[100] Treatment usually does not have to be modified, transfusions are rarely required, and normal erythropoiesis is resumed after cessation of drug. Oral ribavirin was also effective in Lassa fever therapy (2 g initially followed by 1 g/d in three divided doses for ten days)[108] and in prophylaxis of induced sandfly fever (1200 mg/d in three divided doses).[111]

Parallels between in vitro sensitivity of viruses and drug efficacy have been seen providing a single cell substrate is used[103] (see Table 26–6). Viruses in the *Arenaviridae* and *Bunyaviridae* families are most sensitive to inhibition in Vero cell culture and, when tried, the drug has worked well in laboratory animal models or human infections. Flaviviruses require 2 or more times as much ribavirin for inhibition in vitro and the drug has failed to modify yellow fever or dengue infections of rhesus monkeys, even when given prophylactically in IV doses comparable to those used in Lassa fever[112] (F.J. Malinoski, unpublished observations, 1988). Filovirus replication is insensitive to the drug, and treatment of model guinea pig infections is unsuccessful (H.W. Lupton, J. Moe, unpublished observations, 1980). These observations lead one to expect that Rift Valley fever[103] and CCHF[106, 107] would be candidates for ribavirin therapy. These diseases have a shorter duration than arenavirus diseases and therefore there may be a shorter "window" for treatment than with Lassa fever.[103] The low mortality rate (estimated 0.5%) of Rift Valley fever further complicates evaluation of treatment strategies. The most useful approach might be liberal oral treatment of all febrile patients soon after onset of disease, with prevention of the development of HF as a goal.

Prophylactic use of ribavirin in man has only been tested in sandfly fever, but might also have a role in prevention of VHF. Several studies, particularly recent pharmacodynamic studies of human immunodeficiency virus, (HIV)–infected men,[113, 114] suggest that oral doses of ribavirin of 1200 mg/day will be well tolerated by most, but not all, normal people. Increasing dose levels will lead to more frequent problems with significant anemia. Based on available data, 5 mg/kg every eight hours (ie, about 1 g/d) should be an acceptable dose. In diseases of short incubation and short duration, such as Rift Valley fever or CCHF, prophylaxis for a period of seven to ten days would be reasonable based on sandfly fever studies in man[111] or Rift Valley fever in monkeys.[103] The situation is more complicated in arenavirus diseases where the time elapsed between natural infection and beginning of clinical recovery usually is 14 days or longer. In several lethal animal arenavirus models, administration of prophylactic ribavirin for 7 to 10 days was followed by development of viremia and death several days after cessation of treatment (D. Jones, G.A. Eddy, P.B. Jahrling, unpublished data, 1979); in other arenavirus-infected animals, 14 days prophylaxis was sufficient.[97, 101, 104] Thus, until more experience is available, prophylaxis of arenavirus diseases in man should be carried out for at least 14 days. Regardless of the disease, clinical monitoring of fever, symptoms, and hematocrit should be carried out during and after prophylaxis with subsequent serologic studies to detect asymptomatic seroconversion.

Other pharmacologic properties of ribavirin are relevant. The drug is teratogenic in laboratory rodents and should not be used in pregnancy.[100, 115] Acutely, there is insufficient penetration into the brain for therapy of intracranial infections.[100, 101] Resistance has not been seen to the drug.[100, 101, 104]

Antibody therapy also has a place in hemorrhagic fevers (see Table 26–6). Convalescent plasma is the treatment of choice in Argentine or Bolivian hemorrhagic fever. Its use in Lassa fever[92, 116] and CCHF[117] is limited by the low neutralizing antibody titers and the consequent need for careful donor selection. Combinations of ribavirin and antibody can achieve therapeutic ends in Lassa virus-infected macaques,[116] impossible with either alone. Lassa virus specific IgG concentrates for IV use are under evaluation as alternative or supplemental therapy.[92] In HFRS an active immune response is already evolving in most patients, but plasma containing virus-neutralizing antibodies has been used empirically in prophylaxis of high-risk exposures.

While potentially effective in prophylaxis of some VHFs, alpha interferon has no obvious role in therapy. The single exception is Rift Valley fever; in the primate model, fatal hemorrhagic fever is often associated with a late and low interferon response, suggesting that exogenous interferon could be helpful.[93, 118, 119] Gamma interferon exerts an antiviral effect on arenaviruses, which are resistant to alpha interferon, and deserves further exploration in therapy of Lassa and Argentine HF.[120, 121]

The following maintain microbiologic containment facilities for these organisms and should be considered for consultation:

Argentina: Instituto Nacional de Estudios Sobre Virosis Hemorragicas, Casilla Correo 195, 2700 Pergamino, Argentina

Central African Republic: Institute Pasteur, Bangui, Central African Republic

France: Institut Pasteur, 28 Rue du Docteur Roux Paris, Cedex 15, France

Kenya: Virus Research Center, Nairobi, Kenya

Senegal: Institute Pasteur, B.P. 220, Dakar, Senegal

South Africa: National Institute for Virology, Private Bag

Table 26–6
Therapeutic Alternatives in the Viral Hemorrhagic Fevers

	Disease	In Vitro Neutralization by Convalescent Sera	In Vitro Interferon Sensitivity	In Vitro Ribavirin Sensitivity
Arenaviridae	Lassa fever	+	Low	Yes
	Argentine HF	+ +	Low	Yes
Bunyaviridae				
Phlebovirus	Rift Valley fever	+ + +	Yes	Yes
Nairovirus	Crimean-Congo HF	+	Yes	Yes
Hantavirus	HFRS	+ + +	Yes	Yes
Filoviridae	Marburg virus disease or Ebola HF	±	Low	No
Flaviviridae				
Mosquito-borne flavivirus	Yellow fever	+ + +	Yes	Low
	Dengue	+ + +	Yes	Low
Tick-borne flaviviruses	Kyasanur Forest disease, Omsk HF	+ + +	?	?

HF = hemorrhagic fever; HFRS = hemorrhagic fever with renal syndrome.

8

710   *C. J. Peters, E. D. Johnson, and K. T. McKee, Jr.*

X4, Sandringham, Johannesburg, South Africa

United Kingdom: Center for Applied Microbiology and Research, Special Pathogens Unit, Salisbury, Porton Down, Wiltshire, SP4 OJG, England

USA: United States Army Medical Research Institute of Infectious Diseases, Medical Division, Ft Detrick, Frederick, MD 21701 USA

USA: Centers for Disease Control, Special Pathogens Branch, Atlanta, GA 30333 USA

REFERENCES

1. Martini GA, Siegert R (eds): *Marburg Virus Disease*. New York, Springer-Verlag, 1971.
2. Pattyn SR (ed): *Ebola Virus Haemorrhagic Fever*. Amsterdam, Elsevier/North-Holland, 1978.
3. Kiley MP, Bowen ETW, Eddy GA, et al: Filoviridae: A Taxonomic home for Marburg and Ebola viruses? *Intervirology* 1982; 18:24–32.
3a. Jahrling PB, Geisbert TW, Dalgard DW, et al: Preliminary report: Isolation of Ebola virus from monkeys imported to the USA. *Lancet* 1990; 335:502–505.
4. Murphy FA, Simpson DIH, Whitfield SG, et al: Marburg virus infection in monkeys. *Lab Invest* 1971; 24:279–291.
5. Peters D, Muller G, Slenczka W: Morphology, development, and classification of the Marburg virus, in Martini GA, Siegert R (eds): *Marburg Virus Disease*. New York, Springer-Verlag, 1971, pp 68–83.
6. Almeida JD, Waterson AP, Simpson DIH: Morphology and morphogenesis of the Marburg agent, in Martini GA, Siegert R (eds): *Marburg Virus Disease*. New York, Springer-Verlag, 1971, pp 84–97.
7. Murphy FA, van der Groen G, Whitfield SG, et al: Ebola and Marburg virus morphology and taxonomy, in Pattyn SR (ed): *Ebola Virus Haemorrhagic Fever*. Amsterdam, Elsevier/North-Holland, 1978, pp 61–84.
8. Ellis DS, Stamford S, Tvoey DG, et al: Ebola and Marburg viruses. II. Their development within Vero cells and the extracellular formation of branched and torus forms. *J Med Virol* 1979; 4:213–225.
9. Ellis DS, Bowen ETW, Simpson DIH, et al: Ebola virus: A comparison, at ultrastructural level, of the behavior of the Sudan and Zaire strains in monkeys. *Br J Exp Pathol* 1978; 59:584–593.
10. Ellis DS, Simpson DIH, Francis DP, et al: Ultrastructure of Ebola virus particles in human liver. *J Clin Pathol* 1978; 31:201–208.
11. Bowen ETW, Platt GS, Lloyd G, et al: A comparative study of strains of Ebola virus isolated from Southern Sudan and Northern Zaire in 1976. *J Med Virol* 1980; 6:129–138.
12. Kiley MP, Regnery RL, Johnson KM: Ebola virus: Identification of virion structural proteins. *J Gen Virol* 1980; 49:333–341.
13. Buchmeier MJ, DeFries RU, McCormick JB, et al: Comparative analysis of the structural polypeptides of Ebola viruses from Sudan and Zaire. *J Infect Dis* 1983; 147:276–281.
14. Kiley MP, Cox NJ, Elliott LH, et al: Physiochemical properties of Marburg virus: evidence for three distinct virus strains and their relationships to Ebola virus. *J Gen Virol* 1988; 69:1957–1967.
15. Elliott LH, Kiley MP, McCormick JB: Descriptive analysis of Ebola virus proteins. *Virology* 1985; 147:169–176.
16. Regnery RL, Johnson KM, Kiley MP: Virion nucleic acid of Ebola virus. *J Virol* 1980; 36:465–469.
17. Kiley MP, Wilusz J, McCormick JB, et al: Conservation of the 3; pr terminal nucleotide sequences of Ebola and Marburg virus. *Virology* 1986; 149:251–254.
18. Sanchez A, Kiley MP: Identification and analysis of Ebola virus messenger RNA. *Virology* 1987; 157:414–420.
19. Bowen ETW, Simpson DIH, Bright WF, et al: Vervet monkey disease: Studies on some physical and chemical properties of the causative agent. *Br J Exp Pathol* 1969; 50:400–407.
20. ven der Groen G, Elliot LH: Use of betapropiolactone inactivated Ebola, Marburg and Lassa intracellular antigens in immunofluorescent antibody assay. *Ann Soc Belg Med Trop* 1982; 62:49–54.
21. Elliot LH, McCormick JB, Johnson KM: Inactivation of Lassa, Marburg, and Ebola viruses by gamma irradiation. *J Clin Microbiol* 1982; 16:704–708.
22. Johnson KM, Elliot LH, Heymann DL: Preparation of polyvalent viral immunofluorescent intracellular antigens and use in human serosurveys. *J Clin Microbiol* 1981; 14:527–529.
23. Lupton HW: Inactivation of Ebola virus with ^{60}Co irradiation. *J Infect Dis* 1981; 143:291.
24. Cox NJ, McCormick JB, Johnson KM, et al: Evidence for two subtypes of Ebola virus based on oligonucleotide mapping of RNA. *J Infect Dis* 1983; 147:272–275.
25. Webb PA, Johnson KM, Wulff H, et al: Some observations on the properties of Ebola virus, in Pattyn SR (ed): *Ebola Virus Haemorrhagic Fever*. Amsterdam, Elsevier/North-Holland, 1978, pp 91–94.
26. Johnson KM, Webb PA, Lange JV, et al: Isolation and partial characterization of a new virus causing acute haemorrhagic fever in Zaire. *Lancet* 1977; 1:569–571.
27. Richman DD, Cleveland PH, McCormic JB, et al: Antigenic analysis of strains of Ebola virus: Identification of two Ebola virus serotypes. *J Infect Dis* 1983; 147:268–271.
28. Slenczka W, Wolff G: Biological properties of the Marburg virus, in Martini GA, Sieger R (eds): *Marburg Virus Disease*. New York, Springer-Verlag, 1971, pp 105–108.
29. Hofman H, Kunz C: Cultivation of the Marburg virus (Rhabdovirus simiae) in cell cultures, in Martini GA, Siegert R (eds): *Marburg Virus Disease*. New York, Springer-Verlag, 1971, pp 112–116.
30. van der Groen G, Webb PA, Johnson KM, et al: Growth of Lassa and Ebola viruses in different cell lines, in Pattyn SR (ed): *Ebola Virus Haemorrhagic Fever*. Amsterdam, Elsevier/North-Holland, 1978, pp 255–260.
31. McCormick JB, Bauer SP, Elliott LH, et al: Biologic differences between strains of Ebola virus from Zaire and Sudan. *J Infect Dis* 1983; 147:264–267.
32. Kunz C, Hofmann H: Some characteristics of the Marburg virus, in Martini GA, Siegert R (eds): *Marburg Virus Disease*. New York, Springer-Verlag, 1971, pp 109–111.
33. Simpson DIH, Zlotnik I, Rutter DA: Vervet monkey disease. Experimental infection of guinea pigs and monkeys with the causative agent. *Br J Exp Pathol* 1968; 49:458–464.
34. Hennessen W: Epidemiology of "Marburg virus" disease, in Martini GA, Siegert R (eds): *Marburg Virus Disease*. New York, Springer-Verlag, pp 161–165.
35. Report of WHO/International Study Team: Ebola haemorrhagic fever in Zaire, 1976. *Bull WHO* 1978; 56:271–293.
36. Report of WHO/International Study Team: Ebola haemorrhagic fever in Sudan, 1976. *Bull WHO* 1978; 56:247–270.
37. Viral haemorrhagic fever surveillance. *Weekly Epidemiol Rec* No. 44, Nov 2, 1979.
38. Smith DH, Isaacson M, Johnson KM, et al: Marburg-virus disease in Kenya. *Lancet* 1982; 1:816–820.
39. Conrad JL, Isaacson M, Smith EB, et al: Epidemiologic investigation of Marburg virus disease, southern Africa, 1975. *Am J Trop Med Hyg* 1978; 27:1210–1215.
40. Swanepoel R: Viral haemorrhagic fever in South Africa: history and national strategy. *S Afr J Sci* 1987; 83:80–88.
41. Heymann DL, Weisfeld JS, Webb PA, et al: Ebola hemorrhagic fever: Tandala, Zaire, 1977–1978. *J Infect Dis* 1980; 142:372–376.
42. Tomori O, Fabiyi A, Sorungbe A, et al: Viral hemorrhagic fever antibodies in Nigerian populations. *Am J Trop Med Hyg* 1988; 38:407–410.

43. Knobloch J, Albiez EJ, Schmitz H: A serological survey on viral haemorrhagic fevers in Liberia. *Ann Virol (Inst Pasteur)* 1982; 133E:125–128.

44. Ivanhoff B, Duquesnoy P, Languillat G, et al: Haemorrhagic fever in Gabon. I. Incidence of Lassa, Ebola and Marburg viruses in Haut-Ogooue. *Trans R Soc Trop Med Hyg* 1982; 76:719–720.

45. Bouree P, Bergmann JF: Ebola virus infection in man: a serological and epidemiologic survey in the Cameroons. *Am J Trop Med Hyg* 1983; 32:1465–1466.

46. Gonzalez JP, McCormick JB, Saluzzo JF, et al: Les fièvres hémorragiques africaines d'origine virale. Contribution a leur étude en République centrafricaine. *Ent Med Parasitol* 1983; 21:119–130.

47. Johnson ED, Peters CJ, Gonzalez JP, et al: Ebola hemorrhagic fever (EHF), preliminary seroepidemiological investigation in the Central African Republic. Presented at the Fourth International Conference on the Impact of Viral Diseases on the Development of African and Middle East Countries, Rabat, Morocco, April 14–19, 1985.

48. van der Groen G, Johnson KM, Webb PA, et al: Results of Ebola antibody surveys in various population groups, in Pattyn SR (ed): *Ebola Virus Haemorrhagic Fever.* Amsterdam, Elsevier/North-Holland, 1978, pp 203–208.

49. Johnson BK, Ocheng D, Gitau LG, et al: Viral haemorrhagic fever surveillance in Kenya, 1980–1981: *Trop Geogr Med* 1983; 35:43–47.

50. Blackburn NK, Searle L, Taylor P: Viral haemorrhagic fever antibodies in Zimbabwe school children. *Trans R Soc Trop Med Hyg* 1982; 76:803–805.

51. Teepe RGC, Johnson BK, Ocheng D, et al: A probable case of Ebola virus haemorrhagic fever in Kenya. *Southeast Afr Med J* 1983; 60:718–722.

52. Slenczka W, Wolff G, Siegert R: A critical study of monkey sera for the presence of antibody against the Marburg virus. *Am J Epidemiol* 1971; 93:496–505.

53. Johnson BK, Gitau LG, Gichogo A, et al: Marburg, Ebola and Rift Valley fever virus antibodies in East Africa primates. *Trans R Soc Trop Med Hyg* 1982; 76:307–310.

54. Johnson KM, Scribner CL, McCormick JB: Ecology of Ebola virus: A first clue? *J Infect Dis* 1981; 143:749–751.

55. Stansfield SK, Scribner CL, Kaminski RM, et al: Antibody to Ebola virus in guinea pigs: Tandala, Zaire. *J Infect Dis* 1982; 146:483–486.

56. Gear JSS, Cassel GA, Gear AJ, et al: Outbreak of Marburg virus disease in Johannesburg. *Br Med J* 1975; 5:489–493.

57. Martini GA: Marburg virus disease. Clinical syndrome, in Martini GA, Siegert R (eds): *Marburg Virus Disease.* New York, Springer-Verlag, 1971, pp 1–9.

58. Emond RTD, Evans B, Bowen ETW, et al: A case of Ebola virus infection. *Br Med J* 1977; 2:541–544.

59. Siegert R, Slenczka W: Laboratory diagnosis and pathogenesis, in Martini GA, Siegert R (eds): *Marburg Virus Disease.* New York, Springer-Verlag, 1971, pp 157–160.

60. Spence IM, Gear JHS: Marburg virus disease—an indicator case in South Africa. *S Afr Med J* 1982; 62:796.

60a. Geisbert TW, Jahrling PB: Use of immunoelectron microscopy to demonstrate Ebola virus during the 1989 United States epizootic. *J Clin Pathol* in press.

61. Wulff H, Johnson KM: Immunoglobulin M and G responses measured by immunofluorescence in patients with Lassa or Marburg virus infections. *Bull WHO* 1979; 57:631–635.

62. Gedigk P, Bechtelsheimer H, Korb G: Pathologic anatomy of the Marburg virus disease, in Martini GA, Siegert R (eds): *Marburg Virus Disease.* New York, Springer-Verlag, 1971, pp 50–53.

63. Jackob H: The neuropathology of the Marburg disease in man, in Martini GA, Siegert R (eds): *Marburg Virus Disease.* New York, Springer-Verlag, 1971, pp 54–61.

64. Rippey JJ, Schepers NJ, Gear JHS: The pathology of Marburg virus disease. *S Afr Med J* 1984; 66:50–54.

65. Baskerville A, Bowen ETW, Platt GS, et al: The pathology of experimental Ebola virus infection in monkeys. *J Pathol* 1978; 125:131–138.

66. Johnson ED, McKee KT Jr, Jaax N, et al: Experimental Ebola hemorrhagic fever (EHF): a model for rational therapy. Presented at the Fourth International Conference on the Impact of Viral Diseases on the Development of African and Middle East Countries, Rabat, Morocco, April 14–19, 1985.

67. Fisher-Hoch SP, Platt GS, Neild GH, et al: Pathophysiology of shock and hemorrhage in a fulminating viral infection (Ebola). *J Infect Dis* 1985; 152:887–894.

68. Zlotnik I: Marburg agent disease: Pathology. *Trans R Soc Trop Med Hyg* 1969; 63:310–323.

69. Simpson DIH, Bowen ETW, Bright WF, et al: Vervet monkey disease: Experimental infection of monkeys with the causative agent, and antibody studies in wild-caught monkeys. *Lab Anim* 1968; 2:75–81.

70. Bowen ETW, Baskerville A, Cantell K, et al: The effect of interferon on experimental Ebola virus infection in Rhesus monkeys, in Pattyn SR (ed): *Ebola Virus Haemorrhagic Fever.* Amsterdam, Elsevier/North-Holland, 1978, pp 245–252.

71. Lupton HW, Lambert RD, Bumgardner DL, et al: Inactivated vaccine for Ebola virus efficacious in guinea pig model. *Lancet* 1980; 2:1294–1295.

71a. Peters CJ, Johnson ED, Jahrling PB, et al: Filoviruses, in Morse S (ed): *Emerging Viruses.* Princeton, NJ, Princeton University Press, 1990; in press.

71b. CDC: Update: Ebola-related filovirus infection in nonhuman primates and interim guidelines for handling nonhuman primates during transit and quarantine. *MMWR* 1990; 39:22–24.

71c. CDC: Update: Filovirus infection in animal handlers. *MMWR* 1990; 39:221.

71d. CDC: Update: Filovirus infections among persons with occupational exposure to nonhuman primates. *MMWR* 1990; 39:266–267.

72. Smorodintsev AA, Kazbintsev LI, Chudakov VG: *Virus Hemorrhagic Fevers.* Leningrad, 1963, pp 245. Published in English by Israel Program for Scientific Translations, Jerusalem, 1964.

73. Peters CJ, Johnson KM: Hemorrhagic fever viruses (evolving concepts in viral pathogenesis illustrated by selected diseases in humans), in Notkins AL, Oldstone MBA (eds): *Concepts in Viral Pathogenesis.* New York, Springer-Verlag, 1984, pp 325–337.

74. Johnson KM, Peters CJ: Viral hemorrhagic fevers, in Conn RB (ed): *Current Diagnosis.* Philadelphia, Saunders, 1985, pp 212–218.

75. Lupton HW, Peters CJ, Eddy GA: Rift Valley fever: Global spread or global control? *Proc US Anim Health Assoc* 1983, pp 261–275.

76. van der Groen G, Trexler PC: A look at the P4 virus containment laboratory. *Prog Med Virol* 1982; 28:192–207.

77. Trexler PC, Emond RTD, Evans B: Negative-pressure plastic isolator for patients with dangerous infections. *Br Med J* 1977; 2:559–561.

78. Hutchinson JGP, Gray J, Flewett TH, et al: The safety of the Trexler isolator as judged by some physical and biological criteria: A report of experimental work at two centres. *J Hyg Camb* 1978; 81:311–319.

79. Clausen L, Bothwell TH, Isaacson M, et al: Isolation and handling of patients with dangerous infectious disease. *S Afr Med J* 1978; 53:238–242.

80. Clayton AJ, Best HR: Controlling the exotic diseases: 1. Isolation facilities. *Can Med Assoc J* 1980; 123:863–867.

81. Clayton AJ: Containment aircraft transit isolator. *Aviat Space Environ Med* 1979; 50:1067–1072.

82. Report of a WHO expert committee: Viral haemorrhagic fevers. *World Health Organization, Technical Report Series* No. 721, Geneva, 1985, pp 5–126.

83. Centers for Disease Control: Management of patients with suspected viral hemorrhagic fever. *MMWR* 1988; 37(S-3):1–16.

84. Galbraith NS, Berrie JRH, Forbes P, et al: Public health aspects of viral haemorrhagic fevers in Britain. *R Soc Health J* 1978; 98:152–160.

85. Low GC, Fairley NH: Laboratory and hospital infections with Yellow Fever in England. *Brit Med J* 1931; 1:125–128.
86. Langmuir AD: Changing concepts of airborne infection of acute contagious diseases: a reconsideration of classic epidemiologic theories. *Ann NY Acad Sci* 1980; 353:35–44.
87. Fenner F, Henderson DA, Arita I, Jezek Z, Ladnyi ID: Smallpox and Its Eradication. World Health Organization, Geneva, 1988, pp 169–208.
88. Josephson A, Gombert ME: Airborne transmission of nosocomial varicella from localized zoster. *J Infect Dis* 1988; 158:238–241.
89. Zweighaft RM, Fraser DW, Hattwick MAW, et al: Lassa fever: response to an imported case. *N Engl J Med* 1977; 297:297–301.
90. Cooper CB, Gransden WR, Webster M, et al: A case of Lassa fever: experience at St Thomas's Hospital. *Br Med J* 1982; 285:1003–1005.
91. Openheimer L: A case of Lassa fever. *Br Med J* 1982; 285:1576–1577.
92. Peters CJ, Jahrling PB, Liu CT, et al: Experimental studies of arenaviral hemorrhagic fevers. *Curr Top Microbiol Immunol* 1987; 134:5–68.
93. Peters CJ, Liu CT, Anderson GW Jr: Pathogenesis of viral hemorrhagic fevers: Rift Valley fever and Lassa fever contrasted. *Rev Infect Dis* 1989; S743–749.
94. Mitrakul C, Poshyachinda M, Futrakul P, et al: Hemostatic and platelet kinetic studies in dengue hemorrhagic fever. *Am J Trop Med Hyg* 1977; 26:975–984.
95. Lee M, Cho BY, Park S: Hematologic manifestations of Korean hemorrhagic fever. Presented at Proceedings of the Fourth Meeting of Asian-Pacific Division of International Society of Hematology, Korea, June 25–29, 1979.
96. Cummins D, Fisher-Hoch S, Bennett D: Detection of a plasma inhibitor of platelet function in patients with severe Lassa fever. Presented at the 36th Annual Meeting of the American Society of Tropical Medicine and Hygiene, Los Angeles, CA, 1987.
97. Fisher-Hoch SP, Mitchell SW, Sasso DR, et al: Physiological and immunologic disturbances associated with shock in a primate model of Lassa fever. *J Infect Dis* 1987; 155:465–474.
98. Milei J, Bolomo NJ: Myocardial damage in viral hemorrhagic fevers. *Am Heart J* 1982; 104:1385–1391.
99. Canonico PG, Kende M, Luscri BJ, et al: In-vivo activity of antivirals against exotic RNA viral infections. *J Antimicrob Chemother* 1984; 14(suppl):27–41.
100. Canonico PG: Ribavirin: a review of efficacy, toxicity and mechanisms of antiviral activity, in Hahn FE (ed): *Antibiotics*. Heidelberg, Springer-Verlag, 1983, Vol 6: *Modes and Mechanisms of Microbial Growth Inhibitors*. pp 161–186.
101. Stephen EL, Jones DE, Peters CJ, et al: Ribavirin treatment of *Toga-, Arena-* and *Bunyavirus* infections in subhuman primates and other laboratory animal species, in Smith RA and Kirkpatrick W (eds): *Ribavirin: A Broad Spectrum Antiviral Agent*. New York, Academic Press, 1980, pp 169–183.
102. Jahrling PB, Hesse RA, Eddy GA, et al: Lassa virus infection of rhesus monkeys: pathogenesis and treatment with ribavirin. *J Infect Dis* 1980; 141:580–589.
103. Peters CJ, Reynolds JA, Slone TW, et al: Prophylaxis of Rift Valley fever with antiviral drugs, immune serum, an interferon inducer, and a macrophage activator. *Antiviral Res* 1986; 6:285–297.
104. Kenyon RH, Canonico PG, Green DE, et al: Effect of ribavirin and tributylribavirin on Argentine hemorrhagic fever (Junin virus) in guinea pigs. *Antimicrob Agents Chemother* 1986; 29:521–523.
105. Huggins JW, Kim GR, Brand OM, et al: Ribavirin therapy for Hantaan virus infection in suckling mice. *J Infect Dis* 1986; 153:489–497.
106. Watts DM, Ussery MA, Peters CJ: Effects of ribavirin on the replication of Crimean-Congo hemorrhagic fever. Presented at the Annual Meeting of the American Society for Virology, Chapel Hill, NC, May 31–June 4, 1987.
107. Berezina LK, Leont'eva NA, Kondrashina NH, et al: Influence of ribavirin on the reproduction of bunyaviruses in cell culture and in experiments on white mice. *Vopr Virusol* 1983; 5:627–629.
108. McCormick JB, King IJ, Webb PA, et al: Lassa fever, effective therapy with ribavirin. *N Engl J Med* 1986; 341:20–26.
109. Huggins JW, Hsiang CM, Cosgriff TM, et al: Intravenous ribavirin therapy of hemorrhagic fever with renal syndrome (HFRS). *Antiviral Res* 1988; 9:123.
110. Enria DA, Briggiler AM, Levis S, et al: Preliminary report, tolerance and antiviral effect of ribavirin in patients with Argentine hemorrhagic fever. *Antiviral Res* 1987; 7:353–359.
111. MacDonald C, McKee K Jr, Huggins J, et al: Ribavirin (RB) prophylaxis of sandfly fever-Sicilian (SFS) infection in human volunteers. Presented at the 86th Annual Meeting of the American Society for Microbiology, Washington, DC, March 23–28, 1986.
112. Peters CJ, Huggins JW, Jahrling PB: Antiviral therapy for Yellow Fever. Annals of the International Symposium on Yellow Fever and Dengue, Rio de Janeiro, Brazil, May 15–19, 1988 (in press).
113. Roberts RB, Laskin OL, Laurence J, et al: Ribavirin pharmacodynamics in high-risk patients for acquired immunodeficiency syndrome. *Clin Pharmacol Ther* 1987; 42:365–373.
114. Laskin OL, Longstreth JA, Hart CC, et al: Ribavirin disposition in high-risk patients for acquired immunodeficiency syndrome. *Clin Pharmacol Ther* 1987; 42:546–555.
115. Ferm VH, Willhite C, Kilham L: Teratogenic effects of ribavirin on hamster and rat embryos. *Teratology* 1978; 17:93–102.
116. Jahrling PB, Peters CJ, Stephen EL: Enhanced treatment of Lassa fever by immune plasma combined with ribavirin in cynomolgus monkeys. *J Infect Dis* 1984; 149:420–427.
117. Shepherd AJ, Swanepoel R, Leman PA: The antibody response in Crimean-Congo hemorrhagic fever. *Rev Infect Dis* 1989; S801–806.
118. Morrill JC, Jennings GB, Johnson AJ, et al: Pathogenesis of Rift Valley fever in rhesus monkeys: role of interferon response. *Arch Virol* 1990; 110:195–212.
119. Morrill JC, Jennings GB, Cosgriff TM, Gibbs PH, Peters CJ: Prevention of Rift Valley fever in rhesus monkeys with interferon-α. *Rev Infect Dis* 1989; 11:S815–S825.
120. Saavedra M, Levis S, Tiano E, Falcoff R, Maiztegui J: Sensibilidad del virus Junin a los interferones α y γ. 30th Reunion de la Sociedad Argentina de Investigación Clínica, Mar del Plata, Argentina, November 1985.
121. Leist TP, Eppler M, Zinkeragel RM: Enhanced virus replication and inhibition of lymphocytic choriomeningitis virus disease in anti-gamma interferon-treated mice. *J Virol* 1989; 63:2813–2819.

Orbiviruses and Other Reoviruses

Robert B. Craven

Orbiviruses are insect-borne viruses (arboviruses) primarily of veterinary importance.[1] The genus name is derived from their doughnut-shaped capsomers visualized under the electron microscope. Although classified as arboviruses, unlike the majority of that group they are relatively resistant to inactivation by detergents or lipid solvents. They grow well in a number of tissue culture lines.

The genus is divided into 12 serogroups of which four contain viruses known to infect or produce disease in humans: Colorado tick fever group, Changuinola group, Corriparta group, and Kemerovo group. Among the veterinary diseases produced by orbiviruses are African horse sickness, bluetongue disease, epizootic hemorrhagic disease, and equine encephalosis. Representatives of the genus are found throughout the world.

STRUCTURE AND BIOLOGY OF ORBIVIRUSES

Orbiviruses contain double-stranded RNA (dsRNA) arranged in ten segments except for the members of the Colorado tick fever serogroup which have 12 segments of dsRNA.[1] Compared with the other reoviruses, orbiviruses are less stable at low pH. They are described as varying in size from 50 to 90 nm and are ico-

sahedral in shape with 92 capsomers. The capsid is double-layered protein. The outer layer is diffuse and unstructured while the inner layer is organized in pentameric-hexameric units. Molecular virologic studies of the orbiviruses that infect man have yet to be done, with most research to this point having concentrated on the viruses of veterinary significance.

Orbiviruses may be isolated from their vectors or from mammals by a variety of methods, including mice, chick embryos, and a number of tissue culture cell lines such as Vero, LLC-MK-2, and BHK-21. Serologically, they can be detected by neutralization test, complement fixation (CF), indirect fluorescent antibody (IFA) test, and gel immunoprecipitation.

COLORADO TICK FEVER

Colorado tick fever, caused by a virus belonging to the family *Reoviridae*, is a zoonotic infection of rodents transmitted to man by the bite of the wood tick, *Dermacentor andersoni,* in the Rocky Mountains and more western regions of the United States. It is a denguelike disease of relatively low frequency and should be considered in the differential diagnosis of febrile illness in patients with an appropriate exposure history.

History

As early as 1850, physicians in Colorado described an entity called "mountain fever" but were unable to distinguish it with certainty from a number of infections including Rocky Mountain spotted fever (RMSF), typhus, typhoid fever, malaria, etc. In 1930, Becker first gave the disease its present name, Colorado tick fever (CTF), and described some of its symptoms.[2, 3] Referring to the disease as "American mountain tick fever," Toomey reviewed the older literature in three articles published in 1931 and 1932.[4–6] In 1940, Topping et al reported clinical findings in 11 patients and reviewed the epidemiology of CTF in Colorado. They summarized quite accurately many of the salient clinical and epidemiologic facts about the disease as they are presently known.[7]

In 1946, Florio et al infected human volunteers and demonstrated that CTF was not a mild form of RMSF, nor was it dengue, which it closely resembled clinically.[8] In 1950, Florio and his group isolated CTF virus from *D andersoni* ticks collected in an endemic area. Their laboratory studies of transmission showed that *D andersoni* could be infected at any stage of development (larval, nymphal, or adult) and that if ticks were infected at an early stage of their development, infection would persist into adulthood (transstadial transmission). They erroneously concluded that transovarial transmission of CTF virus occurred.[9]

Structure and Biology

CTF viral particles are spherical, 80 nm in outer diameter with an inner core diameter of 50 nm. An icosahedral architecture has been demonstrated for the capsid which has 92 doughnut-shaped capsomers on its surface. The viral genome consists of dsRNA arranged in 12 segments. This multisegmented genome provides for the possibility of natural recombination (reassortment) of genes. Other characteristics of the virus include relative stability at room temperature, resistance to deoxycholate and lipid solvents, and instability at acidic pH. Electron micrographs of CTF virus growing in cell culture reveal production of mature virions, intracytoplasmic matrices, and tubular or fibrillar structures.[10, 11] Antigenic variants of CTF virus have been described by both neutralization tests and RNA-RNA blot hybridization. Variations are greatest when comparisons are made between isolates obtained from ticks and rodent hosts, from ticks and human hosts, or from rodents and humans.[12, 13] The closest antigenic relative of CTF virus is Eyach virus which has been isolated in West Germany from *Ixodes ricinus* ticks and in France from *Ix ricinus* and *Ix ventalloi* ticks.[14] CTF virus and Eyach virus differ from other viruses in their genus in that they have 12 RNA segments compared to ten for the other members of the genus. In spite of this morphogenetic difference, the two viruses are assigned to the genus *Orbivirus* of the family *Reoviridae.*

Epidemiology

Incidence and Distribution

CTF is a disease which is reported at the option of the states to the US Public Health Service, Centers for Disease Control (CDC). Colorado annually reports between 100 and 300 cases, but the disease is underreported from there and from other western states as well. There is a strong seasonal trend[15]; cases occur between February and July with the majority in May and June. Variations in the seasonal peak occur from one geographic region to another or within the same area, depending on climatic factors and abundance of the vector and host populations. *D andersoni* requires a certain minimal amount of ground moisture for optimum survival. Thus, factors such as rainfall, snow-melt run-off, type of ground cover, altitude, and solar radiation are important. At lower elevations, temperatures rise more quickly earlier in the spring and dry up the ground moisture sooner than at the cooler, higher elevations. Similarly, the success in feeding of the wood tick depends on the fortunes of its natural hosts which must deal, in turn, with such factors as the severity of winter and the amount of food and ground cover available.

The geographic distribution of CTF reflects the range of the vector tick, which occurs at altitudes from 4000 to 10,000 feet. Although more commonly recognized or reported as a disease in Colorado, CTF occurs in several western states and Canada; however, because of the tourism in these endemic areas, imported CTF cases can be encountered almost anywhere in the free world. In the western United States, the following states have documented the occurrence of CTF by laboratory confirmation of human cases or the transmission of CTF virus in nature: Colorado, Wyoming, Montana, South Dakota, Utah, Idaho, Nevada, Washington, Oregon, California, and New Mexico. In Canada, the virus is known to be present in British Columbia and Alberta.

No differences in susceptibility to infection due to age or sex are known; however, severe manifestations such as hemorrhage and encephalitis are more frequent in children. The reported incidence in males exceeds that for females by a ratio of 3:1 because of their greater opportunity for exposure during occupational and recreational activities. Outdoor exposures (camping, fishing, ranching, cutting lumber, etc) in endemic areas during the time of peak adult tick activity are associated with a risk of infection.

Ecology of the Virus

The basic transmission cycle of CTF virus involves immature (larval and nymphal) *D andersoni* ticks and a limited number of rodent species. Large mammals such as deer and elk, although serving as hosts for the adult ticks, play no recognized role in virus perpetuation. Infection with CTF virus produces no apparent illness in the natural hosts, and the successful persistence of the virus in the enzootic cycle is aided by the lengthy viremia in small mammals (rodents) which are fed upon by larvae and nymphs. The virus is passed transstadially from nymphal to adult ticks, the latter having a host preference for larger mammals, including man. Viremias in infected hosts can persist for over a month and can be prolonged in hibernating animals, thus providing one possible mechanism for overwintering of the virus, although the importance of this mechanism in nature has not been established.[16-21] The remarkable length of viremia even in hosts with neutralizing antibody appears to be due to the protected location of the virus within the erythrocytes of the host.[22, 23]

Although it is possible for *D andersoni* to reach adulthood in 1 year during the warmer months from spring to early fall, the cycle from larvae to adults is usually 2 to 3 years.[15] In the spring, enzootic transmission is reinitiated when infected nymphs feed upon susceptible small mammal hosts, which then develop protracted viremias and are fed upon by other nymphal or larval ticks. A viremia in the range 10^2 to 10^3 mouse LD_{50} (median lethal dose) per milliliter is required to infect adult *D andersoni*.[24]

Four species of rodents have been identified as important amplifying hosts; the golden-mantled ground squirrel, the Columbia ground squirrel, the yellow pine chipmunk, and the least chipmunk.[18-20] Other species also have been found to be naturally infected, including other ground squirrels and chipmunks, tree squirrels, mice, voles, kangaroo rats, wood rats, rabbits, and hares. The principal hosts for adult ticks have not been clearly defined, but probably include porcupines, elk, and mule deer. These larger animals are excluded from the viral transmission cycle but play an important role in adult tick blood feeding and mating. Like other large mammals, man is also a "dead-end" host since immature ticks do not readily feed on humans and since, even if it feeds on a viremic human, the mature *D andersoni* female cannot pass virus transovarially to her offspring. CTF produces prolonged viremias in humans, and human-to-human transmission via blood transfusion has been documented.[25, 26]

Pathogenesis and Pathology

Soon after infection, CTF virus invades the bone marrow and the erythrocyte precursors. When the mature red blood cell (RBC) finally is produced, it contains within it CTF virus which is then protected from an immune response. This sequestration of virus within the erythrocyte explains both the long period of viremia (up to 120 days) and the extended length of time required before detectable antibodies appear.[22, 23] Both CF and neutralizing (N) antibody may be quite slow in developing (4–6 weeks). Once infected, long-term immunity appears to be the norm, but at least one instance of reinfection has been documented.[27]

Because of the low case-fatality ratio, autopsy findings have only been reported in the literature for one case, and the author has been provided with the findings in one additional case (D.L. Dawson, personal communciation, October 1980).[28] Both deaths occurred in children, a 4-year-old boy and a 10-year-old girl. The most striking finding in both cases was massive gastrointestinal (GI) bleeding. In addition, the girl had disseminated intravascular coagulation (DIC) and acute tubular necrosis of the kidneys. Focal necrotic lesions were noted in multiple organs.

Clinical Features

Symptoms of CTF appear after an incubation period of three to six days. The onset of symptoms is dramatic, with most patients developing high fever, chills, joint and muscle pains, and headache with ocular pains. Nausea and vomiting with anorexia may also be present as complaints. Abnormal physical findings generally consist of fever and conjunctival injection; occasionally, a spleen tip or liver edge is palpable and lymphadenopathy may be present. A fleeting petechial or maculopapular central rash is seen in a minority of patients. Many patients have a biphasic fever pattern with a high fever for one to three days, then defervescence and remission of symptoms for up to two days, followed by a second febrile period of one to three days, often accompanied by more severe symptoms.[27–29]

A more severe clinical picture is occasionally seen in children, who may demonstrate hemorrhagic manifestations ranging from a more pronounced rash to severe GI bleeding and DIC. Children may also exhibit CNS involvement, expressed as aseptic meningitis or encephalitis.[30] In one unfortunate case of double jeopardy, a child was reported as having had concomitant CTF and tick-borne paralysis.[31] In adults, there have been rare reports of orchitis, pericarditis, hepatitis, and symptoms mimicking myocardial infarction.[27–33]

Laboratory Diagnosis

A number of techniques for virus isolation and serodiagnosis of CTF have been developed. Some state health departments in the endemic area provide testing. Those state laboratories that do not routinely provide tests for CTF may forward specimens (see below) to the Centers for Disease Control in Atlanta, Georgia. Possibly because of the intraerythrocytic sequestration of the virus,

both CF and N tests are slow to demonstrate antibody (3–6 weeks and 2–3 weeks, respectively).[34–36] Virus isolation can be performed by inoculation of the patient's blood clot into suckling mice or a continuous tissue culture cell line such as Vero cells. The virus strain isolated can then be identified by CF, N,[34] or immunofluorescent (IF) staining.[37, 38] The most rapid technique for diagnosis utilizes IF staining of slip smears of the acutely ill patient's washed blood clots[38]; experience in this laboratory has consistently shown good specificity for this test but varying sensitivity, especially during the first seven days of illness, when as many as 50% of patients, who will eventually be proved to have CTF by IF or another technique will be negative. Thus, a positive test in the first seven days is good evidence for CTF, but a negative test should be repeated during the second week after onset of illness.[39, 40]

A serum IgM test has been recently described. This test is much more rapidly performed than the N test although it is less sensitive. One of the useful aspects of this test, however, is that IgM antibody declines rapidly after 45 days, and thus the detection of this antibody provides a basis for a presumptive diagnosis of recent infection in a single serum.[41]

Of the serologic tests available, the IFA technique detects antibody more quickly (from four to eight days after onset of illness in some cases) and in higher titer than the CF or N tests.[40] Acute and convalescent blood specimens should be spun down, and both sera and clots in separate tubes should be labeled with appropriate identification and dates of collection. The clots and sera may then be submitted at ambient temperature to an appropriate laboratory if shipping time does not exceed two to three days. If a greater delay is anticipated, the specimen should be shipped frozen.

Prevention and Treatment

No licensed vaccine for CTF is available. Because of the relatively benign nature of the disease and the sporadic numbers of cases reported annually, vaccination will not be a practical public health measure in the foreseeable future. Measures to educate the public about the location of enzootic areas and about the prevention of tick bites are the most appropriate strategies at present. During the spring and early summer, persons who live or work in enzootic zones or pursue recreational activities in these areas should wear long pants and long-sleeved shirts. Pants legs should be tucked into boots or sealed off by rubber bands. After an adult *D andersoni* finds a human host, it does not usually attach and feed before two to six hours, so that ticks can be found on clothing and removed before they attach. Insect repellents containing a high concentration of diethyltoluamide also can be of value when applied to clothing.[42] The skin and scalp should be inspected at least daily for attached ticks. If an attached tick is found, it should be coated with an alcohol, a solvent such as turpentine or nail polish remover, or a hydrocarbon such as gasoline. The tick should be grasped as close to the head as possible, preferably with tweezers or forceps, and gentle traction should be applied away from the skin to facilitate removal of the entire head and mouth-parts. If the tick must be removed with fingers, avoid touching the tick directly by using gauze, paper, a handkerchief, etc., to prevent contamination of the fingers by CTF virus or other possible pathogens. After removal, the bite area should be thoroughly washed and an antiseptic applied. A person with an attached tick should seek immediate medical attention if a febrile illness develops after the bite, since potentially severe bacterial infections requiring antibiotic therapy are also transmitted by *D andersoni* (see below).

Although the antiviral substance ribavirin triacetate has been demonstrated to inhibit CTF virus in mice, its use in humans has not been evaluated and no specific therapy for CTF is available. Treatment of uncomplicated cases is aimed at alleviating symptoms.[43] Most cases of CTF do not require hospitalization, but the difficulty in differentiating early CTF from early RMSF may require some period of observation in the hospital. Symptomatic therapy for CTF should include control of fever by antipyretics, maintenance of adequate hydration, and administration of analgesics as required. Patients with hemorrhagic manifestations frequently have thrombocytopenia, and the antipyretic chosen for them should be acetaminophen since aspirin reduces platelet adhesiveness and may aggravate bleeding. Severe nausea and vomiting may necessitate intravenous (IV) fluid and electrolyte replacement. CNS involvement should be treated the same as aseptic meningitis or encephalitis of other viral origin.[30] Because of the exceptionally long period of viremia, patients with CTF should not donate blood until at least 6 months after the onset of their illness. Occasionally, some patients, after their acute illness, will experience weakness and malaise for 3 or more weeks after onset of their illness. This prolonged illness is observed more frequently beginning at age 30, and its occurrence increases in likelihood with increasing age.[27]

Algorithm for Diagnosis and Management

The appropriate diagnosis of CTF requires a careful history about exposure in an endemic area and whether the patient had an attached tick or saw ticks crawling on his or her skin or clothing. In a series of 228 laboratory-confirmed cases of CTF studied from 1973 to 1974 in Colorado, 90% of the patients recalled having an attached tick (52%) or ticks crawling on their skin or clothing (38%).[27]

Once exposure in an endemic area or to ticks has been ascertained or is suspected, three diseases requiring antibiotic therapy should be excluded; RMSF, tick-borne relapsing fever, and tick-borne tularemia. The differentiation between these diseases on the basis of incubation period and clinical and laboratory findings is displayed in the algorithm shown in Figure 27–1. On occasion, it may be necessary to hospitalize acutely ill patients until a definitive diagnosis can be established.

OTHER ORBIVIRUSES INFECTING MAN

Eyach Virus

Eyach (EYA) virus was isolated from *Ix ricinus* in West Germany in 1976 and is a close antigenic relative of the CTF virus.[44]

It has subsequently been isolated from *Ix ricinus* and *Ix ventalloi* ticks in France. No human disease has been associated with EYA virus in either of these countries, but a study in Czechoslovakia reported the presence of antibody titers to EYA virus in patients with a number of inflammatory neurologic conditions. However, no causal relationship has yet been established.

Changuinola Virus

Changuinola (CGL) virus was isolated by workers from the Gorgas Laboratory in Panama in 1960.[44] While trapping *Lutzomyia spp* mosquitoes, the vector, a mosquito trapper, developed an undifferentiated febrile illness. The virus was isolated from his blood and he subsequently developed CF antibodies. The importance of this virus as a cause of human illness remains to be elucidated.

Kemerovo Virus

Kemerovo (KEM) virus was isolated from *Ix persculatus* ticks in Siberia in 1962.[44] It has also been isolated from the spinal fluid of a man with aseptic meningitis. Neutralizing antibodies to this virus were found in nearly 3% of the population in one serosurvey in Siberia. The virus has also been isolated in Egypt. Human antibodies to Tribec virus, a member of the Kemerovo serogroup, have also been reported from patients with inflammatory neurologic disease in Czechoslovakia.

Reovirus Type III

Biliary atresia of human infants is a disease in which the histopathologic findings resemble those of reovirus-induced cholangitis in mice.[45] Peripheral intrahepatic portal bile ducts revealed inflammation and proliferation in early human disease which progressed to proliferation of portal fibrous tissue resulting in biliary cirrhosis. Mice infected with reovirus type III show pathologic changes resembling those seen in early human disease, but the irreversible progressive fibrosis is not seen in the mouse model. Serologic studies on infants with extrahepatic biliary atresia or neonatal hepatitis implicate reovirus III as the possible cause of these diseases. In contrast to control infants or infants with other causes of cholestasis, infants with extra biliary atresia more frequently have antibodies to reovirus type III (62% antibody-positive); infants with neonatal hepatitis commonly have antibody (50%) to reovirus type III. Only 6% to 12% of control groups had antibody.[46, 47] Antibodies to reovirus type III are commonly found in adults, but studies have suggested that the antibodies found in infants with extrahepatic biliary atresia or neonatal hepatitis are not maternal antibodies.[3]

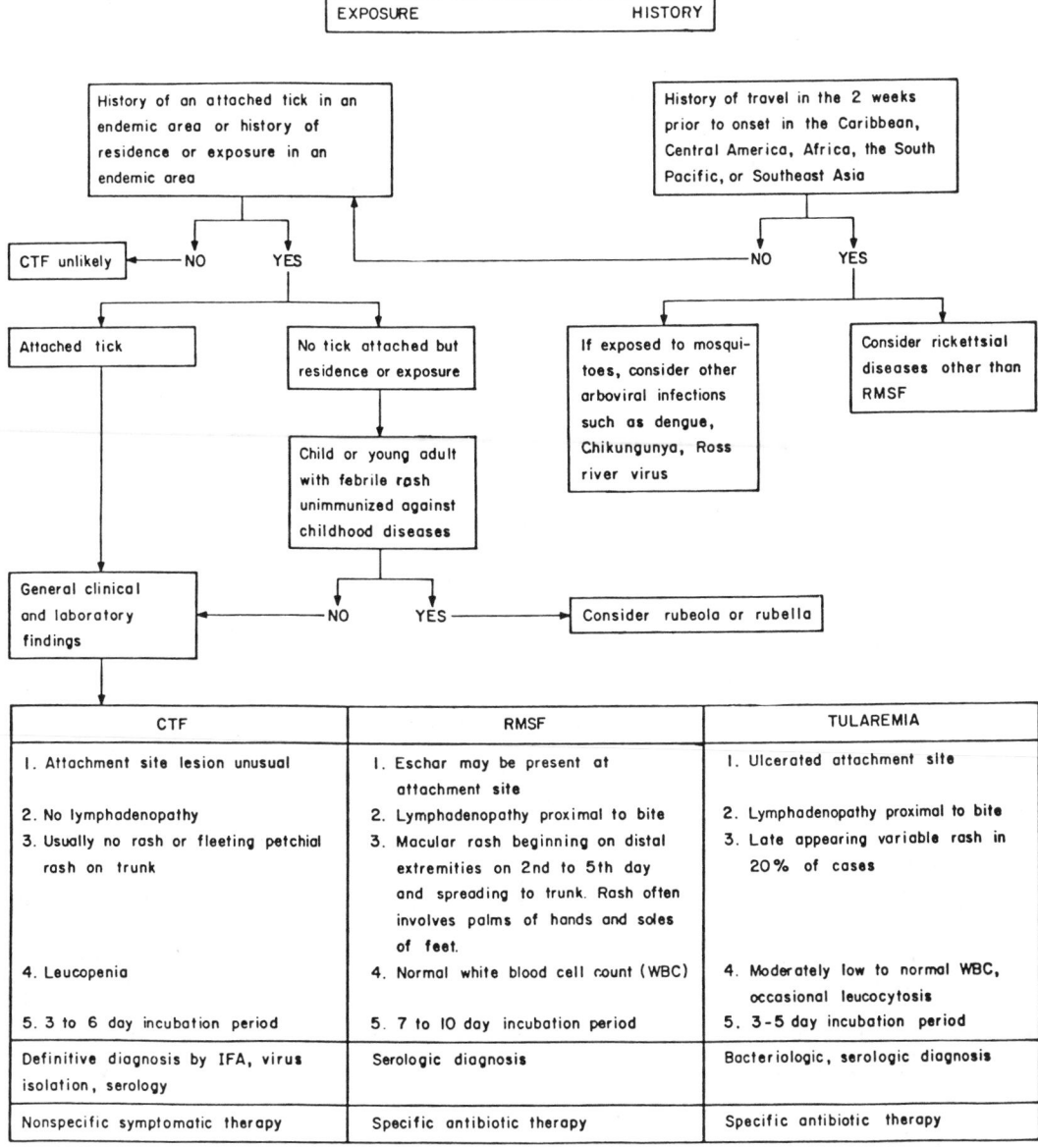

Figure 27–1. Algorithm for the differential diagnosis and management of Colorado tick fever (CTF). RMSF = Rocky Mountain spotted fever; IFA = indirect fluorescent antibody test.

REFERENCES

1. Gorman BM, Taylor J, Walker PJ: Orbiviruses, in Wolfgang J (ed): *The Reoviridae,* New York, Plenum, 1983, pp 287–357.
2. Becker FE: Tick-borne infections in Colorado. I. The diagnosis and management of infections transmitted by the wood tick. *Colo Med* 1930; 27:36–43.
3. Becker FE: Tick-borne infections in Colorado. II. A survey of the occurrence of infections transmitted by the wood tick. *Colo Med* 1980; 27:87.
4. Toomey N: Mountain fever and spotted fever of the Rocky Mountains—clinical studies. *Am Intern Med* 1931; 5:601–612.
5. Toomey N: American mountain tick-fever and spotted fever of Rocky Mountains—comparative epidemiography. *Am Intern Med* 1931; 5:601–612.
6. Toomey N: American mountain tick fever—semiography and nosology, with remarks on pathology and treatment. *Am Intern Med* 1932; 5:912–923.
7. Topping NH, Cullyford JS, Davis GE: Colorado tick fever. *Public Health Rep* 1940; 55:2224–2237.
8. Florio L, Mugrage ER, Stewart MO: Colorado tick fever. *Am Intern Med* 1946; 25:466–471.
9. Florio L, Miller MS, Mugrage ER: Colorado tick fever. Isolation of the virus from *Dermacentor andersoni* in nature and a laboratory study of the transmission of the virus in the tick. *J Immunol* 1950; 64:257–263.
10. Murphy FA, Borden EC, Shope RE, et al: Physicochemical and morphological relationships of some arthropod-borne viruses to bluetongue virus—a new taxonomic group. Electron microscopic studies. *J Gen Virol* 1971; 13:273–288.
11. Murphy FA, Coleman PH, Harrison AK, et al: Colorado tick fever virus: An electron microscopic study. *Virology* 1968; 35:28–40.
12. Karabatsos N, Poland JD, Emmons RW, et al: Antigenic variants of Colorado tick fever virus. *J Gen Virol* 1987; 5:1463–1469.
13. Bodkin DK, Knudson DL: Genetic relatedness of Colorado tick

fever virus isolates by RNA-RNA blot hybridization. *J Gen Virol* 1987; 68:1199–1204.

14. Rehse-Kupper B, Casals J, Rehse E, et al: Eyach—an arthropod-borne virus related to Colorado tick fever virus in the Federal Republic of Germany. *Acta Virol (Praha)* 1976; 20:339–342.

15. Eads RB, Smith GC: Seasonal activity and Colorado tick fever infection rates in Rocky Mountain woodticks, *Dermacentor andersoni* (Acari: Ixodidae) in north-central Colorado, USA. *J Med Entomol* 1983; 20:49–55.

16. Emmons RW: *Experimental Colorado Tick Fever Virus Infection in Wild Rodents: Viremia and Antibody Response in Active and Hibernating Animals.* Thesis, University of California, Berkeley, 1965.

17. Emmons RW: Colorado tick fever: prolonged viremia in hibernating *Citellus lateralis. Am J Trop Med Hyg* 1966; 15:428–433.

18. Burgdorfer W, Eklund CM: Studies on the ecology of Colorado tick fever virus in Western Montana. *Am J Hyg* 1959; 69:127–137.

19. Eklund CM, Kohls GM, Jellison WL: Isolation of Colorado tick fever virus from rodents in Colorado. *Science* 1958; 128:413–414.

20. Burgdorfer W: Colorado tick fever. I. The behavior of CTF virus in the porcupine. *J Infect Dis* 1959; 104:101–104.

21. Burgdorfer W: Colorado tick fever. II. The behavior of CTF virus in rodents. *J Infect Dis* 1960; 107:384–388.

22. Emmons RW, Oshuo LS, Johnson HN, et al: Intraerythrocytic location of Colorado tick fever virus. *J Gen Virol* 1972; 17:185–195.

23. Hughes LE, Casper EA, Clifford CM: Persistence of Colorado tick fever virus in red blood cells. *Am J Trop Med Hyg* 1974; 23:530–532.

24. Rozeboom LE, Burgdorfer W: Development of Colorado tick fever in the Rocky Mountain wood tick, *Dermacentor andersoni. Am J Hyg* 1959; 69:138–145.

25. Philip RN, Casper EA, Cory J, et al: The potential for transmission of arbovirus by blood transfusion with particular reference to Colorado tick fever, in Greenwalt TJ, Jamieson GA (eds): *Transmissible Diseases and Blood Transfusion.* New York, Grune ; aM Stratton, 1975, pp 175–195.

26. Randall WH, Simmons J, Casper EA, et al: Transmission of Colorado tick fever virus by blood transfusion—Montana. *MMWR* 1975; 24:422–423.

27. Goodpasture HC, Poland JD, Francy DB, et al: Colorado tick fever: Clinical, epidemiologic, and laboratory aspects of 228 cases in Colorado in 1973–1974. *Ann Intern Med* 1978; 88:303–310.

28. Eklund CM, Kohls GM, Jellison WL: The clinical and ecological aspects of Colorado tick fever, in Proceedings of the Sixth International Congress on Tropical Medicine and Malaria. 1959, Vol 5, pp 197–203.

29. Earnest MP, Breckinridge JC, Barr RJ, et al: Colorado tick fever. Clinical and epidemiologic features and evaluation of diagnostic methods. *Rocky Mountain Med J* 1971; 68:60–62.

30. Fraser CH, Schiff DW: Colorado tick fever encephalitis. Report of a case. *Pediatrics* 1962; 29:187–190.

31. Anderson RD: Colorado tick fever and tick paralysis in a young child. *Pediatr Infect Dis* 1983; 2:43–44.

32. Hierholzer WJ, Bary DW: Colorado tick fever pericarditis. *JAMA* 1971; 227:825–828.

33. Loge RV: Acute hepatitis associated with Colorado tick fever. *West J Med* 1985; 142:91–92.

34. Gerloff RK, Eklund CM: A tissue culture neutralization test for Colorado tick fever antibody and use of the test for serologic surveys. *J Infect Dis* 1959; 104:174–183.

35. DeBoer CJ, Kung LJ, Koprowski H, et al: Specific complement-fixing diagnostic antigens for Colorado tick fever. *Proc Soc Exp Biol Med* 1947; 64:202–208.

36. Thomas LA, Eklund CM: Use of the complement fixation test as a diagnostic aid in Colorado tick fever. *J Infect Dis* 1960; 107:235–240.

37. Burgdorfer W, Lackman D: Identification of the virus of Colorado tick fever in mouse tissues by means of fluorescent antibodies. *J Bacteriol* 1960; 80:131–136.

38. Emmons RW, Lennette EH: Immunofluorescent staining in the laboratory diagnosis of Colorado tick fever. *J Lab Clin Med* 1966; 68:923–929.

39. Emmons RW, Dondero DV, Devlin V, et al: Serologic diagnosis of Colorado tick fever. A comparison of complement-fixation, immunofluorescence, and plaque-reduction methods. *Am J Trop Med Hyg* 1969; 18:796–802.

40. Gaidamovich SY, Klisenko GA, Shanovan NK: New aspects of laboratory techniques for studies of Colorado tick fever. *Am J Trop Med Hyg* 1974; 23:526–529.

41. Calisher CH, Poland JD, Calisher SB, et al: Diagnosis of Colorado tick fever virus infection by enzyme immunoassays for immunoglobulin M and G antibodies. *J Clin Microbiol* 1985; 22:84–88.

42. Weidhass DE: Rocky Mountain spotted fever tick control. *JAMA* 1978; 239:1661.

43. Smee DF, Sidwell RW, Clark SM, et al: Inhibition of bluetongue and Colorado tick fever orbiviruses by selected antiviral substances. *Antimicrob Agents Chemother* 1981; 20:533–538.

44. Karabatsos N (ed): *International Catalogue of Arboviruses Including Certain Other Viruses of Vertebrates,* ed 3. San Antonio, Tex, American Society of Tropical Medicine and Hygiene, 1985.

45. Bangaru B, Morecki R, Glaser JH, et al: Comparative studies of biliary atresia in the human newborn and reovirus-induced cholangitis in weanling mice. *Lab Invest* 1980; 43:456–462.

46. Morecki R, Glaser JH, Cho S, et al: Biliary atresia and reovirus type 3 infection. *N Engl J Med* 1982; 304:481–484.

47. Glaser JH, Balistreri WF, Morecki R: Role of reovirus type 3 in persistent infantile cholestasis. *J Pediatr* 1984; 105:912–915.

28

Hepatitis B Virus

Larry I. Lutwick

In recent times, medical science has come upon an increasing number of previously unrecognized human pathogens. Usually not truly ''new,'' these organisms have been identified as causes of human disease related to factors such as improved detection techniques, more aggressive medical or surgical therapy, or human population expansion into previously sparsely inhabited areas. The observation of icteric illness with a long incubation and subsequent identification of the hepatitis B virus (HBV) can be classified in this category. Indeed, only with the advent of immunotherapy (vaccines and immune sera) and chemotherapy directed against a variety of pathogens could the disease caused by HBV be recognized as a separate entity.

With as many as 284,000,000 people thought to be currently infected with HBV,[1] this virus is actively replicating in more humans than any other. Not only is HBV impressive in the number of people infected but also in its diversity of clinical manifestations. HBV may exist as a commensal, manifest only as viral antigenemia without liver disease. HBV can cause acute hepatitis that may be anywhere on a spectrum from mild and self-limited to aggressive and destructive disease which may lead to postnecrotic cirrhosis. The liver disease may also be worsened by infection with the delta virus, an agent with which HBV functions uniquely as a helper

virus. In addition, the virus has been strongly associated with one of the most common visceral malignancies worldwide, primary hepatocellular carcinoma (hepatoma). Furthermore, the agent may be associated with polyarteritis nodosa, glomerulonephritis, and a number of other immunologically mediated disorders. HBV is transmissible in a variety of ways, including blood transfusion, sexual contact, neonatal exposure, and perhaps via insect vectors. The spectrum of diseases that it causes and its extraordinary prevalence make HBV a remarkable pathogen. Yet, in the midst of these factors, HBV has been replaced as a major cause of posttransfusion hepatitis in the Western World, and several unique vaccines have been developed that have the possibility of substantially decreasing the morbidity and mortality associated with this agent in years to come.

HISTORY

Specific serologic assays to detect the presence of HBV were developed in the second half of this century. The early epidemiologic reports, therefore, could not clearly distinguish HBV disease from other icteric illnesses, but certainly many of the early reports represent HBV disease. Similarly, the overall detection of transmission of the disease was limited to those cases of overt, symptomatic icteric illness since serum aminotransferase measurements were not used as an assessment of hepatocyte injury until the 1950s.

Lürman in 1885 appears to have been one of the first to suggest a link between parenteral inoculation and icterus.[2] In Germany, he recognized a cluster of nearly 200 jaundiced individuals occurring after smallpox vaccination with virus from a human lymph source. It is surprising that few records of other such events are found because of the common practice of using lymph from the vesicles of vaccinated individuals for further inoculations, and the ever-present art of tattooing.[3] More than likely, icteric illness from other causes (hepatitis A and leptospirosis among them) had hidden the association of needle sticks and icteric illness. With the advent of arsphenamine, the prototype of antimicrobial drugs, links between parenteral therapy and icteric illness began to occur. It is likely that most of the arsenical-associated jaundice in syphilitics and icterus in insulin-treated diabetics represented transmission of viral hepatitis through reused syringes.[4] However, it was difficult to distinguish syringe-transmitted viral hepatitis from direct toxicity of the therapeutic agent (particularly with arsenotherapy).[5]

During the same period that syringe-associated hepatitis was being recognized, a clear-cut association between human blood or blood product administration and a long incubation-type icteric disease was made in both the United States and Europe. One of the earliest circumstances was that of jaundice associated with yellow fever vaccine. As this vaccine was prepared in the 1930s and 1940s, mouse- or egg-passed virus was suspended in normal human serum. This was erroneously believed to be necessary for vaccine virus stability. Findlay and MacCallum in England reported 48 cases of hepatitis and jaundice occurring among 2200 vaccinated individuals over $4\frac{1}{2}$ years.[6] They were able to show that neither yellow fever nor leptospirosis caused the illnesses and suggested that the long incubation period distinguished the illnesses from that of hepatitis A. The most impressive outbreak of vaccine-associated jaundice occurred in United States military personnel during World War II. As reported by Sawyer et al, an estimated 30,000 cases of jaundice occurred among 3 million people receiving the vaccine.[7] The use of vaccine free of human serum eventually eliminated this problem.

If indeed human serum was the vehicle of transmission of this infection, then the direct use of blood, plasma, or serum should also be implicated. In 1938, Propert described a number of cases of jaundice in children inoculated with convalescent measles serum.[8] Similarly, use of pooled convalescent mumps plasma was associated with hepatitis outbreaks. One large series reported 101 cases of hepatitis with an attack rate of 45%.[9–10] Whole blood and pooled human plasma were also linked to jaundice with long incubation periods as reported by Beeson in the United States and Morgan and Williamson in Great Britain.[11, 12] It is from these outbreaks that the terms "homologous serum jaundice" and "serum hepatitis" were derived, and the latter is still commonly used today. The term hepatitis B, introduced by MacCallum,[13] became generally adopted in the 1970s.

A serendipitous discovery by Blumberg and his colleagues in 1963 has become one of the major factors in the further elucidation of the nature of HBV. This discovery and the investigative work that followed culminated in Blumberg being awarded a Nobel Prize in 1976.[14] While investigating protein polymorphism in different population groups, Blumberg discovered a precipitating antigen-antibody complex occurring when the serum of a multiply transfused hemophiliac was reacted with that of an Australian aborigine.[15] The antigen (Australia antigen) was found to be present with varying prevalence in different parts of the world and to be associated with leukemic patients and institutionalized individuals with Down syndrome. Subsequently, the antigen was found to be associated with certain cases of hepatitis, particularly those cases which were posttransfusion in origin.[16–18] The viral marker became known as the hepatitis-associated antigen (HAA) at that time. As the disease became known as hepatitis B, this antigen became referred to as hepatitis B antigen (HBAg) and finally hepatitis B surface antigen (HBsAg). Screening all blood prior to transfusion for HBsAg began on a limited basis in 1969 and was an important factor in decreasing the incidence of hepatitis B as a cause of posttransfusion hepatitis.

A number of equally important observations came directly out of studies performed at the Willowbrook State School in New York where controlled experimental transmission of hepatitis was observed.[19, 20] In an elegant series of experiments by Krugman and his coworkers,[21–23] the natural course of viral hepatitis was described in detail, particularly with relationship to infectivity and modification with globulin. The investigations documented the previously suspected idea that two different agents could produce viral hepatitis, one resembling infectious hepatitis and one serum hepatitis (referred to in the Willowbrook studies as MS-1 and MS-2, respectively). Crossprotection of one type for the other did not occur.[21] It was demonstrated that MS-2 could be transmitted by nonparenteral means, that MS-2 sera and not MS-1 contained the Australia antigen, and that heat-inactivated MS-2 sera could modify infectivity and function as a vaccine to prevent serum hepatitis.[22, 23] These studies, performed meticulously over several decades, clearly delineated the natural history of acute viral hepatitis and, with the discovery of Australia antigen, set the stage for the intensive investigations to follow.

STRUCTURE AND BIOLOGY OF THE AGENT

The hepatitis B virus is the prototype virus of a group of recently described agents that have been referred to as the hepadnaviruses.[24] These agents share common morphologic and biochemical properties, and all exhibit prominent liver tropism with a tendency toward chronic infection. Other members of the group include the woodchuck, ground squirrel, and duck hepatitis viruses.[25–27] Both the woodchuck and ground squirrel viruses are associated with liver cancer as is seen with HBV in humans. All the agents are essentially species-specific and exhibit marked differences in geographic prevalence of infection (Table 28–1). These animal viruses may become vital tools in the investigation of mechanisms of transmission, chronicity, and malignant transformation associated with HBV. Other animal species, in addition, have been found to have circulating antibody reacting with HBV antigen.[28] Whether this reflects other hepadnaviruses or cross-reacting natural antigens is unclear.

Several particulate structures can be found in serum containing HBsAg.[29] The most frequently observed particle is a small sphere approximately 22 nm in diameter (Figure 28–1), which may be somewhat variable in size (14–38 nm).[30] A second particle (Figure 28–2) in the shape of a variable length filament is usually noted in a lesser concentration than the sphere. A third type of particle (see Figure 28–2), 42 nm in diameter, is more complex, having both an outer coat and inner core and has been termed the Dane particle.[31] It has become clear that the small spherical and filamentous forms represent excess HBsAg, also present as the outer coat of the Dane particle, and are not infectious by themselves.

A paucity of information exists regarding the overall number of particles found in plasma. No doubt great variability is present in the absolute and relative concentrations of spheres, filaments, and Dane particles. Kim and Tilles estimated the overall concentration of 22-nm spheres to be about 10^{13} per milliliter of blood.[30] Bond and Hall found about 2000 spheres for every Dane particle

Table 28–1

Characteristics of the Hepadnaviruses

Type	Distribution	Prevalence of Infection	Host Range*
Hepatitis B	Worldwide	0.1%–15%	+ in chimpanzee, gibbon, −1A lower primates, ground squirrel, woodchuck
Woodchuck hepatitis virus	Pennsylvania, Maryland, New Jersey	30%–35%	− in chimpanzee, ground squirrel, mouse
Ground squirrel hepatitis virus	California	0%–50%	+ in tree squirrel, − in hamster, mice, rat
Duck hepatitis virus	China, Illinois, Virginia, California	1%–10%	− in chicken, + in goose

*+ = experimental host; − = no replication.

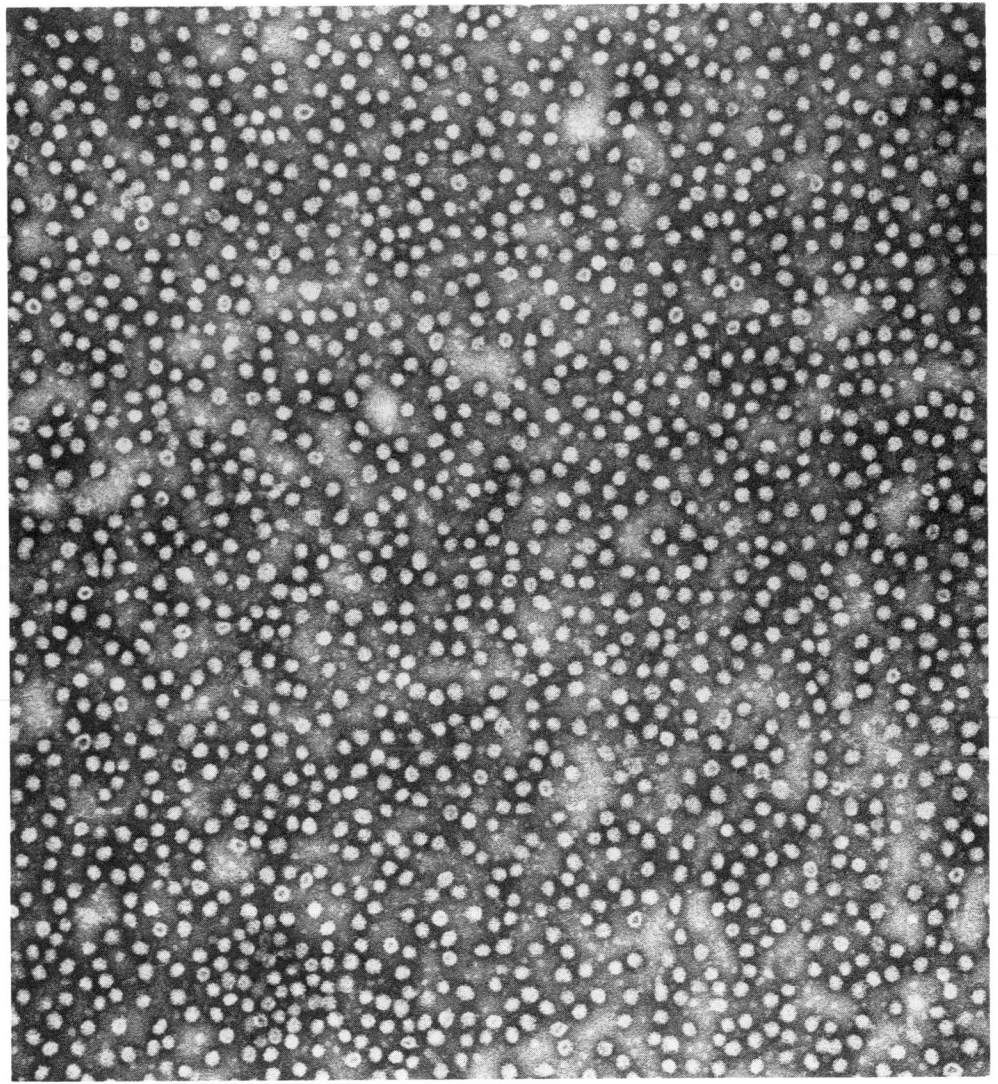

Figure 28–1. Electron photomicrograph of 22-nm spheres of hepatitis B surface antigen, the most common particulate form of hepatitis B virus found in serum (×150,000). (Photo courtesy of Dr John Gerin.)

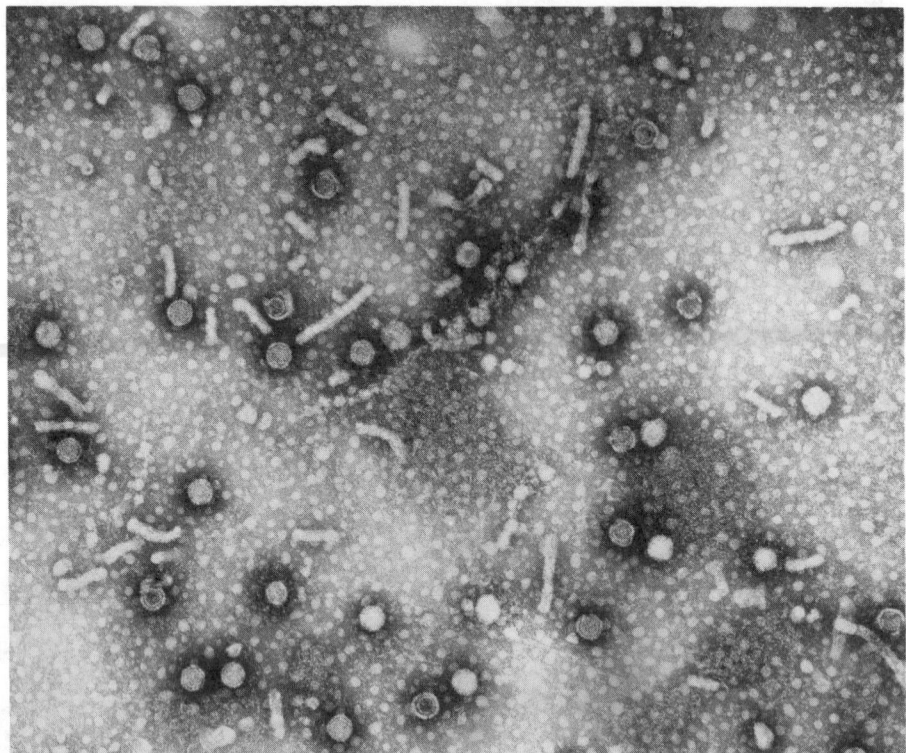

Figure 28–2. Electron photomicrograph of the elongated filamentous forms of hepatitis B surface antigen and the double-shelled 42-nm Dane particles are seen amid the smaller spheres (× 150,000). (Photo courtesy of Dr John Gerin.)

in a single serum,[32] and Almeida has estimated that Dane particles occur in concentrations of between 10^5 to 10^9 in certain sera.[33]

The Dane particle, depicted graphically in Figure 28–3, is thought to be the complete, infectious virus of hepatitis B. In addition to having HBsAg on its surface, the particle internally contains the hepatitis B core antigen (HBcAg). Internal to the core, a small, mostly double-stranded DNA is found together with an endogenous DNA-dependent DNA polymerase enzyme with reverse transcription activity as well and a protein kinase. In addition, the hepatitis B e antigen (HBeAg) is, in part, associated with the internal structure of the Dane particle.

HBV is unique among human viruses in that the major mode of detection of the virus is the measurement of HBsAg, its envelope protein, which is produced in extraordinary quantities as noninfectious material during HBV replication. It has been generally believed that the liver parenchymal cell is the sole site of virus production. There is now evidence, however, that implicates the pancreas as another site for viral replication.[34] In the duck hepadnavirus, evidence for virus replication exists for the pancreas, adrenal gland, renal tubular epithelial cells, some splenic cells and yolk sac cells of the embryonated egg.[35] HBV may additionally replicate in the spleen of chimpanzees.[36]

HBsAg is an antigenically complex glycoprotein that can be divided into several subtypes. Antigenic heterogeneity has been demonstrated by the presence of spurs of nonidentity in immunodiffusion testing.[37] All HBsAg contains a common virus-specific determinant *a* and, in addition, has two almost always mutually exclusive determinants *d* or *y* and *w* or *r*.[37, 38] It is thereby necessary

to recognize four primary subtypes, *adw, ayw, adr,* and *ayr,* although *ayr* is extremely rare. Additional but interrelated variations in subtype have been found with heterotypes of *a* and *w*.[39] Such variation in *a* may account for the rarely reported second infection with HBV since *a* is the most antigenic of the determinants.[40] Other antigenic variants have been reported but have not been well

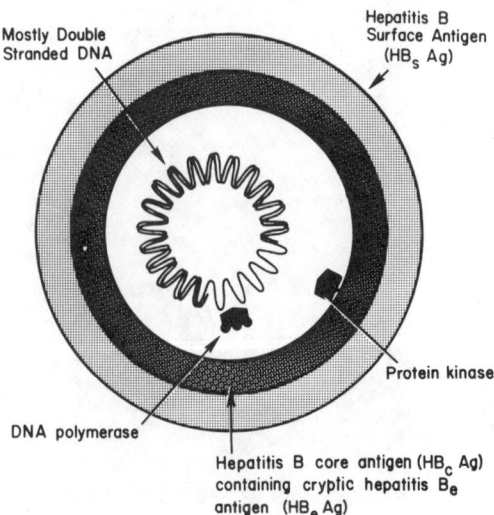

Figure 28–3. Graphic demonstration of the Dane particle and its components.

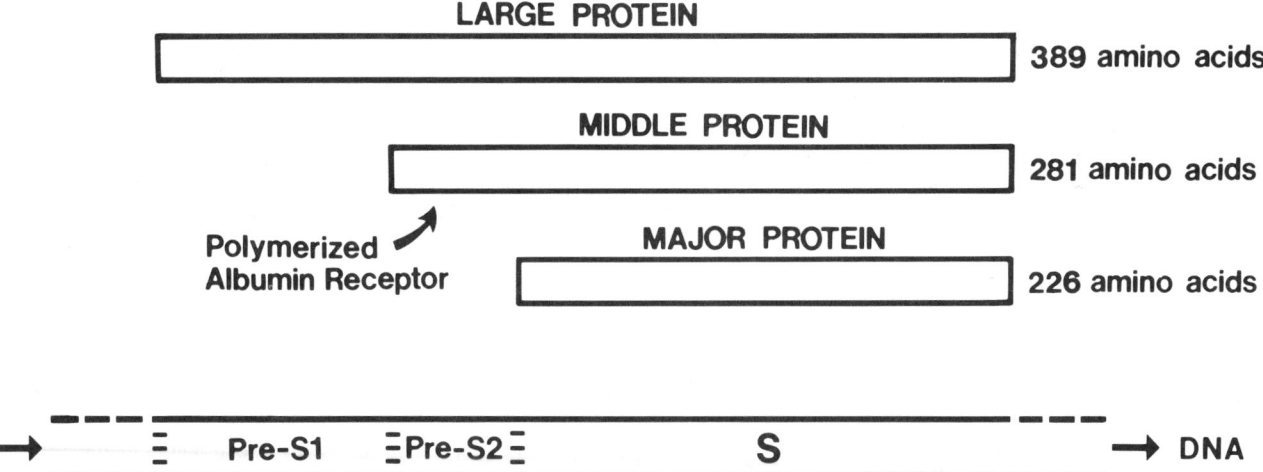

Figure 28–4. Protein products of the S/pre-S region.

evaluated. There is ample evidence from the United States and Europe to suggest that the different subtypes are useful as epidemiologic markers of HBV, that is, transmitted virus will be identical in subtype, and that the subtypes are not markers of virulence or chronicity.[41, 42] HBsAg has been shown to be closely associated with a number of host-produced moieties including albumin, immunoglobulin, transferrin, alpha-2 globulin, complement, and phospholipids.[43]

The surface envelope has been shown to contain three similar moieties, the major, middle, and large proteins.[44] The major protein is the 226-amino acid polypeptide sequenced by Valenzuela et al[45] which exists in a 24-kilodalton (kd) and a 27-kd glycosylated form. Variations in one of the more hydrophilic regions of the protein seem to account for the subtype determinants. The middle protein is 281 amino acids in length and is coded by the S and pre-S2 regions in the HBV genome (Figure 28–4). This protein mainly exists in two glycosylated forms. The 55 amino acids encoded by pre-S2 contain a receptor for polymerized human serum albumin.[46] This may be important in the binding of HBV to hepatocytes. The large protein is produced from transcription and translation of pre-S1, pre-S2, and S and may be glycosylated (41 kd) or non-glycosylated (39 kd).

Heerman et al[47] have found that a single virion contains 300 to 400 major and 40 to 80 middle and large protein molecules. The Dane particle and filamentous structures contain the same composition of proteins but the 22-nm spheres do not. In patients who seem to be actively producing Dane particles, much less large protein but similar ratios of major and middle proteins occur. In patients without active production of Dane particles, very little large or middle protein is found. Tiollais et al[48] speculate that the relative rates of protein synthesis may be regulated at the transcriptional level.

In addition to the presence of HBsAg in blood and blood derivatives, the antigen has been found to be present in many body fluids and excretions. Among those that have been found, albeit not uniformly, to be reactive for HBsAg in individuals with antigenemia are tears,[49] saliva and semen,[50] synovial fluid,[51] urine and feces,[52] breast milk,[53] and vaginal secretions.[54]

Soon after the discovery of the Dane particle, a second antigen

that was different from HBsAg was found to be associated with HBV.[55] Convalescent hepatitis B sera were found to aggregate detergent-treated Dane particle cores (stripped of HBsAg) but not complete virions. No antigenic cross-reactions occur between HBsAg and the core antigen (HBcAg). Isolated 27-nm core particles occur in two populations as determined by buoyant density. The heavier of these particles was shown to contain endogenous DNA polymerase activity.[56] Endogenous polymerase activity is present in cores derived from Dane particles as well as infected liver.[57] Unlike HBsAg, HBcAg is found mostly in the nucleus of the infected hepatocyte by electron microscopy and immunofluorescence. Generally, HBcAg is not found to be circulating in a freely detectable form but may be found after serum is frozen and thawed several times causing some degeneration of Dane particles and uncovering the core antigen. Since the human immune system recognizes HBcAg and produces antibody directed against it, it is assumed that HBcAg must be extracellular at some time during infection, possibly when infected hepatocytes lyse, or be expressed at the cell surface. The core open reading frame allows production of a larger precore/core protein by alternate translation. Although the precore polypeptide seems to direct the core to subcellular organelles,[58a] it does not seem to be essential for the assembly, propagation, or transmission of HBV.[58a]

The third antigen, HBeAg, associated with HBV was originally described by Magnius and Espmark.[59] HBeAg has not been fully characterized, but it exists primarily in a soluble, nonparticulate form in contrast to HBsAg and HBcAg. Although initially some investigators felt that HBeAg might well be a host response to HBV, it is now clear that HBeAg is virus-specific.[60] HBeAg appears to exist in a cryptic form in the core of the Dane particle and can be released from the core by detergent treatment.[61] The 17-kd HBeAg appears to result from processing of both the carboxy and amino groups of the 25-kd precore/core protein.[58] Three different immunotypes of HBeAg have been described, but the significance of this observation is not understood and the nomenclature is unstandardized.[62]

The presence of HBeAg in serum seems to correlate well with Dane particle markers, and serum containing HBeAg is likely to have detectable Dane particle DNA polymerase activity, Dane particles visualizable by electron microscopy, and extractable Dane particle DNA.[63, 64] Since the Dane particle is thought to be the infectious virion, it is assumed that the presence of the e antigen is a marker of the complete virus and therefore for infectivity. In addition to increased infectivity, the presence of HBeAg in chronic carriers of HBsAg may indicate an increased likelihood of a more aggressive hepatic lesion than the presence of anti-HBe.[65] Furthermore, the persistence of HBeAg beyond 8 weeks after onset of symptoms in acute hepatitis B may be prognostic for the occurrence of chronic hepatitis.[66]

HBeAg is usually found only in sera that are reactive for HBsAg. There is one report, however, of four patients from Uganda who had sera reactive for e but not surface antigen.[67] All four patients had additional evidence of HBV infections, either antibody to core antigen or surface antigen or both. The mechanism causing this presumably rare divergence is not known.

Other antigens have been described in association with HBV, including a Dane particle surface antigen which seemed distinct from HBsAg; its confirmation and identity are remaining problems for study.[68] Another antigen, the delta antigen, is immunologically distinct from the surface, core, and e antigens and is not related to the Dane particle.[69, 70] Transmissible to HBV-infected chimpanzees, the antigen can be found in the nuclei of HBV-infected livers and sometimes occurs in the same nucleus as HBcAg but is separable from it.[71] Usually delta is manifest in human HBV infection by the finding of anti-delta antibody in the serum, but treatment of HBsAg preparations with detergents may release the delta antigen in a detectable form.[70] The presence of anti-delta, seen usually only in ongoing or recent HBV infection, seems to correlate with a tendency toward chronic progressive liver disease independent of the presence of HBeAg.[70] Anti-delta of the IgM class is particularly useful to identify ongoing delta infection, while IgG anti-delta may represent previous delta infection.[73]

The delta antigen is associated with a subpopulation of spherical particles that contain delta internal to the HBsAg coat.[72] These particles are 35 to 37 nm in diameter, larger than HBsAg alone. They are associated with a small RNA molecule (50,000 dalton molecular weight). These observations may serve to clarify an early report finding RNA associated with HBsAg.[74] Information to date suggests that delta, now referred to as the hepatitis D virus (HDV), represents a defective hepatitis virus which must have coinfection with HBV or other hepadnavirus for replication. The extent and nature of the dependency of HDV on its helper virus is unknown. Although unique among human pathogenic viruses, similar situations occur in plants, where satellite RNAs and satellite viruses occur. Both groups are dependent for growth on helper viruses replicating in the same cell and both are encapsidated with a protein coat. Satellite RNAs (or virusoids) use the coat of the helper virus (as HDV does) and satellite viruses are encapsidated by proteins translated from the satellite genome itself.[75]

The small RNA of HDV has been cloned[76] and shown to consist of a covalently closed circular molecule of 1678 nucleotides. The single stranded molecule assumes a rod-like structure resulting from the extensive intramolecular base-pairing. HDAg (delta antigen) can be produced using this RNA in a recombinant model. The protein has been shown to be encoded for by a region less than 50% of RNA.[77] Using an immunoblot assay, HDAg has been shown to contain proteins of 27 kd and 29 kd which may be linked together in both HDV particles and infected liver.[78] A third protein of 22 kd may be closely linked to the RNA.

DNA polymerase activity associated with crude pellets of HBsAg was first recognized by Hirschman, Vernace, and Schaffner.[79] Polymerase activity was associated with the Dane particles or purified core particles but not with the 22-nm HBsAg spheres.[80, 81] In addition, it was demonstrated that the reaction was DNA-dependent and was internal to the core particle. Antibodies directed against the polymerase have been reported by some investigators.[82, 83] Recent work could not find a relationship between a serologic response to the viral polymerase and any diagnostic or prognostic significance.[84] The role of the DNA polymerase in the pathogenesis of HBV infection is unclear. In vitro, the polymerase enzyme endogenous to HBV functions to close the single-stranded region of the DNA molecule rather than reproduce an entire nucleic acid copy.[85] The function of the polymerase during in vivo replication of HBV is unknown. It has been suggested from experimental data that replication of the HBV genome occurs through an RNA template as occurs in the reverse transcriptase-containing retroviruses.[86] Miller[87] has demonstrated homology between HBV and retroviruses in a number of nucleotide and protein sequences including protease and ribonuclease H-reverse transcriptase sequences. The relatedness of hepadnaviruses and retroviruses is the subject of current investigation. Additionally, it has been found that the polymerase gene product is required for the packaging of the RNA and this encapsidation function of the enzyme is separate from its polymerase activity.[87a]

Another enzyme, a protein kinase, has been identified in Dane and core particles but not in 22-nm spheres. The kinase appears to selectively phosphorylate the core protein polypeptides.[88] Another viral-coded protein associated with HBV is associated with the X region of the genome which is located in a portion of the genome between the surface and core genes. Feitelson[89] has produced antibodies from synthetic proteins made from the HBxAg region and they appear to bind to core proteins. Antibodies to HBxAg have been found naturally in chronic HBV infections and particularly in sera from patients with hepatocellular carcinoma.[90] The demonstration of transactivation activity[91] by the HBV X gene product, a protein with a molecular weight of 14 kd and which is conserved in integrated HBV sequences, suggests a role of transactivation in HBV-associated oncogenesis. More recently, it has been found that X may exist as a nonstructural fusion protein with C, but HBxAg can be found in its nonfusion state before HBsAg is found and it, independent of HBeAg, can be a marker for infectivity.[91a]

The DNA of HBV has been isolated from purified Dane particles.[92] It is a circular and mostly double-stranded molecule with a molecular weight of about 2×10^6 daltons; very small for a human DNA virus. Several lines of evidence have shown that a variable part, about 25% of the circle, is initially single-stranded and made double-stranded by the polymerase reaction.[85, 93, 94] The structure and genetic organization of the genome is shown in Figure 28–5. The four open reading frames on the long strand of the DNA are pre-S/S (surface antigen and pre-S), C (core antigen), P (polymerase) and X. As noted in Figure 28–5, each reading frame overlaps with at least one other P overlapping the other three. The circular genome is maintained by cohesive base pairing of the two strands at the ends of which are direct repeat areas called DR1 and DR2. The overlapping translational frames and therefore extreme compactness of the genome underscores the sophistication of the virus on an evolutionary aspect.

The use of recombinant DNA technology and molecular cloning methodology have been very useful in assisting the functional role of the Dane particle DNA. *Escherichia coli* recombinant clones containing the HBV genome can produce HBsAg and HBcAg.[97, 98] Moreover, HeLa tissue cell cultures have been transfected with cloned DNA, resulting in marked cytopathic effect (CPE), virus-specific antigen production, and release of Dane particle-like 22-nm spheres into the tissue culture media.[99] These observations demonstrate that the Dane particle DNA codes for the major structural proteins of HBV. More recently, HBV particles as well as expression of four open reading frames of the genome (S,P,C,X) have been demonstrated using transfection of human hepatoma cell lines.[100] This model and the use of transgenic mice containing the HBV genome[101] will allow much more information to be obtained regarding the in vivo workings of HBV. In addition, DNA extracted from liver tissue that is chronically infected with HBV contains HBV DNA.[94] The investigators demonstrated that RNA homologous to the Dane particle DNA is present during infection, thereby showing that the DNA is transcribed into RNA. Some of the DNA homologous to the Dane particle in chronically infected liver exists in a form substantially larger than the Dane particle

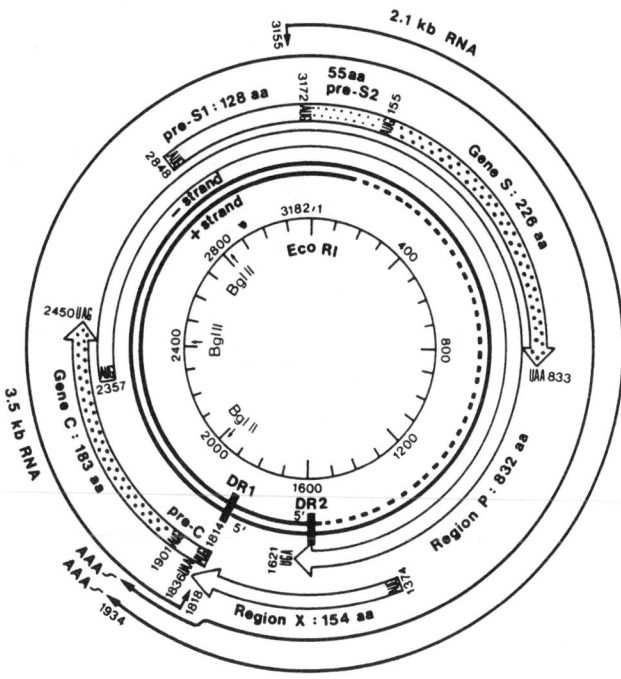

Figure 28–5. The structure and organization of the hepatitis B virus genome. (Reproduced with permission from Tiollais P, et al: Structure, genetic organization and transcription of hepa-DNA viruses, in Zuckerman AJ (ed): *Viral Hepatitis and Liver Disease.* New York, Alan R Liss, 1988; pp 255–300. *Inner circle;* restriction endonuclease activity sites with Eco RI and Bgl II; *next circle;* HBV circular DNA (DR1 = direct repeat area 1, DR2 = direct repeat area 2); *next circle;* open reading frames for pre-S/S (surface), C (core), P (polymerase), X (aa = amino acid length, AUG = initiation sequence, UAA = termination sequence); *outer circle,* RNA transcripts.

circle.[94] This implies that the genome may be integrated into the host cell DNA. Integrated Dane particle DNA sequences have been demonstrated in acute hepatitis B as well as in chronically infected and transformed tissue by other investigators.[102, 103]

It has been suggested that an HBV related virus may exist in man by the finding of HBsAg positivity with nonreactive serologies for anti-HBc by Soursaget et al[104] in Senegal. The infection is not associated with HBeAg and after the loss of HBsAg, anti-HBs does not develop. It does not appear that anti-HBs, acquired naturally or via immunization, protects against this entity which may be a distinct variant of HBV, sharing nonprotective epitopes. It has been referred to HBV$_2$ by Coursaget and some cross reactivity occurs with pre-S2.[105] The prevalence of this variant and its overall significance is yet to be determined. Lee et al[105a] have also reported neonatal HBV infection with HBsAg and HBeAg positivity but negative anti-HBc in 10% of their infected infants. They feel that this pattern may result from the immune incompetency to HBcAg. Other HBV variants are reported by using monoclonal antibody determinations for HBsAg that do not react with the standard assays[105b] and by using the polymerase chain reaction to identify serum HBV DNA in individuals completely seronegative by commercial assay for HBV.[105c] The significance of these findings are yet to be clarified. It is also possible that the variation is in host response to the agent rather than the intrinsic agent itself. However, a patient with chronic carriage of HBsAg and lacking anti-HBc has been described in which mutations and insertions were found in the precore region.[105a]

EPIDEMIOLOGY

According to the US Public Health Service, there were 25,916 reports of hepatitis B in the United States in 1987.[106] This number was 40% of the total reported cases of viral hepatitis and represents a rate of 10.65 cases per 100,000 population. Over the preceding decade, the number of reported cases per 100,000 had risen from 3.02 in 1969 to 8.39 in 1980 but was 11.06 in 1984. It has been estimated that only 10% to 15% of cases of hepatitis are reported, so that perhaps 300,000 cases of overt hepatitis B had occurred.[107] In addition, the proportion of subclinical HBV infections is one half or more.[108, 109] Thus, the true annual incidence of HBV infections in the United States may approximate 600,000, or 320 cases per 100,000 population. No seasonal variation in the incidence of HBV has been noted. A higher incidence of HBV is found in the Pacific and southeastern regions of the United States and lower-than-average incidence in the central United States.[106]

The prevalence of HBV infection can be estimated by testing for HBsAg in blood donors. In the United States, this prevalence is 0.1% to 0.2%.[110] The prevalence distribution is variable, however, with commercial donors having a tenfold higher rate than volunteer donors[111] and certain ethnic groups (eg, Chinese-Americans, blacks, and Puerto Ricans) having higher rates.[112] The prevalence of anti-HBs in the adult population as a marker for previous HBV infection is about 5% to 6% in most studies but is increased among certain high-risk groups as described below.

The incidence and prevalence of HBV infection is variable throughout the world. Occurrence of this infection in other industrialized Western countries is comparable to the United States. In Canada, the overall prevalence of HBsAg was found to be 0.24%

to 0.7% and anti-HBs was about 4%.[113–115] Among the general population in the United Kingdom and France, incidence and prevalence rates similar to the United States are also found.[116, 117] Similar rates occur in West Germany, Switzerland, Sweden, Norway, Holland, and Denmark.

Other areas in Europe, particularly the southern regions, are more endemic for hepatitis B. Greece has a prevalence rate for HBsAg of 5% and anti-HBs of 20% to 50%.[118, 119] Correspondingly, Italy has a 4% rate of HBsAg and a 34% rate of anti-HBs.[120] In addition, Italy was the first area to be shown to have a high prevalence of HDV. Hepatitis B also occurs with a moderately high frequency in many countries of Central and South America. The overall prevalence of HBV in Central and South American blood donors ranges from 0.5% to 2.0% for HBsAg and 7% to 30% for anti-HBs.[121]

The prevalence of HBV is high on the African continent, but data from many areas are sparse. Prevalence rates for HBsAg include Senegal with 10.8%, Uganda with 7.2%, Morocco with 3.3%, and Egypt with 6.2%.[115] Anti-HBs prevalence from Uganda was 50% and from Morocco, 20%. Szmuness estimated an overall HBsAg prevalence of 5% to 8% for the African continent.[110] The Asian continent also has a high prevalence of hepatitis B. The HBsAg prevalence was 5.9% and anti-HBs was 28% in India, and prevalence rates of 9.3% HBsAg and 42% anti-HBs occur in Thailand.[115] A study of volunteer blood donors in India, however, found HBsAg prevalence was 1.6% and demonstrated the variability of these serosurveys depending on the specific population investigated.[122] The prevalence in Iran was found to be 9.8% and 37% for HBsAg and anti-HBs respectively,[123] in Israel 1.8% and 10.1%,[124] Japan 2.1% and 16.4%,[115] and Taiwan 14.7% and 44.6%.[125] Refugees from southeast Asia residing in the United States have been found to have a prevalence rate of HBsAg of 13%.

In Oceania, a reflection of HBV in both Western and Eastern countries is seen. Australia and New Zealand have prevalence rates similar to the United States, with Australia having a 0.3% rate of HBsAg and 3% anti-HBs.[115] Many small isolated Pacific islands, however, are highly endemic for the B agent. In Melanesia, for example, HBsAg prevalence in the Solomon Islands is 12.5% and the Wuvula Islands in Polynesia have a rate of 17.7%.[126, 127] The prevalence of HBsAg globally is shown graphically in Figure 28–6.

In addition to variable prevalence rates throughout the world, the distribution of HBsAg subtypes is different geographically. Subtypes *adw* and *ayw* are distributed in the West; however, within any area differences may occur reflecting local demographic changes. For example, the *d* subtype is predominant over *y* in Germany, whereas the reverse is true in Romania, Greece, and other Mediterranean areas.[115] In the United States, as in most of northern Europe, *d* seems to be the major subtype in blood donors, but *y* is seen more commonly in acute hepatitis and drug addicts.[128, 129] Subtype *adr* represents a significant percentage of HBsAg in the Far East and usually *adr* cases in the West are epidemiologically linked to that region. HBeAg also has a variable distribution throughout the world. HBeAg reactivity in HBsAg carriers was seen in 32% of Taiwanese, 6% of Senegalese, and 4% of Americans.[130]

The age-specific HBsAg prevalence has also been examined.

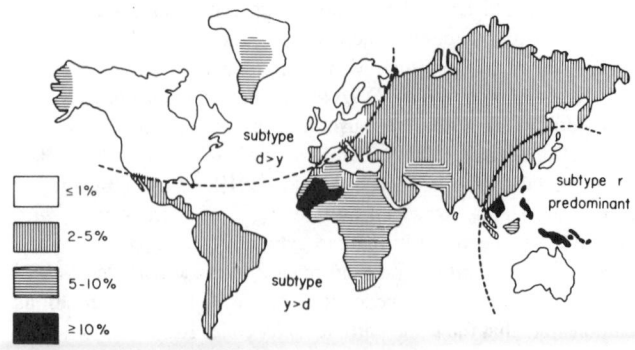

Figure 28–6. Worldwide prevalence of hepatitis B virus and hepatitis B surface antigen subtype.

In highly endemic areas, the highest prevalence rates occur in the pediatric population, often in the 0- to 4-year-old age group.[115] This contrasts with areas of low prevalence where HBV usually appears only in adolescence and young adulthood. HBV infection in the United States is highest in persons 18 to 28 years of age.[130] Age is also an important variable in HBeAg positivity, probably relating to the length of the carrier state. The frequency of e reactivity decreases with increasing age.[130, 131] No difference in acquisition of HBV in relationship to sex under conditions of equal exposure has been found.[132, 133] However, males are more prone to become chronic carriers of HBV. The male-to-female sex ratio among HBsAg carriers is as high as 2.7.[133] Males were predominant in 22 of 23 prevalence studies as reviewed by Blumberg et al, with an overall ratio of 1.58.[134] Similar observations have been reported from Europe and other areas of the world.[115]

The amount of HDV in a population correlates grossly with that of HBV and tends to become greater with the higher density of HBV in the group. In areas of high endemicity of delta such as the Amazon basin of South America, the ratio of D to B approaches 1.0. Other areas with prevalence greater than 30% of anti-HD in HBsAg carriers include central Europe, the Middle East, and the northwestern part of Africa.[135] In Western societies, the highest rates exist in areas where drug abuse is high. Certain populations have not had a significant prevalence of HDV despite high levels of HBV. These populations include the Far East, the peoples of southern African tier, and the Alaskan Eskimos.[135] There is no evidence that any resistance to HDV exists. Rather the differences reflect variability in introduction into each population. Based on analysis of serum immune globulin lots, it appears that HDV has occurred to some degree in the United States since the 1940s.[135a]

Several other variables, many of which are related to one another and to those mentioned above, have been found to be linked in some way to HBV acquisition. These include lower socioeconomic status, lower level of education, history of parenteral drug abuse, dialysis, institutionalization (particularly in individuals with Down syndrome), health care deliverers, and male homosexuals.[130] An increased risk of persistence of infection seems to occur in hemodialysis patients, patients with Down syndrome, and in infants born of chronic carrier mothers. Male homosexuals, possibly related to sexual promiscuity, have a very high rate of anti-HBs. A total prevalence rate of 69% (about 10 times that of male volunteer blood donors) and annual incidence of 7.6% for HBsAg and 11.6% for anti-HBs was found among New York homosexuals.[136] Among health care deliverers, certain subgroups have higher prevalence rates for HBV, including oral surgeons, hemodialysis staff, laboratory technicians, and workers in mental health institutions. The frequency of HBeAg is also variable among HBsAg carriers. Of HBV-carrier dialysis patients, 71% had e antigen whereas the HBeAg positivity in HBsAg carriers who were homosexual, had Down syndrome, or were volunteer blood donors were 61%, 39%, and 9%, respectively.[133] The prevalence of HBeAg was independent of sex and HBsAg subtype.

PATHOGENESIS

Transmission

Infection with HBV is limited to man and several of the higher primates including the chimpanzee and gibbon. No evidence exists that the other hepadnaviruses such as the woodchuck and duck hepatitis viruses can infect man. All infectivity data must be derived in man and primates since a tissue culture system for studying infectious HBV has not been produced.

Classically transmitted by blood or serum, HBV joins a variety of other diseases of differing etiology including hepatitis C, cytomegalovirus, malaria, syphilis, and Chagas disease in this regard. The transfusion of blood containing HBsAg is a substantial risk to the susceptible host for the development of hepatitis B. Hepatitis occurred in 52% of recipients of HBsAg-positive blood as compared to 20% for those receiving only surface antigen-negative units.[138] In another study, susceptible patients developed evidence of HBV infection after transfusion with surface antigen-positive blood in 100% of cases (24% with clinical hepatitis) as compared to 5% with HBsAg-negative transfusions (2% with overt disease).[139] In addition to screening blood for evidence of HBV prior to transfusion, the use of volunteer rather than paid donor blood substantially decreases posttransfusion hepatitis B (and hepatitis C).[140] For example, the incidence of overall posttransfusion hepatitis in a population with 53% commercial donors was 20.1 per 1000 transfused units as compared to 3.7 per 1000 transfused units where all donors were volunteers.[141] Screening for HBsAg and the exclusive use of volunteer blood has decreased the incidence of HBV as a cause of posttransfusion hepatitis from about 25% to under 2%,[138, 142] but because of other agents (hepatitis C), these procedures have had a disappointing effect on the overall incidence of posttransfusion hepatitis.

Dilution experiments in humans and chimpanzees have shown that blood can be highly infectious for HBV. A dilution of 10^{-7} of serum produced HBV infection in two human volunteers.[143] The massive infectious dose that may be given in a unit of surface antigen-positive blood may even overwhelm the immunity of individuals possessing anti-HBs as demonstrated in man and chimpanzees.[144] However, not all susceptible individuals will develop HBV infection after transfusion with blood containing HBsAg.[145] Such donor blood tends to come from individuals who are otherwise healthy, asymptomatic carriers of HBsAg with normal or minimally abnormal liver biopsies and possessing antibody to HBeAg.[146] Not all anti-HBe-positive, HBsAg-positive blood is noninfectious, however, since experimental transmission of HBV by this substance has been demonstrated.[147] Therefore, all HBsAg-positive blood must be considered infectious. The concentration of HDV in one blood specimen was found to be 10^{11} chimpanzee infectious doses with 10^6 infectious doses of HBV in the same inoculum.[147a]

Although blood containing HBsAg may not be infectious for HBV, blood that is nonreactive for HBsAg may be infectious for the virus. Sera that are negative for HBsAg and anti-HBs but reactive for the antibody to core antigen (anti-HBc) have been implicated in posttransfusion hepatitis, particularly if anti-HBc IgM is present.[148] Such sera are thought to contain quantities of HBsAg in levels below the detectable limits of the most sensitive tests but in association with sufficient infectious virions to cause infection. It is not known if every blood with such serologic findings are infectious for HBV, but the transmission would be most likely in a circumstance of high inoculum (ie, blood transfusion) than with a needle stick exposure. A minimum of 10^9 22-nm particles per milliliter of serum is needed for a positive HBsAg test.[149] That a chronic state of low-grade HBV carriage (negative HBsAg, positive anti-HBc, negative anti-HBs) occurs has been demonstrated by Ackerman et al[150] by the analysis of immune complexes removed by physical means.

It has been estimated that screening all donor blood for anti-HBc and discarding all positives would decrease posttransfusion hepatitis of any type in patients by about 6% and decrease the donor pool by 5%.[151] Blood containing both anti-HBc and anti-HBs, however, should be considered noninfectious convalescent material. No significant increase in hepatitis B or non-B hepatitis occurred in individuals receiving anti-HBs-positive blood as compared to anti-HBs-negative blood.[152] It has also been reported that blood obtained during the period prior to HBsAg becoming detectable may also be infectious during a time when HBsAg, anti-HBc, and anti-HBs were all absent.[153]

Since HBV may be present in high concentrations in blood, it is not surprising that most components produced from whole blood can be infectious. Included among these components are fresh frozen plasma, packed red blood cells, and a variety of pooled concentrates such as fibrinogen, factors VIII and IX, and albumin. The observations that certain blood components have a greater propensity to transmit HBV than others (clotting factor concentrates carry the highest risks) may be explained by the fate of HBV during plasma fractionation.[154] HBsAg copurifies with Cohn's fraction III (prothrombin complex) and IV (plasma protein fraction) and less so with fraction I (fibrinogen). HBeAg and Dane particles occur almost entirely in fraction III and minimally with fraction I. Cohn's fraction II (gamma globulin) was found to be free of detectable HBsAg, HBeAg, or Dane particles in the study.[154] Recent reports, however, implicate immunoglobulin produced by Cohn's ethanol fractionation as a source of HBV, but this occurrence appears to be an extremely uncommon event.[155] The use of intravenous (IV) gamma globulin preparations may be associated with hepatitis transmission (hepatitis C) by virtue not so much of the differences in purification techniques from the intramuscular (IM) product, but rather an inoculum effect related to the higher amount of the product infused.[156] The use of reconstituted frozen red blood cells has been suggested to decrease posttransfusion hepatitis presumably due to extensive washing of the cells involved.[157] Experimental transmission of HBV to chimpanzees by reconstituted cells, however, has been demonstrated.[158]

In addition to the infusion of blood and blood products, HBV has been indirectly transmitted by blood in organ transplants, including bone marrow and kidney.[159, 160] In one instance, HBV was inadvertently transmitted to a seronegative individual via a cadaver renal allograft while the other kidney, also transplanted into a seronegative host, did not produce HBV infection. The infectious kidney was implanted after cold storage, but the noninfectious organ underwent cold perfusion for 18 hours before implantation.[161]

Blood-associated transmission may be related to inadvertent needle punctures of health care deliverers, shared drug paraphernalia between parenteral drug abusers, unsterilized and reused medical or dental instruments, or tattooing instruments. The ability of HBV to transmit through such exposures is increased by the presence of HBeAg in the donor.[162] Transmission may occur if blood containing HBV contaminates an open cut, abrasion, or mucous membrane.[163] Hepatitis B surface and e antigens have been demonstrated on environmental surfaces after blood contamination and may persist for weeks.[164] It is unclear how long the material remains infectious. HBV-positive plasma which had been dried and stored for 1 week, however, has been demonstrated to be experimentally infectious.[165]

Bloodsucking insects such as mosquitoes and bedbugs may serve to transmit HBV. In laboratory and natural environments, homogenates of these insects occasionally are found to contain HBsAg.[166, 167] Moreover, bedbugs fed HBsAg-positive blood could maintain this antigen for at least $7^1/_2$ weeks, and antibody conversion to HBsAg occurred in nonpermissive species fed on by the contaminated insects.[168] No clear evidence for multiplication of HBV in the insects has been found nor has transovarial spread of HBV in insects been demonstrated. However, it is possible that insects serve as a frequent mode of spread of HBV in some regions of the world.

Aerosol dissemination of the B virus was suggested in one dialysis unit outbreak of HBV.[169] Airborne transmission of HBV has been reviewed, and it was concluded that aerosol transmission is probably quite rare.[170] Nevertheless, appropriate protection of eyes, nose, and mouth should be maintained if the chance of splatter of infectious material exists.

Nonparenteral means of HBV transmission was originally shown by Krugman, Giles, and Hammond.[21] Family surveys of household contacts of HBV index cases have shown higher prevalence rates for HBV infection than controls. Sexual partners were 2 to 3 times more at risk than other household groups to have evidence of past or present HBV infection.[171, 172] Longitudinal studies have shown 23% of exposed susceptible spouses and/or sexual partners develop evidence of HBV infection in contrast to no HBV infections among other household contacts of acute cases.[173] The rate of symptomatic hepatitis B among the sexual contacts of cases of acute hepatitis B in another study was 27%.[174] As in the case of needle stick exposure, the presence of HBeAg in index cases increased the risk for transmission of HBV to sexual contacts. Recent data have suggested, in vitro, that latex rubber condoms are effective in preventing transmission through semen but natural membrane barriers may not be.[176] Transmission may also occur in household contacts by nonsexual means as is evidenced by a higher anti-HBs prevalence in white family members (mostly children) where Vietnamese orphans (with a high prevalence of HBsAg) have been

placed.[177] A recent review on the horizontal transmission of HBV suggests the low efficiency of nonsexual horizontal spread and requires more data to define the risk of transmission in classrooms and daycare centers.[178] Although clear cut transmission in the daycare setting is not observed,[178a] observations among children born to southeast Asian refugees in the United States continue to support child-to-child transmission of HBV in the household setting.[178b]

The exact mode of transmission of the B virus in nonparenteral cases of HBV is not known. The association of close, intimate contact with transmission together with data showing that body fluids such as saliva, semen, and vaginal secretions often contain HBsAg implicate these substances as infectious vehicles. No direct human studies exist, however, to confirm the infectious nature of these fluids. Although a human bite exposure from a chronic carrier of HBV has been implicated in transmission of the virus,[179] two small epidemiologic studies have failed to demonstrate transmission associated with saliva exchange.[180] Attempts to infect susceptible primates with HBsAg-positive saliva have failed using intranasal or oral administration.[181–183] No transmission occurred even though some saliva pools were from HBeAg-positive individuals and contained Dane particle-like structures. Animals inoculated parenterally with the same saliva, however, developed infection. These observations demonstrate that saliva is a potentially infectious vehicle if introduced parenterally. That saliva can be infectious without parenteral administration has not been demonstrated. As with saliva, parenteral inoculation of semen produced hepatitis B in chimpanzees.[183] Additionally, one animal was infected by intravaginal instillation. Thus, semen may function as a natural vehicle for transmission of HBV. It is likely that saliva, semen, and vaginal fluids function as vehicles most effectively if contaminated with blood and inadvertently applied to a small abrasion or cut during oral or sexual contact.

The virus may also transmit from an infected mother to her newborn. Although not necessarily a true vertical (prepartum) event, the transmission is often referred to as such. True transplacental transmission of infection has been rarely documented. Transmission in the duck hepadnavirus, however, appears to be vertical through eggs laid by viremic females.[184] Although HBsAg can be found in umbilical cord blood, it is difficult to exclude maternal-fetal transfusion at the time of delivery.[185] HBV transmission, however, has been reported in infants delivered by cesarean section from chronic carrier mothers.[186, 187] The lack of anti-HBc IgM at the time of delivery in exposed neonates is evidence against in utero infection occurring commonly.[188] Recent evidence has suggested that either transplacental blood leakage of HBeAg-positive maternal blood induced by threatened abortion or preterm labor producing uterine contractions and placental disruptions, is the major factor associated with HBV intrauterine spread.[189]

Great variability exists in the incidence of transmission from mother to newborn. Investigators in the United States and Greece found little transmission from chronic carrier asymptomatic mothers, with no correlation between cord blood HBsAg positivity and subsequent infection.[190, 191] In contrast, a 32% transmission rate was found in Taiwan, and the risk of transmission correlated with positive cord blood as well as antigenemia in siblings.[192] These disparate results may be explained by the differences in HBeAg positivity in the populations. Neonatal transmission occurs more frequently, but not exclusively, if the mother's blood contains

HBeAg.[193, 194] No transmission of delta antigen has been reported from HBsAg, anti-HBe, anti-delta mothers, although delta has been neonatally transmitted along with HBV by HBsAg, HBeAg, anti-delta mothers.[195] Women who develop acute type B hepatitis late in pregnancy or early in the postpartum period have also been shown to be efficient transmitters of HBV.[190, 194] It is interesting to note that although much has been made regarding the importance of HBeAg positivity in transmission, fulminant B hepatitis in infants seems to be more common in infants born of HBeAg-negative carrier mothers.[196]

The mechanism of transmission in the neonatal setting is unclear. Most likely, transmission occurs during delivery or in the early postnatal period. Postnatally, HBV spread may occur through nonblood vehicles mediated by the close mother-child contact in early life. In particular, breast feeding has been implicated as a transmission mechanism either related to the presence of HBV in milk or to the ingestion of infectious blood or serum exuding from cracked nipples during nursing. However, multiple factors are involved in neonatal transmission, and in a highly endemic area such as Taiwan, breast feeding may be a minor transmission factor.[197, 198] In the Western World, however, where the endemicity of HBV is much lower, it could have a more significant role in transmission. Older children may also acquire HBV by nonparenteral means in highly endemic regions. A 3-month follow-up of Nigerian children between 6 and 24 months of age found 13% with acute hepatitis B and 15% with chronic infection.[199] Transmission has been retrospectively and anecdotally reported from the health care deliverers to patients. A recent study has examined prospectively the risk of transmission in the hospital setting.[200] In this study, 246 patients were exposed a total of 483 times to nine health care deliverers with either acute or chronic hepatitis B. No evidence of transmission was found, suggesting that the risk of spread is less than 1%.

Host Response

Clinical Syndromes

Little is known regarding the early events in HBV infection. Kupffer cells may play a role in the pathogenesis of viral hepatitis since some murine viruses are taken up and inactivated in these littoral cells. Other viruses are taken up by Kupffer cells but replicate only in hepatocytes. Alternatively, some viruses replicate initially in the macrophage.[201] The in vitro isolation and cultivation of human Kupffer cells should make it possible to study the interactions between HBV and these phagocytic cells.[202] Bone marrow lymphoblastoid cell lines isolated from HBV-infected individuals may produce HBsAg in vitro.[203] A specific saturable binding site occurs in the liver for HBsAg and the affinity is organ and species specific.[204, 205] HBsAg binds to polymerized human serum albumin and albumin on the hepatocyte surface may function as a HBV receptor.[206] The site of binding of HBsAg to the polymerized albumin has been localized to the pre-S2 region of HBsAg.[44]

Following entrance of the virus into the hepatocyte, a closed circular viral DNA is formed in the nucleus. The DNA functions as a template for HBV messenger RNA (mRNA) synthesis and for the production of a 3.2-kilobase RNA-positive strand. The use of an RNA for producing negative-strand DNA parallels replication in retroviruses. It is best demonstrated by the continued production

of DNA in the presence of inhibitors of DNA-dependent DNA synthesis. Replication continues with the packaging of the positive RNA template, the polymerase (reverse transcriptase), and primer together with HBcAg into nucleocapsids. Negative-strand DNA is then produced within the core particles with the RNA template being degraded by RNase activity. Positive-polarity DNA strands are then produced with the negative-strand DNA as a template in a circular form. The cores are assembled into intact HBV virions after encapsidation with HBsAg, the glycoprotein envelope. Release may occur at any time following assembly since HBV may be found containing various stages of the nucleic acid assembly.[207, 208] The immediate upstream region of the C gene of HBV, termed pre-C, is not required for the expression of HBcAg or HBeAg. Pre-C, a hydrophobic sequence, causes HBcAg to be associated with the endoplasmic reticulum and results in the secretion of HBeAg.[95] The pre-C transcript may also play a role in the encapsidation of the core to form intact virions.

As shown in Figure 28–5, two major viral-specific poly (A) positive RNA transcripts are found in liver of 2.1 and 3.5 kilobases in length. The smaller RNA is the messenger for the surface antigen and the larger for core and the polymerase. A smaller 1.0-kilobase transcript for x has been found. The regulatory signals for transcription have also been investigated. The pre-S1 area contains a sequence similar to the late promotor of SV40 which may control the synthesis of 2.1-kilobase RNA.[209] An upstream promotor sequence for the larger RNA has been described in the animal hepadnaviruses but not in HBV.[95] The factors controlling the RNA transcripts appear to be different. During viral replication in the hepatocyte, the two transcripts exist in the same amounts; however, in liver with integrated sequences and in murine cells transfected with HBV DNA, the amount of the 2.1 kilobase transcript is at least ten times more than the larger RNA.[210] These observations suggest[48] that the surface antigen gene promotor directs constitutive expression of HBsAg whereas transcription of the C gene seems to be inducible. Shaul[211] and associates have detected a transcriptional enhancer element located upstream from the C gene promoter with a striking preferred activity in human hepatic cells. This observation may also be involved in tissue tropism of the virus. In transgenic mice, sex-related differences in gene expression of the transcripts also occur. Although 2.1-kilobase transcript and HBsAg production are in parallel in males and females early in life, S gene expression increases up to 10 times in males at puberty.[212] This may in part explain sex-related differences in HBV incidence. A glucorticosteroid-responsive element, which has been mapped to the S gene, may also be involved in the expression of HBV gene products.[213]

Although the clinical incubation period of hepatitis B is long, ranging from 60 to 180 days, with a mean of approximately 100 days, the virologic incubation period of HBV may be short. HBsAg has been detected as early as 1 to 2 weeks after experimental parenteral inoculation.[214] HBsAg can be present as early as three days following inadvertent transfusion with an HBsAg-positive unit of blood.[215] During the clinical incubation of HBV, the infected individual, despite being HBsAg-positive, remains well without biochemical or histologic evidence of liver disease. These observations suggest that the HBV by itself is not cytotoxic for the hepatocyte. Recent evidence suggests, however, that expression of HBcAg in hepatocytes in addition to HBsAg may cause cytopathologic changes, whereas HBsAg may not. Yoakum et al[216] introduced the core antigen DNA coding sequence into a hepatoma line producing HBsAg. Significant CPE was noted with the expression of HBcAg.

The early symptoms of acute hepatitis B include fatigue and malaise with or without mild gastrointestinal (GI) distress and with or without the less common but more indicative serum sickness-type illness. The serum sickness is manifested by arthralgias, bilateral symmetric small joint arthritis, and maculopapular and urticarial rashes. This serum sickness type of illness occurs in as many as 10% of patients with acute HBV infection. It is not pathognomonic for HBV, as similar illnesses may occur with hepatitis C. The transient appearance of circulating complement-fixing (CF) immune complexes, which cause the activation of both the classic and alternative complement pathways, may be responsible for the symptoms.[217] The serum sickness phase tends to abate when the classic symptoms of hepatitis develop, but serum aminotransferases are usually elevated during the immunologic event. Serum aminotransferases (alanine aminotransferase [ALT or SGPT] and aspartate aminotransferase [AST or SGOT]) must be elevated to biochemically confirm the diagnosis of hepatitis.

The acute hepatic manifestations of hepatitis B are indistinguishable from those of other varieties of viral or toxic hepatitis and range from asymptomatic aminotransferase elevations to severe icteric disease. As many as 50% or more of HBV infections are anicteric. In general, the symptoms of nausea, vomiting, anorexia, and right upper quadrant abdominal pain are most prominent during the initial week of illness; these symptoms and the jaundice fade in the second or third week of illness. Although the sense of well-being continues to improve, the patient may have some mild to moderate constitutional symptoms or periods of increased fatigue for months. A small percentage (0.2%–0.5%) of icteric hepatitis B cases develop into acute fulminant hepatitis manifested by encephalopathy, coagulopathy, and fluid electrolyte imbalance. This severe form of hepatitis B carries a high fatality rate.[218] Another uncommon form of acute hepatitis B is subacute hepatic necrosis, and a significant proportion of these patients may progress to postnecrotic cirrhosis.[219]

Although most cases of acute hepatitis B clinically and serologically recover within 4 weeks with normalization of liver function abnormalities and clearance of HBsAg, about 10% of patients may have persistent surface antigenemia and elevated aminotransferases with or without associated constitutional symptoms. About half of these will have mild, nonprogressive, nonaggressive disease (chronic persistent hepatitis) which resolves generally within 12 months, and the others have more progressive and histologically more aggressive disease (chronic active hepatitis). Only time and histologic examination of the liver distinguish the benign prognosis of chronic persistent hepatitis from chronic active hepatitis.[220] Prospectively following individuals simultaneously infected with HBV and HDV revealed no tendency toward chronicity, but increased activity of hepatitis has been observed in HBV carriers subsequently infected with HDV.[195] It appears that it is common for carriers of HBV when superinfected with HDV to develop a severe inflammatory hepatitis which cannot be distinguished from acute fulminant hepatitis. This phenomenon has been observed in an endemic setting in the mountains of northern Columbia[221] (so-called Santa Marta hepatitis) and in the Yucpa Indians of Venezuela.[222] Superinfection of HBV (no IgM-anti-HBc present) as a

cause of fulminant hepatitis not due to HDV was found in 18% of fulminant cases, suggesting the other factors or other viruses besides HDV may behave as HDV in this scenario.[223] Individuals infected simultaneously with HBV and HDV have a usually less aggressive course than superinfection, but serologic difficulties with diagnosis may occur (see below). The natural history of chronic active hepatitis is variable, but gradual progression to postnecrotic cirrhosis may occur in the ensuing years.[224] Because of the increased inflammatory response with HDV, cirrhosis associated with it may develop one to two decades earlier than with HBV alone or with hepatitis C. Persistence of HBsAg in the blood does not necessarily connote inflammatory liver disease since it is common to find asymptomatic individuals with normal serum aminotransferase levels who are surface antigen positive. Such individuals, termed chronic healthy carriers, usually do not have a history of icteric illness and often have normal or only mild inflammatory changes seen on liver biopsy. These carriers may continue to be positive for decades, perhaps for a lifetime.

In many areas of the globe, primary hepatocellular carcinoma (PHC) is the most common visceral malignancy in man. Overall, there is good correlation between the prevalence rates of HBsAg and PHC in different populations.[225] Also, the frequency of HBV markers is significantly higher in PHC patients compared to the general population; this observation is true in areas of both high and low HBsAg prevalence.[226] In addition, a carefully done case-control study found a higher prevalence of HBV in PHC patients as compared to individuals with malignancies other than PHC.[227] Prospective follow-up of HBV-associated cirrhosis compared to HBV-independent cirrhosis also revealed a fourfold higher incidence of PHC among the HBV group.[228] PHC can occur in HBV-infected noncirrhotic liver as well.[229] Even more impressively, prospective evaluation of Taiwanese HBsAg carriers revealed an incidence of PHC 233 times higher than among noncarriers.[230]

Whether HBV is directly oncogenic is not known, but the evidence discussed earlier, that HBV DNA is found to be integrated into the cellular genome in chronically infected liver and transformed tissue culture cells, suggests oncogenic potential for this virus. PHC is probably multifactorial in origin but HBV most likely plays a major role in the development of the malignancy. It is likely that a variety of factors, including environmental, viral and host, may be related to the oncogenesis. A recent report by Trowbridge and colleagues, however, suggests that amplification of c-*myc,* a cellular proto-oncogene, may be an important step.[231] In addition, nucleic acid hybridization studies have shown integrated HBV DNA sequences in some PHC patients without HBsAg in the serum and even without anti-HBc.[232] Although the mycotoxin aflatoxin is also epidemiologically linked to PHC, the toxin may be predisposing to the HBV carrier state rather than having a direct carcinogenic effect in humans.[226]

In addition to the long-term manifestations of postnecrotic cirrhosis and PHC on the liver, HBV may occasionally manifest itself in other organ systems. Not only can a serum sickness-like illness with arthralgias and arthritis be associated with acute infection, arthritis may also be associated with chronic hepatitis B.[232a] Some cases of polyarteritis nodosa or glomerulonephritis may be linked to HBV and are likely related to antigen-antibody complex deposition. Since the duck hepadnavirus appears to replicate in renal epithelial cells,[233] it is possible that some glomerulonephritis may be related to direct replication of HBV. As many as 30% of polyarteritis cases may be linked to HBV infection.[234] Except for HBsAg reactivity and elevated aminotransferases, HBV-related polyarteritis is indistinguishable from polyarteritis cases not associated with HBV infection.[235] Glomerulonephritis of several histologic types has been associated with HBV infection.[236, 237] HBsAg, immunoglobulin, and complement are deposited along glomerular capillary walls; HBeAg has been found in this location as well.[238] The entity essential mixed cryoglobulinemia, which is associated with purpura, arthralgia, and rapidly progressive glomerulonephritis, has also been linked to HBV infection.[239] Other manifestations which have been rarely linked to HBV infection include myopericarditis,[240] encephalopathy,[241] polymyositis,[242] and Guillain-Barré syndrome.[243] In addition, the Gianotti-Crosti syndrome (papular acrodermatitis of childhood), a nonrelapsing erythematopapular dermatitis seen on the face and extremities, appears to be an uncommon cutaneous manifestation of acute HBV infection.[244]

Immunologic Response to Infection

Some weeks after HBsAg appears in the blood and about the time that aminotransferases begin to rise (Figure 28–7), the humoral immune response to HBV is first detectable. Initially, antibody that is directed against HBcAg appears.[245] Although anti-HBs may be produced during the surface antigenemic period, it is usually undetectable, being complexed with HBsAg. Its presence may be indicated by serum anticomplementary activity or direct visualization by electron microscopy. Antibody to pre-S1 may be found at this time, occurring perhaps before anti-HBc.[246] Anti-HBc antibody levels, initially of the IgM subclass and then IgG, continue to rise during acute infection to high titers in early convalescence. HBeAg becomes detectable late in the incubation period and remains detectable for a variable time during acute disease. After HBeAg is cleared from the serum, anti-HBe becomes detectable either immediately or within several weeks.[214, 247]

Following surface antigen clearance, there is often a "window" when neither HBsAg nor anti-HBs is present.[245] During this window, which can last weeks to months, high levels of anti-HBc (including IgM anti-HBc) are found. Blood for transfusion obtained inadvertently from asymptomatic cases of hepatitis B during this period may transmit hepatitis B.[148] It is presumed that HBsAg and infectious HBV replication continue at a level below detection by current tests during this window. It is not unusual to find anti-HBs titers continuing to rise 6 to 12 months following recovery from acute hepatitis B. In contrast to anti-HBc, the individuals with the highest titers of anti-HBs exhibit the shortest periods of HBsAg positivity. Antibody directed against pre-S2 develops in acute hepatitis B, usually after the peak of aminotransferase ele-

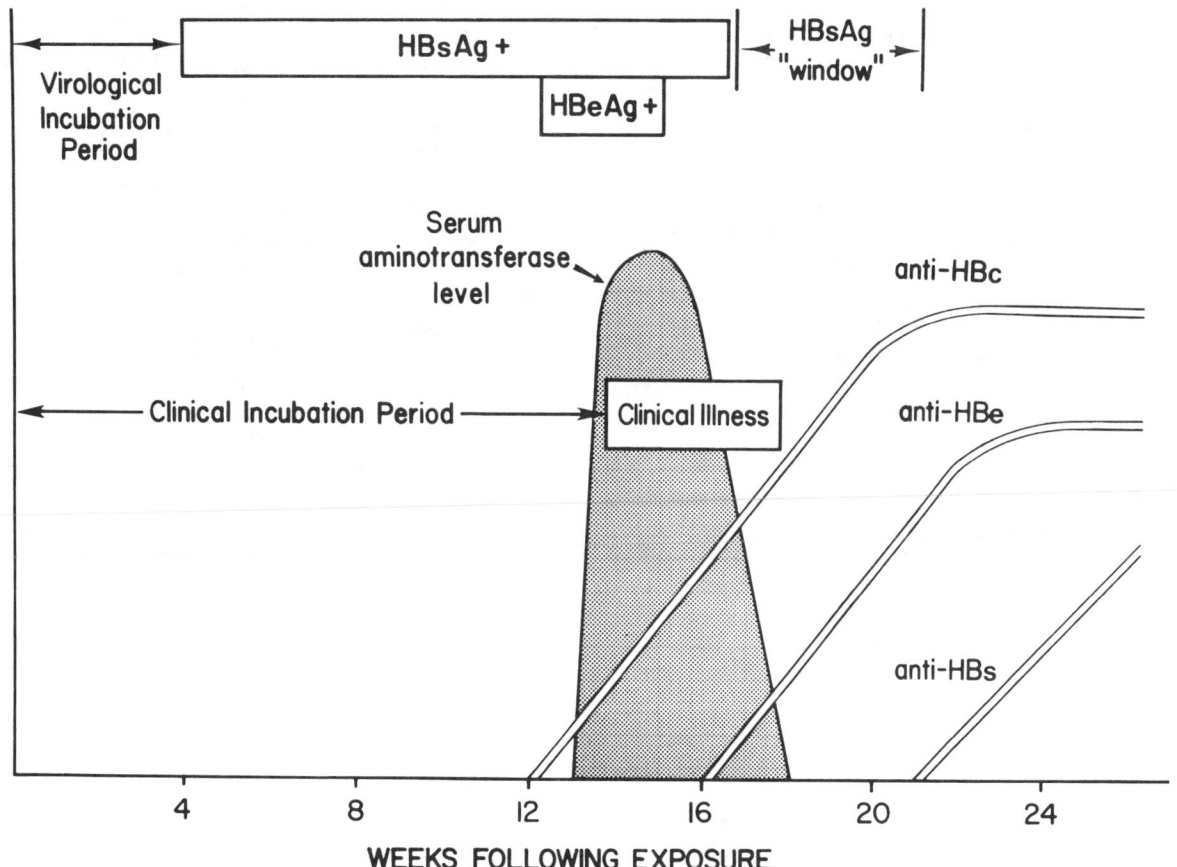

Figure 28–7. Serologic course of acute hepatitis B with resolution. The short virologic incubation period and hepatitis B surface antigen (HBsAg) "window" are illustrated. HBeAg = HBe antigen; anti-HBc(e,s) = antibodies to HB core (e, surface) antigen.

vation and substantially prior to anti-HBs.[249] It may persist into convalescence in as many as 40% of immune hosts.

In convalescence, the three serum antibodies can be found for some time. Anti-HBe seems to wane first.[203] Anti-HBe has been found only rarely in sera without other serologic evidence of HBV infection; the significance of this is unknown.[250] Anti-HBs is protective and usually signifies immunity against future infection. Anti-HBc has also been demonstrated to persist for a number of years after the acute infection. Anti-HBc is not protective in experimental situations.[251]

Anti-HBc titers remain at high levels, indicating continuing HBcAg production, in patients who do not clear HBsAg. HBeAg may also continue to circulate in these patients. However, chronic carriers may eventually lose HBeAg and develop anti-HBe.[252] This seroconversion is often associated with a diminished activity of chronic inflammation, as indicated by lower serum aminotransferases. Postnecrotic cirrhosis may have already developed, however, in these subjects. Some chronic HBsAg carriers seem to have a specific B lymphocyte defect for anti-HBs production.[253] Additionally, some defects in regulatory T cells were found to contribute to this abnormality. It has been found that in inbred strains of mice the antibody response to administered HBsAg is H-2 restricted.[254] Furthermore, it has been indicated[255] that the nonresponder mice were characterized by the defective generation of HBV antigen-specific T cell proliferation responses. Nonspecifically stimulating T cell helper functions may therefore enhance the humoral response. In addition, the carrier state of HBV may involve the production of anti-idiotype antibodies directed against anti-HBs rather than the direct non-production of the antibody itself. This antibody may result in further suppression of anti-HBs through a defective feedback mechanism.[256] Alternatively, the induction of T cells which manifest suppressor functions downregulating anti-HBs production can maintain the carrier state. Sylvan and Hellström postulate that this may be consequence of interactions of pre-S1, pre-S2 and HBsAg with human albumin exhibited on the envelope of HBV.[257]

During infection with delta virus, replication of HBsAg appears to be suppressed and HBsAg may be transiently undetectable. Rizzetto et al estimated that 1% to 3% of acute coinfection with HBV and HDV will not produce HBsAg at detectable levels and 20% to 30% will produce a biphasic (D then B) illness. Rizzetto[135] also suggests that in superinfections of B with D, 2% to 10% will terminate the B carrier state and in 2% to 3% HBsAg will disappear, anti-HBs will develop, and HBsAg will then recur. It is of interest that in HDV superinfection, the resultant HDV found in the blood will take the HBsAg subtype of the pre-existing HBV strain rather than that of the subtype of HBV found with the transmitted HDV, if the subtypes differ. Using commercially available assays for HDAg and anti-HD, discrepancies occurred in the sensitivity of HDAg detection in different kits.[258] The authors recommend testing for HDAg in the first two weeks of illness if a sensitive assay is used, and seroconversion to anti-HD IgG used for late diagnosis, 2 to 5 weeks after onset of illness. Although uncommon, HD antigenemia can persist without anti-HD developing, as has been described in two immunodeficient individuals.[259] It has been reported that HDV may persist following superinfection and clearance of HDAg and anti-HD, as recently shown by the demonstration of serum HDV RNA with absent HDAg in serum and liver from chimpanzees infected two years previously.[260]

The cell-mediated immune response (CMI) appears to be important in the pathophysiology of liver cell damage as well as in the eventual clearance of the virus. It has been proposed that hepatocyte necrosis results from sensitized lymphocytes reacting with viral antigens on the infected cell surface.[261] In fact, CMI responses can be demonstrated in acute hepatitis B, but some studies find CMI activity to HBsAg during acute infection, and others find this only in convalescence.[261, 262] Some correlation exists between the peak aminotransferase level and the leukocyte migration index.[261] In addition, natural killer (NK) cell activity was found to be increased during chronic HBV infection.[263] Leukocyte migration inhibition has been found using liver-specific lipoprotein (LSP) as an antigen and suggests that "autoimmunity" may have some role to play in acute hepatitis.[264] Further work has suggested that focal necrosis in HBV infection represents T cell lysis of virus-containing cells, while periportal "piecemeal" necrosis may reflect an autoimmune response to a liver antigen.[265] However, other studies were unable to demonstrate increased HBsAg or LSP cytotoxic effector cell activity in either NK or T cell populations in patients with acute or chronic hepatitis B.[266]

Increased specific CMI responsiveness to HBsAg has been found in chronic carriers of HBV with biochemical evidence of liver disease as compared to those with normal aminotransferases.[267] It is possible that the degree of HBV-induced inflammation does not correlate with CMI response to HBsAg but rather to the CMI response to HBcAg when expressed on hepatocytes. Vento et al[268] found T cell sensitization to HBcAg but not HBsAg in chronic HBV liver disease. The weight of the evidence suggests that the more intense the CMI response, the higher the degree of hepatocyte damage and the lower the tendency toward chronicity. On one end of the spectrum of disease is acute fulminant hepatitis, which has a low chance of developing into chronic infection, and at the other end of the spectrum of disease is the asymptomatic chronic carrier state without an acute icteric event and normal aminotransferases.

An extrinsic defect of T lymphocyte erythrocyte rosette activity (suppressor cell function) in hepatitis A and HBV infection has been described.[269] This defective suppressor cell function is modulated by rosette inhibitory factor (RIF), a low-density lipoprotein. The RIF-mediated defect has been found in seven of eight individuals with chronic active hepatitis B and ten of ten with unresolved acute hepatitis B, but in zero of nine with resolved acute hepatitis B.[269] Another study, however, found only 44% of patients with acute hepatitis B displaying such abnormal activity.[270] Furthermore, suppressor cell dysfunction inversely correlated with aminotransferase elevation.[271] Immunoregulatory very low-density lipoproteins can be extracted from the liver which may modulate immunologically mediated liver damage in situ but do not have an identifiable circulating counterpart.[272] RIF also has suppressive effect on anti-HBs synthesis which seems to be due to inhibition of specific T helper cell function.[273]

Because of the correlations relating to CMI response and inflammation and clearance of HBV, it would be expected that in human immunodeficiency virus (HIV) disease the degree of hepatitis inflammation would be diminished. A recent study, however failed to show a relationship between indication for hepatic inflammation and HBV replication with currently available tests of CMI, including T cell levels.[274]

LABORATORY DIAGNOSIS OF INFECTION

An algorithm for the diagnosis of hepatitis B is shown in Figure 28–8. Ideally, all HBV serologic tests should be performed by third-generation assays such as radioimmunoassay (RIA), passive hemagglutination, or enzyme-linked immunosorbent assay (ELISA). The hallmark of ongoing HBV infection is the detection of HBsAg in the blood. In general, recent clinical and biochemical evidence of hepatitis in association with surface antigen positivity are taken as indicators of acute HBV disease. However, an undiagnosed chronic carrier of HBsAg may develop acute hepatitis of other etiology including hepatitis A, alcohol, or drug toxicity. The correct diagnosis can be made by the absence of anti-HBc of the IgM class in the surface antigen carrier with non-B hepatitis.[275]

The clinical diagnosis of acute hepatitis B infection with negative HBsAg can be suggested with a positive IgM anti-HBc, a positive high-titer anti-HBc with negative anti-HBs, or demonstrable seroconversion to anti-HBs.[276] Seroconversions are useful only in the absence of administration of immunoglobulin or blood. In addition, some individuals who have chronic hepatitis B may not be HBsAg positive, manifesting disease only by anti-HBc without anti-HBs. In fact, nucleic acid hybridization techniques have found HBV sequences in some individuals with chronic hepatitis without any HBV marker in the serum.[232] Whether these patients truly have HBV rather than hepatitis C remains to be clearly determined. Other similar studies have found HBV sequences even in individuals with anti-HBs, suggesting that this antibody may not always indicate clearance of the virus in toto.[277] The finding of anti-HBs in the setting of elevated aminotransferases does not definitively make the diagnosis of acute HBV infection; it signifies HBV exposure of unknown age. Seroconversion to anti-HBs without anti-HBc is considered to represent an "immunization" response which occurs as a result of noninfectious challenge with HBsAg.[248] Persons exposed to HBV may seroconvert to anti-HBs and not to anti-HBc, suggesting that natural immunization response may occur.[278] In prevalence surveys, a significant number of individuals can be found to be anti-HBs-positive but anti-HBc-negative; this may represent remote HBV infection with waning of anti-HBc levels or previous immunization with noninfectious HBsAg.

Individuals can also be identified whose only evidence of HBV infection is IgG-anti-HBc. It is not entirely clear how many of these individuals have "old" HBV and waned anti-HBs, are low-grade carriers of HBV or have false-positive antibodies. The most important delineation is whether or not these individuals are susceptible to HBV and therefore need to be vaccinated against HBV. Recent evidence has suggested that anti-HBc alone often represents a false-positive by virtue of a primary not amnestic response to hepatitis B vaccine.[279]

The chronic asymptomatic carrier state is manifest by HBsAg positivity and normal aminotransferases. It is important to differentiate this status from the incubation period of hepatitis B. The distinction can be made by the detection of anti-HBc, which will be positive in high titer in the chronic carrier and negative during the incubation period of HBV. In addition, the individual, during the incubation period of acute hepatitis B, will eventually manifest the biochemical and virologic changes found in acute hepatitis. The HBsAg-positive patient can be assessed for the degree of potential infectivity by measuring HBeAg. Epidemiologic data suggest that HBsAg, HBeAg-positive individuals are more infectious than patients who are HBsAg, anti-HBe-positive. Although HBV is transmitted by needle stick, sexual contact, or neonatal contact, "casual" transmission of HBV is uncommon. For this reason, HBsAg, HBeAg-positive chronic carriers should not be considered highly infectious under ordinary circumstances, including health care delivery.

It is not uncommon (10%–30%) to find acutely or chronically infected individuals to manifest both HBsAg and anti-HBs. This serologic observation is more common in chronic active hepatitis than in acute or chronic persistent disease and may represent HBsAg of one subtype and anti-HBs of a heterologous subtype.[280] The observation in general, however, is of little or no practical significance.[281]

Table 28–2 summarizes the interpretation of HBV serologies.

PREVENTION AND TREATMENT OF HEPATITIS B

A number of modalities are available to prevent transmission of HBV to immunologically naive (anti-HBs-negative) and therefore susceptible persons. Selectively screening high-risk groups for HBsAg will identify infected patients but all patients should have health care delivered using "universal precautions" to avoid contact with blood and body secretions since many carriers will be in low risk groups. Just as important is the employment of immunologic methods to prevent transmission of HBV. These methods include passive immunization and active immunization with vaccine.

Immunoglobulin Prophylaxis of Hepatitis B

It had been generally accepted dogma through the mid-1970s that standard immune serum globulin (ISG) had no beneficial role in the prevention of hepatitis B. ISG produced prior to screening of donor blood for HBV had either low or unmeasurable levels of anti-HBs.[282] Free anti-HBs in some sera was being complexed with HBsAg in other sera during the process of ISG pooling. Subsequent purification of the gamma globulin fraction removed the antigen-antibody complexes. Since routine screening for HBsAg in donor blood was instituted in 1972, the mean anti-HBs titer in ISG has risen substantially.[283] Although some early prophylaxis studies showed no benefit from ISG, pools eventually shown to contain anti-HBs were able to decrease the incidence of hepatitis B in American military personnel stationed in Korea; the prophylactic effect lasted about 6 months.[284] In addition, a hyperimmune globulin with an anti-HBs titer of 1:250,000 protected or modified the course of experimental HBV infection.[285] Subsequently, the efficacy of hyperimmune hepatitis B globulin (HBG) or ISG (with or without anti-HBs) in preventing HBV infection in either preexposure or postexposure circumstances has been extensively evaluated.

Preexposure prophylaxis has been examined among hemodialysis patients and staff in centers with high endemic rates of infection. These studies have been summarized by Seeff.[286] In two

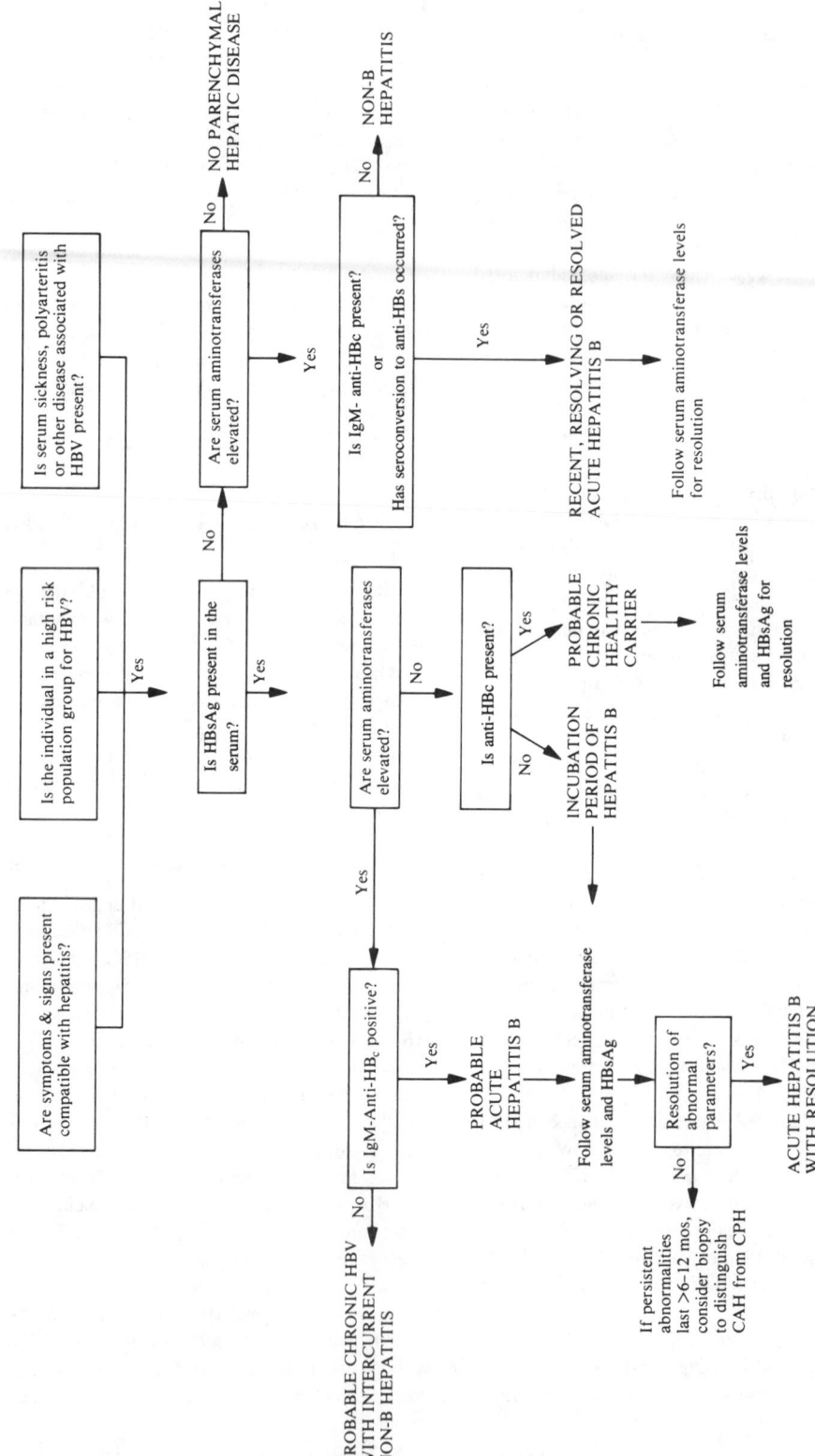

Figure 28–8.
Algorithm for the evaluation of the HBsAg-positive state. HBV = hepatitis B virus; HBsAg = HB surface antigen; anti-HBc(s) = antibodies to HB core surface antigen; HDV = hepatitis delta virus; CAH = chronic active hepatitis; CPH = chronic persistent hepatitis.

Table 28–2
Interpretation of Common Hepatitis B Serology Patterns*

HBsAg§	HBeAg	Anti-HBc	Anti-HBe	Anti-HBs	Significant
−	−	−	−	−	Susceptible to HBV Early in HBV incubation period
+	−	−	−	−	Incubation period of HBV Early in acute HBV Possible HBV variant infection
+	+	+	−	−	Acute HBV infection† Chronic HBV‡ (high infectivity)
+	−	+	−	−	Acute HBV† in e antigen "window" Chronic HBV‡ using insensitive e antigen testing
+	−	+	+	−	Acute HBV† after HBeAg clearance Chronic HBV‡ (low infectivity)
+	±	+	±	+	HBsAg and anti-HBs present together likely has no different significance than if anti-HBs were absent
−	−	+	±	−	HBsAg window following acute infection† thought to be infectious by blood transfusion Possible false-positive anti-HBc Chronic HBV‡ with low-grade HBsAg production
−	−	+	±	+	Convalescence from HBV
−	−	−	−	+	Immunization response Convalescence from HBV with waning anti-HBc and anti-HBe Recent passive immunoprophylaxis by immunoglobulin

*Not all tests are necessary in every clinical situation.
†Particularly if IgM anti-HBc is present.
‡The type of chronic infection depends on aminotransferase levels and liver histology.
§HBsAg may be transiently unreactive in patients acutely infected with hepatitis D virus (HDV). In appropriate epidemiologic settings. HDAg and anti-HDAg are appropriate tests to investigate this possibility. Anti-HBc IgM (in acute HBV) or IgG (in acute and chronic HBV) may be the only positive serology in HDV co- or superinfection. HBsAg = hepatitis B surface antigen; HBeAg = HB e antigen; anti-HBc,e,s = antibodies to HB core (e, surface) antigen; HBV = HB virus.

small studies, HBG was no more efficacious than ISG containing anti-HBs activity. However, in a large multicenter project in the United States, HBG was more effective than ISG with a lower titer of anti-HBs.[287] There are no standard recommendations, however, from public health officials regarding the use of HBG or ISG in the preexposure settings. Postexposure efficacy trials of immunoglobulins have involved needle stick contacts, sexual contacts of acute cases, and neonatal exposures. Two large studies have been reported regarding needle stick exposures of health care deliverers. One study compared HBG against two ISG preparations of lower anti-HBs titers and found no major difference in the overall incidence of hepatitis.[288] However, an apparent prolongation of the incubation period occurred in the HBG group. Another study compared HBG against ISG containing no anti-HBs and found a lower incidence of subsequent overt disease following HBG but no difference in asymptomatic infection between the two groups.[289] A significant percentage of the placebo group, however, developed anti-HBs without anti-HBc. The "placebo" ISG employed has been subsequently shown to contain low levels of HBsAg that were detectable only after concentration and that accounted for this substantial number of seroconversions to anti-HBs alone.[290] Despite somewhat unclear data and a major difference in cost, most institutions use HBG for postexposure prophylaxis following needle stick exposure when the needle is contaminated with HBV. HBG in a dose of 0.06 mL/kg is given soon after exposure and followed by vaccination against the virus to produce long-lasting immunity. This regimen is currently recommended by the PHS.[291] An algorithm for the management of needle stick exposures is shown in Figure 28–9.

The prevention of HBV by HBG has been compared to prevention by ISG without anti-HBs (placebo) among sexual contacts of patients with acute hepatitis B.[174] The incidence of symptomatic hepatitis B was significantly higher in the ISG group. In another study, however, HBG was no better than ISG containing anti-HBs in preventing symptomatic hepatitis B among sexual contacts of patients with acute hepatitis B, but the incidence of subclinical infection was higher in the ISG group.[292] Current recommendations in the United States advise prophylaxis for sexual partners of patients with HBV, for patients who report sexual contact with an HBV acutely infected person based on the above studies with a recommendation for the use of HBG at 0.06 mL/kg IM, with the dose given within 2 weeks of last exposure. If the index becomes a chronic carrier, then the contact should be vaccinated for long-lasting immunity. Any sexual contact of a chronic carrier of HBV should receive similar treatment. Vaccination is optional in initial treatment of heterosexual contacts of persons with acute HBV.

The efficacy of immunoglobulin prophylaxis has also been evaluated in neonates born to HBsAg-positive carrier mothers. A single dose of HBG conferred no protection as compared with placebo.[293] However, multiple doses of HBG administered for 6 months with the initial dose given soon after birth may confer protection, particularly in prevention of the chronic carrier state.[294, 295] Current recommendations by the PHS advise 0.5 mL HBG to be given to all infants born of HBsAg positive mothers as soon as possible after birth regardless of HBeAg status and advise vaccinating the child as well.[291] It has recently been recommended that all pregnant women should be screened for HBsAg, not just those with a high risk history for HBV.[296] This practice will avoid missing infected mothers in low risk groups.

Because of the poor prognosis of hepatocellular carcinoma, it is advisable to institute programs for the early detection of the malignancy in individuals with chronic inflammatory and fibrotic disease associated with HBV. These programs, pioneered in Japan, utilize alpha-fetoprotein screening and ultrasonography as well as other imaging techniques.[296a]

HBV Vaccine

Although passive prophylaxis with immunoglobulin can be useful, the inherent problems of undetected carriers and unrecognized exposure make either HBG or ISG inadequate as the primary preventive method. Preexposure prophylaxis with a vaccine to produce long-lasting immunity is a more practical objective. Early reports demonstrated that boiling serum for one minute inactivated the infectivity of HBV and conferred protection against challenge with HBV.[23] The major problem in the production of HBV vaccine has been the lack of an adequate tissue culture cell line or other in vitro system to produce HBsAg. Because of this drawback, the first commercial HBV vaccines were prepared from plasma obtained from healthy HBsAg carriers. Several vaccines were produced in the United States and Europe that differed primarily in the techniques of HBsAg purification. Most of these vaccines are inactivated with formalin for 48 to 72 hours and prepared as alum precipitates prior to injection. The alum precipitation results in increased immunogenicity because of aluminum hydroxide utility as a vaccine adjuvant.

Since this HBV vaccine is manufactured from plasma, it is unique among currently available vaccines, and concerns have arisen regarding its safety. Potential hazards include transmission of HBV, hepatitis C agent, or other pathogens; induction of autoimmune liver disease through contamination of the vaccine with liver-specific proteins; and possible oncogenicity.[297, 298] This vaccine has been extensively safety-tested in chimpanzees and man. The current multistep purification and inactivation procedures and safety-testing techniques are adequate to obviate the first two con-

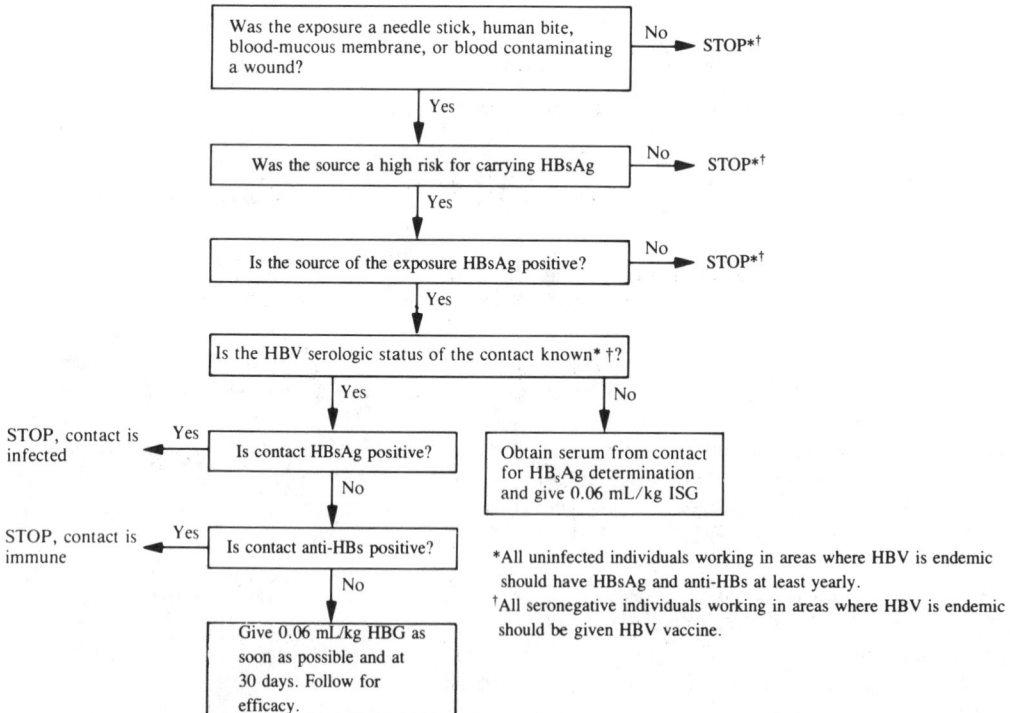

Figure 28–9. Algorithm for the management of exposure to hepatitis B. HBsAg = hepatitis B surface antigen; ISG = immune serum globulin; HBG = hepatitis B globulin; PHS = Public Health Service.

cerns. Each lot of vaccine is tested in primates to assess infectivity and purification. Some concern has been voiced regarding spread of HIV via this vaccine. There is no evidence of such an association. Evidence supporting the absence of such a relationship includes the following: all three inactivation steps in the vaccine manufacture inactivate HIV[299]; there are no documented HIV seroconversions in vaccinees; there are no cases of acquired immunodeficiency syndrome (AIDS) in low-risk vaccinees and no higher risk of AIDS in high-risk vaccinees. Available evidence suggests that no oncogenic agent is purified with the vaccine, and HBsAg by itself is not oncogenic. Toxicity of the vaccine has been assessed in clinical trials in the United States and France. In data collected from more than 1 million vaccinees, adverse effects are mild-to-moderate arm tenderness, and the overall incidence of adverse reactions did not differ with the placebo group.[300, 301] Rare reports of hypersensitivity reactions have occurred with the product. The inciting factor in the vaccine can be the preservative thimerosol[302] or the formalin.[303] Follow-up studies have shown that the alum-precipitated vaccine is highly immunogenic. Approximately 95% of initially seronegative vaccines developed anti-HBs after the recommended three-dose regimen.[300, 301] Antibodies are seemingly long-lasting. A recent study[304] suggested that as many as 50% of homosexual individuals may revert to seronegativity to anti-HBs after 5 years but no real increase in clinical HBV infection occurred. A recent PHS publication did not recommend routine vaccine boosters.[291] In another study involving health care workers,[305] 29% had lost anti-HBs by 45 months. The final decision on the use of boosters will depend on evidence of failure to protect from clinically significant disease related to HBV. This has not occurred even though up to 50% of adult vaccinees may have low or undetectable anti-HBs at 7 years.[291] The booster recommendation may in fact differ from one high-risk group to another since the response to HBV vaccine is suboptimal in such populations as hemodialysis patients and individuals infected with HIV. As yet, the only individuals who developed a true HBsAg reactive event as a manifestation of reversion to antibody negativity were HIV antibody positive.

Randomized, double blind, placebo-controlled trials of this vaccine have been performed in different population groups with a high risk of HBV acquisition. Vaccine conferred significant protection for both hemodialysis staff and patients, although the latter group had a somewhat lower immune response.[301, 306] Among homosexual males, the vaccine was also highly efficacious.[300] None of the vaccinees who developed anti-HBs subsequently developed clinical hepatitis B or asymptomatic antigenemia. A reduction of the incidence of HBV infection was noted to begin 75 days after vaccination and suggests that vaccination may have some efficacy as postexposure prophylaxis. The degree of immunity in vaccinated chimpanzees was found to be high as reflected by protection against highly infectious blood.[307] Vaccination of children under age 2 years in an endemic area of Africa reduced the incidence of HBsAg carriage by 85% in susceptible children.[308] In addition, 95% of neonates developed anti-HBs after a three-dose regimen, even when the initial dose was given at less than 1 month of age.[309] These findings may result in a significant impact on the morbidity of HBV infection in endemic areas by vaccination early in life. In follow-up studies on vaccinated neonates in Taiwan, the pro-

tective efficacy of the plasma-derived vaccine at 5 years was 100%.[309a] The combination of immunoglobulin and a multiple-dose course of vaccine also appears to be an adequate method of both initial and long-lasting protection.[310]

Thus it appears that vaccination against hepatitis B can effectively prevent infection and the HBsAg carrier state. The source of the plasma vaccine and its cost (in the United States, about $120 for the series) has sparked continued research into different modes of administration and sources of antigen. A number of small studies have investigated the intradermal route of immunization using one tenth of the IM dose. This 2-μg dose produced seroconversion rates similar to the IM 20-μg dose[311, 312] but anti-HBs titers of only about 50% of the standard regimen. The lower peak titer likely will produce a shorter duration of detectable antibody and perhaps of immunity. Currently, this mode of vaccination is not approved for use in the United States for HBV.

Recombinant DNA technology has produced a number of bacterial, yeast, insect, and mammalian cells able to produce HBsAg potentially useful for vaccine technology. The first two marketed in the United States are produced in *Saccaromyces cerevisiae*. The vaccine is the protein product of 226 base residues of the open reading frame encoding HBsAg introduced by a vector plasmid into the baker's yeast. The gene product is a 24-kd nonglycosylated molecule purified by filtration and chromatography producing a particle morphologically similar and immunologically indistinguishable from the plasma based vaccine. About 25% of the plasma product is glycosylated. As with the plasma product, it is formalin-treated, alum-absorbed, and thimerosol is added as a preservative. The antibody produced using this vaccine seems identical in specificity, avidity, and reactivity to the plasma vaccine.[313] The first yeast derived vaccine licensed in the United States uses 10-μg doses at 0, 1, and 6 months (one half of the dose of the plasma vaccine). Although seroconversion rates are similar between the two products, the peak antibody levels had generally been lower with the yeast vaccine and therefore persistence of antibody may be shorter with this product. Concern about the immunogenicity of this product at the 10-μg dose,[314] and the fact that this yeast product had clearly been shown only to be efficacious when used in neonates and combined with globulin, had led to reformation of the seed lot and purification techniques to produce higher antibody responses[315] at the same antigen challenge. A second US licensed yeast vaccine has also produced appropriate antibody response and its protective efficacy has been demonstrated in high-risk humans.[316]

It appears that any of these products is efficacious in the prevention of hepatitis B and should be utilized in susceptible individuals in several groups at high risk for the acquisition of HBV.[291] These groups include primary health care personnel (particularly oral surgeons and hemodialysis staff), laboratory workers involved with blood or blood products, male homosexuals, institutionalized patients, and inhabitants (particularly children) of highly endemic areas. It is also recommended for the spouses (and also family) of chronic HBV carriers; and when combined with immunoglobulin, for infants born of HBV-infected mothers; and following needle stick exposures of HBV patients. Additionally, because of horizontal household risk in high risk groups such as Asians,[178b] it is recommended that all children in this category be immunized.[291]The vaccine must be given IM in adults in the deltoid region as gluteal injections produce a suboptimal antibody response, especially in those above 40 years old.[316a]

One system to circumvent the limited amount of viral antigen produced in the yeast system and avoid contaminating yeast proteins which can potentially be associated with allergic phenomena (although only rare problems have been noted[316b]) is the baculovirus *Autographo californica* nuclear polyhedrosis virus used as an expression vector in cultured insect cells. Replication produces a large inclusion body called polyhedron that accounts for 20% to 50% of the cell protein mass but is not essential for viral replication. It therefore is ideal as a recombinant system and has been used to produce HBsAg,[317] which is additionally produced glycosylated—HBsAg's natural state. This and other systems are also using the genes for the pre-S region which in some studies increases the antigenicity of HBsAg.[317, 318]

Another strategy for the production of a vaccine for hepatitis B is the introduction of the HBsAg gene into vaccinia virus, the smallpox vaccine agent, which can be expressed producing an anti-HBs response during its replication in the host. This system clearly is immunogenic in rabbits,[319] a nonpermissive host, and it has the advantage of great stability and portability (important factors in the eradication of smallpox), low cost, and introduction of multiple immunogens at one time. It is also possible to produce vaccines using synthetic polypeptide subunits of HBsAg that stimulate neutralizing antibody. Indeed, small polypeptides, 15 to 40 amino acids long, have been shown to be antigenic for HBsAg in nonpermissive hosts.[320, 321] Immunization using anti-idiotypic antibodies which mimic the neutralizing site of the target antigen is also an area of potential utility and has been used in a number of antigenic situations. Human anti-idiotype antibody is immunogenic as HBsAg in mice and hamsters.[322]

The rational use of vaccines for HBV can produce a major decrease in the amount of hepatitis B, especially in a finite, easily attackable setting such as health care delivery. Recent data[323] confirm the high prevalence of HBV exposure in health care workers and prospectively document the high incidence over time of new infections in such workers unprotected by vaccination. It clearly reiterates the need for aggressive immunization approaches in health care workers. Because HBV rates have not been controlled on an overall basis, it is very likely that universal immunization during childhood will eventually be utilized.[323a] The protection imparted by vaccination against HBV can produce a major decrease in the amount of primary hepatocellular carcinoma if high-risk individuals, particularly in the Third World, can be immunized. This vaccine, therefore, may represent the first cancer vaccine.

Two additional issues regarding vaccination relate to preimmunization screening for susceptibility and postimmunization screening for seroconversion. In immunizing high-risk populations such as health care deliverers who have had time at risk (unlike first-year medical or nursing students), it is cost-effective to test for previous infection since as many as 13% to 20% may manifest immunity and will not benefit from the vaccine. There has been much discussion about which HBV serologies ought to be done for susceptibility screening. Screening possibilities are shown in Table 28–3 with the pros and cons of each test. Overall, however, nonsusceptibility is defined as an anti-HBs positivity greater than 10 RIA units. An anti-HBs is considered positive at 2.1 RIA units,

Table 28–3

Hepatitis B Virus Vaccine—Prevaccination Susceptibility Testing

Test	Pro	Con
Anti-HBs	It is the protective antibody by natural or vaccine exposure	False-positives may occur but rarely if anti-HBs ≥ 10 IU/L Neither a positive nor negative test can completely rule out active infection
Anti-HBc	As a single test, it may allow detection of infected and immune hosts, decreasing cost of screening	False-positive reactions may allow susceptible individuals to remain at risk; it is not the protective antibody
HBsAg	Identifying infected individuals can aid in decreasing transmission and make them aware of their infections	Concern exists about discrimination against the chronic carrier health care deliverer

For abbreviations, see footnote, Table 28–2.

but to avoid low-level false-positives the higher level is used for immunity. When possible, anti-HBs titers should be expressed in international units where 10 IU/L is considered immunity.

Postvaccination, most vaccinees will produce anti-HBs in the immune range. The length of persistence of anti-HBs greater than 10 IU/L is directly related to the initial height of antibody. The length of vaccine-induced immunity seems to be longer than the anti-HBs reactivity.[304] Some vaccinees do not respond with immunity-associated levels of anti-HBs. Nonresponders are more likely to be older than 40, obese or members of high-risk debilitated groups such as hemodialysis patients. There is no consensus regarding the management of this state. Most do not respond to further boosters with any significant anti-HBs titer. These individuals are often of specific DR and complement phenotypes.[324] It is possible that pre-S-containing vaccines or changes in the route or adjuvant of the vaccine will be useful.[325] Milich and colleagues[326] have reported that HBcAg-specific T helper cells can facilitate B cell production of antibody against HBsAg as well as HBcAg despite the antigens being on separate molecules. They also reported that the core-specific T helper cells could induce anti-HBs production in nonresponder mice. These observations may account for reports of HBcAg vaccination in protecting against HBV.[327] Vaccines containing HBcAg with HBsAg may also be able to circumvent the problem of nonresponders to HBV envelope vaccines. Although it would seem that nonresponders to HBsAg vaccines would be more likely to have problems clearing HBsAg when infected, this does not appear to be the case.

Treatment of Infection

Most cases of acute hepatitis B are mild and self-limited, and there is little need for specific treatment in these patients. No unequivocal and reproducible data exist to suggest that specific treatment can decrease the morbidity or the propensity toward chronicity of HBV infection. Although a flavonoid, (+)-cyanidanol-3[(+)-catechin], has been reported to alleviate symptoms and hasten clearance in acute hepatitis B,[328] another study suggested only that aminotransferase levels were lowered more rapidly in the convalescent period of the disease without any statistical effect on HBsAg clearance.[329] The immunoadjuvant levamisole has also been administered to patients with acute hepatitis B.[330] HBsAg clearance was facilitated and more rapid normalization of aminotransferase levels occurred in treated patients, but additional studies have not been published.

In acute fulminant hepatitis B, many investigators had believed corticosteroids to be efficacious because of the presumed immunologic factors involved in the pathogenesis. However, several well-designed studies of fulminant or severe acute hepatitis B have not shown a therapeutic benefit to corticosteroid use; in fact, the corticosteroid therapy may be associated with excess mortality.[218, 331, 332] Infusion of plasma containing anti-HBs was believed effective in an uncontrolled study.[333] Controlled efficacy trials with immune sera or immune sera combined with exchange transfusion, however, demonstrated no therapeutic benefits to anti-HBs in acute fulminant hepatitis B.[334, 335] More recently, several individuals with fulminant hepatitis (not all were B virus) were reported to be benefited by interferon.[336] The mechanism of interferon effect may be through activation of cellular enzymes such as $2',5'$-oligoadenylate synthetase ($2',5'$-AS), which may be involved with destroying viral mRNAs intracellularly. Assaying $2',5'$-AS in peripheral mononuclear cells reflects interferon activation. A recent study did correlate the disappearance of HBV markers with waves of $2',5'$-AS activity, but elevated $2',5'$-AS activity at presentation had no prognostic significance.[337] More studies are necessary prior to any optimistic posture being taken. Maneuvers such as cross-circulation with higher primates and exchange transfusion have been employed with variable success, but no convincing data exist for their use in this devastating form of HBV. Preliminary data published recently have suggested that prostaglandin E can have a beneficial effect in fulminant hepatitis B.[337a]

In chronic hepatitis B, particularly chronic active hepatitis, corticosteroids have been used. Although controlled trials have shown that symptomatic, non-B chronic active hepatitis can be modified by corticosteroids, the response of chronic active hepatitis caused by HBV is less clear.[338, 339] Some investigators have found corticosteroids efficacious in the treatment of HBsAg-positive chronic acute hepatitis.[340] Other studies found treatment failure and death more frequent among the steroid-treated patients.[341, 342] Because of conflicting data, less reliance is placed on corticosteroid therapy in the treatment of aggressive chronic hepatitis B. In addition, corticosteroid treatment modifies virus-specific parameters in the host. Dane particle DNA polymerase and other factors correlating with potential increased infectivity are found more often in steroid-treated individuals and these markers of infectivity disappear on discontinuance of steroid treatment.[343] This diminution of HBV parameters can result in clearance of all HBV markers of active infection, albeit uncommonly. In addition, intermittent cancer chemotherapy has been recently reported to reactivate HBV infections from an asymptomatic carrier state to acute inflammation.[344]

Immunologic manipulations other than steroids have been attempted in the treatment of chronic hepatitis B. Passive infusion of anti-HBs-containing immunoglobulin had no lasting effects.[345] Anecdotally, two persons who were both primary hypogammaglobulinemic and chronic HBeAg HBV carriers did lose HBeAg (not HBsAg) and normalize AST levels following treatment with murine monoclonal antibody directed against HBsAg.[346] Transfer factor was used without clinical or biochemical changes,[347] although one anecdotal report suggested that transfer factor had a beneficial effect.[348] Other cellular immune adjuvants such as levamisole,[349] BCG vaccine,[350] immune RNA[351] and recombinant interleukin 2[351a] have been employed in treatment of chronic hepatitis B, but more data are necessary for efficacy evaluation of these manipulations. A small study of BCG vaccine in HBeAg-reactive HBV carriers revealed no clear response.[352]

There has been a great deal more investigation using the antiviral immunostimulant interferon in treating chronic hepatitis B disease. Human leukocyte interferon suppresses, sometimes permanently, Dane particle markers and occasionally results in clearance of HBsAg.[353] Although the response is variable, this finding has been reproduced using leukocyte interferon[354] or human fibroblast interferon,[355] and in chimpanzees, using the endogenous interferon inducer, polyriboinosinicpolyribocytidylic acid-poly-L-lysine carboxymethyl cellulose.[356] More recent studies have shown the utility of recombinant alpha interferon in chronic[357] as well as decompensated HBV infection[358] and studies using beta interferon[359] as well as a combination of recombinant alpha and gamma interferon have also shown promise.[360] The purine nucleoside adenine arabinoside (vidarabine) has been moderately effective in suppressing HBV in chronic infection[361, 362] in initial studies in 1978. Further studies with this compound and its more soluble form, adenine arabinoside monophosphate, have shown response, some long-term, in follow-up after treatment.[363] The nucleoside has also been used in tandem with a course of corticosteroids[364] as well as alternating with alpha interferon.[365] A targeting strategy linking the monophosphate to lactosaminated human albumin (which selectively enters hepatocytes) has shown some promise, especially in lessening the risk of the neurologic toxicity of the drug.[366]

Adenine arabinoside may work through inhibition of the Dane particle DNA polymerase enzyme after being phosphorylated to the triphosphate form.[367] Other compounds can be shown to inhibit the polymerase reaction including phosphonoformic acid[368] and the DNA intercalating agents, ethidium bromide, chloroquine, quinacrine, and chlorpromazine.[369, 370] Although chronic woodchuck hepatitis virus did not respond to phosphonoformate (foscarnet) treatment, some success in fulminant hepatitis B with or without delta has been reported.[371] Zidovudine and $2',3'$ dideoxycytidine, the reverse transcriptase inhibitors used for HIV infection, also have activity against HBV DNA polymerase.[372, 372a] Recently, acyclovir, an antiherpes drug which is thought to be active through viral thymidine kinase, has been reported to suppress in vivo Dane particle parameters.[373] Since HBV is not known to have a thymidine kinase, the mechanism of this reported effect is unclear. Clinical trials of acyclovir alone have been shown to effect polymerase activity and HBeAg reactivity with a more prominent response in patients treated with alpha interferon and acyclovir together.[374] Finally, an extract from *Phyllanthus niruri,* a plant used traditionally in southern India to treat jaundice, has shown activity in the woodchuck hepatitis model.[375] These agents may portend a promising era in the treatment of chronic hepatitis B, and with vaccine to prevent new infections, this common infection may well be better controlled.

REFERENCES

1. Maynard JE, Kane MA, Alter MJ, et al: Control of hepatitis B by immunization: global perspectives, in Zuckerman AJ (ed):*Viral Hepatitis and Liver Disease*. New York, Alan R Liss, 1988, pp 967–969.
2. Lürman: Eine Icterusepidemie. *Berlin Klin* 1885; 22:20–23.
3. MacCallum FO: Historical perspectives. *Can Med Assoc J* 1972; 106:423–426.
4. Sherwood PM: An outbreak of syringe-transmitted hepatitis with jaundice in hospitalized diabetic patients. *Ann Intern Med* 1950; 33:380–396.
5. Soffer LJ: Postarsphenamine jaundice. *Am J Syph Gon Ven Dis* 1937; 21:309–338.
6. Findlay GM, MacCallum FO: Note on acute hepatitis and yellow fever immunization. *Trans R Soc Trop Med Hyg* 1937; 31:297–308.
7. Sawyer WA, Meyer KF, Eaton MD, et al: Jaundice in army personnel in the western region of the United States and its relation to vaccination against yellow fever. *Am J Hyg* 1944; 39:337–432, 40:35–107.
8. Propert SA: Hepatitis after prophylactic serum. *Br Med J* 1938; 2:677–678.
9. Beeson PB, Chesney G, McFarlan AM: Hepatitis following injection of mumps convalescent plasma. I. Use of plasma in the mumps epidemic. *Lancet* 1944; 1:814–815.
10. McFarlan AM, Chesney G: Hepatitis following injection of mumps convalescent plasma. II. Epidemiology of the hepatitis. *Lancet* 1944; 1:816–821.
11. Beeson PB: Jaundice occurring one to four months after transfusion of blood or plasma. *JAMA* 1943; 121:1332–1334.
12. Morgan HV, Williamson DAJ: Jaundice following administration of human blood products. *Br Med J* 1943; 1:750–753.
13. Anonymous: Homologous serum hepatitis. *Lancet* 1947; 2:691–692.
14. Blumberg BS: Australia antigen and the biology of hepatitis B. *Science* 1977; 197:17–25.
15. Blumberg BS, Alter JH, Visnich S: A "new" antigen in leukemia sera. *JAMA* 1965; 191:541–546.
16. London WT, Sutnick AI, Blumberg BS: Australia antigen and acute viral hepatitis. *Ann Intern Med* 1969; 70:55–59.
17. Prince AM: An antigen detected in the blood during the incubation period of serum hepatitis. *Proc Natl Acad Sci USA* 1968; 60:814–821.
18. Prince AM, Hargrove RL, Szmuness W, et al: Immunologic distinction between infectious and serum hepatitis. *N Engl J Med* 1970; 282:987–991.
19. Ward R, Krugman S, Giles JP, et al: Infectious hepatitis. Studies of its natural history and prevention. *N Engl J Med* 1958; 258:407–416.
20. Krugman S, Ward R, Giles JP: The natural history of infectious hepatitis. *Am J Med* 1962; 32:717–728.
21. Krugman S, Giles JP, Hammond J: Infectious hepatitis. Evidence for two distinctive clinical, epidemiological and immunological types of infection. *JAMA* 1967; 200:365–373.
22. Krugman S, Giles JP: Viral hepatitis. New light on an old disease. *JAMA* 1970; 212:1019–1029.
23. Krugman S, Giles JP, Hammond J: Hepatitis virus: Effect of heat on the infectivity and antigenicity of the MS-1 and MS-2 strain. *J Infect Dis* 1970; 122:432–436.
24. Robinson WS: Genetic variation among hepatitis B and related viruses. *Ann NY Acad Sci* 1980; 354:371–378.
25. Summers J, Smolec JM, Snyder R: A virus similar to human hepatitis B virus associated with hepatitis and hepatoma in woodchucks. *Proc Natl Acad Sci USA* 1978; 75:4533–4537.
26. Marion PL, Oshiro LS, Regnery DC, et al: A virus in Beechey ground squirrels which is related to hepatitis B virus of man. *Proc Natl Acad Sci USA* 1980; 77:2941–2945.
27. Mason WS, Seal G, Summers J: Virus of Pekin ducks with structural and biological relatedness to human hepatitis B virus. *J Virol* 1980; 36:829–836.
28. Hoofnagle JH, Schafer DF, Ferenci P, et al: Antibody to hepatitis B surface antigen in nonprimate animal species. *Gastroenterology* 1983; 84:1478–1482.
29. Bayer ME, Blumberg BS, Werner B: Particles associated with Australia antigen in the sera of patients with leukemia, Down's syndrome and hepatitis. *Nature* 1968; 218:1057–1059.
30. Kim CY, Tilles JG: Purification and biophysical characterization of hepatitis B antigen. *J Clin Invest* 1973; 52:1176–1186.
31. Dane DS, Cameron CH, Briggs M: Virus-like particles in serum of patients with Australia-antigen-associated hepatitis. *Lancet* 1970; 1:695–698.
32. Bond HE, Hall WT: Separation and purification of hepatitis-associated antigen into morphologic types by zonal ultracentrifugation. *J Infect Dis* 1972; 125:263–268.
33. Almeida JD: Individual morphological variations seen in Australia antigen positive sera. *Am J Dis Child* 1972; 123:303–309.
34. Shimoda T, Shikata T, Karasawa T, et al: Light microscopic localization of hepatitis B virus antigens in the human pancreas. *Gastroenterology* 1981; 81:998–1005.
35. Mason WS, Taylor JM: Experimental systems for the study of hepadnavirus and hepatitis delta virus infection. *Hepatology* 1989; 9:635–645.
36. Lieberman HM, Tung WW, Shafritz DA: Splenic replication of hepatitis B in the chimpanzee chronic carrier. *J Med Virol* 1987; 21:347–359.
37. LeBouvier GL: The heterogeneity of Australia antigen. *J Infect Dis* 1971; 123:671–675.
38. Bancroft WH, Mundon FK, Russell PK: Detection of additional antigenic determinants of hepatitis B antigen. *J Immunol* 1972; 109:842–848.
39. Soulier JP, Courouce-Pauty AM: New determinants of hepatitis B antigen (Au or HB antigen). *Vox Sang* 1973; 25:212–234.
40. Gerin JL, Faust RM, Holland PV: Biophysical characterization of the *adr* subtype of hepatitis B antigen and preparation of anti-*r* sera in rabbits. *J Immunol* 1975; 115:100–105.
41. Mosley JW, Edwards VM, Meihaus JE, et al: Subdeterminants *d* and *y* of hepatitis B antigen as epidemiologic markers. *Am J Epidemiol* 1972; 95:529–535.
42. Halmosdi G, Vallo D, Matkovics A: The changing subtypes of hepatitis B surface antigen in Hungary and the lack of correlation with severity and chronicity of the disease. *Infection* 1977; 5:149–151.
43. Vnek J, Prince AM, Hashimoto N, et al: Association of normal serum protein antigens with chimpanzee hepatitis B surface antigen particles. *J Med Virol* 1978; 2:319–333.
44. Stibbe W, Gerlich WH: Structural relationships between minor and major proteins of hepatitis B surface antigen. *J Virol* 1983; 46:626–628.
45. Valenzuela P, Gray P, Quiroga M, et al: Nucleotide sequence of the gene coding for the major protein of hepatitis B virus surface antigen. *Nature* 1979; 280:815–819.
46. Machida A, Kishimoto S, Ohnuna H, et al: A polypeptide containing 55 amino acid residues coded by the pre-S region of hepatitis B virus DNA bears the receptor for polymerized human as well as chimpanzee albumins. *Gastroenterology* 1984; 86:910–918.
47. Heermann KH, Geldmann U, Schwartz W, et al: Large surface proteins of hepatitis B virus containing the pre-S sequence. *J Virol* 1984; 52:296–402.
48. Tiollais P, Purcell C, Dejean A: The hepatitis B virus. *Nature* 1985; 317:489–495.
49. Darrell RW, Jacob GB: Hepatitis B surface antigen in human tears. *Arch Ophthal* 1978; 96:674–676.
50. Heathcote J, Cameron CH, Dane DS: Hepatitis-B antigen in saliva and semen. *Lancet* 1974; 1:71–73.

51. Primack WA, Schoeneman M, Spitzer A, et al: Hepatitis B surface antigen in synovial fluid during chronic renal failure: A potential danger to medical personnel. *Transplant Proc* 1977; 9:1673–1674.

52. Tripatzis I: Australia antigen in urine and feces. *Am J Dis Child* 1972; 123:401–404.

53. Linneman CC, Goldberg S: HBAg in breast milk. *Lancet* 1974; 2:155.

54. Darani M, Gerber M: Hepatitis B antigen in vaginal secretions. *Lancet* 1974; 2:1008.

55. Almeida JD, Rubenstein D, Stott EJ: New antigen-antibody system in Australia-antigen-positive hepatitis. *Lancet* 1971; 2:1225–1227.

56. Hruska JF, Robinson WS: The proteins of hepatitis B Dane particle cores. *J Med Virol* 1977; 1:119–131.

57. Fields HA, Hollinger FB, Desmyter J, et al: Biochemical and biophysical properties of hepatitis B core particles derived from Dane particles and infected hepatocytes. *Intervirology* 1977; 8:336–350.

58. Bruss V, Gerlich WH: Formation of transmembranous hepatitis Be-antigen by cotranslational in vitro processing of the viral precore protein. *Virology* 1987; 61:3322–3325.

58a. Schlicht HJ, Salfield J, Schaller H: The duck hepatitis B virus pre-c region encodes a signal sequence which is essential for synthesis and secretion of processed core proteins but not for virus formation. *J Virol* 1987; 61:3701–3709.

59. Magnius LO, Espmark JA: New specificities in Australia antigen positive sera distinct from the Le Bouvier determinants. *J Immunol* 1972; 109:1017–1021.

60. Takahashi K, Imai M, Miyakawa Y, et al: Duality of hepatitis B e antigen in serum of persons infected with hepatitis B virus: Evidence for the nonidentity of e antigen with immunoglobulins. *Proc Natl Acad Sci USA* 1978; 75:1952–1956.

61. Takahashi K, Akabane Y, Gotanda T, et al: Demonstration of hepatitis B e antigen in the core of the Dane particles. *J Immunol* 1979; 122:275–279.

62. Murphy B, Tabor E, McAuliffe V, et al: Third component, HBeAg/3 of hepatitis B e antigen system identified by three different double-diffusion techniques. *J Clin Microbiol* 1978; 8:349–350.

63. Hindman SH, Gravelle CR, Murphy BL, et al: "e" antigen, Dane particles, and serum DNA polymerase activity in HBsAg carriers. *Ann Intern Med* 1976; 85:458–460.

64. Werner BG, O'Connell AP, Summers J: Association of e antigen with Dane particle DNA in sera from asymptomatic carriers of hepatitis B surface antigen. *Proc Natl Acad Sci USA* 1977; 74:2149–2151.

65. Feinman SV, Berris B, Sinclair JC, et al: e antigen and anti-e in HBsAg carriers. *Lancet* 1975; 2:1173–1174.

66. Villarejos VM, Visoná KA, Eduarte ACE: e-antigen and age in acute and chronic type B hepatitis. *J Med Virol* 1978; 2:117–125.

67. Tabor E, Ziegler JL, Gerety RJ: Hepatitis B e antigen in the absence of hepatitis B surface antigen. *J Infect Dis* 1980; 141:289–292.

68. Alberti A, Diana S, Scullard GH, et al: Detection of a new antibody system reacting with Dane particles in hepatitis B virus infection. *Br Med J* 1978; 2:1056–1058.

69. Rizzetto M, Canese MG, Aricò S, et al: Immunofluorescence detection of new antigen-antibody system (δ/anti-δ) associated to hepatitis B virus in liver and serum of HBsAg carriers. *Gut* 1977; 18:997–1003.

70. Rizzetto M, Shih JW-K, Gocke DJ, et al: Incidence and significance of antibodies to delta antigen in hepatitis B virus infection. *Lancet* 1979; 2:986–990.

71. Rizzetto M, Canese MG, Gerin JL, et al: Transmission of the hepatitis B virus-associated delta antigen to chimpanzees. *J Infect Dis* 1980; 141:590–602.

72. Rizzetto M, Hoyer B, Canese MG, et al: δ agent: Association of δ antigen with hepatitis B surface antigen and RNA in serum of δ-infected chimpanzees. *Proc Natl Acad Sci USA* 1980;

73. Smedile A, Lavarini C, Crivelli O, et al: Radioimmunoassay detection of IgM antibodies to the HBV-associated delta antigen: Clinical significance in delta infection. *J Med Virol* 1982; 9:131–138.

74. Józwiak W, Koscielak J, Madalínski K, et al: RNA of Australia antigen. *Nature (New Biol)* 1971; 229:92–94.

75. Diener TO: Autonomous and helper-dependent small pathogenic RNAs of plants: viroids and satellites, in Rizzetto M, Derin JL, Purcell RH (eds): *The Hepatitis Delta Virus and Its Infection.* New York, Alan R Liss, 1986, pp 3–18.

76. Wang K-S, Choo Q-L, Weiner AJ, et al: The viroid-like hepatitis delta (δ) genome: synthesis of a viral antigen in recombinant bacteria, in Rizzetto M, Gerin JL, Purcell RH (eds): *The Hepatitis Delta Virus and Its Infection.* New York, Alan R Liss, 1986, pp 71–82.

77. Makino S, Chang M, Sheih C, et al: Molecular cloning and sequencing of human hepatitis delta virus RNA. *Nature* 1987; 329:343–346.

78. Gerlich WH, Heerman KH, Ponzetto A, et al: Proteins of hepatitis delta virus, in Rizzetto M, Gerin JL, Purcell RH (eds): *The Hepatitis Delta Virus and Its Infection.* New York, Alan R Liss, 1986, pp 97–104.

79. Hirschman SZ, Vernace SJ, Schaffner F: DNA polymerase in preparations containing Australia antigen. *Lancet* 1971; 1:1099–1103.

80. Kaplan PM, Greenman RL, Gerin JL, et al: DNA polymerase associated with human hepatitis B antigen. *J Virol* 1973; 12:995–1005.

81. Robinson WS, Greenman RL: DNA polymerase in the core of the human hepatitis B virus candidate. *J Virol* 1974; 13:1231–1236.

82. Cappel R, De Cuyper F, Van Beers D: e antigen and antibody, DNA polymerase and inhibitors of DNA polymerase in acute and chronic hepatitis. *J Infect Dis* 1977; 136:617–622.

83. Bradley DW, Murphy BL, Smith JL, et al: Naturally occurring antibody against unusually high serum DNA polymerase activity. *Nature* 1976; 259:594–596.

84. Chang L-J, Dienstag J, Ganem D, et al: Detection of antibodies against hepatitis B virus polymerase antigen in hepatitis B virus-infected patients. *Hepatology* 1989; 10:332–335.

85. Summers J, O'Connell A, Millman I: Genome of hepatitis B virus: Restriction enzyme cleavage and structure of DNA extracted from Dane particles. *Proc Natl Acad Sci USA* 1975; 72:4597–4601.

86. Summers J, Mason WS: Properties of the hepatitis B-like viruses relates to their taxonomic classification. *Hepatology* 1982; 2:61S–66S.

87. Miller RH: Retroviruslike organization of the hepatitis B virus genome, in Zuckerman AJ (ed): *Viral Hepatitis and Liver disease.* New York, Alan R Liss, 1988, pp 301–303.

87a. Hirsch RC, Lavine JE, Chang L-J, et al: Polymerase gene products of hepatitis B viruses are required for genome RNA packaging as well as reverse transcription. *Nature* 1990; 344:552–555.

88. Albin C, Robinson WS: Protein kinase activity in hepatitis B virus. *J Virol* 1980; 34:297–302.

89. Feitelson MA: Products of the "X" gene in hepatitis B and related viruses. *Hepatology* 1986; 6:191–198.

90. Moriarty AM, Mitomura K, Thornton GB: Detection of antibody to hepatitis B viral X determinant in chronic hepatitis B viral infection, in Zuckerman AJ (ed): *Viral Hepatitis and Liver Disease.* New York, Alan R Liss, 1988, pp 345–350.

91. Wollenstein M, Hofschneider PH: Translocation by a product of the X gene of hepatitis B virus, in Zuckerman AJ (ed): *Viral Hepatitis and Liver Disease.* New York, Alan R Liss, 1988, pp 331–340.

91a. Feitelson MA, Clayton MM, Blumberg BS: X antigen/antibody markers in hepadnavirus infections. *Gastroenterology* 1990; 91:1071–1078.

92. Robinson WS, Clayton DA, Greenman RL: DNA of a human

hepatitis B virus candidate. *J Virol* 1974; 14:384–391.

93. Hruska JF, Clayton DA, Rubenstein JRL, et al: Structure of hepatitis B Dane particle DNA before and after the Dane particle DNA polymerase reaction. *J Virol* 1977; 21:666–672.

94. Lutwick LI, Robinson WS: DNA synthesized in the hepatitis B Dane particle DNA polymerase reaction. *J Virol* 1977; 21:96–104.

95. Tiollais P, Buendia M-A, Brechot C, et al: Structure, genetic organization and transcription of hepadna viruses, in Zuckerman AJ (ed): *Viral Hepatitis and Liver Disease.* New York, Alan R Liss, 1988, pp 295–300.

96. Miller RH, Kaneko S, Chung CT, et al: Compact organization of the hepatitis B virus genome. *Hepatology* 1989; 9:322–327.

97. Burrell CJ, Mackay P, Greenaway PJ, et al: Expression in *Escherichia coli* of hepatitis B virus DNA sequences cloned in plasmid pBR322. *Nature* 1979; 279:43–47.

98. Edman JC, Hallewell RA, Valenzuela P, et al: Synthesis of hepatitis B surface and core antigens in *E. coli*. *Nature* 1981; 291:503–506.

99. Hirschman SZ, Price P, Garfinkel E, et al: Expression of cloned hepatitis B virus DNA in human cell cultures. *Proc Natl Acad Sci USA* 1980; 77:5507–5511.

100. Jeng K-S, Hu C-P, Lo SJ, et al: Production of hepatitis B virus by transfection of cloned hepatitis B virus DNA in a hepatomic cell line, in Zuckerman AJ (ed): *Viral Hepatitis and Liver Disease.* New York, Alan R Liss, 1988, pp 355–359.

101. Purcel C, Hadchouel M, Salmon A-M, et al: The use of transgenic mice containing hepatitis B virus DNA as a model for HBV infection, in Zuckerman AJ (ed): *Viral Hepatitis and Liver Disease.* New York, Alan R Liss, 1988, pp 381–388.

102. Béchot C, Hadchoel M, Scotto J, et al: State of hepatitis B virus DNA in hepatocytes of patients with hepatitis B surface antigen-positive and negative liver diseases. *Proc Natl Acad Sci USA* 1981; 78:3906–3910.

103. Marion PO, Salazar FH, Alexander JJ, et al: State of hepatitis B viral DNA in a human hepatoma cell line. *J Virol* 1980; 33:795–806.

104. Coursaget P, Yvonnet B, Bourdil C, et al: HBsAg positive reactivity in man not due to hepatitis B virus. *Lancet* 1987; 2:1354–1358.

105. Budkowska A, Dubreuil P, Ouattara A, et al: Hepatitis B virus type 2. *Lancet* 1988; 1:990.

105a. Lee S-D, Lo K-J, Tsai Y-T, et al: HBsAg carrier infants with serum anti-HBc negativity. *Hepatology* 1989; 9:102–104.

105b. Wands JR, Marciniak RA, Isselbacher KJ, et al: Demonstration of previously undetected hepatitis B viral determinants in an Australian aboriginal population by monoclonal anti-HBs antibody radioimmunoassays. *Lancet* 1982; 1:997–980.

105c. Thiers V, Nakajima E, Kremsdorf D, et al: Transmission of hepatitis B from hepatitis-B-seronegative subjects. *Lancet* 1988; 2:1273–1276.

105d. Bhat RA, Ulrich PP, Vyas GN: Molecular characterization of a new variant of hepatitis B virus in a persistently infected homosexual man. *Hepatology* 1990; 11:271–276.

106. Centers for Disease Control: *Hepatitis Surveillance,* Report No. 52, US Public Health Service, April 1989.

107. Marier R: The reporting of communicable diseases. *Am J Epidemiol* 1977; 105:587–590.

108. Schober A, Thomssen R, Kaboth U, et al: Inapparent infections in the course of Australia-SH-antigen positive hepatitis. *Am J Dis Child* 1972; 123:404–405.

109. Szmuness W, Prince AM, Hirsch RL, et al: Familial clustering of hepatitis B infection. *N Engl J Med* 1973; 289:1162–1166.

110. Szmuness W: Recent advances in the study of the epidemiology of hepatitis B. *Am J Pathol* 1975; 81:629–650.

111. Cherubin CE, Prince AM: Serum hepatitis specific antigen (SH) in commercial and volunteer sources of blood. *Transfusion* 1971; 11:25–27.

112. Szmuness W, Hirsch RL, Prince AM, et al: Hepatitis B surface antigen in blood donors: Further observations. *J Infect Dis* 1975; 131:111–118.

113. Moore BPL, Perrault RA: Hepatitis B antigenemia among blood donors: The changing scene. *Can Med Assoc J* 1975; 112:53–54.

114. Sinclair JC, Feinman SV, Wrobel DM, et al: Hepatitis B surface antigen and antibody in asymptomatic blood donors. *JAMA* 1976; 235:1014–1017.

115. Sobeslavsky O: Prevalence of markers of hepatitis B virus infection in various countries: A WHO collaborative study. *Bull WHO* 1980; 58:621–628.

116. Barr A, Dow BC, MacVarish I: HBsAg detection-results of comparative large scale testing of blood donations. *Med Lab Sci* 1979; 36:109–114.

117. Caretta M, Benamon D, Drouet J, et al: Screening of HB antigen and detection of corresponding antibodies of Groupamatic equipment. *Vox Sang* 1977; 33:175–186.

118. Papaevangelou G, Karaboyia-Karafyllidis P, Kryiakidou A: Prevalence and epidemiologic significance of antibody to hepatitis B core antigen in Greece. *Am J Epidemiol* 1977; 106:502–506.

119. Trichopoulos D, Tabor E, Gerety RJ, et al: Hepatitis B and primary hepatocellular carcinoma in a European population. *Lancet* 1978; 2:1217–1219.

120. Minoja CM, Melloni GF, Lureti GF, et al: Comparative study of the incidence of HBsAg and HBsAb in a random group of patients and in the normal population. *Boll Soc Ital Biol Sper* 1977; 53:822–827.

121. Mazzur S, Nath N, Fang C, et al: Distribution of hepatitis B virus (HBV) markers in blood donors of thirteen Western hemisphere countries: Proceedings of the Red Cross Latin American Workshop. *Bull Pan Am Health Organ* 1980; 14:44–51.

122. Thyagarajan SP, Subramanian S, Solomon S, et al: Incidence of hepatitis B surface antigen and antibody in patients with liver disease, blood donors, and leprosy patients—A preliminary report. *Indian J Med Res* 1978; 67:528–538.

123. Farzadegan H, Harbour C, Ala F: The prevalence of hepatitis B surface antigen and its antibody in blood donors and high risk groups in Iran. *Vox Sang* 1979; 37:182–186.

124. Sandler SG, Nath N, Biber Y: Seroepidemiology of hepatitis B virus in Israel. *Am J Epidemiol* 1977; 106:76–82.

125. Chen DS, Sung JL: Hepatitis B virus infection and chronic liver disease in Taiwan. *Acta Hepatogastroenterology* 1978; 24:423–430.

126. Austin FJ, Maguire T, Miles JAR: The occurrence of hepatitis B antigen and antibody in some population groups in the Southwest Pacific region. *Am J Trop Med Hyg* 1974; 23:489–494.

127. Gaxotte P, Coulaud JP, Salmot J, et al: Hepatitis B antigenemia on Wuvulu Island. *Am J Trop Med Hyg* 1978; 27:1037–1040.

128. Dodd RY, Holland RV, Ni LY, et al: Hepatitis B antigen: Regional variation in incidence and subtype ratio in the American Red Cross donor population. *Am J Epidemiol* 1973; 97:111–115.

129. Nordenfelt E, Le Bouvier G: The distribution of subtypes in various Swedish populations positive for hepatitis B antigen. *Scand J Infect Dis* 1973; 5:279–283.

130. Szmuness W, Harley EJ, Ikram H, et al: Sociodemographic aspects of the epidemiology of hepatitis B, in Vyas GN, Cohen SN, Schmid R (eds): *Viral Hepatitis: Etiology, Epidemiology, Pathogenesis and Prevention.* Philadelphia, Franklin Institute Press, 1978, pp 297–320.

131. Ohbayashi A, Matsuo Y, Mozai T, et al: Decreasing frequency of *e* antigen with age in serum of symptom-free carriers of hepatitis B antigen. *Lancet* 1975; 2:577–578.

132. Allen JG, Sayman WA: Serum hepatitis from transfusion of blood. *JAMA* 1962; 180:1079–1085.

133. Grady GF, Bennett AJE: Risk of post-transfusion hepatitis in the United States. *JAMA* 1972; 220:692–701.

134. Blumberg BS, Sutnick AI, London WT, et al: Sex distribution of Australia antigen. *Arch Intern Med* 1972; 130:227–231.

135. Rizzetto M, Ponzetto A, Bonino F, et al: Hepatitis delta virus

infection: clinical and epidemiological aspects, in Zuckerman AJ (ed): *Viral Hepatitis and Liver Disease.* New York, Alan R Liss, 1988, pp 389–394.

135a. Ponzetto A, Hoofnagle JH, Seeff LB: Antibody to the hepatitis B virus-associated delta-antigen in immune serum globulins. *Gastroenterology* 1984; 87:1213–1216.

136. Szmuness W: Large-scale efficacy trials of hepatitis B vaccines in the USA: Baseline data and protocols. *J Med Virol* 1979; 4:327–340.

137. Szmuness W, Neurath AR, Stevens CE, et al: Prevalence of hepatitis B "e" antigen and its antibody in various carrier populations. *Am J Epidemiol* 1981; 113:113–121.

138. Gocke DJ: A prospective study of post-transfusion hepatitis. The role of Australia antigen. *JAMA* 1972; 219:1165–1170.

139. Goldfield M, Bill J, Colosino F: The control of transfusion-associated hepatitis, in Vyas GN, Cohen SN, Schmid R (eds): *Viral Hepatitis: Etiology, Epidemiology, Pathogenesis and Prevention.* Philadelphia, Franklin Institute Press, 1978, pp 405–417.

140. Barker LF, Gerety RJ: The clinical problem of hepatitis transmission. *Prog Clin Biol Res* 1976; 11:163–182.

141. Alter HJ, Holland PV, Purcell RH, et al: Posttransfusion hepatitis after exclusion of commercial and hepatitis-B antigen-positive donors. *Ann Intern Med* 1972; 77:691–699.

142. Seeff LB, Wright EC, Zimmerman HJ, et al: VA cooperative study of post-transfusion hepatitis, 1969–1974. Incidence and characteristics of hepatitis and responsible risk factors. *Am J Med Sci* 1975; 270:355–362.

143. Barker LF, Murray R: Relationship of virus dose to incubation time of clinical hepatitis and time of appearance of hepatitis-associated antigen. *Am J Med Sci* 1972; 263:27–33.

144. Trepo CG, Prince AM: Absence of complete homologous immunity in hepatitis B infection after massive exposure. *Ann Intern Med* 1976; 85:427–430.

145. Reinicke V, Dybkjaer E, Poulsen H, et al: A study of Australia-antigen-positive blood donors and their recipients with special reference to liver histology. *N Engl J Med* 1972; 286:867–870.

146. Magnius LO, Lindholm A, Lundin P, et al: A new antigen-antibody system. Clinical significance in long-term carriers of hepatitis B surface antigen. *JAMA* 1975; 231:356–359.

147. Berquist KR, Maynard JE, Murphy BL: Infectivity of serum containing HBsAg and antibody to e antigen. *Lancet* 1976; 1:1026–1027.

147a. Ponzetto A, Hoyer BH, Popper H, et al: Titration of the infectivity of hepatitis D virus in chimpanzees. *J Infect Dis* 1987; 155:72–78.

148. Hoofnagle JH, Seeff LB, Bales ZB, et al: Type B hepatitis after transfusion with blood containing antibody to hepatitis B core antigen. *N Engl J Med* 1978; 298:1379–1383.

149. Gerety RJ, Tabor E, Hoofnagle JH, et al: Tests for HBV-associated antigen and antibodies, in Vyas GN, Cohen SN, Schmid R (eds): *Viral Hepatitis: Etiology, Epidemiology, Pathogenesis and Prevention.* Philadelphia, Franklin Institute Press, 1978, pp 121–138.

150. Ackerman Z, Gazitt Y, Wands JR, et al: Unmasking of circulating hepatitis B surface antigen (HBsAg) following removal of immune complexes from serum of hepatocellular carcinoma, in Zuckerman AJ (ed): *Viral Hepatitis and Liver Disease.* New York, Alan R Liss, 1988, pp 783–785.

151. Holland PV: Available methods to further reduce post-transfusion hepatitis, in Szmuness W, Alter HJ, Maynard JE (eds): *Viral Hepatitis: 1981 International Symposium.* Philadelphia, Franklin Institute Press, 1982, pp 563–571.

152. Aach RD, Alter HJ, Hollinger FB, et al: Risk of transfusion blood containing antibody to hepatitis-B surface antigen. *Lancet* 1974; 2:190–193.

153. Rinker J, Galambos JT: Prospective study of hepatitis B in thirty-two inadvertently infected people. *Gastroenterology* 1981; 81:686–691.

154. Trepo C, Hantz O, Jacquier MF, et al: Different fates of hepati-

155. John TJ, Ninan GT, Rajagopalan MS, et al: Epidemic hepatitis B caused by commercial human immunoglobulin. *Lancet* 1979; 1:1074.

156. Björkander J, Cunningham-Rundles C, Lundin P, et al: Intravenous immunoglobulin prophylaxis causing liver damage in 16 of 77 patients with hypogammaglobulinemia or IgG subclass deficiency. *Am J Med* 1988; 87:107–111.

157. Carr JB, de Quesada AM, Shires DL: Decreased incidence of transfusion hepatitis after exclusive transfusion with reconstituted frozen erythrocytes. *Ann Intern Med* 1973; 78:693–695.

158. Alter HJ, Tabor E, Meryman HT, et al: Transmission of hepatitis B virus infection by transfusion of frozen-deglycerolized red blood cells. *N Engl J Med* 1978; 298:637–642.

159. Falk PM, Feig SA, Gitnick GL, et al: Transplantation of hepatitis B surface antigen positive bone marrow. *Transfusion* 1978; 18:242–243.

160. Wolf JL, Perkins HA, Schreeder MT, et al: The transplanted kidney as a source of hepatitis B infection. *Ann Intern Med* 1979; 91:412–413.

161. Lutwick LI, SyWassink JM, Corry RJ, et al: The transmission of hepatitis B by renal transplantation. *Clin Nephrol* 1983; 19:317–319.

162. Grady G: Relation of e antigen to infectivity of HBsAg-positive inoculations among medical personnel. *Lancet* 1976; 2:492–494.

163. Kew MC: Possible transmission of serum (Australia-antigen-positive) hepatitis via the conjunctiva. *Infect Immun* 1973; 7:823–824.

164. Zachoval R, Frösner G, Deinhardt F, et al: Persistence of hepatitis B virus antigen in dried blood. *Lancet* 1981; 1:778.

165. Bond WW, Favero MS, Peterson NJ, et al: Survival of hepatitis B virus after drying and storage for one week. *Lancet* 1981; 1:550–551.

166. Newkirk MM, Downe AER, Simon JB: Fate of ingested hepatitis B antigen in blood-sucking insects. *Gastroenterology* 1975; 69:982–987.

167. Wills W, Lazouzé B, London WT, et al: Hepatitis-B virus in bedbugs (*Cimex hemipterus*) from Senegal. *Lancet* 1977; 2:217–219.

168. Jupp PG, McElligott SE: Transmission experiments with hepatitis B surface antigen and the common bedbug (*Cimex lectularius L.*). *S Afr Med J* 1979; 56:54–57.

169. Almeida JD, Chisholm GD, Kulatilake AE, et al: Possible airborne spread of serum-hepatitis virus within a haemodialysis unit. *Lancet* 1971; 2:849–850.

170. Peterson NJ: An assessment of the airborne route in hepatitis B transmission. *Ann NY Acad Sci* 1980; 353:157–166.

171. Irwin GR, Allen AM, Bancroft WH, et al: Hepatitis B antigen and antibody. Occurrence in families of asymptomatic HB Ag carriers. *JAMA* 1974; 227:1042–1043.

172. Heathcote J, Gateau P, Sherlock S: Role of hepatitis B antigen carriers in nonparenteral transmission of the hepatitis-B virus. *Lancet* 1974; 2:370–372.

173. Koff RS, Slavin MM, Connelly LJD, et al: Contagiousness of acute hepatitis B. Secondary attack rates in household contacts. *Gastroenterology* 1977; 72:297–300.

174. Redeker AG, Mosley JW, Gocke DJ, et al: Hepatitis B immune globulin as a prophylactic measure for spouses exposed to acute type B hepatitis. *N Engl J Med* 1975; 293:1055–1059.

175. Perrillo RP, Gelb L, Campbell C, et al: Hepatitis B e antigen, DNA polymerase activity, and infection of household contacts with hepatitis B virus. *Gastroenterology* 1979; 76:1319–1325.

176. Minuk GY, Bohme CE, Bowen TS, et al: Efficacy of commercial condoms in the presentation of hepatitis B virus infections. *Gastroenterology* 1987; 93:710–714.

177. Vernon TM, Wright RA, Kohler PF, et al: Hepatitis A and B in the family unit. Nonparenteral transmission by asymptomatic children. *JAMA* 1976; 234:2829–2831.

178. Davis LG, Weber DJ, Lemon SM: Horizontal transmission of hepatitis B virus. *Lancet* 1989; 1:889–893.

178a. Shapiro ED: Lack of transmission of hepatitis B in a day care center. *J Pediatr* 1987; 110:90–92.

178b. Franks AL, Berg CJ, Kane MA, et al: Hepatitis B virus infection among children born in the United States to Southeast Asian refugees. *N Engl J Med* 1989; 321:1301–1305.

179. MacQuarrie MB, Forghani B, Wolochow DA: Hepatitis B transmitted by a human bite. *JAMA* 1974; 230:723–724.

180. Center for Disease Control: Lack of transmission of hepatitis B to humans after oral exposure to hepatitis B surface-antigen-positive saliva. *MMWR* 1978; 27:247–248.

181. Bancroft WH, Snitbhan R, Scott RM, et al: Transmission of hepatitis B virus to gibbons by exposure to human saliva containing hepatitis B surface antigen. *J Infect Dis* 1977; 135:79–85.

182. Alter HJ, Purcell RH, Gerin JL, et al: Transmission of hepatitis B to chimpanzees by hepatitis B surface antigen-positive saliva and semen. *Infect Immun* 1977; 16:928–933.

183. Scott RM, Snitbhan R, Bancroft WH, et al: Experimental transmission of hepatitis B virus by semen and saliva. *J Infect Dis* 1980; 142:67–71.

184. Tsiquaye KN, McCaul TF, Zuckerman AJ: Maternal transmission of duck hepatitis B virus in pedigree Pekin ducks. *Hepatology* 1985; 5:622–628.

185. Papaevangelou G, Kremastinou T, Prevedourakis C, et al: Hepatitis B antigen and antibody in maternal blood, cord blood, and amniotic fluid. *Arch Dis Child* 1974; 49:936–939.

186. Buchholz HM, Frösner GG, Ziegler GB: HB Ag carrier state in an infant delivered by caesarean section. *Lancet* 1974; 2:343.

187. Stokes J, Berk JE, Malamut LL, et al: The carrier state in viral hepatitis. *JAMA* 1954; 154:1059–1065

188. Goudeau A, Lesage G, Denis F, et al: Lack of anti-HBc IgM in neonates with carrier mothers argues against transplacental transmission of hepatitis B virus infection. *Lancet* 1983; 2:1103–1104.

189. Lin H–H, Lee T–Y, Chen D–S, et al: Transplacental leakage of HBeAg–positive maternal blood as the most likely route in causing intrauterine infection with hepatitis B virus. *J Pediatr* 1987; 111:877–881.

190. Schweitzer IL, Mosley JW, Ashcavai M, et al: Factors influencing neonatal infection by hepatitis B virus. *Gastroenterology* 1973; 65:277–283.

191. Papaevangelou G, Hoofnagle J, Kremastinou T: Transplacental transmission of hepatitis-B virus by symptom-free chronic carrier mothers. *Lancet* 1974; 2:746–748.

192. Stevens CE, Beasley RP, Tsui J, et al: Vertical transmission of hepatitis B antigen in Taiwan. *N Engl J Med* 1975; 292:771–774.

193. Okada K, Kamiyama I, Inomata M, et al: e antigen and anti-e in the serum of asymptomatic carrier mothers as indicators of positive and negative transmission of hepatitis B virus to their infants. *N Engl J Med* 1976; 294:746–749.

194. Gerety RJ, Schweitzer IL: Viral hepatitis type B during pregnancy, the neonatal period, and infancy. *J Pediatr* 1977; 90:368–374.

195. Smedile A, Dentico P, Zanetti A, et al: Infection with the delta agent in chronic HBsAg carriers. *Gastroenterology* 1981; 81:992–997.

196. Shiraki K, Tanimoto K, Yanadak K, et al: Pediatric fulminant hepatitis—a national study of 105 cases. *Shonika* 1985; 26:1–7.

197. Krugman S: Vertical transmission of hepatitis B and breast-feeding. *Lancet* 1975; 2:916.

198. Beasley RP, Stevens CE, Shiao I–S, et al: Evidence against breast-feeding as a mechanism for vertical transmission of hepatitis B. *Lancet* 1975; 2:740–741.

199. Tabor E, Gerety RJ: Hepatitis B virus infection in infants and toddlers in Nigeria: The need for early intervention. *J Pediatr* 1979; 95:647–650.

200. LaBrecque DR, Muhs JM, Lutwick LI, et al: The risk of hepatitis B transmission from health care workers to patients in a

hospital setting—a prospective study. *Hepatology* 1986; 6:205–208.

201. Mims CA: Aspects of the pathogenesis of virus disease. *Bacterial Rev* 1964; 28:30–71.

202. Kirn A, Steffan AM, Bingen A, et al: Uptake of viruses by Kupffer cells isolated from human liver. *Lancet* 1980; 2:585–586.

203. Romet–Lemonne J–L, McLane MF, Elfassi E, et al: Hepatitis B virus infection in cultured human lymphoblastoid cells. *Science* 1983;221:667–669.

204. Lutwick LI, Hebert MG: The affinity of hepatitis B surface antigen for human hepatic tissue. *Gastroenterology* 1980; 79:1035.

205. Lutwick LI, Hebert MB, Sklamberg T: Specificity of hepatitis B virus affinity for human hepatic tissue. *J Med Virol* 1982; 9:101–109.

206. O'Neill SP: Interaction of hepatitis B surface antigen with polymerized human serum albumin. *J Med Virol* 1979; 4:177–185.

207. Miller RH, Marion PL, Robinson WS: Hepatitis B DNA–RNA hybrid molecules in particles from infected liver are converted to viral DNA during an endogenous DNA polymerase reaction. *Virology* 1984; 193:69–72.

208. Miller RH, Tran CT, Robinson WS: Hepatitis B virus particles in plasma and liver contain viral DNA–RNA hybrid molecules. *Virology* 1984; 139:53–63.

209. Cattaneo R, Will H, Hernandez N, et al: Signals regulating hepatitis B surface antigen transcription. *Nature* 1983; 305:336–338.

210. Pourcel C, Louise A, Gervais M, et al: Transcription of the hepatitis B surface antigen gene in mouse cells transformed with cloned viral DNA. *J Virol* 1982; 42:100–105.

211. Shaul Y, Rutter WJ: A human hepatitis B viral enhancer element. *EMBO J* 1985; 4:427–430.

212. Farza H, Salmon AM, Hadehouel M, et al: Hepatitis B surface antigen gene expression is regulated by sex steroids and glucocorticoids in transgenic mice. *Proc Natl Acad Sci USA* 1987; 84:1187–1191.

213. Tur–Kaspa R, Burk RD, Shaul Y, et al: Hepatitis B virus DNA contains a glucocorticoid responsive element. *Proc Natl Acad Sci USA* 1986; 83:1627–1631.

214. Krugman S, Overby LR, Mushahawar IK, et al: Viral hepatitis, type B. Studies on natural history and prevention re-examined. *N Engl J Med* 1979; 300:101–106.

215. Ukkonen P: Rapid appearance of HBsAg after inoculation. *Lancet* 1979; 2:480.

216. Yoakum GH, Korba EB, Lechne JF, et al: High frequency transfection and cytopathology of the hepatitis B virus core antigen gene in human cells. *Science* 1983; 232:385–389.

217. Wands JR, Mann E, Alpert E, et al: The pathogenesis of arthritis associated with acute hepatitis-B surface antigen-positive hepatitis. *J Clin Invest* 1975; 55:930–936.

218. Gregory PB, Knauer CM, Kempson RL, et al: Steroid therapy in severe viral hepatitis. A double-blind, randomized trial of methylprednisolone versus placebo. *N Engl J Med* 1976; 294:681–687.

219. Ware AM, Eigenbrodt EH, Combes B: Prognostic significance of subacute hepatic necrosis in acute hepatitis. *Gastroenterology* 1975; 68:519–524.

220. de Groote J, Desmet VJ, Gedigk P, et al: A classification of chronic hepatitis. *Lancet* 1968; 2:626–628.

221. Villanueva A, Fraser P, Garcia R, et al: Fulminant hepatitis in the Sierra Nevada, in Zuckerman AJ (ed): *Viral Hepatitis and Liver Disease.* New York, Alan R Liss, 1988, pp 415–420.

222. Handler SC, DeMonzon M, Ponzetto A, et al: Delta virus infection and severe hepatitis: an epidemic in the Yucpa Indians of Venezuela. *Ann Intern Med* 1984; 100:339–344.

223. Saracco G, Macagno S, Rosina F, et al: Serologic markers with fulminant hepatitis in persons positive for hepatitis B surface antigen. *Ann Intern Med* 1988; 108:380–383.

224. Dudley FJ, Scheuer PJ, Sherlock S: Natural history of hepatitis-associated antigen-positive chronic liver disease. *Lancet* 1972; 2:1388–1393.

225. Szmuness W: Hepatocellular carcinoma and the hepatitis B virus: Evidence for a causal association. *Prog Med Virol* 1978; 24:40–69.

226. Lutwick LI: Relationship between aflatoxin, hepatitis B virus and hepatocellular carcinoma. *Lancet* 1979; 1:755–757.

227. Prince AM, Szmuness W, Michon J, et al: A case/control study of the association between primary liver cancer and hepatitis B infection in Senegal. *Int J Cancer* 1975; 16:376–383.

228. Obata H, Hayashi N, Motoika Y, et al: A prospective study on the development of hepatocellular carcinoma from liver cirrhosis with persistent hepatitis B infection. *Int J Cancer* 1980; 25:741–747.

229. Shikata T, Yamazaki S, Uzawa T: Hepatocellular carcinoma and chronic persistent hepatitis. *Acta Pathol Jpn* 1977; 27:297–304.

230. Beasley RP, Lin C-C, Hwang L-Y, et al: Hepatocellular carcinoma and hepatitis B virus. A prospective study of 22707 men in Taiwan. *Lancet* 1981; 2:1129–1131.

231. Trowbridge R, Fagan EA, Davison F, et al: Amplification of the c-*myc* gene locus in a human hepatic tumor containing integrated hepatitis B virus DNA, in Zuckerman AJ (ed): *Viral Hepatitis and Liver Disease*. New York, Alan R Liss, 1988, pp 764–768.

232. Brechot C, Purcel C, Hadchovel M, et al: State of hepatitis B DNA in liver disease. *Hepatology* 1982; 2:27S–34S.

232a. Schumacher HR, Gall EP: Arthritis in acute hepatitis and chronic active hepatitis. *Am J Med* 1974; 57:655–664.

233. Halpern MS, Egan J, Mason WS, et al: Viral nucleic acid synthesis and antigen accumulation in pancreas and kidney of Pekin ducks infected with duck hepatitis B virus. *Proc Natl Acad Sci USA* 1983; 80:4865–4869.

234. Gocke DJ, Hsu K, Morgan C, et al: Association between polyarteritis and Australia antigen. *Lancet* 1970; 2:1149–1153.

235. Sergent JS, Lockshin MD, Christian CL, et al: Vasculitis with hepatitis B antigenemia: Long term observations in nine patients. *Medicine* 1976; 55:1–18.

236. Brzosko WJ, Krawczynski K, Nazarewicz T, et al: Glomerulonephritis associated with hepatitis B surface antigen immune complexes in children. *Lancet* 1974; 2:477–482.

237. Kohler PF, Cronin RE, Hammond WS, et al: Chronic membranous glomerulonephritis caused by hepatitis B antigen-antibody immune complexes. *Ann Intern Med* 1974; 81:448–451.

238. Takekoshi V, Tanaka M, Miyakawa Y, et al: Free "small" and IgG-associated "large" hepatitis B e antigen in the serum and glomerular capillary walls of two patients with membranous glomerulonephritis. *N Engl J Med* 1979; 300:814–819.

239. Levo Y, Gorevic PD, Kassab HJ, et al: Association between hepatitis B virus and essential mixed cryoglobulinemia. *N Engl J Med* 1977; 296:1501–1504.

240. Miller AB, Waggoner DM: Cardiac disease, hepatic disease, and hepatitis B antigen. *Ann Intern Med* 1973; 79:276.

241. Rosenberg RN, Neuwelt EA, Kirkpatrick J, et al: Encephalopathy associated with cryoprecipitable Australia antigen. *Ann Neurol* 1977; 1:298–300.

242. Mihas AA, Kirby JD, Kent SP: Hepatitis B antigen and polymyositis. *JAMA* 1978; 239:221–222.

243. Niermeijer P, Gips CH: Guillain-Barré syndrome in acute HBsAg-positive hepatitis. *Br Med J* 1975; 4:732–733.

244. Gianotti F: Papular acrodermatitis of childhood and other papulovesicular acro-located syndromes. *Br J Dermatol* 1979; 100:49–59.

245. Krugman S, Hoofnagle JH, Gerety RJ, et al: Viral hepatitis, type B. DNA polymerase activity and antibody to hepatitis B core antigen. *N Engl J Med* 1974; 290:1331–1335.

246. Klinkert M, Theilman N, Pfaff E, et al: Pre-S1 antigens and antibodies early in the course of acute hepatitis B virus infection. *J Virol* 1986; 58:522–525.

247. Frösner GG, Brodersen M, Papaevangelou G, et al: Detection of HBeAg and anti-HBe in acute hepatitis by a sensitive radioimmunoassay. *J Med Virol* 1978; 3:67–76.

248. Hoofnagle JH, Seeff LB, Bales ZB: Serologic responses in HB, in Vyas GN, Cohen SN, Schmid R (eds): *Viral Hepatitis: Etiology, Epidemiology, Pathogenesis and Presentation*. Philadelphia, Franklin Institute Press, 1978, pp 219–242.

249. Alberts A, Cavalletto D, Pontisso P, et al: Antibody response to pre-S2 and hepatitis B virus induced liver damage. *Lancet* 1988; 1:1421–1424.

250. Hess G, Arnold W, Gahl GM, et al: Significance of antibody to hepatitis B e antigen (anti-HBe) in HBsAg-negative individuals. *Vox Sang* 1981; 40:95–98.

251. Markenson JA, Gerety RJ, Hoofnagle JH, et al: Effects of cyclophosphamide on hepatitis B virus infection and challenge in chimpanzees. *J Infect Dis* 1975; 131:70–83.

252. Realdi G, Alberti A, Rugge M, et al: Seroconversion from hepatitis B e antigen to anti-HBe in chronic hepatitis B virus infection. *Gastroenterology* 1980; 79:195–199.

253. Dusheiko GM, Hoofnagle JH, Cooksley WG, et al: Synthesis of antibodies to hepatitis B virus by cultured lymphocytes from chronic hepatitis B surface antigen carriers. *J Clin Invest* 1983; 71:1104–1113.

254. Milich DR, Chisari FV: Genetic regulation of the immune response to hepatitis B surface antigen. I. H-2 restriction of the murine humoral immune response to the *a* and *d* determinants of HBsAg. *J Immunol* 1982; 129:320–325.

255. Milich DR, Alexander H, Chisari FV: Genetic regulation of the immune response to hepatitis B surface antigen (HBsAg). III. Circumvention of nonresponsiveness in mice bearing HBsAg nonresponder haplotypes. *J Immunol* 1983; 130:1401–1407.

256. Troisi CL, Hollinger FB: Detection of an IgM antiidiotype directed against anti-HBs in hepatitis B patients. *Hepatology* 1985; 5:758–762.

257. Sylvan SPE, Hellström UB: Immunological mechanism in asymptomatic carriers of HBsAg, in Zuckerman AJ (ed): *Viral Hepatitis and Liver Disease*. New York, Alan R Liss, 1988, pp 704–710.

258. Dubois F, Goudeau A: Kinetics of delta antigen and delta antibody in acute delta hepatitis: evaluation with different enzyme immunoassays. *J Clin Microbiol* 1988; 26:1329–1342.

259. Grippon P, Ribiere Q, Cadranel JF, et al: Long term delta antigenemia without appearance of delta antibody in two immunodeficient patients. *Hepatology* 1987; 7:1156.

260. Negro F, Bergmann KF, Baroudy BM, et al: Chronic hepatitis D virus (HDV) in hepatitis B virus carrier chimpanzees experimentally superinfected with HDV. *J Infect Dis* 1988; 158:151–159.

261. Dudley FJ, Fox RA, Sherlock S: Cellular immunity and hepatitis-associated Australia antigen liver disease. *Lancet* 1972; 1:723–726.

262. Tong MJ, Wallace AM, Peters RL, et al: Lymphocyte stimulation in hepatitis B infections. *N Engl J Med* 1975; 293:318–322.

263. Dienstag JL, Savarese AM, Bhan AK: Increased natural killer cell activity in chronic hepatitis B virus infection. *Hepatology* 1982; 2:107S–115S.

264. Lee WM, Reed WD, Osman CG, et al: Immune responses to the hepatitis B surface antigen and liver-specific lipoprotein in acute type B hepatitis. *Gut* 1977; 18:250–257.

265. Thomas HC, Montano L, Goodall A, et al: Immunological mechanisms in chronic hepatitis B virus infection. *Hepatology* 1982; 2:116S–121S.

266. Chisari FV, Bieber MS, Josepho CA, et al: Functional properties of lymphocyte subpopulations in hepatitis B virus infection. II. Cytotoxic effector cell killing of targets that naturally express hepatitis B surface antigen and liver-specific lipoprotein. *J Immunol* 1981; 126:45–49.

267. Beutner KR, Tiku ML, Ogra PL: Hepatitis B surface antigen-specific cell-mediated immune responses in human chronic hepatitis B surface antigen carriers. *Infect Immun* 1978; 21:480–488.

268. Vento S, Hegarty JE, Alberti A, et al: T lymphocyte sensitization to HBcAg and T cell-mediated unresponsiveness to HBsAg in hepatitis B virus-related chronic liver disease. *Hepatology* 1985; 5:192–197.

269. Chisari FV, Routenberg JA, Fiala M, et al: Extrinsic modulation of human T-lymphocyte E rosette function associated with prolonged hepatocellular injury after viral hepatitis. *J Clin Invest* 1977; 59:134–142.

270. Anderson DS, Chisari FV: Deficient adherent and mitogen induced suppressor cell function in hepatitis. *Gastroenterology* 1979; 76:1271.

271. Chisari FV, Castle KL, Xavier C, et al: Functional properties of lymphocyte subpopulations in hepatitis B virus infection. I. Suppressor cell control of T lymphocyte responsiveness. *J Immunol* 1981; 126:38–44.

272. Chisari FV: Regulation of lymphocyte function and viral transformation by hepatic bioregulatory molecules. *Hepatology* 1982; 2:97S–106S.

273. Sanders GE, Perrillo RP: Suppression of T helper function: on immunoregulatory effect of rosette inhibiting factor in hepatitis B virus infection. *Hepatology* 1985; 5:392–396.

274. Rector WB, Govindarajan S, Horsburgh CR, et al: Hepatic inflammation, hepatitis B replication, and cellular immune function in homosexual males with chronic hepatitis B and antibody to human immunodeficiency virus. *Am J Gastroenterol* 1988; 83:262–266.

275. Gerlich WH, Luer W, Thomassen R, et al: Diagnosis of acute and inapparent hepatitis B virus infections by measurement of IgM antibody to hepatitis B core antigen. *J Infect Dis* 1980; 142:95–101.

276. Irwin GR, Allen RG, Segal HG, et al: Serodiagnosis of hepatitis B virus infection by antibody to core antigen. *J Infect Dis* 1977; 136:31–36.

277. Shafritz D: Hepatitis B virus DNA molecules in the liver of HBsAg carriers: Mechanistic considerations in the pathogenesis of hepatocellular carcinoma. *Hepatology* 1982; 2:35S–41S.

278. Lutwick LI, SyWassink JM, Fredrickson MA: The risk of transmission of hepatitis B in the hospital environment. Evidence for natural immunization. Presented at the Fourth Annual VA Nursing Research Conference, Chicago, Oct 30, 1981.

279. McMahon BJ, Helminiak C, Parkinson AJ, et al: Effect of hepatitis B vaccine in patients positive for antibody to hepatitis B core antigen only. *Hepatology* 1987; 7:1025.

280. Shiels MT, Taswall HF, Czaja AJ, et al: Frequency and significance of concurrent hepatitis B surface antigen and antibody in acute and chronic hepatitis B. *Gastroenterology* 1987; 93:675–680.

281. Dienstag JL: Concurrent hepatitis B surface antigen and antibody and the clonal selection theory of antibody diversity. *Gastroenterology* 1987; 93:899–904.

282. Hoofnagle JH, Gerety RJ, Barker LF: Antibody to hepatitis B surface antigen in immune serum globulin. *Transfusion* 1975; 15:408–413.

283. Grady GF, Rodman M, Larsen LH: Hepatitis B antibody in conventinoal γ-globulin. *J Infect Dis* 1975; 132:474–477.

284. Ginsberg AL, Conrad ME, Bancroft WH, et al: Prevention of endemic HAA-positive hepatitis with gamma globulin. *N Engl J Med* 1972; 286:562–566.

285. Krugman S, Giles JP, Hammond J: Viral hepatitis, type B (MS-2 strain): Prevention with specific hepatitis B immune serum globulin. *JAMA* 1971; 218:1665–1670.

286. Seeff L: Immunoprophylaxis and treatment of viral hepatitis B. *Semin Liv Dis* 1981; 1:69–80.

287. Prince AM, Szmuness W, Mann MK, et al: Hepatitis B immune globulin: Final report of a controlled multicenter trial of efficacy in prevention of dialysis-associated hepatitis. *J Infect Dis* 1978; 137:131–144.

288. Grady GF, Lee VA: Hepatitis B immune globulin—Prevention of hepatitis from accidental exposure among medical personnel. *N Engl J Med* 1975; 293:1067–1070.

289. Seeff LB, Wright EC, Zimmerman HJ, et al: Type B hepatitis after needle-stick exposure—Prevention with hepatitis B immune globulin. Final report of the Veterans Administration cooperative study. *Ann Intern Med* 1978; 88:285–293.

290. Hoofnagle JH, Seeff LB, Bales ZB, et al: Passive-active immunity from hepatitis B immune globulin. Re-analysis of the Veterans Administration cooperative study of needle stick hepatitis. *Ann Intern Med* 1979; 91:813–818.

291. Centers for Disease Control: Protection against viral hepatitis: Recommendations of the Immunization Practices Advisory Committee (ACIP). *MMWR* 1990; 39(RR-2):1–26.

292. Perrillo R, Campbell C, Costigan D: Immune serum globulin (ISG) and hepatitis B immune globulin (HBIG) for sexual exposure to acute type B hepatitis: Further observations from a randomized, controlled trial. *Hepatology* 1981; 1:536.

293. Beasley RP, Stevens CE: Vertical transmission of HBV and interruption with globulin, in Vyas GN, Cohen SN, Schmid R (eds): *Viral Hepatitis; Etiology, Epidemiology, Pathogenesis and Prevention*. Philadelphia, Franklin Institute Press, 1978, pp 333–345.

294. Stevens CE, Beasley RP, Lin C-C, et al: Perinatal hepatitis B virus infection: Use of hepatitis B immune globulin, in Szmuness W, Alter JH, Maynard JE (eds): *Viral Hepatitis: 1981 International Symposium*. Philadelphia, Franklin Institute Press, 1981, pp 527–535.

295. Beasley RP, Hwang L-Y, Lin C-C, et al: Hepatitis B immune globulin (HBIG) efficacy in the interruption of perinatal transmission of hepatitis B virus carrier state. Initial report of a randomised double-blind placebo controlled trial. *Lancet* 1981; 2:388–393.

296. Centers for Disease Control: Prevention of perinatal transmission of hepatitis B virus: prenatal screening of all pregnant women for hepatitis B surface antigen. *MMWR* 1988; 32:341–346, 351.

296a. Okuda K: Early recognition of hepatocellular carcinoma. *Hepatology* 1986; 6:729–738.

297. Purcell RH, Gerin JL: Hepatitis B vaccines: On the threshold. *Am J Clin Pathol* 1978; 70S:159–169.

298. Zuckerman AJ: Safety of hepatitis B vaccines containing intact 20 nm particles. *Lancet* 1979; 1:547–548.

299. Francis DP, Feorino PM, McDougal S, et al: The safety of hepatitis B vaccine: inactivation of the AIDS virus during routine vaccine manufacture. *JAMA* 1986; 256:869–872.

300. Szmuness W, Stevens CE, Harley EJ, et al: Hepatitis B vaccine. Demonstration of efficacy in a controlled clinical trial in a high-risk population in the United States. *N Engl J Med* 1980; 303:833–841.

301. Crosnier J, Jungers P, Couroucé AM, et al: Randomised placebo-controlled trial of hepatitis B surface antigen vaccine in French haemodialysis unit: 1. Medical staff. *Lancet* 1981; 1:455–459.

302. Lohiya G: Asthma and urticaria after hepatitis B vaccination. *West J Med* 1987; 147:341.

303. Ring J: Exacerbation of eczema by formalin-containing hepatitis B vaccine in formaldehyde-allergic patient. *Lancet* 1986; 2:522–523.

304. Hadler SC, Francis DP, Maynard JE, et al: Long-term immunogenicity and efficacy of hepatitis B vaccine in homosexual men. *N Engl J Med* 1986; 315:209–214.

305. Hadler SC: Are booster doses of hepatitis B vaccine necessary? *Ann Intern Med* 1988; 108:457–458.

306. Crosnier J, Jungers P, Couroucé AM, et al: Randomised placebo-controlled trial of hepatitis B surface antigen vaccine in French haemodialysis units: II. Haemodialysis patients. *Lancet* 1981; 1:797–800.

307. Karasawa T, Shikata T, Abe K, et al: Efficacy of hepatitis B vaccine in chimpanzees given transfusions of highly infective blood. *J Infect Dis* 1983; 147:327–335.

308. Maupas P, Chiron J-P, Barin F, et al: Efficacy of hepatitis B vaccine in prevention of early HBsAg carrier state in children. *Lancet* 1981; 1:289–292.

309. Barin F, Goudeau A, Denis F, et al: Immune responses in neonates given hepatitis B vaccine. *Lancet* 1982; 1:251–253.

309a. Lo K-J, Lee S-D, Tsai Y-T, et al: Long-term immunogenicity and efficacy of hepatitis B vaccine in infants born to HBeAg-positive HBsAg-carrier mothers. *Hepatology* 1988; 8:1647–1650.

310. Szmuness W, Stevens CE, Oleszko WR, et al: Passive-active

immunisation against hepatitis B: Immunogenicity studies in adult Americans. *Lancet* 1981; 1:575–577.

311. Redfield RR, Innis BL, Scott RM, et al: Clinical evaluation of low-dose intradermally administered hepatitis B vaccine, a cost reduction strategy. *JAMA* 1985; 254:3203–3206.

312. Halsey NA, Reppert EJ, Margolis HS, et al: Intradermal hepatitis B vaccination in an abbreviated schedule. *Vaccine* 1986; 4:228–232.

313. Hollinger FB: Hepatitis B vaccines—to switch or not to switch. *JAMA* 1983; 257:2631–2636.

314. Gerety RJ, Ellis RW: Plasma-derived vs recombinant hepatitis B vaccine. *JAMA* 1987; 258:1434.

315. Gerety RJ, Ellis RW, Zajac BA, et al: Two superb vaccines against hepatitis B in Mexican standoff. *JAMA* 1988; 259:2402–2404.

316. Andre FE, Safary A: Clinical experience with a yeast-derived hepatitis B vaccine, in Zuckerman AJ (ed): *Viral Hepatitis and Liver Disease*. New York, Alan R Liss, 1988, pp 1025–1030.

316a. Lindsay KL, Herbert DA, Gitnick GL: Hepatitis B vaccine: Low postvaccination immunity in hospital personnel given gluteal injections. *Hepatology* 1985; 5:1088–1090.

316b. Brightman CAJ, Scadding GK, Dumbreck LA, et al: Yeast-derived hepatitis B vaccine and yeast sensitivity. *Lancet* 1989; 1:903.

317. Scully LF, Kang CY: Production and secretion of hepatitis B surface antigen and pre-S2 plus HBsAg using a baculovirus expression vector, in Zuckerman JA (ed): *Viral Hepatitis and Liver Disease*. New York, Alan R Liss, 1988, pp 365–371.

318. Milich DR, Thornton GB, Neurath AR, et al: Enhanced immunogenicity of the pre-S region of hepatitis B surface antigen. *Science* 198; 228:1195–1198.

319. Smith GL, Machett M, Mass B: Infectious vaccinia virus recombinants that express hepatitis B virus surface antigen. *Nature* 1983; 302:490–495.

320. Lerner RA, Green N, Alexander H, et al: Chemically synthesized peptides predicted from the nucleotide sequence of the hepatitis B virus genome elicit antibodies reactive with the native envelope protein of Dane particles. *Proc Natl Acad Sci USA* 1981; 78:3404–3407.

321. Dreesman GR, Sanchez Y, Ionescu-Matiu I, et al: Antibody to hepatitis B surface antigen after a single inoculation of uncoupled synthetic HBsAg peptides. *Nature* 1982; 295:158–160.

322. Korec E, Hlozánek I, Stará J, et al: Antiidiotypic antibody as a prospective vaccine against hepatitis B. In Zuckerman AJ (ed): *Viral Hepatitis and Liver Disease*. New York, Alan R Liss, 1988, pp 1102–1105.

323. Gibas AL, Ryan DM, Dienstag JL: Prevalence and incidence in health workers of hepatitis B infection in the prevaccination era. *Hepatology* 1987; 7:1119.

323a. Hoofnagle JH: Toward universal vaccination against hepatitis B virus. *N Engl J Med* 1989; 321:1333–1334.

324. Craven DE, Awdeh ZL, Kunches LM, et al: Nonresponsiveness to hepatitis B vaccine in health care deliverers. *Ann Intern Med* 1986; 105:356–360

325. Nagafuchi S, Kashiwagi S: Reversal by intradermal hepatitis B vaccination of unresponsiveness to HBsAg. *Lancet* 1987; 2:1522–1523.

326. Milich DR, McLachlan A, Thornton GB, et al: Antibody production to the nucleocapsid and envelope of the hepatitis B virus primed by a single synthetic T cell site. *Nature* 1987; 329:547–549.

327. Tabor E, Gerety RJ: Possible role of immune responses to hepatitis B core antigen in protection against hepatitis B infection. *Lancet* 1987; 1:172.

328. Blum AL, Berthet P, Doelle W, et al: Treatment of acute viral hepatitis with (+)-cyanidanol-3. *Lancet* 1977; 2:1153–1155.

329. Piazza M, Guadagnino V, Picciotto L, et al: Effect of (+)-cyanidanol-3 in acute HAV, HBV, and non-A, non-B viral hepatitis. *Hepatology* 1983; 3:45–49.

330. Par A, Barna K, Hollos I, et al: Levamisole in viral hepatitis. *Lancet* 1977; 1:702.

331. Redeker AG, Schweitzer IL, Yamahiro HS: Randomization of corticosteroid therapy in fulminant hepatitis. *N Engl J Med* 1976; 294:728–729.

332. Ware AJ, Cuthbert JA, Shorey J, et al: A prospective trial of steroid therapy in severe viral hepatitis. The prognostic significance of bridging necrosis. *Gastroenterology* 1981; 80:219–224.

333. Gocke DJ: Fulminant hepatitis treated with serum containing antibody to Australia antigen. *N Engl J Med* 1971; 284:919.

334. Acute Hepatic Failure Study Group: Failure of specific immunotherapy in fulminant type B hepatitis. *Ann Intern Med* 1977; 86:272–277.

335. Gateau P, Opolon P, Nusinovici V, et al: Passive immunotherapy in HBsAg fulminant hepatitis. Results on antigenemia and survival. *Digestion* 1976; 14:304–310.

336. Levin S, Hahn T: Interferon system in acute viral hepatitis. *Lancet* 1982; 1:592–594.

337. Chousterman S, Chousterman M, Hagege H, et al: Interferon system in acute viral hepatitis B: pattern of activation in patients during progress to complete recovery, in Zuckerman AJ (ed): *Viral Hepatitis and Liver Diseases*. New York, Alan R Liss, 1988, pp 831–833.

337a. Sinclair SB, Greig PD, Blendis LM, et al: Biochemical and clinical response of fulminant viral hepatitis to administration of prostaglandin E. *J Clin Invest* 1989; 84:1063–1069.

338. Soloway RD, Summerskill WHJ, Baggenstoss AH, et al: Clinical, biochemical, and histological remission of severe chronic active liver disease: A controlled study of treatment and early prognosis. *Gastroenterology* 1972; 63:820–833.

339. Wright EC, Seeff LB, Berk PD, et al: Treatment of chronic active hepatitis. An analysis of three controlled trials. *Gastroenterology* 1977; 73:1422–1430.

340. Tsuji T, Naito K, Tokuyama K, et al: Followup ten years after corticosteroid therapy for chronic active hepatitis type B. *Hepatogastroenterology* 1980; 27:85–90.

341. Schalm SW, Summerskill WHJ, Gitnick GL, et al: Contrasting features and responses to treatment of severe chronic active liver disease with and without hepatitis Bs antigen. *Gut* 1976; 17:781–786.

342. Lam KC, Lai CL, Ng RP, et al: Deleterious effect of prednisolone in HBsAg positive chronic active hepatitis. *N Engl J Med* 1981; 304:380–386.

343. Sagnelli E, Manzillo G, Maio G, et al: Serum levels of hepatitis B surface and core antigens during immunosuppressive treatment of HBsAg positive chronic active hepatitis. *Lancet* 1980; 2:395–397.

344. Hoofnagle JH, Dusheiko GM, Schafer DF, et al: Reactivation of chronic hepatitis B virus infection by cancer chemotherapy. *Ann Intern Med* 1982; 96:447–449.

345. Reed WD, Eddleston ALWF, Cullens H, et al: Infusion of hepatitis-B antibody in antigen-positive active chronic hepatitis. *Lancet* 1973; 2:1347–1351.

346. Lever AML, Waters J, Brook MG, et al: Treatment of chronic hepatitis B virus infection with monoclonal antibody to the hepatitis B virus surface antigen in two patients with hypogammaglobulinemia, in Zuckerman AJ (ed): *Viral Hepatitis and Liver Disease*. New York, Alan R Liss, 1988, pp 961–962.

347. Tong MJ, Nystrom JS, Redeker AG, et al: Failure of transfer factor therapy in chronic active type B hepatitis. *N Engl J Med* 1976; 295:209–211.

348. Kohler PF, Trembath J, Merrill DA, et al: Immunotherapy with antibody, lymphocytes, and transfer factor in chronic hepatitis B. *Clin Immunol Immunopathol* 1974; 2:465–471.

349. Chadwick RG, Jain S, Thomas HC, et al: Levamisole in the treatment of HBs antigen positive chronic active liver disease. *Gut* 1977; 18:A979.

350. Brzosko WJ, Debski R, Derecka K: Immunostimulation for chronic active hepatitis. *Lancet* 1978; 2:331.

351. Shi-Shan L, Chang-Fu L, Fu-Ying H, et al: Preparation and clinical use of HBsAg immune RNA. *Lancet* 1982; 1:197–198.

351a. Nishioka M, Kagawa H, Shirai M, et al: Effects of human recombinant interleukin 2 in patients with chronic hepatitis B. *Am J Gastroenterol* 1987; 82:438–442.

352. McGilchnit AJ, Follett E: Bacillus Calmette-Guérin in vaccine as immunotherapy in chronic hepatitis B, in Zuckerman AJ (ed): *Viral Hepatitis and Liver Disease.* New York, Alan R Liss, 1988, pp 963–964.

353. Greenberg HB, Pollard RB, Lutwick LI, et al: Effect of human leukocyte interferon on hepatitis B virus infection in patients with chronic active hepatitis. *N Engl J Med* 1976; 295:517–522.

354. Scullard GH, Alberti A, Wansbrough-Jones MH, et al: Effects of human leucocyte interferon on hepatitis B virus replication and immune responses in patients with chronic hepatitis B infection. *J Clin Lab Immunol* 1979; 1:277–282.

355. Kingham JGC, Gangoly NK, Shaari ZD, et al: Treatment of HBsAg positive chronic active hepatitis with human fibroblast interferon. *Gut* 1978; 19:91–94.

356. Purcell RH, Gerin JL, London WT, et al: Modification of chronic hepatitis B virus infection in chimpanzees by administration of an interferon inducer. *Lancet* 1976; 2:757–761.

357. Dusheiko GM, Kassianides C, Song E, et al: Loss of hepatitis B surface antigen in three controlled trials of recombinant alpha-interferon for treatment of chronic hepatitis B, in Zuckerman AJ (ed): *Viral Hepatitis and Liver Disease.* New York, Alan R Liss, 1988, pp 963–964.

358. Kassionides C, DiBisceglie AM, Hoofnagle JH, et al: Alpha-interferon therapy in patients with decompensated chronic type B hepatitis, in Zuckerman AJ (ed): *Viral Hepatitis and Liver Disease.* New York, Alan R Liss, 1988, pp 840–843.

359. Suzuki H, Iehida F, Fujisawa K, et al: Double-blind controlled study of the antiviral effect of human interferon-B on chronic active hepatitis, in Zuckerman AJ (ed): *Viral Hepatitis and Liver Disease.* New York, Alan R Liss, 1988, pp 864–867.

360. Caselman WH, Eisenburg J, Hofschneider PH, et al: Interferon-beta and gamma therapy of chronic active hepatitis B: a controlled trial, in Zuckerman AJ (ed): *Viral Hepatitis and Liver Disease.* New York, Alan R Liss, 1988, pp 875–878.

361. Pollard RB, Smith JL, Neal EA, et al: Effect of vidarabine on chronic hepatitis B virus infection. *JAMA* 1978; 239:1648–1650.

362. Chadwick RG, Bassendine MF, Crawford EM, et al: HBsAg-positive chronic liver disease: Inhibition of DNA polymerase activity by vidarabine. *Br Med J* 1978; 2:531–533.

363. Hoofnagle JH, Davis GL, Hanson RG, et al: Treatment of chronic type B hepatitis with multiple ten-day courses of adenine arabinoside monophosphate. *J Med Virol* 1985; 15:121–128.

364. Perillo R, Regenstein F, Bodicky C, et al: Prolonged follow-up of chronic active hepatitis treated with prednisone withdrawal followed by ARA-AMP. *Hepatology* 1985; 5:1009.

365. Smith CI, Kitchen LW, Scullard GH, et al: Vidarabine monophosphate and human leukocyte interferon in chronic hepatitis B infection. *JAMA* 1982; 247:2261–2265.

366. Fiume L, Torrani Cerenzia MR, Bonino F, et al: Inhibition of hepatitis B virus replication by vidarabine monophosphate conjugated with lactosaminated serum albumin. *Lancet* 1988; 2:13–15.

367. Hess G, Arnold W, Meyer zum Büschenfelde K-H: Inhibition of hepatitis B virus deoxyribonucleic acid polymerase by the 5'-triphosphates of 9-β-D-arabinofuranosyladenine and 1-β-D-arabinofuranosylcytosine. *Antimicrob Agents Chemother* 1981; 19:44–50.

368. Nordenfelt E, Oberg B, Helgstrand E, et al: Inhibition of hepatitis B Dane particle DNA polymerase activity by pyrophosphate analogs. *Acta Pathol Microbiol Scand* 1980; 88B:169–175.

369. Hess G, Arnold W, Moller B, et al: Inhibition of hepatitis B virus specific DNA polymerase by intercalating agents. *Med Microbiol Immunol* 1980; 168:25–34.

370. Hirschman SZ, Garfinkel E: Inhibition of hepatitis B DNA polymerase by intercalating agents. *Nature* 1978; 271:681–683.

371. Hedin G, Weiland O, Ljunggren K, et al: Treatment with foscarnet of fulminant hepatitis B and fulminant hepatitis B and D coinfection, in Zuckerman AJ (ed): *Viral Hepatitis and Liver Disease.* New York, Alan R Liss, 1988, pp 947–952.

372. Nordenfelt E, Löfgren B, Chattopadhyaya J, et al: Inhibition of hepatitis B virus DNA polymerase 3'-azido-3'-deoxythymidine triphosphate but not by threo analogue, in Zuckerman AJ (ed): *Viral Hepatitis and Liver Disease.* New York, Alan R Liss, 1988, pp 944–946.

372a. Kassianides C, Hoofnagle JH, Miller RH, et al: Inhibition of duck hepatitis B virus replication by 2',3'-dideoxycytidine. *Gastroenterology* 1989; 97:1275–1280.

373. Alexander GJM, Fagan EA, Hegarty JE, et al: Controlled clinical trial of acyclovir in chronic hepatitis B virus infection. *J Clin Microbiol* 1987; 21:81–87.

374. Schlam SW, Heytink RA, van Buuren HR, et al: Acyclovir enhances the antiviral effect of interferon in chronic hepatitis B. *Lancet* 1985; 2:358–360.

375. Venkateswaran PS, Millman I, Blumberg BS: Effects of an extract from *Phyllanthus nirum* on hepatitis B and woodchuck hepatitis viruses: in vitro and in vivo studies. *Proc Natl Acad Sci USA* 1987; 84:274–278.

29

Hepatitis Delta Virus

Stephen C. Hadler
Howard A. Fields

The hepatitis delta virus (HDV), the third of the agents of viral hepatitis to be identified and characterized, has opened new avenues for investigating human viruses and understanding mechanisms of disease. Since its discovery in 1977, HDV has been characterized as a unique human virus which is dependent on hepatitis B virus (HBV) to cause infection and disease, yet which greatly augments the severity of both acute and chronic liver disease in the HBV-infected host.[1-3] Molecular virology studies of the HDV genome have shown a low-level insignificant homology to HBV and no homology to other animal viruses. The HDV genome, however, has the closest relationship to certain plant pathogens—viroids, and plant satellite viruses and RNAs—some of which are dependent on other plant viruses to cause disease.[4]

Dependence on HBV dictates that the epidemiology and clinical syndromes caused by HDV be closely related to those of its host virus. The high endemicity of HBV infection worldwide and its versatility of transmission mechanisms (by bloodborne or sexual routes) assure HDV of a large potential host population. HDV can cause infection in two ways: (1) by coinfection with HBV of an HBV-susceptible host, and (2) by superinfection of an HBV car-

rier.[5] The consequences of the two types of HDV infection differ markedly. Coinfection with HBV results in acute hepatitis, which can be fulminant, but which, like HBV infection alone, is usually self-limited with resolution of both diseases. Superinfection of an HBV carrier, while also initially inducing acute or fulminant hepatitis, usually progresses to chronic HBV infection and chronic hepatitis. Chronically HDV-HBV-infected persons carry the major burden of disease and are the major reservoir for HDV infection worldwide.

HDV is now known to account for a significant proportion of liver disease previously attributed to HBV alone. Worldwide, HDV coinfection or superinfection can be found in about one third of fulminant hepatitis B cases, and in parts of northern South America and Africa HDV is implicated in causing outbreaks of fulminant hepatitis. More importantly, HDV accounts for between 20% to 40% of HBV-associated chronic liver disease worldwide, particularly chronic active hepatitis (CAH) and cirrhosis. Neverthelsss, HDV has not been directly implicated in HBV-associated primary liver cancer, and, in general, HDV must be viewed in the context of bring an accessory virus to HBV.[2-3]

HISTORY

The HDV was discovered by Rizzetto and colleagues during studies on hepatitis B core antigen (HBcAg) in livers of chronic HBV patients.[1] While studying liver biopsies from patients seropositive for hepatitis B surface antigen (HBsAg) by direct immunofluorescence (IF), Rizzetto and coworkers noted that one particular human serum containing anti-HBc activity stained not only core particles demonstrable by electron microscopy but also stained biopsies devoid of core particles. These HBcAg-negative biopsies remained negative after staining with other reference antisera against HBcAg. Further study using these same HBcAg-positive and HBcAg-negative biopsies which stained with other sera containing anti-HBc activity suggested that there were two distinct nuclear antigenic specificities. The staining—always confined to the nuclei of hepatocytes and appearing as diffuse, granular, or globular fluorescence—was different from the uniformly finely speckled fluorescence of nuclei containing HBcAg.

Initially, this newly identified antigen-antibody system, designated delta, was thought to be an HBV-related marker until chimpanzee transmission studies in 1979–1980 characterized HDV as a separate virus, but one which required HBV infection to cause infection.[5] Following these studies, which characterized the basic virologic and clinical events of both HBV-HDV coinfection and HDV superinfection of HBV carriers, progress in developing laboratory tests, and defining the basic virology of the agent and its basic epidemiology was rapid. Serologic tests for hepatitis delta antigen (HDAg) and antibodies to HDAg (anti-HD) became the initial tools for study of HDV, but were rapidly improved and enhanced by IgM-specific anti-HD assays in the early 1980s.[6, 7] The clinical consequences of HDV, initially thought to be primarily chronic hepatitis, were quickly expanded to include fulminant hepatitis.[8, 9] In addition, the pathogenesis of HDV disease and its unresponsiveness to immunosuppressive drugs was defined.[10] Most recently, the use of molecular virologic techniques have led to the characterization of the virus and a better understanding of the nature of its dependency on HBV.[4, 11, 12] Furthermore, probes of HDV RNA and immunoblots for HDAg have contributed to a better definition of chronic HDV infection and relative infectivity for epidemiologic and prevention purposes.[13, 14]

While the progress in understanding the biology and clinical consequences of HDV have been remarkable, the origin of HDV remains obscure. Although initially discovered in Italy, the highest HDV prevalence is found in widely separated areas including northern South America, northern Kenya, and Romania.[15–17] Historically, HDV infection has been linked to fulminant hepatitis occurring in northern South America since the 1930s and antibodies have been found in immunoglobulin produced in the United States in the 1940s.[18] Movement into drug-abusing communities in Europe and Australia in the early 1970s suggest later introduction into developed countries from some higher endemicity foci.[19, 20] Nevertheless, the true geographic origin of HDV is not likely to be identified.

STRUCTURE AND BIOLOGY

The HDV is the only member of a new class of defective animal viruses containing a single negatively stranded, closed circular molecule of RNA, 1.7 kilodaltons (kd) in size, and dependent on the presence of an hepadnavirus for its pathogenic expression.[4] This dependence was initially demonstrated by experimental transmission of the virus to chimpanzees chronically infected with HBV.[5, 21] The observation has been extended to woodchucks and to Pekin ducks in which the respective hepadnaviruses provided the necessary helper functions.[22, 23] It is thought that the major helper function is the synthesis of coat protein composed of HBsAg which the HDV uses to encapsulate the genome.

The genomic structure (closed circular RNA with rodlike secondary structure) and putative replication intermediates[11] has led to the hypothesis that HDV may belong to a group of transmissible disease-causing agents of plants known as viroids.[24] There are, however, important differences between HDV and viroids. The

HDV genome is at least 4 times larger and both genomic and antigenomic RNA species have been detected within infected cells,[11, 24] a feature not yet detected in viroids.[25] HDV also differs from viroids in that HDV is encapsulated while viroids are thought to be naked RNA. Thus, these characteristics suggest that HDV may more closely resemble two groups of encapsulated RNAs of plants, the satellite viruses and the satellite RNAs,[24, 26] both of which require a helper virus for replication. The satellite viruses encode their own coat protein, whereas the satellite RNAs depend on the helper virus to provide the coat. A subgroup of the satellite RNAs, previously known as virusoids, have small circular genomes of less than 400 bases that become encapsulated. The remainder of the satellite RNAs and the satellite viruses have genome sizes of up to 1.2 kilobases in length, more comparable to the HDV genome size. Because HDV codes for its own antigen,[4] it most closely resembles a satellite virus, although retaining certain features of viroids, virusoids, and satellite RNAs.

Transmission studies in chimpanzees and woodchucks using sera obtained from chronically HDV-infected individuals were essential in providing source material from which the HDV could be isolated, purified, and characterized. Sera obtained from patients demonstrating intrahepatic expression of the HDAg were often devoid of detectable HDAg activity in serum, presumably because of cocirculating high titers of anti-HD that interfered with the immunologic detection assay for the antigen. An analysis of serial specimens obtained from experimentally infected chimpanzees revealed, however, that the HDAg could be detected in acute phase serum prior to development of anti-HD activity.[5] This material allowed Rizzetto et al to begin to characterize the virus.[6, 21]

Physical characterization of HDV in acute phase serum demonstrated that the HDAg is associated with a discrete subpopulation of HBsAg-enveloped particles with a bouyant density of about 1.25 g/mL in cesium chloride and a sedimentation coefficient intermediate between that of the 22-nm HBsAg particle and the complete virion (HBV).[21, 27] Electron microscopic examination of acute phase sera revealed a predominant morphologic form with a diameter of 35 to 37 nm that shares common antigenic determinants with HBsAg. Immunoprecipitation studies have demonstrated that to detect the HDAg the serum must be first treated with detergents, indicating that this antigen is an internal component of this subpopulation of HBsAg-coated particles. Both the HDV RNA and the HDAg are found within the enveloped particle, but not as a defined core structure as is found with hepadnaviruses (Figure 29–1).[27] The envelope of HDV particles has been studied by Bonino et al by purifying the particles from the serum of an experimentally infected chimpanzee and analyzing the envelope proteins by immunoblots.[28] The HBsAg envelope of HDV contains all known HBsAg proteins; however, its protein envelope composition is more similar to that of the 22-nm particles of HBsAg than to that of complete HBV, indicating that HDV does not require the pre-S1 protein region which is always found in the envelope of complete HBV (see Fig 29–1). Alberti et al have shown that the expression of the polymerized human serum albumin receptor activity, found in the pre-S2 region, in sera of patients infected with HDV is variable and depends, as in HBV infection alone, on the hepatitis B e antigen (HBeAg)-antibody to HBeAg (anti-HBe) status.[29]

The HDAg was first isolated by treatment with 6 mol/L guan-

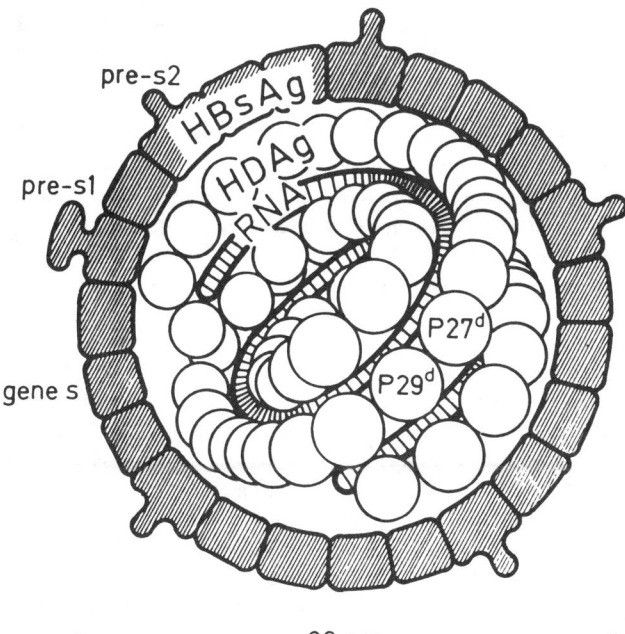

Figure 29–1. Schematic of hepatitis D delta virus particle. See text. (From Zyzik E, et al: Proteins of the hepatitis delta virus in serum and liver, in Robinson W, et al: *Hepadna Viruses.* New York, Alan R Liss, 1987, pp 565–571. Used by permission.)

idine hydrochloride of extracted and sonicated material from the nuclei of a human liver obtained at autopsy. Equilibrium centrifugation, gel filtration, and chemical and enzymatic treatments revealed HDAg to be a protein of approximately 68 kd with a bouyant density of 1.28 g/mL in CsCl, stable to heat, acid, nucleases, and glycosidases, and inactivated by alkali and proteases.[6]

Several groups of investigators, using immunoblot techniques, have identified two major polypeptides with molecular weight values between 24 and 29 kd, detectable within the interior of HDV obtained from serum and from liver tissue of humans and experimentally infected animals.[14, 28, 30] These proteins were both stained by polyclonal anti-HD antibodies and by the available human monoclonal anti-HD antibody, suggesting they share common determinants.[31] The sizes of these polypeptides have varied in different laboratories, but have remained consistent among different species investigated in the same laboratory. Variations are likely related to experimental techniques rather than true differences in molecular weight. Smaller species of polypeptides have been detected in some studies, and also react with the anti-HD monoclonal antibody[14, 32]; these polypeptides were not found consistently and appear most likely due to proteolysis.[30]

Thus, these two polypeptides appear to be the major structural components of HDAg resident within HDV particles, and because they share common epitopes, are believed to be derived from a single gene.[14] Products of in vitro translation of HDV-specific RNA from infected livers have produced proteins of similar size detectable by both polyclonal and monoclonal antibodies; in contrast, HDV RNA isolated from serum is not translated in vitro into HDAg.[31] This is consistent with the concept that the HDAg gene is encoded on the antigenomic strand.

The exact molecular derivation of the two large polypeptides

has remained unclear. Pohl et al speculated that these polypeptides could be generated by splicing of different RNA species,[31] by posttranslational modifications of a single translation product,[14] or by translation from two different initiation sites in the same open reading frame. Immunologic analysis of viral extracts and recombinant expressed antigen in bacteria and yeast has revealed, however, that only one open reading frame found in the antigenomic sequence encodes for the epitope shared by both HDV-specific polypeptides.[33] Furthermore, these authors observed nine sites of sequence heterogeneity within the HDAg coding region, one of which encoded an amber (TAG) stop codon 195 amino acids from the first in-frame methionine of the predicted polypeptide. It is probable that the larger molecular weight species of 214 amino acids occurs as a result of partial host suppression of the first stop codon after amino acid position 195, whereas the smaller polypeptide represents the translation product terminating at the first TAG codon. Thus, a translational suppression of the first stop codon may occur in vivo such that both polypeptides are synthesized from a single template. Alternatively, a heterogeneous population of RNA genomes may exist such that both polypeptides are the translation products of two different mRNAs transcribed from distinct genomes.

The predicted amino acid sequence of the HDV-specific proteins based on published nucleotide sequence data indicates a protein containing highly charged amino acids in the N-terminal two thirds and uncharged amino acids at the C-terminus.[34, 35] The abundance of highly basic amino acid residues suggests that the HDAg may interact with the HDV RNA. In experiments by Chang et al[36] both recombinant expressed antigen and antigen prepared in vitro were shown to bind the genomic RNA of HDV. In addition, the protein was shown to be phosphorylated at the serine residues and accumulate in the nuclei of transfected COS 7 cells. Collectively, these data suggested that the HDAg is a nucleocapsid protein which interacts directly with the viral RNA and may play an important role in HDV RNA replication and pathogenesis.

Initial studies by Rizzetto et al demonstrated that HDV RNA found in the 35- to 37-nm virus particles was unusually small (molecular weight of 5×10^5).[21] Further studies by Hoyer et al revealed a size of approximately 1.75 kilobases.[37] Binding studies showed that the RNA species does not have a 3′ poly (A) tail, indicating that the HDV RNA was negatively stranded. Since these initial reports on the nature of HDV RNA, a number of studies describing the molecular biology of HDV have been published, greatly contributing to our understanding of the genomic organization and replication strategy.

In 1986, Denniston et al published the first partial sequence of HDV RNA, sequencing a complementary-strand cDNA (complementary DNA) fragment of 166 base pairs cloned into the plasmid vector pBR322 and designated pKD3.[38] Using pKD3 as a probe, Wang et al[4] sequenced overlapping cDNA clones to determine the structure of the entire genome, obtaining a circular molecule of 1679 nucleotides (revised from 1678).[4, 39] Additional evidence of a circular genome was provided by electron microscopy and electrophoresis.[40] The sequence analysis by Wang et al showed a high GC content (60%), and an inherent ability to self-anneal in an intramolecular fashion to form a covalently closed, stable, double-stranded RNA secondary structure in which 67% of the residues are base-paired. In addition, several palindromic sequences, and viroid and virusoid consensus sequences were observed. The HDV RNA sequence and the complementary anti-HDV RNA strand contain numerous open reading frames (ORFs). One ORF (ORF5) from the antigenomic strand, when subcloned into an expression system, produced a fusion protein which reacted by immunoblot with anti-HD-positive sera. This fusion protein induced in rabbits anti-HD which identified HDAg-specific polypeptides by immunoblots. The fact that eukaryote ribosomes cannot translate circular RNA molecules and the observed inability of an in vitro rabbit reticulocyte lysate to translate the HDV genome provided additional evidence that HDV is a negative-stranded virus.[34]

A complete nucleotide sequence of HDV RNA obtained directly from acute phase human material was derived by Makino et al.[35] Sequence analysis revealed human HDV RNA contains 1683 nucleotides, is present as a circular molecule, and has an overall homology with the chimpanzee sequence of 89%, with domains of relative conservation and of more pronounced divergence. This contrasts with the nearly identical sequences published from chimpanzees. Nevertheless, with only minor changes, the viroid and virusoid consensus sequences were present and one ORF (ORF2) corresponded with the ORF5, the putative gene for HDAg, reported by Wang et al.[34] Saldanha et al also derived a partial sequence of human HDV RNA, noting a 20% overall difference with the chimpanzee sequence and failing to find the viroid consensus sequence.[41] The function of the viroid and virusoid sequences is speculative and may be important for replication.

Kuo et al cloned and sequenced the HDV RNA extracted from the liver of a woodchuck infected with the same strain of HDV sequenced by Wang.[42] The complete sequence showed equal length (1679 nucleotides) and 98.5% homology with the chimpanzee sequence. The nine discrepancies represented only single-base changes with no insertions or deletions. Since no substantial nucleotide changes were observed during interspecies adaptation of HDV to woodchucks, the woodchuck model probably represents a good animal model system to study HDV replication. The overall homology between the woodchuck sequence and the human HDV sequence published by Makino et al[35] was 89%, which included not only single-base changes, but also three insertions and seven deletions. The extent of sequence differences between laboratories appears likely due to different strains of HDV rather than to the consequences of serial experimental transmission.

By using computer analysis, an unbranched rod structure has been predicted with 70% of the nucleotides base-paired. It has been speculated that the rodlike structure may have significance for the life cycle of HDV by conferring nuclease resistance and stability, facilitating RNA polymerase binding, or triggering a response within the infected cell.

Chen et al, using strand-specific cDNA as probes, have studied both the virion and intracellular RNA from livers of infected chimpanzees and woodchucks.[11] They found that only one polarity of HDV RNA was packaged into virions. Infected livers contained as many as 300,000 copies of genomic strand RNA per cell, some of which had a circular conformation. Also present in these livers were RNA species complementary to the virion RNA, although the genomic RNA was 5 to 22 times more abundant than this antigenomic strand. Some of the antigenomic circular RNA was complexed with genomic RNA; these double-stranded species could be replicative forms of the genome. These features are unusual

for an animal virus system and most closely resemble a rolling-circle replication strategy, as described for plant viroids.[24] Furthermore, these similar features allow the speculation that the HDV RNA, like a viroid, once inside a permissive cell can replicate without the helper hepadnavirus and that the helper HBV may simply provide the envelope proteins needed for transmission. Because both circular genomic and circular antigenomic species have been detected within HDV-infected liver cells, a double rolling-circle model, one for the genomic and the other for the antigenomic strand, has been proposed.[43]

In the rolling-circle models of replication, RNA cleavage and ligation are needed to produce progeny monomer circles. Sharmeen et al[44] have shown that the antigenomic strand of HDV RNA can undergo self-cleavage in vitro, as previously described for the genomic and antigenomic RNAs of plant viroids.[45, 47] This self-cleavage occurs at a specific site located almost adjacent to the 3' end of the HDAg coding region. This cleavage event may have a role not only in genome replication, but also in RNA processing, helping to produce a functional mRNA for the translation of the HDAg by facilitating the process of poly(A) addition.

The role of the helper hepadnavirus has been investigated by studying the replication events in primary woodchuck hepatocytes obtained from both woodchuck hepatitis virus (WHV)-infected and uninfected animals. These cells were inoculated with HDV derived from an experimentally infected woodchuck.[12] The primary cultures were able to support both the early events of HDV adsorption and penetration and the intermediate events of genome replication. The release of progeny virions was not, however, demonstrated. At ten to 14 days after infection, significant amounts of both circular genomic and circular antigenomic HDV-specific RNA were detected. The amounts of HDV RNA and the ratio of genomic RNA to antigenomic RNA were comparable to those previously reported in infected cells obtained from experimentally infected chimpanzees and woodchucks. Although the inoculum contained the WHV, the authors have not been able to infect primary hepatocytes with WHV. This observation argues against a helper hepadnavirus role during the intermediate replicative events. To complete the HDV replication cycle, genomic RNA has to be packaged into virions and released from the cell, the step which appears to be dependent on the presence of the helper hepadnavirus to provide the synthesis of the envelope proteins.

In summary, during the past several years there has been considerable evidence supporting the original hypothesis by Hoyer et al[37] that the structure and replication of the HDV genome are analogous to plant viroids, virusoids, and satellite RNAs:[24]

1. The HDV RNA is a closed circular single-stranded molecule of approximately 1700 nucleotides which has the ability to fold on itself by internal base pairing to produce an unbranched rod structure.[11, 34, 42]
2. Within infected hepatocytes there is both genomic and antigenomic RNA, although the antigenomic RNA is found in lower concentration.[11, 12]
3. Most of the genomic and antigenomic RNAs are circular and monomeric; multimeric lengths of genomic and antigenomic RNAs can be found in infected hepatocytes albeit present in small amounts relative to monomeric RNA.[11]
4. Antigenomic RNA can undergo in vitro self-cleavage.[44]

Although the rolling-circle replication strategy for HDV is speculative, the hypothesis remains viable and offers numerous possibilities for further research.

ANIMAL MODELS

Shortly after the initial discovery by Rizzetto et al[1] using IF of the new delta antigen-antibody system, the potential pathogenicity and transmissibility of HDV were confirmed by transmission studies in chimpanzees.[5] These studies have led to our understanding of the natural history of HDV infection. Chimpanzees were inoculated with sera obtained from two carriers of HBsAg who expressed large amounts of intrahepatic HDAg in their livers. These inocula were introduced into HBV-susceptible animals, into HBsAg chronic carrier chimpanzees, and into animals immune to HBV infection. HBV infection and HDV markers did not develop in the animals immune to HBV infection. However, inoculation of sera into animals susceptible to HBV infection resulted in development of hepatitis B and synthesis of HDV markers, causing HBV-HDV coinfection (Figure 29-2A). Similarly, inoculation into HBV carrier chimpanzees resulted in development of biochemical hepatitis during which HDAg and anti-HD were expressed (superinfection, Figure 29-2B).

Experimental HBV-HDV coinfections can result in moderate to severe hepatitis characterized by the simultaneous expression in hepatocytes of the HDAg and HBcAg, and a single episode of elevated liver enzymes. Anti-HD and anti-HBc may appear at approximately the same time and follow parallel courses. Nevertheless, an alternative course of sequential expression in the liver, first HBcAg followed by the HDAg, has been observed, and although found less frequently, the reverse has also been seen. The order of expression of HBV and HDV markers is probably determined by the relative titers of infecting viruses. In the case of sequential expression, a bimodal distribution of abnormal levels of alanine aminotransferase (ALT) in the serum may be observed. The HDAg, however, is not detected until after HBsAg is detected in the serum. In experimental coinfection, anti-HD activity is often transient and is relatively low in titer. Smedile et al demonstrated that the transient anti-HD was primarily of the IgM class.[7]

In chimpanzees with circulating HBsAg at the time of inoculation, HDV infections (superinfection) tended to be more severe, although less often producing clinical symptoms than in humans. Synthesis of HDAg occurred earlier and its extent and duration were greater than in animals previously unexposed to HBV (see Figure 29-2B).[5, 48] In these chronic HBsAg carrier chimpanzees an episode of hepatitis occurred coincident with the synthesis of HDAg in the liver. The synthesis of preexisting HBV products, HBsAg and HBcAg, as well as HBV DNA and viral DNA polymerase, however, were diminished. Bimodal hepatitis has occasionally been observed in superinfected chimpanzees. Superinfections resulted in a quantitatively greater abundance of anti-HD activity in the serum, persisting for longer than the HDAg in liver and perhaps for life.

These studies demonstrated that the HDAg was a marker for a transmissible pathogenic agent that requires the presence of HBV to express its pathogenic potential, and infection with this virus interferes with HBV replication. These studies have also shown that in superinfections the HBsAg on the surface of the HDV virus

is determined by the subtype preexisting in the chronic carrier animal and not by the HBV subtype found in the inoculum.

Successive passage of the HDV in chronic HBsAg carrier chimpanzees resulted in a progressive shortening of the incubation period before the appearance of HDAg and a progressive increase in severity of the associated episode of hepatitis.[48] Initially, none of these experimentally infected chimpanzees appeared to develop chronic infection with HDV, as evidenced by the disappearance of HDAg from the liver and plasma which was paralleled by the appearance of anti-HD in the serum. In contradistinction to early HDV transmission studies in HBsAg chronic carrier chimpanzees, Fields et al demonstrated the reappearance and persistence of HDAg in the hepatocytes coinciding with a second and third abnormal elevation of ALT activity, indicating establishment of a persistent HDV infection.[49] Negro et al, using a sensitive HDV RNA hybridization assay on stored sera, found that greater than 50% of chimpanzees previously superinfected with HDV and presumed to

COINFECTION

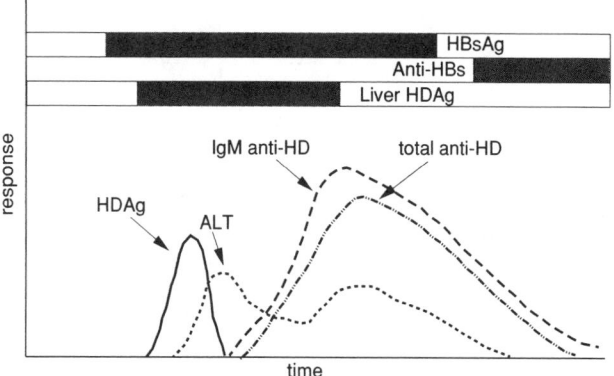

SUPERINFECTION

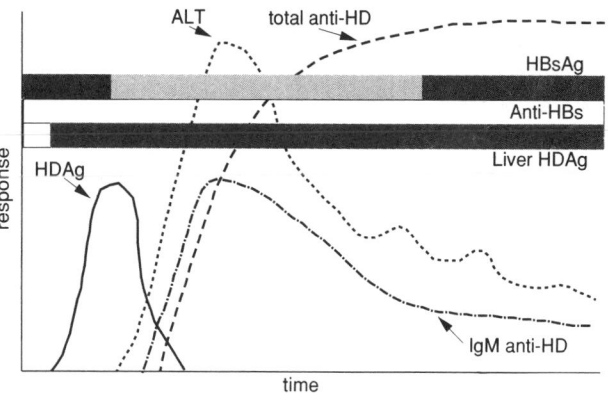

Figure 29-2. A, schematic diagram of serologic course of hepatitis B virus-hepatitis D virus coinfection. **B,** schematic diagram of serologic course of hepatitis D virus superinfection of hepatitis B virus carrier. ALT = serum alanine aminotransferase; anti-HD = antibodies to hepatitis D antigen; HBsAg = hepatitis B surface antigen; Anti-HBs = antibodies to HBsAg; HDAg = hepatitis D antigen; anti-HD = antibodies to HDAg.

have developed acute, self-limited HDV infection, had detectable signs of ongoing HDV replication an average of 2.4 years after inoculation.[50] HDAg remained undetectable in both serum and the liver by both IF and immunoblot assays. Thus, the application of improved methods for detecting the HDV genome in serum resulted in the conclusion that persistent HDV infection is a frequent occurrence in superinfected chimpanzees.

Fields et al have followed this persistent infection for more than 3 years.[49] Hepatocyte abnormalities observed in this chimpanzee by electron microscopy included vacuoles, proliferated endoplasmic reticulum, and tubules[51] similar to those seen in hepatitis C virus (HCV) infection and classified by Pfeifer et al.[52] The tubular and reticular abnormalities coincided with HDAg expression in liver biopsies and abnormal ALT levels in the serum during the first three cycles. However, a fourth ALT elevation was observed during the third year of infection, accompanied by these ultrastructural abnormalities but without HDAg detected in the liver (authors' unpublished observations, 1987). Canese et al reported identical ultrastructural changes in chimpanzees infected with the same inocula.[53]

Several possibilities exist to explain this enigmatic fourth ALT elevation: (1) HCV contamination of the inoculum (which could have occurred during the two previous successive chimpanzee passages or could have been present in the original inoculum; (2) reactivation of HBV infection; (3) reactivation of a quiescent HCV infection; or (4) immune clearance of HDV, which may induce an ALT elevation similar to that often seen following the immune clearance of HBsAg after an HBV infection.

In addition to similar ultrastructural changes, HDV and HCV infections in chimpanzees share another common feature. Shimizu et al established two cloned cell lines of lymphocytes that produce antibodies reactive by IF with liver biopsies obtained from animals infected with HCV.[54] (K. Krawczynski, personal communication). These antibodies have been shown by immunoperoxidase electron microscopy on HCV-infected liver biopsies to bind to structures originally described by Pfeifer et al.[52] More recently, Shimizu et al reported that these antibodies also react with liver biopsy specimens from chimpanzees infected with HDV.[55]

The results of several investigators suggested that both HCV and HDV may induce similar cellular changes independently, or alternatively, the original inoculum used for chimpanzee transmission studies was contaminated with HCV.[49, 51, 53–55] Shimizu reported several lines of evidence which suggested that the HDV inoculum was not contaminated with HCV:[55] (1) ultrastructural changes and antibody reactivity were present in an HDV-infected chimpanzee inoculated with dilutions of sera up to and including the terminal dilution of 10^{-11}, a dilution far exceeding the usual titer of HCV; (2) these features were present in an HDV-infected chimpanzee inoculated with an ultrafiltrate from a 30-nm membrane ultrafilter too small to pass HCV; and (3) these features were present in an HDV-infected chimpanzee inoculated with antihemophilic factor that was heated under conditions that would inactivate HCV but not HDV.[56]

Fields et al[57] (authors' unpublished observations, 1987) used the woodchuck animal model to rescue the HDV from any potential contamination and cotransmission of HCV. Following transmission from a chimpanzee to a woodchuck, HDV was rescued from this animal by inoculation of acute phase woodchuck sera into another chimpanzee acutely infected with HBV. This chimpanzee

demonstrated ultrastructural changes and Shimizu antibody reactivity during HDV-induced disease. Because the woodchuck is susceptible to HDV but not to HCV, these data support the concept that the original inoculum was not contaminated with HCV and that the identical ultrastructural changes and Shimizu antibody reactivity represent similar cellular changes common to both HDV and HCV virus infections.

Available evidence from chimpanzee transmission studies suggests that successful HDV infection depends on an obligatory helper function provided by HBV. Ponzetto et al have shown that the eastern woodchuck (*Marmota monax*) infected with the WHV, a hepadnavirus with similar characteristics and tissue tropism to HBV, can support HDV infection.[22] HDV of human origin from a second chimpanzee passage was inoculated into four woodchucks chronically infected with WHV. The animals developed HDV infection, with serologic patterns similar to those previously observed in humans and in chimpanzees. The HDAg in woodchuck sera circulated as an internal component of a particle similar in size to the human HDV but was encapsulated by the woodchuck hepatitis surface antigen. The HDAg, however, from infected woodchucks had similar biophysical properties to the HDAg from chimpanzee livers. On second passage in woodchucks, a greater expression of HDAg in the liver was observed, and the level of HDAg in circulation was higher than that obtained in the first passage, suggesting successful adaptation of HDV to the helper functions of WHV.

Subsequently, Ponzetto et al have subpassaged HDV in woodchucks through five generations.[58] HDAg in serum remained undetectable until the fourth passage, although HDV RNA became detectable in serum by sensitive hybridization techniques during the first passage. Furthermore, with successive passages, HDV RNA appeared in the sera after shorter incubation periods, from 6 weeks at first passage to 2 weeks at fifth passage. Chronic HDV infection was demonstrated in four of five animals for which a 6-month follow-up was available. The chronic infections resembled chronic HDV infections in humans with HDAg detectable in liver biopsies and HDV RNA detectable in the sera. Electron microscopic examination of woodchuck liver biopsies revealed characteristic electron-dense undulating structures very similar to those described by Pfeifer et al[52] in the liver of chimpanzees infected with HCV and to the features described in acute HDV infection. Using chronic phase chimpanzee sera, Fields et al have also demonstrated that woodchucks were susceptible to HDV infection resulting in the establishment of a persistent infection lasting for greater than 500 days.[57] The inoculum used for this woodchuck transmission experiment was obtained from a first-passage chimpanzee 400 days after inoculation, further demonstrating a persistent HDV viremia in a chimpanzee.

In addition to chimpanzees and woodchucks, the Pekin duck, chronically infected with the duck hepatitis virus (DHV), has been shown to support the replication of HDV.[23] In ten ducks, 2.5 to 6 months old, inoculated with HDV-positive sera, transient HDAg was detected in six animals, appearing 1 to 2 weeks postinoculation. HDV-specific RNA was detected in three of five animals by molecular hybridization. Confirmation of this observation was made by Freiman et al.[59] Because the Pekin duck is easy to house and maintain, it should provide an excellent model to study the biology of HDV.

Animal models will continue to play an important role in con-

Table 29-1
Known Mechanisms of Hepatitis Delta Virus (HDV) Transmission

Exposure Type	Groups at Risk
Direct parenteral	
Contaminated needles	Parenteral drug abusers
Blood product transfusion	Hemophiliacs
	Blood recipients (rare)
Perinatal	Infants born to HBeAg-positive HBV-HDV carrier mothers
Indirect/inapparent parenteral	
Via open skin lesions	Persons living in areas of high HBV-HDV endemicity
Via environmental contamination	Hemodialysis units, butcher shops
Uncertain	Institutionalized mentally handicapped
	Household contacts of HBV-HDV carriers
Sexual	Heterosexual contacts of:
	Acute HBV-HDV infections
	HBV-HDV carriers
	Homosexual men

HBV = hepatitis B virus; HBeAg = hepatitis B e antigen.

tributing to our understanding of HDV infection. While the molecular biology of the virus is rapidly being unraveled, animal models will continue to be required to understand the pathophysiology of infection. Furthermore, animal models can be used to define whether a vaccine composed of recombinant expressed antigen would afford protection for chronic HBV carriers who are at risk of developing severe liver disease as the result of HDV superinfection, and to determine the effect of various antiviral treatment modalities for those individuals who are already chronically infected.

EPIDEMIOLOGY

The epidemiologic features of HDV infection strongly parallel those of HBV, as would be expected from its status as a dependent virus. HDV shares with HBV similar reservoirs of infection and transmission pathways (Table 29–1). Worldwide prevalence of HDV infection tends to parallel that of HBV, being highest in nations or subpopulations with highest HBV prevalence. However, HDV epidemiology differs in several important respects, such as the relative efficiency of the bloodborne and sexual routes of transmission and in its lack of uniform distribution on a regional and local basis throughout the world.

Persons who are susceptible to HDV infection include those susceptible to HBV, and HBV carriers. Numerous studies have shown that persons and chimpanzees immune to HBV due to prior infection are not susceptible to HDV infection.[5, 48, 60] Similarly, persons vaccinated with hepatitis B vaccine and who develop protective levels of antibody against HBV can be presumed protected against HDV infection.

The reservoir of HDV infection includes both persons with acute and chronic or persistent HDV infection. Transmission studies in chimpanzees have demonstrated infectivity of blood from persons with both acute and chronic HDV infection, and that levels

of HDV viremia may vary widely both in an absolute sense and relative to HBV. The initial inoculum, obtained from a human with chronic HDV infection, co-transmitted HBV and HDV in experimentally infected chimpanzees when given undiluted, but transmitted only HBV when diluted to 10^{-8}.[5] After serial passage in HBV carrier chimpanzees, an HDV acute phase serum infectivity titer of 10^{12}/mL was obtained, five orders of magnitude higher than HBV infectivitity for the same inoculum.[48]

Recent studies using sensitive hybridization assays for HDV RNA and immunoblot assays for HDAg have further characterized infectivity patterns. First-generation probes have detected HDV RNA in 61% of cases of acute HDV infection, in 58% of those with chronic HDV liver disease, but in none of HBV carriers with anti-HD without evidence of chronic liver disease. In persons with chronic liver disease, HDV RNA was detected most often in those with CAH (92%) and infrequently in those with inactive cirrhosis.[13] Studies in experimentally infected animals have also shown that about half of chronically infected animals have detectable HDV RNA, at estimated levels of 2.6 to 6×10^7 genomes per milliliter, but also have suggested that highest levels of viremia occur during the acute phase of infection.[50] This is supported by epidemiologic data from an HDV endemic area which show that persons with acute HDV superinfection are at much higher risk of transmitting HDV to household contacts than are persons with chronic HDV infection.[61]

Thus, persons with either acute or active chronic HDV infection evidenced by liver inflammation or HDAg in liver are clearly viremic and should be considered infectious to others. Whether HBV carriers with anti-HD antibodies but without HDV RNA in serum or HDAg in liver are actually HDV carriers potentially infectious to others, or have inactive or healed disease without infectivity, awaits evaluation by more sensitive assays.

The known pathways for HDV transmission are limited to those described for HBV transmission, and include apparent and inapparent exposure to blood or blood-derived body fluids, and sexual contact (see Table 29–1). Bloodborne transmission through direct exposure to contaminated blood products or shared needles is an efficient pathway of transmission, as shown by animal transmission studies and by the high frequency of HDV infection among parenteral drug abusers who share needles and hemophiliacs who receive clotting factors prepared from large donor pools.[5, 19, 62–68] Transmission through single-unit blood transfusion is uncommon due to HBsAg screening of donor blood.[69] Nevertheless, pooled blood products such as factors VIII and IX still pose appreciable risk of HDV transmission despite HBsAg screening of single-donor units.

Transmission of HDV by blood via indirect percutaneous routes is also important. Transmission of HDV among children in developing countries has been associated with high frequencies of open skin lesions due to impetigo, scabies, insect bites, and dermatoses,[9] and transmission in hemodialysis units,[70, 71] and in butcher shops,[72] presumably via environmental contamination, has been observed. Although the environmental stability of HDV has not been directly evaluated, it appears likely the virus can survive for at least short periods in the environment based on these epidemiologic considerations.

Perinatal transmission of HDV from HBV-HDV carrier mothers to infants has been recognized, but is probably of minimal importance. Risk of HDV transmission, like that of HBV, is dependent on the mother's HBeAg status.[73] Only one untreated baby born to an HBeAg-positive HBV and HDV carrier mother has been studied: this infant developed HBV-HDV coinfection and carriage of both viruses. In contrast, among 24 untreated infants born to anti-HBe-positive HBV carrier mothers, only one developed acute HBV-HDV delta coinfection but later seroconverted to anti-HBs-positive. Since most adults with HBV-HDV infection are anti-HBe-positive, the importance of perinatal transmission of HDV appears minimal, in contrast to its central role in HBV transmission.

The transmission of HBV via sexual contact is demonstrated by the high frequency of HDV infection among spouses of HDV carriers,[74] the frequent occurrence of cases of HDV infection among sexual contacts of infected drug abusers during outbreaks of HDV infection,[19, 64, 67] and by reports of cases in homosexual men who deny drug abuse.[75, 76] Sexual transmission, both as coinfection with HBV and as superinfection of HBV carriers, has been observed following both heterosexual and homosexual contact. In homosexual men who deny drug abuse, risk of infection increases with numbers of sexual partners and frequency of rectal intercourse.[75] Nevertheless, data collected in studies of homosexual men suggest that sexual transmission of HDV is less efficient that that of HBV or of blood transmission of HDV. With few exceptions, the prevalence of HDV in homosexual HBV carriers is low (<10%) in contrast to the universally higher frequency (30%–60%) among HBV carrier drug abusers.[62, 77–81] Several investigators have found relatively frequent occurrence of HDV infection in HBV carrier homosexual men in Los Angeles (up to 17%), but have shown that this results primarily from high rates of superinfection of HBV carriers, while rates of HBV-HDV coinfection in this area remain low.[75, 76]

One explanation may be that sexual transmission of both HBV and HDV as coinfections is less efficient than sexual transmission of HDV as a superinfection. Animal studies have shown that the inoculum sufficient to cause superinfection of an HBV carrier is lower than that necessary to cause coinfection.[48] Nevertheless, it appears likely that sexual transmission of HDV in either circumstance is less efficient than is sexual transmission of HBV.

Transmission of HDV by less clearly defined pathways is also likely. Transmission of HDV among HBV carriers in areas of high HBV endemicity is common, even in the absence of obvious exposure to blood. Studies of family contacts of persons with chronic HDV infection in Italy have shown high prevalence of HDV infection among all groups of HBV carrier household contacts, with highest rates in spouses and in siblings, indicating predominantly horizontal transmission.[74] High rates of HDV infection among HBV carriers in some institutions for the developmentally disabled has also recently been recognized.[82, 83] In these settings, inapparent exposure of susceptible persons to HDV-containing inocula must be postulated, and could include transmission via shared objects (toothbrushes or razors), via human bites, or through exposure of open skin lesions to infective material in the environment, routes documented for HBV transmission. Whether body fluids (saliva, semen) other than blood or blood-derived fluids contain HDV virus has not been studied. Semen and vaginal secretions may be presumed infectious based on evidence of sexual transmission, but whether saliva, a possible vehicle for HBV transmission, may also

be a potential vehicle for HDV is unknown. There is no reason to believe that disease transmission pathways that are absent in HBV transmission—fecal-oral, waterborne, or airborne—occur for HDV.

HDV infection occurs worldwide, with frequencies largely determined by HBV endemicity, but with major departures in some areas of high HBV endemicity, and a variable distribution in many other areas. Numerous studies permit creation of a comparative world map of HDV distribution (Figure 29–3).[2, 3, 15, 20, 84, 85] Available data must be compared cautiously as they often deal with small numbers of participants and widely varying study populations. In particular, data on HDV prevalence have been derived from studying asymptomatic HBV carriers, acute hepatitis B cases, or persons with chronic hepatitis or cirrhosis. Because HDV infection augments the severity of acute and chronic HBV hepatitis, HDV prevalence is usually 3 to 10 times higher among persons with chronic hepatitis than among asymptomatic HBV carriers, and in those with fulminant compared to acute hepatitis in the same population. When considering relative frequency of HDV infection in various populations, it is most useful to determine frequency in asymptomatic HBV carriers and in persons with chronic hepatitis B and compare these with frequencies in the same segments of other populations.

Given these considerations, several patterns of HDV infection occur worldwide and can be related to relative HBV endemicity in the population. Patterns of HDV endemicity may be broadly defined as: (1) very low when HDV prevalence is 0% to 2% in asymptomatic HBV carriers and less than 10% in chronic hepatitis B cases; (2) low when HDV prevalence in asymptomatic HBV carriers is 3% to 9% and in chronic hepatitis B or cirrhosis cases is 10% to 25%; (3) moderate when prevalence in asymptomatic HBV carriers is 10% to 19% and in chronic hepatitis B cases 30% to 60%; and (4) high when prevalence in asymptomatic carriers is above 20% and in chronic hepatitis B cases is above 60%.

Worldwide, HDV prevalence tends to be low in regions with low HBV endemicity except in certain HBV risk groups; variably low to moderate in areas with moderate (2%–5% in HBV carriers) HBV endemicity; and highly variable in areas with high HBV (6%–15% in HBV carriers) endemicity (see Fig 29–3). In areas with low HBV endemicity—North America, western and northern Europe, temperate South America, Australia, and New Zealand—HDV prevalence in asymptomatic HBV carriers and in chronic hepatitis cases is uniformly less than 10% and 25%, respectively.[2, 3, 15, 84] In these countries, HDV infection is found most commonly in adults at high risk of HBV, particularly parenteral drug abusers, immigrants from HDV endemic areas, and in hemophiliacs. Cases are less frequently identified in persons from other HBV risk groups such as homosexual men, hemodialysis patients, and in the mentally retarded, although high rates of transmission among the latter two groups have been reported in a few localities. Thus, in these areas, HDV penetration is limited, even though cases have been identified in the United States since the 1960s.[75]

In countries with moderate HBV endemicity, including most countries of southern and eastern Europe, North Africa and the Middle East, the Soviet Union and the Indian subcontinent, and much of Central Ameria and tropical South America, the prevalence of HDV infection is low to moderate.[84–89] For example,

Figure 29–3. Prevalence of hepatitis D virus infection worldwide. See text under Epidemiology for key to prevalence.

within Italy, HDV endemicity is variable, being low in northern and central Italy, but moderate in southern Italy and Sicily.[86] Patterns of transmission in northern Italy closely resemble those of northern Europe, HDV being found most commonly in drug abusers or immigrants from southern Italy, without significant penetration into other HBV risk groups.[87] In southern Italy, however, HDV infection is endemic in the general population, and its presence is not related to drug abuse.[74] In such areas, intrafamilial and sexual transmission are the major sources of infection. Interestingly, prevalence in some parts of eastern Europe appears high, reaching 50% and 90% in chronic hepatitis B cases in the southern Soviet Union, and in Romania, respectively.[17, 90] The prevalence of both HBV and HDV in Romania is the highest reported from Europe.

Prevalence of HDV infection in high HBV endemicity areas would be expected to be high due to the presence of large populations of susceptible HBV carriers; nevertheless, HDV prevalence varies widely within this group. HDV prevalence is highest in the high HBV endemicity regions of northern South America—the western Amazon basin in Brazil, the Santa Marta region of Colombia, and in indigenous Indians in Venezuela.[9, 15, 91, 92] In these areas, HDV prevalence among asymptomatic HBV carriers exceeds 20%, and among chronic hepatitis cases reaches 80% to 90%. Recent studies have established that fulminant hepatitis historically reported in these regions is largely due to HDV superinfection in HBV carriers.[9, 18, 92] Within these regions, HDV transmission occurs primarily among HBV carrier children and young adults, most likely by bloodborne transmission through open skin lesions among children and sexual transmission among adults.[9, 61] Despite the high endemicity, local disease distribution may be variable, being absent in some villages located adjacent to other villages in which all HBV carriers are infected with HDV.

HDV prevalence in sub-Saharan Africa is widely variable, from moderate to high in northern Kenya to virtually absent in persons from southern Africa (South Africa and Zimbabwe).[16, 84, 93–96] Areas with presumed high prevalence also include the Central African Republic, where outbreaks of fulminant HDV hepatitis identical to those in northern South America have been recently described, and Niger.[96, 97] Marked variation in prevalence is evident among different tribal groups within individual countries.[16, 95] For example, in Kenya, among asymptomatic HBV carriers HDV prevalence varies from 1% in the south to 31% in the north, underscoring the variable penetration of HDV into HBV endemic areas.[16]

Finally, HDV prevalence in the Far East is very low among Orientals in all areas studied (China, Indochina, Philippines, Japan), despite the very high rates of HBV carriage.[20, 65, 84, 98, 99] The disease, however, is not entirely absent in any of these countries, and has been found in high frequency in drug abusers in Taiwan, and in hemophiliacs in Japan.[100] HDV prevalence reaches high levels in some Pacific island groups but is absent in others.[15, 20] The high penetration into Pacific island groups makes unlikely the possibility that HDV has been introduced only recently into the Pacific region, and suggests instead that specific factors (behavioral or racial) may have retarded HDV penetration into Oriental populations.

HDV infection in the United States follows the pattern in other low HBV endemicity areas, with low prevalence in the general population but higher risk among drug abusers and in certain other groups. HDV infection is not yet a reportable disease, nor is it included in the International Classification of Diseases (ICD-9) and so disease load cannot be estimated directly. Nevertheless, HDV prevalence in asymptomatic HBV carriers is between 1.4% and 8.0% and the frequency in chronic hepatitis B cases is 20% to 30%.[15, 80, 101–103] Similarly, the prevalence of HDV in uncomplicated acute hepatitis B cases is 1.7% to 8.2%, and in fulminant hepatitis B cases between 16% and 34%.[15, 104] From these data, and current estimates of HBV carrier rates and disease load, it can be estimated that there are 60,000 to 70,000 HDV carriers in the United States, and that up to 850 persons die due to chronic HDV infection (800) or fulminant (50) HDV infection each year. Similarly, among the approximately 26,000 reported cases of acute hepatitis B, 1300 to 1500 have HDV coinfection or superinfection, and the true acute disease load is between 3 to 10 times higher due to underreporting.

The two clearly defined high-risk groups for HDV in the United States include parenteral drug abusers (prevalence 20%–53% in HBV carriers) and hemophiliacs (prevalence 48%–60%).[15, 66, 75, 101] Prevalence has been variable but generally low in homosexual men (0%–13%), hemodialysis patients, and the mentally retarded (0%–30%). HDV is absent among high HBV risk populations such as Alaskan natives and Asians, except Indochinese refugees among whom prevalence is a low 2% to 8%. Pacific islanders under US jurisdiction have variable prevalence (0%–10%) with HDV, reaching 10% prevalence in American Samoa, infection mainly occurring in older adults with little evidence of chronic liver disease.[15]

Although in general, HDV, like HBV, is predominantly an endemically transmitted disease and penetrates only slowly through susceptible populations, outbreaks of HDV hepatitis are being recognized with increasing frequency, particularly among parenteral drug abusers and in areas of high HBV endemicity. Outbreaks among parenteral drug abusers have been reported from several areas of Europe and the United States.[63, 64, 67] Cases predominantly involve HBV-HDV coinfection and often have high case fatality rates (up to 17%). In two areas (Sweden and Australia) the emergence of HDV infection into drug-abusing communities during the 1970s has been observed.[19, 20] Most recently, an outbreak of HBV with some HDV coinfection has been documented among butchers in Australia, presumably linked to blood transfer through contaminated knives and skin wounds acquired during work.[72]

HDV outbreaks in HBV endemic areas were first described among Venezuelan Indians, and shown to result from HDV superinfection of HBV carriers.[9] Such outbreaks produce fulminant hepatitis with distinctive hepatic histopathologic findings, and cause death not only from fulminant or massive necrosis, but also subacute necrosis and rapidly progressive chronic hepatitis.[105, 106] Outbreaks of HDV superinfection have now been reported from several regions of northern South America and the Central African Republic, and are potential hazards in any area with high HBV endemicity.[9, 18, 92, 97] In the United States, one recent study has indicated wide HDV transmission among mentally retarded HBV carriers in a large institution in the United States during the 1950s and 1960s.[83] Disease transmission occurred when facilities for the retarded were overcrowded and understaffed, and was associated with high mortality due to fulminant and chronic hepatitis. Transmission has not been documented since reform of such facilities led to improved living standards. Given its similarity to HBV, other HDV outbreaks resulting from bloodborne or sexual transmission are likely to be identified in the future.

Host Response, Pathogenesis of HDV Infection

Although both HBV-HDV coinfection and HDV superinfection

usually cause clinical acute hepatitis during the initial stages of infection, the long-term outcomes differ markedly, the former almost always ending in resolution of both HBV and HDV infection, while the latter usually leads to persistent HDV infection and ultimately manifestations of chronic liver disease.[5, 107] Because of the ability to cause persistent viral infection, HDV superinfection plays the central role in disease spread and maintenance in the community.

HBV-HDV coinfection occurs following exposure of an HBV-susceptible person or animal to an inoculum containing both viruses. Early stages of infection are rarely observed in humans but have been characterized in chimpanzees.[5, 48] After an incubation period typical for hepatitis B (6 weeks to 6 months), coinfection produces replication of HBV virus, followed by replication of HDV, with synthesis of viral antigens in liver. Onset of liver inflammation, ALT elevations, and symptoms most often coincide with appearance of HDAg in the liver.[2, 3]

Acute hepatitis in humans caused by HBV-HDV coinfection is indistinguishable from other types of viral hepatitis. Between 10% and 20% of cases develop a biphasic course of illness, in which a second peak of ALT elevation may follow the first by 2 to 5 weeks, an uncommon finding in acute hepatitis due to HBV alone or to other viruses.[62, 108, 109] HBV-HDV coinfection only rarely leads to development of the HBV-HDV carrier state. In the largest studies, Moestrup and Caredda and their colleagues found that 2% to 4% of persons with coinfection became HBV carriers.[108, 109] This risk appears to be lower than the 5% to 10% risk of developing the HBV carrier state following acute HBV infection in adults, but is higher than the frequency observed in hospitalized patients with acute HBV infection (0.5%).[110]

HBV-HDV coinfection causes fulminant hepatitis at a rate significantly exceeding that of HBV infection alone. Markers of HDV infection are found 2 to 5 times more frequently among persons with HBV fulminant hepatitis than among persons with uncomplicated acute HBV infection.[8, 104] A recent summary of data worldwide has shown that HBV-HDV coinfection accounts for 3% to 25% of fulminant hepatitis B cases, with the lowest rates in Asia (India, Taiwan), but with high frequencies in Italy, Egypt, and the United States.[111] Reported case fatality rates in large series of cases have varied widely, reaching 17% in one outbreak.[64] During epidemics of HBV and HDV coinfection among drug abusers, Shattock and Lettau and coworkers have shown that fulminant infection, as well as severe illness requiring hospitalization, is more common among HBV-HDV-coinfected persons than in those with HBV infection alone.[63, 64]

The serologic manifestations of HDV in acute HBV-HDV coinfection include variably detectable HDAg during early illness, followed by appearance of antibodies during later stages of illness and convalescence (see Figure 29–2A). HDAg can be detected in a variable proportion (16%–86%) of such patients one to ten days after illness onset, depending on test sensitivity and stage of illness at presentation.[108, 109, 112–114] Antibodies to HDV appear within 1 to 3 weeks of illness onset; IgM anti-HD predominates in coinfection, and IgG antibodies may not always develop.[7] Generally, antibody titers remain modest and drop below detectability several months to several years after infection, leaving no lasting evidence of prior HDV coinfection.

HDV superinfection of an HBV carrier also initially produces an episode of acute hepatitis, followed by establishment of persistent HDV infection and often chronic liver disease.[107, 109, 115] Studies in chimpanzees have shown that the incubation period following exposure of an HBV carrier to an inoculum containing HDV ranges from 2 to 8 weeks.[5, 48] The incubation period in chimpanzees is inversely related to the HDV titer of the inoculum, although HDV titer does not appear to affect disease severity.[116] Because of the established presence of HBV infection, replication of HDV can commence immediately throughout the liver and lead to rapid development of disease.

HDV superinfection produces an episode of acute hepatitis in 50% to 70% of those infected.[108, 117, 118] Infection can occur without acute illness, as evidenced by detection of HDV antibodies in HBV carrier blood donors without prior history of hepatitis.[119] Acute hepatitis produced by HDV superinfection is clinically indistinguishable from other types of acute hepatitis; biphasic illness often seen in coinfection is rarely observed in superinfection.[108, 109]

Fulminant hepatitis is an unusually frequent outcome of HDV superinfection of hepatitis B carriers. In studies of HBV-associated fulminant hepatitis in eight countries worldwide, HDV superinfection accounted for 14% of cases ranging from 0% to 2% in some parts of Europe and Asia to 33% of cases in the Central African Republic.[111] Superinfection of HBV carriers is the primary cause of unusualy severe hepatitis in northern South America, with mortality approaching 20% in outbreaks. In fulminant HDV superinfection in South America and Africa, a characteristic histopathologic picture involving eosinophilic necrosis and microvesicular fatty infiltration forming morula cells has been described and found to differ from that observed in fulminant cases in Europe and North America.[92, 97, 105, 106, 120] The histopathologic picture appears similar to that of toxic hepatitis of pregnancy or due to drugs, with sparse cellular infiltrate, suggesting direct cytotoxicity.[105]

The establishment of persistent HDV infection following superinfection, with the potential consequences of chronic hepatitis and cirrhosis, is the most important feature of differentiating its clinical course from HBV-HDV coinfection. Several investigators have shown that almost all persons who acqure HDV superinfection remain HBV carriers, that most develop high titers of anti-HD antibodies, and that the majority maintain IgM anti-HD, HDV RNA in serum, and continue to express HDAg in the liver, all indicative of continued viral replication.[7, 13, 107, 15, 121] Nevertheless, HDV superinfection may not always lead to persistent HDV infection. HBV carriers with HDV superinfection may lose detectable HBsAg in the serum and develop anti-HBs, during either the acute or chronic phases of HDV infection.[108, 122] This is likely related to the HDV inhibition of HBV replication documented during acute superinfection[5, 123, 124]; however, this event is relatively infrequent (<10% of cases) and may not differ in frequency from the spontaneous clearance of HBsAg in chronic HBV infection. In addition, a few investigators have reported evidence of transient HDV superinfection of HBV carriers, with HDV markers detected only during acute hepatitis, but disappearing during convalescence.[125] Few such cases have been well documented and the existence of a transient HDV superinfection remains controversial.

The outcome of chronic HDV infection has been extensively studied in patients with chronic liver disease, but less frequently among asymptomatic patients and among population-based cohorts of persons unselected for status of chronic liver disease. Almost all data indicate that HDV superinfection changes the course of basically indolent HBV infection to one of progressive chronic active hepatitis not responsive to conventional drug treatment.[10, 125] A cohort study of Venezuelan Indians who acquired chronic HDV infection following the outbreaks in 1979 provides the most striking evidence.[61] In this study, 45% of HBV carriers with HDV infection developed moderate-to-severe chronic liver disease within 2 to 5 years after HDV infection, and only 30% had no evidence of liver inflammation. In contrast, only 4% of HBV carriers without HDV infection had moderately severe disease, and 82% had no evidence of chronic liver disease. In general, seroprevalence studies in populations worldwide show that HDV infection is found 2 to 5 times more frequently in persons with CAH or cirrhosis than in asymptomatic HBV carriers, consistent with this conclusion.[60, 65, 77, 126]

Studies of persons presenting with chronic HBV liver disease almost invariably identify a sizable proportion (20%–80%) to have evidence of HDV infection, depending on the prevalence of HDV in the population. In general, HDV infection is found more frequently in persons with CAH or active cirrhosis than in those with chronic persistent hepatitis (CPH), suggesting greater severity even among patients selected for presence of chronic liver disease.[60, 103, 117, 126, 127] Chronic liver disease patients with HDV infection are usually younger than those with HBV alone, indicating more rapid disease progression.[126]

Long-term follow-up of persons with chronic HBV-HDV hepatitis has generally shown a progressive course of disease unresponsive to anti-inflammatory drugs. Bonino et al have shown that persons with chronic HDV disease usually present 15 to 30 years after an episode of acute hepatitis; histopathologic changes in the first decade are dominated by CAH, but in later decades by inactive cirrhosis.[118] Studies in adults in Italy and the United States and of children in Italy have demonstrated that about 40% of persons presenting with chronic active HDV hepatitis will show progression to cirrhosis within several years, that few show histologic evidence of disease regression, and that about 40% maintain stable, but active disease.[10, 128] Characteristic of HDV infection are relatively severe necroinflammatory changes during the first several years of infection, but which subside in inactive cirrhosis cases.[118, 129] An accelerated course of CAH with necroinflammatory changes and with progression to cirrhosis within 2 years is well described for HDV infection but rare with HBV alone.

The histopathologic findings of chronic HDV infection are not unique, although they show certain characteristic features. Early chronic HDV infection tends to produce greater inflammation than HBV alone or hepatitis C, with a pattern of eosinophilic cellular necrosis, and degeneration without lymphocytic infiltration.[2, 3, 130] HDAg can be detected in cell nuclei in quantities proportional to disease severity; this, combined with the paucity of inflammatory cells, suggests the virus is directly cytotoxic rather than inducing immunologically mediated injury. Ultrastructural changes include electron-dense 20- to 30-nm nuclear granularity (also seen in hepatitis C) but not the cytoplasmic alterations seen in experimental animals.[53] Unusual autoantibodies, including antibodies to microsomal membranes, the based cell layer of the rat forestomach, and thymic epithelial cells, can be detected in 50% of cases but are of uncertain significance.[2, 3, 131]

HDV chronic liver disease does not appear to be responsive to drug treatment (with steroids and/or anti-inflammatory drugs), and in one study children with HDV infection were significantly more likely to have disease progression than those without HDV infection.[10, 128] Several authors have reported no difference in the rate of disease progression in adults with HDV-positive chronic liver disease compared to those without HDV infection. The likely explanation is that persons studied in chronic liver disease clinics tend to have severe and progressive disease, and that within these populations HDV infection per se does not predict disease progression.[117] Rather, the more important effect of HDV infection is the shifting of persons who previously had no or mild liver disease into an active disease status which brings them to the attention of physicians treating chronic liver disease patients.

HDV-infected persons without illness have been identified among HBV carrier blood donors, families of persons with chronic HDV hepatitis, and in general population-based studies.[60, 65, 74, 89, 119] Nevertheless, in one study, a significant proportion (38%) of asymptomatic HBV-HDV carriers had abnormal liver function tests and 16% had occult CAH or cirrhosis or both, findings which were uncommon among HBV carriers without HDV infection.[119]

In several settings, including certain Greek island populations, mentally retarded HDV-HBV carriers in Illinois, and in American Samoa, moderate HDV prevalence with low frequency of chronic liver disease has been observed.[15, 83, 89] In the first two settings, epidemiologic data indicate that outbreaks of HDV superinfection occurred in the past, and persons with evidence of HDV infection now appear to be those with milder disease who survived the severe acute and chronic sequelae of HDV infection.

With the exceptions noted previously, HDV superinfection results in indefinite persistence of high titers of anti-HD antibody. Clinical studies have shown that the titer of total anti-HD antibody only weakly reflects histologic activity of the disease but that the presence of high-titer IgM anti-HD correlates well with activity of chronic disease.[7, 119, 121] IgM anti-HD appears to be a relatively specific indicator of active viral replication, with HDAg detectable in the liver and HDV RNA detectable in serum.[13, 119, 121]

HDV infection has not been directly associated with development of HBV-associated primary hepatocellular carcinoma (PHC). Most studies have failed to find evidence of HDV infection in more than a small percentage of such cases and this prevalence is usually exceeded by HDV prevalence among CAH or active cirrhosis cases in the same population.[93, 98, 117, 126, 132] It has been suggested that because HDV infection leads to more rapid progression of chronic liver disease, infected patients may die of cirrhosis before PHC can develop. Thus, while pathogenic issues must be resolved by future studies, it must be concluded that HDV infection is not necessary for PHC induction by HBV.

Laboratory Detection Methodology

The initial methodology for the detection of HDAg in liver biopsy material evolved from the direct IF staining of liver specimens as used by Rizzetto et al when they discovered the HDAg-anti-HD system.[1] Human sera containing high titer-anti-HD and low-titer anti-HBc were subsequently identified and labeled to study liver biopsy or autopsy tissue from persons with chronic liver disease. Immunoperoxidase (IP) staining techniques for the detection of HDAg in frozen sections and in biopsies embedded in paraffin and araldite were developed by several investigators.[53, 133–135] Both IF and IP staining of liver tissue using standard reference reagents continue to be research tools to identify the presence of chronic HDV infection.

Concurrent with animal transmission studies in chimpanzees, Rizzetto et al developed a solid phase competitive inhibition radioimmunoassay (RIA) specific for anti-HD.[6] The standard anti-HD serum was obtained from an HBsAg carrier with chronic persistent hepatitis whose serum contained a high anti-HD titer by IF and a low anti-HBc titer. The standard HDAg was isolated from the nuclei of liver cells obtained at autopsy from an HBsAg carrier who died of chronic liver disease. This assay was used by Rizzetto et al to elucidate the incidence and significance of anti-HD in HBV infections, as well as to monitor transmission in chimpanzee studies.[5, 60]

Crivelli et al developed a competitive inhibition enzyme immunoassay (EIA) for detection of anti-delta using similar reagents and demonstrated that the sensitivity of EIA was intermediate between that of IF and RIA.[136] Fields et al developed a blocking EIA using purified IgG fractions from two different high-titered anti-HD sera.[49] This improved the specificity of the assay and in comparative sensitivity studies with the RIA and with a commercially available kit (Abbott Laboratories, North Chicago, Ill) this blocking EIA had the highest sensitivity. Recently Puig et al[137] demonstrated equivalent sensitivity and specificity of a blocking EIA for the detection of anti-HD using recombinant expressed HDAg in *Escherichia coli* as compared to the EIA using HDAg derived from infected chimpanzee liver.

An RIA for the detection of IgM antibodies to the HDAg was first developed by Smedile et al using the IgM-capture technique.[7] The assay is based on the selective binding of IgM from test sera to anti–human IgM (μ-chain-specific), and utilized HDAg extracted from the liver of an experimentally infected chimpanzee. The IgM anti-HD assay appears useful in detecting acute HDV infection and in the serologic differentiation of active HDV disease from nonpathogenic or past HDV infection. Dimitrakakis et al used this assay to distinguish between coinfection and superinfection.[112] Transient IgM anti-HD has been observed in patients coinfected with HDV, while prolonged elevated IgM levels are found in HDV carriers with chronic liver disease. Farci et al extended these studies and demonstrated that IgM anti-HD activity persisted in high titers over many years in patients with unremitting or progressive liver disease but declined or disappeared in the patients whose disease improved or resolved.[121]

One of the major limitations to widespread utilization of generic immunoassays for the detection of anti-HD is the requirement of antigen derived from liver material. Shattock and Morgan reported, however, that HDAg derived from serum could be used in place of antigen from liver.[138] These authors reported the development of a sensitive EIA for the detection of HDAg in serum after treatment with polysorbate (Tween) 20 to release the antigen from the HBsAg envelope. This assay appears to be much more sensitive than earlier assays, and can detect HDAg early during the initial week of illness in about 80% of HBV-HDV coinfections. The assay incorporates a dissociating buffer to disrupt immune complexes in serum before addition of the specimen to the assay, and this likely accounts for the higher sensitivity.

Epidemiologic and serologic studies in humans have suggested

Table 29–2
Laboratory Markers of Hepatitis Delta Virus (HDV) Infection

	Blood/ Tissue	Method	Stage of Illness				
			Early Acute	Acute	Convalescent*	Chronic	
						Symptomatic	No Disease
Delta antigen	Serum	RIA,† EIA†	+	±	–	–	–
		Immunoblot	+ +	+	–	+	?
	Liver	IF, IP	+ +	+ +	–	+ +	–
Delta antibody	Serum	RIA, EIA					
IgM			±	+ +	±	+ +	–
IgG			±	+ +	±	+ + +	+ +
Delta RNA	Serum	cDNA or RNA Hybridization	+	+ +	–	+ +	–

RIA = radioimmunoassay; EIA = enzyme immunoassay; IF = immunofluorescence; IP = immunoperoxidase; cDNA = complementary DNA; + = detectable, – = not detectable, ± = may be detectable.
†In HDV–hepatitis B virus coinfection.
*Must treat serum with detergent.

that chronic HDV viremia occurs frequently following superinfections, as evidenced by detection of HDAg in liver and infectivity to others.[5, 10] Despite the apparent improved sensitivity for the detection of HDAg in sera reported by Shattock and Morgan,[138] this assay is not capable of identifying HDAg activity in chronic phase sera. The recent availability of cDNA probes, obtained by reverse transcription of the HDV RNA, provided the basis for a method developed by Smedile et al for the detection of HDV RNA in serum by dot-blot hybridization.[13] Among 22 HBsAg carriers demonstrating intranuclear expression of HDAg in liver biopsies, 80% had detectable levels of serum HDV RNA by dot-blot hybridization assay. Smedile extended these findings by extracting and isolating HDV RNA from 1 mL of serum specimens, using proteinase K, chloroform, and phenol, and subjecting these to both a slot-blot hybridization assay and a northern blot analysis using nick-translated DNA probes from cloned material.[139] This assay detected HDV RNA in 58% of cases of chronic HDV infection, and 61% of cases of acute hepatitis. The majority had full-length viral RNA by northern blot analysis. The sensitivity of the hybridization assay has been improved 100- to 1000-fold by using radiolabeled RNA probes produced by the Riboprobe system (Promega Biotec, Madison, Wisc). A comparison with an immunoblot assay for HDAg demonstrated that the hybridization assay using RNA probes was more sensitive. Rasshofer et al using a spot-hybridization assay and radiolabeled RNA probes demonstrated that the assay could detect 1 pg of cloned cDNA after an exposure period of four days.[140] However, in these studies, not all patients with HDAg in liver tissue were positive for serum HDV RNA. One reason for this discrepancy may be a low level of HDV replication, with secretion of only small amounts of HDV particles into the serum.

Immunoblot assays for the detection of HDAg from acute and chronic phase sera and liver tissue from various human and animal sources have been developed by Bergmann and Gerin[14] and Bonino et al.[28] In the studies of Bergmann and Gerin, liver tissue extracted with guanidine HCl, or serum specimens pelleted by ultracentrifugation through 20% sucrose, were separated by 12% polyacrylamide gel electrophoresis (PAGE), transferred to nitrocellulose, and HDV-specific polypeptides identified by incubation with anti-

HD sera followed by ^{125}I-labeled protein A and autoradiography.[14] The results demonstrated that serum from acutely infected chimpanzees contained HDAg-specific polypeptides which temporally correlated with the detection of HDAg by RIA. Unlike the RIA or EIA for the detection of antigen, the immunoblot assay is unaffected by the presence of cocirculating antibody. As a result, Bergmann and Gerin were able to demonstrate for the first time the detection of HDAg in the serum of carriers of HDV.[14] The assays developed by Bonino et al differ primarily in using immunostaining with peroxidase-labeled anti-IgG.[28]

The research diagnostic laboratory now has excellent assays available for the detection and monitoring of HDV infections. Both the immunoblot assay and the molecular hybridization assay are more sensitive and more useful than either RIA or EIA for the detection of HDAg in sera (Table 29–2). Since these assays are noninvasive they can be used in the research setting to monitor the course of HDV infections and the effects of various treatments without the necessity of obtaining a liver biopsy.

LABORATORY DIAGNOSIS OF CLINICAL DISEASE

Testing for HDV infection should be considered in persons with clinical syndromes of acute and chronic hepatitis, and might be considered, in epidemiologic studies, for HBV carriers without overt disease. Serologic tests for HDV antibodies are the primary clinical tools for diagnosis; tests for total anti-HD are commercially available in many countries; and tests for IgM anti-HDV and HDAg are currently under review in the United States, and are available in Europe. Tests for HDV RNA in serum, HDAg by immunoblot techniques, and HDAg in liver remain tools of research facilities.

Accurate diagnosis of HDV infection in persons with acute hepatitis requires use of serologic tests for HBV (HBsAg and IgM anti-HBc) and HDV (anti-HD, and IgM anti-HD or HDAg if available) (Table 29–3). Acute HBV-HDV coinfection is diagnosed in persons with positive IgM anti-HBc (indicative of acute HBV infection) and a positive marker for HDV. Accurate diagnosis of HDV in this situation requires use of HDAg (during the first week after onset) or IgM anti-HD assays (second or third week after onset); anti-HD detectable by total anti-HD assays may not become positive, or may appear late (2–3 weeks after onset) in such cases. Lack of wide availability of the former tests may result in underdiagnosis in a clinical setting.[112-114]

Acute HDV superinfection is diagnosed by finding HDV markers in a person with acute hepatitis with positive HBsAg but negative IgM anti-HBc (indicative of the HBV carrier state). HDAg may be present in early acute illness, but both the IgM and IgG total anti-HD usually appear rapidly, and the test for total anti-HD usually becomes strongly positive during acute illness. In cases of fulminant hepatitis, HDV markers in serum may be negative despite demonstrable HDAg in liver.

Diagnosis of chronic HDV hepatitis is made in persons with clinical chronic hepatitis who are positive for HBsAg and for anti-HD in serum. Active cases can be distinguished in the presence of active liver inflammation by the presence of IgM anti-HD and HDV RNA in serum and HDAg in liver.[7, 13, 121] Persons with chronic HDV infection but who lack evidence of liver disease or HDV replication in liver or serum may have quiescent or possibly resolved HDV infection.

PREVENTION

Prevention of HDV infection has two focuses: (1) prevention of HBV infection and possible HBV-HDV coinfection in HBV-susceptible persons, and (2) prevention of HDV superinfection in HBV carriers. General measures to prevent HBV transmission, which include sterilization of needles and instruments that penetrate the skin, use of barrier techniques to minimize contact with human blood in a medical setting, and screening of blood for HBsAg, are effective in preventing both HBV and HDV infection.[141] Routine screening of blood donors for HBsAg has made posttransfusion HBV and HDV infection uncommon; this risk has been reduced further by exclusion of anti-HBc-positive blood units as currently recommended to prevent parenterally transmitted non-A, non-B hepatitis.[142] Nevertheless, risk for recipients of pooled plasma products (eg, hemophiliacs) remains.

Plasma-derived and recombinant hepatitis B vaccines, available since 1982, are highly effective in inducing protective antibodies and preventing HBV infection.[141, 143] Vaccination of persons susceptible to HBV should prevent HDV coinfection, and is now the primary tool to prevent this infection worldwide. The development of vaccines by numerous countries should gradually increase availability and decrease vaccine cost, allowing vaccination programs to become routine in developing areas where HBV infection is acquired during childhood.

Prevention of HBV superinfection in HBV carriers is more difficult, as neither passive prophylaxis with immunoglobulins nor vaccines currently exist to prevent infection. Furthermore, it is uncertain whether immunoprophylaxis that induces anti-HD antibodies will protect against infection, since the HDAg is sequestered inside the virus particle. At present, prevention can only be based on awareness of HBV carrier status and counseling on the prevention of possible blood exposures. In low hepatitis B endemicity areas, counseling HBV carriers against parenteral drug abuse may be useful; for hemophiliac HBV carriers avoidance of pooled-donor plasma products would be ideal but may be impractical. In closed institutional settings, such as hemodialysis units or mental institutions, HDV testing of all HBV carriers followed by cohorting of those positive for HDV separately from HDV-negative persons has been proposed.[83] In HBV endemic areas, HDV transmission among HBV carriers has been linked to poor sanitation and frequent open skin lesions; improvement of basic living conditions and prevention or treatment of skin disease may offer the most practical approaches to prevention.[9]

TREATMENT

Treatment of HDV infection remains in investigational stages. Studies in Italy among adults and children with CAH have shown no evidence that HDV infection is responsive to steroids or anti-inflammatory drugs such as azathioprine.[10, 126] Several investigations are now studying the effect of alpha interferon (α-IF) on chronic HDV infection. High doses (5×10^6 units/d) of α-IF appear to suppress HDV replication in 50% or more of such cases, resulting in disappearance of HDAg from liver and HDV RNA from serum, and in a similar proportion, a decrease in ALT levels.[144, 145] Liver biopsies show decrease in hepatocellular necrosis and inflammatory cell infiltrates as well. Unfortunately, cessation of treatment almost always has led to recurrence of liver inflammation and reappearance of HDV RNA after some months. Hence, α-IF appears to suppress HDV replication in many cases, but rarely

Table 29–3
Clinical Diagnosis of Hepatitis Delta Virus (HDV) Infection

| Clinical Illness | Serologic Results | | | | | Interpretation |
| | HBV | | HDV | | | |
	HBsAg	IgM Anti-HBc	HDAg	IgM Anti-HD	Total Anti-HD	
Acute hepatitis	+ or −	+	−	−	−	Acute HBV
	+ or −	+	+ or	+ or	+	HBV-HDV coinfection
	+	−	+ or	+ or	+	HDV superinfection
Chronic hepatitis	+	−	−	−	−	Chronic HBV
	+	−	−	+	+	Chronic HBV-HDV
Asymptomatic	+	−	−	+	+	Occult chronic HBV-HDV
	+	−	−	−	+	Chronic HBV with quiescent HDV

HBV = hepatitis B virus; HBsAg = hepatitis B surface antigen; Anti-HBc = antibodies to hepatitis B core antigen; HDAg = hepatitis delta antigen; Anti-HD = antibodies to HDAg.

causes permanent clearance of viral replication; therefore, sustained treatment appears necessary at this time.

Orthotopic liver transplantation has been attempted in end-stage chronic HDV infection. Because most such cases have low HBV infectivity (anti-HBe-positive), it is hoped that combination of liver transplantation and immunoprophylaxis with hepatitis B vaccine and hepatitis B immune globulin (HBIG) would prevent recurrence of HBV and HDV infection in the new liver.[146] Among seven such patients who survived long enough to be assessed, five had evidence of HBV-HDV reinfection, including one who died of fulminant hepatitis and three who had only limited evidence of reinfection. Two persons have survived without evidence of reinfection. Hence, liver transplantation can be considered in such patients, although the real chance of reinfection must be considered. Attempts to improve prophylactic treatment with antiviral drugs are being considered.

Treatment of fulminant HBV-HDV infection with phosphonoformate (foscarnet), an HBV DNA polymerase inhibitor, is being evaluated in Sweden with promising results.[147] This study has shown survival of three fourths of patients with HBV-HDV coinfection who developed fulminant hepatitis with at least grade II coma; expansion of such studies is under way. Treatment of at least two cases of fulminant HBV-HDV coinfection with orthotopic liver transplantation has been attempted in France, with short-term survival[148]; the available report does not address whether HDV reinfection recurred in these cases. To date, there are no reports dealing with treatment of fulminant HDV superinfection of HBV carriers.

REFERENCES

1. Rizzetto M, Canese MG, Arico S, et al: Immunofluorescence detection of new antigen-antibody system (delta/anti-delta) associated to hepatitis B virus in liver and in serum of HBsAg carriers. *Gut* 1977; 18:997–1003.
2. Bonino F, Smedile A: Delta agent (type D) hepatitis. *Semin Liver Dis* 1986; 6:28–33.
3. Rizzetto M, Ponzetto A, Bonino F, et al: Hepatitis delta virus infection: Clinical and epidemiological aspects, in Zuckerman AJ (ed): *Viral Hepatitis and Liver Disease.* New York, New York, Alan R Liss, 1988, pp 389–394.
4. Wang KS, Choo QL, Weiner AJ, et al: The viroid-like structure of the hepatitis delta genome: synthesis of a viral antigen in recombinant bacteria. *Prog Clin Biol Res* 1987; 234:71–82.
5. Rizzetto M, Canese MG, Gerin JL, et al: Transmission of the hepatitis B virus-associated delta antigen to chimpanzees. *J Infect Dis* 1980; 141:590–602.
6. Rizzetto M, Shih JWK, Gerin JL: The hepatitis B virus-associated delta antigen: isolation from liver, development of solid-phase radioimmunoassays for delta antigen and anti-delta and partial characterization of delta antigen. *J Immunol* 1980; 125:318–324.
7. Smedile A, Lavarini C, Crivelli O, et al: Radioimmunoassay detection of IgM antibodies to the HBV-associated delta antigen: clinical significance in delta infection. *J Med Virol* 1982; 9:131–138.
8. Smedile A, Farci P, Verme G, et al: Influence of delta infection on severity of hepatitis B. *Lancet* 1982; 2:945–947.
9. Hadler SC, Monzon M, Ponzetto A, et al: Delta virus infection and severe hepatitis—An epidemic in the Yucpa Indians of Venezuela. *Ann Intern Med* 1984; 100:339–344.
10. Rizzetto M, Verme G, Recchia S, et al: Chronic hepatitis in carriers of hepatitis B surface antigen, with intrahepatic expression of delta antigen—An active and progressive disease unresponsive

to immunosuppressive treatment. *Ann Intern Med* 1983; 98:437–441.
11. Chen PJ, Kalpana G, Goldberg J, et al: Structure and replication of the genome of the hepatitis delta virus. *Proc Natl Acad Sci USA* 1986; 83:8774–8778.
12. Taylor J, Mason W, Summers J, et al: Replication of human hepatitis delta virus in primary cultures of woodchuck hepatocytes. *J Virol* 1987; 61:2891–2895.
13. Smedile A, Rizzetto M, Denniston K, et al: Type D hepatitis: the clinical significance of hepatitis D virus RNA in serum as detected by a hybridization-based assay. *Hepatology* 1986; 6:1297–1302.
14. Bergmann KF, Gerin JL: Antigens of hepatitis delta virus in the liver and serum of humans and animals. *J Infect Dis* 1986; 154:702–706.
15. Maynard JE, Hadler SC, Fields HA: Delta hepatitis in the Americas: an overview. *Prog Clin Biol Res* 1987; 234:493–505.
16. Greenfield C, Farci P, Osidiana V, et al: Hepatitis delta virus infection in Kenya. Its geographic and tribal distribution. *Am J Epidemiol* 1986; 123:416–423.
17. Tapalaga P, Forzani B, Hele C, et al: HDV Infection in Romania (abstr.). *Prog Clin Biol Res* 1987; 234:425.
18. Buitrago B, Hadler SC, Popper H, et al: Epidemiologic aspects of Santa Marta hepatitis over a 40 year period. *Hepatology* 1986; 6:1292–1296.
19. Hansson BG, Moestrup T, Widell A, et al: Infection with delta agent in Sweden: Introduction of a new hepatitis agent. *J Infect Dis* 1982; 146:472–478.
20. Dimitrakakis M, Crowe S, Gust I: Prevalence of delta infection in the western Pacific region. *J Med Virol* 1986; 18:335–339.
21. Rizzetto M, Hoyer BH, Canese MG, et al: Delta agent: association of delta antigen with hepatitis surface antigen and RNA in serum of delta-infected chimpanzees. *Proc Natl Acad Sci USA* 1980; 77:6124–6128.
22. Ponzetto A, Cote PJ, Popper H, et al: Transmission of the hepatitis B virus-associated delta agent to the eastern woodchuck. *Proc Natl Acad Sci USA* 1984; 81:2208–2212.
23. Ponzetto A, Rapicetta M, Forzani B, et al: Hepatitis delta virus infection in Pekin ducks chronically infected by the duck hepatitis B virus. *Prog Clin Biol Res* 1987; 234:47–49.
24. Riesner D, Gross HJ: Viroids. *Annu Rev Biochem* 1985; 54:531–564.
25. Diener TO: Viroids. *Adv Virus Res* 1983; 28:241–283.
26. Chirgwin JM, Przybyla AE, MacDonald RJ, et al: Isolation of biologically active ribonucleic acid from sources enriched in ribonuclease. *Biochemistry* 1979; 18:5294–5299.
27. Bonino F, Hoyer B, Shih JWK, et al: Delta hepatitis agent: structural and antigenic properties of the delta-associated particle. *Infect Immun* 1984; 43:1000–1005.
28. Bonino F, Heermann KH, Rizzetto M, Gerlich WH: Hepatitis delta virus: protein composition of delta antigen and its hepatitis B virus-derived envelope. *J Virol* 1986; 58:945–950.
29. Alberti A, Pontisso P, Fraiese A, et al: Virus-associated receptor for polymerized human serum albumin and antibody to the receptor in HBV and HDV infection. *Prog Clin Biol Res* 1987; 234:61–70.
30. Roggendorf M, Pahlke C, Bohm B, et al: Characterization of proteins associated with hepatitis delta virus. *J Gen Virol* 1987; 68:2953–2959.
31. Pohl C, Baroudy BM, Bergmann KF, et al: A human monoclonal antibody that recognizes viral polypeptides and in vitro translation products of the genome of the hepatitis D virus. *J Infect Dis* 1987; 156:622–629.
32. Puig J, Anderson LA, and Fields HA: Purification and western blot analysis of the delta hepatitis antigen derived from infected liver, in Robinson W, Koike K, Will H (eds): *Hepadna Viruses.* New York, New York, Alan R Liss, 1987, pp 579–590.
33. Weiner AJ, Choo QL, Wang KS, et al: A single antigenomic open reading frame of the hepatitis delta virus encodes the epitope(s) of both hepatitis delta antigen polypeptides p24 and p27. *J Virol* 1988; 62:594–599.

34. Wang KS, Choo QL, Weiner AJ, et al: Structure, sequence and expression of the hepatitis delta viral genome. *Nature* 1986; 323:508–514.

35. Makino S, Chang MF, Shieh CK, et al: Molecular cloning and sequencing of a human delta virus RNA. *Nature* 1987; 329:343–346.

36. Chang MF, Baker SC, Soe LH, et al: Human hepatitis delta antigen is a nuclear phosphoprotein with RNA-binding activity. *J Virol* 1988; 62:2403–2410.

37. Hoyer B, Bonino F, Ponzetto A, et al: Properties of delta-associated ribonucleic acid. *Prog Clin Biol Res* 1983; 143:91–97.

38. Denniston KJ, Hoyer BH, Smedile A, et al: Cloned fragment of the hepatitis delta virus RNA genome: sequence and diagnostic application. *Science* 1986; 232:873–875.

39. Houghton M: Structure sequence and expression of the hepatitis delta viral genome. *Nature* 1987; 328:456.

40. Kos A, Dijkema R, Arnberg AC, et al: The hepatitis delta virus possesses a circular RNA. *Nature* 1986; 323:558–560.

41. Saldanha JA, Thomas HC, Monjardino JP: Cloning and characterization of a delta virus cDNA sequence derived from a human source. *J Med Virol* 1987; 22:323–331.

42. Kuo MYP, Goldberg J, Coates L, et al: Molecular cloning of hepatitis delta virus RNA from an infected woodchuck liver: sequence, structure, and applications. *J Virol* 1988; 62:1855–1861.

43. Branch AD, Robertson HD: A replication cycle for viroids and other small infectious RNA's. *Science* 1984; 223:450–455.

44. Sharmeen L, Kuo MYP, Dinter-Gottlieb G, et al: Antigenomic RNA of human hepatitis delta virus can undergo self-cleavage. *J Virol* 1988; 62:2674–2679.

45. Forster AJ, Symons RH: Self-cleavage of plus and minus RNAs of a viroid and a structural model for active sites. *Cell* 1987; 49:211–220.

46. Hutchins CJ, Rathjen PD, Forster AJ, et al: Self-cleavage of plus and minus RNA transcripts of avocado sunblotch viroid. *Nucleic Acids Res* 1986; 14:3627–3640.

47. Prody GA, Bakos JT, Buzayan JM, et al: Autolytic processing of dimeric plant virus satellite RNA. *Science* 1986; 231:1577–1580.

48. Purcell RH, Gerin JL, Rizzetto M, et al: Experimental transmission of the delta agent to chimpanzees. *Prog Clin Biol Res* 1983; 143:79—89.

49. Fields HA, Govindarajan S, Margolis HS, et al: Experimental transmission of the delta virus to a hepatitis B chronic carrier chimpanzee with the development of persistent delta carriage. *Am J Pathol* 1986; 122:308–314.

50. Negro F, Bergmann KF, Baroudy BM, et al: Chronic hepatitis D virus (HDV) infection in hepatitis B virus carrier chimpanzees experimentally superinfected with HDV. *J Infect Dis* 1988; 158:151–159.

51. Govindarajan S, Fields HA, Humphrey C, et al: Pathologic and ultrastructural changes of acute and chronic delta hepatitis in an experimentally infected chimpanzee. *Am J Pathol* 1986; 122:315–322.

52. Pfeifer V, Thomssen R, Legler K, et al: Four types of cytoplasmic alterations in hepatocytes of infected chimpanzees: Experimental non-A, non-B hepatitis. *Virchows Arch (Cell Pathol)* 1980; 33:233–243.

53. Canese MG, Rizzetto M, Arico S, et al: An ultrastructural and immunohistochemical study on the delta antigen associated with the hepatitis B virus. *J Pathol* 1979; 128:169–175.

54. Shimizu YK, Oomura M, Abe K, et al: Production of antibody associated with non-A, non-B hepatitis in a chimpanzee lymphoblastoid cell line established by in vitro transformation with Epstein-Barr virus. *Proc Natl Acad Sci USA* 1985; 82:2138–2142.

55. Shimizu YK, Purcell RH, Gerin JL, et al: Relation between non-A, non-B and delta hepatitis: Studies with monoclonal antibodies. *Prog Clin Biol Res* 1987; 234:51–60.

56. Purcell RH, Gerin JL, Popper H, et al; Hepatitis B virus, hepatitis non-A, non-B virus and hepatitis delta virus in lyophilized antihemophilic factor: relative sensitivity to heat. *Hepatology* 1985; 5:1091–1099.

57. Fields HA, Krawczynski K, Humphrey CD, et al: Passage of chimpanzee delta infection from woodchuck to chimpanzee (abstr.). *Prog Clin Biol Res* 1987; 234:113.

58. Ponzetto A, Forzani B, Smedile A, et al: Acute and chronic delta infection in the woodchuck. *Prog Clin Biol Res* 1987; 234:37–46.

59. Frieman J, Williams G, Dimitrakakis M, et al: Transmission of hepatitis delta virus to the Pekin duck, in Zuckerman AJ (ed): *Viral Hepatitis and Liver Disease.* New York, New York, Alan R Liss, 1987, pp 442–443.

60. Rizzetto M, Shih JWK, Gocke DJ, et al: Incidence and significance of antibodies to delta antigen in hepatitis B virus infection. *Lancet* 1979; 2:986–990.

61. Hadler SC, Rivero D, Monzon M: Ongoing studies of delta infection in the Yucpa Indians (abstr.). *Hepatology* 1985; 5:964.

62. Raimondo G, Smedile A, Gallo L, et al: Multicenter study of prevalence of HBV associated delta infection and liver disease in drug addicts. *Lancet* 1982; 1:249–251.

63. Shattock AG, Irwin FM, Morgan BM, et al: Increased severity of acute hepatitis in drug abusers with simultaneously acquired hepatitis B and hepatitis D virus infections. *Br Med J* 1985; 290:1377–1380.

64. Lettau L, McCarthy JG, Smith MH, et al: An outbreak of severe hepatitis due to delta and hepatitis B viruses in parenteral drug abusers and their contacts. *N Engl J Med* 1987; 317:1256–1261.

65. Rizzetto M, Purcell RH, Gerin JL: Epidemiology of HBV-associated delta agent: Geographical distribution of anti-delta and prevalence in polytransfused HBsAg carriers. *Lancet* 1980; 1:1215–1218.

66. Ponzetto A, Seeff L, Buskell-Bales Z, et al: Hepatitis B markers in the United States drug addicts with special emphasis on delta hepatitis virus. *Hepatology* 1984; 4:1111–1115.

67. Caredda F, Rossi E, Monforte AA, et al: An outbreak of delta agent among a group of drug addicts and their contacts. *J Infect Dis* 1984; 149:286–287.

68. Rizzetto M, Morello C, Manucci PM, et al: Delta infection and liver disease in hemophiliac carriers of hepatitis B surface antigen. *J Infect Dis* 1982; 145:18–22.

69. Rosina F, Saracco G, Rizzetto M: Risk of post-transfusion infection with the delta virus: A multicenter study. *N Engl J Med* 1985; 312:1488–1491.

70. Lettau LA, Alfred HJ, Glew RH, et al: Nosocomial transmission of delta hepatitis. *Ann Intern Med* 1986; 104:631–635.

71. Marinucci G, Valeri L, DiGiacomo C, et al: Spread of delta infection in a group of hemodialysis carriers of HBsAg. *Prog Clin Biol Res* 1983; 143:151–154.

72. Mijch AM, Barnes R, Crowe SM, et al: An outbreak of hepatitis B and D in butchers. *Scand J Infect Dis* 1987; 19:179–184.

73. Zanetti RA, Tanzi E, Ferroni P, et al: Vertical transmission of the HBV associated delta agent. *Prog Clin Biol Res* 1983; 143:127–132.

74. Bonino F, Caporaso N, Dentico P, et al: Familiar clustering and spreading of hepatitis delta virus infection. *J Hepatol* 1985; 1:221–226.

75. DeCock KM, Govindarajan S, Chin KP, et al: Delta hepatitis in the Los Angeles area: A report of 126 Cases. *Ann Intern Med* 1986; 105:108–114.

76. Solomon RE, Kaslow RA, Phair JP, et al: Human immunodeficiency virus and hepatitis delta virus in homosexual men. *Ann Intern Med* 1988; 108:51–54.

77. Hoy JF, Hansson BG, Dimitrakakis M, et al: Delta agent in Melbourne. *J Med Virol* 1984; 13:339–345.

78. Jacobson IM, Dienstag JL, Werner BG, et al: Epidemiology and clinical impact of hepatitis D virus (delta) infection. *Hepatology* 1985; 5:188–191.

79. Tedder RS, Briggs M, Howell DR: UK prevalence of delta infection. *Lancet* 1982; 2:764–765.

80. Mushawar IK, Decker RH: Prevalence of delta antigen and anti-delta detected in immunoassays in various HBsAg populations (abstr.), in Vyas GN, Dienstag JL, Hoofnagle JH (eds): *Viral Hepatitis and Liver Disease,* Orlando, Fla, Grune & Stratton, 1984, p 617.

81. Hess G, Lange W, Bienzle U: Delta infection in Germany. *Prog Clin Biol Res* 1987; 234:433–434.

82. Marinucci G, DiGiacomo C, Morganti D, et al: Delta agent diffusion in institutionalized Down's syndrome patients. *Ital J Gastroenterol* 1983; 15:69.

83. Hershow RC, Chomel BB, Graham DR, et al: Hepatitis D virus infection in Illinois State facilities for the developmentally disabled: epidemiology and clinical manifestations. *Ann Intern Med* 1989; 109:779–785.

84. Ponzetto A, Forzani B, Parravicini PP, et al: Epidemiology of hepatitis delta virus infection. *Eur J Epidemiol* 1985; 1:257–263.

85. Purcell RH, Gerin JL: Epidemiology of the delta agent: An introduction. *Prog Clin Biol Res* 1983; 143:113–119.

86. Smedile A, Lavarini C, Farci P, et al: Epidemiologic patterns of infection with the hepatitis B virus associated delta agent in Italy. *Am J Epidemiol* 1983; 117:223–229.

87. Antonori S, Re T, Pastecchia C, Caredda F: Diffusion of HDV in Milan. *Prog Clin Biol Res* 1987; 234:383–384.

88. Toukan AU, Abu-El-Rub OA, Abu-Laban SA, et al: The epidemiology and clinical outcome of hepatitis delta virus infection in Jordan. *Hepatology* 1987; 7:1340–1345.

89. Hadziyannis SJ, Hatzikis A, Papaioannou C, et al: Endemic hepatitis delta virus infection in a Greek community. *Prog Clin Biol Res* 1987; 234:181–202.

90. Ketiladze ES, Vyazov SO, Chernovetsky MA, et al: Delta infection in patients and HBsAg carriers (Russia). *Prog Clin Biol Res* 1987; 234:461–466.

91. Ljunggren KE, Patarroyo ME, Engle R, et al: Viral hepatitis in Colombia: A study of the "hepatitis of the Sierra Nevada de Santa Marta." *Hepatology* 1985; 5:299–304.

92. Bensabath G, Hadler SC, Pereira-Soares MC, et al: Hepatitis delta virus infection and Labrea hepatitis: prevalence and role in fulminant hepatitis in the Amazon basin. *JAMA* 1987; 258:479–483.

93. Kew MC, Dusheiko GM, Hadziyannis SJ, et al: Does delta infection play a part in the pathogenesis of hepatitis B virus related hepatocellular carinoma? *Br Med J* 1984; 228:17–27.

94. Tsega E, Mengesha B, Hansson BG, et al: Hepatitis A, B and delta infection in Ethiopia: A serologic survey with demographic data. *Am J Epidemiol* 1986; 123:344–351.

95. Goudsmit J, van der Waals F, Ponzetto A, et al: Infections with the hepatitis B virus associated delta agent in an isolated West African community. *J Trop Med Hyg* 1984; 87:257–262.

96. Saubiran G, Le Bras M, Marini P, et al: High HBsAg and anti-delta carrier rate among asymptomatic Africans living on the campus of the University of Niamey, Niger. *Trans R Soc Trop Med Hyg* 1987; 81:998–1000.

97. Lesbourdes JL, Trepo C, Ravisse P, et al: Infection with hepatitis delta virus. *N Engl J Med* 1986; 314:517–518.

98. Chen D-S, Lai M-Y, Sung J-L: Delta agent infection in patients with chronic liver diseases and hepatocellular carcinoma—An infrequent finding in Taiwan. *Hepatology* 1984; 4:502–503.

99. Roggendorf M, Mai K, Thian G, et al: Prevalence of hepatitis delta virus in different provinces in China. *Prog Clin Biol Res* 1987; 234:487–491.

100. Lee S-D, Wang J-Y, Wu J-C, et al: Hepatitis B and D virus infection among drug abusers in Taiwan. *J Med Virol* 1986; 20:247–252.

101. Shiels MT, Czaja AJ, Taswell HF, et al: Frequency and significance of delta antibody in acute and chronic hepatitis B: A United States experience. *Gastroenterology* 1985; 89:1230–1234.

102. Nath N, Mushawar IK, Fang CT, et al: Antibodies to delta antigen in asymptomatic hepatitis B surface antigen-reactive blood donors in the United States and their association with other markers of hepatitis B virus. *Am J Epidemiol* 1985; 122:218–225.

103. Govindarajan S, Kanel GC, Peters RG: Prevalence of delta antibody among chronic hepatitis B virus infection patients in the Los Angeles area: Its correlation with liver biopsy diagnosis. *Gastroenterology* 1983; 85:160–162.

104. Govindarajan S, Chin KP, Rededker AG, et al: Fulminant B viral hepatitis: Role of delta agent. *Gastroenterology* 1984; 86:1417–1420.

105. Popper H, Thung SN, Gerber MA, et al: Histopathologic studies of severe delta agent infection in Venezuela Indians. *Hepatology* 1983; 3:906–912.

106. Buitrago B, Popper H, Hadler SC, et al: Specific histologic features of a delta type hepatitis widespread in northern South America. *Hepatology* 1986; 6:1285–1291.

107. Smedile A, Dentico P, Zanetti A, et al: Infection with the delta agent in chronic HBsAg carriers. *Gastroenterology* 1981; 81:992–997.

108. Moestrup T, Hansson GB, Widell A, et al: Clinical aspects of delta infection. *Br Med J* 1983; 286:87–90.

109. Caredda F, Antinori S, Re T, et al: Course and prognosis of acute HDV infection. *Prog Clin Biol Res* 1987; 234:267–276.

110. Tassopoulas NC, Papavangelou GJ, Sjorgren MH, et al: Natural history of acute hepatitis B surface antigen positive hepatitis in Greek adults. *Gastroenterology* 1987; 92:1844–1850.

111. Saracco G, Macaguo S, Rosina F, et al: Serologic markers with fulminant hepatitis in persons positive for hepatitis B surface antigen. A worldwide epidemiologic and clinical survey. *Ann Intern Med* 1988; 108:1380–1383.

112. Dimitrakakis M, Water MJ, Wooton A, et al: Detection of IgM antibodies to delta antigen after coinfection and superinfection with the delta virus. *J Med Virol* 1986; 20:305–311.

113. Buti M, Esteban R, Jardi R, et al: Serological diagnosis of acute D virus (delta) hepatitis: Sensitivity and specificity of HD-Ag determination. *J Med Virol* 1986; 18:81–85.

114. Aragona M, Macagno S, Caredda F, et al: Serological response to the hepatitis delta virus in hepatitis D. *Lancet* 1987; 1:478–480.

115. Farci P, Smedile A, Lavarini C, et al: Delta hepatitis in inapparent carriers of hepatitis B surface antigen. A disease simulating acute hepatitis B progressive to chronicity. *Gastroenterology* 1983; 85:669–673.

116. Ponzetto A, Hoyer BH, Popper H, et al: Titration of the infectivity of hepatitis D virus in chimpanzees. *J Infect Dis* 1987; 155:72–78.

117. Colombo M, Cambieri R, Rumi MG, et al: Long-term delta superinfection in hepatitis B surface antigen carriers and its relationship to the course of chronic hepatitis. *Gastroenterology* 1983; 85:235–239.

118. Bonino F, Negro F, Baldi M, et al: The natural history of chronic delta hepatitis. *Prog Clin Biol Res* 1987; 234:145–152.

119. Arico S, Aragona M, Rizzetto M, et al: Clinical significance of antibody to the hepatitis delta virus in symptomless HBsAg carriers. *Lancet* 1986; 2:356–357.

120. Fonseca JCF, Gayotto LC, Ferreira LC, et al: Labrea hepatitis—Hepatitis B and delta antigen expression in liver tissue: Report of three autopsy cases. *Rev Inst Med Trop Sao Paulo* 1985; 27:224–227.

121. Farci P, Gerin JL, Aragona M, et al: Diagnostic and prognostic significance of the IgM antibody to the hepatitis delta virus. *JAMA* 1986; 255:1443–1446.

122. Frommel D, Allain JR, Courouce AM, et al: Long-lasting abatement of HBsAg synthesis induced by acute delta infection. *Lancet* 1983; 1:656–657.

123. Hadziyannis SJ, Sherman M, Leiberman HM, et al: Liver disease activity and hepatitis B virus replication in chronic delta antigen positive hepatitis B virus carriers. *Hepatology* 1985; 5:544–547.

124. Krogsgaard K, Kryger P, Aldershvile J, et al: Delta infection and suppression of hepatitis B virus replication in chronic HBsAg carriers. *Hepatology* 1987; 7:12–15.

125. Tassopoulos N, Roumeliotou-Karayannis A, Papavangelou G: Acute delta hepatitis and hepatitis B antigen carriage. *Ann Intern Med* 1986; 105:804–805.

126. Craxi A, Raimondo G, Longo G, et al: Delta agent infection in acute hepatitis and chronic HBsAg carriers with and without liver disease. *Gut* 1984; 25:1288–1290.

127. Weller IVD, Karayiannis P, Lok ASF, et al: Significance of

delta-agent infection in chronic hepatitis B virus infection: A study in British carriers. *Gut* 1983; 24:1061–1063.

128. Farci P, Barbera C, Navone C, et al: Infection with the delta agent in children. *Gut* 1985; 26:4–7.

129. Govindarajan S, DeCock KM, Redeker AG: Natural course of delta superinfection in chronic hepatitis B virus infected patients: Histopathologic study with multiple liver biopsies. *Hepatology* 1986; 6:640–644.

130. Verme G, Amoroso P, Lettieri G, et al: A histological study of hepatitis delta virus liver disease. *Hepatology* 1986; 6:1303–1307.

131. Zauli D, Crespi C, Bianchi FB, Pisi E: Preliminary characterization of autoantibodies associated with chronic hepatitis delta virus infections, in Zuckerman AJ (ed): *Viral Hepatitis and Liver Disease*. New York, New York, Alan R Liss, 1988, pp 412–414.

132. Govindarajan S, Hevia F, Peters RL: Prevalence of delta antigen/antibody in B-virus-associated hepatocellular carcinoma. *Cancer* 1984; 15:1692–1694.

133. Stocklin E, Gudat F, Krey G, et al: Delta antigen in hepatitis B: Immunohistology of frozen and paraffin embedded liver biopsies and relation to HBV infection. *Hepatology* 1981; 1:238–242.

134. Recchia S, Rizzi R, Acquarira F, et al: Immunoperoxidase staining of HBV-associated delta antigen in paraffinated liver specimens. *Pathologica* 1981; 73:773–777.

135. Govindarajan S, Lim B, Peters RL: Immunohistochemical localization of the delta antigen associated with hepatitis B virus in liver biopsy sections embedded in araldite. *Histopathology* 1984; 8:63–68.

136. Crivelli O, Rizzetto M, Lavarini C, et al: Enzyme-linked immunosorbent assay for detection of antibody to the hepatitis B surface antigen-associated delta antigen. *J Clin Microbiol* 1981; 14:173–177.

137. Puig J, Fields HA: Development of an enzyme immunoassay using recombinant-expressed antigen to detect hepatitis delta virus antibodies. *J Clin Microbiol* 1989; 27:2222–2225.

138. Shattock AG, Morgan BM: Sensitive enzyme immunoassay for the detection of delta antigen and anti-delta using serum as the delta antigen source. *J Med Virol* 1984; 13:73–82.

139. Smedile A, Baroudy BM, Bergmann KF, et al: Clinical significance of HDV RNA in HDV disease. *Prog Clin Biol Res* 1987; 234:235–241.

140. Rasshofer R, Buti M, Esteban R, et al: Demonstration of hepatitis D virus RNA in patients with chronic hepatitis. *J Infect Dis* 1988; 157:191–195.

141. Centers for Disease Control: Recommendations for protection against viral hepatitis. *MMWR* 1985; 34:313–324, 329–335.

142. Stevens CE, Aach RD, Hollinger FB, et al: Hepatitis B virus antibody in blood donors and the occurrence of non-A, non-B hepatitis in transfusion recipients: an analysis of the Transfusion Transmitted Virus Study. *Ann Intern Med* 1984; 101:733–738.

143. Centers for Disease Control: Update on hepatitis B prevention. *MMWR* 1987; 36:353–365.

144. Hoofnagle JH, Di Biscegle: Therapy of chronic viral hepatitis: Chronic hepatitis D and Non-A, Non-B hepatitis, in Zuckerman AJ (ed): *Viral Hepatitis and Liver Disease*. New York, New York, Alan R Liss, 1988, pp 823–830.

145. Rosina F, Saracco G, Lattore U, et al: Treatment of chronic delta hepatitis with alpha-2 recombinant infection, in Zuckerman AJ (ed): *Viral Hepatitis and Liver Disease*. New York, New York, Alan R Liss, 1988, p 857.

146. Rizzetto M, Macaguo S, Chiaberge E, et al: Liver transplantation in hepatitis delta virus disease. *Lancet* 1987; 2:469–471.

147. Hedin G, Weiland O, Ljunggren K, et al: Treatment with foscarnet of fulminant hepatitis B and fulminant hepatitis B and D coinfection, in Zuckerman AJ (ed): *Viral Hepatitis and Liver Disease*. New York, New York, Alan R Liss, 1988, pp 961–962.

148. Bismuth H, Samuel D, Gugenbheim J, et al: Emergency liver transplantation for fulminant hepatitis. *Ann Intern Med* 1987; 107:337–341.

30

Bloodborne Non-A, Non-B Hepatitis

Stephen M. Feinstone

Non-A, non-B hepatitis (NANBH) was first recognized about 15 years ago although its existence had been suspected by some investigators for several years before it was definitely demonstrated. At this time there are two distinct forms of NANBH recognized. The first resembles hepatitis B (HB) in many respects and has been referred to as parenterally transmitted NANBH, though it most likely is transmitted by ways other than percutaneous exposure to contaminated blood or blood products. The second resembles hepatitis A (HA) and has been referred to as enterically transmitted NANBH, or hepatitis E (HE), and is the subject of Chapter 31. While other viruses such as Epstein-Barr virus (EBV), cytomegalovirus (CMV), and yellow fever virus are known to cause hepatitis, they do so as part of a generalized viral infection of which the hepatitis is only a part and are therefore not considered to be hepatitis viruses.

Recently, the genome of the virus that seems to be responsible for the majority of NANBH has been cloned as complementary DNA (cDNA), sequenced, and partially expressed.[1, 1a, 1b] The virus itself is still not well characterized but appears to be related to the flaviviruses and is now designated hepatitis C virus (HCV). The disease caused by this virus is called hepatitis C (HC). Because there may be other viruses still unrecognized that cause hepatitis and because most of the studies referred to in this chapter were done before HCV was identified and we do not know precisely the contribution of HCV to these studies, the use of NANBH is maintained in this chapter unless there was specific evidence for HC.

HISTORY

The separation of the transmissible forms of hepatitis into the categories infectious hepatitis (type A) and serum hepatitis (type B) was established in the studies conducted during and following World War II.[1c] The elegant series of investigations by Dr Krugman and his associates during the 1960s defined further these two classic forms of the disease and described many of their distinctive characteristics.[2] Although it is curious that NANBH did not reveal itself during Krugman's Willowbrook studies (see Chapters 18 and 28), the universal exposure of the patients to HA virus (HAV) and HB virus (HBV) may have masked the cases of NANBH. It is not surprising therefore that the existence of NANBH was generally not suspected during this era. The development of specific serologic assays first for HB and then for HA caused rapid changes in the epidemiologic concepts of viral hepatitis and ultimately established the existence of NANBH. However, even prior to the discovery of the Australia antigen there were several pieces of epidemiologic data that suggested the existence of more than two forms of viral hepatitis. First, more than two attacks of viral hepatitis had been reported in drug addicts.[3] Second, it was noted in two studies that the incubation period of posttransfusion hepatitis had a unimodal distribution peaking at about 7 weeks.[4, 5] If all transfusion-associated hepatitis (TAH) were type B one would expect a longer incubation period of approximately 6 to 12 weeks. However, if some of these cases were indeed HA where the incubation period was generally thought to be 3 to 4 weeks, one would expect a bimodal distribution of the incubation periods. Therefore, it was unlikely that HAV was a significant cause of posttransfusion hepatitis. In 1974, Prince et al analyzed a group of posttransfusion hepatitis cases that had no serologic relationship to HB and had incubation periods longer than that accepted for HA infections.[6] There was also no serologic evidence for CMV infections in these patients. Thus, it was concluded that some TAH cases were not due to HAV, HBV or CMV, but probably due to some unrecognized agent.

After the development of the immune electron microscopy (IEM) test for HAV and its antibody (anti-HA),[7] Feinstone and colleagues studied a group of 17 posttransfusion hepatitis patients in whom HB had been excluded by highly sensitive serologic tests. No serologic evidence for HAV infections could be found in any of these patients by IEM, nor could their hepatitis be attributed to EBV or CMV.[8] From this and subsequent studies it became clear that HAV was not a common cause of TAH, and that there must be a new infectious agent responsible for non-type B TAH. This type of hepatitis was designated NANBH because it was undefined other than its lack of relatedness to hepatitis type A or B. It was not known what the nature of the agent was or even if there was only one NANBH agent. By applying serologic techniques to eliminate HAV or HBV as the cause of hepatitis, investigators have described much of the epidemiology of NANBH and by use of the chimpanzee infectivity model have partially characterized the virus(es).

After considerable effort by many laboratories around the world during the past 15 years it appears that the NANBH agent has been at least partially identified by means of molecular cloning and expression techniques.[1, 1a] As specific tests for the virus and antibody to the virus are now a reality, much of the previous "knowledge" about NANBH may change. However, many of the concepts developed prior to the specific HC test have been confirmed with the new technology.

DESCRIPTION OF THE AGENT

That NANBH is caused by a transmissible agent has been documented in both human and animal studies. It is known that the disease can be transmitted from person to person by blood transfusion. Human volunteer studies were done in the 1950s in which known icterogenic serum samples from various sources were inoculated into volunteers. These studies were later reevaluated by Hoofnagle et al[9] using new serologic assays. He showed that nine volunteers developed HC after inoculation with one of three sera that did not contain hepatitis B surface antigen (HBsAg). There was no evidence for HAV, HBV, CMV, or EBV infections in any of these patients. In another study serial passage of NANBH was performed inadvertently in a volunteer experiment designed to study the transmission of malaria by blood. Again, retrospective analysis of these volunteers showed that they had NANBH.[10] The hepatitis observed in both of these studies in which human vol-

unteers were inoculated with blood or serum from other humans was typical for NANBH observed in recent prospective studies on TAH. There was a generally mild acute illness but many of the volunteers developed persistently elevated or fluctuating aminotransferase levels.

In 1978 the first reports of successful transmission of NANBH to chimpanzees were published by Alter et al,[11] Tabor et al,[12] and Hollinger et al.[13] These and subsequent experiments by other laboratories using chimpanzees[14–17] and marmosets[18] proved that NANBH is an infectious disease. Infectious inocula have included serum or plasma from patients with either acute or chronic NANBH, and from patients with community-acquired disease as well as transfusion-associated disease. In addition, several plasma products made from large pools of plasma collected from perhaps thousands of donors, including factor VIII concentrate,[14, 18] factor IX concentrate,[16] and fibrinogen[17] have been shown to be infectious. Several strains of NANBH have been serially passaged in chimpanzees.[18] The disease in chimpanzees resembles the human illness but is generally quite mild, and little increase in virulence is associated with chimpanzee passage. Incubation periods usually fall between 4 and 16 weeks. Chronic disease has been observed in chimpanzees and chronic infections have been documented by transmission of the disease by serum obtained from a chimpanzee with the chronic hepatitis to another animal.[19] Liver biopsies from infected chimpanzees have histologic findings consistent with viral hepatitis.[20]

The chimpanzee model has been useful for studying several aspects of the disease and the infectious agent. A detailed pathologic examination on serial chimpanzee biopsies has revealed some distinctive aspects of HC compared to hepatitis A or B.[20] Degeneration of hepatocytes was diffuse throughout the entire lobule and consisted of cytoplasmic clumping, hydropic changes, and fat vacuolization with cell membranes remaining intact. There was prominent portal inflammation during the acute phase. The most distinctive feature observed in these biopsies was an activation of the sinusoidal lining cells but with a very limited lymphocyte reaction. Chimpanzees exhibiting evidence of chronic infection also have histologic changes noted in liver biopsies consistent with mild chronic hepatitis. Pathologic studies in humans have confirmed many of these findings in chimpanzees.[21]

Electron microscopic studies of liver biopsies from experimentally infected chimpanzees have revealed some unusual structures (see Figure 30–1).[15, 22, 23] The endoplasmic reticulum has been observed to be rolled and fused into tubular structures composed of two unit membranes with an electron-dense material between them. These structures were temporally associated with disease and generally disappeared when liver function returned to normal. Essentially identical structures termed undulating membranes or confronting cisternae have now been described in several conditions including in lymphocytes from patients with acquired immunodeficiency syndrome (AIDS).[24] Recent data suggest that these structures are a response to interferon.[25] This may indicate that the NANBH virus is a potent interferon inducer. While such structures have been observed in humans with NANBH, they are not common. They have not been reported in chimpanzees with either HAV or HBV infections, but they are seen in chimpanzees with delta hepatitis.[26] Nuclear particles, originally thought to be

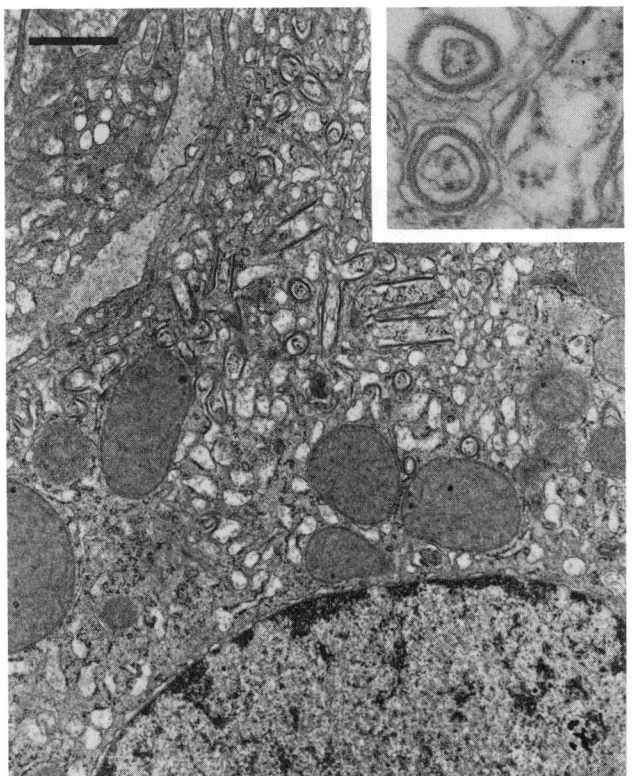

Figure 30–1. Electron micrograph of chimpanzee hepatocyte during acute hepatitis C (HC). The typical cytoplasmic tubules are seen in both cross and longitudinal section. These tubular structures have been called fused membranes, undulating membranes, and confronting cisternae. They are seen in chimpanzee hepatocytes during acute HC and hepatitis D virus infections and have also been observed in lymphocytes from patients with acquired immunodeficiency syndrome. Bar = 100 nm. (Reproduced with permission from Feinstone SM, et al: Non-A, non-B hepatitis in chimpanzees and marmosets. *J Infect Dis* 1981; 144:588–598.)

specific for at least one form of NANBH have now been described in a variety of situations and are clearly not specific for NANBH.[15, 27]

Though chimpanzee inoculation studies have been useful for characterizing the agent(s) of NANBH, the problem of how many viruses are responsible for this disease remains unresolved. Multiple bouts of NANBH have been recognized, especially in drug addicts and multiply transfused patients such as hemophiliacs.[3, 28, 29] It is not known if these multiple attacks are new infections or exacerbations of chronic infections. Cross-challenge studies in chimpanzees have yielded confusing results. Two immunologically distinct agents seem to have been transmitted to chimpanzees.[30–33] These agents provide homologous but not heterologous immunity, and one causes the typical cytoplasmic tubules (see below) in hepatocytes while the other does not, and one is sensitive to extraction with chloroform and the other is not. However, Brotman et al have been able to produce disease in chimpanzees by reinoculating a large dose of the identical material used to produce the initial infection.[34] Therefore, second cases of NANBH may be either reinfection with the original agent, reactivation of a chronic or latent infection, or infection with a serologically and perhaps virologically distinct agent. The issue of

whether more than one type of NANBH virus exists will be quickly settled when the appropriate samples are tested with the new test that seems to be specific for the most common form of NANBH.

In other chimpanzee studies the NANBH agent has been shown to be inactivated by heat[35, 36] and formalin.[35, 37] It appears that the agent causing the most common type of NANBH is sensitive to lipid solvents such as chloroform.[38, 39] This indicates that the virus contains essential lipids as part of its structure and therefore it may be an enveloped virus or have a lipoprotein coat like HBV. There may be a second agent of NANBH that is not sensitive to lipid solvents and therefore would be in a completely distinct viral category.[33]

NANBH infectivity was shown to pass a 220-nm filter by Prince et al in 1978.[39] This observation was extended by Bradley and colleagues who showed that the agent passed an 80-nm filter[40] and by He and colleagues who found that the agent passed a 50- but not a 30-nm filter.[41] These filtration studies have now been shown to be detecting HCV infections.

The picture of a small (<50 nm) lipid-containing agent leaves very few possibilities among the known groups of viruses. These include the hepadnaviruses, the hepatitis D (HD) agent, and the togaviruses. New information from the molecular cloning studies by Houghton and colleagues suggests that the virus is more similar to the flaviviruses or the closely related pestiviruses than any other viral family (M. Houghton, personal communication, June 1988).

The exact nature of the agent(s) of NANBH had been highly controversial over the years since the initial description of the existence of the disease. There have been extensive searches made in many laboratories around the world. Numerous serologic tests have been described, viruslike particles have been reported, viruslike enzymes have been detected, and nucleic acids have been detected and even cloned. While any one of these past reports might have been correct, no test of any sort had been able to reliably detect the virus, any specific viral product, or antibody to any viral antigen. While it is not definitively known at this time how many different agents are responsible for NANBH or if there are different serotypes of these agents, it appears that at least one of the viruses, and probably the most important one, of NANBH is now being characterized by molecular and serologic techniques.

Several reports have suggested a relationship between HBV and the causative agent of NANBH. The NANBH agent could be a variant of HBV expression or perhaps an entirely different hepadnavirus related to HBV in the same way that the duck or woodchuck hepatitis B viruses are related to HBV. This hypothesis had several attractive features. A hepadnavirus etiology for NANBH fits with the limited information on the physical and chemical properties of the virus. In addition, HB and NANBH share some epidemiologic and clinical features (see below). Antigens that cross-react with HBsAg, core (HBcAg), and e (HBeAg) antigens have been reported in patients with putative NANBH.[42–44] Wands and colleagues have developed monoclonal antibodies against HBsAg and used these antibodies to construct radioimmunoassays (RIA) for HBsAg that they claim are more sensitive than conventional RIAs based on polyclonal antibodies.[45] Using this RIA, Wands et al found some patients who had been diagnosed as having NANBH to have HBsAg in their serum, and the disease could be transmitted to chimpanzees which also developed the antigen in their serum.[46, 47]

In addition to the possible serologic relationship between

NANBH and type B hepatitis, there were also reports of a genetic relationship. Both patients believed to have NANBH and chimpanzees experimentally infected with human blood derivatives thought to contain the NANBH agent have been studied for the presence of DNA in either their serum or in liver biopsies that would hybridize with specific HBV DNA probes. Such hybridizable sequences have been detected in both serum and liver, often in association with the antigen detected by the Wands monoclonal antibody.[46–49] It seems possible that some cases of NANBH are actually misdiagnosed HBV infections. In contrast, other laboratories have reported no HBV hybridizable sequences in NANBH specimens.[50, 51] Nonetheless, it may also be possible that some NANBH may be caused by a replication-deficient HBV. Such a virus must be capable of growing only to low titers and expressing little if any excess HBsAg. In addition, the anti-HBc response in these patients and animals must be either limited or the core antigen toward which the antibody is directed must be poorly cross-reactive with the standard HBcAg. The studies of TAH as well as the chimpanzee inoculations that have been performed seem to contradict the relatedness between HBV and common NANBH. In these studies there was no protection in HBV-seropositive patients or chimpanzees against infection by the NANBH agent whether the anti-HB was secondary to an HBV infection or vaccination. HBV-seropositive chimpanzees did not express an antibody booster response following NANBH infection[50, 52] (Feinstone, unpublished observation, 1980). This possible similarity of NANBH to HBV will be resolved by isolation, cloning, and sequencing the genome of the NANBH agent that cross-reacts with HBV.

In 1984 Seto and colleagues reported the detection of reverse transcriptase activity in the serum of patients with NANBH.[53] According to their report, this enzyme activity was associated with a particle that had some of the physical characteristics of a retrovirus. This report was followed by the detection of particles in infected chimpanzee hepatocytes that were said to resemble retroviruses,[54] and the detection and purification of a glycoprotein with a molecular weight of about 77,000.[55] While one report has confirmed the reverse transcriptase reactivity,[53] many laboratories with retrovirus expertise have not been able to reproduce these results.[56] The proof of these findings depends on their utility in identifying patients with NANBH and to this date neither the reverse transcriptase nor the glycoprotein tests have been shown to have such utility.

At the time of this writing, a group of the Chiron Corporation led by Michael Houghton reports that they have been successful in obtaining complementary DNA (cDNA) clones of the NANBH virus RNA genome. They have sequenced these clones and expressed a peptide from one of them that is reactive with antibody in the serum of some patients convalescent from HC and, more importantly, in patients who are chronically infected by the virus either as inapparent carriers or with chronic disease. Therefore this antibody test may be useful for screening blood donors. Characterization of this RNA genome has revealed that it is approximately 10,000 bases in length, plus (message) sense, and has a single open reading frame (M. Houghton, personal communication, October 1988). This finding appears to be the most important yet reported and may finally lead to a fuller understanding of the virus, the disease, and its clinical and epidemiologic characteristics. It would seem that a specific test for diagnostics as well as screening

blood donors is at hand. It must be realized that many of the concepts that will be discussed in the remainder of this chapter may be revised by the application of a specific test. Indeed the very name of this disease will likely be changed by the time this book appears.

EPIDEMIOLOGY

Without specific tests that can identify patients with NANBH or patients who have had NANBH in the past, a complete understanding of the epidemiology of this disease is not possible. Though the disease has been best studied in the posttransfusion setting where the time of exposure is known, the source may be known, and the patient can be followed prospectively, NANBH certainly occurs without prior transfusion, known exposure to blood or blood products, or another known parenteral inoculation of any kind.

The epidemiology of NANBH resembles the epidemiology of HB both as a transfusion-associated disease and also an infection transmitted by apparently nonparenteral exposure. From the transfusion studies it has become clear that a carrier state of NANBH exists and that these carriers frequently have no overt signs of the disease. The carriers undoubtedly are the source of most of the new infections that occur. The question is, however, just how does transmission occur outside the obvious percutaneous exposure to blood or blood products which could not account for the majority of cases of this disease. What body fluids contain the infectious agent? By what routes is the agent infectious? When do patients excrete the virus, or when are they most likely to infect their contacts? Though NANBH has been detected in essentially every epidemiologic situation in which HB has been implicated, it cannot be predicted that its mode of spread in the population is identical to HB. However, the similarities between the epidemiology of HBV and HC virus should aid in developing strategies for control of the disease, and the availability of a specific test will enhance our understanding of the epidemiology.

Besides the transfusion of whole blood, NANBH has been documented following inoculation of plasma or plasma products such as fibrinogen, factor VIII, and factor IX concentrates.[14, 16, 17, 57, 58] NANBH has not been reported following inoculation of albumin or gamma globulin plasma fractions. Plasma products produced from large pools of plasma collected from many individuals are especially dangerous. There have been animal data presented that the agent contained in the factor VIII fraction is different from the agent in factor IX.[59]

As with HB, NANBH has been reported in high frequency in patients in renal dialysis centers,[60] and occasionally in people living in institutions such as those for the mentally ill or mentally handicapped, prisons, and hospitals.[61] In a prospective study by the Transfusion Transmitted Viruses Study (TTVS) group, 2.9% of nontransfused hospitalized patients developed NANBH during a 6-month follow-up compared with 10.2% of transfused patients. This may indicate a low-level nosocomial spread of the disease without blood transfusion.[62] However, the possibility of percutaneous exposure always exists in hospitalized patients or in people living in institutions or prisons.

Other forms of percutaneous exposure have also been documented to transmit NANBH. Illicit intravenous (IV) drug abuse is an important mode of transmission in modern, urban societies.

Such cases have been reported from several cities around the world.[63-69] Mosley et al[28] and Norkrans et al[29] reported multiple episodes of hepatitis in patients from an urban population, some of whom were drug abusers. These multiple episodes generally included cases of HA, HB, and NANBH. A few patients in these studies had more than one episode of acute NANBH. Whether the multiple episodes of NANBH were caused by different agents, reinfection by the same agent, or exacerbation of a chronic but quiescent infection has not been determined.

The transmission of NANBH by sexual contact has not been well studied. There are few reports of secondary cases among family members or sexual contacts of acutely or chronically infected individuals.[70] However, it would seem that the sexual mode of spread may be important for maintaining the large number of chronic carriers in the community. Studies on the relative frequency of NANBH among prostitutes have not been performed, but Szmuness et al followed a group of 1083 male homosexuals in a placebo-controlled, double blind randomized trial of an HB vaccine.[71] During an 18-month follow-up period there were a total of 174 hepatitis events documented. Of these, 122 were HB, 17 were HA, eight were due to CMV, and two were diagnosed as EBV infections. There were 15 cases that were classified as NANBH, ten in vaccinees and five in the placebo group. Although this rate of NANBH was low compared with HB, it is a rather high rate of hepatitis compared to the general population. In addition, NANBH may be underdiagnosed because only clinically apparent cases or cases with elevated liver function tests at the time of a follow-up examination could be diagnosed. In addition, the number of individuals at risk for NANBH in the above study could not be determined without some means of assessing prior exposure. The conclusion is that male homosexual contact is possibly a mechanism for transmission of NANBH.

The possibility of vertical transmission of NANBH was investigated by Tong et al[72] who found that six out of eight infants of mothers who had NANBH in the third trimester of pregnancy developed mild hepatitis, whereas none of three infants whose mothers had NANBH during the second trimester developed hepatitis. From these very preliminary data it cannot be stated with certainty that these infants indeed had NANBH or if they acquired it by intrauterine exposure, at the time of birth or shortly after birth.

As with HB, sporadic community-acquired cases of NANBH occur. These cases have no identifiable source and thus the mode of spread is not understood. Most studies of sporadic hepatitis from various locations in the world have shown that NANBH occurs in this setting. The actual proportion of the total sporadic cases diagnosed as NANBH in various reports ranged between 9% in Athens[73] to 45% in Baltimore.[67] The relative frequency of NANBH cases to HBV or HAV infections probably depends to a large extent on the rate of HA and HB cases in that particular locality. Nevertheless, NANBH accounts for a substantial proportion of sporadic cases of hepatitis in every geographic area in which it has been studied to date.[64-69,74-79] It should be recognized that the vast majority of NANBH cases must occur without overt exposure to blood. It has been estimated that 1% to 7% of blood donors are carriers of the NANBH virus. Very few of these donors have ever had a blood transfusion or other parenteral exposure to blood or blood products. These patients must have acquired their infections

by other mechanisms—most likely close personal contact in much the same way as HB is acquired. It has been speculated that sporadic community-acquired NANBH is a different disease than the TAH, that this form of the disease does not progress to chronic hepatitis, and it probably is caused by the agent responsible for the enterically transmitted NANBH. However, in an ongoing study of viral hepatitis in four sentinal counties being conducted by the Centers for Disease Control (CDC), Alter et al[80] reported that among 131 patients diagnosed as having NANBH, 43% had a history of exposure, including 20% transfused and 23% with IV drug use. Of the remainder, 3% were health care workers and 2% household contacts of patients with NANBH. Persistently elevated liver enzymes were observed in 66 (50%) of the 131 patients. There was no significant difference in the proportion of patients with chronic hepatitis among patients with a known exposure to blood compared with patients who had only a known contact with patients with NANBH and patients who had no known exposure of any kind. Based on these results there is no reason to suspect that the hepatitis with these two different modes of transmission was caused by different agents.[80] These results have now been specifically confirmed by the new serologic assay for HCV infection. Alter has found that about 90% of patients with community acquired NANBH seroconvert to antibody to the HCV related antigen within 6 months of the onset of their disease.[80a]

As with HB there has been a slight male preponderance of NANBH cases. The age of acquisition of NANBH outside the transfusion setting also seems to resemble HB in that young adults are the most likely to acquire this disease. This may reflect illicit drug use or sexual exposure to multiple partners in this age group. Comparison studies on the prevalence on NANBH in specific population groups such as socioeconomic class have not been done. However, from studies of TAH, again it appears that populations likely to have a high frequency of HB exposure and therefore high carrier rates are also more likely to be transmitters of NANBH. Several studies have pointed out the relative high risk of NANBH carriers among commercial blood donors compared to volunteer donors.[81-83] Goldfield et al[83] showed that there was a reduction in overt hepatitis cases from 28.4 cases per 1000 transfusion episodes with all commercial blood to 13.2 per 1000 transfusion episodes with mixed commercial and volunteer blood to 2.0 cases per 1000 transfusion episodes with all volunteer blood when all blood were prescreened by RIA for HBsAg. These studies also showed that there was an increased hepatitis risk from blood donated by military "volunteers" compared to community volunteer donors. This presumably reflects the lower socioeconomic level of the military population compared to the community volunteer donors. Thus, the hepatitis risk of blood is dependent more on the actual population from which the blood is obtained than on whether or not the blood donors were paid. A similar observation was reported in the TTVS, which was a multicenter study. One hospital that used all volunteer blood had a very high rate of posttransfusion hepatitis. This hospital drew its blood donor volunteers from a predominantly low socioeconomic group living in the area surrounding the hospital. Thus, as with type B hepatitis, lower socioeconomic groups seem to be at a higher risk for infection by NANBH and subsequently are more likely to be carriers than the rest of the population.

The carrier rate of NANBH in blood donors can be estimated

from the large studies of posttransfusion hepatitis. In the TTVS[62] the overall rate of hepatitis was 10% and ranged from a low of 4% at the St Louis center to a high of 18% in Houston. Since the average number of blood units transfused per patient in St Louis was 4.2, it could be crudely estimated that approximately 1% of the blood units in that locality were contaminated. However, in Houston, where the blood donor population was from a lower socioeconomic group, the rate of hepatitis was 18% with a mean of 2.4 units of blood transfused per patient. In this group it could be estimated that perhaps as many as 7.5% of the donors were carriers of NANBH. In the TTVS 19 of 275 patients who received a single-unit transfusion developed NANBH. This would indicate an overall carrier rate of at least 6.9%, although a disproportionately high number of these hepatitis cases came from the Houston center where the blood donors were probably not representative of the general population. The attack rate for recipients of a single unit of blood ranged from 1.0% at the St Louis center to 11.5% at the Houston center. In the Veterans Administration cooperative study,[82] single unit transfusions resulted in NANBH in approximately 1.0% of the recipients of volunteer blood and in about 5.4% of recipients of commercial blood. If more than 1% of American volunteer blood donors are carriers of NANBH, it is an astoundingly high figure and is at least 10 times greater than the rate of HB carriage in the same population. Application of the specific test for HCV infection has revealed that about 0.25% to 1% of normal blood donors in the United States and western Europe are positive in this test. In Spain the overall prevalence in healthy subjects without risk factors was 1.2%, while in West Germany it was 0.42%. High risk groups studied in Spain showed that 85% of prospectively followed patients with post-transfusion NANBH and 62% of patients with chronic liver disease and a history of transfusion were antibody positive. In other high risk groups the seropositivity rate was 70% of hemophiliacs, 70% of intravenous drug abusers, 20% of patients on chronic dialysis, 8% of homosexual men who were also HIV positive, and 42% of patients with

chronic hepatitis, including cryptogenic, alcoholic, and biliary cirrhosis and autoimmune hepatitis.[83a, 83b, 83c]

In summary, the epidemiologic patterns of NANBH follow those of HB in a general way. The exact mode of transmission without apparent percutaneous exposure is not known but it must be assumed that this nonapparent parenteral exposure accounts for most infections and the high carrier rate in the general population. The carrier rate of NANBH as estimated from studies of posttransfusion hepatitis is very high, ranging from approximately 0.25% to 1% in volunteer blood donors to more than 10% in donors from certain lower socioeconomic groups. Hepatitis occurring in a transfusion setting today is predominantly type C. Sporadic community-acquired hepatitis may be due to any of the types of viral hepatitis. Epidemic hepatitis in developed countries is usually due to type A hepatitis but there may occasionally be small outbreaks of hepatitis that are due to HBV or NANBH virus infections, and type B or NANBH cases may be intermingled with the HA cases of an epidemic and these cases often are not correctly diagnosed. In addition, the second form of NANBH termed enterically transmitted NANBH, or hepatitis E (HE) (see Chapter 31), is perhaps the most important cause of sporadic and epidemic hepatitis in certain parts of the world.

CLINICAL FEATURES

There are no clinical features of NANBH that can distinguish any individual case from type A or B or other hepatitis. Each clinical form of viral hepatitis that occurs with HBV also occurs with NANBH. Typical acute disease with apparent complete recovery, acute fulminant hepatitis,[84, 85] relapsing hepatitis with intervening periods of normal liver function, chronic infection without apparent illness, and chronic infection with active liver disease and cirrhosis have all been documented. The two most typical characteristics of this disease are relapsing hepatitis and chronic hepatitis (Figure 30–2). Patients are frequently encountered who

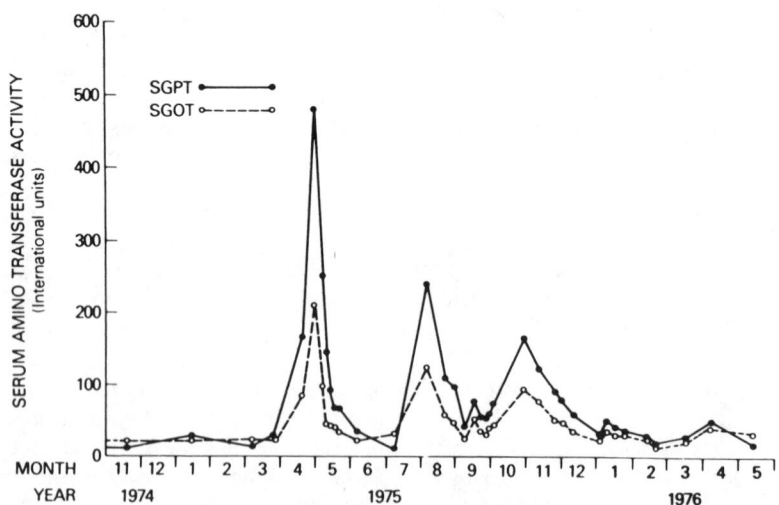

Figure 30–2. Clinical course of a patient with hepatitis C (HC) depicting a relapsing pattern of hepatitis with three distinct periods of aspartate (AST, SGOT) and alanine (ALT, SGPT) aminotransferase elevations. This pattern is often seen in patients with HC. (Reproduced with permission from Feinstone SM, Purcell RH: Non-A, non-B hepatitis. *Ann Rev Med* 1978; 29:359–366.)

have a typical acute hepatitis syndrome with resolution only to be followed by one or more episodes of recurrent illness. This pattern may or may not be associated with eventual chronic illness. A large proportion of NANBH cases develop chronic hepatitis, which can range from mild disease to severe chronic active hepatitis (CAH) and may lead to cirrhosis.[86-89]

Acute Hepatitis

In transfusion-associated NANBH the peak alanine aminotransferase (ALT) levels typically average about 600 IU/L. Only about a quarter of these patients are icteric, and other signs and symptoms of acute viral hepatitis are less prominent in NANBH compared with HB.[88]

While NANBH is generally thought to be a relatively mild acute disease, fulminant cases have been reported. Among 20 fulminant hepatitis cases studied by Mathiesen et al,[85] four were classified as HA, nine as HB, one as mixed HA and HB, and six as NANBH. In another study, the Acute Hepatic Failure Study Group reported that 64 of 188 cases of fulminant hepatitis were thought to be NANBH and that only 13% of these patients survived.[84] Without specific tests it is not possible to know if these cases were due to the same agent(s) that causes the less severe acute and chronic forms of the disease or even if they had an infectious etiology. In chimpanzee transmission studies at the National Institutes of Health (NIH)[18] plasma from two cases of fulminant NANBH failed to transmit disease to recipient chimpanzees while plasma from patients with acute and chronic community-acquired and TAH successfully transmitted disease to chimpanzees. It is possible that the titer of virus drops during the terminal stages of fulminant hepatitis because the liver cannot support the replication of the virus. However, a proven transmissible agent was not demonstrated in these cases of fulminant NANBH.

Relapsing Hepatitis

When patients with acute NANBH are followed carefully, they may seem to recover only to relapse either clinically or biochemically (see Fig 30–2). This relapsing nature of the disease is one of its most typical features and occurs much less frequently in HB. Rarely, single relapses have been reported to occur shortly after acute HA.[90] Whether these relapses represent exacerbations of chronic infections, reappearance of latent infections or, less likely, reinfection with the same or different NANBH virus, is not known at this time.

In posttransfusion studies the reported rate of NANBH cases that had elevated enzymes for more than 6 months varied between 10% and 70% as reviewed by Dienstag.[91] In 75 carefully followed patients at the NIH, Alter and colleagues found that 51 (68%) had ALT elevations persisting for more than 1 year after transfusion.[92, 93] A recent report of 676 consecutive transfused patients done in Milan, Italy in which blood donors with elevated ALT levels were excluded, 96 patients developed hepatitis and 92 were diagnosed as type NANBH.[94] Even though the hepatitis was completely asymptomatic in 68 of these patients, 60% had elevated ALT levels 1 year after the onset of the acute disease.

Long-term prospective follow-up studies have not been performed so the natural history of chronic NANBH is not completely known. A number of patients have been biopsied to determine the nature of their chronic liver disease.[91] The important finding of these studies is that all ranges of histologic lesions of chronic hepatitis have been observed, from chronic persistent hepatitis (CPH) to CAH to cirrhosis with and without portal hypertension. Though patients who were biopsied in these studies probably represented the more severe end of the spectrum of the chronic patients, the severity of their lesions could not be predicted on clinical findings.

Di Bisceglie et al biopsied 50 patients who were referred to NIH for a treatment trial.[95] The duration of hepatitis in these patients ranged between 6 months and 20 years with a mean of 3.9 years. Twelve patients (24%) had cirrhosis and most of these patients had their disease for several years. Three patients developed cirrhosis with clinical signs of portal hypertension within 12 months of the onset of their disease following blood transfusion. These three were 58, 63, and 68 years old while the mean age of the group was 43 and the mean age of all the 12 patients with cirrhosis was 49.8. Thus serious chronic liver disease is a common finding in NANBH and cirrhosis seems to correlate with the duration of the infection and the age of the patient. Older patients are perhaps more likely to experience the rapid onset of cirrhosis.

The rate of chronic liver disease following sporadic NANBH has been reported to be between 0% and 20% in different studies.[80, 89] It has been suggested that the rate of chronic disease following community-acquired NANBH is lower than the rate following transfusion. However, Alter and colleagues have found no difference in the chronic disease rate in patients with NANBH acquired from parenteral exposure to blood compared with patients who had no known exposure when these patients were carefully evaluated.[80] It seems likely that most chronic carriers of NANBH acquired their infections from the community, not from blood transfusion, and that it is these carriers who are responsible for the posttransfusion HC, and therefore the sporadic community-acquired cases are likely to be caused by the same agent(s) responsible for the posttransfusion cases.

NANBH in hemophiliacs after administration of factor VIII concentrate has been reported to occur in some patients following very short incubation periods, but in other patients after incubation periods within the range reported for posttransfusion hepatitis. Six hemophiliacs in England developed NANBH following treatment with one batch of factor VIII. The incubation periods were ten days in one patient and between 21 and 28 days in the other five.[60] Six hemophiliacs with nine episodes of NANBH were reported in the United States.[61] Eight of the nine episodes occurred with incubation periods of ten days or less, and the other was 19 days. These patients all had a similar history of not having received blood products for more than 1 year prior to the factor VIII that preceded the episode of hepatitis. Although four of the nine bouts of hepatitis seemed to be recurrent episodes, all the patients recovered without evidence of chronic disease.

Factor VIII has been used to experimentally infect chimpanzees[14, 18] with NANBH and it seems that many (if not all) lots of commercial factor VIII concentrate are contaminated. The disease reported in chimpanzees was not distinctive in any way compared with the HC transmitted to chimpanzees by plasma from patients with posttransfusion hepatitis. In addition, the reported studies of posttransfusion hepatitis have included many patients with incubation periods of less than 1 month. Patients with a hepatitislike illness prior to 2 weeks after transfusion have usually been excluded from the posttransfusion studies. Thus it is not known if these cases of short-incubation-period HC following administration of factor VIII concentrate are due to a different agent, a high-dose inoculum, or an unusual host response to the infectious agent. It is hard to imagine, however, that there could be an agent present in the factor VIII concentrate that is not present in the whole plasma.

Extrahepatic Manifestations

It is not known if the NANBH virus replicates outside the liver but there is little evidence of extrahepatic pathologic changes. Cases of agranulocytosis and aplastic anemia with hepatitis have often been classified as NANBH,[96] but other than the rare occurrence of prodromal arthritis, the extrahepatic manifestations frequently seen in HBV infections have not been reported in NANBH.

Hepatocellular Carcinoma

The relationship of chronic HBV to hepatocellular carcinoma (HCC) is well established,[97] though the mechanism of oncogenesis is not understood. Since NANBH may lead to chronic liver disease, including cirrhosis, it is possible that NANBH is an important cause of HCC not related to HBV infections. Kiyosawa et al reported a case of HCC that developed in a man 18 years after he contracted NANBH from a blood transfusion.[98] During this 18-year-period he had five liver biopsies and his course from acute to chronic hepatitis to cirrhosis and finally to HCC was well documented. Okuda et al[99] performed a retrospective analysis of 113 patients with nonalcohol-related chronic liver disease and HCC. Twenty-three of these patients had no HBV markers and were therefore diagnosed as NANBH while 35 were HBsAg-positive and 55 had serologic evidence of past HBV infections. Okuda et al speculated that NANBH virus infections may have played an important role either directly or indirectly through the induction of cirrhosis, not only in the 23 NANBH patients but also in at least a portion of the 55 patients with serologic evidence of past HBV infections.[99] The exact importance of NANBH in HCC awaits the availability of specific tests.

Several recent reports have established a strong association between chronic HCV infection and HCC. In Spain 72 out of 96 patients (75%), in Italy 86 out of 132 (65%), in South Africa 110 out of 380 (29%), and in Japan 138 out of 253 (54.5%) were positive for anti-HCV. While HBV was also common in these patients, 44.5% in Spain, 16% in Italy, 7 % in South Africa, and 43% in Japan had anti-HCV without evidence of present or past infections with HBV.[99a–99d]

IMMUNE RESPONSE

There is presently very little known about the immune response in HC because a serologic test has only recently become available and is not yet widely distributed. It has been revealed that this test detects antibody in the serum of patients in the late acute, convalescent, and chronic stages of HC. It is not known at this time if this test detects an antibody that is directed against a major antigen of the virus, the importance of this antibody in the immune response, or how many other antigens are expressed by this virus.

Once the whole virus is isolated in quantity these questions can be answered.

Dienstag et al[100] reported finding immune complexes in the sera of 13 out of 22 patients with transfusion-associated NANBH, including six out of 12 with acute and seven out of 19 with chronic disease. In addition, one out of two chimpanzees that had been experimentally infected demonstrated immune complex formation during the acute illness. It has not been shown that these complexes consist of the infectious agent or an antigenic component of that agent and its antibody.

There have been reinoculation studies in chimpanzees that seem to show protection from rechallenge.[30–32] However, successful in vitro neutralization experiments have not been reported. In addition, Brotman et al[34] has been able to induce disease in chimpanzees by reinoculating a large dose of the same inoculum that was used in the initial infection. If the chimpanzees that were reinoculated did not have an antibody response but were in fact chronically infected without apparent illness, it is likely that rechallenge experiments would give results simulating protection from antibody, and reinfections may be superinfections or exacerbations of chronic infections. Application of specific assays for HCV infection should define if protective antibodies exist.

There have been reports indicating that administration of immune serum globulin prior to transfusion may have at least a modifying effect on transfusion-associated NANBH illness. Reduction in either icteric or chronic disease has been reported in transfused patients who received immune serum globulin prophylaxis,[82, 87] which may indicate the presence of antibody in these pooled immune globulin preparations. However, no study has yet demonstrated that administration of immune serum globulin can prevent either infection or illness.

Many of the serologic tests that have been proposed or published for NANBH have been shown to be nonspecific and may represent a variety of reactants such as rheumatoidlike factors[101] or other autoimmune responses that seem to occur with a high frequency in NANBH. The role that these nonspecific reactants play in NANBH is not clear.

LABORATORY DIAGNOSIS OF INFECTIONS

Numerous serologic tests have been described in the past to detect antigens and antibodies associated with NANBH. None of these tests have proved useful for diagnosing patients with the disease or for screening blood donors who may be asymptomatic carriers. Essentially all of these tests are nonspecific and will not be discussed further. The recent announcement of the cloning of specific viral cDNA sequences and the expression of a peptide antigen recognized by antibody in the serum patients in late acute, chronic, or early convalescent stages of HC may quickly lead to the availability of specific diagnostic tests. This approach has solved the major difficulty in developing a serologic assay for HC, which was insufficient antigen to be detected in any known antigen-antibody reaction. The availability of cloned cDNA and genomic sequence data will also permit the detection of viral nucleic acid with a high degree of sensitivity using hybridization or amplification techniques.

At the present the diagnosis of HC is still based on the clinical and epidemiologic situation and the exclusion of other forms of viral hepatitis by serologic testing (see Chapters 18 and 28). It should be remembered that CMV has been implicated in TAH, and that hepatitis is a frequent occurrance in EBV infections. It is important to exclude these two viruses as well as nonviral causes of hepatitis, if the clinical situation warrants, before a presumptive diagnosis of NANBH can be made. It has been difficult to prove that CMV is responsible for posttransfusion hepatitis even though it was well known to be transmitted through blood transfusion. It could be shown that a seroresponse to CMV occurred in approximately the same percentage of transfusion recipients who did not develop hepatitis compared with those who did develop hepatitis.[81] A careful analysis by Alter et al[92] of posttransfusion cases at NIH where very few HB infections still occur revealed that 15% were probably caused by CMV as judged by a sensitive indirect hemagglutination assay for anti-CMV. These CMV patients seemed to form a subset of the NANBH cases in that they generally had short incubation periods, and they were all nonicteric with low maximum ALT levels, averaging 177 IU/L compared with 655 IU/L for the other HC cases. None of the CMV cases showed evidence of chronic disease. Though it seems established that CMV can cause TAH, this infection is a less serious health threat compared with type B and HC because of the mild and transient nature of the disease.

At this time HE is very rare in the United States and western Europe, but imported cases have been reported and it seems likely that this disease will begin to appear in the developed world. Diagnostic tests suitable only for the research laboratory have been developed. Routine diagnostic tests may eventually be available if the epidemiology of this disease changes so that it is important to test for it in this country (see Chapter 31).

Surrogate tests, serum ALT levels, and anti-HBc are now being used in an attempt to screen out high-risk blood donors (see below). These tests seem to have value in reducing the rate of TAH, but they cannot be considered diagnostic tests for individual patients, epidemiologic studies, and even research applications.

Histopathologic changes characteristic of NANBH have been described that may aid in the diagnosis in patients with chronic liver disease but not in acute hepatitis, because liver biopsy is rarely performed on these patients in the United States. Two typical lesions have been observed by light microscopy in liver biopsies from patients with either acute or chronic HC.[21, 102] First was an eosinophilic alteration of hepatocytes associated with a large number of acidophilic bodies. Second was an activation of the sinusoidal lining cells. Portal and periportal inflammation was observed but was mild relative to the degree of parenchymal reaction. The lesions were similar in both the acute and chronic cases though changes of chronic hepatitis, including cirrhosis, have been observed.

In chimpanzees with acute and chronic HC a characteristic electron microscopic change has been regularly observed (see Fig 30–1). Cytoplasmic tubules (cylindrical confronting cisternae) consisting of double-unit membranes presumably formed from rolled and fused rough endoplasmic reticulum are seen in correlation with the disease state.[103, 104] These structures have also been seen in human biopsies[105] but at a much lower frequency than in chimpanzees where they can be seen in almost every hepatocyte during active disease. Precisely the same structures have been observed in chimpanzees with HD (coexisting with HBV infection) but not

in HAV- or HBV-infected chimpanzees.[103, 106] In addition, similar structures have been observed in lymphocytes from patients with AIDS.[107] The exact nature of these structures and what role they have in the replication of the NANBH virus is not known, but recent data suggest that these structures are a response to interferon.[25]

Shimizu and colleagues have developed monoclonal antibodies from EBV-immortalized peripheral blood lymphocytes from chimpanzees and humans convalescent from NANBH.[108] They were able to select antibodies that reacted with acute phase liver biopsies but not preinfection biopsies by an indirect immunoflourescence assay (IFA).[108] Using immune electron microscopy (IEM), the authors found that these antibodies were directed against clusters of microtubular or filamentous structures that were seen commonly in chimpanzee hepatocytes during NANBH. Like the cytoplasmic fused membrane tubules, this structural antigen was also seen in liver biopsies from chimpanzees with HD but not type A or B hepatitis.[109] Again, it has been difficult to see this reactivity in humans, but using immunoperoxidase Shimizu has been able to see what is likely to be the same antigen in human biopsies (Y.K. Shimizu, personal communication, 1988). The nature of the antigen is not completely known at this time but it is believed to be a host-coded antigen. Preliminary data also seem to indicate that the appearance of this antigen is also related to interferon (Y.K. Shimizu, personal communication, 1988). While increased levels of plasma interferon in NANBH has not been reported, it is possible that the NANBH virus is a potent inducer of local interferon in the liver. It is curious that patients with NANBH make antibody to a host-coded antigen that seems to be produced in response to interferon. Whether this host response plays a role in pathogenesis can only be a matter for speculation at this time.

A serologic test based on the work by Houghton et al has recently been approved for use in screening blood donors. This test is based on the detection of antibody to a portion of the HCV genome cloned as cDNA and expressed in a yeast expression system. The antigen termed C100 is derived from the portion of the genome that probably codes for the NS4 protein. This is a nonstructural protein that has an unknown function. However, people who are chronically infected generally carry antibody to this protein, which makes it useful for screening blood donors. Patients who are recently infected seroconvert an average of 5 months after exposure but a few develop antibody much later or not at all.[108] Therefore, this test has limited utility as a diagnostic tool for an acutely ill patient. It is assumed that new diagnostic methods will soon be developed that will overcome the limitations of the original test. It is also difficult to judge the number of false positives and false negatives in the present test but both seem to occur.

PREVENTION

Until this time efforts at prevention of NANBH have focused primarily on elimination of high-risk individuals as blood donors and inactivation of the HC virus in pooled plasma products such as factor VIII concentrate. With a specific test now available it is possible to identify most carriers with a high degree of accuracy. In addition, the expression of antigens associated with HCV will allow for a better understanding of the immune response in this disease and the possible preparation of a vaccine.

Without specific serologic tests it has been very difficult to identify the mode of transmission of HC in the general population and thereby develop a strategy for preventing new infections. However, the situation in the transfusion setting has been felt to be serious enough to investigate nonspecific methods for detection of likely carriers among blood donors. These methods have included identification of specific sources of high-risk blood, application of various tests of liver function that may indicate chronic NANBH in donors, and application of certain serologic tests for HB, with the implication that an individual exposed to HBV is also more likely to have been exposed to the NANBH virus since HB and NANBH share many epidemiologic features.

It has long been recognized that commercial blood is more likely to transmit both HB and HC. The NIH clinical center studies[81] showed an 82% reduction in the rate of posttransfusion hepatitis, from 20.1 cases per 1000 units to 3.7 cases per 1000 units transfused following elimination of both commercial sources of blood and institution of routine second-generation testing of donor blood for HBsAg. This reduction occurred in both type B and NANBH cases, but analysis of the data revealed that if only HBsAg screening had been introduced without changing the donor population, the hepatitis reduction would have been only about 25%. Thus it was felt that elimination of commercial blood was the major factor that resulted in the decrease in the rate of TAH. Other studies of TAH have shown the same trend. Goldfield et al[83] reported that when all blood was prescreened for HBsAg by RIA, there were approximately 0.9 cases of icteric hepatitis per 1000 units of all volunteer blood, 7.4 cases per 1000 units of mixed commercial and volunteer blood, and 25 cases per 1000 recipients of all commercial blood. Seventy-eight percent of these cases were NANBH.

Seeff et al[110] reported that in a large VA cooperative study the rate of posttransfusion hepatitis (primarily NANBH) increased in essentially direct proportion to the number of units of commercial blood transfused, rising from about 7% for patients receiving only 1 unit of commercial blood to 37% for those receiving 11 or more units. In addition, when the Hines, Illinois VA Hospital switched from 91.2% commercial blood to 4.1%, the hepatitis incidence among posttransfusion patients fell from 20% to 6.2%. During the same period of time three other hospitals in the study continued to use about 90% commercial blood with no appreciable change in the rate of hepatitis.

The evidence is overwhelming that commercial blood carries a high risk of transmitting hepatitis and that elimination of this source of blood is the single most important measure for reducing TAH NANBH. Blood taken from volunteer donors of low socioeconomic status also carries a higher risk compared with blood from middle-class volunteer donors. Therefore, it may be possible to define a subset of the volunteer donor population that is likely to transmit hepatitis.

At present all blood for transfusion is tested for either the presence of elevated levels of ALT or the presence of anti-HBc. These two tests, together with the elimination of commercial blood donors, has greatly reduced the risk of TAH. The increased risk of hepatitis in transfused patients who received at least 1 unit of blood that had an elevated level of ALT was first recognized in the TTVS.[111] While hepatitis risk increased with the number of

units received that had elevated ALT, the risk was also noted to be increased in recipients of single-unit transfusions when that unit had elevated ALT. It was calculated that exclusion of the blood units with elevated ALT would have resulted in a 30% reduction in the number of hepatitis cases. In an analysis of the multiply transfused heart surgery patients that had been followed prospectively at the NIH, Alter et al found that elimination of elevated ALT blood would have reduced hepatitis about 29% with a 1.6% loss in donors.[112]

In these same studies of TAH it was shown that there was an association between the presence of anti-HBc in donor blood and the development of hepatitis in the recipient. Stevens et al reported that the rate of HC was about threefold higher in recipients of anti-HBc-positive blood than in patients who received only anti-HBc-negative blood.[113] Studies by Alter at NIH have confirmed the TTVS findings.[114] Although anti-HBc may predict high-risk blood donors there is no evidence for a specific antigenic cross-reactivity between HBV and HC. Recipients of this anti-HBc-positive blood did not develop anti-HBc following NANBH. Alter has estimated that elimination of anti-HBc-positive blood would reduce TAH approximately 40% with a loss of donors of 2% to 4%.[114] Specific tests for the HC virus will eliminate the need for these surrogate tests and eliminate much of the cost of time, money, and lost donors. If, however, there prove to be more than one NANBHvirus, surrogate tests may have a continuing role in screening blood donors until specific tests for all the agents are available.

The effect of anti-HCV testing of blood donors on the rate of post-transfusion hepatitis has been tested retrospectively. In a study by Alter et al at the NIH Clinical Center, 18 patients developed HC infections following blood transfusion. Anti-HCV postive donors were identified retrospectively for 14 of these patients, but in 2 of the patients with negative donors all donor samples were not available. Thus, the anti-HCV test would have eliminated 14 out of 16 cases of HC (88%) in whom adequate donor samples were available. In patients with adequate donor samples it was found that 4 out of 12 patients would have had donors excluded by ALT testing and 8 out of 15 would have been excluded by anti-HBc testing. In no case would the surrogate tests have picked up an infectious donor that the anti-HCV testing missed.[108b] In a study from the Netherlands, it was found that the efficacy in reducing post-transfusion hepatitis was 63% for anti-HCV testing, compared to 65% for ALT testing of blood donors. However, anti-HCV testing had a positive predictive value of 16.2% compared to 3.6% for ALT testing, and anti-HCV testing would have eliminated only 0.7% of blood donors compared to 3.6% for ALT testing.[114a] Thus it is certain that the new anti-HCV test will reduce the rate of post-transfusion hepatitis, but it is not yet clear that the surrogate tests can be eliminated.

Methods are now being introduced to inactivate several viral agents that are known to contaminate cell-free blood products. These viruses include not only the HCV agent but also HBV, hepatitis D virus (HDV), human immunodeficiency virus (HIV), human T cell lymphotropic virus I (HTLV-I), CMV, EBV, and the human parvorvirus. The methods include the use of heat, ultraviolet light with β-propiolactone, various organic solvents, and purification.[115-117] The most common method in use at this time is heat, which has been used either on the dry lyophilized product or as a pasteurization process while the produce is still in aqueous solution.[118] The wet heating process seems to be somewhat more effective but neither has been uniformly successful in eliminating all viral agents.[118, 119]

Since many of the viruses that contaminate blood products have lipid envelopes, lipid solvents have been used to inactivate them. Chloroform has been shown to be a very effective inactivating agent but has not been widely used on blood products.[38, 120] Ether has been used in combination with the detergent polysorbate (Tween) 80, but the combination of tri-(*n*-butyl) phosphate with polysorbate 80 for factor IX or with sodium cholate for factor VIII seems to be highly effective.[116]

While a specific test for HC carriers is now available, the experience with HBV indicates that transmission of this virus to chronic users of plasma products made from large pools of plasma is still a problem and inactivation procedures may still be necessary. The ultimate solution may come from the use of synthetic plasma products produced through recombinant DNA technology.[121]

Studies have been performed on the efficacy of passive immunoprophylaxis by immune serum globulin (ISG) for prevention of TAH with mixed results, at this time its use is not recommended. Kuhns et al reported that ISG administered on the seventh and 30th days after transfusion was not effective in reducing NANBH.[122] In contrast, Knodell et al reported that ISG administered prior to cardiac surgery reduced the incidence of both acute and chronic TAH.[87, 123] Seeff found no significant difference in the rate of TAH in recipients of ISG (9.8%) or placebo (12.1%), but icteric hepatitis was reduced from 1.8% to 0.8%. This effect was most pronounced in recipients of commercial blood and elimination of this source of blood would have been much more effective in reducing all forms of hepatitis than the use of ISG.[82]

While little progress has been made in the development of methods of active prophylaxis, the recent expression of a peptide antigen that is recognized commonly by antibody in the serum of patients gives a rational starting place for vaccine development. It might even be possible now to detect this virus growing in cell culture.

THERAPY

The therapy of NANBH, like all the viral hepatitides, remains supportive and is not the subject of this chapter. Chronic NANBH can be a serious, even life-threatening disease. Therefore, the development of effective therapy would have clinical importance.

The use of corticosteroids in viral hepatitis is generally not recommended and does not appear to benefit patients with NANBH.[124] In a recent preliminary report, Hoofnagle and colleagues at the NIH treated ten patients with human alpha interferon and observed surprisingly good results.[125] Using various dosage schedules and durations of treatment the elevated serum levels of ALT declined to normal or near normal. The ALT levels quickly returned to pretreatment levels in two patients in whom treatment was stopped after 4 months, but they declined again when treatment was reinstituted at a lower dosage level. Three of the patients who were treated for 12 months underwent follow-up liver biopsy which showed a marked improvement compared with pretreatment biopsies.

In a later controlled study, Di Bisceglie found that 10 of 21

patients treated with 2 million units of recombinant interferon-alpha 3 times a week for 6 months had a complete normalization of their transaminases and 2 more patients had a greater than 50% reduction. There were no responders in the untreated group.[125a] Davis et al treated 58 patients with 3 million units and 57 with 1 million units of interferon-alpha 3 times a week for 6 months. Forty-six percent of those patients treated with 3 million units and 28% of those treated with 1 million units had either complete or partial response, while only 8% of the control group responded. In both these studies most patients relapsed within 1 year of the cessation of treatment.[125b] Studies are now underway to determine a treatment that will result in a longer lasting or permanent response.

The recent cloning and expression of the genome of the NANBH virus will put such treatment trials on much more objective virologic grounds. As the nature of the virus is revealed, it may be possible to design specific antiviral compounds.

SUMMARY

Posttransfusion hepatitis is now infrequently caused by the hepatitis B virus but is usually due to one or more agents now called the hepatitis C virus(es). Recently the RNA genome of the virus that probably is responsible for most of the NANBH has been cloned as complementary DNA in a lambda phage expression vector. One of the clones expresses an antigen that is useful for the detection of serum antibody. Therefore specific tests for this agent will soon be a reality. This agent can now be specifically diagnosed. This remarkable achievement by the group at the Chiron Corporation caps a 15-year search for the agent and will no doubt begin a new phase of scientific inquiry into this fascinating disease and the virus that causes it. By the time of the next edition of this book, we will all know a great deal more about NANBH hepatitis than we do today.

REFERENCES

1. Choo QL, Kuo G, Weiner AJ, et al: Isolation of a cDNA clone derived from a blood-borne non-A, non-B viral hepatitis genome. *Science* 1989; 244:159–162.
1a. Kuo G, Choo QL, Alter HJ, et al: An assay for circulating antibodies to a major etiologic virus of human non-A, non-B hepatitis. *Science* 1989; 244:162–164.
1b. Houghton M, Choo QL, Kuo G: European Patent Application, no. 88310922.5. Publ no. 0318216, Nov 18, 1988.
1c. MacCallum FO: Early studies of viral hepatitis. *Br Med Bull* 1972; 28:105–108.
2. Krugman S, Giles JP, Hammond J: Infectious hepatitis: Evidence for two distinctive clinical epidemiological, and immunological types of infection. *JAMA* 1967; 200:365–373.
3. Havens WP Jr: Viral hepatitis: multiple attacks in a narcotic addict. *Ann Intern Med* 1956; 44:199–203.
4. Grady GF, Chalmers TC, Boston Inter-Hosptial Liver Group: Risk of post-transfusion viral hepatitis. *N Engl J Med* 1964; 271:337–342.
5. Mosley JW: New patterns of transfusion-associated hepatitis. *Epatologica* 1966; 12:527.
6. Prince AM, Brotman B, Grady GF, et al: Long-incubation post-transfusion hepatitis without serological evidence of exposure to hepatitis B virus. *Lancet* 1974; 2:241–246.
7. Feinstone SM, Kapikian AZ, Purcell RH: Hepatitis A: Detection by immune election microscopy of a virus-like antigen associated with acute illness. *Science* 1973; 182:1026–1028.

8. Feinstone SM, Kapikian AZ, Purcell RH, et al: Transfusion-associated hepatitis not due to viral hepatitis type A or B. *N Engl J Med* 1975; 292:767–770.

9. Hoofnagle JH, Gerety RJ, Tabor E, et al: Transmission of non-A, non-B hepatitis. *Ann Intern Med* 1977; 87:14.

10. Dienstag JL, Krotoski WA, Howard WA, et al: Non-A, non-B hepatitis after experimental transmission of malaria by inoculation of blood. *J Infect Dis* 1981; 143:200–209.

11. Alter HJ, Purcell RH, Holland PV, et al: Transmissible agent in non-A, non-B hepatitis. *Lancet* 1978; 1:459–463.

12. Tabor E, Gerety RJ, Drucker JA, et al: Transmission of non-A, non-B hepatitis from man to chimpanzee. *Lancet* 1978; 1:463–466.

13. Hollinger FB, Gitnick GL, Arch RD, et al: Non-A, non-B hepatitis transmission in chimpanzees: a project of the transfusion-transmitted viruses study group. *Intervirology* 1978; 10:60–68.

14. Bradley DW, Cook EH, Maynard JE, et al: Experimental infection of chimpanzees with antihemophilic (factor VIII) materials: recovery of virus-like particles associated with non-A, non-B hepatitis. *J Med Virol* 1979; 3:253–269.

15. Shimizu YK, Feinstone SM, Purcell RH, et al: Non-A, non-B hepatitis: ultrastructural evidence for two agents in experimentally infected chimpanzees. *Science* 1979; 205:197–200.

16. Wyke RJ, Tsiquaye KN, Thornton A, et al: Transmission of non-A, non-B hepatitis to chimpanzees by factor IX concentrates after fatal complications in patients with chronic liver disease. *Lancet* 1979; 1:520–524.

17. Yoshizawa H, Akahane Y, Itoh Y, et al: Virus like particles in a plasma fraction (fibrinogen) and in the circulation of apparently healthy blood donors capable of inducing non-A/non-B hepatitis in humans and chimpanzees. *Gastroenterology* 1980; 79:512–520.

18. Feinstone SM, Alter HJ, Dienes HP, et al: Non-A, non-B hepatitis in chimpanzees and marmosets. *J Infect Dis* 1981; 144:588–598.

19. Bradley DW, Maynard JE, Popper H, et al: Persistent non-A, non-B hepatitis in experimentally infected chimpanzees. *J Infect Dis* 1981; 143:210–218.

20. Popper H, Dienstag JL, Feinstone SM, et al: The pathology of viral hepatitis in chimpanzees. *Virchows Arch* (Pathol Anat) 1980; 387:91–106.

21. Dienes HP, Popper H, Arnold W, et al: Histologic observations in human hepatitis non-A, non-B. *Hepatology* 1982; 2:562–571.

22. Tsiquaye KN, Bird RG, Tovey G, et al: Further evidence of cellular changes associated with non-A, non-B hepatitis. *J Med Virol* 1980; 5:63–71.

23. McCaul TF, Tsiquaye KN, Tovey G, et al: Application of electron microscopy to the study of structural changes in the liver in non-A, non-B hepatitis. *J Virol Methods* 1982; 4:87–106.

24. Sidhu GS: Ultrastructure of AIDS lymph nodes. *N Engl J Med* 1983; 309:1188.

25. Bockus D, Remington F, Luu J, et al: Induction of cylindrical confronting cisternae (AIDS inclusions) in Daudi lymphoblastoid cells by recombinant alpha-interferon. *Hum Pathol* 1988; 19:78.

26. Canese MG, Rizzetto M, Novara R, et al: Experimental infection of chimpanzees with the HBsAg-associated delta agent: an ultrastructural study. *J Med Virol* 1984; 13:63.

27. De Vos R, Vanstapel MJ, Desmyter J, et al: Are nuclear particles specific for non-A, non-B hepatitis? *Hepatology* 1983; 3:532–544.

28. Mosley JW, Redeker AG, Feinstone SM, et al: Multiple hepatitis viruses in multiple attacks of acute viral hepatitis. *N Engl J Med* 1977; 296:75–78.

29. Norkrans G, Frisner G, Hermodsson S, et al: Multiple hepatitis attacks in drug addicts. *JAMA* 1980; 243:1056–1058.

30. Bradley DW, Maynard JE, Cook EH, et al: Non-A, non-B hepatitis in experimentally infected chimpanzees: cross-challenge and electron microscopic studies. *J Med Virol* 1980; 6:185–201.

31. Hollinger FB, Mosley JW, Szmuness W, et al: Transfusion-transmitted viruses study: Experimental evidence for two non-A, non-B hepatitis agents. *J Infect Dis* 1980; 142:400–407.

32. Yoshizawa H, Itoh Y, Iwakiri S, et al: Demonstration of two different types of non-A, non-B hepatitis by reinjection and cross-challenge studies in chimpanzees. *Gastroenterology* 1981; 81:107–113.

33. Bradley DW, Maynard JE, Popper H, et al: Posttransfusion non-A, non-B hepatitis: Physicochemical properties of two distinct agents. *J Infect Dis* 1983; 148:254.

34. Brotman B, Prince AM, Huima T: Non-A, non-B hepatitis: Is there more than a single blood-borne strain? *J Infect Dis* 1985; 151:618.

35. Yoshizawa H, Itoh Y, Iwakiri S, et al: Non-A, non-B (type 1) hepatitis agent capable of inducing tubular ultrastructures in the hepatocyte cytoplasm of chimpanzees: Inactivation by formalin and heat. *Gastroenterology* 1982; 82:502–506.

36. Hollinger FB, Dolana G, Thomas W, et al: Heat inactivation of a non-A, non-B hepatitis agent and hepatitis B virus in human clotting factor concentrates, abstract. *Hepatology* 1982; 2:705.

37. Tabor E, Gerety RJ: Inactivation of an agent of human non-A, non-B hepatitis by formalin. *J Infect Dis* 1980; 142:767–770.

38. Feinstone SM, Mihalik KB, Kamimura T, et al: Inactivation of hepatitis B virus and non-A, non-B hepatitis by chloroform. *Infect Immun* 1983; 41:816.

39. Prince AM, Brotman B, Van Den Ende MC, et al: Non-A, non-B hepatitis. Identification of a virus specific antigen and antibody. A preliminary report, in Vyas GN, Cohen SN, Schmid R (eds): *Viral Hepatitis*. Philadelphia, Franklin Institute Press, 1978, pp 613.

40. Bradley DW, McCaustland KA, Cook EH, et al: Posttransfusion non-A, non-B hepatitis in chimpanzees: Physicochemical evidence that the tubule-forming agent is a small, enveloped virus. *Gastroenterology* 1985; 88:773.

41. He LF, Alling D, Popkin T, et al: Determining the size of non-A, non-B hepatitis by filtration. *J Infect Dis* 1987; 156:636.

42. Trepo C, Vitvitski L, Hantz O, et al: Identification and detection of virus specific core and e Ag/Ab across reacting with those of hepatitis B in non-A, non-B hepatitis (NANBH). *Gastroenterology* 1980; 79:1060.

43. Trepo C, Vitvitski L, Hantz O, et al: Detection by immunofluorescence of a new "corelike": Ag/Ab system in liver and serum of patients with NANB hepatitis. *Liver* 1981; 1:191.

44. Hantz O, Vitvitski L, Trepo C: Non-A, non-B hepatitis: Identification of hepatitis-B-like virus particles in serum and liver. *J Med Virol* 1980; 5:73.

45. Wands JR, Carlson RI, Schoemaker H, et al: Immunodiagnosis of hepatitis B with high-affinity IgM monoclonal antibodies. *Proc Natl Acad Sci USA* 1981; 78:1214.

46. Wands JR, Lieberman HM, Muchmore E, et al: Detection and transmission in chimpanzees of hepatitis B virus-related agents formerly designated "non-A, non-B" hepatitis. *Proc Natl Acad Sci USA* 1982; 79:7552.

47. Wands JR, Fujita YK, Isselbacher JK, et al: Identification and transmission of hepatitis B virus-related varients. *Proc Natl Acad Sci USA* 1986; 83:6608.

48. Figus A, Blum HE, Vyas GN, et al: Hepatitis B viral nucleotide sequences in non-A, non-B or hepatitis B virus-related chronic liver disease. *Hepatology* 1984; 4:364.

49. Brechot C, Degos F, Lugassy C, et al: Hepatitis B virus DNA in patients with chronic liver disease and negative tests for hepatitis B surface antigen. *N Engl J Med* 1985; 312:270.

50. Fowler MJF, Monjardino J, Weller IV, et al: Failure to detect nucleic acid homology between some non-A, non-B viruses and hepatitis B virus DNA. *J Med Virol* 1983; 12:205.

51. Tassopoulos NC, Papaevangelou GJ, Roumeliotou-Karayannis A, et al: Search for hepatitis B virus DNA in sera from patients with acute type B or non-A, non-B hepatitis. *J Hepatol* 1986; 2:410.

52. Yap SH, Hellings JA, Rijntjes PJM, et al: Absence of detectable hepatitis B virus DNA in sera and liver of chimpanzees with non-A, non-B hepatitis. *J Med Virol* 1985; 15:343.

53. Seto B, Coleman WG, Iwarson S, et al: Detection of reverse

transcriptase activity in association with the non-A, non-B hepatitis agent(s). *Lancet* 1984; 2:941.

54. Fields HA, Berninger M, Nath N, et al: Unrelatedness of factor VIII derived non-A, non-B hepatitis and hepatitis B virus. *J Med Virol* 1983; 11:59.
55. Feinstone SM, Alter HJ, Dienes HP, et al: Non-A, non-B hepatitis in chimpanzees and marmosets. *J Infect Dis* 1981; 144:588.
56. Iwarson S, Schaff Z, Seto B, et al: Retrovirus-like particles in hepatocytes of patients with transfusion-acquired non-A, non-B hepatitis. *J Med Virol* 1985; 16:37.
57. Seto B, Gerety RJ: A glycoprotein associated with the non-A, non-B hepatitis agent(s): Isolation and immunoreactivity. *Proc Natl Acad Sci USA* 1985; 82:4934.
58. Casoli C, Tremolada F, Lori F, et al: Reverse transcriptase activity in post-transfusion non-A, non-B hepatitis: characterisation and association with retrovirus particles in serum. *Serodiagn Immunother Infect Dis* 1987; 1:00.
59. Itoh Y, Iwakiri S, Kitajima K, et al: Lack of detectable reverse transcriptase activity in human and chimpanzee sera with a high infectivity for non-A, non-B hepatitis. *J Gen Virol* 1986; 67:777.
60. Craske J, Dilling N, Stern D: An outbreak of hepatitis associated with intravenous injection of factor-VIII concentrate. *Lancet* 1975; 2:221–223.
61. Hruby MA, Schauf V: Transfusion-related short-incubation hepatitis in hemophilic patients. 1978; 240:1355–1357.
62. Tsiquaye KN, Zuckerman AJ: New human hepatitis virus. *Lancet* 1979; 1:1135–1136.
63. Galbraith RM, Dienstag JL, Purcell RH, et al: Non-A, non-B hepatitis associated with chronic liver disease in a hemodialysis unit. *Lancet* 1979; 1:951.
64. Rakela J, Nugent E, Mosley JW: Viral hepatitis: enzyme assays and serologic procedures in the study of an epidemic. *Am J Epidemiol* 1977; 106:493–501.
65. Hollinger FB, Mosley JW, Szmuness W, et al: Non-A, non-B hepatitis following blood transfusion: Risk factors associated with donor characteristics, in Szmuness W (ed): *Proceedings of the 1981 International Symposium on Viral Hepatitis.* Philadelphia, Franklin Institute Press, 1982, pp 361–376.
66. Norkrans G, Frösner G, Hermodsson S, et al: Clinical epidemiological and prognostic aspects of hepatitis "non-A, non-B"; a comparison with hepatitis A and B. *Scand J Infect Dis* 1979; 11:259–264.
67. Locarnini SA, Gust ID, Ferris AA, et al: A prospective study of acute viral hepatitis with particular reference to hepatitis A. *Bull WHO* 1976; 54:199–206.
68. Dienstag JL, Alaama A, Mosley JW, et al: Etiology of sporadic hepatitis B surface antigen-negative hepatitis. *Ann Intern Med* 1977; 87:1–6.
69. Mathiesen LR, Skinhoj P, Hardt F, et al: The Copenhagen Hepatitis Acuta Programme. Epidemiology and clinical characteristics of acute hepatitis types, A, B, and non-A, non-B. *Scand J Gastroenterol* 1979; 14:849–856.
70. Alter MJ, Gerety RJ, Smallwood LA, et al: Sporadic non-A, non-B hepatitis: Frequency and epidemiology in an urban U.S. population. *J Infect Dis* 1982; 145:886–893.
71. Szmuness W, Stevens CE, Harley EJ, et al: Demonstration of efficacy in a controlled clinical trial in a high-risk population in the United States. *N Engl J Med* 1980; 303:833–841.
72. Tong MJ, Thursby M, Rakela J, et al: Studies on the maternal infant transmission of the viruses which cause acute hepatitis. *Gastroenterology* 1981; 80:999–1004.
73. Papaevengelou G, Decker R, Contoyannis P, et al: Differential sero-diagnosis of sporadic acute viral hepatitis. *Proc Soc Exp Biol Med* 1979; 161:322–325.
74. Guyer B, Bradley DW, Bryan JA, et al: Non-A, non-B hepatitis among participants in a plasmapheresis stimulation program. *J Infect Dis* 1979; 139:634–640.
75. Müller R, Willer H, Frösner GG, et al: The seroepidemiological pattern of acute viral hepatitis: an epidemiological study of viral hepatitis in the Hannover region. *Infection* 1978; 6:65–70.

76. Norkrans G, Frösner G, Hermodsson S, et al: The epidemiological pattern of hepatitis A, B, and non-A, non-B in Sweden. *Scand J Gastroenterol* 1978; 13:873–877.
77. Farrow LJ, Stewart JS, Lamb SGS, et al: Sporadic non-A, non-B hepatitis in west London. *Lancet* 1979; 2:300.
78. Norkrans G, Frösner G, Hermodsson S, et al: The epidemiological pattern of hepatitis A, B, and non-A, non-B in Sweden. *Scand J Gastroenterol* 1978; 13:873–877.
79. Koff RS, Pannuti CS, Pereira MLG, et al: Hepatitis A and non-A, non-B viral hepatitis in Sao Paulo, Brazil: Epidemiological, clinical, and laboratory comparisons in hospitalized patients. *Hepatology* 1982; 2:445–448.
80. Alter MJ, Margolis HS, Krawczynski K, et al: The role of transfusions in the chronic disease burden associated with non-A, non-B hepatitis in the United States. *Transfusion Med Rev* 1988; 2.
80a. Alter MJ, Sampliner RE: Hepatitis C: And miles to go before we sleep. *N Engl J Med* 1989; 321:1538–1540.
81. Alter HJ, Holland PV, Purcell RH, et al: Post-transfusion hepatitis after exclusion of commercial and hepatitis-B antigen-positive donors. *Ann Intern Med* 1972; 77:697.
82. Seeff LB, Zimmerman HJ, Wright EC, et al: A randomized, double-blind controlled trial of the efficacy of immune serum globulin for the prevention of post-transfusion hepatitis: a Veterans Administration Cooperative Study. *Gastroenterology* 1977; 72:111–121.
83. Goldfield M, Bill J, Colosimo F: The control of transfusion associated hepatitis, in Vyas GN, Cohen SN, Schmid R (eds); *Viral Hepatitis.* Philadelphia, Franklin Institute Press, 1978, pp 405–414.
83a. Kuhnl P, Seidl S, Stangel W: Antibody to hepatitis C virus in German blood donors (letter). *Lancet* 1989; 2:324.
83b. Esteban JI, Viladomiu L, Gonzalez A: Hepatitis C virus antibodies among risk groups in Spain. *Lancet* 1989; 2:294–297.
84. Rakela J, and Acute Hepatic Failure Study Group: Etiology and prognosis in fulminant hepatitis, abstract. *Gastroenterology* 1979; 77:33A.
85. Mathiesen LR, Skinoj P, Nielsen JO, et al: Hepatitis type A, B, and non-A, non-B in fulminant hepatitis. 1980; 21:72–77.
86. Berman M, Alter HJ, Ishak KG, et al: The chronic sequelae of non-A, non-B hepatitis. *Ann Intern Med* 1979; 91:1–6.
87. Knodell RG, Conrad ME, Ishak KG: Development of chronic liver disease after acute non-A, non-B post-transfusion hepatitis: Role of g-globulin prophylaxis in its prevention. *Gastroenterology* 1977; 72:902–909.
88. Aach RD, Lander JJ, Sherman LA, et al: Transfusion-transmitted viruses: Interim analysis of hepatitis among transfused and non-transfused patients, in Vyas GN, Cohen SN, Schmid R (eds): *Viral Hepatitis.* Philadelphia, Franklin Institute Press, 1978, pp 383–396.
89. Mathieson LR, Hardt F, Dietrichson O, et al: The role of acute hepatitis type A, B and non-A, non-B in the development of chronic active liver disease. *Scand J Gastroenterol* 1980; 15:49–54.
90. Sjogren MH, Tanno H, Fay O, et al: Hepatitis A virus in stool during clinical relapse. *Ann Intern Med* 1987; 106:221.
91. Dienstag JL: Non-A, non-B hepatitis. I. Recognition, epidemiology and clinical features. *Gastroenterology* 1983; 85:439.
92. Alter HJ, Purcell RH, Feinstone SM, et al: Non-A, non-B hepatitis: prologue, progress and prospects, in Szmuness W (ed): *Proceedings of the 1981 International Symposium on Viral Hepatitis.* Philadelphia, Franklin Institute Press, 1982, pp 279–294.
93. Alter HJ, Hoofnagle JH: Non-A, non-B: Observations on the first decade, in Vyas GN, Dienstag JL, Hoofnagle JH (eds): *Viral Hepatitis and Liver Disease.* Orlando, Fla, Grune & Stratton, 1984, pp 345–354.
94. Colombo M, Oldani S, Donato MF, et al: A multicenter, prospective study of posttransfusion hepatitis in Milan. *Hepatology* 1987; 7:709.
95. Di Bisceglie AM, Kassianides C, Lisker-Melman M, et al: Development of cirrhosis following chronic non-A, non-B hepati-

tis, abstract. *Gastroenterology* 1988; 94:535.

96. Zeldis JB, Dienstag JL, Gale RP: Aplastic anemia and non-A, non-B hepatitis. *Am J Med* 1983; 4:64.

97. Beasley RP, Hwang LY: The epidemiology of hepatocellular carcinoma. in Vyas GN, Dienstag JL, Hoofnagle JH (eds): *Viral Hepatitis and Liver Disease.* Orlando, Fla, Grune & Stratton, 1984, p 209.

98. Kiyosawa K, Akahane Y, Nagata A, et al: Hepatocellular carcinoma after non-A, non-B posttransfusion hepatitis. *Am J Gastroenterol* 1984; 79:777.

99. Okuda H, Obata H, Motoike Y, et al: Clinicopathological features of hepatocellular carcinoma—comparison of seropositive and seronegative patients. *Hepatogastroenterology* 1984; 31:64.

99a. Bruix J, Calvert X, Costa J, et al: Prevalence of antibodies to hepatitis C virus in Spanish patients with hepatocellular carcinoma and hepatic cirrhosis. *Lancet* 1989; 2:1004–1006.

99b. Columbo M, Choo QL, Del Ninno E, et al: Prevalence of antibodies to hepatitis C virus in Italian patients with hepatocellular carcinoma. *Lancet* 1989; 2:1006–1008.

99c. Kew MC, Houghton M, Choo QL, et al: Hepatitis C virus antibodies in southern African blacks with hepatocellular carcinoma. *Lancet* 1990; 335:873–874.

100. Dienstag JL, Bahn AK, Alter HJ, et al: Circulating immune complexes in non-A, non-B hepatitis. *Lancet* 1979; 1:1265–1267.

101. Shiraishi H, Alter HJ, Feinstone SM, et al: Rheumatoid factor-like reactants in sera proven to transmit non-A, non-B hepatitis: A potential source of false-positive reactions in non-A, non-B assays. *Hepatology* 1985; 5:181–187.

102. Omata M, Iwama S, Sumida M, et al: Clinicopathologic study of acute non-A, non-B hepatitis: Histologic features of liver biopsies in acute phase. *Liver* 1981; 1:201.

103. Shimizu YK, Feinstone SM, Purcell RH, et al: Non-A, non-B hepatitis: Ultrastructural evidence for agents in experimentall infected chimpanzees. *Science* 1979; 205:197.

104. Pfeifer V, Thomssen R, Legler K, et al: Experimental non-A, non-B hepatitis: Four types of cytoplasmic alterations in hepatocytes of infected chimpanzees. *Virchows Arch (Cell Pathol)* 1980; 33:233.

105. Watanabe S, Reddy KR, Jeffers L, et al: Electron microscopic evidence of non-A, non-B hepatitis markers and virus-like particles in immunocompromised humans. *Hepatology* 1984; 4:628.

106. Canese MG, Rizzetto M, Novara R, et al: Experimental infection of chimpanzees with the HBsAg-associated delta agent: an ultrastructural study. *J Med Virol* 1984; 13:63.

107. Sidhu GS: Ultrastructure of AIDS lymph nodes. *N Engl J Med* 1983; 309:1188.

108. Shimizu YK, Oomura M, Abe K, et al: Production of antibody associated with non-A, non-B hepatitis in a chimpanzee lymphoblastoid cell line established by *in vitro* transformation with Epstein-Barr virus. *Proc Natl Acad Sci USA* 1985; 82:2138.

108a. Alter HJ, Purcell RH, Shih JW, et al: Detection of antibody to hepatitis C virus in prospectively followed transfusion recipients with acute and chronic non-A, non-B hepatitis. *N Engl J Med* 1989; 321:1494–1500.

109. Shimizu YK, Purcell RH, Gerin JL, et al: Further studies by immunofluorescence of the monoclonal antibodies associated with experimental non-A, non-B hepatitis in chimpanzees and their relation to D hepatitis. *Hepatology* 1986; 6:1329–1333.

110. Seeff LB, Wright EC, Zimmerman HJ, et al: Members of VA hepatitis cooperative studies group. VA cooperative study of post-transfusion hepatitis incidence and characteristics of hepatitis and responsible risk factors. *Am J Med Sci* 1975; 270:355–362.

111. Aach RD, Szmuness W, Mosley JW, et al: Serum alanine aminotransferase of donors in relation to the risk of non-A, non-B hepatitis in recipients. *N Engl J Med* 1981; 304:989–994.

112. Alter HJ, Purcell RH, Holland PV, et al: Donor transaminase and recipient hepatitis. *JAMA* 1981; 246:630.

113. Stevens CE, Aach RD, Hollinger FB, et al: Hepatitis B virus antibody in blood donors and the occurrence of non-A, non-B hepatitis in transfusion recipients: An analysis of the transfusion-transmitted viruses study. *Ann Intern Med* 1984; 101:733.

114. Alter HJ: Posttransfusion hepatitis: clinical features, risk and donor testing, in Dodd RY, Barker LF (eds): *Infections Immunity and Blood Transfusions.* New York, Alan R Liss, 1985, p 47.

114a. van der Poel CL, Reesink HW, Schaasberg W, et al: Infectivity of blood seropositive for hepatitis C virus antibodies. *Lancet* 1990; 335:558–560.

115. Gomperts EH: Procedures for the inactivation of viruses in clotting factor concentrates. *Am J Hematol* 1986; 23:295.

116. Prince AM, Horowitz B, Horowitz MS, et al: The development of virus-free labile blood derivatives—a review. *Eur J Epidemiol* 1987; 3:103.

117. Horowitz B, Wiebe M, Lippin A, et al: Inactivation of viruses in labile blood derivatives II. Physical methods. *Transfusion* 1985; 25:523.

118. Schimpf K, Manucci PM, Kreutz W, et al: Absence of hepatitis after treatment with a pasteurized factor VIII concentrate in patients with hemophilia and no previous transfusions. *N Engl J Med* 1987; 316:918.

119. Colombo M, Mannucci PM, Carnelli V, et al: Transmission of non-A, non-B hepatitis by heat-treated factor VIII concentrate. *Lancet* 1985; 2:1.

120. Quinnan GV, Wells MA, Wittek AE, et al: Inactivation of human T lymphotropic virus, type III (HTLV-III) by heat, chemicals, and irradiation. *Transfusion* 1986; 26:481.

121. Eaton DL, Hass PE, Riddle L, et al: Characterization of recombinant human factor VIII. *J Biol Chem* 1987; 262:3285.

122. Kuhns WJ, Prince AM, Brotman B, et al: A clinical and laboratory evaluation of immune serum globulin from donors with a history of hepatitis: Attempted prevention of posttransfusion hepatitis. *Am J Med Sci* 1976; 272:255–261.

123. Knodell RG, Conrad ME, Ginsberg AL, et al: Efficacy of prophylactic gamma-globulin in preventing non-A, non-B posttransfusion hepatitis. *Lancet* 1976; 1:557.

124. Hoofnagle JH: Chronic hepatitis: The role of corticosteroids, in Szmuness E, Alter HJ, Maynard JE (eds): *Viral Hepatitis* Philadelphia, Franklin Institute Press, 1982, p 573.

125. Hoofnagle JH, Mullen KD, Jones DB, et al: Treatment of chronic non-A, non-B hepatitis with recombinant human alpha interferon. *N Engl J Med* 1986; 315:1575.

125a. Di Bisceglie AM, Martin P, Kassianides C, et al: Recombinant interferon alpha therapy for chronic hepatitis C: A randomized, double-blind, placebo-controlled trial. *N Engl J Med* 1989; 321:1506–1510.

125b. Davis GL, Balart LA, Schiff ER, et al: Treatment of chronic hepatitis C with recombinant interferon alpha: A multicenter randomized, controlled trial. *N Engl J Med* 1989; 321:1501–1506.

31

Hepatitis E

Daniel W. Bradley
Krzysztof Krawczynski
Mark A. Kane

NATURAL HISTORY AND GEOGRAPHIC DISTRIBUTION

EXPERIMENTAL STUDIES IN PRIMATES

HISTOPATHOLOGY IN EXPERIMENTALLY INFECTED
   PRIMATES

VIRUSLIKE PARTICLES

PHYSICOCHEMICAL PROPERTIES OF HE-ASSOCIATED 27- TO
   34-nm VLPS

UNANSWERED QUESTIONS

More than 50 percent of acute viral hepatitis occurring in some developing countries appears to be unrelated to infection by hepatitis A virus (HAV) or hepatitis B virus (HBV) and accumulating evidence suggests that a high proportion of this non-A, non-B hepatitis (NANBH) is enterically transmitted. Epidemics or outbreaks of enterically transmitted NANBH, or hepatitis E (HE), have been documented in the Soviet Union, Nepal, Burma, Pakistan, India, Borneo, Somalia, Sudan, Ivory Coast, Algeria, and Mexico (see below for details). These outbreaks primarily affect young-to-middle-aged adults and are often associated with a high mortality rate in infected pregnant women, approaching 20% in most reported epidemics.[1-5] Several investigators have reported finding 27- to 34-nm viruslike particles (VLPs) in stools of acutely infected cases. Stools containing these small, nonenveloped VLPs have been shown to cause HE in experimentally infected cynomolgus macaques, African green monkeys, chimpanzees, rhesus monkeys, and *Saguinas mystax* monkeys (tamarins).[6-11] Infected primates have been shown to seroconvert to 27- to 34-nm VLPs recovered from stools of cases occurring in the Soviet Union, India, Nepal, Burma, Pakistan, and Mexico, suggesting that HE is caused by one virus or class of serologically related viruses.[6-10] The morphologic features and physicochemical properties of one candidate

virus are very similar to those of some human caliciviruses, a group of viruses that is normally associated with outbreaks of severe diarrhea.[12, 13]

NATURAL HISTORY AND GEOGRAPHIC DISTRIBUTION

A significant proportion of acute viral hepatitis occurring in young-to-middle-aged adults in Asia and the Indian subcontinent appears to be caused by an agent that is serologically unrelated to either HAV or HBV.[14, 15] Disease has been shown to occur in both epidemic and sporadic forms and is primarily associated with the ingestion of fecally contaminated drinking water. The term "enterically transmitted NANBH" has evolved from the waterborne mode of virus transmission and presumed enteric route of natural infection in humans.[16] HE was first documented in New Delhi, India in 1955, when 29,000 cases of icteric hepatitis were identified following widespread fecal contamination of the city's drinking water.[17] A similar epidemic of viral hepatitis occurred between December 1975 and January 1976 in Ahmedabad City, India, again due to contaminated water supplies.[18] Both outbreaks were originally thought to be caused by HAV; however, retrospecitve serologic analysis of paired serum specimens from documented cases revealed that neither HAV nor HBV could be implicated as the etiologic agent.[15] Large epidemics of enterically transmitted viral hepatitis have also been observed in the Kirghiz Republic, USSR.[1] Between 1955 and 1956 more than 10,800 cases of acute viral hepatitis were documented in young-to-middle-aged adults; approximately 18% of infected pregnant women died as a result of acute disease.

The epidemiologic and clinical features of these outbreaks are remarkably similar to those associated with the 1955–1956 New Delhi outbreak. Subsequent outbreaks of epidemic and acute sporadic NANBH were documented in North India[19] and in Kashmir, India.[20] Outbreaks of epidemiologically similar HE have also been reported in Southeast Asia, including Burma[2] and Nepal,[3] and were associated with a high mortality rate in infected pregnant women. Between June 1976 and August 1977, more than 20,000 icteric cases occurred in Mandalay, Burma, with a case fatality ratio of 18% in pregnant women (M. Schreeder, unpublished data, 1977). An epidemic of viral hepatitis involving 10,000 cases in the Kathmandu Valley, Nepal, in 1973 was also reported to be associated with a high mortality rate in infected pregnant women.[4, 21] The occurrence of HE in Pakistan has recently been inferred from the observation of cases of disease imported into the United States.[22] Four Pakistani nationals, three residing in the Los Angeles area and one living in Chicago, were found to have developed HE shortly after returning from Karachi. All four cases were subsequently shown by immune electron microscopy (IEM) to have antibody in their acute phase sera against 27- to 34-nm VLPs in a proven infectious HE case stool (see below).

Outbreaks of HE have also been reported in Africa, including Algeria,[28] Ivory Coast,[5] Eastern Sudan,[24] and Somalia.[24] Between October 1980 and January 1981, more than 780 cases of HE were documented in Algeria and linked to the use of fecally contaminated drinking water. Mostly young adults were affected, and nine of nine infected pregnant women died as a direct result of HE. A similar number of HE cases (N-623) in Tortiya, Ivory Coast were observed between 1983 and 1984.[5] Although no precise figure was given, a high mortality rate among infected pregnant women was noted. More recently, large outbreaks of HE have been documented in Eritrean and Tigrean (Ethiopian) refugees encamped in Eastern Sudan.[24] More than 2000 cases occurred in these refugees between August and September 1985, again due to the use of fecally contaminated water. Several thousand cases of HE were also noted in Ethiopian refugees residing in Tog Wajale and other camps in northwest Somalia;[24] these cases accounted for the majority of acute viral hepatitis observed between 1985 and 1986. The mortality rate among HE-infected pregnant refugee women was greater than 17% and a fecally contaminated environment was again implicated as the vehicle for virus transmission.

HE does not appear to be confined to Asia, the Soviet Union, and North Africa, however. In fact, outbreaks of HE associated with fecally contaminated drinking water have recently been documented in Borneo (I. Lubis and S. Wuryadi, personal communication, 1988), and in two rural villages located south of Mexico City.[25] More than 90 cases of presumed HE were recorded in Huitzililla, Mexico between June and October of 1986. Additional cases of HE were seen in Telixtac, Mexico shortly thereafter. Virologic and serologic studies of case stool and serum specimens, respectively, suggested that the etiologic agent responsible for disease in North America might be similar or identical to that associated with HE in other regions of the world (see below). Tables 31–1 and 31–2 summarize the major epidemiologic and clinical features of HE.

EXPERIMENTAL STUDIES IN PRIMATES

Transmission of human-origin HE to nonhuman primates was first reported by Balayan and coworkers in 1983.[6] Two cynomolgus macaques were intravenously (IV) inoculated with a 10% wt/vol

suspension of a human volunteer stool positive by IEM for 27- to 30-nm VLPs. These animals developed elevations in alanine aminotransferase (ALT) activity between 24 and 36 days after inoculation, excreted 27- to 30-nm VLPs in their preacute phase stools, and seroconverted to morphologically similar VLPs in the inoculum. Andjaparidze and coworkers later reported the successful transmission of HE to African green monkeys, as well as cynomolgus macaques (''cynos''), using HE case stool specimens positive by IEM for 27- to 30-nm VLPs.[8] Although HE was serially passaged in the latter animals, a decreased efficiency of transmission was observed during each successive passage.

Intravenous (IV) inoculation of four *S mystax* tamarins with another acute phase stool suspension obtained from a case of HE in Nepal resulted in biochemical evidence of liver dysfunction in three; small, nonenveloped VLPs were observed in several early acute-illness-phase stool specimens from one animal studied in detail.[7] This animal was also shown by IEM to have seroconverted to 27- to 30-nm contained in the original stool inoculum.

More recently, animal transmission studies have been conducted in cynos, chimpanzees, and tamarins[9, 10] using highly characterized inocula. Table 31–3 summarizes the nature of the inocula used in these studies, including some of those already described above. All inocula were positive by IEM for 27- to 30-nm or 27- to 34-nm VLPs. These particles were reported to specifically react with antibody in acute phase HE case and primate sera (see below). One inoculum, Mexico No. 14, consisted of partially purified virus with particle counts in excess of 300 per five electron microscopic grid squares. Intravenous inoculation of four *S mystax* with a Burma stool pool (inoculum III, Table 31–3) caused increased serum isocitrate dehydrogenase (SICD) activity in three animals, with peak values occurring between 70 and 80 days after inoculation. Three of four cynos inoculated IV with the same material developed elevated ALT activity after an average incubation period of 38 days. Two of three cynos infected with inoculum IV (PAK No. 1) exhibited elevated ALT activity after a similar incubation period. Figure 31–1 illustrates the course of HE in four first-passage cynos following infection with either the Burma or Pakistan inoculum. HE was subpassaged in three of seven *S mystax* and in five of seven cynos using pools of stool suspensions from first-passage animals. One additional passage of virus in five cynos resulted in a significantly shortened incubation period (20 days) and increased severity of disease.[9] Intravenous inoculation of four cynos with a partially purified virus preparation containing a relatively large number of 32- to 34-nm VLPs (inoculum VII, Table 31–3) resulted in elevated ALT activity after incubation periods of 5, 5, 8, and 12 days, respectively (D. Bradley, unpublished findings, 1987).

Twenty-seven- to thirty-four-nanometer VLPs morphologically similar to those found in the human inocula were observed in stool specimens of first, second-, and third-passage cynos and in first- and second-passage *S mystax*.[9] These VLPs were detected by IEM in stools collected just prior to or during the initial increase in liver enzyme activity. Sera from selected animals in each passage of disease were tested by IEM for virus-specific antibody. None of the preinoculation sera from these animals contained antibody to HE-associated 27- to 34-nm VLPs. However, without exception, all acute phase animal sera examined were capable of aggregating the above VLPs when used at final dilutions of 1:60 or 1:75 (data

Table 31-1
Hepatitis E: Geographic Distribution

Site	Dates	No. of Cases	Source of Agent	Highest Age Incidence (yr)	Mortality in Pregnant Women (%)
New Delhi, India	12/55–1/56	29,000	Contaminated city water	15–39	10.5
Ahmedabad City, India	12/75–1/76	2572	Contaminated city water	16–30	High
Mandalay, Burma	6/76–8/77	20,000	Contaminated water	20–29	18
Rangoon, Burma	1982–1983	399	Contaminated water	20–40	12
Kathmandu Valley, Nepal	1973–1974	10,000	ND	20–39	High
Kathmandu Valley, Nepal	1981–1982	6000	ND	15–34	21
Algeria	10/80–1/81	788	Contaminated water	Young adults	100%
Tortiya, Ivory Coast	1983–1984	623		NA	High
Eastern Sudan	8/85–9/85	2012	Contaminated water	Young adults	NA
Tog Wajale, Somalia	1985–1986		Contaminated water	Young adults	17%
Karachi, Pakistan	1986	5	imported to U.S.	Young, middle-aged adults	NA
San Jose, Costa Rica	1976 (reported)	5 (sporadic)	ND		NA
Qatar	1981	91	ND	Young, middle-aged adults	NR
Huitzililla, Mexico	6/86–10/86	94	Contaminated water	15–45	0
Kirghiz Republic, USSR	1955–1956	10,812	ND		18%

ND = not determined but presumed to be contaminated water; NA = not available; NR = not reported; 0 = None.

not shown). Convalescent serum from these same animals was often found to be less reactive in IEM than the matching acute phase serum, indicating that a significant rise in antibody potency (titer) does not normally occur between the acute and convalescent phases of disease (see below).

Transmission of HE to chimpanzees has also been documented.[10] Intravenous inoculation of two animals with stool suspension originating from two cases of HE in India resulted in mild histologic and biochemical hepatitis after an incubation period of approximately 2 to 4 weeks. Both chimpanzees seroconverted to 27-nm VLPs contained in one of the inocula. It is interesting to note that, as in the case of HE-infected cynos and tamarins, acute phase sera from infected chimpanzees appeared to be more reactive than convalescent sera when tested by IEM for antibody against disease-associated VLPs.

Only one report to date has described the transmission of HE to primates by inoculation of acute phase serum from a presumed case of HE.[11] Three adult rhesus monkeys were inoculated intramuscularly (IM) with serum from a sporadic case of HE occurring in New Delhi, India. All three animals developed mild elevations in liver enzyme values indicative of acute hepatitis between 20 and 40 days after inoculation. Two of the monkeys exhibited mild

histologic alterations in acute phase liver biopsy specimens that were consistent with a diagnosis of acute viral hepatitis. Tables 31–4 and 31–5 summarize the salient features of the animal transmission studies described above. Figure 31–2 illustrates, in a comparative fashion, typical immune responses of individuals infected with HAV or HE virus.

Table 31-2
Hepatitis E: Clinical and Epidemiologic Features

1. Transmitted by fecal-oral route, presumably through fecally contaminated water supplies
2. Average incubation period slightly longer than that of hepatitis A
3. Outbreaks may involve up to tens of thousands of cases: primarily occur in Indian subcontinent and Central Asia; also found in USSR, Algeria, Ivory Coast, Sudan, Somalia, Pakistan, Mexico, and Borneo
4. Highest attack rates typically found among individuals between 15 and 40 years of age
5. Associated with high mortality rate (approx 20%) in infected pregnant women

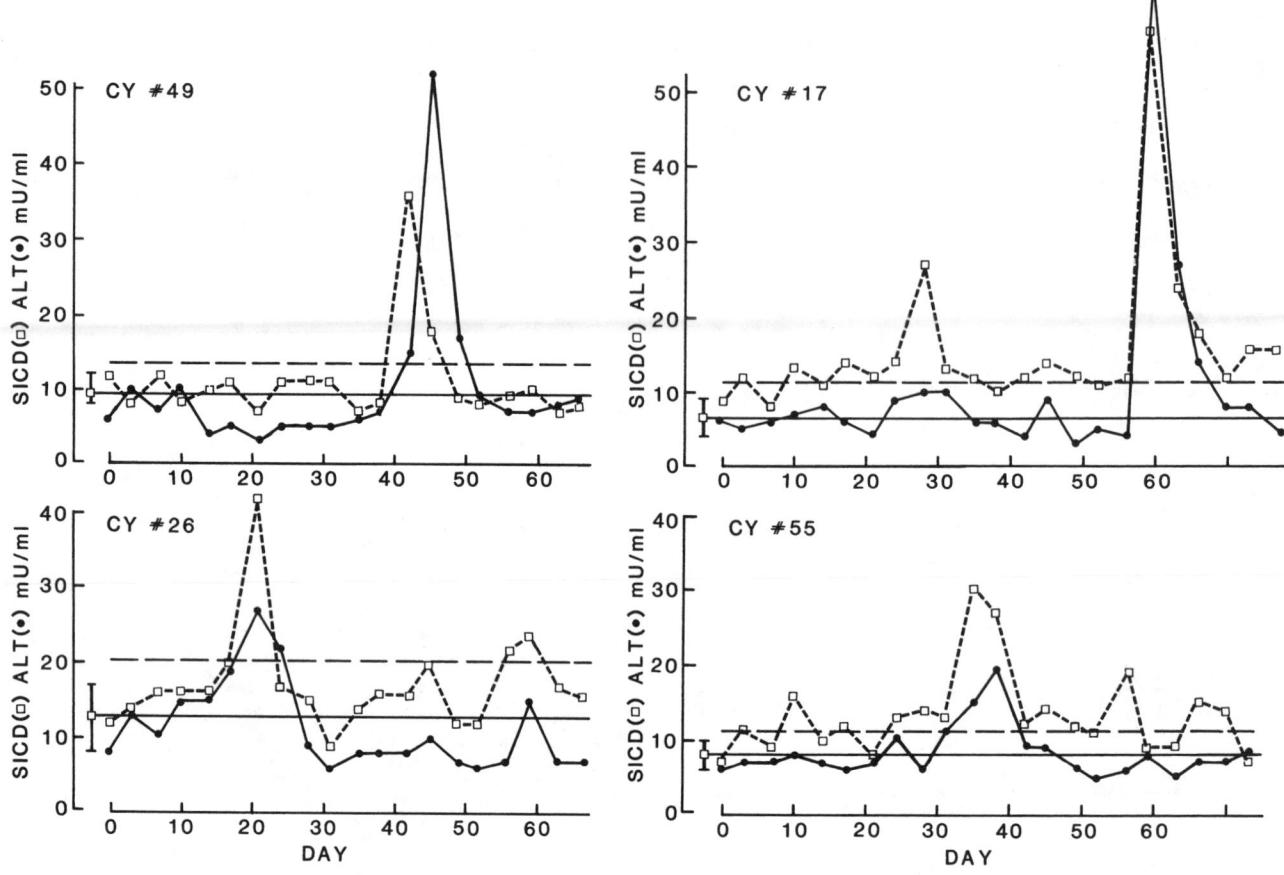

Figure 31–1. First passage of human-origin enterically transmitted non-A, non-B hepatitis (hepatitis E) in cynomolgus (Cy) macaques infected with acute phase case stools from Pakistan (Cy #49) or Burma (Cy #17, 26, 55). Bars and open circles indicate the range and mean of preinoculation alanine aminotransferase (ALT) values. Dashed line represents the 95% confidence limit for the upper level of normal ALT activity. SCID = serum isocitrate dehydrogenase.

Table 31–3
Hepatitis E Inocula for Primate Transmission Studies

Inoculum	Stool Origin	Identification	Stool Composition: No. of Patients (Days After Onset)	Particle Size (nm)	VLPs*	Primate Species Inoculated (No.)
I	Nepal (Kath Valley, 1981–1982)	NHO-464	1(4)	27–32	>200	CH(2), MY(4)
II	USSR (human volunteer, 1981)	(day 42 after inoculation)		27–30	90	CY(2)
III	Burma (Rangoon, 1982)	FVH-8, -9, -11, -12	4(4–7)	27–34†	20–100	MY(4), CY(4)
IV	Pakistan*‡ (Karachi, 1985)	PAK 1	1(7)	27–32	150	CH(2), CY(3)
V	USSR (Tashkent, 1981–1982)	1435	1(−1)	27–34†	300	CH(1)
VI	Africa (Somalia, 1986)	28	1(5)	27–34†	155	
		30	1(5)	27–34†	65	
		414	1(7)	27–34†	160	
VII	Mexico (Telixtac, 1986)	14	1(−2)	27–34†	5–10 (375–1645)	CY(4), CH(4)
VIII	India (Ahmedabad, 1984; Kohlapur, 1981)	Ahmn-84	1 (acute phase)	27	NR	CH(1)
		Kol-81	1 (acute phase)	27	NR	CH(1)

CH = chimpanzees; MY = Saguinas mystax tamarins; CY = cynomolgus macacques; NT = not tested; NR = not reported.
*Number of antibody-coated viruslike particles (VLPs) per five grid squares (immune electron microscopy of 10% wt/vol stool suspension); number of VLPs per five grid squares for partially purified virus shown in parentheses (range for three different preparations).
†Majority of VLPs measured between 32–34 nm.
‡Imported case seen in Los Angeles, August 1985.

Table 31–4
Transmission of Hepatitis E to Nonhuman Primates: Summary

Investigator	Chimpanzee	Cynomolgus Macaque (yr)	Tamarin (Saguinas mystax)	African Green Monkey
Balayan et al[6]	NT	Yes (1983)	NT	NT
Kane et al[7]	No*	NT	Yes (1984)	NT
Bradley et al[9]	Yes†	Yes (1987)	Yes (1987)	NT
Andjaparidze et al[8]	NT	Yes (1986)	NT	Yes (1986)
Arankalle et al[10]	Yes (1988)	NT	NT	NT
Krawczynski et al‡	Yes (1987)	NT	NT	NT

NT = not tested.
*Young chimpanzee.
†Mild alanine aminotransferase elevations after inoculation of inoculum I (see Table 31–3) (unpublished data, 1983).
‡Unreported findings; inoculum was partially purified virus (inoculum VII; see Table 31–3).

Table 31–5
Transmission of Hepatitis E to Nonhuman Primates: Pathogenesis in Cynomolgus Macaques, Tamarins, and Chimpanzees

1. Virus excreted prior to or during the initial increase in alanine aminotransferase or serum isocitrate dehydrogenase activity
2. No demonstrable increase in antibody reactivity between the acute and convalescent phases of disease
3. Immune electron microscopy–reactive antibody in acute phase sera primarily of IgM class
4. 32–34-nm viruslike particles (VLPs) excreted in 1st, 2nd, and 3rd passage cynomolgus macaques are morphologically similar to VLPs found in inocula

HISTOPATHOLOGY IN EXPERIMENTALLY INFECTED PRIMATES

In cynos with elevated ALT activity, degeneration and necroinflammatory changes were observed in liver parenchyma accompanied by inconspicuous or minimal infiltrations in portal tracts. The more advanced changes were compatible with a diagnosis of acute viral hepatitis. Acidophilic degeneration and a coagulative type of liver cell necrosis were also prominent, particularly in animals with the highest ALT values. Acidophilic bodies with pyknotic nuclei or remnants of nuclear chromatin were frequently observed. Spotty liver cell necrosis, activation of sinusoidal macrophages, and occasional accumulation of mononuclear cells in sinuses were also evident. Within intralobular infiltrates histiocytes appeared to outnumber lymphocytes. Sinusoidal macrophages containing diastase-resistant PAS-positive material were occasionally found in lobules and portal tracts.

Needle biopsy liver specimens from HE-infected *S mystax* were usually found to be inadequate for histopathologic evaluation. However, morphologic changes observed in larger tissue specimens obtained from animals necropsied at or near the peak of liver enzyme activity revealed morphologic changes compatible with those of acute viral hepatitis. Intralobular mononuclear infiltrations often delineated foci of liver cell necrosis and contained lymphocytes and histiocytes mixed with a few polymorphonuclear leukocytes. Portal tracts were enlarged by infiltrations composed of lymphocytes and histiocytes.

Acute HE in experimentally infected chimpanzees was asso-

Hepatitis A (HAV)

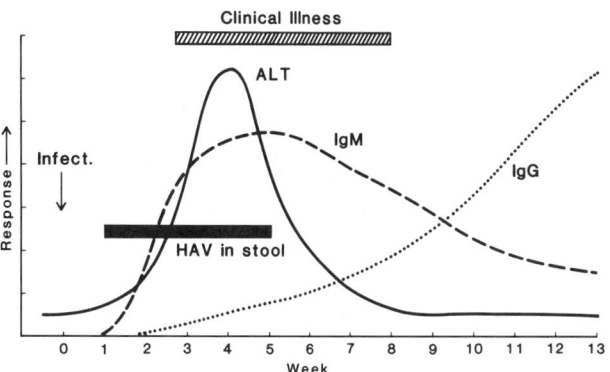

ET-NANBH

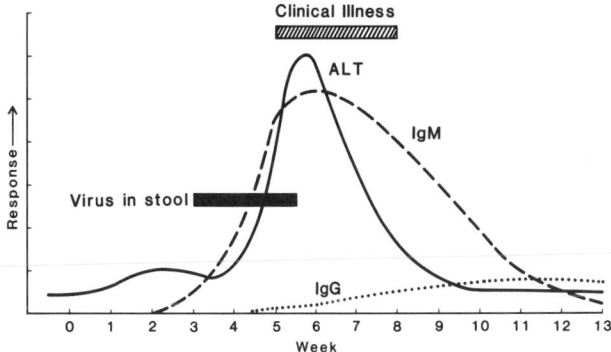

Figure 31–2. Typical responses of individuals infected with either hepatitis A virus or enterically transmitted non-A, non-B hepatitis (ET = NANBH)(hepatitis E) virus. The immune response shown in the case of HE-infected individuals is based on recent immune electron microscopic evidence that suggests convalescent sera are generally of low potency (titer).

ciated with minor alterations in liver tissue, including small areas of focal necrosis, activation of sinusoidal cells, and portal inflammation. A remarkable feature of disease observed in these animals was the relatively small proportion of lymphocytes seen among inflammatory cells.

VIRUSLIKE PARTICLES

The recovery of 27- to 30-nm VLPs from the stools of three of nine sporadic endemic cases of HE in Soviet Central Asia, with subsequent demonstration of their association with disease, provided laboratory support for the notion that epidemic HE is caused by a virus.[6] Transmission of HE to a human volunteer using a pool of 14 stool extracts from these cases, with recovery of morphologically and serologically similar 27- to 30-nm VLPs in the volunteer's acute phase stools, further strengthened the causal relationship between these particles and HE.[6] Identical particles were visualized by IEM in the acute phase stools of cynos that had developed HE after inoculation of a stool extract from the above human volunteer.

Twenty-seven- to twenty-nine-nanometer VLPs were also recovered from the stool of one case of HE occurring in Pune, India.[26] These particles were reportedly aggregated by the patient's own convalescent serum as well as pooled convalescent sera obtained from a HE epidemic in Kolhapur, India. More recently, viruslike particles with a diameter of approximately 27 nm were identified in the stool of one case of HE that was collected during a focal outbreak of disease in Ahmedabad, India.[10] These particles were used to document, by IEM, seroconversion in: (1) a human volunteer with HE;[6] (2) a case of sporadic HE in India; and (3) two experimentally infected chimpanzees. Although the VLPs described in this report were significantly smaller in diameter than those observed in two stools obtained from cases in the USSR and Mexico (see below),[27] there were morphologic similarities, including a rough or "feathery" particle margin, presence of surface indentations, and a conspicuous lack of well-defined, empty capsids.

Other recent studies have yielded electron microscopic and serologic evidence for the strong association of slightly larger VLPs with HE occurring in Nepal,[3] Burma,[9] Pakistan,[22] Tashkent (Uzbekistan, USSR),[26] Somalia,[24] and Mexico.[25] An epidemic of HE in Kathmandu Valley, Nepal provided an opportunity to collect acute phase stools and sera from epidemiologically and serologically characterized cases of disease.[3] IEM examination of nine case stool specimens for VLPs using two different convalescent serum pools (derived from the same outbreak) revealed one that was positive for antibody-aggregated 27- to 32-nm particles. Many of the particles appeared to have characteristic surface indentations and projections. Convalescent (but not preinoculation) serum from an *S mystax* tamarin that had developed HE after inoculation of a case stool positive of 27- to 32-nm VLPs also aggregated the above VLPs. This finding suggested the animal had specifically seroconverted to VLPs contained in the inoculum and further indicated that these particles might be etiologically related to disease. Morphologically and serologically similar 27- to 32-nm VLPs were recovered from stools of the animal just before and during the peak of liver enzyme activity.

Four stools collected from 31 cases of HE in Rangoon, Burma, during a 1982 outbreak were found to be positive by IEM for 27- to 34-nm VLPs.[2, 9] These particles were morphologically similar to those isolated from the Nepal HE case stool, although most particles were slightly larger in diameter and measured between 31 and 35 nm. Aggregation of the Burma stool VLPs by acute phase case sera appeared to result in a much heavier antibody coating than that afforded by the use of convalescent sera.

Table 31–6
Properties of 32 to 34-nm Viruslike Particles Associated With Hepatitis E

1. Sedimentation coefficient approx 183S
2. Degrade when isopyknically banded in CsCl gradient
3. Sensitive to freeze-thawing
4. Particle counts decline in samples stored at $-20°C$
5. Immune aggregates stored at 4 to 8°C spontaneously degrade
6. Storage in liquid N_2 preserves virus capsid integrity
7. May be destroyed by hydrodynamic (shearing) forces during pelleting
8. Has not been cultivated in vitro (BSC-1, Vero, HEK, FRhK-4; 1–3 passes each; 21–28 days per passage)
9. No effect on suckling mice inoculated intracerebrally with 10% wt/vol stool suspension

Morphologically similar VLPs were recovered from the acute phase stool of a Pakistani with HE.[22] These particles displayed the characteristic surface features described above and were most efficiently aggregated by acute phase case sera. Control sera did not aggregate these VLPs, nor did preinoculation serum from a monkey infected with the above Nepal case stool. Acute phase sera from HE cases originating in Pakistan, Nepal, and Burma were uniformly capable of aggregating 27- to 32-nm VLPs in the Pakistani stool; however, as noted, convalescent sera seemed to react less well.

More extensive IEM studies have recently been performed using a stool obtained from a case of HE in Tashkent (Uzbekistan, USSR).[27] These studies strongly suggest that the larger, 32- to 34-nm VLP is etiologically linked to HE (Table 31–6). Normal human sera, including preinoculation serum from a human volunteer and one serum positive for antibody to HAV, failed to aggregate 32- to 34-nm VLPs in the Tashkent No. 1435 stool suspension. Acute phase sera or serum pools from cases of HE occurring in the Soviet Union, Pakistan, Burma, Nepal, Somalia, Sudan, and Mexico were shown to efficiently aggregate the above VLPs; antibody coating on the particles ranged between 2+ and 4+. More convincing evidence for the association between 32- to 34-nm VLPs and disease, however, derives from the demonstrated seroconversion of primates experimentally infected with HE. Cynos infected with Soviet or Burma HE case stools (positive by IEM for 32–34-nm VLPs) were shown to develop acute phase antibody to 32- to 34-nm VLPs in the Tashkent No. 1435 stool suspension.[27] One *S mystax* tamarin infected with the Burma isolate was also shown by IEM to seroconvert to the above VLPs.

Partially purified 32- to 34-nm VLPs derived from the stool of a case of HE occurring in Telixtac, Mexico were also shown to react with acute phase antibody in sera from humans and primates infected with HE.[27] Sera from cases in the Soviet Union, Pakistan, Nepal, Burma, and Mexico were all capable of aggregating 32- to 34-nm VLPs in the Telixtac No. 14 stool; antibody coating on these particles was very heavy, and was rated 4+. Seroconversion of experimentally HE-infected primates was also clearly documented, since all animals tested developed acute phase antibody to the above VLPs. It is important to note that selected cynos from the first, second, and third passage of a Burma HE isolate were shown to acquire virus-specific antibody, thus reinforcing the notion that human-origin HE can be successfully passaged in this species of nonhuman primate.[27]

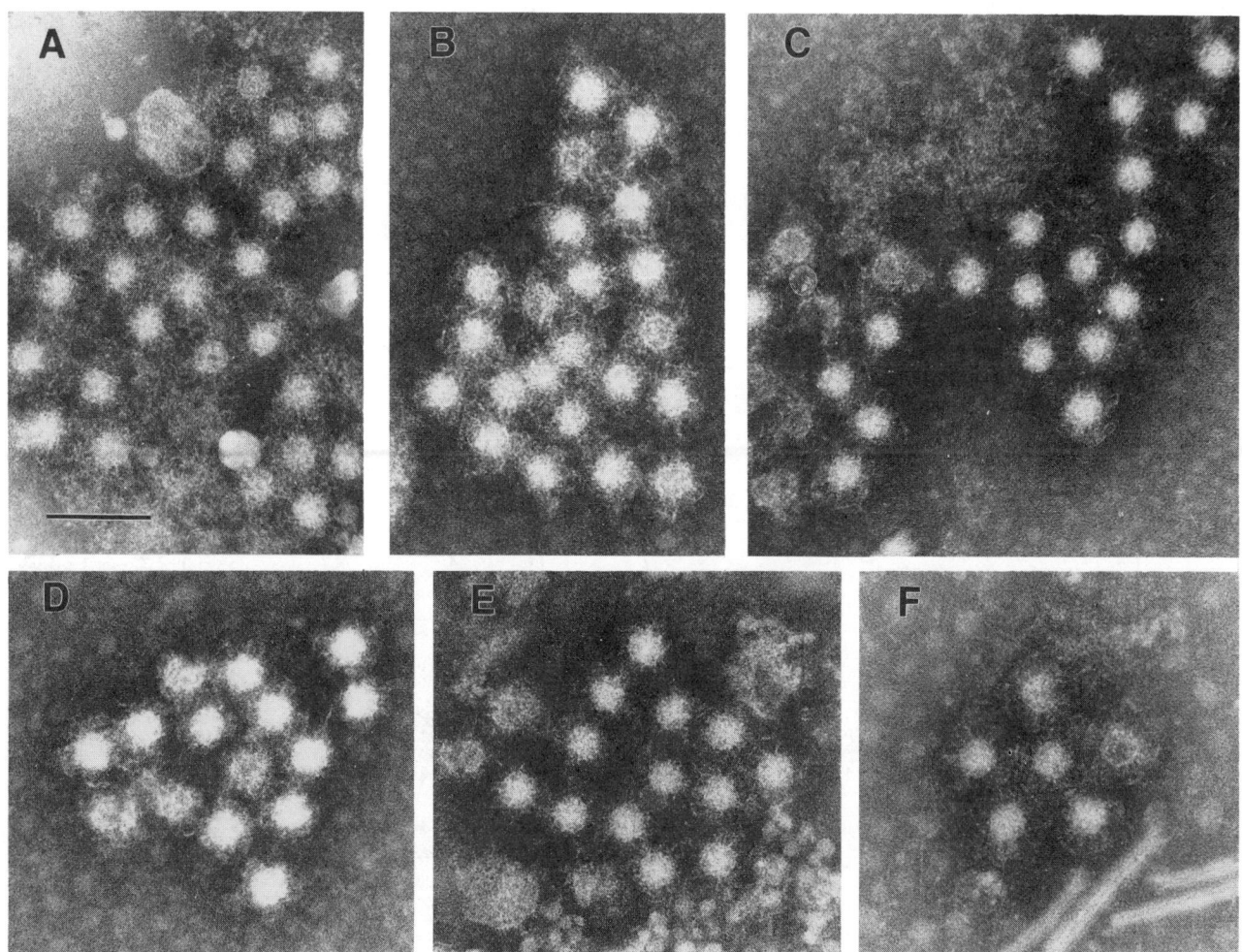

Figure 31–3. Electron micrographs of 32- to 34-nm-diameter viruslike particles recovered from the stools of hepatitis E (HE) cases occurring in the USSR, Somalia, and Mexico. Particles are heavily coated by antibody contained in the patient or primate acute phase serum which was used for immune aggregation. A. Tashkent No. 1435 virus aggregated with antibody from acute phase serum from human volunteer. B,C. Telixtac No. 14 virus (partially purified; 183S peak fraction from rate-zonal gradient) aggregated with antibody from acute phase HE case serum (Mexico No. 4). D. Telixtac No. 14 virus (partially purified) aggregated with antibody from *Saquinas mystax* tamarin acute phase serum. E. Somalia case No. 30 virus (183S peak fraction from rate zonal gradient) aggregated with antibody from Mexico acute phase serum No. 4. F. Tashkent No. 1435 virus coated with antibody from Mexico acute phase serum pool. Bar marker represents 100 nm.

The inconsistency of the above-reported particle diameters may be related to the effects of proteolytic digestion, or to partial denaturation of the virus during passage through the gut.[28] One calicivirus that infects navel orangeworms, for example, has been shown to undergo a reduction in particle diameter from 35 to 38 nm to 27 to 30 nm after treatment with trypsin, a common enzyme found in the frass (excreta) of orangeworms and in the gut of man.[29] In spite of the uncertainty surrounding the physical dimensions of the putative virus of HE, it appears that one virus or class of morphologically and serologically related family of viruses is responsible for disease occurring in Soviet Asia, Asia, North Africa, and North America. Limited cross-challenge studies conducted in cynos further suggest that animals convalescent from a bout of HE induced by an Asian isolate are protected from reinfection by a second (North American) isolate (D. Bradley, unpublished findings, 1987). The latter finding is in agreement with the notion that one virus is responsible for the majority of HE. Figure 31–3 shows antibody-aggregated 32- to 34-nm VLPs identified by IEM in stools of cases occurring in the Soviet Union, Somalia, and Mexico. Antibody used to aggregate these VLPs was derived from human and primate sources representing infections caused by virus isolates from Burma, the Soviet Union, Somalia, and Mexico.

Physicochemical Properties of HE-Associated 27- to 34-nm VLPs

Failure to detect 27- to 34-nm VLPs by IEM in cesium chloride gradient fractions of isopycnically banded stool preparations suggested that the virus of HE is relatively labile and may not survive pelleting from dense salt solutions. It is interesting to note that isopycnically banded Norwalk virus, a morphologically similar

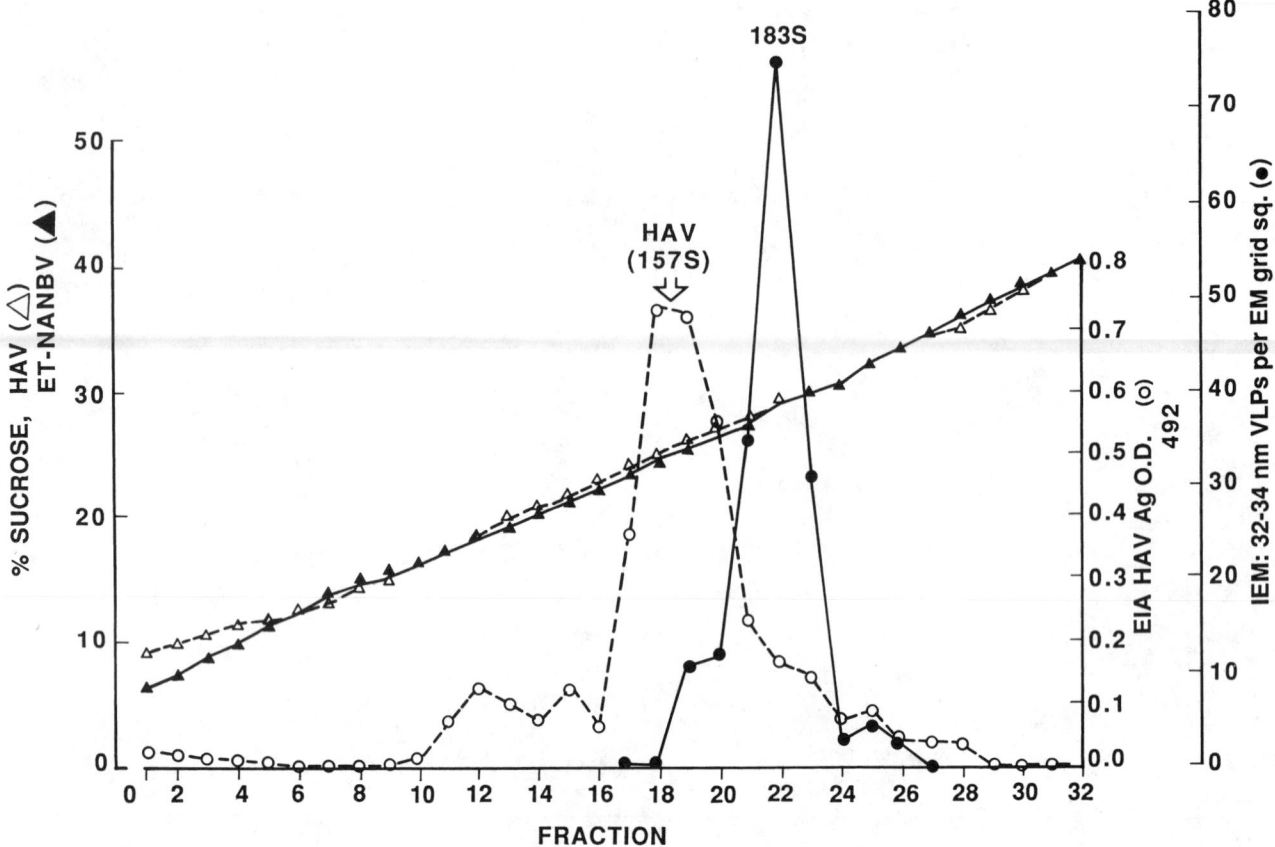

Figure 31–4. Comparative sedimentation profiles of hepatitis A virus (HAV) and enterically transmitted non-A, non-B hepatitis (ET-NANBH) (hepatitis E) virus in sucrose gradients. IEM = immune electron microscopy; VLPs = viruslike particles.

VLP, can only be recovered from CsCl density gradient fractions if they are first dialyzed to remove salt (S. Monroe, personal communication, 1988). Rate-zonal banding of 32- to 34-nm VLPs in linear, preformed sucrose gradients, however, was found to yield partially purified virus suitable for further IEM studies (Fig 31–4). It is of interest to note that 32- to 34-nm VLPs contained in both the Tashkent No. 1435 and Telixtac No. 14 stool suspensions described above sedimented significantly faster in rate-zonal gradients than did HAV run in parallel gradients.[27] The computed sedimentation coefficient of the HE-associated virus was approximately 183S, in contrast to 157S for that of HAV, a member of the *Picornaviridae*.

Other physicochemical properties of the HE-associated VLPs can be inferred from uncontrolled IEM studies of virus-positive stool preparations. Virus particles associated with HE have been shown to be extremely sensitive to freeze-thawing. They also appear to spontaneously degrade when held at 4 to 8°C for periods of time exceeding three to five days. Immune aggregates (virus-antibody complexes) stored at 4 to 8°C also degrade spontaneously. In fact, virus particle counts can decline rapidly (within 24 hours) under such conditions. Storage of 10% wt/vol stool suspension in liquid nitrogen seems to be effective in preserving particle integrity since preparations of partially purified virus made over a 1-year period from frozen stock have revealed similar particle counts by IEM. Table 31–6 summarizes the properties of the larger, undegraded 32- to 34-nm VLPs associated with HE. The histogram in

Figure 31–5 illustrates the range of diameters of virus particles recovered from case stools originating in Burma, the Soviet Union, Somalia, and Mexico. The majority of virus particles measured (78%) had diameters between 31 and 35 nm (mean of length and breadth measurements).

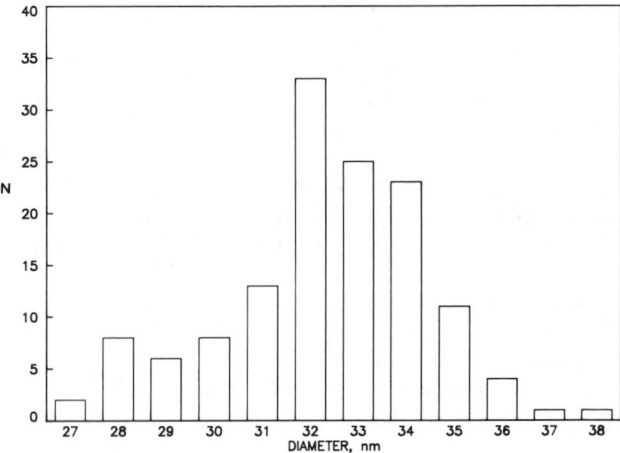

Figure 31–5. Histogram showing the size distribution of hepatitis E–associated viruslike particles.

UNANSWERED QUESTIONS

In developing countries, more than 50% of acute viral hepatitis appears to be caused by agents other than HAV or HBV. It is assumed that a high proportion of HE in these countries is associated with an enterically transmitted agent, since environmental conditions in most endemic areas favor the fecal-oral route of transmission. In this regard, however, the preponderance of clinically apparent HE cases in persons between the ages of 15 and 40 years suggests that infection either occurs subclinically in younger individuals or does not occur at all. The latter presumption is difficult to justify in view of the fact that seroprevalence studies conducted in these countries clearly indicate that nearly all persons acquire anti-HAV antibody before the age of 10. If, on the other hand, younger persons exposed to HE develop subclinical infection, and presumably protective antibody, outbreaks of HE would not be expected to disproportionately affect young-to-middle-aged adults unless waning antibody levels permit reinfection. Clearly, further studies are needed to identify other factors involved in the epidemiology and pathogenesis of HE.

Of perhaps greater importance is the unusually high mortality rate observed in infected pregnant women. Approximately 20% of women in their third trimester of pregnancy succumb to HE infection (or its complications), in contrast to 0.5% to 3.0% of the local or general population suffering from HE. Pregnancy itself does not seem to be the major, predisposing factor since significantly lower mortality rates (3%–8%) are seen in HAV- or HBV-infected pregnant women. In this regard, the unexpectedly high mortality rate observed in HE-infected pregnant women may reflect a unique feature of viral replication or pathogenesis of disease in these women.

Another notable feature of HE is the relatively low incidence of clinical disease observed in case contacts. For example, only 2.4% of household contacts of HE cases developed clinical illness during the 1981–1982 epidemic in Kathmandu Valley, Nepal.[7] This is in sharp contrast to the much higher secondary attack rate of 10% to 20% observed in household contacts of HAV-infected cases occurring in the same region. The relative instability of the 32- to 34-nm VLPs described above may account for the decreased secondary transmission of HE; however, definitive studies of virus stability and infectivity will be required to support or refute this notion.

Finally, many of the physicochemical properties of the larger 32- to 34-nm VLPs described above are similar to those of some calicilike viruses. In fact, the latter viruses are 32 to 38 nm in diameter, possess characteristic surface features, sediment at approximately 180s, are relatively unstable to freeze-thawing, and degrade or disintegrate when pelleted from CsCl density gradient fractions.[30–34] Although it is tempting to speculate that the HE virus is calici-like, its final classification must wait definitive biochemical studies of virion nucleic acid and capsid polypeptide(s) before any assignment to a specific virus group can be made.

ADDENDUM

The virus responsible for HE (HEV) has been cloned and shown to have an approximately 7.6 kb single-stranded, positive-sense RNA genome.[35]

REFERENCES

1. Sergeev NW, Paktoris EA, Ananev WA, et al: General characteristics of Botkin's disease occurring in Kirgiz Republic of USSR in 1955–1956. *Sov Healthcare Kirgizii* 1957; 5:16–23.
2. Myint H, Soe MM, Khin T, et al: A clinical and epidemiological study of an epidemic of non-A, non-B hepatitis in Rangoon. *Am J Trop Med Hyg* 1985; 34:1183–1189.
3. Naidu SS, Viswanathan R: Infectious hepatitis in Delhi (1955–56): a critical study; observations in pregnant women. *Indian J Med Res* 1957; 45:71–76.
4. Hillis A, Shrestha SM, Saha NK: An epidemic of infectious hepatitis in the Kathmandu Valley. *J Nepal Med Assoc* 1973; 11:145–151.
5. Sarthou JL, Budkowska A, Sharma MD, et al: Characterization of an antigen-antibody system associated with epidemic non-A, non-B hepatitis in West Africa and experimental transmission of an infectious agent to primates. *Ann Inst Pasteur (Virology)* 1976; 137E:225–232.
6. Balayan MS, Andjaparidze AG, Savinskaya SS, et al: Evidence for a virus in non-A, non-B hepatitis transmitted via the fecal-oral route. *Intervirology* 1983; 20:23–31.
7. Kane MA, Bradley DW, Shrestha SM, et al: Epidemic non-A, non-B hepatitis in Nepal: recovery of a possible etiologic agent and transmission studies in marmosets. *JAMA* 1984; 252:3140–3145.
8. Andjaparidze AG, Balayan MS, Savinov AP, et al: Fecal-orally transmitted non-A, non-B hepatitis induced in monkeys. *Vopr Virusol* 1986; 1:73–80.
9. Bradley DW, Krawczynski K, Cook EH Jr, et al: Enterically transmitted non-A, non-B hepatitis: Serial passage of disease in cynomolgus macaques and tamarins and recovery of disease-associated 27- to 34-nm viruslike particles. *Proc Natl Acad Sci USA* 1987; 84:6277–6281.
10. Arankalle VA, Ticehurst J, Sreenivasan MA, et al: Etiological association of a virus-like particle with enterically-transmitted non-A, non-B hepatitis. *Lancet* 1988; 2:550–554.
11. Datta R, Panda SK, Tanden BN, et al: Acute sporadic non-A, non-B viral hepatitis of adults in India—epidemiological and immunological studies. *J Gastoenterol Hepatol* 1987; 2:333–345.
12. Nakata S, Chiba S, Terashima H, et al: Humoral immunity in infants with gastroenteritis caused by human calicivirus. *J Infect Dis* 1985; 152:274–279.
13. Cubitt WD, Blacklow NR, Herrmann JE, et al: Antigenic relationships between human caliciviruses and Norwalk virus. *J Infect Dis* 1987; 156:806–814.
14. Khuroo MS: Study of an epidemic of non-A, non-B hepatitis: possibility of another human hepatitis virus distinct from posttransfusion non-A, non-B type. *Am J Med* 1980; 68:818–824.
15. Wong DC, Purcell RH, Sreenivasan MA, et al: Epidemic and endemic hepatitis in India: evidence of a non-A, non-B hepatitis etiology. *Lancet* 1980; 2:876–879.
16. Bradley DW, Maynard JE: Etiology and natural history of posttransfusion and enterically-transmitted non-A, non-B hepatitis. *Semin Liver Dis* 1986; 6:56–66.
17. Viswanathan R: Infectious hepatitis in Delhi (1955–56): A critical study; epidemiology. *Indian J Med Res* 1957; 45(suppl):1–30.
18. Sreenivasan MA, Banerjee K, Pandya PG, et al: Epidemiological investigations of an outbreak of infectious hepatitis in Ahmedabad City during 1975–76. *Indian J Med Res* 1978; 67:197–206.
19. Tandon BN, Joshi YK, Jain SK, et al: An epidemic of non-A, non-B hepatitis in North India. *Indian J Med Res* 1982; 75:739–744.
20. Khuroo MS, Duermeyer W, Zargar SA, et al: Acute sporadic non-A, non-B hepatitis in India. *Am J Epidemiol* 1983; 118:360–364.
21. Shrestha SM, Malla DS: Viral A hepatitis in pregnancy during Kathmandu epidemic. *J Nepal Med Assoc* 1957; 13:58–69.
22. De Cock KM, Bradley DW, Sandford NL, et al: Epidemic non-A, non-B hepatitis in patients from Pakistan. *Ann Intern Med* 1987; 106:227–230.

23. Bellabes H, Benatallah A, Bourguermouh A: Non-A/non-B epidemic viral hepatitis in Algeria: Strong evidence for its water spread, abstracted in Vyas GN, Dienstag JC, Hoofnagle JH (eds): *Viral Hepatitis and Liver Disease*. New York, Grune & Stratton, Inc., 1984, p 637.

24. Centers for Disease Control: Enterically transmitted non-A, non-B hepatitis-East Africa. *MMWR* 1987; 36:241–244.

25. Centers for Disease Control: Enterically transmitted non-A, non-B hepatitis-Mexico. *MMWR* 1987; 36:597–602.

26. Sreenivasan MA, Arankalle VA, Sehgal A, et al: Non-A, non-B epidemic hepatitis: visualization of virus-like particles in the stool by immune electron microscopy. *J Gen Virol* 1984; 65:1005–1007.

27. Bradley DW, Andjaparidze A, Cook EH Jr, et al: Etiologic agent of enterically transmitted non-A, non-B hepatitis. *J Gen Virol* 1988; 69:731–738.

28. Bradley DW, Balayan MS: Virus of enterically transmitted non-A, non-B hepatitis. *Lancet* 1988; 2:819.

29. Hillman B, Morris TJ, Kellen WR, et al: An invertebrate calici-like virus: evidence for partial virion disintegration in host excreta. *J Gen Virol* 1982; 60:115–123.

30. Komolafe O: Effect of storage on the integrity of purified feline calicivirus particles. *Microbios* 1979; 26:137–146.

31. Soergel ME, Smith AW, Schaffer FL: Biophysical comparisons of calicivirus serotypes isolated from pinnepeds. *Intervirology* 1975; 5:239–244.

32. Schaffer FL, Soergel ME: Biochemical and biophysical characterization of calicivirus isolates from pinnipeds. *Intervirology* 1973; 1:210–219.

33. Schaffer FL, Bachrach HL, Brown F, et al: Caliciviridae. *Intervirology* 1980; 14:1–6.

34. Burroughs JN, Brown F: Physico-chemical evidence for the reclassification of the caliciviruses. *J Gen Virol* 1974; 22:281–286.

35. Reyes GR, Purdy MA, Kim JP, et al: Isolation of a cDNA from the virus responsible for enterically transmitted non-A, non-B hepatitis. *Science* 1990; 247:1335–1339.

$$\overline{}\ 32$$

Adenoviruses

Chien Liu

Adenoviruses are ubiquitous. They are a group of important animal viruses and not only owing to their ability to cause illnesses; they have also served as models in studies of molecular biology, genetics, ultrastructure, and virus-host cell interactions. Human adenoviruses are responsible for a wide variety of clinical illnesses ranging from mild upper respiratory diseases in children to large outbreaks of pneumonitis in military recruits. The virus is also responsible for two important conjunctival disorders known as epidemic keratoconjunctivitis and pharyngoconjunctival fever. In addition, a wide variety of systemic disorders including gastroenteritis, myocarditis, polyarthritis, rhabdomyolysis, and skin rashes have been associated with adenovirus infections.

HISTORY

In the early 1950s, while searching for the etiologic agents of the common cold and mild acute respiratory illnesses, two groups of workers independently discovered the adenoviruses. Rowe et al in 1953[1] reported the isolation of an agent which caused spontaneous degeneration of primary tissue culture cells originating from adenoids and tonsils surgically removed from children. Soon after, Hilleman and Werner[2] reported the isolation of similar viral agents from military recruits sick with acute respiratory disease. Different names were used but in 1956, the group name "adenoviruses" was adopted for these newly recognized respiratory tract viruses. At present, 42 serotypes of human adenoviruses have been described.[3] Adenoviruses are found in a number of natural animal hosts including monkeys, cattle, rodents, dogs, and chickens.[4] The general morphology of these viruses from different animals species is remarkably similar.

STRUCTURE AND BIOLOGY OF ADENOVIRUSES

Structure

The virus measures 60 to 90 nm and consists of a naked icosahedral shell known as the capsid. The capsid is composed of 252 capsomers arranged in a 5:3:2 cubic symmetry.[4, 5] The 12 vertex capsomers are called pentons because each is surrounded by five neighboring subunits. Each penton has a fiber, whose length varies with the viral type, and a base plate. The nonvertex capsomers are called hexons, because each is surrounded by six neighboring subunits. Four additional minor capsid proteins (IIIa, VI, VIII, IX) are found in close association with the pentons or hexons. These proteins are felt to maintain virion stability, assist in virion assembly, and form links with the core proteins.[5, 6]

The core is a solid body lying within the capsid. It contains one linear, double-stranded DNA molecule with a molecular weight

Table 32–1
Classification of Human Adenoviruses

Subgenus	Serotypes	Hemagglutination Pattern*	T Antigen Groups	DNA % G + C	Cell Transformation
A	12, 18, 31	IV	A	48	+
B	3, 7, 11, 14, 16, 21, 34, 35	I	B	51	+
C	1, 2, 5, 6	III	C	58	+
D	8, 9, 10, 13, 15, 17, 19, 20, 22, 23, 24, 25, 26, 27, 28, 29, 30, 32, 33, 36, 37, 38, 39	II	D	58	+
E	4	III	?	58	Unknown
F	40, 41, (42)	IV	?	52	+

*I = complete agglutination of rhesus monkey erythrocytes; II = complete agglutination of rat erythrocytes; III = partial agglutination of rat erythrocytes; IV = agglutination of rat erythrocytes only after addition of heterotypic antisera. Adapted from Rosen,[9] Huebner,[10] and Wadell et al.[11]

of approximately 23×10^6 daltons associated with a number of internal core proteins which assist in maintaining genome integrity.[7]

Physical Properties

Adenoviruses have several distinguishing physical characteristics. They retain infectivity for several weeks at 4°C and for months at −25°C.[5] The optimum pH range for infectivity lies between 6.5 and 7.4. Loss of infectivity occurs at 56°C after 2.5 to 5.0 minutes. Adenoviruses are resistant to lipid solvents because of the absence of lipids within their structure. The capsid is sensitive to rapid disruption by 0.25% sodium dodecyl sulfate.

Propagation

The virus can be readily propagated on continuous human cell culture lines such as HeLa, KB, and HEp-2 cells. Embryonated eggs do not support growth. Human embryonic kidney cell culture is preferred for initial viral isolation. In the first 12 to 18 hours of infection, host macromolecular metabolism is markedly reduced and virus replication begins. Within the first six hours, few viral proteins are synthesized, but thereafter viral nucleic acids and proteins are produced in large amounts.[8] The typical cytopathic effects (CPE) observed include cell rounding and clumping. These occur within 14 days of cell culture inoculation.

Methods of Classification

A variety of classification systems have been proposed for human adenoviruses (Table 32–1). In 1960 Rosen[9] grouped serotypes by their ability to agglutinate mammalian red blood cells. Group 1 agglutinated rhesus monkey erythrocytes (Ad 3, 7, 11, 14, 16), group 2 completely agglutinated rat erythrocytes (Ad 8, 9, 10, 13, 15, 17), and group 3 partially agglutinated rat erythrocytes (Ad 1, 2, 4, 5, 6). In 1973 Hierholzer[12] proposed a revised scheme for adenovirus typing by utilizing the fact that many adenoviruses agglutinate the red blood cells of animals other than rats and rhesus monkeys. Thirty-three known serotypes were divided into ten subgroups on the basis of differential hemagglutin-

ation titers with human, monkey, and rat erythrocytes at 37°C. Additional classifications have been proposed which are based on the molecular weight of virion core proteins[13] or the presence of virus-specific proteins known at "T antigens."[12] T antigens represent viral coded polypeptides that are induced in the early stages of infection. Serum from hamsters with adenoviral-induced tumors is reacted with adenovirus-infected human cells. Hamster antibody against the T antigen is then measured by the complement fixation (CF) or immunofluorescence methods. T antigens may be present even in the absence of infectious virus particles, thereby providing a useful marker for adenoviral presence. Green et al[14] extended the groupings of previous workers by placing 31 human adenovirus serotypes into five groups on the basis of DNA genome homologies using liquid-phase molecular hybridization. This system was consistent with the findings of previous workers with respect to the base-ratio content of the viral genome, previous hemagglutination groups, molecular properties of virion substructures, T antigen groups, and epidemiology of human adenoviral infection. Currently, 41 human adenoviruses are divided into six subgenera, A, B, C, D, E, and F.[4, 14] Subgenus F is created to accommodate the newly characterized enteric adenoviruses types 40 and 41. Type 42, recently recovered from the feces of a 14-month-old boy with bowel atresia, will likely be a new candidate of the enteric adenoviruses.[3]

Serologic Typing

Serologic typing of human adenoviruses is useful in epidemiologic studies. The hexons demonstrate both family reactivity (by the CF test) and type specificity (by the neutralization and hemagglutination-inhibition tests). The pentons react as a family-reactive soluble antigen. Fiber antigens are primarily type-specific.[5] In general, the CF test can be readily performed and can detect recent infections with specific serotypes, except in infants in whom the antibody response may be low. CF antibodies become detectable seven days after the onset of illness, and decline over the next 2 to 12 months. Neutralization antibodies develop along with the CF antibodies but persist for longer periods without a substantial decrease in titer.

Oncogenic Potential

Correlations have been made between the base ratios of the different adenoviral types and their respective oncogenic potentials in animals. Serotypes 12, 18, and 31 have the lowest guanine-cytosine DNA base composition (47%–49%) and have the greatest animal oncogenic potential. Adenovirus types 3, 7, 11, 14, 16, and 21 have a ratio of 50% to 53% and are weakly oncogenic. The remainder have ratios between 50% and 60%. Hybridization occurs between closely related adenoviral types and SV40, a similar papovavirus with oncogenic activity. Adenoviruses, to date, have not been found to be oncogenic in humans.

Adeno-Associated Viruses

Adeno-associated viruses (AAV) are small (20–25 nm) defective parvoviruses containing single-stranded DNA which were first noted as contaminants in adenovirus cultures. AAVs are not subunits of adenoviruses but require helper activity from serologically unrelated adenoviruses for active replication.[15, 16] The exact mechanism by which adenoviruses stimulate AAV replication is not known. It has been shown, however, that other DNA or RNA viruses, inactivated adenovirus strains, or cells transformed by adenoviruses which contain T antigens do not support AAV replication.[15] In order for AAV replication to be detected, active adenovirus multiplication or some adenovirus genetic functional units occurring later than T antigen formation are required. Four serotypes have been recognized by CF, immunodiffusion, fluorescent antibody, and neutralization techniques. Human disease has not been associated with these viruses, but they have been shown to be interesting epidemiologic markers for adenoviral infections.

Blacklow et al[17] noted that 30% of children less than 30 months of age had CF antibodies to AAV types 2 and/or 3. Serologic evidence for AAV infection occurred more frequently in children who were ill with adenoviral respiratory disease than in those who were asymptomatic. Parks et al[18] showed that antibody titers by the neutralization method reached a peak at 2 to 3 years of age for types 1, 2, and 3. Type 4 antibodies were rarely found in human sera. Schmidt et al[19] noted a high rate of isolation of AAV

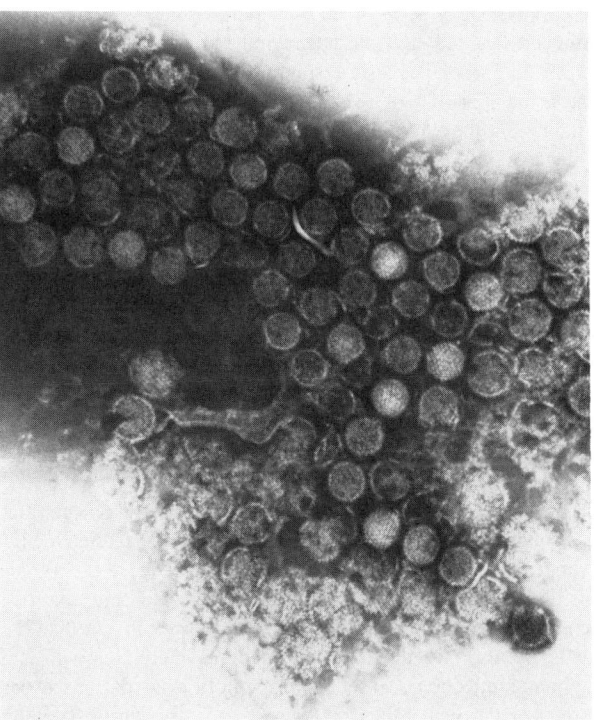

Figure 32–1. Electron micrograph of adenovirus type 5 from clinical specimens, negatively stained (×92,000). (Courtesy of H. D. Mayor, Baylor College of Medicine.)

type 3 in patients affected with conjunctivitis induced by adenovirus type 3. Further elucidation is required to determine the role of adeno-associated viruses in human disease.

ILLNESSES ASSOCIATED WITH ADENOVIRUSES

Adenoviruses cause a wide spectrum of respiratory illnesses in both children and adults (Table 32–2). The prevalence of the endemic serotypes has often been underestimated due to the clinically insignificant illnesses that they frequently cause. In contrast, considerable attention has been generated by the sporadically occurring epidemic serotypes, which have resulted in significant morbidity in closely associated populations such as day care centers and military training camps.

Endemic Respiratory Diseases

In 1953 Rowe et al[1] found evidence for the presence of latent agents which caused spontaneous degeneration of tissue cultures originating from surgically removed adenoids and tonsils. Huebner et al[20] further classified these as "adenoidal-pharyngeal-conjunctival" agents and identified adenoviral serotypes 1 through 6 as a cause of mild upper respiratory diseases (Fig 32–1).

Adenoviruses types 1, 2, and 5 are now recognized as endemic in North America and Europe. These serotypes can be demonstrated as latent infectious agents in 50% to 90% of surgically removed tonsils.[21] Approximately half of the infections caused by these serotypes remain asymptomatic.[22, 23] In those persons with symptomatic illnesses, types 2, 1, 7, 3 and 5 (in that order) account

Table 32–2
Illnesses Associated With Adenoviruses

Illness Category	Common Serotypes
A. Endemic respiratory disease	1,2,5
B. Acute respiratory disease of military recruits	3,4,7,14,21
C. Adenoviral pneumonias	3,4,7b,14,21
D. Epidemic keratoconjunctivitis	8,19
E. Pharyngoconjunctival fever	3,7
F. Less common syndromes	
1. Pertussis syndrome	1,2,3,5
2. Acute hemorrhagic cystitis	1,4,7,11,21
3. Hepatic disorders	3,7
4. Gastroenteritis	9,12,13,18,25,26,27, 28,40,41,42
5. Intussusception	1,2,5
6. Musculoskeletal disorders	7
7. Genital infections	19
8. Skin infections	2,4,7,21
9. Immunocompromised hosts	32,34,35,36

for approximately 95% of all adenoviral isolates.[24] It has been estimated that the endemic adenoviral serotypes are responsible for 2% to 7% of pediatric respiratory diseases in major United States cities[22] and 5% of all childhood respiratory illnesses in Great Britain.[25] By the age of 2 1/2 years, 50% to 70% of children show evidence of adenovirus infection with serotypes 1 and 2 by serum neutralization tests. Thirty percent of the same age group possess neutralizing antibodies to serotypes 3 and 5.[21] When all age groups are considered, serotypes 1 and 2 are isolated most frequently from those with respiratory illnesses, while the epidemic strains 3 and 7 are more frequently isolated from older children and adults.[23, 26]

Transmission of the endemic adenoviral strains occurs through respiratory and fecal excretion of the virus. Prolonged, intermittent excretion (up to 906 days with serotype 2) has been documented, but persistent shedding has not been demonstrated. It is therefore postulated that generation-to-generation transmission of the virus does not occur.[23]

Symptomatic infections with the endemic serotypes occur after an incubation period of five to ten days. Clinical features include fever (in over 80% of cases), pharyngitis (69% of cases), and tonsillitis and cough (63% of cases). Coryza, vomiting, diarrhea, meningeal signs, and pulmonary infiltrates occur in less than half of all patients.[26] Roentgenographic findings in children with viral respiratory infections caused by respiratory syncytial virus, parainfluenza viruses, influenza viruses, and adenoviruses demonstrated that hilar adenopathy was more common in adenovirus infection.[27]

Acute Respiratory Disease in Military Recruits

The epidemic nature of certain adenoviral strains has been recognized since 1954, when Hilleman and Werner[2] associated a newly isolated virus with acute respiratory disease (ARD) in military recruits. Adenovirus types 3, 4, 7b, 14, and 21[28, 29] are now recognized as significant upper and lower respiratory tract pathogens capable of causing outbreaks of pneumonia with occasional sequelae of chronic lung damage. These serotypes account for 22% of all adenoviral strains isolated from epidemics, with types 3 and 4 occurring most frequently (Fig 32–2).[28]

In the United States, serotypes 4 and 7 account for 60% of all acute respiratory illnesses in military recruits who require hospitalization.[30, 31] Serotypes 3, 14, and 21 are less commonly implicated.[32, 33] An intermediate adenoviral strain (Ad 14–11) has been reported to cause upper respiratory disease in a Spanish military camp.[34] This isolate possessed high hemagglutination inhibition titers to Ad 14 and high serum neutralization antibody titers to Ad 11. Although ARD can occur year round, peak epidemics are more prevalent in the fall, winter, and spring months. Up to 80% of recruits have been reported to develop adenoviral infections; of these, as many as 20% may require hospitalization. The yearly median attack rate for new recruits in the United States ranges from 6 to 16.7 cases per 100 each month.[31] The attack rate for seasoned military personnel is considerably lower due to the acquisition of immunity within the first 6 weeks of training.[35] Reported attack rates are similar for recruits in Western European countries. They are considerably lower in Taiwan,[36] Colombia,[37] and Argentina,[38] where immunity probably is acquired early in life, and prior to induction, through close association in crowded living quarters.

Most cases of ARD in recruits are noted by the end of the third week in training. Clinically, the illness is characterized by a three- to four-day history of fever, malaise, nasal congestion, sore throat, hoarseness, headache, and cough. Ten percent of all recruits with symptoms of ARD develop patchy pulmonary infiltrates, predominantly in the lower lobes.[39] However, these chest x-ray findings do not correlate well with the severity of clinical illness.[40] The presence of infiltrates usually extends the duration of the illness to 3 weeks.

In marked contrast to military recruits, adenoviruses are associated with only a very small proportion (0.3%–3.0%) of respiratory illnesses in civilian adult populations, including college students,[41, 42] who also live in closely associated living quarters such as dormitories. The reason for this difference remains unexplained.

Adenoviral Pneumonias

The first cytopathogenic agent, named RI-67, isolated by Hilleman and Werner in 1954[2] was from a serviceman at Fort Leonard Wood, Missouri, with a clinical diagnosis of primary atypical pneumonia (PAP). This agent subsequently was designated as adenovirus type 4. Although type 4 and type 7 adenoviruses are important etiologic agents for ARD, their role in causing significant pneumonitis is minor. On the other hand, sporadic cases of fatal

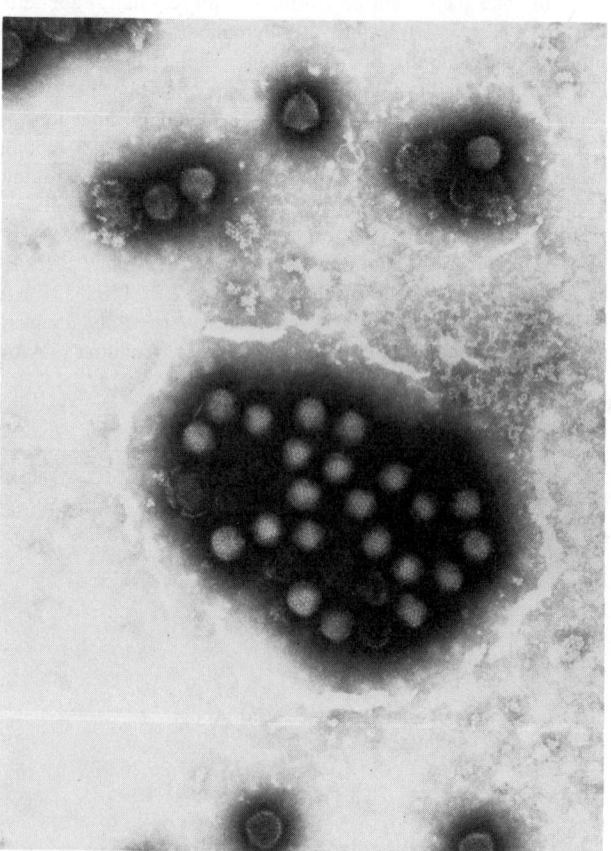

Figure 32–2. Electron micrograph of adenovirus type 4 from clinical specimens negatively stained, magnified (×92,000). (Courtesy of H. D. Mayor, Baylor College of Medicine.)

pneumonia caused by these viruses in military recruits have occurred.[43–45] Adenovirus types 3 and 7 have been responsible for outbreaks of severe or fatal pneumonia in infants and young children from France,[46] Finland,[47] and China.[48] During the Chinese epidemic between October 1958 to January 1959, more than 3000 cases of respiratory illnesses were seen at the Peking Children's Hospital with a fatality rate of 15.5%.[48] Adenovirus serotypes 3 and 7 predominated in this outbreak with other viral agents, such as influenza A virus, occurring less frequently. In other outbreaks, it has been reported that antecedent illnesses such as measles substantially increases the mortality rate of adenoviral infections.[49] A study of Ad 3 infection in Israel involved eight apparently normal children. All eight patients had fever lasting at least seven days, hepatomegaly, diffuse pulmonary infiltrates, and abnormal liver function tests. Six of the patients developed changes in the status of consciousness with three patients having repeated convulsions. Electroencephalographic patterns of the three patients were compatible with encephalopathy. The authors stated that this Ad 3 infection shared the potential of disseminated disease simulating Reye syndrome.[50] Ad 30 was not considered to be a respiratory pathogen previously. However, a fatal case of pneumonia in a newborn caused by Ad 30 was reported in which the suggested mode of transmission was likely to have ascended from the birth canal.[51] The clinical symptomatology of adenoviral pneumonias includes fever, cough, dyspnea, and inspiratory and expiratory wheezing. Roentgenographs show bronchopneumonia with diffuse patchy infiltrates, bronchial wall thickening, streaky peribronchial opacities, and pulmonary hyperinflation.[52] Massive pleural effusions may also be present.[53] Associated extrapulmonary manifestations may include meningoencephalitis, myocarditis, gastroenteritis, conjunctivitis, rashes, rhabdomyolysis, nephritis, hepatitis, and disseminiated intravascular coagulation.[29, 54, 55]

Adenovirus type 7 is frequently associated with severe illnesses. Using DNA restriction techniques, Wadell and associates[29] demonstrated three different genome subtypes: Ad 7 prototype, Ad 7a (vaccine strain), and Ad 7b. Ad 7b was associated with severe epidemics of respiratory illnesses including febrile pneumonias, abdominal symptoms, and meningismus. Analysis of 36 adenovirus isolates collected from several epidemics (Paris, 1956; United States, 1973; England, 1973, 1974, and 1977; Sweden, 1976–1977) showed all of them to be Ad 7b subtype. Wadell et al concluded that genome subtype Ad 7b was responsible for a significant number of severe adenoviral infections and suggested that vaccination of institutionalized children could be considered during years when Ad 7 epidemics appear. Fatal cases of Ad 7 pneumonia show characteristic histopathologic findings with necrotizing bronchitis and bronchiolitis, hyaline membrane formation, and patchy alveolar fibrinopurulent exudates.[56, 57] In areas of consolidation, distinctive halo-outlined eosinophilic intranuclear inclusion bodies are seen in bronchiolar epithelium and alveolar lining cells.[57] In a rare case of Ad 3 pneumonia developing in an adult patient while hospitalized in a respiratory intensive care unit, an open lung biopsy showed hyaline membranes and necrotizing hemorrhagic pneumonitis with occasional intranuclear inclusions.[58]

Epidemics of bronchopneumonia caused by serotype 21 occur less frequently. There have been two widespread outbreaks reported in Polynesian children from Auckland, New Zealand, in 1965[59] and in 1977.[60] In the former epidemic, two (8%) of 25 patients died, and 60% (14/23) of the survivors demonstrated residual lung damage thought to be secondary to obliterative bronchiolitis. Sporadic outbreaks of pneumonitis caused by adenovirus serotype 21 have been reported in adults.[61] Closely related intermediate strains are also capable of causing disease.[62]

Several studies in children with follow-up examination 5 to 13 years after pneumonitis caused by adenovirus types 1, 3, 4, 7, and 21 have shown significant chronic lung damage.[59, 60, 63–66] Between 7% and 64% of the patients who survived the pneumonia developed bronchiectasis. Herbert et al[64] detailed an unusually severe Ad 3 epidemic that occurred in 1964 in 19 North American Indian infants hospitalized in crowded quarters. Of 14 children who developed pneumonitis and were examined on follow-up 8 to 10 years later, ten showed evidence of chronic lung damage. This was manifested by restrictive and obstructive changes on pulmonary function tests, and roentgenographic demonstration of bronchiectasis, pulmonary fibrosis, or atelectasis. Similä et al[63] in Finland reported a 10-year follow-up study on children with Ad 7 pneumonia. Of 22 children examined 9.6 to 12.1 (mean 10.7) years after the pneumonia, 12 had abnormal chest roentgenograms, with six showing bronchiectasis. Six of the ten children with normal chest x-rays and ten of the 12 with abnormal chest x-ray films had abnormal pulmonary function tests. The authors attempted to investigate if there were any factors predisposing children to pulmonary sequelae. They suggested that atopic disposition might predispose these children with pneumonia to asthma and small-airway obstruction, leading to the development of bronchiectasis.

Epidemic Keratoconjunctivitis

Epidemic keratoconjunctivitis (EKC) has been recognized as a disease entity since the late 1880s when several Australian ophthalmologists described a clinical syndrome characterized by conjunctivis, pain, photophobia, and lacrimation followed by superficial corneal erosions and deeper subepithelial corneal infiltrates.[67] In 1930, investigators implicated a viral etiology by demonstrating disease transmission to volunteers through filtered conjunctival washings.[68] The prototype of adenovirus type 8 was first isolated in 1955 from conjunctival scrapings inoculated into HeLa tissue culture cells.[69] Subsequent inoculation of this agent into human volunteers reproduced the features of naturally occurring illness.[70]

Although sporadic reports of outbreaks were noted in the United States before 1941,[71] it was not until the war years when renewed interest was attached to this disease because of the widespread morbidity it caused in industrial and shipyard workers, hampering war production. In the summer of 1941, more than 10,000 cases occurred in the naval shipyards of Pearl Harbor, Hawaii, particularly in those individuals who had sustained minor trauma to the eyes by foreign bodies. The disease spread to the West Coast of the United States during 1941 to 1942 where it was known as "shipyard eye" and subsequently to the East Coast.[72] Hogan and Crawford coined the current term "epidemic keratoconjunctivitis."[73]

Epidemiologic studies of major outbreaks in Western countries have implicated adenovirus type 8,[74–81] type 19,[82–87] and type 37 as the most frequent causative agents. Mixed outbreaks with both viral types are not uncommon. Adenoviral types 3 and 7 have been identified as causes of sporadic outbreaks; types 1, 2, 4, 5, 6, 9, 10, 11, 13, 14, 15, and 29 are rarely implicated.[88, 89]

Typical clinical illness of EKC affects males between 20 and 40 years of age and lasts 4 to 6 weeks. Unilateral or bilateral follicular conjunctivitis develops within the first ten to 15 days of illness associated with a foreign-body sensation, lacrimation, mucopurulent discharge, prominent eyelid edema, and subconjunctival hemorrhage. Associated systemic manifestations occur in 50% of the patients and consist of preauricular adenopathy, pharyngitis, and rhinitis. Less common symptoms include fever, malaise, diarrhea, and vomiting.[84, 89] Keratitis is typically seen in this illness. Within one to seven days after infection, diffuse epithelial keratitis develops. By the end of the first week, focal epithelial lesions occur. After 2 weeks, the conjunctivitis begins to subside and small (1-mm) round subepithelial opacities can be seen in the corneal stroma. Pseudomembrane formation may occur in severe infections resulting in scarring.[77, 87, 90]

Inherent properties of the adenovirus account for the clinical modes of transmission. Tissue culture studies have shown that only a very small proportion of the total amount of virus produced is infectious.[91] This may explain the low rate of transmission despite the absence of demonstrable antibodies to adenovirus type 8 in 88% to 95% of the United States population.[89, 92, 93] Epidemiologic studies have documented that a major factor in the transmission of adenovirus type 8 is the ability to survive long periods of time outside the human body. There is no decline in viral infectivity after six days at 37°C; 2 weeks at 22°C, and 3 months at 4°C, allowing extended survival on fomites.[94] Antecedent eye trauma, concurrent bacterial infection, or direct viral inoculation into the eye predisposes to clinical infection. Cyclic changes in the frequency of isolation of adenovirus from patients with conjunctivitis were shown to correlate with monthly total hours of sunshine. This observation suggested that sunshine may predispose to clinical infection of eyes contaminated with adenovirus.[95] Outbreaks of adenoviral keratoconjunctivitis in medical facilities have been linked to contaminated ophthalmic instruments (tonometers), solutions, or the hands of doctors and nurses.[76–78] The risk of viral infection appears greater when foreign bodies have been removed from the eye. Community outbreaks have occurred in schools, swimming pools, and refugee camps. Direct hand-to-eye[85] contact and fomites, such as contaminated towels,[78, 80] have been implicated. In countries such as Japan, where adenovirus type 8 infection is more common, a different epidemiologic pattern has been described. Young children develop a membranous conjunctivitis, fever, and either respiratory or gastrointestinal (GI) symptoms. The cornea is virtually never involved. When the infection spreads to adult family members, typcial corneal subepithelial opacities occur and systemic symptoms are lacking.[94, 95]

The differential diagnosis of adenoviral keratoconjunctivitis includes herpes simplex and zoster keratoconjunctivitis, ocular vaccinia, acute hemorrhagic conjunctivitis caused by enterovirus 70 (a picornavirus), and chlamydial conjunctivitis. Bacterial conjunctivitis with the Koch-Weeks bacillus, *Haemophilus aegyptius* has also been associated with outbreaks of EKC.[76, 80, 96]

The treatment of epidemic keratoconjunctivitis is symptomatic. Secondary bacterial or herpetic infection should be treated. Topical steroid treatment may delay the appearance of subepithelial corneal infiltrates,[97] but may also contribute to prolonged viral shedding and ultimately delay final corneal healing.[98]

Pharyngoconjunctival Fever

Pharyngoconjunctival fever is a disease manifested by conjunctivitis, fever, and mild pharyngitis commonly associated with adenoviral types 3, 4, and 7.

In 1925 Paderstein[99] noted the association between swimming pools and the development of a febrile illness with conjunctivitis. Subsequent outbreaks were described in the United States[100, 101] and Australia.[102] In 1954 adenoviral type 3 was implicated by a rise in CF and neutralization titers in affected patients.[103] A large outbreak in Washington, DC, by this serotype provided the first opportunity for detailed epidemiologic study.[104] The illness occurs in all age groups; however, it is found to be more severe in children. After an incubation period of five to seven days, unilateral or bilateral conjunctivitis develops. Systemic symptoms of mild throat tenderness and fevers to 104°F frequently accompany the ocular involvement. Physical examination typically shows bulbar and palpebral follicular conjunctivitis, an injected posterior pharynx, and nontender submaxillary or preauricular lymphadenopathy. Gastrointestinal and respiratory symptoms are less commonly seen. The illness lasts seven to eight days[105] with no permanent eye injury.

Adenovirus types 3 and 7 are now recognized[103–108] as common causes of the syndrome. However, types 1, 2, 4, 5, 6, 11, 14, and 19 are occasionally implicated.[109–111] Recently, adenoviral intermediate strains have also been reported to be associated with the syndrome.[112, 113]

Although sporadic outbreaks have been described, most epidemics have been associated with swimming facilities where chlorination was presumed or proved to be inadequate.[104, 107, 114–116] Infection occurs either through direct contact with infected water, or secondarily by person-to-person spread in affected households. Since adenovirus type 3 can be inactivated by chlorine in 180 seconds, transmission of the virus in a well-chlorinated pool is unlikely.[117] Adenovirus type 4 has been isolated from the water of a swimming pool where chlorine levels were below the recommended 0.4 mg/L.[118] Breakpoint chlorination and closing of the pool for the summer stopped the spread of this outbreak of pharyngoconjunctival fever.

The differential diagnosis of pharyngoconjunctival fever includes influenza, herpangina, leptospirosis, epidemic keratoconjunctivitis, and inclusion conjunctivitis.

Management of pharyngoconjunctival fever is symptomatic. Prevention of disease spread can be accomplished by maintaining adequate chlorination levels in public swimming facilities. Infection among household members can be diminished by avoiding contact with contaminated secretions or fomites (such as towels) and through the use of frequent handwashing.[115–117]

Less Common Clinical Syndromes

Adenoviruses are now recognized to cause a number of less frequently seen syndromes, including a pertussis-like illness; renal, musculoskeletal, and hepatic dysfunction; gastroenteritis; and intestinal intussusception. Specific serotypes have also been isolated from skin and genital tract specimens. These rare clinical entities are described below.

Pertussis Syndrome

The role of adenovirus infection in association with clinical pertussis has not been defined. Early studies from the 1930s noted the presence of intranuclear inclusion bodies in lung specimens of children who had died after infection with pertussis.[119, 120] Subsequent work noted the association between adenoviral types 1, 2, 3, and 5 and a pertussis-like disease without actual culture-proven or serologic evidence for *Bordetella pertussis* infection.[121–123] In 1975 Nelson et al[124] reported a significant increase in adenoviral isolates in patients who had positive cultures of *B pertussis*. Adenoviral infections were noted in 18 of 46 patients (39.1%) with positive cultures of *Bordetella* and in 12 of 88 patients (13.6%) with negative cultures. More recent work by Keller et al[125] failed to implicate adenoviruses as the sole agent in causing the pertussis syndrome. When patients with positive cultures for *Bordetella* were compared with patients with negative *Bordetella* cultures, there was no significant difference in the adenovirus isolation rates of 33% (13/39) versus 14% (5/36) for the two groups. The authors considered several possible explanations for the concurrent shedding of pertussis bacilli and adenovirus, including reactivation of latent infection or synergistic interaction. They concluded that, although confirmation of adenovirus infection or recrudescent shedding of adenovirus is frequently found in infants and children, it cannot be considered as a major, primary etiologic agent for the pertussis syndrome.

Acute Hemorrhagic Cystitis

Adenoviral types 1, 4, and 7 were among the first to be isolated from urine specimens.[126, 127] In 1973 Numazaki et al[128] described a large study in Japan in which adenovirus type 11 was isolated from the urine from 20 of 28 patients (71.4%) with the diagnosis of acute hemorrhagic cystitis (AHC). Most affected individuals were between the ages of 6 and 15 years and developed a self-limited disease characterized by gross hematuria, urgency, frequency, and occasionally fever. Mufson et al[129] noted that AHC was the most common diagnosis among children admitted with gross hematuria and symptoms of cystitis at a large United States metropolitan hospital. Of 69 children with AHC, adenovirus type 11 was recovered from the urine of 10 (14%) and adenovirus type 21 from the urine of two (3%). Twelve patients had *Escherichia coli* bacteriuria. These authors concluded that AHC in children has at least two causes. Adenovirus type 11 or *E coli* infection accounted for 40% of the illnesses. The majority of AHC remains unexplained. Steigbigel et al[130] reported the association of red blood cell casts in urinary sediments with adenovirus type 7a infection. In renal transplant patients, AHC caused by adenovirus types 11 and 2 has been reported.[131–134] Newly identified adenovirus serotypes have been isolated from immunocompromised patients. Adenovirus type 34 was first recovered from the urine of a renal transplant recipient.[135] Adenovirus type 35 was initially recovered from the lung and renal tissues of a patient with a fatal case of interstitial pneumonitis 55 days after receiving a cadaveric renal allograft.[136]

Gastroenteritis

Adenovirus-associated gastroenteritis accounts for 15% of all hospitalized cases of viral gastroenteritis.[137] Adenovirus types 9, 12, 13, 18, and 25 through 28 were among the first to be isolated from the stools of children with acute nonbacterial gastroenteritis.[138] Subsequent workers, however, noted the presence of substantial numbers of adenovirus particles in the feces of infants with gastroenteritis which could not be grown by standard tissue culture techniques.[139] These noncultivatable adenoviruses have been linked to sporadic[140] and/or fatal[141] cases of gastroenteritis in children and to occasional hospital ward outbreaks.[142, 143]

A new subgenus F consisting of enteric adenovirus Ad 40 and Ad 41 has been established.[11] More recently, a new candidate, Ad 42 may be added to this subgenus.[3] The enteric adenoviruses differ from all other adenoviruses by their inability to grow in human embryonic kidney cells or in most heteroploid cell lines.[144] The most reliable cell lines for cultivating enteric adenoviruses are the 293 cells and tCMK cells. Serologic differentiation into either Ad 40 or Ad 41 are best performed by serum neutralization titrations on tCMK cells.[145] Clinical manifestations of enteric adenovirus gastroenteritis[146] in children include an incubation period of seven to eight days, followed by a moderate disease with diarrhea and vomiting. Fever and respiratory symptoms are not common. Clinically, patients infected with Ad 40 or with Ad 41 on the whole are quite similar. However, Ad 41-infected children tend to be older (28 vs 15 months) and have more abdominal pain and a more protracted diarrhea. In a longitudinal 29-month study involving 70 families in the metropolitan Washington, DC area, an adenovirus was detected in approximately 6% of children with gastroenteritis. Confirmed enteric adenovirus cases by isolation of the virus in tissue culture or by electron microscopic procedure were found in approximately 2% of episodes of gastroenteritis in children under 2 years of age.[147]

Intussusception

Adenovirus types 1, 2, and 5 are most commonly recovered from stools, throat swabs, and mesenteric lymph nodes of young children with intussusception.[148–150] Serologic studies have noted an increased incidence of recent adenoviral infection with these endemic serotypes prior to intussusception. In 90% of the cases studied, intussusception begins at the distal ileum or the ileocecal valve.[151] Adenoviruses are felt to induce intussusception by altering intestinal motility or by inducing hyperplasia of the lymphoid tissues of the ileum and mesentery.[152] Viral particles have been demonstrated in intranuclear inclusion bodies of epithelial cells from patients with acute appendicitis and ileocecal intussusception.[152, 153]

Musculoskeletal Disorders

Adenoviruses have been associated with rhabdomyolysis[49, 154] and acute nonspecific febrile polyarthritis with clinical findings similar to those seen in juvenile rheumatoid arthritis (Still's disease).[155] Rahal et al[156] described a 9-year-old girl who developed juvenile rheumatoid arthritis after adenovirus type 7 was isolated from pericardial fluid. Panush[157] described a 19-year-old recruit who developed a febrile inflammatory arthritis involving both knees associated with acute respiratory disease, aseptic meningitis, and a macular erythematous rash. Serum C3 was elevated during the acute illness while serum C4 was depressed. Group-specific CF antibodies indicated infection by adenovirus type 7.

Genital Infections

Harnett and Newnham[158] reported the isolation of adenovirus type 19 from urethral and cervical specimens of men and women attending a sexually transmitted diseases clinic in western Australia. Peak incidence of genital infection correlated with cases of conjunctivitis and keratoconjunctivitis in the community at the same time. A possible association between orchitis in a 5-year-old boy and adenovirus has been reported. However, in this patient, coxsackieviruses and lymphocytic choriomeningitis virus were not excluded as etiologic agents.[159]

Skin Infections

Skin eruptions can be rarely seen with adenoviral infections. Morbilliform eruptions have been reported in association with types 2, 4, 7, and 21, but in these cases antecedent infection with measles was not definitively excluded.[160] Other reported exanthems have been described as urticarial, Stevens-Johnson-like, scarlatinaform, or (in adults), rubelliform.[161] Adenovirus type 1 has been isolated from recurrent oral ulcerations. Adenoviral antigen was detectable by immunofluorescent staining in the nuclei of the cells taken directly from the ulcers.[162]

SYSTEMIC ADENOVIRAL INFECTIONS

Viruses with latency such as cytomegalovirus, herpes simplex virus, and varicella-zoster virus are the ones most frequently associated with chronic or life-threatening systemic viral infections in immunocompromised hosts. Since adenoviruses can also establish latency in the infected hosts, their reactivation would be expected in patients following transplantation and immunosuppression. Case reports of disseminated adenoviral infection in bone marrow transplant recipients,[163, 164] and immunocompromised patients[165–168] have been recorded in the literature. Among 262 children receiving liver transplantaton, 22 had developed adenoviral infection.[169] Five had adenoviral hepatitis in the allograft caused by serotype 5. Liver biopsy specimens showed characteristic histopathologic changes with positive viral cultures. The remaining 17 patients had adenoviruses isolated, predominantly serotypes 1 and 2, from urine, stool, throat secretions, and/or blood samples, but none had any detectable visceral infection. In children, a clinical and pathologic syndrome with cerebral edema, fatty liver, and hepatic dysfunction characteristic of Reye syndrome has been reported in association with adenovirus types 3 and 7.[170, 171]

LABORATORY DIAGNOSIS OF INFECTION

Laboratory diagnosis of recent adenoviral infection may be accomplished by isolation of the virus or serologic studies.[172] Viral isolation is best performed in primary human embryonic kidney cell cultures which will show typical CPE within two to 20 days after inoculation with conjunctival, nasopharyngeal, or stool specimens.[64] Patient specimens may yield a more rapid diagnosis by immunofluorescent staining using antiserum prepared in rabbits against a specific adenoviral serotype.[173, 174] In lung specimens the

occurrence of smaller eosinophilic, halo-outlined, intranuclear inclusions and the presence of larger basophilic, intranuclear inclusions in desquamating alveolar lining cells is said to be characteristic of adenoviral infections.[175] The presence of chronic inflammatory cells in conjunctival scrapings offers indirect evidence for viral involvement. CF, neutralization, and hemagglutination-inhibition tests are useful in the retrospective confirmation of a recent infection. Convalescent antibody titer rise occurs ten to 14 days after an acute infection. Type-specific antibody titers may persist as long as 10 years after acute infection. More recent methods for detecting adenoviruses in patient specimens have included immune electron microscopy,[176] counterimmunoelectrophoresis,[177] indirect immunofluorescence, radioimmunoassays, and enzyme-linked immunosorbent assays.[180] The use of DNA probe and monoclonal antibody technology has enabled investigators to study the molecular epidemiology of adenoviral isolates from patients and in situ detection of nucleic acid sequences for rapid and accurate diagnosis of adenoviral infections.[181–187]

ADENOVIRAL VACCINES

The high incidence of ARDs associated with adenoviruses in the military recruit population within the first 6 weeks of training has led to the development of vaccines for immunization against the commonly responsible serotypes: 3, 4, 7, and 21.

Initial research led to the development of bivalent (types 4 and 7) and later trivalent (types 3, 4, and 7) vaccines containing formalin-inactivated adenoviruses. Early trials were promising with a 70% decrease in type-specific diseases,[188] but problems developed subsequently with the finding of variation in the antigenicity of vaccine lots and the contamination of adenovirus seeds for the vaccine by the simian virus SV40.[189]

Couch et al[190] demonstrated that living adenovirus could be administered via an enteric-coated tablet to cause an asymptomatic infection of the GI tract which would induce protection against type-specific respiratory illness. This is in contrast to clinical inoculation of the same virus into the respiratory tract which produces symptomatic disease. Clinical trials with the administration of serotype 4 in enteric-coated tablets substantially reduced the number of hospitalizations for ARD in military trainees.[188] However, suppression of Ad 4 fostered the emergence of Ad 7 in immunized populations.[188] Development of a live virus vaccine using serotype 7 was initially delayed until controlled studies showed that its oncogenic potential in rodents was not similarly present in humans. Subsequent studies using live Ad 7 in orally administered enteric-coated tablets showed that selective GI infection without illness could occur.[192] Specific neutralizing antibody was stimulated in over 95% of infected volunteers within 21 days after immunization. Simultaneous administration of the Ad 4 vaccine with the Ad 7 vaccine was also demonstrated to be a safe and effective means of stimulating neutralizing antibody to both viruses without a loss of immunogenicity or infectivity of either vaccine. Large-scale trials at Fort Dix, New Jersey in 1969 and 1970, comparing the efficacy of immunization with both the Ad 4 and Ad 7 vaccines to the administration of the Ad 4 vaccine alone, showed that the total number of adenovirus-associated diseases was reduced by two thirds in those individuals receiving both vaccines. Ad 7-associated ARD occurred 95% less often in recruits immunized against this serotype.[193, 194] Ad 21 has been responsible for significant, but sporadic outbreaks of ARD in military recruits in the Netherlands[195] and the United States.[196, 197] A vaccine containing live Ad 21 has been developed which successfully induces type-specific neutralizing antibodies when given alone[198, 199] or in conjunction with the Ad 4 and Ad 7 vaccines.[200]

Current monovalent vaccines for use in military recruit populations are prepared by growing the desired vaccine viral serotype initially in primary human embryonic kidney cells (HEK), and then passing the strains over 10 times in WI-38 cells. The lyophilized viruses are then enclosed in standard enteric-coated tablets for human administration. It is recommended that new military trainees be immunized against serotypes 4 and 7 (via two separate orally ingested monovalent vaccines) immediately upon arrival at the training centers to ensure adequate time to develop serum neutralizing antibodies. Live virus vaccines containing Ad 21 are administered only in the event of documented epidemics with this serotype. Since the development of these vaccines, over 10 million people have been immunized without adverse reactions. Transmission of adenoviral infection from vaccinees to close contacts does not appear to be a significant problem. More recently, a double blind controlled clinical study was carried out in the Canadian armed forces by vaccinating 600 recruits with live enteric-coated Ad 4 and Ad 7 attenuated vaccines.[201] Among the seronegative vaccinees, 86% of 188 and 76% of 161 recipients showed antibody response to Ad 4 and Ad 7, respectively. All but one seronegative placebo recipient remained seronegative to both serotypes, which indicated that no naturally occurring Ad 4 or Ad 7 infections were present in this military population at the time of the experiment. This study confirmed that the attenuated adenovirus vaccines were safe and antigenic and did not transmit the infection by contact from vaccinees to others. However, the communicability of live, oral type 4 adenovirus vaccine between married couples and within families with children has been studied. When live enteric Ad 4 vaccine was administered to one partner of each of 39 married couples and a placebo was administered to the other, cross-infection was demonstrated in 70% of the marital partners receiving placebo.[202] Within family groups, adenovirus type 4 was transmitted to one of eight seronegative spouses and to one of 64 susceptible children after maternal vaccination. However, when one of the children in a household was vaccinated, transmission of type 4 adenovirus was demonstrated in three of 23 nonimmune parents and five of 49 susceptible siblings and was associated with mild respiratory tract illness.[203]

Although live adenovirus vaccines of any serotype can be produced, the risk of spread of vaccine virus in immunized children has limited the large-scale testing of vaccines against the common endemic serotypes 1, 2, and 5. Oral vaccines containing these serotypes have been successfully administered to adult volunteers lacking homologous serum antibodies.[204] The role of these vaccines in immunizing children living in institutional quarters remains to be determined.

REFERENCES

1. Rowe WP, Huebner RJ, Gilmore LK, et al: Isolation of a cytopathogenic agent from human adenoids undergoing spontaneous degeneration in tissue culture. *Proc Soc Exp Biol Med* 1953; 84:570–573.

2. Hilleman MR, Werner JH: Recovery of new agent from patients with acute respiratory illness. *Proc Soc Exp Biol Med* 1954; 85:183–188.

3. Wigand R, Adrian TH, Bricout F: A new human adenovirus of subgenus D: Candidate adenovirus type 42. *Arch Virol* 1987; 94:283–286.

4. Wigand R, Bartha A, Dreizin RS, et al: Adenoviridae: Second report. *Intervirology* 1982; 18:169–176.

5. Ginsberg HS: Adenoviruses, in David BD, Dulbecco R, Eisen HN (eds): *Microbiology Including Immunology and Molecular Genetics.* New York, Harper and Row, 1980, pp 1047–1061.

6. Nermut MV: The architecture of adenoviruses: Recent views and problems. *Arch Virol* 1980; 64:175–196.

7. Anderson CW, Baum PR, Gesteland RF: Processing of adenovirus 2-induced proteins. *J Virol* 1973; 12:241–252.

8. Lenk R, Storch T, Maizel JV Jr: Cell architecture during adenovirus infection. *Virology* 1980; 105:19–34.

9. Rosen L: A hemagglutination-inhibition technique for typing adenoviruses. *Am J Hyg* 1960; 71:120–128.

10. Huebner RJ: Adenovirus-directed tumor and T-antigens, in Pollard M (ed): *Perspectives in Virology,* New York, Academic Press, 1967, vol 5, pp 147–166.

11. Wadell G, Allard A, Johansson M, et al: Enteric adenoviruses. *Ciba Found Symp* 1987; 128:63–91.

12. Hierholzer JC: Further subgrouping of the human adenoviruses by differential hemagglutination. *J Infect Dis* 1973; 128:541–550.

13. Wadell G: Classification of human adenoviruses by SDS-polyacrylamide gel electrophoresis of structural polypeptides. *Intervirology* 1979; 11:47–57.

14. Green M, Mackey JK, Wold WSM, et al: Thirty-one human adenovirus serotypes (Ad 1–Ad 31) form five groups (A–E) based upon DNA genome homologies. *Virology* 1979; 93:481–492.

15. Hoggan MD, Blacklow NR, Rowe WP, et al: Studies of small DNA viruses found in various adenovirus preparations: Physical, biological, and immunological characteristics. *Proc Natl Acad Sci USA* 1966; 55:1467–1474.

16. Atchison RW, Casto BC, Hammon WMcD: Adenovirus-associated defective virus particles. *Science* 1965; 149:754–756.

17. Blacklow NR, Hoggan MD, Sereno MS, et al: A seroepidemiologic study of adenovirus-associated virus infection in infants and children. *Am J Epidemiol* 1971; 94:359–366.

18. Parks WP, Boucher DW, Melnick JL, et al: Seroepidemiological and ecological studies of the adenovirus-associated satellite viruses. *Infect Immun* 1970; 2:716–722.

19. Schmidt OW, Cooney MK, Foy HM: Adenoassociated virus in adenovirus type 3 conjunctivitis. *Infect Immun* 1975; 11:1362–1370.

20. Huebner RJ, Rowe WP, Ward TG, et al: Adenoidal-pharyngeal-conjunctival agents. A newly recognized group of common viruses of the respiratory system. *N Engl J Med* 1954; 251:1077–1086.

21. Bell JA, Rowe WP, Rosen L: Adenoviruses. *Am J Public Health* 1962; 52:902—907.

22. Brandt CD, Kim HW, Vargosko AJ, et al: Infections in 18,000 infants and children in a controlled study of respiratory tract disease. I. Adenovirus pathogenicity in relation to serologic type and illness syndrome. *Am J Epidemiol* 1969; 90:484–500.

23. Fox JP, Hall CE, Cooney MK: The Seattle virus watch. VII. Observations of adenovirus infections. *Am J Epidemiol* 1977; 105:362–386.

24. Assaad F, Cockburn WC: A seven-yer study of WHO virus laboratory reports on respiratory viruses. *Bull WHO* 1974; 51:437–445.

25. A collaborative study of the aetiology of acute respiratory infections in Britain 1961–4. A report of the Medical Research Council Working Party on acute respiratory virus infections. *Br Med J* 1965; 2:319–326.

26. Pereira MS: Adenovirus infections. *Postgrad Med J* 1973; 49:798–801.

27. Wilden SR, Chonmaitree T, Swischuk LE: Roentgenographic fea-

tures of common pediatric viral respiratory tract infections. *Am J Dis Child* 1988; 142:43–46.

28. Epidemiology. Adenovirus infections, editorial. *Br Med J* 1971; 2:719.

29. Wadell G, Varsanyi TM, Lord A, et al: Epidemic outbreaks of adenovirus 7 with special reference to the pathogenicity of adenovirus genome type 7b. *Am J Epidemiol* 1980; 112:619–628.

30. Hilleman MR, Gauld RL, Butler RL, et al: Appraisal of occurrence of adenovirus-caused respiratory illness in military populations. *Am J Hyg* 1957; 66:29–41.

31. Dudding BA, Top FH Jr, Winter PE, et al: Acute respiratory disease in military trainees: The adenovirus surveillance program, 1966–1971. *Am J Epidemiol* 1973; 97:187–198.

32. Rose HM, Lamson TH, Buescher EL: Adenoviral infection in military recruits. *Arch Environ Health* 1970; 21:356–361.

33. Van Der Veen J, Oei KG, Abarbanel MFW: Patterns of infections with adenovirus types 4, 7, and 21 in military recruits during a 9-year survey. *J Hyg Camb* 1969; 67:255–268.

34. Hierholzer JC, Pumarola A: Antigen characterization of intermediate adenovirus 14–11 strains associated with upper respiratory illness in a military camp. *Infect Immun* 1976; 13:354–359.

35. Dingle JH, Langmuir AD: Epidemiology of acute respiratory disease in military recruits. *Am Rev Respir Dis* 1968; 97(pt 2):1–65.

36. Tai FH, Grayston JT, Johnson PB, et al: Adenovirus infections in Chinese army recruits on Taiwan. *J Infect Dis* 1960; 107:160–164.

37. Evans AS, Jeffrey C, Niederman JC: The risk of acute respiratory infections in two groups of young adults in Columbia, South America: A prospective seroepidemiologic study. *Am J Epidemiol* 1971; 93:463–471.

38. Evans AS, Cenabre L, Wanat J, et al: Acute respiratory infections in different ecologic settings. I. Argentine military recruits. *Am Rev Respir Dis* 1973; 108:1311–1319.

39. Foy HM, Grayston JT: Adenoviruses, in Evans AS (ed): *Viral Infections of Humans. Epidemiology and Control. (2nd ed)* New York, Wiley, 1982, pp 67–84.

40. Miller LF, Rytel M, Pierce WE, et al: Epidemiology of nonbacterial pneumonia among naval recruits. *JAMA* 1963; 185:92–99.

41. Grayston JT, Lashof JC, Loosli CG, et al: Adenoviruses. III. Their etiological role in acute respiratory disease in civilian adults. *J Infect Dis* 1958; 103:93–101.

42. Evans AS: Clinical syndromes in adults caused by respiratory infections. *Med Clin North Am* 1967; 51:803–818.

43. Levin S, Dietrich J, Guillory J: Fatal nonbacterial pneumonia associated with adenovirus type 4: Occurrence in an adult. *JAMA* 1967; 201:975–977.

44. Dudding BA, Wagner SC, Zeller JA: Fatal pneumonia associated with adenovirus type 7 in three military trainees. *N Engl J Med* 1972; 286:1289–1292.

45. Loker EF, Hodges GR, Kelly DJ: Fatal adenovirus pneumonia in a young adult associated with ADV-7 vaccine administered 15 days earlier. *Chest* 1974; 66:197–199.

46. Chany C, Lepine P, Lelong M, et al: Severe and fatal pneumonia in infants and young children associated with adenovirus infections. *Am J Hyg* 1958; 67:367–378.

47. Similä S, Ylikorkala O, Wasz-Höckert O: Type 7 adenovirus pneumonia. *J Pediatr* 1971; 79:605–611.

48. Teng CH: Adenovirus pneumonia epidemic among Peking infants and preschool children in 1958. *Chin Med J* 1960; 80:331–339.

49. Warner JO, Marshall WC: Crippling lung disease after measles and adenovirus infection. *Br J Dis Chest* 1976; 2:89–94.

50. Levy Y, Nitzan M, Beharab A, et al: Adenovirus type 3 infection with systemic manifestation in apparently normal children. *Isr J Med Sci* 1986; 22:774–778.

51. Sun CC, Duara S: Fatal adenovirus pneumonia in two newborn infants, one case caused by adenovirus type 30. *Pediatr Pathol* 1985; 4:247–255.

52. James AG, Lang WR, Liang AY, et al: Adenovirus type 21 bronchopneumonia in infants and young children. *J Pediatr* 1979; 95:530–533.

53. Cho CT, Hiat WO, Behbehani AM: Pneumonia and massive pleural effusion associated with adenovirus type 7. *Am J Dis Child* 1973; 126:92–94.

54. Wright J, Couchonnal G, Hodges GR: Adenovirus type 21 infection. Occurrence with pneumonia, rhabdomyolysis, and myoglobinuria in an adult. *JAMA* 1979; 241:2420–2421.

55. Benyesh-Melnick M, Rosenberg HS: The isolation of adenovirus type 7 from a fatal case of pneumonia and disseminated disease. *J Pediatr* 1964; 64:83–87.

56. Brown RS, Nogrady MB, Spence L, et al: An outbreak of adenovirus type 7 infection in children in Montreal. *Can Med Assoc J* 1973; 108:434–439.

57. Becroft DMO: Histopathology of fatal adenovirus infection of the respiratory tract in young children. *J Clin Pathol* 1967; 20:561–569.

58. Pingleton SK, Pingleton WW, Hill RH, et al: Type 3 adenoviral pneumonia occurring in a respiratory intensive care unit. *Chest* 1978; 73:554–555.

59. Lang WR, Howden CW, Laws J, et al: Bronchopneumonia with serious sequelae in children with evidence of adenovirus type 21 infection. *Br Med J* 1969; 1:73–79.

60. James AG, Lang WR, Liang AY, et al: Adenovirus type 21 bronchopneumonia in infants and young children *J Pediatr* 1979; 95:530–533.

61. Pearson RD, Hall WJ, Menegus MA, et al: Diffuse pneumonitis due to adenovirus type 21 in a civilian. *Chest* 1980; 78:107–109.

62. Hierholzer JC, Torrence AE, Wright PF: Generalized viral illness caused by an intermediate strain of adenovirus (21/H 21 + 35). *J Infect Dis* 1980; 141:281–288.

63. Similä S, Linna O, Lanning P, et al: Chronic lung damage caused by adenovirus type 7: A ten-year follow-up study. *Chest* 1981; 80:127–131.

64. Herbert FA, Wilkinson D, Burchak E, et al: Adenovirus type 3 pneumonia causing lung damage in childhood. *Can Med Assoc J* 1977; 116:274–276.

65. Becroft DMO: Pulmonary sequelae of epidemic type-21 adenovirus infection: A 13 year followup. *Arch Dis Child* 1979; 54:155–156.

66. Gold R, Wilt JL, Adhikari PK, et al: Adenoviral pneumonia and its complications in infancy and childhood. *J Can Assoc Radiol* 1969; 20:218–224.

67. Fuchs E: Keratitis punctata superficialis. *Wien Klin Wochenschr* 1889; 2:837–841.

68. Wright RE: Superficial punctate keratitis. *Br J Ophthalmol* 1930; 14:257–291.

69. Jawetz E, Kimura SJ, Hanna L, et al: Studies on the etiology of epidemic keratoconjunctivitis. *Am J Ophthalmol* 1955; 40(2); 200–211.

70. Mitsui Y, Hanabusa J, Minoda R, et al: Effects of inoculating adenovirus (APC virus) type 8 into human volunteers. *Am J Ophthalmol* 1957; 43:84–90.

71. Hobson LC: Acute epidemic superficial punctate keratitis. *Am J Ophthalmol* 1938; 21:1153–1155.

72. Jawetz E: The story of shipyard eye. *Br Med J* 1959; 1:873–876.

73. Hogan MJ, Crawford JW: Epidemic keratoconjunctivitis. *Am J Ophthalmol* 1942; 25:1059–1078.

74. Jawetz E, Thygeson P, Hanna L, et al: The etiology of epidemic keratoconjunctivitis. *Am J Ophthalmol* 1957; 43:79–83.

75. Kjer P, Mordhurst CN: Studies on epidemic of keratoconjunctivitis caused by adenovirus type 8. II. Clinical and epidemiological aspects. *Acta Ophthalmol (Copehn)* 1961; 39:984–992.

76. Dawson C, Darrell R: Infections due to adenovirus type 8 in the United States. I. An outbreak of epidemic keratoconjunctivitis originating in a physician's office. *N Engl J Med* 1963; 268:1031–1034.

77. Dawson CR, Hanna L, Wood TR, et al: Adenovirus type 8 keratoconjunctivitis in the United States: III. Epidemiologic, clinical, and microbiologic features. *Am J Ophthalmol* 1970; 69:473–480.

78. Sprague JB, Hierholzer JC, Currier RW, et al: Epidemic keratoconjunctivitis. A severe industrial outbreak due to adenovirus type 8. *N Engl J Med* 1973; 289:1341–1346.

79. Barnard DL, Dean Hart JC, Marmion VJ, et al: Outbreak in Bris-

tol of conjunctivitis caused by adenovirus type 8, and its epidemiology and control *Br Med J* 1973; 2:165–169.

80. Zweighaft RM, Hierholzer JC, Bryan JA: Epidemic keratoconjunctivitis at a Vietnamese refugee camp in Florida. *Am J Epidemiol* 1977; 106:399–407.

81. D'Angelo LJ, Hierholzer JC, Holman RC, et al: Epidemic keratoconjunctivitis caused by adenovirus type 8: Epidemiologic and laboratory aspects of a large outbreak. *Am J Epidemiol* 1981; 113:44–49.

82. Hierholzer JC, Guyer B, O'Day DM, et al: Adenovirus type 19 keratoconjunctivitis. *N Engl J Med* 1974; 290:1436.

83. Guyer B, O'Day DM, Hierholzer JC, et al: Epidemic keratoconjunctivitis: A community outbreak of mixed adenovirus type 8 and type 19 infection. *J Infect Dis* 1975; 132:142–150.

84. O'Day DM, Guyer B, Hierholzer JC: Clinical and laboratory evaluation of epidemic keratoconjunctivitis due to adenovirus types 8 and 19. *Am J Ophthalmol* 1976; 81:207–215.

85. Burns RP, Potter MH: Epidemic keratoconjunctivitis due to adenovirus type 19. *Am J Ophthalmol* 1976; 81:27–29.

86. Vastine DW, West CE, Yamashiroya H, et al: Simultaneous nosocomial and community outbreak of epidemic keratoconjunctivitis with types 8 and 19 adenovirus. *Trans Am Acad Ophthalmol Otolaryngol* 1976; 81:826–840.

87. Keenlyside RA, Hierholzer JC, D'Angelo LJ: Keratoconjunctivitis associated with adenovirus type 37: an extended outbreak in an ophthalmologist's office. *J Infect Dis* 1983; 147:191–198.

88. Ford E, Nelson KE, Warren D: Epidemiology of epidemic keratoconjunctivitis. *Epidemiol Rev* 1987; 9:244–261.

89. Hierholzer JC, Sprague JB: Five-year analysis of adenovirus 8 antibody levels in an industrial community following an outbreak of keratoconjunctivitis. *Am J Epidemiol* 1979; 110:132–140.

90. Darougar S, Pearce R, Gibson JA, et al: Adenovirus type 21 keratoconjunctivitis. *Br J Ophthalmol* 1978; 62:836–837.

91. Jawetz E, Hanna L, Nicholas A, et al: Some biological characteristics of adenovirus type 8. *Am J Hyg* 1958; 67:276–285.

92. Jawetz E, Hanna L, Sonne M, et al: A laboratory infection with adenovirus type 8: Laboratory and epidemiologic observations. *Am J Hyg* 1959; 69:13–20.

93. Jawetz E, Thygeson P, Hanna L, et al: Antibodies to APC virus type 8 in epidemic keratoconjunctivitis. *Proc Soc Exp Biol Med* 1956; 92:91–95.

94. Mitsui Y, Tanaka C, Yamashita K: Change in the constitution with age. Its influence on the clinical symptoms of conjunctivitis. *Am J Ophthalmol* 1955; 39:540–547.

95. Yirrell DL, Darville JM, Armstrong AG, et al: A correlation between the weather and the incidence of ocular adenovirus infections. *Arch Virol* 1986; 91:367–373.

96. Bell SD, McComb De, Murray ES: Adenoviruses isolated from Saudi Arabia. I. Epidemiological features. *Am J Trop Med Hyg* 1959; 8:492–500.

97. Laibson PR, Dhiri S, Oconer J, et al: Corneal infiltrates in epidemic keratoconjunctivitis: Response to double-blind corticosteroid therapy. *Arch Ophthalmol* 1970; 84:36–40.

98. Pettit TH, Holland GN: Chronic keratoconjunctivitis associated with ocular adenovirus infection. *Am J Ophthalmol* 1979; 88:748–751.

99. Paderstein R: Was ist Schwimmbad-Konjunktivitis? *Klin Monatsbl Augenheilkd* 1925; 72:634–642.

100. Bahn C; Swimming bath conjunctivitis. *New Orleans Med Sci J* 1927; 79:586–590.

101. Cockburn TA: Epidemic of conjunctivitis in Colorado: Associated with pharyngitis, muscle pain, and pyrexia. *Am J Ophthalmol* 1953; 36:1534–1539.

102. Derrick EH: Swimming-bath conjunctivitis with report of three probable cases and note on its epidemiology. *Med J Aust* 1943; 2:334–336.

103. Parrott RH, Rowe WP, Huebner RJ, et al: Outbreak of febrile pharyngitis and conjunctivitis associated with type 3 adenoidal-pharyngeal-conjunctival virus infection. *N Engl J Med* 1954; 251:1087–1090.

104. Bell JA, Rowe EP, Engler JI, et al: Pharyngoconjunctival fever. Epidemiological studies of a recently recognized disease entity. *JAMA* 1955; 157:1083–1092.

105. Ward TG, Hueber RT, Rowe WP, et al: Production of pharyngoconjunctival fever in human volunteers inoculated with APC viruses. *Science* 1955; 122:1086–1087.

106. Ryan WR, O'Rourke JF, Iser G, et al: Conjunctivitis in adenoidal-pharyngeal-conjunctival virus infection. *Arch Ophthalmol* 1955; 54:211–216.

107. Caldwell GG, Lindsey NJ, Wulff H, et al: Epidemic of adenovirus type 7 acute conjunctivitis in swimmers. *Am J Epidemiol* 1974; 99:230–234.

108. Buchta RM: Membranous conjunctivitis due to adenovirus type 7 infection. *Clin Pediatr (Phila* 1974; 13:232–234.

109. Tai FH, Lin HM, Chu S, et al: A new form of acute conjunctivitis epidemic in Taiwan. A simultaneous outbreak of adenovirus type II and "acute hemorrhagic conjunctivitis" virus infections. *Chin J Microbiol* 1974; 7:79–87.

110. Taylor JW, Chandler JW, Cooney MK: Acute hemorrhagic conjunctivitis associated with adenovirus type 19, letter. *N Engl J Med* 1975; 292:978–979.

111. Van Bijsterveld OP, de John JC, Muzerie CJ, et al: Pharyngoconjunctival fever caused by adenovirus type 19. *Ophthalmologica* 1978; 177:134–139.

112. Schaap GJ, de Jong JC, van Bijsterveld OP, et al: A new intermediate adenovirus type causing conjunctivitis. *Arch Ophthalmol* 1979; 97:2336–2338.

113. Hierholzer JC, Rodriguez FH: Antigenically intermediate human adenovirus strain associated with conjunctivitis. *J Clin Microbiol* 1981; 13:395–397.

114. Ormsby HL, Aitchison WS: The role of the swimming pool in the transmission of pharyngeal-conjunctival fever. *Can Med Assoc J* 1955; 73:864–866.

115. Cockburn TA, Row WP, Huebner RJ: Relationship of the 1951 Greeley, Colorado, outbreak of conjunctivitis and pharyngitis to type 3 APC virus infection. *Am J Hyg* 1956; 63:250–253.

116. Martone WJ, Hierholzer JC, Keenlyside RA, et al: An outbreak of adenovirus type 3 at a private recreation center swimming pool. *Am J Epidemiol* 1980; 111:229–237.

117. Clarke NA, Stevenson RE, Kabler PW: The inactivation of purified type 3 adenovirus in water by chlorine. *Am J Hyg* 1956; 64:314–319.

118. D'Angelo LJ, Hierholzer JC, Keenlyside RA, et al: Pharyngoconjunctival fever caused by adenovirus type 4: Report of a swimming pool-related outbreak with recovery of virus from pool water. *J Infect Dis* 1979; 140:42–47.

119. Rich AR: On the etiology and pathogenesis of whopping cough. *Bull Johns Hopkins Hosp* 1932; 51:346–359.

120. McCordock HA: Intranuclear inclusions in pertussis. *Proc Soc Exp Biol Med* 1932; 29:1288–1291.

121. Collier AM, Connor JD, Irving WR: Generalized type 5 adenovirus infection associated with the pertussis syndrome. *J Pediatr* 1966; 69:1073–1078.

122. Connor JD: Evidence of an etiological role of adenoviral infection in the pertussis syndrome. *N Engl J Med* 1970; 283:390–394.

123. Sturdy PM, Court SDM, Gardner PS: Viruses and whooping cough. *Lancet* 1971; 2:978–979.

124. Nelson KE, Gavitt F, Batt MD, et al: The role of adenoviruses in the pertussis syndrome. *J Pediatr* 1975; 86:335–341.

125. Keller MA, Aftandelians R, Connor JD: Etiology of pertussis syndrome. *Pediatrics* 1980; 66:50–55.

126. Gutekunst RR, Heggie AD: Viremia and viruria in adenovirus infections. Detection in patients with rubella or rubelliform illness. *N Engl J Med* 1961; 264:374–378.

127. Gresser I, Kibrick S: Isolation of vaccinia virus and type 1 adenovirus from urine. *N Engl J Med* 1961; 265:743–744.

128. Numazaki Y, Kumasaka T, Yano N, et al: Further study of acute hemorrhagic cystitis due to adenovirus type 11. *N Engl J Med* 1973; 289:344–347.

129. Mufson MA, Belshe RB, Horrigan TJ, et al: Cause of acute hem-

802   C. Liu

orrhagic cystitis in children. *Am J Dis Child* 1973; 126:605–609.

130. Steigbigel RT, LaScolea LJ, Marx G: Renal hematuria associated with adenovirus 7a infection. *Am J Dis Child* 1978; 132:208–209.

131. Shindo K, Kitayama T, Ura T, et al: Acute hemorrhagic cystitis caused by adenovirus type 11 after renal transplantation. *Urol Int* 1986; 41:152–155.

132. Harnett GB, Bucens MR, Clay SJ, et al: Acute haemorrhagic cystitis caused by adenovirus type 11 in a recipient of a transplanted kidney. *Med J Aust* 1982; 1:565–567.

133. Fiala M, Payne JE, Berne TV, et al: Role of adenovirus type 11 in hemorrhagic cystitis secondary to immunosuppression. *J Urol* 1974; 112:595–597.

134. Lecatsas G, Prozesky OW, van Wyk J: Adenovirus type 2 associated with haemorrhagic cystitis after renal transplantation. *S Afr Med J* 1974; 48:1932.

135. Hierholzer JC, Atuk NO, Gwaltney JM: New human adenovirus isolated from a renal transplant recipient: Description and characterization of candidate adenovirus type 34. *J Clin Microbiol* 1975; 1:366–376.

136. Stalder H, Hierholzer JC, Oxman MN: New human adenovirus (candidate adenovirus type 35) causing fatal disseminated infection in a renal transplant recipient. *J Clin Microbiol* 1977; 6:257–265.

137. Retter M, Middleton PJ, Tam JS, et al: Enteric adenoviruses: Detection, replication, and significance. *J Clin Microbiol* 1979; 10:574–578.

138. Wilt JC, Hannan CK: Adenoviruses, general properties, in Rhodes AJ, Van Rooyen CE (eds): *Textbrook of Virology.* Baltimore, Williams & Wilkins, 1968, pp 356–363.

139. Gary GW Jr, Hierholzer JC, Black RE: Characteristics of noncultivable adenoviruses associated with diarrhea in infants: A new subgroup of human adenoviruses. *J Clin Microbiol* 1979; 10:96–103.

140. Richmond SJ, Caul EO, Dunn SM, et al: An outbreak of gastroenteritis in young children caused by adenoviruses. *Lancet* 1979; 1:1178–1180.

141. Whitelaw A, Davies H, Parry J: Electron microscopy of fatal adenovirus gastroenteritis. *Lancet* 1977; 1:361.

142. Flewett TH, Bryden AS, Davies H, et al: Epidemic viral enteritis in a long-stay children's ward. *Lancet* 1975; 1:4–5.

143. Middleton PJ, Szymanski MT, Petric M: Viruses associated with acute gastroenteritis in young children. *Am J Dis Child* 1977; 131:733–736.

144. de Jong JC, Wigand R, Kidd AH et al: Candidate adenoviruses 40 and 41: fastidious adenoviruses from human infant stool. *J Med Virol* 1983; 11:215–231.

145. Takiff HE, Strauss SE, Garon CF: Propagation and in vitro studies of previously non-cultivable enteral adenoviruses in 293 cells. *Lancet* 1981; 2:832–834.

146. Uhnoo I, Olding-Stenkvist E, Kreuger A: Clinical features of acute gastroenteritis associated with rotavirus, enteric adenoviruses, and bacteria. *Arch Dis Child* 1986; 61:732–738.

147. Rodriguez WJ, Kim HW, Brandt CD, et al: Fecal adenoviruses from a longitudinal study of families in metropolitan Washington D.C.: Laboratory, clinical, and epidemiologic observations. *J Pediatr* 1985; 107:514–520.

148. Bell TM, Steyn JH: Viruses in lymph nodes of children with mesenteric adenitis and intussusception. *Br Med J* 1962; 2:700–702.

149. Potter CW: Adenovirus infection as an aetiological factor in intussusception of infants and young children. *J Pathol Baeteriol* 1964; 88:263–274.

150. Clarke EJ, Phillips IA, Alexander ER: Adenovirus infection in intussusception in children in Taiwan. *JAMA* 1969; 208:1671–1674.

151. Ravitch MM: Intussusception, in Mustard WT, Ravitch MM, Snyder WH Jr, et al (eds): *Pediatric Surgery.* Chicago, Year Book Medical Publishers, 1969, pp 914–931.

152. Yunis EJ, Hashida Y: Electron microscopic demonstration of ade-

novirus in appendix vermiformis in a case of ileocecal intussusception. *Pediatrics* 1973; 51:566–570.

153. Yunis EJ, Atchison RW, Michaels RH, et al: Adenovirus and ileocecal intussusception. *Lab Invest* 1975; 33:347–351.

154. Meshlinpour H, Vaziri ND: Acute rhabdomyolysis associated with adenovirus infection. *J Infect Dis* 1981; 143:133.

155. Bayer AS: Arthritis associated with common viral infections: Mumps, coxsackievirus, and adenovirus. *Postgrad Med* 1980; 68:55–58, 60, 63–64.

156. Rahal JJ, Millian SJ, Noriega ER: Coxsackievirus and adenovirus infection. Association with acute febrile and juvenile rheumatoid arthritis. *JAMA* 1976; 235:2496–2501.

157. Panush RS: Adenovirus arthritis. *Arthritis Rheum* 1974; 17:534–536.

158. Harnett GB, Newnham WA: Isolation of adenovirus type 19 from the male and female genital tracts. *Br J Vener Dis* 1981; 57:55–57.

159. Naveh Y, Friedman A: Clinical memorandum: Orchitis association with adenoviral infection, letter. *Am J Dis Child* 1975; 129:257–258.

160. Warner JO, Marshall WC: Crippling lung disease after measles and adenovirus infection. *Br J Dis Chest* 1976; 70:89–94.

161. Behbehani AM: A concise review. Common viral exanthems and enanthems. *Kans Med J* 1981; 82:442–446.

162. Sallay K, Kulcsar G, Nasz I, et al: Adenovirus isolation from recurrent oral ulcers. *J Periodontol* 1973; 44:712–714.

163. Landry ML, Neddermann K, Solomon L, et al: Disseminated adenovirus infection in an immunocompromised host. *Am J Med* 1987; 83:555–559.

164. Shields AF, Hackman RC, Fife KH, et al: Adenovirus infections in patients undergoing bone marrow transplantation. *N Engl J Med* 1985; 312:529–533.

165. Rodriguez FH, Liuzza GE, Gold RH: Disseminated adenovirus serotype 31 infection in an immunocompromised host. *Am J Clin Pathol* 1984; 82:615–618.

166. South MA, Dolen J, Beach DK et al: Fatal adenovirus hepatic necrosis in severe combined immunodeficiency. *Pediatr Infect Dis* 1982; 6:416–419.

167. Zahradnik JM, Spencer MJ, Porter DD: Adenovirus infection in the immunocompromised patient. *Am J Med* 1980; 68:725–732.

168. Horwitz MS, Valderrama G, Hatcher V, et al: Characterization of adenovirus isolates from AIDS patients. *Ann NY Acad Sci* 1985; 437:161–174.

169. Koneru B, Jaffe R, Esquivel CO, et al: Adenoviral infections in pediatric liver transplant recipients. *JAMA* 1987; 258:489–492.

170. Brown JM: Reye's syndrome associated with adenovirus type 3 infection. *Med J Aust* 1974; 2: 873–875.

171. Ladisch S, Lovejoy FH, Hierholzer JC, et al: Extrapulmonary manifestations of adenovirus type 7 pneumonia simulating Reye syndrome and the possible role of an adenovirus toxin. *J Pediatr* 1979; 95:348–355.

172. Cooney MK: Adenoviruses, in Lennette EH (ed): *Laboratory Diagnosis of Viral Infections.* New York, Marcel Dekker, 1985, pp 135–146.

173. Kawai T, Fujiwara T, Aoyama Y, et al: Diffuse interstitial fibrosing pneumonitis and adenovirus infection. *Chest* 1976; 69:692–694.

174. Schwartz HS, Vastine DW, Yamashiroya H, et al: Immunofluorescent detection of adenovirus antigen in epidemic keratoconjunctivitis. *Invest Ophthalmol* 1976; 15:199–207.

175. Strano AJ: Light microscopy of selected viral diseases: Morphology of viral inclusion bodies. *Pathol Annu* 1976; 11:53–75.

176. Luton P: Rapid adenovirus typing by immunoelectron microscopy. *J Clin Pathol* 1973; 26:914–917.

177. Hierholzer JC, Barme M: Counterimmunoelectrophoresis with adenovirus type-specific anti-hemagglutinin sera as a rapid diagnostic method. *J Immunol* 1974; 112:987–995.

178. Ariyawansa JP, Tobin JO: Fluorescent antibody responses to adenoviruses in humans. *J Clin Pathol* 1976; 29:411–416.

179. Scott JV, Dressman GR, Spira G, et al: Radioimmunoassay of

human serum antibody specific for adenovirus type 5-purified fiber. *J Immunol* 1975; 115:124–128.

180. Harmon MW, Drake S, Kasel JA: Detection of adenovirus by enzyme-linked immunosorbent assay. *J Clin Microbiol* 1979; 9:342–346.

181. van der Avoort HG, Adrian T, Wigand R, et al: Molecular epidemiology of adenovirus type 21 in the Netherlands and the Federal Republic of Germany from 1960 to 1985. *J Clin Microbiol* 1986; 24:1084–1088.

182. Flomenberg PR, Chen M, Munk G, et al: Molecular epidemiology of adenovirus type 35 infections in immunocompromised hosts. *J Infect Dis* 1987; 155:1127–1134.

183. Adrian T, Wigand R, Richter J: Gasteroenteritis in infants, associated with a genome type of adenovirus 31 and with combined rotavirus and adenovirus 31 infection. *Eur J Pediatr* 1987; 146:38–40.

184. Gomes SA, Nascimento JP, Siqueira MM, et al: In situ hybridization with biotinylated DNA probes: a rapid diagnostic test for adenovirus upper respiratory infections. *J Virol Methods* 1985; 12:105–110.

185. Lehtomaki K, Julkunen I, Sandelin K, et al: Rapid diagnosis of respiratory adenovirus infections in young adult men. *J Clin Microbiol* 1986; 24:108–111.

186. Neumann R, Genersch E, Eggers HJ: Detection of adenovirus nucleic acid sequences in human tonsils in the absence of infectious virus. *Virus Res* 1987; 7:93–97.

187. Singh-Naz N, Naz RK: Development and application of monoclonal antibodies for specific detection of human enteric adenoviruses. *J Clin Microbiol* 1986; 23:840–842.

188. Buescher EL: Respiratory disease and the adenoviruses. *Med Clin North Am* 1967; 51:769–779.

189. Top FH: Control of adenovirus acute respiratory disease in US Army trainees. *Yale J Biol Med* 1975; 48:185–195.

190. Couch RB, Chanock RM, Cate TR, et al: Immunization with types 4 and 7 adenovirus by selective infection of the intestinal tract. *Am Rev Respir Dis* 1963; 88(suppl):394–403.

191. Edmondson WP, Purcell RH, Gundelfinger BF, et al: Immunization by selective infection with type 4 adenovirus grown in human diploid tissue culture. II. Specific protective effect against epidemic disease. *JAMA* 1966; 195:453–459.

192. Top FH, Grossman RA, Bartelloni PJ, et al: Immunization with live types 7 and 4 adenovirus vaccines. I. Safety, infectivity, antigenicity, and potency of adenovirus type 7 vaccine in humans. *J Infect Dis* 1971; 124:148–154.

193. Top FH, Buescher EL, Bancroft WH, et al: Immunization with live types 7 and 4 adenovirus vaccines. II. Antibody response and protective effect against acute respiratory disease due to adenovirus type 7. *J Infect Dis* 1971; 124:155–160.

194. Top FH, Dudding BA, Russell PK, et al: Control of respiratory disease in recruits with types 4 and 7 adenovirus vaccines. *Am J Epidemiol* 1971; 94:142–146.

195. Van der Veen J, Dijkman JH: Association of type 21 adenovirus with acute respiratory illness in military recruits. *Am J Hyg* 1962; 76:149–159.

196. Rose HM, Lamson TH, Buescher EL: Adenoviral infection in military recruits. *Arch Environ Health* 1970; 21:356–361.

197. Top FH Jr, Brandt WE, Russell PK: Adenovirus ARD in basic combat trainees, in *Research in Biological and Medical Sciences: Annual Progress Report,* 1975/1976, Washington, DC, Walter Reed Army Institute of Research, 1976, pp 462–465.

198. Dudding BA, Bartelloni PJ, Scott RM, et al; Enteric immunization with live adenovirus type 21 vaccine. I. Tests for safety, infectivity, immunogenicity, and potency in volunteers. *Infect Immun* 1972; 5:295–299.

199. Scott RM, Dudding BA, Romano SV, et al: Enteric immunization with live adenovirus type 21 vaccine. II. Systemic and local immune responses following immunization. *Infect Immun* 1972; 5:300–304.

200. Takafuji ET, Gaydos JC, Allen RG, et al: Simultaneous administration of live, enteric-coated adenovirus types 4, 7, and 21 vaccines: Safety and immunogenicity. *J Infect Dis* 1979; 140:48–53.

201. Chaloner-Larsson G, Contreras G, Furesz J, et al: Immunization of Canadian armed forces personnel with live types 4 and 7 adenovirus vaccines. *Can J Public Health* 1986; 77:367–370.

202. Stanley ED, Jackson GG: Spread of enteric live adenovirus type 4 vaccine in married couples. *J Infect Dis* 1969; 119:51–59.

203. Mueller RE, Muldoon RL, Jackson GG: Communicability of enteric live adenovirus type 4 vaccine in families. *J Infect Dis* 1969; 119:60–66.

204. Schwartz AR, Togo Y, Hornick RB: Clinical evaluation of live, oral types 1, 2 and 5 adenovirus vaccines. *Am Rev Respir Dis* 1974; 109:233–238.

33

Rotavirus, Enteric Adenoviruses, Norwalk Viruses, Caliciviruses, Astroviruses, and Other Viruses Causing Gastroenteritis*

Robert H. Yolken
Joseph J. Eiden

This work was supported by contract N01-AI-52579 and grants DK 33089 and 1 R29 AI2422-01A1 from the National Institutes of Health.

The infectious nature of acute gastroenteritis has been long recognized. However, while bacterial agents of gastroenteritis have been identified and studied since the end of the last century,[1] numerous studies have documented that many cases of acute gastroenteritis occurring in infants cannot be explained by known bacterial pathogens.[2-4] In 1943, Light and Hodes documented that gastroenteritis could be transmitted from humans to animals by the use of bacterial-free filtrates.[5] This finding and the clinical observations that many patients with acute gastroenteritis also have fever, cough, and rhinorrhea led to the concept that a significant portion of acute gastroenteritis might be caused by viral agents. Extensive attempts to cultivate viruses from stool specimens of children with acute gastroenteritis have failed to establish cultivatable viruses as important causes of infantile diarrhea. While a number of viral agents such as echoviruses, coxsackieviruses, and reoviruses could be cultivated from some children with diarrhea, these viruses could also be cultivated from the stools of children without diarrheal symptoms.[6-8] In addition, large-scale outbreaks of diarrhea caused by these agents were difficult to identify. Thus these viruses are probably not major causes of childhood diarrhea.[9]

The understanding of viral gastroenteritis has been markedly enhanced by the recent application of direct electron microscopic and immunologic techniques to the study of viral gastroenteritis.

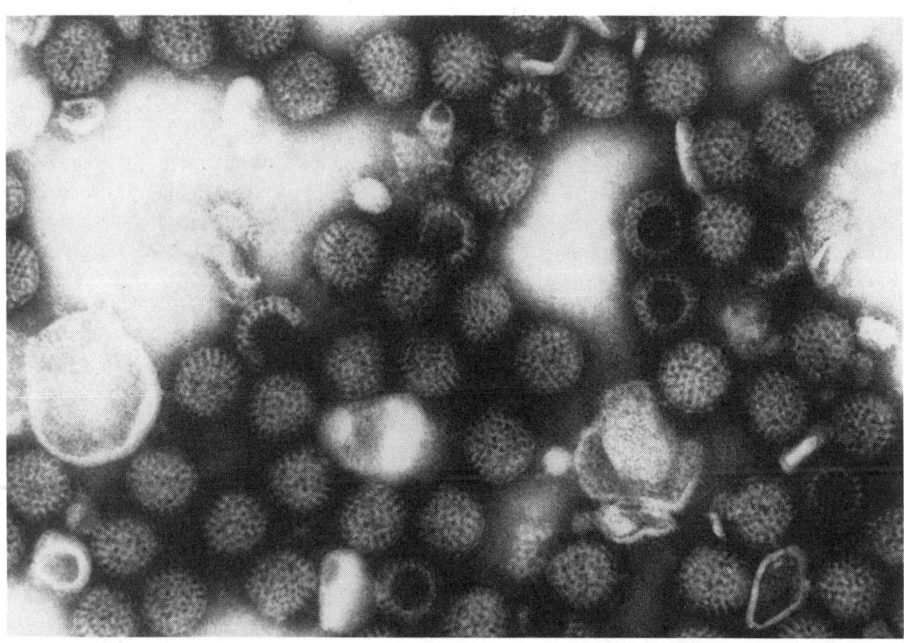

Figure 33–1. Electron microscopic appearance of human rotavirus from a child with acute gastroenteritis. (From Yolken RH, et al: Rotavirus, in Mandell GL (ed): *Principles and Practice of Infectious Diseases, ed 2.* New York, Wiley, 1985. Used by permission.)

Such techniques have led to the discovery of several viral agents associated with gastroenteritis which could not be easily identified by available methods of tissue culture or animal inoculation.[2, 10, 11] Three such viruses that have been extensively studied are rotaviruses,[12] adenoviruses,[13] viruses 27 to 32 nm related to Norwalk virus, and caliciviruses.[2, 14] The three viral agents are quite different in terms of size and nucleic acid content. However, all agents are capable of causing acute infection of the small intestine leading to acute diarrhea with concentrated vomiting and fever.

ROTAVIRUSES

Rotaviruses, one of the six genera of the family *Reoviridae*, are the most extensively studied of the viral agents of acute gastroenteritis. The rotavirus particle is approximately 70 nm in diameter, with a density in cesium chloride of 1.36 g/cm^3.[15, 16] Examination of the virus by means of negative-staining electron microscopy suggests the appearance of a wheel (Figure 33–1), hence the name "rota-" from the Latin. The intact virion consists of a double-layered, protein capsid surrounding a core which contains 11 segments of double-stranded genomic RNA. Each RNA segment appears to code for a single viral protein, and the molecular weights (mol wt) of these proteins range from 20,000 to 125,000 daltons. The RNA segments are between 0.2×10^6 to 2.2×10^6 daltons in mol wt, with a total mol wt of 12×10^6.[17-20] The largest of the RNA segments is designated 1, and the remainder of the segments are numbered in order of decreasing molecular weight.[20] The RNA segments may be separated from one another by means of polyacrylamide gel electrophoresis (PAGE). Although different virus strains can sometimes exhibit similar electropherotypes,[21] PAGE is often useful in distinguishing individual strains of rotaviruses.

Study of several readily cultivatable rotavirus strains, especially the simian rotavirus SA11, has provided valuable information concerning the structure and molecular genetics of these viruses.[22, 23] As revealed in the study of these viruses, the major inner capsid protein of rotaviruses is coded by gene segment 6 and is designated as VP$_6$ (viral protein number 6). This protein is 41,000 daltons in mol wt and composes 80% of the mass of the inner capsid.[24] Other inner capsid proteins include VP$_1$ and VP$_2$ which are coded by RNA segments 1 and 2, respectively. VP$_4$ (previously termed VP$_3$) (mol wt 88,000) and VP$_7$ (mol wt 34,000) are the major outer capsid proteins. VP$_7$ is glycosylated and is encoded by either segment 8 or 9, depending on the virus strain. VP$_4$ is encoded by gene segment 4 and contains the hemagglutination activity associated with some rotavirus strains.[25] Trypsin cleavage of VP$_4$ to VP$_5$ and VP$_8$ increases the infectivity of rotaviruses.[26] Study of reassortant rotaviruses indicates that the enhanced infectivity of some rotavirus strains in tissue culture is also determined by VP$_4$. In addition, inoculation of infant mice with rotavirus reassortants discloses that VP$_4$ is a major determinant of rotavirus virulence.[27] Further investigations are needed in order to identify the proteins associated with other virus-encoded functions, such as RNA-dependent RNA polymerase.

The relationships of individual rotavirus strains to one another are classified to group, subgroup, and serotype specificity.[28-30] Both group-specific and subgroup-specific antigenic determinants are located on the major inner capsid protein, VP$_6$.[28] Two major subgroups, I and II, are currently recognized, and these are distinguished by means of enzyme-linked immunosorbent assay (ELISA), immune adherence hemagglutination assay, and complement fixation (CF). The serotype of rotavirus strains is determined by means of virus neutralization assays.[29, 30] The determinants of serotype specificity were initially identified with antigenic sites on the outer capsid protein, VP$_7$.[31] However, more recent investigations indicate that VP$_4$ also contains antigenic sites important for virus neutralization.[32] Almost all rotaviruses that are isolated from human infection are identified as serotypes 1–4, although two recent human isolates are reported not to react with antisera specific for these serotypes.[33–37] Field isolates of animal rotaviruses appear to be limited to serotypes 3–7.[34]

Until recently, it was believed that there was only one rotavirus group, and all rotaviruses shared a common, group-specific antigen which was encoded by gene segment 6. However, a number of viruses have been identified since 1980 which are morphologically similar to rotaviruses but do not share the group-specific antigen usually associated with rotaviruses. These antigenically distinct rotaviruses are reported from a variety of species, including birds, cows, lambs, pigs, rats, and man.[38–41] Antigenically distinct rotaviruses are known by a number of different names, such as pararotaviruses, rotavirus-like viruses, and novel rotaviruses. Like other rotaviruses, antigenically distinct rotaviruses possess the double-capsid structure characteristic of the rotavirus genus, and they have a genome consisting of 11 segments of double-stranded RNA. However, the antigenically distinct rotaviruses do not react in standard immunoassays based on the group-specific antigen and cannot be diagnosed by those assays. Antigenically distinct rotaviruses also do not react with the neutralization antisera employed in the serotyping of rotaviruses.

In addition, the electropherotypes of the antigenically distinct

rotaviruses are distinctively different from the electropherotype pattern usually associated with rotaviruses. Prior to the recognition of antigenically distinct rotaviruses, all rotaviruses were thought to exhibit a characteristic PAGE pattern of 4-2-3-2, from the four largest segments to the two smallest segments. Considerable variability was recognized among different rotavirus strains, but the overall 4-2-3-2 pattern was highly conserved. In contrast, the electropherotypes of the antigenically distinct rotaviruses have patterns markedly different from the 4-2-3-2 arrangement (Figure 33–2). While these electropherotype patterns are not definitive in the identification of antigenically distinct rotaviruses, they greatly assist in comparing strains.[42–44]

A proposal is currently under evaluation that would result in the designation of several rotavirus groups instead of the use of terms such as pararotavirus, antigenically distinct rotaviruses, rotavirus-like, etc.[45] With this system, the rotaviruses previously associated with wintertime epidemics of infantile gastroenteritis are termed "group A rotaviruses," and the antigenically distinct rotaviruses are separated into groups B, C, D; E, etc. A combination of assays such as electropherotype analysis, nucleic acid hybridization, and serologic tests are employed in order to determine the group specificity of newly discovered rotavirus strains.[45]

Pathophysiology

Knowledge of the pathophysiology of rotavirus infections in humans is limited to the study of a small number of available small-bowel mucosa specimens. Intestinal changes such as villous shortening and microvillous aberrations have been noted in jejunal biopsy specimens obtained from a few infected children.[46, 47] These changes might be related to the deficient absorption of disaccharides that has been noted in some children following rotaviral infection.[48, 49]

A great deal more information is known about rotavirus infection in animals, especially in piglets and calves. Infection with rotavirus in these animals leads to a rapid destruction of columnar epithelial cells. This destruction proceeds temporally from the proximal duodenum to distal ileum[50] and correlates with the appearance of viral antigen detectable by immunofluorescence microscopy. There is no evidence of viral replication or epithelial cell destruction in the stomach or the colon. This sequence of events in the small bowel is followed shortly by the replacement of the damaged epithelial cells with regenerated cells derived from the crypts. These newly formed cells can be deficient in their content of disacchardidases and have abnormal glucose-coupled sodium transport.[51, 52] It is thus likely that the diarrhea that occurs following rotavirus infection is a function of a decreased intestinal absorptive capacity due to villous destruction and the subsequent enzyme deficiency of newly formed epithelial cells.[53] In addition, it is likely that some secretion of fluid into the gut lumen also occurs in response to the epithelial cell damage.

The pathologic lesions associated with group B rotavirus infection have been studied by oral inoculation of laboratory animals. Excretion of virus by experimental animals generally follows within one day postinoculation, and watery diarrhea, anorexia, and weight loss usually begin within one day after feeding of virus. The infection is usually self-limited, but more severe illness and death are sometimes noted in younger animals. Infection with group B rotavirus results in villous epithelial cell atrophy and necrosis sim-

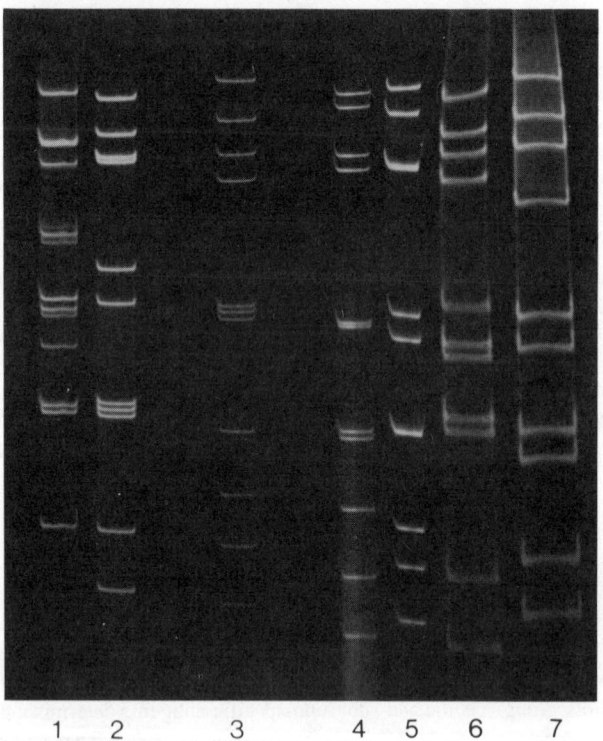

Figure 33–2. Rotavirus, double-stranded RNA genomic segments separated by means of polyacrylamide gel electrophoresis. Lane 1: complex rotavirus electropherotype resulting from infection of an immunodeficient patient with multiple strains of group A rotavirus. Lane 2: SA-11 tissue culture strain of group A rotavirus. Lane 3: group B rotavirus passaged in infant rat. Lane 4: bovine group B rotavirus. Lane 5: Ohio isolate of porcine group B rotavirus. Lane 6: Cowden strain of porcine group C rotavirus. Lane 7: avian group D rotavirus.

ilar to that observed with group A rotaviruses. All regions of the small intestine may be infected, but lesions are reported to be more numerous in the ileum. The group B rotaviruses appear to be distinguished from other rotavirus group by syncytial cell formation in infected tissues.[43]

Epidemiology

Gastroenteritis caused by group A rotavirus infection is largely a disease of infancy. In most areas of the world, the peak of rotavirus infections occurs between 4 months and 3 years of age.[54, 55] While viral particles can be detected in the stools of some newborns, many infections occurring in this age group appear to be asymptomatic or associated with minimal degrees of diarrhea.[56] In addition, while young and middle-aged adult contacts of children occasionally demonstrate a serologic response to infection with rotavirus, the majority of infections occurring in this age group also appear to be asymptomatic.[57] On the other hand, symptomatic outbreaks of rotavirus gastroenteritis have been reported in populations of adults older than 60 years of age. Some of these cases have been associated with severe morbidity.[58,177] Evidence of rotavirus infection has also been found in cases of "traveler's diarrhea" occurring in tourists and students. However, many of these infections occurred concomitantly with infections with other antigens such as *Shigella* spp and toxigenic *Escherichia coli*.[59] In Third World countries, rotavirus infections are estimated to cause more than 800,000 deaths each year in infected infants. In the United States, rotavirus diarrhea is estimated to result in 500,000 physician visits and 67,000 hospitalizations each year.[60]

One striking feature of the epidemiology of rotavirus gastroenteritis is the seasonal variation of infections. Most infections occurring in children living in temperate climates are detected during the winter and early spring months.[55, 58] For example, in the Baltimore area 95% of the infections noted in hospitalized children occurred between January and April. This striking seasonal variation has not been noted in tropical climates.[61] Surveillance of an infant population in rural Bangladesh reveals that cases of symptomatic rotavirus could occur throughout the year. However, an increased rate of infection was noted during the cooler months of the year.[62]

Another interesting feature of rotavirus epidemiology is the fact that the disease is highly prevalent both in developed and undeveloped countries. For example, 90% of children living in the Washington, DC, area show serologic evidence of rotavirus infection during the first 4 years of life. This rate of infection is not significantly different from that found in children living in rural Bangladesh or Central America.[57, 58, 61–63]

Since rotavirus can be found in large quantities in the stools of infected children, it is generally assumed that rotavirus is spread by the fecal-oral route. However, the high rate of prevalence of rotavirus in children living under diverse conditions of sanitation, as well as the marked seasonal variation, has suggested to some investigators that rotaviruses might also be spread by other routes such as by the respiratory tract. This supposition is also supported by the fact that many children with rotavirus gastroenteritis often have concomitant respiratory symptoms such as rhinorrhea and coughing. In addition, children have been shown to have respiratory symptoms associated with a seroresponse to rotavirus without any evidence of gastroenteritis.[64, 65] However, most attempts at identifying rotavirus antigen in respiratory secretions have been unsuccessful. Until this question can be correctly answered, it is advisable to assume that rotavirus can be spread both by the fecal-oral and respiratory routes. Infection control procedures aimed at limiting the spread of rotavirus in a closed population should thus entail methods aimed at the prevention of spread by these routes.

Of the new rotavirus groups, only strains of groups B and C have so far been isolated from human fecal specimens.[38–40, 40a, 42, 66] While occasional human isolates of group C rotavirus are reported, a strain of group B rotavirus is responsible for extensive epidemics of human gastroenteritis in the People's Republic of China.[40, 40a] Infection with this virus has occurred in all age groups, but the frequent isolation of the virus from adults has led to the use of the term "adult diarrhea rotavirus" or ADRV.[40] Outbreaks in China are noted during all seasons, not primarily during the wintertime as reported for group A rotaviruses. Illness with ADRV is characterized by watery diarrhea, vomiting, abdominal cramps, and nausea. Group B rotavirus epidemics have not yet been reported outside of China, but another strain of group B rotavirus has been found in both adults and children in Baltimore.[39] Serologic assays to investigate the prevalence of group B rotavirus have indicated either high or low seroprevalence in human populations.[39, 67, 68] Variations in these results may be due to the differences in interpretation of assay results or differences in the antibodies employed in the assays. Alternatively, these serologic surveys may indicate variation in the prevalence of group B rotavirus infection among human populations in various geographic regions. The true prevalence of group B rotavirus infection among human populations should be clarified with the development of more standardized immunoassays.

Clinical Effects of Infections

Rotavirus gastroenteritis can vary from mild watery diarrhea lasting less than 24 hours to overwhelming and, occasionally, fatal gastroenteritis.[69–72] The hallmark of rotavirus gastroenteritis is vomiting, with virtually all children admitted to the hospital with rotavirus displaying this symptom. Vomiting can occur for up to 48 hours prior to the onset of gastroenteritis. In older children, vomiting may be the principal manifestation of the disease with little or no diarrhea actually occurring. In addition, virtually all of the children with rotavirus gastroenteritis display fevers greater than 38.5°C at some point in their illness. Infected children over 3 years of age often report myalgias and headaches.[73] Most patients have watery stools that are occasionally green in color due to the presence of large amounts of mucus. While a small number of inflammatory cells can often be detected by microscopic examinations of the stools, frankly bloody or purulent stools are seldom found unless there is evidence of coincidental infection with another pathogen such as *Shigella* or *Campylobacter*. Most hospitalized patients have greater than six stools per day at the height of their gastroenteritis. The period of diarrhea in hospitalized patients is as short as two days and as long as 23 days. Most patients continue to excrete virus in their stool for extended periods of time. Such patients may appear as asymptomatic excreters of rotaviruses later in the course of their hospitalization and might serve as reservoirs of virus capable of infecting additional patients.

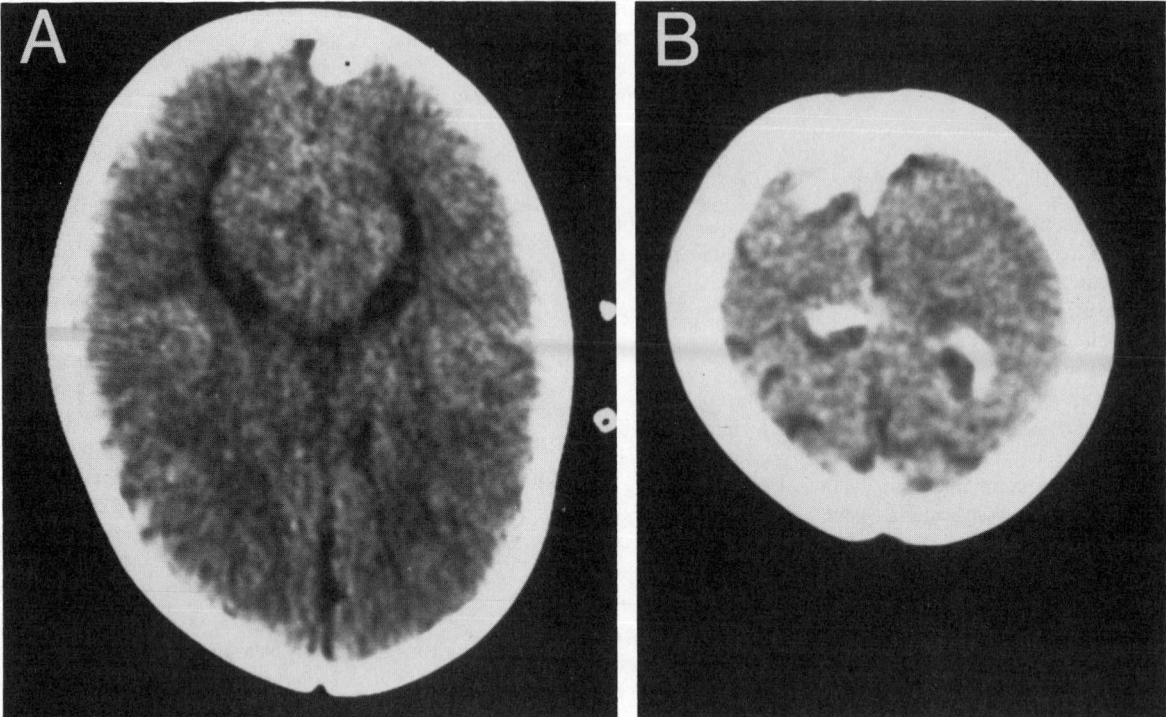

Figure 33–3. A. Computed tomographic (CT) scan of head showing a right medial parietal occipital lobe hematoma located adjacent to the inner table of the calvarium. B. A second CT scan of the head two days later showing small bilateral areas of hemorrhage within the superficial portion of the parietal lobes. (Photo courtesy of Dr Janet S. Kinney.)

The most consistent electrolyte abnormality noted in children with rotavirus diarrhea is metabolic acidosis. Occasionally this acidosis can be severe with serum levels of HCO_3^- falling to levels of less than 10 mEq/L. The majority of children seen at our institution have normal levels of sodium and potassium on admission. However, a small number of children have sodium levels in excess of 150 mEq/L, usually associated with an increased salt intake, and a number have serum sodium levels below 120 mEq/L, often due to the administration of tap water or dilute solutions. Rotavirus infections can also be associated with neurologic abnormalities, ranging from aseptic meningitis to subdural hemorrhage related to severe electrolyte abnormalities.[73] Evidence of subdural or subarachnoid hemorrhage can occasionally be visualized by means of tomographic imaging of the central nervous system (Figure 33–3). Such abnormalities should be considered in children with gastroenteritis who display neurologic abnormalities.

As discussed above, rotavirus displays variable degrees of pathogenicity in neonates. Prospective studies indicate that many infections with rotaviruses in the neonatal age group are relatively asymptomatic.[74] However, some infections can be associated with more severe forms of gastroenteritis. While the diarrhea is often watery, it can be associated with the passage of bloody stools, a phenomenon which occurs rarely, if at all, in older children infected with rotaviruses. In addition, rotavirus infections in premature infants can be associated with necrotizing enterocolitis, a disease of multiple etiologies which is characterized by pneumatosis intestinalis, intestinal perforation, and secondary bacterial infections.[75] Since necrotizing enterocolitis can occur in epidemic

patterns, it is prudent to protect high-risk infants in neonatal intensive care units by the use of isolation procedures appropriate for the identification and containment of enteric pathogens.

The reasons for the great variability in the clinical expression of rotavirus infections in the neonatal age group are not known with certainty. Possible factors include the level of maternal antibodies, the sufficiency of the neonatal immune system, and the structural and functional maturity of the neonate's gastrointestinal (GI) tract. It is also possible that some of the differences can be explained by the genetic makeup of the infecting virus.[76] The identification of factors contributing to the pathogenicity of rotavirus infections in the neonatal period would be important in defining the optimal methods for the diagnosis and management of rotavirus infections in high-risk neonates.

Treatment

The treatment of rotavirus gastroenteritis is directed largely at maintenance of adequate levels of intravascular volume. The mainstay of treatment of outpatients is the replacement of fluid losses by means of the administration of oral fluids. A variety of oral hydration solutions have been utilized for the successful treatment of mild to moderate degrees of dehydration associated with rotavirus gastroenteritis.[77] The main limitation of oral hydration for the treatment of dehydration due to rotavirus gastroenteritis is the high rate of vomiting that occurs during the course of the disease. However, several studies performed in developing and developed countries have indicated that sufficient quantities of oral fluid can be ingested and absorbed to treat children with rotavirus gastroenteritis.[78-80] Children with more serious degrees of dehydration and children unable to take adequate amounts of oral fluids are treated with fluids administered by the intravenous (IV) route. Intravenous rehydration can be performed utilizing standard electrolyte solutions consisting of sodium in concentrations ranging from 40 to 80 mEq/L and potassium concentrations ranging from 10 to 20 mEq/L. Patients with hyponatremia or hypernatremia require rehydration with careful monitoring as does any patient with these conditions.[81] In addition, we have found that many patients with rotavirus gastroenteritis have metabolic acidosis.

The institution of IV fluid therapy usually leads to a decrease in stool output within 48 hours. Oral fluids in the form of electrolyte solutions or clear liquids can also be administered if the fluids can be tolerated by the patient. Since the main limitation on the use of oral fluids is persistent vomiting, one possible means of decreasing the period required for IV hydration would be the use of a safe antiemetic regimen. The development of such a regimen is currently the subject of experimental investigations. The use of drugs such as opium derivatives to decrease GI motility should have no place in the treatment of viral gastroenteritis.[82]

Controlled studies to determine the optimal schedule for the reintroduction of milk and other foods into the diet of children recovering from rotavirus gastroenteritis are unavailable. However, most centers employ a gradual approach to refeeding, first starting children on breast milk or dilute formula when the vomiting and diarrhea have abated.[83] The concentration of formula or breast milk is increased in increment after 24 hours of the lower increment of formula. Children who cannot be increased to full strength within a reasonable period of time are given nonmilk formulas containing soy proteins. A recent study also indicates that soy-based formulas can be used as a primary rehydrating solution, obviating the need for the use of rehydrating solutions totally devoid of proteins.[84] The use of soy- and other vegetable-based protein formulas and of human breast milk as primary rehydrating fluids might be particularly applicable in treating malnourished children with acute viral gastroenteritis since such children can ill afford to be deprived of protein and other nutrients for extended periods of time. Children unable to tolerate soy proteins are then given elemental monosaccharide-based formulas. In our experience a small proportion of children with severe episodes of rotavirus gastroenteritis will require the use of such a disaccharide-free formula for up to 1 month following acute gastroenteritis and, in rare cases, for longer periods of time. It should be noted that the refeeding regimen is generally well tolerated and can be utilized at home as well as in the hospital. The early discharge of children with acute gastroenteritis is to be encouraged in order to decrease the possibility of hospital-acquired illnesses.[85, 86]

One group of patients highly susceptible to rotavirus gastroenteritis are children with abnormal immune systems due to either congenital immunodeficiency syndromes or acquired immunologic defects secondary to cancer chemotherapy. For example, several children have been reported with congenital hypogammaglobulinemia, severe combined immunodeficiency diseases, or aplastic anemia suffering from chronic diarrhea due to rotavirus.[87] Unlike children with normal immune status, these children can have diarrhea due to rotavirus persisting for greater than 3 months. The strains of rotavirus often display unusual RNA patterns as deter-

mined by PAGE (see Figure 33–2, lane B). Two such patients who did not respond to the usual supportive measures were treated with breast milk (Figure 33–4). The breast milk was irradiated to destroy possible endogenous viruses and was treated with lactase to decrease the lactose content of the milk. Both children responded to the breast milk with a decrease in the diarrhea as well as a diminution in the amount of rotavirus found in the stools. We have also utilized human serum immunoglobulin to treat children with chronic rotavirus infection. The administration of immunoglobulin-containing rotavirus antibody to such children has resulted in a decrease in rotavirus excretion due to complexing of antigen with antibody.[88] The administration of human immunoglobulin has also resulted in the prevention of symptomatic neonatal rotavirus infection.[89]

The use of passive antibody or other factors given by the oral route in the form of breast milk or serum antibody should be investigated further to determine its potential role in the treatment of rotavirus and other GI infections which are not adequately cleared in an infected individual by the host immune system. The pathophysiology and treatment of severe viral diarrhea in children with immune impairments due to other states such as secretory IgA deficiency, malignancy, and malnutrition should also be the subject of further investigation.

Diagnosis

The accurate diagnosis of rotavirus gastroenteritis is desirable to optimize the patient treatment plan, prevent nosocomial infections in a closed population, and distinguish infectious from noninfectious disorders of the GI tract. The fact that most human strains are not cultivatable by commonly utilized viral isolation procedures precludes the use of standard viral cultivation techniques for rotavirus diagnosis. In early studies the rapid diagnosis of rotavirus gastroenteritis was accomplished by the direct visu-

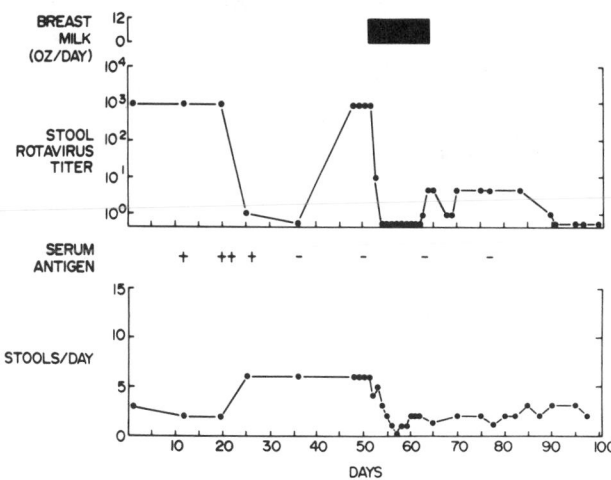

Figure 33–4. Comparison of the number of stools per day, stool rotavirus titer, and results of serum testing for rotavirus antigen in temporal relationship to breast milk administration in a 10-month-old boy with severe combined immunodeficiency. (From Saulsbury F, et al: Chronic rotavirus infection in children with immunodeficiency disease. *J Pediatr* 1980; 91:61–65. Used by permission.)

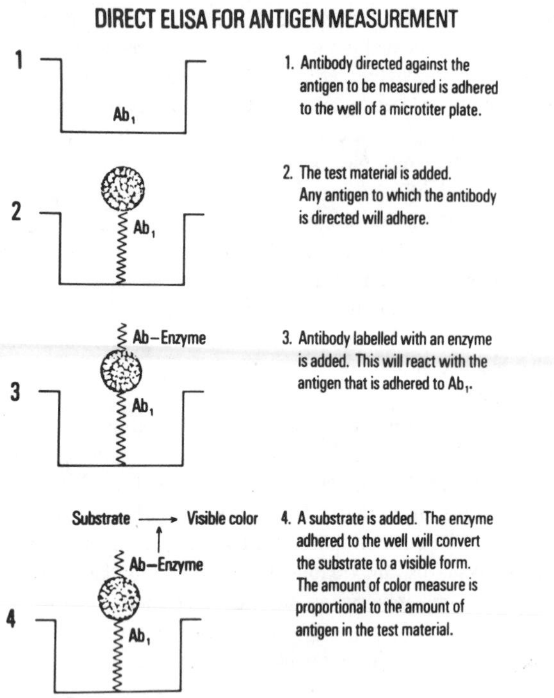

DIRECT ELISA FOR ANTIGEN MEASUREMENT

Figure 33–5. Direct enzyme-linked immunosorbent assay (ELISA) for the detection of viral antigens. (From Kapikian AZ, et al: The gastroenteritis viruses, in Lennette EH, Schmidt N (eds): *Diagnostic Procedures for Viral, Rickettsial and Chlamydial Infections*, ed 5. Washington, DC, American Public Health Association, 1979, pp 927–995. Used by permission.)

alization of viral particles in stool specimens by electron microscopy. However, the scarcity of laboratories capable of performing electron microscopic examination on a routine basis has led to the development of a number of immunoassay systems for the direct detection of rotavirus antigens in stools. The most useful is the technique of enzyme immunoassay also known as ELISA[90] (Figure 33–5).

Enzyme immunoassays are capable of accurately quantitating rotavirus antigen in stool specimens or rectal swabs. While the originally described ELISA systems required four hours to perform, recent modifications allow for the performance of the assay within 20 minutes.[91, 92] The recent availability of commercial enzyme immunoassays for the diagnosis of rotavirus has brought accurate rotavirus diagnosis within reach of most clinicians.[93] Diagnostic tests are specially useful to distinguish rotavirus gastroenteritis from diarrhea due to other causes such as bacterial gastroenteritis, drug reactions, and food allergies. In addition, the immunoassays can be utilized to measure the clearance of viral antigens during recovery as well as to monitor the epidemiology of rotavirus in a hospital environment. In an outpatient setting, rotavirus assays are often utilized to determine the nature of outbreaks of gastroenteritis occurring in the community.[94] It is advisable that such monitoring be continually performed, since it is possible that the striking seasonal variations noted in previous studies might vary in different climates from year to year.

It should be noted in regard to the immunodiagnosis of rotaviruses and other enteric pathogens that there are materials in fecal samples which can react nonspecifically with the antibodies and solid phase components of the assay system. Nonspecifically reacting materials include bacterial cell wall proteins and antibodies directed at animal immunoglobulins.[90] While such nonspecific reactants can occur in any fecal sample, they appear to be particularly prevalent in stools obtained from newborns, probably due to nature of the neonatal fecal flora. Fortunately, nonspecific activity due to these reactants can be decreased by the addition of excess antibodies into the immunoassay reaction mixture. Furthermore, nonspecific binding can be distinguished from specific binding by means of control reactions in which nonantibody immunoglobulins are substituted for the antiviral antibodies in the performance of the immunoassays.[63, 90] Comparative studies have indicated that the specificity of commercially available assays varies depending on assay format and immunoreagents. Care should thus be utilized in the selection of immunoassay systems for clinical use, especially when fecal samples from neonates are being evaluated.

The antigenically distinct rotaviruses cannot be detected by means of commercially available immunoassays which are based on reactivity with the group-specific antigen of group A rotaviruses. Immune electron microscopy (IEM) is valuable in detection of the antigenically distinct rotaviruses, but the scarcity of specific antisera restricts the usefulness of IEM as a routine diagnostic assay for nongroup A rotaviruses. Direct extraction or RNA from fecal specimens followed by PAGE can also be employed to identify the presence of any of the rotavirus groups, but the sensitivity of PAGE is also limited if small quantities of virus are excreted.[40, 95] Cultivation of nongroup A rotaviruses is not yet a practical alternative for routine diagnosis, although one porcine strain of group C rotavirus and an avian group D rotavirus have each been adapted to growth in tissue culture.[96] Advances in in vitro cultivation techniques, the production of monoclonal antibodies, and the application of recombinant DNA techniques for the expression of viral proteins are expected to lead to improvements in the diagnosis and characterization of the nongroup A rotaviruses.[97]

It should be noted in terms of diagnosis that rotaviruses can be encountered in the absence of clinical disease. As discussed above, prolonged shedding can occur in newborns and in infants hospitalized for extensive periods of time. The shedding of rotaviruses in the absence of symptoms has also been encountered in outpatients, particularly those living in environments conducive to the repeated transmission of rotaviruses. In the United States this phenomenon has been best documented in children attending day care centers.[98] Presumably many of these children are undergoing repeated infections which are asymptomatic due to their prior exposure to rotaviruses. The diagnosis of rotaviral shedding by the assays discussed above may be important in the prevention of disease transmission in such environments. Conversely, the detection of rotavirus antigen in a symptomatic child living in such an environment should be interpreted with caution. It is possible in such situations that the child is undergoing an asymptomatic rotavirus infection and that the symptoms are related to other enteric pathogens such as parasites or enteropathogenic bacteria.

Immunity to Rotavirus Infection

Rotavirus remains a common cause of serious gastroenteritis both in developed and underdeveloped countries. The high prevalence of rotavirus infection in areas of the world with modern systems of sanitation suggests that all cases of rotavirus infection will not be prevented by the institution of currently available sanitation techniques. Rather, if the rate of rotavirus infections is to be dramatically decreased, specific immunoprophylactic methods such as vaccination programs will have to be developed.

While a great deal has been learned about the structure and epitope diversity of rotaviral surface proteins, there is still little information available regarding the nature of protection against disease in humans. For example, while studies with monoclonal antibodies indicate a great deal of antigenic diversity, epidemiologic studies indicate that humans undergo a very limited number of symptomatic rotavirus infections. While serologic studies and shedding studies indicate that humans can be infected multiple times, it is generally only the first infection that occurs in children 4 to 15 months of age which is associated with discernible symptoms.[107]

Thus, while it has been shown that children who lack any serum antibody to rotaviruses as measured by solid phase assays are more likely to suffer serious infections, it has been difficult to associate the presence of neutralizing antibodies with protection against individual viral serotypes. This fact suggests that primary infections with rotavirus might be more severe, whereas secondary infections, regardless of viral serotype, might be somewhat modulated in terms of clinical course. In fact, a long-term prospective study indicated that asymptomatic infections occurring in infancy can provide protection against symptomatic infection.[100] Such data provide the rationale for immunization with a limited number of human serotypes, as discussed below.

Thus, while the virus displays multiple ''serotypes'' as defined by in vitro assays, epidemiologic studies raise questions as to the relevance of these determinations in human disease. Possible explanations for this discrepancy include the occurrence of cross-protection due to shared epitopes on VP_4 or VP_7 that are detectable by monoclonal antibodies but which are generally not recognized by neutralization assays using polyclonal reference antisera.[32] It is possible that antibodies to these shared epitopes arise following repeated infections, thus explaining the finding that such infections are often not associated with symptoms of serious disease. It is also possible that the immune response in the intestinal tract is different from that measured in serum and that the presence of neutralizing secretory IgA antibody at the site of viral replication is required for the inhibition of viral infection. This possibility is supported by the fact that colostrum can provide protection in animal model systems[101] and human breast milk contains significant levels of antirotavirus antibodies.[102, 103] However, due to the difficulty in obtaining adequate specimens for analysis, little data exist for the direct evaluation of this hypothesis.

It has also been suggested that cross-protection might be related to T cell–mediated immunity.[104] This hypothesis is supported by the fact that T cells appear to demonstrate cross-reactvity in in vitro systems probably related to the expression of conserved epitopes on internal viral proteins which might be expressed in the cell surface during the course of infection. In addition to these immune-related phenomena, it is also possible that nonimmune factors might play a role in susceptibility of infection. For example, it has been demonstrated in animal model systems that the older animals are protected against the development of symptomatic rotavirus infections even in the absence of functioning T cells or

B cells.[105] This protection is probably related to the maturation of the GI tract in terms of receptors or other aspects of the enteric environment. A more detailed understanding of factors involved in the immune and nonimmunologically mediated protection against infection with human rotaviruses might be important in the development of effective measures for the prevention of rotaviral disease in humans.

Potential for Rotavirus Immunization

The demonstration of disease protection across viral serotypes has encouraged the development of vaccines against rotavirus infection based on immunization with single or limited numbers of viral serotypes. Up to this point in time, most studies have utilized animal strains of rotavirus with the hope that they would provide cross-protection against human strains while being sufficiently attenuated to avoid the development of GI symptoms in the vaccinees. As depicted in Table 33–1, both bovine and simian strains of rotaviruses have been used for this purpose. In the case of the bovine rotaviruses, a highly passaged strain of Nebraska calf diarrhea virus (NCDV) has proved to be quite safe and to provide protection against symptomatic disease in children 6 months to 2 years of age living in Finland.[106] However, less protection has been noted in studies performed in younger infants, perhaps related to the inhibiting effects of persistent maternal antibodies. In addition, lower degrees of efficiency were also noted in children living in less developed countries, a finding that is perhaps related to the high rate of circulation of other enteric viruses in this population and subsequent interference with enteric rotavirus replication. A similar phenomenon probably explains the inhibitory effects that have been noted between rotavirus vaccine efficacy and the contemporaneous administration of oral polio vaccines.[107] It is also possible that these interference phenomena can explain the lack of vaccine efficacy noted in children living on an Apache Indian reservation in Arizona.

More recently, a less highly passaged bovine strain, named WC3, has been shown to prevent rotaviral disease in infants and young children living in urban and suburban areas near Philadelphia.[108] Interestingly, while infants in the vaccine group were clearly protected as compared to a matched group administered placebo, there was little, if any, correlation between the levels of serum antibody attained and disease protection. In fact, a high rate of protection was noted in children who did not have any demonstrable seroresponse to vaccination. This finding illustrates the need for additional studies directed at the elucidation of the immunologic mechanisms involved in viral inhibition and determination of sensitive and specific markers for disease protection.

Additional studies have been performed with a strain of rotaviruses originally isolated from the feces of a rhesus monkey. This virus has the theoretical advantage that its VP_7 is highly homologous to the VP_7 of serotype 3 strains of human rotaviruses and thus might be expected to provide greater cross-protection against some human strains. However, early studies with this virus also indicated that it was less attenuated than the bovine strains and many infants in Finland administered the virus displayed high rates of fever and symptoms of respiratory and GI dysfunction.[109] Later studies have utilized lower doses and have focused on the administration of vaccine to young infants who might be expected to have maternal antibody and thus be partially protected against vaccine side effects. Under such conditions the virus has been administered safely to several populations. In Finland, degrees of protection were attained that were similar to those found with the bovine vaccine. However, the vaccine did not display significant efficacy when administered to children living in New York State or in the Indian reservation in Arizona. Efficacy was noted in a study performed on children living in Venezuela[110]; however, disease in the placebo group in that population was apparently caused by viruses homologous to human serotype 3, a serotype that is not highly prevalent in other populations.

In addition, the vaccine has not been extensively tested in premature infants or others who might not possess a full complement of antibodies and who thus might not be able to limit the intestinal replication of the vaccine strain. Such studies should be performed before the vaccine can be considered for general use in the United States or other countries with large numbers of such infants. Based on this finding, additional studies are being performed using recombinant strains which contain VP_4 from the rhesus strain and VP_7 from human strains. The safety and efficacy of such vaccines is currently the subject of controlled trials in developed and developing countries.[107]

However, the fact that rotavirus infections are generally self-limited suggests that an alternative approach to reducing the morbidity and mortality associated with rotavirus infections might be the promotion of adequate case detection and the use of oral fluid therapy.[83] Since treatment in many areas of the world is based largely on oral fluid replacement, further investigation should be directed at optimizing such passive therapy. Immunoprophylactic measures, including the use of breast milk and oral antibody solutions, should be further developed for the treatment of immunodeficient and malnourished children and for those who do not respond to fluid replacement therapy.

Recent studies on animal model systems suggest additional ways in which oral therapies might be utilized for the prevention or treatment of rotavirus infections. As discussed above, rotaviruses require the presence of proteases for efficient replication. It has been shown that materials containing protease inhibitors can prevent the in vitro and in vivo replication of rotaviruses, and several inhibitors have been shown to prevent the development of rotavirus gastroenteritis in animal models of rotavirus infections.[111] The fact that many food products, such as those derived from soy and other plant and animal sources, contain protease inhibitors raises the possibility that such materials might be utilized for the prevention or treatment of rotavirus infections, perhaps by their addition to orally administered rehydrating solutions. Similarly, the fact that animals generate antibodies with extensive cross-reactivities for human rotaviruses raises the possibility that animal-derived immunoglobulins, perhaps derived from bovine milk[112] or from eggs[113] might also be used for the prevention of rotavirus gastroenteritis. However, the presence of allergies to milk or egg proteins might inhibit this approach. Finally, it has been shown that sialic acid-containing glycoproteins, such as bovine salivary mucin and chicken ovomucoid, can inhibit the in vitro replication of rotaviruses and prevent the development of disease in animal models.[114] The mechanism for this prevention is probably related to the fact that rotaviruses bind strongly to such compounds, perhaps because they are structural analogues of viral receptors. Since there are a number of mucins and other sialic acid-containing glycoproteins which are suitable for human consumption, it is possible that such compounds also might be used for the prevention or treatment of human disease.

Table 33–1
Completed Field Trials of Live Attenuated Rotavirus Vaccines

Site	Vaccine Dose	No. of Doses	Age at Vaccination (mo)	Protection against Rotavirus Diarrhea (%)		Prevalent Rotavirus Serotypes
				All Episodes	Severe Episodes	
A. RIT 4237 vaccine (10^8 PFU)						
Finland	10^8	1	6–8	50	88	1
Finland	10^8	2	6–12	58	82	1
Finland	10^8	1	Newborn	0	80	1, 4
United States	10^8	1	2–6	0	0	1, 2, 4
Rwanda	10^8	1	2–5	0	0	N/A
Gambia	10^8	3	2–6	33	33	2
Peru	10^8	1, 2, or 3	3–18	40	75	1, 2
B. WC-3 vaccine (10^7 PFU)						
United States	10^7	1	3–12	76	100	1
C. RRV-1 vaccine						
Sweden	10^5	1	5–12	45	80	1
Finland	10^4	1	2–4	38	67	1, 4
United States (Rochester)	10^4	1	2–4	0	30	1
United States (Whiteriver)	10^4	1	2–6	0	0	1, 2, 4
Venezuela	10^4	1	1–10	64	90	3

PFU = plaque-forming units; N/A = not available.
Adapted from Programme for Control of Diarrhoeal Diseases.[107]

Table 33–2
Diarrheal Disease in Patients Infected With Enteric Adenoviruses and Other Agents

	Maximum No. Stools/Day			No. Days of Diarrhea	
	No.	Mean	Range	Mean	Range
Enteric adenoviruses	13	8.7	3–13	6.3	0–25
Other adenoviruses	2	7.5	7–8	4.0	2–6
Salmonella	2	8.5	7–10	7.0	4–10
No agent identified	9	9.0	5–15	5.6	2–11

Modified from Yolken et al.[121]

ENTERIC ADENOVIRUS INFECTIONS

Adenoviruses were first recognized as potential enteric pathogens in 1962.[115] However, the role of adenovirus in acute gastroenteritis has been controversial. Some investigators found adenoviruses to be associated with as many as 32% of the cases of actue gastroenteritis occurring in hospitalized children.[116, 117] Other investigators have documented the fact that adenoviruses could also be cultivated from the stools of a large number of asymptomatic children.[117, 118] This controversy has been recently clarified by the finding of the specific serogroups of adenoviruses with a high propensity for causing acute GI illness.[119] In addition to being antigenically distinct, these adenoviruses differ from those colonizing the respiratory tract in that they are not cultivatable in cell lines such as human embryonic kidney cells that allow for the growth of other human adenoviruses.[120] These fastidious enteric adenoviruses must be detected by electron microscopy, immunoassay techniques, or specialized cell lines.[121–123]

As in the case of other enteric viruses, enteric strains of adenoviruses appear to be highly fastidious and will not grow well in cell lines which support the growth of other adenovirus strains. This growth restriction has been shown to be related to a block in an early step in the growth cycle.[124, 124a] Fortunately, the enteric adenoviruses can be passaged in cells coinfected with other strains of rotaviruses or in cells that are chronically infected with deficient strains of virus, presumably because infection under these conditions allows for the early block to be overcome. Grahm's 293 cells, a cell line which is chronically infected with a deficient form of adenovirus type 5, thus serves as a useful cell line for the identification and propagation of enteric adenovirus strains. However, some strains of enteric adenoviruses will also grow in other cell lines, such as Hep 2.[125] The growth patterns of adenoviruses should thus not be used as the sole criteria of whether an individual strain belongs to the enteric groups.

Most of the strains of enteric adenovirus that have been isolated appear to be members of adenovirus group F and have been tentatively characterized as type 40 and type 41 based on their antigenic reactivities. The recent development of monoclonal antibodies against group-reactive and type-specific epitopes[126] should allow for the more efficient detection and characterization of these viral types in clinical samples. In addition, these viruses have been found to display characteristic patterns following digestion with restriction endonucleases (particularly the enzyme SMA 1).[127] Also, viral clones have been identified which react with DNA extracted from adenovirus types 40 and 41 but not with other known strains of adenoviruses.[128] These findings have allowed for the classification of adenoviruses on genetic as well as antigenic criteria.

Studies using these reagents have indicated that most strains of adenoviruses associated with diarrheal disease are closely related to the prototype enteric adenoviruses type 40 and type 41. However, investigators have also identified strains of adenoviruses epidemiologically associated with diarrheal disease which appear to be related to other adenoviral types.[129] The development of animal model systems and other methods for studying the pathogenesis of adenoviral enteric disease should allow for the more precise definition of adenovirus strains capable of causing diarrheal disease in humans. Also, the availability of specific reagents should allow for the widespread use of efficient diagnostic assays by clinicians and investigators and thus for a better understanding of the epidemiology of adenovirus gastroenteritis.

Prospective studies of infantile diarrhea have found rates of enteric adenovirus infection which have ranged from 4% to 8%. The clinical symptoms of the children infected with enteric adenoviruses have generally not varied from those exhibited by children infected with other agents of gastroenteritis (Table 33–2).[121, 130] In most studies, adenovirus was second only to rotaviruses as the most common agent of viral gastroenteritis. Adenoviruses have also been implicated in other enteric diseases. For example, Kagnoff et al[131] found evidence of infection with adenovirus type 12 in patients with celiac disease (nontropical sprue). The association between malabsorption and adenovirus infection is possibly related to the sequence homology between the EIb protein of adenovirus type 12 and the α-gliadin protein known as the activator of celiac disease.[131] The association between adenovirus infection and chronic intestinal disorders is the subject of ongoing investigations in a number of laboratories.

There have been few studies directed at determining the prevalence of infections with enteric adenoviruses by serologic means. However, recently, Shinozaki et al[132] developed a specific neutralization assay for adenovirus types 40 and 41 and found that 48% of adults living in Japan had serologic evidence of infection with one or both of these strains. The analysis of paired sera indicated 19% of the study patients with gastroenteritis had serologic evidence of infection with enteric adenoviruses. We have found similar rates of infection using enzyme immunoassay techniques for antibody measurements (R. Yolken, unpublished observations). The reasons for the higher rates of infection detected by serologic means as opposed to electron microscopic or antigen-detection methods is not known with certainty but is possibly related to the relative sensitivity of the assay systems and to the pattern of viral shedding during the course of infection.

Another population susceptible to infection with enteric-type adenovirus are patients undergoing bone marrow transplantation.[133] In a prospective study of 54 patients with bone marrow trans-

Table 33-3
Relationship of Enteric Pathogens to Clinical Symptoms in Patients With Bone Marrow Transplants

Pathogen	No. of Patients	No. with Indicated Symptoms				
		Vomiting	Diarrhea	Abdominal Cramps	Respiratory Illness	Death
Rotavirus	8	8	4	7	6	5
Adenovirus*	9	8	5	5	4	4
Coxsackievirus*	2	1	2	1	1	2
Rotavirus and adenovirus†	1	1	0	0	0	0
Coxsackievirus and adenovirus*‡	2	1	2	2	2	2
Any viral pathogen	22	19	13§	15§	13‖	13§
C difficile only	9	6	5‖	4	3	4
Any pathogen	31	25	18§	19§	16‖	17‖
No virus or toxin	47	31	6	6	9	6

*Includes one patient coinfected with Clostridium difficile *toxin within 6 weeks of the viral infection.*
†*The onsets of the rotavirus and adenovirus infections were separated by a 4-week interval. The vomiting occurred within five days of the rotavirus infection.*
‡*Both patients were simultaneously infected with coxsackievirus and adenovirus.*
§$P<.002$ *compared to no virus or toxin.*
‖$P<.05$ *compared to no virus or toxin. Statistical analyses were not performed for the individual viruses. Modified from Yolken et al.*[133]

plantation, nine (17%) were found to have gastroenteritis associated with enteric-type adenovirus (Table 33–3, Figure 33–6). The patients ranged in age from 9 to 36 years. The volume of diarrhea ranged from 600 to 3000 mL per day and the diarrhea persisted for seven to 31 days. The cases of adenovirus gastroenteritis in bone marrow transplant patients occurred at the same time of year that the cases of adenovirus gastroenteritis occurred in the pediatric unit. We have also found that enteric adenovirus infections are highly prevalent in infants with prolonged hospitalization and functioning ileostomies or colostomies.[134] These findings suggest that adenovirus may have been transmitted within the hospital environment. Further studies should be performed on the epidemiology of enteric-type adenoviruses to determine the mode of spread of this agent within families and within closed environments.

Diagnosis

The diagnosis of enteric-type adenovirus can be made by immunologic methods. Enzyme immunoassay techniques utilizing both group-reacting antisera directed at common adenovirus antigens and type-specific reagents directed at enteric-type adenoviruses can detect adenoviruses in stool specimens and distinguish enteric-type adenovirus serotypes from other adenoviruses which might not be associated with diarrheal disease.[123, 126] As discussed above, the recent availability of monoclonal antibodies specific for enteric adenoviruses should expand the usefulness of such immunoassay systems. Similarly, nucleic acid hybridization assays have been developed for the detection and identification of enteric-type adenoviruses.[126] The diagnosis of adenovirus gastroenteritis can also be made by the visualization of typical adenoviral particles by electron microscopy. The use of monoclonal antibody-based immune electron microscopy can aid in the detection of adenovirus types 40 and 41 in fecal specimens and distinguishing those adenoviruses that might not be associated with diarrhea.[135] Since the enteric-type adenoviruses do not usually grow in tissue culture cell lines such as human embryonic kidney cells, which are used for the isolation of other adenoviruses, cultivation of virus in these

cell lines cannot be utilized to diagnose adenovirus gastroenteritis. However, specialized cell lines such as Grahm's cells and Chang conjunctive cells appear to support the growth of enteric-type adenoviruses.[120, 136] Adenoviruses isolated in these cell lines can be identified as enteric-type adenoviruses by means of the immunoassays or hybridization assays discussed above or by the examination of viral DNA following restriction enzyme digestion.

The hypothesis that adenoviruses are important causes of gastroenteritis is an attractive one, since certain aspects of adenoviruses, such as the large number of adenovirus serotypes and the ability of adenoviruses to replicate in both GI and respiratory epithelial cells, are consistent with many of the clinical and epidemiologic aspects of acute gastroenteritis. The available assays should be utilized along with well-controlled epidemiologic studies to further define the role of enteric-type adenoviruses as causative agents of gastroenteritis and respiratory disease in both children and adults.

NORWALK AND RELATED VIRUSES

It has been known for a number of years that common-source outbreaks of gastroenteritis can often occur in the absence of in-

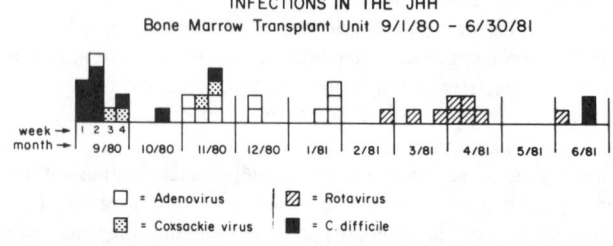

Figure 33–6. Temporal clustering of enteric infections occurring in patients undergoing bone marrow transplantation. (From Yolken RH, et al: Infectious gastroenteritis associated with morbidity and mortality in bone marrow transplantation. *N Engl J Med* 1982; 306:1009–1012. Used by permission.)

fection with identifiable bacterial agents. In 1972, a viral agent associated with such an outbreak was identified by electron microscopy. This agent was given the name Norwalk after the city in Ohio where the outbreak occurred.[137] The virus that caused the outbreak was 32 nm in diameter and had a buoyant density of 1.37 to 1.41g/mL in CsCl.[138] Since the original description of Norwalk virus, a number of similar-sized viruses have been found in fecal specimens obtained from children and adults during sporadic infections as well as during outbreaks of diarrheal disease.[139] These agents have usually been named according to the geographic region of their discovery (eg, Snow Mountain agent,[140] Hawaii agent,[141] etc). Little success has been reported in the adaptation of these viruses to growth in vitro, and this has made it difficult to define the antigenic relationships among these agents. Initial attempts at classification were based on virion morphology as observed by means of IEM.[142] The Norwalk virus and Norwalk-like agents do not appear to possess distinctive morphologic features as observed by means of electron microscopy. Other 27- to 32-nm viruses observed in human fecal specimens more closely resemble the caliciviruses with cuplike indentations on the viral surface.[143, 144] The caliciviruses are also characterized by a genome of plus-strand RNA and the presence of a single major virus polypeptide of 60,000 to 70,000 daltons mol wt.[145]

Recent studies, however, suggest that the Norwalk-like agents and caliciviruses may be more closely related than initially indicated by means of electron microscopy. Both Norwalk virus and a Norwalk-like agent, the Snow Mountain agent, have been reported to contain a single major polypeptide similar in size to the characteristic single protein found in caliciviruses.[146, 147] Additional evidence that the Norwalk-like agents are related to the caliciviruses is provided by examination of acute and convalescent sera obtained from individuals known to be infected with caliciviruses. In a recent study, seroconversion to Norwalk virus was documented in 12 of 20 patients with gastroenteritis due to human calicivirus serotype UK4 and in two of eight patients with serotype UK2 infection.[148] Seroconversion to caliciviruses has not been demonstrated among patients with Norwalk infection. Comparison of the genomic content of these viruses would be important in defining the relationship of the caliciviruses and Norwalk-like agents, but the genomes of Norwalk-like agents have not yet been identified.

Pathologic and Clinical Features

Of the 27- to 32-nm agents, the greatest amount of information concerning the clinical and pathologic features of human infection is available about Norwalk-like viruses through the study of outbreaks as well as administration of the viruses to human volunteers.[149–152] Examination of intestinal biopsy specimens obtained from experimentally infected individuals has shown that, unlike the case with rotavirus, there appears to be little epithelial cell destruction or evidence of mucosal disruption. However, Norwalk virus does appear to cause blunting of the intestinal villi at the distal part of the jejunum.[153, 154] Examination of the mucosa by light microscopy often reveals cytoplasmic vacuolization and inflammatory cell infiltration. Examination of cellular enzymes such as disaccharidase reveals a moderate decrease in levels during the acute phase of gastroenteritis with a rapid return to normal following resolution.[155] Postinfection complications due to disac-

charide deficiency have not been observed following infection with Norwalk virus.

Norwalk virus produces a characteristic picture of gastroenteritis in either human volunteers or individuals ingesting virus from a common source. The onset of diarrhea occurs 24 to 72 hours after ingestion of the virus. As little as 10 mL of a 1:100 dilution of stool filtrate from an infected patient can induce disease. Infection is reduced only minimally by treatment with heat (50–60°C), lipid solvents such as ether, or mild acid.[151] The diarrhea, which is usually mild to moderate in extent, lasts 18 to 36 hours. The diarrhea is often accompanied by vomiting, which in some cases can occur as often as 20 times a day. In addition, many patients infected with Norwalk virus will also have headaches, myalgias, and malaise. These symptoms do not usually persist beyond 72 hours. The occurrence of chronic infection with Norwalk virus or chronic gastroenteritis damage following acute Norwalk virus infection has not been reported.

Immune Responses to the Norwalk Agent

Acute infection with Norwalk viruses usually leads to the development of an immune response to the virus as measured by IEM or immunoassay. However, this serum antibody does not appear to provide protection against symptomatic reinfection.[156, 157] The possibility that reinfection is due to minor antigenic differences among infecting viruses has been excluded in some cases by volunteer studies in which adults have been serially reinfected with aliquots of an identical strain of viruses.[156] In such studies patients who developed diarrhea following ingestion of Norwalk virus were protected from symptomatic reinfection for up to 8 weeks. However, volunteers who were rechallenged beyond that period of time developed clinical illness of similar severity to their initial infection. Interestingly, in these studies there was a subgroup of individuals who did not develop symptomatic gastroenteritis despite initial challenge with large amounts of virus. On rechallenge, these same individuals were protected against illness. Serum levels of antibody to Norwalk virus in individuals resistant to the effect of Norwalk virus were not greater than those of individuals who were susceptible. The possibility that the resistant patients had larger amounts of local antibody in their GI tract was rendered unlikely by the findings that the resistant volunteers had lower levels of anti-Norwalk antibody in jejunal fluids than patients who were susceptible.[157] These findings suggest that susceptibility or resistance to infection with Norwalk virus is based not only on the generation of soluble antibodies but on some as yet undetermined local or systemic mechanism of resistance. An understanding of this mechanism will be required for the development of effective means of immunoprophylaxis.

Epidemiology

Many of the cases of Norwalk virus gastroenteritis have been associated with groups of patients living in a closed environment such as schools, recreational camps, or cruise ships.[139, 157, 158] Other outbreaks have occurred in individuals ingesting contaminated shellfish or water.[159, 160] Seroepidemiologic studies have been performed in an attempt to determine the age-associated acquisition of Norwalk antibody.[157, 161] Only approximately 20% of children living in developed countries such as the United States demonstrate antibody to Norwalk virus by the time they are 5 years old. It is thus unlikely that Norwalk virus is a common cause of infantile gastroenteritis in these geographic populations. However, children living in developing countries such as Bangladesh and Equador have a much higher rate of acquisition of Norwalk antibody. A majority of children living in those countries have serologic evidence of infection with Norwalk virus by 5 years of age. In addition, a number of children with acute gastroenteritis living in developing areas are documented to exhibit a serologic response to Norwalk virus following episodes of acute diarrheal disease.[157] While these agents do not appear to be common among infants hospitalized with severe dehydration, these data indicate that Norwalk virus may be an important cause of mild, infantile gastroenteritis in developing countries.

CALICIVIRUSES

Caliciviruses have been identified as etiologic agents of human gastroenteritis in a number of geographic regions, but the most intensive study of these viruses has been performed in Great Britain and Japan.[162] Caliciviruses have been observed in fecal specimens from 6.6% of children admitted to a London hospital because of diarrhea.[163] These viruses have also been associated with gastroenteritis in Japanese infants and school children.[164] Examination of human sera indicates that the presence of antibody directed against caliciviruses is common among adults living in the United Kingdom, Japan, southeast Asia, and other geographic locations.[165, 166] In the United Kingdom and Japan, the majority of the population appear to acquire anticalicivirus antibodies by age 5 years. Information concerning calicivirus infection in the United States is less complete, but a better understanding of calicivirus epidemiology should be possible in the near future with the wider application of recently developed immunoassays for the detection of calicivirus infection.[99, 165, 167]

Diagnosis of Norwalk Viruses and Caliciviruses

Initially, the diagnosis of Norwalk-like virus and calicivirus infections was accomplished by means of IEM which employed convalescent sera from the infected patient.[137] This technique remains valuable in the identification of these agents in fecal specimens, although solid phase immunoassays are now reported for the detection of Norwalk virus, the Snow Mountain agent, and caliciviruses.[167–170] Since stool specimens may contain only small amounts of these antigens, the diagnosis of infection is often best accomplished by comparison of antibody titers from acute and convalescent paired sera in immunoassay systems. As measured in these assays, infected individuals have a fourfold increase in antibody titer to the virus. Since the immune response can be variable, diagnosis is frequently made in outbreak situations when sera from several members of the outbreak are obtained.

ASTROVIRUSES

Astroviruses were first isolated from infants in Great Britain in 1975 and named for their five- or six-pointed starlike appearance as seen by means of electron microscopy.[171, 172] These viruses are

isolated during outbreaks of gastroenteritis and in sporadic cases of diarrheal illness.[173] Most astrovirus isolates are obtained from infants and children, but adult infection is occasionally reported, as illustrated by an epidemic of astrovirus infection which occurred in a nursing home in Marin County, California in 1978.[174] In some areas, a sharp increase in seroprevalence to the astroviruses is noted between 1 year and 4 years of age, with more than 75% of children seropositive by the age of 10.[175] However, the incidence and prevalence of astrovirus infection in most geographic areas has not yet been explored. Infection is thought to be transmitted via the fecal-oral route from contaminated food and water, as well as person-to-person spread. Outbreaks are noted from ingestion of oysters.[173] The clinical features associated with astrovirus infection are generally mild, with nausea, vomiting, and diarrhea lasting for two to three days in the normal host.[176–179] Systemic complaints including headache, fever, and general malaise are also noted. In contrast to the Norwalk-like agents, astrovirus infection may be most easily diagnosed by means of electron microscopy, since they are excreted in diarrheal feces in quantities of as much as 10^{10} particles per gram.[173]

Investigation of astroviruses has been aided by the large number of virus particles in fecal specimens and the in vitro cultivation of the viruses.[173, 180] At least five serotypes of human astroviruses are described, and these are antigenically distinct from animal astroviruses.[181, 182] The astroviruses also do not cross-react serologically with any of the reported caliciviruses or Norwalk viruses.[173, 185] The astroviruses are similar in size (approximately 28 nm) and density (1.35–1.39 g/mL in CsCl) to the Norwalk and caliciviruses,[183] but they are distinguished by their starlike appearance when examined by means of electron microscopy.[172] In contrast to the single virus-associated protein, which is characteristic of caliciviruses, examination of the astroviruses indicates that they contain either two or four polypeptides of mol wt 32,000 to 36,000 daltons.[183] The viral genome appears to be a single strand of RNA which is polyadenylated.[183] The role of astroviruses in human disease in the United States is the subject of ongoing studies.

CONCLUSIONS

Recent years have seen great strides in the understanding of nonbacterial gastroenteritis. Most of the advances have been accomplished by the identification of viral agents in stool specimens by electron microscopic techniques and the study of the epidemiology of these agents by means of immunoassays. The additional application of these techniques should further increase our understanding of the epidemiology and clinical course of infections with these agents. For example, the widespread availability of immunologic techniques for the diagnosis of noncultivatable adenoviruses should greatly expand the existing knowledge on the role of this virus in acute infectious diarrheal disease. In addition, the availability of immunoassays for the diagnosis of Norwalk and related enteric viruses should improve our understanding of the role of these agents. Similarly, the application of recently developed immunoassays for picornaviruses such as coxsackieviruses should provide greater understanding of the role of these viruses in acute diarrheal disease.[184]

An additional area that requires further study is the nature of the immune response to infection with these agents. The relative importance of serum antibody, local antibody, cell-mediated immunity, and nonimmune factors in protection against these agents needs to be investigated. Furthermore, the number of infecting serotypes and the possibility of antigenic drift in the different viruses needs to be more accurately established. The recent development of monoclonal antibodies to Norwalk virus and related agents should expand the scope and availability of immunoassays for the detection of these agents. These questions will have to be answered before populations at risk can be accurately determined and before effective strategies for immunoprophylaxis can be devised. Additionally, practical techniques for the detection of viral antigen in environmental specimens such as drinking water and effective strategies for elimination of these pathogens from environmental sources need to be developed. The diminution of the rate of acute GI infections and the morbidity and mortality associated with such infections remain important goals of medical research in all areas of the world.

REFERENCES

1. Shiga K: Observations on the epidemiology of dysentery in Japan. *Philippine J Sci* 1906; 1:485.
2. Hardy A, Watt J: Studies of the acute diarrheal diseases. XVIII. *Epidemiol Public Health Rep* 1948; 63:363.
3. Moffett HL, Shulenberger HK, Burkholder ER: Epidemiology and etiology of severe infantile diarrhea. *J Pediatr* 1968; 72:1–14.
4. Wyatt RG, Kalica AR, Mebus CA, et al: Reovirus-like agents (rotaviruses) associated with diarrheal illness in animals and man, in Pollard M (ed): *Perspectives in Virology.* New York, Raven Press, 1978, vol 10, pp 121.
5. Light JS, Hodes JH: Studies on epidemic diarrhea of the newborn: Isolation of a filtrate agent causing diarrhea in calves. *Am J Pediatr Med* 1942; 33:1451.
6. Connor JD, Barrett-Connor E: Infectious diarrheas. *Pediatr Clin North Am* 1967; 14:197–221.
7. Cramblett HJ, Siewers CMF: The etiology of gastroenteritis in infants and children with emphasis on the occurrence of simultaneous mixed viral-bacterial infection. *Pediatrics* 1965; 35:885–889.
8. Yow MD, Melnick JL, Blattner RJ, et al: The association of viruses and bacteria with infantile diarrhea. *Am J Epidemiol* 1970; 92:33–39.
9. Kapikian AZ, Yolken RH, Wyatt RG, et al: Viral diarrhea: Etiology and control. *Am J Clin Nutr* 1978; 31:2219–2236.
10. Blacklow NR, Schreiber DS, Trier JL: Viral enteritis, in Weinstein L, Fields S (eds): *Seminars in Infectious Diseases.* New York, Stratton Intercontinental Medical Book, 1978, p 256.
11. Kapikian AZ, Kim HW, Wyatt RG, et al: Reovirus-like agent in stools: Association with infantile diarrhea and development of serologic tests. *Science* 1974; 185:1049.
12. Bishop RF, Davidson GP, Holmes IH, et al: Virus particles in epithelial cells of duodenal mucosa from children with acute gastroenteritis. *Lancet* 1973; 2:1281.
13. Thornhill TS, Wyatt RG, Kalica AR, et al: Detection by immune electron microscopy of 26–27 nm virus-like particles associated with two family outbreaks of gastroenteritis. *J Infect Dis* 1977; 138:20.
14. Flewett TH, Bryden AS, Davies H: Epidemic viral enteritis in a long-way children's ward. *Lancet* 1975; 1:4–5.
15. Mathews REF: The classification and nomenclature of viruses: Summary of results of meetings of the international committee on taxonomy of viruses in The Hague, September 1978. *Intervirology* 1979; 11:133–135.
16. Woode GN, Bridger JC, Jones JM, et al: Morphological and antigenic relationships between viruses (rotaviruses) from acute gastroenteritis of children, calves, piglets, mice and foals. *Infect Immun* 1976; 14:804–810.
17. Rodger SM, Schnagl RD, Holmes IH: Biochemical and biophysical characterization of diarrhea virus of human and calf origin. *J Virol* 1975; 16:1229–1235.
18. Flewett TH, Bryden AS, Davies H, et al: Relation between viruses from acute gastroenteritis of children and newborn calves. *Lancet* 1974; 2:61–63.
19. Palmer EL, Martin ML, Murphy FA: Morphology and stability of infantile gastroenteritis virus: Comparison with reovirus and bluetongue virus. *J Gen Virol* 1977; 35:403–414.
20. Kalica AR, Sereno NM, Wyatt RG, et al: Comparison of human and animal rotavirus strains by gel electrophoresis of viral RNA. *Virology* 1978; 87:247–255.
21. Clarke IN, McCrae MA: Structural analysis of electrophoretic variation in the genome profiles of rotavirus field isolates. *Infect Immun* 1982; 36:492–497.
22. McCrae MA, McCorquodale JG: Molecular biology of rotaviruses. II. Identification of the protein-coding assignments of calf rotavirus genome RNA species. *Virology* 1982; 117:435–443.
23. Mason BB, Graham DY, Estes MK: Biochemical mapping of the simian rotavirus SA11 genome. *J Virol* 1983; 46:413–423.
24. Novo E, Esparza J: Composition and topography of structural polypeptides of bovine rotavirus. *J Gen Virol* 1981; 56:325–335.
25. Kalica AR, Flores J, Greenberg HB: Identification of the rotaviral gene that codes for hemagglutination and protease-enhanced plaque formation. *Virology* 1983; 125:194–305.
26. Estes MK, Graham DY, Mason BB: Proteolytic enhancement of rotavirus infectivity: Molecular mechanisms. *J Virol* 1981; 39:879–888.
27. Offit PA, Blavat G, Greenberg HB, et al: Molecular basis of rotavirus virulence: Role of gene segment 4. *J Virol* 1986; 57:46–49.
28. Greenberg HB, McAuliffe V, Valdesuso J, et al: Serological analysis of the subgroup protein of rotavirus, using monoclonal antibodies. *Infect Immun* 1983; 39:91–99.
29. Kalica AR, Greenberg HB, Wyatt RG, et al: Genes of human (strain Wa) and bovine (strain UK) rotaviruses that code for neutralization and subgroup antigens. *Virology* 1981; 112:385–390.
30. Kapikian AZ, Cline WL, Greenberg HB, et al: Antigenic characterization of human and animal rotaviruses by immune adherence hemagglutination assay (IAHA): evidence for distinctness of IAHA and neutralization antigens. *Infect Immun* 1981; 33:415–425.
31. Greenberg HB, Kalica AR, Wyatt RG, et al: Rescue of noncultivatable human rotaviruses by gene reassortment during mixed infection with ts mutants of a cultivatable bovine rotavirus. *Proc Natl Acad Sci USA* 1981; 78:420–424.
32. Matsui SM, Offit PA, Vo PT, et al: Passive protection against rotavirus-induced diarrhea by monoclonal antibodies to the heterotypic neutralization domain of VP7 and VP8 fragment of VP4. *J Clin Microbiol* 1989; 27:780–782.
33. Urasawa S, Urasawa T, Tankguchi K, et al: Serotype determination of human rotavirus isolates and antibody prevalence in pediatric populations in Hokkaido, Japan. *Arch Virol* 1984; 81:1–12.
34. Hoshino Y, Wyatt RG, Greenberg HB, et al: Serotypic similarity and diversity of rotaviruses of mammalian and avian origin as studied by plaque-reduction neutralization. *J Infect Dis* 1984; 149:694–702.
35. Matsuno S, Hasegawa A, Mukoyama A, et al: A candidate for a new serotype of human rotavirus. *J Virol* 1985; 54:623–624.
36. Clark HF, Hoshino Y, Bell LM, et al: Rotavirus isolate WI61 representing a presumptive new human serotype. *J Clin Microbiol* 1987; 25:1757–1762.
37. Thouless ME, Bryden AS, Flewett TH, et al: Serological relationships between rotaviruses from different species as studied

by complement fixation and neutralization. *Arch Virol* 1977; 53:287–294.

38. Dimitrov DH, Estes MK, Rangelova SM, et al: Detection of antigenically distinct rotavirus from infants. *Infect Immun* 1983; 41:523–526.

39. Eiden JJ, Vonderfecht S, Yolken RH: Evidence that a novel rotavirus-like agent of rats can cause gastroenteritis in man. *Lancet* 1985; 2:8–11.

40. Hung T, Chen G, Wang C, et al: Waterborne outbreak of rotavirus diarrhea in adults in China caused by a novel rotavirus. *Lancet* 1984; 1:1139–1142.

40a. Fang ZY, Ye Q, Ho MS, et al: Investigation of an outbreak of adult diarrhea rotavirus in China. *J Infect Dis* 1989; 160:948–953.

41. Pedley S, Bridger JC, Chasey D, et al: Definition of two new groups of atypical rotaviruses. *J Gen Virol* 1986; 67:131–137.

42. Rodger SM, Bishop RF, Holmes IH: Detection of a rotavirus-like agent associated with diarrhea in an infant. *J Clin Microbiol* 1982; 16:724–726.

43. Vonderfecht SL, Huber AC, Eiden JJ, et al: Infectious diarrhea of infant rats produced by a rotavirus-like agent. *J Virol* 1984; 52:94–98.

44. Vonderfecht SL, Eiden JJ, Tores A, et al: Identification of a bovine enteric syncytial virus as a non-group A rotavirus. *Am J Vet Res* 1986; 47:1913–1918.

45. Pedley S, Bridger JC, Brown JF, et al: Molecular characterization of rotaviruses with distinct group antigens. *J Gen Virol* 1983; 64:2093–2101.

46. Holmes IH, Ruck BJ, Bishop RF, et al: Infantile enteritis viruses: Morphogenesis and morphology. *J Virol* 1975; 16:937–943.

47. Suzuki H, Konno T: Reovirus-like particles in jejunal mucosa of a Japanese infant with acute infectious nonbacterial gastroenteritis. *Tohoku J Exp Med* 1975; 115:119–211.

48. Mavromichalis J, Evans N, McNeish AS, et al: Intestinal damage in rotavirus and adenovirus gastroenteritis assessed by D-xylose malabsorption. *Arch Pediatr* 1977; 52:589–591.

49. Hyams J: Lactose malabsorption following rotavirus infection. *J Pediatr* 1981; 99:916–917.

50. Mebus CA, Wyatt RG, Kapikian AZ: Pathology of diarrhea in gnotobiotic calves induced by the human reovirus-like agent in infantile gastroenteritis. *Vet Pathol* 1977; 14:273–282.

51. Gall DG: Pathophysiology of viral diarrhea, in: Proceedings of 73rd Ross Conference on Pediatric Research: Etiology, Pathology, and Treatment of Acute Gastroenteritis, Ponte Verde Beach, Fla, March 20–22, 1977.

52. Zissis G, Lambert JP, Fonteyne J, et al: Child-mother transmission of rotavirus. *Lancet* 1976; 1:96.

53. Davidson GP, Butler DG, et al: Ion transport in enteritis caused by human rotavirus. Presented at American Society of Microbiology Annual Meeting, Washington DC, May 1977. Abstract A 20/1043.

54. Blacklow NR, Echeverria P, Smith DA: Serological studies with reovirus-like agents. *Infect Immun* 1976; 13:1563–1566.

55. Kapikian AZ, Kim HW, Wyatt RG, et al: Human reovirus-like agent as the major pathogen associated with "winter" gastroenteritis in hospitalized infants and young children. *N Engl J Med* 1976; 294:964–972.

56. Banatvala JE, Chrystie IL, Totterdell BM: Rotaviral infections in human neonates. *J Am Vet Med Assoc* 1978; 173:527.

57. von Bonsdorff CH, Hovi T, Makala P, et al: Rotavirus infections in adults in association with acute gastroenteritis. *J Med Virol* 1978; 2:21.

58. Brandt CD, Kim HW, Yolken RH, et al: Comparative epidemiology of the rotavirus sero-types and other viral agents associated with pediatric gastroenteritis. *Am J Epidemiol* 1979; 54:339–346.

59. Bolivar R, Conklin RH, Vollet JJ, et al: Rotavirus in traveler's diarrhea—Study of an adult student population in Mexico. *J Infect Dis* 1978; 137:324–327.

60. Institute of Medicine: Prospects for immunizing against rotavirus. Appendix D-13. New Vaccine Development. Establishing Priorities, in *Diseases of Importance in Developing Countries*. Washington, DC, National Academy Press, 1986, vol 2, pp 1–12.

61. Wyatt RG, Yolken RH, Urrutia JJ, et al: Diarrhea associated with rotavirus in rural Guatemala: A longitudinal study of 24 infants and young children. *Am J Trop Med Hyg* 1979; 28:325–328.

62. Taylor P, Black RB, Yolken RH, et al: Oral rehydration therapy of diarrhoea in a rural treatment centre in Bangladesh. *Arch Dis Child* 1980; 55:376–379.

63. Yolken RH: Enzyme immunoassays for detecting human rotavirus, in Kapikian AZ, Tyrrell DAJ (eds): *Virus Infections of the Gastrointestinal Tract*. New York, Marcel Dekker, 1982, pp 51–74.

64. Lewis NM, Parry JV, Davies NA, et al: A year's experience of the rotavirus syndrome and its association with respiratory illness. *Arch Dis Child* 1979; 54:339–346.

65. Goldmatis PN, Chrystie IL, Banatvala JE: Rotavirus and the respiratory tract. *Br Med J* 1979; 4:1551–1553.

66. Matsumoto K, Ha-ano M, Kobayashi K, et al: An outbreak of gastroenteritis associated with acute rotaviral infection in schoolchildren. *J Infect Dis* 1989; 160:611–615.

67. Nakata S, Estes MK, Graham DY, et al: Detection of antibody to group B adult diarrhea rotaviruses in humans. *J Clin Microbiol* 1987; 25:812–818.

68. Penaranda ME, Ho MS, Fang ZY, et al: Seroepidemiology of adult diarrhea rotavirus in China, 1977 to 1987. *J Clin Microbiol* 1989; 27:2180–2183.

69. Kapikian AZ, Yolken RH: Rotavirus. Infectious diseases and their etiologic agents, in Mandell GI, Douglass R, Bennett J (eds): *Principles and Practice of Infectious Diseases*, ed 2. New York, Wiley, 1985, pp 933–944.

70. Gurwith M, Wenman W, Hinde D, et al: A prospective study of rotavirus infection in infants and younger children. *J Infect Dis* 1981; 144:218–224.

71. Carlson JK, Middleton PJ, Zamanski M, et al: Fatal rotavirus gastroenteritis. An analysis of 21 cases. *Am J Dis Child* 1978; 132:477.

72. Delage G, McLaughlin B, Besthaume L: A clinical study of rotavirus gastroenteritis. *J Pediatr* 1978; 93:455.

73. Salmi TT, Arstila P, Koivikko A: Central nervous system involvement in patients with rotavirus gastroenteritis. *Scand J Infect Dis* 1978; 10:29.

74. Valmari R, Pontynen P, Sunila R: Rotavirus infection in a neonatal unit. *J Clin Res* 1984; 16:167–170.

75. Rotbart HA, Nelson WL, Glode MP, et al: Neonatal rotavirus-associated necrotizing enterocolitis: Case control study and prospective surveillance during an outbreak. *J Pediatr* 1988; 112:87–93.

76. Flores J, Midthun K, Hoshino Y, et al: Conservation of the fourth gene among rotaviruses recovered from asymptomatic newborn infants and its possible role in attenuation. *J Virol* 1986; 60:972–979.

77. Sack DA, Chowdhury AMAK, Eusof A, et al: Oral hydration in rotavirus diarrhea: A double-blind comparison of sucrose with glucose electrolyte solution. *Lancet* 1978; 2:280.

78. Nalin DR, Levine MM, Mala L, et al: Comparison of sucrose with glucose in oral therapy of infant diarrhea. *Lancet* 1978; 2:77.

79. Black RE, Merson MH, Taylor PR, et al: Glucose vs sucrose in oral rehydration solutions for infants and young children with rotavirus-associated diarrhea. *Pediatrics* 1981; 67:79–83.

80. Finberg L: The management of the critically ill child with dehydration secondary to diarrhea. *Pediatrics* 1970; 15:1029.

81. Finberg L: Dehydration in infants and children. *N Engl J Med* 1968; 176:458–462.

82. Portnoy R, DuPont H, Pruitt D: Antidiarrheal agents in the treatment of acute diarrhea in children. *JAMA* 1976; 236:844–846.

83. Rees L, Brook CGD: Gradual re-introduction of full-strength milk after acute gastroenteritis in children. *Lancet* 1979; 1:770.

84. Santosham M, Foster S, Reid R, et al: Role of soy-based, lactose-free formula during the treatment of acute diarrhea. *Pediatrics* 1985; 76:292–298.

85. Flewett TH, Bryden AS, Davies H: Epidemic viral enteritis in a long-stay children's ward. *Lancet* 1975; 1:4–5.

86. Stamm WE, Martin SM, Bennett JV: Epidemiology of nosocomial infections. *J Infect Dis* 1971; 136:151–154.

87. Saulsbury F, Winkelstein J, Yolken RH: Chronic rotavirus infection in children with immunodeficiency diseases. *J Pediatr* 1980; 91:61–65.

88. Losonsky G, Johnson J, Winkelstein JA, et al: Oral administration of human serum immunoglobulin in immunodeficient patients with viral gastroenteritis: A pharmacokinetic and functional analysis. *J Clin Invest* 1985; 76:2362–2367.

89. Barnes GL, Hewson PH, McLellan JA, et al: A randomized trial of oral gammaglobulin in low-birth-weight infants infected with rotavirus. *Lancet* 1982; 1:1371–1373.

90. Yolken RH, Stopa PJ, Harris CC: Enzyme immunoassay for the detection of rotavirus antigen and antibody, in Rose N, Friedman H (eds): *Manual of Clinical Immunology,* ed 3. Washington, DC, American Society for Microbiology, 1980, p 692.

91. Yolken RH, Leister FJ: Rapid double determinant enzyme immunoassay for the measurement of human rotavirus. *J Infect Dis* 1982; 146:43–46.

92. Yolken RH, Eiden J, Leister F: Self-contained enzymic membrane immunoassay for detection of rotavirus antigen in clinical samples. *Lancet* 1986; 2:1305–1307.

93. Yolken RH, Leister FL: Evaluation of enzyme immunoassay systems for the detection of human rotavirus. *J Infect Dis* 1981; 144:379.

94. Yolken RH: Rapid diagnosis of viral infections. *Johns Hopkins Med J* 1981; 149:126–131.

95. Herring AJ, Inglis NF, Ojeh CK, et al: Rapid diagnosis of rotavirus infection by direct detection of viral nucleic acid in silver-stained polyacrylamide gels. *J Clin Microbiol* 1982; 16:473–477.

96. Saif LJ, Terrett LA, Miller KL, et al: Serial propagation of porcine group C rotavirus (pararotavirus) in a continuous cell line and characterization of the passaged virus. *J Clin Microbiol* 1988; 26:1277–1282.

97. Eiden JJ, Firoozmand F, Sato S, et al: Detection of group B rotavirus in fecal specimens by dot hybridization with a cloned cDNA probe. *J Clin Microbiol* 1989; 27:422–426.

98. Pickering LK, Bartlett AV, Reves RR, et al: Asymptomatic excretion of rotavirus before and after rotavirus diarrhea in children in day care centers. *J Pediatr* 1988; 112:361–365.

99. Matson DO, Estes MK, Tanaka T, et al: Asymptomatic human calicivirus infection in a day care center. *Pediatr Infect Dis J* 1990; 9:190–196.

100. Bishop RF, Barnes GL, Cipriani E, et al: Clinical immunity after neonatal rotavirus infection. A prospective longitudinal study in young children. *N Engl J Med* 1983; 309:72.

101. Snodgrass DR, Wells PW: Passive immunity in rotaviral infections. *J Am Vet Med Assoc* 1978; 173:565.

102. Ringenbergs M, Albert MJ, Davidson GP, et al: Serotype-specific antibodies to rotavirus in human colostrum and breast milk and in maternal and cord blood. *J Infect Dis* 1988; 158:477–479.

103. Yolken RH, Mata L, Garcia B, et al: Secretory antibody directed against rotavirus in human milk: Measurement by means of enzyme linked immunosorbent assay. *J Pediatr* 1978; 93:916–921.

104. Offit PA, Dudzik KI: Rotavirus-specific cytotoxic T lymphocytes cross-react with target cells infected with different rotavirus serotypes. *J Virol* 1988; 62:127–131.

105. Eiden J, Lederman H, Vonderfecht S, et al: T-cell deficient mice display normal recovery from experimental rotavirus infection. *J Virol* 1986; 57:706–708.

106. Vesikari T, Isolauri E, D'Hondt E, et al: Clinical efficacy of the RIT 4237 live attenuated bovine rotavirus vaccine in infants vaccinated before a rotavirus epidemic. *J Pediatr* 1985; 107:189–194.

107. *Programme for Control of Diarrhoeal Diseases. Sixth Programme Report 1986–1987.* Geneva, World Health Organization, 1988, WHO/CAP/88.28.

108. Clark HF, Furukawa T, Bell LM, et al: Immune response of infants and children to low passage bovine rotavirus (strain WC3). *Am J Dis Child* 1986; 140:250–256.

109. Kapikian AZ, Flores J, Hoshino Y, et al: Rotavirus: The major etiologic agent of severe infantile diarrhea may be controllable by a "Jennerian" approach to vaccination. *J Infect Dis* 1986; 153:815–822.

110. Flores J, Perez-Schaelel I, Gonzalez M, et al: Protection against severe rotavirus diarrhea by rhesus rotavirus vaccine in Venezuelan infants. *Lancet* 1987; 1:882–884.

111. Vonderfecht SL, Wee S-B, Miscuff RL, et al: Protease antagonists inhibit the *in vitro* and *in vivo* replication of rotavirus. *J Clin Invest* 1988; 82:2011–2016.

112. Yolken RH, Losonsky GA, Vonderfecht S, et al: Antibody to human rotavirus in cows milk. *N Engl J Med* 1985; 312:605–610.

113. Yolken RH, Leister F, Wee S-B, et al: Antibodies to rotavirus in chicken's eggs: A potential source of antiviral immunoglobulins suitable for human consumption. *Pediatrics* 1988; 81:291–295.

114. Yolken RH, Willoughby R, Wee S-B, et al: Sialic acid glycoproteins inhibit the *in vitro* and *in vivo* replication of rotaviruses. *J Clin Invest* 1987; 79:148–154.

115. Joncas J, Moisan A, Pavilanis V: Incidence of adenovirus infection: A family study. *Can Med Assoc J* 1962; 87:52–58.

116. Richmond SJ, Dunn SM, Caul EO, et al: An outbreak of gastroenteritis in young children caused by adenoviruses. *Lancet* 1979; 1:1178–1180.

117. Flewett TH, Bryden AS, Davies H: Virus particles in gastroenteritis. *Lancet* 1973; 2:1497.

118. Moffett HL, Shulenberger HK, Burkholder ER: Epidemiology and etiology of severe infantile diarrhea. *J Pediatr* 1968; 72:1–14.

119. Johansson ME, Unhou I, Kidd AH, et al: Direct identification of enteric adenovirus, a candidate new sero-type associated with infantile gastroenteritis. *J Clin Microbiol* 1980; 12:95–100.

120. Gary GW, Hierholzer JC, Black RE: Characteristics of noncultivatable adenoviruses associated with diarrhea in infants: a new subgroup of human adenoviruses. *J Clin Microbiol* 1979; 10:93–103.

121. Yolken RH, Lawrence F, Leister F, et al: Gastroenteritis associated with enteric type adenovirus in hospitalized infants. *J Pediatr* 1982; 10:21–26.

122. Takiff HE, Straus SE, Garon CE: Propagation and in vitro studies of previously noncultivatable enteral adenoviruses in 293 cells. *Lancet* 1981; 2:832–834.

123. Uhnoo I, Wadell G, Svensson L, et al: Two new serotypes of enteric adenoviruses causing infantile diarrhoea. *Dev Biol Stand* 1983; 53:311–318.

124. Takiff HE, Straus SE: Early replicative block prevents the efficient growth of fastidious diarrhea associated adenoviruses in cell culture. *J Med Virol* 1982; 9:93–100.

124a. Mautner V, MacKay N, Steinthorsdottir V: Complementation of enteric adenovirus type 40 for lytic growth in tissue culture by E1B 55K function of adenovirus types 5 and 12. *Virology* 1989; 171:619–622.

125. Perron-Henry DM, Herrmann JE, Blacklow NR: Isolation and propagation of enteric adenoviruses in HEp-2 cells. *J Clin Microbiol* 1988; 26:1445–1447.

126. Wadell G: Molecular epidemiology of human adenoviruses. *Curr Top Microbiol Immunol* 1984; 110:191–220.

127. Brown M, Petric M, Middleton PJ: Silver-staining of DNA restriction fragments for the rapid identification of adenovirus iso-

lates: application during nosocomial outbreaks. *J Virol Methods* 1984; 9:87–98.

128. Takiff HE, Seidlin M, Krause P, et al: Detection of enteric adenoviruses by dot-blot hybridization using highly specific, molecularly cloned viral DNA probes. *J Med Virol* 1985; 16:107–118.

129. Bishai FR, Yolken RH, Chernesky MA, et al: Studies on fastidious adenoviruses in Ontario: a distinct strain associated with gastroenteritis. *J Clin Microbiol* 1986; 23:398–400.

130. Uhnoo I, Olding-Stenkvist E, Kreuger A: Clinical features of acute gastroenteritis associated with rotavirus, enteric adenoviruses, and bacteria. *Arch Dis Child* 1986; 61:732–738.

131. Kagnoff MF, Paterson YK, Kumar PJ, et al: Evidence of the role of a human intestinal adenovirus in the pathogenesis of coeliac disease. *Gut* 1987; 28:995–1001.

132. Shinozaki T, Araki K, Ushijima H, et al: Antibody response to enteric adenovirus types 40 and 41 in sera from people in various age groups. *J Clin Microbiol* 1987; 25:1679–1682.

133. Yolken RH, Bishop CA, Townsend TR, et al: Infectious gastroenteritis associated with morbidity and mortality in bone marrow transplantation. *N Engl J Med* 1982; 306:1009–1012.

134. Yolken RH, Franklin CC: Gastrointestinal adenovirus—an important cause of morbidity in patients with necrotizing enterocolitis and gastrointestinal surgery. *Pediatr Infect Dis* 1985; 4:42–47.

135. Wood DJ, deJong JC, Bijlsma K, et al: Development and evaluation of monoclonal antibody-based immune electron microscopy for diagnosis of adenovirus types 40 and 41. *J Virol Methods* 1989; 25:241–250.

136. Graham FL, Smiley J, Russell WC, et al: Characterization of a human cell line transformed by DNA from human adenovirus type 5. *J Gen Virol* 1977; 36:59–72.

137. Kapikian AZ, Wyatt RG, Dolin R, et al: Visualization by immune electron microscopy of a 27nm particle associated with acute infectious non-bacterial gastroenteritis. *J Virol* 1972; 10:1075–1081.

138. Kapikian AZ, Gerin JL, Wyatt RG, et al: Density in cesium chloride of the 27-nm "8FIIa" particle associated with acute infectious nonmicroscopy. *J Infect Dis* 1974; 129:709–714.

139. Dolin R, Treanor JJ, Madore HP: Novel agents of viral enteritis in humans. *J Infect Dis* 1987; 155:365–376.

140. Morens DM, Zweighaft RM, Vernon TM, et al: A waterborne outbreak of gastroenteritis with secondary person-to-person spread. Association with viral agents. *Lancet* 1979; 1:964–966.

141. Thornhill TS, Wyatt RG, Kalica AR, et al: Detection by immune electron microscopy of 26-to27-nm virus-like particles associated with two family outbreaks of gastroenteritis. *J Infect Dis* 1977; 135:20–27.

142. Caul EO, Appleton H: The electron microscopical and physical characteristics of small round human fecal viruses: an interim scheme for classification. *J Med Virol* 1982; 9:257–265.

143. Flewett TH, Davies H: Calicivirus in man. *Lancet* 1976; 1:311.

144. Madeley CR, Cosgrove BP: Calicivirus in man. *Lancet* 1976; 1:199–200.

145. Schaffer FL, Bachrach HL, Brown F, et al: Caliciviridae. *Intervirology* 1980; 14:1–6.

146. Greenberg HB, Valdesuso JR, Kalica AR, et al: Proteins of Norwalk virus. *J Virol* 1981; 37:994–999.

147. Madore HP, Treanor JJ, Dolin R: Characterization of the Snow Mountain agent of viral gastroenteritis. *J Virol* 1986; 58:487–492.

148. Cubitt WD, Blacklow NR, Herrmann JE, et al: Antigenic relationships between human caliciviruses and Norwalk virus. *J Infect Dis* 1987; 156:806–814.

149. Wyatt RG, Dolin R, Blacklow NR, et al: Comparison of three agents of acute infectious non-bacterial gastroenteritis by cross-challenge in volunteers. *J Infect Dis* 1974; 129:709–724.

150. Johnson PC, Mathewson JJ, Dupont HL, et al: Multiple-challenge study of host susceptibility to Norwalk gastroenteritis in US adults. *J Infect Dis* 1990; 161:18–21.

151. Dolin R, Blacklow NR, DuPont H, et al: Biological properties of Norwalk agent of acute infectious nonbacterial gastroenteritis. *Proc Soc Exp Biol Med* 1972; 140:578–583.

152. Dolin R, Reichman RC, Roessner KD, et al: Detection by immune electron microscopy of the Snow Mountain agent of acute viral gastroenteritis. *J Infect Dis* 1982; 146:184–189.

153. Agus SG, Dolin R, Wyatt RG, et al: Acute infectious nonbacterial gastroenteritis: Intestinal histopathology. Histologic and enzymatic alterations during illness produced by the Norwalk agent in man. *Ann Intern Med* 1973; 79:18–25.

154. Dolin R, Levy AG, Wyatt RG, et al: Viral gastroenteritis induced by the Hawaii agent. Jejunal histopathology and seroresponse. *Am J Med* 1975; 59:761.

155. Levy AG, Widerlite L, Schwartz CJ, et al: Jejunal adenylate cyclase activity in human subjects during viral gastroenteritis. *Gastroenterology* 1976; 70:321–325.

156. Parrino TA, Schreiber DS, Trier JS, et al: Clinical immunity in acute gastroenteritis caused by the Norwalk agent. *N Engl J Med* 1977; 297:86–89.

157. Blacklow NR, Herrmann JE, Cubitt WD: Immunobiology of Norwalk virus. *Ciba Found Symp* 1987; 128:144–161.

158. Greenberg HB, Valdesuso J, Yolken RH, et al: Role of Norwalk virus in outbreaks of nonbacterial gastroenteritis. *J Infect Dis* 1979; 139:564–568.

159. Murphy AM, Grohmann GS, Christopher PJ, et al: A Australia-wide outbreak of gastroenteritis from oysters caused by Norwalk virus. *Med J Aust* 1979; 2:329–333.

160. Morse DL, Guzewich JJ, Hanrahan JP, et al: Widespread outbreaks of clam- and oyster-associated gastroenteritis: role of Norwalk virus. *N Engl J Med* 1986; 314:678–681.

161. Blacklow NR, Cukor G, Bedigian MK, et al: Immune response and prevalence of antibody to Norwalk enteritis virus as determined by radioimmunoassay. *J Clin Microbiol* 1979; 10:903–909.

162. Cubit WD: The candidate caliciviruses. *Ciba Found Symp* 1987; 128:126–143.

163. Cubit WD, McSwiggan DA: Calicivirus gastroenteritis in northwest London. *Lancet* 1981; 1:975–977.

164. Oishi I, Maeda A, Yamazaki K, et al: Calicivirus detected in outbreaks of acute gastroenteritis in school children. *Biken J* 1980; 23:163–168.

165. Nakata S, Chiba S, Terashima H, et al: Prevalence of antibody to human calicivirus in Japan and Southeast Asia determined by radioimmunoassay. *J Clin Microbiol* 1985; 22:519–521.

166. Cubit WD, McSwiggan DA: Seroepidemiological survey of the prevalence of antibodies to a strain of human calicivirus. *J Med Virol* 1987; 21:361–368.

167. Nakata S, Chiba S, Terashima H, et al: Microtiter solid-phase radioimmunoassay for detection of human calicivirus in stools. *J Clin Microbiol* 1983; 17:198–201.

168. Herrmann JE, Kent GP, Nowak NKA, et al: Antigen detection in the diagnosis of Norwalk virus gastroenteritis. *J Infect Dis* 1986; 154:547–548.

169. Madore HP, Tranor JJ, Pray KA, et al: Enzyme-linked immunosorbent assays for Snow Mountain and Norwalk agents of viral gastroenteritis. *J Clin Microbiol* 1986; 24:456–459.

170. Gary GW Jr, Kaplan JE, Stine SE, et al: Detection of Norwalk virus antibodies and antigen with a biotin-avidin immunoassay. *J Clin Microbiol* 1985; 22:274–278.

171. Appleton H, Higgfin PG: Viruses and gastroenteritis in infants. *Lancet* 1975; 1:1297.

172. Madley CR, Cosgrove BP: 28 nm particles in faeces in infantile gastroenteritis. *Lancet* 1975; 2:451–452.

173. Kurtz JB, Lee TW: Astroviruses: human and animal. *CIBA Found Symp* 1987; 128:92–107.

174. Oshiro LS, Haley CE, Roberto RR, et al: A 27-nm virus isolated during an outbreak of acute infectious nonbacterial gastroenteritis in a convalescent hospital: a possible new serotype. *J Infect Dis* 1981; 143:791–795.

175. Kurtz J, Lee T: Astrovirus gastroenteritis: age distribution of

antibody. *Med Microbiol Immunol* 1978; 166:227–230.

176. Kurtz JB, Lee TW, Craig JW, et al: Astrovirus infection in volunteers. *J Med Virol* 1979; 3:221–230.

177. Lewis DC, Lightfoot NF, Cubitt WD, et al: Outbreaks of astrovirus type 1 and rotavirus gastroenteritis in a geriatric in-patient population. *J Hosp Infect* 1989; 14:9–14.

178. Konno T, Suzuki H, Ishida N, et al: Astrovirus-associated epidemic gastroenteritis in Japan. *J Med Virol* 1982; 9:11–17.

179. Ashley CR, Caul EO, Paver WK: Astrovirus-associated gastroenteritis in children. *J Clin Pathol* 1978; 31:939–943.

180. Lee TW, Kurtz JB: Serial propagation of astrovirus in tissue culture with the aid of trypsin. *J Gen Virol* 1981; 57:421–424.

181. Kurtz JB, Lee TW: Human astrovirus serotypes. *Lancet* 1984; 2:1405.

182. Snodgrass DR, Angus KW, Gray EW, et al: Pathogenesis of diarrhoea caused by astrovirus infections in lambs. *Arch Virol* 1979; 60:217–226.

183. Herring AJ, Gray EW, Snodgrass DR: Purification and characterization of ovine astrovirus. *J Gen Virol* 1981; 53:47–55.

184. Yolken RH, Torsch VM: Enzyme-linked immunosorbent assay for the detection and identification of coxsackie viruses A. *Infect Immun* 1980; 31:742–750.

185. Herrman JE, Nowak NA, Perron-Henry DM, et al: Diagnosis of astrovirus gastroenteritis by antigen detection with monoclonal antibodies. *J Infect Dis* 1990; 161:226–229.

34

Herpes Simplex Virus*

H. Reid Mattison
Roselyn J. Eisenberg
Richard C. Reichman

Herpes simplex viruses (HSV) are extremely common human pathogens which cause a broad spectrum of illness, ranging from asymptomatic infections to fulminant disseminated diseases re-

sulting in death.[1] There are two types of HSV, type 1 and type 2. The two types vary in biochemical composition, have different biologic properties, and can be readily distinguished from one another by a variety of immunologic techniques.[2, 3] In general, HSV type 1 (HSV-1) is responsible for orofacial infections, visceral infections in immunocompromised hosts, and herpes simplex encephalitis in adults. HSV type 2 (HSV-2) is more commonly associated with infections of the genital tract, and it causes the majority of neonatal disease. Despite these generalizations, however, there exists considerable overlap in the spectrum of clinical disease caused by these two closely related agents.

In addition to the variety of disease syndromes caused by these viruses, other factors have contributed recently to a general increase in interest in these pathogens. Our knowledge of the biochemistry and molecular biology of HSV has grown enormously in the past 15 years. Concomitantly, our understanding of the complex relationships between HSV and different mechanisms of host defense at both cellular and molecular levels has increased. In addition, some HSV-induced diseases have been among the first viral infections of humans to be treated effectively by antiviral compounds. These successes have provided solid evidence for the utility of antiviral chemotherapy. For example, the first drug to be licensed in the United States for the treatment of an established systemic viral disease was adenine arabinoside. The drug reduces the mortality rate and incidence of neurologic sequelae in patients with biopsy-proven herpes simplex encephalitis.[4, 5] Subsequently, the natural histories of several other HSV-induced syndromes have been demonstrated to be ameliorated by the judicious use of antiviral drugs. These syndromes are discussed in detail below.

HISTORY

As pointed out by Beswick,[6] the word "herpes" has been used

*Supported in part by grants AI 18289, HL 28220, and DE 08239 from the National Institutes of Health, Bethesda, MD.

as a medical term for at least 25 centuries. However, it is probable that in ancient times the word was used to describe conditions as diverse as eczema and skin cancer. Derived from a verb meaning "to creep," herpes appears to have been used initially to describe a variety of spreading cutaneous lesions. Eventually, most medical writers seem to have used the word to describe zoster. Willan and Bateman first differentiated labial herpes and genital herpes from herpes zoster in 1814.[7] In 1873, Vidal demonstrated that HSV was infectious by human inoculation experiments.[8] HSV was transmitted to rabbits in 1920 and was shown to be a filterable agent the following year.[9, 10] In 1930, Andrews and Carmichael discovered that many adults had circulating neutralizing antibody to HSV and that recurrent herpetic disease occurred only in such individuals.[11] The distinction between primary and recurrent disease was first elucidated by Burnet and Williams in 1939.[12] In subsequent years, the recognized clinical spectrum of HSV-induced disease was extended to include eczema herpeticum,[13] vulvovaginitis,[14] keratoconjunctivitis,[15] encephalitis,[16] and meningitis.[17] In the early 1960s, the existence of two distinct antigenic types was discovered.[18] A few years later the observation was made that anatomical site of isolation could be correlated generally with antigenic type.[19] Recently, new techniques, including analysis of thymidine kinase amino acid sequences, have suggested that divergence of HSV into types 1 and 2 occurred approximately 8 to 10 million years ago.[20]

STRUCTURE AND REPLICATION

According to the International Committee on Taxonomy of Viruses, HSV is a member of the family *Herpetoviridae* and the genus *Herpesvirus*.[21] Complete virus particles are approximately 180 to 200 nm in diameter and consist of: (1) a cylindrical core structure around which the viral DNA is wound, (2) an icosahedral capsid approximately 85 to 110 nm in diameter, (3) a granular zone or tegument which surrounds the capsid, and (4) an envelope, which is derived from the host cell as the particles bud from the nuclear membrane[22] (Figure 34–1). HSV is relatively sensitive to heat and must be stored at $-70°C$ if infectivity is to be preserved for significant lengths of time.[23] Like other enveloped viruses, HSV is readily inactivated by lipid solvents such as ether, chloroform, and alcohol.[24] The virus is also sensitive to a variety of types of radiant energy and to many proteolytic enzymes.[25, 26]

Like other herpesviruses, the genome of HSV contains double-stranded DNA. The DNA of HSV-1 has been completely sequenced and contains approximately 70 open reading frames.[27, 28] It is a simple linear molecule, but exhibits unusual structural properties. These properties, along with the mode of replication of HSV DNA, have been reviewed recently.[29, 30] The molecule consists of long (L) and short (S) components which constitute 82% and 18% of the genome, respectively. Each of the components contains largely unique sequences (U_L and U_S), but these are bracketed by relatively small regions which are inverted and repetitive. The reiterated sequences bracketing the L component are designated ab and b'a' and those bracketing the S component a'c' and ca. Because of this arrangement, the L and S regions can invert relative to each other, giving rise to four possible genome populations which differ only in the orientation of these regions. It has been demonstrated that DNA extracted from wild-type viruses consists of equimolar concentrations of all four populations. The DNAs of HSV types 1 and 2 share approximately 50% of their base pairs, although they differ in many sites of cleavage by restriction endonucleases.[31, 32]

The capsid is an icosahedron which is formed by 162 capsomers shaped like long hollow prisms. Twelve of the capsomers are pentagonal, and 150 are hexagonal in shape. They measure 9.5 $\times$ 12.5 nm and have a central hole approximately 4 nm in diameter.[33, 34]

The virion envelope is a membrane which appears by electron microscopy as a three-layered structure analogous to cellular membranes.[35] As noted above, the envelope is obtained by the virus during the process of budding through the inner lamella of the nuclear membrane into the perinuclear cysternae. Other intracellular membranes have also been implicated in the formation of the envelope.[36] Embedded in the evelope are the viral glycoproteins. They appear as numerous protrusions or spikes. Three of the glycoproteins have been analyzed by immune-electron microscopy,[37] and appear to be present on the surface of virions in distinct structures. gB spikes are clustered and appear T-shaped; gC spikes are very long and filamentous; and gD appears as short fringe-like projections.

Infection by HSV begins with the attachment of the virus to a cellular receptor, which may differ for HSV-1 and HSV-2.[38] The virus penetrates the cell via fusion of the viral envelope with the plasma membrane.[39–43] Transcription of the HSV genome appears to occur in three phases.[44] In phase 1, transcription is mediated by host proteins, either alone or possibly in association with virion proteins; in phase 2, transcription appears to be mediated by proteins which are synthesized after infection but before the initiation of viral DNA synthesis; in phase 3, transcription is coupled to the initiation of viral DNA synthesis. These three phases of transcription result in the production of messenger RNAs (mRNA) which eventually lead to the synthesis of three groups of polypeptides: alpha, beta, and gamma.[45] Synthesis of the viral proteins takes place in the cytoplasm, in a coordinately regulated and sequentially ordered cascade.[46–51] HSV-1 genes have been classified into alpha, beta, and gamma groups based on the temporal order and functional requirements for their expression. The transcription of alpha genes does not require the synthesis of new viral proteins.[49] However, mature particles of HSV-1 contain a phosphoprotein of 65 kilodaltons (kd) called VP_{16} which activates expression of alpha genes.[52, 53] Five alpha proteins have been identified: ICP-0, ICP-4, ICP-22, ICP-27, and ICP-47. The genes for ICP-22 and ICP-47 can be deleted from the virus without adverse effects on viral replication.[54, 55] The other three have been implicated to some extent in activation of HSV-1 beta and gamma gene expression.[54, 56–67] Mutants containing deletions of the ICP-0 gene do not exhibit dramatic defects in viral gene expression, even though ICP-0 is a potent activator of gene expression in transfected cells.[66, 68] Most evidence implicates ICP-4 as an important activator of beta and gamma gene transcription.[64, 66, 67] ICP-27 is important for the transactivation of gB and other viral genes[69] and may play a stimulatory role in DNA replication.[69, 70] Beta proteins include most of the nonstructural proteins, such as those involved in DNA replication.[70] The gamma or late genes are the last temporal class of genes to be activated, and their full expression depends on the commencement of viral DNA synthesis.[49, 71] This class includes

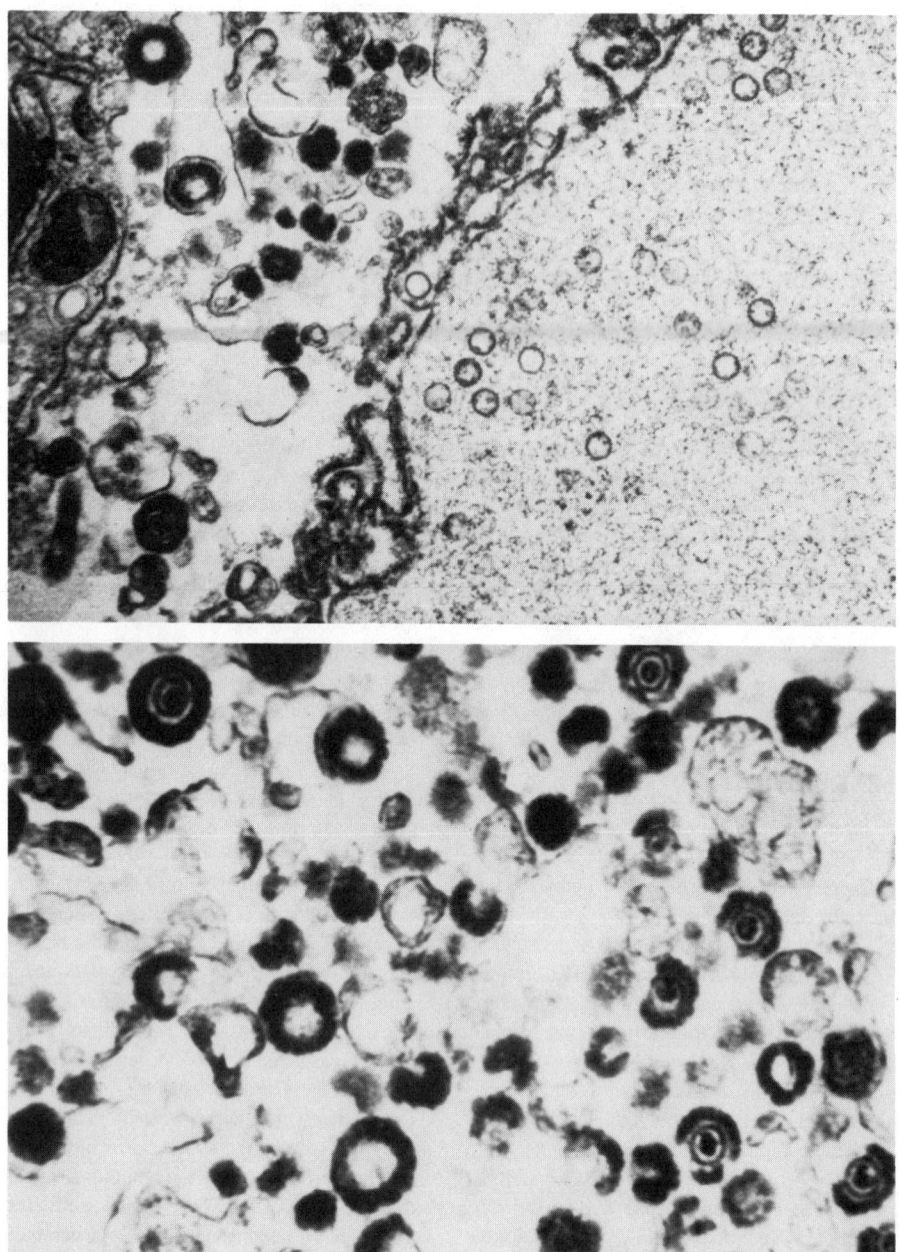

Figure 34–1. Top: Virus particles in nucleus *(at right)*, "budding" through nuclear membrane *(center)*, and in cytoplasm with envelopes *(at left)*. ×16,600 magnification. Bottom: Concentrated preparation of enveloped particles. ×24,400 magnification.

most of the viral structural polypeptides. The structural and some nonstructural proteins are transported back to the nucleus where the nucleocapsids are assembled. Nucleocapsids associate with regions of the inner nuclear lamella modified by viral glycoproteins and bud into the perinuclear space.[72–74] After budding from the inner nuclear membranes, virus particles may traverse the Golgi complex prior to exocytosis.[75] In addition, syncytial strains of HSV cause fusion of infected cells, thus permitting cell-to-cell spread.[74] The virus may remain cell-associated for prolonged periods; enveloped virions may be shed gradually, ejected from cytoplasmic vacuoles, or released during the process of host cell lysis. The complete cycle of viral replication occurs approximately 15 hours

following infection. It is an inefficient process, and results in the production of only one infectious virus particle for every 100 to 1000 which are produced.

Among the nonstructural proteins which are coded for by HSV DNA are DNA polymerases and a thymidine kinase. Inhibition of the functions of these enzymes has proved to be an effective method of antiviral chemotherapy in humans.[76, 77] For example, one mode of action of adenine arabinoside appears to be related to the ability of phosphate derivatives of this compound to interfere with virus-specified DNA polymerases.[78] Acyclovir, or acycloguanosine, has been shown to be a specific substrate for the thymidine of HSV kinase.[79] The virus-specified enzyme selectively phosphorylates acyclovir, which is then taken up by infected cells and further phosphorylated by cellular enzymes to a triphosphate derivative. Acycloguanosine triphosphate has been shown to inhibit HSV synthesis both by inhibiting viral DNA polymerases and by acting as a substrate for the enzyme.[80]

HSV-1 specifies seven membrane glycoproteins, gB, gC, gD, gE, gG, gH, and gI.[39, 81-84] Three of these, gB, gD, and gH, have been shown to be essential for infectivity. Four glycoproteins, gC, gE, gG, and gI, can be deleted from the virus genome with no loss of infectivity in cell culture.[84, 86-91] Antibodies directed to gD and gC inhibit virus adsorption[92] and experiments with liposomes[93] implicate both gB and gD in this process. However, viruses lacking these proteins can adsorb to cells.[94-96] Entry of HSV appears to involve fusion of the virion envelope with the plasma membrane.[97-99] Certain monoclonal antibodies to gD block virion envelope-plasma membrane fusion[97, 100, 101] and fusion of infected cells,[102] suggesting a role for gD in virus penetration. These same monoclonal antibodies exhibit very high titers of virus-neutralizing activity[97, 100-103] and have been shown to recognize the same antigenic site on gD.[103-107] Mutants lacking the gD gene can bind to cells but fail to penetrate,[96] and temperature-sensitive (*ts*) mutants of gB exhibit a similar phenotype.[108] There is also evidence that gH is essential for virus entry or cell-to-cell spread.[100, 108-110] Thus it is suggested that entry is a cooperative process involving at least three of the essential glycoproteins and participation by one or more of the nonessential glycoproteins.

Three of the nonessential glycoproteins appear to modulate the host immune response. Glycoprotein C functions as a C3b receptor on the surface of HSV-1–infected cells.[111] Receptor activity is not found on the surface of HSV-2–infected cells, although purified gC-2 binds C3b.[112] It has been suggested that other HSV-2 glycoproteins may mask this activity on infected cells. Glycoprotein gE binds the Fc fragment of IgG,[113] possibly as a complex with gI.[114, 115] No role has yet been assigned to gG, though its synthesis and processing in HSV-2–infected cells involves cleavage and secretion of a portion of the polypeptide.[116]

Because of their presence on the surface of the virion and in the plasma membrane of infected cells, glycoproteins are targets of the host's immune response to HSV infection. It has been shown that gB, gC, gD, gE, gG, and gH can induce virus-neutralizing antibody.[104, 117-130] In addition, HSV glycoproteins participate in antibody-dependent complement-mediated,[131-133] and antibody-dependent cell-mediated[126, 131, 134] cytotoxic reactions (ADCC). HSV glycoproteins can also stimulate cytotoxic T cells (CTLs), which will lyse HSV-infected cells,[134] and can stimulate a T helper response.[135] Specifically, gB, gC, and gD can act as targets for CTLs[131, 134-140]; gB and gC can be recognized by natural killer (NK) cells[141, 142]; and gC and gD can stimulate a delayed hypersensitivity response.[48] The antigenic structure of gB, gC, and gD is the subject of intense study and many epitopes involved in the humoral response have been identified.[39, 100, 103, 105-107, 143-151] In addition, studies have identified specific T cell epitopes on gD.[152]

EPIDEMIOLOGY

Incidence and Prevalence

Infection with HSV is extremely common and widespread,

occurring in a worldwide distribution with equal frequency in both sexes.[153] While there is no clear-cut seasonal variation in the incidence of HSV infections, some investigators feel that skin infections occur more commonly in the summer months, and herpetic keratitis and labialis more commonly in the winter months.[154] Mucocutaneous HSV infections account for the vast majority of all herpetic infection and illness, with nonmucocutaneous infections being relatively uncommon. For example, although HSV is the most commonly diagnosed cause of sporadic encephalitis in the United States, estimates are that only a few hundred to a few thousand cases occur in the United States each year.[155] Mucocutaneous HSV infections primarily involve oral and genital sites, and less commonly other cutaneous areas. Nonmucocutaneous HSV-induced diseases include keratitis, meningitis, encephalitis, and other visceral infections. HSV infections in neonatal, immunocompromised, and pregnant individuals are occasionally fulminant, but these types of infection are not common.

Seroepidemiologic studies carried out in the 1940s and 1950s, before knowledge of the existence of HSV subtypes, showed that more than 90% of some US populations had antibody to HSV by the fourth decade of life.[156] Subsequent investigation showed the incidence of circulating antibody to HSV to vary considerably with age.[157] Up to approximately 6 months, antibodies which have been acquired transplacentally can be detected in the sera of most newborn infants. The presence of antibody declines through the first 6 months of life, reflecting the loss of maternal antibodies, and approaches zero in children between 6 and 12 months of age. The acquisition of HSV antibodies thereafter generally occurs in two stages, with antibody to HSV-1 acquired in the first decade of life, and antibody to HSV-2 acquired after puberty and into the early adult years. The incidence of antibody to HSV-1 rises rapidly in the first 4 years of life, probably reflecting intrafamilial spread, and remains detectable throughout life. Poor hygiene and crowded living conditions may contribute to the acquisition of HSV-1 infection, and account for an earlier and nearly universal antibody presence in lower socioeconomic groups.[158] A recent report defining the epidemiology of herpesvirus infections in Navajo children showed a high prevalence of infection with HSV-1, and demonstrated the strongest correlate of HSV-1 seropositivity to be sharing of a bed with parents.[158a] Resultant prolonged face-to-face contact with HSV-1–infected parents provided a possible opportunity for transmission. No children were seropositive for HSV-2, which demonstrates the uncommon nonsexual transmission of HSV-2. In contrast, up to 50% of adults in higher socioeconomic groups in Western industrialized settings may lack HSV-1 antibodies.[158] The incidence of antibody to HSV-2 varies with the population studied and reflects past sexual activity.

The prevalence of HSV-2 antibody has been shown to range from 3% in nuns to 80% in prostitutes, with up to 25% of higher and 60% of lower socioeconomic groups being seropositive.[156, 159, 160] Fifteen percent of sampled white middle-class adults between 22 and 45 years of age in metropolitan Toronto were shown to be HSV-2–seropositive.[161] Approximately 16% of over 4,200 individuals between the ages of 15 and 74 sampled in the US from 1976 to 1980 were HSV-2 seropositive. Age and race were demographic factors associated with the presence of HSV-2 antibody. HSV-2 antibody increased from less than 1% in the under-15 age group to 20.2% in the group 30 to 44 years old, and increased only slightly thereafter. High rates were observed in the black population, with HSV-2 antibody present in 41% of blacks and 13.3% of whites.[162]

Transmission

Although a variety of animals can be experimentally infected with HSV, man is the only known natural reservoir. No vector has been demonstrated to spread the virus, and fomites have never been shown to transmit disease. Transmission of the virus occurs as a result of direct contact with infectious secretions or, rarely, by laboratory accidents with infectious materials. Orofacial infections are generally thought to be most commonly acquired as a result of kissing, and genital herpes simplex infections are acquired as a result of either genital-genital, oral-genital, or anal-genital contact. Other instances of close body contact, as occurs during wrestling, for example, have been associated with outbreaks of mucocutaneous HSV infections.[163] Recent reports have documented transmission of HSV by renal and hepatic transplantation.[164–166] In addition, genital herpes has been shown to be transmitted during periods of asymptomatic virus shedding.[167, 168]

PATHOGENESIS

Incubation Period

The incubation period of HSV infections is generally considered to be between two and 12 days, with a mean of approximately six days.[169] However, because primary infection can be asymptomatic, it is possible for an individual to acquire latent infection and not have an outbreak of recognizable disease for periods of years.

Primary and Recurrent Infection

During the initial phases of HSV infection, the virus enters parabasal and intermediate epithelial cells where it multiplies, eventually producing cell lysis. A local inflammatory response ensues, and regional lymph nodes may become involved. Rarely viremia and visceral dissemination may occur, but this is unusual even in immunocompromised individuals. During the course of primary infection, the virus appears to travel centripetally through sensory nerves. This mode of spread is thought to occur intraaxonally, and to result in latent infection of sensory ganglia, as discussed below. Recurrent HSV infections occur almost exclusively in individuals who possess neutralizing antibody to the homologous virus. Such infections are generally felt to be the result of reactivation of latent virus, which travels centrifugally from sensory ganglia to mucocutaneous sites.[170] These recurrent episodes may result in asymptomatic virus shedding or in clinically evident disease. In general, recurrent HSV infections are milder than primary infections. Although reactivation of latent, endogenous virus is thought to account for the bulk of recurrences, recent studies have demonstrated that exogenous reinfection with different virus strains within an HSV type does occur.[171] The frequency with which such reinfection occurs is unknown.

Latency

The hallmark of HSV infections is the establishment of the virus in a latent state following the primary disease episode. The mechanisms responsible for establishment, maintenance, and reactivation of latent HSV remain poorly understood. Following a primary infection, HSV-1 and HSV-2 establish lifelong latent infection in trigeminal and dorsal root ganglia, from which they can be reactivated to produce recurrent mucocutaneous infections.[160, 172–174] Latent HSV-1 has been demonstrated to be present in trigeminal ganglia by organ culture,[175] explant cocultivation,[176–179] and by in vivo reactivation following neurectomy.[180] Although infectious particles are not detectable in latently infected cells, the entire viral genome is present in the form of either circular or concatenated molecules.[181–183] In latently infected mice, most of the HSV-1 DNA is extrachromosomal and may exist in an episomal state.[184] Viral DNA has been detected during HSV-1 latency in the central and peripheral nervous systems of mice and in human brain tissue.[181, 183, 185–187]

Virus-specific transcripts originating from the repeat regions of the genome have been detected during HSV-1 latency in the central and peripheral nervous systems of mice and rabbits,[174, 188–190] and in human trigeminal ganglia.[191, 192] Viral transcripts have been detected during HSV-2 latency in sensory ganglia of guinea pigs[193] and humans.[194, 195] In HSV-1, the region that is transcribed during latency overlaps the immediate early gene ICP-0, which is transcribed in the opposite direction.[174, 190, 196] Three viral transcripts, 2.0, 1.5, and 1.45 kilobases, are present in latently infected mice, but only the 2.0-kilobase transcript has been detected in infected tissue culture cells.[196, 197] There is some evidence that this latency-associated set of genes may be regulated differently from alpha, beta, or gamma genes.[197] No proteins corresponding to the open reading frames of these transcripts have been detected in either acutely or latently infected cells. Thus the role of these transcripts in establishment or maintenance of latency remains to be determined.

Immunologic Responses

Human immunologic responses to HSV infection are complex and incompletely understood. Many components of host defense are felt to be important in resistance to and recovery from HSV infections. Humoral and cell-mediated immunity (CMI) are involved, as are "nonspecific" host responses.[198]

Following primary infection, antibody to HSV antigens can be detected within four to eight days with highly sensitive techniques. As with most other infectious diseases, IgM antibodies develop first, followed by IgG antibodies.[199, 200] IgM antibodies are relatively short-lived, whereas IgG antibodies persist for prolonged periods. It has been demonstrated that an individual's risk of developing recurrent genital herpes is directly related to the presence and titer of neutralizing antibody in convalescent serum to HSV-2 following primary infection with the homologous virus.[201] These studies suggest that the presence of neutralizing antibody may serve as a serologic marker for latent infection. Serum antibody has been shown to neutralize extracellular virus in tissue culture and to lyse certain HSV-infected cells.[202] In addition, it has been observed that the presence of circulating neutralizing antibody in acute phase serum decreases the severity and shortens the duration of first episodes of genital herpes.[203, 204] Thus, serum antibody neutralizes extracellular virus and appears to reduce the extent of infection. However, it does not prevent the recurrence of established disease.

In addition to antibody, it is also known that early complement components contribute to the neutralization of HSV.[205] The absence of certain complement components has been associated with frequent HSV recurrences.[206]

Because recurrent HSV infections are known to occur in the presence of high levels of serum neutralizing antibody against the homologous virus, investigators have searched for possible deficiencies in other host defense mechanisms which might result in the development of recurrent disease. Particular interest has been directed toward evaluation of CMI, both in animal models and in humans. A variety of different measurements of CMI, including lymphocyte transformation, lymphokine production, cell-mediated cytotoxicity, and skin test reactivity, have been examined.[207-212] These studies have provided conflicting evidence regarding the hypothesis that defects in CMI explain the development of recurrent or prolonged HSV disease. In general, skin test reactivity has been demonstrated to be normal in these patients, as has lymphocyte transformation. The production of a variety of lymphokines, including interferon, macrophage inhibitory factor, lymphotoxin, and chemotactic factor, has been reported to be decreased, increased, or normal. Some studies have demonstrated depressed mononuclear cell cytotoxicity in these patients, whereas others have found such assays of CMI to be normal or increased. Macrophage and monocyte functions have been evaluated less extensively.[213, 214] In general, it can be stated that no consistently demonstrable defect in CMI has been demonstrated to explain why some individuals develop recurrent and/or severe HSV disease whereas others do not.

CLINICAL SYNDROMES AND TREATMENT

Orofacial Infections

Primary orofacial infections are thought to be most commonly acquired asymptomatically during childhood.[215] However, symptomatic herpetic gingivostomatitis is a common childhood illness which lasts approximately 3 weeks and is characterized by painful blisters, fever, malaise, irritability, and regional adenopathy.[216] The disease process is localized anteriorly, and generally involves the lips, gums, anterior tongue, and hard palate. When primary oral infections occur in adulthood, they may appear as a severe pharyngitis which is clinically indistinguishable from disease produced by other pathogens such as group A streptococci.[160]

Random sampling of adults reveals approximately one third to have recurrent herpes labialis, defined as a history of cold sores and the presence of antibodies to HSV.[217]

The course of recurrent orofacial infections has been studied in detail.[218, 219] In one study, investigators performed daily examinations of 80 patients with recurrent HSV infections of the lip, carefully documenting the clinical and virologic course of this infection. Oral lesions were noted to progress through characteristic phases of erythema (macule), papule, vesicle, ulcer, crust, and healing. Pain, lesion size, and amount of virus present were maximal in the first 24 hours. Lesions were present for a mean of approximately eight days. In the absence of overt lesions, cultures of oral secretions are reportedly positive for HSV-1 in up to 2% to 9% of adults and in 5% to 8% of children.[220] Recurrence of herpes labialis has been linked to aphthous ulcers, sun exposure,

and oral trauma (eg, dental procedures), but no association has been observed between recurrent herpetic labialis and chapped lips, ethnicity, or phenotype (complexion, hair, and eye color).[217] Of patients reporting a history of recurrent herpes labialis, 28% have recurrences at least twice a year, but the frequency of recurrences appears to decline after 35 years of age.[158]

No controlled studies of antiviral drugs, or of other potentially useful modes of therapy, have been performed in patients with primary orofacial infection due to HSV. An open study using oral acyclovir in the treatment of gingivostomatitis in children demonstrated a reduced duration of virus shedding and lesion healing.[221] However, 36% of treated children continued to develop new lesions during the treatment period. Further investigation is needed before acyclovir can be recommended in the treatment of healthy children with herpetic gingivostomatitis. Management of patients with these infections is therefore limited to maintaining good local hygiene, good hydration, and adequate control of pain.

In contrast to the lack of adequate studies in patients with primary orofacial infections, several well-done, appropriately controlled investigations of treatment of the recurrent form of the disease have been performed. Topically administered antiviral drugs which have been adequately evaluated include idoxuridine, kethoxal, cytosine arabinoside, adenine arabinoside, adenine arabinoside 5'-monophosphate, and acyclovir. A beneficial effect with a topical preparation has been demonstrated with the use of acyclovir cream, a preparation employing propylene glycol as a base instead of the polyethylene glycol preparation of acyclovir ointment that is available in the United States. Clinical trials using acyclovir cream in the treatment of recurrent herpes labialis have shown conflicting results, with some studies reporting modest clinical benefit in the form of decreased healing time, and others failing to demonstrate any significant clinical or antiviral effects.[229-231] Continuous use of acyclovir cream in patients with frequently recurrent herpes labialis has shown a reduction in the number and duration of outbreaks.[232] Acyclovir ointment has not been demonstrated to be effective in the treatment of recurrent labialis caused by HSV.[229, 233, 234] Topical 15% idoxuridine in dimethyl sulfoxide (DMSO) has shown a beneficial effect in the form of accelerated healing and reduced duration of pain when treatment was begun in the prodrome or erythema stages of lesion development. No clinical benefit was demonstrated when treatment was started once the labialis lesion had progressed to the papule stage.[234a] Oral acyclovir treatment initiated at the onset of prodromal labial symptoms has shown a significant antiviral effect with only minimal clinical benefit and a modest reduction in time to healing.[235, 235a] Suppressive oral regimens have demonstrated clear-cut efficacy in reducing the number of recurrences.[236] Suppressive oral acyclovir evaluated in a controlled trial in skiers with a history of frequently recurring HSV labialis resulted in a 73% reduction in outbreaks occurring during ultraviolet exposure on the ski slopes.[237]

Genital Infections

Genital herpes infections have occurred with notably increased incidence and cumulative prevalence in the last two decades.[238-242] Seroepidemiologic investigation has shown that the majority of genital infections are asymptomatic, with less than 25% of HSV-2–seropositive individuals knowingly infected.[161, 241]

Asymptomatic shedding of virus from the genital tract has been reported in 0.3% to 5.4% of males and 0.5% to 8.0% of females.[169, 243, 243a, 243b] Symptomatic episodes of infection in the genital tract occur as either first-episode or recurrent infections. First-episode infections are categorized as either true primary or nonprimary initial infections, depending on the absence or presence of antibodies to HSV in acute sera, respectively. True primary infections are more severe than nonprimary first-episode infections, which likewise are more severe than recurrent infections.[169] Either type 1 or type 2 HSV can cause primary genital HSV infection, with HSV-2 being the predominant pathogen in approximately 70% to 90% of patients.[169] The presentation and clinical course of primary HSV infection, whether caused by HSV-1 or HSV-2, are indistinguishable.[169] However, genital infections caused by HSV-2 are reported to recur 15 times more frequently than those caused by HSV-1.[244] Thus, approximately 98% of recurrent HSV genital infections are caused by type 2 virus.[169] The likelihood of recurrence is also influenced by the presence and titer of neutralizing antibodies in addition to the viral type and anatomical location of infection, but long-term natural history studies to reliably predict whether and/or when recurrences decrease or change over time are not available.[244] The possibility that the frequency of herpetic recurrences diminished spontaneously over time is indirectly raised through studies assessing long-term suppressive acyclovir treatment. One such study showed the mean time to recurrent infection became sufficiently long to withhold further suppressive acyclovir treatment in about one fifth of patients followed for up to 7 years.[244a]

Primary infections are commonly associated with systemic manifestations such as fever, generalized malaise, myalgia, and adenopathy. Many lesions are present in the genital tract, and virus is shed for prolonged periods (mean 15–20 days). The time to complete healing of lesions in primary infections is approximately 3 weeks. Infection of the cervix in women with primary infection occurs in almost all cases. Not uncommon complications associated with primary infections include pharyngitis, meningitis, acute urinary retention, and distal site inoculation. Rarely, more severe complications, such as transverse myelitis, are seen.[244] Disseminated disease resulting in death in an apparently normal, nonimmunocompromised woman has been reported.[246]

Recurrent genital HSV infections are, in general, much milder than primary infections. The duration of virus shedding is usually three to five days, and the time to complete healing of all lesions occurs in a mean of approximately seven to eight days.[247, 248] Systemic manifestations associated with recurrent episodes are rare, but do occur. Shedding of virus from the cervix of women with recurrent disease is seen much less commonly than with primary disease. Generally, about 5% of women with recurrences will have positive cervical cultures during the recurrent episode.[249]

Completely adequate control measure for genital HSV infections do not currently exist. However, treatment with the antiviral drug acyclovir has been demonstrated to shorten the duration of individual episodes of genital HSV infections. Most markedly affected by acyclovir treatment have been first-episode infections, particularly true primary infections.[250–255] In this setting, topical, oral, and intravenous (IV) formulations of the drug have been demonstrated to reduce the duration of virus shedding and lesions. When given systemically, the duration of symptoms and the in-

cidence of complications are also reduced by acyclovir therapy.

In addition to reducing the duration of first-episode infections, orally administered acyclovir also decreases the duration of virus shedding and lesions in recurrent disease.[254, 256] These effects are more pronounced when treatment is begun by the patient early in the course of a recurrent episode.[256] Five percent acyclovir in a polyethylene glycol base (acyclovir ointment), administered topically, shortens the duration of virus shedding in recurrent genital herpes but does not appear to affect the duration of the lesions.[250, 257, 258] Topical acyclovir cream may be a more effective preparation in the treatment of genital HSV infection than acyclovir ointment,[259, 260] and further studies are needed to confirm these findings. Despite the effect on the acute disease, administration of acyclovir in any form does not appear to reduce the incidence or frequency of subsequent recurrent disease.

Many reports have described the use of interferon in the treatment and suppression of primary and recurrent genital HSV infections.[261–268] These studies are difficult to compare due to marked heterogeneity of design. Conflicting results have been reported for topical and subcutaneous interferon use in the treatment of primary and recurrent genital disease, as well as for intermittent subcutaneous interferon suppression of recurrent disease.

Continuous daily oral acyclovir use has shown significant effectiveness in reducing the frequency and duration of recurrent genital HSV episodes.[269–276] Completed trials of continuous acyclovir suppression of recurrent genital herpes for up to 2 years have shown this therapy to remain effective and well tolerated.[277] Effects of chronic oral acyclovir on asymptomatic shedding and transmission of infection need to be determined. One recent report showed the rate of asymptomatic shedding to be unaltered by chronic oral acyclovir.[277a]

Other Mucocutaneous Infections

It is important to recognize that HSV can infect any mucosal or cutaneous surface in normal human hosts. Thus, mucocutaneous HSV infections other than orofacial and genital herpes are not uncommon. Among the most common of such infections are those involving the tips of the fingers, commonly referred to as "herpetic whitlow". Such infections can involve the fingers, thumbs, or the remainder of the hand. Finger and thumb infections account for approximately 90% of herpetic hand infections, with the digital pulp space more commonly infected than the periungual or lateral digit spaces.[278] These infections occur predominantly in health care workers, children, and young adults.[278, 279] They were previously thought to be most commonly an occupational disease of medical personnel,[280] but recent reports have shown a decline in the percentage of cases in a better informed health care population and have defined a bimodal distribution in children and young adults.[278] Herpetic whitlow in children is most commonly caused by autoinoculation of HSV-1 from stomatitis; young adults acquire digital HSV-2 by autoinoculation from genital infection.[281, 282] As in other herpes infections, primary and recurrent digital infections occur, with primary episodes being of greater severity.[282a] Preliminary studies have shown that acyclovir may be useful in the management of these infections.[283]

HSV is also an established cause of proctitis among homosexual men.[284, 285] This infection is often associated with severe anorectal pain and internal as well as external ulcerations. Difficulty in urinating, impotence, and sacral paresthesias are commonly seen, suggesting the possibility of autonomic nervous system dysfunction.[285, 286]

Spontaneously arising herpetic tracheobronchitis has recently been described as a treatable cause of bronchospasm in elderly immunocompetent individuals.[287]

HSV infection should be considered in the differential diagnosis of recurrent cutaneous lesions of compatible appearance, regardless of their location. Treatment of mucocutaneous HSV infections outside of the orofacial and genital areas in nonimmunocompromised humans has not been studied. At the present time, therefore, only supportive care for these infections can be recommended.

Encephalitis

The clinical manifestations of herpes simplex encephalitis have been described by several authors.[288–290] Among the best descriptions of the natural history of this infection are those contained in the reports of placebo-controlled drug studies in which virus isolation from brain tissue was required for diagnosis.[291–293] The mortality rate of untreated disease is approximately 70%, and the great majority of survivors suffer significant neurologic sequelae.

The clinical course of herpes simplex encephalitis is variable; it may begin abruptly or more gradually after a brief nonspecific illness. Prominent features of the disease are headache, fever, behavioral disorders, difficulties with speech, and focal seizures. Olfactory hallucinations may also be present, reflecting the propensity of the infection to affect the temporal lobes. Examination of the cerebral spinal fluid (CSF) usually discloses mild pleocytosis, a normal glucose, and a modestly elevated protein. It is rare for infectious virus to be isolated from the CSF. Histologically, the disease process is characterized by necrotizing hemorrhagic destruction of brain tissue.[294]

The vast majority of patients with biopsy-proven disease will develop evidence of localized brain involvement by electroencephalography, computed axial tomography, and/or technetium brain scan. However, among patients with encephalitis who have evidence of localized disease by at least one of those diagnostic tests, less than half will have herpes simplex encephalitis as determined by culture.[295, 296] Difficulty arises in distinguishing HSV encephalitis from other causes of encephalitis, since the clinical presentation, laboratory findings, and neurodiagnostic assessment does not allow the clinician to readily identify those patients with presumed HSV encephalitis.[296, 297] Despite efforts to develop other methods of diagnosis,[298, 299] the only definitive method of diagnosis available at the present time is demonstration of HSV in brain tissue.[300] Methods of detecting HSV-related antigen or antibody in the CSF have suffered from a lack of sensitivity early in the course of the illness, when decisions of intervention arise.[301, 302] A recent preliminary study reported the detection of HSV DNA using the polymerase chain reaction technique in the CSF of 4 of 4 patients with biopsy-proven HSV encephalitis, and 0 to 6 negative controls. Further study is needed to establish the sensitivity and specificity of this promising technique.[302a] Among those patients who come to biopsy, many will have other diseases for which specific therapy is available.[295, 296] A multicenter report of 432 patients with presumed herpes simplex encephalitis found

biopsy-proven HSV disease present in 45%; of the remaining 55% without evidence of encephalitis, 22% had another diagnosis obtained by biopsy and other means, and in 33% no diagnosis was established.[296] Thus, despite considerable controversy,[303–306] patients who have an illness compatible with herpes simplex encephalitis should be referred to a center that is equipped to establish a specific diagnosis and initiate therapy.

A multicenter study published in 1982,[291] established adenine arabinoside (vidarabine) as an effective therapy for biopsy-proven herpes simplex encephalitis. In that study of 28 patients, treatment reduced mortality from 70% in the placebo group to 28% among vidarabine recipients, one month after disease onset. A subsequent, larger study, which was conducted in an open fashion, confirmed and extended these findings.[295] The latter study also determined that age and level of consciousness at initiation of therapy were important variables influencing outcome. Patients who are under 30 years of age and who are lethargic have a significantly better prognosis than do older patients who are either semicomatose or comatose. Subsequent multicenter investigation comparing vidarabine with acyclovir showed a further reduction in mortality to approximately 20% with the use of acyclovir, establishing this agent as the drug of choice for biopsy-proven encephalitis.[307, 308] Acyclovir treatment also resulted in less long-term functional impairment than was seen with vidarabine treatment.

Neonatal Infections

The incidence of neonatal HSV infection is estimated to vary between 1 in every 2500 to 1 in every 10,000 deliveries per year.[309] Most infections are felt to result from acquisition of HSV-2 by the newborn passing through an infected birth canal, although other modes of transmission do occur.[310–312] Serious perinatal morbidity, including aborted pregnancy, premature labor, intrauterine growth retardation, and transmitted infection, occurs in a significant number of women experiencing symptomatic primary genital herpes during pregnancy, and at an incidence approaching 50% if the primary infection occurs in the third trimester.[309, 313] The majority of infected infants are born to mothers who have no signs or symptoms of active infection at the time of delivery, and antepartum maternal cultures are not predictive of shedding at delivery.[314–316a] The frequency of HSV shedding at delivery was determined to be 0.2% when over 6900 consecutive maternal cultures were obtained, without regard to history of genital herpes, and the majority of women with positive maternal cultures had subclinical infection previously.[314] A 4.1% rate of HSV shedding at delivery is reported in asymptomatic women with a history of genital herpes.[316]

In one recent study, approximately half of the babies infected with HSV were born prematurely.[317] Common complications in premature infants included respiratory distress, bacterial infection, and hypoglycemia. Among infants born at term, approximately two thirds had normal nursery courses and were discharged before the onset of infection. Clinical evidence of neonatal HSV infection is usually seen between five and 17 days of life,[318] and is categorized according to local, disseminated, or CNS (eg, encephalitis) involvement.[319, 319a] In the 1970s, disseminated and CNS disease accounted for over 80% of the cases of neonatal HSV infection, with local infection seen in less than 20% of cases.[319] Local infection now accounts for over 40% of neonatal HSV infections, an increase possibly related to a better awareness and earlier identification of the illness.[319] CNS infection has continued to account for approximately 30% of neonatal HSV infections.[319] Local infections commonly involve the skin, eye, or mouth, and are not themselves fatal infections. However, untreated local infection progresses to CNS or disseminated disease in 75% of cases, and CNS and disseminated disease mortality rates are over 50% and 80%, respectively.[319]

The administration of vidarabine to infants with disseminated or CNS infection has demonstrated a reduction in the mortality rate from 74% to 38%, decreasing from 90% to 70% in disseminated disease, and from 50% to 15% in CNS disease.[320] Approximately 30% of surviving infants were normal at 1 year of age. The severity of sequelae following vidarabine treatment is directly related to the severity of antecedent disease. Trials comparing vidarabine with acyclovir are currently under way, and preliminary results with acyclovir in the treatment of infants with disseminated or CNS disease are similar to those achieved with vidarabine.[297]

Meningitis

Meningismus, with or without objective evidence of inflammation, occurs in approximately 10% to 15% of individuals with primary genital HSV infections. Rarely, recurrent meningitis may be seen in association with recurrent genital herpes.[321] Meningitis caused by HSV is a benign, self-limited "aseptic" meningitis, and is rarely, if ever, associated with direct involvement of the brain or with neurologic sequelae.

Infections in Compromised Hosts

Patients whose immune systems are compromised by disease or chemotherapeutic agents are at greater risk of developing more frequent and more severe HSV infections than are other patients.[322, 323] Asymptomatic shedding of virus occurs frequently in these settings and more serious disease is not uncommon. HSV infections in these patients are usually characterized by progressive extension of local disease rather than by hematogenous dissemination, although the latter occurs occasionally.[324] Thus, innocuous-appearing mucocutaneous infections may become extensive and progress to deep ulcerations. As one would expect, such infections most commonly occur in the orofacial and genital areas. Visceral disease is most frequently observed in the trachea, esophagus, and to a lesser extent, the lungs.[325–327] Particularly susceptible to these infections are individuals who have undergone renal, cardiac, or bone marrow transplantation, as well as those with hematologic or lymphoreticular neoplasms.[328–330] In addition, children with congenital disorders of the thymus may develop unusually severe HSV infections, as may patients with the acquired immunodeficiency syndrome (AIDS).[331–333]

HSV infections of burns are being recognized more frequently. In addition to involved areas, such infections occasionally disseminate to other areas of the skin and rarely to visceral organs.[334] A variety of other skin disorders may also predispose patients to cutaneous dissemination of HSV. The most common of these is eczema, but a similar syndrome may be seen in individuals with pemphigus, Darier's disease, or Sézary syndrome.[335–337]

Treatment of HSV infections in immunocompromised hosts in the past has been limited to supportive care. Acyclovir treatment has been demonstrated to shorten the duration of virus shedding and the duration of lesions in these patients.[338–342] However, the development of HSV resistant to acyclovir may be seen in immunocompromised patients.[342a–342c]

Keratitis

Herpetic keratitis occurs in both primary and recurrent forms.[343] Repeated episodes may result in the formation of dendritic ulcers which can progress to deep stromal keratitis and blindness.[344] Superficial infections respond to a variety of antiviral drugs applied topically,[345] but deep infections are very difficult to treat. All patients in whom herpetic keratitis is suspected should be evaluated by an ophthalmologist.

Syndromes Associated With HSV Infections

HSV has been associated with a variety of neurologic diseases of unknown etiology including Bell's palsy, transverse myelitis, trigeminal neuralgia, and multiple sclerosis.[346–350] These associations are generally based on antibody frequencies in different populations, and the known propensity for HSV to affect neurologic tissue. Whether or not HSV plays a role in the etiology of pathogenesis of any of these diseases remains highly speculative.

LABORATORY DIAGNOSIS OF INFECTION

Although the diagnosis of most mucocutaneous HSV infections can be made on the basis of physical examination and history alone, the definitive diagnosis of any HSV infection is dependent on laboratory diagnostic methods. Laboratory methods for diagnosing HSV include tissue culture; histocytopathology; antigen, antibody, and DNA detection; and assay of HSV-specific enzymes (eg, thymidine kinase).[351, 352] Histologic diagnoses of herpesvirus infections are generally specific, but relatively insensitive. Virus-infected cells may be detected by light microscopy of material scraped from the base of mucocutaneous lesions or by biopsy of specimens of other involved organs. Cells which are actively infected with virus fuse into characteristic multinucleated giant cell forms. In addition to their multinucleated appearance, these cells may contain Cowdry type A inclusion bodies, representing crystalline arrays of virus particles.[353] Virus-infected cells may also be detected when stained according to the Papanicolaou method.[354] All of these cellular changes are not specific for HSV and can also be seen in infections caused by other members of the herpesvirus group such as varicella-zoster virus. Virus particles can be seen by electron microscopy. Characteristic particles may be visualized from material obtained from aspiration of vesicles as well as by biopsy. Immunofluorescent examination of infected tissue represents the most sensitive histologic diagnostic technique.[355] The use of monoclonal antibodies will also allow the virus to be typed by this method.[356]

A variety of assays for antibodies to HSV are available, but are only helpful in the diagnosis of primary infection, because all individuals with established recurrent disease have circulating antibodies directed against the virus. The types of serologic tests available include neutralization, complement fixation, indirect fluorescent antibody, indirect hemagglutination, immune adherence hemagglutination, solid phase radioimmunoassay, and ADCC.[357] Enzyme-linked immunosorbent assay (ELISA) and western blot techniques allow determination of specific subtype antibody levels.[358] Although it is easy to demonstrate the presence of antibody in serum of patients with HSV infections, it is relatively difficult to distinguish antibody directed against type 1 versus antibody directed against type 2. Attempts to distinguish the two different types of antibodies have been made utilizing a variety of techniques, the most common of which is the microneutralization test.[359] The recent recognition of type-specific virus proteins and the ability to produce them in significant concentrations should facilitate our ability to distinguish antibodies directed against the two different virus types in the near future.[360]

The most sensitive and specific method of diagnosis of infections caused by HSV is isolation of virus from infected tissues. HSV can be isolated in a variety of laboratory animals as well as in embryonated eggs; however, the use of tissue culture is considered to be the method of choice by most diagnostic laboratories. The virus grows in a wide variety of primary and continuous cell lines.[361] The system selected depends largely on personal choice and the availability of cell types. The cell types most commonly used include rabbit kidney, human embryonic kidney, human diploid fibroblasts, and Vero cells. Cells are generally seeded into tissue culture tubes and grown to form confluent monolayers. Clinical specimens (0.1–0.2 mL per tube) are then inoculated into two such tubes and incubated for approximately one hour at 34 to 37°C to allow the virus to adsorb. After adsorption, 1 mL of maintenance media is added, and the cultures are reincubated. Cultures are then observed daily for the development of characteristic cytopathic effects (CPE). CPE is generally observed within 48 to 72 hours of inoculation and frequently within 24 hours. Virtually all specimens that contain infectious virus will produce these changes within five days. Observation of the cultures for longer periods is generally not productive.[362] The addition of labeled antibodies to viral cultures to detect viral antigens before a CPE has been employed is a more rapid method of virus identification.[358]

Once a virus isolate has been obtained from clinical specimens, it may be typed as HSV-1 or HSV-2 by a variety of techniques. The most widely used typing methods are those which employ immunologic techniques. Viruses may be typed using immunofluorescent antisera, analysis of neutralization kinetics, or by immunofiltration.[363–365] In addition, an immunoperoxidase method has been employed, as well as a solid phase radioimmunoassay.[366, 367] The recent availability of monoclonal antibodies has facilitated the performance of several of these tests. In addition, the viruses may be typed by DNA hybridization techniques and by restriction endonuclease analysis of viral DNA.[368–371]

Several methods for detection of virus antigens in clinical specimens are under development. Such methods, utilizing monoclonal antibodies or DNA hybridization techniques, may eventually replace virus isolation as the method of choice for rapid and specific diagnosis.[372, 373] Most of these tests require some tissue culture incubation of the virus to amplify the test signal to an acceptable level of sensitivity, which sacrifices diagnostic speed.[374, 375]

PREVENTION

There is no currently available method of prevention other than avoidance of potentially infectious materials. Because of the extremely high prevalence of mucocutaneous HSV infections, and the knowledge that the virus may be excreted asymptomatically, this does not represent a practical control measure.

Vaccination with inactivated whole-virus preparations has been practiced for several years. However, no controlled studies of these preparations have been conducted, and their efficacy rate is unknown.[376]

Both subunit preparations and live virus vaccines are currently undergoing development and evaluation. One very interesting approach to live virus vaccines has been the creation of artificially attenuated strains by deletion of a variety of nonessential genes.[377] These strains afford good protection against primary infection, but do not prevent establishment of latent infections in the host animal. Subunit vaccines consisting of a mixture of HSV glycoproteins are capable of stimulating the immune response in animals and have been shown in animal protection studies to be effective.[378–382] Passive immunization with monoclonal antibodies to gB, gC, gD, gE, and gH[383–387] or immunization with purified gB, gC, or gD[152, 388–391] can protect animals from infection. In addition, immunization with vaccinia virus recombinants that contain gD-1[143, 392, 393] or a synthetic gD-related peptide[394, 395] protected mice against subsequent lethal challenge. Moreover, immunization with the gD-vaccinia recombinant partially protected mice from latent infection,[143, 393] and immunization with a combined gB-gD mixture protected guinea pigs from recurrent infections.[396] However, subunit preparations have not yet been shown to be effective in trials in humans.[397] It remains to be seen whether any vaccine will ameliorate symptoms in previously infected individuals. At present, vaccination would appear to be most appropriate for individuals who have not been previously infected. Thus, the target populations would be very young children and possibly adolescents and young adults.

REFERENCES

1. Hirsch MS: Herpes simplex virus, in Mandell GL, Douglas RG Jr, Bennett JE (eds): *Principles and Practices of Infectious Disease.* New York, Churchill Livingstone, 1990, pp 1144–1153.
2. Stalder H, Oxman MN, Herrmann KL: Herpes simplex virus neutralization: a simplification of the test. *J Infect Dis* 1975; 131:430–432.
3. Nahmias A, Delbuono I, Pipkin J, et al: Rapid identification and typing of herpes simplex virus types 1 and 2 by a direct immunofluorescence technique. *Appl Microbiol* 1971; 22:455–458.
4. Whitley RJ, Soong S-J, Dolin R, et al: Adenine arabinoside therapy of biopsy-proved herpes simplex encephalitis. *N Engl J Med* 1977; 297:289–294.
5. Whitley RJ, Alford CA: Parenteral antiviral chemotherapy of human herpesviruses, in Nahmias AJ, Dowdle WR, Schinazi RF (eds): *The Human Herpesviruses. An Interdisciplinary Perspective.* New York, Elsevier, 1980, pp 478–490.
6. Beswick TSL: The origin and the use of the word herpes. *Med Hist* 1962; 6:214–232.
7. Bateman T: *A Practical Synopsis of Cutaneous Diseases According to the Arrangement of Dr. Willan,* ed 3. London, Longman, Hurst, Orme & Brown, 1814, p 221.
8. Vidal E: Inoculabilité des pustules d'ecthyma. *Ann Dermatol Syphiligr* 1873; 4:350–358.
9. Gruter W: Experimentelle und klinische Untersuchungen über den sogenannten Herpes corneae. *Berl Versamml Dtsch Ophthalmol Ges* 1920; 42:162–167.

832   *H. R. Mattison, R. J. Eisenberg, and R. C. Reichman*

10. Luger A, Lauda E: Zur Ätiologie des Herpes febrilis. *Z Gesamte Exp Med* 1921; 24:289–321.
11. Andrewes CH, Carmichael EA: A note on the presence of antibodies to herpesvirus in post-encephalitic and other human sera. *Lancet* 1930; 1:857–858.
12. Burnet FM, Williams SW: Herpes simplex: A new point of view. *Med J Aust* 1939; 1:637–642.
13. Ruchman I, Welsh AL, Dodd K: Kaposi's varicelliform eruption. Isolation of the virus of herpes simplex from the cutaneous lesions of three adults and one infant. *Arch Dermatol Syph* 1947; 56:846–863.
14. Slavin HB, Gavett E: Primary herpetic vulvovaginitis. *Proc Soc Exp Biol Med* 1946; 63:343–345.
15. Gallado E: Primary herpes simplex keratitis: Clinical and experimental study. *Arch Ophthalmol* 1943; 30:217–220.
16. Smith MG, Lennette EH, Reames HR: Isolation of the virus of herpes simplex and the demonstration of intranuclear inclusions in a case of acute encephalitis. *Am J Pathol* 1941; 17:55–68.
17. Terni M, Carccialanza D, Cassai E, et al: Aseptic meningitis in association with herpes progenitalis. *N Engl J Med* 1971; 285:503–504.
18. Schneweis KE, Brandis H: Typendifferenzen beim Herpes simplex Virus. *Zentralbl Bakteriol Parasitenkunde Infektionskr* 1961; 183:556–558.
19. Dowdle WR, Nahmias AJ, Harwell RW, et al: Association of antigenic type of herpesvirus hominis with site of viral recovery. *J Immunol* 1967; 99:974–980.
20. Gentry GA, Rowe M, Alford G, et al: Sequence analysis of herpesviral enzymes suggest an ancient origin for human sexual behavior. *Proc Natl Acad Sci USA* 1988; 85:2658–2661.
21. Fenner F: The classification and nomenclature of viruses. Summary of results of meetings of the International Committee on Taxonomy of Viruses in Madrid, September, 1975. *J Gen Virol* 1976; 13:463–470.
22. Darlington RW, Moses LH: Herpesvirus envelopment. *J Virol* 1968; 2:48–55.
23. Lycke E, Jeansson S: Herpesviridae: Herpes simplex virus, in Lennette EH, Halonen P, Murphy FA (eds): *Laboratory Diagnosis of Infectious Diseases: Principles and Practices.* New York, Springer-Verlag, 1989, p 217.
24. Kaplan AS, Vatter AE: A comparison of herpes simplex and pseudorabies viruses. *Virology* 1959; 7:394–407.
25. Powell WF: Radiosensitivity as an index of herpes simplex virus development. *Virology* 1959; 9:1–19.
26. Rawls WE: Herpes simplex virus types 1 and 2 and *Herpesvirus simiae*, in Lennette EH, Schmidt NJ (eds): *Diagnostic Procedures for Viral, Rickettsial and Chlamydial Infections,* ed 5. Washington, DC, American Public Health Association, 1979, pp 309–373.
27. McGeoch DJ, Dolan A, Donald S, et al: Sequence determination and genetic content of the short unique region in the genome of herpes simplex virus type 1. *J Mol Biol* 1985; 181:1–13.
28. McGeoch DJ, Dalrymple MA, Davison AJ, et al: DNA sequence of the HSV-1 long unique region. Presented at 12th International Herpesvirus Workshop, Philadelphia, 1987, p 300.
29. Roizman B: The structure and isomerization of herpes simplex virus genomes. *Cell* 1979; 16:481–494.
30. Jongeneel CV, Bachenheimer SL: Structure of replicating herpes simplex virus DNA. *J Virol* 1981; 39:656–660.
31. Cortini R, Wilkie NM: Physical maps for HSV type 2 DNA with restriction endonucleases. *J Gen Virol* 1978; 39:259–280.
32. Morse LS, Buchman TG, Roizman B, et al: Anatomy of herpes simplex virus DNA. IX. Apparent exclusion of some parenteral DNA arrangements in the generation of intertypic (HSV-1 × HSV-2) recombinants. *J Virol* 1977; 24:231–248.
33. Wildy P, Russell WC, Horne RW: The morphology of herpes virus. *Virology* 1960; 12:204–222.
34. Horne RW, Wildy P: Symmetry in virus architecture. *Virology* 1961; 15:348–373.

35. Ben-Porat T, Kaplan AS: Studies on the biogenesis of herpesvirus envelope. *Nature* 1972; 235:165–166.
36. Schwartz J, Roizman B: Similarities and differences in the development of laboratory strains and freshly isolated strains of herpes simplex virus in HEp-2 cells: Electron microscopy. *J Virol* 1969; 4:879–889.
37. Stannard LM, Fuller AO, Spear PG: Herpes simplex virus glycoproteins associated with different morphological entities projecting from the virion envelope. *J Gen Virol* 1987; 68:715–725.
38. Vahlne A, Svennerholm B, Sandberg M, et al: Differences in attachment between herpes simplex type 1 and type 2 viruses to neurons and glial cells. *Infect Immun* 1980; 28:675–680.
39. Spear PG: Glycoproteins specified by herpes simplex viruses, in Roizman B (ed): *The Herpesviruses.* New York, Plenum, 1985, vol 3, pp 315–356.
40. Campadelli-Fiume G, Arsenakis M, Farabegoli F, et al: Entry of herpes simplex virus 1 in BJ cells that constitutively express viral glycoprotein D is by endocytosis and results in degradation of the virus. *J Virol* 1988; 62:159–167.
41. DeLuca N, Bzik DJ, Bond VC, et al: Nucleotide sequences of herpes simplex virus type 1 (HSV-1) affecting virus entry, cell fusion and production of glycoprotein gB (VP7). *Virology* 1982; 122:411–423.
42. Fuller AO, Spear PG: Anti-glycoprotein D antibodies that permit adsorption but block infection by herpes simplex virus 1 prevent virion-cell fusion at the cell surface. *Proc Natl Acad Sci USA* 1987; 84:5454–5458.
43. Para MF, Baucke RB, Spear PG: Immunoglobulin G (Fc) binding receptors on virions of herpes simplex virus type 1 and transfer of these receptors to the cell surface by infection. *J Virol* 1980; 34:512–520.
44. Honess RW, Roizman B: Regulation of herpesvirus macromolecular synthesis. I. Cascade regulation of the synthesis of three groups of viral proteins. *J Virol* 1974; 14:8–19.
45. Roizman B, Kozak M, Honess RW, et al: Regulation of herpesvirus macromolecular synthesis: Evidence for multilevel regulation of herpes simplex 1 RNA and protein synthesis. *Cold Spring Harbor Symp Quant Biol* 1974; 39:687–701.
46. Roizman B: The structure and isomerization of herpes simplex virus genomes. *Cell* 1979; 16:481–494.
47. Roizman B, Batterson W: Herpesviruses and their replication, in Fields BN (ed): *Virology.* New York, Raven Press, 1985, pp 497–526.
48. Clements JB, Watson RJ, Wilkie NM: Temporal regulation of herpes simplex virus type 1 transcription: location of transcripts on the viral genome. *Cell* 1977; 12:275–285.
49. Honess RW, Roizman B: Regulation of herpesvirus macromolecular synthesis. I. Cascade regulation of the synthesis of three groups of viral proteins. *J Virol* 1974; 14:8–19.
50. Jones PC, Roizman B: Regulation of herpesvirus macromolecular synthesis. VIII. The transcription program consists of three phases during which both the extent of transcription and accumulation of RNA in the cytoplasm are regulated. *J Virol* 1979; 72:299–314.
51. Roizman B, Batterson W: Herpesviruses and their replication, in Fields BN, Knipe DM (eds): *Fundamental Virology.* New York, Raven Press, 1986, pp 607–636.
52. Post LE, Mackem S, Roizman B: Regulation of genes of herpes simplex virus: expression of chimeric genes produced by fusion of thymidine kinase with alpha gene promoters. *Cell* 1981; 24:555–565.
53. Campbell MEM, Palfreyman JW, Preston CM: Identification of herpes simplex virus DNA sequences which encode a trans-acting polypeptide responsible for the stimulation of immediate-early transcription. *J Mol Biol* 1985; 180:1–19.
54. Mavromara-Nazos P, Silver S, Hubenthal-Voss J, et al: Regulation of herpes simplex virus type 1 genes: alpha gene sequence requirements for transient induction of indicator genes regulated by beta or late (gamma 2) promoters. *Virology* 1986; 149:152–164.

55. Post LE, Roizman B: A generalized technique for deletion of specific genes in large genomes: alpha gene 22 of herpes simplex virus is not essential for growth. *Cell* 1981; 25:275–284.

56. DeLuca NA, McCarthy AM, Schaffer PA: Isolation and characterization of deletion mutants of herpes simplex virus type 1 in the gene encoding immediate-early regulatory protein ICP4. *J Virol* 1985; 56:558–570.

57. Everett RD: Trans-activation of transcription by herpes-virus products: requirements of two HSV-1 immediate-early polypeptides for maximum activity. *EMBO J* 1984; 3:3135–3141.

58. Everett RD: The product of herpes simplex virus type 1 (HSV-1) immediate-early genes 1, 2, and 3 can activate HSV-1 expression in trans. *J Gen Virol* 1986; 68:2507–2513.

59. Faber SW, Wilcox KW: Association of the herpes simplex virus regulatory protein ICP4 with specific nucleotide sequences in DNA. *Nucleic Acids Res* 1986; 11:1475–1489.

60. Gelman IH, Silverstein S: Identification of immediate-early genes from herpes simplex virus that transactivate the virus thymidine kinase gene. *Proc Natl Acad Sci USA* 1985; 82:5265–5269.

61. Godowski PJ, Knipe DM: Transcriptional control of herpesvirus gene expression: gene functions required for positive and negative regulation. *Proc Natl Acad Sci USA* 1986; 83:256–260.

62. O'Hare P, Hayward GS: Evidence for a direct role of both the 175,000 and 110,000-molecular weight immediate-early proteins of herpes simplex virus in the transactivation of delayed-early promoters. *J Virol* 1985; 53:751–760.

63. O'Hare P, Hayward GS: Three trans-acting regulatory proteins modulate immediate-early gene expression in a pathway involving positive and negative feedback regulation. *J Virol* 1985; 77:723–733.

64. Preston CM: Control of herpes simplex virus type 1 mRNA synthesis in cells infected with wild-type virus or the temperature-sensitive mutant tsK. *J Virol* 1979; 29:275–284.

65. Quinlan MP, Knipe DM: Stimulation of expression of a herpes simplex virus DNA-binding protein by two viral functions. *Mol Cell Biol* 1985; 5:957–961.

66. Sacks WR, Greene CC, Aschman DP, et al: Herpes simplex virus type 1 ICP27 is an essential regulatory protein. *J Virol* 1985; 55:796–805.

67. Watson RJ, Clements JB: A herpes simplex virus type 1 function continuously required for early and late virus RNA synthesis. *Nature* 1980; 285:329–330.

68. Stow ND, Stow EC: Isolation and characterization of a herpes simplex virus type 1 mutant containing a deletion within the gene encoding the immediate-early polypeptide Vmw 110. *J Gen Virol* 1986; 67:2571–2585.

69. Rice SA, Knipe DM: Gene-specific transactivation by herpes simplex virus type 1 alpha protein 27. *J Virol* 1988; 62:3814–3823.

70. Wu CA, Nelson NJ, McGeoch DJ, et al: Identification and mapping of herpes simplex virus type 1 genes required for origin-dependent DNA synthesis. *J Virol* 1988; 62:435–443.

71. Holland LE, Anderson LP, Shipman C, et al: Viral DNA synthesis is required for the efficient expression of specific herpes simplex virus type 1 mRNAs. *Virology* 1980; 10:110–124.

72. Darlington RW, Moss LH III: Herpesvirus envelopment. *J Virol* 1968; 2:48–55.

73. Morgan C, Rose HM, Holden M, et al: Electron microscopic observation on the development of herpes simplex virus. *J Exp Med* 1959; 110:643–656.

74. Nii S, Morgan C, Rose HM: Electron microscopy of herpes simplex virus II. Sequence of development. *J Virol* 1968; 2:517–536.

75. Johnson DC, Spear PG: Monensin inhibits the processing of herpes simplex virus glycoproteins, their transport to the cell surface, and the egress of virions from infected cells. *J Virol* 1982; 43:1102–1112.

76. Mertz GJ: Herpes simplex virus, in Galasso GJ, Whitley RJ, Merigan TC (eds): *Antiviral Agents and Viral Diseases of Man.*

77. New York, Raven Press, 1990, pp 278–279.

77. Overall JC: Antiviral chemotherapy of oral and genital herpes simplex virus infections, in Nahmias AJ, Dowdle WR, Schinazi RF (eds): *The Human Herpesviruses. An Interdisciplinary Perspective.* New York, Elsevier, 1980, pp 447–465.

78. Cohen SS: The lethality of aranucleotides. *Med Biol* 1978; 54:299–326.

79. Elion GB, Furman PA, Fyfe JA, et al: Selectivity of action of an antiherpetic agent, 9-(2-hydroxy-ethoxymethyl) guanine. *Proc Natl Acad Sci USA* 1977; 74:5716–5720.

80. Elion GB: Mechanism of action and selectivity of acyclovir. *Am J Med* 1982; 73:7–13.

81. Ackermann M, Longnecker R, Roizman B, et al: Identification, properties and gene location of a novel glycoprotein specified by herpes simplex virus 1. *Virology* 1986; 50:207–220.

82. Buckmaster EA, Gompels U, Minson AC: Characterisation and physical mapping of an HSV-1 glycoprotein of approximately 115 × 103 molecular weight. *Virology* 1984; 139:408–413.

83. Johnson DC, Frame MC, Ligas MW, et al: Herpes simplex virus immunoglobulin G Fc receptor activity depends on a complex of two viral glycoproteins, gE and gI. *J Virol* 1988; 62:1347–1354.

84. Longnecker R, Roizman B: Clustering of genes dispensable for growth in culture in the S component of the HSV-1 genome. *Science* 1987; 236:573–576.

85. Sarmiento M, Haffey M, Spear PG: Membrane proteins specified by herpes simplex virus. III. Role of glycoprotein VP7 (B2) in virion infectivity. *J Virol* 1979; 29:1149–1158.

86. Zezulak KM, Spear PG: Mapping of the structural gene for the herpes simplex virus type 2 counterpart of herpes simplex virus type 1 glycoprotein C and identification of a type 2 mutant which does not express this glycoprotein. *J Virol* 1984; 49:741–747.

87. Holland TC, Homa FL, Marlin SD, et al: Herpes simplex virus type 1 glycoprotein C-negative mutants exhibit multiple phenotypes, including secretion of truncated glycoproteins. *J Virol* 1984; 52:566–574.

88. Neidhardt H, Schroder CH, Kaerner HC: Herpes simplex virus type 1 glycoprotein E is not indispensable for viral infectivity. *J Virol* 1987; 61:600–603.

89. Longnecker R, Roizman B: Generation of an inverting herpes simplex virus 1 mutant lacking the L-S junction a sequences, an origin of DNA synthesis and several genes including those specifying glycoprotein E and the alpha 47 gene. *J Virol* 1986; 58:583–591.

90. Weber PC, Levine M, Glorioso JC: Rapid identification of non-essential genes of herpes simplex virus type 1 by Tn5 mutagenesis. *Science* 1987; 236:576–579.

91. Longnecker R, Chatterjee S, Whitley RJ, et al: Identification of a herpes simplex virus 1 glycoprotein gene within a gene cluster dispensable for growth in cell culture. *Proc Natl Acad Sci USA* 1987; 84:4303–4307.

92. Fuller AO, Spear PG: Specificities of monoclonal and polyclonal antibodies that inhibit adsorption of herpes simplex virus to cells and lack of inhibition by potent neutralizing antibodies. *J Virol* 1985; 55:475–482.

93. Johnson DC, Wittels M, Spear PG: Binding to cells of virosomes containing herpes simplex virus type 1 glycoproteins and evidence for fusion. *J Virol* 1984; 52:238–247.

94. Cai W, Person S, Warner SC, et al: Linker-insertion nonsense and restriction-site deletion mutations of the gB glycoprotein gene of herpes simplex virus type 1. *J Virol* 1987; 61:714–721.

95. Holland TC, Marlin SD, Levine M, et al: Antigenic variants of herpes simplex virus selected with glycoprotein-specific monoclonal antibodies. *J Virol* 1983; 45:672–682.

96. Ligas MW, Johnson DC: A herpes simplex virus mutant in which glycoprotein D sequences are replaced by β-galactosidase sequences binds to but is unable to penetrate into cells. *J Virol* 1988; 62:1486–1494.

97. Fuller AO, Spear PG: Anti-glycoprotein D antibodies that per-

mit adsorption but block infection by herpes simplex virus 1 prevent virion-cell fusion at the cell surface. *Proc Natl Acad Sci USA* 1987; 84:5454–5458.

98. Johnson DC, Wittels M, Spear PG: Binding to cells of virosomes containing herpes simplex virus type 1 glycoproteins and evidence for fusion. *J Virol* 1984; 52:238–247.

99. Para MF, Baucke RB, Spear PG: Immunoglobulin G (Fc) binding receptors on virions of herpes simplex virus type 1 and transfer of these receptors to the cell surface by infection. *J Virol* 1980; 34:512–520.

100. Highlander SL, Cai W, Person S, et al: Monoclonal antibodies define a domain on herpes simplex virus glycoprotein B involved in virus penetration. *J Virol* 1988; 62:1881–1888.

101. Minson AC, Hodgman TC, Digard P, et al: An analysis of the biological properties of monoclonal antibodies against glycoprotein D of herpes simplex virus and identification of amino acid substitutions that confer resistance to neutralization. *J Gen Virol* 1986; 67:1001–1013.

102. Noble G, Lee GT-Y, Sprague R, et al: Anti-gD monoclonal antibodies inhibit cell fusion induced by herpes simplex virus type 1. *Virology* 1988; 129:218–224.

103. Eisenberg RJ, Cohen GH: Identification and analysis of biologically active sites of herpes simplex virus glycoprotein D, in Crowell RL, Lonberg-Holm K (eds): *Virus Attachment and Entry into Cells.* Washington, DC, American Society for Microbiology, 1986, pp 74–84.

104. Showalter SD, Zweig M, Hampar B: Monoclonal antibodies to herpes simplex virus type 1 proteins, including the immediate early protein ICP4. *Infect Immun* 1981; 34:684–692.

105. Muggeridge MI, Isola VJ, Byrn RA, et al: Antigenic analysis of a major neutralization site of herpes simplex virus glycoprotein D, using deletion mutants and monoclonal antibody-resistant mutants. *J Virol* 1988; 62:3274–3280.

106. Eisenberg RJ, Long D, Pereira L, et al: Effect of monoclonal antibodies on limited proteolysis of native glycoprotein gD of herpes simplex virus type 1. *J Virol* 1982; 41:478–488.

107. Cohen GH, Isola VJ, Kuhns J, et al: Localization of discontinuous epitopes of herpes simplex virus glycoprotein D: Use of a nondenaturing ("native") gel system of polyacrylamide gel electrophoresis coupled with western blotting. *J Virol* 1986; 60:157–166.

108. Gompels R, Minson A: The properties and sequence of glycoprotein H of herpes simplex virus type 1. *Virology* 1986; 153:230–247.

109. Sarmiento M, Haffey M, Spear PG: Membrane proteins specified by herpes simplex virus. III. Role of glycoprotein VP7 (B2) in virion infectivity. *J Virol* 1979; 29:1149–1158.

110. Little SP, Jofre JT, Courtney RJ, et al: A virion associated glycoprotein essential for infectivity of herpes simplex virus type 1. *Virology* 1981; 115:149–160.

111. Friedman HM, Cohen GH, Eisenberg RJ, et al: Glycoprotein C of herpes simplex virus 1 acts as a receptor for the C3b complement component on infected cells. *Nature* 1984; 309:633–635.

112. Eisenberg RJ, Ponce de Leon M, Friedman HM, et al: Complement component C3b binds directly to purified glycoprotein C of herpes simplex virus types 1 and 2. *Microbiol Pathol* 1987; 3:423–435.

113. Baucke RB, Spear PG: Membrane proteins specified by herpes simplex viruses. V. Identification of an Fc-binding glycoprotein. *J Virol* 1979; 32:779–789.

114. Johnson DC, Feenstra V: Identification of a novel herpes simplex virus type 1–induced glycoprotein which complexes with gE and binds immunoglobulin. *J Virol* 1987; 61:2208–2216.

115. Johnson DC, Frame MC, Ligas MW, et al: Herpes simplex virus immunoglobulin G Fc receptor activity depends on a complex of two viral glycoproteins, gE and gI. *J Virol* 1988; 62:1347–1354.

116. Su HK, Courtney RJ: Inducible expression of herpes simplex virus type 2 glycoprotein gG-2 in a mammalian cell line. *J Virol* 1988; 62:3668–3674.

117. Balachandran N, Bachetti S, Rawls WE: Protection against lethal challenge of BALB/c mice by passive transfer of monoclonal antibodies to five glycoproteins of herpes simplex virus type 2. *Infect Immun* 1982; 37:1132–1137.

118. Chan WL: Protective immunization of mice with specific HSV-1 glycoproteins. *Immunology* 1983; 49:343–352.

119. Cremer KJ, Mackett M, Wohlenberg C, et al: Vaccinia virus recombinant expressing herpes simplex virus type 1 glycoprotein D prevents latent herpes in mice. *Science* 1985; 228:737–740.

120. Dix RD, Pereira L, Baringer JR: Use of monoclonal antibody directed against herpes simplex virus glycoproteins to protect mice against acute virus-induced neurological disease. *Infect Immun* 1981; 34:192–199.

121. Gompels R, Minson A: The properties and sequence of glycoprotein H of herpes simplex virus type 1. *Virology* 1986; 153:230–247.

122. Marsden HS: Herpes simplex virus glycoproteins and pathogenesis, in Russell WC, Almond JW (eds): *Molecular Basis of Virus Disease.* New York, Cambridge University Press, 1987, pp 259–288.

123. Para MF, Parish ML, Noble AG, et al: Potent neutralizing activity associated with anti-glycoprotein D specificity among monoclonal antibodies selected for binding to herpes simplex virions. *J Virol* 1985; 55:483–488.

124. Pereira L, Klassen T, Baringer JR: Type-common and type-specific monoclonal antibody to herpes simplex virus type 1. *Infect Immun* 1980; 29:724–732.

125. Powell KL, Buchan A, Sim C, et al: Type-specific protein in herpes simplex virus envelope reacts with neutralizing antibody. *Nature* 1974; 249:360–361.

126. Rector JT, Lausch RN, Oakes JE: Use of monoclonal antibodies for analysis of antibody-dependent immunity to ocular herpes simplex virus type 1 infections. *Infect Immun* 1982; 38:168–174.

127. Schrier RD, Pizer LI, Moorhead JW, et al: Type-specific delayed hypersensitivity and protective immunity induced by isolated herpes simplex virus glycoprotein. *J Immunol* 1983; 130:1413–1417.

128. Sullivan V, Smith GL: Expression and characterization of herpes simplex virus type 1 (HSV1) glycoprotein G by recombinant vaccinia virus: neutralization of HSV1 infectivity with anti-gG antibody. *J Gen Virol* 1987; 68:2587–2598.

129. Cohen GH, Katze M, Hydrean-Stern C, et al: Type-common CP-1 antigen of herpes simplex virus is associated with a 59,000-molecular-weight envelope glycoprotein. *J Virol* 1978; 27:172–181.

130. Eisenberg RJ, Ponce de Leon M, Pereira L, et al: Purification of glycoprotein gD of herpes simplex virus types 1 and 2 by use of monoclonal antibody. *J Virol* 1982; 41:1099–1104.

131. Eberle R, Russell RG, Rouse BT: Cell-mediated immunity to herpes simplex viruses: recognition of type-specific and type-common surface antigens by cytotoxic T cell populations. *Infect Immun* 1981; 34:795–803.

132. Norrild B, Shore SL, Nahmias AJ: Herpes simplex virus glycoproteins: participation of individual herpes simplex virus type 1 glycoprotein antigens in immunocytolysis and their correlation with previously identified glycopolypeptides. *J Virol* 1979; 32:741–748.

133. Rector JT, Lausch RN, Oakes JE: Use of monoclonal antibodies for analysis of antibody-dependent immunity to ocular herpes simplex virus type 1 infections. *Infect Immun* 1982; 38:168–174.

134. Glorioso J, Kees R, Kumel G, et al: Identification of herpes simplex virus type 1 (HSV-1) glycoprotein gC as the immunodominant antigen for HSV-1-specific memory cytotoxic T lymphocytes. *J Immunol* 1985; 135:575–582.

135. Carter VC, Schaffer PA, Tevethia SS: The involvement of herpes simplex virus type 1 glycoproteins in cell-mediated immunity. *J Immunol* 1981; 126:1655–1660.

136. Torseth JW, Cohen GH, Eisenberg RJ, et al: Native and recombinant herpes simplex virus type 1 envelope proteins induce human immune T-lymphocyte responses. *J Virol* 1987; 61:1532–1539.

137. Lawman MJP, Courtney RJ, Eberle R, et al: Cell-mediated immunity to herpes simplex virus: Specificity of cytotoxic T cells. *Infect Immun* 1980; 30:451–461.

138. Rosenthal KL, Smiley JR, South S, et al: Cells expressing herpes simplex virus glycoprotein gC but not gB, gD, or gE are recognized by murine virus-specific cytotoxic T lymphocytes. *J Virol* 1987; 61:2438–2447.

139. Zarling JM, Moran PA, Burke RL, et al: Human cytotoxic T cell clones directed against herpes simplex virus infected cells. IV. Recognition and activation by cloned glycoproteins gB and gD. *J Immunol* 1986; 136:4669–4673.

140. Zarling JM, Moran PA, Lasky LB, et al: Herpes simplex virus (HSV)–specific human T-cell clones recognize HSV glycoprotein D expressed by a recombinant vaccinia virus. *J Virol* 1986; 59:506–509.

141. Bishop GA, Glorioso JC, Schwartz SA: Relationship between expression of herpes simplex virus glycoproteins and susceptibility of target cells to human natural killer activity. *J Exp Med* 1983; 157:1544–1561.

142. Bishop GA, Marlin SD, Schwartz SA, et al: Human natural killer cell recognition of herpes simplex virus type 1 glycoproteins: specificity analysis with the use of monoclonal antibodies and antigenic variants. *J Immunol* 1984; 133:2206–2214.

143. Cohen GH, Dietzschold B, Ponce de Leon M, et al: Localization and synthesis of an antigenic determinant of herpes simplex virus glycoprotein D that stimulates the production of neutralizing antibody. *J Virol* 1984; 49:102–108.

144. Marlin SD, Holland TC, Levine M, et al: Epitopes of herpes simplex virus type 1 glycoprotein gC are clustered in two distinct antigenic sites. *J Virol* 1985; 53:128–136.

145. Seidel-Dugan CM, Ponce de Leon M, Friedman HM, et al: C3b receptor activity on transfected cells expressing glycoprotein C of herpes simplex virus types 1 and 2. *J Virol*, submitted.

146. Bzik DJ, Fox BA, DeLuca NA, et al: Nucleotide sequence specifying the glycoprotein gene, gB, of herpes simplex virus type 1. *Virology* 1984; 133:301–314.

147. Stuve LL, Brown-Shimer S, Pachl C, et al: Structure and expression of the herpes simplex virus type 2 glycoprotein gB gene. *J Virol* 1987; 61:326–335.

148. Marlin SD, Highlander SL, Holland TC, et al: Antigenic variations (mar mutations) in herpes simplex virus glycoprotein B can induce temperature-dependent alterations in gB processing and virus production. *J Virol* 1986; 59:142–153.

149. Highlander SL, Cai W, Person S, et al: Monoclonal antibodies define a domain on herpes simplex virus glycoprotein B involved in virus penetration. *J Virol* 1988; 62:1881–1888.

150. Weijer WJ, Drijfhout JW, Geerligs HJ, et al: Antibodies against synthetic peptides of herpes simplex virus type 1 glycoprotein D and their capability to neutralize viral infectivity in vitro. *J Virol* 1988; 62:501–510.

151. Strynadka NCJ, Redmond MJ, Parker JMR, et al: The use of synthetic peptides to map the antigenic determinants of glycoprotein D of herpes simplex virus. *J Virol* 1988; 62:3474–3483.

152. Wyckoff JH, Osmand AP, Eisenberg RJ, et al: T cell recognition of synthetic peptides corresponding to continuous antibody epitopes of herpes simplex virus type 1 glycoprotein D. *Immunobiology* 1988; 177:134–148.

153. Nahmias AJ, Keyserling H, Lee FK: Herpes simplex viruses 1 and 2, in Evans AS (ed): *Viral Infections of Humans. Epidemiology and Control,* ed 3. New York, Plenum, 1989, p 393–417.

154. Goodman JL: Infections caused by herpes simplex viruses, in Hoeprich PD, Jordan CL (eds): *Infectious Diseases,* ed 4. Philadelphia, Lippincott, 1989, pp 915–930.

155. Workshop on the treatment and prevention of herpes simplex virus infection. *J Infect Dis* 1973; 127:117–119.

156. Nahmias AJ, Roizman B: Infection with herpes-simplex virus 1 and 2. *N Engl J Med* 1973; 289:667–674, 719–725, 781–789.

157. Whitley RJ: Herpes simplex virus, in Fields BN, Knipe DM, Chanock RM, et al (eds): *Virology.* New York, Raven Press, 1990, pp 1843–1888.

158. Straus SE, Rooney JF, Sever JL, et al: Herpes simplex virus infection: Biology, treatment, and prevention. *Ann Intern Med* 1985; 103:404–419.

158a. Becker TM, Magder L, Harrison HR, et al: The epidemiology of infection with human herpesviruses in Navajo children. *Am J Epidemiol* 1988; 127:1071–1078.

159. Nahmias AJ, Gosey WE, Naib ZM, et al: Antibodies to *Herpesvirus hominis* types 1 and 2 in humans. *Am J Epidemiol* 1970; 91:539–546.

160. Corey L, Spear PG: Infections with herpes simplex viruses. *N Engl J Med* 1986; 314:686–691, 749–757.

161. Stavraky KM, Rawls WE, Chiavetta J, et al: Sexual and socio-economic factors affecting the risk of past infections with herpes simplex virus type 2. *Am J Epidemiol* 1983; 118:109–121.

162. Johnson RE, Nahmias AJ, Magder LS, et al: A seroepidemiologic survey of the prevalence of herpes simplex virus type 2 infection in the United States. *N Engl J Med* 1989; 321:7–12.

163. Porter PS, Baughman RD: Epidemiology of herpes simplex among wrestlers. *JAMA* 1965; 194:998–1000.

164. Koneru B, Tzakis A, DePuydt LE, et al: Transmission of fatal herpes simplex infection through renal transplantation. *Transplantation* 1988; 45:653–656.

165. Dummer JS, Armstrong J, Somers J, et al: Transmission of infection with herpes simplex virus by renal transplantation. *J Infect Dis* 1987; 155:202–206.

166. Singh N, Dummer JS, Kusne S, et al: Infections with cytomegalovirus and other herpesviruses in 121 liver transplant recipients: Transmission by donated organ and the effect of OKT3 antibodies. *J Infect Dis* 1988; 158:124–131.

167. Mertz GJ, Coombs RW, Ashley R, et al: Transmission of genital herpes in couples with one symptomatic and one asymptomatic partner: A prospective study. *J Infect Dis* 1988; 157:1169–1177.

168. Rooney JF, Felser JM, Ostrone JM, et al: Acquisition of genital herpes from an asymptomatic sexual partner. *N Engl J Med* 1986; 314:1561–1564.

169. Corey L, Adams HG, Brown ZA, et al: Genital herpes simplex virus infections: Clinical manifestations, course and complications. *Ann Intern Med* 1983; 98:958–972.

170. Roizman B: An inquiry into the mechanisms of recurrent herpes infections of man, in Pollard M (ed): *Perspectives in Virology.* New York, Harper & Row, 1965, p 283.

171. Buchman TG, Roizman B, Nahmias AJ: Demonstration of exogenous genital reinfection with herpes simplex virus type 2 by restriction endonuclease fingerprinting of viral DNA. *J Infect Dis* 1979; 140:295–304.

172. Blyth WA, Hill TJ: Establishment, maintenance, and control of herpes simplex virus latency, in Rouse BT, Lopez C (eds): *Immunobiology of Herpes Simplex Virus Infection.* Boca Raton, Fla, CRC Press, 1984, pp 9–32.

173. Hill TJ: Herpes simplex virus latency, in Roizman B (ed): *The Herpesviruses.* New York, Plenum, 1985, pp 175–240.

174. Stevens JG, Wagner EK, Devi-Rao GB, et al: RNA complementary to a herpesvirus alpha gene mRNA is prominent in latently infected neurons. *Science* 1987; 235:1056–1059.

175. Stevens JG, Cook ML: Latent herpes simplex virus in spinal ganglia of mice. *Science* 1971; 173:843–845.

176. Cook ML, Stevens JG: Latent herpetic infections following experimental viraemia. *J Gen Virol* 1976; 31:75–80.

177. Knotts FB, Cook ML, Stevens JG: Latent herpes simplex virus infection in the central nervous system of rabbits and mice. *J Exp Med* 1973; 138:740–744.

178. Warren KG, Brown SM, Wroblewska Z, et al: Isolation of latent herpes simplex virus from the superior cervical and vagus ganglions of human beings. *N Engl J Med* 1978; 298:1067–1068.

179. Warren KG, Devlin M, Gilden DH, et al: Isolation of herpes simplex virus from human trigeminal ganglia, including from one patient with multiple sclerosis. *J Hyg* 1977; 65:173–192.

180. Walz MA, Price RW, Notkins AL: Latent ganglionic infection with herpes simplex virus types 1 and 2: viral reaction in vivo after neurectomy. *Science* 1974; 184:1185–1187.

181. Rock DL, Fraser NW: Detection of HSV-1 genome in central nervous system of latently infected mice. *Nature* 1983; 302:523–525.

182. Rock DL, Fraser NW: Latent herpes simplex virus type 1 DNA contains 2 copies of the virion DNA joint region. *J Virol* 1985; 55:849–852.

183. Efstathiou S, Minson A, Field HJ, et al: Detection of herpes simplex virus-specific DNA sequences in latently infected mice and in humans. *J Virol* 1986; 57:446–455.

184. Mellerick DM, Fraser NW: Physical state of the latent herpes simplex virus genome in a mouse model system: evidence suggesting an episomal state. *Virology* 1987; 158:265–275.

185. Cabrera CV, Wohlenberg C, Openshaw H, et al: Herpes simplex virus DNA sequences in the CNS of latently infected mice. *Nature* 1980; 288:288–290.

186. Fraser NW, Lawrence WC, Wroblewska Z, et al: Herpes simplex virus DNA in human brain tissue. *Proc Natl Acad Sci USA* 1981; 78:6461–6465.

187. Puga A, Rosenthal D, Openshaw H, et al: Herpes simplex virus DNA and mRNA sequences in acutely and chronically infected trigeminal ganglia in mice. *Virology* 1978; 89:102–111.

188. Deatly AM, Spivak JG, Lavi E, et al: Latent herpes simplex virus type 1 transcription in peripheral and central nervous system tissues of mice map to similar regions of the viral genome. *J Virol* 1988; 62:749–756.

189. Stroop WG, Rock DL, Fraser NW: Localization of herpes simplex virus in the trigeminal and olfactory systems of the mouse central nervous system during acute and latent infections by in situ hybridization. *Lab Invest* 1984; 51:27–38.

190. Rock DL, Nesburn AB, Ghiasi H, et al: Detection of latency-related viral RNAs in trigeminal ganglia of rabbits latently infected with herpes simplex virus type 1. *J Virol* 1987; 61:3820–3826.

191. Croen KD, Ostrove JM, Dragovic LJ, et al: Latent herpes simplex virus in human trigeminal ganglia: detection of an immediate early gene "anti-sense" transcript by in situ hybridization. *N Engl J Med* 1987; 317:1427–1432.

192. Steiner I, Spivak JG, O'Boyle DR II, et al: Latent herpes simplex virus type 1 transcription in human trigeminal ganglia. *J Virol* 1988; 62:3493–3496.

193. Tenser RB, Dawson M, Ressel SJ, et al: Detection of herpes simplex virus mRNA in latently infected trigeminal ganglion neurons by in situ hybridization. *Ann Neurol* 1982; 11:285–291.

194. Galloway DA, Fenoglio C, Shevchuk M, et al: Detection of herpes simplex virus RNA in human sensory ganglia. *Virology* 1978; 95:265–268.

195. Galloway DA, Fenoglio DM, McDougall JK: Limited transcription of the herpes simplex virus genome when latent in human sensory ganglia. *J Virol* 1982; 41:686–691.

196. Spivak JL, Fraser NW: Detection of herpes simplex virus type 1 transcripts during latent infection in mice. *J Virol* 1987; 61:3841–3847.

197. Spivak JL, Fraser NW: Expression of herpes simplex virus type 1 (HSV-1) latency-associated transcripts and transcripts affected by the deletion in avirulent mutant HFEM: evidence for a new class of HSV-1 genes. *J Virol* 1980; 62:3281–3287.

198. Shore SL, Feorino PM: Immunology of primary herpesvirus infections in humans, in Nahmias AJ, Dowdle WR, Schinazi RF (eds): *The Human Herpesviruses. An Interdisciplinary Perspective.* New York, Elsevier, 1980, pp 267–288.

199. Moller-Larsen A, Haahr S, Black FT: Cellular and humoral immune responses to herpes simplex virus during and after primary gingivostomatitis. *Infect Immun* 1978; 22:445–457.

200. Kurtz JB: Specific IgG and IgM antibody responses in herpes

simplex virus infections. *J Med Microbiol* 1974; 7:333–341.

201. Reeves WC, Corey L, Adams HG, et al: Risk of recurrence after first episodes of genital herpes. *N Engl J Med* 1981; 305:315–319.

202. Allison AC: Interactions of antibodies, complement components and various cell types in immunity against viruses and pyogenic bacteria. *Transplant Rev* 1974; 19:3–55.

203. Corey L: The diagnosis and treatment of genital herpes. *JAMA* 1982; 248:1041–1049.

204. Corey L, Holmes KK, Benedetti J, et al: Clinical course of genital herpes: Implications for therapeutic trials, in Nahmias AJ, Dowdle WR, Schinazi RF (eds): *The Human Herpesviruses. An Interdisciplinary Perspective.* New York, Elsevier, 1980, pp 496–502.

205. Daniels CA, Borsos T, Rapp HJ, et al: Neutralization of sensitized virus by purified components of complement. *Proc Natl Acad Sci USA* 1970; 65:528–535.

206. Kapadia A, Gupta S, Good RA, et al: Familial herpes simplex infection associated with activation of the complement system. *Am J Med* 1979; 67:122–126.

207. Lopez C, O'Reilly RJ: Cell-mediated immune responses in recurrent herpesvirus infections. I. Lymphocyte proliferation assay. *J Immunol* 1977; 118:895–902.

208. O'Reilly RJ, Chibbaro A, Anger E, et al: Cell-mediated immune responses in patients with recurrent herpes simplex infections. II. Infection-associated deficiency of lymphokine production in patients with recurrent herpes labialis or herpes progenitalis. *J Immunol* 1977; 118:1095–1102.

209. Reichman RC, Dolin R, Vincent MM, et al: Cell-mediated cytotoxicity in recurrent herpes simplex virus infections in man. *Proc Soc Exp Biol Med* 1977; 155:571.

210. Moller-Larsen A, Haahr S, Black FT: Cellular and humoral immune responses to herpes simplex virus during and after primary gingivostomatitis. *Infect Immun* 1978; 22:445–457.

211. Shore SL, Black CM, Melewicz FM, et al: Antibody-dependent cell-mediated cytotoxicity to target cells infected with type 1 and type 2 herpes simplex virus. *J Immunol* 1976; 116:194.

212. Russell AS: Cell-mediated immunity to herpes simplex virus in man. *J Infect Dis* 1974; 129:142–146.

213. Mogensen SC: Role of macrophages in natural resistance to virus infections. *Microbiol Rev* 1979; 43:1–26.

214. Lopez C, Dudas G: Replication of herpes simplex virus type 1 in macrophages from resistant and susceptible mice. *Infect Immun* 1979; 23:432–437.

215. Nahmias AJ, Roizman B: Infection with herpes-simplex viruses 1 and 2. *N Engl J Med* 1973; 289:667–674, 719–725, 781–789.

216. Kohl S: Postnatal herpes simplex virus infection, in Feigin RD, Cherry JD (eds): *Textbook of Pediatric Infectious Diseases.* Philadelphia, Saunders, 1987, pp 1577–1601.

217. Young TB, Rimm EB, D'Alessio DJ: Cross-sectional study of recurrent herpes labialis. *Am J Epidemiol* 1988; 127:612–625.

218. Spruance SL, Overall JC Jr, Kern ER, et al: The natural history of recurrent herpes simplex labialis. Implications for antiviral therapy. *N Engl J Med* 1977; 297:69–76.

219. Daniels CA, LeGoff SG, Notkins AL: Shedding of infectious virus/antibody complexes from vesicular lesions of patients with recurrent herpes simplex labialis. *Lancet* 1975; 2:524–528.

220. Overall JC Jr: Dermatologic viral diseases, in Gallasso GJ, Merigan TC, Buchanen RA (eds): *Antiviral Agents and Viral Diseases of Man,* ed 2. New York, Raven Press, 1984, pp 247–312.

221. Cizman M, Mozetic M: Oral acyclovir in primary gingivostomatitis. *Proc Eur Soc Paediatr Infect Dis,* Oct 1986.

222. Kibrick S, Katz AS: Topical idoxuridine in recurrent herpes simplex. *Ann NY Acad Sci* 1970; 173:83–89.

223. Underwood GE, Nichol FR: Clinical evaluation of kethoxal against cutaneous herpes simplex. *Appl Environ Microbiol* 1971; 22:588–592.

224. Marks R, Koutts J: Topical treatment of recurrent herpes sim-

plex with cytosine arabinoside. *Med J Aust* 1975; 1:479–480.

225. Adams HG, Benson EA, Alexander ER, et al: Genital herpetic infection in men and women: Clinical course and effect of topical application of adenine arabinoside. *J Infect Dis* 1976; 133(suppl A):A151–A159.

226. Spruance SL, Crumpacker CF, Haines H, et al: Treatment of herpes simplex labialis with adenine arabinoside-5'-monophosphate (ARA-AMP). *N Engl J Med* 1979; 300:1180–1184.

227. Spruance SL, Crumpacker CS, Schnipper LE, et al: Topical 10% acyclovir (ACV) in polyethylene glycol (PEG) for herpes simplex labialis: Results of treatment begun in the prodrome and erythema stages. Presented at the 22nd Interscience Conference on Antimicrobial Agents and Chemotherapy, Miami Beach, Oct 4–6, 1982.

228. Spruance SL, Schnipper LE, Overall JC Jr, et al: Treatment of herpes simplex labialis with topical acyclovir in polyethylene glycol. *J Infect Dis* 1982; 146:85–90.

229. Raborn GW, McGaw WT, Grace M, et al: Treatment of herpes labialis with acyclovir: Review of three clinical trials. *Am J Med* 1988; 85(2A):39–42.

230. Fiddian AP, Yeo JM, Stubbings R, et al: Successful treatment of herpes labialis with topical acyclovir. *Br Med J* 1983; 286:1699–1701.

231. Shaw M, King M, Best JM, et al: Failure of acyclovir cream in treatment of recurrent herpes labialis. *Br Med J* 1985; 219:7–9.

232. Gibson JR, Klaber MR, Harvey SG, et al: Prophylaxis against herpes labialis with acyclovir cream—a placebo-controlled study. *Dermatologica* 1986; 172:104–107.

233. Spruance SL, Schnipper LE, Overall JR, et al: Treatment of herpes simplex labialis with topical acyclovir in polyethylene glycol. *J Infect Dis* 1982; 146:85–90.

234. Spruance SL, Crumpanker CS, Schnipper LE, et al: Early, patient-mitiated treatment of herpes labialis with topical 10% acyclovir. *Antimicrobiol Agents Chemother* 1984; 25:553–555.

234a. Spruance SL, Stewart JCB, Freeman DJ, et al: Early application of topical 15% idoxuridine in dimethyl sulfoxide shortens the course of herpes simplex labialis: A multicenter placebo-controlled trial. *J Infect Dis* 1990; 161:191–197.

235. Raborn GW, McGaw WT, Grace M, et al: Oral acyclovir and herpes labialis: A randomized, double-blind, placebo-controlled study. *J Am Dent Assoc* 1987; 115:38–42.

235a. Spruance SL, Stewart JCB, Rowe NH, et al: Treatment of recurrent herpes simplex labialis with oral acyclovir. *J Infect Dis* 1990; 161:185–190.

236. Meyrick Thomas RH, Dodd HJ, Yeo JM, et al: Oral acyclovir in the suppression of recurrent non-genital herpes simplex virus infection. *Br J Dermatol* 1985; 113:731–735.

237. Spruance SL, Hamill ML, Hoge WS, et al: Acyclovir prevents reactivation of herpes simplex labialis in skiers. *JAMA* 1988; 260:1597–1599.

238. Sexually transmitted disease. *Br J Vener Dis* 1983; 59:134–137.

239. Becker TM, Blount JH, Guinan ME: Genital herpes infections in private practice in the United States, 1966–1981. *JAMA* 1985; 253:1601–1603.

240. Guinan ME, Wolinsky SM, Reichman RC: Epidemiology of genital herpes simplex virus infection. *Epidemiol Rev* 1985; 7:127–146.

241. Becker TM, Stone KM, Cates W Jr: Epidemiology of genital herpes infections in the United States: The current situation. *J Reprod Med* 1986; 31:359–364.

242. Communicable Disease Surveillance Centre: Sexually transmitted disease in Britain 1985. *Commun Dis Rep* 1987; 45:3–6.

243. Corey L, Holmes KK: Genital herpes simplex virus infections: Current concepts in diagnosis, therapy, and prevention. *Ann Intern Med* 1983; 98:973–983.

243a. Brock BV, Selke S, Benedetti J, et al: Frequency of asymptomatic shedding of herpes simplex virus in women with genital herpes. *JAMA* 1990; 263:418–420.

243b. Langenberg A, Benedetti J, Jenkins J, et al: Development of clinically recognizable genital lesions among women previously identified as having "asymptomatic" herpes simplex virus type 2 infection. *Ann Intern Med* 1989; 110:882–887.

244. Lafferty WE, Coombs RW, Benedetti J, et al: Recurrences after oral and genital herpes simplex infection: Influence of site of infection and viral type. *N Engl J Med* 1987; 316:1444–1449.

244a. Straus SE, Croen KD, Sawyer MH, et al: Acyclovir suppression of frequently recurring genital herpes: Efficacy and diminishing need during successive years of treatment. *JAMA* 1988; 260:2227–2230.

245. Craig CP, Nahmias AJ: Different patterns of neurologic involvement in herpes simplex virus types 1 and 2: Isolation of herpes simplex virus type 2 from the buffy coat of two adults with meningitis. *J Infect Dis* 1973; 127:365–372.

246. Whorton CM, Thomas DM, Denham SW: Fatal systemic herpes simplex virus type 2 infection in a healthy young woman. *South Med J* 1983; 76:81–82.

247. Guinan ME, MacCalman J, Kern ER, et al: The course of untreated recurrent genital herpes simplex infection in 27 women. *N Engl J Med* 1981; 304:759–763.

248. Silvestri DL, Corey L, Holmes KK: Ineffectiveness of topical idoxuridine in dimethyl sulfoxide for therapy for genital herpes. *JAMA* 1982; 248:953–959.

249. Harger JH, Pazin GJ, Armstrong AJ, et al: Characteristics and management of pregnancy in women with genital herpes simplex virus infection. *Am J Obstet Gynecol* 1983; 145:784–791.

250. Corey L, Nahmias AJ, Guinan ME, et al: A trial of topical acyclovir in genital herpes simplex virus infections. *N Engl J Med* 1982; 306:1313–1319.

251. Thin RN, Nabarro JM, Parker JD, et al: Topical acyclovir in the treatment of initial genital herpes. *Br J Vener Dis* 1983; 59:116–119.

252. Mindel A, Adler MW, Sutherland S, et al: Intravenous acyclovir treatment for primary genital herpes. *Lancet* 1982; 1:697–700.

253. Corey L, Fife KH, Benedetti JK, et al: Intravenous acyclovir for the treatment of primary genital herpes. *Ann Intern Med* 1983; 98:914–921.

254. Nilsen AE, Aasen T, Halsos AM, et al: Efficacy of oral acyclovir in the treatment of initial and recurrent genital herpes. *Lancet* 1982; 2:571–573.

255. Bryson YJ, Dillon M, Lovett M, et al: Treatment of first episodes of genital herpes simplex virus infection with oral acyclovir. A randomized double-blind controlled trial in normal subjects. *N Engl J Med* 1983; 308:916–920.

256. Reichman RC, Badger GJ, Mertz CJ, et al: Treatment of recurrent genital herpes simplex infections with oral acyclovir: A controlled trial. *JAMA* 1984; 251:2103–2107.

257. Reichman RC, Badger GJ, Guinan ME, et al: Topically administered acyclovir in the treatment of recurrent herpes simplex genitalis: A controlled trial. *J Infect Dis* 1983; 147:336–340.

258. Luby JP, Grann JW Jr, Alexander WJ, et al: A collaborative study of patient-initiated treatment of recurrent genital herpes with topical acyclovir or placebo. *J Infect Dis* 1984; 150:1–6.

259. Fiddian AP, Kinghorn GR, Goldmeier D, et al: Topical acyclovir in the treatment of genital herpes; a comparison with systemic therapy. *J Amtimicrob Chemother* 1983; 12(suppl):67–77.

260. Kinghorn GR, Turner EB, Barton IG, et al: Efficacy of topical acyclovir cream in first and recurrent episodes of genital herpes. *Antiviral Res* 1983; 3:291–301.

261. Eron LJ, Harvey L, Toy C, et al: Interferon in the prevention of genital herpes recurrence. *Antimicrob Agents Chemother* 1986; 30:608–610.

262. Glezerman M, Lunenfeld E, Cohen V, et al: Placebo-controlled trial of topical interferon in labial and genital herpes. *Lancet* 1988; 1:150–152.

263. Kuhls TL, Sacher J, Pineda E, et al: Suppression of recurrent genital herpes simplex virus infection with recombinant alpha 2 interferon. *J Infect Dis* 1986; 154:437–442.

264. Pazin GJ, Harger JH, Armstrong JA, et al: Leukocyte interferon

for treating first episodes of genital herpes in women. *J Infect Dis* 1987; 156:891–989.

265. Friedman-Kien AE, Klein RJ, Glaser RD, et al: Treatment of recurrent genital herpes with topical alpha interferon gel combined with nonoxynol nine. *J Am Acad Dermatol* 1986; 15:989–994.

266. Lassus A, Bergelin I, Paloranta A, et al: Efficacy of interferon and placebo in the treatment of recurrent genital herpes: A double-blind trial. *Sex Transm Dis* 1987; 14:185–190.

267. Eron LJ, Toy C, Salsitz B, et al: Therapy of genital herpes with topically applied interferon. *Antimicrob Agents Chemother* 1987; 31:1137–1139.

268. Mendelson J, Clecner B, Eiley S: Effect of recombinant interferon alpha 2 on clinical course of first episode genital herpes infection and subsequent recurrences. *Genitourin Med* 1986; 62:97–101.

269. Mattison HR, Reichman RC, Benedetti J, et al: Double-blind, placebo-controlled trial comparing long-term suppressive short-term oral acyclovir therapy for management of recurrent genital herpes. *Am J Med* 1988; 85(2A):20–25.

270. Lehrman SN, Douglas JM, Corey L, et al: Recurrent genital herpes and suppressive oral acyclovir therapy. *Ann Intern Med* 1986; 104:786–790.

271. Mindel A, Weller IVD, Faherty A, et al: Prophylactic oral acyclovir in recurrent genital herpes. *Lancet* 1984; 2:57–59.

272. Straus SE, Takiff HE, Seidlin M, et al: Suppression of frequently recurring genital herpes: A placebo-controlled double-blind trial of oral acyclovir. *N Engl J Med* 1984; 310:1545–1550.

273. Douglas JM, Critchlow C, Benedetti J, et al: A double-blind study of oral acyclovir for suppression of recurrences of genital herpes simplex virus infection. *N Engl J Med* 1984; 310:1551–1556.

274. Mindel A, Faherty A, Carney O, et al: Dosage and safety of long-term suppressive acyclovir therapy for recurrent genital herpes. *Lancet* 1988; 1:926–928.

275. Mostow SR, Mayfield JL, Marr J, et al: Suppression of recurrent genital herpes by single daily dosages of acyclovir. *Am J Med* 1988; 85(2A):30–33.

276. Gold D, Corey L: Acyclovir prophylaxis for herpes simplex virus infection. *Antimicrob Agents Chemother* 1987; 31:361–367.

277. Mertz GJ, Eron L, Kaufman R, et al: The Acyclovir Study Group: Prolonged continuous versus intermittent oral acyclovir treatment in normal adults with frequently recurring genital herpes simplex virus infection. *Am J Med* 1988; 85(2A):14–19.

277a. Straus SE, Seidlin M, Takiff HE, et al: Effect of oral acyclovir treatment on symptomatic and asymptomatic virus shedding in recurrent genital herpes. *Sex Transm Dis* 1989; 16:107–113.

278. Gill MJ, Arlette J, Buchan K: Herpes simplex virus infection of the hand. A profile of 79 cases. *Am J Med* 1988; 84:89–93.

279. Gill MJ, Arlette J, Tyrrell DL, et al: Herpes simplex virus infection of the hand: Clinical features and management. *Am J Med* 1988; 85(2A):53–56.

280. Rosato FE, Rosato EF, Plotkin SA: Herpetic paronychia: An occupational hazard of medical personnel. *N Engl J Med* 1970; 283:804–805.

281. Gill MJ, Denhollander C: DNA restriction enzyme analysis of digital and genital isolates of herpes simplex virus from three patients. *J Infect Dis* 1988; 158:242–243.

282. Glogau R, Hanna L, Jawetz E: Herpetic whitlow as part of genital virus infection. *J Infect Dis* 1977; 136:689–692.

282a. Gill MJ, Arlette J, Buchan KA: Herpes simplex virus infection of the hand. *J Am Acad Dermatol* 1990; 22:111–116

283. Gill MJ, Arlette J, Buchan K, et al: Therapy for recurrent herpetic whitlow. *Ann Intern Med* 1986; 105:631–632.

284. Quinn TC, Corey L, Chaffee RG, et al: The etiology of anorectal infections in homosexual men. *Am J Med* 1981; 71:395–406.

285. Goodell SE, Quinn TC, Mkrtichian E, et al: Herpes simplex virus proctitis in homosexual men. Clinical, sigmoidoscopic and histopathological features. *N Engl J Med* 1983; 308:868–871.

286. Samarasinghe PL, Oates JK, MacLennan IPB: Herpetic proctitis and sacral radiculomyelopathy—a hazard for homosexual men. *Br Med J* 1979; 2:365–366.

287. Sherry MK, Klainer AS, Wolff M, et al: Herpetic tracheobronchitis. *Ann Intern Med* 1988; 109:229–233.

288. Olson LC, Buescher EL, Artenstein MS, et al: Herpesvirus infections of the human central nervous system. *N Engl J Med* 1967; 277:1271–1277.

289. Adams H, Miller D: Herpes simplex encephalitis: A clinical and pathological analysis of 22 cases. *Postgrad Med J* 1973; 49:393–397.

290. Nolan DC, Lauter CB, Lerner AM: Idoxuridine in herpes simplex virus (type 1) encephalitis: Experience with 29 cases in Michigan. *Ann Intern Med* 1973; 78:243–246.

291. Whitley RJ, Soong S-J, Linneman C, et al: Herpes simplex encephalitis. *JAMA* 1982; 247:317–320.

292. Boston International Virus Study Group and the NIAID Sponsored Cooperative Antiviral Clinical Study: Failure of high dose 5-iodo-2'-deoxyuridine in the therapy of herpes simplex virus encephalitis: Evidence of unacceptable toxicity. *N Engl J Med* 1975; 292:599–603.

293. Longson MM, Bailey AS, Klapper P: Herpes encephalitis, in Waterson AT (ed): *Recent Advances in Clinical Virology*. Philadelphia, Churchill Livingstone, 1980, vol 2, pp 147–157.

294. Bale JF Jr, Perlman S: Clinical neurology, in Joynt RJ (ed): *Viral Encephalitis*. Philadelphia, Lippincott, 1988, p 43.

295. Whitley RJ, Soong SJ, Hirsch MS, et al and the NIAID Collaborative Antiviral Study Group: Herpes simplex encephalitis: Vidarabine therapy and diagnostic problems. *N Engl J Med* 1981; 304:313–318.

296. Whitley RJ, Cobbs CG, Alford CA, et al and the NIAID Collaborative Antiviral Study Group: Diseases that mimic herpes simplex encephalitis: Diagnosis, presentation and outcome. *JAMA* 1989; 262:234–239.

297. Whitley RJ: Herpes simplex virus infections of the central nervous system: A review. *Am J Med* 1988; 85:61–67.

298. Nahmias AJ, Whitley RJ, Visintine AN, et al: Herpes simplex virus encephalitis: Laboratory evaluations and their diagnostic significance. *J Infect Dis* 1982; 145:829–836.

299. Lenine DP, Lauter CB, Lerner AM: Simultaneous serum and CSF antibodies in herpes simplex virus encephalitis. *JAMA* 1978; 240:356–360.

300. Johnson RT, Olson LC, Beuscher EL: Herpes simplex virus infection of the nervous system. Problems in laboratory diagnosis. *Arch Neurol* 1968; 18:260–264.

301. Lakeman FD, Koga J, Whitley RJ: Detection of antigen to herpes simplex virus in cerebrospinal fluid from patients with herpes simplex encephalitis. *J Infect Dis* 1987; 155:1172–1178.

302. Kahlon J, Chatterjee S, Lakeman FD, et al: Detection of antibodies to herpes simplex virus in the cerebrospinal fluid of patients with herpes simplex encephalitis. *J Infect Dis* 1987; 155:38–44.

302a. Rowley AH, Whitley RJ, Lakeman FD, et al: Rapid detection of herpes-simplex-virus DNA in cerebrospinal fluid of patients with herpes simplex encephalitis. *Lancet* 1990; 335:440–441.

303. Barza M, Pauker SG: The decision to biopsy, treat or wait in suspected herpes encephalitis. *Ann Intern Med* 1980; 92:641–649.

304. Braun P: The clinical management of suspected herpes virus encephalitis. A decision-analytic view. *Am J Med* 1980; 69:895–902.

305. Fishman RA: No, brain biopsy need not be done in every patient suspected of having herpes simplex encephalitis. *Arch Neurol* 1987; 44:1291–1292.

306. Hanley DF, Johnson RT, Whitley RJ: Yes, brain biopsy should be a prerequisite for herpes simplex encephalitis treatment. *Arch Neurol* 1987; 44:1289–1290.

307. Whitley RJ, Alford CA, Hirsch MS, et al and the NIAID Collaborative Antiviral Study Group: Vidarabine versus acyclovir

therapy in herpes simplex encephalitis. *N Engl J Med* 1986; 314:144–149.

308. Skoldenberg B, Alestig K, Burman L, et al: Acyclovir versus vidarabine in herpes simplex encephalitis. *Lancet* 1984; 2:707–711.

309. Whitley RJ: Herpes simplex virus infections, in Remington JS, Klein JO (eds): *Infections of the Fetus and Newborn,* ed 3. Philadelphia, Saunders, 1990; pp 282–305.

310. Sullivan-Bolyai JZ, Fife KH, Jacobs RF, et al: Disseminated neonatal herpes simplex virus type 1 from a maternal breast lesion. *Pediatrics* 1983; 71:455–457.

311. Linnemann CC Jr, Light IJ, Buchman TG, et al: Transmission of herpes simplex virus type 1 in a nursery for the newborn: Identification of viral isolates by DNA "fingerprinting." *Lancet* 1978; 1:964.

312. Koskiniemi M, Happonen JM, Jarvenpaa AL, et al: Neonatal herpes simplex virus infection: A report of 43 patients. *Pediatr Infect Dis J* 1989; 8:30–35.

313. Brown ZA, Vontver LA, Benedetti J, et al: Effects on infants of a first episode of genital herpes during pregnancy. *N Engl J Med* 1987; 317:1246–1251.

314. Prober CG, Hensleigh PA, Boucher FD, et al: Use of routine viral cultures at delivery to identify neonates exposed to herpes simplex virus. *N Engl J Med* 1988; 318:887–891.

315. Prober CG, Sullender WM, Yasukawa LL, et al: Low risk of herpes simplex virus infections in neonates exposed to the virus at the time of vaginal delivery to mothers with recurrent genital herpes simplex virus infections. *N Engl J Med* 1987; 316:240–244.

316. Arvin AM, Hensleigh PA, Prober CG, et al: Failure of antepartum maternal cultures to predict the infant's risk of exposure to herpes simplex virus at delivery. *N Engl J Med* 1986; 315:796–800.

316a. Stone KM, Brooks CA, Guinan ME, et al: National surveillance for neonatal herpes simplex virus infections. *Sex Transm Dis* 1989; 16:152–156.

317. Whitley RJ, Nahmias AJ, Visintine AM, et al: The natural history of herpes simplex virus infection of mother and newborn. *Pediatrics* 1980; 66:489–494.

318. Stagno S, Whitley RJ: Herpes virus infections of pregnancy; part II: Herpes simplex virus and varicella-zoster virus infections. *N Engl J Med* 1985; 313:1327–1330.

319. Whitley RJ, Corey L, Arvin A, et al: Changing presentation of herpes simplex virus infection in neonates. *J Infect Dis* 1988; 158:109–116.

319a. Whitley RJ: Natural history and pathogenesis of neonatal herpes simplex virus infections. *Ann NY Acad Sci* 1988; 549:103–116.

320. Whitley RJ, Nahmias AJ, Soong S-J, et al: Vidarabine therapy of neonatal herpes simplex virus infection. *Pediatrics* 1980; 66:495–501.

321. Skoldenberg B, Jeansson S: Herpes simplex virus type 2 in acute aseptic meningitis. *Br Med J* 1973; 2:611.

322. Muller SA, Herrmann EC Jr, Winkelmann RK: Herpes simplex infections in hematologic malignancies. *Am J Med* 1972; 52:102–114.

323. Oxman MN: Herpes stomatitis, in Braude AI, Davis CE, Fierer J (eds): *Medical Microbiology and Infectious Diseases.* Philadelphia, Saunders, 1981, pp 860–879.

324. Naraqi S, Jackson GG, Jonasson AM: Viremia with herpes simplex type 1 in adults. Four nonfatal cases, one with features of chicken pox. *Ann Intern Med* 1976; 85:165–169.

325. Buss DH, Scharyj M: Herpesvirus infection of the esophagus and other visceral organs in adults. *Am J Med* 1979; 66:457–462.

326. Ramsey PG, Fife KH, Hackman RC, et al: Herpes simplex virus pneumonia. Clinical virologic and pathologic features in 20 patients. *Ann Intern Med* 1982; 97:813–820.

327. Chase RA, Pottage JC Jr, Haber MH, et al: Herpes simplex viral hepatitis in adults: Two case reports and review of the literature. *Rev Infect Dis* 1987; 9:329–333.

328. Buss DH, Scharyj M, White DR: Visceral herpesvirus infec-

tions in leukemic patients receiving cytarabine. *JAMA* 1980; 243:1903–1905.

329. Nash G, Ross JS: Herpetic esophagitis. A common cause of esophageal ulceration. *Hum Pathol* 1974; 5:339–345.

330. Greenberg MS, Friedman H, Cohen SG, et al: A comparative study of herpes simplex infections in renal transplant and leukemic patients. *J Infect Dis* 1987; 156:280–287.

331. Cooper MD, Lawdon AR III: Immune deficiency diseases, in Braunwald E, Isselbacher KJ, Petersdorf RG (eds): *Harrison's Principles of Internal Medicine,* ed 11. New York, McGraw-Hill, 1987, pp 1385–1391.

332. Norris SA, Kessler HA, Fife KH: Severe, progressive herpetic whitlow caused by an acyclovir-resistant virus in a patient with AIDS. *J Infect Dis* 1988; 157:209–210.

333. Siegal FP, Lopez C, Hammer GS, et al: Severe acquired immunodeficiency in male homosexuals, manifested by chronic perianal ulcerative herpes simplex lesions. *N Engl J Med* 1981; 305:1439–1444.

334. Foley FD, Major KA, Greenwald MC, et al: Herpesvirus infection in burned patients. *N Engl J Med* 1970; 282:652–656.

335. Pugh RCB, Dudgeon JA, Bodian M: Kaposi's varicelliform eruption (eczema herpeticum) with typical and atypical visceral necrosis. *J Pathol Bacteriol* 1955; 69:67.

336. Hazen PG, Eppes RB: Eczema herpeticum caused by herpesvirus type 2—A case in a patient with Darier disease. *Arch Dermatol* 1977; 113:1085.

337. Orenstein JM, Castadot MJ, Wilens SL: Fatal herpes hepatitis associated with pemphigus vulgaris and steroids in an adult. *Hum Pathol* 1974; 5:489.

338. Wade JC, Newton B, MacLaren C, et al: Intravenous acyclovir to treat mucocutaneous herpes simplex virus infection after marrow transplantation. A double-blind trial. *Ann Intern Med* 1982; 96:265–270.

339. Straus SE, Smith HA, Brickman C, et al: Acyclovir for chronic mucocutaneous herpes simplex virus infection in immunosuppressed patients. *Ann Intern Med* 1982; 96:270–277.

340. Cupps TR, Straus SE, Waldmann TA: Successful treatment with acyclovir of an immunodeficient patient infected simultaneously with herpesviruses. *Am J Med* 1981; 70:882–886.

341. Saral R, Burns WH, Laskin OL, et al: Acyclovir prophylaxis of herpes-simplex-virus infections. A randomized, double-blind, controlled trial in bone-marrow-transplant recipients. *N Engl J Med* 1981; 305:63–68.

342. Saral R: Management of mucocutaneous herpes simplex virus infections in immunocompromised patients. *Am J Med* 1988; 85(2A):57–60.

342a. Englund JA, Zimmerman ME, Swierkosz EM, et al: Herpes simplex virus resistant to acyclovir: A study in a tertiary care center. *Ann Intern Med* 1990; 112:416–422.

342b. Sacks SL, Wanklin RJ, Reece DE, et al: Progressive esophagitis from acyclovir-resistant herpex simplex: Clinical roles for DNA polymerase mutants and viral heterogeneity? *Ann Intern Med* 1989; 111:893–899.

342c. Erlich KS, Mills J, Chatis P, et al: Acyclovir-resistant herpes simplex virus infections in patients with the acquired immunodeficiency syndrome. *N Engl J Med* 1989; 320:293–296.

343. Pavan-Langston D: Ocular antiviral therapy. *Int Ophthalmol Clin* 1980; 20:149–155.

344. McDonnell PJ, Green WR: Keratitis, in Mandell GL, Douglas RG Jr, Bennett JE (eds): *Principles and Practices of Infectious Diseases.* New York, Churchill Livingstone, 1990, pp 981–987.

345. Trifluridine (Viroptic) for herpetic keratitis. *Med Lett Drugs Ther* 1980; 22:46–48.

346. Adour KK, Bell DN, Hilsinger RL: Herpes simplex virus in idiopathic facial paralysis (Bell palsy). *JAMA* 1975; 233:527–530.

347. Finelli PF: Herpes simplex virus and the human nervous system: Current concepts and review. *Milit Med* 1975; 140:765–771.

348. Krohel GB, Richardson JR, Farrell DF: Herpes simplex neuropathy. *Neurology* 1976; 26:596–597.

349. Catalano LW: *Herpesvirus hominis* antibody in multiple scle-

rosis and amyotrophic lateral sclerosis. *Neurology* 1972; 22:473–478.

350. Warren KG, Gilden DH, Brown SM, et al: Isolation of herpes simplex virus from human trigeminal ganglia, including ganglia from one patient with multiple sclerosis. *Lancet* 1977; 2:637–639.

351. Corey L: Laboratory diagnosis of herpes simplex virus infections: Principles guiding the development of rapid diagnostic tests. *Diagn Microbiol Infect Dis* 1986; 4:111S–119S.

352. Vestergaard BF: Laboratory diagnosis of herpes viruses. *Scand J Infect Dis* 1985; 47(suppl):22–32.

353. Cowdry EV: Problem of intranuclear inclusion in virus disease. *Arch Pathol* 1934; 18:527–542.

354. Naib ZM, Nahmias AJ, Josey WE: Cytology and histopathology of cervical herpes simplex infection. *Cancer* 1966; 19:1026–1031.

355. Rubin SJ, Wende RD, Rawls WE: Direct immunofluorescence test for the diagnosis of genital herpes virus infections. *Appl Microbiol* 1973; 26:373–375.

356. Volpi A, Lakeman AD, Pereira L, et al: Monoclonal antibodies for rapid diagnosis and typing of genital herpes infections during pregnancy. *Am J Obstet Gynecol* 1983; 146:813–815.

357. Stewart JA, Herrmann KL: Herpes simplex virus, in Rose NR, Friedman H (eds): *Manual of Clinical Immunology, ed 2.* Washington, DC, American Society for Microbiology, 1980, pp 614–619.

358. Solomon AR: New diagnostic tests for herpes simplex and varicella zoster infections. *J Am Acad Dermatol* 1988; 18:218–221.

359. Rawls WE, Iwamoto K, Adams E, et al: Measurement of antibodies to herpesvirus types 1 and 2 in human sera. *J Immunol* 1970; 104:599–606.

360. Ashley R, Benedetti J, Corey L: Humoral immune response to HSV-1 and HSV-2 viral proteins in patients with primary genital herpes. *J Med Virol* 1985; 17:153–166.

361. Drew WL, Rawls WE: Herpes simplex virus, in Lennette EH, Balows A, Hausler WJ, et al (eds): *Manual of Clinical Microbiology.* American Society of Microbiology, 1985, pp 705–710.

362. Callihan DR, Menegus MA: Rapid detection of herpes simplex virus in clinical specimens using human embryonic lung fibroblasts and primary rabbit kidney cell cultures. *J Clin Microbiol* 1984; 19:563–565.

363. Pauls FP, Dowdle WR: A serologic study of *Herpesvirus hominis* strains by microneutralization tests. *J Immunol* 1967; 98:941–947.

364. Hanna L, Keshishyan H, Jawetz F, et al: Diagnosis of *Herpesvirus hominis* infections in a general hospital laboratory. *J Clin Microbiol* 1975; 1:318–323.

365. Richman DD, Cleveland PH, Oxman MN: A rapid enzyme immunofiltration technique using monoclonal antibodies to serotype herpes simplex virus. *J Med Virol* 1982; 9:299–305.

366. Forghani B, Schmidt NJ, Lennette EH: Solid phase radioimmunoassay for identification of *Herpesvirus hominis* types 1 and 2 from clinical materials. *Appl Microbiol* 1974; 28:661–667.

367. Benjamin DR: Rapid typing of herpes simplex virus strains using the direct immunoperoxidase method. *Appl Microbiol* 1974; 28:568–571.

368. Brautigam AR, Richman DD, Oxman MN: Rapid typing of herpes simplex virus isolates by deoxyribonucleic acid: Deoxyribonucleic acid hybridization. *J Clin Microbiol* 1980; 12:226–234.

369. Arens MQ, Swierkosz EM: Simplified method for typing herpes simplex virus by restriction endonuclease analysis. *J Clin Microbiol* 1983; 17:548–551.

370. Peterson EM, Aarnaes SL, Byran RN, et al: Typing of herpes simplex virus with synthetic DNA probes. *J Infect Dis* 1986; 153:757–762.

371. Schuster V, Matz B, Wiegand H, et al: Nucleic acid hybridization for detection of herpesviruses in clinical specimens. *J Med Virol* 1986; 19:277–286.

372. Goldstein LC, Corey L, McDougall JK, et al: Monoclonal anti-

bodies to herpes simplex viruses: Use in antigenic typing and rapid diagnosis. *J Infect Dis* 1983; 147:829–837.

373. Redfield DC, Richman DD, Albanil S, et al: Detection of herpes simplex virus in clinical specimens by DNA hybridization. *Diagn Microbiol Infect Dis* 1983; 1:117–128.

374. Grossman JH: Diagnostic techniques of evaluating herpes simplex virus infections: Laboratory considerations. *J Reprod Med* 1986; 31:384–389.

375. Friedman HM: Laboratory diagnosis of herpes viruses in the immunocompromised host. *Adv Exp Med Biol* 1986; 202:83–93.

376. Nasemann TH: *Viral Disease of the Skin, Mucous Membranes, and Genitals.* Philadelphia, Saunders, 1977, pp 117–119.

377. Meignier B, Longnecker R, Mavromara-Nazos P, et al: Virulence and establishment of latency by genetically engineered deletion mutants of herpes simplex virus 1. *Virology* 1988; 62:251–254.

378. Ashley R, Mertz G, Clark H, et al: Humoral immune response to herpes simplex virus type 2 glycoproteins in patients receiving a glycoprotein subunit vaccine. *J Virol* 1985; 56:475–481.

379. Cappel R, Sprecher S, Rickaert F, et al: Immune response to a DNA free herpes simplex vaccine in man. *Arch Virol* 1982; 73:61–67.

380. Kitces EN, Morahan PS, Tew JG, et al: Protection from oral herpes simplex virus infection by a nucleic acid-free virus vaccine. *Infect Immun* 1977; 16:955–960.

381. Klein RJ, Burmovici-Klein E, Moser H, et al: Efficacy of a virion envelope herpes simplex virus vaccine against experimental skin infections in hairless mice. *Arch Virol* 1981; 68:73–80.

382. Mertz GJ, Peterman G, Ashley R, et al: Herpes simplex virus type-2 glycoprotein-subunit vaccine: Tolerance and humoral and cellular responses in humans. *J Infect Dis* 1984; 150:242–249.

383. Fujinaga S, Sugano T, Matsumoto Y, et al: Antiviral activities of human monoclonal antibodies to herpes simplex virus. *J Infect Dis* 1987; 155:45–53.

384. Kapoor AK, Nash AA, Wildy P, et al: Pathogenesis of herpes simplex virus in congenitally athymic mice: the relative roles of cell-mediated and humoral immunity. *J Gen Virol* 1982; 60:225–233.

385. Kumel G, Kaerner HC, Levine M, et al: Passive immune protection by herpes simplex virus–specific monoclonal antibodies and monoclonal antibody–resistant mutants altered in pathogenicity. *J Virol* 1985; 56:930–937.

386. Rector JT, Lausch RN, Oakes JE: Identification of infected cell-specific monoclonal antibodies and their role in host resistance to ocular herpes simplex virus type 1 infection. *J Gen Virol* 1984; 65:657–661.

387. Simmons A, Nash AA: Role of antibody in primary and recurrent herpes simplex virus infection. *J Virol* 1985; 53:944–948.

388. Berman PW, Gregory T, Crase D, et al: Protection from genital herpes simplex virus type 2 infection by vaccination with cloned type 1 glycoprotein D. *Science* 1985; 227:1490–1492.

389. Dix RD, Mills J: Acute and latent herpes simplex virus neurological disease in mice immunized with purified virus-specific glycoproteins gB or gD. *J Med Virol* 1985; 17:9–18.

390. Lasky LA, Dowbenko D, Simonsen CC, et al: Protection of mice from lethal herpes simplex virus infection by vaccination with a secreted form of cloned glycoprotein D. *Biotechnology* 1984; 2:527–532.

391. Roberts PL, Duncan BE, Raybould TJG, et al: Purification of herpes simplex virus glycoproteins B and C using monoclonal antibodies and their ability to protect mice against lethal challenge. *J Gen Virol* 1985; 66:1073–1085.

392. Paoletti E, Lipinskas BR, Samsonoff C, et al: Construction of live vaccines using genetically engineered poxvirus: biological activity of vaccinia virus recombinants expressing the hepatitis B virus surface antigen and the herpes simplex virus glycoprotein D. *Proc Natl Acad Sci USA* 1984; 81:193–197.

393. Rooney JF, Wohlenberg C, Cremer KJ, et al: Immunization with a vaccinia virus recombinant expressing herpes simplex virus type 1 glycoprotein D: Long-term protection and effect of

revaccination. *J Virol* 1988; 62:1530–1534.

394. Cohen GH, Long D, Eisenberg RJ: Synthesis and processing of glycoproteins gD and gC of herpes simplex virus type 1. *J Virol* 1980; 36:429–439.

395. Eisenberg RJ, Cerini CP, Heilman CJ, et al: Synthetic glycoprotein D-related peptides protect mice against herpes simplex virus challenge. *J Virol* 1985; 56:1014–1017.

396. Stanberry LR, Bernstein LI, Burke RL, et al: Vaccination with recombinant herpesvirus glycoproteins: protection against initial and recurrent genital herpes. *J Infect Dis* 1987; 155:914–920.

397. Mertz GJ, Ashley R, Burke RL, et al: Double-blind, placebo-controlled trial of a herpes simplex virus type 2 glycoprotein vaccine in persons at high risk for genital herpes infection. *J Infect Dis* 1990; 161:653–660.

35

Varicella-Zoster Virus

Victoria Schauf
Richard J. Salo

Chickenpox was recognized rarely in Europe until the sixteenth century. The term "chickenpox" first appeared in the medical literature of the seventeenth century. The name is believed to derive from a resemblance of the vesicles of chickenpox to chickpeas,[1] or from the use of "chicken" to designate a child.[2] However, J.H. Scott-Wilson's child dubbed the disease "itching-pox," and the term may, in fact, derive from the old English *gican* (itch).[3]

An English physician, William Heberden, in 1767, distinguished chickenpox, "so insignificant an illness that an acquaintance with it is not of much use of its own sake" from smallpox, "with which it may otherwise be confounded, and so deceive the persons, who have had it, into a false security, which may prevent them either from keeping out of the way of the small-pox, or from being inoculated."[4] Distinguishing chickenpox (varicella) from smallpox (variola) continued to be of importance until smallpox was eradicated.

Chickenpox results from primary varicella-zoster virus (VZV) infection. A single chickenpox infection confers lifelong immunity to chickenpox in the immunologically normal person. VZV persists in a latent form and, upon reactivation, causes herpes zoster (shingles). Although usually mild and self-limited, both primary varicella-zoster infection and reactivation may be severe in immunocompromised individuals, including those with malignancies or organ transplants. VZV infection has emerged as an important problem due to improved control of many other childhood infections and due to increased duration of life in both normal and immunocompromised individuals.

Control of chickenpox and zoster would be highly desirable in view of the morbidity and mortality VZV infections and their complications produce. Immunocompromised individuals, pregnant women, newborn babies, and the elderly are especially vulnerable to these complications. The disease may be quite severe, even in normal adults.

STRUCTURE AND BIOLOGY

The etiologic agent of chickenpox and shingles is VSV.[5] Viruses isolated from vesicles of chickenpox and from shingles are indistinguishable in morphology, antigenic composition,[6] restriction endonuclease cleavage patterns,[7] and cytopathologic[8] and histopathologic effects. Additionally, herpes zoster vesicle fluid produces varicella in exposed susceptibles.

VZV is classified as a herpes virus because of its morphology (Figure 35–1),[9] its DNA, and its production in infected cells of characteristic eosinophilic (type A) intranuclear inclusions.[8] The virion consists of an irregular outer envelope, a nucleocapsid, and

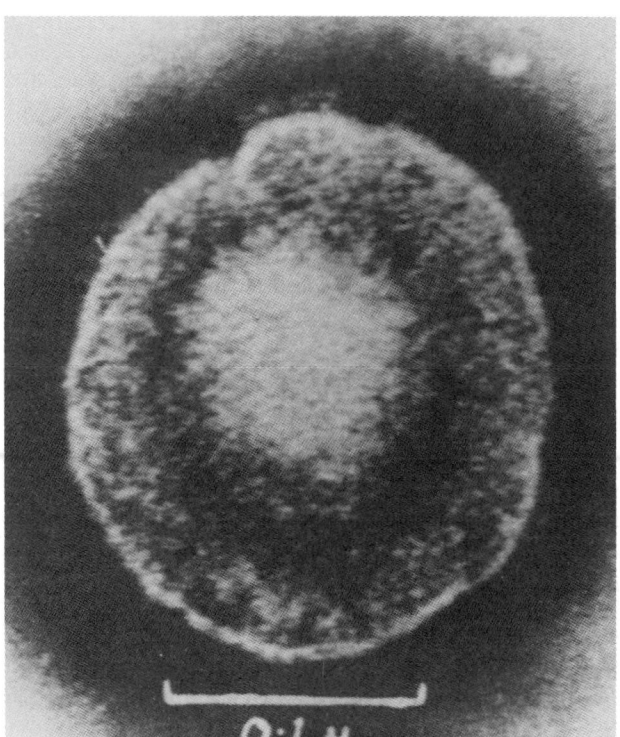

Figure 35–1. The virion of varicella-zoster virus. (From Almeida JD, et al: Morphology of varicella (chicken pox) virus. *Virology* 1962; 16:353–355. Used by permission.)

a core. Amorphous protein, the tegument, is present between the envelope and the nucleocapsid. The virions vary in size, averaging 200 nm in diameter. The capsid is composed of 162 capsomers, as in the case of herpes simplex virus. VZV cannot be distinguised morphologically from herpes simplex virus. However, in the past, electron microscopic identification of virus in vesicle fluid was used to distinguish chickenpox from smallpox or vaccinia caused by the unrelated pox group of viruses. There is a single VZV serotype; however, different isolates possess unique restriction endonuclease cleavage patterns.[10] VZV and herpes simplex virus are antigenically similar[11, 12] and their DNAs hybridize to each other.[13]

The DNA of the VZV genome is linear, double-stranded, and 80×10^6 daltons in size.[14] In agreement with this electron microscopic study, the electrophoretic migration rates of restriction endonuclease fragments indicate the genome is 72 to 80×10^6 daltons.[15] As with some other herpesviruses, the viral DNA by itself can infect tissue culture cells.[14] As determined by sequence analysis, there are 124,884 base pairs and 70 genes distributed equally between the two DNA strands.[16] At least 58 transcripts ranging in size from approximately 0.8 to 6.5×10^6 daltons have been identified and mapped by northern blot analysis of total RNA from virus-infected cells.[17] Neither the gene specificity nor the regulation of these transcripts is known. It is assumed that temporal regulation occurs as in herpes simplex virus transcription.

Numerous VZV proteins, both structural and nonstructural, have been identified and characterized. The virion contains 30 to 33 proteins ranging in size from 16,000 to 280,000 daltons.[18–20]

The reported differences in size and number of proteins are probably due to the difficulty of preparing high-titered purified virus, variation in electrophoretic conditions, and the heterogeneity of the glycosylated proteins. A consensus nomenclature for the glycoprotein genes and their glycosylated products present in the envelope of virions has been developed.[21] To avoid confusion with preexisting nomenclatures of either VZV or herpes simplex virus glycoproteins, the glycoprotein genes are designated by Roman numerals as gpI through gpV. Specific glycoproteins are identified according to molecular weights ($\times 10^{-3}$), for example, gpI(92) is a 92×10^3–dalton glycoprotein product of the gpI gene. The gpI, gpII, and gpIII glycoproteins are on the outer surface of the membrane of infected cells,[22] and the gpI group of glycoproteins is more abundant in the virion envelope than is gpII or gpIII.[23] The glycoproteins of gpIV have been identified also[24]; however, the glycoprotein of gpV has not.[21] In a recent review, the synthesis, molecular weight, and reactivity of these glycoproteins are discussed in detail.[25]

Other viral genes and gene products characterized include thymidine kinase,[26–29] DNA polymerase,[30] DNA binding proteins,[31, 32] and a putative VZV immediate-early gene.[33] Knowledge of viral proteins may have implications for antiviral chemotherapy. The kinetic behavior of the virus-induced thymidine kinase differs from the host enzyme, raising the possibility of developing antiviral agents based on the unique viral thymidine kinase.[34] The VZV thymidine kinase also differs from the corresponding enzyme in herpes simplex virus.[34] Thus, antiviral agents binding to viral thymidine kinase could differ in their activities against various herpesviruses. Restriction endonuclease analysis of the DNA of VZV isolates has shown that epidemiologically distinct isolates are unique.[35] This technique is a powerful tool which has been applied epidemiologically in confirming the identity of VZV from varicella and zoster,[7] and in distinguishing vaccine from wild-type virus.[36, 37]

VZV can be propagated in human embryonic tissue culture cells including fibroblasts, kidney cells, or amnion cells. Under certain laboratory conditions, VZV produces persistent infection.[38] Although some nonhuman primate cell cultures are also susceptible to VZV infection, VZV replicates most efficiently in human embryonic tissue.[39] In these cells, after two to 28 days of incubation, VZV produces a cytopathic effect (CPE) characterized by syncytia formation resulting in plaques that extend peripherally to involve the entire culture. Chromosomal breakage has been observed in leukocytes from children with chickenpox[40] and in VZV-infected cell cultures.[41] Infectious particles are almost entirely cell-associated. As a result of this, substantial amounts of purified cell-free virus are not readily available for analysis and characterization of virions and viral replication. The best yields after sonication of infected cells physically dislodged from culture flasks are 10^4 to 10^5 infectious units per milliliter.[42–44] The instability of VZV also adds to the difficulty of obtaining substantial amounts of infectious virus.

VZV persists following primary infection. The virus has been isolated during herpes zoster from thoracic ganglia by cocultivation with Vero cells.[45] However, attempts to demonstrate latency by recovering VZV from ganglia in the absence of clinical herpes zoster have been negative so far.[46] By using radioactive nucleic acid probes, VZV DNA has been detected in normal thoracic ganglia[47] and in normal trigeminal ganglia.[48] VZV RNA has been detected also in normal trigeminal ganglia.[49, 50] Virus isolated from zoster lesions has the same restriction endonuclease cleavage patterns as earlier isolates from the same patient during primary chickenpox, supporting the thesis that zoster results from latent viral reactivation.[7] The frequency of varicella-zoster disease in immunocompromised patients with renal transplants or malignancy is indirect evidence of viral persistence,[51] which, with reactivation can result in severe or fatal infection.

Improved understanding of VZV pathogenesis, prevention, and treatment would be possible if an adequate animal model system were available. There are a number of simian viruses that produce varicella-like exanthems in subhuman primates, and they are serologically related to VZV and herpes simplex viruses.[52] Although gorillas may become infected with VZV,[53] constraints on the use of gorillas preclude such animals as an animal model system. Weanling guinea pigs have been infected with VZV resulting in nasopharyngeal viral replication, viremia, animal-to-animal transmission, and seroconversion.[54] Exanthems are not apparent in such animals. However, congenitally hairless Hartley guinea pigs infected with VZV do develop a papular, often erythematous, exanthem.[55] These investigators suggest that the lower body temperature, 39.3°C versus 38.3°C, is more permissive for virus replication. This animal model system may prove useful. At this time, the powerful new tools of contemporary biology will continue to provide a better understanding of the epidemiology, pathogenesis, laboratory diagnosis, prevention, and treatment of VZV infections.

EPIDEMIOLOGY

Chickenpox

Chickenpox and shingles produce such characteristic findings that most epidemiologic studies were based on diagnosis by history or physical examination. However, the clinical history of chickenpox is not entirely accurate, with both false-negative and false-positive histories documented. Susceptibility or immunity to VZV infection can best be determined by the fluorescent antibody to membrane antigen (FAMA) technique. In a survey of 200 healthy blood donors, Groth and associates[56] found 97.5% had antibodies by FAMA. Fewer had a history of chickenpox (65%) or complement-fixing (CF) antibody (69%), suggesting that clinical history and/or CF antibody titer are less reliable indicators of varicella immunity than is FAMA positivity.

Varicella is worldwide in distribution and endemic in cities in the United States. Surveillance data for chickenpox in the United States are based on passive reporting, which is often incomplete, with severe cases more likely to be reported than mild cases.[57] Accordingly, the reported death-to-case and encephalitis-to-case ratios may be artificially high. In the mid-1980s there were approximately 200,000 chickenpox cases per year reported with over 100 cases per 100,000 population,[58] an increase from 88 cases per 100,000 population in the previous decade. Chickenpox is greatly underreported, with an estimated 3 million cases annually in the United States.[59, 60]

In 1985 chickenpox continued to be the second most frequently reported disease in the United States.[58] The reported cases were estimated to represent about 6% of all cases. The peak incidence occurs during winter and spring. Most cases were in children, with the highest incidence observed at 5 to 9 years of age.

Chickenpox is a highly communicable disease. The attack rate for institutionalized, susceptible, FAMA–negative children is about 80%.[61] The secondary attack rate after household contact was 87% for children with a negative or unknown history of chickenpox.[62] Since the tertiary attack rate in household contacts in this study was also high (71%), it is likely that no more than 4% of childhood chickenpox is unrecognized. Therefore, individuals who do not recall having chickenpox are likely to be immune if they recall household or other close contact with chickenpox.

In the United States, 97.5% of healthy adults have serologic evidence of previous varicella-zoster infection, although only 70% of young adults give a history of having had chickenpox. In older adults, a positive history is less frequent. Since inapparent varicella is uncommon, it is likely that with increasing age people forget that they have had chickenpox.

Deaths from chickenpox dropped from approximately 100 per year or seven per 10,000 reported cases in the 1970s[57] to approximately 50 per year or two per 10,000 in 1984.[58] Although this decrease is unexplained, it is hoped that the beneficial effects of passive immunoprophylaxis and/or antiviral chemotherapy may have played a role. Although varicella deaths have decreased twofold in the last decade, measles deaths have fallen 20-fold in the same period with aggressive use of active immunization. Since chickenpox reporting is incomplete and the more severe cases are more likely to be reported, death-to-case ratios are probably overestimated.

In recent years, the highest chickenpox death-to-case ratio occurred in individuals at or over 20 years of age.[57, 59] In contrast, during the 1940s, in Massachusetts, chickenpox deaths occurred predominantly in the first year of life.[63] The death-to-case ratio remains high for infants.[59]

Reporting of encephalitis caused by chickenpox accounted for approximately 13% of all diagnosed encephalitis.[59] Chickenpox and chickenpox-associated encephalitis occur at the same rates in males and females. No race-specific differences are known.

Data from Czechosolvakia show annual winter peaks of chickenpox.[64] More cases per 100,000 population and a higher percentage of cases were reported than in the United States, presumably due to differences in the method of notification. Disease incidence was highest in children 3 to 4 years old. Local and temporal differences in age-specific incidence of chickenpox may be related to different ages of school entry or to viral interference where many other infections predominate.

In the United States, Switzerland, and Czechoslovakia, at least 90% of older children, young adults, and neonates, including low-birth-weight infants, have serologically demonstrable varicella immunity.[56, 64–66] Transplacental acquisition of maternal antibody occurs early enough in development that even 1500-g babies have 90% seropositivity.[67] Transplacental antibody disappears rapidly over the first 6 months of life.[65]

In modern years, chickenpox is a childhood disease in developed countries. In contrast, in England in 1900, almost 20% of chickenpox patients were 18 years of age or older. In Massachusetts, the proportion of cases among younger children increased from the 1940s to the 1950s.[63]

Seronegativity is much higher (19.5%) in healthy young adults in Israel.[68] Seronegativity was also more frequent in parturient women immigrants from tropical countries than in native-born parturients in New York City.[65] These reports are consistent with other experience suggesting that more adults develop chickenpox in tropical and subtropical countries than in temperate zones.[69] Because of the greater severity of chickenpox in the adult population, the impact of the disease may be increased in regions where many cases occur in adults.[70]

A nurse who emigrated from the tropics to Britain developed varicella on exposure to a patient with shingles.[71] Adult-onset varicella was more frequent in Chicago health care workers born in Asia than in those born in the United States.[72] Maretić and Cooray[70] also noted that chickenpox is an occupational disease of health care workers in Ceylon. Although varicella-zoster infection is worldwide, regional differences in susceptibility exist. Patterns in age-related susceptibility might be determined by urbanization, sanitation, and/or the presence of other competing infections in the community.

Exposures on pediatric wards may involve large numbers of susceptibles. Nosocomial chickenpox occurred in 13 of 24 susceptible children hospitalized with a child with varicella pneumonia treated with mechanical ventilation in a positive-air-pressure isolation room.[73] Exposure to chickenpox in the hospital is life-threatening in immunosuppressed children. Outbreaks of varicella-zoster infection have also occurred in hospitalized geriatric and cancer patients.[74, 75] Nosocomial spread in newborn nurseries is infrequent because of a high degree of passive immunity and because of low rates of transmission from infant to infant and mother to infant.[76]

Screening hospital personnel with no history of chickenpox for varicella immunity by FAMA or skin test allows measures to prevent nosocomial spread to be implemented (see Prevention). Such measures are likely to be cost-effective.[77, 78]

Zoster

Herpes zoster does not show a seasonal prevalence, nor do epidemics of zoster occur. In a community-based study in Rochester, Minnesota, during 1945–1959, the incidence of herpes zoster was 1.3 per 1000 population.[79] The incidence increased markedly with age and, also, over the 15-year observation period. In private practices in Great Britain, the annual incidence was three to five cases per 1000.[80] About 20% of the adult population have experienced herpes zoster. Most patients give no history of contact with either zoster or chickenpox. Contact with zoster in nonimmune persons may result in varicella. The reverse does not usually occur.

There is no sexual or racial predilection for herpes zoster. In contrast to chickenpox, the incidence of shingles increases with advancing age. The severity of shingles also increases with increasing age.

Analyses of restriction endonuclease fragments of VZV DNA show that clinical shingles is the manifestation of a single VZV strain, in that cleavage patterns from isolates from different locations from each patient were the same[81, 82]; the VZV strain that caused chickenpox in a child with Wiskott-Aldrich syndrome caused zoster 3 months later[7]; and the vaccine strain reemerged causing zoster in a child with acute lymphocytic leukemia 21 months after immunization.[37] In a single incident, different restriction enzyme patterns were observed from a lesion and the corresponding spinal ganglion of an individual, suggesting multiple strains of VZV can

be present in the same human host.[83] More than one attack of herpes zoster seems possible, although virologic documentation of such recurrences is lacking.[84] VZV can survive without a supply of people susceptible to chickenpox and without a known animal reservoir. Viral latency and reactivation as herpes zoster allows survival of the virus and spread in a population under such conditions.

PATHOGENESIS

Infection

Chickenpox is highly communicable from one to four days before until five days after the onset of rash. New vesicle formation and viral shedding persist longer in immunocompromised patients with chickenpox or shingles, thus increasing the period of communicability. Crusted lesions and scabs are not infectious. Chickenpox develops ten to 23 days after exposure of a susceptible person to chickenpox or herpes zoster, with a usual incubation period of 13 to 17 days. The incubation period of congenital varicella may be shorter. Chickenpox is transmitted by direct contact. Although VZV can be recovered with regularity only from vesicles, airborne transmission has been documented.[73]

The pathogenesis of varicella is believed to resemble that described by Fenner for mousepox, which has been used as a model for acute exanthematous infections.[85] During the incubation period, viral replication occurs in the mucosa and lymph nodes of the head and neck with a primary viremia between days 4 and 6. About 1 week after the primary viremia, viral replication in viscera leads to a secondary viremia which infects the skin and results in the appearance of the vesicular skin rash. It is thought that CNS infection may result from local spread or either viremia.

Herpes zoster is a manifestation of reactivation of latent VZV and is not a manifestation of primary infection. Herpes zoster may be somewhat less communicable than chickenpox since the respiratory tract is rarely involved and since zoster patients have partial immunity to the virus. Herpes zoster exposure does not result in herpes zoster. Exposure to herpes zoster poses a considerable threat of significant VZV infection to nonimmune adults and immunocompromised patients of all ages.

Ordinarily, chickenpox is mild and self-limited, even in adults who often experience a more severe illness than children. A one- or two-day prodrome of malaise and fever occurs more often in adults than children. The lesions of varicella are the presumed result of a viremia. Circulating mononuclear cell infection is responsible for the viremia.[86] The first skin lesions appear on the scalp and face and rapidly progress from macule to papule to vesicle to scab. The intraepidermal vesicles contain VZV and multinucleated giant cells with eosinophilic Cowdry type A inclusion bodies. The lesions are pruritic. Characteristically, lesions of all stages of evolution are present in each involved skin area (Figure 35–2). Denuded lesions are also present as an enanthem, and form ulcers. The lesions occur in a series of three to five crops in about three days, with the lowest density peripherally. The greatest concentration is on the trunk, and the scabs fall off in about 1 week. The fever disappears with the last new lesions in uncomplicated chickenpox. Infectivity is lost when the last of the vesicles become scabs. Scarring is unusual unless secondary infection is present.

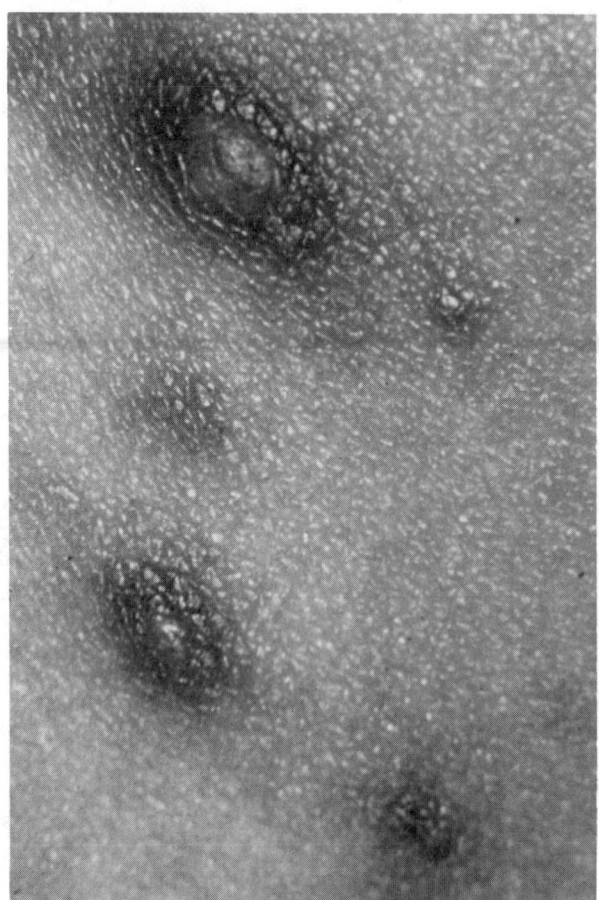

Figure 35–2. Lesions of all stages of evolution are present in each involved skin area. (Photograph courtesy of Leon LeBeau, PhD.)

The typical chickenpox exanthem may be modified in areas covered by warm clothing, diapers, bandages, and by exposure to sunlight, pressure, irritations, or other rashes including eczema.[87] In these areas, the rash erupts sooner, and intensifies, and the vesicles are relatively uniform in size and stage of development. The usual development of crops of lesions is not evident in these areas.

Although most VZV infections can be diagnosed by physical examination, occasionally laboratory confirmation is desirable. For example, lesions of herpes simplex have been observed that were umbilicated and erupted in crops with lesions in all stages present at one time.[88, 89] Most of these patients were immunocompromised. Herpes simplex infection of preexisting dermatitis or dermatosis (eczema herpeticum) can also resemble chickenpox.

In herpes zoster, it is likely that activation of VZV in a sensory ganglion results in viral passage down the axon, although it has been suggested that some cases result from reinfection.[90] A limited varicelliform or erythematous eruption is distributed unilaterally over one to three contiguous dermatomes. Trauma, irradiation, immunosuppressive medications, underlying malignancy, or waning cell-mediated immunity (CMI) may precipitate shingles; however, most outpatients with shingles do not have an associated malignancy.[80] The dermatomal distribution of zoster lesions is illustrated in Figure 35–3. In adults, a three- to four-day painful prodrome precedes the eruption of a crop of vesicles.[91] Regional lymphadenopathy is usually present. Pain and lymphadenopathy may also occur without an eruption. Headache, fever, and malaise occur occasionally. Skin of the affected dermatome may have hyperesthesia or hypoesthesia. Motor paralysis may be present. The eruption lasts up to 16 days if new lesions develop only in the first 48 hours. Continued vesiculation may result in lesions persisting for over 1 month.[92] Unlike chickenpox, the zoster eruption may leave scars. The thoracic nerves are most often involved, with cervical, trigeminal, lumbar, and sacral involvement occurring less often. The distribution pattern of zoster by frequency of attacks resembles the classical centripetal distribution of varicella.[80]

Herpes zoster may be difficult to diagnose during the preeruptive prodrome which may, on occasion, last for weeks. The characteristic eruption may not occur in some instances. Visceral pain, before the eruption, may mimic pleurisy, myocardial infarct, ulcer, peritonitis, ureteral colic, or cystitis. Genitourinary tract complaints include dysuria, lumbar pain and/or tenderness, polyuria, frequency, urinary retention, and impotence. Pyuria and hematuria may be found.

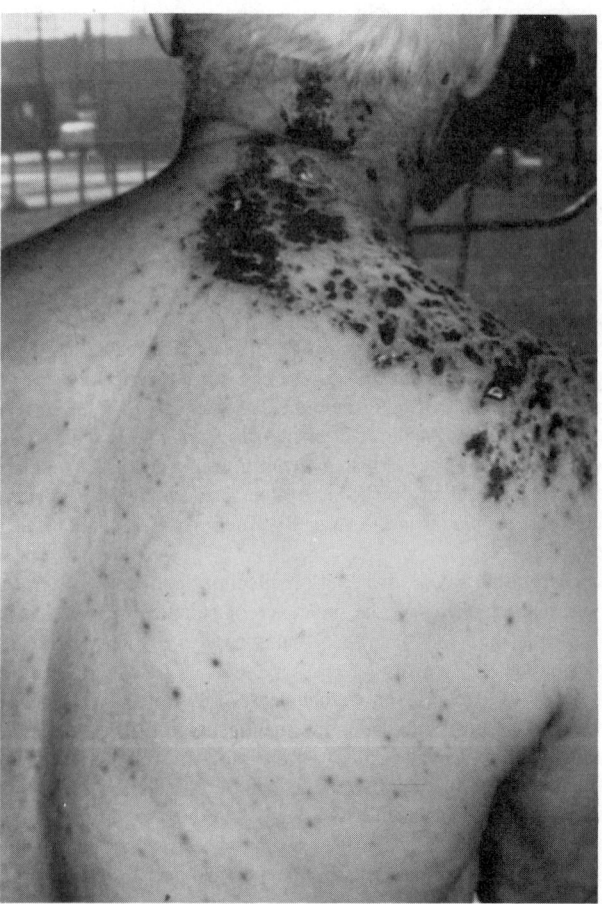

Figure 35–3. Distribution of zoster in a dermatome. (Photograph courtesy of Leon LeBeau, PhD.)

Before the onset of the vesicular eruption, generalized zoster with lymphadenitis may mimic lymphoma.[93] Zoster-type lesions have also been described with enteroviral[94] and herpes simplex infections.[95]

Although herpes zoster is uncommon in childhood, it occurs even in infants. The incidence of herpes zoster reported for Rochester, Minnesota, 1960–1981, ranged from 20 per 100,000 person-years for ages 0 to 4 years to 63 per 100,000 person-years for ages 15 to 19.[96] In infants, it is likely that zoster represents reactivation of latent virus with maternal varicella having occurred during pregnancy.[97] Childhood zoster occurs in children with early onset of chickenpox, and the relative risk for childhood zoster is increased for children experiencing chickenpox in the first year of life.[96, 98, 99] Herpes zoster is a milder disease in normal children than in adults.[98] Morbidity as judged by requirement for hospitalization or postherpetic pain was less than for adults in the same population.[96]

Patients with immune suppression and malignancy are at increased risk for herpes zoster (see below). However, patients with herpes zoster who do not have an overt malignancy are not at increased risk for subsequent cancer.[96, 100] Such patients do not require investigation or surveillance for occult cancer. Since 1984, it has been shown that the development of herpes zoster in otherwise asymptomatic individuals at high risk for acquired immunodeficiency syndrome (AIDS) may represent an early clinical sign of impending development of an immunodeficiency.[101–103] In Africa, the presence of herpes zoster in young and middle-aged patients was highly (>90%) predictive of human immunodeficiency virus (HIV) seropositivity.[104]

Immunity

Immunity to chickenpox is usually lifelong. Reactivation of the primary infection results in herpes zoster. IgG, IgM, and IgA antibodies against VZV are detectable in serum within five days after the onset of varicella.[105] After chickenpox, normal individuals have CF antibody and IgM and IgA FAMA transiently and IgG FAMA antibody persistently.[105] Dependent on the methodology and time of collecting serum samples, IgG antibodies are reactive against "early" VZV proteins synthesized before DNA synthesis,[106] approximately 14 VZV-specific polypeptides,[107] and an array of glycosylated and nonglycosylated VZV proteins.[108] The IgM antibody response during the first week after the onset of varicella is against an average of seven VZV proteins.[109] The persistent IgG antibodies are directed against VZV gpII, gpIII, and the major nucleocapsid protein.[107, 108]

VZV-specific antibody prevents or modifies primary infection, but not subclinical or clinical reinfection or reactivation.[36, 105] The mechanism whereby antibody prevents varicella infection is unknown. However, small amounts of specific antibody and nonimmune leukocytes are able to inactivate cell-associated VZV.[110] Seroconversion is not required for recovery from chickenpox or shingles. Patients with agammaglobulinemia may recover normally, and patients with cellular immunodeficiency may not survive even though they undergo seroconversion.

Cellular immunity appears to be more important than humoral immunity in controlling the progress of VZV infection. Early immunologic changes include increase in number of large lymphocytes in blood and activation of the interferon system.[111] Specific cellular immunity is acquired after primary infection.[112] Early VZV-specific lymphocyte transformation correlated inversely with the number of cutaneous lesions.[111] Lymphocyte transformation to VZV gpI, gpIII, and p 170 has been demonstrated, but is of unknown significance.[113] Human leukocytes can inactivate VZV in vitro.[114] Recovery from VZV infection is associated with development of persisting cellular immunity, even in immunocompromised patients with malignancies.[115] A VZV antigen skin test for testing delayed hypersensitivity has been developed in Japan.[116] Erythematous reactions of greater than or equal to 5 mm diameter correlate well with the presence of neutralizing antibody and resistance to disease. Individuals with negative skin tests are susceptible.

Cellular immunity is transiently decreased during acute herpes zoster.[117, 118] Specific cellular immunity is decreased in the elderly, who are also at greatest risk for herpes zoster.[119] On the other hand, VZV antibody titers do not decline with age.[120]

A rapid increase in VZV antibody titer occurs during herpes zoster.[105, 108] The antibodies are reactive against the same viral proteins as convalescent sera from individuals with chickenpox[107, 108] and against additional viral antigens.[108] Also, circulating immune complexes have been demonstrated.[121] Monocytes in early herpes zoster have decreased ability to support the proliferative response of lymphocytes to allogeneic lymphocytes (mixed lymphocyte reaction). These monocytes also have decreased survival in culture and contain herpeslike virus particles.[122]

Immunocompromised Patient

Chickenpox is of greater severity in children with congenital[123] or acquired defects in cellular immunity,[123a] with life-threatening complications such as pneumonia, encephalitis, and coagulopathy known to occur in the course of progressive varicella. Varicella was more severe in children receiving cancer therapy than in the general population or in patients who had completed therapy.[124] Viremia has been demonstrated before and during the eruption in children with malignancies and with malignant progressive varicella.[125, 126] Prolonged fever often heralds visceral dissemination or bacterial superinfection. Among 17 children in remission and off all therapy, there were no instances of visceral dissemination and no deaths.[124] In 60 patients receiving anticancer therapy, four (7%) died from disseminated varicella, varicella pneumonia, and/or encephalitis. Deaths were all in the group of children with leukemia or lymphosarcoma. Dissemination was more frequent with absolute lymphopenia, although it was not related to type or status of the malignancy. Secondary bacterial infection was common. Only one child had received specific passive prophylaxis within 72 hours of exposure.

Prophylaxis or treatment with immune serum globulin did not protect from dissemination or death. Discontinuing anticancer therapy after exposure or onset of lesions was associated with reduced frequency of dissemination. Reinstitution of therapy did not produce relapse of varicella. In a recent study, progression of varicella was reported in approximately one half of immunocompromised children.[127] Presentation often included unexplained abdominal or back pain. Inappropriate secretion of antidiuretic hormone (ADH) was also noted. There were four deaths among the 15 children with progressive varicella and none among those without progression. One instance of severe back and abdominal pain associated with coagulopathy, splenic infarction, and total functional asplenia in disseminated varicella was reported.[128]

Bone marrow transplant patients have a high mortality from varicella.[129] Varicella in children undergoing immunosuppression for renal transplant is, on occasion, severe or fatal. Severe disease characterized by prolonged fever and lesion formation, thrombocytopenia, and/or hepatitis occurred in eight of 18 children and death in one of these eight.[130] Severe varicella was likely with azathioprine therapy continued for three or more days after onset of rash. Therapy with azathioprine could be stopped for the duration of the rash without loss of the graft.

Varicella was also fatal in children receiving corticosteroid therapy for other nonmalignant diseases.[131, 132] In these children, the rash was often hemorrhagic, and visceral involvement was present. Severe varicella, death from varicella, and reactivation of varicella have been reported in children with nephrotic syndrome treated with cyclophosphamide and adrenal corticosteroids.[133] In contrast, varicella was not unusually severe in steroid-dependent children with asthma.[134]

Herpes zoster is rarely present in the usual hospital population, affecting 0.1% to 0.3% of admissions.[135] However, certain patient groups are at increased risk for herpes zoster, which may also be of increasing severity and duration and may result in dissemination. Predisposing host factors include active or advanced tumor, immunosuppressive drugs, irradiation, and/or splenectomy.[136] Splenectomy does not appear to increase the risk of shingles in patients with nonmalignant diseases.[137] Many immunocompromised patients have decreased cellular immunity to VZV antigens.[118] One fourth of 102 patients with Hodgkin's disease studied prospectively experienced zoster during a 24-month period.[90] The frequency was 8.7% among patients with other types of lymphoma and less than 2% in patients with other malignancies. In a retrospective study of 1130 patients with lymphomas treated at Stanford University from 1959 to 1969, 11.4% experienced VZV infection.[136] Most of these infections were zoster. Zoster is as frequently seen in children with cancer as in adults.[138] Cardiac,[139] bone marrow,[129] and renal transplant patients have an increased frequency of zoster. Herpes zoster is common in patients with systemic lupus erythematosus.[140]

Dissemination of herpes zoster, rare except in the immunocompromised patient, occurs in approximately one fourth of patients with Hodgkin's disease and in about one half of children receiving immunosuppressive therapy for cancer. Severe herpes zoster infections have also been described in AIDS.[141, 142] Dissemination of herpes zoster usually occurs six to ten days after the onset of the lesions in the dermatome(s). Viremia has been demonstrated before or at the onset of dissemination beyond the infected dermatome.[143] Interferon production in vesicle fluid is delayed in lesions of disseminated zoster as compared to localized zoster.[144] Dissemination of herpes zoster is also more frequent in the absence of specific immune adherence agglutination antibody.[145]

Where immunosuppressive treatment is especially aggressive, herpes zoster may persist for weeks to months.[146] Although such patients have a VZV antibody response, cellular immunity and interferon production are defective. Such patients may require a decrease in immunosuppressive medications and/or antiviral treatment (see Treatment).

Atypical disseminated zoster resembles chickenpox because the lesions are not first distributed in a dermatome. However, subclinical reinfection with chickenpox has been documented only rarely.[36] Serologic and virologic studies may be required to distinguish the entities.[36]

The mortality from disseminated zoster is less than 5%, except in marrow transplant recipients, where it is higher. Morbidity results from prolonged skin eruption, visceral involvement, CNS involvement, and postherpetic neuralgia, which may persist for months. Visceral involvement has resulted in small-bowel obstruction and in myocardial lesions. Direct CNS invasion has been demonstrated in postmortem material. In addition, renal transplant patients may experience rejection in association with herpes zoster and/or decreases in immunosuppressive regimen because of herpes zoster.[147]

Fetus and Neonate

Varicella occurs in only 5 per 10,000 pregnancies in the United States,[148] because most people have acquired immunity by adulthood. More complete surveillance than has been performed to date, or cohort studies on a national basis, are required to obtain enough affected infants to demonstrate the relative risk of congenital malformations, prematurity, or fetal death with gestational VZV infection. Limited prospective surveillance has failed to show excessive risk of these events.[149–151]

Gestational varicella is usually not a serious infection for the mother unless varicella pneumonia develops. The infection does pose a threat to the fetus and newborn infant, although the degree of risk is uncertain. Clinical or immunologic evidence of intrauterine varicella after maternal varicella was reported in approximately one fourth of prospectively studied pregnancies. One half of the infections were asymptomatic.[152] Maternal varicella pneumonia resulted in fetal or neonatal morbidity and/or mortality in all but three of 17 reported cases.[153] VZV can be transmitted congenitally and perinatally. Infections manifest in infants within ten days of birth are considered congenital in view of the ten- to 23-day incubation period of varicella. Approximately 25% of women with varicella developing in the last 2 to 3 weeks of pregnancy will have congenitally infected infants. The incubation period for congenital infection is nine to 15 days and, rarely, even less.[76]

Maternal chickenpox rash beginning four days or less before delivery may be transmitted to the fetus or baby with an attack rate of 17% and may lead to severe disseminated neonatal infection with pneumonia, skin lesions, and hemorrhages, and this has a case fatality rate of over 30%.[154] When maternal chickenpox begins five to 17 days before delivery, the infant may develop a mild varicella infection, although fatalities rarely occur. The severe course of chickenpox transmitted near term may relate to the absence of protective maternal antibody. In contrast, chickenpox acquired after the neonatal period poses little risk to the infant.

On rare occasions, infants have been identified with a constellation of congenital malformations following maternal VZV infection in the first and second trimesters of pregnancy. These infants may have low birth weight, cutaneous scars preceded by skin ulcers, hypoplasia or paralysis with muscular atrophy of a limb, rudimentary digits, convulsions, psychomotor retardation, cortical atrophy, chorioretinitis, and/or cataracts.[155] The cutaneous scars may have a dermatomal distribution. In a survey report, five of eight affected infants died. Even third-trimester varicella has been associated with scars and limb atrophy.[156] Satisfactory virologic or serologic documentation of the origin of these malformations from VZV infection is often lacking. Some affected infants had elevated serum IgM or persistent varicella-zoster antibody.

Exposure of nonimmune women to VZV poses a small risk of severe congenital anomalies. For example, in one study of 38 women with gestational varicella (11 first- and 11 second-trimester), one delivered an infant with congenital varicella syndrome.[152] Combining these first-trimester results with results of two other prospective studies gives a first-trimester risk of symptomatic intrauterine VZV infection of three of 61 infants (4.9%).[149, 152, 157]

Infants whose first manifestation of VZV infection is herpes zoster have experienced primary varicella infection in utero.[97] A suggested association between childhood leukemia and other malignancies following in utero exposure to varicella was not supported by results of a large, retrospective comparison of varicella history in mothers of cancer cases versus mothers of controls.[158]

Gestational herpes zoster seems unlikely to produce congenital infection, since women with zoster are likely to have protective antibody and to transfer it to the fetus. Additionally, viremia in such women may be absent or limited by the presence of antibody. Herpes zoster with dissemination from viremia seems likely to be able to affect the fetus. Although there are a few case reports of congenital defects in infants of mothers with herpes zoster during pregnancy, these defects have not been shown to have resulted from maternal zoster.

Complications

Although most varicella infections are mild and self-limited with fewer complications than measles, many types of complications may occur. It is estimated that there are approximately 4000 varicella hospitalizations annually.[60] Most are for children; however, adults have tenfold the risk. Since chickenpox is a systemic infection, involvement of any part of the body is possible. Varicella pneumonia is the most common complication in adults.[60] In contrast, bacterial skin infections are most frequent in preschool children. Varicella encephalitis is common after five years of age. Reye syndrome was common in childhood, but is now declining. Other reported complications have been associated with viral dissemination and related necrotic and inflammatory changes or with bacterial superinfection. These include dehydration, diarrhea, carditis, meningitis, Guillain-Barré syndrome, transverse myelitis, parotiditis, laryngitis, empyema, pulmonary embolism, arthritis, thrombocytopenia, coagulation defects, purpura, conjunctivitis, blepharitis, keratitis, orchitis, glomerulonephritis, nephrosis, gangrene, hepatitis, appendicitis, gastritis, prolonged eruption, exacerbation of underlying disease, overdose of antipruritic agents, impetigo, cellulitis, and abscesses. Intraocular and neuroophthalmologic complications include uveitis, bilateral cataract, optic neuritis, internal ophthalmoplegia, and ocular motor palsy.[159]

Although complications are more likely in adults, neonates, and in immunocompromised individuals, there is a substantial occurrence of life-threatening complications even in children with no underlying disease. Many pregnant women undergo uncomplicated VZV infection[160]; however, maternal and fetal morbidity and mortality are high if the pregnant woman develops pneumonia.[153] Deaths from varicella in the United States were mainly due to bacterial superinfections in the preantibiotic era.[161] In contrast, deaths now occur primarily from viral pneumonia, hemorrhagic processes, and disseminated viral infection in the immunocompromised host.

Varicella pneumonia is a serious complication of chickenpox in pregnant women and other adults, immunosuppressed children, and neonates. Approximately 15% of adults with chickenpox develop pulmonary involvement.[162] Many cases have no clinical evidence of pneumonia; however, in others the clinical picture may be one of extensive involvement. Pulmonary involvement is rare in normal children. In pregnancy, maternal mortality from varicella pneumonia usually ranges from 10% to 30% and even up to 45%.[76, 152, 153]

Symptoms of cough, dyspnea, tachypnea, bloody sputum, pleuritis, and chest pain occur within one to six days of onset of rash.[163] Fever, tachypnea, retractions, cyanosis, and mucosal lesions may be noted. Auscultatory findings may be absent. Heart failure may develop. Nonspecific x-ray changes include nodular infiltrates which may have a peribronchial distribution and pleural effusions. A significant diffusion defect may persist.[164] The CBC does not reliably distinguish varicella from bacterial pneumonia. Sputum cultures reflect the respiratory flora and do not necessarily allow distinction of primary varicella pneumonia from bacterial superinfection.

In varicella pneumonia, the lungs show focal necrosis, consolidation in a peribronchiolar distribution, mononuclear infiltration, and intranuclear inclusion bodies. Hyaline membranes may be present. The pleura may be involved. Cells containing intranuclear inclusion bodies may also be found in sputum.

Bacterial pneumonia is a complication of varicella which occurred more often in the preantibiotic era than now and more often in children than adults.[161, 165] The distinction between varicella and bacterial pneumonia in individuals with chickenpox is based on a composite, including the age of the patient, time of onset in relation to rash, CBC, blood cultures, and x-ray picture.

Varicella pneumonia is also to be distinguished from another pulmonary complication, pulmonary embolism. Pulmonary embolism has been reported in conjunction with varicella pneumonia,[166, 167] although the prevalence is unknown.

A variety of varicella CNS complications occur infrequently and include encephalitis, aseptic meningitis, bacterial meningitis, acute cerebellar ataxia, transverse myelitis, optic neuritis, neuromyelitis optica (Devic syndrome), Guillain-Barré syndrome, ophthalmoplegia, and Reye syndrome.[168–170] Direct viral involvement in the pathogenesis of CNS complications has been documented rarely in chickenpox. Intranuclear inclusions have been demonstrated at autopsy in the CNS of a few immunocompromised individuals with varicella encephalitis.[171] VZV has not been isolated from the CNS in chickenpox, although it has in herpes zoster. Since most patients with acute cerebellar ataxia recover, direct histologic examination of CNS for virus is not possible. However, VZV antigens have been shown in CSF cells in two children with cerebellar ataxia, and VZV antibody has been detected in CSF of varicella patients with encephalitis or transverse myelitis.[172, 173] There were approximately one to two chickenpox-encephalitis cases per 10,000 chickenpox cases in recent years.[58-60] For chickenpox encephalitis, the death-to-case ratio is highest for individuals at or over 20 years of age.[59, 63] The death-to-case ratio for all ages was 13.6% in recent years, down from 19% reported in 1962.[59, 63] Disproportionate reporting of severe cases and adult cases, and inclusion of cases with pneumonia or Reye syndrome may lead to a high estimate of mortality. However, children presenting with acute cerebellar ataxia have an excellent prognosis with no reported mortality in two series.[60, 174]

Encephalitis most often occurs three to seven days after onset of the rash.[175] However, the CNS signs may precede the rash or develop as late as 20 days after onset of the rash. Complaints include headache, malaise, vomiting, alterations of consciousness, delirium, psychosis, and seizures. Fever, meningeal signs, hypotonia, and ataxia are commonly found. Cerebellar signs are predominantly found. Increased intracranial pressure may be present. Coma, neurologic sequelae, and death occur infrequently. The CSF examination may reveal lymphocytes, polymorphonuclear leukocytes, and increased protein concentration. Pathologic findings include perivascular lymphocytic accumulations and demyelination.

Reye syndrome at one time approximated encephalitis in frequency as a complication of varicella. Among reported Reye syndrome cases, 10% to 30% were associated with varicella.[176, 177] Concomitant with restriction of aspirin use in pediatrics, Reye syndrome has declined.[178] The course of chickenpox complicated by Reye syndrome differs from uncomplicated chickenpox. Recurrent vomiting three to five days after onset of the chickenpox rash develops in Reye syndrome.[179] Signs of encephalopathy varying from subtle behavioral changes to deep coma and seizures accompany the vomiting (see Chapter 45). Hyperammonemia, hypoglycemia, and/or elevation of transaminases are found. In contrast to encephalitis, there is no inflammatory cellular response in CSF or tissues. Patients dying with Reye syndrome have marked fatty infiltration of liver and brain, and cerebral edema.

Purpura is relatively unusual in chickenpox. However, varicella was the most frequent cause of acute postinfectious thrombocytopenia in the series of Hirsch and Dameshek.[180] Chickenpox frequently is an antecedent illness in children with immune thrombocytopenia. One classification of purpuric chickenpox included (1) febrile purpura, (2) malignant chickenpox with purpura, (3) postinfectious purpura, (4) purpura fulminans, (5) anaphylactoid purpura, and (6) hemorrhagic gangrene or nephritis with secondary infection from streptococci or *Corynebacterium diphtheriae*.[181]

Febrile purpura refers to the occurrence of a hemorrhagic varicella eruption in the presence of thrombocytopenia. Purpura may be associated with mucosal bleeding. The course of febrile purpura is usually short and self-limited. However, fatal intracerebral hemorrhage has been reported.[182] Malignant chickenpox with purpura occurs in individuals with overwhelming, disseminated varicella infection involving CNS and lungs. Thrombocytopenia with skin and mucosal bleeding is present. Mortality is high. Postinfectious purpura occurring late in varicella and lasting several weeks is usually associated with thrombocytopenia.

Purpura fulminans resulting in progressive hemorrhagic gangrene, toxicity, shock, and frequently death is also associated with thrombocytopenia. The presence of thrombus formation and coagulation defects resembling the Shwartzman phenomenon indicate that purpura fulminans complicating varicella results from dissem-

inated intravascular coagulation (DIC).[183] The pathogenesis of some cases of purpuric varicella has been elucidated. VZV-like particles were demonstrated in megakaryocytes of a boy with malignant chickenpox with purpura.[184] Platelet survival was markedly decreased with associated increase in megakaryocytic mass and presence of platelet-associated antiplatelet antibody in four children with febrile purpura, suggesting that thrombocytopenia resulted from immune-mediated platelet destruction.[185] Although purpuric varicella has been said to result from DIC,[186] this mechanism has been documented only for purpura fulminans. Group A β-hemolytic streptococcal infection of varicella vesicles may on rare occasions result in hemorrhagic gangrene. The progression from cellulitis to gangrenous lesion distinguishes this complication from purpura fulminans, which starts as an ecchymotic lesion and may be associated with other bleeding manifestations.[187]

When varicella occurs in children with tuberculosis, there is a decrease in purified protein derivative (PPD) reactivity and an increase in hilar adenopathy.[188] However, in most cases the clinical course of both diseases is unaffected. An association of chickenpox and cryptosporidiosis has been reported at a day care center.[189] During concomitant outbreaks, children with a recent history of chickenpox more often had *Cryptosporidium*-positive stools than those without a recent history of chickenpox. Resolution of both tuberculosis and cryptosporidiosis is dependent on cellular immunity, which may be transiently decreased in chickenpox.

Secondary bacterial infection of varicella lesions resulting in impetigo, cellulitis, erysipelas, lymphadenitis, abscess, and gangrene is less a problem in current times than when reported by Bullowa and Wishik in 1935.[161] Nevertheless, group A β-hemolytic streptococci and *Staphylococcus aureus* superinfections of skin and soft tissue still may spread, producing septicemia, pneumonia, arthritis, osteomyelitis, and/or gangrene. Bullous varicella is an uncommon variation of chickenpox, in which bullae are interspersed with the usual varicella lesions. Epidermolytic toxin-producing staphylococci have been recovered from the bullous lesions.[190, 191]

Bacterial and nonbacterial arthritis complicate varicella in the week after onset of the rash, on rare occasions. Bacterial infection may result from hematogenous spread of bacteria from skin lesions. In the absence of bacterial infection, varicella virus may infect the joint and produce arthritis.[192] Varicella arthritis occurs in the absence of severe disseminated varicella.

Significant cardiac involvement occurs quite rarely. Pericarditis has been reported.[193] Focal inflammatory lesions were found in the myocardium of seven of 11 patients who died of other varicella complications with no clinical manifestation of cardiac disease.[194] There are several case reports of children with varicella developing supraventricular or ventricular arrhythmias, some of which were fatal. Inflammation of the myocardium and conducting system have been demonstrated. Intranuclear inclusions in the myocardium are rarely demonstrable.

Complications can occur in the gastrointestinal (GI) tract. In rural Guatemala, a chickenpox epidemic involved many children in the first years of life.[195] Acute diarrheal disease occurred simultaneously in 80% of malnourished and in only 2% of well-nourished children. In the presence of varicella and diarrhea and malnutrition, kwashiorkor occurred in five of 27 instances. Involvement of the esophagus has also been noted.

Although clinical hepatitis and/or dissemination of VZV to the liver occur rarely, subclinical hepatic changes were commonly observed in uncomplicated chickenpox.[176] The frequent elevation of alanine aminotransferase (AST) was not associated with CNS changes or any other abnormalities and did not presage the development of Reye syndrome.

A number of rare events in chickenpox have been described including hemolytic uremic syndrome, anaphylactoid purpura, and localized scleroderma.[196, 197] Because of the frequency of chickenpox, one would expect occasional coincidental associations between chickenpox and various other diseases. Whether or not these associations are related, other than by coincidence, is unknown.

In herpes zoster, complications have been divided into neurologic (neuralgia, motor, neuropathy, Guillain-Barré syndrome, and inflammatory), ocular, visceral, cutaneous, and other.[198] Prolonged postherpetic neuralgia is a serious and common sequel to shingles in the aged. Herpes zoster has been associated with some cases of acute peripheral facial palsy.[199] Sacral nerve zoster can produce constipation, urinary retention, and cystitis. Other peripheral neuropathies may occur. Flaccid paralysis is an occasional complication.[200] Encephalitis, meningitis, and myelitis occur. One form of encephalitis produces a syndrome of ophthalmic zoster and contralateral hemiplegia. Even in uncomplicated zoster, mild pleocytosis or increase in CSF protein concentration is not unusual. VZV, viral antigens, and/or antiviral antibodies have been found in CSF of individuals with nervous system complications of herpes zoster.[173, 201–203]

Herpes zoster with involvement of the ophthalmic branch of the trigeminal nerve may lead to conjunctivitis, keratitis, corneal ulcers, iridocyclitis, and ophthalmoplegia. Many other ocular complications of zoster have been described.[204] A few extradermatomal vesicles in a healthy person do not presage dissemination.

LABORATORY DIAGNOSIS

Chickenpox and herpes zoster can usually be diagnosed on clinical grounds. Laboratory confirmation of VZV infection is not routinely used. However, virus isolation or serologic studies are helpful in the diagnosis of zoster. Laboratory studies are desirable when there is any uncertainty about clinical diagnosis and when prophylactic and/or therapeutic intervention may be required.

VZV can be isolated from vesicle fluid early after onset of the rash and on occasion from blood or CSF. Development of detectable CPE in tissue culture cells may require six to eight days. Rapid diagnosis may be desirable.

Demonstration of VZV antigens in cells scraped from the vesicle base by direct immunofluorescence is a rapid, sensitive technique.[205] A Tzanck smear demonstrating multinucleated giant cells with eosinophilic intranuclear inclusions (Cowdry type A) in scrapings of a vesicle base or electron microscopic examination of vesicle fluid (see Figure 35–1) supports a diagnosis of either VZV or other herpesvirus infections.

There are many assays for antibodies to VZV. Tests for neutralizing antibodies have been developed, but are very time-consuming. The FAMA technique, an indirect immunofluorescence test to detect antibody to a membrane antigen of the virus, is more sensitive and specific than the CF test and is the reference procedure for determining VZV immunity.[206, 207] Immunofluorescence, immunoperoxidase, and radioimmunoassays for VZV

seroconversion are more sensitive than CF assays.[206, 208–210] Rises in CF antibody titer can also be demonstrated. Unlike the FAMA, the CF antibody does not persist; therefore a high CF titer may indicate recent infection. Seroconversions with heterologous herpesviruses occur and are most often found with the CF assay. In addition to FAMA, commercially available enzyme-linked immunosorbent assay (ELISA) tests may prove useful in determining prior immunity.[207, 211]

For optimal clinical usefulness, rapid diagnostic methods, which can be available before an IgG antibody response occurs, are needed. IgM to VZV can be detected by FAMA as early as the second day of the chickenpox.[212] The IgM antibodies are also found in herpes zoster. An ELISA for VZV IgM using *S aureus*–absorbed test sera was reported to be 100 times more sensitive than the FAMA.[213] Antibody to early antigens of VZV appears early in chickenpox and shingles.[106] VZV antigen detection by ELISA also shows promise for rapid diagnosis.[214]

Diagnosis of congenital varicella syndrome is not confirmed by virus isolation since virus is not present at birth. However, antibody may not decline after birth as passively acquired antibody does.

Screening hospital staff and high-risk individuals with a doubtful or negative varicella history for VZV antibody by immunofluorescence identifies those at risk for infection.[215] Such data are useful in minimizing nosocomial varicella and in allocating supplies of varicella zoster immune globulin (VZIG).

PREVENTION

Infection Control

Chickenpox and zoster are both contagious, presumably by direct contact, droplet, or aerosol transmission, until all lesions are crusted. Thus, children should not return to school or day care until all lesions are crusted, approximately seven days after onset of rash.[216]

Nosocomial varicella and herpes zoster pose a serious threat to nonimmune patients with compromised immune function. Strict isolation is recommended for chickenpox, disseminated zoster, or localized zoster in the immunocompromised patient and for exposed susceptible inpatients.[216, 217] Applying this principal to puerperal varicella, the mother and infant would be placed separately in strict isolation. Isolation of susceptible newborn infants from infected siblings is also recommended. Guidelines for prevention for the nursery and obstetric service have been proposed.[76] For localized zoster in immunologically normal individuals, drainage/secretion precautions are used. Based on the above discussion, exposed, nonimmune hospital personnel would not care for susceptible patients during the late period of incubation and disease.

Immunoglobulins and Transfer Factor

The appreciation that VZV infection is a serious and sometimes fatal event in certain groups of nonimmune individuals led to evaluation of passive immunization as a means of preventing or modifying the infection. Human immune serum globulin (ISG) administered intramuscularly (IM) within three days of exposure did not reduce the varicella attack rate of normal family contacts; however, at high doses, fever and rash were decreased.[62] Other products evaluated for passive immunization include zoster immune globulin (ZIG), zoster immune plasma, and ISG of known high varicella antibody titer.[218-226] VZIG, an immune globulin with high titer of antibody to varicella-zoster virus prepared from high-titer plasma from outdated blood bank blood, is available and is currently recommended for passive immunization.[227] ZIG and VZIG are equally effective in reducing chickenpox severity in immunocompromised children.[228]

VZIG is distributed in the United States by the American Red Cross, and it can be requested through the nearest regional distribution center.[229] Use of VZIG has been based on the epidemiology of varicella, the nature of disease in various groups of people, the limited availability of FAMA results, and the availability and cost of VZIG.[229-231] Recent recommendations for VZIG use have been published by the Immunization Practices Advisory Committee and the American Academy of Pediatrics.[216, 229]

VZIG use has been discussed for several categories of susceptible, exposed patients including neonates, immunocompromised children and adults, and normal adults, including pregnant women.[152, 229, 232, 233] Expanded use to include pregnant women and the entire neonatal period has been discussed.[152, 232, 233]

VZIG may modify the infection, prolonging the incubation period; however, it is not totally effective. For example, severe varicella was reported in several infants who had received VZIG.[234, 235]

In addition to VZIG, for individuals receiving immunosuppressive therapy the outcome may be further modified by decreasing or interrupting immunosuppression if this is possible. However, for corticosteroid-dependent patients, corticosteroids are necessary.

It was reported that an intravenous (IV) immunoglobulin product contains VZV antibodies.[236] On administration to patients, resulting VZV antibody titers were similar to those achieved with VZIG.

Preexposure administration of a single dose of transfer factor prepared from lymphocytes of adults convalescing from chickenpox was reported effective in preventing chickenpox in subsequently exposed children with acute lymphocytic leukemia.[237] Leukemic children in remission receiving transfer factor developed VZV cellular immunoreactivity.[238] These effects were not confirmed in a study of patients following bone marrow transplantation.[239]

Vaccine

Active immunization offers several advantages over passive immunization or chemotherapy. Susceptible immunodeficient patients may be restricted in their activities for fear of VZV exposure or may be exposed without recognizing the need for VZIG or its timely use. If varicella occurs, it may be so severe that antiviral chemotherapy is not successful. VZIG is expensive and indications for protection are broader than the indications for usage. Exposed susceptible patients may require interruption of necessary chemotherapy or immunosuppressive therapy on multiple occasions. Active immunization of normal susceptible individuals could decrease varicella complications, nosocomial spread, and exposure of high-risk individuals.[240] The morbidity and mortality that occur from varicella and the preliminary data showing safety and immunogenicity formed the basis for conducting larger trials to determine the uses of the vaccine.[241-243]

Arguments against widespread use of the varicella vaccine were raised by Brunell.[244] These included (1) the mild course of most VZV infections; (2) the unknown risk of latency with a live herpesvirus vaccine; (3) the unknown risk of herpes zoster as a result of reactivation of latency; (4) the availability of modes of passive prevention; (5) the unknown duration of immunity; and (6) the risk of delaying varicella to adulthood when it produces more morbidity and mortality than in childhood.

Japanese investigators reported, in 1974, the development of a live attenuated varicella vaccine, the Oka strain.[245] A VZV isolate from K. Oka, a 3-year-old boy with chickenpox, was serially cultivated in human embryonic lung cells at 34°C and then in guinea pig embryo cells.[245, 246] Vaccine virus differs from wild-type virus by improved growth on guinea pig embryo cells[246] and by restriction endonuclease cleavage patterns of DNA.[246, 247] The injection of the Oka vaccine strain induced antibodies in high-risk and normal children with no serious adverse effects.[245] A preliminary study detected no contact infection in susceptible institutionalized children exposed to vaccine recipients;[248] however, transmission from leukemic children to household contacts has been reported.[249-251] The vaccine appeared to interrupt nosocomial spread of varicella. This vaccine has been extensively evaluated and licensed in Japan.

The Oka strain vaccine was administered to steroid-treated, chickenpox-susceptible hospitalized children on exposure to VZV infection.[252] All vaccinated children underwent seroconversion without symptoms. Protection lasted up to 9 months. The vaccine was used successfully to protect susceptible contacts even after household exposure[253] or institutional exposure.[252] The varicella skin test was used to identify susceptibles for immunization.[254] Skin tests converted five days after vaccination and before seroconversion as determined by neutralization. Japanese trials in immunocompetent children have shown a high degree of seroconversion, protection on subsequent exposure, persistence of FAMA or neutralizing antibodies, and persistence of skin test reactivity.[255-257] Confirmatory data from a large United States trial showed 100% efficacy and 94% seroconversion in children.[258] Although there were pain and redness at the injection site and rashes reported, the vaccine was well tolerated. The protective efficacy in eight trials worldwide ranged from 90% to 100%.[259] The number of vaccine virus plaque-forming units (PFU) required to produce seroconversion has been reported to range from 5 to 600 in several reports about various populations.[259, 260] There is preliminary evidence of seroconversion and efficacy in healthy adults.[251, 259] In healthy seropositive adults, aged 55 to 65 years, VZV CMI responses increased after varicella vaccination.[261] A small study combining varicella vaccine with measles, mumps, and rubella vaccine for healthy children suggested the combination to be immunogenic, safe, and cost-effective.[262]

Immune responses to vaccine have been evaluated comparing pre- and postimmunization status or comparing immunity after natural infection to that after immunization. IgG antibody titers were reported to be higher after natural infection and serum and nasopharyngeal IgA responses were limited to natural infection.[263] VZV-specific lymphocyte proliferative responses developed after immunization.[260] Many antibody responses can be detected after natural infection or immunization with VZV. Although it has not yet been possible to identify which responses are required to prevent breakthrough reinfection,[264] western blot analysis may help distinguish secondary from primary antibody responses.[265] The persistence of antibody into adulthood is unknown and not assured. Herpes zoster was extremely rare after immunization in these subjects.

The Oka strain vaccine was also given to susceptible children with acute leukemia in remission or other malignant disease.[266] Chemotherapy was suspended for 1 week before and 1 week after vaccination. The vaccine was immunogenic and appeared to be safe and protective. Subsequent studies in children with acute leukemia support the preliminary findings.[66, 267] Further evaluation of the vaccine showed it was immunogenic in children with acute leukemia or other malignancies without suspension of anticancer therapy.[268] Although rash and fever were more frequent than in those vaccinated with suspension of chemotherapy, only one child had severe varicella symptoms.

In further studies in susceptible leukemic children in the United States varicella vaccine had a protective efficacy of approximately 80%.[269, 270] The seroconversion rate improved with a booster dose. The varicella which occurred in some vaccinees was often mild, suggesting that the vaccine-induced immunity had modified the infection. In the immunocompromised, the vaccine may produce local reaction, fever, rash, and household transmission of vaccine virus. The incidence of zoster was not increased,[271] nor was the incidence of leukemic relapse.[269] Restriction endonuclease analysis of VZV DNA was used to show that early rash within 6 weeks of immunization is due to vaccine virus and that breakthrough infections due to wild-type virus may also occur.[272] Herpes zoster after immunization has been shown to be caused by wild-type or vaccine virus.

One cost-benefit analysis for varicella vaccine suggested that vaccination of 15-month-old children with a safe and effective vaccine with long-lasting immunity, with other assumptions of the model, would reduce costs by 66% and produce $7 savings for each dollar spent on a vaccination program.[59] The savings would come from reducing the expenses related to a universal illness, not from eliminating a severe disease. The model did not include immunocompromised individuals, who would be most likely to benefit. Costs for nosocomial varicella have also been estimated.[273] Although a licensed varicella vaccine is available in Japan and Europe, licensure has not been provided in the United States at this writing. Possible target populations for licensed vaccine under consideration include healthy children and young adults, institutionalized susceptible populations, immunocompromised susceptible children, susceptible health care workers, and the aged.

TREATMENT

Nonspecific Measures

Both chickenpox and shingles are usually mild, self-limited infections which require no therapy. In contrast to the treatment of complicated varicella or varicella in an individual of increased susceptibility, treatment of uncomplicated chickenpox should be limited and should not, in itself, cause harm. Salicylate use has been associated with Reye syndrome and with salicylate toxicity and is not recommended in chickenpox.[216, 274, 275] Treatment of chickenpox is limited to simple measures to control fever and itching and to prevent superinfection.

Treatment of herpes zoster in the immunologically normal individual is directed at controlling the pain of the acute process and at postherpetic neuralgia.[276] Treatments for acute herpes zoster include topical therapy, systemic analgesics, and corticosteroids, with antiviral agents reserved for exceptional situations and complications.[276, 277] For ocular herpes zoster, mydriatics and topical or systemic corticosteroids may also be used. Treatment of postherpetic neuralgia has been attempted with tricyclic antidepressants, phenothiazines, prolonged electrical stimulation, and local anesthetics. Although controlled trials of some of these therapies are lacking, some individuals have apparently benefited from them.[278]

Antibiotics are useful for varicella and herpes zoster when evidence of secondary bacterial infection is present. Although corticosteroids have numerous drawbacks, they may be useful in some varicella complications. Diagnosis and treatment of complications of varicella is aimed at early identification and support of the affected system(s). Hospitalization may be necessary for treatment, particularly in groups with a high case fatality rate, for example, in young infants.

Individuals who are corticosteroid-dependent require sufficient doses for stress. When the patient can tolerate reduction or discontinuation of immunosuppressive drugs, this may promote recovery from VZV infection.

Transfer Factor

Immunotherapy has also been attempted for VZV infection in patients with malignancy. Transfer factor from pooled dialyzable leukocyte extracts from varicella-immune donors seemed to accelerate cessation of vesicle formation and initiation of crust formation in patients with malignancy and localized zoster or disseminated varicella-zoster and to increase serum interferon concentration.[279] Controlled trial data for therapeutic use are not available.

Antiviral Therapy

The immunocompromised patient may have more frequent and more prolonged VZV infections. Although the outcome of zoster in the immunosuppressed host may be good with temporary withdrawal of immunosuppressive therapy, chickenpox may progress to visceral involvement in nonimmune, immunocompromised children with cancer. Chickenpox has a case fatality rate of about 8% in such children. Because of the importance of VZV infection in immunocompromised patients, several antiviral agents have been evaluated. The importance of controlled trials has been emphasized since the demonstration that cytosine arabinoside had an adverse effect on disseminated zoster and was contraindicated for VZV.[280]

Several nucleoside analogues developed as antiviral agents interfere with viral DNA synthesis. Some also show mutagenicity, animal teratogenicity, or toxic effects against systems with rapidly dividing cells. Evaluation of the viral infection, its severity, and the immunologic background of patients is necessary to judge the potential risks and benefits of antiviral therapy. A therapeutic trial of antiviral therapy is appropriate for life-threatening herpesvirus infections.[281]

Adenine arabinoside is a purine analogue which inhibits nuclear DNA synthesis. For immunocompromised patients with malignancy and herpes zoster, early IV administration of adenine arabinoside accelerated clearance of virus from vesicles, cessation of new vesicle formation, and time to total pustulation.[282] Adenine arabinoside was also reported effective and relatively safe in chickenpox and herpes zoster in immunocompromised patients.[283, 284] In Britain, adenine arabinoside was used without controlled trials for immunologically normal adults with severe varicella and for purpura fulminans in zoster and was combined with VZIG and topical idoxuridine for VZV infection in patients with reticuloendothelial neoplasia.[285, 286] Undesirable effects include thrombophlebitis and GI, hematologic, skin, and CNS toxicity. A comparative study of adenine arabinoside versus acyclovir demonstrated clinical and virologic superiority of acyclovir for VZV infection in severely immunocompromised patients.[287] The toxicity profile of the two agents differed.

Acyclovir, a derivative of guanine, is active against herpesviruses. Acyclovir is selective in being taken up by infected cells, in its phosphorylation by viral induced thymidine kinase, and in its ability to inhibit viral DNA polymerase. The therapeutic ratio is favorable. Acyclovir has inhibitory activity against VZV, which is severalfold less susceptible than herpes simplex virus.[288] Acyclovir is effective in halting the progression of herpes zoster in immunocompromised patients.[289, 290] In a placebo-controlled trial in immunosuppressed children with chickenpox, acyclovir recipients did not develop varicella pneumonitis, whereas almost half of the placebo recipients did.[291] In case reports, relapse of VZV infection after acyclovir was noted.[292]

Acyclovir use has been suggested for neonatal varicella although controlled trial data are not available.[293] Severe neonatal varicella may occur without VZIG, and even despite use of VZIG.[232, 234, 235] In scant reports, acyclovir treatment appeared beneficial in some infants. One study of acyclovir for varicella in otherwise healthy children was reported,[293a] and others are underway.

Oral and IV acyclovir have shown some beneficial antiviral and clinical effects in normal adults with herpes zoster; however, the benefits of routine treatment in individuals not at risk for dissemination may not be sufficient to balance the costs.[198, 294–296] In elderly or febrile patients or those with recent onset of pain, IV acyclovir improved healing and reduced pain.[297] Controlled trial data are limited and reported effects marginal in normal adults with chickenpox.[298]

Acute herpes zoster ophthalmicus has been treated with topical idoxuridine, adenine arabinoside, or acyclovir.[299] Oral acyclovir was reported to produce clinical improvement and decrease ocular inflammatory complications and pain and has been recommended for ophthalmic zoster in immunologically normal patients.[198, 300]

Acyclovir has been recommended for VZV pneumonia in normal adults following good outcomes in uncontrolled use.[198, 301, 302] Only a few instances of treatment of varicella pneumonia in the third trimester of pregnancy with acyclovir have been reported.[303–306] Transplacental passage of acyclovir may occur and could have fetal effects.[307]

Other antiviral agents have been evaluated and have no efficacy,[308] appear less promising,[309] or have been evaluated only in vitro or in single clinical trials.[310–315] In a single controlled trial, adenosine monophosphate was reported to decrease viral shedding, improve healing, and relieve pain.[316]

The interferons, a family of glycoproteins with antiviral properties, immunomodulatory activities, and inhibitory effects on cell division, are among the agents for treatment of VZV infection. High interferon titers in vesicles are associated with recovery from zoster. Infection with measles virus is associated with an interferon response and modifies concomitant chickenpox infection, as judged by a reduction in the total number of vesicles.[317] Polyinosinic acid–polycytidilic acid, an interferon inducer, elevated serum and vesicle fluid interferon concentrations and increased lymphoproliferation to VZV antigen in patients with lymphoma or leukemia and VZV infection.[318]

Studies of human leukocyte interferon for herpes zoster in cancer patients were based on previous demonstrations of delay of the interferon response in patients with dissemination or in those with prolonged disease, in vitro interferon sensitivity of VZV[319, 320] virus, and promising results of earlier clinical trials.[321, 322] In a randomized, double blind, placebo-controlled trial, human leukocyte interferon improved the course of localized herpes zoster in cancer patients by decreasing spread within the primary dermatome and to distal cutaneous or visceral sites and by decreasing neuralgia.[323] Early treatment administered IM was required for efficacy. Fever and bone marrow suppression occurred regularly. A shorter course of interferon also diminished distal cutaneous spread and postherpetic neuralgia, but failed to affect the disease in the primary dermatome.[324]

The efficacy of interferon in herpes zoster suggests that interferon might have efficacy in immunocompromised children with varicella infection. In a small preliminary controlled trial of human leukocyte interferon in the treatment of varicella in children with cancer, interferon was well tolerated.[325] Visceral involvement was more frequent in recipients of placebo; however, statistical significance was not achieved. The spontaneous recovery of most placebo recipients underlined the need to exclude uncontrolled trials in this kind of clinical evaluation. Since the interferon dose and the number of patients evaluated were low, a second study was performed.[326] Interferon was effective in reducing the number of days of new lesion formation and in reducing the number of patients with life-threatening dissemination. Dose-dependent, reversible, adverse effects are experienced with human leukocyte interferon use. Recombinant human alpha interferon also has prophylactic and therapeutic efficacy for simian varicella virus in monkeys and in human beings for herpes zoster.[327, 328] The therapeutic efficacy for herpes zoster was similar to acyclovir; however, interferon was less well tolerated.

Levin and Leary[329] have suggested the possibility of combining human leukocyte interferon and acyclovir to lower the toxicity of each while achieving clinical efficacy. Low concentrations of interferon increased synergistically the antiviral effect of acyclovir against VZV and reduced the persistence of VZV in acyclovir-treated tissue culture cells. The combination had no increased activity against division of human fibroblasts or proliferation of peripheral blood mononuclear cells. Synergy has also been demonstrated in vitro against VZV strains between other antiherpes agents and human leukocyte interferon.[330] In a simian varicella virus monkey infection model, synergy between gancyclovir and recombinant human beta interferon was reported.[331] Clinical and virologic superiority of the combination was evident.

Acyclovir resistant VZV has been isolated from patients with AIDS.[332] Resistance may result from a single point mutation in the viral thymidine kinase gene.[333] The potential for developing resistance and the expanded use of acyclovir indicate the need for further investigation of synergistic combinations of antiviral agents.

REFERENCES

1. Lerman SJ: Why is chickenpox called chickenpox? *Clin Pediatr* 1981; 20:111–112.
2. Room A: *Room's Dictionary of Distinguishables*. Boston, Routledge & Kegan Paul, 1981, p 27.
3. Scott-Wilson JH: Why "chicken" pox?, letter. *Lancet* 1978; 1:1152.
4. Heberden W: Variolae pusillae: The chicken-pox, in *Commentaries on the History and Cure of Diseases*. New York, Hafner, 1962, pp 446–452.
5. Weller TH: Serial propagation in vitro of agents producing inclusion bodies derived from varicella and herpes zoster. *Proc Soc Exp Biol Med* 1953; 83:340–346.
6. Weller TH, Witton HM: The etiologic agents of varicella and herpes zoster: Serologic studies with the viruses as propagated in vitro. *J Exp Med* 1958; 108:869–889.
7. Straus SE, Reinhold W, Smith HA, et al: Endonuclease analysis of viral DNA from varicella and subsequent zoster infection in the same patient. *N Engl J Med* 1984; 311:1362–1364.
8. Weller TH, Witton HM, Bell EJ: The etiologic agents of varicella and herpes zoster: Isolation, propagation, and cultural characteristics in vitro. *J Exp Med* 1958; 108:843–869.
9. Almeida JD, Howatson AF, Williams MG: Morphology of varicella (chicken pox) virus. *Virology* 1962; 16:353–355.
10. Richards JC, Hyman RW, Rapp F: Analysis of the DNAs from seven varicella-zoster virus isolates. *J Virol* 1979; 32:812–821.
11. Schmidt NJ, Lennette EH, Magoffin RL: Immunological relationship between herpes simplex and varicella-zoster viruses demonstrated by complement-fixation, neutralization and fluorescent antibody tests. *J Gen Virol* 1969; 4:312–328.
12. Schmidt N: Further evidence for common antigens in herpes simplex and varicella-zoster viruses. *J Med Virol* 1982; 9:27–36.
13. Davison A, Wilkie N: Location and orientation of homologous sequences in the genomes of five herpes viruses. *J Gen Virol* 1983; 64:1927–1942.
14. Dumas AM, Geelen JLMC, Maris W, et al: Infectivity and molecular weight of varicella-zoster virus DNA. *J Gen Virol* 1980; 47:233–235.
15. Straus SE, Aulakh HS, Ruyechan WT, et al: Structure of varicella-zoster virus DNA. *J Virol* 1981; 40:516–525.
16. Davison AJ, Scott JE: The complete DNA sequence of varicella-zoster virus. *J Gen Virol* 1986; 67:1759–1816.
17. Ostrove JM, Reinhold W, Fan C-M, et al: Transcription mapping of the varicella-zoster virus genome. *J Virol* 1985; 56:600–606.
18. Shemer Y, Leventon-Kriss S, Sarov I: Isolation and polypeptide characterization of varicella-zoster virus. *Virology* 1980; 106:133–140.
19. Shiraki K, Okuno T, Yamanishi K, et al: Polypeptides of varicella-zoster virus (VZV) and immunological relationship of VZV and herpes simplex virus (HSV). *J Gen Virol* 1982; 61:255–269.
20. Grose C, Friedrichs WE, Smith GC: Purification and molecular anatomy of the varicella-zoster virion. *Biken J* 1983; 26:1–15.
21. Davison AJ, Edson CM, Ellis RW, et al: New common nomenclature for glycoprotein genes of varicella-zoster virus and their glycosylated products. *J Virol* 1986; 57:1195–1197.
22. Grose C, Litwin V: Immunology of the varicella-zoster virus glycoproteins. *J Infect Dis* 1988; 157:877–881.
23. Keller PM, Neff BJ, Ellis RW: Three major glycoprotein genes of varicella-zoster virus whose products have neutralization epitopes. *J Virol* 1984; 52:293–297.
24. Davison AJ, Waters DJ, Edson CM: Identification of the products of a varicella-zoster virus glycoprotein gene. *J Gen Virol* 1985; 66:2237–2242.
25. Grose C: Varicella-zoster virus: pathogenesis of human diseases, the virus and viral replication, and the major viral glycoproteins and proteins, in Hyman RW (ed): *Natural History of Varicella-Zoster Virus*. Boca Raton, Fla, CRC Press, 1987, pp 1–65.
26. Dobersen MJ, Jerkofsky M, Greer S: Enzymatic basis for the selective inhibition of varicella-zoster virus by 5-halogenated analogues of deoxycytidine. *J Virol* 1976; 20:478–486.
27. Ogino T, Otsuka T, Takahashi M: Induction of deoxypyrimidine kinase activity in human embryonic lung cells infected with varicella-zoster virus. *J Virol* 1977; 21:1232–1235.
28. Yamanishi K, Matsunaga Y, Ogino T, et al: Biochemical transformation of mouse cells by varicella-zoster virus. *J Gen Virol* 1981; 56:421–430.
29. Sawyer M, Ostrove J, Felser J, et al: Mapping of the varicella-zoster virus deoxypyrimidine kinase gene and preliminary identification of its transcript. *Virology* 1986; 149:1–9.
30. Miller RL, Rapp F: Varicella-zoster virus-induced DNA polymerase. *J Gen Virol* 1977; 36:515–524.
31. Shiraki K, Yamamoto T, Yamanishi K, et al: DNA binding proteins induced by varicella-zoster virus in human cells. *Biken J* 1982; 25:185–189.
32. Roberts C, Weir A, Hay J, et al: DNA-binding proteins present in varicella-zoster virus-infected cells. *J Virol* 1985; 55:45–53.
33. Felser JM, Straus SE, Ostrove JM: Varicella-zoster virus complements herpes simplex virus type 1 temperature-sensitive mutants. *J Virol* 1987; 61:225–228.
34. Cheng Y-C, Tsou TY, Hackstadt T, et al: Induction of thymidine kinase and DNase in varicella-zoster virus-infected cells and kinetic properties of the virus-induced thymidine kinase. *J Virol* 1979; 31:172–177.
35. Straus SE, Hay J, Smith H, et al: Genome differences among varicella-zoster virus isolates. *J Gen Virol* 1983; 64:1031–1041.
36. Gershon AA, Steinberg SP, Gelb L, et al: Clinical reinfection with varicella-zoster virus. *J Infect Dis* 1984; 149:137–142.
37. Williams DL, Gershon AA, Gelb LD, et al: Herpes zoster following varicella vaccine in a child with acute lymphocytic leukemia. *J Pediatr* 1985; 106:259–261.
38. Leventon-Kriss S, Gotlieb-Stematsky T, Vonsover A, et al: Infection and persistence of varicella-zoster virus in lymphoblastoid Raji cell line. *Med Microbiol Immunol* 1979; 167:275–283.
39. Taylor-Robinson D, Caunt AE: Varicella virus, in Gard S, Haullauer C, Meyer KF (eds): *Virology Monographs*. New York, Springer-Verlag, 1972, vol 12, pp 1–88.
40. Aula P: Chromosome breaks in leukocytes of chickenpox patients. *Hereditas* 1962; 48:451–453.
41. Benyesh-Melnick M, Stich HF, Rapp F, et al: Viruses and mammalian chromosomes. III. Effect of herpes zoster virus on human embryonal lung cultures. *Proc Soc Exp Biol Med* 1964; 117:546–549.
42. Caunt AE, Taylor-Robinson D: Cell-free varicella-zoster virus in tissue culture. *J Hyg Camb* 1964; 62:413–424.
43. Brunell PA: Separation of infectious varicella-zoster virus from human embryonic lung fibroblasts. *Virology* 1967; 31:732–734.
44. Schmidt NJ, Lennette EH: Improved yields of cell-free varicella-zoster virus. *Infect Immun* 1976; 14:709–715.
45. Bastian FO, Rabson AS, Yee CL, et al: *Herpesvirus varicellae*: Isolated from human dorsal root ganglia. *Arch Pathol* 1974; 97:331–333.
46. Plotkin SA, Stein S, Snyder M, et al: Attempts to recover varicella virus from ganglia. *Ann Neurol* 1977; 2:249.
47. Gilden DH, Rozenman Y, Murray R: Detection of varicella-zos-

ter virus nucleic acid in neurons of normal human thoracic ganglia. *Ann Neurol* 1987; 22:377–380.

48. Gilden DH, Vafai A, Shtram Y, et al: Varicella-zoster virus DNA in human sensory ganglia. *Nature* 1983; 306:478–480.

49. Hyman RW, Ecker JR, Tenser RB: Varicella-zoster virus RNA in human trigeminal ganglia. *Lancet* 1983; 2:814–816.

50. Tenser RB, Hyman RW: Latent herpes virus infections of neurons in guinea pigs and humans. *Yale J Biol Med* 1987; 60:159–167.

51. Joncas JH: Persistence, reactivation, and cell transformation by human herpesviruses: Herpes simplex 1,2 (HSV-1, HSV-2), cytomegalovirus (CMV), varicella-zoster (VZV), Epstein Barr virus (EBV). *Can J Microbiol* 1979; 25:254–260.

52. Harbour DA, Caunt AE: The serological relationship of varicella-zoster virus to other primate herpesviruses. *J Gen Virol* 1979; 45:469–477.

53. Myers MG, Kramer LW, Stanberry LR: Varicella in a gorilla. *J Med Virol* 1987; 23:317–322.

54. Myers MG, Duer HL, Hausler CK: Experimental infection of guinea pigs with varicella-zoster virus. *J Infect Dis* 1980; 142:414–420.

55. Myers MG, Harrison CJ, Stanberry LR: Expression of exanthem in varicella zoster virus (VZV) infected hairless guinea pigs. *Pediatr Res* 1988; 23:377A.

56. Groth KE, McCullough J, Balfour HH Jr: Varicella immunity in adults. *Minn Med* 1980; 63:87–89.

57. Preblud SR, D'Angelo LJ: Chickenpox in the United States. *J Infect Dis* 1979; 140:257–260.

58. Centers for Disease Control: Summary of notifiable diseases, United States, 1985. *MMWR* 1987; 34:1–21.

59. Preblud SR: Varicella: complications and costs. *Pediatrics* 1986; 78(suppl):728–735.

60. Guess HA, Broughton DD, Melton LJ, et al: Population-based studies of varicella complications. *Pediatrics* 1986; 78(suppl):723–727.

61. Gershon AA, Krugman S: Seroepidemiologic survey of varicella: Value of specific fluorescent antibody test. *Pediatrics* 1975; 56:1005–1008.

62. Ross AH: Modification of chicken pox in family contacts by administration of gamma globulin. *N Engl J Med* 1962; 267:369–376.

63. Gordon JE: Chickenpox: An epidemiological review. *Am J Med Sci* 1962; 244:362–389.

64. Trlifajova J, Svandova E, Havrlantova M, et al: Varicella morbidity in Czechoslovakia. *J Hyg Epidemiol Microbiol Immunol* 1980; 24:192–199.

65. Gershon AA, Raker R, Steinberg S, et al: Antibody to varicella-zoster virus in parturient women and their offspring during the first year of life. *Pediatrics* 1976; 58:692–696.

66. Just M, Berger-Hernandez R, Buergin-Wolff A: Initial experience with varicella zoster. *Monogr Paediatr* 1979; 11:54–57.

67. Raker RK, Steinberg S, Drusin LM, et al: Antibody to varicella zoster virus in low-birth-weight newborn infants. *J Pediatr* 1978; 93:505–506.

68. Leventon-Kriss S, Yoffe R, Rannon L, et al: Seroepidemiologic aspects of varicella zoster virus infections in an Israeli Jewish population. *Isr J Med Sci* 1978; 14:766–770.

69. Sinha DP: Chickenpox—A disease predominantly affecting adults in rural West Bengal, India. *Int J Epidemiol* 1976; 5:367–374.

70. Maretić Z, Cooray MPM: Comparisons between chickenpox in a tropical and a European country. *J Trop Med Hyg* 1963; 66:311–315.

71. Hastie IR: Varicella-zoster virus affecting immigrant nurses, letter. *Lancet* 1980; 2:154–155.

72. Nelson KE, Yamashiroya H, McLane MP: Primary varicella infections in health care workers (HCW). Presented at 20th Interscience Conference on Antimicrobial Agents and Chemotherapy, New Orleans, 1980. Abstract No. 281.

73. Leclair JM, Zaiz JA, Levin MJ, et al: Airborne transmission of chickenpox in a hospital. *N Engl J Med* 1980; 302:450–453.

74. Rahman M: Outbreak of chickenpox and herpes zoster in a geriatric hospital. *Br J Clin Pract* 1979; 33:291–293.

75. Morens DM, Bregman DJ, West CM, et al: An outbreak of varicella-zoster virus infection among cancer patients. *Ann Intern Med* 1980; 93:414–419.

76. Young NA, Gershon AA: Chickenpox, measles and mumps, in Remington JS, Kelin JO (eds): *Infectious Diseases of the Fetus and Newborn Infant*. Philadelphia, Saunders, 1983, pp 375–427.

77. Myers MG, Rasley DA, Hierholzer WJ: Hospital infection control for varicella-zoster virus (VZV) infection. *Pediatrics* 1982; 70:199–202.

78. Steele RW, Coleman MA, Fiser M, et al: Varicella zoster in hospital personnel: skin test reactivity to monitor susceptibility. *Pediatrics* 1982; 70:604–608.

79. Ragozzino MW, Melton LJ, Kurland LT, et al: Population-based study of herpes zoster and its sequellae. *Medicine* 1982; 61:310–316.

80. Hope-Simpson RE: The nature of herpes zoster: A long-term study and new hypothesis. *Proc R Soc Med* 1965; 58:9–20.

81. Pichini B, Ecker JR, Grose C, et al: DNA mapping of paired varicella-zoster virus isolates from patients with shingles. *Lancet* 1983; 2:1223–1225.

82. Takayama M, Takayama N, Hachimori K, et al: Restriction endonuclease analysis of viral DNA from a patient with bilateral herpes zoster lesions. *J Infect Dis* 1988; 157:392–393.

83. Hondo R, Yogo Y, Kurata T, et al: Genome variation among varicella-zoster virus isolates derived from different individuals and from the same individuals. *Arch Virol* 1987; 93:1–12.

84. Epstein E: Recurrences of herpes zoster. *Cutis* 1980; 26:378–379.

85. Grose C: Varicella-zoster virus infections: chickenpox (varicella) and shingles (zoster), in Glaser R, Gotlieb-Stematsky T (eds): *Human Herpesvirus Infections: Clinical Aspects*. New York, Marcel Dekker, 1982, pp 85–150.

86. Ozaki T, Ichikawa T, Matsui Y, et al: Viremic phase in nonimmunocompromised children with varicella. *J Pediatr* 1984; 104:85–87.

87. Findlay GH, Forman L, Hull PR: Actinic chickenpox: Light-distributed varicella eruption. *S Afr Med J* 1979; 55:989–991.

88. Naraqi S, Jackson GG, Jonasson OM: Viremia with herpes simplex type 1 in adults: Four nonfatal cases, one with features of chicken pox. *Ann Intern Med* 1976; 85:165–169.

89. Long JC, Wheeler CE Jr, Briggaman RA: Varicella-like infection due to herpes simplex. *Arch Dermatol* 1978; 114:406–409.

90. Schimpff S, Serpick A, Stoler B, et al: Varicella-zoster infection in patients with cancer. *Ann Intern Med* 1972; 76:241–254.

91. Becker LE: Herpes zoster: A geriatric disease. *Geriatrics* 1979; 9:41–47.

92. Burgoon CF Jr, Burgoon JS, Baldridge GD: The natural history of herpes zoster. *JAMA* 1957; 164:265–269.

93. Patterson SD, Larson EB, Corey L: Atypical generalized zoster with lymphadenitis mimicking lymphoma. *N Engl J Med* 1980; 302:848–851.

94. Meade RH III, Chang T-W: Zoster-like eruption due to echovirus 6. *Am J Dis Child* 1979; 133:283–284.

95. Kalman CM, Laskin OL: Herpes zoster and zosteriform herpes simplex virus infections in immunocompetent adults. *Am J Med* 1986; 81:775–778.

96. Guess HA, Broughton DD, Melton LJ, et al: Epidemiology of herpes zoster in children and adolescents: a population-based study. *Pediatrics* 1985; 76:512–517.

97. Brunell PA, Kotchmar GS Jr: Zoster in infancy: Failure to maintain virus latency following intrauterine infection. *J Pediatr* 1981; 98:71–73.

98. Brunell PA, Miller LH, Lovejoy F: Zoster in children. *Am J Dis Child* 1968; 115:432–437.

99. Latif R, Shope TC: Herpes zoster in normal and immunocompromised children. *Am J Dis Child* 1983; 137:801–802.

100. Ragozzino MW, Melton LJ, Kurland LT, et al: Risk of cancer after herpes-zoster: A population-based study. *N Engl J Med* 1982; 307:393–396.

101. Rowland Payne CME, Farthing C, Byrom N, et al: Shingles in seven homosexuals. *Lancet* 1984; 1:103–104.

102. Cone LA, Schiffman MA: Herpes zoster and the acquired immunodeficiency syndrome. *Ann Intern Med* 1984; 100:462.

103. Friedman-Kien AE, Lafleur FL, Gendler E, et al: Herpes zoster: A possible early clinical sign for development of acquired immunodeficiency syndrome in high-risk individuals. *J Am Acad Dermatol* 1986; 14:1023–1028.

104. Colebunders R, Mann JM, Francis H, et al: Herpes zoster in African patients: a clinical predictor of human immunodeficiency virus infection. *J Infect Dis* 1988; 157:314–318.

105. Brunell PA, Gershon AA, Uduman SA, et al: Varicella-zoster immunoglobulins during varicella latency, and zoster. *J Infect Dis* 1975; 132:49–54.

106. Gerna G, Cereda PM, Cattaneo E, et al: Antibody to early antigens of varicella-zoster virus during varicella and zoster. *J Infect Dis* 1979; 140:33–41.

107. Zweerink HJ, Neff BJ: Immune response after exposure to varicella zoster virus: characterization of virus-specific antibodies and their corresponding antigens. *Infect Immun* 1981; 31:436–444.

108. Weigle KA, Grose C: Molecular dissection of the humoral immune response to individual varicella-zoster viral proteins during chickenpox, quiescence, reinfection, and reactivation. *J Infect Dis* 1984; 149:741–749.

109. Palumbo PE, Arvin AM, Koropchak CM: Investigation of varicella-zoster virus–infected cell proteins that elicit antibody production during primary varicella using immune transfer method. *J Gen Virol* 1984; 65:2141–2147.

110. Gershon AA, Steinberg SP: Inactivation of varicella zoster virus in vitro: Effect of leukocytes and specific antibody. *Infect Immun* 1981; 33:507–511.

111. Arvin AM, Koropchak CM, Williams BRG, et al: Early immune response in healthy and immunocompromised subjects with primary varicella-zoster virus infection. *J Infect Dis* 1986; 154:422–429.

112. Jordan GW, Merigan TC: Cell-mediated immunity to varicella-zoster virus: In vitro lymphocyte responses. *J Infect Dis* 1974; 130:495–501.

113. Arvin AM, Kinney-Thomas E, Shriver K, et al: Immunity to varicella-zoster viral glycoproteins, gp I (gp 90/58) and gp III (gp 118), and to a nonglycosylated protein, p. 170. *J Immunol* 1986; 137:1346–1351.

114. Gershon AA, Steinberg S, Smith M: Cell-mediated immunity to varicella-zoster virus demonstrated by viral inactivation with human leukocytes. *Infect Immun* 1976; 13:1549–1553.

115. Gershon AA, Steinberg SP: Cellular and humoral immune responses to varicella-zoster virus in immunocompromised patients during and after varicella-zoster infections. *Infect Immun* 1979; 25:170–174.

116. Kamiya H, Ihara T, Hattori A, et al: Diagnostic skin test reactions with varicella virus antigen and clinical application of the test. *J Infect Dis* 1977; 136:784–788.

117. Russell AS, Maini RA, Bailey M, et al: Cell-mediated immunity to varicella-zoster antigen in acute herpes zoster (shingles). *Clin Exp Immunol* 1972; 14:181–185.

118. Arvin AM, Pollard RB, Rasmussen LE, et al: Selective impairment of lymphocyte reactivity to varicella-zoster virus antigen among untreated patients with lymphoma. *J Infect Dis* 1978; 137:531–540.

119. Miller AE: Selective decline in cellular immune response to varicella-zoster in the elderly. *Neurology* 1980; 30:582–587.

120. Gershon AA, Steinberg SP: Antibody responses to varicella-zoster virus and the role of antibody in host defense. *Am J Med Sci* 1981; 282:12–17.

121. Nielsen H, Ølholm P, Feldt-Rasmussen U, et al: Circulating immune complexes and complement-fixing antibodies in patients with varicella-zoster infection. *Scand J Infect Dis* 1980; 12:21–26.

122. Twomey JJ, Gyorkey F, Norris SM: The monocyte disorder with herpes zoster. *J Lab Clin Med* 1974; 83:768–777.

123. Lux SE, Johnston RB Jr, August CS, et al: Chronic neutropenia and abnormal cellular immunity in cartilage-hair hypoplasia. *N Engl J Med* 1970; 282:231–236.

123a. Jura E, Chadwick EG, Josephs SH, et al: Varicella-zoster virus infections in children infected with human immunodeficiency virus. *Pediatr Infect Dis J* 1989; 8:586–590.

124. Feldman S, Hughes WT, Daniel CB: Varicella in children with cancer: Seventy-seven cases. *Pediatrics* 1975; 56:388–397.

125. Feldman S, Epp E: Detection of viremia during incubation of varicella. *J Pediatr* 1979; 94:746–748.

126. Myers MG: Viremia caused by varicella-zoster virus: Association with malignant progressive varicella. *J Infect Dis* 1979; 140:229–233.

127. Morgan ER, Smalley LA: Varicella in immunocompromised children: incidence of abdominal pain and organ involvement. *Am J Dis Child* 1983; 137:883–885.

128. Warrier I, Ravindranath Y: Splenic infarction and total functional asplenia in disseminated varicella. *J Pediatr* 1986; 109:305–307.

129. Atkinson K, Meyers JD, Storb R, et al: Varicella-zoster virus infection after marrow transplantation for aplastic anemia or leukemia. *Transplantation* 1980; 29:47–50.

130. Feldhoff CM, Balfour HH Jr, Simmons RL, et al: Varicella in children with renal transplants. *J Pediatr* 1981; 98:25–31.

131. Haggerty RJ, Eley RC: Varicella and cortisone, letter. *Pediatrics* 1956; 18:160–162.

132. Gershon A, Brunell PA, Doyle EF: Steroid therapy and varicella, letter. *J Pediatr* 1972; 81:1034.

133. Resnick J, Schanberger JE: Varicella reactivation in nephrotic syndrome treated with cyclophosphamide and adrenal corticosteroids. *J Pediatr* 1973; 83:451–454.

134. Falliers CJ, Ellis EF: Corticosteroids and varicella: Six-year experience in an asthmatic population. *Arch Dis Child* 1965; 40:593–599.

135. Dolin R, Reichman RC, Mazur MH, et al: Herpes zoster-varicella infections in immunosuppressed patients. *Ann Intern Med* 1978; 89:375–388.

136. Goffinet DR, Glatstein EJ, Merigan TC: Herpes zoster-varicella infections and lymphoma. *Ann Intern Med* 1972; 76:235–240.

137. Manning DM, Luparello FJ, Arena VC Jr: Herpes zoster after splenectomy: A study of patients without malignancy. *JAMA* 1980; 243:56–58.

138. Feldman S, Hughes WT, Kim HY: Herpes zoster in children with cancer. *Am J Dis Child* 1973; 126:178–184.

139. Rand KH, Rasmussen LE, Pollard RB, et al: Cellular immunity and herpesvirus infections in cardiac-transplant patients. *N Engl J Med* 1977; 296:1372–1377.

140. Moutsopoulos HM, Gallagher JD, Decker JL, et al: Herpes zoster in patients with systemic lupus erythematosus. *Arthritis Rheum* 1978; 21:798–802.

141. Quinnan GV, Masur H, Rook AH, et al: Herpesvirus infections in the acquired immune deficiency syndrome. *JAMA* 1984; 252:72–77.

142. Ryder JW, Croen K, Kleinschmidt-DeMasters BK, et al: Progressive encephalitis three months after resolution of cutaneous zoster in a patient with AIDS. *Ann Neurol* 1986; 19:182–188.

143. Feldman S, Chaudhary S, Ossi M, et al: A viremic phase for herpes zoster in children with cancer. *J Pediatr* 1977; 91:597–600.

144. Stevens DA, Merigan TC: Interferon, antibody, and other host factors in herpes zoster. *J Clin Invest* 1972; 51:1170–1178.

145. Mazur MH, Whitley RJ, Dolin R: Serum antibody levels as risk factors in the dissemination of herpes zoster. *Arch Intern Med* 1979; 139:1341–1345.

146. Gallagher JG, Merigan TC: Prolonged herpes-zoster infection associated with immunosuppressive therapy. *Ann Intern Med* 1979; 91:842–846.

147. Hurley JK, Greenslade T, Lewy PR, et al: Varicella-zoster infections in pediatric renal transplant recipients. *Arch Surg* 1980; 115:751–752.
148. Sever J, White LR: Intrauterine viral infections. *Annu Rev Med* 1968; 19:471–486.
149. Siegel M: Congenital malformations following chickenpox, measles, mumps, and hepatitis: Results of a cohort study. *JAMA* 1973; 226:1521–1524.
150. Siegel M, Fuerst HT, Peress NS: Comparative fetal mortality in maternal virus diseases: A prospective study on rubella, measles, mumps, chickenpox, and hepatitis. *N Engl J Med* 1966; 274:768–771.
151. Siegel M, Fuerst HT: Low birth weight and maternal virus diseases. *JAMA* 1966; 197:680–684.
152. Paryani SG, Arvin AM: Intrauterine infection with varicella-zoster virus after maternal varicella. *N Engl J Med* 1986; 314:1542–1546.
153. Harris RE, Rhoades ER: Varicella pneumonia complicating pregnancy: Report of a case and review of literature. *Obstet Gynecol* 1965; 25:734–740.
154. Meyers JD: Congenital varicella in term infants: Risk reconsidered. *J Infect Dis* 1974; 129:215–217.
155. DeNicola LK, Hanshaw JB: Congenital and neonatal varicella. *J Pediatr* 1979; 94:175–176.
156. Bai PVA, John TJ: Congenital skin ulcers following varicella in late pregnancy. *J Pediatr* 1979; 94:65–67.
157. Enders G: Varicella-zoster virus infection in pregnancy. *Prog Med Virol* 1984; 29:166–196.
158. Blot WJ, Draper G, Kinlen L, et al: Childhood cancer in relation to prenatal exposure to chickenpox. *Br J Cancer* 1980; 42:342–344.
159. Appel I, Frydman M, Savir H, et al: Uveitis and ophthalmoplegia complicating chickenpox. *J Pediatr Ophthalmol* 1977; 14:346–348.
160. Brunell PA: Varicella-zoster infections in pregnancy. *JAMA* 1967; 199:315–317.
161. Bullowa JGM, Wishik SM: Complications of varicella: I. Their occurrence among 2,534 patients. *Am J Dis Child* 1935; 49:923–926.
162. Weber DM, Pellecchia JA: Varicella pneumonia. *JAMA* 1965; 192:572–573.
163. Triebwasser JH, Harris RE, Bryant RE, et al: Varicella pneumonia in adults. *Medicine* 1967; 46:409–423.
164. Bocles JS, Ehrenkranz NJ, Marks A: Abnormalities of respiratory function in varicella pneumonia. *Ann Intern Med* 1964; 60:183–195.
165. Weinstein L, Meade RH: Respiratory manifestations of chickenpox: Special consideration of the features of primary varicella pneumonia. *Arch Intern Med* 1956; 98:91–99.
166. Glick N, Levin S, Nelson K: Recurrent pulmonary infarction in adult chickenpox pneumonia. *JAMA* 1972; 222:173–177.
167. Brown GD, Eron LJ: Fatal pulmonary embolism in an adolescent with chickenpox. *South Med J* 1979; 72:1489–1490.
168. Chusid MJ, Williamson SJ, Murphy JV, et al: Neuromyelitis optica (Devic disease) following varicella infection. *J Pediatr* 1979; 95:737–738.
169. McCarthy JT, Amer J: Postvaricella acute transverse myelitis: A case presentation and review of the literature. *Pediatrics* 1978; 62:202–204.
170. Singer J: Postvaricella suppurative meningitis. *Am J Dis Child* 1979; 133:934–935.
171. Takashima S, Becker LE: Neuropathology of fatal varicella. *Arch Pathol Lab Med* 1979; 103:209–213.
172. Peters ACB, Versteeg J, Lindeman J, et al: Varicella and acute cerebellar ataxia. *Arch Neurol* 1978; 35:769–771.
173. Gershon A, Steinberg S, Greenberg S: Varicella-zoster-associated encephalitis: detection of specific antibody in cerebrospinal fluid. *J Clin Microbiol* 1980; 12:764–767.
174. Johnson R, Milbourn PE: Central nervous system manifestations of chickenpox. *Can Med Assoc J* 1970; 102:831–834.
175. Bouthton CR: Varicella-zoster in Sydney: II. Neurological complications of varicells. *Med J Aust* 1966; 2:444–447.
176. Pitel PA, McCormick KL, Fitzgerald E, et al: Subclinical hepatic changes in varicella infection. *Pediatrics* 1980; 65:631–633.
177. Hurwitz ES, Nelson DB, Davis C: National surveillance for Reye syndrome: a five-year review. *Pediatrics* 1982; 70:895–900.
178. Centers for Disease Control: Reye syndrome—United States, 1985. *MMWR* 1986; 35:66–74.
179. Glasgow AM, Gold MB: The interval between varicella and Reye's syndrome. *Am J Dis Child* 1979; 133:653.
180. Hirsch EO, Dameshek W: "Idiopathic" thrombocytopenia: Review of eighty-nine cases with particular reference to the differentiation and treatment of acute (self-limited) and chronic types. *Arch Intern Med* 1951; 88:701–728.
181. Charkes ND: Purpuric chickenpox: Report of a case, review of the literature and classification by clinical features. *Ann Intern Med* 1961; 54:745–754.
182. Tobin JD Jr, ten Bensel RW: Varicella with thrombocytopenia causing fatal intracerebral hemorrhage. *Am J Dis Child* 1972; 124:577–578.
183. Hørder M: Purpura fulminans following varicella. *Dan Med Bull* 1968; 15:221–224.
184. Espinoza C, Kuhn C: Viral infection of megakaryocytes in varicella with purpura. *Am J Clin Pathol* 1974; 61:203–208.
185. Feusner JH, Slichter SJ, Harker LA: Mechanisms of thrombocytopenia in varicella. *Am J Hematol* 1979; 7:255–264.
186. McKay DG, Margaretten W: Disseminated intravascular coagulation in virus diseases. *Arch Intern Med* 1967; 120:129–152.
187. Smith EWP, Garson A Jr, Boyleston JA, et al: Varicella gangrenosa due to group A beta-hemolytic *Streptococcus. Pediatrics* 1976; 57:306–310.
188. Belsey MA: Tuberculosis and varicella infections in children. *Am J Dis Child* 1967; 113:444–448.
189. Stehr-Green JK, Juranck DJ, McCaig L, et al: Chickenpox and infection with cryptosporidiosis. *Am J Dis Child* 1986; 140:1213.
190. Melish ME: Bullous varicella: Its association with the staphylococcal scalded skin syndrome. *J Pediatr* 1973; 83:1019–1021.
191. Wald ER, Levine MM, Togo Y: Concomitant varicella and staphylococcal scalded skin syndrome. *J Pediatr* 1973; 83:1017–1019.
192. Priest JR, Urick JJ, Groth KE, et al: Varicella arthritis documented by isolation of virus from joint fluid. *J Pediatr* 1978; 93:990–992.
193. Mandelbaum T, Terk BH: Pericarditis in association with chickenpox. *JAMA* 1959; 170:191–194.
194. Hackel DB: Myocarditis in association with varicella. *Am J Pathol* 1953; 29:369–378.
195. Salomon JB, Gordon JE, Scrimshaw NS: Studies of diarrheal disease in Central America: Associated chickenpox, diarrhea and kwashiorkor in a Highland Guatemalan village. *Am J Trop Med Hyg* 1966; 15:997–1002.
196. Sharman VL, Goodwin FJ: Hemolytic uremic syndrome following chickenpox. *Clin Nephrol* 1980; 14:49–51.
197. Spirer Z, Ilie B, Pick IA, et al: Localized scleroderma following varicella in a three-year-old girl with IgA deficiency. *Acta Pediatr Scand* 1979; 68:783–785.
198. Sawyer MH: Treatment and prevention of varicella-zoster virus infections, in Staus SE (moderator): Varicella-zoster virus infections: biology, natural history, treatment, and prevention. *Ann Intern Med* 1988; 108:221–237.
199. Tovi F, Sidi J, Haikin H, et al: Viral infection and acute peripheral facial palsy. *Israel J Med Sci* 1980; 16:576–580.
200. Chapman BA, Beaven DW: An unusual case of flaccid paralysis of both lower limbs following herpes zoster. *Aust NZ J Med* 1979; 9:702–704.
201. Bieger C, VanScoy RE, Smith TF: Antibodies to varicella zoster in cerebrospinal fluid. *Arch Neurol* 1977; 34:489–491.

202. Peters ACB, Versteef J, Bots GTAM, et al: Nervous system complications of herpes zoster: Immunofluorescent demonstration of varicella-zoster antigen in CSF cells. *J Neurol Neurosurg Psychiatry* 1979; 42:452–457.
203. Andiman WA, White-Greenwald M, Tinghitella T: Zoster encephalitis: isolation of virus and measurement of varicella-zoster specific antibodies in cerebrospinal fluid. *Am J Med* 1982; 73:769–772.
204. Pavan-Langston D: Herpes simplex and herpes zoster kertouveitis: Diagnosis and management. *Bull NY Acad Med* 1977; 53:731–748.
205. Drew LW, Mintz L: Rapid diagnosis of varicella-zoster virus infection by direct immunofluorescence. *Am J Clin Pathol* 1980; 73:699–701.
206. Williams V, Gershon A, Brunell PA: Serologic response to varicella zoster membrane antigens measured by indirect immunofluorescence. *J Infect Dis* 1974; 130:669–672.
207. Demmler GJ, Steinberg SP, Blum G, et al: Rapid enzyme-linked immunosorbent assay for detecting antibody to varicella-zoster virus. *J Infect Dis* 1988; 157:211–212.
208. Gerna G, Achilli G, Chambers RW: Determination of neutralizing antibody and IgG antibody to varicella-zoster virus and of IgG antibody to membrane antigens by the immunoperoxidase technique. *J Infect Dis* 1977; 135:975–979.
209. Haikin H, Leventon–Kriss S, Sarov I: Antibody to varicella–zoster virus–induced membrane antigen: Immunoperoxidase assay with air–dried target cells. *J Infect Dis* 1979; 140:601–604.
210. Friedman MG, Leventon–Kriss S, Sarov I: Sensitive solid–phase radioimmunoassay for detection of human immunoglobulin G antibodies to varicella–zoster virus. *J Clin Microbiol* 1979; 9:1–10.
211. Landry ML, Cohen SD, Mayo DR, et al: Comparison of fluorescent-antibody-to-membrane-antigen test, indirect immunofluorescence assay, and a commercial enzyme-linked immunosorbent assay for determination of antibody to varicella-zoster virus. *J Clin Microbiol* 1987; 25:832–835.
212. Cradock-Watson JE, Ridehalgh MKS, Bourne MS: Specific immunoglobulin responses after varicella and herpes zoster. *J Hyg Camb* 1979; 82:319–336.
213. Hacham M, Leventon-Kriss S, Sarov I: Enzyme-linked immunosorbent assay for detection of virus-specific IgM antibodies to varicella-zoster virus. *Intervirology* 1980; 13:214–222.
214. Ziegler T: Detection of varicella–zoster viral antigens in clinical specimens by solid–phase enzyme immunoassay. *J Infect Dis* 1984; 150:149–154.
215. Grandien M, Appelgren P, Espmark A, et al: Determination of varicella immunity by the indirect immunofluorescence test in urgent clinical situations. *Scand J Infect Dis* 1976; 8:65–69.
216. Committee on Infectious Diseases, American Academy of Pediatrics, in Peter G (ed): *Report of the Committee on Infectious Diseases (The Red Book)*. Elk Grove Village, Ill, American Academy of Pediatrics, 1988, pp 457–462.
217. Garner JS, Simmons BP: Guideline for isolation precautions in hospitals. *Infect Control* 1983; 4:245–325.
218. Brunell PA, Ross A, Miller LH, et al: Prevention of varicella by zoster immune globulin. *N Engl J Med* 1969; 280:1191–1194.
219. Brunell PA, Gershon AA, Hughes WT, et al: Prevention of varicella in high risk children: A collaborative study. *Pediatrics* 1972; 50:718–722.
220. Gershon AA, Steinberg S, Brunell PA: Zoster immune globulin: A further assessment. *N Engl J Med* 1974; 290:243–245.
221. Winsnes R: Efficacy of zoster immunoglobulin in prophylaxis of varicella in high-risk patients. *Acta Pediatr Scand* 1978; 67:77–82.
222. Geiser CF, Bishop Y, Myers M, et al: Prophylaxis of varicella in children with neoplastic disease: Comparative results with zoster immune plasma and gamma globulin. *Cancer* 1975; 35:1027–1030.
223. Balfour HH Jr, Groth KE: Zoster immune plasma prophylaxis

of varicella: A follow-up report. *J Pediatr* 1979; 94:743–746.
224. Gershon AA, Piomelli S, Karpatkin M, et al: Antibody to varicella-zoster virus after passive immunization against chickenpox. *J Clin Microbiol* 1978; 8:733–735.
225. Groth KE, McCullough J, Marker SC, et al: Evaluation of zoster immune plasma: Treatment of cutaneous disseminated zoster in immunocompromised patients. *JAMA* 1978; 239:1877–1879.
226. Stevens DA, Merigan TC: Zoster immune globulin prophylaxis of disseminated zoster in compromised host. *Arch Intern Med* 1980; 140:52–54.
227. Zaia JA, Levin MJ, Wirght GG, et al: A practical method for preparation of varicella–zoster immune globulin. *J Infect Dis* 1978; 137:601–604.
228. Zaia JA, Levin MJ, Preblud SR, et al: Evaluation of varicella–zoster immune globulin: protection of immunosuppressed children after household exposure to varicella. *J Infect Dis* 1983; 147:737–743.
229. Centers for Disease Control: Varicella–zoster immune globulin for the prevention of chickenpox. *MMWR* 1984; 33:84–100.
230. Grady GF, Leszczynski J, Wright GG: Varicella-zoster immune globulin—United States. *MMWR* 1981; 30:15–23.
231. Stiehm RE: Standard and special human immune serum globulins as therapeutic agents. *Pediatrics* 1979; 63:301–319.
232. Rubin L, Leggiadro R, Elie MT, et al: Disseminated varicella in a neonate: implications for immunoprophylaxis of neonates postnatally exposed to varicella. *Pediatr Infect Dis* 1986; 5:100–102.
233. Wurzel CL, Rubin LG, Krilov LR: Varicella zoster immunoglobulin after postnatal exposure to varicella: survey of experts. *Pediatr Infect Dis* 1987; 6:466–468.
234. Bakshi SS, Miller TC, Kaplan M, et al: Failure of varicella-zoster immunoglobulin in modification of severe congenital varicella. *Pediatr Infect Dis* 1986; 5:699–702.
235. King SM, Gorensek M, Ford-Jones EL, et al: Fatal varicella-zoster infection in a newborn treated with varicella-zoster immunoglobulin. *Pediatr Infect Dis* 1986; 5:588–589.
236. Paryani SG, Arvin AM, Koropchak CM, et al: Comparison of varicella zoster antibody titers in patients given intravenous immune serum globulin or varicella zoster immune globulin. *J Pediatr* 1984; 105:200–205.
237. Steele RW, Myers MG, Vincent MM: Transfer factor for the prevention of varicella-zoster infection in childhood leukemia. *N Engl J Med* 1980; 303:355–359.
238. Steele RW: Transfer factor and cellular reactivity to varicella-zoster antigen in childhood leukemia. *Cell Immunol* 1980; 50:282–289.
239. Bowden RA, Siegel MS, Steele RW, et al: Immunologic and clinical responses to varicella-zoster virus–specific transfer factor following marrow transplantation. *J Infect Dis* 1985; 152:1324–1327.
240. Schiff GM: Active immunizations for adults. *Annu Rev Med* 1980; 31:441–451.
241. Kempe CH, Gershon AA: Varicella vaccine at the crossroads. *Pediatrics* 1977; 60:930–931.
242. Sabin AB: Varicella–zoster virus vaccine. *JAMA* 1977; 238:1731–1733.
243. Plotkin SA: Varicella vendetta: Plotkin's plug, letter. *Pediatrics* 1977; 59:953–954.
244. Brunell PA: Varicella–zoster virus vaccine, letter. *JAMA* 1978; 239:1034–1035.
245. Takahashi M, Otsuka T, Okuno Y, et al: Live vaccine used to prevent the spread of varicella in children in hospital. *Lancet* 1974; 2:1288–1290.
246. Hayakawa Y, Toriqoe S, Shiraki K, et al: Biologic and biophysical markers of a live varicella vaccine strain (Oka): identification of clinical isolates from vaccine recipients. *J Infect Dis* 1984; 149:956–963.
247. Martin JH, Dohner DE, Wellinghoff WJ, et al: Restriction endonuclease analysis of varicella zoster vaccine and wild-type DNAs. *J Med Virol* 1982; 9:69–76.

248. Asano Y, Yazaki T, Ito S, et al: Contact infection from live varicella vaccine recipients, letter. *Lancet* 1976; 1:965.

249. Brunell PA, Shehab Z, Geiser C, et al: Administration of live varicella vaccine to children with leukemia. *Lancet* 1982; 2:1069–1072.

250. Gershon AA, Steinberg SP, Gelb L, et al: Live attenuated varicella vaccine: Efficacy for children with leukemia in remission. *JAMA* 1984; 252:355–362.

251. Gershon AA, Steinberg SP, Gelb L, et al: Live attenuated varicella vaccine use in immunocompromised children and adults. *Pediatrics* 1986; 78(suppl):757–762.

252. Asano Y, Nakayama H, Yazaki T, et al: Protective efficacy of vaccination in children in four episodes of natural varicella and zoster in the ward. *Pediatrics* 1977; 59:8–12.

253. Asano Y, Nakayama H, Yazaki T, et al: Protection against varicella in family contacts by immediate inoculation with live varicella vaccine. *Pediatrics* 1977; 59:3–7.

254. Baba K, Yabuuchi H, Okuni H, et al: Studies with live varicella vaccine and inactivated skin test antigen: Protective effect of the vaccine and clinical application of the skin test. *Pediatrics* 1978; 61:550–555.

255. Asano Y, Takahashi M: Clinical and serologic testing of a live varicella vaccine and two-year follow-up for immunity of the vaccinated children. *Pediatrics* 1977; 60:810–814.

256. Asano Y, Albrecht P, Vujcic LK, et al: Five-year follow-up study of recipients of live varicella vaccine using enhanced neutralization and fluorescent antibody membrane antigen assays. *Pediatrics* 1983; 72:291–294.

257. Asano Y, Nagai T, Miyata T, et al: Long-term protective immunity of recipients of the OKA strain of live varicella vaccine. *Pediatrics* 1985; 75:667–671.

258. Weibel RE, Neff BJ, Kuter BJ, et al: Live attenuated varicella virus vaccine: efficacy trial in healthy children. *N Engl J Med* 1984; 310:1409–1415.

259. Arbeter AM, Starr SE, Plotkin SA: Varicella vaccine studies in healthy children and adults. *Pediatrics* 1986; 78(suppl):748–756.

260. Arbeter AM, Starr SE, Weibel RE, et al: Live attenuated varicella vaccine: immunization of healthy children with the OKA strain. *J Pediatr* 1982; 100:886–893.

261. Berger R, Luescher D, Just M: Restoration of varicella-zoster virus cell-mediated immune response after varicella booster vaccination. *Postgrad Med J* 1985; 61(suppl 4):143–145.

262. Arbeter AM, Baker L, Starr SE, et al: Combination measles, mumps, rubella, and varicella vaccine. *Pediatrics* 1986; 78(suppl):742–747.

263. Bogger-Goren S, Baba K, Hurley P, et al: Antibody response to varicella-zoster virus after natural or vaccine-induced infection. *J Infect Dis* 1982; 146:260–265.

264. Brunell PA, Novelli VM, Keller PM, et al: Antibodies to the three major glycoproteins of varicella-zoster virus: search for the relevant host immune response. *J Infect Dis* 1987; 156:430–435.

265. Dubey L, Steinberg SP, LaRussa P, et al: Western blot analysis of antibody to varicella-zoster virus. *J Infect Dis* 1988; 157:882–888.

266. Izawa T, Ihara T, Hattori A, et al: Application of a live varicella vaccine in children with acute leukemia or other malignant diseases. *Pediatrics* 1977; 6:805–809.

267. Nakagawa H, Katsushima N: Use of live varicella vaccine in children with acute leukemia. *Tohoku J Exp Med* 1978; 126:393–395.

268. Ha K, Baba K, Ikeda T, et al: Application of live varicella vaccine to children with acute leukemia or other malignancies without suspension of anticancer therapy. *Pediatrics* 1980; 65:346–350.

269. Gershon AA: Live attenuated varicella vaccine. *Annu Rev Med* 1987; 38:41–50.

270. Gershon AA, Steinberg SP, and the Varicella Vaccine Collaborative Study Group of the National Institute of Allergy and Infectious Diseases: Persistence of immunity to varicella in children with leukemia immunized with live attenuated varicella vaccine. *N Engl J Med* 1989; 320:892–897.

271. Lawrence R, Gershon AA, Holzman R, et al: The risk of zoster after varicella vaccination in children with leukemia. *N Engl J Med* 1988; 318:543–548.

272. Gelb LD, Dohner DE, Gershon AA, et al: Molecular epidemiology of live, attenuated varicella virus vaccine in children with leukemia and in normal adults. *J Infect Dis* 1987; 155:633–640.

273. Weber DJ, Rutala WA, Parham C: Impact and costs of varicella prevention in a university hospital. *Am J Public Health* 1988; 78:19–23.

274. Mortimer EA Jr, Lepow ML: Varicella with hypoglycemia possibly due to salicylates. *Am J Dis Child* 1962; 103:583–590.

275. Fleisher G, Henry W, McSorley M, et al: Life-threatening complications of varicella. *Am J Dis Child* 1981; 135:896–899.

276. Portenoy RK, Duma C, Foley KM: Acute herpetic and postherpetic neuralgia: clinical review and current management. *Ann Neurol* 1986; 20:651–664.

277. Juel-Jensen BE, MacCallum FO, Mackenzie AMR, et al: Treatment of zoster with idoxuridine in dimethyl sulphoxide: Results of two double-blind controlled trials. *Br Med J* 1970; 4:776–780.

278. Mehta M: Shingles: A belt of roses from Hell. *Br Med J* 1979; 3:346.

279. Wisnes R, Froland SS, Degré MI: Effect of transfer factor and zoster immunoglobulin in patients with varicella–zoster infection and malignancy. *Scand J Infect Dis* 1978; 10:21–27.

280. Stevens DA, Jordan GW, Waddell TF, et al: Adverse effect of cytosine arabinoside on disseminated zoster in a controlled trial. *N Engl J Med* 1973; 289:873–875.

281. Aronson MD, Phillips CR, Gump DW, et al: Vidarabine therapy for severe herpesvirus infections: An unusual syndrome of chronic varicella and transient immunologic deficiency. *JAMA* 1976; 235:1339–1342.

282. Whitley RJ, Ch'ien LT, Dolin R, et al: Adenine arabinoside therapy of herpes zoster in the immunosuppressed: NIAID Collaborative Antiviral Study. *N Engl J Med* 1976; 294:1193–1199.

283. Whitley R, Hilty M, Haynes R, et al: Vidarabine therapy of varicella in immunosuppressed patients. *J Pediatr* 1982; 101:125–131.

284. Whitley RJ, Soong S-J, Dolin R, et al: Early vidarabine therapy to control the complications of herpes zoster in immunosuppressed patients. *N Engl J Med* 1982; 307:971–975.

285. Juel-Jensen B: Severe chickenpox and purpura fulminans in zoster treated with vidarabine. *J Antimicrob Chemother* 1976; 2:261–264.

286. Busk CMA, Earl HM, Wrigley PFM, et al: Triple drug therapy of herpes zoster infection occurring in patients with reticuloendothelial neoplasia—A preliminary study. *J Antimicrob Chemother* 1980; 6:733–736.

287. Shepp DH, Dandliker PS, Meyers JD: Treatment of varicella-zoster virus infection in severely immunocompromised patients. *N Engl J Med* 1986; 314:208–212.

288. Biron KK, Elion GB: In vitro susceptibility of varicella-zoster virus to acyclovir. *Antimicrob Agents Chemother* 1980; 18:443–447.

289. Selby PJ, Jameson B, Watson JG, et al: Parenteral acyclovir therapy for herpesvirus infections in man. *Lancet* 1979; 2:1267–1270.

290. Balfour HH Jr, Bean B, Laskin OL, et al: Acyclovir halts progression of herpes zoster in immunocompromised patients. *N Engl J Med* 1983; 308:1448–1453.

291. Prober CG, Kirk LE, Keeney RE: Acyclovir therapy of chickenpox in immunosuppressed children—A collaborative study. *J Pediatr* 1982; 101:622–625.

292. van Weel–Sipman MH, van der Meer JWM, deKoning J, et al: Severe atypical recurrent varicella in childhood leukemia, letter. *Lancet* 1981; 1:147–148.

293. Williams H, Latif A, Morgan J, et al: Acyclovir in the treatment of neonatal varicella. *J Infect* 1987; 15:65–67.

293a. Balfour HH Jr, Kelly JM, Suarez CS, et al: Acyclovir treatment of varicella in otherwise healthy children. *J Pediatr* 1990; 116:633–639.

294. Bean B, Braun C, Balfour HH Jr, et al: Acyclovir therapy for acute herpes zoster. *Lancet* 1982; 2:118–121.

295. Jeul-Jensen BE, Khan JA, Pasvol G: High-dose intravenous acyclovir in the treatment of zoster: a double-blind placebo-controlled trial. *J Infect* 1983; 6(suppl 1):31–36.

296. McKendrick MW, McGill JI, White JE, et al: Oral acyclovir in acute herpes zoster. *Br Med J* 1986; 293:1529–1532.

297. Peterslund NA, Seyer-Hansen K, Ipsen J, et al: Acyclovir in herpes zoster. *Lancet* 1981; 2:827–830.

298. Al-Nakib W, Al-Kandari S, El-Khalik DMA, et al: A randomized controlled study of intravenous acyclovir (Zovirax) against placebo in adults with chickenpox. *J Infect* 1983; 6(suppl 1):49–56.

299. McGill J, Chapman C: A comparison of topical acyclovir with steroids in the treatment of herpes zoster keratouveitis. *Br J Ophthalmol* 1983; 67:746–750.

300. Cobo LM, Foulks GN, Liesegang T, et al: Oral acyclovir in the treatment of acute herpes zoster ophthalmicus. *Ophthalmology* 1986; 93:763–770.

301. Van Der Meer JWM, Thompson J, Tan WD, et al: Treatment of chickenpox pneumonia with acyclovir. *Lancet* 1980; 2:473–474.

302. Chitkara R, Gordon RE, Khan FA: Acyclovir in the treatment of primary varicella pneumonia in non-immunocompromised adults. *NY State J Med* 1987; 87:237–238.

303. Landsberger EJ, Hager WD, Grossman JH III: Successful management of varicella pneumonia complicating pregnancy. A report of three cases. *J Reprod Med* 1986; 31:311–314.

304. Hockberger RS, Rothstein RJ: Varicella pneumonia in adults: a spectrum of disease. *Ann Emerg Med* 1986; 15:931–934.

305. Hankins GDV, Gilstrap LC III, Patterson AR: Acyclovir treatment of varicella pneumonia in pregnancy. *Crit Care Med* 1987; 15:336–337.

306. Eder SE, Apuzzio JJ, Weiss G: Varicella pneumonia during pregnancy. Treatment of two cases with acyclovir. *Am J Perinatol* 1988; 5:16–18.

307. Greffe BS, Dooley SL, Deddish RB, et al: Transplacental passage of acyclovir. *J Pediatr* 1986; 108:1020–1021.

308. Feldman S, Hayes RA, Chaudhary S, et al: Inosiplex for localized herpes zoster in childhood cancer patients: Preliminary controlled study. *Antimicrob Agents Chemother* 1978; 14:495–497.

309. Galbraith AW: Treatment of acute herpes zoster with amantadine hydrochloride (Symmetrel). *Br Med J* 1973; 4:693–695.

310. De Clercq E, Degreef H, Wildiers J, et al: Oral (E)-5-(2-bromo-vinyl)-2'-deoxyuridine in severe herpes zoster. *Br Med J* 1980; 281:1178.

311. Bruni L, Califano A, DeAngelis G, et al: Preliminary results of a clinical trial relative to the use of rifamycin SV in the treatment of herpes zoster. *J Int Med Res* 1980; 8:1–6.

312. DeClercq E, Descamps J, Ogata M, et al: In vitro susceptibility of varicella-zoster virus to E-5-(2-bromovinyl)-2'-deoxyuridine and related compounds. *Antimicrob Agents Chemother* 1982; 21:33–38.

313. Machida H, Kuninaka A, Yoshino H: Inhibitory effects of antiherpesviral thymidine analogs against varicella-zoster virus. *Antimicrob Agents Chemother* 1982; 21:358–361.

314. Baba M, Shigeta S: Antiviral activity of glycyrrhizin against varicella-zoster virus in vitro. *Antiviral Res* 1987; 7:99–107.

315. Peterslund NA, Esmann V, Geil JP, et al: Open study of 2-amino-9-(hydroxyethoxymethyl)-9H-purine (desciclovir) in the treatment of herpes zoster. *J Antimicrob Chemother* 1987; 20:743–751.

316. Sklar SH, Blue WT, Alexander EJ, et al: Herpes zoster. The treatment and prevention of neuralgia with adenosine monophosphate. *JAMA* 1985; 253:1427–1430.

317. Merigan TC, Waddell D, Grossman M, et al: Modified skin lesions during concurrent varicella and measles infections. *JAMA* 1968; 204:333–335.

318. Patel PA, Yoonessi S, O'Malley J, et al: Cell-mediated immunity to varicella-zoster virus infection in subjects with lymphoma or leukemia. *J Pediatr* 1979; 94:223–230.

319. Neumann-Haefelin D, Sundmacher R, Sauter B, et al: Effect of human leukocyte interferon on vaccinia- and herpes zoster virus-infected cell cultures and monkey corneas. *Infect Immun* 1975; 12:148–155.

320. Rasmussen L, Holmes AR, Hofmeister B, et al: Multiplicity-dependent replication of varicella-zoster virus in interferon-treated cells. *J Gen Virol* 1977; 35:361–368.

321. Emödi G, Rufli T, Just M, et al: Human interferon therapy for herpes zoster in adults. *Scand J Infect Dis* 1975; 7:1–5.

322. Emödi G, Rufli T: Antiviral action of interferon in man: Use of interferon in varicella-zoster infections in man. *Tex Rep Biol Med* 1977; 35:511–515.

323. Merigan TC, Rand KH, Pollard RB, et al: Human leukocyte interferon for the treatment of herpes zoster in patients with cancer. *N Engl J Med* 1978; 298:981–987.

324. Merigan TC, Gallagher JG, Pollard RB, et al: Short-course human leukocyte interferon in treatment of herpes zoster in patients with cancer. *Antimicrob Agents Chemother* 1981; 19:193–195.

325. Arvin AM, Feldman S, Merigan TC: Human leukocyte interferon in the treatment of varicella in children with cancer: A preliminary controlled trial. *Antimicrob Agents Chemother* 1978; 13:605–607.

326. Arvin AM, Kushner JH, Feldman S, et al: Human leukocyte interferon for the treatment of varicella in children with cancer. *N Engl J Med* 1982; 306:761–765.

327. Soike KF, Kramer MJ, Gerone PJ: In vivo antiviral activity of recombinant type alpha interferon A in monkeys with infections due to simian varicella virus. *J Infect Dis* 1983; 147:933–938.

328. Duschet P, Schwarz T, Soyer P, et al: Treatment of herpes zoster. Recombinant alpha interferon versus acyclovir. *Int J Dermatol* 1988; 27:193–197.

329. Levin MJ, Leary PL: Inhibition of human herpesviruses by combinations of acyclovir and human leukocyte interferon. *Infect Immun* 1981; 32:995–999.

330. Baba M, Ito M, Shigeta S, et al: Synergistic antiviral effects of antiherpes compounds and human leukocyte interferon on varicella-zoster virus in vitro. *Antimicrob Agents Chemother* 1984; 25:515–517.

331. Soike KF, Eppstein DA, Gloff CA, et al: Effect of 9-(1,3-dihydroxy-2-propoxymethyl) guanine and recombinant human beta interferon alone and in combination on simian varicella virus infection in monkeys. *J Infect Dis* 1987; 156:607–614.

332. Jacobson MA, Berger TG, Fikrig S, et al: Acyclovir-resistant varicella zoster virus infection after chronic oral acyclovir therapy in patients with the acquired immunodeficiency syndrome (AIDS). *Ann Intern Med* 1990; 112:187–191.

333. Sawyer MH, Inchauspe G, Biron KK, et al: Molecular analysis of the pyrimidine deoxyribonucleoside kinase gene of wild-type and acyclovir resistant strains of varicella zoster virus. *J Gen Virol* 1988; 69:2585–2593.

36

Epstein-Barr Virus

Gary R. Fleisher

The Epstein-Barr virus (EBV) was discovered in 1964[1] and was subsequently shown to be the cause of infectious mononucleosis,[2] almost a half century after Sprunt and Evans[3] described this disease. The lag period between the delineation of the clinical disease and the etiologic agent has led, at times, to confusion in the use of certain terms: infectious mononucleosis, infectious mononucleosis syndrome, and Epstein-Barr virus infection. Therefore, it is appropriate to define these terms precisely at the outset of this chapter (Figure 36–1):

1. Infectious mononucleosis (IM) refers to an illness charac-

terized by the constellation of fatigue, fever, pharyngitis, lymphadenopathy, and splenomegaly and caused by the EBV.

2. The infectious mononucleosis syndrome has the same clinical characteristics as IM but may result from an infection with agents other than EBV, most notably cytomegalovirus (CMV) or toxoplasmosis, or as a reaction to noninfectious insults, such as the hypersensitivity response occasionally seen after the administration of phenytoin. Until the etiology is verified, a patient with the aforementioned clinical manifestations should be considered to have the infectious mononucleosis syndrome; the term IM is reserved for those cases in which EBV is found to be the cause. Patients with infectious mononucleosis usually, but not necessarily, develop a heterophil antibody (HA) response.

3. An Epstein-Barr virus infection refers to any infection caused by EBV, regardless of the associated clinical syndrome. Thus the term includes not only IM but also asymptomatic seroconversion and unusual manifestations, such as encephalitis.

Throughout this chapter, a series of abbreviations are used to refer to the virus, viral- and virus-associated antigens, and EBV-related diseases. Table 36–1 provides a listing of these terms.

HISTORY

The history of EBV in its early years is really the history of IM. Despite the fact that civilization has led to the conquest of many diseases by the application of scientific knowledge, this same progress has created an opportunity for the emergence of new diseases, IM being among these. Not until 1920, did Sprunt and Evans[3] describe an illness that unquestionably represented IM as it is now defined. The lack of prior descriptions rested not upon oversight but rather on the infrequency of this disease under conditions of crowding and inadequate sanitation.[4]

Subsequent to the initial clinical report, improved diagnostic criteria for IM were introduced. In 1923, Downey and McKinlay[5] detailed the hematologic abnormalities that occur with IM. While searching for HAs in patients with rheumatic fever in 1932, Paul and Bunnell[6] discovered such antibodies in their control group

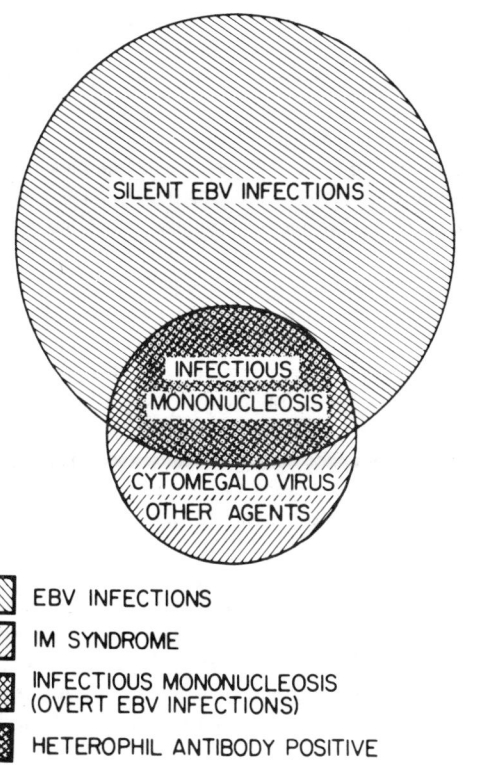

EBV INFECTIONS

IM SYNDROME

INFECTIOUS MONONUCLEOSIS
(OVERT EBV INFECTIONS)

HETEROPHIL ANTIBODY POSITIVE

Figure 36–1. Definition of clinical terms. EBV = Epstein-Barr virus; IM = infectious mononucleosis.

among four individuals who had IM. Later, HA were shown to consistently appear in IM but also to develop in serum sickness and to be present occasionally in well patients. To overcome the diagnostic difficulties created by the occurrence of HA in conditions other than IM, Davidsohn[7] in 1937 advanced the differential absorption test which distinguished IM-specific HA from those

unrelated to IM. He showed that beef red blood cells but not guinea pig kidney extract adsorbed the IM-specific HA, a different pattern being observed in patients with serum sickness or naturally occurring (Forsmann) antibodies.

In 1958, Mr Denis Burkitt[8] described a tumor of the jaw among African natives distributed in a geographic band across the continent, an event seemingly unrelated to the history of EBV at the time. Electron microscopy, performed on cells cultured from specimens of such tumors by Epstein and colleagues[1] in 1964, demonstrated viral particles in some of the lymphoblasts, resembling members of the herpesvirus family. In 1966, Drs Gertrude and Werner Henle[9] developed an indirect immunofluorescent assay (IFA) for antibodies to this virus (now called EBV), allowing for subsequent investigations into its epidemiology. Shortly thereafter, a technician in the Henle laboratory, previously shown to lack antibodies to EBV, developed IM. When testing of her postillness serum then showed the appearance of antibodies to EBV, the Henles postulated, in 1968, that this virus caused IM.[2] Further studies, in collaboration with Niederman and McCollum at Yale University, convincingly proved the etiologic role of EBV in this disease.[10] Using sera collected prospectively from entering freshmen who were followed during their college years, these investigators showed that EBV-specific antibodies were absent prior to the development of IM and appeared subsequently in every case.

Since the discovery of EBV, advances have occurred in both the serodiagnosis and molecular virology of this agent. These techniques have allowed confirmation of the role of EBV in Burkitt's lymphoma (BL)[11] and provided evidence of an association with a second malignancy, nasopharyngeal carcinoma (NPC).[12]

BIOLOGY

Physical Properties

EBV belongs to the herpes group of viruses and has the characteristic morphology displayed by the other members. The in-

Table 36–1
Abbreviations and Descriptions of Viral Antigens

Abbreviations		Description
EBNA	Epstein-Barr virus–associated nuclear antigen	Nonstructural viral antigen; antibody to the antigen develops after a primary infection
EBV	Epstein-Barr virus	Whole virion
EA	Early antigens	Nonstructural antigens formed early in viral replications
EA(D) or D	Diffuse early antigen	Early antigen found diffusely in cytoplasm and nucleus of infected cells; IgG antibody to EA(D) is usually found in acute infectious mononucleosis (IM) but rarely in silent primary infection
EA(R) or R	Restricted early antigen	Early antigen restricted to the cytoplasm of infected cells; antibody to EA(R) is often found in silent primary infection but rarely in acute IM
MA	Membrane antigen	EBV-induced antigens which appear in the cell membranes of
EMA	Early membrane antigen	infected lymphocytes; some appear early (EMA) and others late
LMA	Late membrane antigen	(LMA) after infection; certain MAs do not evoke an antibody
LYDMA	Lymphocyte-detected membrane antigen	response but are detected by the reactions of lymphocytes (LYDMA)
VCA	Viral capsid antigen	Structural antigen; IgM antibody is present in silent primary infection or acute IM but not in EBV-associated tumors; IgG antibody forms after all infections

fectious virus particle consists of three components: a doughnut-shaped central core, or nucleoid; an icosahedral-shaped capsid; and an outer envelope. Individual virions are 180 to 200 nm in diameter.[1, 13, 14]

The core of the virus contains the viral DNA, which is double-stranded in condensed form.[15] The EBV genome has a size of slightly over 100×10^6 daltons, giving it the potential to code for 100 to 200 average-sized proteins.[16, 17] The buoyant density of the EBV DNA is 1.718 g/cc, corresponding to a guanosine-to-cytosine ratio of 58%.[18] Surrounding the core is a capsid composed of hollow, tubular protein subunits (capsomers).[14] There are 162 capsomers, each 12 μm in length and having the characteristic 5:3:2 symmetry of the herpesvirus group.[19] The nucleocapsid is 100 nm in diameter. Acrylamide gel electrophoresis has identified more than 30 different polypeptides associated with the virus.[20] An envelope, derived from the host cell membrane, surrounds the nucleocapsid. This structure incorporates a number of viral proteins that were inserted into the host cell membrane before assembly of complete virus particles began.[21–23]

Biologic Properties

EBV gains access to man via the oropharynx.[24] Presumably, it initially infects B lymphocytes which have specific receptors for the virus but are only moderately permissive for EBV.[25–27] Recent evidence suggests that infection occurs also in the nasopharyngeal, oropharyngeal, or salivary epithelium.[28–33] Following infection of cells in the pharynx, the virus is disseminated, either by viremia or by the circulation of infected B lymphocytes. Rocchi and colleagues[34] estimated that one of every 5000 lymphocytes contained EBV during acute IM, but that this number declined over several months to one per 10,000,000 or fewer.

EBV produces two types of cellular infections in humans. It may either cause a lytic infection, leading to cell death, or a latent infection, immortalizing the infected cell.[35–37] Based on these patterns, two types of virus are defined: lytic and transforming. Virus recovered in nature from healthy carriers or from patients with IM or EBV-related tumors is always of the transforming type.[38–40] Only a single strain of lytic virus has been identified (HR-1), having arisen as a result of a laboratory accident.[41]

In some B lymphocytes, EBV causes a productive infection leading to cell death (Figure 36–2). The first antigens expressed are the Epstein-Barr virus-associated nuclear antigen (EBNA) and the early membrane antigens (EMA), including the lymphocyte-detected membrane antigen (LYDMA).[42–44] Subsequently, two early antigens (EA) are formed, which interfere with cellular metabolism and bring about the synthesis of viral DNA.[45] These early antigens are classified as EA(D), diffuse early antigen, or EA(R), restricted early antigen, depending on their fixation and staining properties. The viral DNA then directs the formation of viral capsid antigen

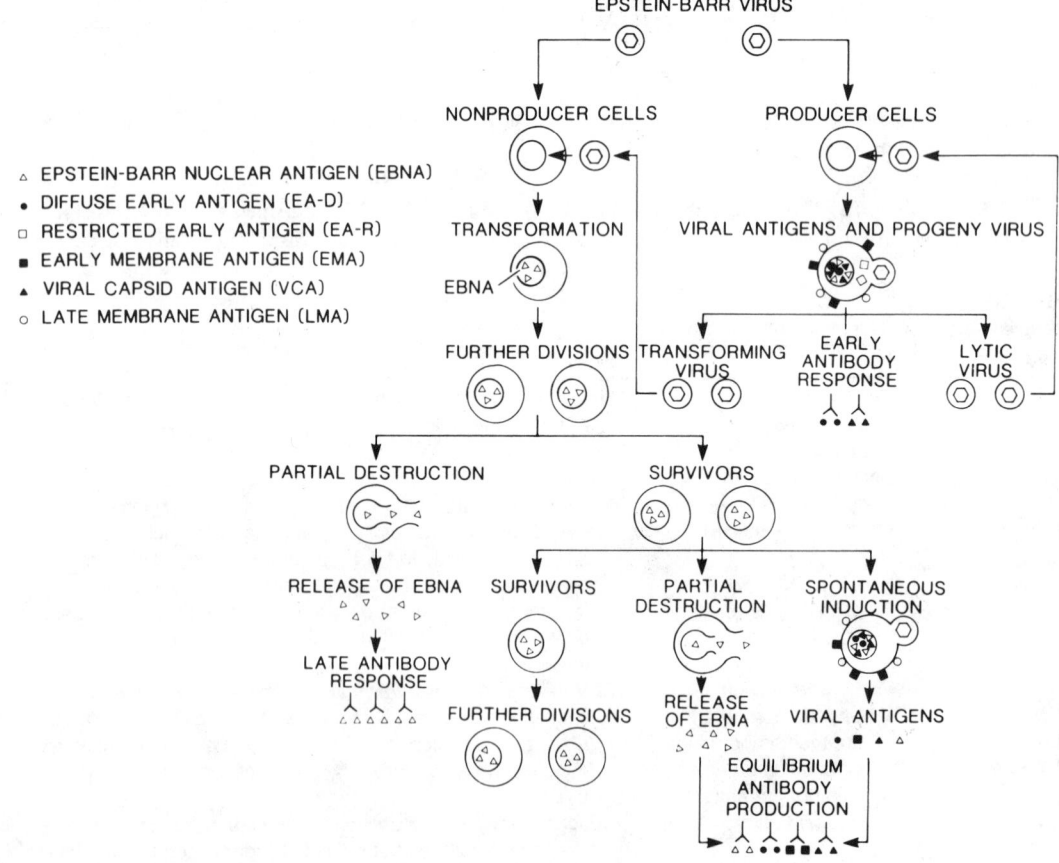

Figure 36–2. Schematic representation of Epstein-Barr virus at the cellular level.

(VCA) and late membrane antigen (LMA).[46] Lastly, virus assembly occurs, leading to cell lysis;[35, 47] EBNA, EMA, LMA, and EA are not incorporated into the structure of the virus. Both lytic and transforming virus are presumably released during this process. Additionally, EBV can also cause a nonproductive infection, becoming latent in the lymphocytes.[48–50] Such cells show no evidence of infection until they are cultured, leading to activation of the latent virus in some of the cells. This latent infection with EBV transforms lymphocytes, permitting their indefinite replication in vitro under appropriate conditions. Such cells harbor multiple copies of the viral DNA in plasmids or linearly integrated into cellular DNA in the nucleus and express EB nuclear and membrane antigens.[51–53]

In the host, transformed lymphocytes undergo a variable number of replications. While some persist in the circulation for life, others experience a different fate. Activated T lymphocytes may identify transformed lymphocytes as being infected with EBV on the basis of viral-induced membrane antigens and attack such cells.[54–56] Their destruction releases EBNA, leading to the formation of antibodies against this antigen. Additionally, a few latently infected lymphocytes that escape the T cell dragnet may spontaneously undergo lytic cycles. The virus that is then released perpetuates the persistent infection, and the viral antigens introduced into the circulation maintain the antibody response at a constant level.

Relationship of EBV to Lymphoid Cell Lines

Two types of EBV-carrying cell lines can be grown in culture. They consist of: (1) the lymphoblastoid cells established either from the blood of EBV-seropositive individuals or the exposure of uninfected B lymphocytes, particularly from cord blood, to the virus in cell culture, and (2) the cells obtained from specimens of Burkitt's lymphoma.[57] The BL lines have a monoclonal origin, are aneuploid, produce tumors when injected subcutaneously into mice, and have characteristic surface glycoproteins. Using chromosome banding techniques, they have been shown to have a reciprocal translocation of a portion of chromosome 8 to chromosome 14 and vice versa. On the other hand, the lymphoblastoid cell lines are polyclonal, diploid, nontumorigenic, and covered with surface glycoproteins with different characteristics than those found on cells from BL lines.

EBV-carrying cell lines can be further divided into producer and nonproducer lines. In producer lines, such as EB3 or P3HR1, a small proportion of the cells are undergoing a lytic cycle at any given point in time. They contain VCA and EA and release mature virions. Nonproducer cell lines, such as Raji, do not contain VCA or EA nor do they release virus under the usual conditions of cell culture, but they do harbor EBV genomes, as indicated by positive EBNA staining and nucleic acid hybridization studies. Depression of the resident viral genome with antimetabolite drugs (5'-bromodeoxyuridine or 5-iodo-2'-deoxyuridine), manipulation of the growing conditions (arginine deprivation), or superinfection with lytic (HR-1) virus induces nonproducer cells to enter into a lytic cycle.[58, 59]

Animal Models

Infection with EBV occurs transiently in certain animal species,

but no satisfactory model of IM or the latent persistent infection has been described. Werner and colleagues did produce a seroconversion and mild tonsillitis following the intratonsillar injection of either EBV or EBV-infected autochthonous lymphocytes into seronegative gibbons.[60] Following the administration of infected lymphocytes to squirrel monkeys, the animals transiently developed HA and anti-VCA but no clinical illness or persistent infection. Several animal species develop lymphomas in response to inoculation of EBV including owl monkeys and marmosets.[61, 62] Shope and colleagues[62] inoculated marmosets with EBV, inducing silent seroconversions, transient lymphoproliferation, or diffuse lymphomas. These lymphomas were not analogous to BL in humans in that they were polyclonal and emerged rapidly after infection.

EPIDEMIOLOGY

Epstein-Barr Virus Infection

General Considerations

The EBV has a worldwide distribution, having been shown to infect populations in every continent and even the inhabitants of remote islands and jungles.[63–67] However, the seroepidemiology varies in different regions depending on the socioeconomic status and customs of the people.[3, 63–83] A high population density and/or poverty both contribute to crowded living conditions that favor the spread of the virus. On the other hand, a sparse population and affluence allow for a more spacious existence and limit close contact until adolescence when intimacy creates an opportunity for spread.

Depending on the living conditions and socioeconomic status of the population, three seroepidemiologic patterns of EBV infection have emerged (Figure 36–3). In the underdeveloped countries and those with a high population density (such as China or Japan), over 90% of children have antibodies to EBV by their third birthday.[63, 69] However, infections are often delayed into late childhood or adolescence among individuals in the developed nations, particularly among affluent families.[70–83] There is a biphasic curve of acquisition among socioeconomically advantaged people that peaks in the first 2 years of life and again in late adolescence and early

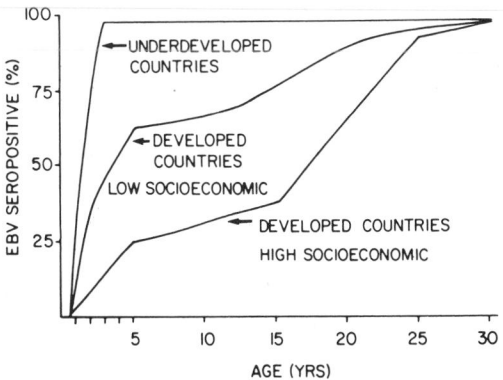

Figure 36–3. Seroepidemiology of Epstein-Barr virus (EBV) in the developed and underdeveloped countries.

Table 36–2
Incidence of Infectious Mononucleosis in the General Population

Author(s)	Study Years	Locations	Inclusion Criteria			Reporting Sources			No. of Cases	Rate per 100,000*
			Clinical	HA	WBC	Hospitals	Labs	Offices		
Henke et al[94]	1950–1969	Rochester, Minn	100%	100%	100%	+	+	+	776	99
Heath et al[93]	1968–1969	Atlanta	100%	100%	90%	−	+	−	575	45
Davidsohn[92]	1960–1969	Aberdeen, Scotland	100%	100%	90%	+	+	+	1258	44
Christine[90]	1948–1967	Connecticut	100%	0%	0%	+	+	+	11,338	46
Penman[89]	1962–1963	Portsmouth, England	100%	76%	100%	−	−	+	17	38
Belfrage[87]	1954–1960	Malmö, Sweden	100%	80%	100%	+	−	−	424	25
Evans[85]	1960–1961	Wisconsin	0%	100%	0%	−	+	−	387	68
Strom[88]	1940–1957	Stockholm	100%	50%	0%	+	−	−	1779	23
Hobson et al[91]	1954–1956	Oxford, England	100%	100%	100%	+	+	+	242	56
Newell[84]	1955	London	0%	100%	0%	+	+	−	1769	1.6

HA = heterophil antibody; WBC = white blood cell count.
Rate given is for last year of study when there was a continually increasing trend.

adulthood; not until the end of the third decade is almost universal seropositivity achieved.

Epidemiology of EBV in Underdeveloped Countries

Seroepidemiologic surveys in the underdeveloped countries have shown a high prevalence of antibodies to EBV. Studies by the Henles[68] in 1969 and Kafuko and colleagues[69] in 1972 found that more than 90% of African children had antibodies to EBV during early childhood. Biggar and colleagues,[4] who followed infants in Ghana for the first 21 months of life, detected seroconversions in 81% by the end of this interval. In several different studies, the prevalence of antibodies by the age of 5 years exceeded a level of 80% among the inhabitants of the Amazon basin, 90% on the Aleutian Islands, 85% in the Mexican highlands, and 90% in the South Pacific.[64–67]

Epidemiology of EBV in Developed Countries

Antibodies to EBV are prevalent among people in the developed countries, increasing with age. In 1969, Porter and colleagues[70] in Houston found antibodies to this virus in 80% of 4-year-old children and 90% of 14-year-old youths of lower socioeconomic status as compared to 60% and 80% of those from more affluent families. Fleisher and colleagues[74] observed that 25% of children between 3 and 24 months of age visiting an urban hospital emergency department in Philadelphia were seropositive as compared to only 10.5% of Finnish children 6 to 23 months of age undergoing cardiac surgery.[73] In the Cleveland family study, only 14% of children of higher socioeconomic status developed antibodies during the first 6 years of life.[72]

After the age of 3 to 5 years, the annual rate of seroconversions declines.[72, 75] None of 59 children in the Cleveland family study contracted an EBV infection between the ages of 6 and 16 years.[72] Evans[75] studied children in grammar schools in New Haven, Connecticut, from impoverished and higher socioeconomic backgrounds. He reported that 16% of the former group were susceptible to EBV at enrollment into elementary school and 50% seroconverted in the ensuing 4 to 5 years, while 63% of the latter group lacked antibodies but only 2.4% seroconverted during the study period.

A second peak in the incidence of EBV occurs among adoles-

cents in the developed countries, particularly after matriculation in college.[76–78] Susceptible individuals, predominantly of higher socioeconomic status, have an increasing frequency of intimate oral contacts at this point in their life. The seroconversion rate among college students is in the range of 10% to 20% annually.

Regardless of socioeconomic status, the prevalence of EBV antibodies approaches 100% by the end of the third decade.[79–83] Fleisher and Bolognese[83] found that 96% of pregnant women of higher socioeconomic status (mean age of 28 years) were seropositive and that 99% of those of lower socioeconomic status (mean age 21 years) had antibodies to EBV. The seropositivity rate for adults of 30 years of age has been reported to be 95% in a rural Louisiana community and 94% in Sweden.[79, 82]

Infectious Mononucleosis

General Considerations

Estimates of the yearly incidence of infectious mononucleosis in the general population have varied from 1.6 to 99 per 100,000 (Table 36–2),[84–94] depending on the population studied, the diagnostic criteria, and the method used for tabulating cases.

Newell[84] and Virtanen[86] reported the lowest incidences of IM, 1.5 and 5.0 per 100,000, respectively, relying on voluntary reporting of cases. Based on hospitalized patients only, Swedish investigators calculated an annual incidence of IM of 25 per 100,000.[87, 88] In 1968, Christine[90] described the experience in Connecticut with 11,338 cases of IM submitted to the state health department over a 20-year period. She found a rate of 46 per 100,000 but made no effort to verify the accuracy of the diagnoses.

Using strict criteria for the diagnosis of IM, two studies in the British Isles and one in Atlanta found yearly incidence rates in the general population from 44 to 56 per 100,000.[91–93] However, when one of these investigators performed a small but incisive survey, designed to detect all cases of IM, he observed an incidence of 100 per 100,000.[92]

Henke and colleagues have compiled the most conclusive data on the incidence of IM, using the excellent medical records available in Rochester, Minnesota.[94] Although their initial calculations suggested a rate of 209 per 100,000, elimination of cases not meeting strict diagnostic criteria led them to revise their estimate

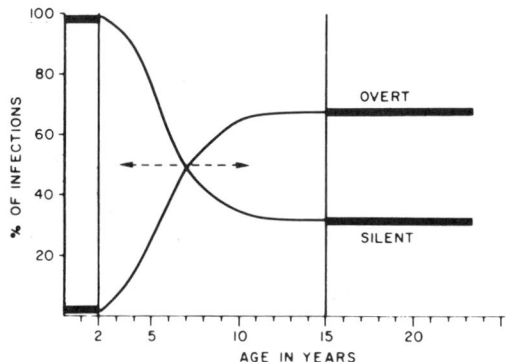

Figure 36–4. Relative frequency by age of silent Epstein-Barr virus infections and infectious mononucleosis.

downward to 99 per 100,000. Taking into account the multiple factors in previous studies that favored either under- or overestimation, it appears that the actual incidence of IM in middle-class communities in the developed countries is approximately 100 per 100,000 annually.

Effect of Socioeconomic Status and Age

The socioeconomic characteristics and age distribution of a population determine the incidence of IM. Opportunities for transmission, which requires close oral contact, are influenced by both of these variables.

The initial exposures occur during the first 2 or 3 years of life when salivary exchange presumably takes place during normal playful activity of childhood. Particularly under conditions of overcrowding, transmission is likely to occur.[4, 63–83] Close contact again becomes common following puberty, and the incidence of IM reaches a second peak in more affluent populations where there are a large number of susceptible adolescents and young adults.[76–78, 84–94]

Only an occasional child, who acquired EBV during the first few years of life, will develop the clinical syndrome of IM. The majority undergo a silent seroconversion. In prospective studies in both developed and underdeveloped countries, young children identified as having current, primary EBV infections did not manifest the constellation of fever, pharyngitis, lymphadenopathy, and splenomegaly.[4, 74] Although sufficient epidemiologic data are lacking to establish a definitive ratio of overt to silent infections, it would appear that fewer than 1 in 100 children who become infected prior to the second birthday develop IM. The ratio of overt

to silent infections appears to increase gradually with age so that one to two thirds of adolescents and young adults who have an EBV infection develop a clinically apparent illness (Figure 36–4).

Figure 36–5 depicts the incidence of IM at various ages in three different studies.[92–94] IM occurs only rarely in the first year of life. In 1930, 2 years before the introduction of the Paul-Bunnell test, Price[95] described the first well-documented case in a child less than 1 year of age; subsequently only five HA-positive cases have been reported in the English language (Table 36–3).[96–99] In 1981, Horwitz and colleagues[100] described two children, ages 10 and 11 months, with HA-negative IM confirmed by EBV-specific serology.

In the decade of life between 3 and 13 years, IM occurs sporadically. In several large series of patients of all ages with IM, 7.5% to 37% of the cases fell in this age range, usually in children more than 5 years old (Figure 36–6).[66, 84–94] Henke and colleagues[94] reported an incidence of IM of 24 per 100,000 from 0 to 5 years and 65 from 5 to 14 years of age. Several investigators have reported large numbers of children with IM, dispelling the oft-quoted notion that the disease is rare in childhood.[101–105]

The incidence of IM makes a sudden, steep upsurge at the age of 13 to 15 years among populations of higher socioeconomic status. Estimates of the annual rate among adolescents in the gen-

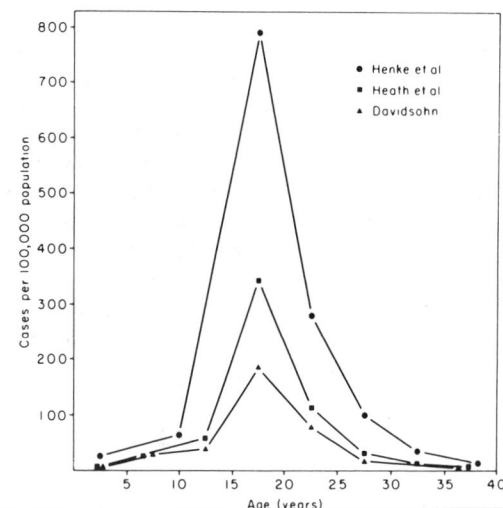

Figure 36–5. Incidence of infectious mononucleosis at various ages in three large studies.

Table 36–3

Infectious Mononucleosis in the First Year of Life

Author	Year	Age	HA Titer	WBC Count Total (per µL)	% Lymph	% AL
Walker[96]	1951	9 wk	1:256	6400	57	23
Woodward et al[97]	1954	4 wk	1:512	189,000	61	5
Gachet and Price[98]	1954	8 mo	1:160	11,000	51	17
		1 yr	1:224	4450	72	8
Phillips and Stone[99]	1956	6 wk	1:2048	26,000	74	14

HA = heterophil antibody; Lymph = lymphocytes; AL = atypical lymphocytes.

eral population have ranged as high as 800 per 100,000 and among college youths of a similar age 4800 per 100,000.[76-78, 92-94]

The incidence of IM decreases markedly after 30 years of age, but there are well-documented cases of patients as old as 86 years.[92-94, 106-110] Between 1950 and 1969, Henke and colleagues[94] identified 12 patients over the age of 35 years with IM in Rochester, Minnesota. Approximately 1.5% of their 776 cases occurred beyond this age, giving an annual incidence of four per 100,000.

Epidemics

Outbreaks of a disease thought to be IM have been reported at various times in the literature. However, even in those epidemics described after the introduction of the Davidsohn modification of the HA test, the diagnosis of IM was generally not well documented and the presence of other pathogens was not excluded.[111, 112] Ginsburg and colleagues encountered the single cluster of IM cases in which the diagnosis was confirmed with EBV-specific serology.[113] They postulated that shared coffee cups or eating utensils may have served as vestors.

Recent Changes in Incidence

Several investigators have suggested an increasing incidence of IM since 1940.[87, 90, 94] Strom[88] reported a fourfold, Christine[90] a tenfold, and Henke and colleagues[94] just less than a twofold rise in incidence over a period of two to three decades. While heightened awareness of the disease and the advent of improved diagnostic techniques may account for some of the increase, these factors do not appear to completely explain the upward trend. Rather, improvements in the socioeconomic status of the population and changes in social customs are most likely responsible.[83]

Within the next few decades, the incidence of IM may well make a downturn. Increasing utilization of day care facilities for preschool children has already been shown to increase the prevalence of cytomegalovirus (CMV) twofold by the age of 2 years.[114] EBV, which has a transmission pattern similar to CMV, may follow the same trend. This would lead to an increase in asymptomatic seroconversions in infants and a decrease in infectious mononucleosis in young adults.

PATHOGENESIS OF INFECTIOUS MONONUCLEOSIS

Transmission

The mode of transmission of EBV in humans remains to be definitively established, but circumstantial evidence suggests that the infection is spread in nature by intimate oral contact. Both experimental data and clinical observations have contributed to our knowledge about transmission of this virus. Investigators in the 1930s and 1940s met with limited, if any, success in attempts to transmit IM from humans to animals or from humans to humans.[115-123] Evans[123] in 1947 and Hoagland[124] in 1955 reviewed these early experiments, noting only two reports of possible transmission to a human volunteer; however, neither case met the clinical, hematologic, and serologic criteria for diagnosis. Subsequently, Evans[125] and Niederman and Scott[126] were unsuccessful in transmitting IM to human subjects by the inoculation or oral instillation of either blood or saliva, regardless of whether the donor was in the incubation or clinical phase of the illness; years later, after the

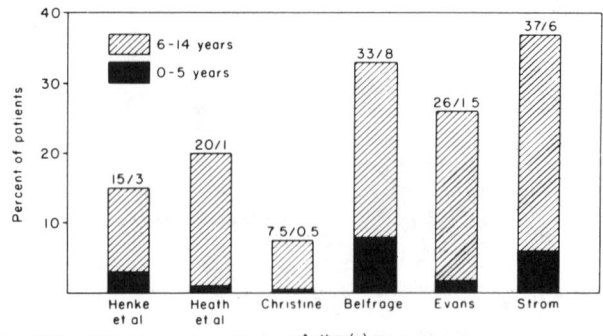

Figure 36–6. Percentage of infectious mononucleosis in children, as reported in several studies (see references 87, 88, 89, 90, 93, and 94).

introduction of EBV-specific serology, sera from these volunteers were retrieved from the freezer and shown to have antibodies to EBV. At the time of these experiments, clinical investigators had long noted the low degree of contagiousness exhibited by patients with IM even in situations allowing for close proximity with other persons. The first clue as to the mode of transmission of IM arose from the observations of Hoagland[124] in 1955. While serving as the physician at the United States Military Academy at West Point, he noted that the incidence of IM peaked in cadets approximately 6 weeks after they returned from their holidays; additionally, he was able to obtain a history of intimate oral contact during the vacation period from 71 of 73 cadets that he questioned personally. These findings led him to postulate that IM was spread by an exchange of saliva as occurred during kissing. Subsequently, Evans[127] reported that 68% of college students with IM had intimate oral contact approximately 60 days prior to their admission to the infirmary as compared to 41.3% of control subjects.

Using EBV-specific serologic techniques, several investigations have now shown spread of the virus within the family.[128-132] Fleisher and colleagues[131] prospectively studied 60 siblings of 35 children with IM and detected seven instances of spread. They noted two patterns of intrafamilial transmission: silent infections among the younger siblings of index cases and clinically apparent IM in the older ones. The occurrence of spread of EBV among siblings points to the role of salivary exchange which could take place during play or via shared drinking cups or utensils. Sumaya and Ench[132] reported a similar pattern of spread among family members in a more extensive study. Within 6 to 9 weeks of the diagnosis of IM in an index case, they reported that 12 of the 112 siblings showed serologic evidence of recent infection; eight developed HA, four in association with IM.

Following the discovery of EBV, studies were performed to assess the requirement for intimate oral contact in the spread of IM. Chang and Golden[38] and Pereira and colleagues[133] first demonstrated the presence of transforming virus, subsequently shown to be EBV, in the saliva of patients with IM. During the first 3 to 6 months after the onset of IM, almost every individual sheds the virus continuously.[134] Years after the primary infection, 5% to 20% of seropositive healthy subjects and 25% to 50% of seropositive immunosuppressed patients excrete EBV in their saliva.[135, 136]

Occasionally the transmission of EBV occurs during the transfusion of blood, but the low incidence of susceptible individuals in the general population limits the opportunity for spread by this route.[109, 137–144] Patients undergoing open heart surgery or receiving multiple transfusions for other reasons are at particular risk.

Incubation

Infectious mononucleosis has a relatively long incubation period which ranges from approximately 30 to 50 days.[124, 131, 145] Perhaps because the incubation period is lengthy, EBV-specific antibodies have usually reached peak titers by the time the disease is clinically apparent. However, 10% to 20% of patients with IM initially have low titers that may increase fourfold or more subsequently, and an occasional individual still lacks detectable antibodies at the time of presentation.

Hoagland,[124] in 1955, first suggested that the incubation period for IM was 5 to 7 weeks. He drew this conclusion from the observation that the incidence of IM peaked at the United States Military Academy at West Point approximately 6 weeks after the cadets returned from their vacations; during the other months of the year, the cadets had limited opportunity for intimate contact since they were confined to the school, which was not yet a co-educational institution. In a study on intrafamilial transmission, Fleisher and colleagues[131] diagnosed IM in two children 2 and 4 weeks after the disease had occurred in a sibling. Taking into account the duration of the illness in the index child prior to seeking medical care and the presence of virus in the saliva before the onset of the symptoms, they postulated an incubation period of approximately 6 weeks. Svedmyr and colleagues[145] prospectively studied a 14-year-old boy after he had kissed a girl who two days later was diagnosed as having IM; this youth denied previous intimate encounters. He developed IM 38 days after his exposure, but lymphoblastoid cell lines (EBNA-positive) were established from his peripheral blood within 13 days of the contact.

Host Response

Common Clinical Syndromes

Infection with EBV commonly elicits one of two responses: an asymptomatic seroconversion or the clinical disease known as infectious mononucleosis. Among the host factors that determine whether or not the infection remains subclinical, age appears to play the most important role. Children who acquire EBV in the first 2 years of life rarely manifest a clinical illness. Biggar and colleagues[4] detected the appearance of antibodies in 21 (81%) of 27 infants bled monthly for 21 months, but none of these children developed IM. Similarly, Fleisher and colleagues[74] noted asymptomatic seroconversions among 14 (18%) of 80 infants with minor illnesses recruited in an urban clinic. With advancing age, a greater percentage of persons who have a primary EBV infection develop IM. Among college students, illness accompanies 33% to 66% of the seroconversions.[76–78]

The onset of IM is generally insidious over five to seven days but may occasionally be abrupt.[146–157] Any of the following clinical manifestations may be preeminent early in the course, leading some investigators to classify the illness into various syndromes. Sore throat (anginal syndrome) is the most severe complaint in 75% to 80% of cases, fever (typhoidal or essential syndrome) in 15% to 20%, and jaundice (hepatic syndrome) in 5% to 10%.[152, 153] An

occasional patient will complain solely of either easy fatigability or lymph node enlargement.[101] However, most patients develop the classic triad of fever, pharyngitis, and lymphadenopathy (Table 36–4).

Symptoms.—Malaise precedes the other symptoms of IM in most individuals. More than 50% of patients experience malaise initially, and the remainder later in the course of the illness. Fever and pharyngitis follow on the heels of malaise, appearing two to five days after its onset. Pharyngeal involvement led to complaints of pain in 70% to 85% of patients in several large series. Among children, however, only 24% of those in one study with HA-positive IM described a sore throat at the time of their initial visit to the physician.[101] Headaches occur in approximately one third of patients with IM and are most commonly frontal in location. Other symptoms are infrequent, including nausea and vomiting (5%–20%), abdominal pain (5%–15%), chills (6%–28%), and myalgias (10%–20%). Although occasional reports in the literature suggest that the abdominal pain in IM may be so severe as to mimic appendicitis, discomfort of this magnitude is rarely encountered.

Signs.—By the time patients with IM seek medical attention, the clinical syndrome has developed fully in the majority to include fever, pharyngitis, adenopathy, and splenomegaly. Fever, the most common sign, occurs in 80% to 90% of the cases of IM, usually peaking at the end of the first week of the illness. It defervesces after 2 weeks in 50% of the patients, and by 4 weeks in 95%.[153] Persistence of fever beyond a month or recurrence of fever once the temperature has returned to normal for 72 hours should trigger a search for an alternative diagnosis or a complication of IM.

Lymphadenopathy ranks second to fever in frequency. Some observers have noted enlarged nodes in all cases and others in only 80% to 90%; variability in reporting may arise from differing criteria for the interpretation of lymphadenopathy. The lymph nodes usually enlarge by the fourth or fifth day of illness and always by the end of the second week. The cervical nodes achieve the largest size, followed by those in the axillary and inguinal regions. Other groups of nodes (supraclavicular, epitrochlear, mediastinal) less commonly reach a degree of enlargement that is clinically appreciated. Among the 96 patients reported by Press and colleagues,[149] 72 had cervical, 28 axillary, 28 inguinal, nine epitrochlear, and three mediastinal adenopathy. The increase in size is mild in one third of the cases, moderate in half, and severe in the remainder; 3% to 5% of patients with IM will develop the "bull-neck" appearance reminiscent of diphtheria. Although almost any cause of pharyngeal inflammation may lead to anterior cervical adenopathy, only EBV and a few other infectious agents produce bilateral enlargement of both the anterior and posterior lymph nodes of the neck. Lymphadenopathy recedes after 3 to 4 weeks in most patients with IM but may occasionally persist for several months.

Inflammation of the pharynx occurs in 75% to 90% of patients with IM and is exudative in half of these cases. The onset of pharyngitis takes place during the first week of illness, usually being present at the first examination. Frequently, the tonsils are moderately to severely enlarged, but they return to their original configuration within 2 to 3 weeks.

Careful palpation of the abdomen detects splenomegaly in 40% to 75% of patients with IM. In those without clinically obvious

Table 36–4
Signs and Symptoms of Infectious Mononucleosis

Author(s) (year)	No. of Patients	Predominant Age of Patients	Percent Meeting Diagnostic Criteria		Time of Evaluation	Symptoms			
			Heterophil Antibody	Hemato-logic		Malaise	Fever	Sore Throat	Headache
Bernstein (1940)[146]	66	Adults	NA	NA	Presentation	NA	NA	77	NA
Contrato (1944)[147]	196	Adults	83	100	Presentation	42	21	50	22
Milne (1945)[148]	111	Adults	90	NA	Presentation	52	13	83	35
Press et al (1945)[149]	196	Adults	71	96	Presentation	34	98	31	35
Mason et al (1951)[150]	100	Adults	91	92	NA	76	79	NA	55
Mankad (1954)[151]	399	Adults	78	100	Presentation	74	50	69	43
Evans (1961)[85]	176	Adults	100	100	NA	NA	NA	76	NA
Hoagland (1960, 1967)[152, 153]	400	Adults	100	100	NA	100	98	76	NA
Baehner et al (1967)[101]	105	Children	100	64	Presentation	24	100	45	NA
Joncas et al (1968)[154]	100	Children, adults	100	100	NA	NA	NA	NA	
Cameron & MacBear†* (1973)[155]	270	Adults	NA	NA	NA	50	60	87	67
Fleisher et al† (1979)[105]	38	Children	95	NA	NA	NA	NA	NA	NA
Sumaya et al† (1985)[156]	47	1–3 yr	32	NA	Presentation	NA	90	65	NA
Sumaya et al† (1985)[157]	66	4–16 yr	84	NA	Presentation	NA	100	75	NA

NA = not available.
*Cases said to be confirmed.
†All cases verified by Epstein-Barr virus–specific serology.

splenomegaly, the spleen may still be larger than normal since it must double in size to be easily felt.[158] The degree of splenic enlargement varies from minimal to massive. In most cases, a firm, but not hard, edge can be palpated from 1 to 5 cm below the left costal margin. Occasionally, however, the spleen will extend to the level of the iliac crest. Since marked splenomegaly is unusual with infections due to hepatitis A or hepatitis B viruses, a patient with jaundice, evidence of liver inflammation, and enlarged spleen needs an evaluation for IM.

The other signs of IM occur in fewer than 25% of the cases. Hepatomegaly and jaundice are each noted in 5% to 10% even though abnormal liver function occurs as a rule.[159, 160] In most series, approximately 10% of the patients are reported to develop periorbital edema, but Hoagland noted swelling in this area in 33% of those individuals that he examined personally.[153] While early investigators reported a high incidence of maculopapular exanthems in cases of IM, the disease was often not confirmed serologically; such eruptions probably occur in fewer than 5% of patients with virologically documented IM. However, the administration of antibiotics to patients may induce the appearance of a rash in a higher percentage.[161–165] Almost 100% of those who receive ampicillin or amoxicillin develop a rash, and 25% to 50% of those given penicillin will have cutaneous involvement. The rare patient with thrombocytopenia during the course of IM may have petechial or purpuric lesions, and this author has cared for two children with erythema multiforme and IM, documented by EBV-specific serology.[166]

Uncommon Nonneoplastic Complications

General Considerations.—Infections with the EBV have been reported to involve virtually every organ system of the body.[157, 167–170] Table 36–5 provides a list of the complications that have been described. While some of these complications may represent either misdiagnoses of IM or chance associations, others either occur frequently enough to attribute a causal role to EBV or are clearly explained pathophysiologically.

Unusual syndromes may accompany IM or occur as the sole manifestation of a primary EBV infection; only with the development of virus-specific serology has the isolated appearance of such syndromes been described. When complications occur in a patient with IM, they may do so before, during, or after the illness. Although estimates have been made as to the frequency of involvement for particular organs, no reliable data exist as to the incidence of complications in general.

Splenic Rupture.—Splenic rupture may infrequently, but dramatically, complicate IM. Infiltration of the spleen by lymphocytes weakens the supporting structures of this organ, predisposing it to rupture.[171–177] Rupture of the spleen may occur after minor trauma or even spontaneously, as initially reported by King[171] in 1941. Rutkow[177] reviewed 107 reported cases of spontaneous splenic rupture, finding 18 instances where the diagnosis of IM met the standard clinical, hematologic, histopathologic, and serologic criteria, and trauma was clearly excluded. In at least two cases, abdominal palpation preceded splenic rupture. In another instance, a Valsalva maneuver during defecation caused left-sided pain and syncope, subsequently shown to be the result of disruption of the spleen.

No accurate estimate is available as to the frequency of splenic rupture. Rawsthorne and colleagues[174] reported only one case in 14 years in Aberdeen, Scotland (population 440,000). Reviewing 50 patients with IM admitted during a 3-year period to St Vincent Hospital in Portland, Oregon, Alberty[176] observed splenic rupture in two. He also reported three fatal cases of splenic rupture in the state of Oregon in 1980. Hoagland[152, 153] observed an incidence of 0.2% in his series of young adults with IM.

Splenic rupture rarely occurs with IM, but this diagnosis demands consideration in any patient who develops abdominal pain, a complaint voiced by only 5% to 15% of patients with uncomplicated illnesses.[146, 155] The additional indicators of splenic rupture

				Signs					
Abdominal Pain, Nausea	Chills	Fever	Lymph-adenopathy	Pharyngitis/ Exudate	Splenomegaly	Hepatomegaly	Rash	Jaundice	Periorbital Edema
NA	NA	98	100	77/26	64	12	2	2	9
9	6	89	84	84/22	41	NA	NA	5	5
28	11	98	92	78/29	43	NA	8	3	5
10	28	98	79	69/NA	69	27	19	5	NA
20	NA	79	95	91/49	51	6	12	0	5
15	11	98	86	80/30	5	4	4	NA	NA
NA	NA	35	92	76/46	40	NA	1	NA	NA
0	NA	98	100	85/22	75	NA	3	10	33
NA	NA	100	83	45/29	47	28	8	5	NA
NA	NA	94	94	NA/69	63	NA	15	8	12
25	NA	NA	95	90/65	50	15	25	10	20
NA	NA	87	95	84/NA	58	26	NA	NA	NA
0	NA	90	92	NA	80	60	34	<5	14
18	NA	100	94	NA	50	30	17	<5	14

are those of free blood in the peritoneum; palpation may elicit tenderness in the left upper quadrant initially and generalized rebound tenderness later. Tachycardia supervenes as the magnitude of the blood loss increases. A falling hematocrit and a neutrophilic leukocytosis may be seen; x-ray occasionally shows an elevation of the left hemodiaphragm. Although splenic rupture may occur at any point during the course of IM, it has been reported most frequently between the second and fourth week after onset.

In addition to rupture, the bulk of the spleen may cause the organ to become displaced. At least one report described a case of wandering spleen in IM.[178]

The outcome of splenic rupture in IM depends on the rapidity of diagnosis and institution of therapy, as with traumatic disruptions. Although early investigators reported a fatality rate of 30%, the more recent experiences point to uniform survival.[175-177] Treatment has consisted of splenectomy, although repair of the organ or even observation might be deemed appropriate by the surgeon in selected cases. As the appreciation of the spleen's role in host resistance has increased, repair or observation has replaced removal in the management of many traumatic lacerations.

Hematologic Complications.—Aplastic anemia is the most serious hematologic complication of IM. Ten cases of pancytopenia have been reported, occurring seven to 49 days after the onset of illness.[179-183] The bone marrow usually appears hypocellular, but may, at times, be hypercellular or contain granulomas.[181] Recovery occurred spontaneously in most cases or, occasionally, following treatment with corticosteroids; however, at least one patient died of this complication.[182]

Less serious but more common than pancytopenia is the oc-

Table 36–5

Reported Complications of Infectious Mononucleosis

Splenic	Respiratory	Ophthalmologic
Rupture	Upper airway obstruction	Conjunctivitis
Wandering spleen	Pneumonia	Uveitis
Hematologic	Pleural effusion	Visual impairment
Aplastic anemia	Mediastinal lymphadenopathy	Other organs
Hemolytic anemia	Cardiac	Orchitis
Thrombocytopenia	Conduction disturbances	Arthritis
Thrombasthenia	Myocarditis	Dermatologic
Agranulocytosis	Pericarditis	Maculopapular exanthems
Neurologic/psychiatric	Gastrointestinal	Petechiae
Encephalitis	Hepatitis	Jaundice
Aseptic meningitis	Reye syndrome	Urticaria
Seizures	Pancreatitis	Infectious
Guillain-Barré syndrome	Mesenteric lymphadenopathy	Streptococcal pharyngitis
Cranial neuropathy	Malabsorption	Systemic bacterial infection
Peripheral neuropathy	Renal	
Subacute sclerosing panencephalitis	Glomerulonephritis	
Depression	Renal hypertrophy	
Psychosis	Hemolytic uremic syndrome	

currence of hemolytic anemia.[184-187] This complication affects 0.5% to 3.0% of the patients with IM and may be the initial manifestation.[153, 187] Most cases are mediated by anti-i antibodies against the erythrocytes.[184-186] The hemolysis usually remains inapparent but may reach a clinically significant level in a few cases, particularly during the second or third week of the illness. Almost all episodes of hemolysis resolve spontaneously.

EBV infections commonly affect the platelets.[166, 188-192] Carter[188] observed at least mild thrombocytopenia in over 50% of patients with IM; however, only seven of 57 had counts less than 100,000/μL. Although severe thrombocytopenia is infrequent, fatal intracranial hemorrhage has been reported with platelet counts below 10,000/μL. Thrombocytopenic purpura may be the sole manifestation of an EBV infection.[192] Although the mechanism for thrombocytopenia remains uncertain, an immune-mediated destruction appears likely on the basis of the bone marrow histology and recent studies demonstrating antiplatelet antibodies.[190] Virtually all cases of thrombocytopenia resolve without specific therapy.

Platelet function abnormalities have also been described in IM. During the course of the illness, Clancy and colleagues[191] observed abnormal platelet aggregation or release of platelet factors in 16 patients. Platelet function returned to normal in these cases following the resolution of their illness.

The neutrophils are infrequently affected by EBV. However, neutropenia and occasional cases of agranulocytosis have been reported.[193]

Neurologic Complications.—EBV can cause a diverse spectrum of neurologic and psychiatric syndromes.[194-208] Serious nervous system disorders have been estimated to affect approximately 1% to 5% of hospitalized patients with IM. Although they may occur as the sole manifestation of an EBV syndrome, most neurologic disturbances have been reported to appear during the course of IM; this may be the result of a failure to pursue a specific serologic diagnosis in the absence of the clinical syndrome of IM. Grose and colleagues[202] detected primary EBV infections, using EBV-specific serology, in seven of 24 cases of Guillain-Barré syndrome and in three of 16 with facial palsy. Only one of their patients had obvious IM and only a few developed HA.

The pathophysiology of the central nervous system manifestations of EBV is unknown. Lymphocytic infiltration may produce a vasculitis and areas of ischemia or an immunologic mechanism may be responsible. Direct viral invasion of neurons seems improbable in view of the inability of EBV to infect any cells other than lymphocytes. Low levels of anti-EBV antibodies in the CSF, as seen in some cases, are most likely the result of spillover from the blood[200]; the single reported recovery of EBV from the CSF may have been due to leakage of peripheral lymphocytes into this fluid and awaits confirmation.[206] Convulsions may occur in patients with IM who have a preexisting seizure disorder due to the enhanced metabolism of certain anticonvulsant drugs during the course of this infection.[207]

Neurologic manifestations occurring with EBV infections include encephalitis, aseptic meningitis, seizures, Guillain-Barré syndrome, optic neuritis, cranial or peripheral neuropathies, subacute sclerosing panencephalitis, depression, and psychosis.[194-208] The encephalitis is usually mild but may occasionally be fatal.[205] The findings in the CSF vary from normal to a mild mononuclear

pleocytosis with or without an increased protein content. Complete recovery of function occurs in almost all survivors.

Depression occurs quite frequently with IM and may persist long after the resolution of all other symptoms. More severe psychiatric disturbances such as psychosis are unusual. A bizarre disorder, the "Alice in Wonderland" syndrome (in which objects appear distorted and change in size), has been reported with IM.[203]

Respiratory Tract Complications.—Complications of EBV infections may affect both the upper and lower portions of the respiratory tract.[209-216] Lymphoid hyperplasia, an expected component of IM, may be unusually marked at the level of the tonsils, causing upper airway obstruction; this occurs in fewer than 1% of cases.[209-211] In most instances, the patient with tonsillar hypertrophy leading to respiratory distress initially develops dysphagia and stridor, but cases of sudden complete obstruction are reported. Although spontaneous regression of the lymphoid hyperplasia is assured, the degree of obstruction may be too severe to allow the disease to take its natural course. Corticosteroids dramatically shrink the tonsils and surrounding tissues in most patients, but the insertion of an artificial airway is occasionally necessary.

Pulmonary complications rarely occur with EBV infections, but the reported spectrum of involvement is diverse.[212-216] Although early reports noted an incidence of radiographic pulmonary changes in as many as 15% of patients, the diagnosis of IM was not well documented in most cases, and coexisting infections were not excluded.[214-216] Fewer than 20 instances of symptomatic pulmonary disease associated with EBV infections have been reported.[212] The manifestations have included isolated pleural effusions, interstitial or lobar pneumonia with and without pleural effusions, and bronchopneumonia. The clinical features of pulmonary involvement are those that would be expected with an infection due to any agent: cough, tachypnea, rales, and, at times, dullness to percussion. Most patients improve without specific therapy.

Mediastinal adenopathy may occur occasionally during the course of IM in a patient with marked generalized lymphadenopathy and should not be considered a complication per se. However, failure to appreciate such nodal enlargement as an expected component of IM has led to invasive diagnostic tests and subsequent iatrogenic mishaps.

Cardiac Complications.—Cardiac complications of IM are unusual except for minor electrocardiographic abnormalities which may be seen in as many as 6% of cases.[217-222] On the basis of the pathologic findings, Reitman and colleagues have postulated that mononuclear cell infiltration of the myocardium could be responsible for the disruption of the conducting system.[218] Most conduction disturbances are detected only if surveillance ECGs are done and consist of nonspecific ST-T wave changes. Occasional patients may develop symptomatic arrhythmias, such as complete heart block. Both myocarditis and pericarditis may occur during the course of IM or as the sole manifestation of an EBV infection.[219, 220] Although spontaneous recovery is the rule, a fatal outcome has been described in at least two cases.[221, 222]

Gastrointestinal Complications.—Hepatitis accompanies most cases of IM.[223-225] Infiltration of the liver with lymphocytes occurs as a rule in IM and presumably disrupts normal hepatic function.[226]

Involvement of this organ usually manifests only as a rise in the serum transaminase levels but may produce jaundice in 5% to 10% of cases. The hepatic manifestations of IM usually resolve promptly, but rare instances of hepatic coma have been described.[227, 228] A single case of posthepatic cirrhosis awaits confirmation, particularly in view of the report of the simultaneous occurrence of IM and hepatitis B virus infection.[229, 230]

In five cases described in the literature, Reye syndrome developed during or shortly after a bout of IM.[231–233] The initial reports relied on the HA test for confirmation of IM, but Fleisher and colleagues described three children with serologically documented EBV infections; two of these three patients developed overt IM but the other had no sign of this disease.

Pancreatic involvement has been described in only a few cases of IM.[234, 235] Reporting on amylase and lipase determinations done on 20 patients, Myhre and Nesbitt[234] found elevations in two individuals without symptoms, suggesting pancreatic disease. Wislocki[235] observed a single instance of pancreatitis, manifested by abdominal pain, vomiting, and an elevated serum amylase level, in an 18-year-old male with HA-positive IM.

Fewer than 15% of patients with IM complain of abdominal discomfort, but massive mesenteric lymphadenopathy may occasionally cause severe pain. At times, this symptom has led to an unnecessary appendectomy. Additionally, a single instance of transient malabsorption during IM has been described.[236]

Renal Complications.—Clinical renal disease is unusual in IM, but an abnormal urinary sediment has been reported in as many as 13% of cases.[237–241] Reported renal manifestations have included glomerulonephritis, renal hypertrophy, and a single instance of hemolytic uremic syndrome. Although some authors have attributed the cause of nephritis during IM to secondary streptococcal pharyngitis, pathologic findings have not been compatible with this diagnosis. Most commonly, biopsy has shown an aggregation of mononuclear inflammatory cells in the interstitium, and focal tubular necrosis. Regardless of the type of renal pathologic changes, the kidneys reverted to normal following recovery from IM in all reported cases.

Other Organ Involvement.—Orchitis has been reported in three males with IM, manifesting as a painful testicular enlargement.[242–244] In the one case from which long-term follow-up was available, azoospermia persisted at least until the final examination at 5 months after the onset of illness.[244]

Musculoskeletal manifestations of IM include myalgia and mild weakness in 10% to 20% of the patients, but arthralgia almost never occurs.[146–155] A single case of arthritis is reported.[245] Although this child recovered without antibiotic or prolonged anti-inflammatory therapy, her joint fluid contained 80,000 WBCs per microliter (90% polymorphonuclear leukocytes), casting some doubt on the presumed viral etiology for the effusion.

Tanner[246] reviewed the ophthalmologic complications of IM, dividing the lesions into two groups: (1) those due to direct involvement of the eye and adnexa, presumably due to lymphocytic infiltration, and (2) those affecting ocular function secondary to involvement of the CNS. Conjunctivitis, periorbital edema, uveitis, optic neuritis, and papilledema fall into the first category. The second group includes extraocular muscle paralysis, ptosis, nystagmus, hemianopsia, and scotomata. Other than periorbital edema, ocular disturbances are rare; spontaneous resolution is the rule.

Dermatologic Manifestations.—Between 5% and 10% of patients with uncomplicated IM develop jaundice and 3% to 5%, a maculopapular exanthem.[146–155, 161–165] Palatal petechiae occur frequently and cutaneous hemorrhage may occur in those cases with marked thrombocytopenia.[188–192, 247] Urticarial eruptions are also seen occasionally.[248, 249] A single case report describes a HA-positive case of IM with a prominent erythematous palmar dermatitis and few systemic signs of illness.[250]

The most curious dermatologic manifestation of IM is the relationship between the administration of antibiotic agents and the appearance of a maculopapular exanthem.[161–165] In virtually 100% of patients who receive ampicillin (or amoxicillin), and in a lesser percentage who take penicillin or other antibacterial drugs, maculopapular lesions erupt within one to three days. Only two of 20 patients challenged with ampicillin after recovery from IM by Nazareth and colleagues developed a rash.[251] This incidence of 10% is compatible with that found in the general population, suggesting that the sensitivity to the drug does not persist.

Secondary Infection.—Some authors have suggested an increased frequency of pharyngeal infection with group A streptococcus in patients with IM, but recent studies have not supported this view.[252–255] Jarvis[254] compared the incidence of streptococcal recovery by throat culture in patients with HA-positive IM and HA-negative controls and found an incidence in the range of 5% in both groups. At the Student Health Service of the University of Pennsylvania, Collins and colleagues noted a 3% to 6% rate of streptococcal colonization of the pharynx both in students with IM and in controls.[256]

Notwithstanding the controversy over the incidence of streptococcal pharyngitis, severe, and even fatal, infections have been described in IM.[255–258] Deaths have occurred from streptococcal sepsis and a streptococcal abscess of the retropharynx.[257, 258]

Death.—Immunologically normal persons almost invariably recover from an EBV infection. However, occasional fatalities have been reported due to neurologic involvement, splenic rupture, airway obstruction, hepatic failure, myocarditis, pneumonia, hemorrhage, granulocytopenia, and other complications. Penman and others estimated that one per 3000 patients with IM died from the disease.[256, 259–261]

Chronic Infectious Mononucleosis.—Cases of chronic or recurrent IM have been reported in the literature on a sporadic basis for a number of years.[262–267] It was not until 1985, however, that the possibility of a distinct syndrome of chronic IM was described in two simultaneous reports.[268, 269]

Jones and colleagues[268] reported on 44 patients referred to them for chronic, undiagnosed illnesses that appeared to be infectious. The disorders were characterized by fatigue, headache or paresthesias, pharyngitis, and lymphadenopathy—persistent or recurrent for more than 1 year, alone or in combination. Thirty-nine of 44 patients had antibodies to EBV, often characterized either by (a) high titers of IgG anti-VCA, anti-EA, and anti-EBNA, or (b) high titers of IgG anti-VCA and anti-EA but low titers of anti-EBNA.

Straus and colleagues[269] described their findings in 23 patients, all of whom had illnesses that included fatigue for at least 1 year as well as antibodies to EBV. These patients displayed, at times, low-grade fever (96%), pharyngitis (57%), adenopathy (48%), and headache (35%). Evaluation of the serologic response to EBV showed high titers of IgG anti-VCA and anti-EA in some but not all patients; in seven cases, anti-EBNA was absent (as compared to 0/23 controls), but the geometric mean titer of 29 was similar to that of 25 measured in controls. Most of the patients had considerable psychosocial problems. Eleven were evaluated by psychiatrists as part of the study; six were considered to have somatization disorders, and one each anxiety neurosis and depression.

At this point, it is certain that (a) a small percentage (<5%) of patients develop, following an episode of otherwise unremarkable IM, a constellation of symptoms including recurrent or persistent fatigue, headache, and pharyngitis, and (b) the same pattern of illness occurs in patients without preceding IM, some with and others without serologic evidence of EBV infection. The role for EBV, as discussed by the authors of the two studies, remains speculative. Findings that cast doubt on a causal association for EBV in a specific syndrome include (a) the vague and variable course of the disease; (b) the absence of serologic evidence for infection in some patients who have the clinical disorder; (c) the inconsistent nature of the serologic pattern; and (d) the known propensity of EBV-specific antibody titers to change with various immunoregulatory disorders. Until the existence of chronic infectious mononucleosis is substantiated and the part played by EBV is defined, physicians must exercise caution in making this diagnosis; on the other hand, patients with these vague complaints should not be dismissed as having a nonorganic condition, as they may be suffering from a persistent infection.

Association of EBV With Burkitt's Lymphoma, Nasopharyngeal Carcinoma, and Other Malignancies

EBV was originally identified by electron microscopy in tumor cells from a patient with BL. Subsequently the association of the virus with this malignancy has become stronger.[270–273] Virtually 100% of African victims of this disease have antibodies to EBV, usually in titers significantly higher than those observed in control subjects.[270–274] BL cells contain EBV, as demonstrated by fluorescent staining for EBNA and nucleic acid hybridization studies.[51–53] Virus can also be recovered from the tumor cells in culture.[275]

BL develops years after primary EBV infection. Among individuals who have had a prior EBV infection, only one per 10 to 100 million circulating lymphocytes carries the EBV genome, but every BL tumor cell contains the viral DNA. This shows that the tumor is monoclonal and arises in every case from one EBV-infected lymphocyte, an unlikely chance occurrence considering the ratio of uninfected to infected cells. Most cases of BL outside of endemic areas are not EBV-associated. However, sporadic cases and even tumor clusters related to EBV occasionally occur in the developed countries.[271, 274, 276]

Similarly, virtually 100% of patients from endemic areas who develop nasopharyngeal carcinoma (NPC) have antibodies to EBV at unusually high titers.[277, 278] The presence of the virus is also demonstrable in the tumor cells by immunofluorescence for EBNA and nucleic acid hybridization.[29–32] Several experiments have suggested that nasopharyngeal epithelial cells may be capable of supporting the replication of EBV, but they have no receptors for EBV, indicating that they are not readily infected.

In both BL and NPC, the initially high titers of antibodies to EBV increase as the tumor burden grows.[270–278] The initiation of effective therapy reduces the tumor mass and thereafter also the level of antibodies. In patients who remain in remission, the antibody spectrum approaches that seen in healthy individuals after a part primary infection. However, concurrent with or preceding a clinical relapse, an upsurge in the antibodies occurs that is proportional to the extent of dissemination.

Although studies have linked EBV infection in late adolescence with Hodgkin's disease, this association may well occur due to unrelated socioeconomic factors.[279–282] Lange and colleagues[283] found no role for EBV in this malignancy.

EBV Infections in the Immunosuppressed Host

Certain groups of patients are peculiarly susceptible to severe disease with this virus. In 1973, Bar and colleagues[36] initially described a kindred in which the males experienced overwhelming IM. Subsequently, Purtilo and coworkers have more extensively categorized the scope of this deficiency, originally known as Duncan syndrome and now referred to as the X-linked lymphoproliferative syndrome (XLP).[284–292] Males in these families have minimal difficulty with infections other than EBV. Following infections with EBV, they die of overwhelming IM, manifest hypogammaglobulinemia, and/or aplastic anemia, or develop lymphoproliferative malignancies. These patients have an impaired humoral immune response to EBV and a deficiency of natural killer (NK) cells.

A single kindred has been described by Fleisher and colleagues[293] with a non-X-linked syndrome of susceptibility to severe EBV infections. The affected members had a deficiency of NK cells but differed from patients with XLP in that they mounted the expected antibody response to the virus and had no sequelae, if they survived.

EBV may reactivate in other immunosuppressed patients but does not usually cause severe infections. However, with profound disturbances of the immune system, as in recipients of cardiac, renal, or liver transplants who receive cyclosporin, unusual infectious syndromes and lymphoproliferative malignancies may occur.[294, 295] Preliminary reports have not shown EBV to be a major problem in patients with acquired immunodeficiency syndrome (AIDS).[296, 297]

Immunologic Response
Humoral

After infection with EBV, the host responds with antibodies to some or all the antigens that are either part of the virus or induced by infection, including viral capsid antigen, early antigens (diffuse and restricted), EBV-determined membrane antigens, and EBV-associated nuclear antigen. Additionally, antibodies may arise that are directed against unrelated antigens found on sheep, horse, or beef red blood cells. Four different patterns of antibody response may emerge at the time of diagnosis, depending on the clinical syndrome: infectious mononucleosis, silent primary infection, Burkitt's lymphoma, or nasopharyngeal carcinoma (Figure 37–7).

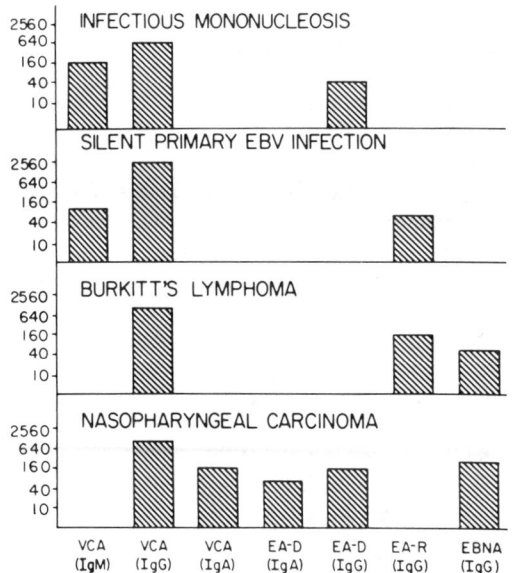

Figure 36–7. Patterns of Epstein Barr virus (EBV)-specific antibody response in various conditions. For key to abbreviations, see Table 36–1.

Infectious Mononucleosis.—Figure 36-8 presents the serologic responses in the course of IM.[298] Within 4 to 6 weeks of infection, antibodies directed against VCA appear in the circulation. Both IgM and IgG antibodies are formed concurrently in all cases, although an occasional patient may have IgM antibodies a few days earlier.[299] These antibodies reach a peak titer in the majority of individuals with IM simultaneously with the appearance of clinical signs, and in the remainder within 2 to 3 weeks of onset. The peak titer of IgG anti-VCA may range from 1:80 to 1:2560 but most frequently falls between 1:320 and 1:1280; that of IgM anti-VCA is usually slightly lower.

Within 6 to 12 weeks of onset, IgM anti-VCA disappears from the circulation.[299] Once it has reached its maximal elevation, IgG anti-VCA persists at this level for several months and then declines, remaining detectable for life at a titer of 1:40 to 1:640 (mean 1:160–1:320). About two thirds of patients with IM transiently produce IgA antibodies to VCA.

Approximately 85% of patients with IM develop IgG antibodies to the EA complex, almost always to the diffuse (D) component, coincident with the clinical syndrome.[300–302] At the time of diagnosis or shortly thereafter, the titer of anti-EA(D) reaches a peak, most often between 1:20 and 1:80. The antibodies usually become undetectable within 3 months of onset but rarely persist for 1 to 2 years. In an occasional patient with IM, antibodies to the restricted component of the EA complex appear transiently at a titer of 1:20 to 1:80 either at the onset of the illness or, more often, several months later.[303] The late emergence of anti-EA(R) takes place both in patients with and without an initial titer of anti-EA(D).

Antibodies to EBV-induced membrane antigens arise shortly after infection and persist for life in a fashion similar to IgG anti-VCA.[304] Neutralizing antibodies parallel the anti–membrane antigen (MA) response and may be identical to such antibodies.[305]

Antibodies to EBNA generally appear only weeks or even months after onset of illness, although an occasional patient may have a low titer (1:2 or 1:5) at the time of diagnosis.[298, 306–308] Presumably, EBNA does not become available for antibody stimulation until after the incubation phase of IM when activated T lymphocytes destroy the EBV genome-carrying B cells.[307] The titer of anti-EBNA rises over a period of several months and persists for life at a low level that varies from 1:5 to 1:80 (mean 1:40) in most individuals.

HAs usually appear in patients with IM at the time of diagnosis, but they may not emerge in some cases until 1 to 4 weeks after onset.[309–313] A very sensitive assay, such as immune adherence hemagglutination (IAHA), detects HAs in more than 85% of pa-

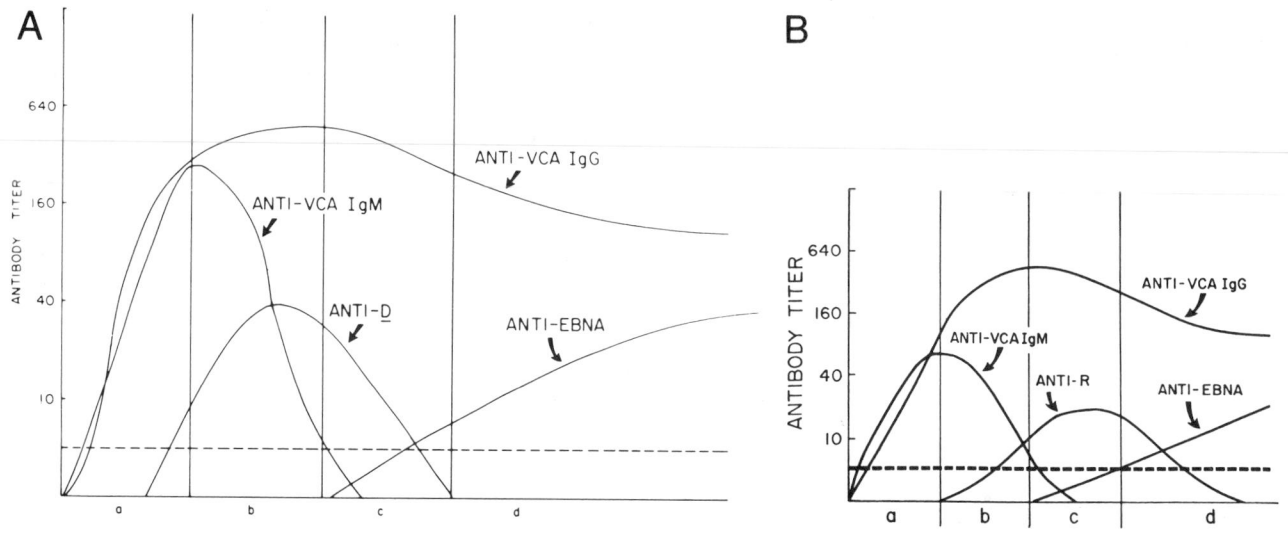

Figure 36–8. A. Evolution of Epstein-Barr virus (EBV)-specific antibody responses in infectious mononucleosis. B. Evolution of EBV-specific antibody responses during asymptomatic seroconversion. For key to abbreviations see Table 36–1.

tients with IM, regardless of their age.[105, 313] However, the geometric mean titer of HA is significantly lower in children under age 5 years as compared to adolescents, and assays that are less sensitive than IAHA may miss the response in 20% to 50% of the cases.[105] HA disappears 2 to 4 months after onset in the majority of patients but occasionally persists as long as 2 years.[312]

Asymptomatic Primary Infections.—The evolution of the antibody response to VCA and EBNA resembles that in IM except that a peak titer of IgM anti-VCA exceeding 1:80 is rarely detected.[7, 74] However, the appearance of antibodies to the EA complex and HA differs markedly. Whereas patients with IM develop anti-EA(D) at the time of diagnosis, those with asymptomatic primary infections manifest a response to the restricted component of the EA complex, and then only several months after seroconversion (Figure 36–8B). Additionally, HA rarely reaches detectable levels in silent infections.

Burkitt's Lymphoma.—Patients with Burkitt's lymphoma usually have titers of IgG antibodies to VCA, MA, the restricted component of the EA complex, and EBNA, but no IgM anti-VCA, anti-EA(D), or HA at the time the tumor is diagnosed.[270–273] VCA-specific IgA antibodies develop at only low titers in no more than 30% of BL patients. High titers of IgG anti-VCA and anti-EA(R) are the rule and are, to a considerable extent, referable to the tumor pattern. When no antibodies to anti-R are detectable or the titers decline following treatment, patients with BL are likely to survive. However, when anti-R antibodies remain elevated or subsequently emerge, an unfavorable outcome is likely. Anti-EA(D) antibodies may appear late in the course and also suggest a poor prognosis. In BL, anti-EBNA titers vary from barely detectable to very high, exceeding the range of control titers at both ends of the scale.

Nasopharyngeal Carcinoma.—Patients with NPC have high titers of IgG antibodies to VCA, MA, the D component of the EA complex, and anti-EBNA.[277, 278] Additionally, they nearly uniformly produce IgA antibodies to VCA and frequently also to the D component of the EA complex, often at substantial titers. An occasional patient develops an apparent low titer of IgM anti-VCA, but these reactions are due to the presence of rheumatoid factor. Anti-EA(R) cannot be measured in the presence of D reactions, and anti-HAs are not observed. Patients who respond well to therapy show slow, steady declines in the antibody titers so that IgA and IgG anti-EA(D) and IgA anti-VCA disappear or persist at barely detectable levels. However, patients who have a less favorable response to therapy continue to produce these antibodies which increase with progression of the disease. Such increases in titers are observed often months before clinical recognition of recurrent tumors or metastases.

Cellular

EBV infects B lymphocytes, which have specific receptors on the surface that are not found on other cells; this infection stimulates rapid proliferation of the B lymphocytes. The total number of B cells in the peripheral circulation increases during the acute phase of IM, reaching a peak within 1 week of onset and declining over the next 3 to 4 weeks.[314–316]

As a response to the B cell proliferation, a corresponding increase in the number of T lymphocytes occurs.[317] During the first week of the illness, there may be a reversal of the usual T/B cell ratio. The number of T lymphocytes in the peripheral circulation continues to rise during the second week of the illness, and then falls over 5 to 6 weeks. Specifically, T suppressor cells are activated which in turn inhibit the B cell proliferation induced by EBV.[318] De Waele and colleagues[319] showed that the increase in T lymphocytes was due to a rise in the number of T suppressor/ cytotoxic cells as determined by labeling with monoclonal antibodies to T cell subsets. They found that the absolute number of T helper cells was in the normal range, so that a reversal of the T helper–suppressor ratio occurred. During clinical recovery, the lymphocyte subset distribution returned to normal.

The development of immunologic techniques for the quantitation of B and T cells has allowed for clarification of the atypical lymphocytosis originally described in patients with IM in the 1920s. Both T and B cells appear in the peripheral circulation as atypical lymphocytes, although the T cells predominate.

Functional changes in cell-mediated immunity (CMI) accompany the alterations in the number of T and B cells. In 1953 Bentzon[320] showed a loss of tuberculin skin test reactivity in patients with IM, and the development of tuberculin anergy was subsequently confirmed by Haider and colleagues.[321] During the first 2 weeks of illness, the cutaneous responses to *Candida albicans* and streptokinase-streptodornase are also diminished. In vitro, the lymphocytes from patients with IM exhibit a decreased responsiveness to mitogens.

During an EBV infection, EBV-specific CMI develops. Cytotoxic T cells active against EBV-transformed cells are found during the acute phase of IM but no longer in convalescence.[54, 322] Additionally, lymphocytes from patients with IM show reactivity to purified preparations of EBV following infection with the virus. ten Napel and The[323] noted such reactivity in no seronegative individuals, seven of 15 patients with IM of less than 21 days' duration, and all subjects studied more than 5 weeks after the onset of the illness. Patients with rheumatoid arthritis show defective EBV-specific T-suppressor cell function.[324]

Several investigations have suggested a role for NK cells in the control of viral infections.[292, 293] Patients with XLP lack NK cells and have a susceptibility to overwhelming illness or the development of lymphoproliferative malignancies following infection with EBV.[292] Fleisher and colleagues[293] have also described one female and two male siblings with deficient NK cell activity, who experienced severe or fatal IM. NK cells may have a role in destroying EBV-infected lymphocytes as soon as membrane antigens appear on the surface but prior to the synthesis of complete virus. By this postulated mechanism, they would limit the amount of virus released as well as the degree of proliferation and thus permit the immune system of the host to control the infection.

LABORATORY DIAGNOSIS

EBV Infections

The definitive diagnosis of an acute primary EBV infection is established by EBV-specific serology.[298] Recovery of the virus does not distinguish between current and past infections.[38–40] In those cases where an EBV infection produces clinically apparent IM, additional tests, such as the HA titer and WBC count and differential, find a place in diagnosis.

Table 36–6
Epstein-Barr Virus Serologic Status

Infection	Antibody Titers			
	IgM Anti-VCA	IgG Anti-VCA	Anti-EA	Anti-EBNA
None	0	0	0	0
Current	+ +	+ +	+	0 or ±
Recent	± or 0	+ + or +	± or 0	0 or ±
Past	0	+	0	+

0 = negative, + + = strongly positive. For abbreviations, see Table 36–1.

Antibodies to VCA, EAs, and EBNA are useful diagnostically.[298] IgG and IgM anti-VCA and IgG antibodies against both diffuse and restricted components of the EA complex are titrated by IFA. IgG antibodies against EBNA are measured in the anti-complement immunofluorescence assay.

Relying on the chronology of the appearance and disappearance of antibodies to the various EBV-specific antigens (as outlined under humoral immune reponse), individuals may be classified into one of four categories in relationship to this virus: no, acute, recent, or past infection (Table 36–6). The serologic criteria for an acute, primary EBV infection manifested as IM are (1) IgM anti-VCA; (2) IgG anti-VCA, usually in high titer but occasionally at an initial low level that rises in 1 to 2 weeks; (3) anti-EA(D) in 85% of cases; and (4) absent or low titers of anti-EBNA.[298] Silent seroconversions are not accompanied by an anti-EA(D) response but may induce a late rise in the anti-EA(R) titer.[3, 74]

Infectious Mononucleosis

Heterophil Antibodies

HAs are IgM antibodies having the capacity to react with certain antigens that are phylogenetically unrelated to the organism producing the antibody response. In addition to occurring during a bout of IM, they may arise without an apparent stimulus (Forssman antibodies) or following other viral infections, lymphoproliferative disorders, or serum sickness.[309–313] Forssman antibodies are adsorbed by suspensions of either beef red blood cells or guinea pig kidney (GPK), and HAs in serum sickness are adsorbed by suspensions of guinea pig kidney but not beef red blood cells.

IM-specific HAs have properties that allow for their detection; these include the agglutination of sheep and horse erythrocytes and the lysis of ox red blood cells. They are adsorbed by suspensions of beef red blood cells but not guinea pig kidney. The first assay described for HA in patients with IM was the Paul-Bunnell test which relied on the agglutination of sheep red blood cells.[6] A modification of this procedure, the Paul-Bunnell-Davidsohn test, was introduced in 1937 and permitted the differentiation of IM-specific HA from antibodies resulting from other conditions (Table 36–7).[7] Subsequently, HAs were found to react more strongly with papain-treated sheep erythrocytes (Wollner test) and with horse erythrocytes.[325, 326] Additionally, the unique ability of IM-specific HA to lyse ox red blood cells was harnessed as a diagnostic assay, eliminating the need for differential adsorption.[309, 310] Recent advances in immunology have permitted the application of agar gel diffusion,[327] latex agglutination,[328] radioimmunoassay (RIA),[329] IAHA,[313] and enzyme-linked immunoadsorption[330] to the detection of the heterophil response.

Tests currently in clinical use include the agglutination of sheep or horse cells with or without differential adsorption, the ox cell hemolysin test, and IAHA. The agglutination of sheep cells is the least sensitive and the least specific assay.[311–313] Approximately 90% of young adults with IM have an HA response detectable by this assay, but nonspecific HAs are also reactive. The substitution of horse erythrocytes increases the sensitivity, but not the specificity, of the assay. To improve the specificity, differential adsorption with suspensions of guinea pig kidney and beef erythrocytes is performed. The IM-specific HA shows less than a threefold decrease after adsorption with GPK and more than a fourfold drop with ox RBCs. In the presumptive test, a titer of 1:40 or greater (or 1:56, depending on the methodology) is considered positive. After differential adsorption with GPK, a titer of 1:40 or greater (or 1:56) indicates IM. However, occasional false-positive results have been reported.[331, 332] Commercial kits (spot tests) relying on the agglutination of sheep or horse erythrocytes have a sensitivity equal to that of the more traditional "tube" tests.[333]

The hemolysis of ox cells by HA, originally described in 1935 by Bailey and Raffel,[309] has subsequently proved to be a reliable technique for the detection of HA.[312] The test has a slightly lower sensitivity than the agglutination assays but is more specific. False-positive reactions occur rarely if at all. The IAHA test appears to be the most specific and sensitive of the assays currently available.[313]

Two factors exert a profound influence on the likelihood of detecting HA in a case of IM: (1) the age of the patient; and (2) the point during the illness at which the test is done. Initially, children were said to develop an HA response less often than young adults. However, subsequent studies have shown that the magnitude rather than the frequency of the response is decreased in childhood (Table 36–8). Using the very sensitive IAHA test, 90% of children as young as 2 years of age have detectable HA, but the geometric mean titer of the response is only one-third that of adolescents and young adults. Thus, tests that lack the sensitivity

Table 36–7
Reaction Patterns of Heterophil Antibodies

Antibody	Unadsorbed	GPK Adsorption	Beef RBC Adsorption
IM-specific	+ + + +	+ + +	0 or +
Serum sickness	+ + +	0 or +	0 or +
Forssman	+ +	0 or +	+ or + +

0 = negative, + + + + = strongly positive; GPK = guinea pig kidney; IM = infectious mononucleosis.

Table 36–8
Heterophil Antibody Response in Childhood

Age Range (years)	Spot Test (% Positive)		Tube Test, % Positive (GMT)		
	Horse Cell	Sheep Cell	IAHA	OCH	PBD
2–5	50	25	90 (400)	65 (150)	70 (175)
6–10	90	50	>90 (700)	80 (600)	80 (500)
11–15	90	70	>90 (1400)	90 (1200)	90 (700)

IAHA = immune adherence hemagglutination; OCH = ox cell hemolysis; PBD = Paul-Bunnell-Davidsohn.

of the IAHA assay may not detect HA in children, particularly those less than 5 years of age.

HAs are usually detectable at the onset of IM, but they may not emerge until the second or third week of illness. In a prospective evaluation of college students, Evans and colleagues[312] found that 15% to 30% of patients, depending on the assay, did not have HAs at onset but developed such antibodies within 4 weeks. Delayed appearance of HA may be associated with a more prolonged course.

Just as the initial detection of HA varies with the assay used, so does the persistence of the antibody. The duration of the response is briefest with the ox cell hemolysin test and longest with the horse cell agglutination assay (Table 36–9). However, the persistence of HA, as measured by horse cell agglutination, may lead to errors in diagnosis of subsequent mononucleosislike illnesses.

White Blood Cells

The initial descriptions of the changes in the WBC count and morphology during the course of IM were provided by Sprunt and Evans[3] in 1920 and Downey and McKinlay[5] in 1923. Refinements in diagnosis have subsequently permitted a more precise enumeration of these alterations. Even so, the data on the leukocyte response during IM in adults has been gathered on patients meeting clinical, hematologic, and serologic, but not virologic, criteria for diagnosis; thus, they may not accurately reflect the full spectrum of the disease.

The common changes in the peripheral blood seen during the course of IM include a leukocytosis, an absolute lymphocytosis, and an increase in the number of atypical lymphocytes.[153, 334] The total leukocyte count is usually normal or mildly increased during the first week of illness, reaching a peak at 14 to 21 days. The highest WBC count usually ranges from 10,000 to 20,000/μL and rarely exceeds 30,000/μL. Although WBC counts greater than

Table 36–9
Percentage of Patients With Persistent Heterophil Antibodies in Infectious Mononucleosis (IM)

Assay	Months Past Onset of IM			
	0	3	12	24
Ox cell hemolysin	>90%	10%		
Sheep cell agglutination	>90%	50%	25%	
Horse cell agglutination	>90%	75%	50%	10%

50,000/μL occasionally occur with IM, elevations greater than 30,000 to 40,000/μL should always raise the suspicion of an alternative diagnosis.[153, 335] As many as 20% of adult patients may develop a leukopenia initially.

Both a relative and an absolute lymphocytosis also occur, achieving maximal levels 2 to 3 weeks after onset. In adults, the percentage of lymphocytes is said always to exceed 50%; however, this level represented a necessary criterion for diagnosis in many early studies.

The most striking finding on the peripheral smear of patients with IM is the occurrence of atypical lymphocytes (Figure 36–9). As originally described by Downey and McKinlay,[5] these lymphocytes may have varying morphologies. Most characteristically they are large mononuclear cells with an eccentric nucleus and abundant cytoplasm that indents when it abuts against an erythrocyte. Atypical lymphocytes usually represent at least 10% and often well over 20% of the WBCs. At times, as many as 90% of the peripheral WBCs may be atypical lymphocytes.

Atypical lymphocytes may also occur in other viral diseases, particularly CMV infections, toxoplasmosis, bacterial endocarditis, streptococcal infections, hypersensitivity states, and occasionally in healthy individuals.[336–338] Only rarely do they exceed 20% of the total WBC count in illnesses other than IM. Although the expected changes in the leukocytes often accompany mild cases of IM, EBV infections do not appear to cause an atypical lymphocytosis in the absence of clinical findings. Fleisher and Paradise[340] studied 45 patients from 1 week to 15 years of age who were not suspected clinically of having IM but who had atypical lymphocytes detected on a peripheral smear obtained for other reasons. The percentage of atypical lymphocytes varied from 5% to 39%, with a mean of 10%. No patient had an acute, primary EBV infection and only one had serologic evidence of a recent exposure, a finding consistent with the expected incidence of asymptomatic seroconversions in childhood.

Both a relative and an absolute neutropenia often develop early in the course of IM.[341] The number of immature forms commonly increases; toxic granules and Döhle bodies may also be present.

Age appears to minimally influence only certain aspects of the leukocyte response in clinically apparent IM. Fleisher and colleagues[342] reviewed the WBC counts and peripheral smears from children who had IM documented by EBV-specific serology and found no difference between the youngest and oldest groups. The total WBC counts at the time of diagnosis ranged from 4400 to 22,800/μL, with a mean of 12,900/μL; the total lymphocytes from 42% to 88%, with a mean of 65%; and the atypical lymphocyte counts from 2% to 83%, with a mean of 22%. In these serologically confirmed cases, 16% of the patients had fewer than 50% lym-

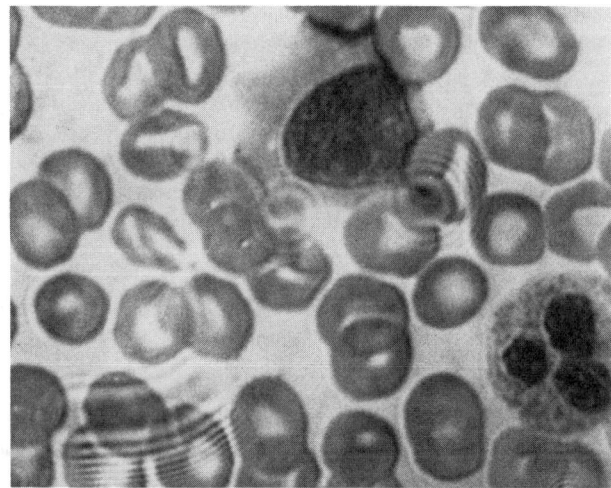

Figure 36–9. Atypical lymphocyte.

phocytes, and 48% of patients fewer than 20% atypical lymphocytes.

Recovery of EBV

Chang and Golden[38] in 1971 and Pereira and colleagues[133] in 1972 first demonstrated the presence of a lymphocyte-transforming agent, later shown to be EBV, in the saliva of patients with IM. Shortly thereafter, Gerber and colleagues[40] found EBV in the oral secretions of occasional healthy individuals seropositive for EBV but not in those who were seronegative. Subsequent studies have shown that 15% to 20% of randomly selected seropositive adults, as many as 50% of immunosuppressed patients seropositive for EBV, and virtually 100% of individuals with acute IM excrete EBV in the oropharynx.[39, 134–136] Thus, the identification of EBV in the saliva confirms a prior infection with the virus but does not distinguish between acute and past infections.

Additional Laboratory Findings

Mild-to-moderate thrombocytopenia occurs in about half the patients with IM.[188] Only rarely does the platelet count decrease sufficiently to cause clinically apparent bleeding. Anemia is not a common finding in IM, but may result from acute hemolysis due to antibodies with anti-i specificity.[184]

From 80% to 100% of patients with IM have elevations of their hepatic enzymes which persist for 3 to 5 weeks.[159, 160] Mild hyperbilirubinemia may occur; however, clinically apparent jaundice is quite unusual.[146–155] The serum bilirubin rarely exceeds 10 mg/dL.

A wide variety of transient immunologic changes occur in IM, probably as a result of nonspecific stimulation of B lymphocytes by EBV.[334] Elevations of cold agglutinins, Weil-Felix titers, febrile agglutinins, and false-positive serologic tests for syphilis have been described in occasional cases. Increases in the levels of all classes of immunoglobulins are usually present.[343]

Several early reports suggested an increased incidence of group A streptococcal pharyngitis in patients with IM, but this has not been confirmed. In a prospective study of IM in college students, Collins found a similar incidence in students with IM and controls.[256]

Histologic Features

During the course of IM, infected B lymphocytes proliferate and may invade almost any organ. Custer and Smith[344] autopsied nine patients who died of IM and found perivascular lymphocytic infiltrates in all tissues except the bone marrow. Lymph nodes obtained by either biopsy or autopsy show diffuse hyperplasia but retain their basic nodal architecture; large numbers of atypical lymphocytes are seen.[345] A marked lymphocytic infiltration of the spleen occurs, often thinning the supporting structures of this organ. Although the liver is only occasionally dysfunctional, large numbers of mononuclear cells are usually apparent in the portal areas.

Differential Diagnosis

The combination of a compatible clinical syndrome and a positive HA test points almost unequivocably to the diagnosis of IM. However, HA-negative cases of IM present a problem in differential diagnosis until the results of EBV-specific serology become available. While CMV causes most of these illnesses, other infectious agents may produce clinical pictures that also overlap with IM.[346, 347] These include toxoplasmosis, viral hepatitis, rubella, and streptococcal pharyngitis.

CMV mononucleosis closely resembles IM except that the pharyngeal involvement is less severe. Additionally, the degree of atypical lymphocytosis is not as marked. Toxoplasmosis causes almost no pharyngitis and minimal hepatitis; often an exanthem occurs as well. With rubella infections, the adenopathy generally remains confined to the head and neck, and organomegaly is absent. Similarly, streptococcal pharyngitis does not involve the distal lymph nodes or the abdominal organs.

PREVENTION AND TREATMENT

Vaccine

Currently, there is neither a vaccine against EBV nor any immediate prospect for development of one. Such a vaccine would be desirable for the prevention of IM and perhaps of the EBV-associated tumors: BL and NPC. Additionally, use of the vaccine in endemic areas for BL and NPC could potentially confirm the etiologic role of EBV in these malignancies.

Because of the oncogenic potential of EBV, any vaccine preparation would have to be devoid of viral nucleic acid. Either a live attenuated or conventionally inactivated viral vaccine would raise the specter of iatrogenic oncogenicity. Vaccines have proved effective in animal herpesvirus infections such as Marek's disease of chickens,[348] but further studies are needed to evaluate nucleic acid–free preparations.

The antigens responsible for eliciting a neutralizing antibody response in humans infected with EBV are located on the membranes of B lymphocytes; these membrane antigens form a portion of the viral envelope that is derived from altered cell membranes. Purification of such antigens from isolated cell membranes has become technically feasible in recent years. Epstein and colleagues have been able to prevent the development of EBV-induced tumors in cottontop tamarins using preparations containing MA.[349] However, a large amount of additional work will be necessary before considering the use of candidate vaccines in humans.

Treatment of Infection

General Measures

Lacking any specific antiviral therapy directed against EBV, the physician is left with providing primarily symptomatic treatment. Bed rest is necessary during the acute phase of illness, compliance with such a recommendation being enforced by the debilitating nature of the disease rather than the admonitions of the caretakers. Either aspirin or acetaminophen provides some relief from the hyperpyrexia that is almost invariably present early in the course. Even in mild cases of IM, avoidance of contact sports is advisable for 6 weeks to lessen the chance of splenic rupture; in cases with persistent splenomegaly, such activities should be proscribed at least until the spleen has returned to its normal size.

Corticosteroids

Corticosteroids offer some relief for acute symptoms, although specific recommendations for their administration remain somewhat arbitrary due to insufficient data.[351–357] Antila and colleagues[352] in 1962 found a shorter duration of fever in steroid-treated patients only if the drug was administered during the first four days of the illness, suggesting a limited utility for this therapy since many patients are not seen until later in their course. Breen and Talukar[353] noted a more rapid resolution of fever, pharyngitis, and lymphadenopathy with the use of steroids, but no statistical significance was shown. The controlled double blind study of Klein and colleagues[355] stands as the best effort to date that shows a significant short-term difference in the duration of sore throat in steroid-compared to placebo-treated patients; however, by the third day of therapy, the two groups had equally frequent symptoms. Extending these observations, Prout and Dalrymple[357] observed that corticosteroid therapy enabled hospitalized students to leave the infirmary more rapidly than those who received a placebo, although the difference was not significant.

Bender[354] was the first to stratify patients with IM by clinical severity before analyzing the response to treatment. He noted a significant decrease in the mean number of febrile days among moderately ill patients given steroid as compared to placebo (14 vs six days of fever, respectively). Addressing the psychiatric effects of IM, Bolden[356] found steroids led to a more rapid, but not statistically significant, resolution of malaise and depression.

Steroids have been used widely for the treatment of patients with IM who develop massive tonsillar hypertrophy causing obstruction of the airway. Although controlled trials are lacking, the consensus of clinical opinion suggests a beneficial effect in this situation.

Collins et al evaluated the efficacy of prednisone for the treatment of patients with IM, confirmed by EBV-specific serology, of varying degrees of severity.[358] Students with mild disease who received steroids improved somewhat more rapidly than placebo recipients during the first week of therapy; the experience with more severe illness was limited. At all grades of severity, the spectrum and pattern of EBV-specific antibodies evolved in a nearly similar fashion in both groups. Two students in the steroid-treated group developed significant complications: a peritonsillar abscess and diabetes mellitus. The potential complications of steroids have not been adequately addressed by most of the studies

on patients with IM. These potent agents may cause hypertension, diabetes mellitus, and psychiatric disturbances even with short-term usage.

Since many patients with IM either have mild disease initially or improve rapidly with symptomatic therapy alone, the routine administration of steroids in all cases would seem to engender unnecessary risks. These agents should be reserved for patients with signs of upper airway compromise, marked systemic toxicity, and persistence of significant symptoms (other than fatigue) beyond 1 to 2 weeks, hemolytic anemia, or thrombocytopenia. If treatment is necessary, prednisone is the agent of choice in a dosage of 2 mg/kg/day (maximum 60-80 mg) for seven to 14 days.

Additional Therapies

Numerous treatments have been used without proven success for patients with IM including gamma globulin,[359] pancreatic DNAase,[360] Methisazone,[361] interleukin-2,[362] metronidazole,[363] tinidazole,[364] and acyclovir. Recent reports from the Scandinavian literature describing a favorable response to metronidazole and tinidazole await more adequate studies.[363, 364] Presumably, these agents decrease the anaerobic flora in the throat and do not directly attack the virus. While acyclovir has demonstrated efficacy against EBV in cell culture, controlled trials have not demonstrated clinical benefit.[365]

Algorithm for Diagnosis and Management of EBV Infection and IM

The approach to the diagnosis of IM varies first with the type of clinical illness (Figure 36–10). Neither an atypical lymphocytosis nor an HA response is likely to accompany asymptomatic

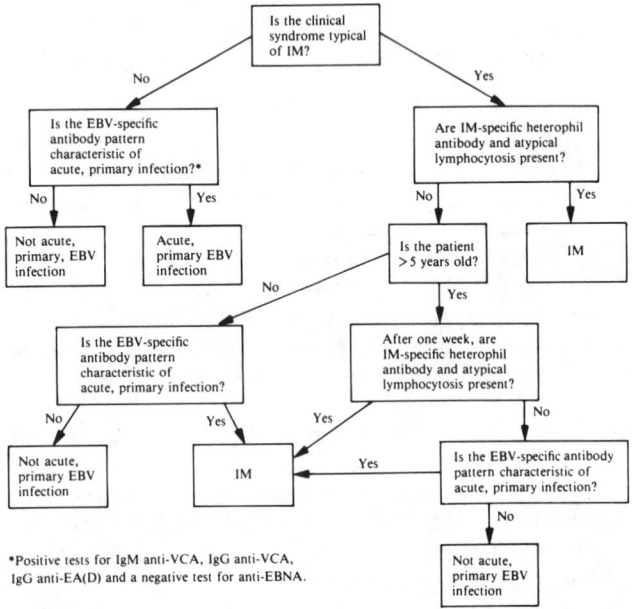

Figure 36–10. Algorithm for the diagnosis of Epstein-Barr virus infections and infectious mononucleosis. For key to abbreviations, see Table 36–1.

seroconversions or isolated uncommon manifestations such as encephalitis or pneumonitis. Thus, diagnosis in the patient who does not have the features of IM requires EBV-specific serology in all cases.

On the other hand, the majority of patients, albeit fewer young children than adolescents, develop both HAs and atypical lymphocytosis during the course of IM. Although testing for the full spectrum of antibodies to EBV provides the ultimate confirmation, these assays are frequently difficult to obtain. Fortunately, the clinician can rely on the HA test and the peripheral leukocyte response in the majority of the cases of IM.

Whenever the initial clinical diagnosis is IM, an HA test and WBC count with differential should be performed. The presence of a significant titer of IM-specific HA and an atypical lymphocytosis confirms the clinical diagnosis with a quite high degree of certainty, and EBV serodiagnostic tests are unnecessary in routine practice. However, failure to detect an HA response or the expected changes in the leukocytes mandates further testing. Since the child less than 5 years of age commonly does not mount an HA response detectable by the usual assays, EBV-specific serology is indicated to make a diagnosis expeditiously. In contrast, more than 90% of older children, adolescents, and young adults develop HAs, which may arise immediately or be delayed in their appearance. Additionally, lymphocytosis and the number of atypical lymphocytes often do not peak until the second week of the disease. Thus, repeating the HA test and WBC count with differential after 1 week may yet obviate the need for EBV serodiagnosis. Those patients who remain persistently HA-negative and do not develop an atypical lymphocytosis require EBV-specific serology in situations where an etiologic diagnosis is important.

Symptomatic treatment, including rest and antipyretic agents, is appropriate for all patients with IM. Those with upper airway obstruction, hemolytic anemia, thrombocytopenia, or symptoms (other than fatigue) persisting beyond ten to 14 days often respond to therapy with corticosteroids. In the unusual EBV infection that is life-threatening, acyclovir holds the most promise of the currently available experimental therapies.

REFERENCES

1. Epstein MA, Achong BG, Barr YM: Virus particles in cultured lymphoblasts from Burkitt's lymphoma. *Lancet* 1964; 1:702.
2. Henle G, Henle W, Diehl V: Relation of Burkitt's tumor associated herpes-type virus to infectious mononucleosis. *Proc Natl Acad Sci USA* 1958; 59:94.
3. Sprunt TP, Evans FA: Mononuclear leukocytosis in reaction to acute infections ("infectious mononucleosis"). *Johns Hopkins Hosp Bull* 1929; 31:410.
4. Biggar RJ, Henle G, Bocker J, et al: Primary Epstein-Barr virus infections in African infants. II. Clinical and serological observations during seroconversion. *Int J Cancer* 1978; 22:244.
5. Downey H, McKinlay CA: Acute lymphadenosis compared with acute lymphatic leukemia. *Arch Intern Med* 1923; 32:82.
6. Paul JR, Bunnell W: The presence of heterophile antibodies in infectious mononucleosis. *Am J Med Sci* 1932; 183:90.
7. Davidsohn I: Serologic diagnosis of infectious mononucleosis. *JAMA* 1937; 108:289.
8. Burkitt D: A sarcoma involving the jaws of African children. *Br J Surg* 1958; 46:218.
9. Henle G, Henle W: Immunofluorescence in cells derived from Burkitt lymphoma. *J Bacteriol* 1966; 91:1248.
10. Niederman JC, McCollum RW, Henle G, et al: Infectious mononucleosis: Clinical manifestations in relation to EB virus antibodies. *JAMA* 1968; 203:205.
11. Epstein MA, Achong BG: The relationship of the virus to Burkitt's lymphoma, in Epstein MA, Achong BG (eds): *The Epstein-Barr Virus*. Berlin, Springer-Verlag, 1979, p 321.
12. Henle W, Henle G: The association of Epstein-Barr virus with nasopharyngeal carcinoma, in Grundman E, Krüger GRF, Ablashi DV (eds): *Cancer Campaign*. Vol 5: *Nasopharyngeal Carcinoma*. Stuttgart, Gustav Fischer Verlag, 1981.
13. Epstein MA, Henle G, Achong BG, et al: Morphological and biological studies on a virus in cultured lymphoblasts from Burkitt's lymphoma. *J Exp Med* 1965; 121:761.
14. Hummler K, Henle G, Henle W: Fine structure of a virus in cultured lymphoblasts from Burkitt Lymphoma. *J Bacteriol* 1966; 91:1366.
15. Nonoyama M, Pagano JS: Detection of Epstein-Barr viral genome in nonproductive cells. *Nature New Biol* 1971; 233:103.
16. Schulte-Holthausen H, zur Hausen H: Partial purification of the Epstein-Barr virus and some properties of its DNA. *Virology* 1970; 40:776.
17. Jehn U, Lindahl T, Klein G: Fate of virus DNA in the abortive infection of human lymphoid lines by Epstein-Barr virus. *J Gen Virol* 1972; 16:409.
18. Pritchett R, Hayward SD, Kieff E: DNA of Epstein-Barr virus. Comparative studies of the DNA of Epstein-Barr virus from HR1 and B95-8 cells; I Size, structure, and relatedness. *J Virol* 1975; 15:556.
19. Miller G, Lipman S: Release of infectious Epstein-Barr virus by transformed marmoset leukocytes. *Proc Natl Acad Sci USA* 1973; 70:190.
20. Dolynuik M, Pritchett RF, Kieff E: Proteins of Epstein-Barr virus. I. Analysis of the polypeptides of enveloped Epstein-Barr virus. *J Virol* 1976; 17:935.
21. Stewart SE, Lovelace E, Whang JJ, et al: Burkitt tumor: Tissue culture, cytogenetic and virus studies. *J Natl Cancer Inst* 1965; 34:319.
22. O'Conor GT, Robson AS: Herpes-like particles in an American lymphoma: Preliminary note. *J Natl Cancer Inst* 1965; 35:899.
23. Silvestre D, Kourilsky FM, Klein G, et al: Relationship between the EBV-associated membrane antigen on Burkitt lymphoma cells and the viral envelope, demonstrated by immunoferritin labelling. *Int J Cancer* 1971; 8:222.
24. Henle G, Henle W: The virus as the etiologic agent of infectious mononucleosis, in Epstein MA, Achong BG (eds): *The Epstein-Barr Virus*. Berlin, Springer-Verlag, 1979, p 297.
25. Jondal M, Klein G: Surface markers on human B and T lymphocytes. II. Presence of Epstein-Barr virus receptors on B lymphocytes. *J Exp Med* 1973; 138:1365.
26. Yefenof E, Bakacs T, Einhorn L, et al: Epstein-Barr virus receptors, complement receptors, and infectibility of different lymphocyte fractions of human peripheral blood. I. Complement receptor distribution and complement binding by separated lymphocyte subpopulations. *Cell Immunol* 1978; 35:34.
27. Einhorn L, Steinitz M, Yefenof E, et al: Epstein-Barr virus receptors, complement receptors and infectibility of different lymphocyte fractions of human peripheral blood. II. Epstein-Barr virus studies. *Cell Immunol* 1978; 35:43.
28. Lemon SM, Hutt LM, Shaw JE, et al: Replication of EBV in epithelial cells during infectious mononucleosis. *Nature* 1977; 268:268.
29. Wolf H, zur Hausen H, Becker V: EB viral genomes in epithelial nasopharyngeal carcinoma cells. *Nature* 1973; 244:245.
30. Klein G, Giovanella BC, Lindahl T, et al: Direct evidence for the presence of Epstein-Barr virus DNA and nuclear antigen in malignant epithelial cells from patients with poorly differentiated carcinoma of the nasopharynx. *Proc Natl Acad Sci USA* 1974; 71:4737.
31. Huang DP, Ho JHC, Henle W, et al: Demonstration of EBV-associated nuclear antigen in NPC cells from fresh biopsies. *Int J Cancer* 1974; 14:580.

32. Wolf H, zur Hausen H, Klein G, et al: Attempts to detect virus-specific DNA sequences in human tumors. III. Epstein-Barr viral DNA in nonlymphoid nasopharyngeal carcinoma cells. *Med Microbiol Immunol* 1975; 161:15.

33. Sixbey JW, Nedrud JG, Raab-Traub W, et al: Epstein-Barr virus replication in oropharyngeal epithelial cells. *N Engl J Med* 1984; 310:1255.

34. Rocchi G, De Felia A, Ragona G, et al: Quantitative evaluation of Epstein-Barr virus-infected mononuclear peripheral blood leukocytes in infectious mononucleosis. *N Engl J Med* 1977; 296:132.

35. Gergely L, Klein G, Ernberg I: Host cell macromolecular synthesis in cells containing EBV-induced early antigens, studied by combined immunofluorescence and radioautography. *Virology* 1971; 45:22.

36. Bar R, De Lor LC, Clausen KP, et al: Fatal infectious mononucleosis in a family. *N Engl J Med* 1974; 290:363.

37. Klein G, Svedmyr E, Jondal G, et al: EBV-determined nuclear antigen (EBNA)-positive cells in the peripheral blood of infectious mononucleosis patients. *Int J Cancer* 1976; 17:21.

38. Chang RS, Golden HD: Transformation of human leucocytes by throat washings from infectious mononucleosis patients. *Nature* 1971; 234:359.

39. Chang RS, Lewis JP, Abildgaard CF: Prevalence of oropharyngeal excreters of leukocyte transforming agents among a human population. *N Engl J Med* 1973; 289:1325.

40. Gerber P, Lucas S, Nonoyama M, et al: Oral excretion of Epstein-Barr virus by healthy subjects and patients with infectious mononucleosis. *Lancet* 1972; 2:988.

41. Hinuma Y, Konn M, Yamaguchi J, et al: Immunofluorescence and herpes-type virus particles in P3HR-1 Burkitt lymphoma line. *J Virol* 1967; 1:1045.

42. Menezes J, Patel P, Dussault H, et al: Comparative studies on the induction of virus-associated nuclear antigen and early antigen by lymphocyte-transforming (B95-8) and non-transforming (P3HR-1) strains of Epstein-Barr virus. *Intervirology* 1978; 9:86.

43. Einhorn L, Ernberg I: Induction of EBNA precedes the first cellular S-phase after EBV-infection of human lymphocytes. *Int J Cancer* 1968; 21:157.

44. Crawford DH, Rickinson AB, Finerty S, et al: Epstein-Barr (EB) virus genome–containing EB nuclear antigen–negative B-lymphocyte populations in blood in acute infectious mononucleosis. *J Gen Virol* 1978; 38:449–460.

45. Takata K, Ostato T: Analysis of transformation of human lymphocytes by Epstein-Barr virus. I. Sequential occurrence from the virus-determined nuclear antigen synthesis, to blastogenesis to DNA synthesis. *Intervirology* 1978; 11:30.

46. Ernberg I, Klein G, Kourilsky FM, et al: Differentiation between early and late membrane antigen on human lymphoblastoid cell lines infected with Epstein-Barr virus. I. Immunofluorescence. *J Natl Cancer Inst* 1974; 53:61.

47. Henle W, Henle G, Zajac B, et al: Differential reactivity of human sera with EBV-induced "early antigens." *Science* 1970; 169:188.

48. Rickinson AB, Jarvis JE, Crawford DH, et al: Observations on the type of infection by Epstein-Barr virus in peripheral lymphoid cells of patients with infectious mononucleosis. *Int J Cancer* 1974; 14:704.

49. Diehl V, Henle G, Henle W, et al: Demonstration of a herpes group virus in cultures of peripheral leukocytes from patients with infectious mononucleosis. *J Virol* 1968; 2:663.

50. Nilsson K, Klein G, Henle W, et al: The establishment of lymphoblastoid lines from adult and fetal human lymphoid tissue and its dependence on EBV. *Int J Cancer* 1971; 8:443.

51. zur Hausen H, Schulte Holthausen H, Klein G, et al: EBV DNA in biopsies of Burkitt tumours and anaplastic carcinomas of the nasopharynx. *Nature* 1970; 228:1056.

52. Lindahl T, Klein G, Reedman B, et al: Relationships between Epstein-Barr virus (EBV) DNA and the EBV-determined nuclear antigen (EBNA) in Burkitt lymphoma biopsies and other lympho-proliferative malignancies. *Int J Cancer* 1974; 13:764.

53. Nonoyama M, Huang CH, Pagano JS, et al: DNA of Epstein-Barr virus detected in tissue of Burkitt's lymphoma and nasopharyngeal carcinoma. *Proc Natl Acad Sci USA* 1973; 70:3265.

54. Svedmyr E, Jondal M: Cytotoxic effector cells specific for B cell lines transformed by Epstein-Barr virus are present within patients with infectious mononucleosis. *Proc Natl Acad Sci USA* 1975; 72:1622.

55. Royston I, Sullivan JL, Perlman PO, et al: Cell-mediated immunity to Epstein-Barr-virus-infected mononuclear peripheral blood leukocytes in infectious mononucleosis. *N Engl J Med* 1975; 293:1159.

56. Hutt LM, Huang YT, Pascomb HE, et al: Enhanced destruction of lymphoid cell lines by peripheral blood leukocytes taken from patients with infectious mononucleosis. *J Immunol* 1975; 115:143.

57. Nilsson K: The nature of lymphoid cell lines and their relationship to the virus, in Epstein MA, Achong BG (eds): *The Epstein-Barr Virus.* Berlin, Springer-Verlag, 1979, p 225.

58. Gerber P: Activation of Epstein-Barr virus by 5 bromodeoxyuridine "virus free" free human cells. *Proc Natl Acad Sci USA* 1972; 69:83.

59. Hampar R, Derge JG, Nonoyama M, et al: Programming of events in Epstein-Barr virus activated cells induced by 5-iodo-deoxyuridine. *Virology* 1974; 62:71.

60. Werner J, Pinto CA, Haff RF, et al: Response of gibbons to inoculation of Epstein-Barr virus *J Infect Dis* 1972; 126:678.

61. Epstein MA, Hunt RD, Rabin H: Pilot experiments with EB virus in owl monkeys *(Aotus trivigatus)* I. Reticuloproliferative disease in inoculated animals. *Int J Cancer* 1973; 12:309.

62. Shope T, Dechaira D, Miller G: Malignant lymphoma in cotton top marmosets after inoculation with Epstein-Barr virus. *Proc Natl Acad Sci USA* 1973; 70:2487.

63. Levy JA, Henle G: Indirect immunofluorescent tests with sera from African children and cultured Burkitt lymphoma cells. *J Bacteriol* 1966; 92:275.

64. Black FL, Woodall JP, Evans AS, et al: Prevalence of antibody against viruses in the Tiriyo, an isolated Amazon tribe. *Am J Epidemiol* 1970; 91:430.

65. Lang DJ, Garruto RM, Gajdusek DC: Early acquisition of cytomegalovirus and Epstein-Barr virus antibody in several isolated Melanesian populations. *Am J Edipemiol* 1977; 105:480.

66. Tischendorf P, Shramek GJ, Balagtas RC, et al: Development and persistence of immunity to Epstein-Barr virus in man. *J Infect Dis* 1970; 122:401.

67. Golubjatnikov R, Allen VD, Steadman S, et al: Prevalence of antibodies to Epstein-Barr virus, cytomegalovirus and toxoplasma in a Mexican highland community. *Am J Epidemiol* 1973; 97:116.

68. Henle G, Henle W, Clifford P, et al: Antibodies to Epstein-Barr virus in Burkitt's lymphoma and control groups. *J Natl Cancer Inst* 1969; 43:1147.

69. Kafuko GW, Henderson BE, Kirya BG et al: Epstein-Barr virus antibody levels in children from the West Nile District of Uganda. *Lancet* 1972; 1:706.

70. Porter DD, Wimberly I, Benyish-Melnick M: Prevalence of antibodies to EB virus and other herpesviruses. *JAMA* 1969; 208:1675.

71. Pereira MS, Blake JM, Macrae AD: EB virus antibody at different ages. *Br Med J* 1969; 4:526.

72. Henle G, Henle W: Observations on childhood infections with the Epstein-Barr virus. *J Infect Dis* 1970; 121:303.

73. Tallqvist H, Henle W, Klemola E, et al: Antibodies to Epstein-Barr virus at the ages of 6 to 23 months in children with congenital heart disease. *Scand J Infect Dis* 1973; 5:159.

74. Fleisher G, Henle W, Henle G, et al: Primary infection with Epstein-Barr virus in infants in the United States: Clinical and serological observations. *J Infect Dis* 1979; 139:553.

75. Evans AS: Epidemiology of Epstein-Barr virus infection and disease, in Nahmias AJ, Dowdle WR, Schinazi RF, et al (eds): *The human Herpesviruses.* New York, Elsevier, 1981, p 172.

76. University Health Physicians and PHLS Laboratories: Infectious mononucleosis and its relationship to EB virus antibody. *Br Med J* 1971; 4:643.

77. Hallee TJ, Evans AS, Niederman JC, et al: Infectious mononucleosis at the United States Military Academy. *Yale J Biol Med* 1974; 47:182.

78. Sawyer RN, Evans AS, Niederman JC, et al: Prospective studies of a group of Yale University freshmen. I. Occurrence of infectious mononucleosis. *J Infect Dis* 1971; 123:263.

79. Demissie A, Svedmyr A: Age distribution of antibodies to EB virus in Swedish females as studied by indirect immunofluorescence on Burkitt cells. *Acta Pathol Microbiol Scand* 1969; 75:457.

80. Lehane DE: A seroepidemiologic study of infectious mononucleosis: The development of EB virus antibody in a military population. *JAMA* 1970; 212:2240.

81. Niederman JC, Evans AS, Subrahmanyan L, et al: Prevalence, incidence, and persistence of EB virus antibody in young adults. *N Engl J Med* 1970; 282:361.

82. Sumaya CV, Henle W, Henle G, et al: Seroepidemiologic study of Epstein-Barr virus infections in a rural community. *J Infect Dis* 1975; 131:403.

83. Fleisher G, Bolognese R: Seroepidemiology of Epstein-Barr virus in pregnancy. *J Infect Dis* 1982; 145:537.

84. Newell KW: The reported incidence of glandular fever, and analysis of a report of the Public Health Laboratory Service. *J Clin Pathol* 1957; 10:20.

85. Evans AS: Infectious mononucleosis. Observations from a public health laboratory. *Yale J Biol Med* 1961; 34:261.

86. Virtanen S: Incidence of infectious mononucleosis antibodies in blood donors. *Acta Pathol Microbiol Scand* 1962; 56:530.

87. Belfrage S: Infectious mononucleosis: An epidemiological and clinical study. *Acta Med Scand* 1962; 171:531.

88. Strom J: Infectious mononucleosis—Is the incidence increasing? *Acta Med Scand* 1960; 168:35.

89. Penman HG: The incidence of glandular fever. *J Hyg Camb* 1966; 64:457.

90. Christine BW: Infectious mononucleosis. *Conn Health Bull* 1968; 82:115.

91. Hobson EC, Lawson B, Wigfield M: Glandular fever: A field study. *Br Med J* 1958; 1:845.

92. Davidsohn RJL: A survey of infectious mononucleosis in the North-East Regional Hospital Board area of Scotland, 1960–1969. *J Hyg Camb* 1970:68:393.

93. Heath CW, Brodsky AL, Potolsky AI: Infectious mononucleosis in a general population. *Am J Epidemiol* 1972; 95:46.

94. Henke CE, Kurland LT, Elveback LR: Infectious mononucleosis in Rochester, Minn, 1950 through 1969. *Am J Epidemiol* 1973; 98:483.

95. Price JP: Infectious mononucleosis. *Am J Dis Child* 1930; 40:581.

96. Walker SH: Infectious mononucleosis manifested by diarrhea. *US Armed Forces Med J* 1951; 2:1875.

97. Woodward WK, Thiele RL, Fuller R: Marked lymphocytic reaction in a one-month-old infant with probable infectious mononucleosis. *J Pediatr* 1954; 45:717.

98. Gachet FS, Price WC: Infectious mononucleosis in infants and children. *J Fla Med Assoc* 1954; 41:280.

99. Philips KD, Stone DGH: Glandular fever at the age of 6 weeks. *Br Med J* 1956; 2:1222.

100. Horwitz C, Henle W, Henle G, et al: Clinical and laboratory evaluation of infants and children with EBV-induced infectious mononucleosis. *Blood* 1981; 57:433.

101. Baehner RL, Shuler SE: Infectious mononucleosis in children. *Clin Pediatr* 1967; 6:393.

102. Starling KA, Fernbach DJ: Infectious mononucleosis in the preschool child. *JAMA* 1968; 203:294.

103. Schmitz H, Volz D, Krainick-Riechert C, et al: Acute Epstein-Barr virus infections in children. *Med Microbiol Immunol* 1972; 158:58.

104. Ginsburg CM, Henle W, Henle G, et al: Infectious mononucleosis in children: Evaluation of Epstein-Barr virus-specific serology. *JAMA* 1977; 237:781.

105. Fleisher GR, Lennette ET, Henle G, et al: Incidence of heterophil-antibody responses in children with infectious mononucleosis. *J Pediatr* 1979; 94:723.

106. Schultz AL, Hall WH: Clinical observation in 100 cases of infectious mononucleosis and the results of treatment with penicillin and aureomycin. *Ann Intern Med* 1952; 36:1498.

107. Dunnett WN: Infectious mononucleosis. *Br Med J* 1963; 1:1187.

108. Evans AS: Infectious mononucleosis: Recent developments. *GP* 1969; 6:127.

109. Blacklow NR, Watson BR, Miller G, et al: Mononucleosis with heterophil antibodies and EB virus infection: Acquisition by an elderly patient in hospital. *Am J Med* 1971; 51:549.

110. Horwitz CA, Henle W, Henle G, et al: Clinical and laboratory evaluation of elderly patients with heterophil–antibody positive infectious mononucleosis. *Am J Med* 1976; 61:333.

111. Halcrow JPA, Owen LM, Rodger NO: Infectious mononucleosis with an account of an epidemic in an EMS Hospital. *Br Med J* 1943; 2:443.

112. Wechsler FH, Rosenblum AH, Sills CT: Infectious mononucleosis: Report of an epidemic in an army post. *Ann Intern Med* 1946; 25:113.

113. Ginsburg CM, Henle G, Henle W: An outbreak of infectious mononucleosis among the personnel of an outpatient clinic. *Am J Epidemiol* 1976; 104:571.

114. Pass R, Hutto C: Group day care and cytomegaloviral infections of mothers and children. *Rev Infect Dis* 1986; 8:599.

115. Bland JOW: Discussion on glandular fever. *Proc R Soc Med* 1931; 25:155.

116. Nyefelt A: Klinishce und experimentelle Untersuchungen über die Monoukeose infecktiöse. *Folia Haematol* 1932; 47:1.

117. Wising PJ: Some experiments with lymph gland material from cases of infectious mononucleosis. *Acta Med Scand* 1939; 98:328.

118. Bang J: Experiments with the transfer of infectious mononucleosis to monkeys–with negative results. *Acta Med Scand* 1942; 111:291.

119. Jullianelle JA, Bierbaum OS, Moore CV: Studies on infectious mononucleosis. *Ann Intern Med* 1944; 20:281.

120. Sohier R, Lepine P, Sautter V: Recherches sur la transmission expérimentale de la mononucleose infectieuse au singe et à l'homme. *Ann Inst Pasteur* 1940; 65:50.

121. Wising PJ: Successful transmission of infectious mononucleosis to man by transfusion of heparinized blood. *Acta Med Scand* 1942; 109:507.

122. Bang J: Experiments with the transfer of infectious mononucleosis to man. *Acta Med Scand* 1943; 123:304.

123. Evans AS: Experimental attempts to transmit infectious mononucleosis to man. *Yale J Biol Med* 1947; 20:19.

124. Hoagland RJ: The transmission of infectious mononucleosis. *Am J Med Sci* 1955; 229:262.

125. Evans AS: Further experimental attempts to transmit infectious mononucleosis to man. *J Clin Invest* 1950; 29:508.

126. Niederman JC, Scott RB: Studies on infectious mononucleosis: Attempts to transmit the disease to human volunteers. *Yale J Biol Med* 1965; 38:1.

127. Evans AS: Infectious mononucleosis in University of Wisconsin students: Report of a five-year investigation. *Am J Hyg* 1960; 71:342.

128. Joncas J, Mitnyan C: Serological response of the EBV antibodies in pediatric cases of infectious mononucleosis and their contacts. *Can Med Assoc J* 1970; 102:1260.

129. Wahren B, Lantorp K, Sterner G, et al: EBV antibodies in family contacts of patients with infectious mononucleosis. *Proc Soc Exp Biol Med* 1970; 133:934.

130. Nye FS, Lambert HP: Epstein-Barr virus antibody in cases and contacts of infectious mononucleosis; a family study. *J Hyg Camb* 1973; 71:151.

131. Fleisher GR, Pasquariello PS, Warren WS, et al: Intrafamilial transmission of Epstein-Barr virus infections. *J Pediatr* 1981; 98:16.

132. Sumaya CV, Ench Y: Epstein-Barr virus infections in families: The role of children with infectious mononucleosis. *J Infect Dis* 1986; 154:842.

133. Pereira MS, Field AM, Blake JM, et al: Evidence for oral excretion of EB virus in infectious mononucleosis. *Lancet* 1972; 1:710.

134. Miller G, Niederman JC, Andrews L: Prolonged oropharyngeal excretion of Epstein-Barr virus after infectious mononucleosis. *N Engl J Med* 1973; 288:229.

135. Golden HD, Chang RS, Prescott W, et al: Leukocyte transforming agent: Prolonged excretion by patients with mononucleosis and excretion by normal individuals. *J Infect Dis* 1973; 127:471.

136. Strauch B, Siegel N, Andrews L, et al: Oropharyngeal excretion of Epstein-Barr virus by renal transplant recipients and other patients treated with immunosuppressive drugs. *Lancet* 1974; 1:234.

137. Kreel I, Zaroff LI, Cauter JW, et al: A syndrome following total body perfusion. *Surg Gynecol Obstet* 1960; 111:317.

138. Holswade GR, Engle MA, Redo SF, et al: Development of viral diseases and a viral-disease-like syndrome after extracorporeal circulation. *Circulation* 1963; 27:812.

139. Smith DR: A syndrome resembling infectious mononucleosis after heart surgery. *Br Med J* 1964; 1:945.

140. Paloheima JA, Halonen PI: A case of mononucleosis-like syndrome after blood transfusion from a donor with asymptomatic mononucleosis. *J Cardiovasc Surg* 1965; 6:558.

141. Solem JG, Jorgensen W: Accidentally transmitted infectious mononucleosis. *Acta Med Scand* 1969; 186:433.

142. Gerber P, Walsh JH, Rosenblum EN, et al: Association of EB-virus infection with the post-perfusion syndrome. *Lancet* 1969; 1:593.

143. Turner RA, MacDonald RN, Cooper BA: Transmission of infectious mononucleosis by transfusion of pre-illness plasma. *Ann Intern Med* 1972; 77:751.

144. Purtilo DT, Paquin LA, Sakamoto K, et al: Persistent transfusion-associated infectious mononucleosis with transient acquired immunodeficiency. *Am J Med* 1980; 68:437.

145. Svedmyr E, Ernberg I, Seeley J, et al: Virologic, immunologic, and clinical observations during the incubation, acute, and convalescent phases of infectious mononucleosis. *Clin Immunol Immunopathol* 1984; 30:437.

146. Bernstein A: Infectious mononucleosis. *Medicine* 1940; 19:85.

147. Contrato AW: Infectious mononucleosis: A study of one hundred and ninety-six cases. *Arch Intern Med* 1944; 73:449.

148. Milne J: Infectious mononucleosis. *N Engl J Med* 1945; 233:727.

149. Press JH, Shlevin EL, Rosen AP: Infectious mononucleosis: A study of 96 cases. *Ann Intern Med* 1945; 22:546.

150. Mason RW, Adams EK: Infectious mononucleosis. *Am J Med Sci* 1951; 239:447.

151. Mankad VR: Infectious mononucleosis: An analysis of 399 hospital cases. *Student Med* 1954; 3:19.

152. Hoagland RJ: The clinical manifestations of infectious mononucleosis: A report of two hundred cases. *Am J Med* 1960; 240:21.

153. Hoagland RJ: *Infectious Mononucleosis.* New York, Grune & Stratton, 1967, p 1.

154. Joncas J, Chiasson JP, Turcotte S, et al: Studies on infectious mononucleosis: III. Clinical data, serologic and epidemiologic findings. *Can Med Assoc J* 1968; 98:848.

155. Cameron D, MacBear LM: A Clinical Study of Infectious Mononucleosis and Toxoplasmosis. Baltimore, Williams & Wilkins, 1973, p 1.

156. Sumaya CV, Ench Y: Epstein-Barr virus infectious mononucleosis in children: I. Clinical and general laboratory findings. *Pediatrics* 1985; 75:1003.

157. Sumaya CV, Ench Y: Epstein-Barr virus infectious mononucleosis in children. II. Heterophil antibody and viral-specific responses. *Pediatrics* 1985; 75:1011.

158. Dommerby H, Stangerup SE, Stangerup M, et al: Hepatosplenomegaly in infectious mononucleosis. *J Laryngol Otol* 1986; 100:573.

159. Baron DN, Bell JL, Demmett WN: Biochemical studies on hepatic involvement in infectious mononucleosis. *J Clin Pathol* 1965; 18:209.

160. Rosalki SB, Jones TG, Verney AF: Transaminase and liver function studies in infectious mononucleosis. *Br Med J* 1960; 1:929.

161. Brown GL, Kanwor BS: Drug rashes in glandular fever. *Lancet* 1967; 2:1418.

162. Harden SA: Ampicillin and mononucleosis. *Br Med J* 1971; 4:364.

163. Patel BM: Skin rash with infectious mononucleosis and ampicillin. *Pediatrics* 1967; 40:910.

164. Pullen H, Wright N, Murdoch JM: Hypersensitivity reactions to antibacterial drugs in infectious mononucleosis. *Lancet* 1967; 2:1176.

165. Kerns DL, Shira JE, Go S, et al: Ampicillin rash in children: Relationship to penicillin allergy and infectious mononucleosis. *Am J Dis Child* 1973; 125:187.

166. Radel EG, Schorr, JB: Thrombocytopenic purpura with infectious mononucleosis. *J Pediatr* 1963; 63:46.

167. Evans AS: Complications of infectious mononucleosis: Recognition and management. *Hosp Pract* 1967; 3:24.

168. Smith JN: Complications of infectious mononucleosis. *Ann Intern Med* 1956; 44:861.

169. Karzon DT: Infectious mononucleosis. *Adv Pediatr* 1976; 22:231.

170. Alpert G, Fleisher GR: Complication of infection with Epstein-Barr virus during childhood: A study of children admitted to hospital. *Pediatr Infect Dis* 1984; 3:304.

171. King R: Spontaneous rupture of the spleen in infectious mononucleosis. *N Engl J Med* 1941; 224:1058.

172. Smith EB, Custer RP: Rupture of the spleen in infectious mononucleosis. *Blood* 1946; 1:317.

173. Garfield S, Gentry JH: Rupture of the spleen in infectious mononucleosis. *US Armed Forces Bull* 1959; 10:91.

174. Rawsthorne CB, Cole TB, Kyle J: Spontaneous rupture of the spleen in infectious mononucleosis. *Br J Surg* 1976; 57:396.

175. Salusky SB, Wallace RB, Silverstein MN, et al: Ruptured spleen in infectious mononucleosis. *Arch Surg* 1967; 94:349.

176. Alberty R: Surgical implications of infectious mononucleosis. *Am J Surg* 1981; 141:559.

177. Rutkow IM: Rupture of the spleen in infectious mononucleosis: A critical review. *Arch Surg* 1978; 113:718.

178. Burns CP, Kellermeyer RW: Wandering spleen—An unusual complication of infectious mononucleosis. *Ohio State Med J* 1970; 66:385.

179. Read JT, Hellwig FC: Infectious mononucleosis: An analysis of 300 cases with 3 characterized by rare hematologic findings. *Arch Intern Med* 1945; 75:376.

180. Mir MA, Delamore IW: Aplastic anemia complicating infectious mononucleosis. *Scand J Haematol* 1973; 11:314.

181. Martin MPR: Atypical infectious mononucleosis with bone marrow granulomas and pancytopenia. *Br Med J* 1977; 5:300.

182. Van Doornik MC, Van 'T Veer-Korthof ET, et al: Fatal aplastic anemia complicating infectious mononucleosis. *Scand J Haematol* 1978; 20:52.

183. Lazarus KH, Baehner RL: Aplastic anemia complicating infectious mononucleosis: A case report and review of the literature. *Pediatrics* 1981; 67:907.

184. Jenkins WJ, Koster HG, March WL, et al: Infectious mononucleosis: An unsuspected source of anti-i. *Br J Haematol* 1965; 11:480.

185. Wilkinson LS, Petz LD, Garraty G: Reappraisal of the role of anti-i in haemolytic anemia in infectious mononucleosis. *Br J Haematol* 1973; 25:715.

186. Bowman HS, Marsh WL, Schumacher HR, et al: Anto anti-N immunohemolytic anemia in infectious mononucleosis. *Am J Clin Pathol* 1974; 61:465.

187. Einzig M, Neerhout R: Hemolytic anemia in infectious mononucleosis. *Clin Pediatr* 1969; 8:171.

188. Carter RL: Platelet levels in infectious mononucleosis. *Blood* 1965; 25:817.

189. Goldstein E, Porter DY: Fatal thrombocytopenia with cerebral hemorrhage in mononucleosis. *Arch Neurol* 1969; 20:533.

190. Ellman L, Carvalho A, Jacobson BM, et al: Platelet autoantibody in a case of infectious mononucleosis presenting as thrombocytopenic purpura. *Am J Med* 1973; 55:72.

191. Clancy R, Jenkins E, Firken B: Platelet defect of infectious mononucleosis. *Br Med J* 1971; 2:646.

192. Andiman WA: Primary Epstein-Barr virus infection and thrombocytopenia during late infancy. *J Pediatr* 1976; 89:435.

193. Penman H: Extreme neutropenia in glandular fever. *J Clin Pathol* 1968; 21:48.

194. Bernstein TC, Wolff HG: Involvement of the nervous system in infectious mononucleosis. *Ann Intern Med* 1950; 33:1120.

195. Karpinski FE: Neurologic manifestations of infectious mononucleosis in childhood. *Pediatrics* 1952; 10:265.

196. Heinz EG, Quinn EL: Aseptic meningitis in siblings with infectious mononucleosis. *Henry Ford Hosp Med Bull* 1966; 14:229.

197. Bonforte RJ: Convulsion as a presenting sign of infectious mononucleosis. *Am J Dis Child* 1967; 114:429.

198. Silverstein A, Steinberg S, Nathanson M: Nervous system involvement in infectious mononucleosis. The haralding and/or major manifestation. *Arch Neurol* 1972; 26:353.

199. Gilbert JW, Culibras A: Cerebellitis in infectious mononucleosis. *JAMA* 1972; 20:727.

200. Joncas JH, Chicoine L, Thivierge R, et al: Epstein-Barr virus antibodies in the cerebrospinal fluid. *Am J Dis Child* 1974; 127:282.

201. Feorino PM, Humphrey D, Hochberg F, et al: Mononucleosis-associated subacute sclerosing panencephalitis. *Lancet* 1975; 2:530.

202. Grose C, Henle W, Henle G, et al: Primary Epstein-Barr virus infections in acute neurologic diseases. *N Engl J Med* 1975; 292:392.

203. Copperman JM: "Alice in Wonderland" syndrome as a presenting symptom of infectious mononucleosis in children. *Clin Pediatr* 1977; 16:143.

204. Weintraub MI: Bilateral facial palsy: A rare presentation of infectious mononucleosis. *Clin Pediatr* 1977; 16:1158.

205. Lange BJ, Berman PH, Bender J, et al: Encephalitis in infectious mononucleosis: Diagnostic considerations. *Pediatrics* 1976; 58:877.

206. Halsted CC, Chang RS: Infectious mononucleosis and encephalitis: Recovery of EB virus from spinal fluid. *Pediatrics* 1979; 64:258.

207. Leppik IE, Ramani V, Sawchuk RJ, et al: Increased clearance of phenytoin during infectious mononucleosis. *N Engl J Med* 1979; 300:481.

208. McKee KT, Wright PF, Kilroy AW, et al: Herpes encephalitis after infectious mononucleosis. *South Med J* 1981; 74:238.

209. Yeager HP: Airway obstruction in infectious mononucleosis. *Arch Otolaryngol* 1964; 83:617.

210. Lee M: Respiratory obstruction in glandular fever. *J Laryngol Otol* 1969; 83:617.

211. Gutgesell HP: Acute airway obstruction in infectious mononucleosis. *Pediatrics* 1971; 47:141.

212. Offit PA, Fleisher GR, Koven NL, et al: Severe Epstein-Barr virus pulmonary involvement. *J Adolesc Health Care* 1981; 2:221.

213. Fermaglich DR: Pulmonary involvement in infectious mononucleosis. *J Pediatr* 1975; 86:93.

214. McCort JJ: Infectious mononucleosis with special reference to roentgenologic manifestations. *Am J Roentgenol* 1949; 62:645.

215. Arendt J: The roentgenologic aspect of infectious mononucleosis. *Am J Roent Radiat Ther* 1950; 64:950.

216. Lander P, Palayew MS: Infectious mononucleosis—A review of chest roentgenographic manifestations. *J Can Assoc Radiol* 1974; 25:303.

217. Hoagland RS: Mononucleosis and heart disease. *Am J Med Surg* 1964; 248:1.

218. Reitman MJ, Zirin HJ, Deangelis CJ: Complete heart block in Epstein-Barr myocarditis. *Pediatrics* 1978; 62:847.

219. Shapiro SC, Dimich I, Steier M: Pericarditis as the only manifestation of infectious mononucleosis. *Am J Dis Child* 1973; 126:662.

220. Miller H Uriccio JF, Phillips RW: Acute pericarditis associated with infectious mononucleosis. *N Engl J Med* 1953; 249:136.

221. Fish M, Barton HR: Heart involvement in infectious mononucleosis. *Arch Intern Med* 1950; 101:636.

222. Frishman W, Kraus ME, Zabkar J, et al: Infectious mononucleosis and fatal myocarditis. *Chest* 1977; 72:535.

223. Finkel M, Parker GW, Fonselau HA: The hepatitis of infectious mononucleosis: Experience with 235 cases. *Milit Med* 1964; 129:553.

224. Hsia DY, Gellis SS: Hepatic dysfunction in infectious mononucleosis in children. *Am J Dis Child* 1952; 84:175.

225. Mathison AK: Hepatitis in infectious mononucleosis. *Can Med Assoc J* 1952; 66:426.

226. Hoagland RJ, McCluskey RT: Hepatitis in mononucleosis. *Ann Intern Med* 1955; 43:1019.

227. Harries JT, Ferguson WA: Fatal infectious mononucleosis with liver failure in two sisters. *Arch Dis Child* 1968; 43:480.

228. McMahon JM, Elliot LW, Green RC: Infectious mononucleosis complicated by hepatic coma. *Am J Gastroenterol* 1969; 51:200.

229. Hodge J, Gorham W: Massive bleeding esophageal varices incident to infectious mononucleosis, cirrhosis of the liver and portal hypertension. *Am J Surg* 1960; 90:369.

230. Madhavan T: Hepatitis and infectious mononucleosis. *JAMA* 1973; 225:314.

231. Rahal JJ, Henle G: Infectious mononucleosis and Reye's syndrome: A fatal case with studies for Epstein-Barr virus. *Pediatrics* 1971; 46:776.

232. Dorm JM, Glick TH, Shannon DL, et al: Complications of infectious mononucleosis: A fatal case in a 2-year old child. *Am J Dis Child* 1974; 128:239.

233. Fleisher G, Schwartz J, Lennette ET: Primary Epstein-Barr virus in association with Reye syndrome. *J Pediatr* 1980; 97:935.

234. Myhre J, Nesbitt S: Pancreatitis in infectious mononucleosis. *J Lab Clin Med* 1949; 34:1671.

235. Wislocki LC: Acute pancreatitis in infectious mononucleosis. *N Engl J Med* 1966; 275:322.

236. Corbus H: Protein-losing enteropathy in infectious mononucleosis. *California Med* 1968; 109:378.

237. Tennant FS: The glomerulonephritis of infectious mononucleosis. *Tex Rep Biol Med* 1968; 26:603.

238. Woodroffe NJ, Kow PG, Meadows R, et al: Nephritis in infectious mononucleosis. *Q J Med* 1974; 43:451.

239. Wallace M, Leet G, Rothwell P: Immune complex-mediated glomerulonephritis with infectious mononucleosis. *Aust NZ J Med* 1974; 4:192.

240. Shashaty GG, Atamer M: Hemolytic uremic syndrome associated with infectious mononucleosis. *Am J Dis Child* 1974; 127:720.

241. Ablow RC, Drew L, Seys Y: Renal enlargement associated with infectious mononucleosis. *Pediatr Radiol* 1975; 3:114.

242. Rolston LS, Sarki AK, Powers WT: Orchitis as a complication of infectious mononucleosis. *JAMA* 1960; 173:1348.

243. Wolnisty C: Orchitis as a complication of infectious mononucleosis. *N Engl J Med* 1962; 266:88.

244. Parnes LR: Infectious mononucleosis with orchitis: Report of a case. *J Am Coll Health Assoc* 1968; 17:90.

245. Adebenojo FM: Monoarticular arthritis: An unusual complication of infectious mononucleosis. *Clin Pediatr* 1972; 11:549.

246. Tanner OR: Ocular manifestations of infectious mononucleosis. *Arch Ophthalmol* 1954; 51:229.

247. Szczepanska A: Petechial rash on the palate in infectious mononucleosis. *Lancet* 1956; 2:1163.

248. Cowdrey SC, Reynolds JS: Acute urticaria in infectious mononucleosis. *Ann Allergy* 1969; 27:182.

249. Africk JA, Halprin KM: Infectious mononucleosis presenting as urticaria. *JAMA* 1969; 209:1524.

250. Petrazzi J: Infectious mononucleosis manifesting as palmar dermatitis. *Arch Dermatol* 1971; 164:207.

251. Nazareth I, Mortimer P, McKendrick GDW: Ampicillin sensitivity in infectious mononucleosis—Temporary or permanent? *Scand J Infect Dis* 1972; 4:229.

252. Schultz AL, Hall WH: Clinical observations in 100 cases of infectious mononucleosis and the results of treatment with penicillin and aureomycin. *Ann Intern Med* 1952; 36:1498.

253. Chietien J, Esswein J: How frequent is bacterial superinfection of the pharynx in infectious mononucleosis? *Clin Pediatr* 1976; 15:424.

254. Jarvis WR: A study of β-hemolytic streptococcal pharyngitis in patients with infectious mononucleosis. *Clin Pediatr* 1980; 19:463.

255. Penman H: Fatal infectious mononucleosis: A critical review. *J Clin Pathol* 1970; 23:765.

256. Collins M, Fleisher G, Fager S: Incidence of beta-hemolytic streptococcal pharyngitis in adolescents with infectious mononucleosis. *J Adolesc Health Care* 1984; 5:96.

257. DuBois DR, Baehner RL: Infectious mononucleosis associated with fatal beta hemolytic streptococcal infection. *Clin Pediatr* 1979; 18:511.

258. Heilmeyer L, Begeman H, in Bergmann G, Frey W, Schwiegk H (eds): *Blut und Blutkrankheiten,* ed 4, Berlin, Springer-Verlag, 1972, p 568.

259. Lukes R, Cox F: Clinical and morphological findings in 30 fatal cases of infectious mononucleosis. *Am J Pathol* 1958; 34:586.

260. Shinton NK, Hawkins CF: A fatal case of glandular fever. *Lancet* 1976; 2:708.

261. Neel EU: Infectious mononucleosis: Death due to agranulocytosis and pneumonia. *JAMA* 1976; 236:1493.

262. Kaufman RE: Recurrences in infectious mononucleosis. *Am Pract* 1950; 1:673–676.

263. Patterson JK, Pinninger JL: Recurrent infectious mononucleosis. *Br Med J* 1955; 2:476.

264. Bender CE: Recurrent mononucleosis. *JAMA* 1962; 182:954–956.

265. Graves S Jr: Recurrent infectious mononucleosis. *J Ky Med Assoc* 1970; 1:790–793.

266. Fry J: Infectious mononucleosis: some new observations from a 15-year study. *J Fam Pract* 1980; 10:1087–1089.

267. Isaacs R: Chronic infectious mononucleosis. *Blood* 1948; 3:858–861.

268. Jones JF, Ray G, Minnich LL, et al: Evidence for active Epstein-Barr virus infection in patients with persistent, unexplained illness: Elevated anti-early antigen antibodies. *Ann Intern Med* 1985; 102:1.

269. Straus SE, Tosato G, Armstrong G, et al: Persisting illness and fatigue in adults with evidence of Epstein-Barr virus infection. *Ann Intern Med* 1985; 102:7.

270. Henle W, Henle G, Gunven P, et al: Patterns of antibodies to Epstein-Barr virus-induced early antigens in Burkitt's lymphoma. Comparison of dying patients with long-term survivors. *J Natl Cancer Inst* 1973; 50:1163.

271. Epstein AL, Henle W, Henle G, et al: Surface marker characteristics and Epstein-Barr virus studies of two established North American Burkitt's lymphoma cell lines. *Proc Natl Acad Sci USA* 1976; 73:228.

272. Nkrumah F, Henle W, Henle G, et al: Burkitt's lymphoma: Its clinical course in relation to immunologic reactivities to Epstein-Barr virus and tumor related antigens. *J Natl Cancer Inst* 1976; 57:1051.

273. Henle W, Henle G: Antibodies to the R component of the EBV-induced early antigens in Burkitt's lymphoma may exceed in titer antibodies to the EBV viral capsid antigen. *J Natl Cancer Inst* 1977; 58:785.

274. Ziegler JL, Anderson M, Klein G, et al: Detection of Epstein-Barr virus DNA in American Burkitt's lymphoma. *Int J Cancer* 1976; 17:701.

275. Klein G, Clifford P, Klein E, et al: Search for tumor—Specific immune reactions in Burkitt lymphoma patients by the membrane immunofluorescence reaction. *Proc Natl Acad Sci USA* 1966; 55:1628.

276. Judson SC, Henle W, Henle G: A cluster of Epstein-Barr virus-associated American Burkitt's lymphoma. *N Engl J Med* 1977; 297:464.

277. Henle W, Henle G, Ho HC, et al: Antibodies to EB virus in nasopharyngeal carcinoma, other head and neck neoplasms and control groups. *J Natl Cancer Inst* 1970; 44:225.

278. Henle W, Ho HC, Henle G, et al: Antibodies to Epstein-Barr virus-related antigens in nasopharyngeal carcinoma. Comparison of active cases and long term survivors. *J Natl Cancer Inst* 1977; 51:361.

279. Rosdahl N, Larson SO, Clemmesen J: Hodgkin's disease in patients with previous infectious mononucleosis. *Br Med J* 1974; 2:253.

280. Carter CD, Brown TM, Herbert JT, et al: Cancer incidence following infectious mononucleosis. *Am J Epidemiol* 1977; 105:30.

281. Kvale G, Korby EA, Pederson E: Hodgkin's disease in patients with previous infectious mononucleosis. *Int J Cancer* 1979; 23:593.

282. Gutensohn N, Cole P: Childhood social environment and Hodgkin's disease. *N Engl J Med* 1981; 304:135.

283. Lange B, Henle W, Meyers JD, et al: Epstein-Barr virus-related serology in marrow transplant recipients. *Int J Cancer* 1980; 26:151.

284. Purtilo DT: Fatal infectious mononucleosis in familial lymphohistiocytosis. *N Engl J Med* 1974; 291:736.

285. Purtilo DT, Yang JPS, Allegra S, et al: The pathogenesis and hematopathology of the X-linked recessive lymphoproliferative syndrome. *Am J Med* 1977; 62:225.

286. Purtilo DT, De Florio D, Yang JPS, et al: Variable phenotypic expression on an X-linked recessive lymphoproliferative syndrome. *N Engl J Med* 1977; 297:1077.

287. Purtilo DT, Bhawan J: Immunopathology of fatal infectious mononucleosis in an X-linked lymphoproliferative syndrome. *Lab Invest* 1978; 38:31.

288. Purtilo DT, Bhawan J, De Nichola L, et al: Epstein-Barr virus infections in the X-linked recessive lymphoproliferative syndrome. *Lancet* 1978; 1:798.

289. Purtilo DT, Cassel C, Yang JPS, et al: X-linked recessive progressive combined variable immunodeficiency (Duncan's disease). *Lancet* 1975; 1:935.

290. Purtilo DT, Paquin LA, Defono D, et al: Immunodiagnosis and immunopathogenesis of the X-linked recessive lymphoproliferative syndrome. *Semin Hematol* 1979; 16:309.

291. Sakamoto K, Fried HS, Purtilo DT: Antibody response to Epstein-Barr virus in families with X-linked lymphoproliferative syndrome. *J Immunol* 1980; 125:921.

292. Sullivan JL, Byron KS, Brewster FE, et al: Deficient natural killer cell activity in X-linked lymphoproliferative syndrome. *Science* 1980; 210:543.

293. Fleisher G, Starr S, Koven N, et al: A non-X-linked syndrome with susceptibility to severe Epstein-Barr virus infections. *J Pediatr* 1982; 100:727.

294. Breinig MK, Zitelli B, Starzl TE, et al: Epstein-Barr virus, cytomegalovirus, and other viral infections in children after liver transplantation. *J Infect Dis* 1987; 156:273.

295. Hanto DW, Frizzera G, Galz-Pecznlska KF, et al: Epstein-Barr virus-induced B-cell lymphoma after renal tranplantation. *N Engl J Med* 1982; 306:913.

296. Fackler JC, Nagel JE, Adler WH, et al: Epstein-Barr virus infection in a child with acquired immunodeficiency syndrome. *Am J Dis Child* 1985; 139:1000.

297. Hellmann D, Cowan MJ, Ammann AJ, et al: Chronic active EB virus in infections in two immunodeficient patients. *J Pediatr* 1983; 103:585.

298. Henle W, Henle G, Horowitz CA: Epstein-Barr virus-specific diagnostic tests in infectious mononucleosis. *Hum Pathol* 1974; 5:551.

299. Schmitz H, Scherer M: IgM antibodies to Epstein-Barr virus in infectious mononucleosis. *Arch Gesamte Virusforsch* 1972; 37:332.

300. Henle W, Henle G, Zajac B, et al: Differential reactivity of human sera with EBV-induced "early antigens." *Science* 1970; 169:188.

301. Henle G, Henle W, Klein G: Demonstration of two distinct components in the early antigen complex of Epstein-Barr virus infected cells. *Int J Cancer* 1971; 8:272.

302. Henle W, Henle G, Niederman JC, et al: Antibodies to early antigens induced by Epstein-Barr virus in infectious mononucleosis. *J Infect Dis* 1971; 124:58.

303. Horowitz CA, Henle W, Henle G, et al: Clinical evaluation of patients with infectious mononucleosis and development of antibodies to the RX component of the Epstein-Barr virus–induced early antigen complex. *Am J Med* 1975; 58:330.

304. Klein G, Pearson G, Henle G, et al: Relation between Epstein-Barr viral and cell membrane immunofluorescence in Burkitt tumor cell II: Comparison of cells and sera from patients with Burkitt's lymphoma and infectious mononucleosis. *J Exp Med* 1968; 128:1011.

305. Hewetson JF, Rocchi G, Henle W, et al: Neutralizing antibodies against Epstein-Barr virus in healthy populations and patients with infectious mononucleosis. *J Infect Dis* 1973; 128:283.

306. Reedman BM, Klein G: Cellular localization of an Epstein-Barr virus (EBV)–associated complement-fixing antigen in producer and nonproducer lymphoblastoid cell lines. *Int J Cancer* 1973; 11:499.

307. Henle G, Henle W, Horowitz CA: Antibodies to Epstein-Barr virus–associated nuclear antigen in infectious mononucleosis. *J Infect Dis* 1974; 130:231.

308. Henle W, Guerra A, Henle G: False-negative and prozone reactions in tests for antibodies to Epstein-Barr virus–associated nuclear antigen. *Int J Cancer* 1974; 13:751.

309. Bailey GH, Raffel S: Hemolytic antibodies for sheep and ox erythrocytes in infectious mononucleosis. *J Clin Invest* 1935; 14:228.

310. Mason JK: An ox cell hemolysin test for the diagnosis of infectious mononucleosis. *J Hyg* 1951; 49:471.

311. Lee CL, Davidsohn I, Slaby R: Horse agglutinins in infectious mononucleosis. *Am J Clin Pathol* 1968; 49:3.

312. Evans AS, Niederman JC, Cenabre LC, et al: A prospective evaluation of heterophil and Epstein-Barr virus–specific IgM antibody tests in clinical and subclinical infectious mononucleosis: Specificity and sensitivity of the tests and persistence of antibody. *J Infect Dis* 1975; 132:5.

313. Lennette ET, Henle G, Henle W, et al: Heterophil antigen in bovine sera detected by immune adherence hemagglutination with infectious mononucleosis sera. *Infect Immun* 1978; 19:923.

314. Sheldon PJ, Hemsted EH, Holborow EJ, et al: Thymic origin of atypical lymphocytes in infectious mononucleosis. *Lancet* 1973; 2:1153.

315. Ernberg RN, Eberle BJ, Williams RC: T- and B-cells in peripheral blood during infectious mononucleosis. *J Infect Dis* 1974; 130:104.

316. Pattengale PK, Smith RW, Perlen E: Atypical lymphocytes in acute infectious mononucleosis: Identification by multiple T and B lymphocyte markers. *N Engl J Med* 1974; 291:1145.

317. Mangi RL, Niederman JC, Kelleher JE, et al: Depression of cell-mediated immunity during acute infectious mononucleosis. *N Engl J Med* 1974; 291:1149.

318. Tosato G, Magrath I, Koski I, et al: Activation of suppressor T cells during Epstein-Barr-virus-induced infectious mononucleosis. *N Engl J Med* 1979; 301:1133.

319. De Waele MD, Thielemans C, Van Camp BKG: Characterization of immunoregulatory T cells in EBV-induced infectious mononucleosis by monoclonal antibodies. *N Engl J Med* 1981; 304:460.

320. Bentzon JW: The effect of certain infectious diseases on tuberculin allergy. *Tubercle* 1953; 34:34.

321. Haider S, Coutinho M, Emond RTD: Tuberculin anergy and infectious mononucleosis. *Lancet* 1973; 2:74.

322. Pearson GR, Orr TW: Antibody-dependent lymphocyte cytotoxicity against cells expressing Epstein-Barr virus antigens. *J Natl Cancer Inst* 1976; 54:485.

323. ten Napel CHH, The TH: Lymphocyte reactivity in infectious mononucleosis. *J Infect Dis* 1980; 141:716.

324. Tosato G, Steinberg AD, Blaese RM: Defective EBV-specific suppressor T-cell function in rheumatoid arthritis. *N Engl J Med* 1981; 305:1238.

325. Wollner D: Über die serologische Diagnose der infektiösen Mononukleose nach Paul-Bunnell mit nativen und fermentierten Hammel-Erythrozyten. *Zitschr Immunitätsforsch* 1955; 112:290.

326. Davidsohn I, Lee CL: Serologic diagnosis of infectious mononucleosis. *Am J Clin Pathol* 1964; 41:115.

327. Milgram F, Loza U, Kano K: Double diffusion in gel tests with Paul-Bunnell antibodies of infectious mononucleosis sera. *Int Arch Allergy Appl Immunol* 1975; 48:82.

328. Levey BA, Lo TM, Caldwell KE, et al: Latex test for serodiagnosis of infectious mononucleosis. *J Clin Microbiol* 1980; 11:256.

329. Fletcher MA, Lo TM, Levey BA, et al: Immunochemical studies of infectious mononucleosis. VI. A radioimmunoassay for the detection of infectious mononucleosis heterophile antibody and antigen. *J Immunol Methods* 1977; 14:51.

330. Halbert SP, Anken M, Henle W, et al: Detection of infectious mononucleosis heterophil antibody by a rapid, standardized enzyme-linked immunosurbent assay procedure. *J Clin Microbiol* 1982; 15:610.

331. Horwitz CAW, Henle W, Henle G, et al: Persistently false positive rapid tests for infectious mononucleosis. *Am J Clin Pathol* 1979; 72:807.

332. Schumacher HR, Austin RM, Stass SA: False positive serology in infectious mononucleosis. *Lancet* 1979; 1:722.

333. Rippey JH, Bowman HE: Infectious mononucleosis test performance on CAP survey specimens. *Am J Clin Pathol* 1979; 72:363.

334. Finch SC: Laboratory findings in infectious mononucleosis, in Carter RL, Penman HG (eds): *Infectious Mononucleosis.* Oxford, England, Blackwell Scientific Publications, 1969, p 47.

335. Shipp JC, Baden H: Leukemoid reaction in infectious mononucleosis: An infrequent manifestation simulating leukemia. *Arch Intern Med* 1959; 104:619.

336. Litwins J, Liebowitz S: Abnormal lymphocytes (virocytes) in virus diseases other than infectious mononucleosis. *Acta Haematol* 1951; 5:223.

337. Dougherty TF, Frank JA: The quantitative and qualitative responses of blood lymphocytes to stress stimuli. *J Lab Clin Med* 1953; 42:530.

338. Fichtilius KE, Vahlquist B: Incidence of atypical mononuclear cells in the peripheral blood of children. *Acta Pediatr Scand* 1955; 44:541.

339. Wood TA, Frenkel TP: The atypical lymphocyte. *Am J Med* 1967; 42:923.

340. Fleisher GR, Paradise J: Atypical lymphocytosis in children. *Ann Emerg Med* 1981; 10:424.

341. Cantow EF, Kostinas JE: Studies on infectious mononucleosis. IV. Changes in the granulocytic series. *Am J Clin Pathol* 1966; 49:43.

342. Fleisher GR, Paradise JE, Lennette ET: Leukocyte response in childhood infectious mononucleosis. *Am J Dis Child* 1981; 135:699.

343. Sutton RN, Reynolds K, Almond JP, et al: Immunoglobulins and EB virus antibodies in infectious mononucleosis. *Clin Exp Immunol* 1973; 13:359.

344. Custer RP, Smith EB: The pathology of infectious mononucleosis. *Blood* 1948; 3:830.

345. Gall EA, Stout HA: The pathology of the lymph nodes of infectious mononucleosis. *Am J Pathol* 1940; 16:433.

346. Kelmola E, Henle G, Henle W, et al: Infectious mononucleosis-like disease with negative heterophil agglutination test. Clinical features in relation to Epstein-Barr virus and cytomegalovirus antibodies. *J Infect Dis* 1970; 121:608.

347. Horwitz CA, Henle W, Henle G, et al: Heterophil negative infectious mononucleosis and mononucleosis-like illness. Laboratory confirmation of 43 cases. *Am J Med* 1967; 63:947.

348. Churchill AE, Payne LN, Chubb RC: Immunization against Ma-

rek's disease using a live attenuated virus. *Nature* 1969; 221:744.

349. Epstein MA, Morgan AJ, Finerty S, et al: Protection of cottontop tamarins against Epstein-Barr virus–induced malignant lymphoma by a prototype subunit vaccine. *Nature* 1985; 318:287.

350. Maki DG, Reich RM: Infectious mononucleosis in the athlete: diagnosis, complications, and management. *Am J Sports Med* 1982; 10–62.

351. Mason WR, Adams EK: Infectious mononucleosis. *Am J Med Sci* 1958; 236:447.

352. Antila V, Makela TE, Klemola E: Corticotropin in the treatment of infectious mononucleosis. *Acta Med Scand* 1962; 171:345.

353. Breen GE, Talukar PK: Corticosteroids in the acute infections. *Lancet* 1965; 1:158.

354. Bender CE: The value of corticosteroids in the treatment of infectious mononucleosis. *JAMA* 1967; 199:97.

355. Klein E, Cochran JF, Buck RL: The effects of short-term corticosteroid therapy on the symptoms of infectious mononucleosis pharyngotonsilitis: A double blind study. *J Am Coll Health Assoc* 1969; 17:446.

356. Bolden KJ: Corticosteroids in the treatment of infectious mononucleosis. *J R Coll Gen Pract* 1972; 22:87.

357. Prout C, Dalrymple W: A double blind study of eighty-two cases of infectious mononucleosis treated with corticosteroids. *J Am Coll Health Assoc* 1966; 15:62.

358. Collins M, Fleisher G, Kreisberg J, et al: Role of steroids in the treatment of infectious mononucleosis in the ambulatory college student. *J Am Coll Health* 1984; 33:101.

359. Bower AG, Affeldt JE, West H: The treatment of the anginose type of infectious mononucleosis with gamma globulin. *J Pediatr* 1949; 34:58.

360. Demin AA: DNA-ase in treatment of infectious mononucleosis. *Lancet* 1976; 1:417.

361. Sinha AK: A pilot trial of methisazone in infectious mononucleosis and chickenpox. *Br J Clin Pract* 1971; 25:177.

362. Kawa HK, Franco E, Doi S, et al: Successful treatment of chronic active Epstein-Barr virus infection with recombinant interleukin-2. *Lancet* 1; 1987:157.

363. Hedstrom SA, Mardh PA, Repa T: Treatment of anginose infectious mononucleosis with metronidazole. *Scand J Infect Dis* 1978; 10:7.

364. Murkland WG, Lungberg C, Nord CE, et al: Evidence of tinidazole interference in the oropharyngeal inflammatory process during infectious mononucleosis. *Scand J Infect Dis* 1976; 6:503.

365. Anderson J, Skoldenberg B, Henle W, et al: Acyclovir treatment in infectious mononucleosis: a clinical and virological study. *Infection* 1987; 15:S14.

37

Cytomegaloviruses

Sirus Naraqi

Human cytomegalovirus (CMV) is a ubiquitous agent belonging to the herpesvirus group. Like other members of the herpesvirus group, CMV possesses the cardinal characteristics of latency-reactivation and potential oncogenicity. CMV infection is prevalent throughout the world. Most infections are asymptomatic. Clinically apparent CMV infections constitute a small proportion of infected individuals. Clinical manifestations of CMV infection vary with the age of acquisition of the virus and range from mild and self-limited to severe and fatal disease. The major clinical syndromes are cytomegalic inclusion disease in neonates, heterophil-negative mononucleosis in previously healthy individuals, and interstitial pneumonia in immunocompromised hosts.

The awareness of the significance of CMV infection in individual patient care, as well as in public health, has steadily increased since the isolation of CMV in the 1950s:

1. CMV is the most common cause of virus-induced mental retardation in the Western World, where congenital infection occurs in about 1% of all neonates each year; at least 10% of these children have or will develop significant and permanent brain damage.

2. In organ allograft recipients and in patients with malignancies, connective tissue diseases or other conditions who are maintained on immunosuppressive agents, CMV infection is commonly associated with allograft rejection or loss, causes significant morbidity, and contributes to mortality. CMV infection also predisposes these patients to severe or fatal bacterial, fungal, and parasitic infections by causing further immunosuppression. Similar observations have been made in patients with acquired immunodeficiency syndrome (AIDS).

3. CMV has been linked to Kaposi's sarcoma and carcinomas of the prostate, cervix and colon. Although the exact nature of this relationship is unknown, these findings may be of major significance.

Effective therapeutic or preventive measure for CMV infection are not available at the present time. Although the efficacy of CMV hyperimmune globulin and vaccine in altering the severity of the disease in bone marrow and renal allograph recipients has been shown, more studies are needed to evaluate the practical role and widespread use of these preventive measures. There is also concern about the potential long–term side effects of the vaccine.

HISTORY

The recovery of human CMV was first accomplished independently in three different laboratories in the United States and was reported in 1956 and 1957.[1–3] Smith isolated two CMV strains from the salivary gland and kidney of two dying infants. Both tissues contained cytomagalic inclusion bodies.[1] Rowe et al recovered three CMV strains from surgically removed adenoid tissue of three asymptomatic children.[2] Weller et al isolated three CMV strains from liver biopsy specimens and/or urine of three infants with congenital CMV disease.[3] Each of these strains was identical or closely related.[4, 5]

CMV was initially called "salivary gland virus" or "salivary gland inclusion disease virus." Weller et al, in 1960, proposed the term "cytomegaloviruses," which is derived from "cytomeg-alia" originally used by Goodpasture and Talbot in 1921 to indicate the significant enlargement and alteration of infected cells.[4, 6]

Prior to recovery of the virus, CMV infection had been long recognized by pathologists. The first description of the histologic features of infection is attributed to Ribbert who, in 1881, noted the characteristic cells in the kidney of a stillborn infant, but could not interpret the findings. In 1904, Jesionek et al and later Ribbert reported the findings of these cells in a variety of tissues from neonates and infants.[7, 8] Initially, these cells were called protozoanlike cells and were thought by many workers to be a protozoa. However, over the next several decades, the similarities of these cells to those infected by varicella-zoster virus and herpes simplex virus and to the salivary gland inclusions of guinea pigs and mice led to the consideration of a viral cause,[6, 9] and to the recovery of the virus shortly after the beginning of the modern tissue culture era. CMV mononucleosis, the cardinal feature of symptomatic infection in previously healthy individuals, was first described by Klemola and Kaariainen in 1965.[10]

VIRUS STRUCTURE AND BIOLOGY

Classification

CMV is a member of the genus *Herpesvirus* and belongs to the family ***Herpetoviridae***.[11, 12] The common basic characteristics of the herpesvirus group include fairly large size, enveloped DNA, cell association (latency), and potential oncogenicity. It is the cell association which may produce persistent inapparent infections with members of the herpesvirus group which reactivates under appropriate conditions. Human herpesviruses include herpes simplex virus types 1 and 2 (HSV-1, HSV-2), varicella-zoster virus (VZV), Epstein-Barr virus (EBV), and CMV. Human herpesvirus type 6 (HHV-6) appears to be another newly identified member of this group.[13]

Morphology, Size, and Composition

Morphologically, CMV is indistinguishable from other members of the herpesvirus group. The complete virion is 150 to 200 nm in diameter, icosahedral in shape, and consists of an inner core, a capsid, and an envelope (Figure 37–1). The inner core (genome) is 64 nm in diameter and consists of a linear double-stranded DNA molecule with a molecular weight of 100×10^6 to 150×10^6. While DNAs of various CMV strains demonstrate at least 80% homology by reassociation kinetics, the DNA homology with herpes simplex, murine CMV, and simian CMV is reported to be less than 5%. The capsid is 110 nm in diameter, is made of protein, and has 162 capsomers. The envelope contains lipoprotein and is comprised of a single or double membrane. There are at least 33 structural proteins, some of which reside in the envelope and are glycosylated. The analysis of glycoproteins, by monoclonal antibodies or by other means, demonstrates that several antigenically distinct CMV glycoproteins exist and that some are targets of virus neutralizing antibody.[14–21]

Physicochemical Characteristics

CMV is a labile virus and is readily inactivated by lipid solvents (20% ether for two hours), low pH (below 5), heat (37°C for one hour or 56°C for 0.5 hour), and ultraviolet light (five minutes).

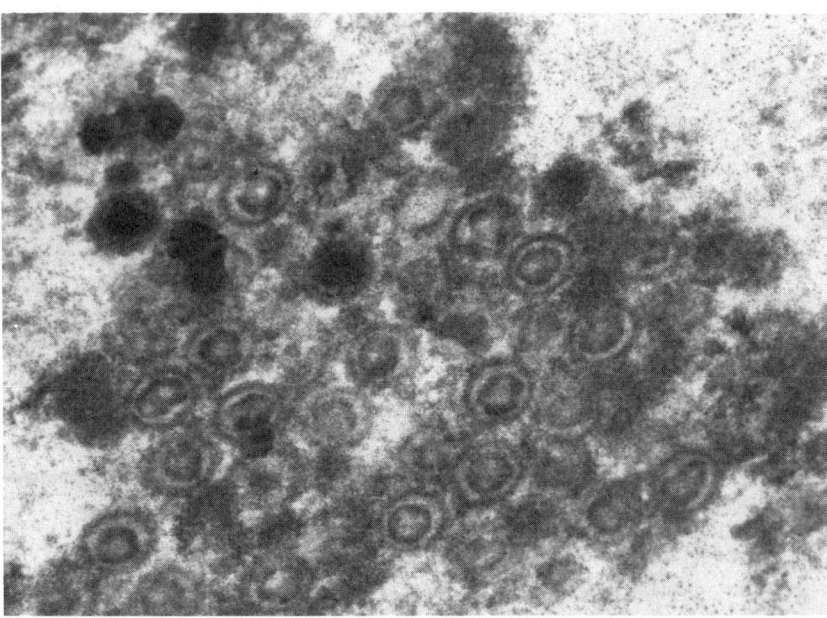

Figure 37–1. Electron micrograph of cytomegalovirus (strain AD169) in human lung fibroblasts.

Preservation of infectivity can best be achieved by freezing the suspension of the infected cells in bicarbonate-free diluent. Addition of sucrose phosphate or 30% to 50% sorbitol adds to the viability. The optimal temperature for storage is −190°C (liquid nitrogen) and results in little or no loss of infectivity. The virus can be kept at −70°C for several months, but storage at −20°C results in complete loss of infectivity over a short period of time. At 4°C, CMV could be stored for several days without an appreciable decrease in the virus titer. Cell-free virus can be obtained by sonication of infected cells and can be kept indefinitely at −190°C. CMV can survive in environmental surfaces for several hours.[14–17, 22–24]

Replication

CMV replication is relatively slow. Virus enters the host cell by fusion of the virus envelope with the cell membrane or via phagocytosis. Infectious particles are first detected by electron microscopy one to several days after inoculation of susceptible tissue culture. During this latent period, however, viral DNA and protein can be detected in the infected cell. Virus particles are made and assembled in the nucleus, attain an envelope by budding through the inner nuclear membrane while exiting, and then migrate through the cytoplasm in vacuoles. Defective virus particles with incomplete DNA may also be formed. These defective particles (dense bodies and noninfectious enveloped particles) lack DNA, and are noninfectious. They may prove useful in development of vaccine because they can provoke immune response without having the risk of latency or oncogenesis.[14–17, 25–31]

Tissue Culture Characteristics

CMV is species-specific, and human strains do not grow in animal cells. Human fibroblasts are the only cells that readily support the growth of CMV in vitro despite the fact that epithelial cells are generally infection in vivo.[14–17] The in vitro growth of human CMV in homologous epithelial cell lines is limited. However, growth of CMV in vitro has been achieved in a variety of tissues including cell cultures derived from human brain, choroid plexus, bone marrow, umbilical vein endothelium, and arterial smooth muscle. It has also been shown that CMV grows in a special subset of bone marrow stem cells which may explain the presence of CMV in peripheral blood cells. Culture supernatants of permissive and nonpermissive cells infected with CMV contain a growth factor which enhances DNA synthesis of target cells. Productive infection of CMV in human fibroblasts and epithelial cells is enhanced by pretreatment with dexamethasone or 5-iodo-2′-deoxyuridine (IUDR).[32]

Cytopathic effect (CPE) of CMV in tissue culture is characteristic and appears several days to several weeks (usually seven to 12 days) following the inoculation of clinical specimens, depending on the amount of virus in the inoculum (Figure 37–2). Occasionally, blind passage of inoculated tissue culture and a longer observation period may be needed for recovery of the virus. Sonication and centrifugation of specimens may also result in increased yield. When large amounts of virus are present in the inoculum, CPE or generalized cell rounding may appear in 24 hours. The CPE consists of small round or elongated foci of rounded, greatly enlarged, refractile cells that enlarge slowly (over several weeks) in size and in number. The virus is highly cell-associated and spread occurs from infected to contiguous cells. However, cell-free virus is present in vivo in the urine of infected patients and in vitro in the supernatant of tissue culture of adapted strains. Characteristic CPE and restricted growth in human fibroblast cell lines are usually sufficient to identify CMV. Identification can be confirmed by tissue staining or by immunofluorescent, complement-fixation (CF), or neutralization techniques, and/or by DNA analysis studies.[1–3, 15, 28, 29]

Strain Variation

CMV isolates from various human sources usually share a common antigen. Antigenic heterogeneity, however, is well recognized and was initially noted by various serologic techniques.[4, 33] No definitive serogrouping has been made yet, but it is suggested that there are three and possibly more serologically distinct strains. This antigenic heterogeneity can cause false–negative results in indirect hemagglutination and antibody assays in a small percentage of sera with antibody to CMV. Various strains may also produce distinguishable CPE and plaque morphology.[34] Distinct differences in the CPE of genital and oral isolates of CMV in tissue culture have been noted occasionally.[35]

DNA of various CMV strains has been shown to share at least 80% homology. However, different human CMV isolates are not identical and exhibit great diversity when studied by DNA-DNA reassociation kinetics or by restriction endonuclease technique.[36] Although no genetic grouping has been possible, these differences are distinct and can be used to trace the source of the virus in an outbreak. Several strains of CMV (AD169, Davis, Towne) are well adapted to tissue culture growth and are widely used for research studies or for vaccine production. AD169 strain has a very broad reactivity and is recommended for routine laboratory diagnostic work.[1–3, 14–17]

Antigenicity

CMV possesses a broad antigenic mosaic. However, antigens responsible for the production of various antibodies have not been well defined. Two CF antigens have been described. The first antigen, which containe at least two polypeptides, is soluble, stable at 4°C, and withstands repeated freezing and thawing but loses its potency at 37°C or with boiling. The other antigen, which is primarily made of nucleocapsids, is virus-associated and is prepared by the treatment of infected cells with glycine buffer.[37–39] The antigens responsible for neutralizing or immunofluorescent antibodies are found in the envelope of mature virions (glycoproteins).[21] There is no known cross-reaction between human CMV antigens with other human herpesviruses or animal CMVs, except for some simian CMVs which show some degree of cross-reactivity with human strains (see CMV and Animals, below).[14, 15]

Some degree of antigen cross-reactivity which has been found between CMV and other human herpesviruses when sensitive techniques are used appear to have pathogenicity and evolutionary rather than clinical or diagnostic significance.

Sequential immunofluorescent antibody studies indicate that CMV replication produces immediate-early, early, and late CMV antigens. These terms refer to the time of production of the antigens in the virus replication cycle. Immediate-early antigens appear in the nucleus of CMV-infected cells one to three hours after infection. Early antigens appear in the cytoplasm or membrane about three hours after infection. Late antigen appears in the nucleus and cytoplasm within six to 24 hours after infection. A membrane antigen can be detected on the surface of infected cells at the end of the CMV replication cycle. Detection of these antigens by monoclonal antibodies in cell cultures infected with clinical specimens or in tissue sections is considered to be a marker of viral infection. A cytoplasmic paranuclear inclusion and an intranuclear inclusion can easily be identified in the infected cell at this stage; immediate-early and early antigens are virus-induced nonstructural proteins and appear before DNA synthesis; late antigen is a viral-induced structural protein and appears after DNA synthesis. Early antigen is obtained by infecting human fibroblasts with CMV in the presence of cytosine arabinoside, which inhibits DNA synthesis and prevents viral replication, thus also inhibiting formation of viral structural protein.[40–42]

Antibody Response

The process of virus replication in the host results in the production of anti-CMV antibodies of the IgG, IgM, and IgA classes. These antibodies may last from several weeks to several months or persist for a lifetime, and can be detected by a variety of methods. Antibody may also be produced against pre-early (immediate), early, or late viral antigens.[14, 15]

CMV-specific IgG antibody may be detected by CF, neutralization, indirect hemagglutination (IHA), immunofluorescent antibody testing (IFA), radioimmunoassay (RIA), immune adherence hemagglutination (IAHA), latex agglutination (LA), enzyme-linked immunosorbent assay (ELISA), and other newer techniques. CF antibody is produced against most, but not all, CMV strains and may first be detected 1 week to several months after infection.[1, 15, 43] Neutralizing antibody is the most specific but is less broadly reactive; it appears later than CF antibody but lasts longer and detects antigenic heterogeneity better.[1–3, 43] The IHA technique detects IgM as well as IgG antibodies and is more sensitive than the CF or neutralization techniques. IFA appears earlier and is more sensitive than the CF or neutralization methods. Fluorescent antibody receptors are found in both the cytoplasm and nucleus of the infected cells. CMV induces receptors for the Fc portion of IgG in the cytoplasm of infected human fibroblasts. This receptor is seen one to several days after infection and results in nonspecific cytoplasmic staining in IFA tests. As a result, a positive reading of the IFA test should be restricted to nuclear staining. The anticomplement immunofluorescent test (ACIF) is an extension of the IFA technique and offers the advantages of lack of nonspecific

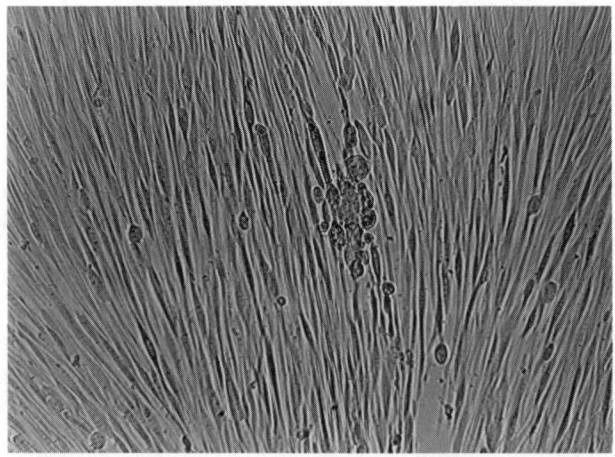

Figure 37–2. Cytopathic effects of cytomegalovirus (strain AD169) in human lung fibroblasts, five days after inoculation.

cytoplasmic reaction and easier interpretation. Techniques such as RIA, IAHA, or ELISA are more sensitive methods for the detection of CMV-specific IgG antibody.[44-49] Subclasses of CMV-specific IgG are produced following CMV infection, but their diagnostic value needs further studies.

CMV-specific IgM can be detected in the serum of patients by IFA, RIA, ELISA, or other techniques. Antibody may be directed toward the nucleus or membrane of the infected cells. IgM antibody may be produced in both primary and recurrent infection and may last for a year or longer. The use of monoclonal antibody to detect CMV-specific IgM will improve the sensitivity of testing. CMV-specific IgA antibody may be produced in body secretions (saliva, cervical secretion, or breast milk) or may be found in serum and can be detected by the same techniques that are used for IgM antibody detection. Titers of antibody to early antigen fall several months after infection while antibody to late antigen may persist for a year or longer. The presence of antibody to early antigen may not indicate active virus replication.[50-56]

The use of monoclonal antibodies by IFA or ELISA has facilitated the characterization of glycoproteins of CMV, has helped to detect a number of immediate-early and early antigens, has shown serologic heterogeneity, and may assist in the development of new subunit vaccines. They have also proved useful in rapid in vitro diagnosis of CMV infection. Furthermore, monoclonal antibodies directed to some groups of viral proteins have been shown to neutralize human CMV in vitro; this observation may provide a new means for passive immunotherapy for immunoprophylaxis of CMV infection.[20, 27, 45]

Histopathology

CMV infection may be localized in the salivary glands or be generalized with involvement of many organs. CMV can replicate in epithelial, fibroblast, and endothelial cells and in macrophages, lymphocytes, and a variety of other cells. The process of CMV replication in cells, both in vivo and in vitro, results in greatly enlarged rounded cells (25–40 μm in diameter). These cells contain intranuclear as well as intracytoplasmic inclusion bodies (Figure 37–3). Intranuclear inclusions are about 10 μm in size, stain red by hematoxylin and eosin, and are separated from the nuclear membrane by a clear zone or halo (owl-eyed).[14, 15, 27] Cell enlargement is visualized within six hours after infection. A paranuclear eosinophilic inclusion is seen within 24 hours. The basophilic nuclear inclusion appears 48 to 72 hours after infection. Margination of nucleoli is also observed. Multinucleated giant cells with intranuclear inclusions are occasionally encountered with CMV. They may be seen in epithelial or fibroblast cell lines and may result from cytophagocytosis or fusion of infected cells.[30, 35, 57, 58] Inclusion bodies have been seen in almost every human organ, and electron microscopic studies show that they contain clusters of virions.[18, 26, 27]

CMV and Animals

CMV is highly host-restricted. Species-specific virus is found in most mammals.[14, 15, 59, 60] There is no experimental animal model for studying human CMV. All attempts to infect animals with human CMV have failed. A CMV strain (Colburn) that was isolated form the brain of a child with encephalopathy has been shown

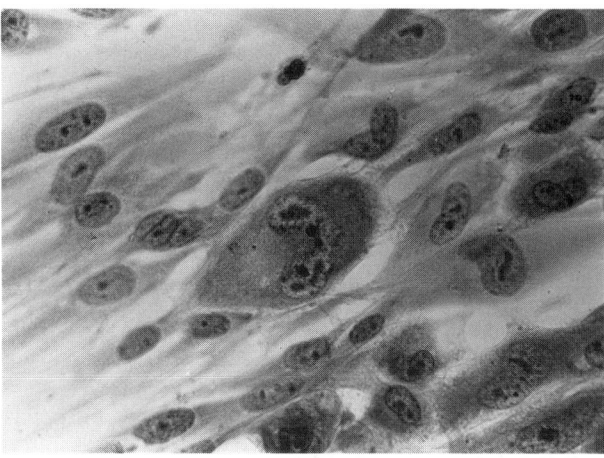

Figure 37–3. Cytomegalic inclusion bodies (strain AD169) in human lung fibroblasts (Papanicolaou's stain).

to cause productive infection in marmosets.[61] However, the DNA of this strain is more related to simian CMV; thus its human origin is not well established. Murine CMV and, to a lesser degree, guinea pig and simian CMV have been studied extensively in an attempt to clarify the pathogenesis of infection in humans. Although useful information on the pathogenesis of these animal viruses has been accumulated, particularly with regard to congenital infection, reactivation due to immunosuppression, mononucleosis-like syndrome and vaccination, applicability of these data to human CMV is not known.[62-64] Simian CMV has some CF and neutralizing antigens in common with human CMV, and it grows in human cells. However, this relationship is generally unidirectional. Human CMV does not replicate in other animal cells, but abortive infection has been observed in a variety of nonhuman cells such as bovine, murine, simian, hamster, and guinea pig cells. Production of antibody to CMV has been accomplished in guinea pigs, goats, monkeys, and rabbits. Such hyperimmune antibodies have been useful in confirmation of antigen variability of human CMV strains and in serologic diagnosis of CMV infection.[14, 15, 65-69]

EPIDEMIOLOGY IN THE GENERAL POPULATION

Prevalence of Antibody

CMV is a ubiquitous agent. Studies on the general populations of all continents, including the inhabitants of isolated parts of the world such as Eskimos and Pacific islanders, indicate that the majority of the world population experiences CMV infection during their lifetime.[70-75] Serologic studies indicate that CMV antibody is present in the cord blood of the majority of neonates. This passively acquired antibody declines in the first few months of life. CMV antibody reappears later in life following primary infection, and its prevalence increases as age increases.[75] (Figure 37-4). Rowe et al demonstrated CF antibodies to CMV in 53% of a series of unselected adults in the United States between the ages of 18 and 25 years and in 81% of a similar group over the age of 35 years.[2] A similar trend has been found in different parts of the world.[74] Socioeconomic status is a factor of major significance in the prevalence of CMV infection. In developing nations, the age

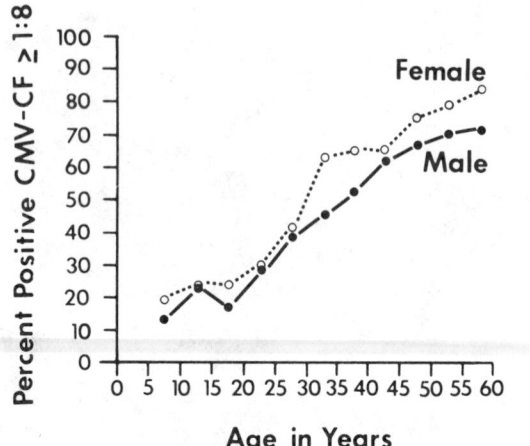

Figure 37–4. Prevalence of antibody to cytomegalovirus (CMV) in general population by age and sex, based on complement-fixing (CF) antibody measurement in 4824 middle-class individuals in the United States. (From Wentworth BB, Alexander ER: Seroepidemiology of infections due to members of the herpesvirus groups. *Am J Epidemiol* 1971; 94:496-507. Used by permission.)

at CMV acquisition is much younger than in industrialized ones. By school age, about 90% or more of the children in the developing world are CMV–seropositive. This has been attributed to living under crowded conditions, poor hygienic standards and/or a large number of people handling the infants (extended family).[73, 74] Among the individuals within an age group, antibody prevalence is higher in blacks than in whites, in women than in men, in sexually active persons than in nuns, and in persons with blood group A than in other blood groups.[14, 15, 70-76]

Prevalence of Virus Excretion

CMV may be excreted in the urine, saliva, and other body excretions of asymptomatic individuals. Some of these individuals may be in the convalescent phase of a CMV illness, but most have no known history of recent or past CMV illness.

Urine and Oral Secretions

The prevalence of CMV shedding from urine or throat of various age groups of the general population is shown in Table 37–1. CMV is excreted from the urine of approximately 0.5% to 25% of all live neonates, 10% to 29% of preschool children, 10% to 15% of school-age children, and 0% to 2% of adults.[77-83] The rate of virus shedding in urine or throat is high in certain populations. It may occur in the urine of 12% of pregnant women, in 14% of homosexual men, and in 75% of some groups of immunocompromised hosts. Excretion of CMV from urine is more prevalent and almost twice that of throat in a given group.[84-86]

Cervical Secretions

An average of 10% of nonpregnant young women excrete CMV from the cervix. This rate increases in pregnant women and in women with sexually transmitted diseases. The rate of cervical excretion in pregnant women declines in early gestation and then increases with gestational age; cervical excretion may reach 28% in the third trimester. CMV has been isolated from the cervix of

13.3% of (nonpregnant) women examined because of suspected sexually transmitted diseases but in none of 76 women having routine pelvic examination. The rate of cervical excretion of CMV in patients with documented past or active gonococcal infection has been found to be higher than that of patients with no documented gonorrhea (14.3% as compared to 4.8%).[84, 87-92]

Semen

CMV is excreted in the semen of asymptomatic CMV-seropositive individuals and in that of patients with CMV mononucleosis.[93-95] In patients with mononucleosis, the virus is present in the extracellular fluid of semen and persists for a long time after recovery from the disease.[93] The titer of CMV in semen is much higher than that of CMV in urine, suggesting local replication of the virus in the genital organs. The rate of CMV excretion in semen may be higher among homosexuals or AIDS patients, or patients with sexually transmitted diseases. CMV is found in the semen of more than 10% of homosexuals, patients with venereal diseases, or with AIDS as compared to 5% of young heterosexual adults.[93-96]

Breast Milk

CMV has been isolated from the breast milk of asymptomatic CMV-seropositive women, despite the presence of CMV-specific IgG and IgA. CMV shedding is observed only in CMV-seropositive mothers and the rate ranges form 14% to 70%. The virus titer in milk appears to be low and virus may persist for many months. Virus excretion in milk may be a major source of CMV transmission in the first two years of life and may or may not be associated with excretion from other sites. More than two thirds of CMV-seropositive donors of breast milk may shed CMV in their milk. Therefore, the transmission of infection to seronegative infants fed from human milk banks is a source of concern.[97-101]

Feces

Rarely, CMV has been isolated from the feces of patients with CMV-induced gastrointestinal (GI) lesions. Eight percent (3/36) of CMV-seropositive children studied by repeated culture of rectal swab have been found to excrete CMV in their feces. The rates of virus excretion from the urine and throat of these children were 89% and 36%, respectively. All fecal excreters had disseminated CMV infection with documented GI involvement in one, while urine and throat excreters were asymptomatic. Virus shedding in the stool was intermittent and was achieved after two to nine specimens were cultured in each child. All fecal excreters had virus in their saliva as well.[103]

Table 37–1
Prevalence of Cytomegalovirus (CMV) Excretion From Urine in Different Age Groups of General Population

Age Group	CMV Excretion (%)
Newborn	0.3–2.5
<5 yr	9.4–29
5–15 yr	9.5–15
>15 yr	0–2.6

Data from references 77–83.

Table 37–2
Rate of Cytomegalovirus Excretion From Cervix and Urine of Pregnant Women According to Stages of Pregnancy

Pregnancy Trimester	Cervix				Urine
	Numazaki et al[91] No.(%)*	Montgomery et al[115] No.(%)*	Stagno et al[88] No.(%)†	Chandler et al[90†] No.(%)*	Reynolds et al[119] No.(%)*
First	0/30(0)	1/14(2)	3/183(1.6)	21/241(9.3)	1/82(1.2)
Second	6/62(9.6)	3/23(7)	29/359(6.1)	28/194(14)	12/276(4.3)
Third	17/61(27.8)	4/26(12)	42/317(11.3)	29/128(23)	18/305(5.9)
Total	23/153(15.1)	14/175(8.9)	63/659(9.5)	78/563(14)	31/663(4.8)

*Number of subjects with virus/number tested.
†Only seropositive women were tested.

Tears

CMV has been isolated from the tears of patients with CMV mononucleosis[104] or chorioretinitis.[105] The rate of CMV excretion in tears in the general population is not known. CMV was recovered from serial cultures of tears or conjunctival swabs of eight of 41 children with acute lymphocytic leukemia; three of these children had chorioretinitis (19%). All had CMV in the urine or saliva as well.[105]

Tissues

CMV was isolated from autopsy tissues (lung and kidney) of 8.8% of 502 unselected subjects; about half had malignancies or organ allografts.[106] Viral cultures of donated allograft kidneys done at the time of transplantation surgery yielded a very low rate of CMV isolation.[107] The prevalence of CMV infection in postmortem tissues, as detected by the presence of inclusion bodies, appears to be high in children and low in adults. CMV inclusion bodies were found in the submaxillary salivary glands of 12% of 183 autopsied children less than 17 months old.[108] However, a review of 502 unselected autopsies revealed inclusion bodies in one or more of various tissues in only 2.4% of the subjects.[109]

Annual Rate of CMV Acquisition

The annual rate of acquisition of CMV in the general population varies with the age and the type of population under study. The most common age of acquiring CMV is the first year of life. At birth, only 0.5% to 2.5% of neonates have CMV infection as demonstrated by virus shedding.[77] However, at the end of the first year of life, 8% to 60% of infants in the Western World excrete CMV.[80, 82] The infection rate is higher in Japan and in low socioeconomic groups.[81, 83, 91] The rate of CMV acquisition after the first year of life gradually decreases until it levels off in older children and adults. The yearly rate of CMV infection in the general population can be estimated from viral or serologic studies in the general population. The yearly rate is 5% to 10% before the age of 4 and 5% or less between 4 and 15 years of age. The rate of infection in young adults is approximately 1% per year. In developing countries most people acquire CMV infection early in life and before school age or adulthood.[70–83]

EPIDEMIOLOGY IN SPECIFIC GROUPS

Pregnant Women

Prevalence

Prospective studies indicate that 45% to 91% of pregnant women have CMV antibody in their sera prior to conception or at the time of their first antenatal clinic visit.[91, 110–118] These figures are similar to the normal population and vary with age, geographic area, multigravidity, sexual behavior, race, and socioeconomic status.[70–75] CMV excretion from the urine is observed in 1.2% to 12% of pregnant women.[84, 111, 115, 117, 119] Cervical excretion is more common and is seen in 8.9% to 28% of this population.[84, 91, 92, 115, 119] The rate of CMV excretion from the cervix or urine increases with gestational age (Table 37–2) and is higher in younger mothers, primigravida women, unmarried women, and low socioeconomic groups.[88, 91, 115, 119] It has been proposed that the overall rate of cervical excretion of CMV in pregnancy is not different from that of the general population of similar demographic characteristics and that early stages of pregnancy suppress the rate of virus excretion.[88]

The risk of developing active CMV infection during pregnancy, as demonstrated by virus shedding and/or a significant antibody rise, is from 1% to 15%.[88, 91, 110, 111, 114, 116, 117] Infection may occur at any stage of pregnancy and may be primary or recurrent. Primary infection is more common in women with high socioeconomic status. Furthermore, in a population with similar socioeconomic status, pregnant women with primary CMV infection are often younger, primigravida, white, and married.[114] Most primary or reactivated infections during pregnancy are asymptomatic.

In Utero Transmission

The natural history of CMV infection during pregnancy, its mechanism of transmission to the fetus, and the risk of development of fetal damage are complex and differ from other common intrauterine infections. Factors such as the type of maternal infection (primary or recurrent), fetal age at the time of in utero transmission, or difference in the virulence of different virus strains are potential factors that alone or in combination may influence the outcome of pregnancy. Unlike rubella infection, which is clinically apparent, CMV is transmitted in utero during the acute phase of the primary maternal infection, and causes most damage during early gestation, CMV infection during pregnancy frequently is asymptomatic and occurs in pregnant women with prior CMV antibody. Furthermore, a clear-cut relationship between fetal damage and gestational age at the time of acquisition of CMV infection is not apparent.[116] Table 37–3 shows the rate of active CMV infection during pregnancy and its risk of in utero transmission in several large studies. The rate of active CMV infection during pregnancy is similar in CMV-immune (1.6%) and nonimmune (1.4%) pregnant women.[114] Infection in immune mothers (recur-

Table 37–3
Risk of Active* Cytomegalovirus Infection in Pregnant Women and Its Transmission to Fetus

Population	Authors	No. of Women Studied	No. of Women Infected (%)	No. of Babies Infected (%)
Serosusceptible women (primary)	Peckham et al (1983)[120]	6511	38(0.6)	28(73)
	Griffiths & Baboonian (1984)[116]	3716	32(0.8)	6(19)
	Grant et al (1981)[118]	1841	13(0.7)	5(38)
	Kumar et al (1984)[125]	1404	14(1)	7(50)
	Stagno et al (1982)[114]	1382	21(1.5)	11(52)
	Ahlfors et al (1982)[121]	1218	14(1.2)	6(43)
	Monif et al (1972)[110]	664	4(0.6)	4(100)
	Stern & Tucker (1973)l[111]	270	11(4.1)	5(45)
	Total	17006	147(0.86)	72(49)
Seroimmune women (recurrent)				
	Peckham et al (1983)[120]	8278	35(0.4)	7(20)
	Ahlfors et al (1982)[121†]	3164	?	12(?)
	Grant et al (1981)[118]	2420	12(0.5)	0(0)
	Stagno et al[112]	2330	338(14)‡	20(6)
	Kamada et al (1983)[123]	1156	20(1.7)	3(15)
	Stern & Tucker (1973)[111]	770	8(10)	0(0)
	Griffiths & Baboonian (1984)[126†]	725	?	1(?)
	Nankervis et al (1984)[113]	710	121(17)	11(10)
	Stagno et al (1977)[112]	208	30(14)	7(7)
	Leinikki et al[117]	124	10(9)	0(0)
	Total	15996	574(3.5)	48(8.3)

*Number with virus shedding and/or seroconversion.
†Excluded from total.
‡Highest possible estimate based on cervical excretion.

rent) is usually due to reactivation of latent virus and on a worldwide basis is more common than the primary infection (due to socioeconomic factors).

The risk of in utero transmission of CMV to the fetus during maternal infection may be estimated from comparison of the rate of congenitally infected infants[77] (1%–2%) to the rate of maternal infection (1%–2%).[114] Indeed some prospective reports indicate that 100% of infected mothers with primary infection transmit CMV to their fetuses. Other studies, however, indicate a transmission rate of 25% to 50% during the primary infection of the mother (see Table 37–3). In women known to be immune before conception, CMV transmission to fetus occurs, but it is very rare. In a study of 725 neonates born to such mothers, only one (0.14%) was found to have congenital CMV infection. The previous offspring of this mother had also suffered from congenital CMV infection.[126a] On the other hand, the prevalence of active CMV infection in mothers at term, as indicated by virus shedding in the urine or cervix, is as high as 14%.[119] As a result, perinatal infections are much more common than congenital ones. Different reports estimate a 26% to 57% rate of perinatal infection, and mothers appear to be the major source (milk or cervical secretions). Perinatal CMV infection may rarely be congenital (in utero, transplacental) when transmission of the virus occurs late in pregnancy with insufficient time for development of positive neonatal features or cultures.[117, 119, 122]

The risk of transmission of CMV to the fetus is higher in primary infection. However, on a worldwide basis, recurrent infections during pregnancy account for the majority of cases of congenital CMV infection. The relationship between fetal age and risk of in utero transmission of maternal CMV infection is not well understood (Table 37–4). Whether maternal infection in early gestational age increases the risk of in utero transmission, as suggested by some studies, is not known.[110, 111] Abortion in mothers with CMV infection during various stages of pregnancy has given mixed results.[114, 127, 128] So has the follow-up on the outcome of pregnant mothers with infection in the first, second, or third trimester of gestation.[111, 113, 116, 118] In larger series, the risk of transmission appears to be higher when CMV infection occurs in late pregnancy[113, 114, 119] and is highest when the mother is infected at term. Two separate reports[111] indicated that all women who were actively

Table 37–4
Relationship Between Gestational Age, Fetal Transmission, and Neonatal Disease in Primary Maternal Cytomegalovirus Infection*

Stage of Pregnancy	No. of Maternal Infections	No. of Babies With Infection	No. of Babies With Disease
First trimester	18	8	4
Second trimester	44	13	2
Third trimester	49	21	1
Total	111	42	7

*Adequate data are not available for gestational age in seroimmune mothers.
Adapted from Monif et al,[110] Stern and Tucker,[111] Stagno et al,[114] Griffiths and Baboonian,[116] Grant et al,[118] Ahlfors et al,[121] Kumar et al,[125] and Stern et al.[126b]

infected at term (virus excretion from cervix or urine) gave birth to infected babies. The transmission rate at term was 57% in another report.[119] This high transmission rate by infected mothers at term may be explained in part by perinatal rather than in utero acquisition of the virus. More studies are needed to confirm the notion that cellular immunity plays a part in preventing in utero transmission of CMV.

Fetal Damage

Little is known about the likelihood of fetal damage caused by CMV following in utero transmission or about the factors influencing the degree of this damage. The majority of congenital CMV infections are clinically silent at birth regardless of the type or the time of maternal infection. While almost all of the congenital infection which results from reactivation of infection produces no brain damage in offspring, about one fourth of infected infants whose mothers had primary infection during pregnancy, asymptomatically or symptomatically, show some evidence of brain damage in early childhood (see Table 37–4).

The incidence of clinically detectable damage is higher in the offspring of mothers with primary infection (25%) than in the offspring of mothers with recurrent infection (0%).[114] However, although uncommon, symptomatic infection or severe brain damage has been noted in the offspring of immune mothers.[129, 130] Socioeconomic status might influence the fetal damage indirectly. In high socioeconomic groups, most women are seronegative; therefore, the majority of congenital infections are the result of primary infection, which causes more brain damage (50%). In low income groups, however, congenital infection is more often the result of recurrent infection, and brain damage is rare (18%).[114]

The role of gestational age at the time of fetal infection is not known. Clinically apparent infection and brain damage have been observed as the result of maternal CMV infection in every trimester of pregnancy.[110, 116, 129] Another potential factor is the difference in the virulence of virus strains that may cause in utero infection. However, it has been observed that the same strain of CMV has caused different degrees of disease in two siblings born 3 years apart from two consecutive pregnancies.[131]

Congenital infection may also occur in the second offspring of mothers who have already given birth to a congenitally infected child.[130–133] These children are usually asymptomatic. Although the possibility exists that a subsequent fetus becomes infected with CMV when a previous sibling has been born with clinically apparent or inapparent congenital CMV infection, the likelihood of this occurring does not appear to be very high. The infection in the second offspring may be symptomatic on rare occasions. Among 14 infants delivered to mothers whose previous offspring had had symptomatic congenital CMV infection, no evidence of congenital CMV infection was found at birth or at follow-up.[131–133]

Day Care Centers

A high prevalence of CMV infection in children one to five years of age who attend day care centers has been reported. Using viruria as an indicator of infection, 21% to 59% of the children are found to be infected with the highest rate observed among one to two-year-old infants. This rate is several times higher than that of children with comparable demographic features who are kept at home. Infant-to-infant transmission in day care centers may play a major role in this increased prevalence as suggested by DNA studies of virus isolates, by a lower rate of infection in the cohort infants staying at home, and by dissimilar antibody rates in mothers and infants.[134–136]

Homosexual Men

Homosexual men, as compared to the general population or to heterosexual men, have a significantly higher prevalence of CMV antibody, CMV excretion in urine or semen, and CMV mononucleosis. A study in San Francisco indicated that the prevalence of CMV antibody in homosexual men (94%) was significantly higher than that of the age-matched controls of heterosexual men attending a sexually transmitted disease clinic (54%) or that of male volunteer blood donors (43%). CMV was isolated from the urine of 7.4% of 190 homosexual men but from none of 101 heterosexual men attending the same clinic. A retrospective survey found that homosexual men are at significantly higher risk than heterosexual men for developing CMV mononucleosis. The yearly attack rates of primary and recurrent CMV infection among homosexual men are reported to be 27% and 6%, respectively. More than a third of CMV seropositive homosexual men may shed the virus, usually for a prolonged period of time. The number of sexual partners, the practice of anal-receptive intercourse, and the duration of homosexual activity are important factors in the prevalence of CMV infection in this group.[85, 137–139]

Prostitutes and Patients With Sexually Transmitted Diseases

In one study, 90% of prostitutes were found to have CMV antibody, a rate twice or more higher than that of blood donors, pregnant women and kidney or heart transplant candidates.[140]

A higher prevalence of CMV antibody is found in patients with sexually transmitted disease.[141, 142] CMV antibody is present on 90.2% of women with suspected sexually transmitted diseases as compared to 56.4% of those undergoing routine pelvic examination. The prevalence is also higher among women with gonococcal infection (82.9%) as compared to patients without gonococcal infection (50%). In women attending sexually transmitted diseases clinic, age at first sexual intercourse and the number of sexual partners correlate with CMV seropositivity. An attack rate of 13% is observed in CMV-seronegative women.[89, 141, 142]

Patients With AIDS

Patients with AIDS have a high prevalence of CMV infection. The syndrome, which occurs mainly in homosexual men, hemophiliacs, drug addicts, and some ethnic groups as well as their children and heterosexual partners, is caused by human immunodeficiency virus (HIV). CMV is a major complication in this group of patients and contributes to the morbidity and mortality. Almost all AIDS patients suffer from CMV infection or disease and more than two thirds shed the virus in urine or throat.[143, 144]

Blood Donors and Recipients

Primary infection, reactivation of latent virus, or reinfection with a new strain of CMV may occur following blood transfusion.

The prevalence of antibody to CMV among blood donors is 24% to 75% in the United States and Europe.[145–147] This rate approaches 100% in certain areas of the world such as Japan and Africa.[74] While CMV can be commonly isolated from peripheral leukocytes of patients with active CMV infection, attempts to isolate CMV from the leukocytes of blood donors have been largely unsuccessful except for one study by Diosi et al,[147] who found that two of 35 healthy asymptomatic blood donors had occult viremia.[145–150] The prevalence of CMV viruria in blood donors in one study was reported to be 3%.[151]

Following blood transfusion or perfusion, as many as 21% to 54% of patients develop serologic evidence of CMV infection. Increases in antibody titers occur in both seronegative and seropositive recipients. Patients may be asymptomatic or may develop posttransfusion CMV mononucleosis or CMV hepatitis.[145, 146, 152, 153] CMV can be transmitted by fresh (within 24 hours after collection) or stored blood or by granulocyte transfusion. The freshness of blood, presence of leukocytes, number of units, and CMV antibody status of the donor are factors that increase the risk of CMV infection in the recipient. Antibody to CMV does not protect the recipient of leukocyte or blood transfusion from infection. All of the recipients of blood from donors with CMV viruria may develop CMV infection, as indicated by increase in antibody titer or CMV excretion in the urine. On the other hand, transfusion of blood from CMV–seronegative donors to neonates does not result in CMV infection. It has been shown that leukocyte-free or depleted blood is associated with a lower risk of CMV transmission. The value of screening of donor blood for IgM or antibodies to IEA (immediate early antigen) and EA (early antigen) needs further study.[145, 146, 154, 155] The risk of CMV infection after transfusion increases with the number of units transfused. The rate of CMV seroconversion was found to be about 7% in patients who received one unit of blood and rose to 52% in patients receiving 10 to 14 units.[152] Factor VIII does not transmit CMV. Forty-two percent of hemophiliacs in one series were found to have CMV antibodies, a rate similar to their age-related controls in the general population. However, hemophiliacs who acquire AIDS are at greater risk of developing CMV infection and disease.

Recent studies have shown substantially lower transfusion-related CMV infection rates than earlier studies. This change may be attributed to the current practice of transfusion of fewer units, and the use of red blood cells. Most post-transfusion infections are the result of reactivation of latent CMV either in donor or recipient blood leukocytes. While it is not necessary to provide blood from seronegative donors for most patients who receive blood transfusions, CMV-seronegative blood should be used for preterm and newborn infants who require trnsfusion. The rate of CMV infection in neonates receiving unscreened blood transfusion may be as high as 28%.[145, 146]

Immunocompromised Hosts

A high prevalence of CMV infection has been found in various immunocompromised hosts. Infection usually occurs within the first few months after the onset of immunosuppression and is more common in CMV-seropositive patients.[86, 143, 159–164] One to two thirds of renal allographt recipients have CMV antibody prior to transplantation. The overall infection rate after renal transplantation ranges from 60% to 96%. Primary infection in CMV-seronegative recipients was observed in 24% to 53%, while the rate of recurrent infection in CMV-seropositive recipients was 64% to 100%.[86, 159–177] In recipients of bone marrow,[160] heart,[161] or liver[162] allografts, the CMV infection rate has been found to be more than 50%. Patients with malignancies[163] or connective tissue diseases[164] who are maintained on immunosuppressive agents have a high prevalence (30%–60%) of CMV infection as well.

The source as well as the risk factors for development of CMV infection varies in various groups of immunosuppressed patients. The source of the virus may be exogenous (blood transfusion, allograft organs, hospital environment) or endogenous (latent infection). The major source of CMV infection in CMV-seropositive allograft organ recipients appears to be latent virus that is either endogenous (residing in the recipient) or exogenous (residing in and transmitted by blood or the allograft organ). Reinfection by exogenous virus occurs as well, but is infrequent. The reactivation of latent CMV appears to be related to immunosuppression and/or graft-versus-host or host-versus-graft reaction. The importance of immunosuppressive agents is shown by the following observations: (1) CMV infection is seen in almost all patients who are treated with cytotoxic agents regardless of the underlying condition;[160–164] (2) renal or bone marrow allograft patients who do not receive these drugs (such as transplantation in identical twins) do not have a high incidence of CMV infection;[176] (3) there is a close temporal relation between immunosuppressive therapy and the appearance of CMV infection;[165–172] and (4) there is a direct correlation between the degree of immunosuppression and the morbidity of infection.[177] Host-versus-graft or graft-versus-host reaction may also play a role in the reactivation of latent CMV, as suggested by animal studies, but the significance of these immunologic reactions in reactivation of latent CMV in humans is not known.[178] In CMV-seronegative recipients, donated organ and transfusion are the major exogenous sources of CMV infection.

In renal or cardiac transplantation, the CMV immune status of donors as well as that of recipients is of major importance.[161, 173, 174] The risk of development of CMV infection is severalfold greater in CMV-seropositive renal allograft recipients than in their seronegative counterparts. Seronegative recipients who receive a kidney from seronegative donors rarely develop CMV infection, but there is a higher rate of CMV infection in seronegative recipients who receive a kidney from seropositive donors as compared to those whose allograft is from seronegative donors.[172–176] Transfusion, underlying kidney disease, dialysis, splenectomy, and hospital environment do not play a significant role in CMV acquisition by renal allograft recipients.[86, 159, 165–172, 179] In bone marrow transplantation, the immune status of donors or recipients does not appear to play a role, but granulocyte transfusion and allogeneic bone marrow graft are associated with a higher rate of CMV infection.[160, 180] In patients with malignancy and connective tissue diseases, immunosuppressive agents appear to be the major factor for reactivation of latent virus. The role of malignancy as an independent factor is not known.[163, 164, 181] Molecular epidemiology of CMV infection in kidney, heart, and marrow transplant patients has confirmed that reactivated virus is the cause of infection in CMV-seropositive or virus-excreting recipients. It has also revealed that infection or reinfection with a new strain (from donor of organ or blood) occurs, that the virus causing reinfection can disseminate and cause illness, and that viruses isolated form various sites of the same patient are genetically identical.[182-184]

Patients With Burn Injury

A high prevalence of CMV infection occurs following burn injury. Infection may be primary or recurrent and may contribute to development of late bacterial infection in some of these patients.[185, 186] A prospective study of 52 patients with 20% or more body surface burn injury showed that 33% of the patients developed a significant rise in CMV antibody titer. Infection occurred an average of 4 weeks after injury and was more common in patients whose blood contained antibody to CMV on the day of burn. Transfusion of blood products, the extent and degree of burn injuries, and smoke inhalation were not related to the development of CMV infection.[185] Another study showed a 54% rate of CMV urine shedding in 33 children with burn injury. CMV was excreted from urine an average of 8 weeks after burn injury.[186]

PATHOGENESIS

After entering the human body, it is widely believed that CMV spreads via the bloodstream to various organs. The vehicle of the virus transportation in the blood is blood leukocytes. Both mononuclear and polymorphonuclear leukocytes have been implicated. Viremia and virus excretion from various sites occur in the presence of high-titer neutralizing antibody.[148, 149] CMV infection may occur in individuals without prior exposure (primary infection) or in those with prior exposure to the virus (recurrent infection). Primary infection is demonstrated by the absence of specific antibody to CMV prior to infection. Recurrent infection may result

Table 37–5
Characteristics of Lytic and Latent Cytomegalovirus

	Lytic	Latent
Duration of infection	Limited	Lifelong
Fate of infected cells	Death	Normal or extended life*
Virus replication	Yes	No
Virus structure	Complete	Incomplete? (not known)
Inclusion bodies	Present	Absent
Virion seen by electron microscope (EM)	Yes	No
Antigen detected by fluorescent antibody (FA)	Yes	No
Virus DNA detection by hybridization	Yes	Yes
Virus isolation by:		
Tissue cultures	Yes	No
Tissue explantation	Yes?	Yes
Change of status to	Persistence (latency)	Reactivation (lytic)

*Transformed cells initiated from latently infected tissues may show the virus which can be detected by FA, EM, or hybridization, while the examination of the same tissue prior to transformation by the same methods is not revealing.

from reactivation of endogenous latent virus or from reinfection with an exogenous virus. Reinfection may occur as a result of exposure to a different antigenic strain of CMV or to a higher infectious dose of the same virus strain. Differentiation between primary or recurrent infection on clinical grounds is not possible. Either primary or recurrent infection may be asymptomatic or cause mild or severe illness or death. However, in general, recurrent infection is more often asymptomatic and, if symptomatic, produces less severe symptoms than the primary infection.[182-184, 187-194]

Like other herpesviruses, interaction between CMV and the host cell may result in productive infection, latency, and/or cell transformation (Figure 37–5). Productive infection is the result of virus replication, but the mechanism of latency and cell transformation is not known. Table 37–5 shows the characteristics of lytic and latent CMV and compares the two types of infections.

Productive Infections

Productive infection is caused by lytic virus and results in the death of the infected cells. Virus replicates in the nucleus, produces inclusion bodies, and causes lysis of the cell.[195] The virus then spreads to other cells for continuation of the replication cycle. In this system, the infection can be chronic and perpetuated for as long as living susceptible cells are present. Lytic CMV (infectious or overt virus) can be detected by the presence of cytomegalic inclusion bodies, demonstration of the virion by electron microscopy, isolation of the virus by tissue culture, demonstration of CMV-specific antigen by fluorescent antibody techniques, and/or by detection of its genome by DNA hybridization. Lytic infection may be caused by exogenous or reactivated endogenous viruses. The target organ for the induction of CMV disease in lytic infection is highly age-dependent. In fetal or neonatal life, neurons and salivary glands are most sensitive.[196] After birth, CMV infection is commonly asymptomatic, but in symptomatic previously healthy

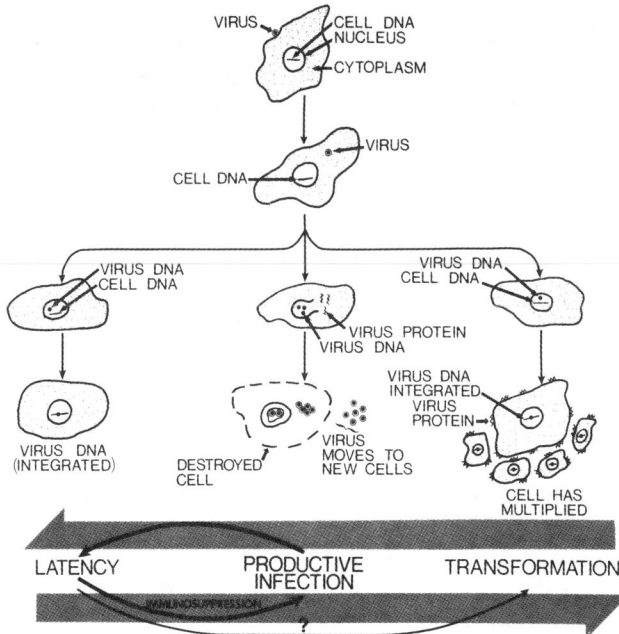

Figure 37–5. Pathogenesis of cytomegalovirus infection; virus-cell interactions.

individuals, lymphoid tissues appear to provide the most susceptible cells.[197] In immunocompromised hosts, lungs are most commonly affected, although other organs may be involved as well.[198]

Latent Infection

Following primary infection, it is believed that CMV, like other herpesviruses, remains latent in the host cells for a lifetime. True viral latency can be defined as the presence of the genome of the virus (or genetic information) in an unexpressed state in the host cell. Latent CMV (noninfectious or covert virus) cannot be recovered from infected tissues by conventional tissue culture methods. However, examination of the same tissue by explanation techniques unmasks and releases the virus in the supernatant or in the monolayers formed around the explants. Viral DNA may also be detected by hybridization. Other methods for detection of latent CMV include the demonstration of the virus particles, its genome, or its antigen by electron microscopy, hybridization, and/or fluorescent antibody techniques in long-term cultures of explanted tissue or in transformed cell lines derived from latently infected tissues. The mechanism of CMV latency in humans is not known, but it is postulated that latently infected cells continue to live while harboring the virus and that the virus may be in a defective form. This coexistence is disturbed under certain natural (pregnancy) or iatrogenic conditions (immunosuppression). Reactivation of latent CMV results in productive infection, which may or may not be associated with clinical manifestations.

Persistent lytic CMV infection should not be confused with CMV latency. The persistent infection is due to a balance between the release of virus and the growth of uninfected susceptible cells. Persistent CMV infection has been demonstrated in several different cell lines and may result in production of a variant strain.[191–201]

The CMV latency-reactivation concept has not been documented in humans, but it is supported by the following observations:

1. A high incidence (over 80%) and lifelong persistence of antibody to CMV in the absence of virus shedding in the general population (1% of normal adults)[15]
2. Occurrence of a high incidence of CMV infection in CMV-seropositive recipients of various organ allografts shortly after transplantation and commencement of immunosuppressive drugs[169]
3. A high incidence of active CMV infection as indicated by virus excretion from the cervix among CMV-seropositive pregnant women[91, 112]
4. Transmission of CMV by kidney,[173, 174] heart,[161] and blood leukocytes[154] in recipients of renal allograft, cardiac allograft, or blood, respectively, even though culture of the donated allografts,[107] and blood leukocytes[145] are negative for CMV
5. A high incidence of CMV excretion following administration of immunosuppressive agents to CMV-seropositive individuals with a variety of illnesses such as leukemia, carcinomas, connective tissue diseases, and other conditions.[163, 164]

Reinfection with different antigenic strains of CMV may be postulated as an explanation for the above-mentioned observations.

However, CMV isolates from the same patients with recurrent CMV infection many years apart are antigenically and genetically identical or very closely related.[131] These findings support the reactivation of endogenous (latent) CMV as the best and most commonly occurring explanation for the above observations. Examination of virus DNA of different isolates has confirmed that while reinfections with new strains occur, reactivation of the patient's strain is the most common cause of recurrent infection.[182–184, 187–194]

CMV is a species-specific virus, and the applicability of data from animal CMV to human CMV is unknown. Experimental studies with murine, guinea pig, and simian CMV also support the latency-reactivation concept. Spleen, lymphocytes, macrophages, salivary glands, and prostate have been suggested as the sites of latent murine CMV.[62–64] The site of CMV latency is not known in humans. In vitro models of CMV latency have been described; hormones, cell inhibitors, and/or lower temperature may be needed for the establishment of these models. The hypothesis that latent CMV may be harbored by most or all organs that are infected during primary infection has not been ruled out. Latent virus may be maintained in a single ubiquitous cell type (such as lymphocytes or macrophages) or in various cell types. Attempts to recover latent CMV from kidney have not yielded positive results.[107] Skin has been suggested as one of the likely sites of CMV latency in humans. CMV has been isolated from one of 43 fibroblast cell lines derived from normal skin. The CMV genome has also been detected in three of these cell lines by DNA hybridization. Lymphoid tissue appears to be another likely site of CMV latency in humans, and the CMV genome has been found to persist in lymphoid cells after congenital infection and in lymphocytes of asymptomatic CMV-seropositive individuals. However, isolation of CMV from blood cells does not implicate these cells as a site of latecy, since CMV may be present simply as a result of their phagocytic activities. It has been shown that CMV-specific cytotoxic T lymphocytes (precursors) are present in peripheral blood of latently infected individuals without preceding overt infection. These cells may be capable of lysing infected cells prior to viral replication and may play a role in controlling reactivation of CMV in individuals with latent infections.[195–209]

Cell Transformation and Oncogenicity

CMV has been shown to increase DNA and RNA synthesis of host cells, a characteristic shared by oncogenic DNA viruses. This may be the result of production of an α-protein by CMV-infected cells which stimulates host cell functions. This reaction is subsequently switched off by a β-protein in productive infection. The ability of human CMV to transform mammalian cells has been shown in human and rodent cells. Exposure of hamster lung fibroblasts to human CMV irradiated with ultraviolet light results in establishment of continuous cell lines that contain CMV-specific antigen on their membranes and within their cytoplasm.[203] These cells produce tumors in hamsters. The new tumor cells also exhibit CMV-specific antigen on their membrane and within their cytoplasm. Antibody to human CMV can also be detected in the serum of hamsters with these tumors. Similar observations have been made in rat cells. The minimum-size fragment of human CMV genome required to initiate transformation in rat cells has been determined.[210–214]

Exposure of human lung fibroblasts to a genital isolate of CMV has resulted in establishment of a continuous cell line.[210] These cells contain CMV-specific antigen on the cell membrane and produce tumors in mice. Transformation of prostatic cells by CMV has also been observed. Prostatic tissue obtained from a child yielded CMV on primary tissue culture. After a number of cell culture passages, a cell line was established that no longer yielded the virus. CMV-specific antigen could be detected on the surface of the cells after exposure of the cultures to 5-iodo-2-deoxyuridine. Nucleic acid hybridization studies revealed that viral DNA was carried by these human prostate cells and that each cell contained ten to 15 genome equivalents of CMV DNA.[200]

CMV does not infect or transform lymphocytes in vitro.[148] CMV can be isolated from blood leukocytes (buffy coat) and genome equivalents of CMV DNA have been found in the blood buffy coat of healthy donors.[204] CMV has also been shown to cause persistent infection of lymphoblast cell lines that originated from B lymphocytes of leukemic patients and of lymphoblastoid cell lines that originated from lymphocytes infected with Epstein-Barr virus.[207] CMV genome, CMV antigens, and infectious virus could be detected in these lines. However, the infection is different from productive infection in susceptible fibroblasts. Only 1% to 10% of the cells show evidence of infection. Cell lines originated from T lymphocytes are not susceptible to CMV, although CMV has been isolated from T lymphocytes.[206]

Association of CMV with carcinomas of the prostate, colon, and cervix and association with Kaposi's sarcoma have been reported. The association consists of the presence of virus particles in electron micrographs of cell lines derived from tumor tissues, demonstration of CMV genome in tumor tissue, and a higher prevalence of antibody to CMV in patients with some of these malignancies as compared to the control population. The significance of this association and the role of CMV as the etiologic agent or cofactor in these malignancies are not known.[211–214]

IMMUNOLOGY

CMV affects humoral as well as cell-mediated immune responses in both normal and immunocompromised hosts. Although cell-mediated immunity (CMI) appears to play a bigger role than humoral immunity, interplay between cellular and humoral immune mechanisms may be more important than either mechanism alone. CMV infection is associated with some degree of immunostimulation as suggested by the presence of atypical lymphocytes in peripheral blood and the occasional presence of various autoantibodies and increased serum immunoglobulins in some CMV-infected patients. However, immunity to CMV is only a marker of previous infection and individuals with humoral and CMI to one strain of CMV may be reinfected by another strain.[16]

Nonspecific Response

A genetic basis of resistance to CMV infection has not been demonstrated in man. The role of macrophages in nonspecific defense against CMV infection is not known.

The role of interferon in CMV infection in man is not well

established. The production of alpha (leukocyte) and beta (fibroblast) interferons which are important parts of the host nonspecific defense against viruses has been studied in a few centers. CMV can induce alpha and beta interferons in vitro. Alpha interferon has been found in alveolar secretions and the plasma of patients with CMV pneumonia, but leukocytes of infants with CMV disease are unable to produce interferon.[16, 215]

There is increasing evidence that natural killer (NK) cells have a role in limiting the severity of virus infection immediately following virus entry and prior to development of specific T cell immunity. NK cells are a novel class of cells found among peripheral blood mononuclear cells; they resemble small lymphocytes and macrophages and have the capacity to lyse virus-infected (and tumor) cells without obvious preimmunization. It has been demonstrated that NK cells can recognize and lyse CMV-infected fibroblasts in vitro and are present in the peripheral blood of CMV-seropositive and -seronegative individuals. Furthermore, recovery from CMV infection in bone marrow allograft recipients has been correlated with both non-T killer cells and cytotoxic T cells.[16, 215]

Humoral Response

Almost all of the described CMV structural proteins have been shown to be immunogenic. Monoclonal antibodies induced against several of these viral proteins are able to neutralize the virus. Normal and immunocompromised hosts develop IgG, IgM, and IgA antibodies to CMV following active infection. Antibody production against CMV is relatively intact in immunosuppressed patients.[216, 217] The humoral immune system plays a protective, but imperfect role in the host defense against CMV infection. IgA antibodies against CMV are present in urine, milk, and saliva of infected individuals but do not prevent virus sheddings from these sites.

CMV disease and viremia occur in the presence of high titers of neutralizing antibody.[149] Infection occasionally occurs in a second offspring of mothers with one congenitally infected child, indicating that maternal antibody does not prevent transplacental transmission of CMV infection.[130–132] Furthermore, there is a higher incidence of CMV infection in organ allograft recipients who are CMV-seropositive prior to transplantation than in those who are not[168, 169] and CMV-seropositive organ allograft recipients can be reinfected with new CMV strains from the donors.[182, 183] However, some protective role for humoral antibody in CMV infection is suggested by several observations: Congenitally infected infants born to CMV-immune mothers have a lower incidence of brain damage and CMV disease. In one series, five of 33 infants born after a primary infection had CMV disease while none of the 27 born after recurrent infection were ill.[114] Antibody may also protect babies from transfusion-induced CMV infection.[156, 157] CMV-seropositive renal and cardiac allograft recipients are not protected against CMV infection but are protected against CMV disease as indicated by the fact that the majority of the infections in these recipients are asymptomatic.[159] In bone marrow allograft recipients, immune donors can protect the recipients from severe CMV infection and administration of CMV immune plasma (obtained by pooling plasma samples having a CF antibody titer of 1:64 or greater) did not prevent CMV infection but significantly reduced the rate of CMV pneumonia or illness.[218] Patients with organ allografts who do not develop a rise in CMV antibody have a high fatality rate from CMV infection.[219] These observations indicate some protective role for humoral antibody. The similar attack rate and case fatality rate observed in CMV-seropositive and CMV-seronegative bone marrow transplant recipients may be explained by the fact that in this particular instance the donor's immune system is being transplanted to the recipient.

Cellular Response

CMI has a crucial role in limiting the spread of CMV infection in patients with mononucleosis and in preventing disease caused by reactivated infection in immunocompromised hosts. All the conditions associated with a high prevalence of CMV infection involve depressed CMI (organ transplantation, malignancy, AIDS, and pregnancy).[220–239] Specific or sensitized thymus-derived lymphocytes appear in the peripheral blood and body secretions of patients with active CMV infection and may be protective against CMV disease. Such T cells are usually HLA-restricted. A protective role of these CMV-specific cytotoxic lymphocytes has been shown in bone marrow and renal transplant patients who develop less or less severe disease when these lymphocytes appear in their peripheral blood.[221–225]

Alteration of T cell subsets occurs in CMV infection. CMV, like other viruses, induces a reversal of the ratio of T helper (OKT4) to T suppressor (OKT8) cells in the peripheral blood of acutely infected individuals. The reversal is the result of a decrease in the number of helper cells and an increase in the number of suppressor cells. Furthermore, in vitro or immune interferon production by cultures of purified T lymphocytes from CMV-seropositive donors is well described. The role of macrophages in the specific cellular response to CMV is not clear. In patients with CMV mononucleosis the presence of CMV-infected monocytes may cause suppression of T cell mitogen response (monocyte suppressor).[222–224]

Acute CMV infection in normal or immunocompromised hosts is associated with depression of both specific and non-specific CMI. Specific depression can be measured by a decrease in the lymphocyte proliferation response to CMV antigen and by decreased interferon production. The nonspecific response has been detected by the same assay using mitogens. The precise mechanism of this suppression of immune response is not known. However, virus replication in lymphocytes and monocytes, which can be detected by induction of early proteins in these cells, may play an important role. Studies using CMV antigen in lymphocyte proliferation assays as a measure of CMI reveal that CMV-infected newborns, pregnant women, and organ allograft recipients (kidney, heart and bone marrow) have a markedly depressed or absent response despite the presence of antibody.[220–239]

In previously healthy individuals with community-acquired CMV mononucleosis, depression of CMI may result in chronic infection or in prolonged virus shedding, in spread of the virus, and in superinfection with other agents. These patients have a diminished response of lymphocyte proliferation to CMV antigen (specific) and a variety of mitogens (nonspecific). These changes are transient and return to normal during convalescence. The major defect appears to be in T lymphocyte function involving proliferative, cytotoxic, and interferon responses. CMV-infected monocytes acting as suppressor cells may be the cause of CMV-induced im-

munosuppression. CMV infection may trigger proliferation and activation of cytotoxic T or T suppressor cells (or both), which may be responsible for immunosuppression. The depression of CMV-specific CMI is usually transient and converts to normal when virus excretion ceases. Abnormal delayed hypersensitivity may also be manifested as the loss of reactivity to skin test antigens in CMV-infected patients.[221–224] In CMV–infected women during pregnancy and shortly after delivery, CMI to CMV is depressed. This depression (both CMV-specific and nonspecific) is transient. Whether CMV infection is the result or the cause of this immunosuppression in pregnant women is not known.[226–228] In congenitally infected children, similar observations have been made.[229, 230]

In immunosuppressed populations, depression of CMI causes reactivation of CMV infection in the majority of CMV-seropositive patients. Immunosuppressive agents and particularly antithymocyte globulin markedly depress CMI while leaving the humoral response relatively intact. This suppression is general, nonspecific, and limited to the first few months following initiation of therapy. It is during this period that most CMV infection occur in immunosuppressed patients. The CMI response becomes similar to normal individuals in long-term survivors. CMV viremia and illness is more common in patients who receive antithymocyte globulin, presumably because their immunosuppression is more severe and more prolonged. Depression of CMI as a result of CMV infection itself has also been documented in organ allograft recipients. This depression appears to be the result of active infection because initial isolation of CMV is associated with further suppression of lymphocyte responses. It has been reported that in living related kidney recipients, T cell ratio inversion is only observed in patients with CMV disease, whereas in recipients of cadaver kidneys it is seen in both primary and reactivated infection. The mechanism of CMV-induced immunosuppression in compromised hosts is not clear. It is suggested that the macrophages as well as T cells that are present in normal individuals with CMV mononucleosis may be deficient in allograft recipients. This depression further predisposes the patients to severe and fatal secondary infection.[231–238]

A low T helper-T suppressor cell ratio is observed in homosexual men who develop primary CMV infection in the absence of acquiring HIV. This observation suggests that CMV is an important cofactor in the immunologic difficulties of patients with AIDS.[239]

Immunologic Aberrations

A variety of immunologic abnormalities have been observed in association with CMV infection. These include circulating immune complexes, cold agglutinins, rheumatoid factor, antibody to nuclear antigen, positive Coombs test, cryoglobulin, and monoclonal gammopathy of IgA, IgM, or IgG types.[240–244] These aberrations are seen in congenital or acquired infection.[241] All these abnormalities are transient and disappear with the resolution of CMV infection. A high incidence of skin rash is also observed in patients with CMV mononucleosis who receive ampicillin, but the mechanism of this reaction is unknown. The induction of autoimmune antibodies following CMV infection may be the result of polyclonal B cell activation on regulatory T cells.[244]

Evasion of host defense mechanisms by CMV has also been suggested based on the following observations: (a) CMV induces

Table 37–6
Sources of Cytomegalovirus Infection in Man

Primary	Recurrent
Prenatal	Reinfection
Transplacental	Different antigenic strains
Intrauterine transfusion	Higher infectious dose of the same strain
Perinatal	Reactivation (of latent virus)
Cervical secretions	Pregnancy
Postnatal	Immunosuppression
Body secretions (breast milk, saliva, urine, semen, tears, feces)	Malignancies?
	Burn injury
Blood or leukocytes transfusion	
Organ allografts	

a receptor for the Fc portion of human IgG in infected cells. The nonspecific binding of IgG molecules via their Fc portion by CMV-infected cells will protect such cells from specific lysis by cytolytic antibody or cytotoxic cells in vivo. (b) In body fluid such as urine, CMV is coated with the host protein microglobulin. Such binding masks the antigenic sites recognized by antibodies and prevents neutralization of the virus.[16]

TRANSMISSION

Natural

Oropharyngeal Route

Advances in molecular biology and the use of restriction endonuclease digestion of DNA to analyze strains of CMV isolates have documented the transmission of CMV from infant to infant, husband to wife, mother to infant, blood or organ donor to recipient patient to medical personnel, and between sexual partners. Furthermore, concurrent infection or reinfection with more than one strain has been documented in immunocompetent and immunocompromised individuals.[182–184, 187–194] Oral transmission of CMV, via the GI or respiratory tract or both, is probably the most common way of acquiring infection under natural circumstances. (Table 37–6). Asymptomatic persons who shed CMV probably serve as the major reservoir of the virus. Close and prolonged contact with infected individuals or infectious secretions appear to be necessary for oral transmission of CMV (such as kissing in transmission by saliva, nursing in transmission by breast milk, and passage through the birth canal in transmission by cervical secretions). Oropharyngeal transmission of CMV in humans has not been shown experimentally but is supported by the following indirect evidence:

1. Individuals with symptomatic or asymptomatic CMV infection excrete the virus in the saliva, urine, and other body secretions for a long period of time. Urine contains as many as 1 million virus particles per milliliter (10^5 TCID$_{50}$ [50% tissue culture infectious dose]/0.1 mL).[15]

2. A higher prevalence of CMV antibody and shedding in children in boarding schools and day care nurseries as compared to those attending day schools or remaining at home.[136]

3. High incidence of CMV infection in close contacts of children with viruria. Attack rates of about 50% have been observed when a CMV-infected member enters a family.[14–17, 136]

4. Presence of CMV in breast milk, a high rate of CMV acquisition in the first 2 years of life, and a higher incidence of CMV infection in breast-fed infants as compared to formula-fed ones.[82, 98]

The remarkable increase in the CMV viruria rate during the first year of life (8%–60% compared to 0.4%–2.5% at birth) suggests that CMV is acquired postnatally in most infants.[82] Maternal CMV excretion from various sites (urine, cervix, saliva, breast milk) suggests that mothers are the most likely source of CMV transmission in early infancy.[98] The role of different maternal secretions in transmission of CMV is suggested by the study of children of women who were shedding CMV in breast milk and not in saliva or urine. Of 28 such mothers, 11 of 19 breast-fed infants and none of the nine exclusively bottle-fed infants developed viruria (58% vs 0%, respectively). There was no CMV transmission to the infants of 26 mothers who excreted CMV in their saliva or urine. Only one infant from 136 mothers who did not excrete CMV from any site developed CMV infection.[98] In another study, consumption of CMV-infected breast milk led to infection in 69% of infants. The infection was asymptomatic except in some low-birth-weight babies.[99]

Epidemiologic evidence suggests that the female genital tract plays a major role in transmission of CMV to infants while passing through the birth canal. The presence of CMV in cervical secretions has been shown to correlate with the rate of CMV infection after birth. Fifty-seven percent of infants of mothers who shed CMV into the genital tract in the third trimester and after birth developed CMV infection as compared to 12% of those whose mothers shed CMV during the first or second trimester.[119] It is presumed that the ingestion of cervical secretions is responsible for CMV transmission through oral mucosa.

Genital Route

There is strong epidemiologic evidence for genital transmission of CMV. Sexual transmission of CMV in adults is supported by several observations:

1. A relatively high rate of CMV excretion in the semen of asymptomatic young men (5%)[94] and in the cervical secretions of asymptomatic young women (10%).[89]

2. A higher incidence of CMV antibody, viruria, and symptomatic infection in homosexual men as compared to heterosexual men with or without sexually transmitted diseases.[85]

3. A higher prevalence of CMV antibody in women suspected of having sexually transmitted diseases (82.9%) or having documented past or active gonorrhea (92.2%) as compared with women having routine pelvic examination (50%) or not having gonorrhea (56.4%).[89]

4. An increase in the rate of acquisition of antibody to CMV in the general population at the peak of sexual activity between adolescence and 40 years of age.[70, 76]

5. The occurrence of CMV infection in sexual but not in nonsexual intimate contacts of patients with CMV infection. CMV mononucleosis developed in two men after sexual contact with a woman who had had a similar illness several months before; CMV was cultured from her urine and cervix. CMV infection also de-

veloped in a new sexual contact of one of the men. The infected woman and men all developed clinical or serologic evidence of CMV infection. However, the roommates of the infected patients remained well.[245]

6. A higher rate of CMV infection in 27 individuals with CMV-infected sex partners. CMV seropositivity is observed in 74% of men whose female partners were seropositive compared with 31% of men whose partners were seronegative. Furthermore, a significantly higher percentage of men whose partners shed CMV from the cervix or urine shed CMV in their semen or urine compared to men whose partners are culture-negative.[246]

7. DNA restriction enzyme typing of CMV isolates from pairs of sex partners has documented the infection with common strains.[246]

The overall influence of the genital route in the spread of CMV in the general population is not known. However, sexual contact may be an important route for transmission of CMV in adults of industrialized countries where about half the population is seronegative at puberty.

Transplacental Route

Symptomatic or asymptomatic pregnant women with primary or nonprimary CMV infection can transmit the virus to their fetuses. The presence of a high titer of CMV in urine of the neonates at birth and/or the presence of CMV-specific IgM antibody in the cord blood of infected children indicates virus replication in fetal life. The embryo from a mother who had CMV mononucleosis during the first trimester of pregnancy contained CMV in various tissues following a therapeutic abortion.[127] The exact mechanism of transplacental transmission of CMV is not known. Infection may occur and be transmitted in any stage of pregnancy.[114, 119, 128] Direct transmission of CMV from the infected placenta to the fetus is possible but does not appear to be common.[247, 248] Viremia seems to be the major mechanism of transmission in the prenatal period. Local reactivation of infection in the cervix of the mother and contiguous spread to the fetus is another potential mechanism of transmission but has not been documented.[249] A rare cause of prenatal transmission of CMV is intrauterine transfusion (iatrogenic).[250]

Iatrogenic
Transfusion

Fresh or stored blood or granulocyte transfusion can transmit CMV infection. CMV viremia has been demonstrated by cultivating leukocytes (buffy coat) of previously healthy adults, children with congenital infection, patients with heterophil-negative mononucleosis, postperfusion syndrome, and various immunocompromising conditions. CMV can be isolated from the mononuclear, polymorphonuclear, or both fractions of peripheral blood leukocytes and not from washed erythrocytes or plasma. These fractions are only 96% to 98% pure, so it is not known whether CMV is present in various leukocytes or infection or a subgroup of them contaminates all fractions. Whether leukocytes support the replication of CMV or merely become carriers of the ingested virus is unknown. Virus appears to reside in the blood leukocytes in latent form because it cannot be recovered by cultivation of leukocytes from asymptomatic seropositive healthy blood donors;

these cells are capable of transmitting CMV.[146–149, 154, 251, 252]

Organ Transplantation

CMV can be transmitted by organ transplantation when an allograft from a seropositive donor is given to a seronegative recipient. Following kidney transplantation, several centers have reported that CMV-seronegative recipients given kidneys from seropositive donors have a greater incidence of CMV infection than the seronegative recipients whose kidney allografts were from seronegative donors.[173, 174] Similar results have been reported following cardiac transplantation.[161] The failure to isolate CMV from donated kidney suggests that the virus is present in the kidney in a latent form. However, attempts to unmask the latent virus by the tissue explantation technique from kidney tissue have been unsuccessful. It is possible that blood leukocytes that are trapped in the allograft organ and not the allograft parenchyma are the source of virus transmission. Recent studies using restriction enzyme analysis have documented the transmission of CMV from renal and cardiac transplant donors to recipients.[107, 182, 183]

Nosocomial

Nosocomial acquisition of CMV by infants in day care centers, nurseries, and hospitals have been reported.[253–255] The risk of nosocomial transmission of CMV from infected patients to other patients, household contacts, or medical personnel is not high. In nurseries housing well and full-term infants, as many as 2.5% of infants may have congenital infections. In intensive care nurseries, as many as 14% of patients may have CMV infection.[255] In pediatric transplantation or oncology units, one also expects a high rate of patients with CMV shedding. The risk of infection is particularly important for nurses of child-bearing age and in pregnant medical personnel in industrialized countries where as many as half of the women of childbearing age are susceptible to CMV. Infant-to-infant transmission in day care centers has also been demonstrated. CMV is usually present in saliva and other secretions of infected individuals and in toys which are often explored orally by infants. Survival of CMV in paper diapers, vaginal tampons, toys, hands, and other environmental surfaces, often for several hours to several days, supports the potential role of fomite and possible nosocomial transmission. However, this does not appear to occur frequently. The rate of CMV transmission from infected infants to parents and household contacts may be as high as 50%.[134–136, 256–258]

A prospective study has shown that the CMV seroconversion rate is higher in nurses than in hospital personnel without patient contact. Over a two-year period, the rate of CMV seroconversion was 0% in hospital employees without patient contact, 4.1% in nurses from neonatal units, and 7.7% in nurses from pediatric wards. This rate is somewhat higher than the annual seroconversion rate of 1% to 2% in the general population, and 0.7% to 4.0% in pregnant women.[254] Although health workers in pediatrics, obstetric and gynecology wards frequently and unknowingly are exposed to patients who shed CMV, this occupational contact confers no greater risk than that faced by young women in the community.[254, 258] In transplantation and dialysis units, several studies indicate that there is no significant nosocomial transmission of CMV from infected patients to other patients or to medical personnel.[254]

Table 37–7
Prevalence of Congenital Cytomegalovirus Infection in Different Parts of the World*

Population	Authors	No. of Infants Studied	No. of Infants Infected (%)	Symptoms at Birth/Follow-up†
North America				
Canada	Larke et al (1980)[77]	15212	64(0.42)	4/8
United States	Reynolds et al (1974)[265]	9100	22(0.24)	?/?
United States	Starr et al (1979)[227]	2147	26((1.2)	1/?
United States	Melish & Hanshaw (1973)[77a]	1963	20(1.1)	1/2
Europe				
England	Peckham et al (1983)[120]	14200	42(0.3)	17/4
England	MacDonald & Tobin (1978)[124]	9233	37(0.4)	11/5‡
Sweden	Ahlfors et al (1982)[121]	2200	7(0.3)	2/0
Denmark	Andersen et al (1979)[77b]	3060	11(0.36)	0/0
Other				
Ivory Coast	Schopfer et al (1978)[126a]	2032	28(1.31)	6/0
Japan	Kamada et al (1983)[123]	2070	11(0.53)	1/0
Brazil	Pannuti et al (1985)[267]	1016	7(0.69)	0/?

*Only studies with more than 1000 children were included. Diagnostic criterion: viruria in the first week of life.
†Number of infants who were symptomatic at birth/number of infants who were asymptomatic at birth but developed symptoms during the follow-up period.
‡Of 27 studied.

INCUBATION PERIOD

The exact incubation period of CMV is unknown. The incubation period may be estimated from the interval between the time of exposure to CMV and the development of symptoms or detection of viruria in individuals with no prior exposure to CMV. This period is 4 to 8 weeks and is similar in infants exposed to CMV in the genital tract at the time of delivery, in breast-fed infants exposed to CMV in mother's milk after birth and in adults with CMV mononucleosis following blood transfusion.[91, 98, 119, 251]

CLINICAL MANIFESTATIONS

Although CMV infection is quite common, CMV disease is rare. The majority of infections are asymptomatic. In symptomatic infection, the clinical manifestations vary with the age of the affected individual, and the severity ranges from mild to fatal illness. A variety of clinical syndromes resulting from involvement of various organs are being increasingly recognized and reported.

Neonatal Infection

Clinical and laboratory evidence of CMV infection in the neonatal period may be present at birth (or within several days thereafter) or may become apparent several weeks later. The former situation is always the result of in utero transmission of CMV (congenital infection), but the latter may result from either in utero or perinatal transmission of the virus (acquired infection). CMV is the most common virus causing congenital infection in the Western Hemisphere. Prospective studies in various parts of the world indicate that 0.5% to 2.5% of all neonates have CMV viruria at birth (Table 37–7). Most of these babies are asymptomatic, but approximately 5% to 10% of infected babies have apparent disease at the time of birth. There is 30% mortality in this subgroup, and almost all the survivors will have permanent neurologic damage.[259–263] Another 10% to 20% with inapparent infection at

birth will develop perceptual, neurologic, or psychomotor complications during preschool years.[264–266] At present it is not possible to predict which infants with asymptomatic congenital CMV infection will develop long-term sequelae.

Perinatal infection may occur in 10% of neonates in the United States and Europe. Most of the infections are inapparent clinically but some infants may show evidence of cytomegalic inclusion disease. The source of CMV may be cervical secretions (at the time of birth), breast milk, or, rarely, blood transfusion (first few days after birth). All postnatal infections are primary type. Congenital infection may result from primary or recurrent maternal infection. The mother's infection is usually asymptomatic, but mononucleosis and a "flu-like" syndrome during pregnancy have been occasionally reported.[114, 132] Primary infection of mothers leads to clinically apparent disease in only 15% of infected neonates.[114] As a rule, recurrent infection does not cause fetal disease, but severe brain damage has been reported rarely.[114, 129, 130]

Fetal infection may result in abortion, stillbirth, prematurity, low birth weight in term infants, or a variety of congenital abnormalities. Associated congenital abnormalities include inguinal hernia, atresia of bile ducts, polycystic kidney, pulmonary and mitral stenosis, ventricular and atrial septal defects, high arched or cleft palate, teeth abnormalities, unusual skin carving, and other defects.[268–270]

The clinical spectrum in term infants may range from asymptomatic to disseminated and fatal disease. Table 37–8 summarizes the major clinical and laboratory findings in severe cases of neonatal CMV infection. Neonates with full cytomegalic inclusion disease usually have jaundice, petechiae, and hepatosplenomegaly as the most common presenting findings. Microcephaly, deafness, chorioretinitis, and neuromuscular disorders are usually present. Laboratory findings include anemia, thrombocytopenia, periventricular calcification of brain, and abnormal liver function tests. Interstitial pneumonia may develop in more severe cases and can have a protracted course.[260] Clinical and laboratory findings may be present at birth or appear shortly afterward. The disease is chronic and, while nonneurologic manifestations are transient and leave no permanent sequelae, the neurologic findings are usually irreversible and result in mental and growth retardation and deafness.[259-263]

Of CNS findings, microcephaly is the most prominent feature of congenital CMV infection. In children with congenital CMV, head size may be normal at birth and become abnormal later. Antibody to CMV is more prevalent in microcephalic children than in normal or hospitalized controls. A review of 239 microcephalic children aged 6 months to 8 years by three groups of investigators showed a 22% incidence of CMV antibody as compared to 6% in the age-matched normal controls. No such difference was found in the level of antibodies to rubella virus or toxoplasma.[268] Of 47 infected neonates who were followed prospectively for at least 1 year, 17% had some CNS defects, the most common one being microcephaly.[264, 265, 267] Intellectual impairment and mental retardation as detected by lower IQ and school failure has been seen in 61% of symptomatic and 30% of asymptomatic congenitally infected children followed prospectively.[264, 265] Hearing defect is the most common CNS abnormality in CMV-infected neonates who are asymptomatic at birth and CMV is the most common cause of congenital viral-induced deafness. In long-term follow-up of children with asymptomatic congenital CMV infection, mild hearing loss has been observed but postnatally infected infants

Table 37-8
Clinical and Laboratory Findings in Neonatal* Cytomegalovirus Infection

	Number (%)
Clinical findings	
Prematurity	15/56(26)
Low birth weight (<2500 g)	48/89(53)
Respiratory distress	5/78(6)
Jaundice	52/76(68)
Petechiae	56/78(71)
Hepatosplenomegaly	67/78(85)
Seizures	10/79(12)
Hearing impairment	14/62(22)
Optic atrophy	6/79(7)
Chorioretinitis	18/90(20)
Impaired vision or blindness[†]	12/79(15)
Neuromuscular disabilities[†] (paresis, spasticity, dystonia)	44/78(56)
Microcephaly	54/90(60)
Mental impairment[†]	51/79(64)
Laboratory findings	
Atypical lymphocytes (5%–41%)	8/30(26)
Anemia and hemolysis	15/26(57)
Thrombocytopenia	41/58(70)
Elevated liver enzymes	29/47(61)
Hyperbilirubinemia	37/56(66)
Interstitial pneumonia	8/27(29)
Urine cytology	19/40(47)
Cerebral calcification	16/89(18)
CSF protein	9/9(100)

*Mostly congenital.
[†]Including findings in long-term follow-up.
Data from Weller and Hanshaw,[259] Medearis,[260] McCracken et al,[261] Berenberg and Nankervis,[262] and Pass et al.[263]

Table 37-9
Etiology of Mononucleosis Syndrome in 555 Cases in Finland*

	Number(%)
Epstein-Barr virus (EBV)	
Heterophil-Positive[†]	442(79)
Heterophil-negative	75(13.5)
Cytomegalovirus (CMV)	
Heterophil-positive	0(0)
Heterophil-negative	38(6.5)
Toxoplasma gondii	
Heterophil-positive	0(0)
Heterophil-negative	2[‡](<1)

*Adapted from Evans.[278]
[†]With further testing with horse red blood cells, 474 patients (92%) of EBV group were heterophil-positive.
[‡]Both had CMV infection as well.

appear to be spared. It may be seen in the absence of decreased mental or other neurologic defects. It is also seen in 17% of children with symptomatic congenital infection at birth. The defect is usually bilateral and may be progressive. Viral antigen and particles are widely distributed in the inner ear, including the organ of Corti and neurons of the eighth nerve.[261-266, 271]

Among nonneurologic findings, chronic liver damage is commonly associated with neonatal CMV disease. In one report, 39% of children with unexplained hepatomegaly had evidence of CMV infection. Abnormal liver function and histology also have been shown in some infected children after many months of follow-up.[272] Tooth defects occur in 40% of symptomatic and 5% of asymptomatic children with congenital CMV infection. The defects consist of generalized yellowish discoloration, absent or hypocalcified enamel causing fractured borders in some teeth, and a tendency to wear down rapidly.[270]

Mononucleosis

The cardinal feature of symptomatic acquired CMV infection in previously healthy individuals is heterophil-negative mononucleosis. It may occur spontaneously or following blood transfusion.[10, 102, 273-278] Mononucleosis is a distinct clinical entity which may be caused by Epstein-Barr virus, CMV, *Toxoplasma gondii,* or several other viruses.[278] The disease consists of fever, tonsillitis, generalized lymphadenopathy, splenomegaly, leukocytosis, and an absolute or relative increase in the number of circulating lymphocytes (>50%) with the presence of many atypical forms (>10%). Other findings such as headache, malaise, myalgia, arthralgia, skin rash, tender hepatomegaly, and abnormal liver function tests are often associated with the syndrome.

CMV mononucleosis accounts for less than 10% of all cases of mononucleosis[278] (Table 37–9). CMV is the most or second most common etiologic agent of heterophil-negative mononucleosis (after Epstein-Barr virus), and it causes about half of all cases of this entity. It is not known what proportion of CMV-induced disease manifests as mononucleosis. Some studies suggest that approximately half the adults who develop symptomatic CMV infection may present with symptoms and signs of mononucleosis.

Table 37–10
Significant Clinical and Laboratory Findings in Cytomegalovirus Mononucleosis

Symptoms	Number(%)
Fever (± chills)	87/107(81)
Malaise	14/26(53)
Myalgia	34/108(31)
Sore Throat*	27/107(25)
Headache	21/108(19)
Abdominal pain†	10/108(9)
Signs	
Temperature	98/103(95)
Tonsilitis	30/107(28)
Splenomegaly	27/108(25)
Lymphadenopathy	18/102(17)
Rash	12/108(11)
Hepatomegaly	1/26(3)
Laboratory	
Lymphocytosis (35%–83%)	108/108(100)
Atypical Lymphocytes (19%–55%)	108/108(100)
Leukocytosis	20/78(25)
Abnormal liver function tests	92/106(86)
High bilirubin	3/106(3)
Elevated serum transaminases	77/96(80)
Cold agglutinins‡	33/105(31)
Urine cytology	5/12(41)

*One patient had exudative tonsillitis.
†Upper quadrant.
‡Titer greater than 1:64, or a four-fold rise.
Adapted from Monif et al,[110] Klemola et al,[273, 275] and Horwitz et al.[276]

Characteristic changes in the peripheral blood smear may or may not be present.[279, 280]

CMV mononucleosis affects all age groups and both sexes; the majority of the patients, however, are in the third and fourth decade of life. The onset of illness is insidious and symptoms may be present from several days to several weeks before medical advice is sought. Table 37–10 shows a summary of symptoms, signs, and laboratory findings observed in CMV mononucleosis. Fever is the most common symptom and may dominate the picture. The fever is usually high and irregular and lasts from 1 to 5 weeks (average 3 weeks). The general condition of the patient is usually good and upper respiratory tract manifestations are notably absent. A rubelliform or maculopapular skin rash occurs in a small portion of the patients. The rash may occasionally be petechial or scaling.[273, 282] Exudative tonsillitis is rare but known to occur. Lymphadenopathy may be mild or prominent. It may be generalized, or it may only involve cervical and axillary areas. Tender hepatomegaly is found occasionally. Lymphocytosis and atypical lymphocytes are part of the syndrome and therefore present in all reported cases. Cases with all the symptoms and signs of mononucleosis but without the characteristic peripheral blood picture have been observed.[279, 280] Occasionally, a leukemoid reaction (leukocyte count >50,000 cells/μL) may be observed. One or more liver function tests are abnormal in almost all cases. However, jaundice is rare, and significant elevation in transaminases (more than twice normal) is seen only in half the patients.[102, 273, 275] The course of CMV mononucleosis is usually mild and self-limited with occasional complications. The reported complications include

vestibulitis, splenic infarction, glomerulonephritis, vasculitis, hemolytic anemia, and thrombocytopenic purpura. Laboratory abnormalities such as lymphocytosis and abnormal liver function tests return to normal within 6 weeks in the majority of patients. However, they may persist from several months to several years in certain patients. Patients may shed the virus from urine, throat, or other secretions long after recovery. Urine cytology may be useful in differentiating active infection from asymptomatic persistent viruria.

Administration of ampicillin to patients with CMV mononucleosis has been associated with the development of skin rash in 80% to 100% of the cases. The mechanism of this skin rash is not known. The rash is usually maculopapular but may be erythematous and occurs a week or so following administration of the drug. The incidence of skin rash in ampicillin-treated patients with CMV mononucleosis is at least 8 times greater than the approximate 10% incidence of skin rash in ampicillin-allergic patients without CMV mononucleosis or in patients with CMV mononucleosis who did not receive ampicillin.[283] Other immunologic aberrations are observed as well. A high rate of significant increase in the titer of cold agglutinins, positive rheumatoid factor, antibody to nuclear antigen, cryoprecipitin, and anticomplementary activity has been detected in the serum of a number of patients with CMV mononucleosis.[273–277] As mentioned previously, reversal of the normal ratio of T4 to T8 cells occurs in CMV mononucleosis and reflects a large absolute increase in T8 and a smaller decrease in T4 cells in peripheral blood. Atypical lymphocytes observed in CMV mononucleosis have been shown to be T lymphocytes. It has been suggested that certain individuals are hypersensitive to CMV and may be most likely to develop mononucleosis following primary infection.[281]

Postperfusion Syndrome

In 1966, it was noted by Kaarianen et al that a mononucleosis-like syndrome caused by CMV may occur following blood transfusion or cardiac surgery.[284] Prospective studies following blood transfusion, cardiac surgery, and tumor surgery have shown an incidence of CMV infection of 30% to 54% several weeks to several months following these procedures.[145–147, 251, 284] Approximately 25% of infected patients develop hepatitis. Infection may be primary or recurrent (reinfection or reactivation).[285] The risk of primary CMV infection following transfusion is reported to be 35% per year as compared to 0.8% per year in blood donors.[155] Seronegative infants who receive blood from one or more seropositive donors have a high incidence of CMV infection of 13.5%.[156–158] The majority of these patients are asymptomatic.[145] CMV is the most common known cause of postperfusion syndrome. Symptomatic infections, which occur in one fourth of patients, are manifested by fever, malaise, hepatosplenomegaly, and lymphocytosis with the presence of atypical lymphocytes. Elevation of liver enzymes and jaundice may or may not be present. Symptoms usually occur several weeks following transfusion. Tonsillitis and lymphadenopathy are usually absent.[251]

Factors contributing to the development of posttransfusion CMV infection are the freshness of the blood (collected within 24 hours), quantity of blood, seropositivity of donor, and presence of leukocytes in the blood product.[145, 146] The presence of antibody in the recipient of blood prior to transfusion is not protective, but transfusion of CMV-seronegative blood to seronegative recipients (neonates and immunosuppressed hosts) prevents postperfusion syndrome.[145, 146] In neonates requiring blood transfusion, an infection rate of 24% is observed in seronegative infants. Of infected babies, 50% develop fatal or serious symptoms.[156–158]

Hepatitis

Hepatitis may occur as the primary manifestation of CMV infection in previously healthy adults.[279, 280] However, CMV does not appear to be a common etiology of viral hepatitis in the general population. It may also occur as a prominent finding in CMV mononucleosis[286] neonatal disease,[259, 263] postperfusion syndrome,[251] or in immunosuppressed patients.[167, 287] CMV is the second most common cause of posttransfusion hepatitis (after hepatitis C) and usually occurs several weeks following transfusion. In CMV mononucleosis, abnormal liver function tests, such as slight elevation of transaminases, are almost always present, but clinical hepatitis is rare.[275] In cytomegalic inclusion disease of neonates, jaundice and hepatomegaly are constant findings. Liver tissue damage may be chronic and last for years. CMV has also been isolated from 39% of children with unexplained hepatomegaly.[272] In immunosuppressed patients, CMV hepatitis is seen in 15% of the patients.[167]

Patients with CMV hepatitis usually present with fever, malaise, anorexia, nausea, vomiting, dark urine, and right upper quadrant pain. Tender hepatomegaly and jaundice are rare. Lymphocytosis and atypical lymphocytes may or may not be present. Liver function tests usually show mild abnormalities. Liver histology shows multiple small areas of focal necrosis, reticuloendothelial hyperplasia, and scattered mononuclear cell infiltrates in portal and central vein areas. Inclusion bodies may be seen and CMV antigen may be detected in liver tissue. Cholestasis and hemolytic anemia may also contribute to jaundice in some patients. Granulomatous changes have been occasionally reported. Fibrosis of portal zones has been observed in several infants with neonatal infection.[259, 260] Liver damage in CMV infection is generally transient and liver function returns to normal within 6 weeks. In chronic liver diseases of adults, CMV does not appear to play a major role, although in neonates hepatitis may last for many months.[259, 288–292]

Pneumonia

Pneumonia may occur as the primary manifestation (without involvement of other organs) or as a part of disseminated CMV infection. It has been recognized in congenital CMV infection as well as in acquired infection of both normal and immunocompromised individuals. In the general population, CMV does not appear to be a common cause of pneumonia. In a study of 443 cases of community-acquired pneumonia requiring hospital admission, less than 1% of the patients had documented pneumonia. Only one of four patients with tissue-documented CMV pneumonia was not immunocompromised. Another 3% had suspected CMV pneumonia.[291] Pneumonia as the sole manifestation of CMV infection may be seen in as many as 20% of clinically apparent infected individuals.[279, 280, 291] In neonates, interstitial pneumonia is seen in 20% of infants with symptomatic, congenital CMV infection.[259–263]

In the first six months of life, as many as half the cases of interstitial pneumonia may be caused by CMV.[293] In immunocompromised hosts, pneumonia is the second most common manifestation of CMV infection (after fever) and the most common cause of interstitial pneumonia in this population. In renal allograft recipients, 47% of the patients whose deaths were complicated by pneumonia showed evidence of CMV pneumonia at postmortem.[166, 294–296] In bone marrow allograft recipients, CMV pneumonia is the most common cause of morbidity in the first few months following transplantation; interstitial pneumonia occurs in 46% or more of these patients, half of which is caused by CMV; two thirds of patients with CMV pneumonia die, and half of all fatal cases are found to have CMV pneumonia at postmortem.[297, 298] CMV pneumonia is also observed in 44% of cardiac transplant and 30% of liver transplant recipients. Other immunosuppressed patients have a high incidence of CMV pneumonia as well.[161–163]

CMV pneumonia may be asymptomatic and discovered by routine roentgenogram in patients with CMV mononucleosis. In symptomatic cases the onset of pneumonia is insidious, and patients complain of fever, malaise, myalgia, arthralgia, dry hacking cough, and shortness of breath of one to ten days duration. Tachypnea and high temperature are usually present, but the rest of the physical examination is insignificant. Cyanosis, increased dullness, and diffuse rales in the lower lungs may occasionally be present.[292–300] Rarely, CMV may cause a clinical picture resembling that of bronchiolitis. Leukopenia and hypoemia are often present. Pulmonary function tests show alveolar capillary blockage compatible with interstitial lung disease. Elevated liver enzymes are present in one third of patients. Chest roentgenograms show a bilateral diffuse reticular or nodular pattern. Streaks or nodular densities of 2 to 4 mm in size are present throughout both lung fields, but they are more prominent in the periphery and basilar areas. Large nodules have also been reported in asymptomatic persons. Sputum cytology may show cells with characteristic inclusion bodies. Lung tissue yields CMV in culture. The titer of virus in the lung may be as high as 10^6 TCID$_{50}$ per gram of tissue. Inclusion bodies may or may not be present in the lung tissues. Histopathologic examination of the lung shows a nodular or reticular pattern of pneumonitis. Diffuse panlobular interstitial infiltrate with inflammatory cells, protein-rich fluid in the alveolar spaces, and hyaline membrane may be observed. CMV inclusion bodies are seen in macrophages as well as in alveolar cells. The spherical lesions seen in nodular form consist of areas of hemorrhage and necrosis of several millimeters in diameter which are sharply demarcated and separated from the unaffected lung tissue.[301]

The symptoms and signs of CMV pneumonia may last from 1 week to several months (usually 2 weeks). The course may be self-limited, with full recovery, or may be progressive, leading to respiratory failure and death. Chest roentgenogram findings usually resolve in several weeks. Premature or newborn infants with CMV pneumonia may have a chronic protracted course.[302] CMV pneumonia is more common in renal and cardiac allograft recipients with primary infection than in those with recurrent infection. In bone marrow recipients the difference in incidence between primary and nonprimary infection is not clear. Severe prolonged leukopenia (< 1500 leukocytes/μL for more than seven days) and severe hypoxemia (PaO$_2$ < 60 mmHg) have been found to be prognostic factors that indicate a poor outcome.[295, 299] Association of CMV pneumonia with other pulmonary pathogens is common, and patients with mixed infection have a worse prognosis.[300] The most common pathogen associated with CMV infection is *Pneumocystis carinii*. Fungi, gram-negative bacilli, and other viruses may also occur concomitantly with CMV.[299, 300]

Any immunosuppressed patient who develops interstitial lung infiltrates should be suspected of having CMV pneumonia. Vigorous diagnostic evaluation which includes lung biopsy should be done to exclude other pathogens. Bronchoscopy is not a reliable diagnostic procedure, since many patients without CMV pneumonia will shed CMV in their throat, which may contaminate bronchoscopy specimens. Rapid reduction of immunosuppressive therapy may be an effective means for the control of CMV pneumonia. However, relapse following resumption of the drugs has been observed.[303]

Chorioretinitis

CMV retinitis occurs in congenital as well as acquired CMV infection in both normal and immunocompromised individuals. Although retinitis has been associated with CMV infection in previously healthy individuals,[304] it occurs most commonly in congenital infection and in patients who are immunosuppressed.[305–308] The incidence of retinitis is estimated to be 4% in immunocompromised hosts[168] and as high as 30% in congenitally infected neonates.[259–263] CMV retinitis is usually indicative of disseminated infection and may be the first sign of this entity. Prolonged viremia may be a factor in the pathogenesis of CMV retinitis.[168, 307]

Patient complaints are usually nonspecific and include blurred vision, scotoma, or decreased visual acuity. Many patients, however, are asymptomatic. At the beginning, one eye is involved in the majority of the cases, but in half of the patients the second eye becomes involved in a few weeks.[307] CMV retinitis has a distinctive ophthalmologic appearance.[308] The lesions evolve through exudative, hemorrhagic, and atrophic stages. Retinal lesions appear as scattered white dots or white granular patches accompanied by irregular sheathing of adjacent vessels. After several weeks, superimposed hemorrhagic patches develop and lesions become confluent. The whitish lesions subsequently lose their granular character and are replaced by gray-brown areas of marked retinal and pigmental epithelial atrophy. This usually indicates the end stage of the inflammatory process; while these changes take place in the center of the lesions, the edges advance. The new lesions appear as satellites to the advancing edge of the old lesions. Histologically, inclusion bodies may be seen in retina, pigment epithelial, and endothelial cells of retinal vessels. Retinal pigment becomes necrotic and loses the capacity to proliferate. Later, all retinal elements are replaced by thin bands of fibrous tissue.

The natural history of CMV retinitis in immunocompromised hosts is a progression from focal to generalized lesions resulting in visual impairment. Half the patients may not progress, especially if their immune status is improved.[307] It takes several weeks to several months for the retinal lesions to take their course. Various degrees of uveitis are associated with chorioretinitis. Microaneurysms of retinal arteries, capillaries, and venules have been reported in CMV retinitis. Retinal detachment or optic atrophy may complicate the illness. Unlike retinal lesions in toxoplasmosis, which do not have discrete edges, in CMV retinitis the lesions

mask the retinal vessels and cause epithelial pigment proliferation. Cessation of immunosuppressive agents may halt the progress of the lesions.[307, 308]

Conjunctivitis and Other Ocular Manifestations

Conjunctivitis has been recognized as the sole manifestation of CMV infection in previously healthy individuals,[279, 280] but the significance of this virus in the overall etiology of conjunctivitis is not known. Conjunctivitis also has been reported in association with CMV mononucleosis. Whether the eye is the portal of entry for the virus in such cases is not known.[104]

CMV has also been isolated from the tears of patients with congenital CMV infection.[105] Nineteen percent of children with CMV in their throat or urine were found to excrete CMV in their tears as well. The source of the virus in tears has not been identified. No correlation has been found between isolation of CMV from tears and the presence or future development of chorioretinitis.[105] Cloudy cornea, strabismus, iritis, uveitis, cataract, optic nerve atrophy, coloboma, and microphthalmia have been associated with CMV infection.

Gastrointestinal Syndromes

CMV GI lesions are usually seen in neonates or immunosuppressed patients as a part of the disseminated infection. About half the patients who die of disseminated CMV disease have GI involvement. The lesions consist of well-circumscribed ulcers with inclusion bodies in the bed or margin of the ulcers. These ulcers may be localized to esophagus, stomach, small bowel, or colon. They may also be generalized and involve most of the GI tract.[310]

Clinical syndromes such as esophagitis, gastritis, pancreatitis, enteritis, pneumatosis intestinale, proctitis, and ulcerative colitis have been observed to be associated with CMV in compromised or noncompromised hosts.[310–313] Clinical and laboratory findings of each syndrome are similar to those caused by other etiologic factors, but biopsy shows characteristic inclusion bodies in affected tissues. Massive GI bleeding and perforation resulting from ulcers or vasculitis involving arterioles, capillaries, and venules has been observed. Proliferating endothelial cells appear to have special susceptibility to CMV infection, and GI ulceration may be the result of necrosis caused by vasculitis in these patients.[313] Acute hemorrhagic pancreatitis may be caused by CMV in neonates and in immunocompromised hosts. In these patients, pancreatitis is usually a part of disseminated disease and may be fatal.[311] The significance of CMV in the etiology of pancreatitis in previously healthy individuals is not known.

Evidence has been presented that CMV may be involved in the pathogenesis of ulcerative colitis and carcinoma of the colon. In one review of reported cases of ulcerative colitis associated with CMV infection, a high mortality, a frequent association with toxic dilatation of the colon, and a clinical course sufficiently severe to require colectomy have been observed.[314] In patients with carcinoma of the colon, long-term culture of the tumor fragments obtained from resected colon yielded CMV in three of eight patients. Normal colons and cases of Crohn's disease were negative.[315] Whether CMV is an opportunistic infection in previously damaged colon or an etiologic factor in the pathogenesis of ulcerative colitis or carcinoma of the colon is not known.

Meningoencephalitis

In the majority of cases of congenital CMV infection, the brain is predominantly involved. The damage is irreversible and causes mental retardation and other neurologic defects.[263] In acquired CMV infection, CNS involvement is relatively rare in normal hosts but has been frequently observed in immunocompromised individuals.[316–319]

Meningitis, encephalitis, or meningoencephalitis in previously healthy adults may be the primary manifestation or part of disseminated CMV infection.[316] Meningitis or brain involvement causes a clinical picture indistinguishable from other viral meningitis or encephalitis. Patients complain of an acute febrile illness with signs of meningeal irritation. Diffuse or focal neurologic defects are present in cases of encephalitis. Examination of cerebrospinal fluid (CSF) reveals increased pressure, mild elevation of protein, and mild-to-moderate CSF pleocytosis with the mononuclear cells being predominant. CSF glucose levels are usually normal but may be low. The EEG may show diffuse dysrhythmia. Virus has been isolated from brain biopsy and CSF. Cytomegalic inclusion bodies or CMV DNA may be seen in neurons or other cells in the brain. Histologic examination of the brain shows a hemorrhagic necrotizing pattern.[316]

In immunocompromised hosts, encephalitis is usually diagnosed at postmortem examination. CSF is usually normal. Meningeal involvement is often absent. Histology shows glial-nodular encephalitis with or without the characteristic inclusion bodies in glial cells, neurons, or other cells. Inflammation and necrosis may or may not be present.[318] A role for CMV in a subgroup of schizophrenic patients has been suggested but has not been established.[320]

Polyneuritis and Myelitis

Polyneuritis may be the primary manifestation of CMV infection or a complication of CMV mononucleosis. Almost all of the reported cases are in previously healthy individuals. CMV causes 10% of all the cases of peripheral neuropathy.[321, 322] The illness usually starts as a mild respiratory infection followed by ascending or descending involvement of limbs (sensory and/or motor). Involvement of the limbs is the most common clinical picture, but involvement of the cranial nerve and respiratory muscles resulting in death has been noted as well. Peripheral blood may or may not show lymphocytosis and atypical lymphocytes.[323, 324] Patients may rarely present with transverse or ascending myelitis[325] (with a sensory level) or with Guillain-Barré syndrome (normal cells, and increased protein in CSF).[324] The clinical course of polyneuritis caused by CMV appears to be similar to that caused by other organisms. The pathogenesis is not understood but direct virus invasion or immune complex deposition has been suggested.

Thrombocytopenic Purpura

Petechiae and thrombocytopenia are common features of neonatal CMV infection and may be observed in more than half of symptomatic neonates.[263] Less commonly they may be associated with CMV mononucleosis in both children and adults.[277, 326] Thrombocytopenia may also occur as the sole manifestation of CMV infection, but its incidence is not known. The mechanism

is not known. The direct effect of CMV on platelets in humans has been suggested by observing inclusion bodies in megakaryocytes in bone marrow.[327] The prognosis is good and the platelet count returns to normal within several weeks regardless of the type of therapy. The beneficial effect of steroids or splenectomy is not well established.[326]

Hemolytic Anemia

Hemolytic anemia may be caused by congenital or acquired CMV infection. It may occur as a distinct entity or as a part of CMV mononucleosis, hepatitis, or congenital infection. Coombs tests may or may not be positive. Death may occur, but in general the course is self-limited. The mechanism of anemia is not known but may be autoimmune in nature.[287, 328, 329]

Vasculitis and Disseminated Intravascular Coagulopathy

Consumption coagulopathy has been reported in patients with congenital as well as acquired CMV infection. Generalized vasculitis and a polyarteritis nodosalike disease have also been reported.[313] The role of CMV immune complex in the pathogenesis of disseminated intravascular coagulopathy or vasculitis is not known.[330–332]

Carditis

Acute pericarditis as a result of pericardial involvement in CMV mononucleosis has been recognized. Myocardial involvement has been reported as a silent feature (demonstrated by ECG changes) of CMV mononucleosis or as a primary manifestation of CMV infection (myocarditis). The patients are usually previously healthy, and the disease may result in death. Histopathologic examination of the heart shows cardiac enlargement and interstitial lymphocytic infiltration in the myocardium with or without involvement of other organs. The significance of CMV in the overall etiology of acute viral pericarditis or viral myocarditis is not known.[277, 279, 330, 333]

Arthritis

Arthralgia and monoarticular arthritis have been reported in the course of CMV infection in immunocompromised patients.[168] Patients have an acute febrile illness with signs of inflammation involving the large joints. CMV has been isolated from synovial fluid.[334]

Cystitis and Nephritis

Association of lower urinary tract symptoms with CMV infection has been reported in previously healthy individuals.[335] Immune complex glomerulonephritis may also be associated with CMV infection. CMV antigens were demonstrated in the glomerular mesangium of a patient with CMV infection who developed focal mesangial proliferative glomerulonephritis during the course of his illness.[336] Cytomegalic inclusion bodies and degenerative changes are commonly found in renal tubules of neonates with disseminated CMV infection. However, in immunosuppressed patients with CMV infection, cytomegalic inclusion bodies are rarely observed in renal tissue. The rate of recovery of CMV from kidney is low despite a high prevalence of viruria.[107] The high rate of CMV isolation from kidney, observed in one report, has not been confirmed.[337] A distinctive diffuse glomerulopathy has been recognized in renal allograft recipients. It is characterized by enlargement or necrosis of endothelial cells, accumulation of mononuclear cells in glomerular capillaries, and granular deposits containing IgM, C3, and, to a lesser extent, IgG along the glomerular basement membrane and mesangial regions. All patients with nephropathy had clinically apparent CMV infection and viremia. This glomerulopathy was acute and associated with renal dysfunction in the absence of histologic evidence of rejection. The pathogenesis is unknown, but an immune complex–mediated mechanism has been suggested. Electron microscopy did not reveal virus particles.[338]

Manifestations in Immunocompromised Hosts

Clinical manifestations of CMV infection in immunocompromised hosts have been extensively studied in renal and bone marrow allograft recipients. CMV infection in immunocompromised hosts is often asymptomatic but may be associated with various clinical manifestations in one third of cases. Most of the symptomatic infections occur in the first several months of immunosuppressive therapy. CMV disease is more common in patients with primary infection. In renal allograft recipients the incidence of clinically apparent CMV infection varies from 13% to 38%. Cadaver graft and administration of antithymocyte globulin are associated with a higher rate of CMV illness. CMV causes recurrent illness in 6% of the patients. CMV disease is more severe in primary infection.[159–172, 339–341]

Fever is the most common syndrome observed in the immunosuppressed patient with symptomatic CMV infection. Fever is usually irregular in pattern, persistent, and often associated with striking malaise, myalgia, arthralgia, anorexia, fatigue, and night sweats. Also it may last for 1 to several weeks and present as a diagnostic problem. It may be associated with leukopenia or lymphocytosis. Pneumonia is the second most common manifestation of infection and may result in respiratory failure and death. CMV pneumonia in bone marrow allograft recipients accounts for one of the two major causes of death.[160] All the manifestations of CMV infection in previously healthy individuals may be observed in this population. The infection may disseminate and cause death.

Association between renal allograft rejection or graft loss and CMV infection has been noted by many investigators, but a cause-and-effect relationship is difficult to establish or exclude. A higher rate of rejection is seen in allograft recipients with CMV infection as compared with noninfected ones. In CMV-infected patients, the rejection rate is higher in primary as compared to recurrent infection. CMV-related graft loss may occur in as many as 50% of renal allograft recipients. Graft survival rate at 6 months is significantly lower in renal allograft recipients with primary CMV infection than in those with recurrent infection or no infection.[339, 340] CMV contributes to the mortality of immunosuppressed patients directly by causing disseminated infection or pneumonia and indirectly by predisposing to fatal superinfection. CMV-related mortality may be observed in 20% of the renal allograft recipients. A subgroup of patients has been identified in both renal and bone marrow allograft recipients who get CMV infection but do not develop a rise in CMV antibody after transplantation. These pa-

tients do poorly and have a mortality rate of about 100%.[219, 339] CMV infection has a significant effect on patient and graft survival among recipients of kidneys from cadaver donors while no such effect is detected among recipients of kidneys from living related donors.[342]

As many as one third of bone marrow transplant patients develop CMV disease. Furthermore, the presence of CMV antibody in the recipients prior to bone marrow transplantation is associated with a higher rate of symptomatic CMV infection.[343]

The clinical manifestations of CMV in AIDS patients is similar to other immunosuppressed groups with a very high rate of CMV pneumonia, GI problems, chorioretinitis, and encephalitis. CMV appears to be the major cause of encephalitis in almost half of the patients with AIDS. Examination of brain tissue by histopathology, detection of CMV antigen, and DNA suggest that CMV and not HIV is the important pathogen.[143]

DIAGNOSIS

The diagnosis of CMV infection cannot be made clinically and requires laboratory confirmation. Clinically, CMV infection should be suspected in: (1) newborn infants with microcephaly, jaundice, hepatosplenomegaly, and/or purpura; (2) in individuals with mononucleosis syndrome when heterophil antobody is negative; and (3) in immunocompromised hosts with fever, pneumonia, or other known syndromes caused by CMV.

Laboratory conformation may be obtained by the following methods: (1) detection of virus markers in various tissues or clinical specimens; these markers include inclusion bodies (histology, or exfoliative cytology), virus antigen (direct fluorescent or ELISA techniques), virus particles (electron microscopy), and/or virus genome (DNA hybridization); (2) isolation of the virus from body secretions or tissue homogenates by using tissue culture techniques; (3) detection of seroconversion or a significant rise in CMV antibody titer by serologic methods. Detection of virus markers may result in rapid diagnosis of infection, while viral culture and serology may take several days to several weeks.

Histology

For many years, the diagnosis of CMV infection was made on the basis of the presence of characteristic inclusion bodies in histologic examination of autopsy tissues. Giemsa, Papanicolaou, or other stains may be used. More recently, identification of inclusion bodies in tissues obtained by biopsy has been used for making the diagnosis in living patients. Inclusions may be observed in any CMV-infected tissue. Although histology is a relatively reliable means for making the diagnosis, its sensitivity is 2 to 6 times less than that of virus isolation. The specificity of histology for diagnosis of CMV is high, but the intranuclear inclusions can occasionally be confused with inclusions of other herpesviruses or adenovirus.[109, 196, 198]

Cytology

Inclusion-bearing cells may be found in urine, saliva, milk, cervical secretion, and touch preparations of CMV-infected tissues. Exfoliative cytology for the detection of CMV-infected cells with characteristic inclusion bodies in the urinary sediment was used in 1952 and for the first time made it possible to diagnose CMV infection in living patients. The specificity of this method is similar to the histologic examination. The sensitivity of this method is poor, and while positive results are helpful, false-negative results are frequently encountered. Freshly collected specimens should be used. Sputum, bronchoalveolar lavage, or urine cytology may be helpful in differentiation of patients with CMV disease from asymptomatic throat or urine excreters. Cytologic imprint of open lung biopsy from patients with CMV pneumonia may rapidly identify most of the cases.[259, 300, 344–346]

Antigen Detection

Detection of viral antigens in the infected tissue or urine using ELISA, RIA, or IFA methods may be of value in rapid diagnosis of CMV infection. IFA is a highly sensitive, specific, and relatively simple method for this purpose. Thin sections (4 nm) or exfoliative cells may be used. The use of monoclonal antibodies has improved this technique. CMV antigens in lung tissue, bronchoalveolar lavage, or urine can be detected within several hours. The technique is rapid and its sensitivity is reported to be comparable to viral culture.[14, 346, 347]

Electron Microscopy

Detection of the virus particles in the urine by electron microscopy has been found useful for the rapid diagnosis of CMV infection in neonates with congenital infection. These patients have a high titer of cell-free virus in the urine. The sensitivity of this method has been reported to be as high as 95% as compared to virus isolation. Other body secretions and tissues may also be used. This method is not specific and herpes simplex virus and other herpesviruses would be confused with CMV. The sensitivity decreases when the virus titer is lower than 10^4.[348, 349]

Viral Culture

Virus isolation from clinical specimens (body secretions, autopsy tissues, or biopsy specimens) is the most reliable and specific method for the diagnosis of CMV infection. The specimen of choice is urine, but saliva, throat swab, circulating leukocytes, cervical secretions, semen, breast milk, and tears can be used as well. Isolation of CMV from stool has been difficult, and the yield is very low. Specimens should be collected and carried fresh to the laboratory for rapid processing (within several hours) because CMV is relatively unstable. If there is a delay in the processing, specimens should be kept at 4°C. Freezing of the specimen results in loss of virus and should be avoided. Skin or embryonic lung fibroblast cell lines are commercially available and are used for virus isolation. The virus, depending on its concentration in the inoculum, produces cytopathic changes within several days to several weeks.[14, 15]

CMV is known to persist in body secretions long after the patient recovers from the disease. Therefore, recovery of CMV establishes the diagnosis of infection but does not necessarily mean that CMV is the cause of the existing disease. In neonates, the differential diagnosis of congenital from perinatal infection may be difficult. Isolation of the virus in the first week of life, however, is a reliable indication of congenital infection. Recovery of CMV

from amniotic fluid may also establish the diagnosis of congenital infection.[350] Various procedures have been used to shorten the time needed for detection of the virus in tissue culture. After inoculation of a specimen onto tissue culture, direct and/or indirect fluorescent antibody techniques can be used to detect the virus antigen in infected tissue culture cells. The sensitivity of this method is 70% at 24 hours and 90% at 72 hours after inoculation of the urine. Use of shell vial and low-speed centrifugation has been shown to enhance and improve the detection of CMV from urine. It is more sensitive and rapid than the conventional tube cell cultures method. Using monoclonal antibody to detect an early antigen of the virus in the nuclei of infected cells, 16 hours postinoculation, increases the sensitivity of virus detection from clinical specimens and reduced the time needed from ten days to less than one day. The sensitivity and specificity of this method are comparable to conventional cell culture.[351, 352]

Viral Serology

CMV antibody is commonly present in the serum of normal individuals. A single positive test which measures CMV-specific IgG antibody is a good indication of present or past exposure to the virus but has no diagnostic significance. A fourfold or greater rise in antibody titer indicates active infection. Specimens should be collected immediately and after 2, 4, and 8 weeks of onset of the illness. Viral serology is more sensitive than virus isolation, but a significant antibody rise may not occur for several weeks. Furthermore, variation in the titer of antibody has been reported in normal populations, and the sensitivity of the various methods of antibody measurement is different.[43–54, 353–355]

CF is simple, reliable, and specific, and was the most widely used routine serologic assay before the enzyme immunosorbent antibody technique became available. The CF test has certain limitations. False-negative results are encountered rarely. CF antibody may disappear following primary infection or it may take a longer time to appear than virus isolation. Rarely, antigen of CMV strains may not cross-react with the AD169 strain of CMV that is generally used for the CF test antigen. Anticomplementary activity, which is seen in approximately 10% of clinical specimens, is another disadvantage of the CF assay.[14, 15]

Neutralization tests are reliable and specific but are too cumbersome and time-consuming for clinical use. Microtechniques have been developed to simplify and shorten the time required for the completion of the neutralization test.[355] Fluorescent antibody (FA) techniques have become widely available and are the preferred diagnostic methods in most laboratories. They are more sensitive, because FA appears earlier and lasts longer than CF antibody. Anticomplementary fluorescent antibody test and the use of monoclonal antibodies eliminate nonspecific fluorescence.[43, 48, 53, 54] Newer serologic methods (such as RIA or ELISA) are also reliable and have replaced other methods in some centers.

Detection of CMV-specific IgG antibody in neonates or adults does not mean active infection because of passive transplacental transfer and lifelong persistence of specific IgG following infection. Detection of CMV-specific IgA antibody[357] in serum or body secretions is not sensitive and does not have practical diagnostic or prognostic value. On the other hand, measurement of CMV-specific IgM antibody is a useful tool for the diagnosis of CMV infection. Specific IgM antibody has the potential value of confirming the diagnosis in a single serum specimen. Furthermore, IgM antibodies do not cross the placenta, and their presence in the cord blood of neonates suggests congenital infection. Detection of CMV-specific IgM antibody has been found useful in diagnosing CMV infection in pregnant women and in patients with mononucleosis. The specificity and sensitivity of CMV-specific IgM detection is dependent on the technique used. The sensitivity of the FA technique is 50% of that of virus isolation, and false-positive reactions may occur in the presence of rheumatoid factor. The RIA technique appears to be very useful, and recent studies suggest 100% specificity and almost 90% sensitivity as compared to virus isolation.[50–54, 358] The specificity and sensitivity of the more readily available and practical ELISA technique appear to be comparable to those of RIA. Competitive ELISA is several times more sensitive than indirect ELISA.[51, 52]

Differential diagnosis between primary and recurrent CMV infection is desirable. Primary infection is diagnosed by demonstration of newly acquired antibody in convalescent phase serum (serconversion). When preillness or acute phase serum is not available, the diagnosis of primary from recurrent infection becomes difficult. Primary CMV infection during early pregnancy can be diagnosed by testing a single serum for CMV-specific IgM by the RIA technique. The test is negative in recurrent infection in early pregnancy and has 86% sensitivity.[358] However, the value of IgM for differentiating between primary and recurrent CMV infection in late pregnancy and in immunocompromised hosts is less clear. In immunosuppressed patients, IgM antibody may last for a year or more following infection and may be produced in both primary and recurrent infection. The value of cytolytic IgM antibody in differentiating recurrent from primary infection needs further study.

Antibody to early antigen may be useful in detecting subclinical CMV infection. In the absence of illness, demonstration of antibody to early antigen from birth onward indicates congenital infection. In contrast to the situation with Epstein-Barr virus, antibody to early antigen indicates active CMV infection, but it does not differentiate primary from recurrent infection. The value of membrane antigen, immediate-early antigen, and late antigen in the diagnosis of primary infection and/or clinical disease needs further study.[40–42, 55, 56]

Viral DNA Studies

Genome Detection

The detection of CMV DNA in exfoliated cells or touch preparations of tissue by nucleic acid hybridization can be accomplished. Recent advances in the area of recombinant DNA technology have led to the use of DNA hybridization using isotopic and nonisotopic probes in the diagnosis of CMV infection. Dot-blot, sandwich, and in situ hybridization have all been applied. The virus has been detected in various clinical specimens such as biopsied tissues, urine, blood buffy coat, bronchial secretions, etc. This technique provides a rapid diagnostic assay and is more sensitive than culture. Its specificity is close to 90%.[359–362]

Genome Analysis

Restriction enzyme analysis of CMV DNA provides the most practical method for determining genetic relatedness of CMV iso-

lates. CMV strains share 80% of their genetic material and tissue culture passages do not produce major genetic differences. Thus, similarity of CMV strains suggests an epidemiologic link. This approach has been used to trace the source of CMV transmission in various clinical situations such as mother to infant, patient to medical personnel, and blood or allograft organ donor to recipient. The method has also been used for separating endogenous infection (reactivation of latent virus) from exogenous (reinfection with different strains). When repeat isolates are genetically or antigenically identical or very similar, the infection is considered endogenous. Most of the CMV strains isolated from congenitally infected infants have been found to be identical to those isolated from infected mothers or siblings. Repeat isolates from women with recurrent CMV infection during consequent pregnancies have also been found to be identical. Similar observations have been made in blood or organ allograft recipients and their donors and in CMV vaccinees. These data suggest endogenous CMV as the most frequent source of recurrent CMV infection in seroimmune pregnant women and in immunosuppressed patients. Reinfection with different strains also occurs but is less frequent.[181–184, 187–189, 192–194, 238, 246, 257]

PROPHYLAXIS

As the most common known viral cause of mental retardation in the Western World, as the most common complication of organ transplantation in humans, causing graft rejection or loss and death, and as a cause of significant morbidity and mortality in various immunocompromised hosts, prevention of CMV infection is highly desirable. However, with a few exceptions there is currently no effective method for prophylaxis against CMV infection.

General Preventive Measures

Person-to-person transmission of CMV needs intimate and close contact with the infected patients. Isolation of patients is not necessary. The efficacy of the use of condom for prevention of sexual transmission of CMV has been suggested.[363] Therapeutic abortion in pregnant women with CMV infection during the early stages of pregnancy has resulted in variable results. Abortion may not be recommended routinely for pregnant women who were merely exposed to CMV. The risk of infection is not 100%, and even those infants whose mothers develop CMV infection during pregnancy may not become infected. It should be kept in mind, however, that in primary maternal infection, the possibility of in utero transmission of the infection is about 50%. In pregnant women who develop primary CMV infection, the risk of giving birth to an infant who will die or develop long-term sequelae is low (probably 2%–4%). This risk is much less in seroimmune women and only rarely have cases of neurologically damaged infants born to women seropositive at the beginning of pregnancy been reported. Routine serologic screening for CMV antibody in women who are pregnant or planning pregnancy is not recommended. Women who develop primary CMV infection during pregnancy whould be counseled about the possible risk to the fetus. The decision to end the pregnancy or not should be made on an individual basis (Tables 37–3 and 37–4). Recovery of CMV from the cervix or urine at or prior to the time of delivery is not an indication for cesarean section (unlike herpes simplex virus infection).[110–126, 364]

Many infants acquire CMV postnatally. The probability that an infant will acquire CMV infection during delivery when the mother is excreting CMV from the cervix is 40% to 57%. Breast feeding may also be a common source of CMV acquisition in the perinatal period. A 58% rate of infection due to breast feeding is observed and is comparable to that of infants exposed to CMV by delivery through an infected cervix. However, healthy term infants who acquire CMV through breast milk do not become ill. On the other hand, premature or immunocompromised seronegative neonates who receive infected milk are at greater risk of developing severe CMV disease. Thus in term infants the benefits of breast feeding outweigh the risk of acquisition of CMV infection and no restriction on the breast feeding of such infants whose mothers are excreting CMV is recommended. The risks and benefits of the use of milk from milk banks for feeding of premature infants should be evaluated on an individual basis. Transmission of CMV by infected milk from milk banks can be prevented by storing at 4°C for one week or more, by warming it at 62°C (Holder pasteurization) for eight minutes, or by freezing it at −20°C for 72 hours or more.[97–101]

There is no benefit in CMV screening for detection of the children who are symptomatic CMV shedders. They should not be excluded from entering day care centers or other institutions. While CMV can be frequently transmitted from infants to infants and mothers, the degree of risk of transmission from infants to day care workers, nurses, and hospital staff is very low. However, routine infection control measures such as hand washing should be used in hospital and day care centers. Screening or transfer of workers is not recommended. In the hospitals, the use of private rooms, gowns, masks, and gloves for the care of patients known or believed to excrete CMV is not necessary. Routine screening of pregnant or nonpregnant female employees for CMV antibody is not recommended. However, these individuals should be educated, through in-service programs, about the epidemiology of CMV, the possible effects on the fetus, and hygienic practices that can help to prevent infection.[364]

Blood transfusion is a major source of primary CMV infection in hospitalized patients. It is estimated that 20% of CMV-seronegative and 10% of CMV-seropositive recipients of multiple blood transfusions develop infection. The risk of acquiring CMV infection in a seronegative group is estimated to be 2.7% per unit of blood. In blood recipients, CMV can be prevented by giving blood from CMV-seronegative donors. In some recipients, this may be possible by screening all donor-recipient pairs for CMV seropositivity and excluding CMV-seropositive individuals as donors to seronegative recipients. This approach, however, is applicable only in areas where a high proportion of the population is seronegative. Although most CMV infections following transfusion in adults are asymptomatic or self-limited, pregnant women and immunosuppressed patients are at risk of getting severe symptomatic CMV infection. The use of blood product from CMV-seronegative donors for this group is most appropriate and is recommended if available. When such blood is not available, frozen or washed RBCs may be used.

In screening of blood donors for CMV antibody, commercially available CF, IHA, IFA, ELISA, and LA all have been and are still being used. CF, IFA, and ELISA are the most commonly used techniques. IHA appears to be the most reliable and LA the

most practical and easiest methods for this purpose. Negative sera by one method can be checked by another more sensitive method to confirm the negative result. A competitive ELISA may prove to be the best for this purpose. This approach, however, is not practical for transfusion in adults because it limits the availability of compatible donors significantly. The use of leukocyte-depleted or frozen red blood cells, while not eliminating the risk of transmission, reduces the risk of CMV transmission and is recommended in adults whenever possible.[145, 146, 158, 364]

Newborns and premature infants constitute a special risk group because they have a high rate of transfusion-induced CMV morbidity and mortality. Since they require small volumes of blood, the transfusion-acquired CMV infection can and should be avoided in seronegative newborn infants by providing blood from seronegative donors.[156–158, 364]

Immunocompromised patients (organ allograft recipients, patients with malignancies, collagen-vascular diseases, AIDS, burns, etc.) are at high risk of morbidity and mortality from CMV. Allograft organs from seropositive donors are the major source of CMV infection in seronegative recipients of kidney or heart transplant grafts. However, reinfection by exogenous virus in seropositive recipients also occurs rarely. The exogenous source of the virus should be minimized whenever possible by giving seronegative recipients organs, blood, or granulocytes from seronegative donors. In bone marrow recipients the factors that influence the incidence of CMV infection are complex. Serologic status of donors and recipients may not prevent CMV infection and seropositive donors may have a protective role against CMV disease. Pretransplant blood transfusions are now routinely given to renal allograft candidates because these transfusions increase the survival of the subsequent graft. Leukocyte transfusion may confer the same benefit. Whenever possible, excluding CMV-seropositive recipients is also desirable.[159–161, 364]

Chemoprophylaxis

Chemoprophylaxis with low-dose adenine arabinoside or acyclovir was found ineffective in prevention of CMV pneumonia following bone marrow transplantation.[365]

Immunoprophylaxis

Passive immunoprophylaxis with either plasma or globulin has been found to be effective in preventing or modifying the manifestation of primary CMV infection in bone marrow transplant recipients. The optimal antibody regimen has yet to be determined. Passive immunoprophylaxis with CMV hyperimmune globulin should be effective in all seronegative patients at the risk of primary infection. However, more clinical trials are needed to study the population at risk. Intravenous immunoglobulin can prevent CMV infection and interstitial pneumonia in seronegative bone marrow recipients.

Leukocyte interferon, given at the time of renal transplantation and regularly thereafter for 14 weeks, did not prevent CMV infection. However, CMV disease was significantly reduced in the interferon group as compared to placebo recipients. In contrast to renal transplant recipients, the prophylactic effect of interferon in bone marrow transplant recipients is not encouraging.[218, 366, 367]

Vaccination

Two experimental models of CMV in other species have been used to explore the efficacy of CMV vaccines. Live and inactivated vaccines in the mouse and guinea pig have been prepared and used with respective species viruses. Protection against wild strains of CMV has been shown in these species. However, because of species specificity, these results have limited value when applied to CMV vaccine in humans. In recent years, two different strains of live human CMV vaccine have been prepared and tested in normal volunteers, prospective renal allograft recipients, and medical personnel. Both vaccines are immunogenic and have not been associated with illness or virus excretion in the urine or throat of vaccinees.[368–371]

A live tissue culture–adapted CMV vaccine was prepared and tested in CMV-susceptible normal volunteers by Elek and Stern in England in 1974.[368] While the vaccine was not effective following oral or intradermal inoculation, it induced CF and neutralizing antibodies following subcutaneous inoculation. Side effects were minimal, and a delayed hypersensitivity reaction was observed at the site of injection. Immunogenicity of this vaccine has been confirmed by others.

Plotkin and coworkers developed a live, attenuated vaccine using a virus strain (Towne–125) that was isolated from a child with congenital CMV infection.[369] It has minimal side effects and stimulates the production of IgM and antibody to early antigen. It also causes a booster response in CMV-seropositive individuals. In healthy volunteers, the Towne virus vaccine results in asymptomatic infection without evidence of virus excretion. This infection produces humoral and cellular immunity. Following subcutaneous administration, the vaccine stimulates the synthesis of neutralizing antibody and results in a lymphocyte stimulation response to CMV antigens. It has minimal local side effects (erythema and induration). In contrast to natural infection, the vaccine does not appear to produce latency and does not cause a reversal in the OKT8/OKT4 reactivity ratio. The safety and immunogenicity of the vaccine has also been shown in women of childbearing age.[372–374] Vaccine studies in CMV-seronegative renal transplant candidates with Towne–125 strain indicated that the vaccine is safe and immunogenic in this population. The efficacy of the vaccine in prevention of CMV disease in renal allograft recipients has been demonstrated. Vaccine trials in the United States have shown that most vaccinees developed cellular and humoral immune responses to CMV. In transplant candidates, this response was lower than that of healthy volunteers. Furthermore, CMV infection occurred in most of the seronegative vaccine-treated or placebo-treated patients who received kidneys from seropositive donors, but the illnesses were less severe in the vaccinees than those in similarly exposed placebo-treated patients. Vaccine-treated patients who received kidneys from seronegative donors never excreted any virus, suggesting that the vaccine virus was not reactivated following transplantation, despite immunosuppressive therapy.[372–374] The notion that vaccination of bone marrow donors may prevent CMV disease in the recipients awaits further investigation.

Two major problems are associated with CMV vaccination. First, unlike measles virus and poliovirus, once CMV is administered, the virus persists in the host in a potentially infectious state (latency) and may become reactivated later. Second, the oncogenic potential of CMV is still unsettled and must be weighed against the benefit obtained from vaccination. It is clear that more work needs to be done to demonstrate the efficacy and safety of CMV vaccine in two important target groups: young women before pregnancy and recipients of organ allografts before transplantation.

TREATMENT

The result of treatment of CMV infection with various agents has been disappointing. Currently, there is no effective treatment for CMV infection. Various chemical compounds that are effective in the treatment of certain other herpesviruses such as idoxuridine, floxuridine, cytosine arabinoside, adenine arabinoside, and acyclovir have been used in the treatment of various patients with CMV disease. Most of the aforementioned drugs are inhibitors of DNA synthesis and are effective against CMV in vitro, but their clinical effect is minimal at best. Ganciclovir ([9 (dihydroxy-2-propoxymethyl)-guanine]), a new antiviral agent which is 10 to 100 times more potent an inhibitor of CMV replication in vitro than acyclovir, has been used in various immunosuppressed CMV-infected patients with some promising results. However, further investigation is needed to prove its efficacy. These agents alone or in combination have been used in isolated cases or clinical trials in the treatment of various CMV syndromes such as congenital and neonatal infection, pneumonia, retinitis, encephalitis, disseminated infection, and mononucleosis, both in immunocompromised and normal hosts, with minimal or no effect.[367, 375] Rifampin has also been shown to inhibit the replication of CMV in vitro. The mode of action is presumed to be blocking a stage in the production of messenger RNA. The effects appear to be transient. No clinical trial has been conducted.[376] CMV is relatively resistant to the effect of interferon, and this resistance may be due to cell association of the virus. Human alpha interferon, transfer factor, and globulin have also been used to treat CMV infection.[367] In most studies these agents have been shown to decrease the titer of the virus in urine or tissue significantly, but have no beneficial clinical effect and do not prevent death.

Immunoglobulins and CMV-specific hyperimmune globulin have been used in the treatment of CMV disease in infants and in bone marrow and renal allograft recipients with promising results.[367]

CONCLUDING REMARKS

During the past four decades, much new information has been accumulated on CMV infection. The bulk of the knowledge is on the virus structure, biology, epidemiology, and clinical features of the infection in normal and immunocompromised hosts and on the long-term sequelae of congenital infection. Areas of immunity, latency, pathogenesis, and oncogenicity are under active investigation, but the progress has been relatively slow owing to the lack of an experimental animal model and the host specificity of the virus. Much remains to be done in the areas of prophylaxis and treatment of CMV infection. Efficacy of experimental vaccine has been shown but more studies are needed to establish its protective effect in various target populations. No available therapeutic agent has been found to be effective in the treatment of CMV infection at the present time.

REFERENCES

1. Smith MG: Propagation in tissue cultures of cytopathogenic virus from human salivary gland virus (SGV) disease. *Proc Soc Exp Biol Med* 1956; 92:424–430.
2. Rowe WP, Hartley JW, Waterman S, et al: Cytopathogenic agent resembling human salivary gland virus recovered from tissue cultures of human adenoids. *Proc Soc Exp Biol Med* 1956; 92:418–424.
3. Weller TH, Macaulay JC, Craig JM, et al: Isolation of intranuclear inclusion producing agents from infants with illnesses resembling cytomegalic inclusion disease. *Proc Soc Exp Biol Med* 1957; 94:4–12.
4. Weller TH, Hanshaw JB, Scott DE: Serologic differentiation of viruses responsible for cytomegalic inclusion disease. *Virology* 1960; 12:130–132.
5. Weller TH, Cytomegaloviruses: The difficult years. *J Infect Dis* 1970; 122:532–539.
6. Goodpasture EW, Talbot FB: Concerning the nature of "protozoan-like" cells in certain lesions of infancy. *Am J Dis Child* 1921; 21:415–425.
7. Jesionek A, Kiolemenoglou B: Ueber einen Befund von protozoenartigen Gebilden in den Organen eines hereditärluetischen Fötus. *Munchen Med Wochensch* 1904; 51:1905–1908.
8. Ribbert H: Ueber protozoenartige Zellen in der Nieren eines syphilitischen Neugeborenen und in der Parotis von Kindern. *Centralbl Allg Pathologie Anat* 1904; 15:945–948.
9. Goodpasture EW: Cellular inclusions and the etiology of virus diseases. *Arch Pathol* 1929; 7:114–132.
10. Klemola E, Kaariainer L: Cytomegalovirus as a possible cause of a disease resembling infectious mononucleosis. *Br Med J* 1965; 2:1099–1102.
11. Fenner F: The classification and nomenclature of viruses: Summary of results of meetings of the international committee on taxonomy of viruses in Madrid September, 1975. *Virology* 1976; 71:371–378.
12. Roizman B: in Roizman B (ed): *The Herpesviruses* Plenum, New York, 1982, vol 1, pp 1–23.
13. Salahuddin SZ, Blashi DV, Markham PD, et al: Isolation of a new virus HBLV, in patients with lymphoproliferative disorders. *Science* 1986; 234:596–601.
14. Reynolds DW, Stagno S, Alford CA: Laboratory diagnosis of cytomegalovirus infections, in Lennette EH, Schmidt NJ (eds): *Diagnostic procedures for Viral Rickettsial and Chlamydial Infections*, ed 5. Washington DC, American Public Health Association, 1979, pp 399–439.
15. Weller TH: The cytomegaloviruses: Ubiquitous agents with protean clinical minifestations. *N Engl J Med* 1971; 285:203–214, 267–274.
16. Krichner H: Immunobiology of infections with human cytomegalovirus. *Adv Cancer Res* 1983; 40:31–105.
17. Griffith PD, Grundy JE: Molecular biology and immunology of cytomegalovirus. *Biochem J* 1987; 24:313–324.
18. Ruebner BH, Hirano T, Slusser RJ, et al: Human cytomegalovirus infections: Electron microscopic and histochemical changes in cultures of human fibroblasts. *Am J Pathol* 1965; 46:477–496.
19. Somogyi T, Colimon R, Michelson S: An illustrated guide to the structure of human cytomegalovirus genome and a review of transcription data. *Prog Med Virol* 1986; 33:99–133.
20. Pereira L, Hoffman M, Tatusuno M, et al: Polymorphism of human cytomegalovirus glycoproteins: characterization by monoclonal antibodies. *Virology* 1984; 139:73–86.
21. Furlini G, Gonezol E, Szokau G, et al: Monoclonal antibodies directed to two groups of viral proteins neutralize human cytomegalovirus in vitro. *Hybridoma* 1987; 6:321–326.
22. Feldman RA: Cytomegaloviruses in stored urine specimens: A quantitative study. *J Pediatr* 1968; 73:611–614.
23. Friis H, Andersen HK: Rate of inactivation of cytomegalovirus in raw banked milk during storage at −20°C and pasteurization. *Br Med J* 1982; 285:1604–1605.
24. Faix RG: Survival of cytomegalovirus on environmental surfaces. *J Pediatr* 1985; 106:649–652.
25. Furukawa T, Fiorette A, Plotkin S: Growth characteristics of cytomegalovirus in human fibroblasts with demonstration of protein synthesis early in viral replication. *J Virol* 1973; 11:991–997.
26. Smith JD, De Harven E: Herpes simplex virus and human cytomegalovirus replication in WI-38 cells. I. Sequence of viral replication. *J Virol* 1973; 12:919–930.
27. Smith JD, De Harven E: Herpes simplex virus and human cytomegalovirus replication in WI-38 cells. II. An ultrastructural study of viral penetration. *J Virol* 1974; 14:945–956.
28. Kanich RE, Craighead JE: Human cytomegalovirus infection of cultured fibroblasts. I. Cytopathologic effects induced by an adapted and a wild strain. *Lab Invest* 1972; 27:263–271.
29. Kanich RE, Craighead JE: Human cytomegalovirus infection of cultured fibroblasts II. Viral replicative sequence of a wild and an adapted strain. *Lab Invest* 1972; 273–282.
30. Knowles WA: *In vitro* cultivation of human cytomegalovirus in thyroid epithelial cells. *Arch Virol* 1976; 50:119–124.
31. Irmiere A, Gibson W: Isolation and characterization of non infectious virion-like particles released from cells infected with human strains of cytomegalovirus. *Virology* 1983; 130:118–133.
32. St Joer S, Rapp F: Cytomegalovirus replication in cells pretreated with 5-iodo-2-deoxyuridine. *J Virol* 1973; 11:986–990.
33. Chiang WT, Wentworth BB, Alexander ER: The use of an immunofluorescence technique for the determination of antibodies to cytomegalovirus strains in human sera. *J Immunol* 1970; 104:992–999.
34. Albrecht T, Weller TH: Heterogenous morphologic features of plaques induced by five strains of human cytomegalovirus. *Am J Clin Pathol* 1980; 648–654.
35. Diosi P, Babusceac L, David C: Distinctive cytopathic properties of cytomegalovirus recovered from the female genital tract. *Am J Clin Pathol* 1973; 59:192–195.
36. Kilpatrick BA, Huang E, Pagano JS: Analysis of cytomegalovirus genomes with restriction endonucleases, HinD III and EcoR-1. *J Virol* 1976; 18:1095–1105.
37. Dreesman GR, Benyesh-Melnick M: Spectrum of human cytomegalovirus complement-fixing antigens. *J Immunol* 1967; 99:1106–1114.
38. Cremer NE, Schmidt NJ, Jensen F, et al: Complement-fixing antibody in human sera reactive with viral and soluble antigens of cytomegalovirus. *J Clin Microbiol* 1975; 1:262–267.
39. Kim KA, Moon HM, Spaienza VJ, et al: Complement-fixing antigen of human cytomegalovirus. *J Infect Dis* 1977; 135:281–288.
40. The TH, Klein G, Langehuysen MMAC: Antibody reactions to virus-specific early antigens (EA) in patients with cytomegalovirus (CMV) infection. *Clin Exp Immunol* 1974; 16:1–12.
41. Geder L: Evidence for early nuclear antigens in cytomegalovirus-infected cells. *J Gen Virol* 1976; 32:315–319.
42. Giraldo G, Beth E, Hammerling U, et al: Detection of early antigens in nuclei of cells infected with cytomegalovirus or herpes simplex virus type 1 and 2 by anti-complement immunofluorescence, and use of a blocking assay to demonstrate their specificity. *Int J Cancer* 1977; 19:107–116.
43. Spencer ES, Andersen HK: The development of immunofluorescent antibodies as compared with complement-fixing and virus neutralizing antibodies in human cytomegalovirus infection. *Scand J Infect Dis* 1972; 4:109–112.
44. Faix RG: Cytomegalovirus antigenic heterogenicity can cause false-negative results in indirect hemagglutination and complement fixation antibody assay. *J Clin Microbiol* 1985; 22:768–771.
45. Volpi A, Britt WJ: Serological heterogenicity of CMV isolates with a monoclonal antibody. *J Infect Dis* 1985; 152:648–649.
46. Balachandraw N, Oba DE, Hutt-Fletcher LM: Antigenic cross-reaction among herpes simplex virus types 1 and 2, Epstein-Barr virus and cytomegalovirus. *J Virol* 1987; 61:1125–1135.

47. Beckwith DC, Halstead DC, Alpaugh K, et al: Comparison of latex agglutination test with five other methods for detecting the presence of antibody against cytomegalovirus. *J Clin Microbiol* 1985; 21:328–331.
48. Brandt JA, Kettering JD, Lewis JE: Immunity to human cytomegalovirus measured and compared by complement fixation, indirect fluorescent antibody, indirect hemagglutination, and enzyme linked immunosorbent assays. *J Clin Microbiol* 1984; 19:147–152.
49. Keller R, Peitchel R, Goldman JN, et al: An IgG-Fc receptor induced in cytomegalovirus-infected human fibroblasts. *J Immunol* 1976; 116:772–777.
50. Hanshaw JB, Steinfeld HF, White CJ: Fluorescent-antibody test for cytomegalovirus macroglobulin. *N Engl J Med* 1968; 279:566–570.
51. Stagno S, Tinker MK, Elrod C, et al: Immunoglobulin M antibodies detected by enzyme-linked immunosorbent assay and radio-immunoassay in the diagnosis of cytomegalovirus infections in pregnant women and newborn infant. *J Clin Microbiol* 1985; 21:930–935.
52. Wreghit TG, Hicks J, Gray JJ, et al: Development of a competitive enzyme-linked immunosorbent assay for detecting cytomegalovirus antibody. *J Med Virol* 1986; 18:119–129.
53. Pass RF, Griffiths PD, August AM: Antibody response to cytomegalovirus after renal transplantation: Comparison of patients with primary and recurrent infection. *J Infect Dis* 1983; 147:40–46.
54. Rasmussen L, Kelsall D, Nelson R, et al: Virus specific IgG and IgM antibodies in normal and immunocompromised subjects infected with cytomegalovirus. *J Infect Dis* 1982; 145:191–199.
55. Grena G, Cereda PM, Cattaneo E, et al: Immunoglobulin G to virus specific early antigens in congenital, primary and reactivated human cytomegalovirus infection. *Immunology* 1978; 22:833–834.
56. Chiba S, Motokawa T, Tamura T, et al: Seroconversion of virus specific pre-early nuclear antigens in infants with primary cytomegalovirus infection. *Infect Immun* 1980; 30:135–139.
57. Garnett HM: Fusion of cytomegalovirus infected fibroblasts to form multinucleated giant cells. *J Med Virol* 1979; 3:271–274.
58. Booth JC, Beesley JE, Stern M: Syncytium formation caused by human CMV in human embryonic lung fibroblasts. *Arch Virol* 1978; 57:143–152.
59. Plummer G: Cytomegaloviruses of man and animals. *Prog Med Virol* 1973; 15:92–125.
60. Smith MG: The salivary gland viruses of man and animals. (cytomegalic inclusion disease) *Prog Med Virol* 1959; 2:171–202.
61. Nigida SM Jr, Falk LA, Wolfe LG, et al: Experimental infection of marmosets with a cytomegalovirus of human origin. *J Infect Dis* 1975; 132:582–586.
62. Bia FZ, Griffiths BP, Fong CKY, et al: Cytomegaloviral infections in the guinea pig: Experimental models for human diseases. *Rev Infect Dis* 1983; 5:177–195.
63. Jordan MC: Latent infection and the elusive cytomegalovirus. *Rev Infect Dis* 1983; 5:205–215.
64. Hudson JB: The murine cytomegalovirus as a model for the study of viral pathogenesis and persistent infections. *Arch Virol* 1979; 62:1–29.
65. Black PH, Hartley JW, Rowe WP: Isolation of a cytomegalovirus from African green monkey. *Proc Soc Exp Biol Med* 1963; 112:601–605.
66. Krech U, Jung M: The development of neutralizing antibodies in guinea pigs following immunization with human cytomegalovirus. *Arch Gesamte Virusforsch* 1969; 28:248–250.
67. Martos LM, Ablashi DV, Gilden RV, et al: Preparation of immune rabbit sera with neutralizing activity against human cytomegalovirus and varicella zoster virus. *J Gen Virol* 1970; 7:169–171.
68. Fioretti A, Furukawa T, Santoli D, et al: Nonproductive infection of guinea pig cells with human cytomegalovirus. *J Virol* 1973; 11:998–1003.
69. Haines HG, Von Essen R, Benyesh-Melnick M: Preparation of specific antisera to cytomegalovirus in goats. *Soc Exp Biol Med* 1971; 138:846–849.
70. Wentworth BB, Alexander ER: Seroepidemiology of infections due to members of the herpesvirus groups. *Am J Epidemiol* 1971; 94:496–507.
71. Stern H, Alexander ER: The incidence of infection with cytomegalovirus in a normal population: A serological study in greater London. *J Hyg Camb* 1965; 63:79–87.
72. Sinha DK, Pauls PF: Cytomegalovirus complement fixation antibody response in Eskimo families. *Pediatrics* 1971; 48:157.
73. Lang DJ, Garruto RM, Gajdusek DC: Early acquisition of cytomegalovirus and Epstein-Barr virus antibody in several isolated Melanesian populations. *Am J Epidemiol* 1977; 105:480–487.
74. Krech U: Complement-fixing antibodies against cytomegalovirus in different parts of the world. *Bull WHO* 1973; 49:103–106.
75. Krech U, Tobin J: A collaborative study of cytomegalovirus antibodies in mothers and young children in 19 countries. *Bull WHO* 1981; 59:605–610.
76. Davis LE, Stewart JA, Garvin S: Cytomegalovirus infection: A seroepidemiologic comparison of nuns and women from a venereal disease clinic. *Am J Epidemiol* 1975; 102:327–330.
77. Larke RPB, Wjeatley E, Saigal S, et al: Congenital cytomegalovirus infection in an urban Canadian community. *J Infect Dis* 1980; 162:641–653.
77a. Melish ME, Hanshaw JB: Congenital cytomegalovirus infection. Developmental progress of infants detected by routine screening. *Am J Dis Child* 1973; 126:190–194.
77b. Andersen HB, Bronstrom K, Hansen KB, et al: A prospective study on the incidence and significance of congenital cytomegalovirus infection. *Acta Paediatr Scand* 1979; 68:329–336.
78. Rowe WP, Hartleh JW, Cramblett MG, et al: Detection of human salivary gland virus in the mouth and urine of children. *Am J Hyg* 1958; 67:57–65.
79. Stern H: Isolation of cytomegalovirus and clinical manifestations of infection at different ages. *Br Med J* 1968; 1:665–669.
80. Levinsohn EM, Foy HM, Kenny GE, et al: Isolation of cytomegalovirus from a cohort of 100 infants throughout the first year of life. *Proc Soc Exp Biol Med* 1969; 32:957–962.
81. Olson LC, Ketusinha R, Mansuwan P: Respiratory tract excretion of cytomegalovirus in Thai children. *J Pediatr* 1970; 77:499–504.
82. Leinikki R, Heinonen K, Pettay O: Incidence of cytomegalovirus infections in early childhool. *Scand J Infect Dis* 1972; 4:1–5.
83. Li F, Hanshaw JB: Cytomegalovirus among migrant children. *Am J Epidemiol* 1967; 88:137–141.
84. Knox GE, Pass RF, Reynolds DW, et al: Comparative prevalence of subclinical cytomegalovirus and herpes simplex virus infections in the genital and urinary tracts of low-income, urban women. *J Infect Dis* 1979; 140:419–422.
85. Drew WL, Mintz L, Sands M, et al: Cytomegalovirus infection in homosexual men. *J Infect Dis* 1981; 143:188–192.
86. Betts RF: Cytomegalovirus infection in transplant patients. *Prog Med Virol* 1982; 28:44–64.
87. Knowles WA, Gardner SD, Fox H: A comparison of cervical cytomegalovirus (CMV) excretion in gynecological patients and post partum women. *Arch Virol* 1982; 73:25–31.
88. Stagno S, Reynolds D, Tsiantos A, et al: Cervical cytomegalovirus excretion in pregnant and nonpregnant women: Suppression in early gestation. *J Infect Dis* 1975; 131:522–527.
89. Jordon MC, Rousseau WE, Nobel GR, et al: Association of cervical cytomegalovirus with venereal disease. *N Engl J Med* 1973; 288:932–934.
90. Chandler SH, Alexander ER, Holmes KK: Epidemiology of cytomegaloviral infection in a heterogenous population of pregnant women. *J Infect Dis* 1985; 152:249–256.
91. Numazaki Y, Yano N, Marizuka T, et al: Primary infection with human cytomegalovirus: Virus isolation from healthy infants and pregnant women. *Am J Epidemiol* 1970; 91:410–417.
92. Alexander ER: Maternal and neonatal infection with cytomega-

lovirus in Taiwan. *Pediatr Res* 1980; 87:308–314.

93. Lang DJ, Kummer JF, Hartley DP: Cytomegalovirus in semen: Persistence and demonstration in extracellular fluids. *N Engl J Med* 1974; 291:121–123.

94. Lang DJ, Kummer JF: Cytomegalovirus in semen: Observations in selected populations. *J Infect Dis* 1975; 132:472–473.

95. Embil JA, Manuel FR, Garner JB, et al: Cytomegalovirus in the semen. *Can Med Assoc J* 1982; 126:391–392.

96. Rinaldo CR, Kingsley LA, Lyter DW, et al: Excretion of cytomegalovirus in semen associated with HTLV-III seropositivity in asymptomatic homosexual men. *J Med Virol* 1986; 20:17–22.

97. Hayes K, Danks DM, Gibas H, et al: Cytomegalovirus in human milk. *N Engl J Med* 1972; 287:177–178.

98. Stagno S, Reynolds DW, Pass RF et al: Breast milk and the risk of cytomegalovirus infection. *N Engl J Med* 1980; 302:1073–1076.

99. Dowrsky M, Yow M, Stagno S, et al: Cytomegalovirus infection of breast milk and transmission in infancy. *Pediatrics* 1983; 72:295–299.

100. Ahlfors K, Ivarsson SA: Cytomegalovirus in breast milk of Swedish milk donors. *Scand J Infect Dis* 1985; 17:11–13.

101. Dowrsky M, Stagno S, Pass RF, et al: Persistence of cytomegalovirus in human milk after storage. *J Pediatr* 1982; 101:440–443.

102. Jordan MC, Rousseau WE, Stewart JA, et al: Spontaneous cytomegalovirus mononucleosis; Clinical and laboratory observation in nine cases. *Ann Intern Med* 1973; 79:153–160.

103. Cox F, Hughes WT: Fecal excretion of cytomegalovirus in disseminated cytomegalic inclusion disease. *J Infect Dis* 1974; 129:732–736.

104. Garau J, Kabins S, DeNosaqus S, et al: Spontaneous cytomegalovirus mononucleosis with conjunctivitis. *Arch Intern Med* 1977; 137:1631–1632.

105. Cox F, Meyer D, Hughes DT: Cytomegalovirus in tears from patients with normal eyes and with acute cytomegalovirus chorioretinitis. *Arch Ophthalmol* 1975; 80:817–824.

106. Smith TF, Holley KE, Keys TR, et al: Cytomegalovirus studies of autopsy tissue.I–Virus isolation. *Am J Clin Pathol* 1975; 63:854–858.

107. Naraqi S, Jackson GG, Jonasson OM, et al: Search for latent cytomegalovirus in renal allografts. *Infect Immun* 1978; 19:699–703.

108. Farber S, Wolback SB: Intranuclear and cytoplasmic inclusions (''protozoan-like bodies'') in the salivary glands and other organs of infants. *Am J Pathol* 1932; 8:123–135.

109. Macasaet FF, Holley KF, Smith TF, et al: Cytomegalovirus studies of autopsy tissue. II—Incidence of inclusion bodies and related pathologic data. *Am J Clin Pathol* 1975; 63:859–865.

110. Monif GRG, Egan EA, Held B: The correlation of maternal cytomegalovirus infection during varying stages in gestation with neonatal involvement. *J Pediatr* 1972; 80:17–20.

111. Stern H, Tucker SM: Prospective study of cytomegalovirus infection in pregnancy. *Br Med J* 1973; 2:268–270.

112. Stagno S, Reynolds DW, Huang E, et al: Congenital cytomegalovirus infection: Occurrence in an immune population. *N Engl J Med* 1977; 296:1254–1258.

113. Nankervis GA, Kumar ML, Cox I, et al: A prospective study of maternal cytomegalovirus infection and its effect on the fetus. *Am J Obstet Gynecol* 1984; 149:435–450.

114. Stagno S, Pass RF, Dworsky ME, et al: The relative importance of primary and recurrent maternal infection. *N Engl J Med* 1982; 306:945–949.

115. Montgomery R, Youngblood L, Medearis DN: Recovery of cytomegalovirus from the cervix in pregnancy. *Pediatrics* 1972; 49:524–531.

116. Griffiths PD, Baboonian C: A prospective study of primary cytomegalovirus infection during pregnancy: final report. *Br J Obstet Gynecol* 1984; 94:307–315.

117. Leinikki P, Cranstrom M-L, Santavuori P: Epidemiology of cytomegalovirus infections during pregnancy and infancy: A prospective study. *Scand J Infect Dis* 1978; 10:165–171.

118. Grant S, Edmond E, Syme J: A prospective study of cytomegalovirus infection in pregnancy: Laboratory evidence of congenital infection following maternal primary and reactivated infection. *J Infect* 1981; 3:24–31.

119. Reynolds DW, Huang E, Thames SD: Cytomegalovirus excretion and perinatal infection. *N Engl J Med* 1973; 289:1–5.

120. Peckham CS, Chin KS, Coleman GC, et al: Cytomegalovirus infection in pregnancy: preliminary findings from a prospective study. *Lancet* 1983; 1:1352–1355.

121. Ahlfors K, Ivarsons A, Johnsson T, et al: Primary and secondary maternal cytomegalovirus infections and their relation to congenital infection. *Acta Paediatr Scand* 1982; 71:109–113.

122. Kumar ML, Nankervis GA, Cooper AR: Postnatally acquired cytomegalovirus infections in infants of CMV excreting mothers. *J Pediatr* 1984; 104:699–673.

123. Kamada M, Komori A, Chiba S, et al: A prospective study of congenital cytomegalovirus infection in Japan. *Scand J Infect Dis* 1983; 15:277–232.

124. MacDonald H, Tobin O'H: Congenital cytomegalovirus. A collaborative study of epidemiological, clinical and laboratory findings. *Dev Med Child Neurol* 1978; 20:471–472.

125. Kumar ML, Gold E, Jacob IB: Primary cytomegalovirus infection in adolescent pregnancy. *Pediatrics* 1984; 74:493–500.

126. Griffiths PD, Baboonian C: Intrauterine transmission of cytomegalovirus in women known to be immune before conception. *J Hyg Camb* 1984; 92:89–95.

126a. Schopfer K, Lauber E, Kreck U: Congenital cytomegalovirus infection in newborn infants of mothers infected before pregnancy. *Arch Dis Child* 1978; 53:536–539.

126b. Stern H, Hannington G, Booth J, et al: An early marker of fetal infection after primary cytomegalovirus infection in pregnancy. *Br Med J* 1986; 292:718–720.

127. Davis LE, Tweed GV, Stewart JA, et al: Cytomegalovirus mononucleosis in a first trimester pregnant female with transmission to the fetus. *Pediatrics* 1971; 48:200–206.

128. Shearer WT, Sohreiner RL, Marshal RE, et al: Cytomegalovirus infection in a newborn dizygous twin. *J Pediatr* 1972; 81:1161–1165.

129. Ahlfors K, Harris S, Ivarsson S, et al: Secondary maternal cytomegalovirus infection using symptomatic congenital infection. *N Engl J Med* 1981; 305:284.

130. Krech U, Konjajev Z, Jung M: Congenital cytomegalovirus infection in siblings from consecutive pregnancies. *Helv Paediatr Acta* 1971; 26:355–362.

131. Stagno S, Reynolds DW, Lakeman A, et al: Congenital cytomegalovirus infection: Consecutive occurrence due to viruses with similar antigenic compositions. *Pediatrics* 1973; 53:778–794.

132. Embil JA, Ozere RL, Haldane EV: Congenital cytomegalovirus infection in two siblings from consecutive pregnancies. *J Pediatr* 1970; 77:417–421.

133. Yeager AS, Martin HP, Stewart JA: Congenital CMV infection. Outcome for the subsequent siblings. *Clin Pediatr* 1977; 16:455–458.

134. Pass RF, Hutto C, Ricks R, et al: Increased rate of cytomegalovirus among parents of children attending day care centers. *N Engl J Med* 1986; 314:1414–1418.

135. Murph JR, Bale JF, Murray JC, et al: Cytomegalovirus transmission in a Midwest day care center: Possible relationship to child care practices. *J Pediatr* 1986; 109:35–39.

136. Pass RF, Hutto C: Group day care and cytomegalovirus infections of mothers and children. *Rev Infect Dis* 1986; 8:599–605.

137. Collier AC, Meyers JD, Cory L, et al: Cytomegalovirus infection in homosexual men: Relationship to sexual practices, antibody to human immunodeficiency and cell mediated immunity. *Am J Med* 1987; 82:593–601.

138. Coutinho RA, Dillen PW, Lent PA, et al: Infection with cytomegalovirus in homosexual men. *Br J Vener Dis* 1984; 60:249–252.

139. Drew WL, Mills J, Levy J, et al: Cytomegalovirus infection and abnormal T-lymphocyte subset ratios in homosexual men. *Ann Intern Med* 1985; 103:61–63.

140. Dannenmenier B, Alle W, Hoferner EW, et al: Incidence of antibodies to hepatitis B, herpes simplex and cytomegalovirus in prostitutes. *Zentralbl Bakteriol Mikrobiol Hyg (B)* 1985; 259:275–283.

141. Chandler SH, Holmes KK, Wentworth RB, et al: The epidemiology of cytomegaloviral infection in women attending a sexually transmitted disease clinic. *J Infect Dis* 1985; 152:597–605.

142. Willmott FE: CMV in female patients attending a VD clinic. *Br J Vener Dis* 1975; 51:278–280.

143. Quinnan GV, Masur H, Rook AH, et al: Herpesvirus infections in the acquired immune deficiency syndrome. *JAMA* 1984; 252:72–77.

144. Halbert SP, Kiefer DJ, Friedman–Kiew AE, et al: Antibody levels for cytomegalovirus, herpes simplex virus and rubella in patients with acquired immune deficiency syndrome. *J Clin Microbiol* 1986; 23:318–321.

145. Tegtmeier GE: Transfusion-transmitted cytomegalovirus infections: Significance and control. *Vox Sang* 1986; 5(suppl 1): 22–30.

146. Adler SP: Transfusion associated cytomegalovirus infection. *Rev Infect Dis* 1983; 5:977–993.

147. Preikasaitis FC, Grancet FC, Smith WK, et al: Transfusion acquired cytomegalovirus infection in cardiac surgery patients. *J Med Virol* 1985; 15:283–290.

148. Rinaldo CR, Black PH, Hisch MS: Interaction of cytomegalovirus with leukocytes from patients with mononucleosis due to cytomegalovirus. *J Infect Dis* 1977; 136:667–678.

149. Fiala M, Edmondson L, Guze LB: Simplified method for isolation of cytomegalovirus and demonstration of frequent viremia in renal transplant patients. *Proc Soc Exp Biol Med* 1973; 144:871–875.

150. Diosi P, Moldovan E, Tomescu N: Latent cytomegalovirus infection in blood donors. *Br Med J* 1969; 4:660–662.

151. Kane RC, Rousseau WE, Noble GR, et al: Cytomegalovirus infection in a volunteer blood donor population. *Infect Immun* 1975; ll:719–723.

152. Prince AM, Szmuness W, Millian SJ, et al: A serologic study of cytomegalovirus infections associated with blood transfusions. *N Engl J Med* 1969; 280:1311–1316.

153. Foster KM, Jack I: A prospective study of the role of cytomegalovirus in post–transfusion mononucleosis. *N Engl J Med* 1969; 280:1311–1316.

154. Winston DJH, Ho WG, Howel CL, et al: Cytomegalovirus infections associated with leukocyte transfusion. *Ann Intern Med* 1980; 93:671–675.

155. Wilhelm JA, Matter L, Schopfer K: The risk of transmitting cytomegalovirus to patients receiving blood transfusions. *J Infect Dis* 1986; 154:169–171.

156. Adler SP, Lawrence LT, Bagget J, et al: Prevention of transfusion-associated cytomegalovirus infection in very low-birth weight infants using frozen blood and donors seronegative for cytomegalovirus. *Transfusion* 1984; 24:333–335.

157. Yeager AS, Grumet FC, Hafleight EB, et al: Prevention of transfusion–acquired cytomegalovirus infections in newborn infants. *J Pediatr* 1981; 98:281–287.

158. Luban NLC, Williams AE, McDonald MG, et al: Low incidence of acquired cytomegalovirus infection in neonates transfused with washed red blood cells. *Am J Dis Child* 1987; 141:416–419.

159. Glenn J: Cytomegalovirus infections following renal transplantation. *Rev Infect Dis* 1981; 3:1151–1178.

160. Winston DJ, Gale RP, Meyer DV, et al: Infectious complications of human bone marrow transplantation. *Medicine* 1979; 58:1–31.

161. PreiKsaitis JK, Rosno R, Grumet C, et al: Infections due to herpesviruses in cardiac transplant recipients: Role of the donor

162. Fulginti VA, Scribner R, Groth CG, et al: Infections in recipients of liver homografts. *N Engl J Med* 1968; 279: 619–626.

163. Duvall CP, Casazza AR, Gromley PM, et al: Recovery of cytomegalovirus from adults with neoplastic disease. *Ann Intern Med* 1966; 64:531–541.

164. Dowling JN, Saslow AR, Armstrong JA, et al: Cytomegalovirus infection in patients receiving immunosuppressive therapy for rheumatologic disorders. *J Infect Dis* 1976; 133:399–408.

165. Hedley-Whyte ET, Craighead JE: Generalized cytomegalic inclusion disease after renal homotransplantation—Report of a case with isolation of virus. *N Engl J Med* 1965; 272:473–475.

166. Hill RB Jr, Rowlands DT, Rifkind D: Infectious pulmonary disease in patients receiving immunosuppressive therapy for organ transplantation. *N Engl J Med* 1964; 271:1021–1027.

167. Luby JPL, Brunett W, Hull AR: Relationship between cytomegalovirus and hepatic function abnormalities in the period after renal transplant. *J Infect Dis* 1974; 129:511–518.

168. Fiala M, Payne JE, Berne TV: Epidemiology of cytomegalovirus infection after transplantation and immunosuppression. *J Infect Dis* 1975; 132:421–433.

169. Naraqi S, Jackson GG, Jonasson OM, et al: Prospective study of prevalence, incidence and source of herpes virus infections in patients with renal allografts. *J Infect Dis* 1977; 136:531–540.

170. Chatterjee SN, Jordon GW: Prospective study of the prevalence and symptomatology of cytomegalovirus infection in renal transplant recipients. *Transplantation* 1979; 28:457–460.

171. Rubin RH, Cosimi AB, Tolkoff-Rubin NE, et al: Infectious diseases syndromes attributable to cytomegalovirus and their significance among renal transplant recipients. *Transplantation* 1977; 24:458–464.

172. Pass RF, Long WK, Whitley RJ, et al: Productive infection with cytomegalovirus and herpes simplex virus in renal transplant recipients: Role of source of kidney. *J Infect Dis* 1978; 137:556–563.

173. Ho M, Suwansirikul S, Dowling JN, et al: The transplanted kidney as a source of cytomegalovirus infection. *N Engl J Med* 1975; 223:1109–1112.

174. Betts RF, Freeman RD, Douglas RG, et al: Transmission of cytomegalovirus infection with renal allograft. *Kidney* 1975; 8:387–394.

175. Tolkoff-Rubin NE, Rubin RH, Keller EE, et al: Cytomegalovirus infection in dialysis patients and personnel. *Ann Intern Med* 1978; 89:625–628.

176. Kanich RE, Craighead JE: Cytomegalovirus infection and cytomegalic inclusion disease in renal homotransplant recipients. *Am J Med* 1966; 40:874–882.

177. Pass RF, Whitley RJ, Diethelm AG, et al: Cytomegalovirus infection in patients with renal transplants: Potentiation by antithymocyte globulin and an incompatible graft. *J Infect Dis* 1980; 142:9–17.

178. Lang DJ: Cytomegalovirus infection in organ transplantation and post transfusion: An hypothesis. *Arch Gesmate Virusforsch* 1972; 37:365–377.

179. May AG, Betts RF, Freeman RB, et al: An analysis of cytomegalovirus infection and HLA antigen matching on the outcome of renal transplantation. *Ann Surg* 1978; 187:110–117.

180. Noel DR, Witherspoon RP, Strobe R, et al: Does graft-versus-host disease influence the tempo of immunologic recovery after allogenic human marrow transplantation? An observation on 56 long-term survivors. *Blood* 1978; 51:1087–1105.

181. Peace RJ: Cytomegalic inclusion disease in adults: A complication of neoplastic disease of the hemopoietic and reticuloendothelial systems. *Am J Med* 1958; 24:48–56.

182. Chou S: Cytomegalovirus infection and reinfection transmitted by heart transplantation. *J Infect Dis* 1987; 155:1954–1956.

183. Chou S: Acquisition of donor strains of cytomegalovirus by renal transplant recipients. *N Engl J Med* 1986; 314:1418–1423.

184. Winston DJ, Huang ES, Miller MJ, et al: Molecular epidemiol-

ogy of cytomegalovirus infections associated with bone marrow transplantation. *Ann Intern Med* 1985; 102:16–20.

185. Pollard RB: Herpes simplex and cytomegalovirus infections in burned patients. Interscience Conference on Antimicrobiol Agents and Chemotherapy. Chicago, 1981. Abstract No. 236.

186. Naraqi S, Kagan RJ, Matsuda R, et al: Cytomegalovirus and herpes simplex infections following severe burn injury, abstracted. *Clin Res* 1982.

187. Huang ES, Alford CA, Reynolds DW, et al: Molecular epidemiology of cytomegalovirus infections in women and their infants. *N Engl J Med* 1980; 303:958–962.

188. Wilfert M, Huang ES, Stagno S: Restriction endonuclease analysis of cytomegalovirus deoxyribonucleic acid as an epidemiologic tool. *Pediatrics* 1982; 70:717–721.

189. Yow MD, Lakeman AD, Stagno S, et al: Use of restriction enzymes to investigate the source of a primary cytomegalovirus infection in a pediatric nurse. *Pediatrics* 1982; 70:713–716.

190. Suwansirikul S, Rao N, Dowling J, et al: Primary and secondary cytomegalovirus infection. *Arch Intern Med* 1977; 137:1026–1029.

191. Adeler SP: The molecular epidemiology of cytomegalovirus transmission among children attending a day care center. *J Infect Dis* 1985; 152:760–768.

192. Spector SA, Hirata KK, Newman TR: Identification of multiple cytomegalovirus strains in homosexual men with acquired immune deficiency syndrome. *J Infect Dis* 1984; 150:953–956.

193. McFarlane, ES, Koment RW: Use of restriction endonuclease digestion to analyse strains of human cytomegalovirus isolated concurrently from an immunocompetent heterosexual man. *J Infect Dis* 1986; 154:167–168.

194. Chandler SH, Handsfield HH, McDougal JK: Isolation of multiple strains of cytomegalovirus from women attending a clinic for sexually transmitted diseases. *J Infect Dis* 1987; 155:655–660.

195. Wright HR Jr, Kasten FH, McAllister RM: Human cytomegalovirus: Observations of intracellular lesion development as revealed by phase contrast, time-lapse cinematography. *Proc Soc Exp Biol Med* 1968; 127:1032–1036.

196. Smith MG, Vellios F: Inclusion disease or generalized salivary gland virus infection. *Arch Pathol* 1950; 50:862–884.

197. Ii K, Hizawa K, Katsuse R: Generalized cytomegalic inclusion disease presenting an infectious mononucleosis syndrome (so called cytomegalovirus mononucleosis) in a previously healthy adult: An autopsy study. *Acta Pathol Jpn* 1972; 22:723–737.

198. Wong TW, Warner NE: Cytomegalic inclusion disease in adults: Report of 14 cases with review of literature. *Arch Pathol* 1962; 74:403–422.

199. Lang DJ, Cheung KS, Schwartz JN, et al: Cytomegalovirus replication and the host immune response. *Yale J Biol Med* 1976; 49:45–58.

200. Sanford EJ, Geder L, Murasko D, et al: Longterm persistence of cytomegalovirus genome in cultured human cells of prostatic origin. *J Virol* 1975; 16:982–990.

201. Williams LL, Blakeslee Jun JR, Boldogh I, et al: Detection of cytomegalovirus genomes in human skin fibroblasts by DNA hybridization. *J Gen Virol* 1980; 51:435–438.

202. Joncas JH, Menezes J, Huang ES: Persistence of CMV genome in lymphoid cells after congenital infection. *Nature* 1975; 258:432–434.

203. Albrecht T, Rapp F: Malignant transformation of hamster embryo fibroblasts following exposure to ultraviolet-irradiated human cytomegalovirus. *Virology* 1973; 55:53–61.

204. Pagano JS: Diseases and mechanisms of persistent DNA virus infection: Latency and cellular transformation. *J Infect Dis* 1975; 132:209–223.

205. Furukawa T, Yoshimura N, Jean J, et al: Chronically persistent infection with human cytomegalovirus in human lymphoblasts. *J Infect Dis A* 1979; 139:211–214.

206. Garnett HM: Isolation of human CMV from peripheral blood T cells of renal transplant patients. *J Lab Clin Med* 1982; 99:92–97.

207. Cockly KD, Rapp F: Analysis of long-term human cytomegalovirus latency in vitro. *Intervirology* 1986; 26:129–193.

208. Shrier RD, Nelson JA, Oldstone MB: Detection of human cytomegalovirus in peripheral blood lymphocytes in a natural infection. *Science* 1985; 230:1048–1051.

209. Rice GPA, Schrier RO, Oldstone MBA: Cytomegalovirus infects human lymphocytes and monocytes: Virus expression is restricted to immediate-early gene products. *Proc Natl Acad Sci* 1984; 81:6134–6138.

210. Geder L, Lausch R, O'Neill F, et al: Oncogenic transformation of human embryo lung cells by human cytomegalovirus. *Science* 1976; 192:1134–1137.

211. Rapp F: Cytomegalovirus and carcinogenesis. *J Natl Cancer Inst* 1983; 72:783–787.

212. Spector DH, Spector SA: The oncogenic potential of human cytomegalovirus. *Prog Med Virol* 1984; 29:45–89.

213. Giraldo G, Beth E: The involvement of cytomegalovirus in acquired immune deficiency and Kaposi sarcoma. *Prog Allergy* 1986; 37:319–331.

214. Nelson JA, Fleckenstein B, John G, et al: Structure of the transforming region of human cytomegalovirus. *J Virol* 1984; 49:109–115.

215. Borysiewiez LK, Rogers B, Morris S, et al: Lysis of human cytomegalovirus infected fibroblasts by natural killer cells: Demonstration of an interferon-independent component requiring expression of early viral proteins and characterization of effector cells. *J Immunol* 1985; 134:2695–2701.

216. Rytel MW, Balay J: Cytomegalovirus and immunity in renal allograft recipients: Assessment of the competence of humoral immunity. *Infect Immun* 1976; 13:1633–1637.

217. Lopez C, Simmon RL, Park BH, et al: Cell-mediated and humoral immune responses of renal transplant recipients with cytomegalovirus infections. *Clin Exp Immunol* 1974; 16:565–573.

218. Winston DJ, Pollard RB, How G, et al: Cytomegalovirus immune plasma in bone marrow transplant recipients. *Ann Intern Med* 1982; 97:11–18.

219. Simmons RL, Matas AJ, Rattazzi LC, et al: Clinical characteristics of the lethal cytomegalovirus infection following renal transplantation. *Surgery* 1976; 82:537–570.

220. Ho M: The lymphocytes in infections with Epstein-Barr virus and cytomegalovirus. *J Infect Dis* 1981; 143:857–862.

221. Oill PA, Fiala M, Schofferman J, et al: Cytomegalovirus mononucleosis in a healthy adult: Association with hepatitis, secondary Epstein-Barr virus antibody response and immunosuppression. *Am J Med* 1977; 62:413–417.

222. Rinaldo CR, Jr, Carney WP, Richter BS, et al: Mechanisms of immunosuppression in cytomegaloviral mononucleosis. *J Infect Dis* 1980; 141:488–495.

223. DeWaele M, Thielemaus C, Camp BV: Immunoregulatory T cells in mononucleosis and toxoplasmosis. *N Engl J Med* 1981; 305:228.

224. Carney WP, Hirsch MS: Mechanisms of immunosuppression in cytomegalovirus mononucleosis. II. Virus-monocyte interactions. *J Infect Dis* 1980; 141:488–495.

225. Borysiewicz LK, Morris S, Page JD, et al: Human cytomegalovirus specific cytotoxic T lymphocytes: requirement for in vitro generation and specificity. *Eur J Immunol* 1983; 13:804–809.

226. Gehrez RC, Christianson WR, Linner KM, et al: Cytomegalovirus-specific humoral and cellular immune responses in human pregnancy. *J Infect Dis* 1981; 143:391–395.

227. Starr SE, Tolpin MD, Friedman HM, et al: Impaired cellular immunity to cytomegalovirus in congenitally infected children and their mothers. *J Infect Dis* 1979; 140:500–505.

228. Faix RG, Zewig SE, Kummer J, et al: Cytomegalovirus-specific cell-mediated immunity during pregnancy in lower socioeconomic class adolescent. *J Infect Dis* 1983; 148:621–629.

229. Gehrz RC, Linner KM, Christianson WR, et al: Cytomegalovirus infection in infancy: Virological and immunological studies. *Clin Exp Immunol* 1982; 47:27–33.

230. Tanaka R, Tanaka A, Oizumi Y, et al: Virus excretion and cell-mediated immunity during cytomegalovirus infection among

healthy infants and children. *J Med Virol* 1986; 18:21–27.

231. Pass RF, Reynolds DW, Whelchel JD, et al: Impaired lymphocyte transformation response to cytomegalovirus and phytohemagglutinin in recipients of renal transplants: Association with antithymocyte globulin. *J Infect Dis* 1981; 143:259–265.

232. Meyers JD, Flournoy N, Thomas ED: Cytomegalovirus infection and specific cell-mediated immunity after marrow transplant. *J Infect Dis* 1980; 142:816–824.

233. Quinnan GV, Kirmani N, Rook AH, et al: Cytotoxic T cells in cytomegalovirus infection. *N Engl J Med* 1981; 307:6–13.

234. Pollard RB, Arvin AM, Gabert P, et al: Specific cell–mediated immunity and infection herpes viruses in cardiac transplant recipients. *Am J Med* 1982; 73:679–687.

235. Metselaar HJ, Rothbarth PH, Wenting GJ, et al: Mononuclear subsets during cytomegalovirus disease in renal transplant recipients treated with cyclosporine and rabbit antithymocyte globulin. *J Med Virol* 1986; 19:95–100.

236. Chatterjee SN, Fiala M, Weiner J, et al: Primary cytomegalovirus and opportunistic infections: Incidence in renal transplant recipients. *JAMA* 1978; 240:2446–2449.

237. Rand RH, Pollard RB, Merigan TC: Increased pulmonary superinfections in cardiac transplant patients undergoing primary cytomegalovirus infection. *N Engl J Med* 1978; 298:951–953.

238. Grundy JE, Super M, Griffiths PD: Reinfection of a seropositive allograft recipient by cytomegalovirus from donor kidney. *Lancet* 1986; 1:159–160.

239. Drew WL, Mills J, Levy J, et al: Cytomegalovirus infection and abnormal T lymphocyte subset ratios in homosexual men. *Ann Intern Med* 1985; 103:61–63.

240. Wager O, Rasanen JA, Hagman A, et al: Mixed cryoimmunoglobulinaemia in infectious mononucleosis and cytomegalovirus mononucleosis. *Int Arch Allergy Appl Immunol* 1968; 34:345–361.

241. Kantor GI, Goldberg LS, Johnson BL, et al: Immunological abnormalities induced by postperfusion cytomegalovirus infection. *Ann Intern Med* 1970; 73:553–558.

242. Stagno S, Volanakis JE, Reynolds DW, et al: Immune complexes in congenital and natal cytomegalovirus infections of man. *J Clin Invest* 1977; 60:838–845.

243. Vodopick H, Chaskes SJ, Solomon A, et al: Transient monoclonal gammopathy associated with cytomegalovirus infection. *Blood* 1974; 44:189–195.

244. Hutt–Fletcher LM, Balachandran N, Elkins MH: B cells activation by cytomegalovirus. *J Exp Med* 1983; 158:2171–2176.

245. Chretien JH, McGinniss CG, Muller A: Venereal causes of cytomegalovirus mononucleosis. *JAMA* 1977; 238:1644–1645.

246. Handsfield HH, Chandles SH, Caina VA, et al: Cytomegalovirus infection in sex partners: Evidence of sexual transmission. *J Infect Dis* 1985; 151:344–348.

247. Rosenstein DK, Navarrete-Reyna A: Cytomegalic inclusion disease: Observation of the characteristic inclusion bodies in the placenta. *Am J Obstet Gynecol* 1964; 89:220–224.

248. Monif GRG, Dische RM: Viral placentitis in congenital cytomegalovirus infection. *Am J Clin Pathol* 1972; 58:445–449.

249. Griffiths PD, Stagno S, Reynolds DW: A longitudinal study of the serological and virological status of 18 women infected with cytomegalovirus. *Arch Virol* 1978; 58:111–118.

250. King-Lewis PA, Gardner SD: Congenital cytomegalic inclusion disease following intrauterine transfusion. *Br Med J* 1969; 2:603–605.

251. Lang DF, Hanshaw JB: Cytomegalovirus infection and the postperfusion syndrome: Recognition of primary infections in four patients. *N Engl J Med* 1969; 280:1145–1149.

252. Armstrong D, Mathew E, Steger L: Post-transfusion cytomegaloviremia and persistence of cytomegalovirus in blood. *Infect Immun* 1971; 3:159–163.

253. Demmler GJ, Yow MD, Spector SN, et al: Nosocomial infections within two hospitals caring for infants and children. *J Infect Dis* 1987; 156:9–16.

254. Yeager AS: Longitudinal, serological study of cytomegalovirus infections in nurses and in personnel without patient contact. *J Clin Microbiol* 1975; 2:448–452.

255. Spector SA, Schmid K, Ticknor W, et al: Cytomegaloviruria in older infants in intensive care nurseries. *J Pediatr* 1979; 95:444–446.

256. Hutto C, Little EA, Ricks R, et al: Isolation of cytomegalovirus from toys and hands in a day care center. *J Infect Dis* 1986; 154:527–530.

257. Adler SP: Molecular epidemiology of cytomegalovirus: evidence of viral transmission to parents from children infected at a day care center. *Pediatr Infect Dis* 1986; 5:315–318.

258. Dowrsky ME, Welch K, Cassday G, et al: Occupational risk for primary cytomegalovirus infection among pediatric health care workers. *N Engl J Med* 1983; 309:950–953.

259. Weller TH, Hanshaw JB: Virologic and clinical observations on cytomegalic inclusion disease. *N Engl J Med* 1962; 266:1233–1244.

260. Medearis DN: Observations concerning human cytomegalovirus infection and disease. *Bull Johns Hopkins Hosp* 1964; 114:181–211.

261. McCracken GH, Shinefield HR, Cobb K, et al: Congenital cytomegalic inclusion disease. *Am J Dis Child* 1969; 117:522–539.

262. Berenberg W, Nankervis G: Long-term follow-up of cytomegalic inclusion disease of infancy. *Pediatrics* 1970; 46:403–410.

263. Pass RF, Stagno S, Myers GJ, et al: Outcome of symptomatic congenital cytomegalovirus infections: Results of long-term longitudinal follow-up. *Pediatrics* 1980; 66:758–762.

264. Hanshaw JB, Scheiner AP, Moley AW, et al: School failure and deafness after "silent" congenital cytomegalovirus infection. *N Engl J Med* 1976; 295:468–470.

265. Reynolds DW, Stagno S, Stubbs G, et al: Inapparent congenital CMV infection with elevated cord IgM levels, causal relation with auditory and mental deficiency. *N Engl J Med* 1974; 290:291–296.

266. Stagno S, Reynolds DW, Amos CS, et al: Auditory and visual defects resulting from symptomatic and subclinical congenital cytomegaloviral and toxoplasma infections. *Pediatrics* 1977; 59:669–678.

267. Pannuti CS, Vilus-Boas LS, Angelo MJO, et al: Congenital cytomegalovirus infection: Occurrence in two socio-economically distinct populations of a developing country. *Rev Inst Med Trop Sao Paulo* 1985; 27:105–107.

268. Hanshaw JB: Congenital cytomegalovirus infection: A fifteen year perspective. *J Infect Dis* 1971; 123:555–561.

269. Hanshaw JB: Developmental abnormalities associated with congenital cytomegalovirus infection. *Adv Teratol* 1973; 4:64–93.

270. Stagno S, Pan RF, Thomas JP, et al: Defects of tooth structure in congenital CMV infection. *Pediatrics* 1982; 69:646–648.

271. Davis GL: Congenital cytomegalovirus and hearing loss: Clinical and experimental observations. *Laryngoscope* 1981; 89:1681–1688.

272. Hanshaw JB, Betts RF, Simon G, et al: Acquired cytomegalovirus infection: Association with hepatomegaly and abnormal liver-function tests. *N Engl J Med* 1965; 272:602–609.

273. Klemola A, Kaariainen L, Von Essen R: Further studies on cytomegalovirus mononucleosis in previously healthy individuals. *Acta Med Scand* 1967; 182:311–322.

274. Nikosklainen J, Leikola J, Klemola E: IgM antibodies specific for Epstein-Barr virus in infectious mononucleosis without heterophil antibodies. *Br Med J* 1974; 2:72–75.

275. Klemola E, Von Essen R, Wager O: Cytomegalovirus mononucleosis in previously healthy individuals. Five new cases and follow-up of thirteen previously published cases. *Ann Intern Med* 1969; 71:11–19.

276. Horwitz CA, Henle W, Henle G, et al: Clinical and laboratory evaluation of cytomegalovirus-induced mononucleosis in previously healthy individuals: Report of 82 cases. *Medicine* 1986; 65:124–134.

277. Cohen JL, Corey GR: Cytomegalovirus infection in normal

host. *Medicine* 1985; 64:100–114.

278. Evans AS: Infectious mononucleosis and related syndromes. *Am J Med Sci* 1978; 276:325–339.

279. Sterner G, Agell BO, Wahren B: Acquired cytomegalovirus infection in older children and adults. *Scand J Infect Dis* 1970; 2:95–103.

280. Calstrom G, Alden J, Belfrage S, et al: Acquired cytomegalovirus infection. *Br Med J* 1968; 2:521–525.

281. Felsenstein D, Carney WD, Iacovicollo VR, et al: Phenotypic properties of atypical lymphocytes in cytomegalovirus–induced mononucleosis. *J Infect Dis* 1985; 152:198–203.

282. Muller-Stamou A, Senn HJ, et al: Epidermolysis in a case of severe cytomegalovirus infection. *Br Med J* 1974; 2:609–610.

283. Klemola E: Hypersensitivity reactions to ampicillin in cytomegalovirus mononucleosis. *Scand J Infect Dis* 1970; 2:29–31.

284. Kaarianen L, Klemola E, Paloheimo J: Rise of cytomegalovirus antibodies in an infectious-mononucleosis-like syndrome after transfusion. *Br Med J* 1966; 1:1270–1272.

285. Chou S, Kim DY, Norman DJ: Transmission of cytomegalovirus by pretransplant leukocyte transfusing in renal transplant candidates. *J Infect Dis* 1987; 155:565–567.

286. Lamb SG, Stern H: Cytomegalovirus mononucleosis with jaundice as presenting sign. *Lancet* 1974; 2:1003–1006.

287. Toghill PJ, Bailey ME, Williams R, et al: Cytomegalovirus hepatitis in the adult. *Lancet* 1967; 1:1351–1354.

288. Bayer WL, Tegtmeier GE, Barbara JAJ: The significance of non–A, non–B hepatitis, cytomegalovirus and the acquired immune deficiency syndrome intransfusion practice. *Clin Hematol* 1984; 13:253–269.

289. Smover DC, Horwitz CA: Liver disease in cytomegalovirus mononucleosis: A light microscopical and immunoperoxidase study of six cases. *Hepatology* 1984; 4:408–412.

290. Clarke J, Craig RM, Saffro R, et al: Cytomegalovirus granulomatous hepatitis. *Am J Med* 1979; 66:264–269.

291. Marrie TJ, Tanigan DT, Haldane EV, et al: Does cytomegalovirus play a role in community–acquired pneumonia? *Clin Invest Med* 1985; 8:286–295.

292. Klemola E, Stenstrom R, Von Essen R: Pneumonia as a clinical manifestation of CMV infection in a previously healthy adult. *Scand J Infect Dis* 1972; 4:7–10.

293. Stagno S, Brasfield D, Brown MB, et al: Infant pneumonitis associated with cytomegalovirus, chlamydia, pneumocystis and *Ureaplasma:* A prospective study. *Pediatrics* 1981; 68:322–329.

294. Craighead JE: Pulmonary cytomegalovirus infection in the adult. *Am J Pathol* 1971; 63:487–500.

295. Ramsey RG, Rubin RH, Talkoff-Rubin NE, et al: The renal transplant patient with fever and pulmonary infiltrates: Etiology clinical manifestations and management. *Medicine* 1980; 59:206–221.

296. Naraqi S, Johasson OM, Jackson GG, et al: Clinical manifestations of infections with herpesvirus after kidney transplantation: A prospective study of various syndromes. *Ann Surg* 1978; 188:234–239.

297. Neiman PE, Reeves W, Ray G, et al: A prospective analysis of interstitial pneumonia and opportunistic viral infection among recipients of allogenic bone marrow grafts. *J Infect Dis* 1977; 136:754–767.

298. Meyers JD, Flournoy N, Thomas ED: Nonbacterial pneumonia after allogenic marrow transplantation: A review of ten years experience. *Rev Infect Dis* 1982; 4:1119–1132.

299. Abdullah PS, Mark JB, Merigan TC: Diagnosis of cytomegalovirus pneumonia in compromised hosts. *Am J Med* 1976; 61:326–332.

300. Pachucki C, Naraqi S: Clinical spectrum of cytomegalovirus pneumonia in immunocompromised hosts. Unpublished data.

301. Beschorner WE, Hutchins GM, Burns WH, et al: Cytomegalovirus pneumonia in bone marrow transplant recipients: Miliary and diffuse patterns. *Am Rev Respir Dis* 1980; 122:107–114.

302. Whitley RJ, Brasfield D, Reynolds DR, et al: Protracted pneumonitis in young infants associated with perinatally acquired cytomegaloviral infection. *J Pediatr* 1976; 89:16–22.

303. Friedman HM, Grossman RA, Plotkin SA, et al: Relapse of pneumonia caused by cytomegalovirus in two recipients of renal transplants. *J Infect Dis* 1979; 139:465–473.

304. Chawla HB, Ford MJ, Munrow JF, et al: Ocular involvement in cytomegalovirus infection in a previously healthy adult. *Br Med J* 1976; 2:281–282.

305. Smith ME: Retinal involvement in adult cytomegalic inclusion disease. *Arch Ophthalmo.* 1964; 72:44–49.

306. Murray HW, Knox DL, Green WR, et al: Cytomegalovirus retinitis in adults: A manifestation of disseminated viral infection. *Am J Med* 1977; 63:574–584.

307. Pollard RB, Egbert PR, Gallagher JG, et al: Cytomegalovirus retinitis in immunosuppressed hosts. I. Natural history and effects of treatment with adenine arabinoside. *Ann Intern Med* 1980; 93:655–664.

308. De Venecia G, Zu Rhein GM, Pratt MB, et al: Cytomegalic inclusion retinitis in an adult: A clinical, histopathologic and untrastructural study. *Arch Ophthalmol* 1971; 86:44–57.

309. Egbert PR, Pollard RB, Gallagher JG, et al: Cytomegalovirus retinitis in immunosuppressed hosts. II. Ocular manifestations. *Ann Intern Med* 1980; 93:644–670.

310. Henson D: Cytomegalovirus inclusion bodies in the gastrointestinal tract. *Arch Pathol* 1972; 93:477–482.

311. Tilney NI, Collins JJ Jr, Wilson RE: Hemorrhagic pancreatitis: A fatal complication of renal transplantation. *N Engl J Med* 1966; 274:1051–1057.

312. Tamura H: Acute ulcerative colitis associated with cytomegalic inclusion virus. *Arch Pathol* 1973; 96:164–167.

313. Goodman MD, Porter DD: Cytomegalovirus vasculitis with fatal colonic hemorrhage. *Arch Pathol* 1973; 96:281–284.

314. Berk T, Gordon SJ, Choi HY, et al: Cytomegalovirus infection of the colon: A possible role in exacerbation of inflammatory bowel disease. *Am J Gastroenterol* 1985; 80:355–360.

315. Hashiro GM, Horikani L, Loh PC: CMV isolation for cell cultures of human adenocarcinoma of the colon. *Intervirology* 1979; 12:84–88.

316. Phillips CA, Fanning WL, Gump DW, et al: CMV encephalitis in immunologically normal adults: Successful treatment with vidarabine. *JAMA* 1977; 238:2299–2300.

317. Jamison RM, Hathron AW: Isolation of CMV from cerebrospinal fluid of a congenitally infected infant. *Am J Dis Child* 1978; 132:63–64.

318. Morgello S, Cho ES, Nielsen S, et al: Cytomegalovirus encephalitis in patients with acquired immune deficiency syndrome. An autopsy study of 30 cases and a review of literature. *Hum Pathol* 1987; 18:289–297.

319. Wiley CA, Schrier RO, Denaro FJ: Localization of cytomegalovirus protein and genome during fulminant central nervous system infection in an AIDS patient. *J Neuropathol Exp Neurol* 1986; 45:127–139.

320. Carter G, Taylor GR, Crow T: Search for viral nucleic acid sequences in the post mortem brains of patients with schizophrenia and individuals who have committed suicide. *J Neurol Neurosurg Psychiatry.* 1987; 50:247–251.

321. Dowling PC, Stuart D, Cook MD: Role of infection in Guillain-Barré syndrome: Laboratory confirmation of herpesviruses in 41 cases. *Ann Neurol* 1981; 9(suppl): 44–45.

322. Kaplan JC, Greenspan JR, Bomgaars M, et al: Simultaneous outbreaks of Guillain-Barré syndrome and Bell's palsy in Hawaii in 1981. *JAMA* 1983; 250:2635–2640.

323. Klemola E, Ewckman N, Haltia K, et al: The Guillain-Barré syndrome associated with acquired cytomegalovirus infection. *Acta Med Scand* 1967; 181:603–607.

324. Leonard JC, Tobin J O'H: Polyneuritis associated with cytomegalovirus infections. *QJ Med* 1971; 40:435–442.

325. Kabins SA, Keller R, Naraqi S, et al: Viral ascending radiculomyelitis with severe hypoglycorrhachia. *Arch Intern Med* 1976; 136:933–935.

326. Chanarin I, Walford DM: Thrombocytopenic purpura in cytomegalovirus mononucleosis. *Lancet* 1973; 2:238–239.

327. Chesney PJ, Taher A, Gilbert EMF, et al: Intranuclear inclusions in megakaryocytes in congenital cytomegalovirus infection. *J Pediatr* 1978; 92:957–958.

328. Coombs RRM: Cytomegalic inclusion body disease associated with acquired autoimmune haemolytic anemia. *Br Med J* 1968; 2:743–744.

329. Franklin AJ: Cytomegalovirus infection presenting as acute haemolytic anemia in an infant. *Arch Dis Child* 1972; 47:474–475.

330. Tiula E, Leiniki P: Fatal cytomegalovirus infection in a previously healthy boy with myocarditis and consumption coagulopathy as presenting signs. *Scand J Infect Dis* 1972; 4:57–60.

331. Hathaway WE, Mull MM, Pechet GS: Disseminated intravascular coagulation in the newborn. *Pediatrics* 1969; 43:233–240.

332. Lin C-S, Penha PD, Krishnan MN, et al: Cytomegalic inclusion disease of the skin. *Arch Dermatol* 1981; 117:282–284.

333. Wilson RSE, Morris TH, Rees KR: Cytomegalovirus myocarditis. *Br Med J* 1972; 34:865–868.

334. Friedman HM, Pincus T, Gibilisco P, et al: Acute monoarticular arthritis caused by herpes simplex virus and cytomegalovirus. *Am J Med* 1980; 69:241–247.

335. Davies JG, Taylor CM, White RHR, et al: Cytomegalovirus infection associated with lower urinary tract symptoms. *Br Med J* 1979; 1:1120.

336. Ozawa T, Stewart JA: Immune-complex glomerulonephritis associated with cytomegalovirus infection. *Am J Clin Pathol* 1979; 72:103–107.

337. Orsi EV, Howard JL, Baturay N, et al: High incidence of virus isolation from donor and recipient tissues associated with renal transplantation. *Nature* 1978; 272:372–373.

338. Richardson WP, Colvin RB, Cheeseman SH, et al: Glomerulopathy associated with cytomegalovirus viremia in renal allografts. *N Engl J Med* 1981; 305:57–63.

339. Peterson PK, Balfour HH, Marker SC, et al: Cytomegalovirus disease in renal allograft recipients: A prospective study of the clinical features, risk factors and impact on renal transplantation. *Medicine* 1980; 59:283–300.

340. Rifkind D, Goodman N, Hill RB: The clinical significance of cytomegalovirus infection in renal transplant recipients. *Ann Intern Med* 1967; 66:1116–1128.

341. Whelchel JD, Pass RF, Diethelm AC, et al: Effect of primary and recurrent cytomegalovirus infections upon graft and patient survival after renal transplantation. *Transplantation* 1979; 28:443–446.

342. Rubin RH, Talkoff-Rubin NE, Oliver D, et al: Multi-center seroepidemiologic study of the impact of cytomegalovirus infection on renal transplantation. *Transplantation* 1985; 40:243–249.

343. Paulin T, Ringden O, Lomnquist B, et al: The importance of pre–bone marrow transplantation serology in determining subsequent cytomegalovirus infection: an analysis of risk factors. *Scand J Infect Dis* 1986; 18:199–209.

344. Fetterman GH: A new laboratory aid in the clinical diagnosis of inclusion disease of infancy. *Am J Clin Pathol* 1952; 22:424.

345. Shulman HM, Hackman RC, Sale GE, et al: Rapid cytologic diagnosis of cytomegalovirus interstitial pneumonia on touch imprints from open lung biopsy. *Am J Clin Pathol* 1982; 77:90–94.

346. Cordonnier C, Escudier E, Nicholas JC, et al: Evaluation of three assays on alveolar lavage fluid in the diagnosis of cytomegalovirus pneumonitis after bone marrow transplantation. *J Infect Dis* 1987; 155:495–500.

347. Naqvi SH, Blair LL: Detection of cytomegalovirus antigen and antibodies in the urine of small infants and children. *J Med Virol* 1986; 18:139–147.

348. Lee KF, Nahmias AJ, Stagno S: Rapid diagnosis of cytomegalovirus infection in infants by electron microscopy. *N Engl J Med* 1978; 99:1266–1270.

349. Montplaisir S, Belloncik S, Leduc NP, et al: Electron microscopy in the rapid diagnosis of cytomegalovirus: Ultrastructural observation and comparison of methods of diagnosis. *J Infect Dis* 1972; 125:533–538.

350. Huikeshoven FJ, Wallenburg HS, Jahoda MGJ: Diagnosis of severe fetal cytomegalovirus infection from amniotic fluid in the third trimester of pregnancy. *Am J Obstet Gynecol* 1982; 142:1953–1054.

351. Stirk PR, Griffiths PD: Use of monoclonal antibodies for the diagnosis of cytomegalovirus infection by the detection of early antigen fluorescent foci (DEAFF) in cell culture. *J Med Virol* 1987; 21:329–337.

352. Paya CV, Wald AD, Smith TF: Detection of cytomegalovirus infections in specimens other than urine by the shell vial assay and conventional tube cell cultures. *J Clin Microbiol* 1987; 25:755–757.

353. Waner JL, Weller TH, Kevy SV: Patterns of cytomegaloviral complement–fixing antibody activity: A longitudinal study of blood donors. *J Infect Dis* 1973; 127:538–543.

354. Horodniceanu F, Michelson S: Assessment of human cytomegalovirus antibody detection techniques: Brief review. *Arch virol* 1980; 64:287–301.

355. Gonczal E, Furlini G, Ianacone J, et al: A rapid microneutralization assay for cytomegalovirus. *J Virol Methods* 1986; 14:37–41.

356. Sarov I, Siqueira–Linhards M, Chardonnet Y, et al: Detection of specific IgA antibodies in serum of kidney transplant patients with recurrent CMV infection. *Intervirology* 1981; 15:228–234.

357. Sarov I, Friedman M, Levy E, et al: Detection of recurrent cytomegalovirus infection in renal transplant patients. *J Infect Dis* 1984; 149:277.

358. Griffiths PD, Stagno S, Pass RF, et al: Infection with cytomegalovirus during pregnancy: Specific IgM antibodies as a marker of recent primary infection. *J Infect Dis* 1982; 145:544–549.

359. Spector SA, Rua JA, Spector DH, et al: Detection of human cytomegalovirus in clinical specimens by DNA-DNA hybridization. *J Infect Dis* 1984; 150:121–126.

360. Buffone GJ, Schimbor CM, Demmler GJ: Detection of cytomegalovirus in urine by nonisotopic DNA hybridization. *J Infect Dis* 1986; 154:163–166.

361. Hilborne LH, Nieberg RK, Cheng L, et al: Direct in situ hybridization for rapid detection of cytomegalovirus in bronchoalveolar lavage. *Am J Clin Pathol* 1987; 87:766–769.

362. Myerson D, Hackman RC, Meyers JD: Diagnosis of cytomegaloviral pneumonia by in situ hybridization. *J Infect Dis* 1984; 150:272–277.

363. Katznelson S, Drew WL, Mintz L: Efficacy of the condom as a barrier to the transmission of cytomegalovirus. *J Infect Dis* 1984; 150:155–157.

364. Onorato IM, Morens DM, Martone WJ, et al: Epidemiology of cytomegaloviral infection: Recommendations for prevention and control. *Rev Infect Dis* 1985; 7:479–497.

365. Saral R, Burns WH, Laskin OL, et al: Acyclovir prophylaxis of herpes–simplex–virus infections. *N Engl J Med* 1981; 305:63–67.

366. Winston DJ, Winston G, Ho MD, et al: Intravenous immunoglobulin for prevention of cytomegalovirus infection and interstitial pneumonia after bone marrow transplantation. *Ann Intern Med* 1987; 106:12–18.

367. Meyers JD: Prevention and treatment of cytomegalovirus infections with interferons and immunoglobulins. *Infection* 1985; 13(suppl2):211–218.

368. Elek SD, Stern H: Development of a vaccine against mental retardation caused by cytomegalovirus infection in utero. *Lancet* 1974; 1:1–5.

369. Plotkin SA, Farquhar J, Zygraic N, et al: Candidate cytomegalovirus strain for human vaccination. *Infect Immun* 1975; 12:521–527.

370. Osborn JE: Cytomegalovirus: Pathogenicity, immunology and vaccine initiative. *J Infect Dis* 1981; 143:618–630.

371. Lang DJ: Cytomegalovirus Immunization: Status, prospects and problems. *Rev Infect Dis* 1980; 23:449–458.

372. Plotkin SA, Smiley ML, Friedman HM, et al: Towne-vaccine induced prevention of CMV disease after renal transplants. *Lancet* 1984; 1:528–530.

373. Plotkin SA, Huang ES: Cytomegalovirus vaccine virus (Towne strain) does not induce latency. *J Infect Dis* 1985; 152:395–397.

374. Fleisher GR, Staff SE, Friedman HM, et al: Vaccination of pe-diatric nurses with live attenuated cytomegalovirus. *Am J Dis Child* 1982; 136:294–296.

375. Collaborative DHPG Treatment Study Group: Treatment of seri-ous cytomegalovirus infections with 9-[(1,3,-dihydroxy-2-pro-poxy)methyl]-guanine in patients with AIDS and other immunodeficiencies. *N Engl J Med* 1986; 314:801–805.

376. Furukawa T, Tanaka S, Plotkin SA: Inhibition of human cyto-megalovirus by rifampin. *J Gen Virol* 1975; 28:355–362.

38

Roseola Infantum (Exanthem Subitum) and Human Herpesvirus 6

Prudence Krieger

ETIOLOGY

EPIDEMIOLOGY

CLINICAL MANIFESTATIONS

LABORATORY FINDINGS

DIFFERENTIAL DIAGNOSIS

MANAGEMENT

HUMAN HERPESVIRUS

Roseola infantum (rose rash of infancy, sixth disease) is the descriptive name of a common syndrome observed in infants beyond the neonatal period. The syndrome consists of three or four days of high fever followed by a generalized macular exanthem at defervescence. John Zahorsky first reported it as an entity separate from rubella in 1910.[1] Some authors prefer the name exanthem subitum (unexpected rash) proposed by Veeder and Hempelmann in 1929,[2] but the disease is most often referred to as roseola. Most efforts to identify an etiologic agent have been unsuccessful. Recently, Yamanishi et al isolated human herpesvirus 6 (HHV-6) from the peripheral blood lymphocytes of four of six roseola patients.[3] Some observers believe the syndrome may be a clinical expression of more than one virus.[4, 5]

ETIOLOGY

Early authors doubted the contagiousness of roseola because of the rarity of secondary cases in clinical practice.[1, 2] In 1927, Cushing reported a small outbreak in a foundling home involving 6 of 10 contacts on a ward.[6] Barenberg and Greenspan recorded a larger outbreak in a similar setting in 1939.[7] Epidemics of Boston exanthem, which have been attributed to echovirus 16, have included multiple cases of infants with roseola-like illnesses.[8-11]

Breese made the first unsuccessful attempt to isolate a virus from the throats and blood of affected infants in 1941.[12] Similar attempts at viral isolation by Berenberg et al in 1949 also failed.[13] In 1950, Kempe et al succeeded in transmitting the illness to a susceptible infant by inoculating him with blood taken from an affected patient on the third day of fever.[14] These investigators similarly infected monkeys using either blood or throat washings from the ill patient. Their results were confirmed by Hellstrom and Vahlquist in human infants.[15] Subsequent researchers reported the presence of a virus in the feces of a 2-year-old patient with roseola,[16] and in the serum of experimentally infected monkeys.[17]

Watson first proposed that roseola is a reaction to several or many different viruses.[4] Support for this hypothesis is strengthened by the occurrence of roseola-like rashes during outbreaks of enterovirus illnesses, including echoviruses 9, 11, 16, 25, 27, and 30 and coxsackieviruses A6, A9, B1, B2, B4, and B5.[4, 5, 8-11, 18-20] Adenoviruses and parainfluenza viruses have also been associated with illnesses resembling roseola.[4, 21, 22] Saitoh et al found rotavirus in the stools of nine patients with the roseola syndrome, although gastrointestinal (GI) symptoms were more prominent in their patients than in most infants with roseola.[23] Gurwith et al found neither rotavirus in the stools of infants with roseola, nor observed roseola-like rashes in infants prospectively identified as infected with rotavirus.[24] Most recently, Yamanishi et al isolated human herpesvirus 6 from the peripheral blood lymphocytes of 4 of 6 infants during the febrile phase of roseola.[3] This virus has also been called human B lymphotropic virus, and was first reported by Salahuddin and associates in 1986.[25] All four of Yamanishi's patients demonstrated seroconversion to their own viral isolates and to human herpesvirus 6 by anticomplement immunofluorescence. Furthermore, ten roseola patients exhibited antibody titer rises to human herpesvirus 6 antigen. Specific antibody began to appear after 7 days of illness, was detectable by 2 weeks, and peaked by 3 weeks after the onset of symptoms.

925

Since the original report of Yamanishi et al., additional investigators have added further evidence that HHV-6 is the etiologic agent of roseola.[26-30] Asano et al. detected mononuclear cell–associated HHV-6 viremia in 26 of 26 blood specimens collected in the first 2 days of roseola fever, and demonstrated neutralizing antibody seroconversion to the virus in 37 of 37 plasma samples drawn later than the eighth day of illness.[27] Ueda et al. showed that 6 of 6 infants with roseola either seroconverted or developed an eightfold increase in antibody titer to HHV-6 using an indirect immunofluorescence method.[28] Yoshiyama et al. have isolated HHV-6 from the blood of 13 of 22 infants with roseola, and demonstrated a fourfold or greater rise in anti-HHV-6 indirect immunofluorescence antibody titers between the acute and convalescent sera from 19 of the 22 infants.[30]

EPIDEMIOLOGY

Roseola occurs worldwide in all socioeconomic groups and equally in both sexes. Several reviewers have considered it the most common exanthematous disease of infancy, even prior to the introduction of measles and rubella vaccine.[6, 12, 31] Breese estimated that approximately 30% of infants might develop the syndrome, but no prospective data are available.[12] Some early reviewers undoubtedly included cases that would not be classified as simple roseola today, which may confuse the epidemiologic and clinical picture in the older literature.[31-33]

Most cases of roseola occur in infants between the ages of 4 months and 2 years, with over half the cases occurring in the second 6 months of life.[12, 34, 35] It is not unusual to see patients between 2 and 4 years of age, and one large series reported a peak incidence between 18 months and 2 years.[13] There are several reports of otherwise typical illness occurring in older children and adults.[12, 36-38] Most series do not report patients below age 3 months, although Zahorsky's youngest patient was 2 weeks old.[39] An interesting 1949 report of an outbreak in a maternity hospital records involvement of 19 newborns as well as five nurses, nine mothers, and four fathers.[40] However, a number of features of this outbreak were atypical, and it is not clear that the illness described was roseola. The author has seen a compatible clinical illness in a 12-day-old infant hospitalized for presumptive sepsis.

In general practice, roseola cases may be seen singly or in small clusters over several days.[12, 41] Small outbreaks in infants' homes have been described.[6, 7] Second cases within families are unusual, perhaps because of the lack of age-susceptible siblings within a family unit.[1, 12] Boston exanthem outbreaks with roseola-like cases of illness are clearly contagious to all age groups within the family unit.[8-11] However, adult patients often fail to develop the typical rash.[8, 9]

Some series report a seasonal predominance with peaks of occurrence in mid-autumn and mid-spring,[13, 34] but most reviews indicate that cases occur year round with approximately equal distribution among the seasons.[12, 35-41]

Antibody to HHV-6 is found in 52% to nearly 100% of adults in studies from several countries.[43-47] Eighty-nine percent to 100% of infants are seropositive at birth as a consequence of actively transported, transplacentally acquired, maternal antibody.[26, 28, 45, 46] Anti-HHV-6 antibody declines to low levels by 4 to 6 months of age.[26, 28, 43, 45, 46] Subsequently, the majority of infants apparently are infected shortly after maternal antibody wanes, with anti-HHV-6 seroprevalence rates of 63% to 92% by 9 to 12 months of age.[26, 28, 43, 45, 46] Thereafter, anti-HHV-6 antibody levels decline with age, and may fall below the range detectable by current methodology.[44, 47]

Human herpesvirus 6 has been found in adult saliva specimens in Australia, and it has been postulated that infection is latent in adults and transmitted horizontally from mother to infant.[46, 48] However, researchers in Japan have not been able to isolate the virus from saliva, and the route of transmission has not been established.[30, 47] Using an indirect immunofluorescence assay, Morris et al. demonstrated that HHV-6 antibody responses are distinct from responses to other herpesviruses.[49]

CLINICAL MANIFESTATIONS

The incubation period of roseola in institutional outbreaks has been between 5 and 15 days with an average of 10 days.[6, 7] However, in most cases seen in clinical practice, no identifiable exposure has taken place.

The usual illness begins with the abrupt onset of high fever in an otherwise apparently well child. The child often does not seem very ill to the parent, although nonspecific symptoms of irritability and malaise may be present at the height of the fever. Anorexia is an inconstant feature and is not as marked as in other common febrile illnesses. One or two episodes of vomiting or loose stools may occur in an occasional patient. The fever is between 102°F and 105°F (38.8–40.5°C) rectally and has been described as either continuous or intermittent with a tendency toward morning remissions.[12, 50] The fever is responsive to antipyretics. It lasts three days in the majority of patients, with a range of two to five days. Occasional patients with very transient or more prolonged fever are mentioned in large series.[12, 13] The temperature returns to normal by either crisis or lysis.

During the febrile phase of roseola, many patients are found to have mildly erythematous fauces and pharynx with occasional red macules on the soft palate. A minority of patients present with mild coryza, minimal conjunctivitis, pinpoint follicular exudate on the tonsils, middle ear effusion, or slight cough. Nontender posterior cervical or occipital adenopathy may be found on physical examination.[51] Palpebral edema has been mentioned as a suggestive diagnostic sign, although this finding is probably common to many febrile childhood illnesses.[52] However, many patients have no abnormal physical findings at all when examined.

The roseolar rash is most often observed at the same time the patient's temperature returns to normal. In some cases, the patient has been afebrile for a few hours to a day before the rash erupts. It is first noticed on the neck or upper trunk and spreads quickly to involve the abdomen, buttocks, and proximal extremities. A few lesions may appear on the forehead and behind the ears, but the face is often spared. The rash is not pruritic. Individual lesions are discrete, rose-pink, oval macules or slightly raised maculopapules measuring 2 to 4 mm in diameter and surrounded by a pale areola. The lesions blanch with pressure and may coalesce in areas of greatest density. Although the rash occasionally disappears within hours, it usually lasts one or two days before fading without residua. Minimal desquamation has been observed rarely.[34]

A febrile convulsion is the most frequently observed complication of roseola.[53] Febrile convulsions have occurred in as many as 6% of patients in some series and may be the presenting feature in an occasional patient.[34] An encephalitis-like picture, possibly due to prolonged seizures, is rare but well documented in the literature.[54, 55] Transient or prolonged neurologic residua, including hemiplegia, epilepsy, and mental retardation, have been described.[56–60] The reported hemiplegia is most often consistent with Todd paralysis. Several authors note the appearance of a bulging fontanelle in infants who have no other central nervous system complications.[31, 57, 58, 61, 22]

Since the discovery of HHV-6 as the probable cause of roseola, investigators have estimated that as many as two thirds of infants who seroconvert to HHV-6 have clinical roseola, but only a small number of patients have been studied.[26] Japanese researchers have demonstrated HHV-6 positive cultures of peripheral blood mononuclear cells in infants with 3-day fevers without rash, and in infants with 1- to 2-day, afebrile, abrupt-onset, rubelliform or morbilliform rashes.[63, 64] Morris et al. have suggested that HHV-6 may produce opportunistic recurrent infections in immunocompromised patients.[65]

LABORATORY FINDINGS

In most patients with roseola, the white blood count shows leukopenia with an absolute granulocytopenia and a relative lymphocytosis of 70% to 90%. The granulocytopenia tends to be progressive and becomes most marked just before the rash appears.[12, 13, 34, 35, 66] At the beginning of the illness, the white count is variable and mild leukocytosis is often present.[13, 31, 35] Atypical lymphocytes and immature granulocytes are not typically seen on the blood smear.[13, 35] There is no increase in the number of monocytes or eosinophils.[13, 35] The white count returns to normal in about a week following recovery from roseola.[13] Nishimura and Igarashi have described postinfectious thrombocytopenia purpura in five patients with otherwise typical roseola.[67]

In patients with symptoms suggesting CNS involvement, a mild increase in cerebrospinal fluid pressure may be found.[31, 55, 60] The CSF analysis is usually normal, although minimal lymphocytosis has been described.[13, 55] Urinalysis occasionally shows trace proteinuria or minimal pyuria, but is usually normal.[31, 34]

Although specific anti-HHV-6 antibody has been detected by both indirect immunofluorescence and virus neutralization assays, these tests are not yet commercially available.[3, 46]

DIFFERENTIAL DIAGNOSIS

The major disease processes to be excluded in the preeruptive, febrile phase of roseola are bacteremia with no localization and early bacterial meningitis.[68] The total white blood cell count is helpful in differentiating roseola from bacteremia.[68] If the count is greater than 15,000 cells per microliter, a blood culture should be obtained. Any patient who presents with a febrile convulsion, a bulging fontanelle, or other signs of CNS irritation must undergo a lumbar puncture. In the patient with an absolute neutrophil count of less than 1000 per microliter, repeat counts must be obtained to exclude cyclic or other neutropenic states.

All too often, the infant with high fever will be given antibiotics. When a roseolar rash ensues, the physician may not be able to exclude drug hypersensitivity.[69] However, if the illness is

typical of roseola, the physician may reasonably prescribe the antibiotic again when indicated.

MANAGEMENT

Other than antipyretics for fever and anticonvulsants for seizures, no treatment is necessary. Isolation is not required.[70]

HUMAN HERPESVIRUS 6

During the culture of peripheral blood leukocytes from patients with acquired immunodeficiency syndrome (AIDS) and/or lymphoproliferative disorders, a cytopathogenic agent has been isolated that has been identified as a herpesvirus. Biologically, genetically, and immunologically, this virus is distinct from herpesvirus types 1 and 2, Epstein-Barr virus, varicella zoster virus, cytomegalovirus (CMV), and nonhuman primate herpesviruses.

Human herpesvirus 6 (HHV-6) is an approximately 20-nm enveloped DNA virus with an icosahedral nucleocapsid made up of 162 capsomers. The morphology of HHV-6 resembles CMV in that they both have tegument-coated cytoplasmic nucleocapsids. However, with HHV-6, the nucleoprotein does not have the beaded appearance and the infected cells do not contain the skein-like structures. HHV-6 induces lytic infection in human cord lymphocytes and grows primarily in T lymphocytes. DNA studies confirm that HHV-6 is distinct from CMV.

Immune electron microscopy has demonstrated the presence of specific antibodies to viral envelope and internal antigens, indicating that this virus is a possible human pathogen. More studies are needed to determine the pathogenesis, epidemiology, and clinical manifestations of HHV-6 infection in man.[25, 71–76]

Similar agents isolated from the culture of mononuclear cells of individuals seropositive with human immunodeficiency virus (HIV) (with or without AIDS) are probably different strains of the same human herpesvirus.[77]

REFERENCES

1. Zahorsky J: Roseola infantilis. *Pediatrics* 1910; 22:60–64.
2. Veeder B, Hempelmann T: A febrile exanthem occurring in childhood (exanthem subitum). *JAMA* 1921; 77:1787–1789.
3. Yamanishi K, Okuno T, Shiraki K, et al: Identification of human herpesvirus-6 as a causal agent for exanthem subitum. *Lancet* 1988; 1:1065–1067.
4. Watson G: The roseolar reaction. *Br Med J* 1974; 4:719–720.
5. Cherry J: Newer viral exanthems. *Adv Pediatr* 1969; 16:233–286.
6. Cushing H: An epidemic of roseola infantum. *Can Med Assoc J* 1927; 17:905–906.
7. Barenberg L, Greenspan L: Exanthem subitum (roseola infantum). *Am J Dis Child* 1939; 58:983–993.
8. Neva F, Feemster R, Gorbach I: Clinical and epidemiological features of an unusual epidemic exanthem. *JAMA* 1954; 155:544–548.
9. Neva F: A second outbreak of Boston exanthem disease in Pittsburgh during 1954. *N Engl J Med* 1956; 254:838–843.
10. Hall C, Cherry J, Hatch M, et al: The return of Boston exanthem: Echovirus 16 infections in 1974. *Am J Dis Child* 1977; 131:323–326.
11. Fujii M: Echovirus type 16 infection (Boston exanthem): Clinical review of 103 cases in Kasahara. *Kansenshogaku Zasshi* 1986; 60:64–69.
12. Breese B: Roseola infantum (exanthem subitum). *NY State J Med* 1941; 41:1854–1859.

13. Berenberg W, Wright S, Janeway C: Roseola infantum (exanthem subitum). *N Engl J Med* 1949; 241:253–259.
14. Kempe C, Shaw E, Jackson J, et al: Studies on the etiology of exanthema subitum (roseola infantum). *J Pediatr* 1950; 37:561–568.
15. Hellstrom B, Vahlquist B: Experimental inoculation of roseola infantum. *Acta Paediatr* 1951; 40:189–197.
16. Neva F, Enders J: Isolation of a cytopathogenic agent from an infant with a disease in certain respects resembling roseola infantum. *J Immunol* 1954; 72:315–321.
17. Reagan R, Chang S, Moolten S, et al: Electron microscopic studies of the roseola infantum (exanthem subitum) virus. *Tex Rep Biol Med* 1955; 13:929–933.
18. St Geme J, Prince J, Scherer W, et al: A clinical study of an exanthem due to ECHO virus type 9. *J Pediatr* 1959; 54:459–467.
19. Cramblett H: Infection with ECHO viruses and observed illnesses in human beings. *Postgrad Med* 1959; 25:359–364
20. Cherry J, Lerner M, Klein J, et al: Coxsackie B5 infections with exanthems. *Pediatrics* 1963; 31:455–462.
21. Fukimi H, Nishikawa F, Kokubu Y, et al: Isolation of adenovirus from an exanthematous infection resembling roseola infantum. *Jpn J Med Sci Biol* 1957; 10:87–91.
22. Jansson E, Wager O, Forssell P, et al: An exanthema subitum-like rash in patients with adenovirus infection. *Ann Paediatr Fenn* 1961; 7:274–282.
23. Saitoh Y, Matsuno S, Mukoyama A: Exanthem subitum and rotavirus. *N Engl J Med* 1981; 304:845.
24. Gurwith M, Gurwith D, Wenman W, et al: Exanthem subitum not associated with rotavirus. *N Engl J Med* 1981; 305:174–175.
25. Salahuddin S, Ablashi D, Markham P, et al: Isolation of a new virus, HBLV, in patients with lymphoproliferative disorders. *Science* 1986; 234:596–601.
26. Takahashi K, Sonoda S, Kawakami K, et al: Human herpesvirus 6 and exanthem subitum. *Lancet* 1988; 1:1463.
27. Asano Y, Yoshikawa T, Suga S, et al: Viremia and neutralizing antibody response in infants with exanthem subitum. *J Pediatr* 1989; 114:535–539.
28. Ueda K, Kusuhara K, Hirose M, et al: Exanthem subitum and antibody to human herpesvirus-6. *J Infect Dis* 1989; 159:750–752.
29. Yoshida T, Yoshiyama H, Suzuki E, et al: Immune response of patients with exanthema subitum to human herpesvirus type 6 (HHV-6) polypeptides. *J Infect Dis* 1989; 160:901–902.
30. Yoshiyama H, Suzuki E, Yoshida T, et al: Role of human herpesvirus 6 infection in infants with exanthema subitum. *Pediatr Infect Dis J* 1990; 9:71–74.
31. Zahorsky J: Roseola infantum: A critical survey of recent literature. *Arch Pediatr* 1947; 64:579–583.
32. Faber H, Dickey L: The symptomatology of exanthem subitum. *Arch Pediatr* 1927; 44:491–496.
33. Zahorsky J: Roseola infantum: A critical survey of some recent literature. *Arch Pediatr* 1940; 57:405–409.
34. Clemens H: Exanthem subitum (roseola infantum): Report of eighty cases. *J Pediatr* 1945; 26:66–77.
35. Juretic M: Exanthema subitum: A review of 243 cases. *Helv Paediatr Acta* 1963; 18:80–95.
36. Zahorsky J: Roseola infantum. *JAMA* 1913; 16:1446–1450.
37. Greenthal R: An unusual exanthem occurring in infants. *Am J Dis Child* 1922; 23:63–65.
38. Cutts M: Exanthem subitum: Report of a case. *Ann Intern Med* 1938; 11:1752.
39. Zahorsky J: Roseola infantum—The rose rash of infants. *Arch Pediatr* 1925; 42:610–613.
40. James U, Freier A: Roseola infantum: An outbreak in a maternity hospital. *Arch Dis Child* 1949; 24:54–58.
41. Greenthal R: Roseola infantum (exanthem subitum). *Wis Med J* 1941; 40:25–27.
42. Nakamura Y, Yanagawa H, Nagai M: Epidemic patterns of infectious diseases from the results of the surveillance of infectious diseases in Japan. *Pediatr Infect Dis J* 1988; 7:262–266.

43. Briggs M, Fox J, Tedder RS: Age prevalence of antibody to human herpesvirus 6. *Lancet* 1988; 1:1058–1059.
44. Brown NA, Sumaya CV, Liu C, et al: Fall in human herpesvirus 6 seropositivity with age. *Lancet* 1988; 2:396.
45. Knowles WA, Gardner SD: High prevalence of antibody to human herpesvirus-6 and seroconversion associated with rash in two infants. *Lancet* 1988; 2:912–913.
46. Yoshikawa T, Suga S, Asano Y, et al: Distribution of antibodies to a causative agent of exanthem subitum (human herpesvirus-6) in healthy individuals. *Pediatrics* 1989; 84:675–677.
47. Yanagi K, Harada S, Ban F, et al: High prevalence of antibody to human herpesvirus-6 and decrease in titer with increase in age in Japan. *J Infect Dis* 1990; 161:153–154.
48. Pietroboni GR, Harnett GB, Bucens MR: Antibody to human herpesvirus 6 in saliva. *Lancet* 1988; 1:1059.
49. Morris DJ, Littler E, Jordan D, et al: Antibody responses to human herpesvirus 6 and other herpesviruses. *Lancet* 1988; 2:1425–1426.
50. Letchner A: Roseola infantum: A review of fifty cases. *Lancet* 1955; 2:1163–1165.
51. McEnery J: Postoccipital lymphadenopathy as a diagnostic sign in roseola infantum (exanthem subitum). *Clin Pediatr* 1970; 9:512–514.
52. Berliner B: A physical sign useful in diagnosis of roseola infantum before the rash. *Pediatrics* 1960; 25:1034.
53. Moller K: Exanthema subitum and febrile convulsions. *Acta Paediatr* 1956; 45:534–540.
54. Wallfield M: Exanthem subitum with an encephalitic onset. *J Pediatr* 1934; 5:800.
55. Holliday P: Pre-eruptive neurological complications of the common contagious diseases—Rubella, rubeola, roseola and varicella. *J Pediatr* 1950; 36:185–198.
56. Rosenblum J: Roseola infantum (exanthema subitum) complicated by hemiplegia. *Am J Dis Child* 1945; 69:234–236.
57. Posson D: Exanthem subitum (roseola infantum) complicated by prolonged convulsions and hemiplegia. *J Pediatr* 1949; 35:235–236.
58. Friedman J, Golomb J, Aronson L: Hemiplegia associated with roseola infantum (exanthem subitum). *NY State J Med* 1950; 50:1749–1750.
59. Windorfer A: Fever persisting for three days and followed by exanthem in infants: Exanthem subitum. *Dtsch Med Wochenschr* 1954; 79:1201.
60. Burnstine R, Paine R: Residual encephalopathy following roseola infantum. *Am J Dis Child* 1959; 98:144–152.
61. Rothman P, Naiditch M: Nervous complications of exanthem subitum. *Calif Med* 1958; 88:39–44.
62. Oski F: Roseola infantum: Another case of bulging fontanel. *Am J Dis Child* 1961; 101:376–378.
63. Suga S, Yoshikawa T, Asano Y, et al: Human herpesvirus-6 infection (exanthem subitum) without rash. *Pediatrics* 1989; 83:1003–1006.
64. Asano Y, Suga S, Yoshikawa T, et al: Human herpesvirus type 6 infection (exanthem subitum) without fever. *J Pediatr* 1989; 115:264–265.
65. Morris DJ, Littler E, Arrand JR, et al: Human herpesvirus 6 infection in renal-transplant recipients. *N Engl J Med* 1989; 320:1560–1561.
66. Becker T, Lampert F: Leukozytenzahl, Differentialblutbild und Blutsenkung bei 9 "klassischen" Infektionskrankheiten. *Klin Pädiatr* 1981; 193:80–87.
67. Nishimura K, Igarashi M: Thrombocytopenic purpura associated with exanthema subitum. *Pediatrics* 1977; 60:260.
68. Teele D, Marshall R, Klein J: Unsuspected bacteremia in young children. *Pediatr Clin North Am* 1979; 26:773–784.
69. Scholleov: Exanthema subitum in pediatric practice: Incidence and significance of the disease in the differential diagnosis of allergic reactions to penicillin. *Cesk Pediatr* 1986; 41:17–19.
70. *Report of the Committee on Infectious Diseases* (Red Book). Elk Grove Village, Ill, American Academy of Pediatrics, 1986.
71. Josephs SF, Salahuddin SZ, Ablashi DV, et al: Genomic analysis

of the human B-lymphotropic virus (HBLV). *Science* 1986; 234:601–603.

72. Biberfeld P, Kramarsky B, Salahuddin SZ, et al: Ultrastructural characterization of a new human lymphotropic DNA virus (human herpesvirus 6) isolated from patients with lymphoproliferative disease. *J Natl Cancer Inst* 1987; 79:933–941.

73. Ablashi DV, Salahuddin SZ, Joseph SF, et al: HBLV (or HHV-6) in human cell lines. *Nature* 1987; 329:207.

74. Lusso P, Salahuddin SZ, Ablashi DV, et al: Diverse tropism of

human B-lymphotropic virus (human herpesvirus 6). *Lancet* 1987; 2:743–744.

75. Downing RG, Sewankambo N, Serwadda D, et al: Isolation of human lymphotropic herpesviruses from Uganda. *Lancet* 1987; 2:390.

76. Tedder RS, Briggs M, Cameron CH, et al: A novel lymphotropic herpesvirus. *Lancet* 1987; 2:390–392.

77. Lopez C, Pellet P, Stewart J, et al: Characteristic of human herpesvirus-6. *J Infect Dis* 1988; 157:1271–1273.

Poxviruses

Derrick Baxby

With one exception poxviruses are unimportant human pathogens; the exception is, or was, smallpox. The last case of naturally acquired smallpox occurred in Somalia in October 1977, and in May 1980 the World Health Assembly accepted the conclusions of the Global Commission for the Certification of Smallpox Eradication[1] that ''Smallpox eradication has been achieved throughout the world.'' Consequently this chapter deals with a virus group whose most important member no longer exists naturally. As recently as the mid-1970s virologists and physicians had to consider smallpox as a serious disease, endemic in some countries, which might be introduced into nonendemic areas at any time. Thankfully this is no longer so.

The family *Poxviridae* is separated into two subfamilies, **Chordopoxvirinae** (poxviruses of vertebrates) and **Entomopoxvirinae** (poxviruses of insects), with some vertebrate poxviruses not yet classified (Table 39–1). Insect poxviruses do not infect vertebrates, and are not discussed here. Poxviruses of vertebrates are placed in six genera. Not all cause human infections, and only those that do are discussed here (Table 39–2). Information about the remainder has recently been summarized elsewhere.[2, 3]

Smallpox was, and molluscum contagiosum is, a specifically human disease. Infection with vaccinia virus is artificial, and the complications of smallpox vaccination will be eliminated as vaccination is discontinued. Human infections caused by cowpox, parapox, and Tanapox viruses are relatively trivial zoonoses. Human monkeypox, clinically indistinguishable from smallpox, is a severe, although rare, zoonosis. Goatpox, sheeppox, fowlpox, and camelpox, although unimportant for human medicine, are important veterinary infections.[2, 3]

HISTORY

The history of smallpox and smallpox vaccination has been reviewed recently.[4, 5] The origins of smallpox are unknown. It is said to have existed in India and China for thousands of years, and the mummified head of Rameses V, who died in 1160 BC, is thought to show smallpox lesions.[1, 4]

Smallpox was established in Europe during the Moorish conquest of Spain and was introduced into America by Spanish con-

Table 39–1
Poxviruses of Vertebrates **(Chordopoxvirinae)**

Genus	Species/Members
Orthopoxvirus	Smallpox, monkeypox, cowpox, vaccinia, camelpox, mousepox
Parapoxvirus	Orf (contagious pustular dermatitis), pseudocowpox (paravaccinia, milker's nodes)
Avipoxvirus	Fowlpox, canarypox, pigeonpox, sparrowpox, etc
Capripoxvirus	Sheeppox, goatpox, lumpy skin disease
Leporipoxvirus	Myxoma, hare fibroma, rabbit fibroma, squirrel fibroma
Suipoxvirus	Pigpox
Unclassified	(a) Raccoon poxvirus, gerbil poxvirus, "carnivore" poxvirus—all orthopoxviruses (b) "Ausdyk" (contagious ecthyma of camels)—probably a parapoxvirus (c) Molluscum contagiosum (d) Tanapox and Yaba poxvirus—serologically related

quistadors in the sixteenth century. Before vaccination was introduced, smallpox deaths in England accounted for 7% to 12% of all deaths and for one third of deaths in young children. About 12% to 20% of smallpox patients died, although in some epidemics the mortality was 40% or higher. If the smallpox mortality in England in the eighteenth century is corrected for the increase in population, it is equivalent to more than 100,000 smallpox deaths each year in the 1970s; similar mortality is now caused by heart disease or cancer.

During this century, variola major persisted in Asia and parts of Africa. A less virulent form, variola minor (alastrim) became established in Europe, America, and parts of Africa. During 1926 to 1930 over 30,000 cases were reported annually in the United States and over 10,000 annually in Britain.[1] The total smallpox cases reported by all countries since 1920 have been tabulated,[1] but the figures for many countries were underestimates until the 1970s.

There were occasional importations of variola major into Europe and North America after World War II. For example, servicemen returning to America in 1946 imported smallpox into Seattle and California, causing 96 cases with 28 deaths.[6] There were five separate importations of variola major into England and Wales in 1961 to 1962 causing 62 cases with 24 deaths.[7] An outbreak occurred in Meschede, West Germany, in 1970 with 20 cases and four deaths.[8]

Attempts were made to prevent smallpox by the deliberate inoculation of smallpox virus (variolation) in the hope that a mild, protective, and nontransmissible disease would result. The practice originated in Asia, China, and Africa, and the introduction of variolation, into England by Lady Mary Wortley Montagu and into America by Cotton Mather and Zabdiel Boylston, in 1721 has been well documented.[9, 10] Variolation was a controversial measure, and its effect has recently been reviewed.[5] Properly done, it did produce a protective infection but had a mortality of about 1 in 200. In the large cities smallpox was ever-present and few people escaped it, so variolation was probably an acceptable risk. The

risk to the community was reduced by isolation and by variolating all the susceptibles at one time.

The most important advance in the control of smallpox was the introduction of vaccination by Edward Jenner in 1796. Whether he "discovered" vaccination or not is irrelevant; it was he who brought it to the attention of others.[5] Critics maintained that, at best, it did not prevent smallpox and that, at worst, it caused or precipitated a variety of diseases including syphilis. The importance of revaccination was not at first appreciated, but it is evident that, whereas smallpox had previously been principally a disease of children, vaccinated children were spared and morbidity switched to adults.

Jenner is assumed to have used cowpox virus but strains of smallpox vaccine (ie, vaccinia virus) are different from cowpox and all other poxviruses.[2, 11] Consequently there has been debate about the origins of vaccinia. The alternatives are that it was derived from (1) smallpox, either by human or animal passage; (2) cowpox, by similar means; (3) cowpox and smallpox by genetic hybridization; (4) an animal poxvirus, such as horsepox which became extinct in the late nineteenth century. The clear differences which exist between vaccinia and cowpox and smallpox viruses make hypothesis (4) the most attractive to this writer.[5]

The historical importance of smallpox should not be forgotten. One of the major infectious diseases of man, it was the first to be controlled by vaccination, the first virus disease for which effective chemoprophylaxis was available, and the first disease to be eradicated.[1]

STRUCTURE AND BIOLOGY OF POXVIRUSES

Structure

Most information is available for vaccinia virus, but the following account can be taken as typical of others. Poxviruses are

Table 39–2
Poxviruses Pathogenic for Man

Virus	Comment
Smallpox	Generalized infection with vesicular rash; mortality 1% to 40% depending on virus strain and immunity; total eradication confirmed 1979
Monkeypox	Rare zoonosis of West and Central Africa; >400 cases 1970 to 1987; mortality 15% but little case-to-case spread
Vaccinia	Complications of smallpox vaccination; encephalitis, eczema vaccinatum, vaccinia gangrenosa; should disappear as vaccination is discontinued
Cowpox	Local hemorrhagic ulcer; restricted to Europe; contact with cattle not necessary; reservoir unknown
Orf, paravaccinia	Painless nodular skin lesion; worldwide; occupational disease of farmers, abbattoir workers, veterinarians, etc
Molluscum	Multiple skin lesions; often sexually transmitted; long-lasting; worldwide
Tanapox	Localized skin nodule with pyrexia; Central Africa

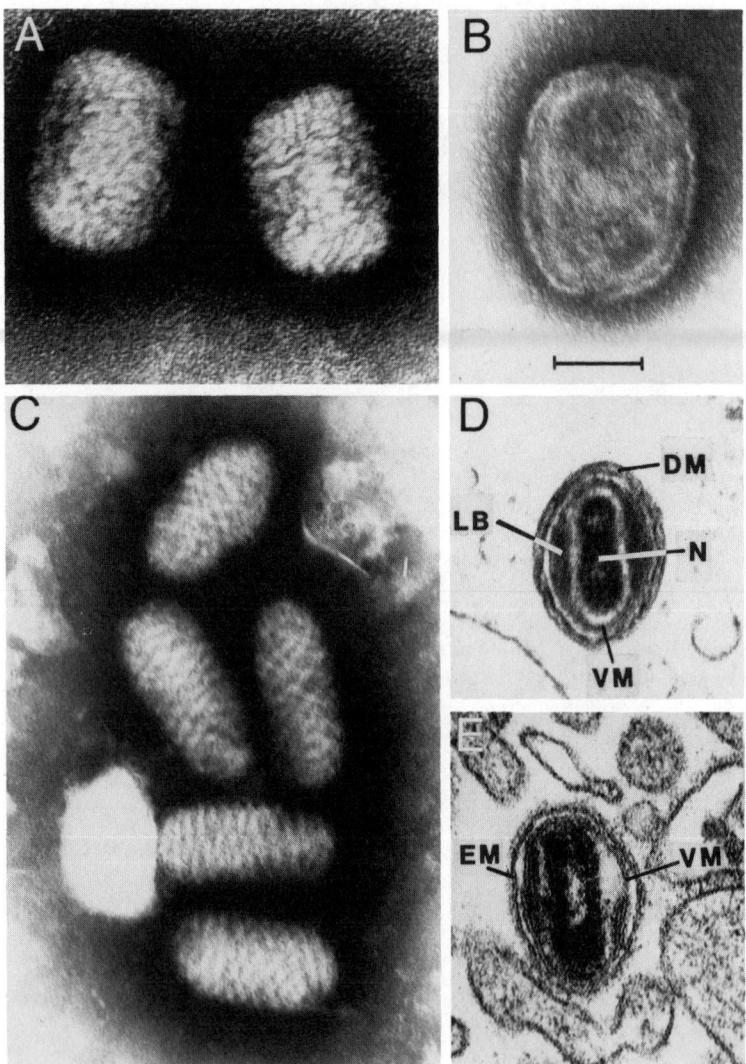

Figure 39–1. A, mulberry (M) form of vaccinia virus, negatively-stained. **B,** capsule (C) form of vaccinia, negatively stained. **C,** M form of pseudocowpox virus, negatively stained. **D,** thin section of intracellular vaccinia virus; N = nucleoid; LB = lateral body; VM = viral membrane; DM = double membrane. **E,** thin section of extracellular vaccinia virus; VM = viral membrane; EM = extra viral membrane. Bar = 150 nm. All figures are same magnification.

the largest and most complex viruses, and a newly isolated virus can be assigned to the poxvirus group by its size and brick-shaped morphology. Poxviruses are assigned to genera (see Table 39–1) on the basis of close serologic and genetic relationships.[2] In addition *Parapoxvirus* species have a different surface structure (see below) which facilitates their recognition.

Initially studies were made on infectious virions extracted from disrupted cells. Very little virus is released naturally, and it was assumed to be identical to that released artificially. However, differences were found between artificially released (intracellular) and naturally released (extracellular) virions,[12] which are important when immunity is discussed (see below).

Vaccinia virus is about 200 × 250 nm and has small surface tubules about 10 nm wide (Figure 39–1,A). Virions showing tubules are referred to as M (mulberry) forms. Also seen is a small proportion of C (capsule) forms (Figure 39–1,B). The two forms

are interconvertible, and the differences are due to variation in the rates of dehydration during specimen preparation.[13]

Parapoxviruses are narrower (160 nm) and the M form has one long surface tubule which winds around the virion (Figure 39–1,C). This gives a characteristic appearance due to superimposition of top and bottom surfaces in electron micrographs.[14]

Internally, poxviruses have a biconcave "nucleoid" or core containing the DNA genome. Two lateral bodies fit into the concavities and the virion is bounded by a viral membrane. Inside the cell the virion is often invested with a double membrane (Figure 39–1,D). When released artificially, virions lose this double membrane. When released naturally, the outer element of the double membrane fuses with the cell membrane as the virus is extruded from the cell. The virus released is thus bounded by the inner element of the double membrane which contains viral antigens not present in intracellular forms (Figure 39–1,E).[12, 15, 16] The extra membrane is very labile and is not usually seen in preparations of extracellular virions, unless care is taken during specimen preparation.

The genome comprises one piece of double-stranded DNA with a molecular weight, in vaccinia, of 120 million. The molecule is cross-linked at each end and forms a closed circle of single-stranded DNA when denatured.[17] Physical maps of the genomes are being prepared, and differences have been detected in the fragments released by endonuclease digestion of DNA from closely related orthopoxviruses.[18, 19] This is probably the most reliable method of defining such species.[11]

Similar work on parapoxviruses is not so well advanced but their genomes show less variation.[20] Traditionally, a division has usually been made between bovine (pseudocowpox) and ovine (orf) infections and recent analyses using DNA probes have provided some evidence for this.[21] However, the differences are probably too minor to warrant placing the viruses in different species. Recent studies on the DNA of molluscum virus have shown that it has the general properties of poxvirus DNA and that two subtypes, based on DNA cleavage patterns, are in circulation.[22]

Recently, nucleotide sequences of some orthopoxvirus genes have been determined including those which code for the hemagglutinin, an envelope protein, a sequence required for growth in human cells, and a sequence which determines the hemorrhagic nature of the cowpox lesion.[23–26]

The isolated DNA of poxviruses is not infectious. Virus-coded enzymes are located in the core and play an essential role in transcribing the viral DNA. These enzymes include a DNA-dependent RNA polymerase, nucleotide transferases and methylases, deoxyribonucleases, and protein kinases, and their roles have been described recently.[15, 27] However, if the DNA of, say, rabbitpox virus is inoculated into cells together with ectromelia virus, infective rabbitpox virus is produced.[28] Evidently, the rabbitpox DNA is transcribed by enzymes provided by ectromelia virus.

Of interest is the finding that the RNA polymerase of vaccinia shows extensive homology with that from pro- and eukaryotes,[29] and that vaccinia and molluscum viruses code for a protein structurally and functionally homologous to epidermal growth factor.[22, 30]

The proteins of vaccinia have been resolved into over 100 polypeptides.[31] Differences have been found in the polypeptide composition of different orthopoxviruses,[32] but the polypeptides of different parapoxviruses are more homogeneous.[33] Poxviruses are antigenically complex and immunodiffusion techniques have detected 20 or more antigens. Some are found only in virus-free supernatants while others can only be extracted from virions.[34] Original reports of slight cross-reaction between different poxvirus genera have been confirmed by monoclonal antibody studies.[35]

Not all orthopoxviruses are antigenically identical and cross-reacting and species-specific neutralizing antigens have been investigated by serum absorption and monoclonal antibody studies.[35, 36] Up to five antigens are involved in the neutralization of orthopoxviruses artificially extracted from cells.[36] Naturally released virions have an extra antigen, and antibody to this antigen will neutralize naturally released but not artificially released virions.[12] The recognition of a monkeypox virus-specific antigen[37] and the development of methods for detection of antibody to it[38] have facilitated searches for the reservoir hosts of monkeypox virus

(see below).[39] Orthopoxviruses produce a hemagglutinin antigen which is easily separable from the virion and is present in the additional membrane of naturally released virus.[40]

There is some similarity between the predicted amino acid sequence of the hemagglutinin and that of several plasma proteins involved in blood coagulation and the virus antigen may function in a similar way, although the virus antigen only agglutinates fowl erythrocytes.[26]

Replication

There is space here for only a brief account of poxvirus replication. However, this topic has been the subject of excellent reviews.[11, 27]

Replication occurs in cytoplasmic factories usually referred to as "B-type" inclusions. These correspond to the classic Guarnieri bodies and contain viruses in various stages of assembly.[15, 41] Some species, for example, ectromelia and cowpox viruses, produce an additional "A-type" inclusion which corresponds to the Marchal or Downie body.[15, 41] In some strains of ectromelia and cowpox viruses the A-type inclusions contain mature virions.[11, 15]

Viral DNA synthesis occurs in the cytoplasm of infected cells, and cellular protein synthesis is inhibited. This facilitates biochemical analysis of poxvirus replication. Also the large size and complex structure of the virion enables virus uncoating and morphogenesis to be studied by electron microscopy.

No special receptors have been identified on the surfaces of poxviruses, and heat-inactivated and antibody-neutralized virions will penetrate susceptible cells, although not as efficiently as fully infectious virus.[42] Although most virions enter cells by pinocytosis and their uncoating commences in cytoplasmic vesicles, the outer membrane of a small proportion fuses with the cell membrane on penetration.[43]

Virus uncoating and the initiation of DNA replication is a complex process. Once inside the cell, viral cores are released by preexisting cellular enzymes and immediate-early transcription of at least part of the genome is accomplished by core enzymes while the genome is still in the core.[44] RNA and protein synthesis is required for delayed-early transcription and as this is accompanied by release of DNAse sensitive DNA it has been assumed that DNA released from the core is transcribed and replicated.[15, 27] Viral DNA is found in incompletely characterized cytoplasmic structures and was thought to be completely uncoated.[45] However, core polypeptides have also been detected in these structures and it has been suggested that the viral DNA is replicated and transcribed from viral cores, or '*deoxyribonucleoproteids*' and that any inoculum DNA sensitive to DNAse is from degraded virions and may play no part in replication or transcription.[46]

The presence of the core enzymes, which can transcribe some of the viral genome, provides an explanation for the phenomenon of nongenetic reactivation by poxviruses. If a heat-inactivated poxvirus is inoculated into a cell along with another live poxvirus, then the inactivated virus will replicate.[47] It is reasonable to assume that the enzymes necessary to complete the uncoating of the heated virus are provided by the active one.[15] The term "nongenetic reactivation" is used because the live poxvirus can be replaced by one which has damaged DNA and functional protein; in this case all the progeny is derived from the heated virus.[47]

Table 39–3
Laboratory Characteristics of Some Orthopoxviruses

	Smallpox	Monkeypox	Vaccinia	Cowpox	Camelpox
Pock on CAM	SOW	SHU*	PHU*-LOW	H*	SOW
Ceiling temperature[†]	37.5–38.5	39	41	40	38.5
Rabbit skin	TrN	IPC	V	IPC	TrN
A-type inclusion	−	−	−	+	−
Diffusible LS antigen	+	+	+	−	+
Specific antigens[‡]	Va	Mo	Va,Vc	−	Va,Vc
Surface antigens[§]	?	Mpx	Vac	Cpx	Cmp
Polypeptides	Spx	Mpx	Vac	Cpx	Cmp

CAM = chick chorioallantoic membrane; SOW = small opaque white; LOW = large opaque white; PHU = pale hemor-
rhagic ulcer; H = hemorrhagic; TrN = transient nodule; IPC = indurated lesion with purple center; V = variable
(TrN-IPC); LS antigen = presence of soluble LS antigen.
Biologic data from Fenner et al.[11]; serologic data from Gispen and Brand-Saathof[37] and Baxby[36]; polypeptide data from
Turner and Baxby.[32]
*Produce white pock mutants.
[†]Highest temperature (°C) which permits pock production on CAM.
[‡]Distribution of three antigens detected by absorbed gel diffusion.
[§]Specificities shown in cross-neutralization tests on absorbed sera.

Detailed comparisons have been made of the messenger RNA (mRNA) and proteins synthesized before and after the replication of viral DNA. Late RNA and proteins are the more complex, and this suggests that there is some control over transcription of inoculum DNA.[48, 49] If viral DNA synthesis is prevented, early protein synthesis continues, showing that one function of late proteins is to shut off the synthesis of some early ones. Biochemical and serologic analyses have shown that different structural and nonstructural antigens are produced before and after DNA replication.[34, 50] Enzymes such as the guanyl- and methyltransferases are synthesized prior to DNA replication, whereas the DNA-dependent RNA polymerase is synthesized late. Thus enzymes that function very early in the newly infected cell are synthesized at different stages of the replication cycle in the infected cell producing the inoculum.[15, 27]

Poxvirus cores can be produced in vitro by chemical treatment of purified virions.[51] The polypeptide composition and morphology of such cores has been compared to the properties of subviral components produced in vivo during uncoating and morphogenesis.[52, 53]

As described above, virus assembly takes place inside cytoplasmic inclusions, and the infectious virions which accumulate inside cells differ in important respects from those which are released naturally.

Although poxviruses replicate in the cytoplasm, and code for enzymes, for example, a DNA-dependent RNA polymerase, to facilitate this, there is evidence that the cell nucleus plays some role in the virus replication cycle, and recent evidence suggests that subunits of the cellular RNA polymerase II are selectively transported into the cytoplasm and used in virus replication.[54]

Poxviruses, with the exception of molluscum contagiosum virus, which has yet to be grown, are perhaps the easiest of viruses to cultivate. All orthopoxviruses produce pocks on the chick chorioallantoic membrane (CAM) and will produce cytopathic effects (CPE) in a wide variety of cell cultures.[11, 55] Laboratory characteristics which are used to identify orthopoxviruses are shown in Table 39–3. Parapoxviruses and Tanapox virus will not grow on the CAM but can be isolated in a number of cell cultures.[55]

SMALLPOX

Although smallpox has been eradicated, a brief account is given here. Not only did new information become available during the eradication campaign, but knowledge of the disease is essential to understand the strategy behind the campaign.

Epidemiology

Incidence

At the beginning of the twentieth century, smallpox was distributed worldwide but was gradually eliminated from some areas, notably Europe and North America. When the Intensified Global Eradication Campaign started in 1967, endemic smallpox was restricted to Asia, Africa south of the Sahara, the Indonesian archipelago, and South America. Table 39–4 shows the number of cases during the final years. Until 1973, India reported 30% to 50% of the total, and in 1974 it reported 87% of the world total of 218,367 cases.[1] Underreporting was common at first. For example, during 1966 to 1967 in a particular area of Bangladesh, 13 cases were reported from five villages. More detailed inquiries detected outbreaks in 23 villages in the area totaling 119 cases and 29 deaths.[56]

The distribution of endemic smallpox was not necessarily uniform. For instance, although the overall incidence in an area of West Pakistan was about 100 per 100,000, the disease never occurred simultaneously in more than 50 of the 1717 villages studied.[57]

Temporal and Geographic Distribution

Smallpox was seasonal and in Bangladesh the same word, *bashunto,* is used to denote "smallpox" and "spring." The factors which governed the seasonal distribution are not clear, and may be more "man-made" than natural.[58] For instance, transmission within families might be increased by overcrowding in rainy periods, while transmission between communities might be increased by the greater mobility during dry periods.

In the twentieth century the geographic distribution reflected the success of control measures. Of greater interest was the geographic distribution of the different viruses involved. Early clinical observations indicated that there were two epidemiologically distinct types of smallpox: that in Asia (variola major) had a high mortality (20%) whereas that in South America and southern Africa (variola minor, alastrim) caused low mortality (<1%). If the source of an outbreak in a nonendemic country was unknown, the differential clinical diagnosis could be made only retrospectively from the mortality. In 1961 a simple laboratory test was introduced which differentiated the two types. Variola major strains produced pocks on the CAM at 38.5°C, whereas variola minor strains would not do so above 37.5°C.[59] The smallpox mortality in Africa varied from less than 1% (eg, Botswana) to 12% (eg, Zaire),[1] and laboratory studies showed that some African strains could be separated from both variola major and minor.[60] It is probably reasonable to regard the strains as forming a spectrum of virulence from variola major in Asia to variola minor in South America, with the disease in Africa caused by variola minor and a variety of strains differing in virulence from the classic types.[1]

Age, Sex, and Other Factors

Smallpox in the unvaccinated was a disease of children. Of 23,546 cases examined in India during 1974 to 1975, 30.7% occurred in children under 5 and 70% in children under 14 years.[61] With no restraint on movement both sexes were equally affected. However, where movement of young females was restricted or where young males traveled in search of work, the incidence was higher in males (64%).[61] The incidence was higher in low socioeconomic groups. This presumably reflected overcrowded conditions. In nonendemic areas there was a high incidence of hospital-associated cases. For example, of 680 cases in Europe during 1950 to 1971, 146 occurred in hospital workers and their families and a further 211 in patients and visitors.[62]

Pathogenesis

Transmission

The eradication campaign was mounted on the assumption that the disease was transmitted, directly or indirectly, from a human case and that there was no animal reservoir. However, some concern was caused by the isolation from monkeypox virus stocks,[63] and animals caught in Indonesia and Zaire,[64, 65] of viruses (so-called "whitepox" viruses) which were indistinguishable from smallpox. These strains were isolated in smallpox laboratories and after detailed inquiries into the circumstances of their isolation, unsuccessful attempts to isolate similar monkeypox "mutants" elsewhere, and detailed study of the strains, it was concluded that they represent contamination with smallpox virus.[1, 66, 67] As such they did not represent an animal reservoir of smallpox.[1]

Smallpox patients were most infectious in the early stages of the illness, but not before and patients transmitted the infection most commonly four to six days after the illness started.[58] At this time oropharyngeal lesions were shedding virus and could infect contacts directly or contaminate bedding, etc.[68, 69] This respiratory virus was thought to be the most important source of infection, but patients were isolated and considered infectious until all the crusts separated.

Airborne transmission of smallpox to other than close contacts has always been a controversial subject.[8] Opponents of the idea of airborne spread usually point to missed cases, or infectious mobile patients before being diagnosed, as the source.[1]

Although indirect infection of, for example, laundry workers, by contaminated bedding has occurred, the most common mode of transmission was via close contact with an infectious patient. It has been said that smallpox was one of the most communicable of diseases. This is not so; only about 30% of susceptible contacts became infected.[70] The picture that emerged was of a disease which spread slowly, required close contact, and in which one case infected relatively few secondary cases.

Transmission was most common among family groups with spread to outside groups through visits to smallpox patients or by ambulatory patients.[58] In Sierra Leone people attending the funeral of a smallpox victim spread infection to 38 villages.[71]

Patients with variola minor were less ill and more mobile than those with variola major, and transmission of the former was often more difficult to control. In one instance in Somalia, infection was transmitted among a group of 46 nomads for 5 months during

Table 39–4

Smallpox Cases Reported to World Health Organization, 1971 to 1979

Year	World	Eastern Mediterranean*	Africa	Southeast Asia†	South America
1971	52,806	7770	26,512	18,505	19
1972	65,153	8308	18,074	38,595	
1973	135,859	9304	5441	121,108	
1974	218,367	7883	4443	206,040	
1975	19,278	14	3935	15,329	
1976	954	39	915		
1977	3234	3229	5		
1978‡	2				
1979					

*Includes Somalia.
†Includes India and Bangladesh.
‡Laboratory-associated cases in England.
Data from Fenner et al.[1]

which time only 19 of 37 susceptibles became infected.[72] Presumably, if the outbreak had not been detected, it would have persisted much longer.

Incubation Period and Prodromal Illness

The incubation period was characteristically 12 days, but contacts were quarantined for 16 to 17 days before those showing no signs of illness were released.

The virus infected via the respiratory mucosa but patients were not infectious at that stage.[58] The virus was transferred to the local lymph nodes from where it spread to internal organs, particularly lymph nodes, spleen, liver, bone marrow, and lungs.[1] Consequently these organs were damaged during the incubation period.

The first clinical sign of infection was a prodromal illness which lasted two to four days, characterized by malaise quickly followed by headache, backache, and a fever which could reach 40.5°C. Rigor was present in 60%, vomiting in 50%, delirium in 15%, and a fleeting erythematous rash in 10%.[58]

The onset of the prodrome coincided with viremia; detection of viremia during the early stages of the rash was a poor prognostic sign.[73] It was during this viremia that virus was distributed to the skin, initiating the characteristic eruption.

Host Response

Clinical

Excellent early accounts,[58, 74, 75] though still valuable, have largely been superseded by the World Health Organization report.[1]

The eruption usually started on the third day of the prodrome; oral lesions would have been present the day before. The exanthem appeared first on the face, spread to the forearms and hands, then to the lower limbs and trunk. The rash was distributed centrifugally—an important diagnostic feature.[74] The lesions were more numerous on the face, hands, and forearms than on the upper arms, and more numerous on the feet and calves than the thighs and trunk. Hollows such as the axillae and front of the elbows were often spared but prominences such as the forehead and knees often had more lesions. The lesions started as macules which quickly became papules. These developed into vesicles by about the fifth day of illness and pustules by about the eighth day. The pustules dried out by the ninth to tenth day to become crusts which

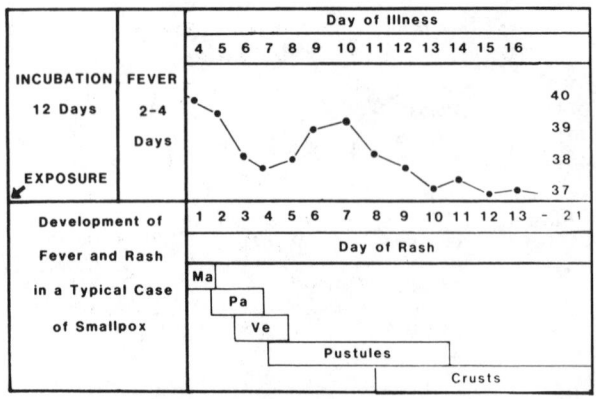

Figure 39-2. Representative clinical chart of a typical case of smallpox. Ma = macules; Pa = papules; Ve = vesicles.

usually became detached by about 3 weeks. The prodromal fever subsided as the eruption appeared and the patients usually felt much better. In many cases a second fever developed about seven to nine days later (Figure 39-2).

When smallpox was still a serious problem, some stressed the dangers of emphasizing too much the "typical" case of smallpox. These would be diagnosed correctly and the unusually severe case, misdiagnosed as, for example, acute leukemia, and the unusually mild case, missed altogether, would cause most danger to the community. Smallpox was usually separated into four clinical varieties (Table 39-5).[1, 58, 68] The figures are a little misleading because relatively fewer modified and ordinary cases would have been admitted to hospital, and the total numbers of vaccinated and unvaccinated people exposed to infection are unknown.

The *hemorrhagic* variety was most serious. In Rao's series of 6932 smallpox cases, there were 200 hemorrhagic patients of whom 192 died.[58] This variety was characterized by hemorrhages into the skin and/or mucous membranes, and patients died before the focal lesions developed. The antibody response was poor, and there was a high titer of virus and antigen in the blood.[76]

The *malignant* or *flat* variety affected 6.7% of Rao's unvaccinated patients and 1.3% of vaccinated patients causing 95% and 66% mortality, respectively.[58] The term "flat" referred to the lesions, sometimes described as "velvety," which remained flush with the skin.[1, 68] They also developed more slowly than in the "typical" case of smallpox.

The *ordinary* or *classic* variety corresponded to the typical case of smallpox (Figure 39-3A), the general progress of which is shown in Figure 39-2. Almost 80% of Rao's patients fell into this category. The case fatality rates were 3% and 30% in the vaccinated and unvaccinated, respectively (see Table 39-5). In the ordinary variety the distribution and evolution of the rash corresponded to the general account given above.

Modified smallpox usually occurred in those with immunity from previous vaccination; 92% of the 937 patients with modified smallpox in Rao's series had previously been vaccinated.[58] The prodrome was usually less severe and the second bout of fever often absent. The lesions developed quicker than usual, the pustular stage was often absent, and crusting could occur as early as the seventh day.

The distinction between ordinary and modified smallpox was not made on the extent of eruption, but on the less severe prodrome and quicker development of the eruption in the latter.

Some highly immune contacts had the prodrome only (*variola sine eruptione*). Subclinical infection in the nonimmune was rare, but studies suggested that it occurred in 30% to 50% of well-vaccinated contacts.[1, 58]

Complications included osteomyelitis or arthritis and conjunctivitis in unvaccinated children, and respiratory problems in probably all unvaccinated cases of ordinary or more severe smallpox.[58, 68] The case fatality rate in pregnant women was 27% in the vaccinated and 61% in the unvaccinated compared to 6% and 35%, respectively, in all cases.[58]

Immunologic Response.—Those who recovered developed a long-lasting immunity. Second attacks occurred in about 1 in 1000 patients and then only after 15 to 20 years.[1, 58]

Both humoral and cellular immune responses were important. Circulating antibodies could be detected by the end of the first

Table 39–5

Age Incidence and Vaccination Status of Varieties of Smallpox Seen at Infectious Diseases Hospital, Madras, 1961 to 1972

Age and Vaccination Status	Clinical Variety										
	Hemorrhagic		Flat		Ordinary		Modified		Total		
	Cases	CF(%)	Cases	CF(%)	Cases	CF(%)	Cases	CF(%)	Cases	PD	CF(%)
Unvaccinated											
0–4	24	100	169	93	1837	37	61	0	2091	59	41
5–24	34	100	48	100	1072	18	12	0	1166	33	23
25–44	16	94	110	100	193	31	2	0	222	6.2	38
44+	11	100	8	88	45	51	1	0	65	1.8	63
Total	85	99	236	95	3147	30	76	0	3544	100	36
Vaccinated											
0–4	1	100	3	100	52	19	34	0	90	2.7	16
5–24	38	100	9	66	1017	2	475	0	1539	45.6	4
25–44	69	91	28	64	1130	3	321	0	1548	45.5	7
44+	7	86	5	60	168	8	31	0	211	6.2	9
Total	115	94	45	66	2367	3.2	861	0	3388	100	6

Rearranged and recalculated from data collected by Rao.[58] CF(%) = case fatality rate; PD = proportionate distributions of patients by age.

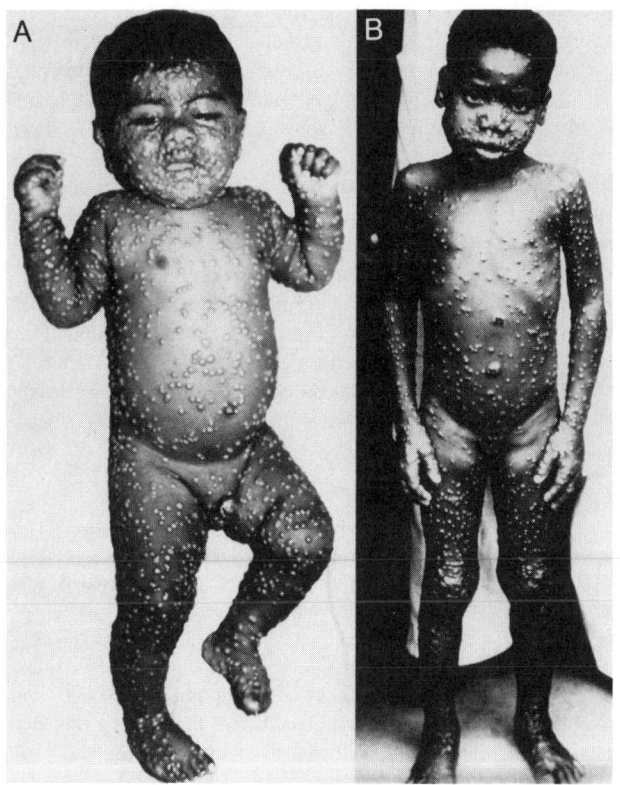

Figure 39–3. A, ordinary variety of smallpox at the vesiculopustular stage. This photograph,[1] in color, was used as one of the "smallpox recognition cards" during the Smallpox Eradication Campaign. (Courtesy of Dr. I. Arita, World Health Organization, Smallpox Eradication Unit.) **B,** human monkeypox in the eighth day of rash. (Courtesy of Dr. J. G. Breman, and *Bulletin of the World Health Organization*.)

week of illness and reached maximum levels by 12 to 21 days.[77] Complement-fixing and hemagglutinin-inhibiting antibodies declined after a few months, but neutralizing antibodies could be detected after 5 years or more.[1, 77] Unfortunately, tests for neutralizing antibody used artificially released virus, and it was antibody to the naturally released forms that was important. Animals immunized with inactivated virus have neutralizing antibody to intracellular virus, but none to extracellular virus. They are not fully immune and their sera will not passively protect. Animals with antibody to extracellular virus are immune, and their sera will passively protect.[78]

The importance of cell-mediated immunity (CMI) was shown by the poor response of people with thymic aplasia who, when vaccinated, produced antibody but not delayed hypersensitivity, and who developed progressive vaccinia.[79] CMI is induced by a viral antigen on the surface of infected cells. Animals immunized with this antigen resist challenge, although their sera neutralize neither intracellular nor extracellular virus and do not passively protect.[80]

Prevention and Treatment

Nothing was available that would successfully treat smallpox once the disease was clinically obvious.

Vaccination.—All countries have discontinued routine vaccination, but the use of recombinant vaccinia vaccines is being considered (see below). Vaccine strains differ in laboratory properties and human pathogenicity[11, 81] and those that produced severe reactions were discontinued. By the late 1960s routine vaccines were prepared from the British (Lister/Elstree), American (Wyeth), and Russian (EM63) strains. An attenuated vaccine (CV1-78) was available for those at risk for whom routine vaccination was inadvisable.[81]

The vaccination reaction was classified as follows.[82] Any reaction producing a vesicle was a *major* reaction. Failure to produce a vesicle was an *equivocal* reaction. The vesicle indicated that virus replication had occurred and immunity had been induced. The major response on revaccination developed more quickly than on primary vaccination. Equivocal primary vaccination was usually due to incorrect technique or low-titer vaccine. Equivocal revaccination was additionally due to hypersensitivity and could be induced by heated virus or antigen.

The effect of vaccination can be seen by comparing the distribution of the different varieties of smallpox in different age groups of vaccinated and unvaccinated individuals (see Table 39–5).[1, 58] The duration of immunity varied in different individuals and immunity too low to prevent infection would usually prevent death. The WHO certificate was valid for 3 years. A disadvantage of this certificate was that it had no provision for recording the result of revaccination. Consequently a "valid" certificate of revaccination did not necessarily mean that the revaccination had been successful. Vaccination of contacts during the incubation period had some effect in reducing morbidity and mortality.[1, 58, 68]

There were no contraindications to vaccination in close contacts. Routine vaccination in nonendemic areas was not offered to the pregnant, the immunosuppressed, and those with eczema, immunologic defects, or leukemia and similar malignancies.

Vaccination should be offered to those working with monkeypox, cowpox, and vaccinia viruses. It will not always prevent, but should reduce the severity of, accidental infection with high-titer laboratory stocks.[83]

In addition to the local lesion, vaccination usually produced a mild febrile illness with axillary involvement. However, certain complications could also occur, particularly in primary vaccinees. Their incidence varied, perhaps due to differences in reporting and in the vaccine strains used.

Postvaccinial Encephalitis.—In England and Wales[84] and the United States[85] the rate per million vaccinations was 2.3 to 2.9, with about 25% mortality. In Holland the incidence dropped from 1 in 4000 to 1 in 21,000 with a change in vaccine strain.[86]

Vaccinees with immunologic defects sometimes developed *vaccinia gangrenosa* (progressive vaccinia, vaccinia necrosum). The incidence in England and Wales[84] and the United States[85] was about 2.6 and 1.0 per million vaccinations, respectively. Although rare, the outcome in those not treated was grave.

Eczematous patients are unusually susceptible to vaccinia virus, and *eczema vaccinatum* was a serious problem in eczematous vaccinees and contacts. In England and Wales during 1961 to 1970 there were 57 cases in vaccinees with seven deaths and 104 cases with 14 deaths in eczematous contacts.[84]

Generalized vaccinia, sometimes misdiagnosed as modified smallpox, was not usually fatal. The estimated incidence in the United States was 290 per million vaccinations.[85] Because vaccination produced an obvious and scratchable lesion, accidental infections, for example, ocular and genital, occurred both in vaccinees and contacts. The estimated incidence in the United States was 525 per million vaccinations.[85]

Military personnel in the United States and the Soviet Union are still vaccinated and vaccination complications are still reported.[87]

Dermal and, to a lesser extent, neurologic complications were treated with anti-vaccinia gammaglobulin and/or methisazone with considerable success.[88, 89]

Serum Prophylaxis.—Anti-vaccinia gammaglobulin, if given to smallpox contacts early in the incubation period, reduced the incidence fourfold.[90]

Chemoprophylaxis.—Various thiosemicarbazones were shown to inhibit the replication of poxviruses in vitro. One derivative, *n*-methylisatin β-thiosemicarbazone (Methisazone, Marboran) was tested on smallpox contacts in Madras.[91] Various dosage schedules were tested, but overall the incidence of smallpox was reduced sixfold and the mortality by fivefold. All the contacts were vaccinated after contact, but this would affect control and test groups equally. This use of methisazone was the first successful application of chemoprophylaxis to virus infections.

ERADICATION OF SMALLPOX

A number of features combined to make smallpox an ideal candidate for eradication: (1) It was a socially acceptable disease with high incidence and mortality. This provided the impetus to eradicate it. (2) There was no animal reservoir. (3) It was not very communicable. (4) It had a relatively long incubation period. (5) During incubation the patient was not infectious. (6) There were no chronic carriers or infectious subclinical cases. (7) Infected patients could be recognized easily. (8) Smallpox virus is immunologically stable and homogeneous and conferred a high degree of immunity. (9) An efficient vaccine was available. Points (2) to (7) meant that the source of infection was the smallpox patient and his immediate environment, and also meant that outbreaks spread slowly and could be controlled quickly.

WHO attached particular importance to the control of smallpox, and from 1958 it encouraged governments to attempt eradication. From 1960 to 1966, 24 countries reported success, but smallpox remained a serious problem in the major endemic areas. The WHO general assembly in 1966 decided to promote an intensified smallpox eradication campaign, which it was hoped would eradicate smallpox within 10 years.

The Plan

The proposed plan stressed the importance of mass vaccination and the development of case detection and reporting systems, and separated the campaign into three phases.[82]

Attack Phase

For areas with a high incidence of smallpox (>5/100,000) and less than 80% of the population vaccinated, the priority was systematic mass vaccination, and improvement of surveillance, reporting, and containment.

Consolidation Phase

For areas with an incidence of less than 5 per 100,000 and where 80% or more had been vaccinated. The objective was the eradication of smallpox from the area. This was to be achieved by maintaining the level of immunity and ensuring that all cases were recognized, isolated, and their contacts vaccinated. Laboratory facilities were developed to identify specimens from all isolated cases. Surveillance activities had to be sufficiently sensitive to confirm the absence of cases. Because of the ease with which smallpox crossed national boundaries, a country from which smallpox had been eliminated was referred to as "smallpox-free," and the term "eradicated" used for continents.

Maintenance Phase

Relevant to areas free of endemic smallpox and intended to ensure that they remained so. Vaccination was continued, but major emphasis was placed on the investigation of every suspect case.

The longest smallpox-free period broken by detection of an endemic case was 8 months and it was proposed that an area could be declared smallpox-free if no cases were detected by intensive searches during a 2-year period. It was acknowledged that certain countries would present special problems and that plans would be modified in the light of experience.[82]

The campaign was coordinated by the WHO Smallpox Eradication Unit headed by Drs D.A. Henderson and I. Arita, which provided epidemiologists, established reference laboratories for diagnosis and vaccine control, and provided expert advice and encouragement. Where possible, campaigns were organized and staffed by nationals of the country concerned. In some cases international campaigns were conducted such as by the Smallpox Eradication and Measles Control Programme organized in 20 countries of Western and Central Africa by WHO and the US Agency for International Development.[1, 70]

Mass Vaccination

Considerable progress was made in developing dried vaccine which would not deteriorate in tropical conditions. The technique of vaccination was simplified, and vaccine conserved, by the introduction of the bifurcated needle[1] (Figure 39–4,A). However smallpox was not eradicated by mass vaccination. In some countries, even though 80% or more had been vaccinated, smallpox circulated in the unvaccinated.[92, 93] In other countries it proved impossible to reach the 80% level.[61]

More important, it became evident that smallpox could be eradicated without mass vaccination.[70]

Surveillance and Containment

Routine Reporting

This was often ineffective. It often underestimated the total incidence, and because the system was often slow, missed cases could spread infection before being traced.[56]

Active Surveillance

The key to smallpox eradication was active surveillance and containment.[70] Advantage was taken of the seasonal incidence, of low communicability, and the fact that not all villages in an area would be affected. Consequently, aggressive activity timed to coincide with the seasonal low incidence rapidly eliminated smallpox without mass vaccination. In 1967 to 1968 Sierra Leone had the highest smallpox attack rate in the world. The eradication campaign started there in January 1968, and the last case occurred in April 1969. Three of the four largest smallpox outbreaks there were

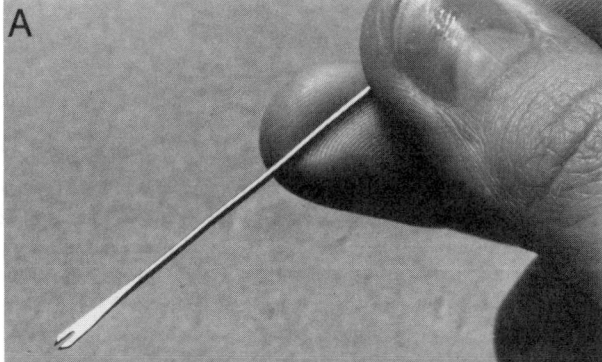
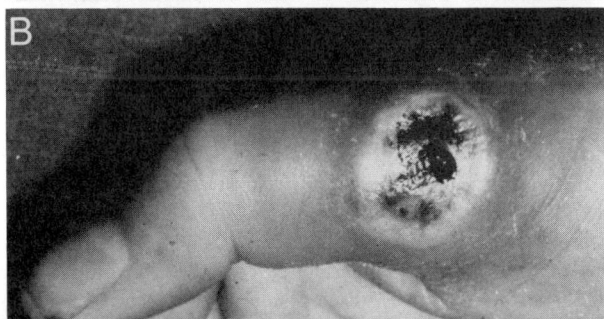
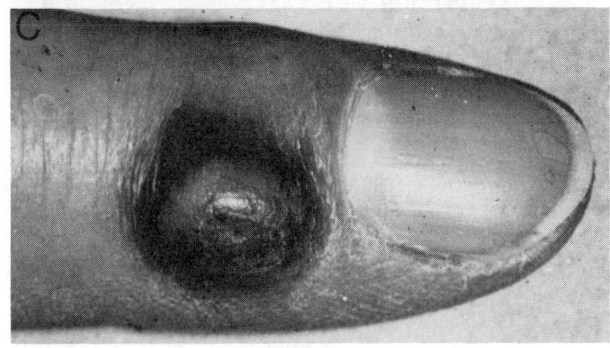

Figure 39–4. A, the bifurcated needle, which greatly facilitated vaccination. **B,** human cowpox. (Courtesy of Mr J. McNae.) **C,** human orf. (Courtesy of Dr. J. Nagington.)

controlled without mass vaccination.[92] Similar successes were reported for the 19 other participating countries in West and Central Africa.[70]

Active surveillance involved trained workers searching for cases. Special recognition cards showing typical cases (see Figure 39–3,A) were shown at schools, markets, etc. Posters were displayed prominently and rewards offered.

Special Searches

India, the main reservoir of variola major, was a particular problem in view of its large area and population (548 million in 1971). In addition to active surveillance measures, a number of special searches were organized. The results were impressive.[61] In Uttar Pradesh 354 cases were reported from 21 districts in the week before the search which detected 5989 new cases in 1483 villages from 47 additional districts. Detailed assessments were made of the effectiveness of the searches to ensure that remote areas were covered.[1, 61] By 1977 smallpox occurred only in Somalia.

Somalia

Although the population of Somalia is not large (3.8 million in 1975), much of it is nomadic and inaccessible. The difficulties in tracing outbreaks were considerable and smallpox could persist for months in nomadic communities.[72]

Transmission was thought to have ended early in 1977, but cases were detected from March 1977 onward and in May the Somali government declared a state of emergency. The problem was not the number of cases, but their widespread distribution in nomadic groups. There were only 3229 cases, but they occurred in 947 outbreaks in 11 of the country's 16 regions. As a result of intensive efforts by Somali and international workers, the last case was detected in October 1977.[93] Ironically the last patient was a hospital cook who had not been vaccinated.[94]

Confirmation of Eradication

This was dependent on intensive searches failing to detect smallpox in the 2 years following the last reported case. The techniques used were those which had detected rare cases in the special searches.[1, 61, 93] After their "last" case had been detected, countries set up "rumor registers," "rash-with-fever" registers, and offered rewards. All suspicious cases were investigated. In India during 1976 to 1977 the techniques that had traced smallpox during 1973 to 1975 detected 833,412 cases of varicella, 629,624 cases of measles, and 146,855 other rash-with-fever cases. Specimens were examined from every suspect case, every outbreak where containment had been started (even in error), and from every varicella outbreak in which a death occurred. No case of smallpox was found.[61]

At the end of its 2-year smallpox-free period each country was visited by an international commission which assessed the evidence and, where necessary, made field visits to remote areas.[1]

Finally an independent Global Commission for the Certification of Smallpox Eradication assessed all the evidence and visited countries where necessary. In late 1979, the Global Commission concluded that smallpox had been eradicated, a conclusion accepted by the WHO general council in May 1980. Despite continued surveillance, no further cases have been reported.[1]

Costs and Benefits

The total cost of the campaign was estimated at US $312 million. Of this $38 million came from the WHO regular budget and $43 million in cash, vaccine, vehicles, etc, from extra donations to WHO. Direct bilateral aid to endemic countries totaled $32 million, made up mainly of vaccine valued at $10.5 million donated to Asia by Russia and $18.5 million donated by the United States to finance the campaign in Western and Central Africa. The endemic countries probably spent $200 million on their own behalf.[1] During these years nonendemic countries were spending large sums on routine vaccination and in controlling the occasional imported epidemic. If smallpox had not been eradicated, these efforts, and similar efforts to control smallpox in endemic areas, would be costing about $10^9 per year.[1]

Unfortunately, in many instances those spared the ravages of smallpox will succumb to other diseases. However, valuable demographic and epidemiologic data have been obtained, and the money saved will, it is hoped, be used for other health projects.

In addition, developing countries now have teams of enthusiastic epidemiologists who will form the nuclei of expanding health services. The eradication of smallpox marks a tremendous achievement in preventive medicine and international cooperation.

The Future

It is most unlikely that there are undiscovered foci of natural smallpox. In the short term we can consider the deliberate or accidental release of smallpox virus as a potential danger. That the former could occur has been acknowledged,[1] and accidental escape of smallpox virus from a laboratory in Birmingham, UK, occurred in 1978. The outbreak was quickly controlled and only two cases resulted.[95] Only two reference laboratories retain smallpox virus and there are proposals to destroy all remaining stocks of the virus.[1] The Global Commission recommended that 200 million doses of vaccine should be stockpiled to cover possible future emergencies.[1]

That smallpox virus could evolve from another orthopoxvirus is a remote possibility that should be measured on an evolutionary time scale. Perhaps more likely is the possibility that an existing orthopoxvirus may develop enhanced virulence for man without actually becoming smallpox virus.

RECOMBINANT VACCINIA VACCINES

With the eradication of smallpox all looked forward to the final end of vaccination and its complications. However recent developments could mean perhaps greater use of smallpox vaccine than ever. A major breakthrough was the demonstration that foreign genes can be inserted into the vaccinia genome.[96, 97] Such recombinant vaccinia strains are still infectious and animals immunized with them usually make antibody to the foreign gene product. The vaccinia genome has spare capacity of at least 25,000 base pairs[98] and this allows multiple copies of the gene, or a number of different genes, to be inserted.[99] The list of genes inserted is extensive; it includes genes from human viruses, for example, hepatitis B[100] and human immunodeficiency virus (HIV),[101] animal viruses such as vesicular stomatitis[102] and rabies,[103] protozoa (eg, *Plasmodium*[104]), and pharmacologically important products such as factor VIII[105] and neuropeptides.[106]

These developments open up the possibility of using the well-established practice of smallpox vaccine production and delivery to facilitate large-scale production of recombinant vaccines for human and animal use and for production of important biopharmaceuticals.[106, 107] Before such strains can be used as vaccines, more information is required on, for example, genetic stability and the nature of the immune response to the foreign gene products. Also, and perhaps more important, one has to consider the incidence of untoward responses in vaccinees. In this respect it is of interest that foreign genes are usually inserted into the vaccinia thymidine kinase gene, thus inactivating it, and that evidence is accumulating that such recombinants are probably attenuated.[108] Epidemiologic factors need also to be considered, particularly if the recombinants are to be used as veterinary vaccines. Of importance here is the possibility that the vaccine strains may spread to other species, perhaps wildlife, and interact with orthopoxviruses already established there.[109]

MONKEYPOX

Monkeypox virus was first isolated from Asiatic monkeys,[110] and although other outbreaks occurred in captive animals relatively little attention was paid to it until 1970 when human cases were reported from Africa.[111]

Epidemiology

Human monkeypox has only been reported from West and Central Africa, particularly Zaire (Figure 39–5) and more than 400 cases had been reported by 1987.[83] Although the first isolations of monkeypox virus were made from captive Asiatic monkeys, the virus is obviously indigenous to parts of Africa. Despite its name there is little evidence that African monkeys become naturally infected and they are unlikely to be a reservoir host. Recent surveys in Zaire have detected monkeypox-specific antibody in a high proportion of squirrels caught in the vicinity of human cases,[39] and the suggestion that squirrels are an important reservoir for the virus in Zaire is sound.

Human Infection

Transmission

Human monkeypox is less communicable than was smallpox, the attack rates among unvaccinated contacts being 12% and greater than 37%, respectively.[112] The precise mode of infection of index cases is unclear but could be through handling infected animals. Person-to-person transmission is uncommon and human transmission beyond four generations has not been recorded.[112, 113]

Clinical Features

The clinical features and pathogenesis of human monkeypox are essentially those of a modified or ordinary case of smallpox (see Figure 39–3,B). However, lymphadenopathy and cropping of lesions is more common in monkeypox.[114, 115] Infection is most common in children and the unvaccinated; a survey in Zaire showed that 262 of 282 cases (95%) were in children less than 15 years old and 247 of those (94%) had not been vaccinated.[115] No deaths have occurred in the vaccinated or in children over 10 but the overall mortality in 250 unvaccinated cases is 11% and 15% in children less than 4.[115]

Control

No human cases have occurred outside the endemic area, and there is little risk of it being introduced into developed countries. Although occasional cases are now being reported in those previously vaccinated,[115] human monkeypox is not considered a serious risk.[1, 116] In view of the severity of infection, those working with monkeypox should be vaccinated.[83]

COWPOX

It is not always appreciated that cowpox only occurs in continental Europe and Britain; there have been no laboratory confirmed cases from other areas. Cowpox was so called because it was isolated from cattle and farmworkers in contact with them. However, recent observations suggest that cowpox is not enzootic in cattle. Serologic and clinical surveys show that bovine cowpox

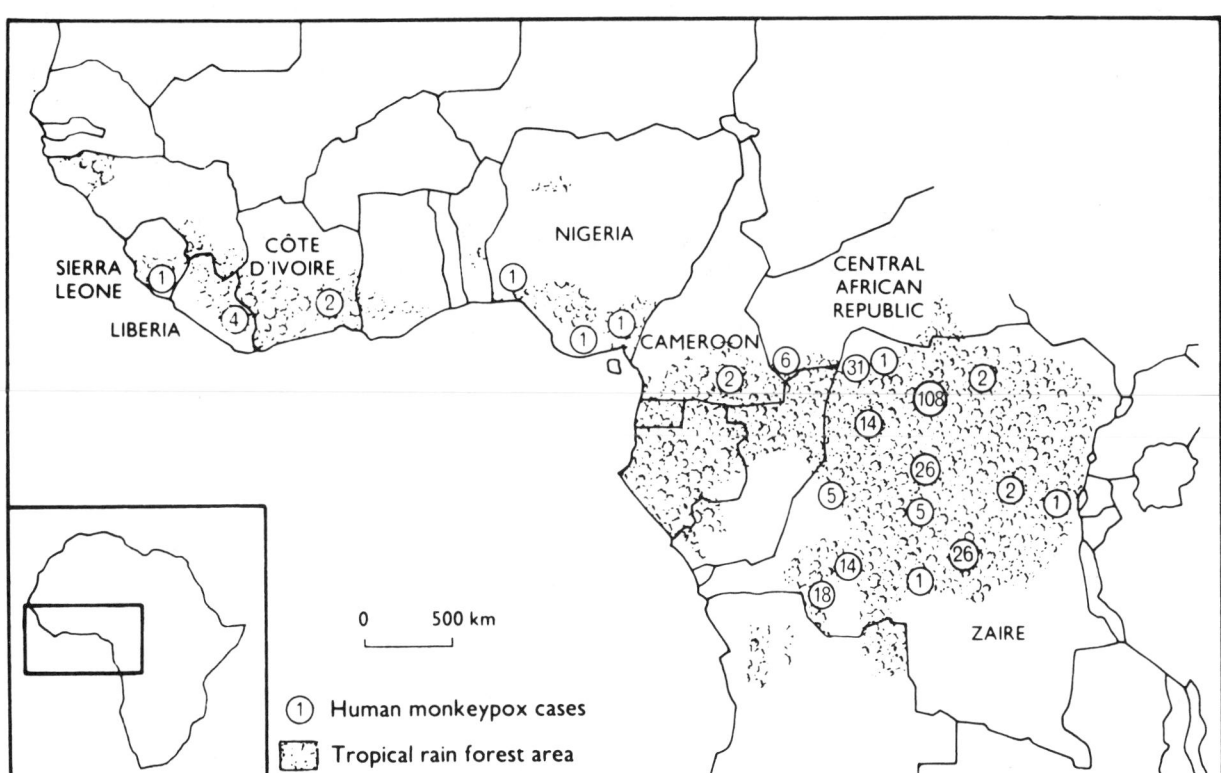

Figure 39–5. Map showing the distribution of human monkeypox cases 1970–1987. (Courtesy of the World Health Organization.)

is extremely rare and human cases occur without contact with cattle.[117] The actual reservoir has not been detected but it is generally believed to be a small wild rodent.[1, 83, 117] Of particular interest is the finding that natural infections occur in domestic cats[3, 83, 118] and the cat is now the most commonly reported host. Human cases have resulted from contact with infected cats.[119]

Human infection is usually more severe than primary vaccination (see Figure 39–4,B) and some patients, particularly children, are admitted to hospital. Lesions occur on the hands and/or face and are usually hemorrhagic.[117] A diagnosis of anthrax is not uncommon.

The possibility of infection from cats should be considered in endemic areas, but the fact that so few human cases are reported suggests that cowpox is not so infectious for humans and/or that most infections are trivial and not reported.[83, 119] Not all human cases are traceable to cats or cows and indirect spread also possibly occurs.

Viruses closely resembling cowpox virus have caused fatal infections of big cats in the Moscow Zoo and of elephants in German zoos and circuses.[120] The ecology and laboratory properties of these viruses are presently under review.

PSEUDOCOWPOX AND ORF

Poxviruses with the characteristic *Parapoxvirus* morphology are enzootic in cattle, sheep, and goats and have a worldwide distribution. Human infection is an occupational hazard of those handling infected animals. The viruses causing ovine and bovine infections are extremely closely related but minor differences have been found by using DNA probes.[21] The viruses can be isolated in tissue culture[55] but reliance is usually placed on the characteristic electron microscopic appearance of the virion for confirmation of diagnosis (see Figure 39–1,C).[55, 121]

Host Response

Attention has been paid to erythema multiforme as a complication of human orf.[121] However, most infections are mild and probably go unreported; consequently the proportion of cases with this complication must be very low. A detailed survey of 119 cases of human orf has been published.[121]

The lesion in man, usually on the fingers, begins as an inflammatory papule. This enlarges to become a large bluish-red granulomatous lesion (see Figure 39–4,C).[121] It usually crusts and regresses without vesicle formation. The lesions may take several weeks to heal, but are surprisingly painless—a useful diagnostic feature.

Immunity is poor and reinfection occurs.[122] It is probable that most people handling infected animals will become infected at some time, many more than once. Management of human cases is supportive. Occasional cases have been treated with idoxuridine,[123, 124] but no trials have been done to prove beneficial effect.

MOLLUSCUM CONTAGIOSUM

Molluscum contagiosum is a common, benign poxvirus disease of the skin and mucous membranes characterized by an umbilicated papule. Although Thomas Bateman published the first description of molluscum contagiosum in 1814, Edward Jenner left a clear account of it, written nearly 20 years earlier, which was not published until 1931.[125] Serial propagation of molluscum contagiosum virus in tissue culture has been reported,[126] but not confirmed by other investigators, although the virus does express some functions in tissue culture.[127, 128] This cytotoxicity may be mistaken for the specific CPE produced by, for example, herpes simplex virus.[129] Molluscum contagiosum virus infection has been thought to be confined to humans, but lesions that are clinically and histologically similar to the human disease have been reported in captive chimpanzees[130] and kangaroos.[131]

Epidemiology

The disease occurs throughout the world with variable frequency. The majority of prevalence studies have been conducted in the South Pacific; one study of children less than 10 years old found a prevalence rate of 22% and an incidence of 6% per year.[132] Lynch has estimated the prevalence rate in the United States to be approximately 1%.[133] In studies from a variety of countries, attack rates for previously uninfected exposed persons range from 12% to 75%.[134] While the disease may develop at any age, the majority of cases are found in children, with boys being affected more frequently than girls.

Pathogenesis
Transmission

Transmission is probably by direct contact or autoinoculation[133]; fomites may also play a role.[135] Experimental transmission to humans has been achieved with an incubation period of 2 to 7 weeks.[127] Outbreaks have been reported among children attending swimming pools, and adults attending Turkish baths, and also among wrestlers; beauty parlors, bath towels, tatooing, and bird mites have also been implicated by various investigators.[127] The influence of poverty, overcrowding, and poor hygiene has been demonstrated by spread within families in Alaska and Fiji.[127] Sexual transmission has been suggested by several workers.[134, 136, 137] Genital infection seems to be more common, or at least more commonly reported. In the United States genital cases have increased tenfold between 1966 and 1983,[138] and in England fourfold from 1971 to 1985.[139] The incidence of subclinical infection is not known, nor is the role of immunity in recovery from infection or in the prevention of reinfection. However, experimental studies show that whereas many immunologically normal adults are resistant to infection, widespread lesions may occur in adults with impaired immunity.[140]

Host Response

The epidermis within the molluscum lesion is markedly hypertrophied and hyperplastic. Infected cells interspersed with normal cells are seen in an area of epithelium spanning six to ten rete ridges. Above the normal-appearing basal layer are pear-shaped lobules of hypertrophied epidermal cells containing multiple cytoplasmic inclusions (molluscum bodies or Henderson-Paterson bodies) which compress the nucleus.[127, 137] These inclusions are made up of multiple nonmembrane-bound vacuoles containing virus particles in various stages of maturation. The lobules are slanted toward the center of the lesion, forming a cup-shaped crater. The mass of infected cells in the crater constitutes the white curdlike core that the clinician recognizes as the "molluscum body." The epidermal lesion is surrounded by a few layers of a circumferentially oriented connective tissue capsule. Inflammatory changes are slight or absent.[127, 137]

The lesions, which begin as minute papules, are usually 3 to 7 mm in diameter. When mature, they are discrete, smooth, waxy, dome-shaped, pearly or flesh-colored papules, usually with a characteristic central umbilication containing a caseous plug which is easily expressed. Often there is a mildly erythematous base. The lesion may appear translucent, which has led to the descriptive colloquial term "water-wart." Most commonly, one to 20 lesions are present. Lesions may be located on any area of the skin and mucous membranes. Distribution of the lesions is usually random, but occasionally multiple small papules are grouped around an initial, larger lesion, and sometimes the papules become confluent in the linear site of a scratch mark. In children, lesions are found anywhere on the trunk and proximal extremities; in adults, lesions are most often confined to the lower abdominal wall, pubic area, inner thighs, and genitalia. Less typical varieties of molluscum contagiosum include hundreds of lesions, giant lesions up to 2 cm in diameter, and isolated lesions on the palms, soles, or face. While lesions are usually asymptomatic, mild pruritus may be present. Lesions near the eyelid may be complicated by conjunctivitis and keratitis. Genital lesions may be inflamed or ulcerated and may be mistaken for lesions produced by herpes simplex virus.[129] An eczematous reaction may develop around some lesions and secondary bacterial infection may occur. Persons with impaired immunity may develop widespread lesions. The duration both of the individual lesion and of the attack is variable. Although most cases resolve within 6 to 9 months, some infections persist for 3 or 4 years.[127]

Diagnosis and Control

The diagnosis of molluscum contagiosum is easily made by the distinctive clinical appearance of the lesions and can be confirmed by microscopic or electron microscopic examination of stained smears of the expressed white core or by biopsy. Molluscum contagiosum must be differentiated from lichen planus, warts, varicella, pyoderma, papillomas, and epitheliomas.

Since the condition is usually self-limiting and lesions heal without scarring in the absence of secondary bacterial infection, treatment is not always sought. Removal of the lesions with a sharp curette or liquid nitrogen is simple, relatively painless, and usually effective. Other forms of treatment include applications of iodine solutions or cantharidin.[141]

TANAPOX

This unclassified poxvirus produces a mild febrile illness with one or two nodular skin lesions. The virus does not grow on the CAM but can be isolated in a variety of cell cultures.[142] It is a simian poxvirus (not "monkeypox" virus) infection initially reported from the Tana River area in Kenya.[142] Opportunity was taken during monkeypox surveys in Zaire to collect data on Tanapox during 1979–1983.[143] Of 357 cases investigated, 264 were confirmed by the virus laboratory. Multiple lesions were rare; 78% of patients had only one lesion and very few had more than three. Lesions were usually found on the torso and were surprisingly few

on the head. It is not thought to present a public health hazard, but infections have been reported in monkey handlers in the United States.[144]

DIAGNOSIS

Human infections with poxviruses are relatively uncommon and the source of infection is usually obvious. In these circumstances an accurate clinical diagnosis can be made if a proper history is taken. The possible exception is cowpox, unless it is remembered that contact with cattle is not necessary and that contact with domestic cats is more significant. Laboratory-acquired infections are possible and physicians should know if any of their patients are virologists working with poxviruses.

Poxviruses, with the exception of molluscum, are among the easiest viruses to cultivate and will present no difficulty to the virus laboratory. Poxviruses can usually be recognized in the electron microscope in scrapings or vesicle fluid from the lesion, and this provides a rapid confirmation of poxvirus infection. If virus is not isolated, virus antigen may be detected in lesion extracts by a variety of methods.[55] Titration of serum antibodies provides a late and relatively poor alternative to virus isolation.

The methods available for poxvirus diagnosis have been reviewed in detail recently.[11, 55] The following scheme is a simple outline of a possible approach to diagnosis.

Generalized Infection

Smallpox and Monkeypox

History.—*There is no reason to suppose that cases of smallpox will occur.* If smallpox is suspected, expert help must be sought immediately. Monkeypox is a rare zoonosis of West and Central Africa, and there is little reason to suppose that cases will be imported into Europe or the United States. Laboratory-acquired infection with monkeypox virus is possible.

Clinical Features.—Febrile prodrome followed by centrifugal vesicular-pustular eruption.

Laboratory Studies.—Electron microscopy of lesion extracts shows typical orthopoxvirus morphology. Isolation on CAM or cell culture and identification as in Table 39–3.

Molluscum Contagiosum

History.—Contact with known case. Increasingly sexually transmitted.

Clinical Features.—Pearly skin nodules with caseous exudate.

Laboratory Studies.—Electron microscopy of exudate shows orthopoxvirus-type morphology. No growth on CAM or in cell culture, and exudate shows no reaction with vaccinia antiserum. Positive serologic reaction with molluscum antiserum if available.

Localized Infection

Cowpox (Rare)

History.—Restricted to Britain and Continental Europe. No particular history; possible contact with cats, cattle, or with zoo or circus animals.

Clinical Features.—Painful hemorrhagic lesions occur on hands and/or face, with pyrexia and general malaise.

Laboratory Studies.—Electron microscopy shows typical orthopoxvirus particles. Isolation on CAM or cell culture, and identification as in Table 39–3.

Vaccinia (Rare)

History.—Recent smallpox vaccination or contact with vaccinee.

Clinical Features.—Secondary vaccinia lesions (oral, genital, ocular, etc), or failure to heal of initial vaccination site.

Laboratory Studies.—Typical orthopoxvirus particles are seen in electron microscope. Isolation on CAM or in cell culture and identification as in Table 39–3.

Treatment.—Methisazone and/or antivaccinia gamma globulin.

Pseudocowpox, Orf

History.—Occupational infection: farm or abattoir worker, veterinary surgeon, student, etc, in contact with infected cattle and/or sheep.

Clinical Features.—Inflamed granulomatous lesion on hands and/or face. Relatively painless.

Identification.—Electron microscopy shows typical parapoxvirus particles. No growth on CAM, but isolation in cell culture.

Tanapox

History.—Relatively rare zoonosis of Central Africa or monkey handler.

Clinical Features.—Febrile prodrome, followed by one or two skin nodules.

Laboratory Studies.—Electron microscopy shows orthopoxvirus-type particles, but lesion extracts show no reaction with antivaccinia serum. No growth on CAM, but isolation in cell cultures. Reaction with Tanapox antiserum if available.

REFERENCES

1. Fenner F, Henderson DA, Arita I, et al: *Smallpox and its Eradication.* Geneva, World Health Organization, 1988.
2. Baxby D: Poxviruses, in Parker MT, Collier LH (eds): *Topley and Wilson's Principles of Bacteriology, Virology, and Immunity,* ed 8. London, Arnold, 1990, vol 4, pp 559–571.
3. Baxby D: Poxvirus infections in domestic animals, in Darai G (ed): *Virus Diseases in Laboratory and Captive Animals.* Boston, Martin Nijhoff, 1988, pp 17–35.
4. Hopkins DR: *Princes and Peasants: Smallpox in History.* Chicago, University of Chicago Press, 1983.
5. Baxby D: *Jenner's Smallpox Vaccine.* London, Heinemann Educational Books, 1981.
6. Palmquist EE: The 1946 smallpox experience in Seattle. *Can J Public Health* 1947;38:213–218.
7. *Smallpox 1961–1962.* London, HMSO, 1962.
8. Wehrle PF, Posch J, Richter KH, et al: An airborne outbreak of smallpox in a German hospital and its significance with respect to other recent outbreaks in Europe. *Bull WHO* 1970; 43:669–679.
9. Miller G: *The Adoption of Inoculation of Smallpox in England and France.* Philadelphia, University of Pennsylvania Press, 1957.
10. Winslow OE: *A Destroying Agent: the Conquest of Smallpox in Colonial Boston.* Boston, Houghton Mifflin, 1974.
11. Fenner F, Wittek R, Dumbell KR: *The Orthopoxiviruses.* Orlando, Fla, Academic Press, 1989.
12. Boulter EA, Appleyard G: Differences between extracellular and intracellular forms of poxvirus and their implications. *Prog Med Virol* 1973; 16:86–108.
13. Harris WJ, Westwood JCN: Phosphotungstate staining of vaccinia virus. *J Gen Microbiol* 1964; 34:491–495.
14. Nagington J, Newton AA, Horne RW, et al: The structure of orf virus. *Virology* 1964; 23:461–472.
15. Dales S, Pogo BGT: Biology of poxviruses. *Virology Monogr* 1981; 18:1.
16. Payne LG, Kristensson K: The mechanism of vaccinia release and its specific inhibition by N_1-isonicotinoyl-N_2-3-methyl-4-chloro-benzoyl-hydrazine. *J Virol* 1979; 32:614–622.
17. Geshelin P, Berns KI: Characterization and localization of the naturally occurring cross-links in vaccinia virus DNA. *J Mol Biol* 1974; 88:785–796.
18. Mackett M, Archard LC: Conservation and variation in *Orthopoxvirus* genome structure. *J Gen Virol* 1979; 45:683–701.
19. Esposito JJ, Knight JC: Orthopoxvirus DNA: a comparison of restriction profiles and maps. *Virology* 1985; 143:230–251.
20. Robinson AJ, Barns G, Fraser K, et al: Conservation and variation in orf virus genomes. *Virology* 1987; 157:13–23.
21. Gassman U, Wyler R, Wittek R: Analysis of parapoxvirus genomes. *Arch Virol* 1985; 83:17–31.
22. Porter CD, Archard LC: Characterization and physical mapping of *Molluscum contagiosum* virus DNA and location of a sequence capable of encoding a conserved domain of epidermal growth factor. *J Gen Virol* 1987; 68:673–682.
23. Shida H: Nucleotide sequence of the vaccinia virus hemagglutinin gene. *Virology* 1986; 150:451–462.
24. Hirt P, Hiller G, Wittek R: Localization and fine structure of a vaccinia virus gene encoding an envelope antigen. *J Virol* 1986; 58:757–764.
25. Gillard S, Spehner D, Drillien R, et al: Localization and sequence of a vaccinia virus gene required for multiplication in human cells. *Proc Natl Acad Sci USA* 1986; 83:5573–5777.
26. Pickup DJ, Ink BS, Hu W, et al: Hemorrhage in lesions caused by cowpox virus is induced by a viral protein that is related to plasma protein inhibitors of serine proteases. *Proc Natl Acad Sci USA* 1986; 83:7698–7702.
27. Moss B: Replication of poxviruses, in Fields BN (ed): *Virology.* New York, Raven Press, 1985, pp 685–703.
28. Sam CK, Dumbell KR: Expression of poxvirus DNA in coinfected cells and marker rescue of thermosensitive mutants by subgenomic fragments of DNA. *Ann Virol (Inst Pasteur)* 1981; 132E:135–150.
29. Broyles SS, Moss B: Homology between RNA polymerases of poxviruses, prokaryotes, and eukaryotes: Nucleotide sequence and transcriptional analysis of vaccinia virus genes encoding 147-kDa and 22-kDa subunits. *Proc Natl Acad Sci USA* 1986; 83:3141–3145.
30. Brown JP, Twardzik DR, Marquadt H, et al: Vaccinia virus encodes a polypeptide homologous to epidermal growth factor and transforming growth factor. *Nature* 1985; 313:491–492.
31. Essani K, Dales S: Biogenesis of vaccinia: Evidence for more than 100 polypeptides in the virion. *Virology* 1979; 95:385–394.
32. Turner A, Baxby D: Structural polypeptides of *Orthopoxvirus:* their distribution in various members and location within the virion. *J Gen Virol* 1979; 45:537–545.
33. Balassu TC, Robinson AJ: Orf virus replication in bovine testis cells: kinetics of viral DNA, polypeptide, and infections virus production and analysis of virion polypeptides. *Arch Virol* 1987; 97:267–281.
34. Wilcox WC, Cohen GH: The poxvirus antigens. *Curr Top Microbiol Immunol* 1969; 47:1–19.
35. Kitamoto N, Tanimoto S, Hiroi K, et al: Monoclonal antibodies to cowpox virus: polypeptide analysis of several major antigens. *J Gen Virol* 1987; 68:239–246.

36. Baxby D: The surface antigens of orthopoxviruses detected by cross-neutralization tests on cross-absorbed antisera. *J Gen Virol* 1982; 58:251–262.

37. Gispen R, Brand-Saathof B: Three specific antigens produced in vaccinia, variola and monkeypox infections. *J Infect Dis* 1974; 129:289–295.

38. Hutchinson HD, Ziegler DW, Wells DE, et al: Differentiation of variola, monkeypox and vaccinia antisera by radioimmunoassay. *Bull WHO* 1977; 55:613–623.

39. Khodakevich L, Szczeniowski M, Manbu-ma-Disu, et al: The role of squirrels in sustaining monkeypox virus transmission. *Trop Geogr Med* 1987; 39:115–122.

40. Payne LG: Identification of the vaccinia haemagglutinin polypeptide from a cell system yielding large amounts of extracellular enveloped virus. *J Virol* 1979; 31:147–155.

41. Kato S, Takahashi M, Kameyama S, et al: A study of the morphological and cyto-immunological relationship between the inclusions of variola, cowpox, rabbitpox, vaccinia (variola origin) and vaccinia IHD and a consideration of the term "Guarnieri body." *Biken's J* 1959; 2:353–363.

42. Joklik WK: The intracellular fate of poxviruses rendered noninfectious by various reagents. *Virology* 1964; 22:620–633.

43. Chang A, Metz DH: Further investigations on the mode of entry of vaccinia virus into cells. *J Gen Virol* 1976; 32:275–282.

44. Kates JR, McAuslan BR: Messenger RNA synthesis by a "coated" viral genome. *Proc Natl Acad Sci USA* 1967; 57:314–320.

45. Dahl R, Kates JR: Intracellular structures containing vaccinia DNA: isolation and characterization. *Virology* 1970; 42:453–462.

46. Zaslavsky V: Uncoating of vaccinia virus. *J Virol* 1985; 55:352–356.

47. Fenner F: Interaction between poxviruses. *Proc R Soc London (B)* 1962; 156:388–414.

48. Cooper JA, Moss B: In vitro translation of immediate early, early and late classes of RNA from vaccinia virus-infected cells. *Virology* 1979; 96:368–380.

49. Oda K, Joklik WK: Hybridization and sedimentation studies on 'early' and 'late' vaccinia messenger RNA. *J Mol Biol* 1967; 27:395–419.

50. Pennington TH: Vaccinia virus polypeptide synthesis: Sequential appearance and stability of pre- and post-replicative polypeptides. *J Gen Virol* 1974; 24:433–444.

51. Easterbrook KB: Controlled degradation of vaccinia virions in vitro: An electron microscopic study. *J Ultrastruct Res* 1966; 14:484–496.

52. Holowczak JA: Uncoating of poxviruses. I. Detection and characterization of subviral particles in the uncoating process. *Virology* 1972; 50:216–232.

53. Sarov I, Joklik WK: Isolation and characterization of intermediates in vaccinia virus morphogenesis. *Virology* 1973; 52:223–233.

54. Moyer RW: The role of the host cell nucleus in vaccinia virus morphogenesis. *Virus Res* 1987; 8:173–191.

55. Nakano JH: Poxviruses, in Lennette EH, Schmidt NJ (eds): *Diagnostic Procedures for Viral, Rickettsial and Chlamydial Diseases,* ed 5. New York, American Public Health Association, 1979, pp 257–308.

56. Thomas DB, McCormack WM, Arita I, et al: Endemic smallpox in rural East Pakistan. II. Methodology, clinical and epidemiological characteristics of cases, and intervillage transmission. *Am J Epidemiol* 1971; 93:361–372.

57. Mack TM, Thomas DB, Khan MM: Epidemiology of smallpox in West Pakistan. II. Determinants of intervillage spread other than acquired immunity. *Am J Epidemiol* 1972; 95:169–177.

58. Rao AR: *Smallpox.* Bombay, Kothari Book Depot, 1972.

59. Nizamuddin M, Dumbell KR: A simple laboratory test to distinguish the virus of smallpox from that of alastrim. *Lancet* 1961; 1:68–69.

60. Bedson HS, Dumbell KR, Thomas WRG: Variola in Tanganyika. *Lancet* 1963; 2:1085–1088.

61. Basu RN, Jezek Z, Ward NA: *The Eradication of Smallpox from India.* Geneva, World Health Organization, 1979.

62. Mack TM: Smallpox in Europe, 1950–1971. *J Infect Dis* 1972; 125:161–169.

63. Marennikova SS, Shelukhina EM, Maltseva NN, et al: Monkeypox virus as a source of whitepox viruses. *Intervirology* 1979; 11:333–340.

64. Gispen R, Brand-Saathof B: 'White' poxviruses from monkeys. *Bull WHO* 1972; 46:585–592.

65. Marennikova SS, Shelukhina EM, Shenkman LS: 'White-wild' (variola-like) poxviruses in rodents of Equatorial Africa. *Acta Virol (Praha)* 1976; 20:80–82.

66. Dumbell KR, Kapsenberg HG: Laboratory investigation of two 'whitepox' viruses and comparison with two variola strains from southern India. *Bull WHO* 1982; 60:381–387.

67. Esposito JJ, Nakano JH, Obijeski JF: Can variola-like viruses be derived from monkeypox virus? an investigation based on DNA mapping. *Bull WHO* 1985; 63:695–703.

68. Christie AB: *Infectious Diseases: Epidemiology and Clinical Practice,* ed 3. London, Churchill Livingstone, 1980.

69. Downie AW, Meiklejohn G, St Vincent L, et al: The recovery of smallpox virus from patients and their environment in a smallpox hospital. *Bull WHO* 1965; 33:615–622.

70. Foege WH, Millar JD, Henderson DA: Smallpox eradication in West and Central Africa. *Bull WHO* 1975; 52:209–222.

71. Hopkins DR, Lane JM, Cummings EC, et al: Two funeral-associated smallpox outbreaks in Sierra Leone. *Am J Epidemiol* 1971; 94:341–347.

72. Foster SO, El Sid AGH, Deria A: Spread of smallpox among a Somali nomadic group. *Lancet* 1978; 1:831–833.

73. Downie AW, McCarthy K, MacDonald A, et al: Virus and virus antigen in the blood of smallpox patients. Their significance in early diagnosis and prognosis. *Lancet* 1953; 2:164–166.

74. Ricketts TF, Byles JB: *The Diagnosis of Smallpox.* London, Cassell, 1908.

75. Dixon CW: *Smallpox.* London, Churchill, 1962.

76. Downie AW, Fedson DS, St Vincent L, et al: Haemorrhagic smallpox. *J Hyg* 1969; 67:619–629.

77. Downie AW, St Vincent L, Goldstein L, et al: Antibody response in non-haemorrhagic smallpox patients. *J Hyg* 1969; 67:609–618.

78. Boulter EA, Zwartouw HT, Titmuss DHJ, et al: The nature of the immune state produced by inactivated vaccinia virus in rabbits. *Am J Epidemiol* 1971; 94:612–620.

79. Fulginiti VA, Kempe CH, Hathaway WE, et al: Progressive vaccinia in immunologically deficient individuals, in Bergsma D, Good RA (eds): *Immunological Deficiency Diseases in Man.* New York, National Foundation, 1968, pp 129–145.

80. Koszinowski U, Ertl H: Role of early viral surface antigens in cellular immune response to vaccinia virus. *Eur J Immunol* 1976; 6:679–683.

81. Galasso GJ, Karzon DT, Katz SL, et al (eds): Clinical and serologic study of four smallpox vaccines comparing variations of dose and route of administration. *J Infect Dis* 1977; 135:131–186.

82. World Health Organization: Smallpox eradication. *WHO Tech Rep Ser* 393, 1968.

83. Baxby D: Human poxvirus infection after the eradication of smallpox. *Epidemiol Infect* 1988; 100:321–334.

84. Dick G: Complications of smallpox vaccination in the United Kingdom, in Regemy RH, Cohen H (eds): *International Symposium on Smallpox Vaccine.* Basel, Karger, 1972, pp 205–215.

85. Lane JM, Millar JD: Risks of smallpox vaccination complications in the United States. *Am J Epidemiol* 1971; 93:238–240.

86. Polak MF: Complications of smallpox vaccination in the Netherlands, 1959–1970, in Regemy RH, Cohen H (eds): *International Symposium on Smallpox Vaccine.* Basel, Karger, 1972 pp 235–242.

87. Redfield RR, Wright DC, James WD: Disseminated vaccinia in a military recruit with human immunodeficiency virus (HIV) disease. *N Engl J Med* 1987; 316:673–676.

88. Kempe CH: Studies on smallpox and complications of smallpox vaccination. *Pediatrics* 1960; 26:176–189.

89. Bauer DJ: *The Specific Treatment of Virus Diseases.* Lancaster, England, MTP Press, 1977.

90. Kempe CH, Bowles C, Meiklejohn G, et al: The use of vaccinia hyperimmune gamma-globulin in the prophylaxis of smallpox. *Bull WHO* 1961; 25:41–48.

91. Bauer DJ, St Vincent L, Kempe CH, et al: Prophylaxis of smallpox with methisazone. *Am J Epidemiol* 1969; 90:130–145.

92. Hopkins DR, Lane JM, Cummings EC, et al: Smallpox in Sierra Leone. II. The 1968–1969 eradication program. *Am J Trop Med Hyg* 1971; 20:697–704.

93. Tulloch J, Jezek Z, Deria A: *Smallpox Eradication in Somalia.* Geneva. WHO (not dated).

94. Deria A, Jezek Z, Markvart K, et al: The world's last endemic case of smallpox: Surveillance and containment measures. *Bull WHO* 1980; 58:279–283.

95. *Report of the Investigation into the Cause of the 1978 Birmingham Smallpox Occurrence.* London, HMSO, 1980.

96. Panicali D, Paoletti E: Construction of poxviruses as cloning vectors: insertion of the thymidine kinase gene from herpes simplex virus into the DNA of infectious vaccinia virus. *Proc Natl Acad Sci USA* 1982; 79:4927–4931.

97. Mackett M, Smith GL, Moss B: Vaccinia virus: a selectable eukaryotic cloning and expression vector. *Proc Natl Acad Sci USA* 1982; 79:7415–7419.

98. Smith GL, Moss B: Infectious poxvirus vectors have capacity for at least 25,000 base pairs of foreign DNA. *Gene* 1983; 25:21–28.

99. Paoletti E, Perkus M, Piccini A, et al: Genetically engineered poxviruses expressing multiple foreign genes, in Lerner RA, Chanock RM (eds): *Vaccines '85.* New York, Cold Spring Harbor Laboratory, 1985, pp 147–150.

100. Smith GL, Mackett M, Moss B: Infectious vaccinia recombinants that express hepatitis B surface antigen. *Nature* 1983; 302:490–495.

101. Hu SK, Kosowski SG, Dalrymple JM: Expression of AIDS virus envelope gene in recombinant vaccinia virus. *Nature* 1986; 320:537–540.

102. Mackett M, Yilma T, Rose J, et al: Vaccinia virus recombinants: expression of VSV genes and protective immunization of mice and cattle. *Science* 1985; 227:433–435.

103. Ruprecht CE, Wiktor TJ, Johnson DH, et al: Oral immunization and protection of raccoons *(Procyon lotor)* with a vaccinia-rabies glycoprotein recombinant virus vaccine. *Proc Soc Natl Acad Sci USA* 1986; 83:7947–7950.

104. Smith GL, Godson GN, Nussenzweig V, et al: *Plasmodium knowlesi* sporozoite antigen: expression by infectious recombinant vaccinia virus. *Science* 1984; 224:397–399.

105. Pavirani A, Meulin P, Harrer H, et al: Choosing a host cell for active recombinant factor VIII production using vaccinia virus. *Biotechnology* 1987; 5:389–392.

106. Hruby DE, Thomas G: Use of vaccinia virus to express pharmaceuticals. *Pharm Res* 1987; 4:92–97.

107. Quinnan GV (ed): *Vaccinia Viruses as Vectors for Vaccine Antigens.* New York, Elsevier, 1985.

108. Buller RML, Smith GL, Kremer K, et al: Decreased virulence of recombinant vaccinia virus expression vectors is associated with a thymidine kinase negative phenotype. *Nature* 1985; 317:813–815.

109. Baxby D, Gaskell CJ, Gaskell RM, et al: Ecology of orthopoxviruses and use of recombinant vaccinia vaccines. *Lancet* 1986; 2:850–851.

110. Magnus P von, Anderson EK, Peterson KB, et al: A pox-like disease in *Cynomologus* monkeys. *Acta Pathol Microbiol Scand* 1959; 46:633–639.

111. Jezek Z, Fenner F: *Human Monkeypox.* Basel, Karger, 1988.

112. Jezek Z, Marennikova SS, Mutumbo M, et al: Human monkeypox: a study of 2510 contacts of 214 patients. *J Infect Dis* 1986; 154:551–555.

113. Jezek J, Arita I, Mutumbo M, et al: Four generations of probable person-to-person transmission of human monkeypox. *Am J Epidemiol* 1986; 123:1004–1012.

114. Arita I, Jezek Z, Khodakevich L, et al: Human monkeypox: a newly emerged orthopoxvirus zoonosis in the tropical rain forests of Africa. *Am J Trop Med Hyg* 1985; 34:781–789.

115. Jezek Z, Szczeniowski M, Paluku KM, et al: Human monkeypox: clinical features of 282 patients. *J Infect Dis* 1987; 156:293–297.

116. Jezek Z, Grub B, Dixon H: Stochastic model for interhuman spread of monkeypox. *Am J Epidemiol* 1987; 126:1082–1092.

117. Baxby D: Is cowpox misnamed? A review of ten human cases. *Br Med J* 1977; 1:1379–1381.

118. Bennett M, Gaskell CJ, Gaskell RM, et al: Poxvirus infection in the domestic cat: some clinical and epidemiological observations. *Vet Rec* 1986; 118:387–390.

119. What's new pussycat? Cowpox. *Lancet* 1986; 2:668.

120. Baxby D, Shackleton WB, Wheeler J, et al: Comparison of cowpox-like viruses isolated from European zoos. *Arch Virol* 1979; 61:337–340.

121. Johannessen JU, Krogh HK, Solberg I, et al: Human Orf. *J Cutan Pathol* 1975; 2:265–283.

122. Robinson AJ, Petersen GV: Orf virus infection of workers in the meat industry. *NZ Med J* 1983; 96:81–85.

123. Hunskaar S: A case of ecthyma contagiosum (human orf) treated with idoxuridine. *Dermatologica* 1984; 168:207.

124. Freeman G, Bron AJ, Juel-Jensen B: Ocular infection with orf virus. *Am J Ophthalmol* 1984; 97:601–604.

125. Woods B: Edward Jenner and molluscum contagiosum. *Br J Dermatol* 1977; 96:91–93.

126. Francis RD, Bradford HB: Some biological and physical properties of molluscum contagiosum virus propagated in tissue culture. *J Virol* 1976; 19:382–388.

127. Postlethwaite R: Molluscum contagiosum. *Arch Environ Health* 1970; 21:432–452.

128. McFadden G, Pace WE, Purres J, et al: Biogenesis of poxviruses: Transitory expression of molluscum contagiosum early functions. *Virology* 1979; 94:297–313.

129. Dennis J, Oshiro LS, Bunter JW: Molluscum contagiosum, another sexually transmitted disease: its impact on the clinical virology laboratory. *J Infect Dis* 1985; 151:376.

130. Douglas JD, Tanner KN, Prine JR, et al: Molluscum contagiosum in the chimpanzee. *J Am Vet Med Assoc* 1967; 151:901–904.

131. Bagnall BG, Witson GR: Molluscum contagiosum in a red kangaroo. *Australas J Dermatol* 1974; 15:115–120.

132. Sturt RJ, Muller HK, Francis GD: Molluscum contagiosum in villages of the West Sepik District of New Guinea. *Med J Aust* 1971; 2:751–754.

133. Lynch PJ: Molluscum contagiosum venereum. *Clin Obstet Gynaecol* 1972; 15:966–975.

134. Overfield TM, Brody JA: An epidemiologic study of molluscum contagiosum in Anchorage, Alaska. *J Pediatr* 1966; 69:640–642.

135. Low RC: Molluscum contagiosum. *Edinburgh Med J* 1946; 53:657–670.

136. Wilkin JK: Molluscum contagiosum venereum in a women's outpatient clinic: A venereally transmitted disease. *Am J Obstet Gynaecol* 1977; 128:531–535.

137. Brown ST, Nalley JF, Kraus SJ: Molluscum contagiosum. *Sex Transm Dis* 1981; 8:227–234.

138. Becker TM, Blount JH, Douglas J, et al: Trends in molluscum contagiosum in the United States. *Sex Transm Dis* 1986; 13:88–92.

139. Oriel JD: The increase in molluscum contagiosum. *Br Med J* 1987; 294:74.

140. Pauly CR, Artis WM, Jones HE: Atopic dermatitis, impaired cellular immunity, and molluscum contagiosum. *Arch Dermatol* 1978; 114:391–393.

141. Funt TR, Mehr KA: Cantharidin: A valuable office treatment of molluscum contagiosum. *South Med J* 1979; 72:1019.

142. Downie AW, Taylor-Robinson CH, Caunt AE, et al: Tanapox: A new disease caused by a pox virus. *Br Med J* 1971; 1:63–68.

143. Jezek Z, Arita I, Szczeniowski M, et al: Human tanapox in Zaire: clinical and epidemiological observations on cases confirmed by laboratory studies. *Bull WHO* 1985; 63:1027–1035.

144. Espana C: A pox disease of monkeys transmissible to man, in El Goldsmith, JM Jankowski (eds): *Medical Primatology, Proceedings of the 2nd Conference on Experimental Medical Surgical Primatology.* Basel, Karger, 1971, pp 694–708.

40

Human Papillomaviruses

A. Bennett Jenson
Wayne D. Lancaster

The human papillomaviruses (HPV) are associated with a variety of proliferative squamous lesions of the skin[1, 2] and mucosal surfaces such as the oral cavity,[3–8] larynx,[9–12] and anogenital tract.[13–26] For years, HPV research was limited for the most part to physical and biochemical characterization of virions obtained from cuta-

neous warts.[27–34] Recent advances in recombinant DNA technology allowed analysis of viral DNA extracted directly from HPV-associated lesions,[35–45] which led to the discovery of multiple papillomavirus (PV) types with anatomical site preference for either cutaneous or mucosal squamous epithelium.[6–8, 11–26, 37–45] Of the more than 50 known types of HPV (Table 40–1), two thirds appear to be cutaneotropic and one third mucosotropic. Cutaneotropic HPVs are usually associated with warts, which are either exophytic (verrucae vulgaris, plantaris) or flat (verrucae plana),[1, 2] whereas mucosotropic HPV are usually associated with benign exophytic or flat condylomata (see Table 40–1)[13–26, 37, 38] and/or latent infections.[44–52] However, the oncogenic potential of HPV is reflected by the association of certain HPV types with varying degrees of premalignant (dysplastic, intraepithelial neoplasia [IN]) squamous lesions and invasive carcinomas, particularly of the uterine cervix of otherwise normal women[13–26, 39–45, 52] and sun-exposed skin of patients with epidermodysplasia verruciformis (EV) (see Table 40–1). Evidence is emerging that the type of HPV determines, in part, the clinical and pathologic appearance, and natural fate of HPV-associated lesions.

HPVs are members of the A (PV) genus of the family *Papovaviridae*; the polyomaviruses constitute the B genus.[53] The genera do not share antigenic determinants[54] or polynucleotide sequence homology.[55] PVs have a larger icosahedral capsid (55 nm vs 45 nm) and a longer supercoiled, double-stranded DNA genome (approximately 8000 vs 5200 base pairs).[56] The genera also differ in biologic properties.[53] PVs are species and tissue-specific, producing hyperplasias, dysplasias, and neoplasias of squamous epithelium of natural hosts. In vitro infection by some PVs, including HPV, result in early gene expression with cellular transformation. The DNA of HPV-16, a highly oncogenic HPV, transforms murine 3T3 cells,[57–59] primary human fibroblasts, and keratinocytes,[60] and in the presence of EJ-ras, primary baby rat kidney epithelial cells.[61] However, culture systems permissive for PV late gene expression

Table 40–1

Classification of Human Papillomavirus Types and the Malignant Potential of the Lesions With Which They Are Most Frequently Associated

Types	Lesions (Malignant Potential)
1, 4	Plantar warts (benign)
2, 26, 28, 29	Common warts (benign)
3, 10, 27	Flat warts (benign)
5, 8	Epidermodysplasia verruciformis (EV) (highly malignant)
6, 11, 34, 39, 41–44	Condylomata (rarely malignant)
7	Butcher's wart (benign)
9, 12, 14, 15, 17, 19–25, 36, 46–50	EV, immunosuppressed patients (benign, rarely malignant)
13, 32	Oral focal epithelial hyperplasia (benign)
16, 18	Condylomata (highly malignant),* bowenoid papulosis (?)
30, 31, 33, 35, 45	Condylomata (intermediately malignant)*

*Particularly cervical lesions

(and productive infections) have not been reported.[62] In contrast, the polyomaviruses give rise to both productive and nonproductive infections in vitro but do not cause tumors in natural hosts.[63]

HISTORY

Warts have created a mystique dating from antiquity since many undergo spontaneous regression frequently attributed to an assortment of unconventional forms of treatment,[64–66] including hypnosis and psychotherapy (reviewed by Bunney[2]). HPV was the first tumor virus to be transmitted experimentally from one host to another. This was accomplished in 1894 by Licht,[67] who transmitted warts from his brother to himself by inoculation of crude wart material. Ciuffo[68] in 1907 and Serra[69] 1 year later demonstrated that warts could be induced by cell-free filtrates of wart material. In 1919, Wile and Kingrey[70] successfully transmitted warts through a succession of human volunteers using sterile extracts. Electron microscopic studies by Strauss et al,[71] Melnick et al,[72] Bunting,[73] and Almeida et al[74] confirmed a viral etiology for cutaneous warts. Melnick,[75] in 1962, grouped the PVs together with the polyomaviruses in the family *Papovaviridae* because both were DNA tumor viruses with physically similar icosahedral capsids and circular, double-stranded DNAs. Reports (reviewed by Rowson and Mahy[1]) of transmission by filtrates of warts, laryngeal papillomas, and genital tract condylomata to human volunteers, some of whom developed cutaneous warts at the site of inoculation, were interpreted as evidence that there was only one type of human wart virus and that the site of infection, and, perhaps, the genetic makeup of the patient, determined the clinical appearance of cutaneous warts and mucosal condylomata and papillomas. However, recent recognition that there are different HPV types (see Table 40–1), some of which have varying degrees of association with premalignant and malignant lesions, particularly of the anogenital tract,[13–26, 37–45, 52] and less frequently the oral cavity[6–8] and aerodigestive tract,[11, 12] has stimulated a new interest in the role of these viruses in benign, premalignant, and malignant squamous lesions.

STRUCTURE AND BIOLOGY

HPV virions are nonenveloped icosahedral capsids (55 nm in diameter) assembled by encapsidation of the DNA genome by 72 capsomers.[76] Virions do not contain lipids and are inactivated by treatment with 0.4% formalin for 72 hours at 4°C.[77] Viral preparations usually contain both complete and empty particles.[27, 56] Complete particles have a sedimentation coefficient of 296 to 300S and a buoyant density of 1.34 g/mL; empty particles have sedimentation coefficients of 168 to 172S and a buoyant density of 1.29 g/mL (tubular capsids are also observed at this density).

Structural viral proteins constitute approximately 88% of the mass of the PV virion.[56] Each PV has a major capsid protein with a molecular weight of approximately 54,000 daltons[31, 33, 34, 78–80] and a minor capsid protein with a weight of approximately 76,600 daltons.[81] Although the nucleotide sequences encoding the major capsid proteins (MCP) are highly conserved among all PVs, the corresponding homologous amino acid residues, recognized immunologically as PV broadly cross-reactive antigenic determinants, have an internal location within the intact virus particle.[82, 83] However, PV type-specific and minimally cross-reactive MCP epitopes are present as nonconformational (linear) and, most likely, conformational epitopes on the surface of the intact viral particle.[83] On the other hand, the minor capsid proteins(s) are poorly conserved, but unlike the topography of MCP antigenic determinants, type-specific and minimally cross-reactive PV minor capsid epitopes are cryptic or internal to the capsid.[81, 84] Four low-molecular-weight polypeptides closely associated with viral DNA have been resolved and are similar to cellular histones.[85] Nonstructural viral proteins have a short half-life and are present in small quantities in infected cells. The exception, however, is the HPV-1 early (E) open reading frame (ORF)–4 gene product, which is found in large quantities in plantar warts.[86]

The physical characteristics of the PV genome based on agarose gel electrophoresis and contour length measurement of DNA molecules by electron microscopy are consistent with a molecular weight of approximately 5×10^6 daltons, corresponding to approximately 8000 base pairs of genetic information, which is sufficient to code for 300,000 daltons of protein.[29, 30] The complete PV genome, either encapsidated within virions or replicating as an extrachromosomal plasmid in infected cells, exists in three forms (Fo); FoI is a covalently closed, circular supercoiled molecule with a sedimentation coefficient of 23S; FoII is an open circular molecule with a sedimentation coefficient of 17S; and, FoIII is a linear molecule with a sedimentation coefficient of 16S.[87, 88] All forms appear to exist as nonintegrated, self-replicating nuclear plasmids in benign and low-grade premalignant lesions.[89–91] However, in many high-grade premalignant lesions, invasive carcinomas, and cervical cancer cell lines associated with HPV-16 and -18, there is site-specific integration of viral genomic DNA in a random distribution into cellular DNA.[91–98]

The genomes of many HPVs, including HPV-1,[99] HPV-6,[100] HPV-16,[101] HPV-18,[102] and HPV-31[103] have been cloned and sequenced. However, knowledge of the genetic organization of HPV has been derived mainly from alignment of the various HPV nucleotide sequences with that of BPV-1, the prototype PV. BPV-1 has been the most extensively studied PV for several reasons, including the availability of virus particles in large quantities from bovine fibropapillomas as well as the capacity of these virions to induce stable transformation of rodent cells in vitro.[104] Based on DNA sequencing, RNA mapping, and functional analysis in in vitro transformation assays, the genome of bovine PV(BPV)–1 appears to be subdivided into three functionally distinct regions (reviewed by Broker and Botchan[104]): (1) the early (E) region, which is required for cellular transformation, episomal replication, and transcriptional control; (2) the long control region (LCR), which contains no long ORF and is the site of origin of DNA replication, promoters, and enhancers; and (3) the late (L) region, which encodes the major and minor capsid proteins. The E region of the PV genome is subdivided into eight ORFs (depending on the PV type) which were arbitrarily designated E1 to E8 based on decreasing lengths of the corresponding nucleotide sequences. All HPV genomes encode for E1, E2, E4, E6, and E7 ORFs, but E3, E5, and E8 ORFs are not highly conserved. The L region is divided into the L1 ORF, which encodes the MCP, and the L2 ORF, which encodes the minor capsid protein. Although the functions of the various E ORFs of HPV-6 and -11 have been assigned by analogy to corresponding ORFs of BPV-1, the general genetic organization

of HPV for this chapter is depicted by the graphic representation of messenger RNAs (mRNAs) from HPV-6 and -11 associated with condylomata (Figure 40–1).[105]

CLASSIFICATION

Unlike most other virus groups, HPV types have been classified by genotyping rather than serotyping. Molecular analysis of the HPV genome was first determined by Crawford.[27, 28, 56] Using stringent hybridization techniques without the aid of various restriction endonucleases, it was concluded that although HPV had similar structures and molecular weights when compared to PV from other species, there was no sharing of polynucleotide sequences among the different genomes analyzed. Thus, the prevailing concept that there was only one PV type for each species was not changed by the first comparative molecular hybridization studies of viruses within this group. However, the advent of recombinant DNA technology provided the opportunity to clone and sequence PV genomes, resulting in homogeneous preparations of viral DNA that could be compared to nucleotide sequences of reference PV

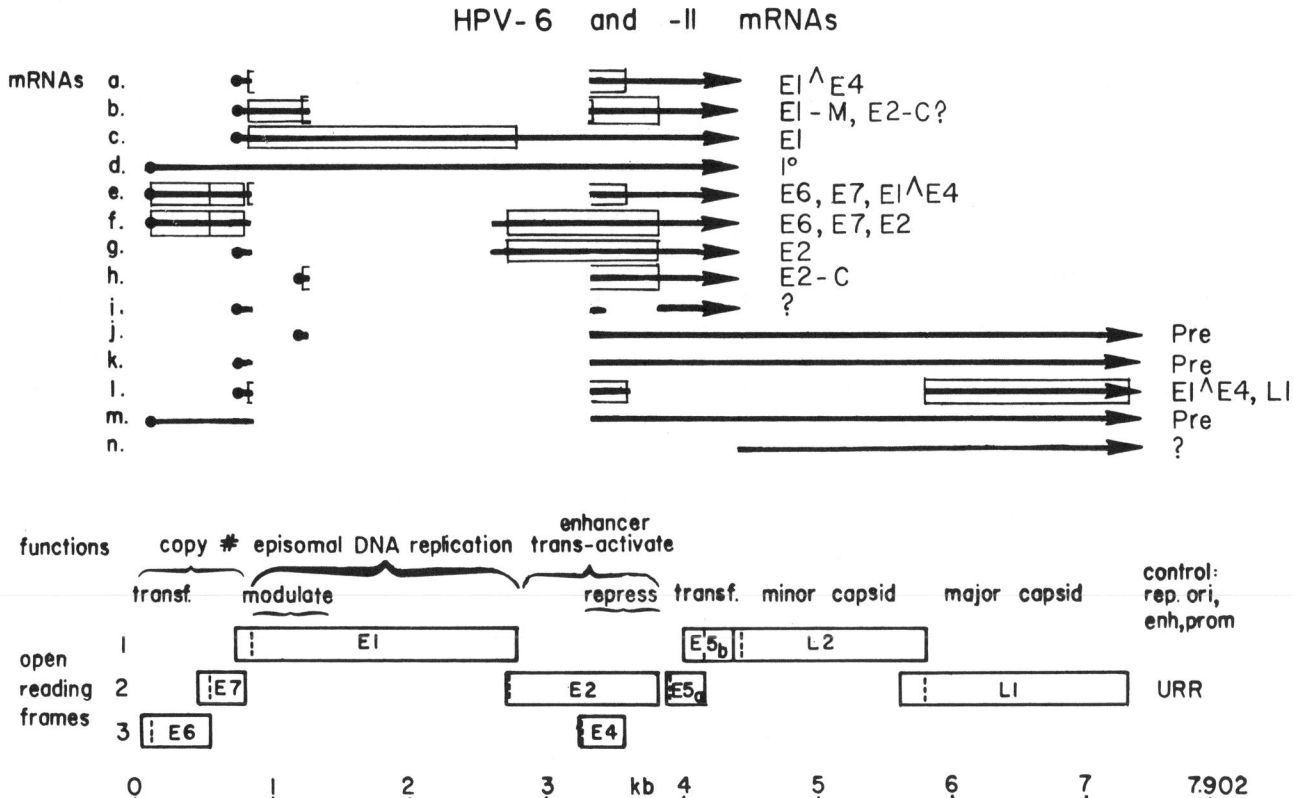

Figure 40–1. Graphic representation of RNAs from human papillomaviruses (HPV-6 and -11) associated with condylomata acuminata. The RNAs were mapped by the electron microscope R–loop method and aligned with DNA sequences of highly homologous HPV-6 and HPV-11 and the open reading frames (ORF) of HPV-6. (This map uses the HPV-6b ORF map.) Beads represent the 5′ ends of the RNAs, arrowheads represent the polyadenylation sites, and gaps signify the intron sequences spliced out of the RNAs; the probably rNA coding regions are boxed and appropriately designated on the right. The functions (transf. = transform; rep. ori. = replication origin; enh = enhancer; prom = promoter, etc.) are assigned by analogy with bovine papillomavirus genetics. The ORFs of the HPV-6 genome are based on the HPV-6b DNA sequence linearized at the conventional position in the upstream regulatory region (URR). The positions of the various early (E) and late (L) ORFs are labeled and boxed (Courtesy of Tom Broker. Adapted from Chow et al.[105])

types.[104-107] It soon became apparent that there was a remarkable plurality of PV, particularly HPV.

The PVs are classified into types or subtypes on the basis of species specificity (human [H], bovine [B], canine [C], etc) and polynucleotide sequence homology. To be classified as a new PV type, there should be a maximum of 50% polynucleotide sequence homology with other known PVs.[108] Those viruses with greater than 50% but less than 100% DNA homology are subtypes. The closely related subtypes usually differ by having one or more distinct restriction endonuclease cleavage patterns. For example, HPV-6 and -11 share about 25% DNA sequence homology,[38, 109] and are thus considered different types; however, HPV types 1a and 1b are subtypes since they are indistinguishable by hybridization and differ only with respect to a limited number of restriction sites.[35] It is of interest, however, that the actual nucleotide sequence homologies of PV are significantly higher than suggested by cross-hybridization studies.[19]

Early studies of endonuclease restriction patterns and physical maps of HPV DNA were dependent on extraction of nonintegrated supercoiled viral DNA from purified virions obtained from productive infections of warts.[29-34, 89, 90] However, the recoverability of virions has always been dependent on the HPV type, the site of infection, and the extent of differentiation of squamous epithelium. Cutaneous warts, particularly plantar and some common warts caused by HPV-1, contain the largest quantity of virions,[110] whereas mucosal papillomas appear to contain the fewest viral particles. Poorly differentiated squamous epithelium such as seen in premalignant and malignant lesions does not readily support productive PV infections.[83] HPV virions that are extracted from the wart/papilloma are usually purified in CsCl equilibrium density gradients. The virions are ruptured by treatment with sodium dodecyl sulfate (SDS), deproteinized by phenol extraction, and supercoiled DNA subsequently isolated in CsCL-ethidium bromide equilibrium density gradients.[29, 30]

With the development of molecular cloning technology, many new HPV types were identified in lesions containing relatively small amounts of viral DNA. Approximately 50% of warts and condylomata are not productively infected[83] but contain variable amounts of HPV DNA. However, even if productively infected, many cutaneous warts and most mucosal condylomata frequently contain only a relatively few viral particles but an abundance of PV DNA. In these instances, supercoiled HPV DNA is extracted directly as a plasmid from infected cells,[35-38, 111-114] usually using modifications of the Hirt differential salt extraction technique.[115] Viral sequences are cleaved with a battery of digestive enzymes while searching for a single cleavage site, which facilitates cloning of the entire viral genome. The vector systems that have been used most frequently are bacterial plasmids, particularly pBR322, and derivatives of bacteriophage lambda. The viral sequences to be cloned are ligated to the vector and then used to transform competent bacterial cells. Most vectors have selective markers such as antibiotic resistance or metabolic pathway inactivation. Once a bacterial colony that contains the proper insert of viral DNA is selected, virtually unlimited amounts of viral and subviral genomic sequences can be prepared from mass culture and manipulated by recombinant DNA technology for detailed characterization.[35, 36, 99-104, 106, 107] Cloned HPV sequences should be of appropriate size,

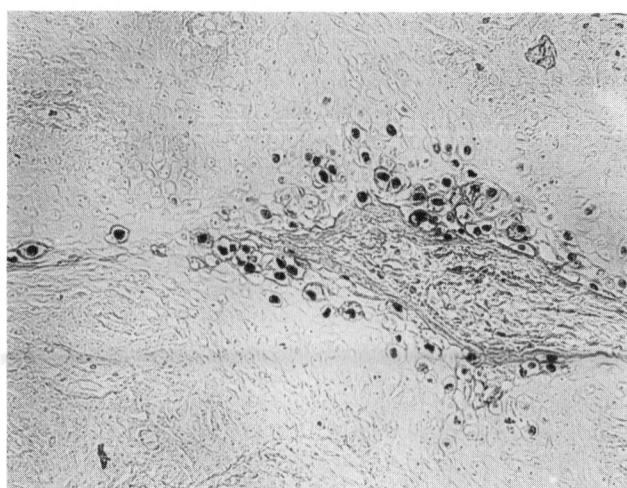

Figure 40–2. In situ hybridization using biotinylated human papillomavirus (HPV)-6,-11 DNA–DNA probe of HPV–6–induced anogenital condyloma. Chromagen precipitate is seen over nuclei of koilocytotic cells in superficial layer of condyloma, which is the location for expression of large amounts of genomic DNA, RNA transcripts, and structural viral proteins. There is no counterstain.

cross-hybridize to known HPV types under conditions of nonstringent hybridization, and have the characteristic PV genome organization.

Detection and typing of HPV DNA sequences, either extracted from exfoliated cells or biopsy tissue or in situ in fixed cells or tissue (Figure 40–2), are generally performed with either the probe or test DNA immobilized on solid supports such as nitrocellulose, nylon membranes, or fixed tissue and/or cells.[116] DNA probes are produced either by nick-translation[117] or random primer synthesis.[118] Of the blotting methodologies such as Southern,[119] dot,[116] and filter hybridization,[120] the southern blot has been used as the "gold standard" since it can be used to interpretate results from nonstringent hybridization and restriction fragment analysis (Figure 40–3A and B) as well as results pertaining to the physical state of the viral genome (episomal or integrated). With this method, DNA is extracted from virions or tissues and cleaved using restriction endonucleases. The DNA fragments are separated by gel electrophoresis, transferred to a membrane, and hybridized with a radiolabeled or biotinylated PV probe under stringent (25°C below the melting temperature of DNA (Tm −25°C) which is the temperature at which the optimal rate of duplex formation occurs, allowing for detection of about 17% base mismatch)[121] or relaxed (43°C below the melting temperature of DNA [Tm −43°C]) conditions.[35, 36, 55, 116] Under relaxed (nonstringent) conditions, thermally stable complexes are formed in at least two regions of the PV genome[122]; as much as 33% base mismatch can be identified by careful choice of hybridization and wash conditions. The kinetics of the hybridization reaction are used to calculate the degree of homology of the PV probe to the test DNA.[123] Alternatively, homology between PV genomes can be determined by saturation hybridization.[124]

Using recombinant DNA hybridization techniques and restriction enzyme digestion analysis, over 50 different HPV types have

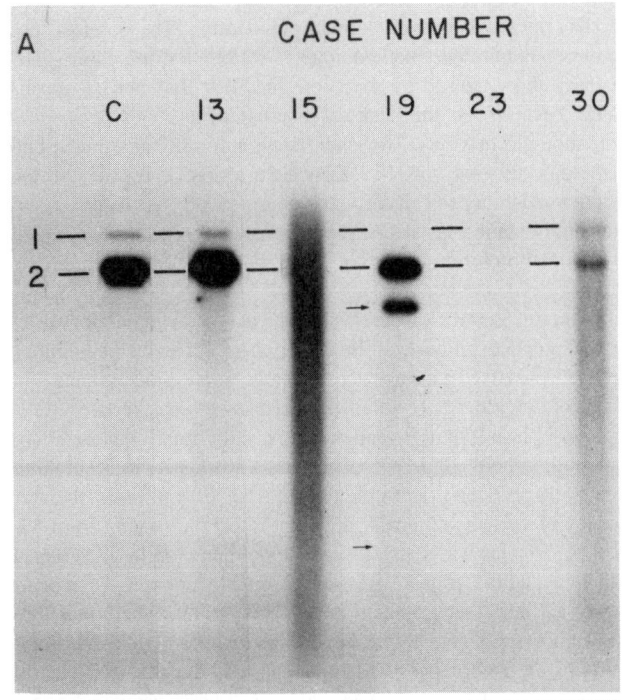

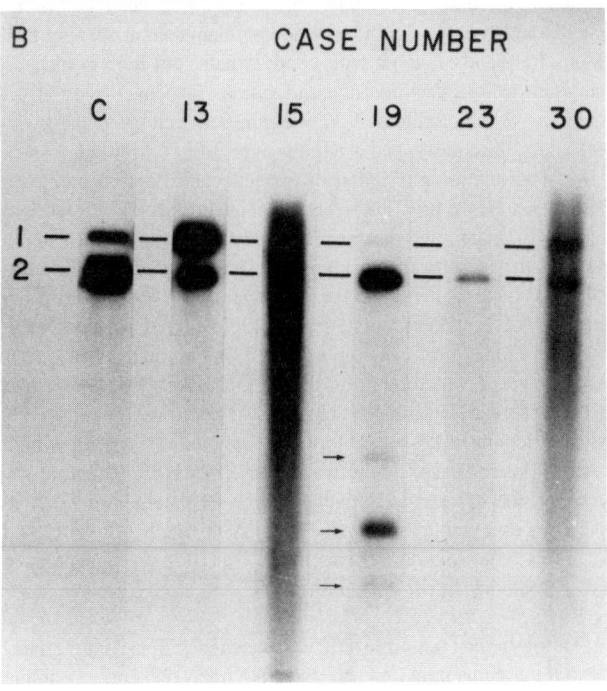

Figure 40–3. Autoradiograms representing hybridization of ³²P-labeled bovine papillomavirus (PV) type 1 (BPV-1) DNA to human papillomavirus type 1 (HPV-1) DNA and DNAs isolated from five cervical biopsies. HPV-1 DNA (10 ng) (lane C) and tissue DNAs were digested with either BamHI (panel A) or HindIII (panel B) and electrophoresed in 0.8% agarose gels. The separated DNA fragments were transferred to nitrocellulose membranes and subsequently hybridized to ³²P-BPV-1 DNA. Bands 1 and 2 represent the migration of circular and linearized HPV-1 DNA, respectively. In both panels **A** and **B**, four of the five cases tested contained DNA sequences to which the BPV-1 probe hybridized. These sequences comigrated with either open circular and/or linear forms of HPV-1 DNA. Arrows indicate migration of low-molecular-weight DNA, present in case 19 (seen in Figure 40–1), that specifically hybridized to the BPV-1 DNA probe. (Performed under relaxed or nonstringent conditions to detect PV genus-specific polynucleotide sequences). (Reproduced with permission from Lancaster WD, et al: Human papillomavirus: Detection of viral DNA sequences and evidence for molecular heterogeneity in metaplasias and dysplasias of the uterine cervix. *Intervirology* 1983; 20:202–212.)

been identified (see Table 40–1)[5–8, 11–25, 37–52, 99–107, 125] (E-M. de Villiers, personal communication, 1988). These HPVs can be broadly categorized into at least three clinicopathologic groups. The first group comprises cutaneotropic HPV (HPV-1, -2, -3, -4, -7, -10, -26, -27, -28, -29) which are invariably associated with benign warts. The second group includes cutaneotropic viruses (HPV-5, -8, -9, -12, -14, -15, -17, -19, -20, -21, -22, -23, -24, -25, -36, -46, -47, -48, -49, -50) which primarily infect the skin of immunologically deficient individuals, particularly those with

EV, a rare familial disorder characterized by varying degrees of decreased cell-mediated immunity (CMI). The third group comprises mucosotropic HPV (HPV-6, -11, -13, -16, -18, -30, -31, -33, -34, -35, -41, -42, -43, -44, -45) which preferentially infect the anogenital tract, and to a lesser extent, the oral cavity and aerodigestive tract of normal individuals. Viruses within each group are more likely to have a higher degree of DNA homology with each other than with HPVs from the other two groups.[125]

The association of HPV with premalignant and malignant le-

Table 40–2
Cofactors in Papillomavirus (PV)-Associated Carcinogenesis

PV	Carcinoma	Cofactor
Rabbit PV (Shope)	Cutaneous	Coal tar
Bovine PV-4	Alimentary tract	Bracken fern
Human papilloma virus (HPV)-5, and -8	Cutaneous in epidermodysplasia verruciformis	Sunlight
HPV-11, and -6	Laryngeal	Irradiation
HPV-16, -16-like, and -18	Anogenital	Multifactorial

sions is strongly suggestive of a causal relationship. Only a few cutaneotropic HPVs, particularly HPV-5 and -8, are associated with premalignant and malignant cancers of the skin of immunosuppressed individuals, usually in areas exposed to sunlight (Table 40–2).[114, 125–128] On the other hand, at least 15 mucosotropic HPVs appear to have varying degrees of association with premalignant and malignant lesions of the anogenital tract, particularly the cervix (see Figure 40–1). The five most prevalent and frequently studied mucosotropic HPVs are HPV-6, -11, -31, -16, and -18.[13–26, 42–48, 52] HPV-6 and -11 are associated with lesions that have low malignant potential, HPV-31 is found in a minority of benign, premalignant, and malignant lesions, and HPV-16 and -18 are associated with the majority of in situ and invasive cancers.[13–26, 42–46] The association of HPV with cancer of the cervix is relatively consistent, although there appear to be geographic variations in the relative frequency of different HPV infections,[19, 42–52] perhaps related to differences in genetic susceptibility and/or prevalence of different HPV type infections in various localized populations.

Although oncogenesis associated with HPV is undoubtedly a multifactorial process (see Table 40–2), there is molecular evidence indicating that the viral genome may undergo changes (integration into cellular DNA and/or modifications in the control region of replicating plasmids) which contribute to the conversion of a noninvasive lesion to the malignant phenotype. For example, HPV-6 and -11 nucleotide sequences do not appear to integrate within cellular DNA, but there are significant modifications in the control region of the replicating plasmid isolated from squamous carcinomas of the anogenital and aerodigestive tract.[129–131] On the other hand, HPV-16 and -18 are invariably episomal in latent infections, condylomata, and low-grade premalignant lesions, but the viral genome is integrated into cellular DNA in most malignant and high-grade premalignant lesions.[91–98] The viral genome is interrupted within the 3′ end of the early region, allowing overexpression of E ORF E6, and E7, which encodes putative viral oncogenes.[92–98] In addition, integrated HPV DNA has been shown to be in the proximity of cellular proto-oncogenes, which are amplified, overexpressed, or both, in late-stage cervical cancer.[132, 133] Whether viral or cellular oncogene activation plays a role in the development of malignancies associated with HPV-16 and -18 is unknown, but available evidence suggests that it is a distinct possibility.

EPIDEMIOLOGY

Relatively little is known about the incidence and prevalence of HPV infection in well-defined populations. The potential use of seroepidemiologic methodology to study HPV infections, particularly those caused by mucosotropic HPV, has not been evaluated because of the lack of standardized PV type-specific immunologic reagents. However, recognition of the clinical and pathologic diversity of HPV-associated lesions coupled with the recent availability of standardized, commercially available molecular hybridization tests for detection of HPV types has provided the foundation for the design of carefully controlled epidemiologic studies.[25]

Although population control studies are not available for HPV, several generalizations can be made about different populations infected by HPV. Laryngeal papillomas occur predominantly in preschool children but exhibit a second lower peak in later life.[11] Verrucae plana (flat or juvenile warts) occur primarily in preschool and grade-school children.[1, 2] Common warts appear to occur more frequently in school-age children and adolescents with the frequency of current, clinically apparent infection varying from 5% to 10%. Plantar warts appear to be more common in adolescents and young adults, probably resulting from higher exposure in communal activities such as bathing and swimming, where moisture and minor trauma to the feet play an important role. Venereal warts of the external genitalia and flat condylomata, particularly of the cervix and glans penis, are most often seen in young, sexually active adults.[13–26] Low-grade premalignant anogenital tract lesions frequently coexist with condylomata, but high-grade premalignant lesions and invasive carcinomas associated with HPV, especially of the uterine cervix, occur in both young (teens, twenties) and, particularly, older adults (over 30).

Most epidemiologic studies of cervical cancer and its precursor lesions (which we now know are associated with HPV infection) as sexually transmitted diseases (STD) were accomplished without knowing the identity of the infectious, etiologic agent. The principle risk factors identified for developing cervical cancer were early age of first intercourse and multiple sexual partners, with the latter being the most important.[134, 135] For many years, herpesvirus type 2 was thought to be the most likely etiologic agent based on seroepidemiologic evidence.[136, 137] However, only HPV has fulfilled most of the criteria for an etiologic agent, which includes the consistent identification of either HPV structural antigens or cell-associated antigens and/or HPV genomic DNA in cancerous and precursor lesions.[13–26] It is now generally accepted that STDs other than those associated with HPV are indicators of sexual behavior rather than of risk of developing cervical cancer.[25, 138, 139]

One particular feature of HPV-associated lesions, particularly those of the anogenital and aerodigestive tract, presents a problem for future epidemiologic studies; HPV-associated lesions such as cutaneous warts, and probably mucosal condylomata, frequently undergo spontaneous regression.[1, 2, 13–26, 64–66, 140] Spontaneous regression is high for cutaneous warts, approaching 25% to 35% in the first 6 months and 35% to 70% within 2 years.[2, 140] The fate of the virus in regressing cutaneous lesions is unknown. However, when HPV-associated mucosal lesions appear to regress or to be effectively treated, the HPV appears to remain in tissue as a latent infection, which cannot be distinguished clinically or pathologically from normal mucosal epithelium.[45–52] This latent state represents the largest reservoir of mucosotropic HPV infections, and reactivation of latent HPV rather than reinfection by sexual transmission may be responsible for recurrence of clinical lesions.

PATHOGENESIS

Transmission

Most of the available evidence that HPVs are transmissible, infectious agents comes from limited epidemiologic studies, case reports, and a few early transmission studies among humans.[1, 2, 25, 67-70] For many years, it has been known that cutaneous warts could be transmitted between individuals, either directly by skin contact, or indirectly from clothing, jewelry, bathroom floors, etc. Warts and mucosal papillomas and condylomata, particularly those occurring at pressure points such as the sole of the foot or in loose traumatized mucosal tissue such as the anogenital tract or larynx, are likely to be multiple and recur after therapy. This is probably due to either autoinoculation or seeding of HPV at the site of recurrent trauma.

Evidence is beginning to accumulate that mucosotropic HPVs are also highly infectious and readily transmitted. There is good evidence that infants may contract the HPV that causes juvenile laryngeal papillomas as they pass through the birth canal of mothers who have genital warts or cervical condylomata.[9, 11] Some cases of oral condylomata occur concurrently in individuals with genital condylomata.[4, 141] The majority of male sexual partners of women with venereal or flat condylomata or intraepithelial neoplastic lesions of the cervix (CIN) have similar penile lesions.[142-145]

Transmission of HPV appears to be particularly effective in two general populations: (1) individuals who are in increased physical contact with others, such as seen in institutionalized patients who have an increased incidence of cutaneous warts,[140] or sexually active persons who have a high rate of exposure to STDs, and (2) patients with acquired or iatrogenic immunosuppression,[146-148] including pregnancy.[148-150] In one study, over a fourth of patients in a mental institution had cutaneous warts, which regressed with the same frequency as in other populations.[140] The increased incidence and severity of wart virus infections in immunosuppressed patients undoubtedly reflect the role of the immune system in HPV infections.[2, 146-148, 150, 151] Although generalized cutaneous warts have been seen in patients with agammaglobulinemia, they appear to be more frequent in patients with decreased cell-mediated responses. All of these observations suggest that HPVs are the transmissible agents that cause cutaneous warts and mucosal condylomata in man.

Incubation Period

HPVs appear to be highly infectious viruses with relatively long incubation periods. The incubation period of cutaneous warts is best assessed by reviewing data from experiments on the transmission of human warts during the first half of the century.[1] Cutaneous warts generally appeared at the site of inoculation within 1 to 3 months, but some incubation periods were as long as 6 to 20 months. The high rate of infectivity of genital warts was first realized in 1954[152] and confirmed in 1971[153] when it was reported that up to 60% of sexual partners of individuals with venereal warts developed similar lesions after an average incubation period of approximately 6 to 8 weeks. The relatively long incubation

period required for development of HPV-associated lesions has also been documented in the only available in vitro, animal model system for growth of HPV-infected tissue.[154, 155] HPV-11–infected human squamous epithelium, particularly cervical and foreskin, implanted beneath the capsule of athymic mice results in the formation of large keratin-filled cysts with the morphologic features of anogenital condylomata rapidly developing from normal-appearing squamous epithelium after an uneventful incubation period of 3 to 4 weeks.

Host Response

All three types of squamous epithelium, (1) cutaneous (keratinized), (2) mucosal (nonkeratinized), and (3) metaplastic, are susceptible to infection by HPV.[156] Generally, the various exophytic cutaneous warts and mucosal condylomata and papillomas are well-circumscribed papillomatous growths that vary in size and color and tend to have a roughened, horny surface (Figure 40–4). However, some of the HPV-associated lesions are flat, such as cutaneous juvenile warts, the pityriasis-like lesions of EV, and anogenital tract flat condylomata and dysplastic lesions, particularly of the cervix and glans penis.[2, 13-26]

It is thought that HPV infection begins in the basal layer of the epithelial cells, presumably from virus released from infected, exfoliated cells that have lodged in cracks of susceptible squamous epithelium.[156] After infection, the PV genome becomes stabilized as an episome, either remaining latent without phenotypic changes in maturing squamous cells, or establishing an active infection with subsequent expression of late and/or early gene functions in

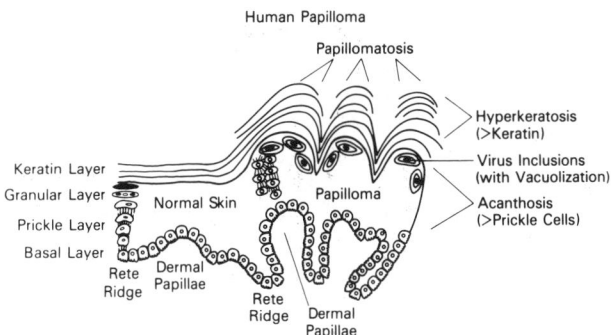

Figure 40–4. Cartoon of the histologic features of normal skin and the histopathologic features of an adjacent papilloma (wart). In the normal skin, there is a basal layer of cells that undergoes division to form a multiple cell layer of prickle cells. The number of prickle cells determines the thickness of the skin, which varies according to location. As the prickle cells are pushed toward the surface, they flatten and develop cytoplasmic keratohyaline granules (granular cells). The granular cells then lose nuclei, and the cytoplasm and keratohyaline granules coalesce into a flat, acellular keratinized layer. In the papilloma, there is a single layer of basal cells but there is hyperplasia of prickle cells (acanthosis) and production of excess keratin (hyperkeratosis), which is associated with the formation of epithelial spikes (papillomatosis). Virus inclusions and/or expression of human papillomavirus structural antigens usually appear in granular cells with degenerative cytoplasmic vacuolization (koilocytotic cells). (Reproduced with permission from Jenson AB, et al: Papillomavirus etiology of oral cavity papillomas, in Hooks J, Jordan W (eds): *Viral Infections in Oral Medicine*. New York, North–Holland Elsevier, 1982.)

differentiating squamous cells resulting in morphologic changes. Early gene expression either increases the rate of cellular proliferation or prolongs the life span of keratinocytes resulting in acanthosis (increase in stratum spinosum or prickle cell layer),[19, 106] whereas late gene expression is associated with the appearance of PV capsid proteins and virion assembly occurring almost exclusively within nuclei of terminally differentiating keratinocytes (see Figure 40–4).[156] The late events that lead up to viral capsid assembly appear to cause degenerative changes in both the cytoplasm (vacuolization or koilocytosis) and nuclei (wrinkling and pyknosis) of differentiating keratinocytes. Viral capsid assembly predominantly occurs in some but not all koilocytes located in the outer differentiating layers of approximately half of warts or condylomata.[82]

Latent infections constitute the largest reservoir for mucosotropic HPV. The concept of latent infection was first proposed by Steinberg et al[157] who recovered HPV-11 DNA from normal-appearing squamous epithelium removed during laryngeal reconstructions of patients with a previous history of laryngeal papillomatosis. Latently infected tissue cannot be distinguished clinically or pathologically from normal mucosal epithelium.[44–52, 157, 158] Latent anogenital tract infections can only be detected in cervical scrapings or biopsies by molecular hybridization techniques employing blots (Southern, dot), since the various in situ hybridization methods have not as yet been sensitive enough to detect either HPV genomic DNA or corresponding transcripts in latently infected cells.[159] Activation of latent infections by mechanical or chemical trauma and regenerating squamous cells has been suggested as a source of recurrent disease which sometimes appears after adequate therapy.[49]

Active HPV infections are characterized by similar histopathologic features in biopsies of most cutaneous warts and many mucosal condylomata and papillomas (see Figure 40–1). Productive HPV infections are manifest by proliferation of prickle cells (acanthosis), degenerative cytoplasmic vacuolization (koilocytosis), nuclear alterations (atypical degenerative changes), and hyperkeratosis (production of excess keratin), particularly in cutaneous warts, or parakeratosis, which is predominantly seen in mucosal condylomata.[156] In exophytic lesions, acanthosis and hyperkeratosis are associated with the formation of numerous papillary projections, collectively referred to as papillomatosis. The epithelial proliferation may also extend downward, resulting in accentuated rete pegs, sometimes referred to as inverted papillomatosis. On the other hand, predominantly flat lesions are not characterized by development of either surface or inverted papillomatosis. Both exophytic and flat HPV-associated cutaneous and mucosal lesions usually have a prominent vascular component, frequently displaying an exuberant capillary proliferation from the underlying dermis or stroma. This accounts for the vascularity of warts and the abnormal vascular patterns seen in cervical condylomata and dysplasia when viewed through the colposcope.

Active HPV infections can also be diagnosed by cytologic examination of exfoliated cells, particularly of the uterine cervix and vagina.[14, 21, 23, 26] This has proved to be a very efficient and reproducible noninvasive screening method for early diagnosis of benign, premalignant, and malignant lesions of the anogenital tracts. Most of the abnormal cells identified by cytologic screening are exfoliated from cervical lesions, which appear to account for up to 95% of invasive carcinomas of the entire anogenital tract. Patients with cervical smears containing cells that only display koilocytotic atypia (HPV cytopathic effect) should be worked up further since up to 37% of patients in some series will have associated premalignant lesions which must be identified by colposcopically directed biopsies.[160]

COMMON CLINICAL SYNDROMES

Cutaneous[1, 2, 29–34, 89, 90, 104, 106, 107, 125]

Verruca vulgaris (HPV-2, -26, -28, -29, and occasionally HPV-1) is the most common (vulgar) of all the warts. It is sessile and exophytic with a crusty papillomatous surface. Common warts can occur singly but are frequently multiple. They are usually located on the hand. Verrucae associated with HPV-2 also occur on the mucocutaneous border of the oral cavity but less frequently than on the skin.[161] Common warts are most frequently seen in young children. Some verrucae disappear, but many are treated for cosmetic reasons. Nonetheless, a small but significant percentage will recur regardless of the form of therapeutic intervention.

Verruca plantaris or plantar warts (HPV-1, -4) are seen mainly in adolescents and young adults. They usually occur as a single lesion on the sole of the foot. Although clinically aggressive, these warts usually respond well to treatment. They are not elevated above the surface of the skin but extend deep into the sole where they are frequently painful. Although many forms of therapy, including irradiation, have been used on these lesions, there are no well-documented reports of malignant transformation.

Verrucae (HPV-3, -10, -27) are flat warts which usually appear over the face and those parts of the extremities other than the hands and feet. They are usually multiple. Since these warts usually appear in children, they are frequently called juvenile warts. Juvenile warts are usually asymptomatic, cause few cosmetic problems, and may persist for a number of years, only to spontaneously disappear within a few weeks.[162–164]

Mucosal

Oral Cavity and Larynx

Focal epithelial hyperplasia, HPV-13, -32,[125, 165] (E-M. de Villiers, personal communication, 1988), occurs only in the oral cavity, appearing clinically to be flat or slightly elevated and either white or the color of the surrounding mucosa.[3, 166, 167] These lesions have been reported to occur primarily in natives of Greenland and North and South America, suggesting the influence of environmental and genetic factors. In Greenland Eskimos, it has been observed primarily in adults, whereas in the Southwest Indians, it has been reported to occur primarily in children. These lesions are usually multiple and spontaneously disappear.

Single oral papillomas (when associated with HPV the type is usually unknown) are the most common benign epithelial tumors of the oral cavity.[168, 169] They are pedunculated with a fibrovascular stalk and usually have a rough papillary appearance to their surface. They can occur in any age group, are usually solitary, and rarely recur after surgical excision.

Multiple papillomas (HPV-6, -11) are clinically and pathologically similar to condylomata, which occur infrequently in the oral cavity.[3–8, 170] Laryngeal papillomas, associated with HPV-11, and

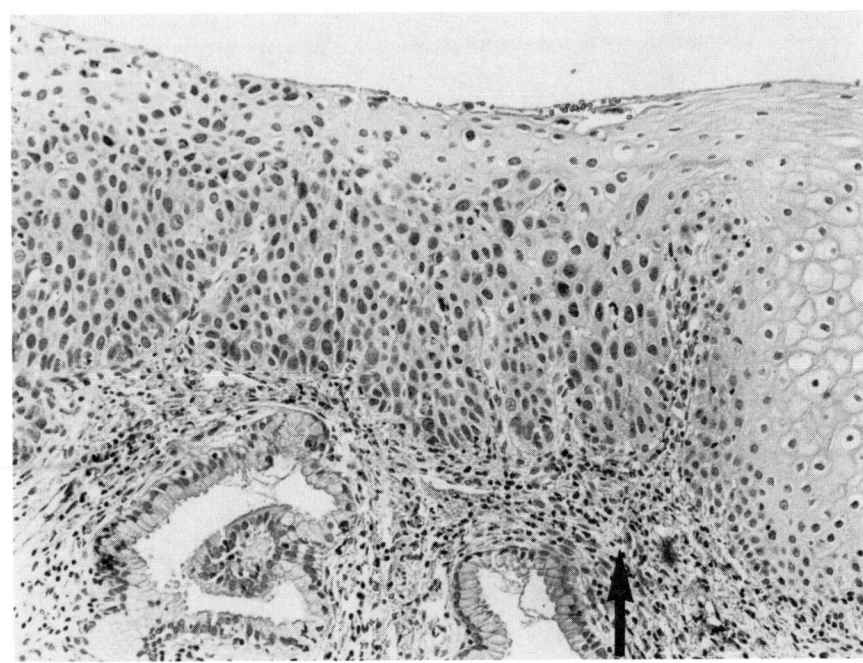

Figure 40–5. Human papillomavirus infection of the transformation zone of the cervix. There is an abrupt transition *(arrow)* from normal glycogenated squamous epithelium of the exocervix to a cervical intranuclear neoplastic (CIN) II lesion within the transformation zone. The exocervical–endocervical junction, where most CIN lesions originate, is anatomically demarcated by submucosal endocervical glands which do not extend beyond the junction.

to a lesser extent HPV-6, are the most common benign epithelial tumors of the larynx.[11, 38, 171] The clinical picture is that of small exophytic papillomas which can coalesce and appear very exuberant. They occur more frequently in children than adults, are typically multiple, and frequently recur after surgical removal. Laryngeal papillomatosis is usually considered a life-threatening condition in children because of the danger of airway obstruction and suffocation; they frequently disappear after puberty. Occasionally papillomas may extend down the trachea and into the bronchi. Malignant transformation may occur after radiation therapy.[172–174]

Anogenital[13–26]

The clinical importance of HPV as a STD is reflected by its impact on society as a major health problem. HPV is one of the most common viral STDs in the United States,[175] and in all populations is associated with up to 90% of cervical cancers, which are responsible for approximately one sixth of cancer deaths in females worldwide.[176] The vast majority of all squamous cancers of the anogenital tract arise from clinically inapparent lesions in the transformation zone of the uterine cervix,[16–26] where it is thought that metaplastic squamous epithelium is particularly susceptible to HPV infection (Figures 40–5 and 40–6). The male anogenital tract is recognized as the "silent" reservoir for sexual transmission of high-risk HPV.[142–145]

HPV infections of the anogenital tract of both sexes generally fall into three categories: (1) latent infections with no clinically or pathologically detectable lesions; latent infections occur in approximately 10% of sexually active individuals and represent the largest reservoir of HPV in the anogenital tract.[44–52, 158, 159] (2) Active infections appear to occur in approximately 2% to 4% of sexually active females resulting in either benign exophytic or flat lesions, or both.[13–26] (3) Intraepithelial neoplasias or invasive carcinomas frequently appear to develop within or adjacent to predominantly flat, but occasionally benign, exophytic lesions.[13–26, 37–48] Flat lesions, which are clinically and morphologically flat, blend in imperceptibly with normal squamous epithelium.[177–179] These HPV-associated flat lesions have been designated subclinical papillomavirus infection (SPI) because they can only be identified clinically after application of acetic acid and colposcopic magnification of the resulting acetowhite area. The designation of SPI, however, may not be appreciated by the pathologist since these clinically inapparent lesions frequently have the characteristic morphology attributed to wart virus infections (Table 40–3).[179]

Condylomata acuminata, so-called venereal warts, are usually associated with HPV-6 (65% of the time) or HPV-11 (20%)[37, 171, 180] frequently occurring on the external genitalia and adjacent anal

Table 40–3
Clinical and Pathologic Diagnoses of Benign Human Papillomavirus–Associated Lesions of the Anogenital Tract

Clinical	Pathologic
Venereal wart	Exophytic condyloma (acuminatum)
Subclinical papillomavirus infection	Flat condyloma (planum) or very mild dysplasia

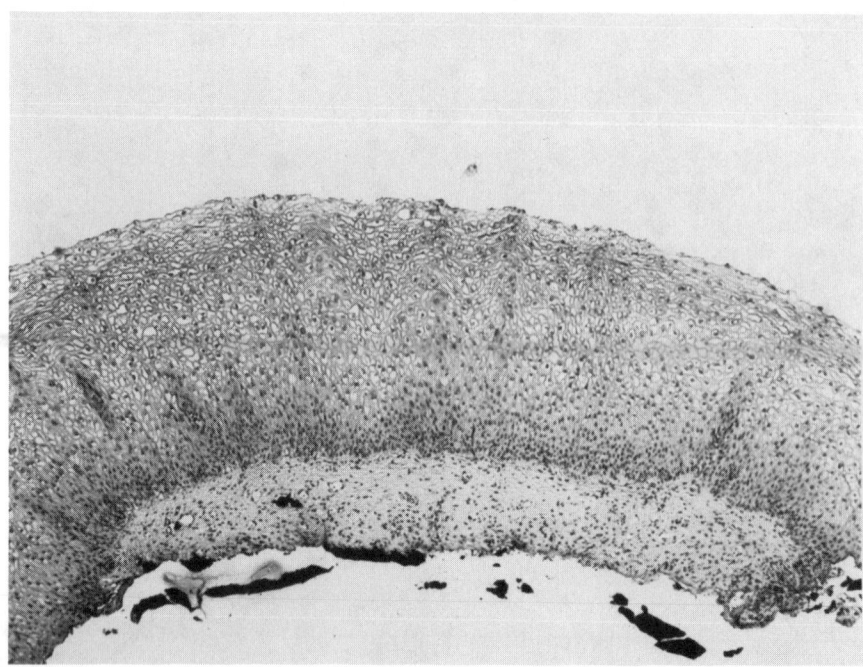

Figure 40–6. Human papillomavirus–16 infection of metaplastic squamous epithelium of the transformation zone of cervix. This flat condyloma is characterized by acanthosis and diffuse koilocytosis extending throughout the upper two-thirds thickness of the epithelium. Capillaries extending through the thickness of the epithelium create small superficial spikes that impart a filiform appearance to the lesion. This condyloma was infectious since superficial koilocytes contained intranuclear capsid antigens (not shown).

and perianal area of both sexes. In females, condylomata may regress spontaneously, persist for years, or undergo a rapid increase in size during pregnancy. Genital warts of long duration appear to have a low risk for undergoing malignant transformation.[181] Many show evidence of mild dysplasia but greater degrees of dysplasia are unusual. Up to 5% of squamous carcinomas of the vulva have been reported to develop in association with condylomata.[181, 182] Perhaps the best clinical evidence of the malignant potential of genital warts occurred in two rare cases in which carcinoma of the vulva in young teenage girls was preceded by condylomata (reviewed by zur Hausen[181]). In males, 15% of squamous carcinomas of the penis have been reported to develop in association with preexisting condylomata.[181, 182] Many penile carcinomas are of the verrucous type with features of giant condyloma acuminatum of Buschke and Lowenstein.[183] Of interest is the observation that circumcision reduces the incidence of penile carcinomas but not the appearance of penile condylomata.[181] Women with vulvar condylomata acuminata and/or sex partners with penile acuminata lesions have a greatly increased risk of having concomitant cervical condylomata acuminata or plana, CIN, or both.

Approximately 10% of normal cervices of sexually active women, 60% to 90% of flat condylomata, 77% to 90% of premalignant lesions of the cervix (dysplastic, CIN), and up to 90% of cervical carcinomas are positive for HPV utilizing nonstringent southern blot hybridizations for HPV.[13–26, 37–52, 104–107, 180] Over half of low-grade lesions of the cervix, condylomata plana and mild dysplasias, have low malignant potential since they are associated with unidentified HPV or HPV-6 or -11.[37 171, 180] However, clinical and histopathologic features of low-grade lesions associated with HPV-6 and -11 are essentially the same as low-grade

lesions associated with HPV with intermediate (HPV-31) or high oncogenic (HPV-16) potential (see Figure 40–6).[156] Although dysplastic lesions or CIN, particularly mild dysplasias or CIN I, appear to represent a heterogeneous group of diseases which are not necessarily premalignant, the majority of invasive cancers appear to develop from CINs which are associated with HPV-16.[13–26] The development of cervical cancer is thought to proceed through a continuum of progressive cellular changes from mild (CIN I) to moderate (CIN II) (see Figure 40–2) to severe dysplasia and/or carcinoma in situ (CIN III).[17, 20, 21, 26, 184–186] This sequence of events has been documented by a number of studies with transit times from mild dysplasia to carcinoma in situ ranging from 84 to 96 months.[184] Most flat condylomata and CIN I lesions will either persist or regress,[13–26] whereas the majority of higher-grade lesions (CIN II and III) will either persist or progress.[184] The rate of development of invasive carcinoma from CIN III lesions is variable but generally occurs in up to two thirds of cases with a transit time of 10 to 15 years.[21, 26]

HPV infections of the male and female anogenital tract appear to be multicentric diseases, represented by latent and active infections, presumably spread throughout the anogenital tract during sexual intercourse. Reid et al[52] reported that when multiple biopsies were used to sample the vulva, vagina, and cervix of each patient with well-documented HPV-associated lesions, half of the women with vulvar lesions also had concomitant cervical infections. Seventy percent of cervical infections were by the same HPV recovered from the vulvar lesions; 30% were associated with different HPVs, implying transmission from different lesions of the same or different sex partners. On the other hand, 50% to 75% of male sex partners of women with flat condylomata or CIN lesions have penile exophytic or flat lesions, or papular lesions, which have some of the clinical characteristics of both acuminate and flat lesions.[142–145] Most of the flat lesions (macules) and some papules occur on the glans penis (Figure 40–7).[142] Clinically, these lesions do not appear to be reliable predictors of either the morphology of the lesion or associated HPV type. Barrasso et al[142] recently showed that if the female sex partners had a proven CIN lesion, the majority of papules and half of the macules would have morphologic evidence of IN, most of which were associated with HPV-16 or -16-like HPV. However, if the female sex partner had flat condyloma of the cervix, then the majority of flat lesions had morphologic evidence of condylomata and were usually associated with HPV-6, -11, or -42.

One of the high-grade dysplastic lesions of external genitalia of both sexes, bowenoid papulosis (Figure 40–8), has been implicated in the transmission and spread of HPV-16.[187, 188] Occurring in young persons, this lesion is multifocal and frequently undergoes regression. A clinically distinct but morphologically similar lesion to bowenoid papulosis, Bowen's disease, is usually single, occurs in older persons, and has the propensity to convert to an invasive cancer. HPV-16 has been reported to replicate as a plasmid as well as with cellular DNA in an integrated state in bowenoid papulosis and Bowen's disease.

UNCOMMON CLINICAL SYNDROMES

Epidermodysplasia verruciformis (HPV-3, -5, -8, -9, -10, -12, -14, -15, -17, -19, -20, -21, -22, -23, -24, -25, -36, -46, -47, -48, -49, -50) or verrucosis generalisata is a rare, autosomal re-

cessive disease characterized by varying degrees of decreased cell-mediated immunity (CMI) and increased susceptibility to HPV infection manifested clinically by polymorphic skin lesions resembling either flat warts or macules indistinguishable from pityriasis rosea.[114, 125–128, 189–193] In approximately 25% of white patients, malignant transformation occurs within the pityriasis rosea–like lesions in sun-exposed areas such as the face and hands. Only lesions containing HPV-5 or -8 appear to progress to premalignant lesions, histopathologically similar to cervical dysplasia, before developing into carcinoma in situ (Bowen's disease) and, eventually, invasive basal cell and squamous cell carcinoma. HPV-5 has been identified in both primary and metastatic malignant lesions from the same patient.[104, 106, 107, 126, 193]

Immunosuppressed patients, particularly those undergoing renal transplantation, also develop pityriasis rosea–like lesions associated with HPV-5, which may undergo malignant transformation.[104, 106, 107, 125, 127] Although warts that are present at the beginning of therapy become aggressive, newly acquired warts are usually seen only after the first year of immunosuppression.[2] Squamous cell carcinomas usually do not develop in patients with immunosuppression of short duration, suggesting that HPV-5 or -8 is acquired from some reservoir which is as yet unknown. Although infection by human immunodeficiency virus (HIV) and development of acquired immunodeficiency syndrome (AIDS) must predispose individuals to development of multicentric HPV infections and, presumably, associated premalignant and malignant lesions, there are other more clinically relevant features of AIDS which have precluded careful study of HPV as a pathogen in these cases.

Butcher's warts, which are clinically indistinguishable from

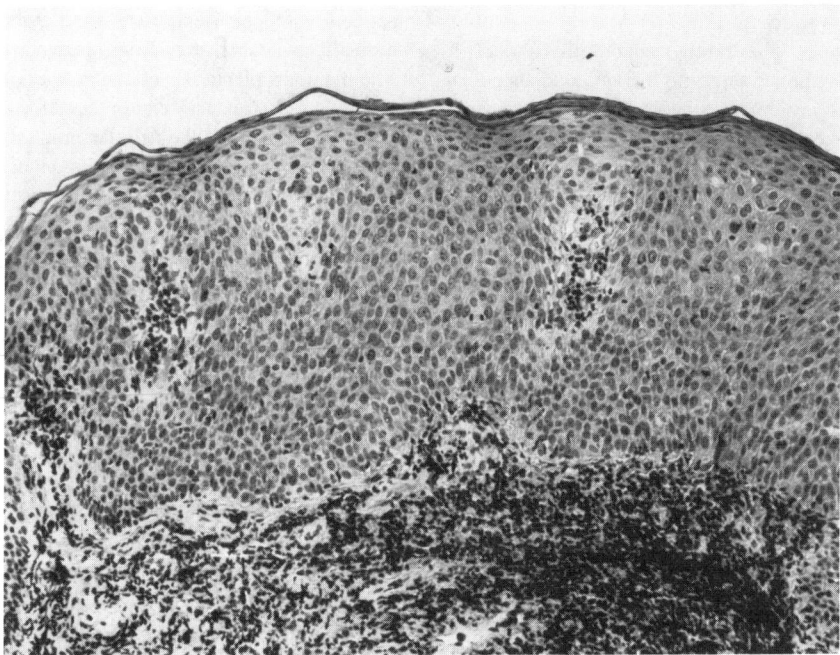

Figure 40–7. Human papillomavirus–16 infection of glans penis. Clinically, this was a nonpigmented papule that turned acetowhite after application of 5% acetic acid. Morphologically, this is a penile intraepithelial neoplasia (PIN) II–III characterized by proliferating basaloid cells that occupy two-thirds to four-fifths of the epithelial thickness. Since this lesion did not support the development of koilocytosis, it is not surprising that immunocytochemical tests were negative for the presence of viral capsid antigen.

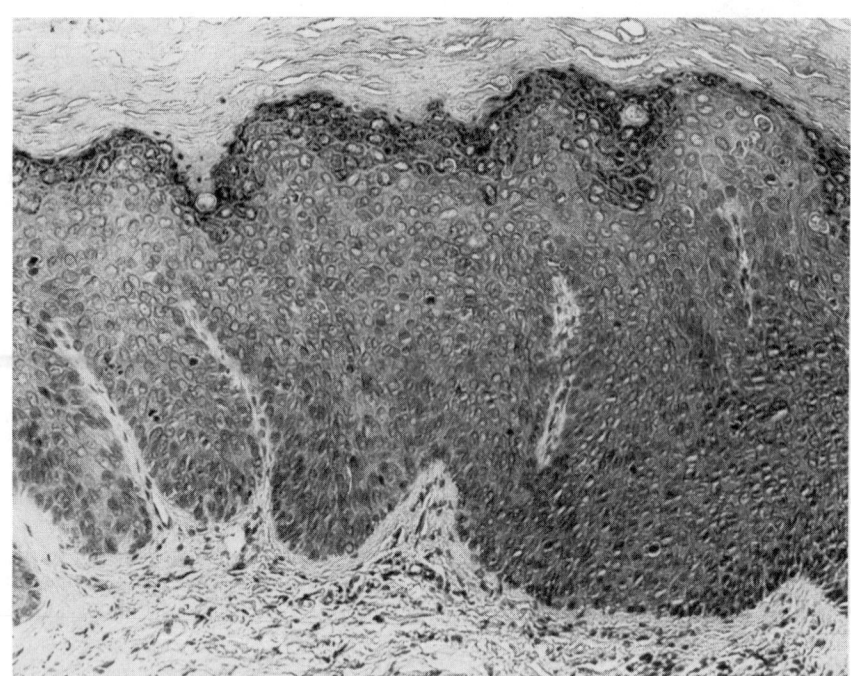

Figure 40–8. Bowenoid papulosis (vulvar intraepithelial neoplasia III lesions) of vulva associated with human papillomavirus–16. There is acanthosis with crowding and an irregular (windblown) appearance of nuclei, many of which are large and pleomorphic extending throughout the thickness of the epithelium.

common warts, are usually multiple and occur on the hands of meat handlers.[194, 195] Although HPV-7 is always associated with butcher's warts, only 25% to 30% of butcher's warts are caused by HPV-7, with HPV-2 the most prevalent HPV type associated with these occupational verrucae.[104, 106, 107, 125]

Conjunctival papillomas, usually associated with HPV-11,[196] are usually multiple, may be refractory to therapy, and anecdotal reports suggest that these lesions may be an occupational hazard for obstetricians and gynecologists.

IMMUNOLOGIC RESPONSES

Available evidence suggests that spontaneous regression or persistence of warts is related to the immunologic responsiveness of the individual (reviewed by von Krogh[151]). Studies of HPV infection suggest that stimulation of cellular immunity is associated with regression of lesions and such immunity is HPV type-specific. Although the humoral response to cutaneotropic HPV infections, particularly HPV-1, has been reported as type-specific,[197] serum antibody responses to HPV infection may also be broadly cross-reactive.[198] Antibody responses have also occasionally been used as a prognostic indicator of spontaneous regression or successful therapy of cutaneous warts. Many of the previous studies of immune responses to HPV infection are, however, difficult to assess in view of our current recognition of the plurality of HPV serotypes.

Cell-Mediated Immunity

An increased incidence of cutaneous warts that are usually flat have been reported in patients with clinical evidence of al-

tered CMI.[146] This has been seen in immunosuppressed patients,[146, 151, 199] patients with cellular immunodeficiency,[147] and patients with weak cutaneous hypersensitivity responses.[200, 201] Specific immunologic defects may be involved, however, since not all patients with persistent warts have evidence of nonspecific abnormalities in CMI. In addition, patients with regressing flat warts will maintain plantar or common warts,[162] suggesting that HPV type-specific structural and/or nonstructural proteins are recognized at the level of the cellular immune response. Morphologic evidence of cell-mediated regression of warts, particularly flat warts, has been reported.[162–164] A perivascular infiltration of mononuclear leukocytes is usually seen in the upper dermis with epidermal invasion localized to the flat wart. Noteworthy is the observation that spontaneous regression or cure following treatment is frequently associated with enhanced specific cellular immunity as tested by cutaneous hypersensitivity to wart virus–associated antigens.[77, 151, 202, 203] Recent reports (reviewed in part by Campion[20]) have suggested that fixed tissue macrophages (Langerhans cells) of squamous epithelium may play a major role in the immunologic response against mucosotropic HPV infections.[176]

Humoral Immunity

Serologic evidence of wart virus infection has been detected by a variety of techniques in various population studies (reviewed by von Krogh[151]). The significance of these studies is unknown because the tests have been performed on different preparations of wart virus material. Patients without wart virus antibodies or with IgM alone are less likely to undergo spontaneous regression or be cured than those with IgM and IgG virus-specific antibodies.[151, 204] Furthermore, after spontaneous or therapeutic cure, IgG antibodies will remain elevated for up to 6 months and as long as 9 years.[205] IgG antibodies are known to be circulating in half of patients who give no history of having warts.[203, 206] Patients with chronic and/or multiple warts are much less likely to have IgG against HPV.[203] Of particular interest is that patients with warts that do not contain virions are less likely to have antibodies.[204] Regardless, the role of serologic tests in evaluating HPV infections must be performed using HPV type-specific polypeptides as antigens. In such a study, Pfister and zur Hausen,[197] using purified HPV-1 polypeptides, demonstrated by radioimmunoassay (RIA) that 40% of an unselected group of individuals had circulating antibody to HPV-1.

LABORATORY DIAGNOSIS OF INFECTION

The multiplicity of HPV types and the relative lack of cross-reactivity of type-specific reagents has until recently impeded an assessment of the role of HPV types in lesions suspected of a HPV etiology. In the past, evidence for the presence of HPV in a particular lesion was mainly inferential, based on the morphologic similarity of the putative HPV-induced lesion to warts or condylomata acuminata, lesions known to be caused by HPV. Identi-

fication of PV particles by electron microscopy offered a direct method (Figure 40–9).[71–74, 110, 209, 210] However, because of the possibility of sampling error, particularly with the mucosal lesions, and the fact that it is a time-consuming, expensive technique, its value diminished as a practical screening technique. Recently, application of immunologic[82] and, particularly, molecular hybridization methods[116] to assay tissues for the presence of PV genus- and HPV type-specific structural antigens and DNA sequences has become possible, and some commercialized kits and standardized reagents are currently available for diagnostic purposes.

Serologic Testing

Serotyping of capsid antigens in productive PV infections has to be performed with well-defined serologic reagents. Polyclonal antisera prepared against detergent-disrupted BPV-1 and HPV-1 particles have been used to detect broadly cross-reactive and genus-specific PV major capsid antigens in approximately 50% of productively infected cutaneous warts and mucosal condylomata.[82] Antisera prepared against intact HPV-1 particles appear to be type-specific since reactivity is only seen with HPV-1–associated lesions,[54, 110] whereas polyclonal antisera generated against intact BPV-1 are cross-reactive with productively infected bovine fibro-

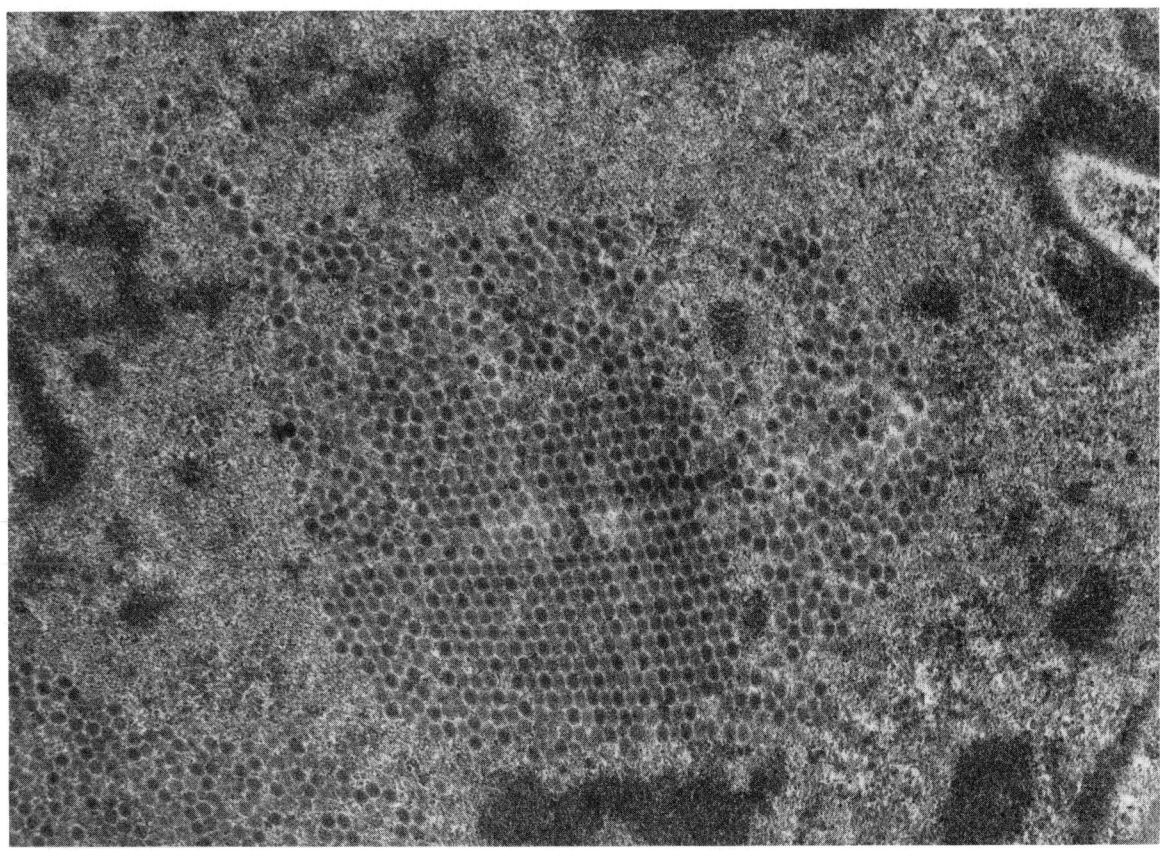

Figure 40–9. Electron micrograph of granular layer-keratin junction in same plantar wart as shown in Figures 40–10 and 40–11. Papillomavirus particles (50–55 nm) in crystalline array fill nucleus of cell immediately prior to undergoing keratinization. (×27,000) (Reproduced with permission from Jenson AB, et al: Human papillomavirus: Frequency and distribution in plantar and common warts. *Lab Invest* 1982; 47:491–497.)

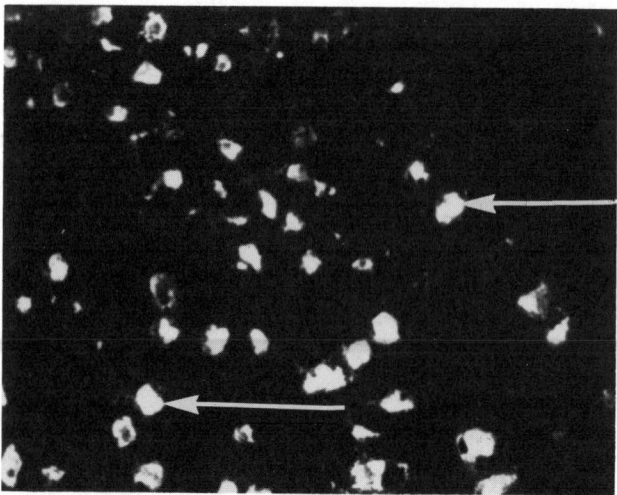

Figure 40–10. Acetone–fixed frozen section of plantar wart containing human papillomavirus 1. Type–specific structural antigens *(arrows)* are seen in many nuclei of cells in upper prickle and granular layer of epithelium. (Fluorescent antibody stain, × 400.) (Reproduced with permission from Jenson AB, et al: Immunologic relatedness of papillomaviruses from different species. *J Natl Cancer Inst* 1980; 64:495–500.)

papillomas induced by either BPV-1 or the closely related BPV-2.[54, 83] On the other hand, PV type-specific monoclonal antibodies (MoAbs) have been prepared by immunization of mice with either intact and/or disrupted PV particles.[83, 211] However, MoAbs generated against detergent-disrupted virions[83] and polyclonal antibodies produced against genetically engineered major capsid proteins[212] may be broadly cross-reactive; in one study, MoAbs were generated against five different broadly cross-reactive major capsid epitopes.[83] At present, only one MoAb has been reported that is reactive with a putatively PV genus-specific antigenic determinant.[83] Polyclonal antibodies generated against minor capsid protein preparations appear to be either type-specific or cross-reactive with closely related PV types,[81, 84] but may be weakly reactive in tissue, perhaps because of the low concentration of minor capsid antigenic determinants. True PV type-specific MoAbs should be capable of distinguishing between closely related PVs, such as BPV-1 and BPV-2, and probably, HPV-6 and -11, as well as among distantly related PVs such as HPV-1, -2, -3, and -4. Thus, serotyping of most HPVs in productively infected lesions is now possible using MoAbs generated against genetically engineered PV capsid proteins, but care should be taken to determine the specificity of such MoAbs.

Genus-Specific Tests

Productive HPV infections, identified by the presence of genus-specific structural proteins using hyperimmune sera prepared against common antigens derived from either HPV or bovine PV, can be demonstrated in acetone-fixed frozen sections by immunofluorescence (Figure 40–10) or formalin-fixed paraffin-embedded sections routinely processed for pathology using immunocytochemical techniques (Figure 40–11).[82] Since 1980, a variety of cutaneous and mucosal lesions have been screened for the presence of the PV common antigen. The frequency of HPV antigenic expression

using these techniques was in 58% of plantar warts; 68% of common warts; 40% to 60% of verrucae (Figure 40–12), multiple papillomas, and condylomata of the oral cavity; 50% of laryngeal papillomas; 50% of vulvar condylomas; 45% to 65% of male urethral papillomas and condylomata; 29% to 45% and 20% of mild (Figure 40–13) and moderate dysplasias, respectively, of the uterine cervix; and 5% of conjunctival papillomas.[82] It is currently unknown why viral antigens are detected in only about half of benign lesions. Although lack of antigen detection may be due to sampling error, limited sensitivity of the test, or denaturing of viral antigens during tissue processing, it probably is related to a cyclic or periodic expression of structural viral antigens by the viral genome, perhaps modulated by the immune response. In a study of 102 laryngeal papillomas, 48% were positive for viral antigens. However, when four or more consecutive recurrences of the same lesion were examined, at least one was always stained positively.[10] Thus, although a positive immunologic reaction for HPV means that the lesion is associated with the virus, a negative reaction does not necessarily exclude an HPV etiology. A positive immunoperoxidase reaction for HPV structural antigens indicates that the lesion is infectious.

Type-Specific Tests

HPV-1, -2, -3, -5, -6, and -16 type-specific viral antigens have been identified by immunofluorescence in frozen sections of cutaneous warts,[81, 110, 128, 190, 213, 214] and venereal warts.[84, 215] Although the immunofluorescence technique is of little practical use for diagnostic purposes in formalin-fixed tissue because of the high background, most antibodies reactive with PV capsid antigens can be successfully utilized to study formalin-fixed warts or condylomata by immunoperoxidase methods.[82] HPV-1 type-specific antigens have been identified in acetone-fixed and formalin-fixed plantar wart tissue using immunocytochemical localization by both type-specific polyclonal[110] and monoclonal antibodies[211, 216] prepared against HPV-1 structural viral antigens. Moreover, the presence of HPV-1 viral antigens in productive plantar wart infections was concordant with the presence of HPV-1–specific nucleotide sequences detected by in situ hybridization utilizing HPV-1 type-specific biotinylated DNA probes.[216] Thus, serotyping of HPV in selective productive infections is possible, but must await development of type-specific immunologic reagents for most HPV infections.

Molecular Hybridization

Molecular hybridization tests detect viral genetic material which is present in the tissue regardless of the state of differentiation of the cells. Variations of this technique have been used on freshly obtained tissues or cells, frozen material, and on formalin-fixed, paraffin-embedded tissue.[116] Molecular hybridization is currently the only method for detection and typing of HPV in latent and active infections. As previously indicated, the southern blot[119] is superior to all of the other HPV nucleic acid detection tests in its sensitivity and specificity. However, the southern blot is labor-intensive, time-consuming, and requires considerable expertise to ensure reproducible results. Dot-blot,[116] which will probably be used in most commercial kits, is as sensitive as the southern, requires little expertise, and is not time-consuming, but has the

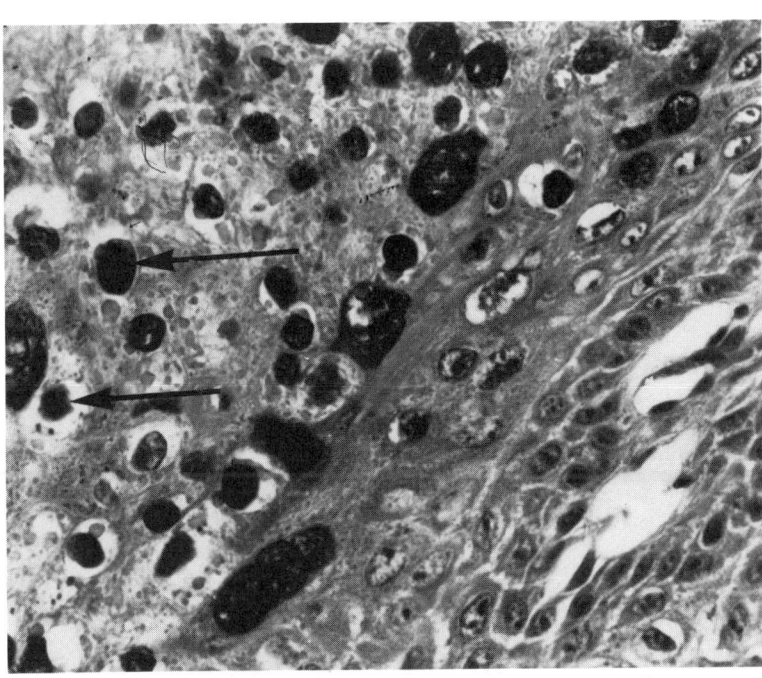

Figure 40–11. Formalin-fixed paraffin–embedded section of same plantar wart as shown in Figures 40–9 and 40–10. Papillomavirus genus-specific (common) structural antigens *(arrows)* are seen in nuclei of koilocytotic granular cells. (Perioxidase–antiperoxidase stain and hematoxylin, × 400.) (Reproduced with permission from Jenson AB, et al: Immunologic relatedness of papillomaviruses from different species. *J Natl Cancer Inst* 1980; 64:495–500.)

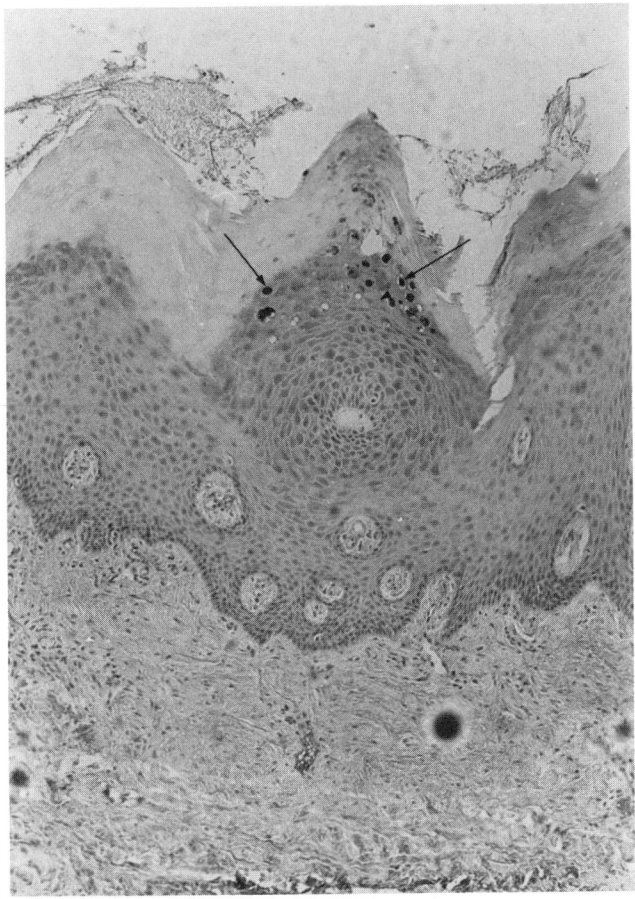

Figure 40–12. Verruca from hard palate of oral cavity. Papillomavirus genus–specific structural antigens are identified by positive peroxidase–antiperoxidase (PAP) reaction *(arrows)*, mainly in koilocytotic cells of granular layer of a single papillary frond. (PAP stain and hematoxylin, × 197.) (Reproduced with permission from Jenson B, et al: Frequency and distribution of papillomavirus structural antigens in verrucae, multiple papillomas, and condylomata of the oral cavity. *Am J Pathol* 1982; 107:212–218.)

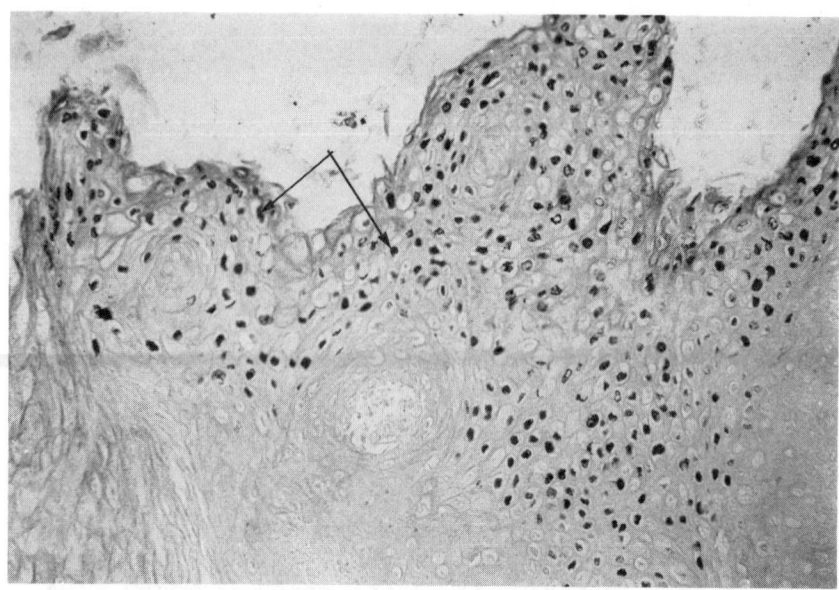

Figure 40–13. Mild cervical dysplasia with prominent epithelial spikes containing numerous cells with intranuclear genus–specific papillomavirus antigens *(arrows).* Papillomavirus DNA of undetermined type was also recovered from this case. (Peroxidase-antiperoxidase stain without counterstain, × 197.) (Reproduced with permission from Lancaster WD, et al: Human papillomavirus: Detection of viral DNA sequences and evidence for molecular heterogeneity in metaplasias and dysplasias of the uterine cervix. *Intervirology* 1983; 20:202–212.)

disadvantage of occasional false-positives and the inability to distinguish between cross-reacting, closely related viruses. Filter in situ hybridization[116, 120] is very rapid and would be useful for screening large number of samples, but it also has the disadvantage of false-positives, which may be more of a problem than the dot-blot.

In situ methods utilizing biotinylated probes are rapidly performed[116, 217] and are specific but at present lack sensitivity. Antisense RNA probes are more sensitive than HPV DNA probes because of the relative nucleic acid concentrations and stability of the RNA-RNA or RNA-DNA hybrid when compared to the DNA-DNA hybrid.[116] However, radioactive DNA[218] (Figure 40–14) and RNA[219] probes are more time-consuming and require considerable expertise (particularly for the RNA probes) when compared to biotinylated DNA probes.

Since none of the commercially available kits offer a version of the southern blot, the utilization of commercial kits for screening for HPV infections is limited to detecting only the HPV DNA sequences which are complementary to the HPV probes included in the kit. However, the sensitivity of the probes used in the HPV dot-blot hybridization kits is approximately 90% to 95% of that reported for the southern blot under stringent conditions.

Depending on the hybridization detection method, the prevalence of HPV types varies considerably in biopsies of cervical lesions. For example, Fuchs et al,[45] using southern blot stringent hybridization conditions designed to detect only HPV-6, -11, -16 (and HPV-16 related), and -18, resulted in a prevalence of these HPV types in 50% of CIN (all grades). In comparison, Lorincz et al,[44] using nonstringent southern blot hybridization capable of detecting a wide variety of HPVs, showed an overall prevalence of HPV in 77% of all grades of CIN. The higher detection frequency for HPV sequences by nonstringent southern blot hybrid-

ization is also reflected in prevalence data for cervical cancers. Fuchs et al[45] detected known HPV types in 68% of invasive cervical cancers whereas Lorincz et al[44] detected both known and unknown HPV types in 83% of cancers.

A comparison of prevalence of HPV in exfoliated cervical cells with cytologic evidence of CIN indicates a wide variation in detection of viral sequences, even when the same technique is employed. Data from filter in situ hybridization studies, which used stringent hybridization conditions to detect HPV-6 or -11, -16, and -18, varied from 35%[51] to 68%[46] in prevalence estimates of HPV in cervical scrapings showing evidence of condylomata, CIN, or both. Nonstringent southern blot hybridization, on the other hand, detected HPV sequences in 92% of samples.[44, 48] It is clear that stringent hybridization assays give a much lower detection rate than nonstringent assays, presumably because of the multiplicity of HPV types, some of which are unknown, in the anogenital tract.

The relatively high false-negative rates generally reported for cytologic screening have been used as one of the major arguments for advocating that cervical smears should be repeated yearly for all sexually active women. Proponents of HPV typing of cervical scrapings have argued that immunosuppressed women or sexually active women with borderline or equivocal cervical smears should be screened by DNA hybridization tests for the presence of HPV. If the test is positive, then the cervical scraping should be reevaluated or repeated (if it is not a representative specimen) to minimize the possibility of a false-negative (with only occasional cells showing significant cytologic abnormalities). If the clinician is satisfied that the cytologic findings and other diagnostic procedures are truly negative for active or productive HPV infection, the diagnosis (by exclusion) is that of a latent HPV infection. Women with latent HPV infections should be followed at regular intervals for the rest of their lives since they appear to be at increased risk for development of condylomata or CIN. Thus, the results of HPV detection tests provide another parameter to take into consideration for appropriate clinical management of gynecologic patients.

TREATMENT

Bunney,[2] in her assessment of a 10-year program evaluating cutaneous wart cures in approximately 14,000 patients, concluded that 70% to 80% of patients could have been cured of warts by simple methods applied either at home or in the clinic. Whether warts are treated or left alone is usually the prerogative of the individual patient. Although most warts are usually treated for cosmetic reasons, others are treated because they cause discomfort or are truly disabling. Since warts frequently undergo spontaneous regression, treatment should not result in permanent damage such as excessive scarring or disfigurement.

In general, cutaneous warts that respond most favorably to treatment are usually single, of short duration, and found in children.[2] Home treatment of warts includes topical application of salicylic acid and formalin or glutaraldehyde; podophyllin or strong acids or bases should be used under supervision. Cryotherapy is the most universally utilized treatment for warts, although surgical intervention may be indicated in some cases. Laser treatment, particularly for plantar warts, has also recently become a popular treatment. Perhaps the best biologic reason for not routinely recommending surgical intervention is that surgical extirpation of the wart is not associated with enhancement of the immunologic response such as is seen following multiple topical or freeze-thawing treatments that appear to facilitate recognition of HPV-associated antigens by the immunologic system.[2, 220] Quick removal of the bulk of wart virus antigens without concomitant exposure to the immune system is probably the main reason for the high recurrence rates of warts following surgery. Other treatments, such as interferon and retinoic acid, appear promising but are experimental at this time.

The duration of treatment and criteria for cure of cutaneous warts are important factors for clinical management of these lesions. Bunney[2] suggests that 12 weeks after beginning treatment is an adequate length of time to expect warts to disappear. Since failure to completely eradicate the initial lesion is the main reason for recurrence, a valid criterion for cure is the appearance of a normal skin after disappearance of the wart(s).

Evaluation of anogenital exophytic and flat lesions of the vagina, and external genitalia of both sexes is dependent on visualization of acuminate lesions and a high index of suspicion for detecting the flat lesions, which are best delineated by application of acetic acid and subsequent acetowhitening of the lesion.[22, 26, 142–145, 177–179, 221] On the other hand, evaluation of women with HPV infections of the cervix is largely dependent on the detection of cytologic abnormalities in cervical scrapings followed by colposcopy and target-directed biopsies to: (1) determine the location, size, and distribution of the cervical lesion(s) clinically, and (2) determine the highest grade of CIN or the presence of cancer by histopathology. When the lesion extends into the endocervical canal and cannot be visualized by colposcopy, diagnostic endocervical curettage and/or conization is necessary.[21, 26, 177, 221]

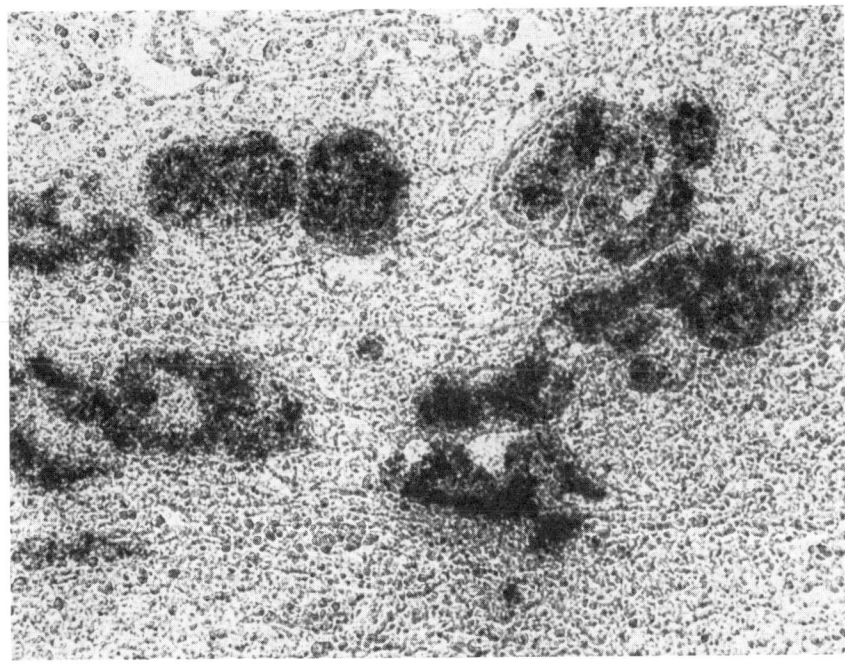

Figure 40–14. In situ hybridization using a 35S-labeled human papillomavirus (HPV)-16 DNA–DNA probe outlines lymph node metastasis from HPV-16–associated squamous carcinoma of the cervix following irradiation of the primary lesion. The high intensity of silver stains over clusters of malignant cells suggests that an unusually high copy number of HPV-16 genome is present, perhaps related to viral mutagenesis as a result of the radiation therapy.

Treatment of anogenital tract lesions takes into consideration that up to 95% of invasive cancers of the anogenital tract of both sexes develop within the transformation zone of the uterine cervix.[13–26, 177–179, 221] Treatment of HPV-associated lesions of the cervix is usually accomplished by obliteration of the entire transformation zone, by the most conservative method possible, usually by either cryotherapy or by laser. Although this approach is both curative and preventive since up to 86% of treated individuals will not have recurrent lesions, the causative HPV appears to persist as a latent infection for the life of the individual. On the other hand, treatment of HPV-associated lesions of the vagina of the female and external genitalia and surrounding perianal and anal areas of both sexes has generally been directed at eradication of only discrete lesions by a variety of methods including trichloro-acetic acid (TCA) application. Recurrent clinical disease is sometimes controlled by topical treatment with such drugs as TCA, 5-fluorouracil,[222] and interferon.[223] Treatment of invasive cancer depends on the stage of disease, location in the anogenital tract, and includes radical surgery and radiotherapy.

VACCINATION

Vaccination offers potential prevention and/or cure for cutaneous warts and HPV-associated papillomas of the mucosal surfaces. It is apparent that effective vaccination will utilize either type-specific structural or nonstructural antigens and that the lesions to be targeted will be those of the anogenital area that are sexually transmitted and are at risk of malignant transformation.[181] Future vaccines will depend on the progress made in the molecular virology of HPV and the development of expression vectors capable of synthesizing highly purified, immunogenic structural and nonstructural HPV proteins. Otherwise, the use of an autogenous vaccine derived from the patient's own lesion is the only alternative for vaccination because of the possibility of potentially harmful biologic contaminants associated with heterologous vaccines.

Most cutaneous warts either spontaneously regress or can be cured by simple treatment. Approximately 20% to 30% of these lesions will be recalcitrant to therapy. Although presumably associated with general or specific immunologic defects, half of the recalcitrant warts may disappear after vaccination of patients with formalin-inactivated HPV[77]; all patients cured developed a positive IgG response and delayed hypersensitivity reaction to the HPV preparation.

Vaccination of persons at high risk for developing or transmitting anogenital HPV-associated lesions appears to be indicated for several reasons. First, many of these are sexually transmitted and reinfection or infection by another mucosotropic HPV by sexual partners may occur. Second, up to 90% of squamous carcinomas of the cervix are associated with HPV, with the majority associated with HPV-16.[13–26, 39–46] Thus, any vaccination program directed at preventing cervical cancer would include a vaccine against HPV-16. Third, 5% to 15% of squamous carcinomas of the vulva and penis appear to arise in preexisting condylomata, usually of long duration. Fourth, successful autogenous vaccination appears to be higher for venereal warts (up to 80%) than

cutaneous warts.[224] Fifth, recombinant DNA technology should provide the necessary biologic materials in the near future for vaccination. Evaluation of the efficacy of vaccination for lesions of the anogenital area, however, will depend on well-controlled epidemiologic studies and clinical trials with evaluation of humoral (possibly secretory IgA) and cell-mediated responses to type-specific viral and viral-associated cellular antigens. Regardless, preventive measures to avoid transmission of these viruses are much preferable to the best cure.

SUMMARY

HPVs are a heterogeneous group of oncogenic viruses that replicate as true plasmids in latent infections and benign (warts, papillomas) and low-grade dysplastic lesions, and as an integrated genome in many high-grade dysplastic (cervical dysplasias, dysplasias of vulva and penis, including bowenoid papulosis), and malignant (anogenital carcinomas) lesions of squamous epithelium. HPVs are either cutaneotropic or mucosotropic. The largest reservoir for mucosotropic HPVs are latent infections which cannot be distinguished clinically or pathologically from normal mucosa. Spontaneous regression or successful topical or cryosurgical treatment of warts or condylomata appears to be dependent on either naturally acquired or iatrogenically related stimulation of HPV type-specific cellular immunity. Since the majority of latent, benign, and low-grade mucosotropic HPV-associated lesions do not appear to progress to a higher-grade lesion, various cocarcinogens and host susceptibility factors such as depressed host immunity are generally considered necessary for malignant transformation to occur. Integration of the viral genome of HPV-16 and -18, in particular, into cellular DNA, and modification of the control region of the viral genome without integration, such as seen with some HPV-6 and -11 infections, appears to be associated with conversion of nonmalignant lesions to the malignant phenotype. Thus, specific types of HPV appear to be necessary but not sufficient to cause the development of high-grade premalignant lesions and invasive cancer.

Research on HPV has benefited more from recombinant DNA technology than any other area in virology, mainly because HPV cannot as yet be grown in cell culture or transmitted to other animal species, other than HPV-11 infection of human mucosal epithelium implanted underneath the renal capsule of athymic mice. Future use of recombinant DNA technology in HPV research should (1) allow even more HPVs to be identified and characterized; (2) permit the products of early and late gene regions to be synthesized in bacterial expression vectors and used as immunogens for development of reagents to detect HPV types in surgical biopsies or exfoliative cytologic preparations, to detect serologic evidence of previous HPV infections, and to be utilized for vaccination purposes; and (3) continue to provide important information about mechanisms involved in carcinogenesis.

Acknowledgment

The authors acknowledge the help of Ann Jenson in preparation of the manuscript.

REFERENCES

1. Rowson KEK, Mahy BWJ: Human papova (wart) virus. *Bacteriol Rev* 1967; 31:110–131.
2. Bunney MH: *Viral Warts: Their Biology and Treatment.* New York, Oxford University Press, 1982.
3. Praetorius-Clausen F: Rare oral viral disorders (molluscum contagiosum, localized keratoacanthoma, verrucae, condyloma acuminatum and focal epithelial hyperplasia). *Oral Surg* 1972; 34:604–618.
4. Jenson AB, Lancaster WD, Hartman DP, et al: Frequency and distribution of papillomavirus structural antigens in verrucae, multiple papillomas, and condylomata of the oral cavity. *Am J Pathol* 1982; 107:212–218.
5. Lutzner K, Kuffer R, Blanchet-Bardon C, et al: Different papillomaviruses as the causes of oral warts. *Arch Dermatol* 1982; 118:393–399.
6. de Villiers EM, Neuman C, Le JY, et al: Infection of the oral mucosa with defined types of human papillomavirus. *Med Microbiol Immunol* 1986; 174:287–294.
7. Naghashfar Z, Sawada E, Kutcher MJ, et al: Identification of genital tract papillomaviruses HPV-6 and HPV-16 in warts of the oral cavity. *J Med Virol* 1985; 17:313–324.
8. Loning T, Ikenberg H, Becker J, et al: Analysis of oral papillomas, leukoplakias, and invasive carcinomas for human papillomavirus type related DNA. *J Invest Dermatol* 1985; 84:417–420.
9. Cook TA, Cohn AM, Brundschwig JP, et al: Laryngeal papilloma: Etiologic and therapeutic considerations. *Am J Otol* 1973; 82:649–655.
10. Lack EE, Jenson, Smith HG, et al: Immunoperoxidase localization of human papillomavirus in laryngeal papillomas. *Intervirology* 1980; 14:148–154.
11. Mounts P, Shah KV, Kashima H: Viral etiology of juvenile- and adult-onset squamous papilloma of the larynx. *Proc Natl Acad Sci USA* 1982; 79:5425–5429.
12. Brandsma JL, Steinberg BM, Abramson AL, et al: Presence of human papillomavirus type 16 related sequences in verrucous carcinoma of the larynx. *Cancer Res* 1986; 46:2185–2188.
13. zur Hausen H: Genital papillomavirus infections. *Prog Med Virol* 1985; 32:15–21.
14. Meisels A, Morin C, Casas-Cordero M: Lesions of the uterine cervix associated with papillomavirus and their clinical consequences. *Adv Clin Cytol* 1984; 2:1–31.
15. Crum CP, Levine RU: Human papilloma virus infection and cervical neoplasia: new perspectives. *Int J Gynecol Pathol* 1984; 3:376–388.
16. Obalek S, Jablonska S, Orth G: HPV-associated intraepithelial neoplasia of external genitalia. *Clin Dermatol* 1985; 3:104–113.
17. Jenson AB, Lancaster WD, Kurman RJ: Uterine cervix, in Henson D, Albores-Saavedra (eds): *The Pathology of Incipient Neoplasia.* Philadelphia, WB Saunders, 1986, pp 249–263.
18. Lancaster WD, Kurman RJ, Jensen AB: Papillomaviruses in anogenital neoplasms, in Luderer AA, Weetal HH (eds): *The Human Oncogenic Viruses.* Clifton NJ, Humana Press, 1986, pp 153–183.
19. Pfister H: Human papillomaviruses and genital cancer. *Adv Cancer Res* 1987; 48:113–147.
20. Campion MJ: Clinical manifestations and natural history of genital human papillomavirus infection. *Obstet Gynecol Clin North Am* 1987; 14:363–388.
21a. Ferenczy A, Winkler B: Cervical intraepithelial neoplasia and condyloma, in Kurman RJ (ed): *Blaustein's Pathology of the Female Genital Tract,* ed 3. New York, Springer-Verlag, 1987, pp 177–217.
21b. Ferenczy A, Winkler B: Carcinoma and metastatic tumors of the cervix, in Kurman RJ (ed): *Blaustein's Pathology of the Female Genital Tract,* ed 3. New York, Springer-Verlag, 1987, pp 218–256.
22. Wilkinson EJ, Friedrich EG Jr: Diseases of the vulva, in Kurman RJ (ed): *Blaustein's Pathology of the Female Genital Tract.* New York, Springer-Verlag, 1987, pp 36–96.

23. Koss L: Cytologic and histologic manifestations of human papillomavirus infections of the female genital tract and their clinical significance. *Cancer* 1987; 60:1942–1950.
24. Syrjanen KJ: Biology of human papillomavirus (HPV) infections and their role in squamous cell carcinogenesis. *Med Biol* 1987; 65:21–39.
25. Koutsky LA, Galloway DA, Holmes KK: The epidemiology of genital papillomavirus infection. *Epidemiol Rev* 1989; 12.
26. Richart RM: Causes and management of cervical intraepithelial neoplasia. *Cancer* 1987; 60:1951–1959.
27. Crawford LV, Crawford EM: A comparative study of polyoma and papilloma viruses. *Virology* 1963; 21:258–263.
28. Crawford LV: A study of human papilloma viruses DNA. *J Mol Biol* 1965; 13:362–372.
29. Favre M, Orth G, Croissant O, et al: Human papillomavirus DNA: Physical map. *Proc Natl Acad Sci USA* 1975b; 72:4810–4814.
30. Gissmann L, zur Hausen H: Human papillomaviruses: Physical mapping and genetic heterogeneity. *Proc Natl Acad Sci USA* 1976; 73:1310–1313.
31. Gissmann L, Pfister H, zur Hausen H: Human papillomaviruses (HPV): Characterization of four different isolates. *Virology* 1977a; 76:569–580.
32. Orth G, Favre M, Croissant O: Characterization of a new type of human papillomavirus that causes skin warts. *J Virol* 1977b; 24:108–120.
33. Favre M, Breitburd F, Croissant O, et al: Structural polypeptides of rabbit, bovine, and human papilloma viruses. *J Virol* 1975; 15:1239–1247.
34. Pfister H, Gissmann L, zur Hausen H: Partial characterization of the proteins of human papillomaviruses (HPV-1) 1–3. *Virology* 1977; 83:131–137.
35. Heilman CA, Law M-F, Israel MA, et al: Cloning of human papillomavirus genomic DNAs and analysis of homologous polynucleotide sequences. *J Virol* 1980; 36:395–407.
36. Howley PM, Israel MA, Law M-P, et al: A rapid method for detecting the mapping homology between heterologous DNAs. *J Biol Chem* 1979; 254:4876–4883.
37. Gissmann L, de Villiers E-M, zur Hausen H: Analysis of human warts (condylomata acuminata) and other genital tumors for human papillomavirus type 6 DNA. *Int J Cancer* 1982; 29:143–146.
38. Gissmann L, Diehl V, Schultz-Coulton H-J, et al: Molecular cloning and characterization of human papillomavirus DNA derived from laryngeal papilloma. *J Virol* 1982; 44:393–400.
39. Durst M, Gissmann L, Ikenberg H, et al: A new type of papillomavirus DNA from a cervical carcinoma and its prevalence in cancer biopsy samples from different geographic regions. *Proc Natl Acad Sci USA* 1983; 80:3812–3815.
40. Boshart M, Gissmann L, Ikenberg H, et al: A new type of papillomavirus DNA, its presence in genital cancer biopsies and in cell lines derived from cervical cancer. *EMBO J* 1984; 3:1151–1157.
41. Durst M, Kleinheinz A, Hotz M, et al: The physical state of human papillomavirus type 16 DNA in benign and malignant genital tumors. *J Gen Virol* 1985; 66:1512–1522.
42. Yoshikawa H, Matsukura T, Yamamoto E, et al: Occurrence of human papillomavirus types 16 and 18 DNA in cervical carcinomas from Japan: age of patients and histological type of carcinomas. *Jpn J Cancer Res* 1985; 76:667–671.
43. McCance DJ, Campion MJ, Clarkson PK, et al: Prevalence of human papillomavirus type 16 DNA sequences in cervical intraepithelial neoplasia and invasive carcinoma of the cervix. *Br J Obstet Gynaecol* 1985; 92:1101–1105.
44. Lorincz A, Temple GF, Kurman RJ, et al: The oncogenic association of specific human papillomavirus types in cervical neoplasia. *J Natl Cancer Inst* 1987; 79:671–677.
45. Fuchs PG, Girardi F, Pfister H: Human papillomavirus DNA in normal, metaplastic, preneoplastic and neoplastic epithelia of the cervix uteri. *Int J Cancer* 1988; 41:41–45.
46. Schneider A, Kraus H, Schuhmann R, et al: Papillomavirus infection of the lower genital tract: Detection of viral DNA in gyneco-

logical swabs. *Int J Cancer* 1985; 35:443–448.

47. Toon PG, Arrand JR, Wilson LP, et al: Human papillomavirus infection of the uterine cervix of women without cytological signs of neoplasia. *Br Med J* 1986; 293:1261–1264.

48. Lorincz AT, Temple GF, Campbell GE, et al: Correlation of cellular atypia and human papillomavirus DNA sequences in exfoliated cells of the uterine cervix. *Obstet Gynecol* 1986; 68:508–512.

49. Ferenczy A, Mitao M, Nagai N, et al: Latent papillomavirus and recurring genital warts. *N Engl J Med* 1985; 313:784–788.

50. MacNab JCM, Walkinshaw SA, Cordiner JW, et al: Human papillomavirus in clinically and histologically normal tissue of patients with genital cancer. *N Engl J Med* 1986; 315:1052–1058.

51. de Villiers E-M, Wagner D, Schneider A, et al: Human papillomavirus infections in women with and without abnormal cervical cytology. *Lancet* 1987; 2:703–706.

52. Reid R, Greenberg M, Jenson AB, et al: Sexually transmitted papillomaviral infections. I. The anatomic distribution and pathologic grade of neoplastic lesions associated with different viral types. *Am J Obstet Gynecol* 1987; 156:212–222.

53. Melnick JL, Allison AC, Butel JS, et al: *Papovaviridae Intervirology* 1974; 3:106–120.

54. Jenson AB, Rosenthal JD, Olson C, et al: Immunologic relatedness of papillomaviruses from different species. *J Natl Cancer Inst* 1980; 64:495–500.

55. Law M-F, Lancaster WD, Howley PM: Conserved nucleotide sequences among the genomes of papillomaviruses. *J Virol* 1979; 32:199–207.

56. Crawford LV: Nucleic acids of tumor viruses. *Adv Virus Res* 1969; 14:89–152.

57. Tsunokawa Y, Takebe N, Kasamatsu T, et al: Transforming activity of human papillomavirus type 16 DNA sequences in a cervical cancer. *Proc Natl Acad Sci USA* 1987; 83:2200–2203.

58. Yasumoto S, Burkhardt AL, Doniger J, et al: Human papillomavirus type 16 DNA-induced malignant transformation of NIH 3T3 cells. *J Virol* 1986; 57:572–577.

59. Yasumoto S, Doniger J, DiPaolo JA: Differential early viral gene expressing in two stages of human papillomavirus type 16 DNA-induced malignant transformation. *Mol Cell Biol* 1987; 7:2165–2172.

60. Piris L, Yasumoto S, Feller M, et al: Transformation of human fibroblasts and keratinocytes with human papillomavirus type 16 DNA. *J Virol* 1987; 61:1061–1066.

61. Matlashewski G, Schneider J, Banks L, et al: Human papillomavirus type 16 DNA cooperates with activated ras in transforming primary cells. *EMBO J* 1987; 6:1741–1746.

62. Butel J: Studies with human papillomavirus modeled after known papovavirus systems. *J Natl Cancer Inst* 1972; 48:285–299.

63. Lancaster WD, Olson C: Papovavirus infections of vertebrate animals. *Comp Diagn Viral Dis* 1981; III:69–98.

64. Bett WR: Wart I bid thee begone. *Practitioner* 1951; 166:77–80.

65. Clarke GHV: The charming of warts. *J Invest Dermatol* 1965; 14:15–21.

66. Rolleston JD: Dermatology and folklore. *Br J Dermatol* 1940; 43:43.

67. Licht C de F: Om vonters smitsomhed. *Ugeskr Laeger* 1894; 1:368–369.

68. Ciuffo G: Imnesto positivo con filtrato di verruca colgare. *G Ital Mal Vener* 1907; 48:12–17.

69. Serra A: Ricerche isologiche e sperimentali sul condiloma capo e la verruca volgare. Contributo all'etiologica, patogenesi, filtrabilita. *G Ital Mal Vener* 1908; 49:11–42.

70. Wile UJ, Kingrey LB: The etiology of common warts: Preliminary report of an experimental study. *JAMA* 1919; 73:970–973.

71. Strauss MJ, Bunting H, Melnick JL: Virus-like particles and inclusion bodies in skin papillomas. *J Invest Dermatol* 1949; 15:433–444.

72. Melnick JL, Bunting H, Banfield WG, et al: Electron microscopy of viruses of human papilloma, molluscum contagiosum, and vaccinia, including observations on the formation of virus within the cell. *Ann NY Acad Sci* 1952; 54:1214–1225.

73. Bunting H: Close-packed array of virus-like particles within cells of a human skin papilloma. *Proc Soc Exp Biol Med* 1953; 84:327–332.

74. Almeida JD, Howatson AF, Williams MG: Electron microscope study of human warts: Sites of virus production and nature of the inclusion bodies. *J Invest Dermatol* 1962; 38:337–345.

75. Melnick JL: Papova virus group. *Science* 1962; 135:1128–1130.

76. Klug A, Finch JT: Structure of viruses of the papilloma-polyoma type. I. Human wart virus. *J Mol Biol* 1965; 11:403–423.

77. Viac J, Thivolet J, Chardonnet Y: Specific immunity in patients suffering from recurring warts before and after repetitive intradermal tests with human papillomavirus. *Br J Dermatol* 1977; 97:365–370.

78. Orth G, Breitburd F, Favre M: Evidence for antigenic determinants shared by the structural polypeptides of (Shope) rabbit papillomavirus and human type 1. *Virology* 1979; 91:243–255.

79. Pass F, Maizel JV: Wart-associated antigens. II. Human immunity to viral structural proteins. *J Invest Dermatol* 1973; 60:307–311.

80. Spira G, Estes MK, Dreesman GR, et al: Papovavirus structural polypeptides; Comparison of human and rabbit papilloma viruses with simian virus 40. *Intervirology* 1974; 3:220–231.

81. Komly CA, Breitburd F, Croissant O, et al: The L2 open reading frame of human papillomavirus type 1a encodes a minor structural protein carrying type-specific antigens. *J Virol* 1986; 60:813–816.

82. Jenson AB, Kurman RJ, Lancaster WD: Detection of papillomavirus common antigens in lesions of the skin and mucosa. *Clin Dermatol* 1985; 3:56–63.

83. Cowsert L, Lake P, Jenson AB: Topographical and conformational epitopes of bovine papillomavirus type 1 defined by monoclonal antibodies. *J Natl Cancer Inst* 1987; 79:1053–1057.

84. Tomita Y, Shirasawa H, Sekine H, et al: Expression of human papillomavirus type 6b L2 open reading frame in *Escherichia coli*: L2-B-galactosidase fusion proteins and their antigenic properties. *Virology* 1987; 158:8–14.

85. Favre M, Breitburd F, Croissant O, et al: Chromatin-like structures obtained after alkaline disruption of bovine and human papillomaviruses. *J Virol* 1977; 21:1205–1209.

86. Breitburd F, Croissant O, Orth G: Expression of human papillomavirus type-1 E4 gene products in warts. *Cancer Cells* 1987; 5:115–122.

87. Gissmann L, zur Hausen H: Physical characterization of the deoxyribonucleic acids of different human papilloma viruses (HPV). *Med Microbiol Immunol* 1978; 166:3–11.

88. Howley PM, Law M-P, Heilman C, et al: Molecular characterization of papillomavirus genomes. *Cold Spring Harbor Symp Quant Biol* 1980; 7:233–247.

89. Howley PM: The human papillomaviruses. *Arch Pathol Lab Med* 1982; 106:429–432.

90. Lancaster WD, Olson C: Animal papillomaviruses. *Microbiol Rev* 1982; 46:191–207.

91. Shirasawa H, Tomita Y, Kubota K, et al: Transcriptional differences of the human papillomavirus type 16 genome between precancerous lesions and invasive carcinomas. *J Virol* 1988; 62:1022–1027.

92. Schwarz E, Freeze UK, Gissmann L, et al: Structure and transcription of human papillomavirus sequences in cervical carcinoma cells. *Nature* 1985; 314:111–114.

93. Di Luca DS, Pilotti B, Stefanon A, et al: Human papillomavirus type 16 DNA in genital tumors: a pathological and molecular analysis. *J Gen Virol* 1986; 67:583–589.

94. Shirasawa H, Tomita Y, Kubota K, et al: Detection of human papillomavirus type 16 DNA and evidence for integration into the cell DNA in cervical dysplasias. *J Gen Virol* 1986; 67:2011–2015.

95. Schneider-Maunoury S, Croissant O, Orth G: Integration of human papillomavirus type 16 DNA sequences: a possible early event in the progression of genital tumors. *J Virol* 1987; 61:3295–3298.

96. Shirasawa H, Tomita Y, Sekiya S, et al: Integration and transcription of human papillomavirus type 16 and 18 sequences in

cell lines derived from cervical carcinomas. *J Gen Virol* 1987; 68:583–591.

97. Smotkin D, Wettstein FO: Transcription of human papillomavirus type 16 early genes in a cervical cancer and a cancer-derived cell line and identification of the E7 protein. *Proc Natl Acad Sci USA* 1986; 83:4680–4684.

98. Schneider-Gadicke A, Schwarz E: Different human cervical carcinoma cell lines show similar transcription patterns of human papillomavirus type 18 early genes. *EMBO J* 1986; 5:2285–2292.

99. Danos O, Katinka M, Yaniv M: Human papillomavirus 1a complete DNA sequence: A novel type of genome organization among papovaviridae. *EMBO J* 1982; 1:231–236.

100. Schwarz E, Durst M, Demankowski C, et al: DNA sequence and genome organization of human genital papillomavirus type 6b. *EMBO J* 1983; 2:2341–2348.

101. Seedorf K, Krammer G, Durst M, et al: Human papillomavirus type 16 DNA sequence. *Virology* 1985; 145:181–185.

102. Cole ST, Danos O: Nucleotide sequence and comparative analysis of the human papillomavirus type 18 genome; Phylogeny of papillomaviruses and repeated structure of the E6 and E7 gene products. *J Mol Biol* 1987; 193:599–608.

103. Lorincz A, Lancaster W, Temple G: Cloning and characterization of a new human papillomavirus from a woman with dysplasia of the uterine cervix. *J Virol* 1986; 58:225–229.

104. Broker TR, Botchan M: Papillomaviruses: Retrospectives and prospectives, in Butcham M, Grodzicker T, Sharp PA (eds): *Cancer Cells 4/DNA Tumor Viruses: Control of Gene Expression and Replication.* Cold Spring Harbor, NY, Cold Spring Harbor Laboratory, 1986, pp 17–36.

105. Chow LT, Nasseri M, Wolinsky SM, et al: Human papillomavirus types 6 and 11 mRNAs from genital condylomata acuminata. *J Virol* 1987; 61:2581–2588.

106. Pfister H: Biology and biochemistry of papillomaviruses. *Rev Physiol Biochem Pharmacol* 1983; 99:111–181.

107. Gissmann L: Papillomaviruses and their association with cancer in animals and in man. *Cancer Surv* 1984; 3:161–181.

108. Coggin JR, zur Hausen H: Workshop on papillomaviruses and cancer. *Cancer Res* 1979; 39:545–546.

109. Gissmann L, de Villiers E-M, zur Hausen H: Analysis of human warts (condylomata acuminata) and other genital tumors for human papillomavirus type 6 DNA. *Int J Cancer* 1982; 29:143–146.

110. Jenson AB, Sommer S, Payling-Wright C, et al: Human papillomavirus: Frequency and distribution in plantar and common warts. *Lab Invest* 1982; 47:491–497.

111. de Villiers E-M, Gissmann L, zur Hausen H: Molecular cloning of viral DNA from human genital warts. *J Virol* 1981; 40:932–935.

112. Green M, Brackmann KH, Sanders PR, et al: Isolation of a human papillomavirus from a patient with epidermodysplasia verruciformis: Presence of related viral DNA genomes in human urogenital tumors. *Proc Natl Acad Sci USA* 1982; 79:4437–4441.

113. Lancaster WD, Kurman RJ, Sanz L, et al: Human papilloma virus: Detection of viral DNA sequences and evidence for molecular heterogeneity in metaplasias and dysplasias of the uterine cervix. *Intervirology* 1983; 20:202–212.

114. Ostrow RS, Bender M, Niimura M, et al: Human papillomavirus DNA in cutaneous primary and metastasized squamous cell carcinomas from patients with epidermodysplasia verruciformis. *Proc Natl Acad Sci USA* 1982; 79:1634–1638.

115. Hirt B: Selective extraction of polyoma DNA from infected mouse cell cultures. *J Mol Biol* 1967; 26:365–369.

116. Lorincz A: Detection of human papillomavirus infection by nucleic acid hybridization. *Obstet Gynecol Clin North Am* 1987; 14:451–469.

117. Rigby P, Rhodes D, Dieckmann M, et al: Labeling deoxyribonucleic acid to high specific activity in vitro by nick translation with DNA polymerase I. *J Mol Biol* 1977; 113:237–251.

118. Feinberg FP, Vogelstein B: A technique for radiolabeling DNA restriction endonuclease fragments to high specific activity. *Anal Biochem* 1983; 132:6–13.

119. Southern EM: Detection of specific sequences among DNA fragments separated by gel electrophoresis. *J Mol Biol* 1975; 93:503–517.

120. Wagner D, Ikenberg H, Boehm N, et al: Identification of human papillomavirus in cervical smears by deoxyribonucleic acid in situ hybridization. *Obstet Gynecol* 1984; 64:767–772.

121. Hyman RW, Brunovskis I, Summers WC: DNA base sequence homology between coliphages T7 and 0/2 and between T3 and 0/II as determined by heteroduplex mapping in the electron microscope. *J Mol Biol* 1973; 77:189–196.

122. Law MF, Lancaster WD, Howley PM: Conserved sequences among the genomes of the papillomaviruses. *J Virol* 1979; 32:199–207.

123. Sharp PA, Pettersson U, Sambrook: Viral DNA in transformed cells. I. A study of the sequences of adenovirus 2 DNA in a line of transformed rat cells using specific fragments of the viral genome. *J Mol Biol* 1974; 86:709–726.

124. Lancaster WD, Olson C: Demonstration of two distinct classes of bovine papilloma virus. *Virology* 1978; 89:372–379.

125. Pfister H: Papillomaviruses: General description, taxonomy, and classification, in Salzman NP, Howley PM (eds): *The Papovaviridae.* New York: Plenum, 1987, vol 2, pp 1–38.

126. Jablonska S: Human papillomavirus and oncogenesis. *Z Hautkr* 1982; 57:551–552, 555–560, 563, 566.

127. Lutzner M, Croissant O, Cudasse M-F, et al: A potentially oncogenic human papillomavirus (HPV-5) found in two renal allograft recipients. *J Invest Dermatol* 1979; 75:353–356.

128. Pfister H, Gassenmaier A, Nurnberger F, et al: Human papillomavirus 5-DNA in a carcinoma of an epidermodysplasia verruciformis patient infected with various human papillomavirus types. *Cancer Res* 1983; 43:1436–1441.

129. Rando RF, Groff DE, Chirikjian JG, et al: Isolation and characterization of a novel human papillomavirus type 6 DNA from an invasive vulvar carcinoma. *J Virol* 1986; 57:353–356.

130. Boshart M, zur Hausen H: Human papillomaviruses in Buschke-Löwenstein tumors: Physical state of the DNA and identification of a tandem duplication in the noncoding regions of a human papillomavirus type 6 subtype. *J Virol* 1986; 58:963–966.

131. Byrne JC, Tsao MS, Fraser RS, et al: Human papillomavirus-11 DNA in a patient with chronic laryngotracheobronchial papillomatosis and metastatic squamous-cell carcinoma of the lung. *N Engl J Med* 1987; 317:873–878.

132. Durst M, Croce C, Gissmann L, et al: Papillomavirus sequences integrate near cellular oncogenes in some cervical carcinomas. *Proc Natl Acad Sci USA* 1987; 84:1070–1074.

133. Riou GF, Barrois M, Dutronquay V, et al: Presence of papillomavirus DNA sequences, amplification of c-*myc* and c-Ha-*ras* oncogenes and enhanced expression of c-*myc* in carcinomas of the uterine cervix, in Howley PM, Broker TM (eds): *Papillomaviruses: Molecular and Clinical Aspects.* New York, Alan R Liss, p 47.

134. Rotkin ID: A comparison review of key epidemiological studies in cervical cancer related to current searches for transmissible agents. *Cancer Res* 1973; 33:1353–1367.

135. Kessler I: Venereal factors in human cervical cancer: evidence from marital clusters. *Cancer* 1977; 39:1912–1919.

136. Rawls WE, Tompkins WAE, Melnick JL: The association of herpesvirus type 2 and carcinoma of the uterine cervix. *Am J Epidemiol* 1969; 89:547–557.

137. Nahmias AJ, Josey WE, Naib ZM, et al: Antibodies to herpesvirus hominis types 1 and 2 in humans. II. Women with cervical cancer. *Am J Epidemiol* 1970; 91:547–552.

138. Vonka V, Kanka J, Jelinek J, et al: Prospective study on the relationship between cervical neoplasia and herpes simplex type-2 virus. I. Epidemiological characteristics. *Int J Cancer* 1984; 33:49–60.

139. Vonka V, Kanka J, Hirsch I, et al: Prospective study on the relationship between cervical neoplasia and herpes simplex type-2 virus. II. Herpes simplex type-2 antibody presence in sera taken at enrollment. *Int J Cancer* 1984; 33:61–66.

140. Massing AM, Epstein WL: Natural history of warts. A two-year

study. *Arch Dermatol* 1963; 87:306–310.

141. Summers L, Booth DR: Intraoral condyloma acuminatum. *Oral Surg* 1974; 38:273–278.

142. Barrasso R, De Brux J, Croissant O, et al: High prevalence of papillomavirus-associated penile intraepithelial neoplasia in sexual partners of women with cervical intraepithelial neoplasia. *N Engl J Med* 1987; 317:916–923.

143. Levine RU, Crum CP, Herman E, et al: Cervical papillomavirus infection and intraepithelial neoplasia: a study of male sexual partners. *Obstet Gynecol* 1984; 64:16–20.

144. Sedlacek TV, Cunnane M, Carpiniello V: Colposcopy in the diagnosis of penile condyloma. *Am J Obstet Gynecol* 1986; 154:494–496.

145. Rosemberg SK: Subclinical papillomaviral infection of male genitalia. *Urology* 1985; 26:554–557.

146. Morison WL: Viral warts, herpes simplex and herpes zoster in patients with secondary immune deficiencies and neoplasms. *Br J Dermatol* 1975; 92:625–630.

147. Reid TMS, Fraser NG, Kernohan IR: Generalized warts and immune deficiency. *Br J Dermatol* 1976; 95:559–564.

148. Sillman FH, Sedlis A: Anogenital papillomavirus infection and neoplasia in immunodeficient women. *Obstet Gynecol Clin North Am* 1987; 14:537–558.

149. Schneider A, Hotz M, Gissmann L: Increased prevalence of human papillomaviruses in the lower genital tract of pregnant women. *Int J Cancer* 1987; 40:198–201.

150. Fife KH, Rogers RE, Zwicki BW: Symptomatic and assymptomatic cervical infections with human papillomavirus during pregnancy. *J Infect Dis* 1987; 156:904–911.

151. von Krogh G: Warts: Immunologic factors of prognostic significance. *Int J Dermatol* 1979; 95:195–204.

152. Barrett TJ, Silbar JD, McGinley GP: Genital warts—a venereal disease. *JAMA* 1954; 154:333–334.

153. Oriel JD: Natural history of genital warts. *Br J Vener Dis* 1971; 47:1–13.

154. Kreider JW, Howlett MK, Wolfe SA, et al: Morphological transformation of human uterine cervix with papillomavirus from condylomata acuminata. *Nature* 1985; 317:639–640.

155. Kreider JW, Howett MK, Leure-Dupree AE, et al: Laboratory production in vivo of infectious human papillomavirus type 11. *J Virol* 1987; 61:590–593.

156. Jenson AB, Kurman RJ, Lancaster WD: Tissue effects of and host response to human papillomavirus infection. *Obstet Gynecol Clin North Am* 1987; 14:397–406.

157. Steinberg BM, Topp WC, Schneider PS, et al: Laryngeal papillomavirus infection during clinical remission. *N Engl J Med* 1983; 308:1261–1264.

158. Nuovo GJ, Nuovo MA, Cottral S, et al: Histological correlates of clinically occult human papillomavirus infection of the uterine cervix. *Am J Surg Pathol* 1988; 12:198–204.

159. Wilbur DC, Reichman RC, Stoler M: Detection of infection by human papillomavirus in genital condylomata. A comparison study using immunocytochemistry and in situ nucleic acid hybridization. *Am J Clin Pathol* 1988; 89:505.

160. Soutter WP, Wisdom S, Brough AK, et al: Should patients with mild atypia in a cervical smear be referred for colposcopy? *Br J Obstet Gynaecol* 1986; 93:70–74.

161. Eversole LR, Laipis PJ, Green TL: Human papillomavirus type 2 DNA in oral and labial verruca vulgaris. *J Cutan Pathol* 1987; 14:319–325.

162. Berman A, Berman BE: Efflorescence of new warts: A sign of involution: Histopathological findings. *Arch Dermatol* 1977; 113:1219–1221.

163. Berman A, Winkelmann RK: Flat warts undergoing involution: Histopathological findings. *Arch Dermatol* 1977; 112:1219–1221.

164. Tagami H, Ogino A, Rakigawa M, et al: Regression of plane warts following spontaneous inflammation. A histopathological study. *Br J Dermatol* 1974; 90:147–154.

165. Henke RP, Milde-Langosch K, Loning T, et al: Human papillomavirus type 13 and focal epithelial hyperplasia of the oral mu-

166. cosa: DNA hybridization on paraffin-embedded specimens. *Virchows Arch* 1987; 411:193–198.

166. Jenson AB, Openshaw H, Hooks JL, et al: Herpes and other virally-induced oral diseases, in Slavkin HC, Cohen DW (eds): *Current Advances in Oral Biology*. Bristol, Pa, Distributions System, 1979, pp 1–45.

167. Jenson AB, Link CC Jr, Lancaster WD: Papillomavirus etiology of oral cavity papillomas, in Hooks J, Jordan W (eds): *Viral Infections in Oral Medicine*. New York, North-Holland Elsevier, 1982, pp 133–146.

168. Abbey LM, Page DG, Sawyer DR: The clinical and histopathologic features of a series of 464 oral squamous cell papillomas. *Oral Surg* 1980; 49:419–428.

169. Greer RO, Goldman HM: Oral papillomas; clinicopathologic evaluation and retrospective examination for dyskeratosis in 110 lesions. *Oral Surg* 1974; 38:435–440.

170. Summers L, Booth DR: Intraoral condyloma acuminatum. *Oral Surg* 1974; 38:273–278.

171. Gissmann L, Wolnik L, Ikenberg H, et al: Human papillomavirus types 6 and 11 DNA sequences in genital and laryngeal papillomas and in some cervical cancers. *Proc Natl Acad Sci USA* 1983; 80:560–563.

172. Galloway TC, Soper GR, Elsen J: Carcinoma of the larynx after irradiation for papilloma. *Arch Otolaryngol* 1960; 72:289–294.

173. Putney FJ: Borderline malignant lesions of the larynx. *Arch Otolaryngol* 1955; 61:381–385.

174. Walsh TE, Beamer PR: Epidermoid carcinoma of the larynx occurring in 2 children in conjunction with papilloma of the larynx. *Laryngoscope* 1960; 60:1110–1124.

175. Becker TM, Stone KM, Alexander ER: Genital human papillomavirus infection: a growing concern. *Obstet Gynecol Clin North Am* 1987; 14:389–396.

176. Lancaster WD, Jenson AB: Viruses in human cancer II. Papillomaviruses. *Oncol Overview* 1987; April:5–9.

177. Reid R, Scalzi P: Genital warts and cervical cancer. VII. An improved colposcopic index for differentiating benign papillomaviral infections from high grade cervical intraepithelial neoplasia. *Am J Obstet Gynecol* 1985; 153:611–618.

178. Coppleson M: Colposcopic features of papillomaviral infection and premalignancy in the female lower genital tract. *Obstet Gynecol Clin North Am* 1987; 14:471–494.

179. Reid R, Herschman BR, Crum CP, et al: Genital warts and cervical cancer. V. The tissue basis of colposcopic change. *Am J Obstet Gynecol* 1984; 149:293–303.

180. Gissmann L, Boshart M, Dürst M, et al: Presence of human papillomavirus in genital tumors. *J Invest Dermatol* 1984; 83:26S–28S.

181. zur Hausen H: Human papillomaviruses and their possible role in squamous cell carcinomas. *Curr Top Microbiol Immunol* 1977; 78:1–30.

182. Boxer RJ, Skinner DG: Condyloma acuminata and squamous carcinoma. *Urology* 1977; 9:72–78.

183. Bushke A, Lowenstein L: Über carcinomähnliche Condylomata acuminata des Penis. *Arch Dermatol Syph* 1931; 163:30–46.

184. Richart RM, Barron BA: Followup of patients with cervical dysplasia. *Am J Obstet Gynecol* 1969; 105:386–393.

185. Nasiell K, Nasiell M, Vaclavinkova V: Behavior of moderate cervical dysplasias during long-term follow-up. *Obstet Gynecol* 1983; 61:609–614.

186. Spriggs AI: Natural history of cervical dysplasia. *Clin Obstet Gynecol* 1981; 8:65–69.

187. Ikenberg H, Gissmann L, Gross G, et al: Human papillomavirus type 16-related DNA in genital Bowen's disease and in Bowenoid papulosis. *Int J Cancer* 1983; 32:563–565.

188. Obalek S, Jablonska S, Beaudenon S, et al: Bowenoid papulosis of the male and female genitalia; risk of cervical dysplasia. *J Am Acad Dermatol* 1988; 14:433–444.

189. Lewandowsky F, Lutz W: Ein Fall einer bisher nicht beschriebenen Hauterkrankung (Epidermo-dysplasia verruciformis). *Arch Dermatol Syph* 1922; 141:193–203.

190. Jablonska S, Dabrowski J, Jakkubowicz K: Epidermodysplasia verruciformis as a model in studies on the role of papovaviruses in oncogenesis. *Cancer Res* 1972; 32:583–589.

191. Jablonska S, Orth G, Jarzabek-Chorzelska M, et al: Immunological studies in epidermodysplasia verruciformis. *Bull Cancer* 1978; 65:183–190.

192. Jablonska S, Orth G, Jarzabek-Chorzelska M, et al: Twenty-one years of follow-up studies of familial epidermodysplasia verruciformis. *Dermatologica* 1979; 158:309–327.

193. Ostrow RS, Bender M, Niimura M, et al: Human papillomavirus DNA in cutaneous primary and metastasized squamous cell carcinomas from patients with epidermodysplasia verruciformis. *Proc Natl Acad Sci USA* 1982; 79:1634–1638.

194. Orth G, Jablonska S, Favre M, et al: Identification of papillomaviruses in butcher's warts. *J Invest Dermatol* 1981; 76:97–102.

195. Ostrow RS, Kryzek R, Pass F, et al: Identification of a novel human papillomavirus in cutaneous warts of meathandlers. *Virology* 1981; 108:21–27.

196. Lass JH, Grove AS, Papale JJ, et al: Detection of human papillomavirus DNA sequences in conjunctival papilloma. *Am J Ophthalmol* 1983; 96:670–674.

197. Pfister H, zur Hausen H: Seroepidemiologic studies of human papilloma virus HPV-1 infections. *Int J Cancer* 1978; 21:161–165.

198. Baird PJ: Serological evidence for the association of papillomavirus and cervical neoplasia. *Lancet* 1983; 2:17–18.

199. Spencer ES, Andersen HK: Clinically evident, non-terminal infections with herpes virus and the wart virus in immunosuppressed renal allograft recipients. *Br Med J* 1970; 3:251–254.

200. Brodersen L, Genner J, Brodthagen H: Tuberculin sensitivity in BCG-vaccinated children with common warts. *Acta Derm Venereol (Stockh)* 1974; 54:291–292.

201. Morison WL: Cell-mediated responses in patients with warts. *Br J Dermatol* 1975; 93:553–556.

202. Viac J, Thivolet J, Hegazy MR, et al: Comparative study of delayed hypersensitivity skin reactions and antibodies to human papilloma virus HPV. *Clin Exp Immunol* 1977; 29:240–246.

203. Morison WL: In vitro assay of immunity to human wart antigen. *Br J Dermatol* 1975; 93:545–552.

204. Shirodaria PV, Matthews RS: An immunofluorescent study of warts. *Clin Exp Immunol* 175; 21:329–338.

205. Cubie HA: Serological studies in a student population prone to infection with human papilloma virus. *J Hyg* 1972; 70:677–690.

206. Pyrhonen S: Human wart-virus antibodies in patients with genital and skin warts. *Acta Derm Venereol (Stockh)* 1978; 58:427–432.

207. Oriel JD, Almeida JD: Demonstration of virus particles in human genital warts. *Br J Vener Dis* 1971; 46:37–42.

208. Hills E, Laverty CR: Electron microscopic detection of papillomavirus particles in selected koilocytotic cells in a routine cervical smear. *Acta Cytol* 1979; 23:53–56.

209. Shaffer EL Jr, Reimann EF, Gysland WB: Oral condyloma acuminatum: A case report with light microscopic and ultrastructural features. *J Oral Pathol* 1980; 9:163–173.

210. Ferenczy A, Braun LA, Shah KV, et al: Human papillomavirus (HPV) in condylomatous lesions of the cervix. A comparative ultrastructural and immunohistochemical study. *Am J Surg Pathol* 1981; 5:661–670.

211. Roseto A, Pothier P, Guillemin M-C, et al: Monoclonal antibodies to the major capsid protein of human papillomavirus type 1. *J Gen Virol* 1984; 65:1319–1324.

212. Doorbar J, Gallimore PH: Identification of proteins encoded by the L1 and L2 open reading frames of human papillomavirus 1a. *J Virol* 1987; 61:2793–2799.

213. Chorzelski T, Jarzabek-Chorzelska M, Jablonska S, et al: An immunofluorescence complement/fixation test for detection of human papilloma viruses in various warts and wartlike lesions of epidermodysplasia verruciformis. *Arch Dermatol Res* 1983; 275:53–57.

214. Laurent R, Kienzler JL, Croissant O, et al: Two anatomoclinical types of warts with plantar localization: specific cytopathogenic effects of papillomavirus type 1 (HPV-1) and type 2 (HPV-2). *Arch Dermatol Res* 1982; 274:101–111.

215. Patel D, Shepherd P, Naylor JA, et al: Reactivities of polyclonal and monoclonal antibodies raised to the major capsid protein of human papillomavirus type 16. *J Gen Virol* 1989; 70:69–77.

216. Jenson AB, Lim LY, Singer AE: Comparison of human papillomavirus type 1 serotyping by monoclonal antibodies with genotyping by in situ hybridization of plantar warts. *J Cutaneous Pathol* 1989; in press.

217. Beckmann AM, Myerson D, Daling JR, et al: Detection and localization of human papillomavirus DNA in human genital condylomas by in situ hybridization with biotinylated probes. *J Med Virol* 1985; 16:265–273.

218. Gupta J, Gendelman HE, Naghashfar Z, et al: Specific identification of human papillomavirus type in cervical smears and paraffin sections by in situ hybridization with radioactive probes: a preliminary communication. *Int J Gynecol Pathol* 1985; 4:211–218.

219. Stoler MH, Broker TR: In situ hybridization detection of human papillomavirus DNA and messenger RNA in genital condylomas and a cervical carcinoma. *Hum Pathol* 1986; 17:1250–1258.

220. Rees BR: Warts—A clinicians view. *Cutis* 1981; 28:175–180.

221. Reid R: Human papillomaviral infection: the key to rational triage of cervical neoplasia. *Obstet Gynecol Clin North Am* 1987; 14:407–429.

222. Krebs Hans-B: The use of topical 5-fluorouracil in the treatment of genital condylomas. *Obstet Gynecol Clin North Am* 1987; 559–568.

223. Trofatter KJ Jr: Interferon. *Obstet Gynecol Clin North Am* 1987; 14:569–579.

224. Powell LC, Pollard M, Jenkins JL: Treatment of condylomata acuminata by autogenous vaccine. *South Med J* 1970; 63:202–205.

41

Human Polyomaviruses

Thomas F. Hogan
Billie L. Padgett
Duard L. Walker

HISTORY OF VIRUS ISOLATIONS

**VIRUS-CODED PRODUCTS AND BIOLOGIC
PROPERTIES**

PROTEINS AND ANTIGENIC RELATIONSHIPS
GENOMES OF POLYOMAVIRUSES
REPLICATION IN PERMISSIVE CELLS
CELL TRANSFORMATION
TUMOR INDUCTION IN ANIMALS

EPIDEMIOLOGY

PATHOGENESIS

LABORATORY DIAGNOSIS

PREVENTION AND TREATMENT

Polyomaviruses (Table 41–1) constitute one genus of the family
Papovaviridae.[1] Polyomaviruses are small, 38 to 43 nm, nonenveloped, icosahedral viruses. The capsid or outer shell contains
72 capsomers made of polypeptides. It encloses the viral genome—
one circular, supercoiled molecule of double-stranded DNA, about
3×10^6 daltons molecular weight. The DNA is associated with
histone-type polypeptides of cellular origin.

Three structures can be observed in preparations of extracellular
polyomaviruses negatively stained with phosphotungstic acid. The
"full" icosahedral virion is infectious and has a buoyant density
of 1.34 to 1.35 g/mL in cesium chloride isopyknic gradients (Figure 41–1,A). "Empty" capsids have the same size and external
characteristics as "fulls," but they lack internal nucleoprotein and
therefore are less dense (buoyant density 1.29 g/mL) and are noninfectious. A third, minor form is "filamentous," having the same
diameter as the spherical forms but varying in length. These probably result from aberrant assembly of capsomers and it is not known
whether they are infectious.

The general characteristics of polyomaviruses include intranuclear virion assembly, restricted host cell range in vitro and in
vivo, stability upon heating, and the ability to induce tumors in
experimental animals and malignant transformation of cells in culture.

The existence of human polyomaviruses was first suspected in
1965. By electron microscopy (EM), particles resembling polyomavirus virions were detected in the brains of patients with the
demyelinating disease progressive multifocal leukoencephalopathy
(PML).[2, 3] Six years later, intense efforts to culture polyomaviruses
from human tissues finally led to the isolation of JC virus (JCV)
from human PML brain tissue[4] and BK virus (BKV) from the urine
of a renal transplant recipient.[5]

JCV and BKV are firmly established as human polyomaviruses.
Simian virus 40 (SV40), whose natural host is certain macaque
monkeys, appears to be a zoonosis. SV40 is discussed in this
chapter because (1) the natural history and molecular biology of
SV40 have been well studied, providing useful comparative information; (2) SV40 can lytically infect and transform human cells
in vitro; (3) some humans are seropositive for SV40 neutralizing
antibody; (4) SV40 has occasionally been isolated from humans;
(5) millions of humans have been exposed to SV40 by receiving
SV40-contaminated poliovirus vaccine. However, there is no evidence that SV40 occurs in the human population in human-to-
human passage, so it is not properly viewed as a human polyomavirus. Preliminary serologic and other data suggest that other,
as yet undiscovered, polyomaviruses may also infect humans.[6]

HISTORY OF VIRUS ISOLATIONS

The primate polyomavirus SV40 was discovered in 1960 as a
passenger virus in cultures of rhesus monkey kidney cells. Viral
multiplication was facilitated when cells were cultured in vitro,

Table 41–1
Polyomaviruses (Family *Papovaviridae*)

Virus Designation	Year Isolated
Murine K (pneumonitis) virus (K)	1952
Murine polyomavirus (MPV)	1953
Simian virus 40 (SV40)	1960
Simian (baboon) agent 12 (SA12)	1963
Rabbit kidney vacuolating virus (RKV)	1964
Human BK virus (BKV)	1971
Human JC virus (JCV)	1971
Bovine polyomavirus (BPV)*	1974
African green monkey lymphotrophic papovavirus (LPV)	1979

*Originally identified as "stump-tailed macaque virus" (STMV), bovine polyomavirus was introduced into monkey kidney cell lines by use of bovine serum for cell culture.[442]

removed from the protective effect of neutralizing antibody. Cytopathic effects (CPE) were observed when SV40 was inoculated onto primary cultures of African green monkey kidney cells (GMK) and cell lines derived from GMK. It produced transformation of rodent cells in vitro and pleomorphic, undifferentiated sarcomas after subcutaneous inoculation into newborn hamsters. Since SV40 is more resistant to inactivation by formalin than are enteroviruses, and formalin-inactivated poliovirus vaccines were produced in monkey kidney cells, viable SV40 was inadvertently administered to several million persons during poliovirus vaccination.

The prototypic strains of the two human polyomavirus species, BKV and JCV, were isolated in 1971. Each virus was designated by the initials of the person from whom the virus was isolated. BKV was first isolated in Vero cells from the urine of a 39-year-old man 4 months after renal transplantation.[5] Urinary excretion of cytologically atypical transitional cells with hyperchromatic intranuclear inclusions had been noted in this patient, suggesting viral urinary tract infection. These cells were sloughed from a diseased (stenosed) segment of the transplanted ureter. Hemagglutination-inhibition (HI) antibody to BKV was later found to occur worldwide except for very remote or isolated human populations.[7, 8] Most BKV infections occurred during childhood and adolescence, and reactivation of latent or endogenous BKV infection could occur despite circulating anti-BKV antibody.

JCV was first isolated from the diseased brain of a patient with Hodgkin's lymphoma, dying of the demyelinating disease PML.[4] Previously, thin sections of PML brain tissue had been shown to contain viruslike particles in the nuclei of abnormal oligodendrocytes, the pathognomonic cell for the histologic diagnosis of this uncommon disease. The size and shape of these particles in electron micrographs (33–36-nm spheres), their intranuclear location, and the fact that both filamentous forms and pseudocrystalline arrays of spherical forms were observed, strongly suggested that these particles were in fact polyomavirus virions.[3] Every subsequent EM examination of diseased oligodendrocytes in PML brain tissues confirmed this initial observation. No human polyomavirus was known to exist at that time, but with such cogent indications that a fatal demyelinating disease was caused by one, attempts were made between 1965 and 1971 to isolate the putative agent. In retrospect, these failed primarily because JCV has a very restricted host cell range in vitro and was unable to propagate in the

tissue culture cells used. Success came with the use of primary human fetal glial (PHFG) cells. The isolated agent was shown to be a novel polyomavirus and subsequent studies established that JCV is distinct from BKV. Man, therefore, is the natural host for at least two species of polyomavirus. To date, most BKV isolations have been from human urine, while JCV has been isolated from both human brain and urine.

VIRUS-CODED PRODUCTS AND BIOLOGIC PROPERTIES

After a polyomavirus enters a cell, the virion passes into the nucleus and the capsid disintegrates, "uncoating" the viral DNA. Early messenger RNAs (mRNAs) are then transcribed from a portion of the circular viral DNA. These early mRNAs are translated to nonstructural peptides which enhance viral DNA replication. Thereafter, the viral genome is replicated and late mRNAs are

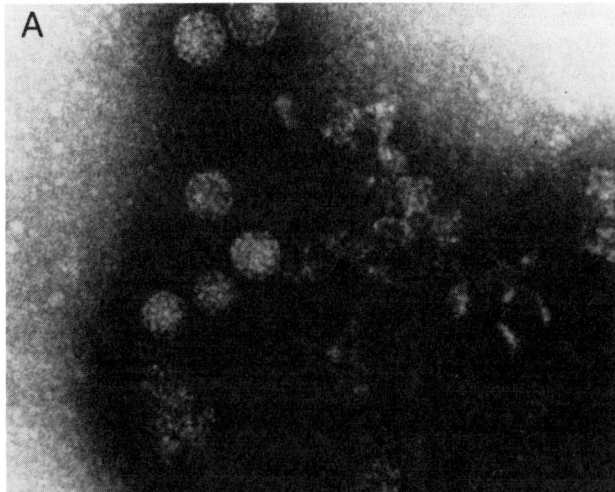
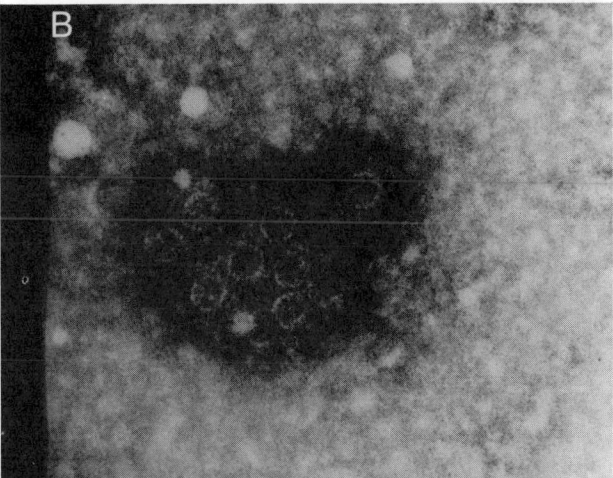

Figure 41–1. A. JC virus (JCV) virions as seen in the electron microscope using negative staining with phosphotungstic acid. **B.** Immune electron microscopy with agglutination of JCV virions after incubation with specific rabbit antiserum against JCV.

transcribed from another portion of the viral DNA. Late mRNAs code for structural proteins (capsomers) used to reassemble infectious virus particles.

Proteins and Antigenic Relationships

In polyomavirus-infected or -transformed cells, mRNA is first transcribed from one half of the circular DNA, the "early region," which is translated to nonstructural peptides. Antibodies against these early peptides are formed by many animals bearing polyomavirus-induced tumors, so the antigens are called "T antigens" and the antibodies "T antibodies." Polyomavirus T antigens were first detected in extracts of SV40-induced tumors by complement fixation (CF) using sera from tumor-bearing hamsters.[9] T antigens, either "large" or "small," are now usually detected by immunofluorescent or histochemical staining procedures. T antigens bind to both viral and host cell DNAs, are associated with initiation of both viral and host cell DNA replication, and are required for both establishment and maintenance of the malignant phenotype in transformed cells.[10, 11] T antigen stimulates both viral genome replication and transcription from late promoter while repressing its own synthesis from early promoter.[12] A shift in JCV and SV40 early RNA initiation sites occurs after DNA replication, when T antigen levels are high. Whether this shift is mediated by T antigen binding to viral DNA and influencing chromatin structure, or by other cellular factors, is still undetermined.[13, 14]

Small t antigen, an enhancing factor in cell transformation,[15–18] may not be needed for in vitro lytic growth of human polyomaviruses.[19, 20] Inability to code for small t antigen has been proposed to explain the low efficiency of stable transformation induced by some BKV strains[21] and small t antigen was not detected in four JCV-induced owl monkey tumor cell lines.[22] Recently, mutants have been constructed to determine the role of small t protein in the biologic activity of JCV.[23]

Serologic and functional cross-reactivity exist among the T antigens of all five primate polyomaviruses. However, there is no reported cross-reactivity between primate and nonprimate polyomavirus T antigens. Although serologic cross-reactions have been demonstrated for JCV, BKV, and SV40 T antigens,[24–26] antigenic specificity can be shown by absorbing antisera with each specific T antigen.[27–30] Immunoprecipitated T antigens of JCV, BKV, and SV40 have been studied and compared by SDS gel electrophoresis[31–33] and by analysis of their tryptic peptides.[31, 34–36] Although similarities can be demonstrated using these methods, T antigens from each specific virus can be shown to be unique.

BKV is capable of supplying early gene functions required by a temperature-sensitive (ts) SV40 mutant for growth at the nonpermissive temperature. This suggests that BKV and SV40 early peptides are functionally similar enough for BKV to "complement" defective SV40 replication.[37–39] By sequence analysis, JCV and SV40 T antigens are 70% homologous, particularly at the amino terminus critical for replication.[40] SV40 T antigen can bind JCV DNA sequences homologous to SV40 DNA–binding sites.[41] However, JCV replication in SV40-transformed cells may not be fully explained by enhancement of JCV replication by SV40 T protein.[42] For example, SV40-transformed human embryonic kidney (HEK) cells express SV40 T antigen. However, transfected BKV DNA replicates but capsid protein is not synthesized in these cells, and transfected JCV DNA cannot use the SV40 T antigen to replicate.[22]

Tumor-specific transplantation antigens (TSTA) are so named because animals immunized with a given polyomavirus reject transplantation of tumors induced in other animals by that virus. TSTAs are found in nuclear and cytoplasmic membranes of cells lytically infected or transformed by polyomaviruses. TSTAs appear 24 hours after infection coincident with the appearance of nuclear T antigen.[43] Partially purified T antigens, like TSTA, can induce immunity to tumor cell transplantation. Thus, the T antigen and TSTA functions may reside on the same polypeptide.[44] Although animals immunized with BKV resist the implantation of BKV-transformed cells more so than SV40-transformed cells,[24, 45] some cross-protection against tumor implantation is demonstrable among primate polyomaviruses.[46]

Other cell polypeptides have been found complexed with T antigens in polyomavirus-transformed cells. These species-specific host cell peptides immunoprecipitate from cell extracts when anti-T antisera are used. Their function is not yet known, but they have been implicated in the disruption of actin-cables noted in virus-infected cells.[47–49] Such cell polypeptides have not been found, however, in JCV-transformed owl monkey cells using monoclonal T antibodies.[22, 50, 51]

Attempts to implicate JCV, BKV, or SV40 with specific human tumors have led to searches for T antigen in human tumor cells and T antibodies in human sera. To date, papovavirus T antigen has not been reproducibly detected in human tumors or in cultures of human tumor cells.[52, 53] Great caution is required in interpreting such studies. T antigen is sensitive to fixation conditions, being destroyed by formalin fixation, paraffin embedding, or fixation of cell monolayers with formalin or glutaraldehyde.[54] The titer and specificity of the T antibody used for detection of T antigen can vary significantly.[55, 56] When standard immunofluorescence (IF) microscopy was compared to anticomplement IF (ACIF) microscopy for detecting JCV or BKV T antigen in transformed cells, ACIF was 30- to 90-fold more sensitive than IF.[30] Expression of T antigen in known polyomavirus-transformed cells can vary. In selected JCV- and BKV-transformed cell lines, T antigen concentration was five- to 35-fold less than in SV40-transformed cell lines.[29]

Tumorigenic but T antigen–negative BKV-transformed hamster cells[57, 58] and BKV-transformed human fetal brain cells[59, 60] have been reported, although BKV (IR strain)-transformed hamster cells contain T antigen.[21] Tumor cells have decreased T antigen expression when repeatedly passaged in animals,[30] when immediately studied as frozen histologic sections without prior passage in vitro,[61] when studied as crowded, confluent cultures and not as subconfluent, growing cultures,[29, 30, 62, 63] and when cells were transformed by polyomavirus at high multiplicity of infection (MOI).[64] When SV40-induced hamster brain tumors were tested for T antigen by fluorescent antibody (FA) staining of cryostat sections, results were equivocal. However, cell cultures derived from these tumors showed T antigen in most cells which intensified during cell passage.[61]

To summarize, BKV, JCV, and SV40 early polypeptides (T antigens) are unique and distinct. However, they are similar enough to produce serologic and sometimes functional cross-reactivity. Factors which appear to influence detection of T antigen in virus-transformed cells include (1) multiplicity of infection (MOI), (2) cell growth rate or metabolic status, (3) cell passage level, (4) IF or histochemical method used, and (5) fixative used to detect T antigen. With current methods for T antigen or T antibody detection, negative results with human tissues are important but cannot provide a definitive answer concerning polyomavirus latency in the cells studied.

After polyomavirus early mRNA transcription occurs, late mRNAs are transcribed and then processed to smaller pieces which are translated to virion capsid (structural) proteins. Capsids of both full and empty virions contain late polypeptides—designated virion polypeptides, VP_1, VP_2, VP_3, etc.,[1-3] based on their molecular weights. In addition, full infectious virions contain viral DNA and histonelike internal polypeptides of cell origin adapted for use by the viral DNA.[65] Although capsid proteins of JCV have not yet been studied, those of BKV, SV40, and murine polyomavirus have similar molecular weights.[66-68] Capsid peptides of several different isolates of BKV have been compared and found to be nearly identical.[69] Capsomers, composed of five to six protein molecules, may exist as morphologically stable, free structures.[70-72] By EM, 9-nm JCV capsomer-like particles were detected and were thought to derive from JCV virions due to virus preparation artifacts.[72]

The polyomavirus virion and its various polypeptides are antigenic. If full or empty intact capsids of JCV, BKV, or SV40 are injected into animals in which virus does not replicate (eg, rabbit or guinea pig), antibodies are produced only against antigenic determinants exposed on the capsid surface. Antibodies specific for BKV or JCV can be detected seven to ten days after a single injection of virus. Virus-specific antisera can be used in IF or immunoperoxidase (IP) staining procedures to identify specific virus antigens in tissues or cultured cells, and to characterize different virus strains.[73, 74] Antibodies produced later, or after multiple injections, react with JCV, BKV, and with SV40.[66, 67, 75, 76] Such antisera demonstrate that a minor antigenic relationship exists between these three distinct primate polyomaviruses—a relationship that does not extend to other members of the *Polyomavirus* genus. These antibodies, which neutralize viral infectivity and prevent virion-mediated hemagglutination (HA), may be detected and quantified by various techniques including neutralization, hemagglutination inhibition (HI), complement fixation (CF), and immune electron microscopy (IEM).

All polyomaviruses have a common internal capsid antigen, exposed after virions are disrupted by detergent (SDS), against which high-titer antisera can be raised. Such antisera will react with any member of the polyomavirus group.[77, 78] Antibodies against this internal determinant do not neutralize infectivity or prevent HA, but they react with and identify unassembled polyomavirus structural peptides present in infected cells using IF or IP staining techniques.

JCV and BKV (but not SV40) can agglutinate human and guinea pig RBCs. HA is produced by both infectious virions and by empty capsids lacking DNA. One HA unit is approximately 3 × 10⁶ physical virions per milliliter.[79] HA disappears when capsids are disrupted to component capsomers. BKV HA titer is highest when assayed at pH 7.0 or less, at 0 to 4°C, and when virus is stored in solution with high NaCl molarity.[79, 80] Virus HA receptors on human RBCs are high-molecular-weight glycoproteins.[81] Gangliosides, cell membrane components capable of determining virus

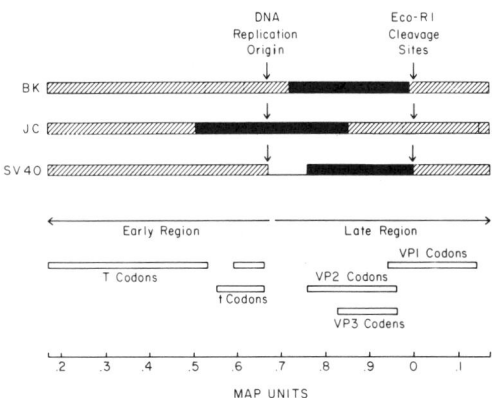

Figure 41–2. Colinear orientation of the physical maps of BK virus (BKV), JC virus (JCV), and simian virus 40 (SV40) genomes with regions of greatest homology shown in black. The bacterial restriction endonuclease Eco-RI cleavage site on each genome is map unit 0; sites of origin of DNA replication are shown at 0.67 map unit. Virus transcriptional regions are shown below the physical maps. (Adapted from Law et al.[105])

receptor specificity, can alter viral infectivity and HA. Gangliosides extracted from human group O RBCs restore the ability of neuraminidase-treated human RBCs to agglutinate with BKV.[82] Human and animal sera may contain nonspecific HA inhibitors which can be eliminated by treatment of sera with neuraminidase or periodate.[79] BKV infectivity can be diminished while leaving HA activity intact by treatment with 0.1% β-propiolactone.[83]

Genome of Polyomaviruses

Except for polypeptides, the only other constituent of polyomavirus virions is DNA (about 3 × 10⁶ daltons, 5000 base pairs, buoyant density 1.60 g/mL in CsCl–ethidium bromide isopyknic gradients). The DNA (genome) is present as a single, double-stranded, covalently closed, supercoiled molecule. As more is learned about JCV and BKV DNAs, the molecular biology of these viruses appears similar to that of SV40.[10] Common polyomavirus DNA functions include (1) replication of each circular, double-stranded viral DNA beginning at a unique site, the origin of replication at 0.67 map unit (Figure 41–2); (2) bidirectional discontinuous replication on both DNA strands terminating opposite to the origin of replication; (3) segregation of daughter molecules by an unknown mechanism with closure of residual DNA gaps by repair enzymes; and (4) two-stage transcription of the genome (early and late) proceeding in opposite directions on separate DNA strands.[39]

When procedures enhancing cell uptake of large molecules are employed, purified DNA is infectious and can transform cells in vitro.[18, 84–86] DNA extracted from a population of polyomavirus virions may contain DNAs of varying sizes, consisting of full-length (5000 base pairs) infectious molecules and various smaller (deleted) molecules which may be either infectious or noninfectious.[87–91] Two different, noninfectious (defective) DNA molecules with major deletions may complement each other to produce fully infectious virus particles if both are present in a single cell.[91, 92] BKV is unique among the polyomaviruses because several strains consist of a mixed population with dual complementary genomes, each with duplication and rearrangements of the viral sequences.[90-93]

Although the DNA molecules composing the genomes of JCV, BKV, and SV40 cannot be distinguished by physical methods, they are readily distinguished by the use of enzymes, restriction endonucleases, that cut them into pieces of differing numbers and sizes.[89, 94-99] The resultant pieces can then be "ordered" to construct a physical map showing location of enzyme cleavage sites.[17, 89, 97, 98, 100] Many restriction endonucleases are now available and their use has resulted in quite detailed physical maps of the polyomavirus genomes.

In light of the antigenic relationships that exist among BKV, JCV, and SV40, it is not surprising that the DNAs of these viruses exhibit relatedness or homology[95, 101, 102] (see Figure 41–2). However, the extent of the observed homology depends on the technique employed to detect it and on the strictness of identity demanded. One technique is to disassociate the two strands of JCV, BKV, or SV40 DNA molecules, mix those from two viruses, and allow the DNAs to reassociate. Homologous regions on heterologous strands will associate, producing hybrid double-stranded molecules which can be detected. By this method, JCV, BKV, and SV40 DNAs exhibit homology in both early and late regions of the viral genome.[95, 101, 103-105] However, by altering the reassociation conditions, significant DNA base mismatching can be demonstrated even in regions with some homology.

Recently, BKV, JCV, and SV40 DNAs have been molecularly cloned using recombinant DNA technology. This has resulted in production of sufficient viral DNA to permit determination of the sequence of the approximately 5000 base pairs that make up each genome. With nucleotide sequence data for the various polyomaviruses, it is possible to compare the various genomes in as much detail as desired. Recombinant DNA technology has solved two major problems encountered with BKV and JCV: (1) avoiding DNA heterogeneity by isolating DNA directly from tissues without cell culture (which generates alterations), and (2) molecular cloning and construction of mutants which can be used to study the function of various genome sequences.[41] As examples, recombinant DNAs representing several isolates of JCV have been constructed and used to transform PHFG cells,[41] and a BKV DNA expression vector (PBK TK-1) has been constructed which persists episomally in human cells and can be shuttled into bacteria.[106]

In 1979, Yang and Wu[107-110] reported the complete nucleotide sequence for BKV (strain MM) encompassing 4963 nucleotide base pairs, and Seif et al[39] accomplished the same for BKV (strain Dun) of 5153 base pairs. Extensive sequence homology between BKV and SV40 DNAs near the beginning of the early genome region and 70% sequence homology in the late genome region was found. DNA from BKV (strain WW) was isolated directly from human urine and cloned. BKV (strain WW) was described in South Africa and was difficult to propagate in cell culture.[111] Restriction mapping showed differences from prototypic BKV DNA, with gain and loss of several restriction endonuclease sites and extensive changes near the origin of replication.[112] Natural variation at the replication origin has been found in both SV40 and BKV,[39, 102, 109, 113, 114] suggesting that this region is susceptible to genetic drift. Reports on genomic variation in SV40 and BKV based on DNAs isolated from culture-propagated virus make it difficult to assess the degree of natural variation.[115-117]

The arrangement of functions within BKV and SV40 genomes

is strikingly similar. BKV, SV40, and polyomavirus have similar palindromes at their replication origins,[118] identical to a T antigen–binding region of SV40 where mutations disrupting a spacer function lead to defects in DNA replication.[119-122] Like SV40, BKV DNA sequences coding for T antigen are noncontiguous segments whose mRNAs are spliced together prior to translation.[110] DNA sequence similarity exists among BKV, SV40, and murine polyomavirus in the region coding for capsid protein VP_1,[118] and BKV sequences for VP_1 overlap those for VP_2 and VP_3.[110]

In 1984, Frisque et al[40] reported the complete nucleotide sequence for JCV (strain MAD-1), encompassing 5130 nucleotide base pairs. Full-length JCV DNA codes for six proteins; large T antigen and small t antigen; the late capsid proteins VP_1, VP_2, and VP_3; and an "agnogene product" encoded in the late leader sequence. JCV DNA homology with SV40 DNA (69%) and BKV DNA (75%) confirms close evolutionary relationship for these three polyomaviruses, although divergent sequences occur in the tandem repeats on the late side of the replication origin.[40] The JCV genome from 0.63 to 0.73 map unit codes several regulatory elements in the amino terminal portion of early viral proteins. JCV and BKV lack sequences here which resemble the third T antigen–binding site of SV40, and JCV lacks a sequence (GGGXGGAG) repeated several times in other polyomaviruses and thought to play a role in DNA replication and/or transcription.[41] JCV DNA can be divided into two subtypes, types 1 and 2, or MAD-1 and HER-1, based on restriction endonuclease cleavage patterns.[123] DNAs of both subtypes vary in the region between 0.67 to 0.72 map units and no two DNAs are identical.[117, 124]

JCV generates defective DNA molecules in cell culture[85, 92, 125] even after one passage.[126] After three or more low-multiplicity passages in PHFG cells, DNA from certain isolates of JCV becomes heterogeneous and deletions of up to 12% occur, most within the region coding for T antigen.[117] Since passage of JCV in PHFG culture does not always induce deleted molecules and sometimes selects for full-length molecules, defective DNAs do not necessarily have a competitive advantage.[126]

JCV DNA extracted from PML brains was compared by restriction endonuclease mapping. After passage at low MOI in PHFG cells, JCV DNA of some isolates remained homogeneous while others became heterogeneous.[127] Thus, the propensity of the JCV genome to sustain deletions was an intrinsic property of each isolate.[126] Induction and maintenance of defective JCV DNA was influenced by the proportion of spongioblasts in PHFG cultures and by the MOI. More defectives were produced in cultures containing semipermissive astrocytes. Deletions were confined to the early region of JCV DNA and appeared nonrandom.[126]

When JCV was isolated from both urine and brain in two PML patients, on restriction analysis the DNAs were mixtures of several different full-length genomes.[128] When these DNAs were molecularly cloned, differences were primarily insertions and deletions in the hypervariable control region of the genome, which appears to be a regular feature of the polyomavirus group.[39, 107-110, 124, 129] The observed variation originated in vivo and not during in vitro isolation, suggesting genetic instability in the JCV genome during its infection of the host.[128, 130] JCV natural genetic variation in brain versus kidney may occur because the MOI in brain is considerably higher than in kidney.[128, 131] However, 3 JCV clones have recently been isolated from urine of non-PML patients and these clones were genetically equivalent to the prototypic strain of PML-derived JCV.[131a]

Hypothetically, JCV hypervariability at the origin of replication should result in DNA heterogeneity in PML brains. However, the supercoiled DNA from any individual PML brain appeared homogeneous at the replication origin, suggesting that selection and amplification of one variant DNA may occur in vivo over time.[124]

Viral transcriptional regulatory elements called "enhancers"[132, 133] increase transcription independent of gene position and orientation,[134-138] exhibit relative host cell specificity,[139] and are required for efficient expression of early viral genes.[140] Apart from a small "core sequence," viral enhancers exhibit sequence divergence even among closely related viruses such as BKV and SV40.[132] Changes in this transcription control region may influence virus host range and may generate new viruses during evolution.[141]

Small changes in enhancer sequences have dramatic effect on host range and oncogenic properties of polyomaviruses. These sequences may have recently diverged and perhaps represent modified enhancer elements derived from host cells.[132] Host cell preference exhibited by viral enhancers suggests that similar transcriptional regulatory elements are associated with host genes controlling specificity of gene expression.[142-144] For example, the human X chromosome fragment "X-rep," which may represent a cell DNA replication origin, has sequence similarity to the BKV origin of replication.[145]

BKV[146] and JCV[123] isolates have variable alterations in the enhancer-promoter region. BKV enhancer regions have been mapped and three regions necessary for promoter function defined.[147] Many BKV variants have a highly conserved structure within this region.[93, 108, 110, 146, 148] BKV early promoter and enhancer regions overlap, in contrast to SV40 where they are separable units. Differences in host range for transformation between BKV and SV40 are determined by viral early gene products rather than by specific enhancer-promoter sequences.[149]

In JCV, the enhancer region consists of 98–base pair tandem repeats at the late side of the viral replication origin.[139] The prototypic JCV genome (MAD-1) differs from SV40 and BKV in early promoter sequences, including two identical control elements called TATA boxes, one in each 98–base pair repeat region, which influence transcription and mRNA cap sites.[41, 139] In JCV-transformed hamster brain cells, the second TATA box early transcripts do not influence size or quantity of early viral proteins, integration patterns of viral DNA, or host cell growth properties.[150]

Replication in Permissive Cells

Polyomavirus replication in permissive cells can be detected by observing CPE or plaque production, by identifying virus particles in cell or culture fluids using EM, by detecting virus antigens in cells using IF or histochemical microscopy, or by observing HA (JCV and BKV) when RBCs are mixed with culture fluids.

In permissive cells infected with BKV and studied by EM, BK virions are typically engulfed by pinocytosis two hours after infection, enter the nucleus after two to 12 hours, remain detectable in the nucleus at 24 hours, enter eclipse phase (uncoated) after 30 hours, and reappear in the nucleus at four days and in the cytoplasm at seven to eight days.[151] CPE may require 2 to 4 weeks to develop.

In PHFG cell culture, BKV produces an extensive and very obvious vacuolation of the cytoplasm (Figure 41–3).[24] Ultraviolet irradiation of virions or exposure to anti-BKV antibody delays the onset of CPE in human fibroblasts.[152]

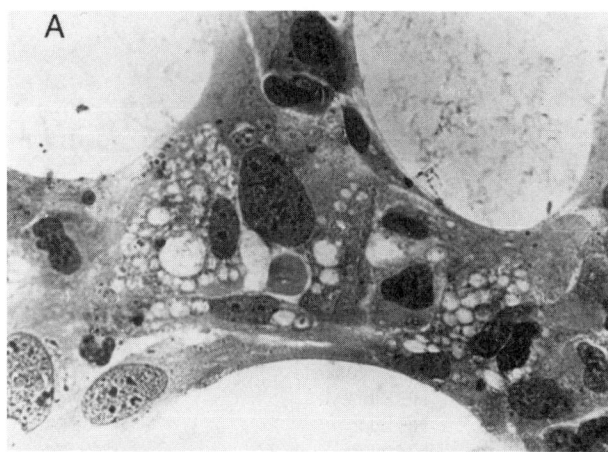
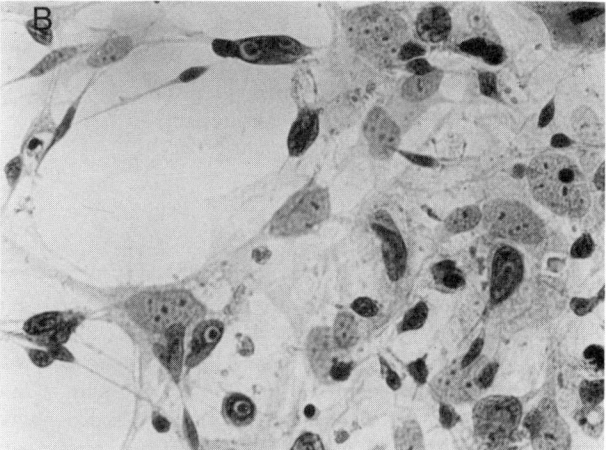
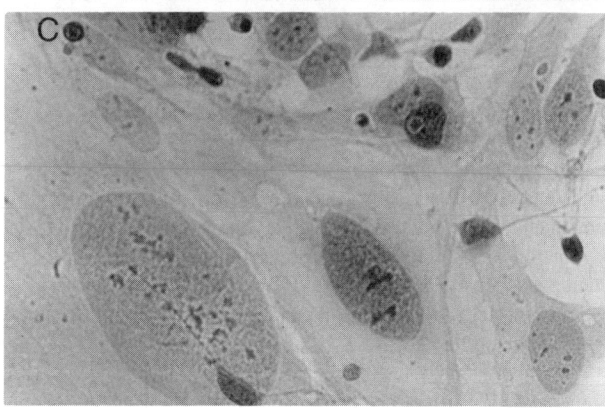

Figure 41–3. A. Primary human fetal glial (PHFG) cells 18 days after infection with BK virus (BKV) showing typical cytoplasmic vacuolization. **B.** PHFG cells 17 days after infection with JC virus (JCV) showing numerous intranuclear inclusions in small cells. **C.** PHFG cells 17 days after infection with JCV showing an enlarged astrocyte with a very large nucleus (normal-sized astrocytes are seen in the opposite corner).

Table 41–2
Cells Permissive For BK Virus (BKV) or JC Virus (JCV) Lytic Growth

	Cells	Initial Report (Reference)
BKV	H Brain	443
	H Fibroblasts	152
	H Endothelium	199
	H Lung (WI-38)	24
	H Lymphocytes	157
	H Urothelium*	154
	HE Fibroblasts	444
	HE Kidney*	200
	HE Lung	413
	HF Brain	24
	HF Liver	65
	HF Pancreas islet cells	158
	M Kidney (Vero)	5
	MF Brain	445
BKV DNA	HE Fibroblasts*	84
(transfection)	HE Kidney*	446
	HE Lung*	84
JCV	H Amnion	170
	H Brain	169
	H Urothelium*	171
	HE Kidney	125
	HF Brain	4
	HF Brain (JCV-transformed)	23
	HF Brain(SV40-transformed)	42
JCV DNA (transfection)	HF Brain	85

H = human; M = monkey; E = embryo; F = fetus.
*Cells reported useful for plaque assays.

Some early-passage human cells and the GMK cell line Vero are permissive for BKV growth (Table 41–2). Many primary human cell cultures are permissive for BKV growth only at low passage levels.[153] In cells supporting BKV plaque production, plaque morphology and size vary even after BKV had been plaque-purified.[153] In permissive human urothelial cells, the optimal temperature for plaque formation is 37°C.[154] In contrast, BKV multiplication in HeLa cells or in Vero cells is enhanced at 38.5°C,[155] and in early-passage, semipermissive monkey kidney cells (CV-1 and other lines) it was enhanced at 40°C.[156]

Human peripheral blood lymphocytes support BKV replication with specific V antigen production and infection of permissive human embryonic fibroblasts (HEF) by lymphocyte lysates.[157] BKV replication is restricted in lymphocytes since V antigen–positive nuclei and virus yield are 100-fold less than in BKV-infected HEF cells. However, antigen–positive nuclei are seen in both B and T lymphocyte cultures.

A human lymphoblastoid cell line (P3HR-1) also supports BKV replication.[157] During the first month, only 1% of nuclei were V antigen–positive and cell lysates had no HA activity. After 40 days' culture and with cell passage, nuclear V antigen increased to 15% and BKV production was sufficient to be detected by HA (16–32 hemagglutination units per milliliter). Receptor-destroying enzyme (RDE) was unnecessary, in contrast to BKV growth in HEF. BKV-exposed peripheral blood monocytes remained negative for BKV antigens for up to 500 days.

Human fetal pancreatic islet cell cultures have been infected with BKV.[158] By the fourth day after infection, about 50% of cells contained BKV T antigen; by the sixth day, 40% contained BKV V antigen. There was no morphologic change up to six days except for the appearance of intranuclear inclusion bodies. Cultures maintained in serum-free (Eagle's) minimum essential medium (MEM) displayed significantly decreased insulin release and increased BKV antigen detection versus cells in 2% to 10% calf serum.[158] Fetal islet cells obtained before 20 weeks were more sensitive to BKV infection than cells obtained thereafter.[158]

In another study,[159] 14-week-old primary human fetal pancreas cells inoculated with BKV at MOI of 1 plaque-forming unit (PFU) per cell exhibited extensive CPE 3 weeks postinoculation. Cells could be subcultured weekly but entered crisis after 12 passages. Intranuclear BKV T antigen was present in 95% and V antigen in 10% to 30%. BKV yield in culture fluids was 104 to 105 TCID (50% tissue culture infectious dose)/mL as determined in human fetal lung cells. By restriction endonuclease mapping, viral DNA was deleted and rearranged, although deletion mutants did not prevent high-level DNA replication and virus multiplication. Despite the continuous presence of BKV T antigen, the transformed phenotype was not observed—no colonies appeared in soft agar and the cells could be passaged only 20 times.

JCV has a very restricted host cell range in vitro (see Table 41–2). It grows well in spongioblasts present in primary cultures of PHFG tissue and, to a limited extent, in astrocytes (the other major cell in these cultures).[160] As the spongioblast is thought to be the precursor of the adult oligodendrocyte, JCV growth in vitro parallels events in PML brain tissue where virions are found almost exclusively in nuclei of oligodendrocytes. Although PHFG cells[161] are permissive for JCV, BKV, and SV40, problems using them include the following: (1) They are difficult to obtain. (2) They are a mixed population of cell types. (3) The ratio of astrocytes to spongioblasts varies. (4) Lytic activity of JCV in the cells is low, growth cycle prolonged, and CPE difficult to recognize. (5) Cells must be maintained several weeks before virus is harvested. (6) Once established in culture, the cells rapidly lose the ability to support JCV replication.[160]

JCV is not a fast-growing, quickly spreading, lytic virus. CPE in PHFG cell cultures is not observed before ten days, even after a large inoculum. CPE is subtle, consisting primarily of enlargement of cells and change from spindle to epithelioid morphology. Intranuclear inclusions may be seen in fixed cells stained with hematoxylin and eosin (see Figure 41–3). Progeny virus is strongly cell-associated with little virus released into culture fluids. After inoculation with four infectious units of JCV per PHFG cell, 10% of cell nuclei contain T antigen at two days and 57% T antigen at five days, although only 2% of nuclei contain V antigen at five days.[160] This is very slow when compared with BKV growth in HEF where V antigen was seen in 6% of cell nuclei two days after inoculation.[151] JCV growth restriction does not involve an early step in the virus-cell interaction such as adsorption, penetration, or uncoating.[85] The long JCV lytic cycle contrasts with that of other papovaviruses.[13, 162]

After JCV infection of PHFG cells, viral DNA replication is detected by day 5, although most DNA replication occurs 3 weeks after infection.[13, 42, 162] This delay is not due to a requirement for several cycles of infection (ie, JCV spread from cell to cell), since most PHFG cells already express JCV T antigen by day 7,[42, 160] but viral HA titers are not substantial before day 21. In PHFG cells, JCV replicates better at 39°C than at 37°C and the higher temperature is now recommended for JCV primary isolations from brain.[127]

JCV (MAD-1) viral DNA cloned in an *Escherichia coli* plasmid vector was used to transfect PHFG cells. After 4 to 5 weeks, the cultures developed characteristic CPE and produced viral particles capable of agglutinating human type O RBCs.[163] Glial cells became enlarged, balloonlike, then detached from the surface and floated in columns. All virus particles detected by HA were initially attached to and/or contained in these "floater" cells. JCV DNA transfection resulted in a slower time course of virion production, reflecting a decreased efficiency of DNA uptake.[163]

JCV host cell restriction may be regulated at several levels. First, enhancer-mediated cell tropism may allow JCV to exploit a given cell only if the cell has enhancer sequences similar to JCV sequences.[164] JCV enhancer-promoter activity, as measured by chloramphenicol acetyl transferase (CAT) expression assays, was limited to PHFG and hamster glial cells.[139, 165] Second, JCV DNA synthesis may require additional species-specific replication factors found only in primate cells. The rodent glial cell line HJC produces JCV T antigen, but the virus does not replicate well in these cells despite T antigen production.[165] Third, in PHFG cells, JCV early promoter activity is greater than late promoter activity, whereas in nonpermissive CV-1 cells, the opposite occurs.[139] Constitutive expression of the late promoter may be deleterious to the JCV lytic cycle in nonglial cells.[13] Fourth, JCV T antigen interacts less efficiently with homologous and heterologous polyomavirus regulatory sequences than does SV40 or BKV T antigen. Perhaps T antigen recognition sites are absent in JCV, contributing to the restricted lytic and transforming activities of JCV in vitro.[166] Finally, nuclear factor I (NF-I) is a host-coded protein with high affinity for specific sites in the host cell genome. NF-I is highly conserved in tissues of higher vertebrates. NF-I enhances viral replication in vitro[167] and recognition sites for NF-I are present in the BKV enhancer region.[167] Perhaps similar sites are missing in JCV.

JCV DNA replicates in some primate cells that are already producing either JCV or SV40 T antigen. SV40 mutant-transformed PHFG cells (designated SVG)[168] support replication of JCV to the same degree as primary PHFG cells.[42] JCV DNA transfection also induces JCV replication in SVG.[165] However, SVG cells do not lessen the time required for JCV multiplication in culture.[42] SV40 T antigen is constitutively expressed in SVG cells, but does not interact efficiently with JCV; possibly, recombination of SV40 and JCV DNA sequences occurs.[23] SVG cells are astroglial, supporting the concept that JCV replication can occur in astroglial cells.[165]

Replication origin mutants of JCV were used to establish transformed PHFG cell lines (designated POJ for "PHFG cells transformed by Ori-JCV"). These cells support the lytic growth of JCV, constitutively express a functional T protein, and complement the replication defect of JCV early-region mutants.[23] POJ cells remain permissive until crisis at passage level 35 to 40 and should facilitate the study of JCV.[23] POJ represents the first permissive cell system for JCV that constitutively produces a wild-type JCV T protein.[23]

Limited JCV growth occurs in other human cells: adult brain,[169] amnion,[170] and embryonic kidney.[125] However, large numbers of defective virions are detected in virus pools prepared from these cells[23] and they are not suitable for routine, large-scale growth and isolation of JCV. JCV growth and isolation from clinical specimens have been noted in human urothelial cells (HUC)[171, 172] cultured from urine of newborns.[173] HUC cultures could be established in 28 of 112 urine specimens (25%) and were maintained for two to 13 passages. Microbial contamination was the primary cause of failure to establish HUC cultures.[174] BKV could be plaqued in[154] and JCV replicates in HUC.[174] JCV HA was detected in culture fluids at 11 days postinoculation, was highly cell-associated, and HA titers were increased 32- to 64-fold by treatment with RDE. Nuclei were positive for both T and V antigen, and morphologically normal cells expressed these antigens. JCV CPE was distinguishable from that of BKV. Primary isolation of JCV from PML brain was less efficient in HUC cells than in PHFG cells. Thus, HUC cells represent an in vitro correlate of one in vivo target tissue for JCV and BKV[174] and may prove quite useful, although neither they nor PHFG cultures are available commercially.

Although monkey cells are the natural "permissive" host for SV40, exhibiting CPE and cytolysis, the virus can multiply lytically to a certain extent in various primary human fetal cells,[161, 175, 176] in a human glioblastoma cell line,[177] and in human endothelial cells.[178]

Cell Transformation

Human polyomaviruses have the ability to transform the morphology and growth characteristics of certain cells in vitro. The transformed cells exhibit characteristics of tumor cells. Growth requirement for serum and cell doubling time decrease, while saturation density and efficiency of cell plating on plastic or in agar increase. If virus-infected cells meet several of these criteria but cannot be subcultured indefinitely or do not form colonies in agar, they have undergone "abortive" or "partial" transformation respectively.[179]

In most transformed cells, either complete or partial polyomavirus genomes are covalently linked (integrated) to host cell DNA.[180-183] The process of integration involves cleavage of the circular viral genome to give a linear molecule, cleavage of the chromosomal DNA, insertion of viral DNA, and union of cut ends. Sites of DNA cleavage for integration appear numerous both within the virus genome and within the host cell DNAs.[180, 181, 183] In addition, transformed cells may contain nonintegrated, free or episomal, viral DNAs.[59, 180-183]

In BKV- or SV40-transformed cells, virus DNA is often nonintegrated.[21, 59, 60, 90, 180, 184-186] When infectious BKV was rescued from lines of virion-free, BKV-transformed hamster, rat, and mouse cells using Sendai virus fusion with permissive cells, efficiency of BKV rescue strongly correlated with content of free viral DNA per cell.[187] However, excision of integrated BKV genomes as a first step in the rescue process was not excluded, since free BKV DNA was not detected in two cell lines from which it was possible to rescue BKV.[187] Variability in BKV transformed cell expression of T and V antigens and in BKV DNA integration patterns has been noted.[188]

In JCV-transformed hamster cell lines and tumors,[150, 189] and in JCV-transformed PHFG (POJ) cells,[23] viral DNA sequences are integrated into the host cell genome at a minimum of four to five unique sites. JCV transformation requiring multiple integration sites could explain the low transforming activity of this virus, since multiple integration events in a given cell would be statistically unlikely.[23]

Mechanisms of cell transformation by human polyomaviruses are currently under intense study. Early-region sequences near the origin of replication influence the cell transformation efficiency of BKV and SV40.[142, 144, 148, 190, 191] When enhancer-promoter sequences are switched between BKV and SV40, they (1) are interchangeable for T antigen induction and cell transformation, (2) influence cell transformation efficiency, but (3) do not influence type of cell transformed.[149]

BKV plaque formation on HEK cells is directly proportional to, and transforming ability is inversely proportional to, the number of 68–base pair repeats in the viral enhancer region.[148, 190, 192] Wild-type BKV has three 68–base pair tandem repeats in its transcriptional control region, forms clear large plaques on HEK cells, and rarely transforms hamster or rat cells. BKV mutants with only two 68–base pair elements form small turbid plaques in human cells and transform rat cells inefficiently. BKV mutants with only one 68–base pair element form very small plaques in human cells and transform rat cells efficiently. Thus, reducing the number of 68–base pair repeats slows BKV lytic growth but increases its transforming efficiency.[192] When BKV DNAs are cloned, reiteration of a 13–base pair sequence in an origin-distal portion of the 68–base pair element is essential for efficient growth in HEK cells; duplication of the origin-proximal end is not required.[193] BKV (strain IR), isolated from a human pancreatic islet cell tumor, is less efficient than prototypic BKV in transforming hamster cells or inducing hamster brain tumors.[194] This strain has a 253–base pair deletion and an 80–base pair insertion in the early region of the genome. The deletion abolishes expression of small T antigen; the insertion rearranges the first and second enhancer elements.

Cell transformation and tumor induction by BKV appears to be a multistep process involving more than one gene.[195–197] The Ha-ras oncogene, isolated from T24/EJ human bladder carcinoma cells, has transforming activity due to a single point mutation resulting in a change in one amino acid. Ha-ras alone does not transform primary HEK cells and BKV DNA alone only partially transforms these cells. However, primary HEK cells transfected with both cloned BKV DNA and human Ha-ras oncogene are fully transformed.[196] In similar experiments, malignant undifferentiated sarcomas were induced in 73% of newborn Syrian hamsters by subcutaneous inoculation of recombinant DNA containing the BKV early-region and the activated Ha-ras oncogene; neither gene inoculated independently was tumorigenic.[197] Similarly, when BALB/C mouse kidney cells partially transformed by BKV were transfected with various human tumor cell DNAs, hepatoma and Burkitt lymphoma cell DNAs produced full transformation.[195] Although human tumor cell DNA sequences disappeared during serial passage, the mouse kidney cells continued to exhibit anchorage independence in agar and contained integrated BKV DNA after 20 passages. Presumably, amplification and/or rearrangement of the BKV genome occurred while the human tumor DNA sequences were present, resulting in fully transformed cell clones.[195]

JCV or JCV DNA has produced abortive transformation of human fetal glial[23, 150, 198] and human vascular endothelial cells.[199] When molecularly cloned JCV DNA was used to transform human amnion cells, the JCV genome was present as a circular episomal element rather than an integrated part of the cell genome.[86] Hamster glial cells have been transformed by four isolates of JCV as well as by extracted JCV DNA.[18] In general, polyomaviruses transform nonpermissive cells incapable of supporting viral growth. Given the very few kinds of cells permissive for JCV, it is somewhat surprising that successful stable transformation has been limited to human amnion and hamster glial cells (Table 41–3).

BKV or BKV DNA has transformed hamster, mouse, rat, rabbit, monkey, and human cells (see Table 41–3). Cell transformation is dose-dependent between multiplicity of infection 2 and 100.[200–203]

Rodent cells are nonpermissive for SV40 but may undergo malignant transformation. Human cells appear intermediate—in some cases producing infectious SV40, in others undergoing transformation. SV40 or SV40 DNA transforms both fetal and newborn human kidney cells,[176] human endothelial cells (abortive),[178] human fetal astrocytes,[161] human adult brain explants,[204, 205] and human skeletal muscle cells.[206] A DNA replication-defective mutant of SV40 transforms human fibroblasts and kidney cells.[50, 207] An origin-defective mutant of SV40 transforms human fetal glial cells which grow rapidly and are capable of lytic infection by JCV.[42]

Table 41–3

Cells Transformed In Vitro by BK Virus or JC Virus

Virus	Initial Report (Reference)
BK	
Hamster	
Brain	443
Embryo	202
Kidney	200
Human	
Embryo fibroblasts	186
Embryo kidney	184
Fetal brain	59
Monkey	
Kidney (African green monkey)	447
Kidney (rhesus)	448
Mouse	
Embryo	448
Kidney	448
Kidney (nude mice)	449
Rabbit	
Brain	448
Kidney	450
Liver	448
Rat	
Embryo	52
Kidney	84
Lung fibroblasts	52
JC	
Hamster	
Brain	18
Human	
Amnion	86
Endothelium	199
Fetal brain	23, 150

Table 41–4

Hamster Tumors Induced by JC Virus (JCV), BK Virus (BKV) and Simian Virus 40 (SV40) Polyomaviruses After Inoculation by Various Routes

Site and Histology	JCV*	BKV	SV40
Central nervous system			
Choroid plexus papilloma	+	+	
Ependymona	+	+	+
Glioblastoma	+		
Medulloblastoma	+		
Meningioma	+		
Neuroblastoma	+	+	
Pineocytoma	+	+	
Retinoblastoma	+		
Lymph nodes			
Histocytic lymphoma (reticulum cell sarcoma)		+	+
Pancreas			
Malignant insulinoma		+	
Miscellaneous			
Anaplastic sarcoma			+
Hemangioma	+		
Leiomyosarcoma	+		
Osteosarcoma		+	+
Rhabomyosarcoma		+	

See text for references.
JCV also has induced malignant glioblastomas in owl and squirrel monkey brains.[214, 215]

These cells (SVG) are "partially transformed" since they grow to high saturation density but do not show anchorage independence.[42] SVG culture morphology started as a mixture of cell types but evolved to a homogeneous population of astroglial cells which contain glial fibrillary acidic protein (GFAP).[42]

Tumor Induction in Animals

BKV, JCV, and SV40 frequently induce tumors after injection into newborn Syrian hamsters by various routes—subcutaneous (SC), intravenous (IV), intracerebral (IC), or intraperitoneal (IP) (Table 41–4). Although spontaneous brain tumors are very rare in the Syrian hamster,[208] JCV given IC is highly oncogenic, inducing several brain tumor histologic types.[208, 209] In one study, 83% of newborn hamsters developed brain tumors within 6 months of inoculation; 95% of these tumors were cerebellar medulloblastomas.[208, 210] Using various routes of inoculation, JCV has also induced visceral sarcomas, peripheral neuroblastomas, and pineocytomas, as well as other intracranial tumors.[208]

During prolonged cell culture of a JCV-induced hamster medulloblastoma, about half of all tumor cells became positive for GFAP, vimentin, and T antigen, and a new clonal cell line (I-23) was established which was subcutaneously transplantable to hamsters.[211] GFAP, a major protein of intermediate filaments, is a cell-specific marker for astrocytes and astrocytomas.[212] I-23 closely resembled human astrocytoma when transplanted, and the transplanted tumor cells retained GFAP and vimentin but lost common papovavirus T antigen.[211, 212]

When JCV (strain Tokyo 1), isolated from human PML brain and serologically identical to JCV (strain MAD-1), was inoculated IC into newborn hamsters, all developed brain tumors in a period averaging 5 months. The tumors were cerebellar medulloblastoma (20) and plexus tumor (two). Although JCV-Tokyo 1 was given into the right cerebral hemisphere, no microscopic tumors were ever observed in the cerebrum or internal organs.[213] Medulloblastomas originated in cells of the neonatal external granular level, which then migrated inward carrying integrated JCV DNA and expressing T antigen and phenotypic transformation.[213] Immunocytochemical studies on the medulloblastoma cells using both glial (GFAP) and neuronal markers (NSE) were negative.[213]

Of great interest, IC inoculation of JCV induces cerebral gliomas in adult owl monkeys and squirrel monkeys,[214, 215] making JCV the first human virus shown to induce brain tumors in any primate. The appearance of brain tumors in two monkey species suggests that the virus, rather than the host species, is responsible.[215] Brain tumors have not occurred in control monkeys, in monkeys inoculated with BKV or SV40 and observed for up to 36 months,[216] or in rhesus monkeys inoculated with JCV.[208]

Half of adult owl monkeys developed cerebral glioblastomas 16 to 34 months after IC inoculation of JCV. All animals developed HI antibody against V antigen within 1 month whether or not they developed brain tumors. HI antibody levels persisted for a prolonged period at constant levels in only three monkeys, suggesting that JCV replication was not prolonged in most animals. T antibody developed in 22 of 23 monkeys, usually 5 or more months postinoculation. Time prior to T antibody detection was highly variable but some animals had sustained titers suggesting persistent JCV genomic expression. T antibody levels did not correlate well with tumor growth, and several animals reverted to seronegative when tumors became evident.[217]

Attempts to isolate or rescue JCV from owl monkey brain tumors failed.[218] However, hybridization with ^{32}P-labeled probes detected JCV DNA in all brain tumors examined. Viral DNA was integrated into cellular DNA at a limited number of sites, indicating that the tumors were clonal. Since only a small piece of each tumor was tested, different cell clones with different integration patterns could exist in other parts of these tumors.[218] The JCV genome was integrated in two or more tandem copies in all but one of the tumors examined, possibly reflecting the need for an uninterrupted copy of a vital portion of the genome (presumably the region coding for T antigen). Although a complete copy of the JCV genome was present, there was very limited genomic expression since there was no detectable virus production and T antigen expression was very limited.[218]

All ten squirrel monkeys injected IC with JCV DNA (strain MAD-1) developed T antibody. During the first year, four animals died; of the remaining six, four developed astrocytomas 14 to 29 months postinoculation. All tumors were high grade with multiple mitotic figures. When fibronectin and GFAP were studied in these brain tumors, histochemical patterns included (1) similarity to grade 4 human astrocytoma, (2) poorly differentiated astrocytoma with minimal vascular proliferation, and (3) focal monstrocellular glial proliferation.[216]

Initial reports on BKV inoculation in newborn hamsters indicated very low oncogenicity. Given IC, BKV induced malignant ventricular papillary ependymomas,[27, 219–221] ventricular choroid plexus papillomas,[222] and pancreatic insulinomas.[219] Combining data from six separate reports, SC inoculation of BKV produced local sarcomas in 14% of 354 newborn or adolescent hamsters.[221–226]

However, after immunosuppression with antithymocyte serum, 75% of newborn hamsters inoculated SC developed tumors.[222] Injected IV, BKV induced abdominal lymphoma (reticulum cell sarcoma) in two (2%) of 89 hamsters.[221] BKV DNA was not oncogenic in hamsters after SC or IV inoculation, although it induced tumors at low frequency when inoculated IC.[227]

In contrast to the preceding studies, Uchida et al[220] reported a high incidence of tumor induction in newborn hamsters after injection of their stock BKV: 79% developed osteosarcoma or insulinoma after SC inoculation; 64% developed osteosarcoma, rhabdomyosarcoma, or insulinoma after IP inoculation; 86% developed brain tumors (ependymoma, choroid plexus papilloma, neuroblastoma, pinealoma), abdominal tumors (insulinoma or peritoneal tumors), osteosarcoma, or other tumors after IC inoculation; malignant and metastasizing islet cell tumors developed after IV inoculation.[220, 227] Thus, BKV was polyoncogenic with a tumor spectrum similar to that of JCV. Further, uncloned BKV stocks may contain mutants capable of inducing specific types of tumors. One plaque morphology mutant of BKV, PM-522, produced more brain tumors and malignant insulinomas, but fewer osteosarcomas, than did WT-BKV.[190]

Outbred Wistar rats have an extremely long latent period for BKV-induced tumors.[228] However, all newborn inbred strain AS rats injected with BKV developed tumors. T antibody response at a critical time postinoculation (1.5–30 months) inhibited tumor induction, although HI titers did not influence tumor induction. Possibly, T antibody–mediated lysis of transformed cells prevented tumor development in this model.[229] Intracerebral inoculation of BKV has reportedly induced malignant ependymomas in outbred mice.[221]

Attempts to induce primate tumors by inoculating SV40 have failed. Monkeys infected with SV40 and then given cyclophosphamide had a tenfold increase in neutralizing antibody levels (vs SV40 alone) but no tumors or obvious histopathologic changes developed.[230] When injected IC into newborn hamsters, SV40 induced malignant ventricular ependymomas.[231] Inoculated IV, SV40 induced leukemia, lymphoma, and osteogenic and anaplastic sarcoma. When virus was neutralized by antisera prior to injection, tumors did not develop.[232, 233] The SV40 early gene region expressed in transgenic mice has been associated with choroid plexus papillomas.[234] T antigen expression was highest in tumor tissues, and large T antigen (but not small t antigen) was required for tumor induction. Deleting a short segment of SV40 enhancer DNA changed the spectrum of pathology from choroid plexus papilloma to hepatocellular carcinoma, islet cell carcinoma, and demyelinating peripheral neuropathy.[139]

EPIDEMIOLOGY

Worldwide serologic surveys in normal populations for HI antibodies have confirmed that JCV and BKV are ubiquitous, common infections of childhood and adolescence. Some children and some adults have antibody against JCV or BKV but not against both, indicating that the viruses circulate independently. Antibody titers persist throughout life, although many surveys show a slight decline in anti-BKV titers after early adulthood (Figure 41–4). JCV or BKV HI antibodies have been found in a few individuals in isolated native groups in Brazil, Malaysia, and the South Pacific

basin, but isolated virgin populations also exist.[8, 235] BKV seems to have penetrated more deeply into remote areas than JCV.[236]

For JCV, most persons become seropositive around age 10 years,[237] although antibody can be acquired well into middle age[236]; for BKV, most children are seropositive by age 5.[7, 238] For JCV, the prevalence of antibodies in adult populations in the United States,[8, 235] urban Brazil,[235] and Tokyo[239, 241] is in the 70% to 90% range. For BKV, the prevalence of antibodies in adults ranges from 10% seropositive in Iceland[8] to 60% to 80% seropositive in England,[7] Finland,[242] the United States,[238] and China.[243] No significant sex difference in prevalence of antibodies has been observed.

There is serologic evidence for JCV and/or BKV reactivation in 5% to 10% of women during pregnancy, although few primary infections occur (Table 41–5).[244–248] In pregnant women initially seronegative against JCV or BKV, none had titer rises against either virus; in seropositives, five (5%) of 92 had titer increases against BKV and nine (16%) of 57 against JCV.[249, 250] Most women with elevated or rising BKV HI titers during pregnancy had BKV-specific IgM antibody detectable for up to 6 months postdelivery.[251] Polyomavirus multiplication during pregnancy probably results from the immune alterations known to occur during pregnancy since

Table 41–5

JC Virus (JCV) or BK Virus (BKV) Fourfold Hemagglutination-Inhibition Titer Increases Observed in Various Clinical Settings*

	(No. of Titer Rises/ No. of Persons Tested)		
	JCV	BKV	References
Normals			
Adults	0/16	1/16	336
Children[†]	—	11/66	242
Pregnant women	—	6/80	244
	—	3/33	247
	13/100	5/100	248
	13/430	18/1235	245, 246
Acute viral syndromes			
Adults	—	3/77	283
Children	—	1/82	357
	—	7/177	284
Renal transplantation	—	26/69	413
	—	13/17	460
	—	10/33	461
	—	8/20	339
	—	8/41	334
	18/61	11/61	336
	40/342	77/342	250
Malignancy			
Leukemia, acute lymphocytic (children)	11/29	11/29	‡
Carcinomas	4/30	3/30	359
	—	20/29	361
Lymphomas	8/29	8/29	359
Miscellaneous	—	3/76	252

*Since the number of sera tested and study duration varied in these reports, results likely underestimate the actual incidence of active JCV and BKV infection in these groups.
†Part of a study on respiratory illnesses; four of 11 children with titer increases had acute respiratory illness of unknown etiology noted between specimens.
‡Hogan et al, unpublished data, June 1990.

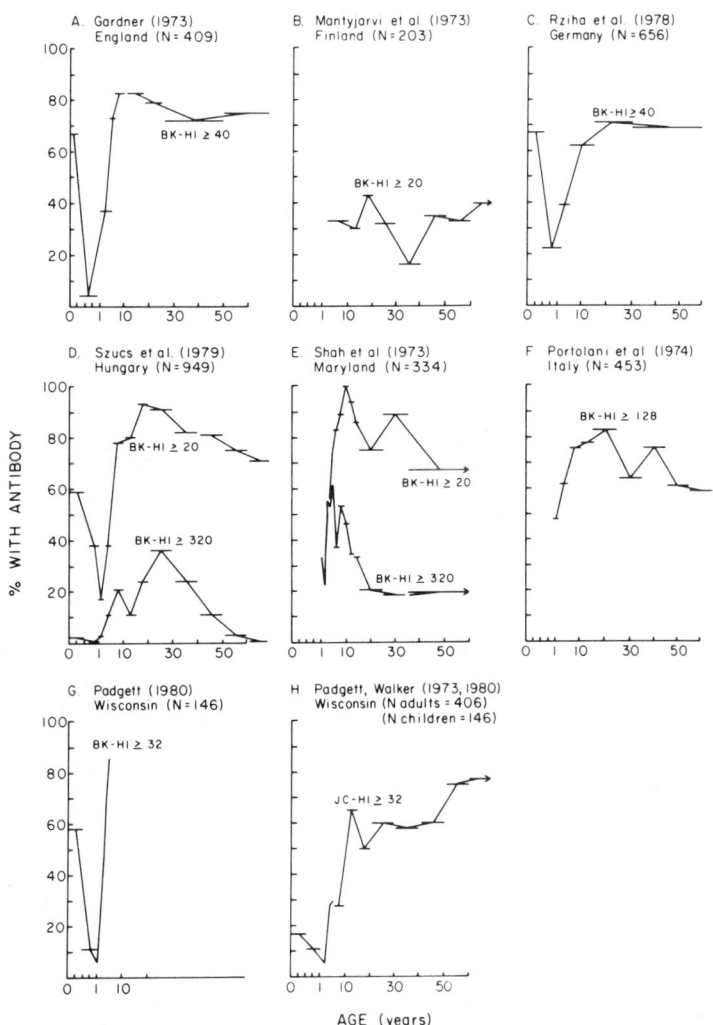

A. Gardner (1973) England (N = 409)

B. Mantyjarvi et al. (1973) Finland (N = 203)

C. Rziha et al. (1978) Germany (N = 656)

D. Szucs et al. (1979) Hungary (N = 949)

E. Shah et al. (1973) Maryland (N = 334)

F. Portolani et al. (1974) Italy (N = 453)

G. Padgett (1980) Wisconsin (N = 146)

H. Padgett, Walker (1973, 1980) Wisconsin (N adults = 406) (N children = 146)

Figure 41–4. Panels A–H depict percent of tested sera seropositive for hemagglutination-inhibition (HI) antibody against BK virus or JC virus at specific ages. Populations surveyed, numbers of sera tested, and HI values used to determine seropositivity are shown at the top of each panel.[7, 198, 237, 238, 242, 252, 462, 463]

most women stop shedding virus after parturition.[246] Whether human intrauterine infection with JCV or BKV occurs is still unresolved. BKV and JCV have not been isolated from human fetal kidneys.[198] Testing umbilical cord bloods for IgM antibodies against JCV or BKV has yielded both positive[244, 252, 253] and negative[245–254] results. In one negative study, samples included umbilical cord sera from seven neonates whose mothers showed definite evidence for either BKV or JCV activity during pregnancy.[249, 250] However, limitations in using serologic data to infer congenital transmission include the following: (1) Congenital infection may lead to fetal death or transient IgM antibody response. (2) Few primary infections may occur during pregnancy in humans. In mice, polyomavirus congenital transmission only occurs when mice have primary infection (not reactivation) during pregnancy.[255, 256] In one study, none of 14 human fetuses were at risk for primary infection with BKV, lacking both BKV maternal antibody and interferon in amniotic fluid.[257] (3) Large numbers of sera must be tested to rule out infrequent congenital transmission.[249, 250] Transplacental trans-

mission may possibly occur, but further study is needed to clarify this.

There is no evidence for animal reservoirs for JCV or BKV and no reason to think that spread is other than from man to man. Although 72% of rabbit sera and 13% of swine sera in Tokyo reportedly had HI antibodies against BKV, nonspecific inhibitors of HI in animal sera most likely led to false-positive results.[258] No antibody against JCV was found in sera from common pets, common laboratory animals, or from five species of monkeys.[160] Small, commonly used laboratory animals respond to JCV inoculation with the formation of anti-V antibodies only, without signs of infection. However, three species of primates injected with JCV developed anti-T as well as anti-V antibodies, indicating at least a limited amount of early viral protein synthesis.[259]

The high prevalence of JCV and BKV antibodies and lack of an animal reservoir indicate a high degree of communicability among children. However, no study of young children undergoing primary infection has yet established the route of transmission or

Table 41–6
Urinary Tract Infection By Human Polyomaviruses*

Associated Conditions	No. Positive/No. Studied	References
A. Defined adult patient groups (some repeatedly studied)		
Carcinoma	5/37(14%)	352
	5/54(9%)	359
	1/2—	353
Diabetes	3/84(6%)	352
Lymphoma	6/60(10%)	359
Normals		
Urine	1/16(6%)	336
	12/3648(0.3%)	352
	1/X—	353
Cadaver kidney, ureter	11/29(38%)	261, 332
	2/14(14%)	323
Pregnant women	24/1235(2%)	245, 246
Progressive multifocal leukoencephalopathy	7/9(78%)	323
Transplantation		
Bone marrow	15/45(33%)	341, 342
	25/53(47%)	345, 347
	5/21(24%)	348
Renal	17/80(21%)	5
		329, 330, 413
	10/300(3%)	420
	7/51(14%)	451
	3/41(7%)	334
	12/61(20%)	336
	9/91(10%)	335
	31/48(65%)	337
	8/13(62%)	353
Urology clinic patients (benign diseases)	9/48(19%)	353
B. Isolated observations in adults†		
Anemia	2	418, 419
Carcinoma, miscellaneous	6	452
		453
		252
Leukemia	1	452
Lymphoma	5	328
		415
		453
		252
Nephrotic syndrome	1	415
Progressive multifocal leukoencephalopathy	4	328
		131
		294
Systemic lupus	1	454
Transplantation		
Bone marrow	2	452
		455
Renal	11	416, 418
		456
		457
		331
C. Defined groups of children (some repeatedly studied)		
Acute upper respiratory infection	1/177(0.6%)	285
Leukemia, acute lymphocytic	3/42(7%)	‡
Miscellaneous acute and chronic illnesses	0/150(0%)	282

D. Isolated observations in children†		
Congenital defects	2	252
Cystitis	2	458
		350
Immunodeficiency	7	19
		252
Leukemia, acute lymphocytic	2	252
Nephritis	1	459

*Urinary tract infections have usually been asymptomatic, recognized by identifying polyomavirus in urine or urothelium using viral culture, electron microscopy, urinary cytology with indirect immunofluorescence microscopy, or hybridization with molecular probes.
†Number positive are shown.
‡Hogan et al, unpublished observations, June 1990.

virus excretion. By analogy with murine polyomavirus[260] and with SV40,[261] infection may occur by aerosol inhalation or oral ingestion of virus with excretion occurring via the urinary tract. JCV and/or BKV urinary excretion has been reported in 2% of pregnant women studied by urinary cytology, EM, or viral culture, in 20% to 65% of adults after organ transplantation, and in 10% of children or adults with malignancies (Table 41–6). JCV or BKV have occasionally been isolated from the urine of normal persons.[73] The above serologic and urinary excretion data have provided substantial evidence that both JCV and BKV establish persistent latent infections that can reactivate during periods of immunosuppression. Further evidence for JCV and BKV latency has recently come from studies detecting JCV and BKV genomes (by molecular hybridization) in 10% and 34% of human kidneys obtained from random autopsies.[262, 263]

From 1% to 30% of feral rhesus monkeys (the natural host for SV40) or those in breeding colonies have been seropositive for antibodies against SV40.[264–266] In adult monkeys, SV40 infection appears to be an asymptomatic, latent infection, although virus can be isolated from kidney explants or cell cultures derived from seropositive animals. Experimentally, young rhesus monkeys have been infected by intranasal, intragastric, or SC inoculation of SV40. Virus was not recoverable from throat or rectal swabs, but virus and neutralizing antibody appeared in urine up to 2 months postinfection and SV40 was isolated from kidney in one monkey 30 weeks postinoculation.[261] Other species of monkeys have also been infected after parenteral inoculation of SV40. Asymptomatic viruria has been demonstrable for several weeks and isolation of SV40 has been possible from renal explants.[267]

In man, SV40 infection appears to be a zoonosis found in persons exposed to infected monkeys or to SV40-contaminated biologic products. Low titers of SV40 neutralizing antibody were found in 14 of 161 human sera (9%) from persons in northern India living contiguous to a large population of rhesus monkeys.[268] Seropositivity was related to duration of exposure to monkeys. Only one (6%) of 17 individuals working for monkey export firms less than 5 years had antibody, while nine of 20 (45%) working for longer periods had antibody.

In the United States and Western Europe, there is no known natural reservoir for SV40. However, millions of humans were exposed to SV40-contaminated poliovirus vaccine from 1955 to 1961. Approximately half of those receiving such vaccine developed anti-SV40 neutralizing antibody and in some, antibody levels persisted for at least 3 years, suggesting continued antigenic stimulus over time.[269] Shah et al[270] found that almost 20% of children in Maryland exposed to contaminated vaccine were seropositive.

Low levels of SV40 neutralizing antibody have been found in some humans with no known exposure to SV40. This has raised the question whether this antibody is truly against SV40, or is antibody against JCV or BKV cross-reacting with SV40.[8, 238, 270–272] SV40 can induce neutralizing antibody production in humans after virus inhalation[273, 274] and can be recovered from stools up to 1 month after oral ingestion.[275] However, natural infection of humans with SV40 appears to be extremely rare since SV40 has rarely been isolated from humans,[276–281] the significance of these isolations is unknown, and the source of the individual's exposure to SV40 in such cases has been conjectural.

PATHOGENESIS

Although serologic surveys have indicated that infections with JCV and BKV are very frequent and most occur in childhood, we know very little about the primary infections in either children or adults. Most primary infections by either virus appear to be subclinical or inapparent. For example, in one study of 150 children ages 0 through 10 who attended a pediatric clinic for various acute or chronic illnesses, no isolations of BKV were made from urine, feces, or throat or nasal swabs.[282] However, four immunocompetent children have been reported whose primary BKV infection (BKV seroconversion) appeared to be a respiratory infection.[242, 283] Another study of children with acute upper respiratory illness found that seven of 177 (4%) seroconverted to BKV during the course of their illness[284] and BKV was isolated from the urine of one child (with tonsillitis) concomitant with the BKV seroconversion.[285] Further, BKV DNA has now been detected (by molecular hybridization) in surgically excised tonsils from five of 12 children with recurrent respiratory infection—strongly suggesting that tonsils represent a site of BKV infection and persistence.[284] Whatever the nature of the primary infection, viremia probably occurs since JCV and BKV reach the urinary tract and JCV reaches multiple organs, including the brain.[286, 287]

JCV has been well established as an opportunistic human pathogen, causing the rare demyeliminating disease PML.[286, 287] JCV multiplies in nuclei of infected oligodendrocytes in the patient's brain, producing enlarged hyperchromatic nuclei with crystalline arrays of JC virions identifiable by IF and EM (see Figure 41–5A and B). Cytotoxicity and cytolysis result in patchy (multifocal) demyelination in the cerebral hemispheres, cerebellum, or spinal cord. Further, since the C-terminal sequences of JCV, BKV, and SV40 T antigens are shared with myelin basic protein, immunopathologic damage to myelin is a theoretical possibility in PML, although the histopathology does not suggest an immunopathologic process.[54, 288]

Progressive neurologic impairment and death often occur within months of diagnosis. A presumptive diagnosis of PML can be made on the clinical evidence of signs and symptoms of multifocal, progressive CNS disease in a person suspected to have impaired resistance to viral infection. A tentative diagnosis may be strongly reinforced if computed tomography (CT) or magnetic resonance imaging (MRI) show areas of decreased density in the brain.[289] However, a firm diagnosis requires brain biopsy (or autopsy tissue)

to demonstrate polyomavirus in the lesions. Characteristic histopathologic changes can be seen by light microscopy, and EM demonstrates papovavirus virions in oligodendrocytes. By EM, there is close association between polyomavirus virions and membranes, particularly the myelin of oligodendroglial cells.[290] Virions are also seen in phagocytosed myelin in the cytoplasm of macrophages, which could explain why polyomavirus antigen has been found on the plasma membrane of macrophages by in situ hybridization.[54] Virus-specific fluorescent antisera can be applied to frozen sections to identify the virus present in infected oligodendrocytes,[25, 25a, 291, 292] or antiserum can be mixed with virions extracted from the tissue and EM used to observe aggregation of the virions (see Figure 41–1,B).[75, 76]

PML advances by progressive enlargement of lesions and continual appearance of new lesions. Early involvement of scattered oligodendrocytes in histologically normal areas remote from signs of demyelination occurs.[293, 294] Itoyama et al[293] investigated the sequence of demyelinization in PML. They used peroxidase-an-

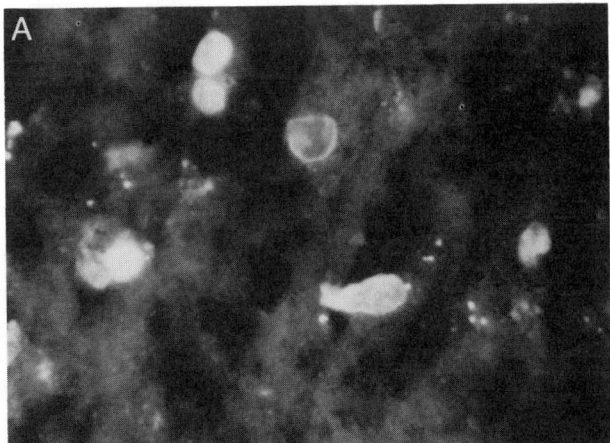
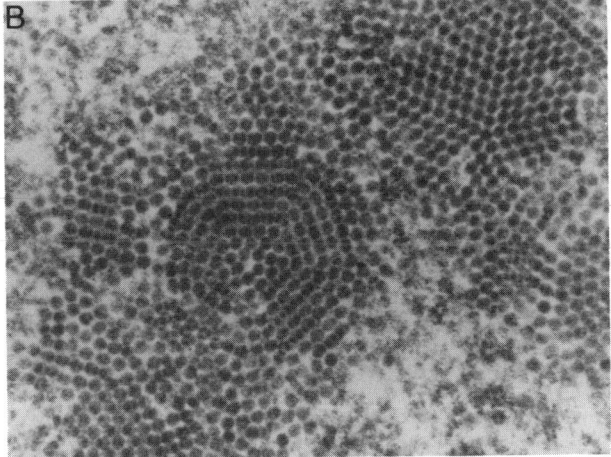

Figure 41–5. A. Frozen section of progressive multifocal leukoencephalopathy (PML) brain tissue stained by indirect immunofluorescence with antiserum specific for JC virus (JCV). Several nuclei are positive for JCV antigen. Very small spots are autofluorescent material present in all brain tissue. **B.** Electron micrograph of human PML brain showing intranuclear arrays of polyomavirus virions. (Courtesy of Dr Gabriel ZuRhein.)

tiperoxidase (PAP) methods to study adjacent paraffin sections of PML lesions with antibodies against JCV, myelin-associated glycoprotein (MAG), and myelin basic protein (MBP). At the outer edge of PML lesions, single oligodendrocytes with viral nuclear antigen were detected; inside this area was a zone with numerous infected oligodendrocytes, intact myelin, but decreased synthesis of MAG; next inward was a zone with myelin breakdown; finally, there was a zone of complete demyelinization, increased number of macrophages, and decreased numbers of infected oligodendrocytes.

Occasionally, PML may spontaneously arrest.[295] In a review of 52 confirmed PML cases, 38 (73%) died within 6 months of developing symptoms and 14 (27%) survived more than 6 months—including six (12%) who underwent remission or disease stabilization.[74] PML usually develops in a clinical setting of immunosuppression, endogenous or exogenous,[296, 297] with depressed cell-mediated immunity (CMI). However, PML without known immunosuppression, termed "primary PML," has occasionally been reported.[2, 294, 298–304] PML in children with congenital severe combined immunodeficiency suggests that the disease can be part of a primary JCV infection, while PML occurring in renal transplant recipients known to have pretransplant JCV HI antibody implies viral reactivation. Recently, JCV DNA was reportedly detected in the CNS of several patients without PML, and the author hypothesized that reactivated or persistent JCV infection can be associated with PML.[305] Although serum or CSF antibody levels have not been clearly related to virus activity or disease development,[74] examination of CSF by isoelectric focusing in two cases of PML showed IgG oligoclonal bands, suggesting intrathecal immunogobulin synthesis.[306] Few data are available concerning cellular immunity, specific or nonspecific, during PML.[296] Cellular inflammatory reactions in the form of perivascular mononuclear cells are usually lacking or are relatively sparse in PML. However, in those patients who have unusually slow progression of the disease or have a remission, an inflammatory response of lymphocytes or plasma cells is frequently present.[286, 287, 307]

DNA can be extracted from diseased brain and JCV DNA sequences identified by restriction endonuclease analysis or by molecular hybridization.[124, 127, 129, 308] Since these methods have not always been applied to potential cases of PML, the incidence of this disease in defined patient populations has been difficult to establish. However, PML incidence will undoubtedly increase together with the number of individuals immunocompromised due to organ transplantation, cancer chemotherapy, improved care of congenital immunodeficiency syndromes, and the acquired immunodeficiency syndrome (AIDS). PML has recently been documented as a complication of AIDS.[309] About 40% of AIDS patients have neurologic symptoms, many at initial presentation,[310] and 2% to 10% have developed PML.[309–322] Thus, PML occurs in AIDS at much higher frequency and appears to be more aggressive than in other immunosuppressed conditions.[54]

In PML, organs other than the CNS are infected by JCV. Nonintegrated, nondefective JCV DNA sequences were detected in focal areas in one kidney, with highest concentration in the renal medulla and almost none in the renal cortex. By in situ hybridization, epithelial cells lining the collecting tubules were the predominant site of viral infection. By EM, no virions were seen in renal tissue.[131]

In a second study, tissues from ten PML patients were examined by hybridization for human polyomavirus DNA sequences. Viral proteins were not identified by FA methods but nonintegrated viral DNA was found by hybridization in the kidneys of seven of nine PML patients. In three patients, viral DNA was also found in liver, lung, lymph node, and spleen. Even though JCV DNA was found in extraneural organs, the amount present was small compared with the brain.[323]

JCV has been suspected to arrive in PML brain by replication in lymphocytes, where it would be protected from circulating JCV antibody.[263] Recent data support this hypothesis.[294] Two PML patients were studied by in situ DNA hybridization and immunocytochemistry. One (with AIDS) had JCV DNA in mononuclear cells in the bone marrow and spleen; the second (without recognized underlying disease or immunosuppression) had JCV DNA in bone marrow B lymphocytes. In the first patient, mononuclear cells with JCV were found in the Virchow-Robin spaces of the brain and infected glial cells were found in perivascular areas. Thus, JCV appears to latently infect mononuclear cells in the bone marrow which circulate, enter the perivascular spaces of the brain, and infect glial cells.[294] Although JCV DNA (but not V antigen) was also found in the renal medulla of these PML patients, no other systemic organs contained detectable JCV DNA or viral antigens.[294] Detection of JCV DNA in lymphocytes suggested viral replication, since at least 200 to 1000 copies of genome per cell were required for a positive signal to be identified by this technique.[294] Infection of lymphocytes with JCV did not appear to require coinfection with HIV or other lymphotropic viruses.[294]

Although JCV can induce tumors in rodents and primates, it has never induced PML-like lesions in animal brains. Recently, however, the restricted cell tropism of JCV was overcome in transgenic mice containing the early gene region (the portion of DNA encoding JCV T antigen) in all cells.[324] These mice developed a "dysmyelinating syndrome" with severity related to level of JCV early-region expression in the brain. T antigen expression occurred mostly in oligodendrocytes, and was the primary cause of dysmyelination since affected cells did not myelinate axons properly. JCV T antigen expression was greatest in brain and lung, lower in heart and kidney, absent in liver, intestine, or spleen. Significantly, every cell in these mice contained the same JCV DNA sequences, yet only cerebral oligodendrocytes were altered by viral gene expression.[324] Peripheral nerves and myelin appeared normal. This transgenic mouse model for PML links JCV T antigen production with arrested maturation of oligodendrocytes and inhibited myelin production.[324, 325] Spontaneous PML-like lesions have been found in eight of 400 macaque monkey brains (2%) at necropsy.[326] SV40 was isolated from two of these eight brains.[327] However, this PML-like illness has been found too rarely to be a model for diagnosis and treatment of human PML.

In addition to JCV pathogenicity in PML, both JCV and BKV urothelial infection and urinary excretion can occur (see Tables 41–6 and 41–7; Figure 41–6). Both viruses have been isolated from human urine and observed sites of urothelial infection have included renal papilla,[328] ureter,[5, 329, 330] and urinary bladder.[331] BKV and JCV persistence has been found in normal cadaver kidneys using DNA-DNA hybridization.[261, 323, 332] BKV DNA was detected in 34% and JCV DNA in 10% of cadaver kidneys, both DNAs as full-length copies, and both equally frequent in renal cortex and

Table 41-7
Patients Reported With Ureteral Stenosis and Polyomavirus Urinary Excretion After Renal Transplantation

Patients With Ureteral Stenosis	Urine Cytology	Urine EM	Virus Species	Concurrent Serum HI Titer Rise	Ureter Histo-pathology or Positive EM	References
1	+	+	BKV culture	BKV	+	5
2, 3, 4, 5	+	+				329
6	+	+	BKV culture	BKV	+	330
7	+	+	BKV IEM*		+	330
8	+	+	BKV			340
9	+	+	BKV/JCV IFM†	JCV and BKV		336
10	+	−	JCV IFM†	JCV		336
11	+	+	JCV IFM†			336

EM = electron microscopy; HI = hemagglutination-inhibition; BKV = BK virus; IEM = immune electron microscopy; JCV = JC virus; IFM = immunofluorescence microscopy.
*BKV identified in urine by immune electron microscopy and urine culture positive for an unspecified polyomavirus.
†Virus identified in cells excreted in urine by indirect immunofluorescence microscopy using specific antisera.

medulla. Not every piece of kidney contained viral DNA, suggesting focal distribution throughout the kidney, and one of seven cadaver ureters contained low levels of JCV DNA.[332]

Numerous, otherwise normal, persons sporadically shed papovaviruses in urine sediments by urine cytology for periods of up to 6 months.[333] In organ transplant recipients, 10% to 40% studied over several years have had urinary excretion (see Table 41–6). Occasionally, virologic findings have been compared to clinical events. In one study,[334] three (7%) of 41 patients had BKV urinary excretion after renal transplantation. Although no clinical syndrome could be clearly linked to this excretion, two of the three excreters developed pancreatitis and died while only two of 38 nonexcreters had this complication. In a second report,[335] polyomavirus excretion in nine (10%) of 91 patients was not clearly related to episodes of transplant rejection or changes in serum creatinine. In a third report,[336] polyomavirus excretion in 12 (20%) of 61 renal transplant recipients was associated with severe diabetes mellitus, arteriooclusive disease, and ureteral stricture.

In a fourth report[337] involving 48 prospectively studied renal transplant patients, 65% had polyomavirus and 63% had cytomegalovirus (CMV) urinary excretion. Half of the polyomavirus and 93% of CMV excretion occurred in the first 3 months posttransplant. Cytology was useful for identifying polyomavirus but not CMV infections; 68% of polyomavirus-infected patients excreted inclusion-bearing cells. Three patients had symptoms possibly associated with polyomavirus infection—ureteric stenosis, vomiting, and pericarditis. Although renal function declined in eight patients (26%) during polyomavirus infection, 25 of 31 polyomavirus-infected patients (81%) retained functioning grafts at the end of the study.

On longitudinal serologic study of 342 renal transplant patients, primary BKV infection occurred in 32% and reactivation in 20%; primary JCV infection occurred in 20% and reactivation in 9%.[249, 250] When the donor was seropositive for BKV and the recipient ser-

onegative, there was a higher risk of infection with BKV than with any other combination of donor and recipient serology.[249, 250] In other serologic studies, BKV IgM antibody has been found in renal dialysis or renal allograft patients with either primary or reactivated BKV infections.[338] BKV IgM antibody has persisted in some transplant recipients for up to 3 years.[338, 339]

Stricture or narrowing of the ureter occurs in up to 5% of patients after renal transplantation.[335] Several reports have now linked BKV or JCV with ureteral narrowing after renal transplantation (see Table 41–7). B.K., the renal transplant patient from whose urine BKV was originally isolated, had this postoperative complication.[5] In another patient with narrowing documented by intravenous pyelography (IVP), virus urinary excretion ceased and the IVP normalized after exogenous immunosuppression was decreased.[340] In 12 renal transplant recipients excreting polyomavirus in the urine, three developed distal ureteral stricture (Figure 41–7) and two of these three lost function of the transplanted kidney. In contrast, only four of 48 persons without stricture lost transplant function.[336]

In a prospective study of bone marrow transplant recipients, 15 of 45 patients (33%) had BKV (13) or JCV (two) urinary excretion during the initial stages of hematopoietic reconstitution. Excretion was associated with sudden increases in serum bilirubin, aspartate aminotransferase, and alkaline phosphatase, but did not appear related to graft-versus-host disease.[341, 342]

Hemorrhagic cystitis occurs in 20% to 30% of bone marrow transplant recipients followed for up to 8 years posttransplant.[343] Acute, early-onset hemorrhagic cystitis has frequently been attributed to acrolein, a cyclophosphamide metabolite toxic to the bladder epithelium. Recently, urinary reactivation of BKV was proposed to account for a substantial proportion of late-onset, long-lasting hemorrhagic cystitis in recipients of bone marrow transplants.[344–346] Fifty-three recipients were prospectively studied for BKV or JCV urinary excretion by enzyme-linked immunosorption assays (ELISA) of urine supernatants and DNA hybridization assays on urinary cells. By dot hybridization, BKV DNA was detected in 1.8% of patients pretransplant, and in one control urine (from a pregnant diabetic). Posttransplant, BKV excretion was found in 47% of patients as the result of virus reactivation. Hemorrhagic cystitis lasting 1 week or more was associated with BKV viruria, occurring in 15 of 19 BKV-excreting patients. JCV was seldom reactivated in bone marrow transplant recipients, but was recovered from one of two patients with BKV-negative cystitis.[345] Urine sediments sometimes hybridized with both BKV and JCV probes.[345, 347] More hemorrhagic cystitis occurred in allogeneic than in syngeneic or autologous marrow recipients.

However, two independent but synchronous events may be taking place here—urinary reactivation of BKV and hemorrhagic cystitis.[333, 348] Urinary polyomavirus excretion is known to occur in persons without symptomatic hemorrhagic cystitis and in those who have not had bone marrow transplants. Reviewing 20-year-old data on the CPE of cyclophosphamide,[349] Koss[333] noted urinary

viral inclusions typical of BKV which had not previously been recognized as viral. BKV urinary excretion may be mistakenly diagnosed as bladder cancer, leading to extensive and costly testing, including cystoscopic bladder biopsies.[333] Transient nonhemorrhagic cystitis was observed in a 3 1/2-year-old boy excreting urinary inclusion–bearing cells typical of human polyomaviruses. BKV was isolated from the urine, and the HI titer against BKV was 8192 (while less than 8 against JCV). The child was generally in good health and had no recognized immune impairment.[350, 351] Polyomavirus-infected cells were detected by urinary cytology in 12 of 3648 patients without severe disease, three of 84 patients with diabetes, and five of 37 patients with cancer receiving various therapies. None of these patients had hemorrhagic cystitis, although many had vague urinary symptoms that subsided spontaneously.[352] By hybridization, urinary JCV and BKV DNA were detected in 20% of patients attending one urologic clinic. Most patients had both viral DNAs detected, no obvious bacterial infection, and a variety of urologic diseases. One control, a healthy

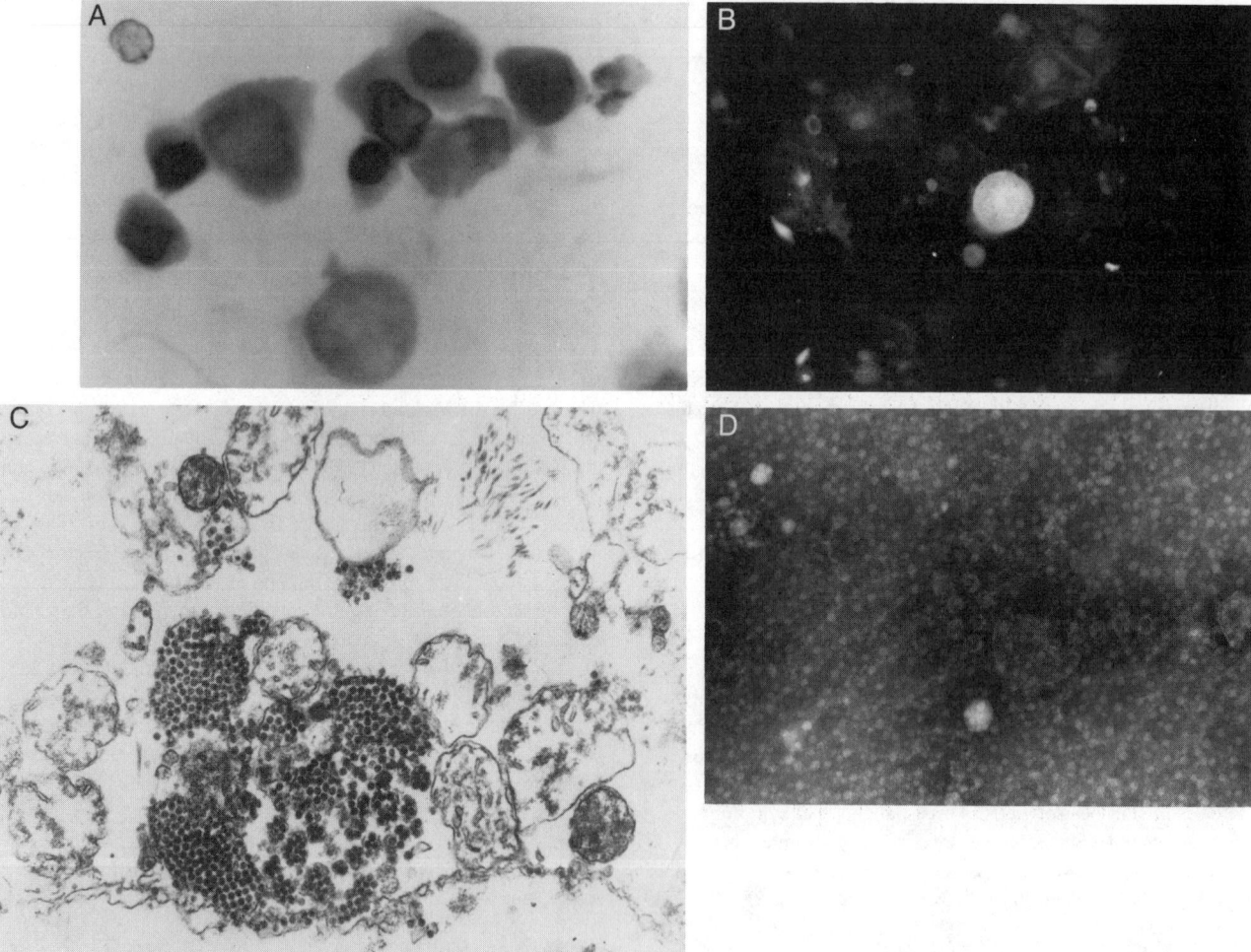

Figure 41–6. A. Cells in urine sediment with enlarged nuclei containing typical glassy intranuclear viral inclusions. **B.** Polyomavirus intranuclear antigen in cells in urine identified by indirect immunofluorescence microscopy using rabbit antisera raised against JC virus. **C.** Polyomavirus virions associated with membranous cell components found in urinary sediment by electron microscopy. (Courtesy of Dr Gabriel ZuRhein.) **D.** Antibody-coated polyomavirus virions in human urine sediment identified by negative staining electron microscopy.

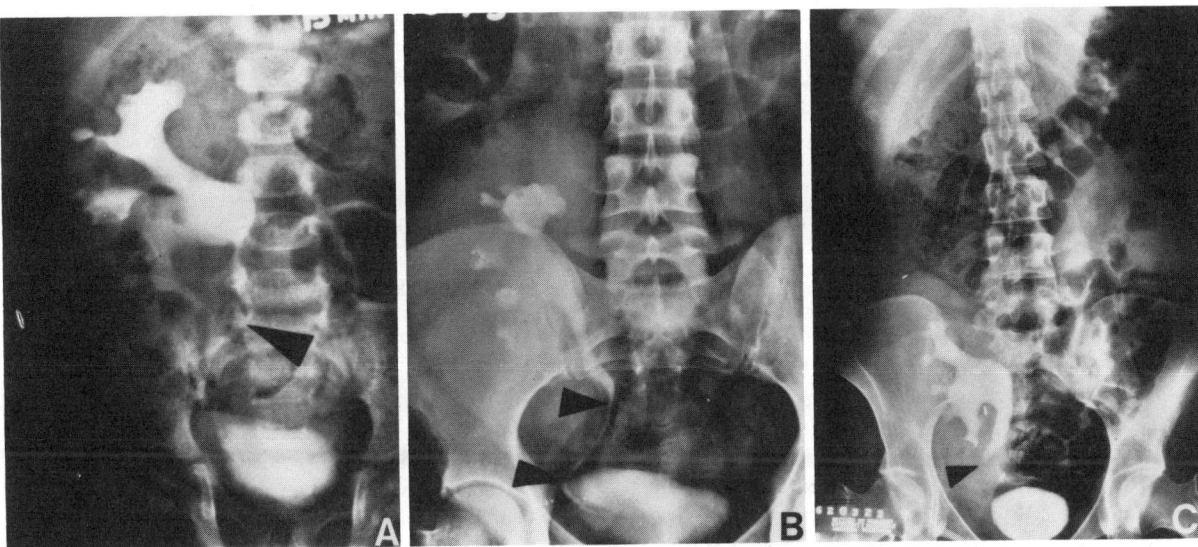

Figure 41-7. A-C. Ureteral narrowing *(arrows)* noted by intravenous pyelography in three renal transplant recipients who excreted inclusion-bearing cells.

physician, was urine cytology–positive, EM-positive, culture-negative, and hybridot-positive for both BKV and JCV DNA (in this paper, the number of controls was not given).[353] Finally, BKV viruria occurring in five of 21 allogeneic bone marrow transplant recipients 2 to 3 months posttransplant has been linked with acute graft-versus-host disease grade 1 or 2.[348]

BKV-specific humoral immunity and CMI were prospectively examined weekly in 19 allogeneic bone marrow transplant recipients and results compared to BKV urinary shedding. During the 15 weeks posttransplant, 11 patients (58%) shed detectable quantities of BKV urinary antigens at least once. Excreters maintained BKV-specific IgG at pretransplant levels, whereas antibody levels steadily declined in BKV nonexcreters. Mean antibody titers before and after a positive urinary antigen assay were higher than titers in those with negative assays. When BKV excreters were compared with nonexcreters, no significant difference in lymphoproliferative response to BKV test antigen was noted. This may have been related to: (1) low proliferative response to BKV in normal subjects, (2) timing of antigen exposure, since BKV urinary excretion usually occurred 2 months posttransplant while antigen-specific CMI may take 1 year or more to return to normal posttransplant,[354] or (3) the BKV exposure level may determine the magnitude of CMI and humoral responses. When donor cellular or humoral immune studies were compared with recipient excretion of BKV, no correlation was found with donor immunity versus recipient BKV excretion.[355]

Other than respiratory infections and PML (mentioned above), attempts to associate JCV and/or BKV infection with miscellaneous diseases by serologic methods have been negative (see Table 41-5). For example, patients with various neurologic diseases,[356] chronic illnesses,[357] or congenital defects[252] have had BKV HI titers similar to those in normal persons.

Because JCV and BKV induce cell transformation in vitro and tumor induction in experimental animals, these viruses have been considered potentially oncogenic for man. Several serologic studies in cancer patients and searches for virions, T or V antigens,

and viral DNA sequences in human cancer tissues have been done. When JCV and/or BKV antibody levels in cancer patients were compared with those in normals, antibody prevalence and/or mean antibody titers have been similar in both groups.[252, 358, 359] In no type of malignancy has HI or T antibody prevalence been 100%. Although an occasional patient's serum contains T antibody, the significance of this is uncertain.[357] In one study, BKV HI titers were inversely related to survival in patients with renal adenocarcinoma[360]; however, no such association was noted for either JCV or BKV HI titers in patients with acute lymphocytic leukemia (Hogan et al, unpublished data, June 1990), lymphoma, or various solid tumors.[359] Repetitive serologic testing of individual patients with cancer has been infrequent. In one such study, 25% of patients with malignant melanoma and 40% of those with lymphoma had fourfold titer increases against JCV or BKV. Evidence for concurrent polyomavirus urinary excretion was sparse and the clinical significance of these infections was undetermined.[359]

Paired sera from 21 women whose children had cancer and 15 women with cervical carcinoma in situ were titrated for BKV antibodies. There was no observed association between BKV infection and either malignancy in the offspring or cervical carcinoma in situ.[361]

In another study, the IgG and IgM antibody response to BKV was measured in sequential sera from 29 children under treatment for cancer. At diagnosis, IgG and IgM antibody prevalence and IgG geometric mean titers (GMT) were the same as in healthy children. Primary infections occurred at similar ages in the two groups. Significant titer increases, detectable IgM antibody, and/or seroconversion were shown in 20 patients (69%); 13 patients (45%) demonstrated positive IgM at least once, a remarkably high number with specific IgM activity in this patient group.[362] However, specific symptoms were not found during primary infection or reactivation of BKV in any patient.

Finally, many have tried to identify JCV or BKV genomes in human tumor tissues—particularly brain or kidney tumors. A viral etiology for human medulloblastoma was recently proposed,[212] based on seasonal variation in the incidence of this tumor noted in Japan, with increased risk between midsummer and early autumn.[363] Brain tumors reported in PML patients have included oligodendroglioma,[364] multifocal glioma,[365] and reticulum cell sarcoma.[366] Papovaviruses have been isolated from several human brain tumors,[19, 185, 367] BKV or SV40 DNA sequences have been identified in brain tumors,[19, 185, 367–371] and T antigen has been found in nuclei within sections of brain tumors or cells grown from brain tumors.[56, 372–374] However, these positive findings have not been confirmed in other studies.[375–377] For example, no T antigen was found in cell cultures from 80 different human brain tumors,[52] or in 69 Japanese brain tumor cell cultures studied at various passage levels.[53]

When three adult pancreatic islet cell tumors were surgically removed and tested by blot hybridization, BKV DNA was detected in one adenoma and BKV (strain-IR) was rescued by transfection of HEF cells. No BKV T antibody was detected in the patient's serum[21] and low-titer V antibody suggested that viral DNA was not present in the tumor as a consequence of an acute or persistent infection.[21] Recently, BKV DNA has been detected by southern blot hybridization in 19 of 74 (26%) human brain tumors and in four of nine (44%) human pancreatic islet tumors. The strongest association was with glioblastoma, where nine of 18 tumor samples were positive for BKV DNA.[378] BKV DNA was episomal, at low copy number (0.2–2.0 genome equivalents per cell), and tumors expressed low levels of T antigen. Transfection of tumor DNA into human AGF cells rescued BKV from six brain tumors and two pancreatic islet tumors. Restriction endonuclease mapping of the rescued genomes showed differences from wild-type BKV but similarities to one another and to BKV-IR.[21, 378]

In Germany, genomic DNA from 29 human brain tumors of 11 different types, and an equal number of control brain specimens, were tested for JCV, SV40, and BKV DNA sequences by southern blot analysis.[379] No hybridization was obtained with JCV- or SV40-specific probes. However, BKV-specific sequences were found in 11 (46%) of 24 tumors, particularly in meningioma (five of six) and neurinoma (three of three). No hybridization was found in CNS tissue from patients without CNS tumors. BKV DNA was integrated at different sites within chromosomal DNA, and no episomal BKV DNA was present.[379]

BKV DNA was cloned from cell DNA from a human kidney carcinoma. Restriction fragments revealed that BKV origin and promoter regions were overrepresented in the tumor-derived clone.[380] In another study, however, BKV DNA was not found in cervical, vulvar, labial, or kidney carcinomas.[378]

In summary, no spontaneous cerebral tumor of man or animal has yet been proved to have a viral etiology, and papovaviruses have not been shown to produce tumors in their natural hosts.[381] While it appears unlikely that JCV or BKV is the sole cause of any given kind of human tumor, polyomavirus infection could still be an important contributing factor in the genesis of some malignancies.[379] Possibly, BKV or JCV genes are only involved in the initiation of transformation, and their presence simply reflects events occurring much earlier in the natural history of the tumor.[378]

SV40 has also been investigated as a possible cause of human tumors using serology (screening for T antigen), molecular probes for viral genomes in tumor tissues, or attempting virus isolation.

To date, most studies have been equivocal or negative[53, 55, 56, 358, 372–375, 382–384] and few isolations of SV40 from human tumors have been reported.[279, 385]

A slight increase in neural tumors was reported in children whose mothers received SV40-contaminated poliovirus vaccine during pregnancy,[386] as was a slight increase in malignant melanoma in 1 million German children born between 1959 and 1961, most of whom received SV40-contaminated poliovirus vaccine.[385] However, United States cancer mortality rates during the period SV40-contaminated poliovirus vaccine was administered (1950–1959) showed no increase,[387] and children who received poliovirus vaccine as newborns did not have an excess incidence of cancer up to 20 years later.[388, 389] Recently, SV40 antibody titers were determined in stored sera from mothers exposed to killed poliovirus vaccine during pregnancy. No sample from eight mothers whose infants had neurologic tumors[386] had antibodies to SV40. Thus, the association between SV40-exposed women and neurologic tumors in offspring was not likely due to SV40.[390] Although it seems very unlikely that SV40 is of major concern for tumor induction in man, careful follow-up of laboratory workers or others heavily exposed to SV40 seems prudent.[391]

LABORATORY DIAGNOSIS

Progressive multifocal leukoencephalopathy can be diagnosed by finding characteristic histopathologic abnormalities in brain or spinal cord. Specific identification of JCV in diseased brain can be made using IF or histochemical microscopy, IEM, or virus culture in spongioblast-rich human fetal brain cells.[292, 296]

Recently, PAP methods have been used to detect human polyomavirus T or V antigens either in tissue sections from formalin-fixed paraffin embedded blocks (FFPE)[293, 392, 393] or from frozen tissues.[54] FFPE facilitates long-term tissue storage, with superior preservation of cell morphology and macromolecules versus cryopreserved tissue.[394, 395] A method which covalently binds FFPE tissue sections to glass microscope slides and which is suitable for in situ hybridization has been described. Using the organosilane method of Maples,[394] 100% tissue adhesion is possible with little nonspecific probe binding, staining, or autoradiographic artifacts. The method can adhere viable cells or human metaphase chromosomes to glass slides and is applicable to studies using cryosections or cultured cells.[396] JCV nucleic acid sequences have been successfully detected in FFPE PML brain tissue using this method. Using tissue fixed in formalin for up to 5 years and stored in paraffin blocks up to 20 years, PAP detected JCV V antigen in 35 of 36 PML patient brains.[392, 393]

In another study, the PAP technique detected nuclear T antigen in frozen brain sections from five PML patients. More cells expressed T antigen in the nucleus than expressed structural V antigen. T antigen was always diffusely nuclear, while V antigen was concentrated at the nuclear margin, with occasional cytoplasmic staining. Endothelial cells did not express either T or V antigen.[54] Recently, monoclonal antibody (TAB416) was used to detect JCV nuclear antigen in PML brain tissue.[26]

Molecular probes can detect JCV or BKV DNA sequences in unfixed cells, fresh or frozen tissues of interest. A highly specific and sensitive hybridot assay using a radiolabeled probe has found

JCV DNA in brain biopsy and postmortem brain samples. The hybridot assay was positive in all cases where PML was confirmed by virus isolation or EM. However, test reliability for tissues undergoing prolonged storage was unknown.[397, 398]

A JCV biotinylated DNA probe was used for in situ hybridization on FFPE or frozen sections of brain tissue from three patients with PML. The method was less sensitive than radiolabeled probes for detecting low copy numbers of viral DNA, but was as sensitive as PAP for antigen detection in FFPE tissue. Further, this method could be performed in conjunction with standard histologic counterstains and immunostains and was superior for morphologic preservation of cell structure.[395]

Molecular hybridization to detect JCV DNA in neural or extraneural tissue has been done using DNA extraction and cloning.[124, 129, 323] Hybridization studies should incorporate positive and negative controls, such as test probes on both animal tumors of known papovavirus origin and on normal tissues.[381] Gel electrophoresis and Southern blotting have been used directly on isolated genomes to identify JCV.[128, 332] In one study, viral DNA was isolated directly from PML brain, was cloned into a plasmid vector, and was subjected to restriction endonuclease analysis. Restriction fragments were almost identical to those of prototypic JCV.[72]

Titration of sequential serum samples to detect fourfold JCV antibody titer increase or examination of CSF for antiviral antibodies have not been extensively studied in PML patients and their diagnostic usefulness is unknown.[296] CSF chemistry is usually normal, although atypical oligoclonal bands (suggesting antibody synthesis) have been noted in two patients.[306]

Electroencephalographic abnormalities during PML may be of diagnostic help.[400–402] Also, CT scanning has been used for early detection of PML brain lesions.[403–412] However, initial brain CT scans in patients with AIDS and PML have been misinterpreted as "toxoplasmosis," so CNS lesions in such patients require biopsy and both light microscopy and EM for correct diagnosis.[412] Contrast-enhancing abnormalities on CT do not exclude the diagnosis of PML and may suggest complex pathology (eg, PML with malignancy).[411] Initial CT scans in PML may be less abnormal than clinical findings. Although lesions enlarge progressively on serial CT scans, they often lag behind clinical symptom evolution. MRI may be more sensitive than CT for detecting PML lesions. However, skull x-rays or radionuclide brain scans have not proved clinically useful nor has direct study of CSF for virus-infected, cytologically atypical cells.[296]

Polyomavirus multiplication in the urinary tract can lead to excretion of cytologically atypical, inclusion-bearing cells in the urine. These can easily be identified by light microscopy after Papanicolaou or hematoxylin and eosin staining of fixed urine sediments (see Figure 41–6).[329, 413] Viral antigen in infected cell nuclei can often be identified using JCV- or BKV-specific antisera and indirect IF microscopy on acetone-fixed urine sediments (see Figure 41–6).[336, 414] Further, thin sections of urinary cell pellets or even of single inclusion-bearing cells recovered from stained urine sediments can be examined by EM for the presence of polyomavirus virions (see Figure 41–6).[415] Polyomavirus virions can be sedimented from fresh urine, negatively stained with phosphotungstic acid, and identified by direct examination using EM (see Figure 41–6).[336, 414, 416–420] Specific identification of free polyomavirus virions in urine as JCV or BKV is theoretically possible using IEM.[76, 330] In practice, however, this cannot always be done because the virions may already be antibody-coated and clumped when excreted.[336, 414]

Hybridot assay for BKV and JCV DNA has detected viral DNA in the urine of 62% of renal allograft recipients and in 20% of nonimmunosuppressed patients attending a genitourinary clinic. Forty-four percent of urines from the renal transplant patients were positive by cytology and 75% by DNA hybridization, indicating that the hybridot assay was more sensitive than cytologic screening.[353] Hybridization was observed when a control sample contained 7×10^4 viral particles, while inclusion-bearing cells contain approximately 10^7 virus particles.[421]

JCV and BKV can be isolated from urine samples by using permissive cell monolayers, but virus cultivation is relatively slow and expensive. Maintenance of cell cultures for 4 weeks or longer may be needed to allow development of hemagglutinin or EM-visible virions in culture fluids, virus-specific nuclear antigens in infected cell nuclei, or visible CPE (see Figure 41–3). Just as brain biopsy is currently a valid approach to early diagnosis of PML, biopsy of kidney, ureter, bladder, or other parenchymal sites may prove important for initiation of effective antiviral therapy if JCV or BKV multiplication is proved to be pathogenic at sites outside the brain.

Titration of sequentially obtained sera for HI antibody against JCV or BKV may establish the diagnosis of polyomavirus infection but does not specify the involved organ site (see Table 41–5). Current data from patients with PML and from renal transplant recipients suggest that HI titer increases against JCV or BKV do not always correlate with disease activity in brain[296] or urinary tract.[336, 359, 414] Serum antibody levels in PML patients are not usually different from the normal adult population, and increased antibody levels are rarely found in active PML. Presumably, this is because the infection progresses so slowly that antibody levels have been stabilized before the disease becomes clinically overt.

ELISA has been used to detect BKV or JCV antibodies,[422, 423] both IgG[423] and IgM,[424] or viral antigens.[425] ELISA serologic results have been similar to IF or HI titers, and were reproducible on successive days. ELISA is well suited for large-scale seroepidemiologic studies since automated spectrophotometric equipment can provide rapid objective numerical data.[422] For detecting viral antigens in urine, chromogenic or fluorogenic ELISA substrates have been used. ELISA permits rapid testing of samples compared with culture or EM. Reagents are stable and, after initial standarization, the assays are relatively simple to perform.[425] Treatment of urine by RDE may increase ELISA sensitivity for antigen detection in urine specimens.[347, 425]

Solid phase RIA has also been used to measure IgG and IgM antibody against BKV. By RIA, IgG titers showed good agreement with HI titers. Use of crude BKV antigen obviates the need for virus purification, although both crude antigen and purified virus were associated with a prozone effect.[338] IgM-capture solid phase RIA for BKV-specific IgM was more sensitive than either HI or IEM, and allowed large numbers of sera to be examined easily for BKV-specific IgM.[253]

Neutralizing assays are more sensitive than HI for detecting serum antibody to BKV.[248] However, conventional neutralization tests are time-consuming and difficult to interpret because CPE may be hard to distinguish from degenerative changes in uninfected cells.[426] An IP neutralization test has been developed to detect neutralizing antibody against BKV using IP staining of BKV structural antigen in cell culture. Sensitivity is the same as HI and ELISA. Most individuals develop neutralizing antibodies to BKV after infection, and sera with only IgM antibody can neutralize BKV infectivity.[427]

Lymphoproliferative assays for studying CMI to BKV or JCV have recently been developed. Positive response to UV-inactivated antigen prepared from BKV-infected fibroblasts was observed in 15 BKV-seropositive individuals. This initial study determined that: (1) lymphocytes from BKV-immune individuals proliferate in vitro in response to authentic BKV-antigen, (2) nonimmune lymphocytes do not proliferate, (3) lymphocyte response does not correlate with serum BKV antibody titer, and (4) BKV antigen provides a valid means of assessing CMI status of individuals to BKV.

PREVENTION AND TREATMENT

It is theoretically possible to prevent primary JCV or BKV infection by vaccination. However, no efforts in this direction have been made as yet because primary infecton is asymptomatic and has not often been associated with subsequent illness or morbidity. Further, it seems unlikely that improved sanitation would influence the incidence of primary JCV or BKV infection, since these viruses have been found even in countries with high levels of sanitation.[8]

Recognized JCV or BKV infection in adults is usually concurrent with a documented illness associated with immunosuppression or immunodeficiency. When an asymptomatic, nonpregnant adult who is not receiving immunosuppressive drugs has polyomavirus multiplication detected, the possibility of undiagnosed malignancy, infection, or immunodeficiency must be considered. If one of these is present, therapeutic efforts may involve treatment of the underlying illness, minimizing exogenous immunosuppression,[340, 429] bolstering the patient's immune system with improved nutrition and correction of vitamin deficiencies, or therapeutic trial of nonspecific biologic response modifiers (such as levamisole or interferon).

Human leukocyte interferon (alpha interferon) administered twice weekly for brief periods was reported ineffective for decreasing BKV urinary excretion in renal transplant recipients.[334] In a recent report, biopsy-proven PML worsened after beta interferon was given IV, but improved after the interferon was given intrathecally.[430]

The use of antiviral chemotherapy for patients with PML has been reviewed.[296] Negative results for levamisole,[321] iododeoxyuridine,[431, 432] cytosine arabinoside (ara-C),[433-435] and adenine arabinoside (ara-A)[405, 430, 436] have been reported, as have positive responses to cytosine arabinoside (ara-C).[303, 401, 408, 437, 438] Recently, complete remission from PML was observed after intrathecal ara-C was used in a patient with non-Hodgkin's lymphoma. Of note, this patient had not improved while receiving intravenous ara-C.[438a] Although multiple therapeutic modalities have been suggested,[401, 405, 408, 432, 434, 436-440] at present, no definitive therapeutic recommendation can be made for patients actively infected with JCV or BKV. Variations in the course of PML with apparent "remissions"[74, 295, 441] cast doubt on reports of beneficial treat-

ments[408] in single patients and underline the need for multicenter therapeutic clinical trials in PML.[304]

REFERENCES

1. Melnick JL, Allison AC, Butel JS, et al: Papovaviridae. *Intervirology* 1974; 3:106–120.
2. Silverman L, Rubinstein LJ: Electron microscopic observations on a case of progressive multifocal leukoencephalopathy. *Acta Neuropathol* 1965; 5:215–224.
3. Zu Rhein GM, Chou SM: Particles resembling papova viruses in human cerebral demyelinating disease. *Science* 1965; 148:1477–1479.
4. Padgett BL, Walker DL, ZuRhein GM, et al: Cultivation of papova-like virus from human brain with progressive multifocal leucoencephalopathy. *Lancet* 1971; 1:1257–1260.
5. Gardner SD, Field AM, Coleman DV, et al: New human papovavirus (BK) isolated from urine after renal transplantation. *Lancet* 1971; 1:1253–1257.
6. Zur Hausen H, Gissmann L, Mincheva A, et al: Characterization of a lymphotropic papovavirus, in Essex M, Todaro G, zur Hausen H (eds): *Viruses in Naturally Occurring Cancers*, Book A: Cold Spring Harbor Conferences on Cell Proliferation. Cold Spring Harbor, NY, Cold Spring Harbor Laboratory, 1980, pp 365–372.
7. Gardner SD: Prevalence in England of antibody to human polyomavirus (BK). *Br Med J* 1973; 1:77–78.
8. Brown P, Tsai T, Gajdusek DC: Seroepidemiology of human papovaviruses. *Am J Epidemiol* 1975; 102:331–340.
9. Black PH, Rowe WP, Turner HC, et al: A specific complement-fixing antigen present in SV40 tumor and transformed cells. *Proc Natl Acad Sci USA* 1963; 50:1148–1155.
10. Khoury G, Lai CJ, Solomon D, et al: The human papovaviruses and their potential role in human diseases, in Hiatt HH, Watson JD, Winsten JA (eds): *Origins of Human Cancer, Book B: Mechanisms of Carcinogenesis. Cold Spring Harbor Conferences on Cell Proliferation.* Cold Spring Harbor, NY, Cold Spring Harbor Laboratory, 1977, pp 971–988.
11. Tegtmeyer P, Rundell K: The role of the papovavirus gene A in oncogenic transformation, in Hiatt HH, Watson JD, Winsten JA (eds): *Origins of Human Cancer, Book B: Mechanisms of Carcinogenesis. Cold Spring Harbor Conferences on Cell Proliferation.* Cold Spring Harbor, NY, Cold Spring Harbor Laboratory, 1977, vol 4, pp 957–969.
12. Grinnell BW, Berg DT, Walls J: Activation of the adenovirus and BK virus late promoters: effects of the BK virus enhancer and trans-acting viral early proteins. *Mol Cell Biol* 1986; 6:596–605.
13. Kenney S, Natarajan V, Salzman NP: Mapping 5' termini of JC virus late RNA. *J Virol* 1986A; 58:216–219.
14. Khalili K, Feigenbaum L, Khoury G: Evidence for a shift in 5'-termini of early viral RNA during the lytic cycle of JC virus. *Virology* 1987; 158:469–472.
15. Bouck N, Beales N, Shenk T, et al: New region of simian virus 40 genome required for efficient viral transformation. *Proc Natl Acad Sci USA* 1978; 75:2473–2477.
16. Sleigh MJ, Topp WC, Hanich R, et al: Mutants of SV40 with an altered small t protein are reduced in their ability to transform cells. *Cell* 1978; 14:79.
17. Martin JD, Frisque RJ, Padgett BL, et al: Restriction endonuclease cleavage map of the DNA of JC virus. *J Virol* 1979; 29:846–855.
18. Frisque RJ, Rifkin DB, Walker DL: Transformation of primary hamster brain cells with JC virus and its DNA. *J Virol* 1980; 35:265–269.
19. Takemoto KK, Rabson AS, Mullarkey MF, et al: Isolation of papovavirus from brain tumor and urine of a patient with Wiskott-Aldrich syndrome. *J Natl Cancer Inst* 1974; 53:1205–1207.
20. Shenk TE, Carbon J, Berg P: Construction and analysis of viable deletion mutants of simian virus 40. *J Virol* 1976; 18:664–671.

21. Caputo A, Corallini A, Grossi MP, et al: Episomal DNA of a BK virus variant in a human insulinoma. *J Med Virol* 1983; 12:37–49.

22. Major EO: JC virus T protein expression in owl monkey tumor cell lines, in Sever JL, Madden DL (eds): *Polyomaviruses and Human Neurological Diseases.* New York, Alan R Liss, 1983, vol 105, pp 290–298.

23. Mandl C, Walker DL, Frisque RJ: Derivation and characterization of POJ cells, transformed human fetal glial cells that retain their permissivity for JC virus. *J Virol* 1987; 61:755–763.

24. Takemoto KK, Mullarkey MF: Human papovavirus, BK strain: biological studies including antigenic relationships to simian virus 40. *J Virol* 1973; 12:625–631.

25. Walker DL, Padgett BL, ZuRhei GM, et al: Current study of an opportunistic papovavirus, in Zeman W, Lennette EH (eds): *Slow Virus Diseases.* Baltimore, Williams & Wilkins, 1973, pp 49–58.

26. Stoner GL, Ryschkewitsch CF, Walker DL, et al: A monoclonal antibody to SV40 large T-antigen labels a nuclear antigen in JC virus-transformed cells and in progressive multifocal leukoencephalopathy (PML) brain infected with JC virus. *J Neuroimmunol* 1988; 17:331–345.

27. Costa J, Yee C, Tralka TS, et al: Brief communication: Hamster ependymomas produced by intracerebral inoculation of a human papovavirus (MMV). *J Natl Cancer Inst* 1976; 56:863–864.

28. Dougherty RM: A comparison of human papovavirus T antigens. *J Gen Virol* 1976A; 33:61–70.

29. Beth E, Cikes M, Schloen L, et al: Interspecies-, species- and type-specific T antigenic determinants of human papovaviruses (JC and BK) and of simian virus 40. *Int J Cancer* 1977; 20:551–559.

30. Beth E, Cikes M, Giraldo G: Microfluorometric analysis of anti-complement and indirect immuno-fluorescence tests for human papovavirus (JCV and BKV) T antigens. *Int J Cancer* 1978; 21:1–5.

31. Rundell K, Tegtmeyer P, Wright PJ, et al: Identification of the human papovavirus T-antigen and comparison with the simian virus 40 protein A. *Virology* 1977; 82:206–213.

32. Rundell K, Tegtmeyer P: Human papovavirus T-antigens: Identification and comparison with the simian virus 40 A protein, in Schlessinger D (ed): *Microbiology 1978.* Washington, DC, American Society for Microbiology, pp 435–438.

33. Farrell MP, Mantyjarvi RA, Pagano JS: T antigen of BK papovavirus in infected and transformed cells. *J Virol* 1978; 25:871–877.

34. Simmons DT, Takemoto KK, Martin MA: Relationship between the methionine tryptic peptides of simian virus 40 and BK virus tumor antigens. *J Virol* 1977; 24:319–325.

35. Simmons DT, Martin MA: Common methionine-tryptic peptides near the amino-terminal end of primate papovavirus tumor antigens. *Proc Natl Acad Sci USA* 1978; 75:1131–1135.

36. Simmons DT, Takemoto KK, Martin MA: Properties of simian virus 40 and BK virus tumor antigens from productively infected and transformeds cells. *Virology* 1978B; 85:137–145.

37. Mason DH, Takemoto KK: Complementation between papovavirus and a simian virus 40 tsA mutant. *J Virol* 1976; 17:1060–1062.

38. Lai CJ, Goldman ND, Khoury G: Functional similarity between the early antigens of simian virus 40 and human papovavirus BK. *J Virol* 1979; 30:141–147.

39. Seif I, Khoury G, Dhar R: The genome of human papovavirus BKV. *Cell* 1979A; 18:963–977.

40. Frisque RJ, Bream GL, Cannella MT: Human polyomavirus JC virus genome. *J Virol* 1984; 51:458–469.

41. Frisque RJ: Regulatory sequences and virus-cell interactions of JC virus, in Sever JL, Madden DL (eds): *Polyomaviruses and Human Neurological Diseases.* New York, Alan R Liss, 1983, vol 105, pp 41–59.

42. Major EO, Miller AE, Mourrain P, et al: Establishment of a line of human fetal glial cells that supports JC virus multiplication. *Proc Natl Acad Sci USA* 1985; 82:1257–1261.

43. Tevethia SS: Immunological controls in simian papovirus SV40-induced neoplasia, in Essex M, Todaro G, zur Hausen H (eds): *Viruses in Naturally Occurring Cancers, Book A: Cold Spring Harbor Conferences on Cell Proliferation.* Cold Spring Harbor, NY, Cold Spring Harbor Laboratory, 1980, vol 7, pp 357–363.

44. Rogers MJ, Law LW, Appella E: Subcellular distribution of the tumor-specific transplantation antigen of simian virus 40-transformed cells. *J Natl Cancer Inst* 1977; 59:1291–1295.

45. Karjalainen HE, Laaksonen AM, Mantyjarvi RA: Tumour specific transplantation antigen in hamster tumour cells induced with BK virus. *J Gen Virol* 1978; 41:171–174.

46. Seehafer J, Downer DN, Gibney DJ, et al: Evidence for the expression of TSTA in BKV-transformed cells: cross-reaction with SV40 TSTA. *Virology* 1979B; 95:241–243.

47. Lane DP, Crawford LV: T-antigen is bound to a host protein in SV40-transformed cells. *Nature* 1979; 278:261–263.

48. Simmons DT: Characterization of tau antigens isolated from uninfected and simian virus 40 infected monkey cells and papovavirus-transformed cells. *J Virol* 1980; 36:519–525.

49. Rundell K, Major EO, Lampert M: Association of cellular 56,000- and 32,000-molecular-weight protein with BK virus and polyoma virus t-antigens. *J Virol* 1981; 37:1090–1093.

50. Major ED, Matsumura P: Human embryonic kidney cells: Stable transformation with an origin-defective simian virus 40 DNA and use as hosts for human papovarvirus replication. *Mol Cell Biol* 1984; 2:379–382.

51. Major EO, Traub RG: JC virus T protein during productive infection in human fetal brain and kidney cells. *Virology* 1986; 148:221–225.

52. Greenlee JE, Becke LE, Narayan D, et al: Failure to demonstrate papovavirus tumor antigen in human cerebral neoplasms. *Ann Neurol* 1978A; 3:479–481.

53. Kosaka H, Sano Y, Matsukado Y, et al: Failure to detect papovavirus-associated T antigens in human brain tumor cells by anti-complement immunofluorescence. *J Neurosurg* 1980; 52:367–370.

54. Stoner GL, Ryschkewitsch CF, Walker DL, et al: JC papovavirus large tumor (T)-antigen expression in brain tissue of acquired immune deficiency syndrome (AIDS) and non-AIDS patients with progressive multifocal leukoencephalopathy. *Proc Natl Acad Sci USA* 1986; 83:2271–2275.

55. Shah KV: Investigation of human malignant tumors in India for simian virus 40 etiology. *J Natl Cancer Inst* 1969C; 42:139–145.

56. Zimmermann W, Scherneck S, Geissler E, et al: Demonstration of SV40-related tumour antigen in human meningiomas by different hamster SV40-T-antisera. *Acta Virol* 1981; 25:199–204.

57. Oliver DM, Lambert M, Major EO: Comparison of wild-type BK virus DNA and BK virion DNA rescued from virus-transformed BHK cells. *Virology* 1980; 103:1–10.

58. Yogo Y, Furuno A, Watanabe S, et al: Occurrence of free defective viral DNA in a hamster tumor induced by human papovavirus BK. *Virology* 1980; 103:241–244.

59. Takemoto KK, Linke H, Miyamura T, et al: Persistent BK papovavirus infection of transformed human fetal brain cells. I. Episomal viral DNA in cloned lines deficient in T-antigen expression. *J Virol* 1979B; 29:1177–1185.

60. Takemoto KK: Human polyoma viruses: Evaluation of their possible involvement in human cancer, in Essex M, Todaro G, zur Hansen H (eds): *Viruses in Naturally Occurring Cancers, Book A: Cold Spring Harbor Conferences on Cell Proliferation.* Cold Spring Harbor, NY, Cold Spring Harbor Laboratory, 1980, vol 7, 311–319.

61. Becker LE, Narayan O, Johnson RT: Studies of human papovavirus tumor antigen in experimental and human cerebral neoplasms. *Can J Neurol Sci* 1976; 3:105–109.

62. Swetly P, Watanabe Y: Cell cycle–dependent transcription of SV40 DNA in SV40-transformed cells. *Biochemistry* 1974; 13:4122–4126.

63. Stenman S, Zeuthen J, Ringertz NR: Expression of SV40 T-anti-

gen during the cell cycle of SV40-transformed cells. *Int J Cancer* 1975; 15:547–554.

64. Watanabe S, Yoshiike K, Yuasa Y, et al: Natural occurrence of a deletion mutant of human papovavirus BK capable of inducing T antigen. *J Gen Virol* 1981; 54:431–435.

65. Seehafer J, Salmi A, Scraba DG, et al: A comparative study of BK and polyoma viruses. *Virology* 1975; 66:192–205.

66. Mullarkey MF, Hruska JF, Takemoto KK: Comparison of two human papovaviruses with simian virus 40 by structural protein and antigenic analysis. *J Virol* 1974; 13:1014–1019.

67. Barbanti-Brodano G, Minelli GP, Portolani M, et al: Structural proteins of a human papovavirus (BK virus): a comparison with the structural proteins of simian virus 40. *Virology* 1975; 64:269–271.

68. Wright PJ, Di Mayorca G: Virion polypeptide composition of the human papovavirus BK: comparison with simian virus 40 and polyoma virus. *J Virol* 1975B; 15:828–835.

69. Wright PJ, Bernhardt G, Major EO, et al: Comparison of the serology, transforming ability and polypeptide composition of human papovaviruses isolated from urine. *J Virol* 1976A; 17:762–775.

70. Kiselev NA, Klug A: The structure of viruses of the papilloma-polyoma type. *J Mol Biol* 1969; 40:155–171.

71. Friedman T: In vitro reassembly of shell-like particles from disrupted polyoma virus. *Proc Natl Acad Sci USA* 1971; 68:2574–2578.

72. Tenser RB, Sommerville KW, Mummaw JG, et al: Isolation of JC virus capsomer-like structures from progressive multifocal leukoencephalopathy brain. *J Neurol Sci* 1986; 72:243–254.

73. Gibson PE, Gardner SD: Strain differences and some serological observations on several isolates of human polyomaviruses, in Sever JL, Madden DL (eds): *Polyomaviruses and Human Neurological Diseases.* New York, Alan R Liss, 1983, vol 105, pp 119–132.

74. Padgett BL, Walker DL: Virologic and serologic studies of progressive multifocal leukoencephalopathy, in Sever JL, Madden DL (eds): *Polyomaviruses and Human Neurological Diseases.* New York, Alan R Liss, 1983, vol 105, pp107–117.

75. Penny JB, Narayan O: Studies of the antigenic relationships of the new human papovaviruses by electron microscopy agglutination. *Infect Immun* 1973; 8:299–300.

76. Albert AE, Zurhein GM: Application of immune electron-microscopy to the study of the antigenic relationships between three new human papovaviruses. *Int Arch Allergy* 1974; 46:405–416.

77. Shah KV, Ozar HL, Ghazey HN, et al: Common structural antigen of papovaviruses of the simian virus 40-polyoma subgroup. *J Virol* 1977A; 21:179–186.

78. Shah KV, Daniel RW, Kelly TJ: Immunological relatedness of papovaviruses of the simian virus 40-polyoma subgroup. *Infect Immun* 1977; 18:558–560.

79. Mantyjarvi RA, Arstila PP, Meurman OH: Hemagglutination by BK virus, a tentative new member of the papovavirus group. *Infect Immun* 1972; 6:824–828.

80. Kende M, Uj M, Szucs G: BK virus haemagglutinin. *Acta Microbiol Acad Sci Hung* 1979; 26:179–184.

81. Seganti I, Mastromarino P, Superti F, et al: Receptors for BK virus on human erythrocytes. *Acta Virol (Praha)* 1981; 25:177–181.

82. Sinibaldi L, Viti D, Goldoni P, et al: Inhibition of BK virus haemagglutination by gangliosides. *J Gen Virol* 1987; 68:879–883.

83. Pitko VM, Pyokari P, Nase L, et al: Effect of beta-propiolactone on infectivity and haemagglutination of the BK virus. *Acta Pathol Microbiol Scand (B)* 1975; 83:141–144.

84. van der Noordaa JV: Infectivity, oncogenicity and transforming ability of BK virus and BK virus DNA. *J Gen Virol* 1976; 30:371–373.

85. Frisque RJ, Martin JD, Padgett BL, et al: Infectivity of the DNA from four isolates of JC virus. *J Virol* 1979; 32:476–482.

86. Howley PM, Rentier-Delrue F, Heilman CA, et al: Cloned human polyomavirus JC DNA can transform human amnion cells. *J Virol* 1980A; 36:878–882.

87. Martin MA, Gelb LD, Garon C, et al: Characterization of "heavy" and "light" SV40-like particles from a patient with PML. *Virology* 1974; 59:179–189.

88. Miao R, Dougherty RM: Characterization of human papovavirus RFV: comparison with SV40 and BKV. *J Gen Virol* 1977; 35:67–75.

89. Yang RCA, Wu R: Cleavage map of BK virus DNA with restriction endonucleases MboI and HaeIII. *J Virol* 1978; 27:700–712.

90. Pater A, Pater MM, Di Mayorca G: The arrangement of the genome of the human papovavirus, RF Virus. *J Virol* 1980; 36:480–487.

91. Pater MM, Pater A, Di Mayorca G: Genome analysis of MG virus, a human papovavirus. *J Virol* 1981; 39:968–972.

92. Yoshiike K, Miyamura T, Chan HW, et al: Two defective DNA's of human polyomavirus JC adapted to growth in human embryonic kidney cells. *J Virol* 1982; 42:395–401.

93. Pater MM, Pater A, Di Mayorca G: BK virus and its variants: association with tumors and transformed cells, in Sever JL, Madden DL (eds): *Polyomaviruses and Human Neurological Diseases.* New York, Alan R Liss, 1983, vol 105, pp 485–494.

94. Osborn JE, Robertson SM, Padgett BL, et al: Comparison of JC and BK human papovavirus with simian virus 40: Restriction endonuclease digestion and gel electrophoresis of resultant fragments. *J Virol* 1974; 13:614–622.

95. Osborn JE, Robertson SM, Padgett BL, et al: Comparison of JC and BK human papovaviruses with simian virus 40: DNA homology studies. *J Virol* 1976; 19:675–684.

96. Khoury G, Howley PM, Garon C, et al: Homology and relationship between the genomes of papovaviruses, BK virus and simian virus 40. *Proc Natl Acad Sci USA* 1975; 72:2563–2567.

97. Yang RCA, Wu R: Physical mapping of BK virus DNA with Sac I, Mbo II, and Alu I restriction endonucleases. *J Virol* 1978; 28:851–864.

98. Freund J, Di Mayorca G, Subramanian KN: Mapping and ordering of fragments of BK virus DNA produced by restriction endonucleases. *J Virol* 1979; 27:915–925.

99. van der Noordaa JV, De Jong W, Pauw W, et al: Transformation and T antigen induction by linearized BK virus DNA. *J Gen Virol* 1979; 44:843–847.

100. Yang RCA, Wu R: BK virus DNA: cleavage map and sequence analysis. *Proc Natl Acad Sci USA* 1978C; 75:2150–2154.

101. Howley PM, Khoury G, Takemoto KK, et al: Polynucleotide sequences common to the genomes of the simian virus 40 and the human papovaviruses JC and BK. *Virology* 1976; 73:303–307.

102. Howley PM: DNA sequence of human papovavirus BK. *Nature* 1980; 284:124–125.

103. Howley PM, Martin MA: Uniform representation of the human papovavirus BK genome in transformed hamster cells. *J Virol* 1977; 23:205–208.

104. Newell N, Lai CJ, Khoury G, et al: Electron microscope study of the base sequence homology between simian virus 40 and human papovavirus BK. *J Virol* 1978; 25:193–201.

105. Law MF, Martin JD, Takemoto KK, et al: The colinear alignment of the genomes of papovaviruses JC, BK and SV40. *Virology* 1979; 96:576–587.

106. Milanesi G, Barbanti-Brodano G, Negrini M, et al: BK virus-plasmid expression vector that persists episomally in human cells and shuttles into *Escherichia coli. Mol Cell Biol* 1984; 4:1551–1560.

107. Yang RCA, Wu R: BK virus DNA sequence coding for the amino terminus of the T-antigen. *Virology* 1979A; 92:340–352.

108. Yang RCA, Wu R: Comparative study of papovavirus DNA: BKV(MM), BKV(WT) and SV40. *Nucleic Acids Res* 1979; 7:651–663.

109. Yang RCA, Wu R: BK virus DNA sequence: extent of homology with simian virus 40 DNA. *Proc Natl Acad Sci USA* 1979; 76:1179–1183.

110. Yang RCA, Wu R: BK virus DNA: complete nucleotide sequence of a human tumor virus. *Science* 1979; 206:456–562.

111. Mew RT, Lecatsas G, Prozesky OW, Barley EH: Characteristics of BK papovavirus DNA prepared directly from human urine. *Intervirology* 1981; 16:14–19.

112. Chauhan S, Lecatsas G, Harley EH: Genome analysis of BK (WW) viral DNA cloned directly from human urine. *Intervirology* 1984; 22:170–176.

113. Howley PM: Molecular biology of SV40 and the human polyomaviruses BK and JC, in Klein G (ed): *Viral Oncology.* New York, Raven Press, 1980, pp 489–550.

114. Tegtmeyer P: Genetics of SV40 and polyoma virus, in Tooze J (ed): *DNA Tumor Viruses. Molecular Biology of Tumor Viruses, part 2, ed 2.* NY, Cold Spring Harbor Laboratory, 1981, pp 297–337.

115. Carroll D, Hansen J, Maryon E, et al: SV40 defectives selected during low multiplicity passage on A172 human glioblastoma cells. *Virology* 1979; 96:576–587.

116. O'Neill FJ, Carroll D: Amplification of papovavirus defectives during serial low multiplicity infections. *Virology* 1981; 112:800–803.

117. Grinnell BW, Martin JD, Padgett BL, et al: Naturally occurring and passage-induced variation in the genome of JC virus, in Sever JL, Madden DL (eds): *Polyomaviruses and Human Neurological Diseases.* New York, Alan R Liss, 1983, vol 105, pp 61–77.

118. Soeda E: The primary sequence of the late region of polyoma virus DNA II. The expression of the late genes and comparison with DNA sequences of SV40 and BKV. *Nucleic Acids Res* 1979; 6:157–160.

119. Bergsma DJ, Olive DM, Hartzell SW, et al: Territorial limits and functional anatomy of the SV40 replication origin. *Proc Natl Acad Sci USA* 1982; 79:381–385.

120. Delucia AL, Lewton BA, Tjian R, et al: Topography of simian virus 40 A protein–DNA complexes: Arrangement of pentanucleotide interaction sites at the origin of replication. *J Virol* 1983; 46:143–150.

121. Deb S, Delucia AL, Baur CP, et al: Domain structure of the simian virus 40 core origin of replication. *Mol Cell Biol* 1986; 6:1663–1670.

122. Li JJ, Peden KWC, Dixon RAF, et al: Functional organization of the SV40 origin of DNA replication. *Mol Cell Biol* 1986; 6:1117–1128.

123. Martin JD, King DM, Slauch JM, et al: Differences in regulatory sequences of naturally occurring JC virus variants. *J Virol* 1985; 53:306–311.

124. Grinnell BW, Padgett BL, Walker DL: Comparison of infectious JC virus DNAs cloned from human brain. *J Virol* 1983; 45:299–308.

125. Miyamura T, Yoshiike K, Takemoto KK: Characterization of JC papovavirus adapted to growth in human embryonic kidney cells. *J Virol* 1980; 35:498–504.

126. Martin JD, Padgett BL, Walker DL: Characterization of tissue culture–induced heterogeneity in DNAs of independent isolates of JC virus. *J Gen Virol* 1983; 64:2271–2280.

127. Grinnell BW, Martin JD, Padgett BL, et al: Is progressive multifocal leukoencephalopathy a chronic disease because of defective interfering particles or temperature-sensitive mutants of JC virus? *J Virol* 1982; 43:1143–1150.

128. Dorries K: Progressive multifocal leucoencephalopathy: analysis of JC virus DNA from brain and kidney tissue. *Virus Res* 1984; 1:25–38.

129. Rentier-Delrue F, Lubiniecki A, Howley PM: Analysis of JC virus DNA purified directly from human progressive multifocal leukoencephalopathy brains. *J Virol* 1981; 38:761–769.

130. Martin JD, Foster GC: Multiple JC virus genomes from one patient. *J Gen Virol* 1984; 65:1405–1411.

131. Dorries K, ter Meulen V: Progressive multifocal leucoencephalopathy: detection of papovavirus JC in kidney tissue. *J Med Virol* 1983; 11:307–317.

131a. Myers C, Frisque RJ, Arthur RR: Direct isolation and characterization of JC virus from urine samples of renal and bone marrow transplant patients. *J Virol* 1989; 63:4445–4449.

132. Rosenthal N, Kress M, Gruss P, et al: BK viral enhancer element and a human cellular homolog. *Science* 1983; 222:749–755.

133. Herbomel P, Bourachot B, Yaniv M: Two distinct enhancers with different cell specificities coexist in the regulatory region of polyoma. *Cell* 1984; 39:653–662.

134. Moreau P, Hen R, Wasylyk B, et al: The SV40 72 base pair repeat has a striking effect on gene expression both in SV40 and other chimeric recombinants. *Nucleic Acids Res* 1981; 9:6047–6068.

135. Banerji J, Rusconi S, Schaffner W: Expression of a β-globin gene is enhanced by remote SV40 DNA sequences. *Cell* 1981; 27:299–308.

136. Fromm M, Berg P: Deletion mapping of DNA required for SV40 early region promoter function in vivo. *J Mol Appl Genet* 1982; 1:457–481.

137. Gluzman Y, Shenk T (eds): *Enhancers and Eukaryotic Gene Expression.* Cold Spring Harbor, NY, Cold Spring Harbor Laboratory, 1983.

138. Khoury G, Gruss P: Enhancer elements. *Cell* 1983; 33:313–314.

139. Kenney S, Natarajan V, Strike D, et al: JC virus enhancer-promoter active in human brain cells. *Science* 1984; 226:1337–1339.

140. Benoist C, Chambon P: In vivo sequence requirements of the SV40 early promoter region. *Nature* 1981; 290:304–310.

141. Watanabe S, Yoshiike K: Evolutionary changes of transcriptional control region in a minute-plaque viable deletion mutant of BK virus. *J Virol* 1986; 59:260–266.

142. Laimins LA, Khoury G, Gorman C, et al: Activation of SV40 genome by 72 base pair tandem repeats from simian virus 40 and Moloney murine sarcoma virus. *Proc Natl Acad Sci USA* 1982; 79:6453–6457.

143. Byrne BJ, Davis MS, Yamaguchi Y, et al: Definition of the simian virus early promoter region and demonstration of a host range bias in the enhancement effect of the simian virus 40 72 base pair repeats. *Proc Natl Acad Sci USA* 1983; 80:721–725.

144. Kriegler M, Botchan M: Enhanced transformation by a simian virus 40 recombinant virus containing a Harvey murine sarcoma virus long terminal repeat. *Mol Cell Biol* 1983; 3:325–339.

145. Riley DE, Reeves R, Gartler SM: Xrep, a plasmid-stimulating X chromosomal sequence bearing similarities to the BK virus replication origin and viral enhancers. *Nucleic Acids Res* 1986; 14:9407–9423.

146. ter Schegget J, Sol CJ, Baan EW, et al: Naturally occurring BK virus variants (JL and Dik) with deletions in the putative early enhancer-promoter sequences. *J Virol* 1985; 53:302–305.

147. Deyerle KL, Cassill JA, Subramani S: Analysis of the early regulatory region of the human papovavirus BK. *Virology* 1987; 158:181–193.

148. Watanabe S, Soeda E, Uchida S, et al: DNA rearrangement affecting expression of the BK virus transforming gene. *J Virol* 1984; 51:1–6.

149. de Ronde A, MacDonald M, Sol C, et al: The early enhancer-promoter of BKV and host range for transformation. *Intervirology* 1987; 27:38–44.

150. Mandl CW, Frisque RJ: Characterization of cells transformed by the human polyomavirus JC virus. *J Gen Virol* 1986; 67:1733–1739.

151. Maraldi NM, Barbanti-Brodano G, Portolani M, et al: Ultrastructural aspects of BK virus uptake and replication in human fibroblasts. *J Gen Virol* 1975; 27:71–80.

152. Shah KV, Hudson C, Valis J, et al: Experimental infection of human foreskin cultures with BK virus a human papovavirus. *Proc Soc Exp Biol Med* 1976; 153:180–186.

153. Seehafer J, Carpenter P, Downer DN, et al: Observations on the growth and plaque assay of BK virus in cultured human and monkey cells. *J Gen Virol* 1978; 38:383–387.

154. Sack GH, Felix JS, Lanahan AA: Plaque formation and purification of BK virus in cultured human urinary cells. *J Gen Virol* 1980; 50:185–189.

155. Taguchi F, Kajioka J, Hara K, et al: Effect of the incubation temperature on the multiplication of BK virus, a human papovavirus. *Kitasato Arch Exp Med* 1978B; 51:57–60.

156. Miyamura T, Takemoto KK: Helper function of adenovirus replication in monkey cells by BK human papovavirus. *Virology* 1979; 98:279–282.

157. Portolani M, Piani M, Gazzanelli A, et al: Restricted replication of BK virus in human lymphocytes. *Microbiologica* 1985; 8:59–66.

158. Sato S, Makino M, Kawana R: A serum-deprived human embryo pancreatic islet cell culture system: a culture method suitable for double-label antibody technique to detect virus infection of beta cells. *Jpn J Med Sci Biol* 1983; 36:85–95.

159. van der Noordaa JV, van Strien A, Sol CJ: Persistence of BK virus in human foetal pancreas cells. *J Gen Virol* 1986; 67:1485–1490.

160. Padgett BL, Rogers CM, Walker DL: JC virus, a human polyomavirus associated with progressive multifocal leukoencephalopathy: additional biological characteristics and antigenic relationships. *Infect Immun* 1977; 15:656–662.

161. Shein HM: Transformation of astrocytes and destruction of spongioblasts induced by a simian tumor virus (SV40) in cultures of human fetal neuroglia. *J Neuropathol Exp Neurol* 1967; 26:60–76.

162. Kenney S, Natarajan V, Selzer G, et al: Mapping 5′ termini of JC virus early RNAs. *J Virol* 1986B; 58:651–654.

163. Miller NR, Major EO, Wallen WC: Transfection of human fetal glial cells with molecularly cloned JCV DNA, in Sever JL, Madden DL (eds): *Polyomaviruses and Human Neurological Diseases.* New York, Alan R Liss, 1983, vol 105, pp 29–40.

164. Spriggs DR: Transgenic mice and the language of cells. *J Infect Dis* 1987; 155:596–597.

165. Feigenbaum L, Khalili K, Major E, et al: Regulation of the host range of human papovavirus JCV. *Proc Natl Acad Sci USA* 1987; 84:3695–3698.

166. Chuke WF, Walker DL, Peitzman LB, et al: Construction and characterization of hybrid polyomavirus genomes. *J Virol* 1986; 60:960–971.

167. Nowock J, Borgmeyer U, Puschel AW, et al: The TGGCA protein binds to the MMTV-LTR, the adenovirus origin of replication, and the BK virus enhancer. *Nucleic Acids Res* 1985; 13:2045–2061.

168. Gluzman Y, Frisque R, Sambrook J: Origin-defective mutant of SV40. *Cold Spring Harbor Symp Quant Biol* 1979; 44:293–300.

169. Wroblewska Z, Wellish M, Gilden D: Growth of JC virus in adult human brain cell cultures. *Arch Virol* 1980; 65:141–148.

170. Takemoto KK, Howley PM, Miyamura T: JC human papovavirus replication in human amnion cells. *J Virol* 1979A; 30:384–389.

171. Beckmann AM, Shah KV: Growth of human papovavirus JC in human urothelial cells. Presented at the 21st Interscience Conference on Antimicrobial Agents and Chemotherapy. Chicago, Nov 5, 1981. Abstract 226.

172. Beckmann AM, Shah KV, Padgett BL: Propagation and primary isolation of papovavirus JC in epithelial cells derived from human urine. *Infect Immun* 1982; 38:774–777.

173. Felix J, Sun T, Littlefield J: Human epithelial cells cultured from urine: Growth properties and keratin staining. *In Vitro* 1980; 16:866–874.

174. Beckmann AM, Shah KV: Propagation and primary isolation of JCV and BKV in urinary epithelial cell cultures, in Sever JL, Madden DL (eds): *Polyomaviruses and Human Neurological Diseases.* New York, Alan R Liss, 1983, vol 105, pp 3–14.

175. Shein HM, Enders JF: Multiplication and cytopathogenicity of simian vacuolating virus 40 in cultures of human tissues. *Proc Soc Exp Biol Med* 1962A; 109:495–500.

176. Shein HM, Enders JF: Transformation induced by SV40 in human renal cell cultures. I. Morphology and growth characteristics. *Proc Natl Acad Sci USA* 1962B; 48:1164–1172.

177. O'Neill FJ: Propagation of simian virus 40 in a human cell line. *Virology* 1976; 72:287–289.

178. Gimbrone MA, Fareed GC: Transformation of cultured human vascular endothelium by SV40 DNA. *Cell* 1976; 9:685–693.

179. Dulbecco R, Ginsberg HS: Virology: Tumor viruses, in Davis BD, Dulbecco R, Eisen HN, et al (eds): *Microbiology,* ed 2. Hagerstown, Md, Harper & Row, 1973, pp 1418–1449.

180. Chenciner N, Meneguzzi G, Corallini A, et al: Integrated and free viral DNA in hamster tumors induced by BK virus. *Proc Natl Acad Sci USA* 1980A; 77:975–979.

181. Chenciner N, Grossi MP, Meneguzzi G, et al: State of viral DNA in BK virus-transformed rabbit cells. *Virology* 1980B; 103:138–148.

182. Grossi MP, Corallini A, Poli F, et al: Analysis of BK-virus transformed cells and BK-virus induced tumors by DNA-DNA reassociation kinetics. *Arch Virol* 1981; 67:345–354.

183. Meneguzzi G, Chenciner N, Corallini A, et al: The arrangement of integrated viral DNA is different in BK-virus transformed mouse and hamster cells. *Virology* 1981; 111:139–153.

184. Purchio AF, Fareed GC: Transformation of human embryonic kidney cells by human papovavirus, BK. *J Virol* 1979; 29:763–769.

185. Krieg P, Amtmann E, Jonas D, et al: Episomal simian virus 40 genomes in human brain tumors. *Proc Natl Acad Sci USA* 1981; 78:6446–6450.

186. Grossi MP, Caputo A, Meneguzzi G, et al: Transformation of human embryonic fibroblasts by BK virus, BK virus DNA and a subgenomic BK virus DNA fragment. *J Gen Virol* 1982; 63:393–403.

187. Burrington MG, Seehafer J, Downer DN, et al: Rescue of BKV from BKV-transformed hamster, rat, and mouse cells: correlation with levels of nonintegrated viral DNA. *Virology* 1984; 138:168–173.

188. Hara K, Yogo Y, Uchida S: Transformation of human embryonic kidney cells by a viable deletion mutant of BK virus. *Microbiol Immunol* 1983; 27:1067–1077.

189. Wold WSM, Green M, Mackey JK, et al: Integration patterns of human JC virus sequences in two clones of a cell line established from a JC virus-induced hamster brain tumor. *J Virol* 1980; 33:1225–1228.

190. Watanabe S, Yoshiike K, Nozawa A, et al: Viable deletion mutant of human papovavirus BK that induces insulinomas in hamsters. *J Virol* 1979; 32:934–942.

191. Watanabe S, Yoshiike K: Change of DNA near the origin of replication enhances the transforming capacity of human papovavirus BK. *J Virol* 1982B; 42:978–985.

192. Watanabe S, Yoshiike K: Decreasing the number of 68-base-pair tandem repeats in the BK virus transcriptional control region reduces plaque size and enhances transforming capacity. *J Virol* 1985; 55:823–825.

193. Hara K, Oya Y, Kinoshita H, et al: Sequence reiteration required for the efficient growth of BK virus. *J Gen Virol* 1986; 67:2555–2559.

194. Pagnani M, Negrini M, Reschiglian P, et al: Molecular and biological properties of BK virus-IR, a BK virus variant isolated from a human tumor. *J Virol* 1986; 59:500–505.

195. Iwamura Y, Mitamura K, Yanagi K, et al: Transforming potential of DNA of the human PLC/PRF/5 hepatoma cell line. *Intervirology* 1986; 26:223–227.

196. Pater A, Pater MM: Transformation of primary human embryonic kidney cells to anchorage independence by a combination of BK virus DNA and the Harvey-ras oncogene. *J Virol* 1986; 58:680–683.

197. Corallini A, Pagnani M, Viadana P, et al: Induction of malignant subcutaneous sarcomas in hamsters by a recombinant DNA containing BK virus early region and the activated human c-Harvey-ras oncogene. *Cancer Res* 1987B; 47:6671–6677.

198. Padgett BL, Walker DL: Human papovavirus JCV: Natural history, tumorigenicity, and interaction with human cells in culture, in *Viruses in Naturally Occurring Cancers, Book A: Cold Spring Harbor Conferences on Cell Proliferation.* Cold Spring Harbor, NY, Cold Spring Harbor Laboratory, 1980, vol 7, pp 339–371.

199. Fareed GC, Takemoto KK, Gimbrone MA: Interaction of simian virus 40 and human papovaviruses BK and JC with human vascular endothelial cells, in Schlessinger D (ed): *Microbiology 1978*. Washington, DC, American Society for Microbiology, 1978, pp 427–431.

200. Major EO, Di Mayorca G: Malignant transformation of BHK 21 clone 13 cells by BK virus—a human papovavirus. *Proc Natl Acad Sci USA* 1973; 70:3210–3212.

201. Major EO, Fiori M, Di Mayorca G, et al: BK, a human polyomavirus, its biology, biochemistry and association with human tumors, in Hiatt HH, Watson JD, Winsten JA (eds): *Origins of Human Cancer. Cold Spring Harbor Conferences on Cell Proliferation*. Cold Spring Harbor, NY, Cold Spring Harbor Laboratory, vol 4, pp 989–1007.

202. Seehafer J, Salmi A, Colter JS: Isolation and characterization of BK virus transformed hamster cells. *Virology* 1977; 77:356–366.

203. Seehafer J, Downer DN, Salmi A, et al: Isolation and characterization of BK virus–transformed rat and mouse cells. *J Gen Virol* 1979A; 42:567–573.

204. Santoli D, Wroblewska Z, Gilden D, et al: Establishment of continuous multiple sclerosis brain cultures after transformation with PML-SV40 virus. *J Neurol Sci* 1975; 24:385–390.

205. Santoli D, Wroblewska Z, Gilden DH, et al: Human brain in tissue culture. III. PML-SV40 induced transformation of brain cells and establishment of permanent lines. *J Comp Neurol* 1975; 161:317–328.

206. Miranda A, Babiss L, Fisher P: Transformation of human skeletal muscle cells by SV40. *Proc Natl Acad Sci USA* 1983; 80:6581–6585.

207. Boast S, LaMantia G, Lania L, et al: High efficiency of replication and expression of foreign genes in SV40 transformed human fibroblasts. *EMBO J* 1983; 2:2327–2331.

208. Zu Rhein GM: Studies of JC virus-induced nervous system tumors in the Syrian hamster: A review, in Sever JL, Madden DL (eds): *Polyomaviruses and Human Neurological Diseases*. New York, Alan R Liss, 1983, pp 205–221.

209. Walker DL, Padgett BL, ZuRhein GM, et al: Human papovavirus (JC): induction of brain tumors in hamsters. *Science* 1973; 181:674–676.

210. Zu Rhein GM, Varakis JN: Perinatal induction of medulloblastomas in Syrian golden hamsters by a human polyoma virus (JC). *Natl Cancer Inst Monogr* 1979; 51:205–208.

211. Inoya H, Ikeda K, Tomonaga M, et al: Establishment of 2 GFAP positive cell lines derived from hamster medulloblastoma induced by JC virus (Japanese). *Igaku No Ayumi* (in press) 1986.

212. Takakura K, Inoya H, Nagashima K, et al: Viral neurooncogenesis. *Prog Exp Tumor Res* 1987; 30:10–20.

213. Nagashima K, Yasui K, Kimura J, et al: Induction of brain tumors by a newly isolated JC virus (Tokyo-1 strain). *Am J Pathol* 1984; 116:455–463.

214. London WT, Houff SA, Madden DL, et al: Brain tumors in owl monkeys inoculated with a human polyomavirus (JC virus). *Science* 1978; 201:1246–1249.

215. Rieth KG, Di Chiro G, London WT, et al: Experimental glioma in primates: a computed tomography model. *J Comput Assis Tomogr* 1980; 4:285–290.

216. McKeever PE, Chronwall BM, Houff SA, et al: Glial and divergent cells in primate central nervous system tumors induced by JC virus isolated from human progressive multifocal leukoencephalopathy (PML), in Sever JL, Madden DL (eds): *Polyomaviruses and Human Neurological Diseases*. New York, Alan R Liss, 1983, vol 105, pp 239–251.

217. Wallen WC, London WT, Traub RG, et al: Antibody responses to JC virus-associated antigens by tumor-bearing owl monkeys, in Sever JL, Madden DL (eds): *Polyomaviruses and Human Neurological Diseases*. New York, Alan R Liss, Inc, 1983, pp 261–270.

218. Miller NR, London W, Padgett BL, et al: The detection of JC viral genome in owl monkey tumors, in Sever JL, Madden DL (eds): *Polyomaviruses and Human Neurological Diseases*. New York, Alan R Liss, 1983, pp 271–288.

219. Uchida S, Watanabe S, Aizawa K, et al: Induction of papillary ependymomas and insulinomas in the Syrian golden hamster by BK virus, a human papovavirus. *Gann* 1976; 67:857–865.

220. Uchida S, Watanabe S, Aizawa K, et al: Polyoncogenicity and insulinoma-inducing ability of BK virus, a human papovavirus, in Syrian golden hamsters. *J Natl Cancer Inst* 1979; 63:119–126.

221. Corallini A, Barbanti-Brodano G, Bortoloni W, et al: High incidence of ependymomas induced by BK virus, a human papovavirus (MMV). *J Natl Cancer Inst* 1977; 59:1561–1563.

222. Greenlee JE, Narayan O, Johnson RT, et al: Induction of brain tumors in hamsters with BK virus. *Lab Invest* 1977; 36:636–641.

223. Nase LM, Karkkainen M, Mantyjarvi RA: Transplantable hamster tumors induced with the BK virus. *Acta Pathol Microbiol Scand* 1975; 83:347–352.

224. Shah KV, Daniel RW, Strandberg JD: Sarcoma in a hamster inoculated with BK virus, a human papovavirus. *J Natl Cancer Inst* 1975; 54:945–950.

225. Dougherty RM: Induction of tumors in Syrian hamsters by a human renal papovavirus, RF strain. *J Natl Cancer Inst* 1976B; 57:395–398.

226. ter Schegget J, Voves J, van Strien A, et al: Free viral DNA in BK virus-induced hamster tumor cells. *J Virol* 1980; 35:331–339.

227. Corallini A, Altavilla G, Carra L, et al: Oncogenicity of BK virus for immunosuppressed hamsters. *Arch Virol* 1982; 73:243–253.

228. Noss G, Stauch G, Mehraein P, et al: Oncogenic activity of the BK type of human papovavirus in newborn wistar rats. *Arch Virol* 1981; 69:239–251.

229. Noss G, Stauch G: Oncogenic activity of the BK type of human papovavirus in inbred rat strains. *Arch Virol* 1984; 81:41–51.

230. Cole GA, Shah KV: Experimental simian virus 40 infection of normal and immunosuppressed spider monkeys. *Acta Virol (Praha)* 1974; 18:65–69.

231. Kirschstein RL, Gerber P: Ependymomas produced after intracerebral inoculation of SV40 into newborn hamsters. *Nature* 1962; 195:299–300.

232. Diamandopoulos GT: Leukemia, lymphoma, and osteosarcoma induced in the Syrian golden hamster by simian virus 40. *Science* 1972; 174:173–175.

233. Diamandopoulos GT: Induction of lymphocytic leukemia, lymphosarcoma, reticulum cell sarcoma, and osteogenic sarcoma in the Syrian golden hamster by oncogenic DNA simian virus 40. *J Natl Cancer Inst* 1973; 50:1347–1365.

234. Palmiter RD, Chen HY, Messing A, et al: SV40 enhancer and large T-antigen are instrumental in development of choroid plexus tumors in transgenic mice. *Nature* 1985; 316:457–460.

235. Candeias JAN, Baruzzi RG, Pripas S, et al: Prevalence of antibodies to the BK and JC papovaviruses in isolated populations. *Rev Saude Publica* 1977; 11:510–514.

236. Walker DL, Padgett BL: The epidemiology of human polyomaviruses, in Sever JL, Madden DL (eds): *Polyomaviruses and Human Neurological Diseases*. New York, Alan R Liss, 1983, vol 105, pp 99–106.

237. Padgett BL, Walker DL: Prevalence of antibodies in human sera against JC virus, an isolate from a case of PML. *J Infect Dis* 1973; 127:467–470.

238. Shah KV, Daniel RW, Warszawski RM: High prevalence of antibodies to BK virus, an SV40-related papovavirus, in residents of Maryland. *J Infect Dis* 1973; 128:784–787.

239. Yasui K, Ogiwara H, et al: Biological characteristics of JC-virus isolated from PML-brain and its antibody prevalence in Tokyo. Presented at 29th Japanese Virology Congress, Tokyo, October 1981.

240. Taguchi F, Kajioka J, Miyamura T: Prevalence rate and age of acquisition of antibodies against JC virus and BK virus. *Microbiol Immunol* 1982; 26:1057–1064.

241. Mashiko J, Nakamura K, Shinozaki T, et al: A serological study of JC virus. Prevalence of antibody with respect to age and native place (Japanese). *Teikyo Med J* 1982; 5:299–304.

242. Mantyjarvi RA, Meurman OH, Vihma L, et al: A human papovavirus (BK), biological properties and seroepidemiology. *Ann Clin Res* 1973; 5:283–287.

243. Jing-ping L, Jun X: BK virus antibody in population of various age groups in Beijing. *Chin Med J* 1986; 99:595–596.

244. Taguchi F, Nagaki D, Saito M, et al: Transplacental transmission of BK virus in human. *Jpn J Microbiol* 1975; 19:395–398.

245. Coleman DV, Daniel RA, Gardner SD, et al: Polyomavirus in urine during pregnancy. *Lancet* 1977; 2:709–710.

246. Coleman DV, Wolfendale MR, Daniel RA, et al: A prospective study of human polyomavirus infection in pregnancy. *J Infect Dis* 1980; 142:1–8.

247. Borgatti M, Costanzo F, Portolani M, et al: Evidence for reactivation of persistent infection during pregnancy and lack of congenital transmission of BK virus, a human papovavirus. *Microbiologica* 1979; 2:173–178.

248. Shah KV, Daniel RW, Madden D, et al: Serological investigation of BK papovavirus infection in pregnant women and their offspring. *Infect Immun* 1980; 30:29–35.

249. Andrews C, Shah KV, Rubin R, et al: BK papovavirus infections in renal transplant recipients: Contribution of donor kidneys. *J Infect Dis* 1982; 145:276.

250. Andrews CA, Daniel RW, Shah KV: Serologic studies of papovavirus infections in pregnant women and renal transplant recipients, in Sever JL, Madden DL (eds): *Polyomaviruses and Human Neurological Diseases*. New York, Alan R Liss, 1983, vol 105, pp 133–141.

251. Gibson PE, Field AM, Gardner SD, et al: Occurrence of IgM antibodies against BK and JC polyomaviruses during pregnancy. *J Clin Pathol* 1981; 34:674–679.

252. Rziha HJ, Bornkamm GW, zur Hausen H: BK virus: I. Seroepidemiologic studies and serologic response to viral infection. *Med Microbiol Immunol (Berl)* 1978; 165:73–81.

253. Rziha HJ, Belohradsky BH, Schneider U, et al: BK virus. II. Serologic studies in children with congenital disease and patients with malignant tumors and immunodeficiencies. *Med Microbiol Immunol (Berl)* 1978; 165:83–92.

254. Brown DW, Gardner SD, Gibson PE, et al: BK virus specific IgM responses in cord sera, young children and healthy adults detected by RIA. *Arch Virol* 1984; 82:149–160.

255. McCance DJ, Mims CA: Transplacental transmission of polyoma virus in mice. *Infect Immun* 1977; 18:196–202.

256. McCance DJ, Mims CA: Reactivation of polyoma virus in kidneys of persistently infected mice during pregnancy. *Infect Immun* 1979; 25:998–1002.

257. Taguchi F, Kajioka J, Shimada N: Presence of interferon and antibodies to BK virus in amniotic fluid of normal pregnant women. *Acta Virol (Praha)* 1985; 29:299–304.

258. Iwasaki K, Yano K, Yanagisawa Y, et al: Seroepidemiological study of BKV infection in Tokyo. *Annu Rep Tokyo Metropol Hyg Inst (Japan)* 1974; 25:69–72.

259. Padgett BL, Walker DL: New human papovaviruses. *Prog Med Virol* 1976; 22:1–35.

260. Eddy BE: Polyoma virus, in Gard S, Hallauer C, Meager KF (eds): *Virology Monographs 7*. New York, Springer-Verlag, 1969, pp 1–114.

261. Shah KV, Willard S, Myers RE, et al: Experimental infection of rhesus with simian virus 40 (SV40). *Proc Soc Exp Biol Med* 1969B; 130:196–203.

262. Heritage J, Chesters PM, McCance DJ: The persistence of papovavirus BK DNA sequences in normal human renal tissue. *J Med Virol* 1981; 8:143–150.

263. McCance DJ: Persistence of animal and human papovaviruses in renal and nervous tissues, in Sever JL, Madden DL (eds): *Polyomaviruses and Human Neurological Diseases*. New York, Alan R Liss, 1983, vol 105, pp 343–357.

264. Shah KV, Southwick CH: Prevalence of antibodies to certain viruses in sera of free-living rhesus and of captive monkeys. *Indian J Med Res*. 1965; 53:488–499.

265. Shah KV, Morrison JA: Comparison of three rhesus groups for antibody patterns to some viruses: absence of active simian virus 40 transmission in the free-ranging rhesus of Cayo Santiago.

266. Yang CS, Kuo CH, Chen CY: A study on natural infection of simian virus 40 (SV40) in Taiwan monkeys. *(Macaca cyclopis)*. *J Form Med Assoc*. 1967; 66:143–148.

267. Ashkenazi A, Melnick JL: Induced latent infection of monkeys with vacuolating SV- 40 papova virus. Virus in kidneys and urine. *Proc Soc Exp Biol Med*. 1962; 8:367–372.

268. Shah KV: Neutralizing antibodies to simian virus 40 (SV40) in human sera from India. *Proc Soc Exp Biol Med*. 1966; 121:303–307.

269. Gerber P: Patterns of antibodies to SV40 in children following the last booster with inactivated poliomyelitis vaccines. *Proc Soc Exp Biol Med*. 1967; 125:1284–1287.

270. Shah KV, McCrumb FR, Daniel RW, et al: Serologic evidence for a simian-virus-40-like infection of man. *J Natl Cancer Inst*. 1972; 48:557–561.

271. Shah KV, Ozar HL, Pond HS, et al: SV40 neutralizing antibodies in sera of US residents without history of polio immunization. *Nature*. 1971; 231:448–449.

272. Shah KV, Daniel RW, Murphy GP: Antibodies reacting to simian virus 40 T antigen in human sera. *J Natl Cancer Inst*. 1973; 51:687–690.

273. Morris JA, Johnson KM, Auslisio CG, et al: Clinical and serologic responses in volunteers given vacuolating virus (SV40) by respiratory route. *Proc Soc Exp Biol Med*. 1961; 108:56–59.

274. Brown P, Morris JA: Serologic response to BK virus following human infection with SV40. *Proc Soc Exp Biol Med*. 1976; 152:130–131.

275. Melnick JL, Stinebaugh S: Excretion of vacuolating SV40 virus (papova virus group) after ingestion as a contaminant of oral poliovaccine. *Proc Soc Exp Biol Med*. 1962; 109:965–968.

276. Weiner LP, Herndon RM, Narayan O, et al: Isolation of virus related to SV40 from patients with progressive multifocal leukoencephalopathy. *N Engl J Med*. 1972; 286:385–390.

277. Weiner LP, Herndon RM, Narayan O, et al: Further studies of a simian virus 40-like virus isolated from human brain. *J Virol*. 1972; 10:147–149.

278. Sack GH, Narayan O, Danna K, et al: The nucleic acid of an SV40-like virus isolated from a patient with progressive multifocal leukoencephalopathy. *Virology*. 1973; 51:345–350.

279. Soriano F, Shelburne CE, Gokcen M: Simian virus 40 in a human cancer. *Nature*. 1974; 249:421–424.

280. Brandner G, Burger A, Neumann-Haefelin D, et al: Isolation of simian virus 40 from a newborn child. *J Clin Microbiol*. 1977; 5:250–252.

281. Scherneck S, Geissler E, Janisch W, et al: Isolation of a SV40-like virus from a patient with progressive multifocal leukoencephalopathy. *Acta Virol (Praha)*. 1981; 25:191–198.

282. Possati L, Bartolotta E: Attempts to isolate BK virus from children affected by various diseases. *Acta Virol (Praha)*. 1981; 25:254–255.

283. van der Noordaa JV, Wertheim-Van Dillon P: Rise in antibodies to human papovavirus BK in clinical disease, letter. *Br Med J*. 1977; 1:1471.

284. Goudsmit J, Wertheim-van Dillen P, van Strien A, et al: The role of BK virus in acute respiratory tract disease and the presence of BKV DNA in tonsils. *J Med Virol* 1982; 10:91–99.

285. Goudsmit J, Baak ML, Slaterus KW, et al: Human papovavirus isolated from the urine of a child with acute tonsilitis. *Br Med J*. 1981; 283:1363–1364.

286. Walker DL: Progressive multifocal leukoencephalopathy: An opportunistic viral infection of the central nervous system, in Vinken PJ, Bryun GW (eds): *Handbook of Clinical Neurology*. Amsterdam, North-Holland Publishing Co, 1978, vol 18, pp 307–329.

287. Walker DL: Progressive multifocal leukoencephalopathy, in Vinken PJ, Bruyn GW, Klawans HL (eds): *Handbook of Clinical Neurology*. Amsterdam, Elsevier, 1985, vol 3, pp 503–524.

288. Stoner GL: *Abstract Trans Am Soc Neurochem* 1985; 16:210.

Am J Epidemiol. 1969A; 89:308–315.

289. Levy JD, Cottingham KL, Campbell RJ, et al: Progressive multifocal leukoencephalopathy and magnetic resonance imaging. *Ann Neurol* 1986; 19:399–401.

290. Mazlo M, Tariska I: Morphological demonstration of the first phase of polyomavirus replication in oligodendroglial cells of human brain in progressive multifocal leukoencephalopathy (PML). *Acta Neuropathol (Berl)* 1980; 49:133–143.

291. Narayan O, Penney JB, Johnson RT, et al: Etiology of progressive multifocal leukoencephalopathy. Identification of papovavirus. *N Engl J Med* 1973; 289; 1278–1282.

292. Walker DL: Biology of JC virus, a human papovavirus in Schlessinger D (ed): *Microbiology 1978.* Washington, DC, American Society for Microbiology, 1978, pp 432–434.

293. Itoyama Y, Webster H DEF, Sternberger NH, et al: Distribution of papovavirus, myelin-associated glycoprotein, and myelin basic protein in progressive multifocal leukoencephalopathy lesions. *Ann Neurol* 1982; 11:396–407.

294. Houff SA, Major EO, Katz DA, et al: Involvement of JC virus–infected mononuclear cells from the bone marrow and spleen in the pathogenesis of progressive multifocal leukoencephalopathy. *N Engl J Med* 1988; 318:301–305.

295. Price RW, Nielsen S, Horten B, et al: Progressive multifocal leukoencephalopathy, a burnt out case. *Ann Neurol* 1983; 13:485–490.

296. Willoughby E, Price RW, Padgett BL, et al: Progressive multifocal leukoencephalopathy (PML): In vitro cell-mediated immune responses to mitogens and JC virus. *Neurology* 1980; 30:256–262.

297. Newton P, Aldridge RD, Lessells AM, et al: Progressive multifocal leukoencephalopathy complicating systemic lupus erythematosus. *Arthritis Rheum* 1986; 29:337–343.

298. Stam FC: Multifocal leukoencephalopathy with slow progression and very long survival. *Psychiatr Neurol Neurochir* 1966; 69:453–459.

299. Fermaglich J, Hardman JM, Earle KM: Spontaneous progressive multifocal leukoencephalopathy. *Neurology* 1970; 20:479–484.

300. Arseni C, Nereantiu F: Progressive multifocal leukoencephalopathy. *Eur Neurol* 1971; 5:270–280.

301. Bolton CF, Rozdkilsky B: Primary progressive multifocal leukoencephalopathy. *Neurology* 1971; 21:72–77.

302. Faris AA, Martinez AJ: Primary progressive multifocal leukoencephalopathy. A central nervous system disease caused by a slow virus. *Arch Neurol* 1972; 27:257–260.

303. Rockwell D, Ruben FL, Winkelstein A, et al: Absence of immune deficiencies in a case of progressive multifocal leukoencephalopathy. *Am J Med* 1976; 61:433–436.

304. Zochodne DW, Kaufmann JCE: Prolonged progressive multifocal leukoencephalopathy without immunosuppression. *J Can Sci Neurol* 1987; 14:603–607.

305. Dorries K: Evidence for human polyomavirus JC infection in the central nervous system of non-PML patients. *Zentralbl Bakteriol Mikrobiol Hyg (A)* 1988; 268:146.

306. Mazzarello P, Poloni M, Ceroni M, et al: Is progressive multifocal leukoencephalopathy associated with intrathecal IgG synthesis? *J Neuroimmunol* 1985; 10:167–172.

307. Richardson EP Jr, Webster HD: Progressive multifocal leukoencephalopathy: its pathological features, in Sever JL, Madden DL (eds): *Polyomaviruses and Human Neurological Diseases.* New York, Alan R Liss, 1983, vol 105, pp 191–203.

308. Dorries K, Johnson RT, ter Meulen V: Detection of polyoma virus DNA in PML-brain tissue by (in situ) hybridization. *J Gen Virol* 1979; 42:49–51.

309. Miller JR, Barrett RE, Britton CB, et al: Progressive multifocal leukoencephalopathy in a male homosexual with T-cell immune deficiency. *N Engl J Med* 1982; 307:1436–1438.

310. Levy RM, Bredesen DE, Rosenblum ML: Neurological manifestations of the acquired immunodeficiency syndrome (AIDS): Experience at UCSF and review of the literature. *J Neurosurg* 1985; 62:475–495.

311. Bedri J, Weinstein W, DeGregorio P, et al: Progressive multifocal leukoencephalopathy in acquired immunodeficiency syndrome. *J Med* 1983; 309:492–493.

312. Reichert CM, O'Leary TJ, Levens DL, et al: Autopsy pathology in the acquired immunodeficiency syndrome. *Am J Pathol* 1983; 112:357–382.

313. Snider WD, Simpson DM, Nielsen S, et al: Neurological complications of acquired immune deficiency syndrome: Analysis of 50 patients. *Ann Neurol* 1983; 14:403–418.

314. Bernick C, Gregorios JB: Progressive multifocal leukoencephalopathy in a patient with acquired immunodeficiency syndrome. *Arch Neurol* 1984; 41:780–782.

315. Moskowitz LB, Gregorios JB, Hensley GT, et al: Cytomegalovirus: induced demyelination associated with acquired immunodeficiency syndrome. *Arch Pathol Lab Med* 1984; 108:873–877.

316. England JD, Hsu CY, Garen PD, et al: Progressive multifocal leukoencephalopathy occurring with the acquired immune deficiency syndrome. *South Med J* 1984; 77:1041–1043.

317. Elkins CM, Leon E, Grenell SL, et al: Intracranial lesions in the acquired immunodeficiency syndrome: radiological (computed tomographic) features. *JAMA* 1985; 253:393–396.

318. Kleihues P, Lang W, Burger PC, et al: Progressive diffuse leukoencephalopathy in patients with acquired immunodeficiency syndrome (AIDS). *Acta Neuropathol* 1985; 68:333–339.

319. Krupp LB, Lipton RB, Swerdlow ML, et al: Progressive multifocal leukoencephalopathy: Clinical and radiographic features. *Ann Neurol* 1985; 17:344–349.

320. Speelman JD, ter Schegget J, Bots GTAM, et al: Progressive multifocal leukoencephalopathy in a case of acquired immunodeficiency syndrome. *Clin Neurol Neurosurg* 1985; 87:27–33.

321. Dupuis M, Xavier FGF, Gonsette RE, et al: Progressive multifocal leukoencephalopathy mimicking multiple sclerosis as only clinical manifestation of an acquired immunodeficiency syndrome. *Acta Neurol Belg* 1986; 86:285–296.

322. Berger JR, Kaszovitz B, Post JD, et al: Progressive multifocal leukoencephalopathy associated with human immunodeficiency virus infection. *Ann Intern Med* 1987; 107:78–87.

323. Grinnell BW, Padgett BL, Walker DL: Distribution of nonintegrated DNA from JC papovavirus in organs of patients with progressive multifocal leukoencephalopathy. *J Infect Dis* 1983B; 147:669–675.

324. Small JA, Scangos GA, Cork L, et al: The early region of human papovavirus JC induces dysmyelination in transgenic mice. *Cell* 1986; 46:13–18.

325. Trapp BD, Small JA, Pulley M, et al: Dysmyelination in transgenic mice containing JC virus early region. *Ann Neurol* 1988; 23:38–48.

326. Gribble DH, Haden CC, Schwartz LW, et al: Spontaneous progressive multifocal leukoencephalopathy (PML) in macaques. *Nature* 1975; 254:602–604.

327. Holmberg CA, Gribble DH, Takemoto KK, et al: Isolation of simian virus 40 from rhesus monkeys *(Macaca mulatta)* with spontaneous progressive multifocal leukoencephalopathy. *J Infect Dis* 1977; 136:593–596.

328. Zu Rhein GM, Varakis J: Papovavirions in urothelium of a treated lymphoma patient. *Lancet* 1974; 2:783–784.

329. Coleman DV, Field AM, Gardner SD, et al: Virus-induced obstruction of the ureteric and cystic duct in allograft recipients. *Transplant Proc* 1973B; 5:95–98.

330. Coleman DV, Mackenzie EFD, Gardner SD, et al: Human polyomavirus (BK) infection and ureteric stenosis in renal allograft recipients. *J Clin Pathol* 1978; 31:338–347.

331. Gerber MA, Shah KV, Thung SN, et al: Immuno-histochemical demonstration of common antigen of polyomaviruses in routine histologic tissue sections of animals and man. *Am J Clin Pathol* 1980; 73:794–797.

332. Chesters PM, Heritage J, McCance DJ: Persistence of DNA sequences of BK virus and JC virus in normal human tissues and in diseased tissues. *J Infect Dis* 1983; 147:676–684.

333. Koss LG: BK viruria and hemorrhagic cystitis, letter. *N Engl J Med* 1987; 316:108–109.

334. Cheeseman SH, Black PH, Rubin RH, et al: Interferon and BK papovavirus—clinical and laboratory studies. *J Infect Dis* 1980; 141:157–161.

335. Traystman MD, Gupta PK, Shah KV, et al: Identification of viruses in the urine of renal transplant recipients by cytomorphology. *Acta Cytol* 1980; 24:501–510.

336. Hogan TF, Borden EC, McBain JA, et al: Human polyomavirus infections with JC virus and BK virus in renal transplant patients. *Ann Intern Med* 1980B; 92:373–378.

337. Gardner SD, MacKenzie EF, Smith C, et al: Prospective study of the human polyomaviruses BK and JC and cytomegalovirus in renal transplant recipients. *J Clin Pathol* 1984; 37:578–586.

338. Zapata M, Mahony JB, Chernesky MA: Measurement of BK papovavirus IgG and IgM by radioimmunoassay (RIA). *J Med Virol* 1984; 14:101–114.

339. Flower A, Banatvaia JE, Chrystie IL: BK antibody and virus-specific IgM responses in renal transplant recipients, patients with malignant disease, and healthy people. *Br Med J* 1977; 2:220–223.

340. Harrison P, Mackenzie EF, Poulding JM: BK virus in search of a disease, letter. *Lancet* 1978; 2:1150.

341. O'Reilly RJ, Lee FK, Grossbard E, et al: Papovavirus excretion following marrow transplantation—incidence and association with hepatic dysfunction. *Transplant Proc* 1981; 13:262–266.

342. O'Reilly RJ, Lee F, Grossbard E, et al: Papovavirus excretion following marrow transplantation: incidence and association with hepatic dysfunction. *Transplant Proc* 1981; 13:262–266.

343. Ambinder RF, Burns W, Forman M, et al: Hemorrhagic cystitis associated with adenovirus in bone marrow transplantation. *Arch Intern Med* 1986; 146:1400–1401.

344. Rice SJ, Bishop JA, Apperley J, et al: BK virus as cause of haemorrhagic cystitis after bone marrow transplantation, letter. *Lancet* 1985; 2:844–845.

345. Arthur RR, Shah KV, Baust SJ, et al: Association of BK viruria with hemorrhagic cystitis in recipients of bone marrow transplants. *N Engl J Med* 1986; 315:230–234.

346. Apperley JF, Rice SJ, Bishop JA, et al: Late-onset hemorrhagic cystitis associated with urinary excretion of polyomaviruses after bone marrow transplantation. *Transplantation* 1987; 43:108–112.

347. Arthur RR, Beckmann AM, Li CC, et al: Direct detection of the human papovavirus BK in urine of bone marrow transplant recipients: comparison of DNA hybridization with ELISA. *J Med Virol* 1985; 16:29–36.

348. Verdonck LF, Dekker AW, Rozenberg-Arska M, et al: BK viruria and hemorrhagic cystitis, letter. *N Engl J Med* 1987; 316:109.

349. Forni AM, Koss LG, Geller W: Cytological study of the effect of cyclophosphamide on the epithelium of the urinary bladder in man. *Cancer* 1964; 17:1348–1355.

350. Mininberg DT, Watson C, Desquitado M: Viral cystitis with transient secondary vesicoureteral reflux. *J Urol* 1982; 127:983–985.

351. Padgett BL, Walker DL, Desquitado MM, et al: BK virus and non-haemorrhagic cystitis in a child, letter. *Lancet* 1983B; 1:770.

352. Kahan AV, Coleman DV, Koss LG: Activation of human polyomavirus infection—detection by cytologic technics. *Am J Clin Pathol* 1980; 74:326–332.

353. Cobb JJ, Wickenden C, Snell ME, et al: Use of hybridot assay to screen for BK and JC polyomaviruses in non-immunosuppressed patients. *J Clin Pathol* 1987; 40:777–781.

354. Witherspoon RP, Matthews D, Storb R, et al: Recovery of in vivo cellular immunity after human marrow grafting: Influences of time postgrafting and acute graft-versus-host disease. *Transplantation* 1984; 37:145–150.

355. Drummond JE, Shah KV, Saral R, et al: BK virus specific humoral and cell mediated immunity in allogeneic bone marrow transplant (BMT) recipients. *J Med Virol* 1987; 23:331–344.

356. Meurman OH, Mantyjarvi RA, Salmi AA, et al: Prevalence of antibodies to a human papova virus (BK virus) in subacute sclerosing panencephalitis and multiple sclerosis patients. *Neurology* 1972; 203:191–194.

357. Corallini A, Barbanti-Brodano G, Portolani PG: Antibodies to BK virus structural and tumor antigens in human sera from normal persons and from patients with various diseases, including neoplasia. *Infect Immun* 1976; 13:1684–1691.

358. Shah KV, Daniel RW, Stone KR, et al: Investigation of human urogenital tract tumors of papovavirus etiology: brief communication. *J Natl Cancer Inst* 1978; 60:579–582.

359. Hogan TF, Padgett BL, Walker DL, et al: Survey of human polyomavirus (JCV, BKV) infections in 139 patients with lung cancer, breast cancer, melanoma, or lymphoma, in Sever JL, Madden DL (eds): *Polyomaviruses and Human Neurological Diseases.* New York, Alan R Liss, 1983, vol 105, pp 311–324.

360. Pyrhonen S, Mantyjarvi R, Tykka H, et al: BK and herpes simplex virus antibodies in renal cell carcinoma. *Med Biol* 1978; 56:194–200.

361. Madden DL, Iltis J, Tzan N, et al: Frequency of antibody to BK antigen in women whose children developed malignancies and women who developed detectable carcinoma in situ of the cervix during this pregnancy, in Sever JL, Madden DL (eds): *Polyomaviruses and Human Neurological Diseases.* New York, Alan R Liss, 1983, vol 105, pp 149–156.

362. Flaegstad T, Traavik T, Kolmannskog S, et al: BK virus infection in children with cancer: Serological response studied by haemagglutination inhibition, neutralization, and IgG- and IgM-class specific ELISA tests. *J Med Virology* 1988; 24:33–44.

363. Yamakawa Y, Fukui M, Kinoshita K, et al: Seasonal variation of birth incidence of children with cerebellar medulloblastoma (Japanese) *Neurol Med Chir (Tokyo)* 1982; 22:1002–1008.

364. Richardson EP Jr: Progressive multifocal leukoencephalopathy. *N Engl J Med* 1961; 265:815–823.

365. Castaigne P, Rondot P, Escourolle R, et al: Leukoencephalopathie multifocale progressive et "gliomes" multiples. *Rev Neurol* 1974; 130:379–392.

366. GiaRusso MH, Koeppeu AH: Atypical progressive multifocal leukoencephalopathy and primary cerebral malignant lymphoma. *J Neurol Sci* 1978; 35:391–398.

367. Scherneck S, Luebbe L, Nisch G, et al: *Int J Cancer* 1979; 24:523–531.

368. Fiori M, Di Mayorca G: Occurrence of BK virus DNA in DNA obtained from certain human tumors. *Proc Natl Acad Sci USA* 1976; 73:4662–4666.

369. Meinke W, Goldstein DA, Smith RA: Simian virus 40-related DNA sequences in a human brain tumor. *Neurology* 1979; 29:1590–1594.

370. Ibelgaufts H, Jones KW: *Acta Neuropathol (Berl)* 1982; 56:118–122.

371. Geissler E, Scherneck S, Prokoph H, et al: in Giraldo GA, Beth E (eds): *The Role of Viruses in Human Cancer.* Amsterdam, Elsevier, 1984, vol 2, pp 265–279.

372. Weiss AF, Portmann R, Fischer H, et al: Simian virus 40-related antigens in three human meningiomas with defined chromosome loss. *Proc Natl Acad Sci USA* 1975; 72:609–613.

373. Weiss AF, Zang KD, Birkmayer GD, et al: SV40 related papovaviruses in human meningiomas. *Acta Neuropathol (Berl)* 1976; 34:171–174.

374. Tabuchi K, Kirsch WM, Low M, et al: Screening of human brain tumors for SV40-related T antigen. *Int J Cancer* 1978; 21:12–17.

375. Cikes M, Beth E, Giraldo G, et al: A search for an association between simian virus 40 and human meningiomas, in Hiatt HH, Watson JD, Winsten JA (eds): *Origins of Human Cancer, Book B: Mechanisms of Carcinogenesis.* Cold Spring Harbor, NY, Cold Spring Harbor Laboratory, 1977, pp 1009–1011.

376. Israel MA, Martin MA, Takemoto KK, et al: Evaluation of normal and neoplastic human tissue for BK virus. *Virology* 1978; 90:187–196.

377. Wold YSM, Mackey JK, Brackman KH, et al: Analysis of human tumors and human malignant cell lines for BK virus-specific DNA sequences. *Proc Natl Acad Sci USA* 1978; 75:454–458.

378. Corallini A, Pagnani M, Viadana P, et al: Association of BK virus with human brain tumors and tumors of pancreatic islets. *Int J Cancer* 1987; 39:60–67.

379. Dorries K, Loeber G, Meixensberger J: Association of polyomaviruses JC, SV40, and BK with human brain tumors. *Virology* 1987; 160:268–270.

380. Knepper JE, diMayorca G: Cloning and characterization of BK virus–related DNA sequences from normal and neoplastic human tissues. *J Med Virol* 1987; 21:289–299.

381. Johnson RT: Evidence for polyomaviruses in human neurological diseases, in Sever JL, Madden DL (eds): *Polyomaviruses and Human Neurological Diseases.* New York, Alan R Liss, 1983, vol 105, pp 183–190.

382. Shah KV, Palma LD, Murphy GP: The occurrence of SV40 neutralizing antibodies in sera of patients with genitourinary carcinoma. *J Surg Oncol* 1971A; 3:443–450.

383. Costa J, Yee C, Rabson AS: Absence of papovavirus T antibody in patients with malignancies. *Lancet* 1977; 2:709–710.

384. May G, Fischer H, Zang KD: SV40-related T-antigen expression in human meningiomas with normal and G-22-monosomic karyotype. *J Gen Virol* 1979; 43:697–700.

385. Geissler E, Scherneck S, Waehite H, et al: Further studies on the relationship of SV40-like viruses to human tumors, in Essex M, Todaro G, zur Hausen H (eds): *Viruses in Naturally Occurring Cancers, Book A: Cold Spring Harbor Conferences on Cell Proliferation.* Cold Spring Harbor, NY, Cold Spring Harbor Laboratory, 1980, vol 7, pp 343–356.

386. Heinonen OP, Shapiro S, Monson, et al: Immunization during pregnancy against poliomyelitis and influenza in relation to childhood malignancy. *Int J Epidemiol* 1973; 2:229–235.

387. Fraumeni JF Jr, Ederer F, Miller RW: An evaluation of the carcinogenicity of simian virus 40 in man. *JAMA* 1963; 185:713–718.

388. Fraumeni JF Jr, Stark CR, Gold E, et al: Simian virus 40 in polio vaccine: Follow-up of newborn recipients. *Science* 1970; 16:59–60.

389. Mortimer EA, Lepow ML, Gold E, et al: Long-term follow up of persons inadvertently inoculated with SV40 as neonates. *N Engl J Med* 1981; 305:1517–1518.

390. Rosa FW, Sever JL, Madden DL: Absence of antibody response to simian virus 40 after inoculation with killed-poliovirus vaccine of mothers of offspring with neurologic tumors. *N Engl J Med* 1988; 318:1469.

391. Shah KV, Nathanson N: Human exposure to SV40: Review and comment. *Am J Epidemiol* 1976; 103:1–12.

392. Budka H, Shah KV: Papova viral antigens in PML brains. *J Neuropathol Exp Neurol* 1982; 41:366.

393. Budka H, Shah KV: Papovavirus antigens in paraffin sections of PML brains, in Sever JL, Madden DL (eds): *Polyomaviruses and Human Neurological Diseases.* New York, Alan R Liss, 1983, pp 299–309.

394. Maples JA: A method for the covalent attachment of cells to glass slides for use in immunohistochemical assays. *Am J Clin Pathol* 1985; 83:356–363.

395. Aksamit AJ, Mourrain P, Sever JL, et al: Progressive multifocal leukoencephalopathy: investigation of three cases using in situ hybridization with JC virus, biotinylated DNA probe. *Ann Neurol* 1985; 18:490–496.

396. Tourtellotte WW, Verity AN, Schmid P, et al: Covalent binding of formalin fixed paraffin embedded brain tissue sections to glass slides suitable for in situ hybridization. *J Virol Methods* 1987; 15:87–99.

397. Gibson PE, Gardner SD, Porter AA: Detection of human polyomavirus DNA in urine specimens by hybridot assay. *Arch Virol* 1985; 84:233–240.

398. Gibson PE, Gardner SD, Field AM: Use of a molecular probe

399. for detecting JCV DNA directly in human brain material. *J Med Virol* 1986; 18:87–95.

399. Singer RH, Ward DC: Actin gene expression visualized in chicken muscle tissue culture by using in situ hybridization with a biotinylated nucleotide analog. *Proc Natl Acad Sci USA* 1982; 79:7331–7335.

400. Farrell DF: The EEG in progressive multifocal leukoencephalopathy. *Electroencephalogr Clin Neurophysiol* 1969; 26:200–205.

401. Richardson EP Jr: Progressive multifocal leukoencephalopathy, in Vinken PJ, Bruyn GW (eds): *Handbook of Clinical Neurology. Multiple Sclerosis and Other Demyelinating Diseases.* Amsterdam, North-Holland, 1970, vol 9, pp 485–499.

402. Marriott PJ, O'Brien MD, Mackenzie CK, et al: Progressive multifocal leucoencephalopathy: Remission with cytarabine. *J Neurol Neurosurg Psychiatry* 1975; 38:205–209.

403. Paxton R, Ambrose J: The EMT scanner: a brief review of the first 650 patients. *Br J Radiol* 1974; 40:530–565.

404. Conomy JP, Weinstein MA, Agamanolis D, et al: Computed tomography in progressive multifocal leukoencephalopathy. *AJR* 1976; 127:663–665.

405. Bosch EP, Cancilla PA, Cornell SH: Computed tomography in progressive multifocal leukoencephalopathy. *Arch Neurol* 1976; 33:216.

406. Wolinsky JS, Johnson KP, Rand K, et al: Progressive multifocal leukoencephalopathy: Clinical pathologic correlates and failure of a drug trial in two patients. *Trans Am Neurol Assoc* 1976; 101:81–82.

407. Carroll BA, Lane B, Norman D, et al: Progressive multifocal leukoencephalopathy: Diagnosis by computerized tomography. *J Radiol* 1977; 122:137–146.

408. Durham DS, Fryer JA, O'Neill BJ, et al: Progressive multifocal leukoencephalopathy, CT and pathological features. *Med J Aust* 1980; 2:502–504.

409. Peters ACB, Versteeg J, Bots, GTAM, et al: Progressive multifocal leukoencephalopathy: Immunofluorescent demonstration of simian virus 40 antigen in CSF cells and response to cytarabine therapy. *Arch Neurol* 1980; 37:497–501.

410. Guilleux MH, Steiner RE, Young IR: MR imaging in PML. *AJNR* 1986; 7:1033–1035.

411. Shafran B, Roke ME, Barr RM, et al: Contrast enhancing lesions in progressive multifocal leukoencephalopathy: A clinicopathological correlation. *Can J Neurol Sci* 1987; 14:600–602.

412. Orenstein JM, Jannotta F: Human immunodeficiency virus and papovavirus infections in acquired immunodeficiency syndrome: An ultrastructural study of three cases. *Hum Pathol* 1988; 19:350–361.

413. Coleman DV, Gardner SD, Field AM: Human polyomavirus infection in renal allograft recipients. *Br Med J* 1973A; 3:371–375.

414. Hogan TF, Padgett BL, Walker DL, et al: Rapid detection and identification of JC virus and BK virus in human urine using immunofluorescence microscopy. *J Clin Microbiol* 1980; 11:178–183.

415. Coleman DV, Russell WJI, Hodgson J, et al: Human papovavirus in Papanicolaou smears of urinary sediment detected by transmission electron microscopy. *J Clin Pathol* 1977; 30:1015–1020.

416. Lecatsas G, Prozesky OW, Van Wyk J, et al: Papova virus in urine after renal transplantation. *Nature* 1973; 241:343–344.

417. Lecatsas G, Schoub BD, Prozesky OW: Development of a new human polyoma virus strain (MG). *Arch Virol* 1976A; 51:327–333.

418. Lecatsas G, Schoub BD, Prozesky OW, et al: Polyoma virus in urine in aplastic anemia. *Lancet* 1976; 1:259–260.

419. Lecatsas G, Pretorius F, Crewe-Brown H, et al: Polyomavirus in urine in pernicious anemia. *Lancet* 1977; 2:147.

420. Lecatsas G, Crewe-Brown H, Boes E, et al: Virus-like particles in pregnancy urine. *Lancet* 1978; 2:433–434.

421. Dulbecco R: Oncogenic viruses, in Davis BD, Dulbecco R, Ei-

sen HN, et al (eds): *Microbiology*. New York, Harper & Row, 1980, pp 1232–1261.

422. Iltis JP, Cleghorn CS, Madden DL, et al: Detection of antibody to BK virus by enzyme-linked immunosorbent assay compared to hemagglutination inhibition and immunofluorescent antibody staining, in Sever JL, Madden DL (eds): *Polyomaviruses and Human Neurological Diseases*. New York, Alan R Liss, 1983, vol 105, pp 157–168.

423. Flaegstad T, Traavik T: Detection of BK virus antibodies measured by enzyme-linked immunosorbent assay (ELISA) and two haemagglutination inhibition methods: a comparative study. *J Med Virol* 1985; 16:351–356.

424. Flaegstad T, Traavik T: Detection of BK virus IgM antibodies by two enzyme-linked immunosorbent assays (ELISA) and a hemagglutination inhibition method. *J Med Virol* 1985; 17:195–204.

425. Arthur RR, Shah KV, Yolken RH, et al: Detection of human papovaviruses BKV and JCV in urines by ELISA, in Sever JL, Madden DL (eds): *Polyomaviruses and Human Neurological Diseases*. New York, Alan R Liss, 1983, vol 105, pp 169–176.

426. Goldstein SC, Trallca TS, Rabson AS: Mixed infection with human polyomavirus (BK). *Br Med J* 1984; 13:33–40.

427. Flaegstad T, Traavik T, Christie KE, et al: Neutralization test for BK virus: plaque reduction detected by immunoperoxidase staining. *J Med Virol* 1986; 19:287–296.

428. Drummond JE, Shah KV, Donnenberg AD: Cell-mediated immune responses to BK virus in normal individuals. *J Med Virol* 1985; 17:195–204.

429. Schlitt M, Morawetz RB, Bonnin J, et al: Progressive multifocal leukoencephalopathy: Three patients diagnosed by brain biopsy, with prolonged survival in two. *Neurosurgery* 1986; 18:407–414.

430. Tashiro K, Moriwaka F, Maruo Y, et al: Progressive multifocal leucoencephalopathy with magnetic resonance imaging verification and therapeutic trials with interferon. *J Neurol* 1987; 234:427–429.

431. Castaigne P, Escourolle R, Derouesne C, et al: Un cas de leukoencephalopathie multifocale progressive. Étude anatomoclinique et immunologique. *Rev Neurol* 1973; 128:85–94.

432. Tarsy D, Holden M, Segarra JM, et al: 5-Iodo-2'-deoxyuridine (IUDR); NSC-39661) given intraventricularly in the treatment of progressive multifocal leukoencephalopathy. *Cancer Chemother Rep* 1973; 57:73–78.

433. Castleman B, Scully RE, McNeeley BU: Weekly clinicopathological exercises, case 19-1972. *N Engl J Med* 1972; 286:1047–1054.

434. Conomy JP, Beard S, Matsumoto H, et al: Cytarabine treatment of progressive multifocal leukoencephalopathy. *JAMA* 1974; 229:1313–1316.

435. Van Horn G, Bastian FO, Morhe JJ: Progressive multifocal leukoencephalopathy: Failure of response to transfer factor and cytarabine. *Neurology* 1978; 28:794–979.

436. Rand KH, Johnson KP, Rubinstein LJ, et al: Adenine arabinoside in the treatment of progressive multifocal leukoencephalopathy: use of virus-containing cells in the urine to assess response to therapy. *Ann Neurol* 1977; 1:458–462.

437. Bauer WR, Turel AP, Johnson KP: Progressive multifocal leukoencephalopathy and cytarabine. Remission with treatment. *JAMA* 1973; 226:174–176.

438. Buckman R, Wiltshaw E: Progressive multifocal leucoencephalopathy successfully treated with cytosine arabinoside. *Br J Haematol* 1976; 34:153–155.

438a. O'Riordan T, Daly PA, Hutchinson M, et al: Progressive multifocal leukoencephalopathy—remission with cytarabine. *J Infect* 1990; 20:51–54.

439. Selhorst JB, Ducy KF, Thomas JM, et al: PML: Remission and immunologic reversals, abstract. *Neurology (NY)* 1978; 28:337.

440. Smith CR, Sima AAF, Salit IE, et al: Progressive multifocal leukoencephalopathy: Failure of cytarabine therapy. *Neurology (NY)* 1982; 32:200–203.

441. Hedley-Whyte ET, Smith BP, Tyler HT, et al: Multifocal leukoencephalopathy with remission and five-year survival. *J Neuropathol Exp Neurol* 1966; 25:107–116.

442. Parry JV, Richmond JE, Gardner SD: Polyomavirus in fetal rhesus monkey kidney cell line used to grow hepatitis A virus. *Lancet* 1983; 1:994.

443. Tanaka R, Koprowski H, Iwasaki Y: Brief communication: Malignant transformation of hamster brain cells in vitro by human papovirus BK. *J Natl Cancer Inst* 1976; 56:671–673.

444. Lecatsas G, Prozesky OW, Scheepers F: The cytopathology and development of the human polyomavirus (BK). *Arch Gesamte Virusforsch* 1974; 45:319–327.

445. Oster-granite ML, Narayan O, Johnson RT, et al: Studies of cultured human and simian fetal brain cells. II. Infections with human (BK) and simian (SV40) papovaviruses. *Neuropathol Appl Neurobiol* 1978; 4:443–445.

446. Howley PM, Mullarkey MF, Takemoto KK, et al: Characterization of human papovavirus BK DNA. *J Virol* 1975; 15:173–181.

447. Bradley MK, Dougherty RM: Transformation of African green monkey kidney cells with the RF stain of human papovavirus BKV. *Virology* 1978; 85:231–240.

448. Portolani M, Borgatti M: Stable transformation of mouse, rabbit, and monkey cells and abortive transformation of human cells by BK virus, a human papovavirus. *J Gen Virol* 1978; 38:369–374.

449. Costa J, Howley PM, Legallais F, et al: Oncogenicity of a nude mouse cell line transformed by a human papovavirus. *J Natl Cancer Inst* 1977B; 58:1147–1149.

450. Mason DH, Takemoto KK: Transformation of rabbit kidney cells by BKV (MM) human papovavirus. *Int J Cancer* 1977; 19:391–395.

451. Mackenzie EF, Poulding JM, Harrison PR, et al: Human polyoma virus (HPV)—significant pathogen in renal transplantation. *Proc Eur Dial Transplant Assoc* 1978; 15:352–360.

452. Reese JM, Reissing M, Daniel RW, et al: Occurrence of BK virus and BK virus-specific antibodies in the urine of patients receiving chemotherapy for malignancy. *Infect Immun* 1975; 11:1375–1381.

453. Gardner SD: Implication of papovaviruses in human diseases, in Kurstak EK, Kurstak C (eds): *Comparative Diagnosis of Viral Diseases*. New York, Academic Press, 1977, vol 1, pp 41–84.

454. Taguchi F, Hara K, Kajioka J, et al: Isolation of BK virus from a patient with systemic lupus erythematosus (SLE). *Microbiol Immunol* 1979; 23:1131–1132.

455. Pauw W, Choufoer J: Isolation of a variant of BK virus with altered restriction endonuclease pattern. *Arch Virol* 1978; 57:35–42.

456. Dougherty RM, Distefano HS: Isolation and characterization of a papovavirus from human urine. *Proc Soc Exp Biol Med* 1974; 146:481–487.

457. Jung M, Krech U, Price PC, et al: Evidence of chronic persistent infections with polyomaviruses (BK type) in renal transplant recipients. *Arch Virol* 1975; 47:39–46.

458. Hashida Y, Gaffney PC, Yunis EJ: Acute hemorrhagic cystitis of childhood and papova-like particles. *J Pediatr* 1976; 89:85–87.

459. Rosen S, Harmon W, Krensky AM, et al: Tubulo-interstitial nephritis associated with polyomavirus (BK type) infection. *N Engl J Med* 1983; 308:1192–1196.

460. Shah KV, Daniel RW, Zeigel RF, et al: Search for BK and SV40 virus reactivation in renal transplant recipients. *Transplantation* 1974; 17:131–134.

461. Krech U, Jung M, Price PC, et al: Virus infections in renal transplant recipients. *Immun Forsch* 1975; 148:341–345.

462. Portolani M, Marzocchi A, Barbanti-Brodano G, et al: Prevalence in Italy of antibodies to a new human papovavirus (BK virus). *J Med Microbiol* 1974; 7:543–546.

463. Szucs G, Kende M, Uj M: Haemagglutination-inhibiting antibodies to BK virus in Hungary. *Acta Microbiol Acad Sci Hung* 1979; 26:173–178.

42

Virus-Induced Subacute Spongiform Encephalopathies (Kuru and Creutzfeldt-Jakob Disease)

Colin L. Masters

HISTORY AND NOMENCLATURE

STRUCTURE AND BIOLOGY OF THE AGENTS

CONVENTIONAL BIOLOGIC PROPERTIES
UNCONVENTIONAL BIOLOGIC PROPERTIES
PHYSICAL PROPERTIES AND PHYSICOCHEMICAL INACTIVATION
  PROFILE

EPIDEMIOLOGY

PATHOGENESIS

TRANSMISSION
INCUBATION
CLINICOPATHOLOGIC SYNDROMES

LABORATORY DIAGNOSIS OF INFECTION

PREVENTION AND TREATMENT

**PRECAUTIONS IN HANDLING POTENTIALLY
  INFECTED MATERIALS FROM PATIENTS WITH
  CREUTZFELDT-JAKOB DISEASE**

**RELATIONSHIP OF ALZHEIMER'S DISEASE TO
  CREUTZFELDT-JAKOB DISEASE**

In a scheme of viral infections of the central nervous system (CNS), the subacute spongiform encephalopathies form a distinct group where the causative agents are best described as unconventional viruses, since their purification and exact physical identification are yet to be achieved. As so often occurs in nature, the same virus may give rise to many different syndromes of infection, depending on such variables as the strain of virus, age and immune status of the host, the genetic background of the host, and the route of inoculation and dose of inoculum. The syndromic clas-

sification of virus infections of the CNS in Table 42–1 emphasizes some of these variables, but more importantly, it draws attention to the fact that the unconventional virus infections result in diseases that are clinically and pathologically distinct from those associated with conventional virus infections. Table 42–1 also indicates that there are a number (the list could easily be expanded) of diseases of the CNS where a viral etiology is thought possible, yet not identified to date.

This chapter covers only a few of the more important features of the virus-induced spongiform encephalopathies. For those interested in more detailed reviews, reference should be made to the monographs edited by Prusiner and Hadlow,[1] and Prusiner and McKinley.[2]

HISTORY AND NOMENCLATURE

For many years, scrapie, a naturally occurring disease of sheep and goats, was known to be caused by a transmissible agent. Clinically, scrapie was an endemic disease of the nervous system, subacute, steadily progressive, and invariably fatal. Pathologically, the brain showed areas of gliosis, neuronal loss, and a vacuolation of neurons and neuropil, and no inflammatory response. The term "scrapie" was used to describe one aspect of the altered behavior of animals, a tendency to scrape their coats against fences, as if pruritus were a dominant symptom. Veterinary research had demonstrated that the disease was transmissible from animal to animal by parenteral inoculation and that the causative agent could infect laboratory mice, where studies of its pathogenesis and physicochemical properties became more practical. Scrapie was then classified as a "slow infection," akin to other animal diseases (visna, maedi, infectious adenomatosis, and Aleutian mink

Table 42–1
Outline of Virus Infections of the Central Nervous System

I. Conventional virus infections
  1. Syndromes of acute meningitis, encephalitis
     a. Alpha-, flavi- and bunyaviruses (Chapters 21, 23)
     b. Polioviruses and other enteroviruses (Chapter 17)
     c. Herpes simplex viruses (Chapter 34)
     d. Arenaviruses (Chapter 20)
  2. Syndromes of para- or postinfectious encephalitis, myelitis, radiculitis
     a. Associated with childhood infections—measles, chickenpox, mumps, rubella (Chapters 12, 13, 25, 35)
     b. Associated with respiratory infections—influenza, parainfluenza, adenoviruses (Chapters 10, 11, 32)
     c. Reye syndrome (Chapter 45)
     d. Guillain-Barré syndrome—many different viruses
  3. Syndrome of congenital infections
     a. Cytomegalovirus (Chapter 37)
     b. Rubella (Chapter 25)
     c. Herpesviruses (Chapters 34–37)
  4. Syndromes of reactivation of a latent infection
     a. Herpes zoster (shingles)—varicella-zoster virus (Chapter 35)
     b. Herpes simplex viruses (Chapter 34)
  5. Syndromes of encephalitis in a host with an ineffective immune response or infection by a defective virus
     a. Progressive multifocal leukoencephalopathy—polyomaviruses (Chapter 40)
     b. Subacute sclerosing panencephalitis—measles, rubella (Chapters 13, 25)
     c. Acquired immunodeficiency syndrome (AIDS)–human immunodeficiency virus (HIV) (Chapter 9)

II. Unconventional virus infections (this chapter)
   Man   Kuru
            Creutzfeldt-Jakob disease (CJD)
            Gerstmann-Sträussler syndrome (GSS)
   Animals Scrapie of sheep, goats, and cows
            Transmissible mink encephalopathy (scrapie in mink)
            Scrapie in captive mule deer, elk, and other animals

III. Diseases suspected of conventional or unconventional virus infection
   Multiple sclerosis (measles virus?)
   Encephalitis lethargica (influenza?)
   Parkinson's disease ⎱
   Alzheimer's disease ⎰ (unconventional virus?)

disease) where an infectious agent, after a long incubation period, caused a progressive subacute to chronic fatal disease.[3] It was not long before the term slow infection became corrupted into terms like "slow virus" or "slow virus disease."

Scrapie remained in the realms of veterinary science until Hadlow[4] drew attention to the pathologic similarities between scrapie and kuru. Kuru was, and is, a human disease confined to a small population in the eastern highlands of Papua, New Guinea. First described in 1957 by Gajdusek and Zigas,[5] kuru was seen as a progressive cerebellar degeneration. The more remarkable features of kuru were (1) its restriction to a single linguistic group of highland New Guineans; (2) its high incidence within this group with women and children being especially vulnerable; (3) the clinical features of a progressive cerebellar ataxia, extrapyramidal signs, and a steadily progressive unremitting course ending in death within a year of onset; and (4) the pathologic changes of neuronal loss, gliosis, and spongiform change, without any suggestion of inflammatory response. All attempts to isolate a conventional virus from the brain were unsuccessful, and many hypotheses were generated to explain the disease in terms of the previously known progressive heredofamilial brain degenerations. When the pathologic similarities between scrapie and kuru were appreciated, it

took several years before the transmissibility of kuru to primates could be established.[6] Chimpanzees inoculated intracerebrally with kuru brain suspension developed a similar clinical and pathologic syndrome after a 1- to 2-year incubation period. It was not long after that the host range for experimentally transmitted kuru was extended to other primate species.

It is now generally accepted that kuru was naturally transmitted by cannibalism: affected patients died, and their remains were eaten by relatives and clansmen, women and children tending to receive the internal viscera and brain. With the cessation of cannibalism in the 1950s, the incidence of kuru progressively declined, in a fashion consistent only with the conjectured method of transmission.[7, 8] Arising from the original pathologic descriptions of kuru,[9] a similarity was recalled to the syndrome of Jakob and Creutzfeldt. In the early 1920s the German neuropathologists Jakob and Creutzfeldt independently described a series of patients with a subacute progressive cerebral degeneration.[10–13] Jakob's contribution was more significant, in that he identified what is now recognized as the condition of subacute spongiform encephalopathy (for a detailed appraisal of the original descriptions, see Masters and Gajdusek[14]). In time, Creutzfeldt-Jakob disease (CJD), or subacute spongiform encephalopathy, became defined as a subacute pro-

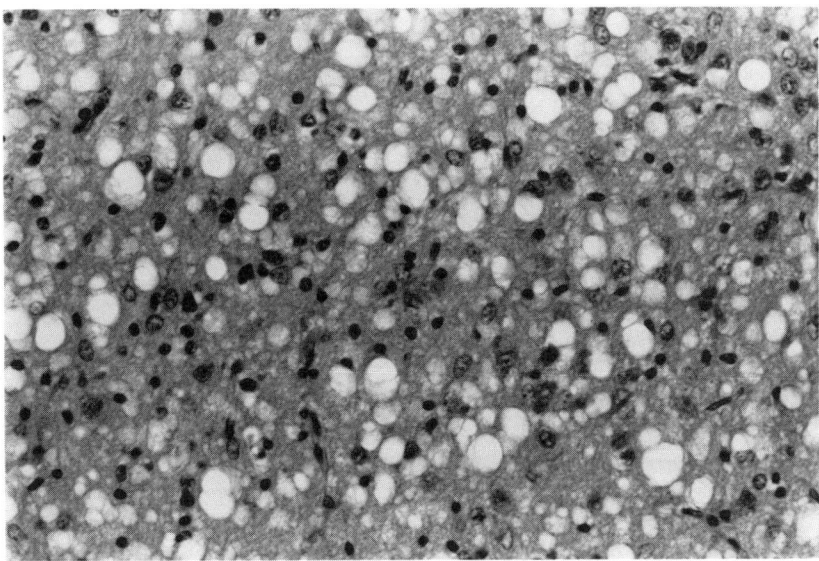

Figure 42–1. Photomicrograph of the cerebral cortex of a squirrel monkey experimentally infected with the Cruetzfeldt-Jakob disease virus. There is a widespread vacuolation of the neuropil, which is typical of a spongiform encephalopathy. Astrocytic nuclei are prominent, and there is a loss of neurons (hematoxylin and eosin; approximate magnification ×150). (From material supplied by Dr D. C. Gajdusek.)

gressive syndrome of dementia, extrapyramidal, pyramidal, and cerebellar signs, myoclonus, and EEG abnormalities, which pathologically was seen as a diffuse neuronal degeneration, gliosis, and spongiform change.[14, 15] The pathologic changes in common between CJD and kuru led to the trial inoculations of CJD brain material into chimpanzees, which, after incubation periods ranging from 2 to 5 years, resulted in the demonstration of its transmissibility.[16]

During the 1970s, the major thrust of research was in purification of the infectious agent. From these studies, two novel concepts emerged in the 1980s. There is a fibrillar structure closely linked to expression of disease (the scrapie-associated fibril, SAF),[17] and there is an altered host-encoded protein (PrP) which copurifies with infectivity.[18] PrP is the major constituent of the SAF, and aggregates to form amyloid fibrils in vitro[19] and in situ.[20] Prusiner[21] coined the term ''prion'' for the PrP protein and the infectious agent itself, to emphasize the essential requirement of *pro*tein for *in*fectivity (correctly formed, this acronym would spell ''proin''). The proin terminology is not yet acceptable, because of the implication-connotation that the protein (PrP) itself is infectious—a concept that may yet prove to be correct but which has not been formally proved to date.

This chain of events, simplified in retrospect, therefore led to the discovery of a new class of infective agents, having in common the unusual clinical properties of subacute progressive cerebral degeneration, without signs of febrile response, and pathologically marked as spongiform encephalopathies, since the vacuolation of the neurons and neuropil was the only distinctive morphological change in common between the naturally occurring and experimentally transmitted disease (Figure 42–1).

STRUCTURE AND BIOLOGY OF THE AGENTS

Scrapie virus was the first of this group of viruses to be adapted

to serial passage in mice and other small rodents. Consequently, most of our knowledge of the biologic behavior and physicochemical properties of these viruses derive from studies of scrapie in mice and hamsters. To date, studies with the isolates from kuru and CJD brains have shown no fundamental differences from the strains of scrapie, except in restrictions in host range. More recently, rodent-adapted strains of kuru and CJD viruses have become available, but the data presented below pertain largely to scrapie. It is important to emphasize one inherent difficulty encountered in the study of these agents: the only reliable assay system is that of a bioassay, in which end point titration must be carried out, and with long incubation periods (more than 5 years in some systems), the turnaround period for experiments is extraordinarily time-consuming. In spite of these difficulties, a coherent picture of the nature of these unconventional viruses is emerging. Little can be said of the absolute physical structure of these viruses, since to date none have been purified to homogeneity, nor have any ultrastructural studies shown convincing evidence of a specific viral particle. The biologic properties of these viruses are summarized in Tables 42–2 and 42–3 under two categories: conventional and unconventional. Their physical properties are summarized in Tables 42–4 and 42–5.

Conventional Biologic Properties

The use of the word ''virus'' applied to these agents is justified when their conventional biologic properties are considered: they titrate cleanly from cell-free preparations, are filterable to 25- to 50-nm average pore diameter, and replicate in high titer in the brains of experimentally infected animals. The kinetics of replication have been documented for scrapie in the hamster. From 2 to 3 weeks after intracerebral inoculation with 10^7 LD_{50} (median lethal dose) units, there is a steady increase in virus titer (approximately 0.5 log per week) until the terminal phase of illness where the titer reaches $10^{11} LD_{50}$ units. The earliest pathologic changes

Table 42–2
Conventional Biologic Properties

1. Filterable and titrate cleanly (most individuals succumb to high LD_{50} in susceptible species, espeicaly when host-adapted strain used)
2. Replicate in high titers (up to 10^8 to 10^{10} infectious units per gram in brain)
3. Replicate first in lymph nodes, spleen, and thymus, and then in brain, when inoculated by routes other than intracerebral; Evidence for spread of virus along neural pathways, and from the spleen to the thoracic cord via autonomic nerves
4. Restriction of host range and adaptability to new host
5. Strain differences (as judged by host specificity, incubation period, topography of brain lesions, ability to induce amyloid plaques, and the selection for different isolates from the same "wildstock" virus)
6. Genetic control of the host influencing susceptibility or resistance to infection
7. Interference between slow-replicating and fast-replicating strains
8. Limited replication in tissue culture
9. Essential protein component for replication (as demonstrated by protease digestion; chemical modification by diethylpyrocarbonate, butanedione; inactivation by detergents such as sodium dodecyl sulfate; ionic inactivation with guanidinium, thiocyanate, trichloroacetic acid; denaturation by urea and phenol)

(spongiform change and gliosis) are detectable 5 to 7 weeks after inoculation, and increase in severity during the clinical evolution of the disease (from 7–8 weeks until death at 11–12 weeks). Routes of inoculation other than intracerebral cause a remarkable increase in incubation period, and it has been shown that the virus replicates first in the spleen and other lymphoreticular tissues before establishing itself in the CNS. It is possible that the virus gains access to the CNS through a mechanism of neural spread along nerves to the spinal cord, then into the brainstem, cerebellum, and finally, the cerebral hemispheres.[22]

The viruses show, on the one hand, a marked restriction of host range and, on the other, a ready adaptability to a new host once the primary passage is achieved. Thus scrapie, a natural disease of sheep and goats, readily passaged in the same species, will only rarely "take" in other species such as mice, hamsters, and certain primates (squirrel monkeys are good examples). All attempts to transmit scrapie to guinea pigs, rats, and certain other primates (especially the chimpanzee) have failed. Most primary cases of kuru and CJD will readily passage into nonhuman primates (especially the squirrel monkey and chimpanzee) and, we suspect, between humans given the appropriate circumstance. But it is only with difficulty that a small proportion of primary cases of kuru and CJD can be transmitted to lower species such as mice, rats, hamsters, and cats.

Table 42–3
Unconventional Biologic Properties

1. Long incubation period
2. Lack of immunogenicity or host immune response
3. Chronic progressive illness without remission or relapse
4. Induction of spongiform change, neuronal loss, and gliosis
5. Absence of specific viral particle by electron microscopy
6. Specific nucleic acid not yet identified, and resistance to procedures that attack nucleic acids (resistant to low pH, nucleases, UV irradiation at 237 nm, zinc hydrolysis, photochemical inactivation with psoralens, chemical modification to hydroxylamine)
7. Unaffected by immunosuppression, immunopotentiation, or most antiviral drugs; splenectomy or other factors which alter splenic function may vary the course of infection
8. No cytopathic effect in tissue culture
9. Unusual spectrum of resistance to certain physical and chemical treatments
10. Induction of amyloid/scrapie–associated fibril and conversion of normal host-encoded protease-sensitive protein (PrP) to protease-resistant homologue

Table 42–4
Physical Properties

1. Filterable to 25- to 50-nm average pore diameter
2. Stable at 90°C for 30 min, but effectively inactivated by autoclaving (121°C, 15 psi, 1h)
3. Hydrophobic with a strong tendency for aggregation of the infectious unit with itself and with cellular elements
4. Continuum of size ranges from 40S–>500S on rate-zonal sucrose gradients
5. Target size determined by ionizing radiation ranges from 64,000–150,000 daltons
6. Gel filtration after zwitterionic detergent treatment gives $\leq$ 50,000 mol wt
7. Density range 1.08–1.30 g/mL

Table 42–5
Physicochemical Inactivation Profile

1. Resistant or only partially inactivated by
   Aldehydes and related compounds (formaldehyde,
      glutaraldehyde, β-propriolactone)
   Nucleases (RNAse, DNAse)
   Heat (80°C)
   UV and ionizing radiation
   Mild organic solvents (ethanol, xylenes)
   Weak chaotropic ions (Cl⁻, Br⁻, acetate)
   Nonionic and nondenaturing anionic detergents

2. Moderately inactivated by
   Ether
   Acetone
   Ethylene oxide

3. Effectively inactivated by
   Autoclaving (121°C, 15 psi, 1 h)
   Proteases (pronase, trypsin, proteinase K)
   Denaturing detergents (sodium dodecyl sulfate)
   Strong chaotropic ions (thiocyanate, trichloroacetate)
   Harsh organic solvents (phenol, chloroform, 2-chloroethanol)
   Strong oxidizing agents (periodate, hypochlorite, permanganate)
   Urea
   Sodium hydroxide

Upon successful primary passage, all viruses show adaptability in that the incubation period falls during second and third passages, and then often reaches a plateau. In some models with high passage levels, the incubation period can then be related to the dose of inoculum. A confounding factor in all these types of experiments, however, has become apparent with the demonstration that different strains of the viruses exist, and that their replication and pathogenesis are controlled by a complex interplay with host genetics.[23] Thus, certain breeds of sheep are quite resistant to most strains of scrapie; different strains of mice show significantly different incubation periods for the same strain of scrapie and also show differences in the topography and nature of the pathologic lesions within the brain. Only a few of these complex variables have been elucidated: two recessive alleles in mice control the incubation period (the *Sinc* gene) and a dominant gene (*Sip*) in sheep controls susceptibility to infection.[23]

Attempts to propagate these viruses in tissue culture have met with limited success. Low titers of scrapie have been maintained in a mouse L cell line.[24]

Unconventional Biologic Properties

Some of the unconventional biologic properties of these viruses have been alluded to above. Their long incubation periods immediately set them apart from most other viral infections. The fact that kuru still occurs more than three decades after the cessation of cannibalism suggests that incubation periods of the naturally occurring diseases will exceed 30 years.[8] In the experimentally transmitted diseases, incubation periods of up to 10 years have been observed, although with host adaptation, incubation periods as short as 60 days have been achieved. The kinetics of replication of the viruses in experimental models exclude in most instances the concept of "latency," where the virus may remain inactive for long periods. It is more likely that the viruses continually

replicate in various host tissues and become clinically manifest only when they have gained access to the CNS and reach a critical titer. The possibility of genomic integration, well established for retroviruses, cannot be excluded for the viruses causing spongiform encephalopathy. Indeed, the familial occurrence of these diseases suggest that genomic integration may be pertinent, although other mechanisms such as genetic susceptibility are equally likely.[25]

The complete absence of any detectable immunogenicity or specific host immune response is difficult to explain. In its native hydrophobic state, the virus may be only weakly antigenic.[21] It is also possible that the virus is so intimately related to a normal cellular protein that no antigenic sites are exposed. The possibility that the virus is in fact a modified host-encoded protein would also readily explain the lack of any immune response (see below).

The clinical course of the illness and the pathologic changes induced by these viruses are also quite atypical for conventional virus infections. Some experimental models of conventional virus infection of the nervous system will induce vacuolation and spongiform change, and of these, the murine retrovirus, which causes a polioencephalomyelopathy, has a close resemblance to the spongiform encephalopathy of scrapie, kuru, and CJD.[26] Although this retrovirus can be readily identified within the infected brain, its mechanism of action in causing the spongiform change is not understood.

The identification of a modified host-encoded protein (PrP) and its filamentous aggregates which copurify with infectivity[17–20] has raised the possibility that the modified PrP is an integral component (if not the sole component) of the virus. The PrP molecule is a 33- to 35-kilodalton (kd) glycosylated membrane protein, localized to neurons in the brain.[27–29] Both normal and scrapie-associated PrP are derived from the same gene,[30] and the level of expression of this gene does not change during the infectious process.[28] How the normal PrP is changed into a protease-resistant fibrillar aggregate during the infectious process is now being investigated.[31] A central role for this protein in the replication of the infectious agent is now demonstrated by the linkage of the PrP gene to a gene which controls the incubation period (*Sinc* gene).[32]

A fundamental question, yet to be settled, is whether these viruses have a nucleic acid genome, either DNA or RNA. Certain physical properties suggest that a nucleic acid is not an integral part of the infectious particle; these properties include resistance to low pH, nucleases, UV irradiation at 237 nm, zinc hydrolysis, photochemical inactivation with psoralens, and chemical modification by hydroxylamine.[21] Some conventional viruses share one or more of these physical properties. An answer to this question must await better techniques for purification.

Attempts to alter the course of infection by immunosuppression or immunopotentiation have failed, although some variables that affect splenic function can alter the incubation period. For example, removal or absence of the spleen increases the incubation period after peripheral routes of inoculation. Most antiviral drugs are ineffective in reducing viral titer.

Physical Properties and Physicochemical Inactivation Profile

Some of the physical properties outlined in Table 42–4 suggest that the monomeric form of the virus is very small, but they must be interpreted cautiously. Thus, the known tendency of the virus for self-aggregation may yield falsely low values in irradiation inactivation studies. In any event, as smaller and smaller conventional viruses are discovered,[33] the apparent size of the unconventional viruses becomes less paradoxical.

The physicochemical inactivation profile listed in Table 42–5 illustrates the point that these viruses are inactivated by a number of processes which are easily amenable for use in routine disinfecting and sterilization. The aspects are discussed in more detail in the section on precautions, below.

EPIDEMIOLOGY

The duration of both kuru and CJD ranges from 6 months to a year, and therefore the incidence and prevalence are approximately equal. The incidence of kuru has steadily declined since the cessation of cannibalism in the 1950s. At the height of the kuru epidemic 40 years ago, over 90% of deaths in adult women were from kuru. Since that time, kuru has progressively disappeared, first among children, and successively thereafter among adolescents and recently among young adults. The youngest living patient is now over 30 years of age. No one born in a village since cannibalism ceased has ever developed kuru, although the disease continues to affect people born earlier in the same villages. Each year new patients are 1 or 2 years older than those of the previous year.

There have been several hundred kuru orphans under surveillance, that is, children born since 1957 to mothers who were dying of kuru. Not one orphan has yet developed kuru. More than 300 of these children are now over 15 years old; some are over age 30. The conclusion is that the many children with kuru who filled Okapa Hospital in the 1950s were not infected by their mothers but rather by some other mechanism. In spite of intensive studies, no genetic factor has been identified which may have predisposed or prevented infection with kuru.

The epidemiologic characteristics of CJD have been reviewed by Brown.[34] In our epidemiologic study of more than 1400 cases of CJD,[35] the disease was shown to have a worldwide distribution, documented in more than 50 countries. At present, we have recorded more than 2000 cases of CJD worldwide, and the latest figures for the United States show an average annual mortality of 0.43 death per million. Epidemic clustering of cases has not been found in the United States, France, Chile, or Japan, where careful searches have been undertaken. However, several foci have been identified in Czechoslovakia, Italy, Hungary, and Israel. The very high incidence of CJD in Libyan-born Israeli Jews (more than 30 per million) remains unexplained, although a high familial incidence has been detected.[36]

Since the only demonstrated transmission of CJD between humans has been iatrogenic (contaminated surgical instruments, contaminated organ transplants, and contaminated batches of growth hormone prepared from human pituitaries), it is of some concern that the incidence of previous surgery or other neurologic diseases seem to be increased in patients with CJD. A recent study from Japan also found a significantly increased incidence of surgical operations and physical injuries in patients with CJD compared with controls. Analysis of occupations of cases of CJD did not reveal any particular groups at increased risk.

The virus causing scrapie is closely related to that causing CJD; when inoculated into nonhuman primates, scrapie produces a disease indistinguishable from CJD. The question arises, can scrapie cause CJD in man? There is no evidence that persons living in areas in which scrapie is endemic are at a greater risk of developing CJD than those living in nonendemic areas. The worldwide pattern of distribution of scrapie does not correlate with the distribution of CJD.[35] For example, in Australia, where overt scrapie has not been detected in more than 20 years, the incidence of CJD is close to that of the United States and France, where scrapie is endemic. Similarly, within the United States, the states with the largest number of reported outbreaks of scrapie (Illinois, Texas, Indiana, Ohio, and California) do not have the highest rates of reported CJD. Such a comparison is of limited value, however, since scrapie-infected material may have been widely disseminated in meat throughout the country. Although it has been suggested that the high incidence of CJD among Libyan-born Israelis might be related to their habits of eating sheep eyes or brain, natural scrapie has not yet been reported in the Middle East.

The demonstration that both scrapie and CJD can be transmitted to the squirrel monkey by the oral route[37] suggests that the zoonotic spread of scrapie is indeed possible. Even in these experiments, however, the possibility that the monkeys infected themselves through mucosal or skin defects has not yet been excluded. Such a mechanism is probably operative in mink that have been fed on scrapie-infected tissue and could be expected since the subcutaneous and intradermal routes of inoculation are also effective in causing infection.

Up to 15% of all cases of CJD have a family history of disease consistent with autosomal dominant transmission.[25] The onset of disease in familial cases is significantly earlier than in sporadic cases. There is no evidence of a maternal effect or of prenatal vertical transmission of the virus. Temporal and spatial separations between affected members demonstrates that incubation periods ranging at least from one to four decades are to be expected. Affected siblings tend to die at the same age and not at the same time, which is consistent with some form of vertical transmission (either prenatal or early postnatal), assuming rather uniform incubation periods. The precise mechanism of spread of the virus in familial CJD remains unknown. The data are consistent with the hypothesis of a genetically inherited susceptibility to infection which is acquired in early infancy or childhood. Since the PrP gene is linked to a gene which controls the incubation period in mice,[32] it is possible that further research will show that the human PrP gene is in some fashion operating in the expression of the familial form of CJD.

PATHOGENESIS

Transmission

The epidemiologic features of kuru point strongly to transmission by cannibalism, a form of transmission that is entirely consistent with the biologic properties of the virus determined experimentally. The regular disappearance of kuru is inconsistent with the existence of any natural reservoir of kuru besides man: with animal or insect vectors, with genomic integration of an infectious agent or other types of in utero transmission, or with neonatal infection including transmission by milk. None of those modes of infection would explain the regular pattern with which kuru has actually disappeared. Moreover, there has been no convincing evidence that case-to-case transmission by noninvasive bodily contact has ever occurred, provided one allows that the act of cannibalism involves some form of invasive inoculation, as through mucosal defects or breaks in the skin or conjunctiva.

There are three broad categories to explain the occurrence of CJD: (1) case-to-case transmission, including lateral contact transmission, vertical or familial transmission, and transmission resulting from iatrogenic contamination; the possibilities of asymptomatic subclinical infection and an inherited susceptibility or resistance to infection must also be taken into account; (2) activation of an endogenous or latent virus infection, through either some environmental trigger or a genetically determined mechanism; and (3) zoonotic transmission of the scrapie virus from sheep, goats, or other animals.

Of these three main hypotheses, the zoonotic transmission of scrapie is, at present, the most difficult to test. In spite of the fact that CJD occurs where overt scrapie is absent, details concerning subclinical infection of scrapie in domestic animals are unknown. Although five species of monkeys developed a disease indistinguishable from CJD after inoculation with the scrapie virus, to date the chimpanzee has remained unaffected, despite intracerebral inoculation with large doses of scrapie. Activation of an endogenous (latent) virus infection cannot be excluded on the basis of present evidence, but it seems unlikely.

Within the hypothetical category of case-to-case transmission, most mechanisms now demonstrated for the spread of hepatitis B virus can also be invoked to explain the spread of CJD virus. However, the iatrogenic spread of CJD is the only mechanism that has been clearly demonstrated; it is a mechanism consistent with the presumed mode of transmission of human kuru and one that is most consistent with the biologic behavior of the CJD virus in experimental studies.

One must conclude that the natural mechanism of spread and the reservoir of the CJD virus remain unknown at present. Future case-control studies will be directed at determining the relative contribution of iatrogenic transmission, while at the same time investigating the other conjectural modes of transmission.

Incubation

The long incubation period of these virus infections is emphasized above as a hallmark of their unconventionality. The youngest patient with kuru was 4 years old and died at age 5; this sets a minimum known incubation period of this disease. Since current patients with kuru came from villages where cannibalism ceased more than three decades ago, an upper limit of the incubation period will be at least 30 years. The factors governing these variable incubation periods are unknown, but one might postulate the effect of route of inoculation and dose of inoculum.

The confirmed iatrogenic transmission of CJD by direct intracerebral[38] or intraocular[39] inoculation yielded an incubation period of less than 2 years. Conversely, the familial occurrence of CJD[25] suggests that incubation periods may exceed four to five decades. Experimental studies have clearly shown that peripheral routes of inoculation result in variable "takes" with exceedingly long incubation periods in some instances.

Clinicopathologic Syndromes

Common Syndromes

The clinical and pathologic characteristics of kuru have been well described.[5, 7, 9] More recent observations of kuru have been limited by the scarcity of cases as the disease progressively disappears. Clinically, kuru differs from CJD most noticeably in the absence of a profound dementia. This clinical difference in the two diseases is difficult to correlate with the pathologic findings: in kuru, the cerebral cortex is involved in all cases studied to date. However, the degree of cerebral cortical involvement in kuru appears to be less than that seen in the typical case of CJD.

In the early reports on the pathologic changes in human kuru, the presence or absence of spongiform change was not clearly stated. In retrospect, realizing the pathognomonic significance of this change, we have been able to review the sections of 22 cases of human kuru, and in all, the presence of a typical spongiform encephalopathy was found. Another point of some interest is the occurrence of amyloid plaques (kuru plaques) in more than 70% of cases of human kuru. These kuru plaques occur more frequently in cases with a longer duration of illness and may provide a clue to the pathogenesis of the amyloid plaque of Alzheimer's disease.[40]

The clinical characteristics of transmissible CJD have been reviewed by Roos et al[15] and Traub et al.[41] CJD presents as a subacute dementia, evolving over weeks to several months and is accompanied by pyramidal, extrapyramidal, and cerebellar signs. Although the mean age at death is 57 years,[35] CJD may occur in the late teens and early twenties. At variable stages in the progression of the disease, myoclonus with periodic sharp-wave complexes in the EEG appear. Dividing the course of the illness into three stages, Bernoulli et al[42] found a characteristic pattern in the presentation of CJD, in that sensorimotor disintegration (disturbances of stance, gait, and motor control, visual disturbances, dizziness, and vertigo) was a prominent early feature of the first stage, where there is only a subjective awareness of physical or mental disorder, insufficient to impair the patient's normal daily activities. In the second stage of the illness, there are unequivocal signs of neurologic disease, usually spasticity with extrapyramidal and cerebellar signs and impairment of mental function sufficient to cause an alteration in the patient's day-to-day activities. In the third (and terminal) stage of illness, there is an incapacitating dementia, usually with severe myoclonus. Myoclonus may appear intermittently in the first and second stages, but it remains discrete. Although previous authors have tried to subdivide CJD into different subtypes based on clinical presentation (eg, Heidenhain's syndrome with occipital cortical involvement or the ataxic form of CJD with prominent cerebellar signs), an analysis of these types of cases shows an overlapping of clinical and pathologic features to an extent that such subclassifications have little practical benefit. While it is correct to keep these clinical variants in mind, the typical case of CJD presents little diagnostic difficulty at a time when the patient has entered the final stage of disease. The pathology of CJD is discussed in the following section.

Uncommon Syndromes

Variant forms of kuru are not described. Many cases with early kuru symptoms which resolved are recorded, but in most instances, these can be attributed to a form of hysterical conversion reaction. While the majority of cases of CJD present the typical clinical and pathologic features of spongiform encephalopathy, in the past few years we have recognized several distinct variants. Most outstanding were a series of cases with chronic cerebellar ataxia, dementia, and amyloid plaque deposition in the brain.[40] These cases, some of which are transmissible as spongiform encephalopathies to animals, bear a close resemblance to the Gerstmann-Sträussler syndrome. The amyloid plaque deposition in these cases is intermediate in morphology to the amyloid plaque of Alzheimer's disease and the kuru plaque. Immunocytochemically, however, the amyloid in kuru, CJD, and the Gerstmann-Sträussler syndrome is composed of the PrP molecule. In contrast, the amyloid plaque in Alzheimer's disease is composed of the A4 protein (see below).

Increasingly, white matter degeneration is being recognized in cases of CJD occurring to an extent that cannot be accounted for by secondary myelin loss. In one Japanese case, virus isolated from the brain caused extensive white matter degeneration in the experimentally infected rodents. We presume that this isolate and others from Japan represent differing strains of the CJD virus. Two unique cases of transmissible spongiform encephalopathy have been described. One patient, a neurosurgeon, presented with a disseminated vasculitis and brainstem and spinal cord signs.[43] The other was a patient without any of the typical clinical or pathologic signs of CJD, whose brain biopsy inoculum caused an experimental spongiform encephalopathy in hamsters.[44] This patient recovered from a briefly incapacitating neurologic illness. Such a virus isolation, if confirmed in similar situations, could be taken as evidence either for widespread subclinical infection or as evidence that the CJD virus can cause an acute neurologic illness with recovery.

Arising from Jakob's original descriptions, a concept developed of a distinct nosologic entity of motor neuron disease, spasticity, and dementia, with or without extrapyramidal signs. These syndromes of motor neuron disease with dementia have been grouped together under the heading of ''amyotrophic CJD.'' The amyotrophic form of CJD is clinically and pathologically distinct from the transmissible spongiform encephalopathies. It is an ''untransmissible'' disease based on present criteria and shares features more in common with the usual sporadic and familial forms of uncomplicated motor neuron disease (amyotrophic lateral sclerosis).

LABORATORY DIAGNOSIS OF INFECTION

There are no laboratory tests for definitive diagnosis short of direct transmission experiments. In the absence of facilities for these tests, confirmatory diagnosis is made on histopathologic changes in the CNS. The isolation of scrapie-associated filaments and visualization by electron microscopy is also proving to be of some diagnostic value.[17]

The neuropathology of spongiform encephalopathy as seen in CJD has been reviewed.[46] A distinction was drawn between the fine vacuolation of the neuropil which is characteristic of the disease (spongiform change) and the rather coarse loosening of the brain parenchyma associated with severe gliosis which is a nonspecific change (status spongiosus). Spongiform change was most severe and readily apparent in cases of relatively short duration (6 months or less), whereas status spongiosus with concomitant gliosis

was seen in those cases of longer duration. This distinction between spongiform change and status spongiosus is not merely semantic, but is of practical diagnostic value. That the spongiform change is pathognomonic is confirmed from the study of the lesions in the brains of experimentally infected animals (see Figure 42–1). By far the majority of cases of typical CJD present little diagnostic problem when the spongiform change is well developed in the cerebral cortex, striatum, medial thalamus, and molecular layer of the cerebellum. In biopsy material of cerebral cortex, care must be taken to rule out ice-crystal artifact as a cause of vacuolation; diagnosis is virtually impossible from frozen sections, and apart from the possible dangers of handling frozen material (see section on precautions), frozen sections of biopsy material in cases of adult-onset dementia have little diagnostic value. Frozen biopsy and autopsy material, however, is extremely valuable for transmission studies and further research.

Several types of histologic change present difficulty in interpretation. First, vacuolation may occur in the most superficial layers of the cerebral cortex, the molecular layer, and subpial zone. This type of vacuolation has proved to be nonspecific, being present in association with an anoxic or metabolic derangement preceding death. Usually in these types of cases, spongiform change is not seen in the striatum, thalamus, or cerebellum. No case where vacuolation has been restricted to the superficial cortical layers has been transmitted as spongiform encephalopathy to experimental animals. Second, vacuolation may be restricted to a perinuclear distribution in cortical neurons. This presumably artifactual change, when observed in isolation, also has no diagnostic significance. Third, in some cases of spongiform encephalopathy of long duration (9 months and longer), the severity of neuronal loss and gliosis in the cerebral cortex masks the presence of discrete spongiform vacuolation in the neuropil. In such cases, examination of severely affected cortex in isolation from the remaining areas of brain presents a nonspecific picture of severe cortical degeneration, indistinguishable from the many types of severe CJD that we have examined to date. From inspection of subcortical areas (such as striatum, thalamus, mesencephalon, and molecular layer of cerebellum), where the pathologic process is not as advanced as in the cerebral cortex, one can usually identify the pathognomonic spongiform change. Fourth, in occasional cases of Alzheimer's disease, and other chronic degenerative conditions, isolated and rare vacuoles are seen which, at a light and electron microscopic level, are randomly distributed through the cortical gray matter. In Alzheimer's disease, these vacuoles are occasionally seen in the region of the subiculum and parahippocampal gyrus. The significance of these changes is uncertain, and there is no evidence at present to suggest that the occurrence of these widely scattered vacuoles is indicative of the presence of a virus capable of inducing a spongiform encephalopathy.

PREVENTION AND TREATMENT

There is no known specific treatment for these infections. Affected patients are treated symptomatically. There is, however, hope for prevention of the disease. Kuru has been virtually eliminated by the cessation of cannibalism. If CJD is caused, in a significant proportion of cases, by iatrogenic transmission, then proper attention to disinfecting contaminated materials will lead to a reduction in incidence (see next section). In the absence of any detectable specific immune response, the prospect for a vaccine is remote.

PRECAUTIONS IN HANDLING POTENTIALLY INFECTED MATERIALS FROM PATIENTS WITH CREUTZFELDT-JAKOB DISEASE

With the recognition of person-to-person transmission of CJD, and the publication of guidelines in handling potentially infectious CJD material,[47] the medical community overreacted to a degree that the care of patients with CJD is being jeopardized, biopsies and autopsies are being refused, and irrational decisions are being made in the general handling of potentially infectious material. Such reactions are based largely on the fear of the unknown. This section attempts to place the problem in a rational perspective (see also references 48–52).

First, there is no evidence in the natural history of CJD or kuru for transmission by noninvasive bodily contact, although the high proportion of cases of familial CJD suggests that this may be one possible mechanism. Moreover, no infectious virus has yet been documented in external secretion (tears, saliva, feces, urine, sweat) or the skin or hair of CJD patients. There is no epidemiologic evidence that medical or ancillary personnel are at increased risk of developing CJD.[35] The demonstration of infectious virus in the CSF, blood, and viscera means that appropriate precautions should be taken when handling this material, or when using instruments exposed to this material. But the general nursing care of a patient with CJD should pose no special problem, provided that open wounds are dealt with appropriately. This would mean that there is no indication for isolation or barrier nursing of a CJD patient, either in hospital or in a nursing home environment. No special risks in the home nursing of a patient are seen. Linen and other materials in contact with open wounds or bedsores should be autoclaved or soaked for 1 hour in 0.5% sodium hypochlorite (a tenfold dilution of household bleach).[49] More recent inactivation studies on the CJD virus have shown that sodium hydroxide (either 1N or 0.1N) is very effective,[53] and offers marked advantages over sodium hypochlorite as it is far less corrosive to fabrics or metal instruments (with the exception of aluminum). Contaminated skin may be placed in contact with a 1N solution of sodium hydroxide for five minutes, then washed with water or a mild (0.1N) hydrochloric acid solution.[53] Instruments (such as venipuncture needles, syringes) which come into contact with blood, CSF, or other viscera should be disinfected or discarded by incineration, calling for no more than routine hospital practice. Medical laboratory personnel and technicians should take the same care as that already exercised in handling blood, CSF, or other body fluids potentially infectious for the hepatitis viruses or specimens obtained from patients with such diverse infectious diseases as acquired immunodeficiency syndrome (AIDS), tuberculosis, poliomyelitis, and leprosy. Reassurance must be given that there are no definitive cases of laboratory-acquired CJD infection.

The continuing need for cerebral biopsy and necropsy in cases not only of CJD, but also of all chronic degenerative diseases of the nervous system, has been stressed by Baringer et al.[51] With adequate precautions, there is no reason for a neurosurgeon to refuse to perform a brain biopsy if the appropriate medical indi-

cations in favor of biopsy are present. The same applies to general surgical procedures performed on patients with CJD. These precautions consist primarily of attention to the adequate sterilization of instruments, usually by autoclaving. Instruments that cannot be autoclaved should be soaked in sodium hypochlorite (0.5%), but notice should be taken that this strong oxidizing agent will damage metal surfaces. As noted above, solutions of sodium hydroxide (1N or 0.1N) may also be used without fear of damaging nonaluminum metallic surfaces. Care should be taken to avoid accidental self-inoculation with contaminated instruments. As a rule, there is no indication for a frozen section to be performed in this type of patient coming to cerebral biopsy.

Similarly, there is no reason why an autopsy should be refused on the grounds of a clinical diagnosis of CJD. The recommendations of the Howie report[52] seem appropriate. Instruments and materials can be adequately disinfected as outlined above. After fresh tissue is taken from the brain, cord, and viscera for virologic and other research studies, specimens for histopathology can be fixed in 10% formalin. After fixation, blocks can be taken and then autoclaved, while in 10% formalin. This will not cause any deleterious effect on subsequent processing. The processing of histologic tissues requires no added precautions other than care taken to avoid cutting oneself on the microtome knife and that solutions used during the processing should be either autoclaved or incinerated. Again, it should be emphasized that there is no evidence that histopathologists and laboratory technicians are at increased risk of developing CJD, in spite of their handling of tissues (previously without special precautions) for at least the last 40 years.

Mortuary attendants and undertakers should be advised to avoid accidental self-inoculation during the preparation of the body for burial. Certainly, there is no indication against embalming and no reason to vary the usual procedure of burial after the body is prepared.

RELATIONSHIP OF ALZHEIMER'S DISEASE TO CREUTZFELDT-JAKOB DISEASE

Alzheimer's disease shares a number of clinical and pathologic features in common with CJD. Clinically, many patients with Alzheimer's disease with rapid deterioration develop myoclonus and an abnormal EEG similar to that seen in CJD. Pathologically, there is a spectrum of amyloid deposition which overlaps in both diseases.[40] At the present time, scrapie in mice is the only model available for the study of cerebral amyloid deposition. Vacuolation at a light and electron microscopic level is seen in some cases of Alzheimer's disease (see above), but usually not to a degree that a distinction between the two diseases cannot be made. CJD occurs rarely in families with Alzheimer's disease, but more commonly, familial Alzheimer's disease occurs with one or more members developing a syndrome of rapidly progressive dementia and myoclonus, but with changes of Alzheimer's disease in the brain.[25] The most intriguing relationship to emerge has been the recognition that the Alzheimer's disease amyloid is derived from a glycosylated membrane protein.[54, 55] This protein, termed A4, therefore shows that a similar mechanism may operate in both Alzheimer's disease and in the unconventional virus diseases in that host-encoded proteins are rendered amyloidogenic. Overall, there is no direct evidence that Alzheimer's disease is causally related to CJD, but the indirect and circumstantial evidence outlined above provides an impetus for further research in this area.

REFERENCES

1. Prusiner SB, Hadlow WJ (eds): *Slow Transmissible Disease of the Nervous System. Volume I: Clinical, Epidemiological, Genetic and Pathological Aspects of the Spongiform Encephalopathies. Volume 2: Pathogenesis, Immunology, Virology, and Molecular Biology of the Spongiform Encephalopathies.* New York, Academic Press, 1971, p 472.
2. Prusiner SB, McKinley MP (eds): *Prions: Their Structure, Biology, and Diseases.* New York, Academic Press, 1987.
3. Sigurdsson B: Observations on three slow infections of sheep. *Br Vet J* 1954; 110:255–270, 307–322, 341–354.
4. Hadlow WJ: Scrapie and kuru. *Lancet* 1959; 2:289–290.
5. Gajdusek DC, Zigas V: Degenerative disease of the central nervous system in New Guinea. The endemic occurrence of "kuru" in the native population. *N Engl J Med* 1957; 257:974–978.
6. Gajdusek DC, Gibbs CJ Jr, Alpers M: Experimental transmission of a kuru-like syndrome to chimpanzees. *Nature* 1966; 209:794–796.
7. Gajdusek DC: Unconventional viruses and the origin and disappearance of kuru. *Science* 1977; 197:943–960.
8. Alpers MP: Epidemiology and ecology of kuru, in Prusiner SB, Hadlow WJ (eds): *Slow Transmissible Diseases of the Nervous System. Volume I: Clinical, Epidemiological, Genetic, and Pathological Aspects of the Spongiform Encephalopathies.* New York, Academic Press, 1979, pp 67–90.
9. Klatzo I, Gajdusek DC, Zigas V: Pathology of kuru. *Lab Invest* 1959; 8:799–847.
10. Creutzfeldt HG: Über eine eigenartige herdförmige Erkrankung des Zentralnervensystems. *Z Gesamte Neurol Psychiatr* 1920; 57:1–18.
11. Jakob A: Über eigenartige Erkrankungen des Zentralnervensystems mit bemerkenswertem anatomischem Befunde (spastische Pseudosklerose-Encephalomyelopathie mit disseminierten Degenerationsherden). *Dtsch Z Nervenheilk* 1921; 70:132–146.
12. Jakob A: Über eigenartige Erkrankungen des Zentralnervensystems mit bemerkenswertem anatomischem Befunde (spastiche Pseudosklerose-Encephalomyelopathie mit disseminierten Degenerationsherden). *Z Gesamte Neurol Psychiatr* 1921; 64:147–228.
13. Jakob A: Die extrapyramidalen Erkrankungen, in Foerster O, Wilmanns K (eds): *Monographien aus dem Gesamtgebiete der Neurologie und Psychiatrie.* Berlin, Julius Springer, 1923; 37:215–245.
14. Masters CL, Gajdusek DC: The spectrum of Creutzfeldt-Jakob disease and the virus-induced subacute spongiform encephalopathies, in Smith WT, Cavanagh JB (eds): *Recent Advances in Neuropathology.* Edinburgh, Churchill Livingstone, 1982, vol 2, pp 139–163.
15. Roos R, Gajdusek DC, Gibbs CJ Jr: The clinical characteristics of transmissible Creutzfeldt-Jakob disease. *Brain* 1973; 96:1–20.
16. Gibbs CJ Jr, Gajdusek DC, Asher DM, et al: Creutzfeldt-Jakob disease (spongiform encephalopathy): Transmission to the chimpanzee. *Science* 1968; 161:388–389.
17. Merz PA, Somerville RA, Wisniewski HM, et al: Abnormal fibrils from scrapie-infected brain. *Acta Neuropathol* 1981; 54:63–74.
18. Bolton DC, McKinley MP, Prusiner SB: Identification of a protein that purifies with the scrapie prion. *Science* 1982; 218:1309–1311.
19. Prusiner SB, McKinley MP, Bowman KA, et al: Scrapie prions aggregate to form amyloid-like birefringent rods. *Cell* 1983; 35:349–358.
20. Bendheim PE, Barry RA, DeArmond SJ, et al: Antibodies to a scrapie prion protein. *Nature* 1984; 310:418–421.
21. Prusiner SB: Novel proteinaceous infectious particles cause scrapie. *Science* 1982; 216:136–144.
22. Kimberlin RH, Walker CA: Pathogenesis of mouse scrapie: Evidence for neural spread of infection to the CNS. *J Gen Virol* 1980; 51:183–187.
23. Dickinson AG, Fraser H: An assessment of the genetics of scrapie in sheep and mice, in Prusiner SB, Hadlow WJ (eds): *Slow Transmissible Diseases of the Nervous System. Volume I: Clinical, Epidemiological, Genetic, and Pathological Aspects of the Spongiform Encephalopathies.* New York, Academic Press, 1979, pp 367–385.
24. Clarke MC: Infection of cell cultures with scrapie agent, in Prusiner SB, Hadlow WB (eds): *Slow Transmissible Diseases of the Nervous System. Volume 2: Pathogenesis, Immunology, Virology, and Molecular Biology of Spongiform Encephalopathies.* New York, Academic Press, 1979, pp 225–233.
25. Masters CL, Gajdusek DC, Gibbs CJ Jr: The familial occurrence of Creutzfeldt-Jakob disease and Alzheimer's disease. *Brain* 1981; 104:535–558.
26. Brooks BR, Swarz JR, Johnson RT: Spongiform polioencephalomyelopathy caused by a murine retrovirus. I. Pathogenesis of infection in newborn mice. *Lab Invest* 1980; 43:480–486.
27. Bolton DC, Meyer RK, Prusiner SB: Scrapie PrP 27–30 is a sialoglycoprotein. *J Virol* 1985; 53:596–606.
28. Oesch B, Westaway D, Wälchli M, et al: A cellular gene encodes scrapie PrP 27–30 protein. *Cell* 1985; 40:735–746.
29. Kretzschmar HA, Prusiner SB, Stowring LE, et al: Scrapie prion proteins are synthesized in neurons. *Am J Pathol* 1986; 122:1–5.
30. Basler K, Oesch B, Scoff M, et al: Scrapie and cellular PrP isoforms are encoded by the same chromosomal gene. *Cell* 1986; 46:417–428.
31. Hope J, Multhaup G, Reekie LJD, et al: Molecular pathology of scrapie-associated fibril protein (PrP) in mouse brain affected by the ME7 strain of scrapie. *Eur J Biochem* 1988; 172:271–277.
32. Westaway D, Goodman PA, Mirenda CA, et al: Distinct prion proteins in short and long scrapie incubation period mice. *Cell* 1987; 51:651–662.
33. Tischer I, Gelderblom H, Vettermann W, et al: A very small porcine virus with circular single-stranded DNA. *Nature* 1982; 295:64–66.
34. Brown P: An epidemiologic critique of Creutzfeldt-Jakob disease. *Epidemiol Rev* 1980; 2:113–135.
35. Masters CL, Harris JO, Gajdusek DC, et al: Creutzfeldt-Jakob disease: Patterns of worldwide occurrence and the significance of familial and sporadic clustering. *Ann Neurol* 1979; 5:177–188.
36. Neugut RH, Neugut AI, Kahana E, et al: Creutzfeldt-Jakob disease: Familial clustering among Libyan-born Israelis. *Neurology* 1979; 29:225–231.
37. Gibbs CJ Jr, Amyx HL, Bacote A, et al: Oral transmission of kuru, Creutzfeldt-Jakob disease, and scrapie to nonhuman primates. *J Infect Dis* 1980; 142:205–208.
38. Bernoulli C, Siegfried J, Baumgartner G, et al: Danger of accidental person-to-person transmission of Creutzfeldt-Jakob disease by surgery. *Lancet* 1977; 1:478–479.
39. Duffy P, Wolf J, Collins G, et al: Possible person-to-person transmission of Creutzfeldt-Jakob disease. *N Engl J Med* 1974; 290:692–693.
40. Masters CL, Gajdusek DC, Gibbs CJ Jr: Creutzfeldt-Jakob disease virus isolations from the Gerstmann-Sträussler syndrome. With an analysis of the various forms of amyloid plaque deposition in the virus-induced spongiform encephalopathies. *Brain* 1981; 104:559–588.
41. Traub RD, Gajdusek DC, Gibbs CJ Jr: Transmissible virus dementia. The relation of transmissible spongiform encephalopathy to Creutzfeldt-Jakob disease, in Kinsbourne M, Smith L (eds): *Aging and Dementia.* Flushing, New York, Spectrum Publications, 1977; pp 91–172.
42. Bernoulli CC, Masters CL, Gajdusek DC, et al: Early clinical features of Creutzfeldt-Jakob disease (subacute spongiform encephalopathy), in Prusiner SB, Hadlow WJ (eds): *Slow Transmissible Diseases of the Nervous System. Volume I: Clinical, Epidemiological, Genetic and Pathological Aspects of the Spongiform Encephalopathies.* New York, Academic Press, 1979, pp 229–251.

43. Schoene WC, Masters CL, Gibbs CJ Jr, et al: Transmissible spongiform encephalopathy (Creutzfeldt-Jakob disease). Atypical clinical and pathological findings. *Arch Neurol* 1981; 38:473–477.

44. Manuelidis EE, Manuelidis L, Pincus JH, et al: Transmission, from man to hamster, of Creutzfeldt-Jakob disease with clinical recovery. *Lancet* 1978; 2:40–42.

45. Salazar AM, Masters CL, Gajdusek DC, et al: Syndromes of amyotropic lateral sclerosis and dementia: Relation to transmissible Creutzfeldt-Jakob disease virus. *Ann Neurol* 1983; 14:17–26.

46. Masters CL, Richardson EP Jr: Subacute spongiform encephalopathy (Creutzfeldt-Jakob disease). The nature and progression of spongiform change. *Brain* 1978; 101:333–344.

47. Gajdusek DC, Gibbs CJ Jr, Asher DM, et al: Precautions in the medical care of, and in handling materials from, patients with transmissible virus dementia (Creutzfeldt-Jakob disease). *N Engl J Med* 1977; 297:1253–1258.

48. Chatigny MA, Prusiner SB: Biohazards of investigations on the transmissible spongiform encephalopathies. *Rev Infect Dis* 1980; 2:713–724.

49. Brown P, Gibbs CJ Jr, Amyx HL, et al: Chemical disinfection of Creutzfeldt-Jakob disease virus. *N Engl J Med* 1982; 306:1279–1282.

50. Centers for Disease Control: Precautions in taking care of patients with suspected Creutzfeldt-Jakob disease, in *National Nosocomial Infections Study Report*. Annual Summary 1979, issued March 1982. US Dept of Health and Human Services, Public Health Services, Atlanta, Centers for Disease Control, 1982; pp 35–36.

51. Baringer JR, Gajdusek DC, Gibbs CJ Jr, et al: Transmissible dementias: Current problems in tissue handling. *Neurology* 1980; 30:302–303.

52. Howie J (chairman): *Code of Practice for the Prevention of Infection in Clinical Laboratories and Post-mortem Rooms*. London, HMSO, Dept of Health and Social Security, 1978.

53. Brown P, Rohwer RG, Gajdusek DC: Sodium hydroxide decontamination of Creutzfeldt-Jakob disease virus. *N Engl J Med* 1984; 310:727.

54. Masters CL, Simms G, Weinman NA, et al: Amyloid plaque core protein in Alzheimer disease and Down syndrome. *Proc Natl Acad Sci USA* 1985; 82:4245–4249.

55. Kang J, Lemaire H-G, Unterbeck A, et al: The precursor of Alzheimer's disease amyloid A4 protein resembles a cell-surface receptor. *Nature* 1987; 325:733–736.

43

Parvoviruses

M. J. Anderson

HISTORY

Electron microscopy of stool samples yielded the first specimen of a human parvovirus.[1] These fecal parvoviruses are often termed "small round featureless viruses" or "SRFVs" and have been described in association with gastrointestinal (GI) symptoms following the consumption of bivalve shellfish.[2] However SRFVs may also be found in stool specimens from asymptomatic individuals, so that their precise pathogenic role is uncertain.[3] Often referred to as "parvovirus-like" are the fecal pathogens Norwalk virus, and Ditchling agent; these viruses are not parvoviruses. Their size (27 nm) is at the upper end of the range for parvoviruses, and their surface structure resembles that of caliciviruses more than that of parvoviruses. Definitive classification of these agents awaits their biochemical characterization.

In 1975 a second type of parvovirus was found in human material, in the serum of asymptomatic blood donors. This virus, now called parvovirus B19, was discovered by chance, as an agent responsible for false-positive reactions in counterimmunoelectrophoresis tests for hepatitis B virus surface antigen. These tests used human serum as a source of antibody, and the detector serum contained, in addition to anti-hepatitis B surface antigen, antibody to a number of other viruses including human parvovirus.[4] Electron microscopy of serum specimens giving these false-positive reactions revealed naked icosahedral particles with a diameter of 20 nm (Figure 43–1). In 1983, the precise chemical nature of the virus was described permitting its identification as an autonomous human parvovirus,[5, 6] thus obviating the need for the variety of names such as "human parvovirus-like agent," "serum parvovirus-like virus," and "B19," after one of the original 11 isolates which had been used in the intervening 8 years. Although only a single serotype is recognized, the name B19 has been recommended by the International Committee for the Taxonomy of Viruses, and is achieving widespread usage.

Most recently, a third type of parvovirus has been recovered from human tissue: RA-1, an autonomous parvovirus, was isolated in suckling mice inoculated with synovial tissue from cases of rheumatoid arthritis.[7] The biology, epidemiology, and pathogenesis of this agent in the human population remains to be determined.

Thus, although three distinct autonomous parvoviruses are known to infect man, only one, B19, has been shown conclusively to be pathogenic. This was not always so; for some 5 years following its discovery those B19 infections detected were either found to be asymptomatic, detected by chance in the screening of donated blood for hepatitis B virus, or associated with mild nonspecific symptoms.[8] Certain properties of autonomous parvoviruses, such as their requirement for their hosts cells to be actively dividing, would seem to confer definite pathogenic potential. Among animals parvovirus infections are a significant cause of morbidity and fetal loss. In 1980, the pathogenic potential of B19 began to be realized with the appreciation of its causal association with the

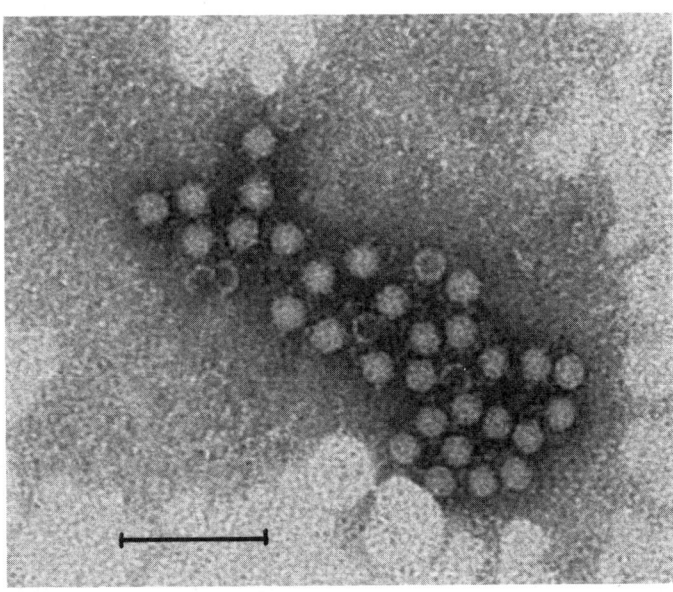

Figure 43–1. Immune electron micrograph of human parvovirus B19, from plasma of an asymptomatic blood donor. Bar = 100 nm.

aplastic crisis of chronic hemolytic anemias.[9] More recently, the common manifestation of B19 infection has been found to be erythema infectiosum (EI), or fifth disease,[10] uniting a virus in search of a disease with an obviously infectious condition of hitherto unknown etiology.

PROPERTIES OF THE VIRUS

Classification

Parvoviruses infect a wide spectrum of host species. Within the family ***Parvoviridae*** are three genera: densoviruses, dependoviruses, and parvoviruses. Densoviruses or densonucleosis viruses are viruses of invertebrates, infecting only hosts of the order Insecta. Dependoviruses are defective parvoviruses requiring coinfection with a helper virus for their own replication to proceed; first described in association with adenovirus infections, in the past these viruses were called "adeno-associated" viruses, or AAVs. Although dependoviruses have been described infecting a number of mammalian species, including man, no causal link has been shown between AAV infection and disease. The third genus within the ***Parvoviridae*** is formed of autonomous parvoviruses capable of independent replication. It is with the autonomous parvovirus B19 which infects man that this chapter is concerned.

Physical and Biologic Characteristics

B19 virus is a naked icosahedral virus with a diameter of 22 nm, and buoyant density in cesium chloride of 1.3 to 1.4 g/dL. The capsid comprises two structural proteins, VP_1 and VP_2, of molecular weight 83 kilodaltons (kd) and 58 kd; VP_2 is the predominant species. Together these account for between 60% and 80% of the virion mass.

B19 is currently regarded as existing as a single serotype, antigenically unrelated to either the human fecal parvoviruses[11] or RA-1. Unlike the majority of autonomous parvoviruses, B19 has not been reported as able to agglutinate erythrocytes from any

animal species. Systems for the in vitro growth of B19 in tissue culture are not widely available (see below), so that extensive neutralization studies have not yet been carried out. However, by analogy with the feline and canine parvoviruses[12] the existence of several overlapping neutralizing epitopes on the capsid may be predicted. Minor antigenic drift has been noted in these animal viruses,[13] but the existence of subtypes of B19 has yet to be fully investigated; minor differences inferred by differential binding of monoclonal antibodies to different isolates have been reported[14]; however, epidemiologic data would suggest that infection with B19 confers lifelong immunity, a pattern consistent with there being a single neutralization serotype.

The genome of B19 is a single piece of single-stranded DNA, 5.5 kilobases in length. Unlike most other autonomous parvoviruses, B19 packages plus and minus strands into separate virions with almost equal efficiency.[6, 7] Parvovirus DNA is organized as a linear coding region, bounded at each end by palindromic sequences which fold into hairpin duplexes.[15] In the genome of B19 these hairpins are almost twice as long as those found in autonomous animal parvoviruses, and are believed to be inverted terminal repeats.[16] This property, like the equal packaging of both strands, is a property shared by B19 and dependoviruses. Although all the evidence available suggests that B19 is an autonomous parvovirus, these similarities suggest that it is possible that B19, like the dependoviruses, may be capable of integration into the host chromosome.[17]

The coding regions of the B19 genome are confined to the plus strand, and comprise two open reading frames. That at the 3' end codes for nonstructural proteins and that at the 5' end for the structural proteins. Restriction endonuclease analysis of 17 isolates collected between 1972 and 1984 indicates that the genome is relatively stable.[18]

Parvovirus particles are classically regarded as highly stable. B19 infectivity is resistant to ether, chloroform, DNAse, and RNAse. Little resistance to acid (0.5N HCl) or alkali (0.05N NaOH) was noted in one report[19]; the same work reports infectivity completely destroyed by heating to 56°C for five minutes although heating to 45°C for 30 minutes had no effect. It should be noted, however, that prolonged storage, and repeated freeze-thaw cycles are believed to compromise parvovirus integrity, decreasing resistance to extremes of heat, and salt concentration.[20]

Replication

Infection of cells by autonomous parvoviruses may result in either productive viral replication or in an interrupted form of replication in which there is restricted viral activity. Virus adsorbs onto host cell receptors, which are probably protein, and whose expression appears to be under developmental control; differentiating cultures of murine teratoma cells yield only a single cell type supporting the replication of the minute virus of mice (MVM),[21] and a similar window of susceptibility in terminally differentiating erythroid precursor cells has been shown for B19.[19, 22] Following adsorption, the virions seem to be transported to the nucleus and uncoated, either as the virion penetrates the nucleus or very soon thereafter. These steps may proceed regardless of the stage of the host cell in the mitotic cycle; following the liberation of the genome, pathways diverge, depending on whether the infection is productive or incomplete.

The end result of productive parvovirus replication is the lysis of mitotically active cells; mitosis is required for DNA replication and lysis for the release of progeny virus. Within the nucleus, following uncoating, DNA synthesis occurs so that a duplex is formed of one parent, virion strand and one new DNA strand. The synthesis of this DNA is dependent on some cell function(s) found only in late S phase. The duplex DNA is replicated, and at the same time transcription and translation occur with the formation of both structural and nonstructural proteins. Capsid proteins begin to accumulate before the peak of virion synthesis, and are not themselves cytotoxic. Newly formed DNA is excised from the double-strand replicative form and packaged within the capsids. Nonstructural proteins are cytotoxic, and may be involved in the ensuing degeneration of nuclear and cytoplasmic membranes permitting release of progeny virus.[20] Ultrastructural study of cells undergoing productive parvovirus replication reveals abnormal mitochondrial structure and vacuolation, nucleolar degeneration, and margination of chromatin.[23]

In autonomous parvoviruses of animals, two types of incomplete replication have been observed which, while they have not yet been described in B19 infections, may well occur, and have implications for the pathogenesis of B19. *Restrictive replication* may occur in cells penetrated by virus, but at the "wrong" stage of differentiation to support productive replication; in in vitro cultures there is a small subpopulation of fully permissive cells in which the virus replicates in the normal way. The majority of the cell population supports only restricted replication with a small amount (about 5%–20% of normal levels) of viral DNA replication, but no capsid synthesis or excision of replicative-form DNA to single strands. Infection of such cultures is chronic and results in a low level of virion production, but no obvious cytopathic effect (CPE) due to the small proportion of permissive cells. This stable dynamic relationship may break down when a mutation occurs in the portion of the genome coding for coat protein, which results in a "host range mutant," capable of productive, lytic infection of the whole cell population.

Cryptic infection may occur when a virus penetrates a cell not in S phase and thus unable to supply those functions required by the virus for DNA synthesis. The virus may persist within the cell until the cell enters S phase when the viral replicative process is resumed. Cryptic infection thus offers the potential for persistent, low levels of viral replication in vivo in tissues where the rate of cell turnover is low.[20]

In Vitro Culture

To date the only in vitro culture systems known to support B19 replication comprise erythroid progenitor cells; B19 virus does not replicate in the common conventional cell lines, nor in the hemopoietic cell lines K562, KMDE-2, or KG1. Suspension cultures of human bone marrow cells have been most widely used,[24] but peripheral blood[22] and fetal liver (author's unpublished observation) also provide sources of susceptible erythroid progenitors.

Bone marrow cells are cultured in the presence of erythropoietin to foster differentiation of cells of the erythroid series. Peak titers of virus (up to 200-fold the amount of input virus under optimal conditions) are found two days after inoculation; although some virus is released into the supernatant the majority of virus remains cell-associated. Due to the depletion of susceptible cells, with more prolonged culture levels of viral replication fall.[24]

EPIDEMIOLOGY

To date, parvovirus antigen has been in short supply; the unsuitability of the in vitro systems described above for the large-scale production of virus means that the bulk of antigen available for serologic studies has been obtained from the blood of individuals acutely infected with B19. Since in most cases the peak of the viremia is not accompanied by a specific disease syndrome, and is often entirely asymptomatic, such infected individuals cannot be identified clinically and large-scale screening of healthy persons is required. At the present time most virus stocks have been obtained by testing voluntarily donated units of blood. Among the blood donor population in the United Kingdom the incidence of viremia is of the order of 1 in 40,000 during epidemic periods.[25] Large-scale serologic surveys have not yet been carried out, and much of our knowledge of the epidemiology of B19 has therefore been gained by inference—by analysis of the patterns of B19-associated disease.

B19 virus has a worldwide distribution and is active throughout the year. In temperate climates infection is most common in the late winter, spring, and early summer months. Outbreaks of infection occur during these months and these are often centered on elementary schools where up to 40% of children may be clinically affected. During these outbreaks cases also occur in adults in contact with affected children.

Clinical observations of the frequency of EI—the common clinical result of B19 infection—among different age groups reflect the antibody profile of the population estimated by small-scale serologic surveys: antibody is most commonly acquired between the ages of 4 and 10 years, after which the frequency of seropositivity continues to rise but less rapidly; among the blood donor population some 60% are seropositive.[26]

In addition to the seasonality seen in temperate regions, longer-term cycles of virus activity are noted. In the United Kingdom there are peaks every 4 to 5 years, but in Jamaica the cycle seems somewhat shorter; outbreaks of aplastic crisis (the complication of infection common to patients with underlying chronic hemolytic anaemia) occur every 3 to 4 years.[27]

Case-to-case intervals, which are determined by the interval between acquisition and excretion of the virus and are irrespective of the type of disease, will be of the order of six to 11 days, according to predictions permitted by experimental infections in human volunteers.[28] This prediction accords well with observations of outbreaks of both erythema infectiosum and aplastic crisis.

The common route of transmission of B19 is respiratory; the virus can be detected in throat swabs or gargle specimens for some five days, beginning 1 week after the acquisition of virus. However, during infection a high-titer viremia develops providing a second possible source of infection, and bloodborne transmission has been documented in recipients of both whole blood and factor VIII.[29]

PATHOGENESIS

The pathogenesis of B19 disease involves two components. The first is due to the lytic infection of susceptible dividing cells; the second is dependent on interactions between viral products and the immune response.

Lytic infection with B19 parallels the situation in animal parvovirus infections, in which disease is apparent in tissues in which a high proportion of the cells are susceptible to infection and have a high mitotic rate. The most sensitive target organ in B19 infection is the erythropoietic cell series; as noted above, B19 productively infects erythroid precursor cells, and in vivo this results in the arrest of erythrocyte production by the bone marrow. In the hematologically normal individual this arrest is not clinically apparent although bone marrow aspirates obtained from volunteers experimentally infected with B19 show a complete absence of erythrocyte precursors ten days after inoculation.[30] In individuals with shortened red cell survival, this arrest results in the transient profound anemia of the aplastic crisis. In the fetus, immaturity of the immune responses permits the persistence of B19 infection and the concomitant abrogation of red cell production, leading to hydrops fetalis.[31–33]

Some eight days after acquisition of virus, viremia reaches peak levels of 10^{11} or more particles per milliliter of blood. This high-titer viremia may be accompanied by symptoms of the prodrome—malaise pyrexia, and chills—but the pathogenesis of these symptoms has not been defined. At the same time, mild upper respiratory tract symptoms may be noted (E. Grilli, T. Hoskins, and M. Anderson, unpublished observations, December 1988).[34] The presence at this time of virus in respiratory tract secretions suggests these symptoms are likely due to viral replication in the respiratory tract.

The second phase of B19 disease is dependent on the immune response and becomes manifest toward the end of the infection when virus is only rarely detectable (E. Grilli, T. Hoskins, and M. Anderson, unpublished observations, December 1988),[35] but virus-specific IgM is present. This phase is characterized by the disease erythema infectiosum.

Infection without a rash occurs most commonly in children and adult males although the reasons for this have not been defined.

The speed of development of the immune response may play a part; certainly the absence of a rash does not indicate anergy to B19 since immune-mediated arthropathy occurs not infrequently in patients with no history of rash.

IMMUNE RESPONSES

The serologic response to B19 infection documented in the controlled experimental infection of volunteers accords well with data obtained in the investigation of naturally acquired infection. B19-specific IgM antibody is first detectable as viremia wanes nine to ten days after inoculation, and rises rapidly to reach peak concentrations within 1 week. During the early part of the immune response much of the antibody circulates as IgM-virus immune complexes which do not fix complement. Specific IgG is not detectable until the viremia has cleared, 2 weeks after the initiation of infection, and concentrations rise more slowly so that peak levels may not be attained until 4 weeks after acquisition of the virus.[28]

CLINICAL SYNDROMES

As mentioned above, both dependoviruses and autonomous parvoviruses infect man. Dependovirus infections have not been associated with disease and of the three serologically distinct autonomous parvoviruses which infect man, only one, B19, has been unequivocally associated with specific disease syndromes.

Erythema Infectiosum (EI)

The common manifestations of B19 infection is a mild febrile illness with a maculopapular rash of variable intensity. Particularly in children, the first sign of illness is often a marked erythema of the cheeks (''slapped cheek'' appearance); in adults this is less common but the rash is often followed by joint involvement. These are the symptoms of EI or fifth disease. Although this syndrome has been known to clinicians for over 100 years, and long regarded as of infectious etiology, it was only recently that B19 virus was recognized as the cause.[11] Following the initial report, outbreaks throughout the world have been investigated and found to share this etiology.[35–37] The use of specific laboratory tests for the diagnosis of B19 infection reveals a spectrum of disease in which EI occupies a central position.[34]

A search of the literature reveals a conspicuous absence of prodromal symptoms in EI. The results of studies in volunteers,[28] however, supported early findings[9] of a febrile episode, with nonspecific symptoms of malaise, myalgia, headache, and chills accompanying the viremic phase of B19 infection. During this illness virus may be detected in respiratory tract secretions and a recent study (E. Grilli, T. Hoskins, and M. Anderson, unpublished observations, December 1988) showed that virus replication in the respiratory tract may be associated with sore throat so that the clinical picture may be one of a ''flu-like'' illness.

Following the prodromal illness, infected individuals are symptom-free for about 1 week before the onset of the second, exanthematous, phase of the illness. The exanthem in classic EI occurs in three stages.[38] The first begins some 18 days after the acquisition of virus, and is characterized by the appearance on the cheeks of a bright red rash, the edges of which may be slightly raised. The second stage begins one to four days later with the appearance of an erythematous, maculopapular rash on the trunk and limbs. The rash is initially discrete but spreads to involve large areas. Toward the end of this phase there is central clearing of the rash to give the characteristic lacy or reticular pattern. The third stage of the exanthem is highly variable in duration, lasting from 1 to 3 or more weeks, and consists of changes in the intensity of the rash with periodic complete evanescence and recrudescence. These fluctuations are related to environmental factors such as exposure to sunlight, and temperature.

The most common complication in EI is joint involvement. In children this is relatively rare, occurring in less than 10% of cases. In adult women, on the other hand, arthropathy is the norm, occurring in more than 80% of cases of exanthematous infection. There is a range of severity from mild arthralgia to frank arthritis, although age and sex both play a role in determining the type of disease. In children the sexes are affected equally, and the arthropathy is often asymmetric, of greater severity and duration than that which is common in adults. Among adults, the vast majority of those affected are women in whom the common form of presentation is an abrupt-onset symmetric arthritis affecting the small joints of the hand, wrists, ankles, knees, or any combination of these. Recovery is complete within 2 weeks of onset in more than two thirds of cases, and most have recovered in 4 weeks. In many respects B19 arthropathy resembles that of acute rubella, and as is the case in rubella, may occur without an accompanying rash.[39]

Aplastic Crisis

Aplastic crisis in sickle cell anemia was the first defined disease syndrome to be associated with B19 infection.[9] The first association was made by diagnosing infection using counterimmunoelectrophoresis to detect either viral antigen or seroconversion in children attending a sickle cell clinic in London, England,[9] and others attending a much larger clinic in Kingston, Jamaica.[40] Soon after this, the development of a specific test for IgM antibody to the virus permitted diagnosis in more cases where only early convalescent sera were available.[41] In the years following these first reports, the association between B19 infection has been confirmed both in outbreaks[42] and sporadic cases. Moreover, it is clear that it is not only patients with sickle cell anemia who develop aplastic crises with B19 infection; any underlying chronic hemolytic anemia predisposes to this complication, and thus patients with hereditary spherocytosis, β-thalassemia intermedia, pyruvate kinase deficiency, hereditary erythrocytic multinuclearity associated with a positive acidified (HAMS) test (HEMPAS), or autoimmune hemolytic anemia may all suffer aplastic crisis with B19 infection.[43–46] Patients receiving chemotherapy for leukemia, including those in remission, may also develop aplastic crises and in these patients the anemia may be more prolonged, probably as a result of the infection being more persistent in these immunosuppressed patients.[47]

In all of these patients, the absolute reticulocytopenia of B19 infection, which occurs also in hematologically normal individuals,[28, 30] results in the depression of hemoglobin concentrations to critical levels. With the resolution of infection, reticulocytes reappear in the peripheral blood and hemoglobin concentrations return to the normal steady-state values for these patients.

B19 infection does not invariably result in aplastic crisis in patients with chronic hemolytic anemia. Some individuals escape this effect if they have been recently transfused[40, 41]; this may be due either to a protective effect of transfused antibody or to the substitution of longer-lived, donated erythrocytes for the patients' own fragile ones, or to a combination of these two.

Infection in Pregnancy

In animal species, autonomous parvovirus infection in pregnant animals carries a poor prognosis for the infected fetus, the nature and extent of the damage being determined by the stage of fetal development and cell differentiation. In human infections with B19 a similar pattern is emerging.

During B19 infection a high-titer viremia develops during which the virus may cross the placenta. Although infection in the mother is acute and self-resolving, it appears that passively transferred antibody is insufficient to control and eradicate B19 virus from the fetus, so that viral replication may continue for some weeks in fetal tissues.

Although the number of documented cases of B19 infection in pregnancy is still small, it is becoming apparent that infection in the first trimester is associated with an increased risk of fetal loss; spontaneous and missed abortion is more common in women infected with B19 than in pregnancies which are not so complicated. Fetal losses in these women show a clustering in time, occurring 4 to 6 weeks after the onset of symptoms of EI in the mother.[48]

Second-trimester infection is associated with the development of hydrops fetalis.[31–33] It is likely that fetal hydrops develops as a result of a process similar to that which occurs in aplastic crisis; lytic infection of erythroid precursor cells causes a reduction in fetal hemoglobin concentrations. Because the fetus is unable to clear the virus, this cycle of lytic infection persists so that the fetus succumbs to what is in effect a chronic aplastic crisis. The time lag between maternal infection and fetal death may be as much as 12 weeks, and fetuses examined at postmortem show virus (detected by in situ hybridization) in all tissues together with hepatic iron deposition from the extensive hemolysis.[33, 49]

Infection in the third trimester has only very occasionally been documented; it is likely that this is because rubella-like illness is only rarely investigated at this late stage of pregnancy since the *clinically* diagnosed virus, rubella, constitutes no risk to the fetus at this time. However, a stillbirth of a macerated fetus was reported occuring at 39 weeks gestation after a clinically normal pregnancy in one such case.[50]

The overall incidence of maternal B19 infection cannot be stated with certainty, although prospective studies of unselected pregnancies are currently under way. Undoubtedly many pregnancies continue to term with the delivery of normal babies. Congenital abnormality has not been recorded at the present time in any liveborn baby exposed to B19 in utero, and in the largest documented study of a clinically identified outbreak of EI, teratogenicity was not observed.[51]

Complications
Cytopenias

Studies of B19 infection in volunteers indicate that in addition to reticulocytopenia, transient lymphopenia, neutropenia and thrombocytopenia are common results of B19 infection.[28, 30] To date these effects appear in the main not to be of sufficient severity or duration to cause distress. They may occasionally be detected during detailed investigation of patients in whom B19 infection is not suspected, and thence lead to clinical concern and overinvestigation.[52, 53] Thrombocytopenia associated with a purpuric rash and bruising has been reported.[54]

Purpura

Vascular purpura has been noted in a number of cases of B19 infection. In the majority of these cases the nonnecrotic, petechial, purpura develops during the viremia, and is not associated with abnormally low platelet counts. Occasionally such cases are diagnosed as Henoch-Schönlein purpura, and the petechiae are accompanied by abdominal pain and large-joint arthralgia.[55, 56]

Nephropathy

Toward the end of the viremia B19 virus-IgM immune complexes circulate, affording the possibility of renal damage, and virus may be excreted in the urine.[35] It is therefore to be expected that some renal damage may occur in B19 infection. Since urinary protein determinations are not part of the routine investigation of patients with rash illness, the incidence of renal involvement in B19 infection is unknown.

Only two documented cases are known to the author. The first occurred in 1985 in a young boy who experienced microscopic hematuria for some weeks following a B19 infection which presented with rash and arthropathy (J. Kurtz and M. Anderson, unpublished observations, May 1987). The second occurred in 1986 in a 44-year-old woman who presented with a typical B19 illness of rash and arthritis and 3 weeks later suffered acute nephritis. Her urinary output dropped to 200 mL per 24 hours and the urine contained blood and protein. At the same time her blood pressure was raised and she suffered edema, especially of the face and legs. She required furosemide for 4 weeks to maintain a satisfactory urinary output and continued to have microscopic hematuria for some months (M. Anderson and J. Cresswell, unpublished observations, March 1989).

Hepatitis

In 1975, the discovery of B19 virus in the serum of a patient suffering acute hepatitis[4] raised the possibility that B19 might be one of the elusive hepatitis C viruses. However, examination of sera from cases of hepatitis C for B19 virus (P. P. Mortimer and B. J. Cohen, unpublished observations) and B19-specific IgM antibody (author's unpublished observations) suggest that this virus is not a common cause of hepatitis.

Biochemical analysis of the blood of infected volunteers did not reveal any abnormality during B19 infection. In some individuals, however, slight liver damage does occur although this is not sufficiently severe to manifest as frank jaundice and is usually only found by accident during detailed investigation of patients with unusually severe B19 infections (author's unpublished observations).

Infection in Immunosuppressed Patients

Recently, a case of persistent B19 infection in a child with

Nezelof syndrome has been described. The child has remained severely anemic and neutropenic for more than 1 year, with episodes of clinical improvement coinciding with temporary absence of virus from the blood.[24] The frequency with which B19 establishes persistent infection in immunosuppressed patients is at present unknown; it is to be expected that with increasing application of diagnostic tests for B19 infection, more cases will be identified and one may speculate that these will be associated with anemia and cytopenias.

DIAGNOSIS

It is clear from Figure 43–2 that B19 infection in aplastic crisis and upper respiratory tract disease may be diagnosed by the detection of virus. This may be accomplished by testing a throat swab, or, preferably, a serum specimen. Sera which do not contain detectable virus should be examined for B19-specific IgM.

In marked contrast to the situation in respiratory tract disease and aplastic crisis, the diagnosis of B19 infection in EI relies upon the detection of specific IgM antibody, since the disease occurs late in the course of infection when virus is only rarely demonstrable in serum.

The diagnosis of intrauterine infection presents a third situation; since the effects of fetal infection seem only to become apparent clinically after some weeks, IgM is often no longer detectable in maternal serum. Diagnosis therefore relies on the examination of

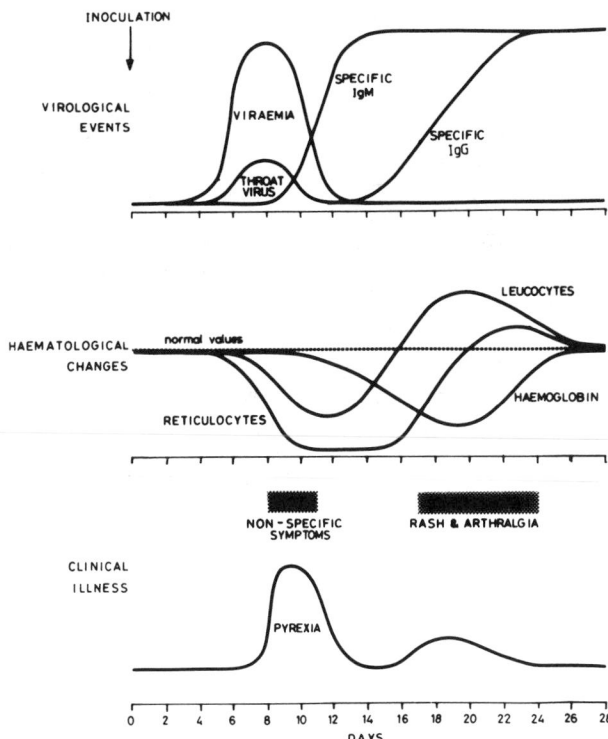

Figure 43–2. Schematic representation of the virologic, hematologic, and clinical events in B19 virus infection. (Reproduced with permission from Anderson MJ: Human parvoviruses, in Zuckerman AJ, Banatvala JE, Pattison JR (eds): *Principles and Practice of Clinical Virology.* New York, Wiley, 1987, p 510.

fetal material. Since the pathologic changes are likely caused by persistent infection in the fetus, and the fetus may not have mounted a detectable immune response, demonstration of virus either in fetal blood taken by cordiocentesis or in fetal tissue at autopsy provides the most reliable diagnosis.

Virus Detection

B19 virus may be detected in blood by electron microscopy, counterimmunoelectrophoresis, radio- or enzyme immunoassay for antigen, or by DNA-DNA hybridization. Because of the relatively low concentrations of virus in throat swab specimens, only immunoassay and hybridization are sufficiently sensitive for use with these specimens.

The simplest and most rapid of these tests is counterimmunoelectrophoresis of the patient's serum against anti-B19 antibody.[40] A positive result should be confirmed by either direct or immune electron microscopy (see Figure 43–1). This test will reveal B19 in some 30% of serum specimens taken within 24 hours of the onset of symptoms[57] and has the advantage of yielding results in one hour.

Radioimmunoassay and Enzyme Immunoassay

B19-specific antigen may be detected in serum or throat swab specimens by assays based on class-specific antibody tests by substituting the patient's sample for "antigen" in the test, and a known anti-B19 antibody positive serum for "test serum." These tests are described more fully below. Samples to be tested for antigen in this way should be tested diluted 1 in 2 in assay diluent containing twice the normal concentration of polysorbate (Tween) 20.

These assays permit the detection of virus in some 60% of serum samples taken within one day of the onset of symptoms in cases of aplastic crisis.[57]

DNA-DNA Hybridization

B19 DNA may be detected in any fluid specimen by dot-blot hybridization.[57] Tissue samples should be digested with proteinase K, the nucleic acid extracted with phenol and chloroform and spotted onto the membrane. It is desirable to confirm positive results obtained with material extracted from tissue samples by fractionating the extracted DNA by agarose gel electrophoresis, transferring the DNA to a filter by Southern blotting and testing this for B19-specific sequences. This is necessary since background levels of DNA in these samples are clearly much higher than those in serum or throat swab specimens.

Cloned viral genome labeled with ^{32}P has been most widely used as an indicator system in B19 hybridization tests. Although biotinylated probes may also be used, there is a loss of sensitivity of some 10%.[58]

Very recently, the use of in situ hybridization to detect B19 DNA in formalin-fixed, paraffin-embedded tissue sections has been described. This technique has the added advantage of permitting localization of the virus in tissue specimens, as well as being applicable to material obtained for histopathologic purposes in cases where B19 infection is not initially suspected.[33, 49]

At the time of this writing, the polymerase chain reaction (PCR) is being used to detect viral genome sequences in a number of diseases. This technique is potentially more sensitive than DNA-DNA hybridization, and preliminary work indicates that the window in which B19 is detectable may be considerably broadened by the application of this technique (S. Adler, personal communication).

Antibody Detection

Anti-B19 antibody may be detected by immune electron microscopy or counterimmunoelectrophoresis, although neither of these techniques permits the identification of the class of antibody.

The most widely used tests are class-specific and depend on the antibody-capture principle, in which one class of patient antibody is bound to a solid phase coated with antibody to human μ or γ chains. The specificity of the bound antibody is determined by the addition of B19 virus antigen to the solid phase, and bound antigen detected by the addition of monoclonal anti-B19 antibody which may be tagged with either an enzyme or radiolabel. Most tests for B19-specific antibody currently employ an additional step where the bound monoclonal antibody is detected by the addition of labeled anti-mouse immunoglobulin.

B19-specific IgM may be detected in these tests for 2 to 3 months after the onset of symptoms.[26] Specific IgG is detectable for very much longer, although since the antibody-capture method is dependent on the relative concentration of IgG which is specific for B19, antibody may not be detectable lifelong (author's unpublished observation). For this reason these tests must be interpreted with care, since patients with no detectable IgG may nevertheless have experienced previous B19 infection.[28]

The source of B19 antigen for use in these assays is currently the serum or plasma of acutely infected individuals, and may be used without purification.[26] It is to be expected that alternative sources of antigen may become available in the near future; the expression of B19-specified proteins in *Escherichia coli* has been described,[59, 60] and the production of structural proteins which self-assemble to capsidlike structures has been achieved by the transfection of Chinese hamster ovary cells (N. S. Young, personal communication).

TREATMENT AND PREVENTION

There is no specific antiviral therapy for B19 infection. Symptomatic therapy in EI is rarely necessary, although arthropathy may be troublesome and may be relieved with aspirin or ibuprofen.

Cases of aplastic crisis require transfusion with erythrocytes until a satisfactory hemoglobin concentration is attained.

The levels of viremia in persistent infection in the immunosuppressed may be reduced by the administration of normal human immunoglobulin, which contains anti-B19 antibody (N. S. Young, personal communication).

There is no vaccine for parvovirus B19. The virus is spread primarily by the respiratory route, but since the majority of clinically apparent cases are either no longer infectious, or only slightly so, the isolation of patients with EI serves no useful role. Patients with aplastic crisis are likely to be infectious; since B19 infection may have grave consequences in hematology patients (the immunosuppressed and those with hemolytic anemias) care should be taken to isolate suspected cases of B19 infection from such patients.

The majority of persons infected with B19 are asymptomatic at the time virus excretion is at its peak; control of outbreaks, and the prevention of infection in those at risk of serious complication, including pregnant women, is thus difficult to achieve.

REFERENCES

1. Paver WK, Caul EO, Ashley CR, et al: A small virus in human faeces. *Lancet* 1973; 1:664–665.
2. Dunnet WN, Thorn RG, Ayling RG: Food poisoning from oysters. *Comm Dis Rep* 1984; 36:3.
3. Caul EO: Small round human fecal viruses, in Pattison JR (ed): *Parvoviruses and Human Disease.* Boca Raton, FL, CRC Press, 1988, pp 139–164.
4. Cossart YE, Field AM, Cant B, et al: Parvovirus-like particles in human sera. *Lancet* 1975; 1:72–73.
5. Summers J, Jones SE, Anderson MJ: Characterisation of the agent of erythrocyte aplasia as a human parvovirus. *J Gen Virol* 1983; 64:2527–2532.
6. Clewley JP: Biochemical characterisation of a human parvovirus. *J Gen Virol* 1984;65:241–244.
7. Simpson RW, McGinty L, Simon L, et al: Association of parvoviruses with rheumatoid arthritis of humans. *Science* 1984; 223:1425–1428.
8. Scheerson JM, Mortimer PP, Vandervelde EM: Febrile illness due to a parvovirus. *Br Med J* 1980; 2:1580.
9. Pattison JR, Jones SE, Hodgson J, et al: Parvovirus infections and hypoplastic crises in sickle cell anaemia. *Lancet* 1981; 1:664–665.
10. Anderson MJ, Lewis E, Kidd IM, et al: An outbreak of erythema infectiosum associated with human parvovirus infection. *J Hyg* 1984; 93:85–93.
11. Paver WK, Clarke SKR: Comparison of human fecal and serum parvovirus-like viruses. *J Clin Microbiol* 1976; 4:67–70.
12. Parrish CR, Carmichael LE: Antigenic structure and variation of canine parvovirus type-Z, feline panleukopenia virus and mink enteritis virus. *Virology* 1983; 129:401–414.
13. Parrish CR, Have P, Foreyt WJ, et al: The global spread and replacement of canine parvovirus strains. *J Gen Virol* 1988; 69:1111–1116.
14. Cohen BJ: Laboratory tests for the diagnosis by infection with B19 virus, in Pattison JR, (ed): *Parvoviruses and Human Disease.* Boca Raton, Fla, CRC Press, 1988, pp 69–84.
15. Bourguignon GJ, Tattersall PJ, Ward DC: DNA of minute virus of mice: self-priming, non-permuted, single stranded genomes with a 5′ terminal hairpin duplex. *J Virol* 1976; 20:290–306.
16. Shade RL, Blundell MC, Cotmore SJ, et al: Nucleotide sequence and genome organization of human parvovirus B19 isolated from an aplastic crisis. *J Virol* 1986; 58:921–927.
17. Cheung AKM, Hoggan MD, Hauswirth WW, et al: Integration of the adeno-associated virus genome into cellular DNA in latently infected human Detroit 6 cells. *J Virol* 1980; 33:739–748.
18. Morinet F, Tratschin J-D, Perol Y, et al: Comparison of 17 isolates of the human parvovirus B19 by restriction enzyme analysis. *Arch Virol* 1986; 90:165–172.
19. Young NS, Mortimer PP, Moore JG, et al: Characterisation of a virus that causes transient aplastic crisis. *J Clin Invest* 1984; 73:224–230.
20. Tattersall P, Cotmore SF: The nature of parvoviruses, in Pattison JR, (ed): *Parvoviruses and Human Disease.* Boca Raton, Fla, CRC Press, 1988, pp 5–42.
21. Tattersall P: *Replication of Mammalian Parvoviruses.* Cold Spring Harbor, NY, Cold Spring Harbor Laboratory, 1978.
22. Duncan JR, Capellini MD, Anderson MJ, et al: Aplastic crisis due to parvovirus infection in pyruvate kinase deficiency. *Lancet* 1983; 2:14–16.
23. Young N, Harrison M, Moore J, et al: Direct demonstration of the human parvovirus in erythroid progenitor cells infected in vitro. *J Clin Invest* 1984; 74:2024–2030.
24. Young N: Hematologic and hematopoietic consequences of B19 parvovirus infection. *Semin Hematol* 1988; 25:159–172.
25. Anderson MJ: The emerging story of a human parvovirus-like agent. *J Hyg* 1982; 89:1–8.
26. Cohen BJ, Mortimer PP, Pereira MS: Diagnostic assays with monoclonal antibodies for the human serum parvovirus-like virus (SPLV). *J Hyg* 1983; 91:113–130.
27. Serjeant GR, Goldstein AR: B19 virus infection and the aplastic crisis, in Pattison JR, (ed): *Parvoviruses and Human Disease.* Boca Raton, Fla, CRC Press, 1988, pp 85–92.
28. Anderson MJ, Higgins PG, Davis LR, et al: Experimental parvoviral infection in man. *J Infect Dis* 1985; 152:257–265.
29. Mortimer PP, Luban NLC, Kelleher JF, et al: Transmission of serum parvovirus-like virus by clotting factor concentrates. *Lancet* 1983; 2:482–484.
30. Potter CG, Potter AC, Hatton CSR, et al: Variation of erythroid and myeloid precursors in the bone marrow and peripheral blood of volunteer subjects infected with human parvovirus (B19). *J Clin Infect* 1987; 79:1486–1492.
31. Brown T, Anand A, Ritchie LD, et al: Intrauterine human parvovirus infection and hydrops fetalis. *Lancet* 1984; 2:1033–1034.
32. Bond PR, Caul EO, Usher J, et al: Intrauterine infection with parvovirus. *Lancet* 1986; 1:448–449.
33. Anderson MJ, Khousam MN, Maxwell DJ, et al: Human parvovirus B19 and hydrops fetalis. *Lancet* 1988; 1:535.
34. Anderson MJ, Cohen BJ: Human parvovirus B19 infections in the United Kingdom 1984–1986. *Lancet* 1987; 1:738–739.
35. Chorba T, Coccia P, Holman C, et al: The role of parvovirus B19 in aplastic crisis and erythema infectiosum (fifth disease). *J Infect Dis* 1986; 154:383–393.
36. Okabe N, Kobyashi S, Tatsuzawa O, et al: Detection of antibodies to human parvovirus in erythema infectiosum (fifth disease). *Arch Dis Child* 1984; 59:1016–1019.
37. Plummer FA, Hammond GW, Forward K, et al: An erythema infectiosum-like illness caused by human parvovirus infection. *N Engl J Med* 1985; 313:74–79.
38. Anderson MJ, Cherry JD: *Textbook of Pediatric Infectious Diseases,* ed 2. Philadelphia, Saunders, 1987.
39. Anderson MJ: Rash illness due to B19 virus, in Pattison JR (ed): *Parvoviruses and Human Disease.* Boca Raton, Fla, CRC Press, 1988, pp 93–104.
40. Serjeant GR, Mason K, Topley JM, et al: Outbreak of aplastic crisis in sickle cell anaemia associated with parvovirus-like agent. *Lancet* 1981; 2:595–597.
41. Anderson MJ, Davis LR, Hodgson J, et al: Occurrence of infection with a parvovirus-like agent in children with sickle cell anaemia during a two year period. *J Clin Pathol* 1982; 35:744–749.
42. Saarinen UM, Chorba TL, Tattersall P, et al: Human parvovirus B19-induced epidemic acute red cell aplasia in patients with hereditary hemolytic anemia. *Blood* 1986; 67:1411–1417.
43. Kelleher JH, Luban NLC, Mortimer PP, et al: The human serum "parvovirus." A specific cause of aplastic crisis in hereditary spherocytosis. *J Pediatr* 1983; 102:720–722.
44. Rao KRP, Patel AR, Anderson MJ, et al: Infection with a parvovirus-like virus and aplastic crisis in chronic haemolytic anaemia. *Ann Intern Med* 1983; 98:930–932.
45. West NC, Meigh RE, Mackie M, et al: Parvovirus infection associated with aplastic crisis in a patient with HEMPAS. *J Clin Pathol* 1986; 39:1019–1020.
46. Bertrand Y, Lefrere JJ, Leverger G, et al: Autoimmune hemolytic anemia revealed by human parvovirus linked erythroblastopenia. *Lancet* 1985; 2:382.
47. van Horn DK, Mortimer PP, Young NS, et al: Human parvovirus associated red cell aplasia in the absence of underlying hemolytic anemia. *Am J Pediatr Hematol Oncol* 1986; 8:235–238.
48. Hall S, Anderson MJ, Caul EO, et al: The outcome of human parvovirus (B19) infection in pregnancy: a prospective study, abstract read before *European Association Against Virus Disease,* Davos, Switzerland, September 1987.
49. Porter HJ, Khong TY, Evans MF, et al: Parvovirus as a cause of

hydrops fetalis: detection by in situ hybridisation. *J Clin Pathol* 1988; 41:381–383.

50. Knott PD, Welply GAC, Anderson MJ: Serologically proven intrauterine infection with parvovirus. *Br Med J* 1984; 289:1660.

51. Ager EA, Chin TDY, Poland JP: Epidemic erythema infectiosum. *N Engl J Med* 1966; 275:1326–1331.

52. Neild G, Anderson MJ, Hawes S, et al: Parvovirus infection after renal transplant. *Lancet* 1986; 2:1226–1227.

53. Saunders PWG, Reid MM, Cohen BJ: Human parvovirus induced cytopenias: a report of five cases. *Br J Haematol* 1986; 53:407–410.

54. Mortimer PP, Cohen BJ, Rossiter MA, et al: Human parvovirus and purpura. *Lancet* 1985; 2:730–731.

55. Lefrere JJ, Courouce A-M, Muller JY, et al: Human parvovirus and purpura. *Lancet* 1985; 2:730.

56. Lefrere JJ, Bougeois H: Human parvovirus associated with erythroblastopenia in iron deficiency anaemia. *J Clin Pathol* 1986; 39:1277–1278.

57. Anderson MJ, Jones SE, Minson AC: Diagnosis of human parvovirus infection by dot-blot hybridization using cloned viral DNA. *J Med Virol* 1985; 15:163–172.

58. Cunningham DA, Pattison JR, Craig RK: Detection of parvovirus DNA in human serum using RNA hybridisation probes. *J Virol Methods* 1988; 19:279–288.

59. Rayment F, Talbot P: Molecular cloning and expression of human parvovirus antigens, Abstract. Presented at *Second Parvovirus Workshop,* Oxford, England, June 1987.

60. Berman ML, Sisk WP: Expression of human parvovirus B19 structural protein in *Escherichia coli* and immunoenzymatic detection of antiviral antibodies in human serum, abstract. Presented at *Second Parvovirus Workshop,* Oxford, England, June 1987.

44

Kawasaki Syndrome

Marian E. Melish
Nyven J. Marchette

Kawasaki syndrome or mucocutaneous lymph node syndrome is an acute febrile exanthematous disease of children. Although it is currently of unknown etiology, the clinical and epidemiologic features strongly suggest an infectious etiology. The illness was first recognized and described in 1967 by Dr. Tomisaku Kawasaki of Japan.[1, 2] It was recognized independently in the United States by our group in 1974.[3, 4] Since its first description in English in 1974, Kawasaki syndrome has been recognized worldwide in children of diverse ethnic groups.[5–51]

The illness was at first considered to be a severe acute febrile, but ultimately benign, self-limited disease. Early in their experience, however, Japanese clinicians recognized that a small proportion of patients, approximately 2%, died suddenly during the subacute phase of the illness at a time when they were thought to be recovering.[52] The cause of death was massive myocardial infarction due to thrombosis of aneurysmally dilated coronary arteries. These patients all had severe coronary artery vasculitis with variable involvement of other systemic blood vessels. Pathologic changes in fatal Kawasaki syndrome are indistinguishable from those of infantile periarteritis nodosa, a rare but well-described pediatric condition which had previously been disgnosed exclusively at autopsy. It is now recognized that there is a spectrum of cardiac involvement in Kawasaki syndrome ranging from asymptomatic ECG to echocardiogram abnormalities to severe clinical cardiac disease.[53–57]

Kawasaki syndrome has now been well defined clinically and pathologically. Although the etiology of this illness remains unknown, effective therapy has been discovered and considerable progress has been made in understanding the pathogenesis. In this chapter, we cover clinical manifestations and pathology, areas of which we have some understanding, before moving on to areas currently under investigation: epidemiology, etiology, and pathogenesis.

CLINICAL ASPECTS

At the present time the diagnosis of Kawasaki syndrome is based on strict adherence to clinical criteria together with exclusion of other clinically similar disease (Figure 44–1). The principal diagnostic criteria are listed in Table 44–1. To make a diagnosis the patient should meet five of six criteria. In practice, most patients have all of the first five criteria while the sixth, lymphadenopathy, is seen in approximately 70% of patients in Japan but in less than half of those seen in Hawaii.

The clinical course of the illness is best described as triphasic, consisting of the acute febrile phase, a subacute phase, and a convalescent phase. The first phase begins abruptly with the onset of fever, followed within one to three days by most of the other principal diagnostic criteria: conjunctival injection, changes in the

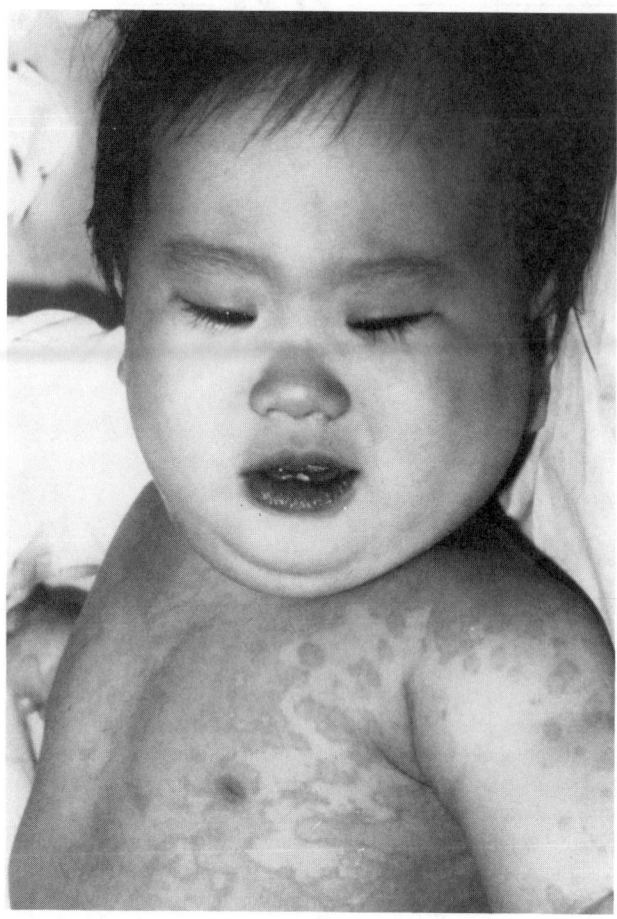

Figure 44–1. Child with acute Kawasaki syndrome demonstrating confluent erythematous plaque-like rash and red, swollen, cracked lips.

lip and mouth, swelling of hands and feet, erythematous rash, and lymphadenopathy. The associated features of aseptic meningitis, diarrhea, and hepatic dysfunction may occur during this period, which lasts from seven to 14 days. Rash, lymphadenopathy, and fever tend to subside together, ushering in the subacute phase which is characterized by persistent anorexia and irritability. Thrombocytosis and desquamation are rare features of this phase. Arthritis, arthralgia, myocardial dysfunction, when they occur, usually begin in this period, which lasts from approximately the tenth to the 25th day after onset of fever. The convalescent phase lasts from the period when all signs of illness have disappeared until the sedimentation rate has returned to normal, usually 6 to 8 weeks from onset. For the great majority of children, the illness is a self-limited one, although the prognosis in each individual depends on the extent and severity of the cardiovascular disease.

Principal Criteria

Fever

Fever, the first sign of the illness, begins abruptly without a well-defined or distinctive prodrome. It is typically high, reaching 40°C (104°F) or more and has a remittent pattern of several spikes per day with no temperature readings below 37.8°C (100°F). Fever

persists for more than five days, the average duration being 11 days (range five to 23 days).

Conjunctival Injection

Conjunctivae show discrete vascular injection involving both bulbar and palpebral surfaces. There is no exudate, discharge, or corneal ulceration, thus differentiating the conjunctival involvement of Kawasaki syndrome from that of other forms of conjunctivitis.

Mouth Changes

Changes in the mouth consist of (1) erythema and fissuring of the lips, (2) diffuse erythema of the oropharynx, and (3) hypertrophic papillae of the tongue, creating a strawberry appearance. These three abnormalities appear simultaneously within one to three days following onset of fever. The urethra is involved in 70% of cases, but vaginal and rectal mucous membranes remain unremarkable.

Extremity Changes

Changes in the hands and feet constitute the most distinctive features of the syndrome. In the acute phase of the illness, soon after the onset of fever, firm indurative edema of the hands and feet develops. The palms and soles are diffusely and deeply erythematous during this stage. These acute changes persist for the duration of the febrile stage.

In the subacute phase of the illness, generally 14 to 20 days from the onset of fever, desquamation of the skin of the finger and toe tips begins under the nails and progresses to involve the entire surface of the palms and soles.

In the convalescent phase, approximately 2 months from onset of illness, deep transverse grooves (Bow's lines) appear across each finger- and toenail, usually growing out with the nail.

Exanthem

The erythematous rash occurs simultaneously with or soon after onset of fever. It is a deeply erythematous exanthem that takes multiple forms. The most common form of rash is a generalized pruritic urticarialike exanthem with large irregular raised erythematous plaques. The second most common form is a deeply er-

Table 44–1
Principal Diagnostic Criteria of Kawasaki Syndrome

	Frequency (%)
I. Fever lasting longer than 5 days	100
II. Conjunctival injection	>90
III. Changes in mouth 　　A. Red cracked lips 　　B. Strawberry tongue 　　C. Oropharyngeal erythema	>90
IV. Polymorphous erythematous rash	>90
V. Changes in extremities consisting of: 　　A. Acute edema of hands and feet 　　B. Acute erythema of palms and soles 　　C. Subacute peeling of palms and soles 　　D. Convalescent transverse nail groove	>90
VI. Cervical lymphadenopathy	50–70

Table 44–2
Associated Features of Kawasaki Syndrome

	Frequency (%)
Urethritis	70
Arthritis/arthralgia	35/45
Aseptic meningitis	25
Gastrointestinal symptoms	25
Myocarditis	20
Coronary artery aneurysms	20
Hepatic involvement	10

ythematous maculopapular morbilliform eruption. Rare (less than 5% of cases), the rash has a scarlatiniform or erythema marginatum character. The rash generally persists for the duration of fever. In the convalescent phase there is perianal desquamation in approximately 80% of patients, while patchy desquamation of other areas such as knees, elbows, and trunk occurs in only 10% of cases.

Lymphadenopathy

Lymphadenopathy is the least constant of the principal features. It is cervical and unilateral, with a single, firm, enlarged lymph node mass measuring greater than 1.5 cm in diameter. Although occasionally erythematous, the swelling is rarely warm, tender, or fluctuant. The lymph node enlargement generally ''melts away'' at the time of defervescence.

Associated Features

The variable associated features of Kawasaki syndrome attest to its multisystem involvement (Table 44–2). Pyuria from urethritis is seen in approximately 70% of patients in the acute stage. True renal involvement in Kawasaki syndrome is so unusual that whenever it is encountered it should prompt serious reconsideration of the diagnosis. Azotemia, elevated creatinine, and hypertension are not seen.

Arthritis is seen in 35% to 40% of patients. Occurring late in the acute febrile state or developing in the subacute period, large joints such as knees, hips, and elbows are most commonly affected. The arthritis may have considerable associated effusion which persists for 2 to 4 weeks but is ultimately self-limited. The cell count of this inflammatory joint fluid ranges from 20,000 to 200,000/mL and consists primarily of polymorphonuclear cells.[58]

Central nervous system effects are seen in nearly all patients. Pronounced irritability and changes of mood are characteristic of the syndrome. Approximately one third have severe lethargy, with some patients progressing to semicoma or coma during the febrile stage. Aseptic meningitis with 25 to 100 WBC per microliter of CSF is seen in approximately one fourth of patients with Kawasaki syndrome. The CSF pleocytosis is predominantly lymphocytic with normal glucose and protein values.

Gastrointestinal manifestations are also seen in approximately one fourth of patients and consist of diarrhea and abdominal pain.

Hepatitis, with modest to moderate bilirubin elevations and moderate elevations of serum transaminases, is seen during the acute febrile phase of illness in about one tenth of patients. An unusual complication, that of acute hydrops of the gallbladder, has been reported in both Japanese[59] and American patients.[22, 32, 60, 61] Presenting late in the acute febrile phase of the illness or in early

convalescence, it manifests itself as a right upper quadrant abdominal mass. Ultrasound examination is useful in diagnosing this complication. The acute hydrops is a self-limited phenomenon that will disappear spontaneously in 2 to 3 weeks and can be monitored until resolution by repeated ultrasound evaluations.

Cardiac Disease

Clinical cardiac disease occurs in at least 20% of patients with Kawasaki syndrome. During the acute febrile period of disease, severe tachycardia and gallop rhythm are the most common manifestations. Toward the end of the febrile phase (mean time, day 11) more serious cardiac abnormalities appear, including congestive heart failure, pericardial effusion, mitral insufficiency, and cardiac arrhythmias, manifest as first- and second-degree atrioventricular (A-V) block, premature ventricular contractions, or paroxysmal atrial tachycardia. Mitral insufficiency has been reported to be secondary to papillary muscle dysfunction,[62, 63] although pathologic studies have also demonstrated valvular inflammation.[5, 64]

Special diagnostic tests are needed to diagnose coronary artery aneurysms. The most comprehensive studies of coronary angiography performed routinely in all patients with Kawasaki syndrome in the series have demonstrated coronary aneurysms in 17% to 20% of those studied in week 4 of disease.[55, 62, 65, 66] Two-dimensional echocardiography appears to be of almost equal sensitivity in detecting left coronary aneurysms but is less successful in visualizing right coronary lesions.[53] When present, coronary aneurysms are usually bilateral and arise close to the origin.[66] Our experience in Honolulu has demonstrated that aneurysmal dilatations are present in 17% of 107 unselected patients studied in week 4 of illness. Another series detected aneurysms in 11 (14%) of 79 unselected children with Kawasaki syndrome by echocardiogram.[67] Therefore, studies of the natural history of reasonably large groups of unselected patients demonstrate that approximately 20% will develop coronary aneurysms in the subacute phase of disease.

The natural history of coronary lesions has been studied by serial angiography in patients with aneurysms.[66] Regression of lesions occurs regularly, with the most extensive survey indicating that over one half of patients will show resolution of aneurysms within 1 year. The remainder show either persistent aneurysms or narrowed and tortuous arteries.[66] The mechanism of aneurysm resolution has been studied by biopsy or resection of peripheral femoral, axillary, or iliac artery aneurysms after resolution had occurred.[68] Resolution results from a combination of intimal proliferation, thrombosis, and recanalization. Therefore, even though a normal caliber of lumen can be restored, the coronary vessels are likely to remain abnormal. Changes in the coronary arteries may result in premature arteriosclerosis and/or premature myocardial infarction in later life.[68, 69]

At this point, it appears likely that a spectrum of coronary vessel disease ranging from minor asymptomatic vascular inflammation, aneurysm formation, and nonfatal infarction, to fatal termination due to massive infarction occurs in all patients with Kawasaki syndrome. Nonfatal infarction is less common than fatal termination, but classic myocardial infarction with confirmatory ECG and myocardial enzyme changes has been recorded and confirmed by angiography.[70–74] Coronary artery bypass grafting has been performed in a small number of patients with occlusive coronary lesions.[57, 72, 75–78] It has become apparent that children who develop giant aneurysms (aneurysms measuring over 8 mm in diameter) by the third week of disease are at greatest risk for ischemic complications and death.[79] Giant aneurysms occur in approximately one third of those developing coronary abnormalities on echocardiography, or about 7% of all patients.

Minor ECG abnormalities are reported in 40% to 60% of patients in the second to fifth week of disease. The ECG changes consist of PR interval prolongation, nonspecific ST and T wave changes, and transient left ventricular hypertrophy patterns. In our experience, the ECG has not been a sensitive tool for detecting and managing cardiac disease.

Vascular abnormalities presenting in the clinical course of Kawasaki syndrome are uncommon. Aneurysms of brachial and femoral arteries present as painless pulsatile masses during the subacute phase of the illness. Peripheral gangrene of fingers or toes is also seen rarely.[80]

Incomplete Cases

The clinical picture of fully expressed Kawasaki syndrome is distinctive and the course is stereotyped. As we do not have any single pathognomonic clinical sign or diagnostic laboratory test, it remains very difficult to diagnose *formes fruste* or cases with incomplete clinical signs. Patients with mild symptoms or incomplete manifestations may develop serious or fatal cardiac disease. Incomplete cases are particularly likely to be encountered in children under 6 months of age.[81–85]

LABORATORY FEATURES

Laboratory abnormalities in Kawasaki syndrome are generally nonspecific and nondiagnostic. Total WBC counts are elevated in the acute febrile phase of the illness. White count values of over 20,000/μL are seen in over half of the patients, and values of over 30,000 are not uncommon. There is a predominance of polymorphonuclear leukocytes with both mature forms and band forms. The sedimentation rate and C-reactive protein are uniformly elevated from the febrile phase and gradually subside, reaching normal values 6 to 10 weeks following onset of fever.

Thrombocytosis is a universal laboratory feature of Kawasaki disease but, unlike the sedimentation rate and the total WBC count, the platelet count is generally normal during the acute febrile phase of the illness. It rises after the tenth day of the illness, peaking at levels of 600,000 to 1.8 million between the 15th and 25th days of the illness, falling to normal values by the 30th day of illness. The period of thrombocytosis coincides with the period of highest risk of coronary artery thrombosis.

Total immunoglobulin levels of IgG, IgA, and IgM are within normal limits. Kusakawa and Heiner have reported modest to moderate elevations in IgE levels in most of a group of 20 patients with Kawasaki syndrome during the acute or early convalescent phase of the illness. Follow-up specimens had lower IgE values, generally within the normal range. This study was interpreted as demonstrating an acute phase stimulation of IgE responses, possibly indicating a role of IgE in the pathogenesis of the disease.[86]

We have also studied serial IgE values in this syndrome, finding

that three fourths of the 30 patients studied serially demonstrate a pattern of acute rise in IgE level in the second, third, or fourth week of illness followed by a fall in later serum samples. Peak IgE levels covered a wide range, and approximately 50% of peak values were less than 100 IU. Height of IgE response was not correlated with the severity of the disease, or with the presence or absence of arthritis or carditis. It is clear that most children with Kawasaki syndrome show an acute response in IgE. It is unknown whether this response reflects antibody formation to a single antigen or whether it is a nonspecific response. However, measurement of IgE has no diagnostic or prognostic value in this syndrome because of the wide range of responses encountered.[84]

Normal values have repeatedly been obtained for latex fixation, LE cell preparation, antinuclear antibody and *Salmonella* antibodies. Total hemolytic complement (CH50) values have been reported to be normal.[62, 87]

PATHOLOGY

A fatal termination of Kawasaki syndrome is reported in 1.7% of those identified in a nationwide survey in Japan. Our own experience of three deaths among 200 patients studied prospectively is in accord with this rate. Fatal Kawasaki syndrome is more common among males; the male-to-female ratio of fatal cases is 3:1 compared with 1.5:1 for total cases. Seventy-five percent of fatal cases are patients less than 2 years old, compared with 50% of total cases.[61, 88]

In fatal cases of Kawasaki syndrome, the most severe and most important pathologic changes are found in the heart, particularly in the coronary arteries. There is variable involvement of blood vessels elsewhere in the body, some cases showing widespread arteritis particularly affecting medium-sized muscular arteries, while others show only minimal changes and scattered vasculitis outside the heart.[5, 64, 89–93]

The cardiac pathologic findings vary with the stage of the illness during which death occurred. Fujiwara and Hamashima have related pathologic findings to the duration of illness at the time of death.[64] This categorization agrees well with pathologic findings reported in other series. The stages identified are summarized in Table 44–3. Few patients have been studied in stage I, as less than 5% of fatal cases occur during the first ten days of illness. The majority of deaths, approximately 70%, occur from day 11 to day 50, in stages II and III, and these patients therefore constitute the best studied group as well as those with the most "typical" pathologic changes. Late deaths in stage IV, occurring months to years after the clinical illness, primarily show chronic or degenerative changes that appear to date from the earlier acute episode.

Extracardiac pathology in Kawasaki syndrome is variable and generally involves the extraparenchymal portion of musculoelastic arteries producing periarterial inflammation, medial destruction, and intimal inflammation. Arteries most often involved are mesenteric, adrenal, splenic, renal, and those in the spermatic cord. Inflammatory changes are also seen in medium-sized and large veins.[5, 91–93]

Changes seen on skin biopsy during the period of rash are variable and generally nonspecific. Dilatation of the capillary loops of the dermal papillae, variable perivascular infiltration in arteries and arteriolas of the dermis, and mild dermal edema are described.

Table 44-3
Pathology of Kawasaki Syndrome

Stage I—Disease duration <10 days
Acute perivasculitis of coronary arteries
Microvascular angiitis of coronary arteries and aorta
Pancarditis with pericardial, myocardial, endocardial inflammation
Inflammation of atrioventricular conduction system

Stage II —Disease duration 12–18 days
Acute panvasculitis of coronary arteries
Coronary artery aneurysms present
Coronary obstruction and thrombosis
Myocardial and endocardial inflammation less intense

Stage III—Disease duration 28–45 days
Subacute inflammation in coronary arteries
Coronary artery aneurysms present
Myocardial, endocardial inflammation much depressed

Stage IV —Disease duration >50 days
Scar formation, calcification in coronary arteries
Stenosis and recanalization of coronary vessel lumen
Myocardial fibrosis without acute inflammation

Adapted from Fujiwara and Hamashima.[64]

Endothelial fenestrations may be observed by electron microscopy.[94] Immunofluorescent studies for disposition of immunoglobulins and complement are usually negative.

Lymph node changes are very common but nonspecific. Characteristically there is hypertrophy of the germinal centers, with medullary edema and an inflammatory infiltrate consisting of lymphocytes and large atypical mononuclear cells. Unfortunately, because of the totally nonspecific changes seen in skin, muscle, and lymph node, there are no tissues accessible to biopsy that would show pathognomonic changes.

The pathologic features of fatal Kawasaki syndrome are indistinguishable from the pathologic features of what had been known as "infantile periarteritis nodosa" (IPN).[89, 93] There is no persuasive reason to consider them to be separate entities. IPN differs considerably from classic periarteritis nodosa (CPN). Classic PN is a subacute or chronic disease with a duration measured in months to years, whereas fatal Kawasaki syndrome is an acute disease marked by sudden death within 2 months of onset. Hypertension, renal, and/or pulmonary involvement are common in classic PN but rare in Kawasaki syndrome. The pattern of vascular involvement in classic PN differs considerably from that of fatal Kawasaki syndrome.[93]

THERAPY

Intravenous Gamma Globulin

Although the etiologic agent in Kawasaki syndrome has not been discovered, high-dose intravenous (IV) gamma globulin (IVGG) given within the first ten days of onset of the disease has been shown in multiple controlled trials to reduce the frequency of coronary artery aneurysms, the only serious sequela of this condition.[95–97] In the US Multicenter Collaborative Controlled Trial, IV gamma globulin was used at a dose of 400 mg/kg/day for four consecutive days with therapy started in the first ten days of illness. Patients receiving this therapy plus aspirin at a dose of 100 mg/

kg/day were compared with patients who received aspirin alone. IV gamma globulin had a beneficial effect on the clinical course of the illness and on the development of coronary abnormalities. Two thirds of the patients who were treated with gamma globulin, but only 10% of those treated with aspirin alone, became afebrile within 24 hours of starting therapy. Patients treated with gamma globulin plus aspirin had a greater decrease in WBC count and in acute phase reactants than aspirin-treated patients. In the IVGG-plus-aspirin-treated patients coronary abnormalities were found in 8% at 2 weeks posttherapy and 4% at 7 weeks posttherapy. This was a statistically significant reduction from the coronary abnormality rates of 23% and 18% in those receiving aspirin alone. The importance of starting therapy early is demonstrated by the number of patients who had coronary abnormalities when first evaluated, 2.3% in the IVGG-plus-aspirin group and 4.7% in the aspirin-alone patients.[96] It has been demonstrated that the mean time of appearance of first coronary artery abnormality in patients ultimately developing aneurysms is ten days. To be effective in preventing aneurysms, therapy must be started early, preferably in the first week before changes are apparent.

It is impossible at this time to predict which patients will develop coronary aneurysms when seen within the first seven days of illness; therefore, all patients should be treated. Since immunoglobulin for IV use is a biologic product, efficacy and side effects may differ. While multiple products utilized in the United States and in Japan have been found to be efficacious in controlled trials, the frequency of adverse effects has differed markedly with different preparations. The preparation used in the US Multicenter Collaborative Controlled Trial was IVeeGam produced by Immuno AG of Vienna, Austria. This product has proved to be extremely safe. Significant side effects such as chills, fever, and anaphylaxis noted with other gamma globulin preparations have not occurred in over 400 patients treated with IVeeGam in the United States. Higher frequencies and increased severity of adverse effects have been encountered with some other products available in Japan. Concerns about safety and cost of therapy have limited the use of IVGG in Japan. In the United States, two formal cost-benefit analyses indicated that the cost of giving all children IVGG was completely offset by savings from decreased follow-up examinations and reduced numbers of patients needing echocardiograms and angiograms.

Aspirin

Aspirin has been advocated in the treatment of Kawasaki syndrome as it has beneficial effects on platelet aggregation and appears to have modest antifebrile effects when used in large doses. Multiple doses of aspirin have been advocated, but no comparable trials have demonstrated an advantage of one dose over the other. At the present time, it is the general consensus that some dose of aspirin should be provided for its antiplatelet effect in Kawasaki syndrome as all patients have a hypercoagulable state with elevation in platelet count during the second and third weeks of illness, and some degree of coronary artery abnormality. There is no evidence that the dose of aspirin employed has any effect on the frequency or severity of coronary involvement. One series of patients treated with the "antiplatelet" dose of 3 to 5 mg/kg/day had a frequency of coronary aneurysms of approximately 21% over a

3-year experience. Multiple Japanese series of patients treated with 30 mg/kg/day, an "antifebrile" dose, have had coronary aneurysm frequencies averaging 20%.[90, 98] In several series in the United States, a dose of 80 to 120 mg/kg has been employed, an "anti-inflammatory" dose, and coronary aneurysm frequencies of approximately 20% have been seen in these patients.[96, 99] One study purporting to show decreased frequency of coronary aneurysms in patients treated with high-dose aspirin is seriously flawed by the fact that the patient groups were not comparable.[100] At this time, an accepted regimen in North America is to use a high dose of aspirin, 80 to 100 mg/kg/day, until fever is controlled, followed by a reduction to 5 mg/kg/day until the sedimentation rate is normal. In Japan, 30 to 50 mg/kg/day is usually given throughout. Prolonged low-dose aspirin therapy is advisable in all children with coronary abnormalities. This dose of approximately 5 mg/kg/day can be given in a single daily dose and is well tolerated for an indefinite period. It may be interrupted if the child develops varicella or influenza, to minimize the risk of Reye syndrome.

Management

All patients with Kawasaki syndrome should be evaluated as early in the course of their illness as possible and a clinical diagnosis made as soon as feasible. Within the first week of illness, or at least in the first ten days of illness, patients should be started on aspirin and gamma globulin. We recommend aspirin at 80 to 100 mg/kg/day until the fever is controlled, then 3 to 5 mg/kg/day or one-half to 1 80-mg tablet per day. Gamma globulin should be given at a dose of 400 mg/kg/day for four consecutive days IV over two hours. IV gamma globulin treatment is associated with gratifying and prompt decrease in fever in 60% of patients. Very few patients remain febrile for four days or longer. Arthritis appears to develop or progress despite IV gamma globulin treatment. However, the arthritis of Kawasaki syndrome is basically self-limited and rarely persists beyond 6 weeks. Aspirin therapy should be continued until the sedimentation rate and platelet count have returned to normal, approximately 8 weeks after onset of illness. Patients should be admitted to the hospital and monitored until afebrile and stable. After IV gamma globulin has been administered and aspirin begun, the afebrile and stable patient may be discharged and followed with physical examinations on a weekly basis. The echocardiogram should be repeated at approximately 4 weeks after onset. If a 4-week echocardiogram is technically adequate and shows no coronary dilatation, further echocardiograms are unnecessary. Aspirin at low dose should be continued until the sedimentation rate is normal at 2 to 3 months postonset.

If coronary abnormalities are found, patients should be continued on low-dose aspirin (3–5 mg/kg/d or 40–80 mg/d) indefinitely. It is unknown whether dipyridamole (Persantine) therapy in addition to aspirin increases protection against thrombosis. If used, dipyridamole should be given at a dose of 4 mg/kg/day in three doses. Echocardiograms should be repeated at 8 weeks, at 6 months, and then yearly. Unless coronary dilatation is transient, coronary angiography is recommended to delineate the coronary anatomy. Patients with significant aneurysms should be followed by a cardiologist.

Complications

Congestive heart failure occurs in up to 30% of patients and generally responds very well to IV immunoglobulin therapy (IVIG). If congestive heart failure persists despite IVIG and aspirin therapy, cautious digitalis therapy or therapy with afterload reducers has been effective. The duration of congestive heart failure and inflammatory myocardiopathy in Kawasaki syndrome is generally short. Rhythm disturbances such as first-degree heart block and other minor arrhythmias generally resolve spontaneously.

Disseminated intravascular coagulation (DIC) and peripheral vascular compromise are very rare complications of Kawasaki syndrome, occurring in less than 1% of those affected. These complications occur too rarely for systematic study of any treatment; however, heparin with or without IV corticosteroid therapy has been employed. A single-pulse IV injection of methylprednisolone steroid therapy at a dose of 30 mg/kg given after full heparinization has been utilized with some success in patients with severe peripheral vascular compromise who appear to be progressing toward gangrene. Another therapy which has been used in severe peripheral compromise with apparent success is prostaglandin E infusion.[101] These rare complications should be managed by consultation with physicians experienced in the care of Kawasaki syndrome disease.

EPIDEMIOLOGY

Kawasaki disease is predominantly a disease of young children. In Japan and Hawaii, the peak age of occurrence is approximately 1 year, with almost equal numbers affected in the first and second years of life. Eighty percent of patients are less than 4 years of age with the age-specific incidence declining steadily to age 8 years. Very few cases are seen beyond 10 years of age.[98] There have been a number of case reports describing "Kawasaki syndrome" in adults.[102–107] Most of the "adult cases" were examples of another newly described disease, the toxic shock syndrome (TSS).[108, 109] At this time there is little evidence that active Kawasaki syndrome occurs in adults to any appreciable extent. Myocardial infarction and coronary disease presenting in adult life have been linked to Kawasaki syndrome in childhood.[110–114]

The epidemiology of Kawasaki syndrome in Japan demonstrates no clear geographic or urban-rural differences in the incidence of the disease. There is no dramatic seasonal difference in incidence, although a slightly higher incidence was noted in summer. Most cases were sporadic with no evidence of secondary cases in school, home, or neighborhood.[50] In a small case-controlled study in Japan, affected children showed no important differences from neighborhood controls.[115]

Until 1978, Kawasaki syndrome was thought to be an endemic, not an epidemic disease. In 1978, sharply defined clusters of cases were seen in New York City during the winter months[116] and in Honolulu from February through June.[117] A large outbreak involving over 200 cases was described in Ehime, Japan, in February through April 1979.[50] In the 1979 to 1980 winter-spring seasons, sharply defined community-wide outbreaks were seen in Rochester, New York (23 cases),[118] eastern Massachusetts (56 cases),[118] Los Angeles (32 cases),[119] and Honolulu (51 cases).[59] In 1981, a very intense outbreak of 72 cases occurred in Honolulu from February to May. In 1982, an outbreak of more than 23 cases was described in Denver.[120] In the well-studied outbreaks, the illness appeared suddenly, involved the entire community, and affected only children less than 10 years of age. There was no evidence of person-to-person transmission or point-source exposure except for one case of illness in siblings seven days apart in the Honolulu study.[121] In Rochester and Massachusetts the patients were of higher socioeconomic status than controls. In Denver and Honolulu the mean income for patients was significantly above the state mean but patients and controls did not differ. In Rochester and Massachusetts, but not in Hawaii or Denver, cases were more likely than controls to have suffered an upper respiratory illness in the month before onset of the illness.[118] In all studies contact with toxins, household pets, medications, chemicals, fertilizers, herbicides, pesticides, foreign visitors or tourists, and diet did not differ between patients and controls. A nationwide pandemic occurred in Japan in 1985 and was associated with apparent geographic spread of disease.[122]

An intriguing statistically significant association of Kawasaki syndrome and exposure to rug shampoo emerged during a case-controlled study of the outbreak in Denver in 1982. Eleven (48%) of 23 cases compared with 10% and 11% of two matched control groups had household carpets shampooed in the 30 days before onset. In addition, exposed patients were more likely to have walked or crawled on the shampooed rugs within two hours of application.[119] This association focuses attention on the child's environment as a possible source of an infectious agent, vector, or chemical hypersensitivity. An association with exposure to freshly shampooed carpets has been reported in two other outbreaks, but was not found in 11 other small clusters in the United States.[123, 124]

Among 200 children with Kawasaki syndrome seen in Hawaii, children of Japanese ancestry are markedly overrepresented compared to their proportion of the child population, while white children have been markedly underrepresented. Chinese, Polynesian, Filipino, and children of mixed race appear to have an intermediate incidence.[121] In the report from the Centers for Disease Control where cases were passively reported from throughout the United States, the prevalence rate was high among Orientals, intermediate for blacks, and low among whites.[125]

Because the disease appears most prevalent in Japan and among Japanese children in Hawaii, a unique genetic susceptibility is suspected. HLA typing of patients compared with controls has been studied with conflicting results generally not supporting an association of the disease with specific HLA types. No single HLA antigen was common to all cases.[126–130] No systematic study of the prevalence of other genetic markers among cases has yet been reported.

ETIOLOGY

At the present time, the etiology of Kawasaki syndrome remains undiscovered. The clinical picture with its acute onset, fever, multisystem disease, exanthem, and aseptic meningitis together with the regular occurrence of community-wide epidemics and the virtual restriction to young children strongly suggests a highly trans-

missible microbial agent which spreads widely through communities at 2- to 3-year intervals, causing infection in virtually all susceptible children but expressed disease in only a few. The increased incidence noted in Japanese children living in Hawaii[131] compared with whites in the same community suggests that susceptibility to disease may be genetically determined. This pattern of widespread infection with infrequent disease affecting primarily preschool children resembles the epidemiology of both poliomyelitis and of *Haemophilus influenzae* type B disease.

No bacterial agent has ever been consistently isolated from any site in patients with Kawasaki syndrome. Blood cultures are characteristically sterile, and focal bacterial infections are exceedingly rare. This lack of focal infection makes bacterial toxin-mediated disease less likely; however, investigations into a toxin-mediated pathogenesis are in progress.[132] Kato and colleagues have reported occasional isolation from blood culture and lymph node of a variant strain of *Propionibacterium acnes*.[133, 134] They have postulated that this variant strain makes a toxin which can be detected by cytopathic effect (CPE) and have shown slightly higher titer of antibody to *P acnes* in the subacute stage of patients recovering from Kawasaki syndrome than in control children. No patients showed seroconversion. This group has not yet proved a unique association of *P acnes* with Kawasaki syndrome by isolation or antibody studies and their reports remain unconfirmed.

Because of a presumed similarity between Kawasaki syndrome and leptospirosis, it has been suggested that leptospires might be the etiologic agent of the Kawasaki syndrome.[135] In the large experience in Hawaii, however, leptospires have not been recovered by culture and no seroconversion to 22 leptospiral agents has been demonstrated.[121] Ohtaki et al similarly reported failure to implicate leptospires in 14 typical Japanese patients[136] as did Bergeson and Shoenike with four American cases.[6] Therefore, leptospirosis does not appear to be a common etiologic agent among cases of Kawasaki syndrome that are diagnosed by clinicians who are totally familiar with its manifestations.

One group of Japanese investigators has reported finding "rickettsia-like bodies" in skin and lymph node specimens studied by electron microscopy. Similar microbodies were recovered from yolk sack and guinea pig tissues inoculated with blood from one patient. The fine structure of these bodies differs from all previously discovered rickettsia. The agent could not be further characterized and was lost in serial passage.[137, 138]

Extensive efforts to confirm the presence of these rickettsialike bodies have been carried out in Japan with no success, despite meticulous adherence to procedures for rickettsial isolation.[139, 140] No antibody rises to known rickettsial agents have been demonstrated. A rickettsial etiology for Kawasaki syndrome remains unconfirmed at this time.

Japanese investigators have also explored a possible role for house dust mites in either causation or transmission of Kawasaki syndrome. Attempts to confirm a unique association with house dust mites by serologic means in the United States have been negative. Cases and controls from varying geographic locations differ in prevalence of antibody to house dust mites.[124] Kawasaki syndrome cases have neither a higher prevalence or titer of antibodies than controls, and seroconversion to house dust mite antigen during the course of illness has not been demonstrated.

Viruses as Etiologic Agents in Kawasaki Syndrome

The regular occurrence of immunoregulatory abnormalities in patients with acute Kawasaki syndrome manifested as a transient decrease in T suppressor cells has suggested that a lymphotropic retrovirus might be the causative agent. Recurrent disease does occur in Kawasaki syndrome, suggesting that the agent might be a highly cell-associated virus with a potential for latent infection. Two groups have reported finding elevated DNA polymerase activity in patients with Kawasaki syndrome and have suggested that this activity represents retroviral reverse transcriptase.[141, 142] In addition to detecting small amounts of DNA polymerase in supernatants from cultivation of patient lymphocytes, Burns et al reported finding viruslike particles on electron microscopy and demonstrated that the density of the DNA polymerase enzyme was similar to that of reverse transcriptase.[142] These reports have stimulated others to search for evidence of reverse transcriptase. The presence of retroviral reverse transcriptase activity was not detected in six patients studied by Okamoto et al.[143] We have recently concluded a comprehensive study of this problem involving 49 cases of Kawasaki syndrome. While we did detect a slight increase in DNA polymerase activity in supernatants of cultured lymphocytes from Kawasaki syndrome patients between the seventh and 13th day in culture, we found similar increases in febrile control patients. The magnitude and timing of the elevation in DNA polymerase detected in our studies was very similar to that reported by Burns et al. However, the finding of increases of similar magnitude in control patients' lymphocyte culture and analysis of template-primer preference data strongly suggested that the increased activity detected by these sensitive assays was due to host cell DNA polymerase and not to retroviral reverse transcriptase. Serologic study of patients demonstrated no evidence of antibodies to known retroviral agents. In the course of carrying out these studies, we did isolate measles vaccine virus from the T cells of one Kawasaki syndrome patient and demonstrated virus particles by electron microscopy. This experience demonstrates that caution is required in assaying an etiologic role to any viral agent demonstrated by isolation or electron microscopy.[144] If retroviruses are involved in the etiology of Kawasaki syndrome, more sensitive and specific measures will be required to establish their presence.

Herpesviruses have been investigated as potential etiologic agents in Kawasaki syndrome. There are no viral isolation or serologic data implicating infection with cytomegalovirus, herpesviruses 1 or 2, or varicella-zoster virus with Kawasaki syndrome. One Japanese group has developed a hypothesis that the disease is the result of an unusual primary infection with Epstein-Barr virus (EBV). They report the occasional isolation of EBV from patients with Kawasaki syndrome. They have noted an unusual serologic relationship with EBV. They have not demonstrated seroconversion, but in fact have found that most patients have persistent negative antibody tests to EBV with an occasional patient showing antibody present initially followed by persistant loss of EBV antibodies.[145] Our group has extensively evaluated the relationship of herpesviruses to Kawasaki syndrome. In a systematic study of 27 consecutive patients with Kawasaki syndrome we were unable to cultivate EBV. In over 50 attempts, we have never been able to establish a continual cell line from the peripheral blood mononuclear cells of patients with Kawasaki syndrome. Both of these observations argue strongly against a primary infection with EBV as the etiologic agent in Kawasaki syndrome. Occasional patients demonstrated seroconversion to EBV in temporal sequence, which suggested recent or concomitant infection. However, most patients remain seronegative for months to years after their encounter with Kawasaki syndrome. The specific pattern of presence of antibody in the acute stage followed by persistent loss of antibody was not observed in any of our patients.[146]

Viral agents have not been searched for as thoroughly or systematically as bacterial agents. Few case reports have mentioned results of viral cultures. In the two series we have reported in Honolulu, viral cultures of 37 patients were uniformly negative.[3, 121] John et al reported negative viral cultures on four patients,[26] Bergeson and Shoeinke in one.[6] Viral agents have not generally been recovered from Japanese patients, although the thoroughness of virologic investigations is unspecified.

Parainfluenza type 2 virus was isolated and seroconversion demonstrated in a 4-year-old girl with a compatible illness including jaundice and myocarditis.[147] Viruses reported from single cases include parainfluenza, adenovirus type 3, herpes simplex, and echovirus 2.[148] In contrast to our virus searches prior to 1979 when we had negative cultures on 37 patients, our more recent studies have yielded viral isolation in 25 (33%) of 75 patients studied in the first eight days of illness. Of these 25 isolates, eight were most likely unrelated to the present illness as two were vaccine strain polioviruses and five were cytomegalovirus in children with stable positive antibody titers. The remaining seven isolates were common respiratory viruses and enterovirus including respiratory syncytial virus, adenovirus 2, coxsackievirus B5, A9, and echovirus 30 agents, which were known to be prevalent in the community during the child's illness. Seroconversion to these agents was demonstrated by the affected child but was not generally found among those whose viral isolations were negative. Serologic study of Kawasaki syndrome patients to a wide variety of common and exotic viral and other infectious agents including hepatitis A and B, hantaviruses, *Anaplasma* spp, and *Ehrlichia canis* has failed to implicate any agent common to all or any significant portion of patients (M. J. Marchette, K. Elutheson, M. E. Melish, unpublished observations).

Thus, at this time, there is no evidence that a single commonly encountered viral agent is responsible for Kawasaki syndrome. A novel viral agent has not been ruled out and remains the most attractive possibility. Our data, however, suggest that multiple, commonly encountered respiratory and enteroviral agents might act as triggers for Kawasaki syndrome in susceptible hosts. This hypothesis, that Kawasaki syndrome may be triggered by multiple viruses in uniquely susceptible hosts, is compatible with some of the epidemiologic observations. Kawasaki syndrome occurs as sporadic cases but also in sharply defined community-wide epidemics. Epidemics occur in the winter and spring at a time when respiratory viruses are prevalent. The absence of evidence for person-to-person spread of Kawasaki syndrome could be explained by unique host susceptibility to a widely prevalent agent. These epidemiologic features are similar to those of Reye syndrome, an illness which is known to be triggered by multiple viruses, most commonly influenza B and varicella, but which affects only a small number of children during a community-wide outbreak

PATHOGENESIS

Until the etiology of Kawasaki syndrome is discovered, the pathogenesis will likewise remain unknown. Consideration of clinical features, pathology, and epidemiology does lead to some reasonable speculation. While the acute, febrile, self-limited, generally nonrecurrent nature of the illness suggests an acute infectious etiology, the development of arthritis and carditis during the subacute phase of the disease is essentially a rheumatic feature. However, the rheumatic disease is not progressive or chronic and therefore not of the classical collagen-vascular disease variety. This, together with the basic pathologic lesion of a time-limited period of acute vasculitis, suggests that the immunologic response to an acute infection mediates the vasculitis.

Circulating immune complexes have been detected primarily during the subacute and early convalescent period of the disease.[87, 149-152] The presence of circulating immune complexes has been linked to platelet aggregation.[153] Despite the fact that small amounts of circulating immune complexes can be regularly detected in Kawasaki syndrome, the disease does not demonstrate classic immune complex-mediated pathology. Complement levels remain normal throughout the illness and renal disease is absent. The exact role of immune complexes is unclear at this time.

Immunoregulatory abnormalities have been reported in Kawasaki syndrome. These include an acute depression in circulating T8 suppressor cells which results in an elevated T helper-T suppressor ratio. This T cell imbalance has a functional effect as T cells from patients with Kawasaki syndrome stimulate immunoglobulin secretion by normal B cells in vitro and as an increased number of circulating B cells are found to be spontaneously secreting immunoglobulin.[154, 155] Cytotoxic IgG and IgM antibodies directed at endothelial cell antigens have been detected during the acute phase of Kawasaki syndrome.[156, 157] The significance of these newly discovered pathogenic mechanisms in Kawasaki syndrome is not clear at the present time.

The strongest evidence for the participation of immunologic mechanisms in the pathogenesis of the vascular damage comes from the striking efficacy of IV immunoglobulin. This immunologic therapy results in decreased intensity of vasculitis, decreased fever, and decreased acute phase reactants. Moreover, the effect is very rapid suggesting that immunopathogenic mechanisms are "turned off" within hours of exposure to IV gamma globulin. The mechanism of action of IVIG is completely unknown although an effect on immunoregulatory T suppressor cells has been demonstrated.[155] Immunopathogenic mechanisms appear to be a most fruitful area for further research.

REFERENCES

1. Kawasaki T: Acute febrile mucocutaneous syndrome with lymphoid involvement with specific desquamation of the fingers and toes. *Jpn J Allergy* 1967; 16:178–222.
2. Kawasaki T, Kosaki F, Okawa S, et al: A new infantile febrile mucocutaneous lymph node syndrome (MLNS) prevailing in Japan. *Pediatrics* 1974; 54:271–276.
3. Melish ME, Hicks RM, Larson EJ: Mucocutaneous lymph node syndrome in the United States. *Am J Dis Child* 1976; 130:599–607.
4. Melish ME, Hicks RM, Larson EJ: Mucocutaneous lymph node syndrome in the United States. *Pediatr Res* 1974; 8:427.
5. Amano S, Hozama F, Kubagawa H, et al: General pathology of Kawasaki disease. *Acta Pathol Jpn* 1980; 30:681–684.
6. Bergeson PS, Shoenike SL: Mucocutaneous lymph node syndrome. *JAMA* 1977; 237:2299–2302.
7. Bernhardt L: Mucocutaneous lymph node syndrome with encephalopathy in the continental United States. *West J Med* 1976; 125:230–233.
8. Bos SE, Kooi-Voskuyl MJP: The mucocutaneous lymph node syndrome, Kawasaki syndrome (Dutch). *Ned Tijdschr Geneeskd* 1978; 122:1184–1187.
9. Brown JS, Billmeier GJ, Cox F, et al: Mucocutaneous lymph node syndrome in continental United States. *J Pediatr* 1976; 88:81–83.
10. *Canada Diseases Weekly Report,* April 22, 1978.
11. Casenave C, Aufrere AM: Un cas de syndrome adéno-cutanéo-muquex (French). *Arch Fr Pediatr* 1978; 35:555–558.
12. Center for Disease Control: *MMWR* 1976; 25:157–158.
13. Condat JM, Chauvet J, Mourieras P: Kawasaki syndrome in an infant from the Ivory Coast. *Nouv Presse Med* 1981; 10:251.
14. Cook A, Heurex L: Radiographic findings in mucocutaneous lymph node syndrome. *Am J Radiol* 1979; 132:107–109.
15. Corbell L, Delmotte B, Standaert L, et al: Kawasaki disease in Europe—Belgium, letter. *Lancet* 1977; 1:797.
16. Cusid MJ, Tang TT: Fever, diarrhea, anemia, and acrocyanosis in a 2 month old girl. *J Pediatr* 1978; 93:1052–1057.
17. Darby CP, Kyong CU: Mucocutaneous lymph node syndrome. *JAMA* 1976; 236:2295–2297.
18. Della Porta G, Alberti A: Kawasaki disease in Europe—Italy, letter. *Lancet* 1977; 1:798.
19. Dennis MK, Ayoub EM, Graham T, et al: Mucocutaneous lymph node syndrome in Florida. *J Fla Med Assoc* 1977; 64:21–26.
20. Fossard D, Thompson RA: Mucocutaneous lymph node syndrome (Kawasaki disease: Probable solution-complex disorder). *Br Med J* 1977; 1:883.
21. Fowler RN, Stevenson RE, Burton OM, et al: Mucocutaneous lymph node syndrome in South Carolina. *J SC Med Assoc* 1979; 75:11–14.
22. Goldsmith RW, Grebetz D, Strauss L: Mucocutaneous lymph node syndrome in the continental United States. *Pediatrics* 1976; 57:431–434.
23. Gorin R, Sorin M, Meyer A, et al: The mucucutaneous lymph node syndrome in Kawasaki (French). *Sem Hop Paris* 1978; 54:442–447.
24. Gross CW, Chamberlin M: Mucocutaneous lymph node syndrome: A new clinical entity. *Laryngoscope* 1977; 87:1702–1704.
25. Hewitt CJ: Case of Kawasaki disease. *Br Med J* 1977; 1:883–884.
26. Hicsonmez G, Kanra G, Kocak H, et al: Acute febrile mucocutaneous lymph node syndrome. *Clin Pediatr* 1977; 16:480–481.
27. John TJ, De Beneditti CD, Zee ML: Mucocutaneous lymph node syndrome in Arizona. *Am J Dis Child* 1976; 130:613–614.
28. Kim J, Yeo Y, Lee B: Mucocutaneous lymph node syndrome: Clinical observations of eight cases. *Korea N Med J* 1973; 16:1156.
29. Kovacevic M, Gardner HG: Thrombocytosis associated with mucocutaneous lymph node syndrome, letter. *J Pediatr* 1976; 86:688.
30. Lauer BA, Bruhn FW, Todd JW, et al: Mucocutaneous lymph node syndrome in Denver. *Am J Dis Child* 1976; 130:610–612.
31. Lyen KR, Brook CGD: Mucocutaneous lymph node syndrome in two siblings. *Br Med J* 1978; 1:1187.
32. Magilavy DB, Speort DP, Silver TM: Mucocutaneous lymph node syndrome: Report of two cases complicated by gallbladder hydrops and diagnosed by ultrasound. *Pediatrics* 1978; 61:699–702.
33. Miriovsky M, Downing JS: Mucocutaneous lymph node syndrome. *Am Fam Physician* 1978; 17:154–157.
34. Newton-John HF: Kawasaki syndrome in Melbourne. *Aust Paediatr J* 1980; 16:57–62.
35. Nyerges G, Barna M, Molnar L: Mucocutaneous lymph node syndrome: Three cases observed in Hungary. *Acta Paediatr Acad Sci Hung* 1978; 19:1–7.

36. Odom R, Olson EG: Mucocutaneous lymph node syndrome. *Arch Dermatol* 1977; 113:339–340.

37. Reddy AB: Mucocutaneous lymph node syndrome. *IMJ* 1978; 153:326–329.

38. Robinson R: Mucocutaneous lymph node syndrome in California, letter. *J Pediatr* 1976; 88:1069–1070.

39. Ruiz D, Krober MS: Mucocutaneous lymph node syndrome. *Okla State Med Assoc J* 1977; 70:351–353.

40. Russell AS, Zaragoza AJ, Shea R: Mucocutaneous lymph node syndrome in Canada. *Can Med Assoc J* 1976; 112:1210–1211.

41. Sherini A, Vegni M, Elli P, et al: Kawasaki disease in Italy. *Minerva Pediatr* 1980; 32:1111–1116.

42. Scopes JW, Hulse JA: Mucocutaneous lymph node syndrome. *Br Med* 1977; 1:511.

43. Siegel CJ: The mucocutaneous lymph node syndrome. *Clin Pediatr* 1976; 15:1103–1106.

44. Sinniah D, Nagappan N, Choo N: Mucocutaneous lymph node syndrome in Malaysia. *Med J Malaysia* 1979; 34:164–166.

45. Smith AD: Infantile polyarteritis and Kawasaki disease. *Acta Paediatr Scand* 1977; 66:381–384.

46. Stephenson SR: Kawasaki disease in Europe, letter. *Lancet* 1977; 1:373–374.

47. Tanaka N, Sekimoto K, Naoe S: Kawasaki disease: Relationship with infantile periarteritis nodosa. *Arch Pathol Lab Med* 1976; 100:81–86.

48. Taneja A, Saxena U: Mucocutaneous lymph node syndrome: Case report. *Indian Pediatr* 1977; 14:927–931.

49. Valaes T: Mucocutaneous lymph node syndrome (MLNS) in Athens, Greece. *Pediatrics* 1975; 55:295.

50. Withers EH, Long WR, Lynch JB: Mucocutaneous lymph node syndrome: An additional case. *J Tenn Med Assoc* 1977; 70:731.

51. Yanigawa H: Epidemiology of Kawasaki disease (MCLS). *Jpn J Med Sci Biol* 1979; 32:241–243.

52. Yanagisawa M, Kobayashi N, Matsuya S: Myocardial infarction due to coronary thromboarteritis following acute febrile mucocutaneous lymph node syndrome (MLNS) in an infant. *Pediatrics* 1974; 54:277–281.

53. Asai T, et al: Analysis of cardiac involvement in 29 cases with mucocutaneous lymph node syndrome (Japanese). *Jpn J Pediatr* 1973; 26:284.

54. Hosaki J, Abe S, Yoshimatsu A, et al: Observations of coronary arterial lesions in acute febrile mucocutaneous lymph node syndrome (MCLS). *Acta Paediatr Jpn* 1976; 18:8–17.

55. Kato H: Natural history of Kawasaki disease, in Shiokawa Y (ed): *Vascular Lesions of Collagen Diseases and Related Conditions.* Tokyo, University of Tokyo Press, 1977, pp 281–286.

56. Kato H, Koike S, Yamamoto M, et al: Coronary aneurysms in infants and young children with acute febrile mucocutaneous lymph node syndrome. *J Pediatr* 1975; 86:892–898.

57. Kitamura S, Kawashima Y, Kawachi K, et al: Left ventricular function in patients with coronary arteritis due to acute febrile mucocutaneous lymph node syndrome or related diseases. *Am J Cardiol* 1977; 40:156–164.

58. Hicks RV, Melish ME: Rheumatic complaints and analysis of salicylate therapy, abstract. *Arthritis Rheum* 1979; 22:621.

59. Tanaka N, Onouchi Z, Fushiki S: Mucocutaneous lymph node syndrome presenting as acute cholecysititis (Japanese). *Acta Paediatr Jpn* 1976; 18:1–7.

60. Mofenson HC, Greensher J, Molavi M: Gallbladder hydrops: Complications of Kawasaki disease. *NY State J Med* 1980; 80:249–251.

61. Slovis TL, Hight DW, Phillipart AI: Sonography in the diagnosis and management of hydrops of the gallbladder in children with mucocutaneous lymph node syndrome. *Pediatrics* 1980; 65:789–794.

62. Kato H, Koike S: Clinicopathologic studies of disease associated with vasculitis—Kawasaki disease and infantile polyarteritis (Japanese) *Jpn J Clin Med* 1978; 36:753–767.

63. Konishi Y, Tasuta N, Miki S, et al: Mitral insufficiency secondary to mucocutaneous lymph node syndrome. A case report of successful surgical treatment. *Jpn Circ J* 1978; 42:901–909.

64. Fujiwara H, Hamashima Y: Pathology of the heart in Kawasaki disease. *Pediatrics* 1978; 61:100–107.

65. Kato H, Koike S, Yokoyama T: Kawasaki disease: Effect of treatment in coronary artery involvement. *Pediatrics* 1979; 63:175–179.

66. Reference deleted in proof.

67. Reference deleted in proof.

68. Sasaguri Y, Kato H: Regression of aneurysms in Kawasaki disease: A pathological study. *J Pediatr* 1982; 100:225–231.

69. Suzuki A, Kamiya T, Ono Y, et al: Follow-up study of coronary artery lesions due to Kawasaki disease by serial selective coronary arteriography in 200 patients. *Heart Vessels* 1987; 3:159–165.

70. Kegel SM, Dorsey TJ, Rowen M, et al: Cardiac death in mucocutaneous lymph node syndrome. *Am J Cardiol* 1977; 40:282–286.

71. Kusakawa S: Kawasaki disease (Japanese). *Jpn J Clin Med* 1978; 1968–1969.

72. Kusakawa S, Asai T: Juvenile myocardial infarction (Japanese). *Jpn J Clin Med* 1977; 35:2525–2528.

73. Radford DJ, Sandheimer HM, Williams GJ: Mucocutaneous lymph node syndrome with coronary artery aneurysms. *Am J Dis Child* 1976; 130:596–598.

74. Kato H, Ichinose E, Kawasaki T: Myocardial infarction in Kawasaki disease: clinical analyses in 195 cases. *J Pediatr* 1986; 108:923–927.

75. Kitamura S, Kawashima Y, Fujita T, et al: Aortocoronary bypass grafting in a child with coronary artery obstruction due to mucocutaneous lymph node syndrome. *Circulation* 1976; 53:1035–1040.

76. Takeuchi Y, Suma K, Shiroma K, et al: Coronary artery changes in Kawasaki disease and its surgical treatment by aorto-coronary bypass grafting (Japanese). *Jpn J Thorac Surg* 1978; 31:356–361.

77. Wada J, Endo M, Takeo A, et al: Mucocutaneous lymph node syndrome. Successful aorto-coronary bypass homograft in a 10 year old boy. *Chest* 1980; 77:443–446.

78. Ino T, Iwahara M, Boku H, et al: Aorto-coronary bypass surgery for Kawasaki disease. *Pediatr Cardiol* 1987; 8:195–197.

79. Tatara K, Kusakawa S: Long-term prognosis of giant coronary aneurysm in Kawasaki disease: an angiographic study. *J Pediatr* 1987; 111:705–710.

80. Fukushige J, Nihill MR, McNamara DG: Spectrum of cardiac disease in mucocutaneous lymph node syndrome. *Am J Cardiol* 1980; 45:98–107.

81. Kleiman MB, Passo MH: Incomplete Kawasaki disease with facial nerve paralysis and coronary artery involvement. *Pediatr Infect Dis J* 1988; 74:301–302.

82. Schuh S, Laxer RM, Smallhorn JF, et al: Kawasaki disease with atypical presentation. *Pediatr Infect Dis J* 1988; 7:201–203.

83. Cloney DL, Teja K, Lohr JA: Fatal case of atypical Kawasaki syndrome. *Pediatr Infect Dis J* 1987; 6:297–299.

84. Rowley AH, Gonzales-Crussi F, Gidding SS, et al: Incomplete Kawasaki disease with coronary artery involvement. *J Pediatr* 1987; 110:409–413.

85. Burns JC, Wiggins JW Jr, Toews WH, et al: Clinical spectrum of Kawasaki disease in infants younger than 6 months of age. *J Pediatr* 1986; 109:759–763.

86. Kusakawa S, Heiner D: Elevated levels of immunoglobulin E in the acute febrile mucocutaneous lymph node syndrome. *Pediatr Res* 1976; 10:108–111.

87. Eluthesen K, Marchette NJ, Melish ME, et al: Circulating immune complexes, immunoglobulin and complement levels in Kawasaki syndrome. *J Pediatr Infect Dis* submitted.

88. Tanaka N: Kawasaki disease (acute febrile infantile mucocutaneous lymph node syndrome) in Japan: Relationship with infantile

periarteritis nodosa. *Pathol Microbiol* 1975; 43:204–218.

89. Ahlstrom H, Lundstrom NR, Mortensson W, et al: Infantile periarteritis nodosa or mucocutaneous lymph node syndrome. *Acta Paediatr Scand* 1977; 66:193–198.

90. Amano S, Hozama F: Neural involvement in Kawasaki disease. *Acta Pathol Jpn* 1980; 30:365–373.

91. Amano S, Hozama F, Hamashima Y: Pathology of Kawasaki disease I—Pathology and morphology of the vascular changes. *Jpn Circ J* 1979; 43:633–643.

92. Amano S, Hozama F, Hamashima Y: Pathology of Kawasaki disease II—Distribution and incidence of the vascular lesions. *Jpn Circ J* 1979; 43:741–748.

93. Landing BH, Larson EJ: Are infantile periarteritis nodosa with coronary artery involvement and fatal mucocutaneous lymph node syndrome the same? Comparison of 20 patients from North America with patients from Hawaii and Japan. *Pediatrics* 1976; 59:651–662.

94. Hirose S, Hamashima Y: Morphological observations on the vasculitis in the mucocutaneous lymph node syndrome. *Eur J Pediatr* 1978; 1929:17–27.

95. Furusho K, Kamiya T, Nakano H, et al: High dose intravenous gammaglobulin for Kawasaki disease. *Lancet* 1984; 2:1055–1058.

96. Newburger JW, Takahashi M, Burns JC, et al: The treatment of Kawasaki syndrome with intravenous gamma globulin. *N Engl J Med* 1986; 315:341–347.

97. Nagashima M, Matsushima M, Matsuoka H, et al: High-dose gammaglobulin therapy for Kawasaki disease. *J Pediatr* 1987; 110:710–712.

98. Yanagawa H, Kawasaki T, Shigematsu I: Nationwide survey on Kawasaki disease in Japan. *Pediatrics* 1987; 80:58–62.

99. Ichida F, Fatica NS, Engle MA, et al: Coronary artery involvement in Kawasaki syndrome in Manhattan, New York: risk factors and role of aspirin. *Pediatrics* 1987; 80:828–835.

100. Koren G, Rose V, Lavi S, et al: Probable efficacy of high dose salicylates in Kawasaki disease. *JAMA* 1985; 254:767–769.

101. Westphalen MA, McGrath MA, Kelly W, et al: Kawasaki disease with severe peripheral ischemia: treatment with prostaglandin E1 infusion. *J Pediatr* 1988; 112:431–433.

102. Everett ED: Mucocutaneous lymph node syndrome in adults. *JAMA* 1979; 242:542–543.

103. Lee TJ, Vaughan D: Mucocutaneous lymph node syndrome in a young adult. *Arch Intern Med* 1979; 139:104–105.

104. Milgram H, Palmer EL, Slovin SF, et al: Kawasaki disease in a healthy young adult. *Am Intern Med* 1980; 92:467–470.

105. Schlossberg D, Kandra J, Kreiser J: Possible Kawasaki disease in a 20 year old woman. *Arch Dermatol* 1979; 115:1435–1436.

106. Snell GF: Adult Kawasaki disease—Three occurrences in the same patient. *West J Med* 1980; 132:6–7.

107. Butler DF, Hough DR, Friedman SJ, et al: Adult Kawasaki syndrome. *Arch Dermatol* 1987; 123:1356–1361.

108. Davis JP, Chesney PJ, Ward PJ: Toxic shock syndrome. *N Engl J Med* 1980; 303:1429–1435.

109. Shands KN, Schmid GP, Dan DB, et al: Toxic shock syndrome in menstruating women. *N Engl J Med* 1980; 303:1436–1442.

110. Brecker SJ, Gray HH, Oldershaw PJ: Coronary artery aneurysms and myocardial infarction: adult sequelae of Kawasaki disease? *Br Heart J* 1988; 59:509–512.

111. Flugelman MY, Hasin Y, Bassan MM, et al: Acute myocardial infarction 14 years after an acute episode of Kawasaki's disease. *Am J Cardiol* 1983; 52:427–428.

112. Pounder DJ: Coronary artery aneurysms presenting as sudden death 14 years after Kawasaki disease in infancy. *Arch Pathol Lab Med* 1985; 109:874–876.

113. Kohr RM: Progressive asymptomatic coronary artery disease as a late fatal sequela of Kawasaki disease. *J Pediatr* 1986; 108:256–259.

114. Gorgels APM, Braat SHGJ, Becker AE, et al: Multiple aneurysms of the coronary arteries as the cause of sudden death in childhood. *Am J Cardiol* 1986; 57:1193–1194.

115. Yanigawa H, Shigematsu I, Kawasaki T: Epidemiological aspects

116. Jacobs JC: Successful treatment of Kawasaki syndrome with aspirin, abstract. *Pediatr Res* 1978; 12:494.

117. Dean AG, Melish ME, Hicks RV, et al: An epidemic of Kawasaki syndrome in Hawaii. *J Pediatr* 1982; 100:552–557.

118. Bell DM, Brink EW, Nitzin JL, et al: Kawasaki syndrome: Description of two outbreaks in the United States. *N Engl J Med* 1981; 304:1568–1575.

119. Mason W, Wu E, Cote S, et al: Kawasaki syndrome: Epidemiologic evaluation of a cluster of 36 cases, abstract. *Clin Res* 1981; 29:126A.

120. Patriarca PA, Rogers MF, Morens DM, et al: Kawasaki syndrome: Association with the application of rug shampoo. *Lancet* 1982; 2:578–580.

121. Melish ME, Hicks RM, Dean AG, et al: Endemic and epidemic Kawasaki syndrome in Hawaii, abstract. *Pediatr Res* 1981; 15:617.

122. Yanagawa H, Nakamura Y, Kawasaki T, et al: Nationwide epidemic of Kawasaki disease in Japan during winter of 1985–86. *Lancet* 1986; 2:1138–1139.

123. Rauch AM, Kaplan SL, Nihill MR, et al: Kawasaki syndrome clusters in Harris County, Texas, and eastern North Carolina. A high endemic rate and a new environmental risk factor. *Am J Dis Child* 1988; 142:441–444.

124. Klein BS, Rogers MF, Patrican LA, et al: Kawasaki syndrome: a controlled study of an outbreak in Wisconsin. *Am J Epidemiol* 1986; 124:306–316.

125. Morens DM, Anderson LJ, Hurwitz ES: National surveillance of Kawasaki disease. *Pediatrics* 1980; 65:21–25.

126. Hicks RV, Melish ME, Paik R, et al: Kawasaki syndrome: 2 or 10 years later, abstract. *Arthritis Rheum* 1981; 24:S125.

127. Kato H: Personal Communication, December 1980.

128. Kato H, Kimura M, Tsuji K, et al: HLA antigen in Kawasaki disease. *Pediatrics* 1978; 61:252–255.

129. Krensky A, Berenberg W, Grady S, et al: HLA antigens in mucocutaneous lymph node syndrome abstract. *Pediatr Res* 1981; 15:735.

130. Matsuda I, et al: HLA antigens in mucocutaneous lymph node syndrome. *Am J Dis Child* 1977; 131:1417–1418.

131. Melish ME, Ching D: Kawasaki syndrome epidemiology—Hawaii 1971–1986. *Prog Clin Biol Res* 1987; 250:547.

132. Glode MP, Brogden RL, Joffe LS, et al: Microbial toxins and Kawasaki disease. *Prog Clin Biol Res* 1987; 250:81–86.

133. Kato H, Fujimoto T, Inoue O, et al: Variant strain of *Propionibacterum acnes:* a clue to the etiology of Kawasaki disease. *Lancet* 1983; 2:1383–1387.

134. Tomita S, Koga Y, Inoue O, et al: Cytopathogenic protein (CPP) produced by *Propionibacterum acnes* isolated from patients with Kawasaki disease. *Prog Clin Biol Res* 1987; 250:73–80.

135. Wong ML, Kaplan S, Kunkie LM, et al: Leptospirosis: a childhood disease. *J Pediatr* 1977; 90:532.

136. Ohtaki C, Tomiyama T, Suzuki M, et al: Leptospiral antibody and MLNS. *J Pediatr* 1978; 93:896.

137. Hamashima Y, Kishi K, Tasaka K: Rickettsia-like bodies in infantile acute febrile mucocutaneous lymph node syndrome, letter. *Lancet* 1973; 2:42.

138. Tasaka K, Hamashima Y: Studies on rickettsia-like body in Kawasaki disease. Attempts in the isolation and characterization. *Acta Pathol Jpn* 1978; 28:235–345.

139. Shishido A: Failure to confirm the rickettsial etiology of MCLS (Kawasaki disease). *Jpn J Med Sci Biol* 1979; 32:250–251.

140. Shishido A, Adachi Y: Attempts at isolation of rickettsia from blood of patients with Kawasaki disease, in Kawasaki T, Kusakawa S, Shigematsu I (eds): *Progress of Research on Kawasaki Disease* (MCLS) (Japanese). Tokyo, 1976.

141. Shulman ST, Rowley AH: Does Kawasaki disease have a retroviral aetiology? *Lancet* 1986; 2:545–546.

142. Burns JC, Geha RS, Schneeberger EE, et al: Polymerase activity in lymphocyte culture supernatants from patients with Kawasaki

of so-called "Kawasaki disease": Presented to the 15th SEAMOTROP MED Seminar. Bangkok, Thailand, Nov 24–28, 1975.

disease. *Nature* 1986; 323:814–816.

143. Okamoto T, Kuwabara H, Shimotohno K, et al: Lack of evidence of retroviral involvement in Kawasaki disease, letter. *Pediatrics* 1988; 81:599.

144. Melish ME, Marchette NJ, Kaplan JC, et al: Absence of significant RNA-dependent DNA polymerase activity in lymphocyte cultures from patients with Kawasaki disease. *Nature* 1989; 337:288–290.

145. Kikuta H, Taguchi Y, Tomizawa K, et al: Epstein-Barr virus genome-positive T lymphocytes in a boy with chronic active EBV infection associated with Kawasaki-like disease. *Nature* 1988; 333:455–457.

146. Marchette NJ, Melish ME, Hicks R, et al: Lack of correlation between Epstein Barr virus infection and Kawasaki syndrome. *J Infect Dis* submitted.

147. Matsuda I, et al: HLA antigens in mucocutaneous lymph node syndrome. *Am J Dis Child* 1977; 131:1417–1418.

148. Kitayama T: Infectious disease theory of Kawasaki disease with special reference to the theory of virus infection as a triggering factor. *Jpn J Clin Med* 1976; 34:295–297.

149. Mason W, Jordan S, Sakai R, et al: Lack of effect of gamma-globulin infusion on circulating immune complexes in patients with Kawasaki syndrome. *Pediatr Infect Dis J* 1988; 7:94–99.

150. Fossard C, Thompson RA: Mucocutaneous lymph node syndrome (Kawasaki disease): probable soluble-complex disorder. *Br Med J* 1977; 1:883–884.

151. Corbeel L, Delmotte B, Standaert L, et al: Kawasaki disease in Europe, letter. *Lancet* 1977; 1:797.

152. Mason WH, Jordan SC, Sakai R, et al: Circulating immune complexes in Kawasaki syndrome. *Pediatr Infect Dis* 1985; 4:48–51.

153. Levin M, Holland PC, Nokes TJC, et al: Platelet immune complex interaction in pathogenesis of Kawasaki disease and childhood polyarteritis. *Br Med J* 1985; 290:1456–1460.

154. Leung DYM, Siegel RL, Grady S, et al: Immunoregulatory abnormalities in mucocutaneous lymph node syndrome. *Clin Immunol Immunopathol* 1982; 23:100–112.

155. Leung DYM, Chu ET, Wood N, et al: Immunoregulatory T cell abnormalities in mucocutaneous lymph node syndrome. *J Immunol* 1983; 130:2002–2004.

156. Leung DY, Geha RS, Newburger JW, et al: Two monokines, interleukin 1 and tumor necrosis factor, render cultured vascular endothelial cells susceptible to lysis by antibodies circulating during Kawasaki syndrome. *J Exp Med* 1986; 164:1958–1972.

157. Leung DY, Collins T, Lapierre LA, et al: Immunoglobulin M antibodies present in the acute phase of Kawasaki syndrome lyse cultured vascular endothelial cells stimulated by gamma interferon. *J Clin Invest* 1986; 77:1428–1435.

Reye Syndrome

Frederick L. Ruben

Reye syndrome is an enigmatic disease which has been fatal for many children. Since it was first described, interest in the syndrome has become widespread and cases have been reported from around the globe. Reye syndrome may be the direct or indirect consequence of a viral infection. This chapter addresses the virologic aspects of Reye syndrome, but does so in the context of known clinical and epidemiologic features of the syndrome.

HISTORY

Reye, Morgan, and Baral in 1963 described the clinical and pathologic features of 21 children admitted between 1951 and 1962 to a children's hospital in Sydney, Australia.[1] They referred to the condition as fatty degeneration of the viscera of unknown cause.

In the same year and month, Johnson, Scurletis, and Carroll described 16 children from North Carolina who died in a 4-month period in 1962 from an encephalitislike disease.[2] These deaths, they noted, coincided with the peak of influenza B virus activity in the same area. The entity described in these two papers has subsequently been referred to as Reye syndrome in recognition of the meticulous description by Reye and his colleagues. The syndrome was probably not a new one. Brain, Hunter, and Turnbull in 1929[3] noted the association of acute brain swelling with fatty liver producing an encephalitislike picture in children. Nevertheless, case reports were infrequent,[4,5] and interest in the syndrome became widespread only in the 1970s when hundreds of cases were identified.[6] There have been many contributions to the recognition and management of cases of Reye syndrome, and only a few will be mentioned here. Diagnostic criteria,[7] staging of the progression of the syndrome,[8,9] further epidemiologic links with influenza B,[6] histopathologic description of the hepatocellular mitochondrial abnormalities,[10] and monitoring of the intracranial pressure and providing intensive supportive care[11,12] all have helped to understand the manifestations and improve the outcome of Reye syndrome. The recognition of an association between Reye syndrome and salicylate use now appears to have been a landmark.[14] With the warning against the use of aspirin in children there has been a decline in the national incidence of Reye syndrome,[15] suggesting that prevention is possible. Although there are no controlled trials of treatment for Reye syndrome, without supportive intervention many patients would die.

EPIDEMIOLOGY

Incidence and Prevalence

Data on the incidence of Reye syndrome come mainly from United States national figures, which reflect voluntary reporting, and from Ohio and Michigan, where surveillance has been active.[15-18] In the 1970s, as interest in Reye syndrome became more widespread, reporting of cases increased. The following rates are

Table 45–1

Case Reports of Reye Syndrome From Throughout the World

Asia	Europe
India[20]	Austria[34]
Japan[21]	Bulgaria[35]
Korea[22]	Czechoslovakia[36]
Sri Lanka[23]	Finland[37]
Taiwan[24]	France[38]
Thailand[25]	West Germany[39]
	Hungary[40]
Africa	Ireland[41]
Nigeria[26]	Israel[42]
South Africa[27]	Italy[43]
	Poland[44]
Western Hemisphere	Spain[45]
Argentina[28]	Sweden[46]
Brazil[29]	United Kingdom[47]
Canada[30]	
Chile[31]	**Oceania**
Jamaica[32]	Australia[1]
Panama[4]	Malaysia[48]
United States[2]	New Zealand[49]
Uruguay[33]	

Adapted and updated from Chaves-Carballo[4]

for populations less than 18 years old and are given as rate per 100,000. In the United States for the years 1974 and 1979, rates were 0.58 and 1.26. In Ohio for 1973 to 1977, the rate was 1.04, and in Michigan in 1974, the rate was 1.38. In the 1980s, national figures have ranged from 0.88 in 1980 to 0.16 in 1986, with a steady decline in incidence each year. The decline in incidence is impressive since the occurrence of influenza has not declined.

There is a less recognizable and milder form of Reye syndrome called grade I, which is characterized by a quiet and sleepy child who responds to verbal commands.[19] Data from Ohio in 1980–1981 included grade I cases and estimated an overall rate of 3.5, with 2.7 cases of grade I and 0.8 of grade II or higher.[19] These rates were for children under the age of 17 years from the Cincinnati metropolitan area.

In the 1987 and 1988 surveillance years, 36 and 20 cases, respectively, of Reye syndrome were reported to national surveillance. These years have the lowest number of cases since continuous national surveillance was established in December 1976.[15]

Based primarily on published case reports, Reye syndrome has a worldwide distribution. Table 45–1 lists countries from which case reports of Reye syndrome have come. The frequency of Reye syndrome in countries other than the United States is not known; however, reports from Canada,[30] Japan,[50] Thailand,[51] and Malaysia[52] document the occurrence of large numbers of cases over relatively short time periods, suggesting that the syndrome is not uncommon in these countries.

Prevalence of Reye syndrome will vary depending on the occurrence of epidemic influenza B. Numbers of cases increase in association with influenza B outbreaks[6, 53]; clusters of cases also have occurred in association with certain strains of influenza A[54, 55]; cases are sporadic when influenza is absent.

Temporal and Geographic Distribution

In the United States, outbreaks of influenza B in 1969,[56] 1971,[57] 1974,[6] and 1977[16] were accompanied temporally and geographically by large outbreaks of Reye syndrome. The same occurred in 1980 when influenza B was the predominant strain and the highest incidence of Reye syndrome was determined. With the influenza B outbreaks of 1982, 1984, and 1986, the incidence of Reye syndrome declined each period of time.[15, 18] Clusters of cases were also associated with different strains of influenza A including A/Port Chalmers/75 (H3N2)[54] and A/Brazil/78 (H1N1).[55] The association of Reye syndrome with influenza B is much greater than that with influenza A.[6, 53]

In Kalamazoo, Michigan, in 1974 when an influenza B-associated Reye syndrome outbreak was investigated with serologic study, the incidence of Reye syndrome following influenza B was estimated at between 30 and 58 cases per 100,000 cases of influenza B.[17]

In the United States the majority of cases of Reye syndrome occur in the first half of the year and of these most occur in February and March.[6, 13] This seasonality is explained by outbreaks of influenza B during these months.

Information regarding temporal and geographic distribution outside the United States is quite limited. In the Canadian maritime provinces, Reye syndrome occurrence has been related to aerial spray operations for insects.[58] A study in Maine on insect spraying and cases failed to demonstrate any association with Reye syndrome, however underreporting of cases and study power limit the reliability of the results.[59] In Thailand Reye syndrome is closely related to periods of rainfall, mainly in the months July through October.[60]

Numerous studies in the United States,[6, 17, 61, 62] Canada[58] and Thailand[51, 60] have noted that cases of Reye syndrome occur mainly in individuals living in surbaban and rural areas; only a few cases occur in individuals from urban locations.

Age, Sex, Race, Socioeconomic Status, Siblings, Recurrences

Reye syndrome is a disease in which most cases are from the pediatric age group.[5] There continue to be reports of Reye syndrome occurring in adults.[63–73] In the United States in a period between December 15, 1973, and June 30, 1974, there were 379 reported cases of confirmed Reye syndrome, with 316 occurring during influenza B outbreaks.[6] Of those cases related to influenza B, the median age was 11 years, while those cases which were sporadic were younger (median age 6 years).[6] From December 1976 through November 1977, there were 454 reported cases in the United States with a median age of 9 years for cases with a respiratory-influenza prodrome, and a median age of 6 years for those with varicella prodromes.[13] Reye syndrome has also been seen in infants.[13, 16, 74, 75] In surveillance from 1976 through 1977, the incidence in infants, 64 cases 1 year of age or less for a rate of 1.43 cases per 100,000 infants, tripled over that noted in 1973 through 1974.[13]

There does not appear to be a consistent sex predilection in Reye syndrome. In 1974 females accounted for 53% of cases[6];

however, in 1977 males accounted for 56% of cases in the United States, a significantly higher attack rate than for females.[13]

Reye syndrome has been reported more frequently in whites, who constituted 94% of United States cases in 1974[6] and 90% of cases in 1977.[13] In contrast, minority infants (black, Asian-American, and American Indians) had higher attack rates in 1977 than whites, white infants, or all infants.[13] In Ohio for 1973 to 1977, attack rates for whites were higher than for blacks, but not significantly so. In contrast, black infants had attack rates 8 times higher than white infants (P <.001).[16, 76]

Limited data are available on socioeconomic status of families with cases. One report emphasized that infants with Reye syndrome all came from urban, lower socioeconomic environments.[75] In Ohio over the years 1973 to 1977 differences in attack rates for different socioeconomic groups were minor and were not convincing to the investigators.[16] A study from Great Britain reported a significant negative correlation between ranked social class and ranked age at death of Reye syndrome cases. The study included 65 cases with a mean age of 50 months (median age was 25 months).[77]

Reye syndrome has been reported to occur simultaneously or within days in siblings[78–83] and in twins.[84] Limited studies with HLA typing failed to identify a common genetic marker.[80] There are rare reports of recurrences of Reye syndrome.[82, 85]

Association With Viruses

The majority of cases of Reye syndrome occur during outbreaks of influenza B.[6, 13, 16] Influenza A viruses have been recovered from patients with Reye syndrome, and clusters of cases have accompanied outbreaks of influenza A.[53–55] Varicella has preceded a large number of cases of Reye syndrome.[13, 16] Cases following varicella occur sporadically throughout the year and occur in younger patients[5, 13] than those accompanying influenza. A cluster of cases associated with varicella has also been reported.[86]

A host of viruses have been recovered from patients who developed Reye syndrome (Table 45–2). Mixed viral infections have also been associated with Reye syndrome,[54, 100] and there are reports of Reye syndrome following the use of live viral vaccines.[94] Bacterial infection preceding the manifestations of Reye syndrome is rare.[101]

CLINICAL SYNDROME

The following case history[102] illustrates many of the features of Reye syndrome.

A 16-year-old male developed symptoms of an upper respiratory infection. On the second and third days of this infection he stayed home from school. He returned to school on day 4, but was sent home when he became dizzy. His family doctor was consulted and cultured his throat (culture was later negative). On day 5 his dizziness resolved and he felt better. On day 6 he awakened from sleep and began to vomit. This continued despite three 25-mg promethazine hydrochloride rectal suppositories. On the morning of the seventh day his mother found him crawling on the floor, confused, and complaining he could not see. He was rushed to an emergency room where he began to thrash about and scream. He was given thiopental sodium in order to perform a computed tomographic (CT) scan of his head. The scan was negative, and a lumbar puncture showed an elevated opening pressure, colorless fluid without cells, a normal protein and glucose. Blood counts and

arterial blood gases were normal. Blood urea nitrogen (BUN) was normal and glucose was slightly increased. Aspartate aminotransferase (AST) was increased to 4 times normal and ammonia was slightly increased. Over the next few hours he became less responsive, his reflexes were diminished, and he developed bilateral, positive Babinski responses and decerebrate posturing. He was transferred to an intensive care hospital after being given mannitol and being placed on a respirator. On arrival his ammonia had risen markedly. He was placed in intensive care and an intracranial pressure (ICP) monitoring screw was placed in the right frontal area. His initial ICP was low. His EEG showed a slow background rhythm, with a markedly suppressed voltage, compatible with stage IV Reye syndrome. His ICP rose markedly and was managed with appropriate drugs. His BUN and creatinine rose and his ammonia remained high. Over the next three days his EEG began to improve, and his ICP remained low. His urine output increased. On the fourth hospital day the ICP monitor screw was removed; subsequently his respirator tube was removed, and he was able to respond to command. His thought processes, while slow and deliberate, gradually improved. Over the next week he was still improving but was not totally back to normal.

Staging

Several investigators have provided criteria for staging patients with Reye syndrome.[8, 9, 94, 103] These are useful in assessing the severity of the syndrome on presentation. The prognosis tends to correlate with the stage of the syndrome at the time the patient presents. Cases presenting in early stages (I and II) fare better than those presenting in advanced stages (III and IV). Table 45–3 shows the staging system of DeVivo and Keating.[103]

Another system for categorizing severity uses grading of cases, grade I through grade IV, with grade I illness characterized by vomiting, lack of interest, abnormal quietness or lethargy, but with an appropriate response to verbal commands.[104] Grade I cases may go unrecognized.[105] Such cases had a better prognosis when ammonia levels and prothrombin times were less abnormal.[105]

Table 45–2

Viruses Associated With Reye Syndrome

Virus	Subtype	Reference
Adenovirus	1, 2, 3, 7	54, 61, 87
Coxsackie A	9, 10	61, 88
Coxsackie B	2, 4	2, 89
Cytomegalovirus		63
Dengue	1	69, 90
Echovirus	8, 11	3
Epstein-Barr		91, 92
Herpes simplex	Untyped	49
Influenza	A, B	54, 61, many others
Mumps	Vaccine	93, 94
Parainfluenza	2, 3, 4A	61, 93, 95
Poliovirus	1, vaccinelike	94, 96
Respiratory syncytial		54, 97
Rotavirus		98
Rubella	Vaccine	82
Rubeola (measles)	Vaccine	82, 94, 99
Vaccinia	Vaccine	56, 61, 93
Varicella-zoster		16, 56, many others

Adapted from Sullivan-Bolyai and Corey.[5]

Table 45–3

Encephalopathy in Reye Syndrome

Stage	Observations
0	Neurologically normal; chemical evidence of hepatic dysfunction, with elevated serum transaminases and hypoprothrombinemia
I	Oriented to mildly confused; lethargic, vomiting, amnesic; chemical evidence of hepatic dysfunction
II	Agitated delirium and visual unresponsiveness; may be stuporous, obtunded or lightly comatose, with decorticate posturing; sympathetic overactivity and hyperpnea; chemical evidence of hepatic dysfunction
III	Coma, with decerebrate posturing; sympathetic overactivity and hyperpnea; chemical evidence of hepatic dysfunction
IV	Flaccidity, apnea, dilated and nonreactive pupils, circulatory collapse; chemical evidence of hepatic dysfunction

Reproduced with permission from DeVivo DC, Keating JP: Reye syndrome. Adv Pediatr 1976; 22:175–229.

Natural History

The mortality from Reye syndrome left untreated has been high. In the original series by Reye et al,[1] 17 (81%) of 21 cases were fatal. Other series[2, 6, 13, 51, 56, 62, 106] have also had high mortality, despite varying degrees of supportive care. More recently the mortality has been 20%[107] to 35%.[15]

Laboratory Diagnosis

The clinical history and presentation are not definitive in diagnosing Reyes syndrome but should suggest which patients to evaluate further. Laboratory studies must establish the diagnosis.[7, 103] Biochemical abnormalities of the blood found in many cases include the following: elevated liver transaminases (AST, alanine aminotransferase [ALT]),[1, 8, 9] hyperammonemia,[8, 9] increased prothrombin time,[108–110] hypoglycemia,[1, 56] elevated creatine phosphokinase (CPK),[93] acid-base disturbances,[111, 112] azotemia associated with dehydration,[103] leukocytosis,[103] hyperuricemia,[113] elevated free fatty acids,[114, 115] aminoacidemia,[116] organic acidemia,[114, 115] and hypocomplementemia.[118, 119] Serum bilirubin may be slightly increased,[7] but alkaline phosphatase and γ-glutamyl transpeptidase are usually normal.[113] Lactic acidemia[120] and hypercatecholaminemia[121] have more recently been recognized, with elevations in the latter more likely in advanced coma and fatal cases.[121, 122]

Liver biopsy, when done early, has revealed, by light microscopy using fat stains, small droplets of fat within parenchymal cells unaccompanied by inflammation.[1, 123–125] Although not usually biopsied, other organs can also show a similar fatty infiltration.[1, 124] The same liver biopsy material examined by electron microscopy has shown disarray of the matrix of the mitochondria of hepatocytes.[10] Similar mitochondrial abnormalities have been seen in neurons in the cerebral cortex.[126, 127] Both the fatty metamorphosis and the mitochondrial abnormalities are reversible, usually in a matter of days.[104]

Other studies may be abnormal in patients with Reye syndrome, including EEG[128, 129] and CT scans of the head.[130, 132, 133]

The Centers for Disease Control (CDC) put forth a set of criteria for diagnosing Reye syndrome which they used in their epidemiologic investigations.[6, 7] These criteria are as follows:

> Acute onset of a noninflammatory encephalopathy demonstrated by either the presence of less than 8 WBCs per cubic millimeter in the CSF or by histologic sections of brain demonstrating cerebral edema without meningeal or perivascular inflammation combined with (1) fatty metamorphosis of the liver demonstrated either by biopsy or autopsy; (2) an SGOT [AST] level greater than 3 times normal and a blood ammonia level greater than 1.5 times normal; (3) no other explanation for the neurologic or hepatic abnormalities such as known "toxin exposure."[107, 134, 135]

It is obvious that any criteria must also exclude conditions that may mimic Reye syndrome.

Pathogenesis and Pathophysiology

Neither the pathogenesis nor the complete pathophysiology of Reye syndrome has been worked out.[136–144] Mild virus infections usually precede or accompany the onset of Reye syndrome. The actual role that the viral infection plays is not known.[145] Only rarely has uncontrolled or disseminated viral spread occurred.[146, 147] The virus infection usually is in its recovery phase when the symptoms of Reye syndrome begin. At the outset of Reye syndrome, tests of liver function reveal abnormalities that are reversible. Clinical worsening beyond this point is usually caused by cerebral edema which produces alterations in consciousness. This edema can occur abruptly, leading to death or permanent brain damage unless treated.

Many investigators have looked for possible environmental factors that might predispose to Reye syndrome.[30, 56, 62, 148] Insecticides and herbicides have been postulated.[149] Aflatoxins have been implicated in cases of Reye syndrome[49, 150, 151] and have been suggested as a causative factor in Thailand.[51] Poisoning by the ackee fruit can mimic Reye syndrome.[152–154] Serum from Reye syndrome patients contains a factor that uncouples oxidative phosphorylation and alters respiration in mitochondria in vitro.[155, 156] Circulating endotoxin has been demonstrated in Reye syndrome patients.[157]

Recently there has been increased attention to the role of salicylates in the development of Reye syndrome.[158, 159] Initially, two controlled but retrospective studies[14, 159] showed a significant correlation between Reye syndrome and salicylate consumption. Indeed, salicylism can closely mimic Reye syndrome.[160, 161] The Public Health Service task force then set up a pilot study[162] followed by a main study[163] to investigate the possible association between Reye syndrome and salicylates. The pilot study found that significantly more Reye syndrome cases than members of each of four control groups or all controls combined had received salicylates during matched antecedent illnesses.[162] The main study, as in the pilot study, found a strong statistical association with ingestion of salicylates during the antecedent illness and prior to the onset of Reye syndrome.[163] The analysis of the independent risk of aspirin and nonaspirin salicylates revealed a significant association with aspirin (odds ratio, 26; lower 95% confidence limit, 6.4) but the independent risk of nonaspirin salicylates could not be assessed because only two cases were not exposed to aspirin.[163] The conclusion of the latter study was that "a majority of Reye syndrome cases may be attributable to salicylate use."[163]

The US Food and Drug Administration in 1986 mandated a package label warning against the use of aspirin in children with viral infections. This action and the studies cited above have generated editorials and policy assessments in the United States and Great Britain.[164-166] There have been surveys performed in different areas of the United States of aspirin use that have found decreasing trends in aspirin use[167-172] and a concomitant decline in the incidence of Reye syndrome.[169-172] Children receiving aspirin for connective tissue disease appear to be at increased risk for Reye syndrome,[173-175] and there are increasing concerns over the safety of aspirin use for appropriate clinical indications.[176]

The mechanism for the role of aspirin in Reye syndrome is unknown. By the time the patient comes to medical attention, aspirin levels have usually been low and in the nontoxic range.[61] Patients with Reye syndrome, 3 to 10 years after recovery, have shown normal or increased ability to metabolize aspirin.[177]

TREATMENT AND PREVENTION

Early Diagnosis and Prevention

Based on epidemiologic observations, it appears that the early recognition and vigorous management of Reye syndrome can improve survival and reduce damage in survivors.[136, 141, 142, 178] Such early diagnosis requires that a high index of suspicion be common practice by parents[179] and physicians.[180] Suspected patients should have diagnostic laboratory tests performed, should be hydrated and followed very carefully, and if progression of the stages occurs, they should be treated vigorously.[181] The experience of 1977 in the United States suggests that when patients present in the advanced stages (stages III to IV) of Reye syndrome, they can be better managed in experienced medical centers where the complex means of monitoring and supporting such sick patients are more readily available.[178]

Because of the documented association between salicylate use and Reye syndrome,[14, 159] it has been judged prudent in the United States to avoid the use of salicylate-containing drugs for the symptomatic treatment of febrile respiratory illnesses or varicella in children.[181a]

Some children and teenagers are receiving long-term aspirin therapy and are at risk of developing Reye syndrome after an influenza infection. These individuals are target groups for annual influenza vaccination.[181b]

Evolution of Treatment

In the initial descriptions of Reye syndrome, little or nothing that was done for patients seemed to be effective, and the disease ran its natural course.[1, 2] Since that time many procedures have been attempted or advocated for treatment including hypertonic glucose,[8] amino acid infusion,[182, 183] hemodialysis,[184] exchange transfusion,[185, 186] peritoneal dialysis,[187] and cerebral decompression.[188] Several reviews[136, 142, 181, 190] have dealt with the details of therapy. Attempts to compare efficacy of proposed therapies have been undertaken,[190, 191] but are not conclusive. Vigorous supportive care[192-195] and the use of intracranial monitoring[196-201] seem to have the most widespread acceptance as the most effective way of avoiding brain damage for patients with Reye syndrome.[187, 202, 203] Figure 45–1 is an algorithm for diagnosing and treating Reye syndrome.

Prognosis

Before any therapy was used, Reye syndrome was usually fatal.[1, 2] Even when therapy has been successful, studies of survivors have found residual damage manifested as neurologic deficits or intellect problems,[204, 205, 205a] although many survivors recover completely.

MISCELLANEOUS

Conditions Mimicking Reye Syndrome

Although Reye syndrome is now recognized as a distinct entity, there are conditions that can mimic Reye syndrome and must be thought of if the situation warrants other considerations. Salicylism should be considered if salicylate-containing drugs have been used.[160] In young children poisoning with insect repellents,[206] sodium valproate,[207] methyl bromide,[208] and margosa oil[209] have produced a Reye syndrome-like picture including the fatty liver. Other conditions which can mimic Reye syndrome include cold agglutinin autoimmune hemolytic anemia,[210] septicemic plague,[211] hypoglycin poisoning,[212] aflatoxin B toxicity,[213, 214] organic acidemias,[215, 216] ketoaciduria,[215] and carnitine deficiency.[217] Inherited ornithine carbamyltransferase deficiency can also produce a Reye syndrome-like picture.[218-220, 220a]

Animal Models

Several studies have used animals to produce a model that could assist in understanding Reye syndrome in humans. Aflatoxins,[213] chemicals or insecticides combined with viruses,[221-227] hypoglycin,[228-230] influenza A and B,[231, 232] insecticides with virus and salicylates have all been used.[233, 234] A rabbit model,[235] mouse models using influenza B virus alone[236] or with a chemical emulsifier[237] and a ferret model[238] all purport to closely mimic the disease in humans. The relevance of and prospects for animal models were reviewed recently.[239, 240]

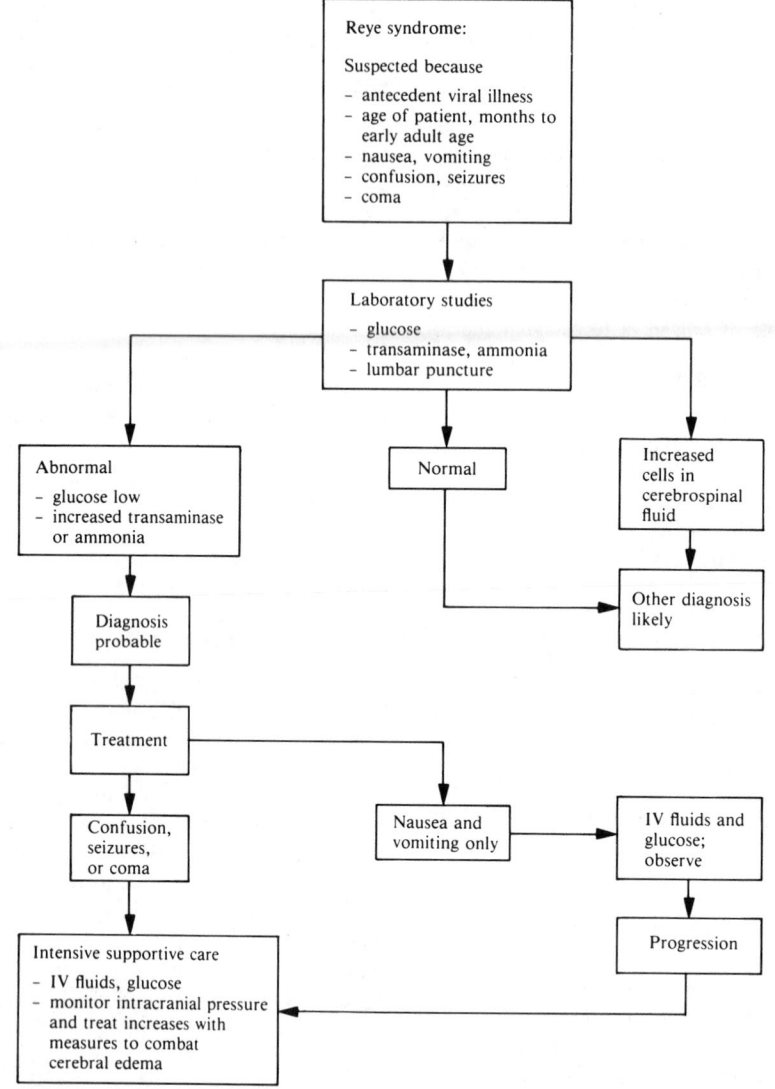

Figure 45–1. Progressions to the diagnosis and treatment of Reye syndrome.

REFERENCES

1. Reye RDK, Morgan G, Baral J: Encephalopathy and fatty degeneration of the viscera. A disease entity in childhood. *Lancet* 1963; 2:749–752.
2. Johnson GM, Scurletis TD, Carroll NB: A study of sixteen fatal cases of encephalitis-like disease in North Carolina children. *NC Med J* 1963; 24:464–473.
3. Brain WR, Hunter D, Turnbull HM: Acute meningo-encephalomyelitis of childhood. *Lancet* 1929; 1:221–227.
4. Chaves-Carballo E: Epidemiology of Reye syndrome. *Adv Neurol* 1978; 19:231–248.
5. Sullivan-Bolyai JZ, Corey L: Epidemiology of Reye syndrome. *Epidemiol Rev* 1981; 3:1–26.
6. Corey L, Rubin RJ, Hattwick MAW, et al: A nationwide outbreak of Reye's syndrome. Its epidemiologic relationship to influenza B. *Am J Med* 1976; 61:615–625.
7. Corey L, Rubin RJ, Bregman D, et al: Diagnostic criteria for influenza B-associated Reye's syndrome: Clinical vs pathologic criteria. *Pediatrics* 1977; 60:702–708.
8. Huttenlocher PR: Reye's syndrome: Relation of outcome to therapy. *J Pediatr* 1972; 80:845–850.
9. Lovejoy FH Jr, Smith AL, Bresnan MJ, et al: Clinical staging in Reye syndrome. *Am J Dis Child* 1974; 128:36–41.
10. Partin JC, Schubert WK, Partin JS: Mitochondrial ultrastructure in Reye's syndrome (encephalopathy and fatty degeneration of the viscera). *N Engl J Med* 1971; 285:1339–1343.
11. David RB, Vries JK, Mamunes P: Intracranial pressure monitoring in Reye's syndrome, in Pollack JD (ed): *Reye's Syndrome.* New York, Grune & Stratton, 1975, pp 309–313.
12. Kindt GW, Waldman J, Kohl S, et al: Intracranial pressure in Reye syndrome. Monitoring and control. *JAMA* 1975; 231:822–825.
13. Morens DM, Sullivan-Bolyai JZ, Slater JE, et al: Surveillance of Reye syndrome in the United States, 1977. *Am J Epidemiol* 1981; 114:406–416.
14. Starko KM, Ray CG, Dominguez LB, et al: Reye's syndrome and salicylate use. *Pediatrics* 1980; 66:859–864.
15. Centers for Disease Control: Reye syndrome surveillance—United States, 1987 and 1988. *MMWR* 1989; 38:325–327.

16. Sullivan-Bolyai JZ, Marks JS, Johnson D, et al: Reye syndrome in Ohio, 1973–1977. *Am J Epidemiol* 1980; 112:629–638.

17. Corey L, Rubin RJ, Thompson TR, et al: Influenza B-associated Reye's syndrome: Incidence in Michigan and potential for prevention. *J Infect Dis* 1977; 135:398–407.

18. Centers for Disease Control: Reye syndrome surveillance—United States, 1986. *MMWR* 1987; 36:689–691.

19. Lichtenstein PK, Heubi JE, Daugherty CC, et al: Grade I Reye's syndrome, a frequent cause of vomiting and liver dysfunction after varicella and upper-respiratory-tract infection 1983; 309:133–139.

20. John TJ, Mammen KC, Date A, et al: Acute encephalopathy with fatty degeneration of the viscera: A study of three cases in India. *Indian J Med Res* 1969; 57:1865–1871.

21. Moriuchi M, Watanabe W: Reye's syndrome: A case report (Japanese). *J Transplant Med* 1974; 28:378–389.

22. Choi JK, Kim CS, Choi IJ, et al: Reye syndrome: Light and electron microscopic studies of 7 cases. *Yonsei Med J* 1978; 19:59–69.

23. De Silva DDS, Chandrasoma PT, Lamabadusuriya SP: Reye's syndrome in Sri Lanka. *Ceylon Med J* 1975; 20:219–224.

24. Chen YK, Lin CA, Huang FY, et al: Reye's syndrome (Chinese). *Acta Paediatr Sin* 1975; 16:158–165.

25. Visudhiphan P, Chatiyanonda K: Isolation of influenza A virus in Reye's syndrome. *Southeast Asian J Trop Med Public Health* 1975; 6:260–263.

26. Mee J, Nirodi NS, Duggan MB: Reye's syndrome: A report of two cases from Northern Nigeria. *East Afr Med J* 1979; 56:86–91.

27. Human DG: Reye's syndrome. *South Afr Med J* 1976; 50:1450–1451.

28. Fuksman de Cherjovsky RB: Morphological findings in the thymus in children with Reye's syndrome, in Crocker JFS (ed): *Reye's Syndrome.* New York, Grune & Stratton, 1979, vol 2, pp 263–279.

29. Moren OM: Reye's syndrome (encephalopathy and fatty degeneration of the viscera). *J Pediatr* 1978; 44:349–353.

30. Bagnell PC, Crocker JFS, Ozere RL: Reye's syndrome in Canada's maritime provinces. *Chemosphere* 1978; 7:565–571.

31. Cordero J, Olivos P, Zacarias J, et al: Toxic encephalopathy with fatty metamorphosis of the viscera. Reye's syndrome. *Rev Chil Pediatr* 1974; 45:483–490.

32. Johnson BE, Hanchard B: Reye's syndrome: A case report. *West Indian Med J* 1979; 28:124–128.

33. Quian J, Alberti M, Lapides C, et al: Reye's syndrome. *Arch Pediatr Uruguay* 1978; 49:163–171.

34. Mutz I, Grubbauer HM, Wilkmann E, et al: The clinical course of Reye's syndrome. *Wien Kiln Wochenschr* 1974; 86:745–749.

35. Kerekovski I, Tzonev I, Gheorghieva M: Reye's syndrome with a relapsing course. *Pediatriya* 1979; 18:508–513.

36. Dvorackova I, Vortel V, Hroch M: Encephalitic syndrome with fatty degeneration of viscera. *Arch Pathol* 1966; 81:240–246.

37. Salmi TT, Arstila P, Koivikko A: Central nervous system involvement in patients with rotavirus gastroenteritis. *Scand J Infect Dis* 1978; 10:29–31.

38. Micheau M, Fontan D, Patty J, et al: Reye's syndrome. *Bordeaux Med* 1978; 11:433–444.

39. Jacobi H, Altemeier KH, Kuenzer W: Coagulation analysis in Reye's syndrome. *Monatsschr Kinderheilkd* 1975; 123:573–574.

40. Czinner A, Lukacs FV, Balazs M: Morphologic and biochemical observations of an infant with Reye's syndrome. *Kinderarzlt Prax* 1978; 46:10–15.

41. Kearney PJ, Deasy PF, O'Donohoe NV: The diagnosis and management of Reye's syndrome. *Ir Med J* 1975; 68:169–174.

42. Mogilner BM, Freeman JS, Blashar Y, et al: Reye's syndrome in three Israeli children. Possible relationship to warfarin toxicity. *Isr J Med Sci* 1974; 10:1117–1125.

43. Cerutti F, Sacchetti C, Foa R: Notes on a case of Reye's syndrome. *Minerva Pediatr* 1977; 29:357–361.

44. Szlachetka R: Clinical picture of acute encephalopathy associated with fatty degeneration of viscera (Reye's syndrome). *Neurol Neurochir Pol* 1976; 26:321–330.

45. Cartig J, Garcia-Tornel S, Nadal-Amat J, et al: Reye's syndrome (6 cases). *Bull Soc Catalana Pediatr* 1977; 37:284–291.

46. Jonsson M, Kollberg H: Reye's syndrome. An expanding disease? *Lakartidningen* 1980; 77:2202–2204.

47. Turel AP Jr, Levinsohn MW, Derakhshan I, et al: Reye syndrome and cerebellar intracytoplasmic inclusion bodies. *Arch Neurol* 1975; 32:624–628.

48. Leong ASY: Reye's syndrome in Malaysian children. A report of 3 autopsy cases. *J Singapore Paediatr Soc* 1976; 18:38–42.

49. Becroft DMO: Syndrome of encephalopathy and fatty degeneration of viscera in New Zealand children. *Br Med J* 1966; 2:135–140.

50. Yamashita F, Massashi Y, Okada S, et al: Reye's syndrome in Japan: Epidemiology, clinical features and indicators for mortality and the sequelae, in Crocker JFS (ed): *Reye's Syndrome.* New York, Grune & Stratton, 1979, vol 2, pp 51–67.

51. Olson LC, Bourgeois CH Jr, Cotton RB, et al: Encephalopathy and fatty degeneration of the viscera in Northeastern Thailand. Clinical syndrome and epidemiology. *Pediatrics* 1971; 47:707–716.

52. Juggi JS, Iyngkaran H, Prathap K: Hyperammonemia in Reye's syndrome, in Crocker JFS (ed): *Reye's Syndrome.* New York, Grune & Stratton, 1979, vol 2, pp 411–432.

53. LaMontagne JR: Summary of workshop on influenza B viruses and Reye's syndrome. *J Infect Dis* 1980; 3:452–465.

54. Ruben FL, Michaels RH: Reye syndrome with associated influenza A and B infection. *JAMA* 1975; 234:410–412.

55. Halsey NA, Hurwitz ES, Meiklejohn G, et al: An epidemic of Reye syndrome associated with influenza A (H1N1) in Colorado. *J Pediatr* 1980; 97:535–539.

56. Glick TH, Likosky WH, Levitt LP, et al: Reye's syndrome: An epidemiologic approach. *Pediatrics* 1970; 46:371–377.

57. Hochberg FH, Nelson K, Janzen W: Influenza type B-related encephalopathy. The 1971 outbreak of Reye syndrome in Chicago. *JAMA* 1975; 231:817–821.

58. Crocker JFS, Ozere RL: The incidence and etiology of Reye's syndrome in Eastern Canada, in Crocker JFS (ed): *Reye's Syndrome* New York, Grune & Stratton, 1979, vol 2, pp 3–12.

59. Wood RB, Bogdan GF: Reye's syndrome and spruce budworm insecticide spraying in Maine, 1978–1982. *Am J Epidemiol* 1986; 124:671–677.

60. Dhiensiri K, Sinavatana P, Lertsookprasert S: Reye's syndrome in Northeastern Thailand, in Crocker JSF (ed): *Reye's Syndrome II.* New York, Grune & Stratton, 1979, vol 2, pp 77–96.

61. Linnemann CC, Shea L, Partin JC, et al: Reye's syndrome: Epidemiologic and viral studies, 1963–1974. *Am J Epidemiol* 1975; 101:517–526.

62. Ruben FL, Streiff EJ, Neal M, et al: Epidemiologic studies of Reye's syndrome: Cases seen in Pittsburgh, October 1973–April 1975. *Am J Public Health* 1976; 66:1096–1098.

63. Morse RS, Holmes AW, Levin S: Reye's syndrome in an adult. *Am J Dig Dis* 1975; 20:1184–1190.

64. Varma RR, Riedel DR, Komorowski RA, et al: Reye's syndrome in nonpediatric age groups. *JAMA* 1979; 242:1373–1375.

65. Comazzi G, Ricciardiello PT, Andreoni M, et al: Clinical picture of Reye's syndrome in an adult. *Minerva Med* 1980; 71:1945–1948.

66. Vanholder R, DeReuck J, Sieben-Praet M, et al: Reye's syndrome in an adult. *Eur Neurol* 1979; 18:367–372.

67. Atkins JN, Haponik EF: Reye's syndrome in the adult patient. *Am J Med* 1979; 67:672–678.

68. Davis LE, Kornfeld M: Influenza A virus and Reye's syndrome in adults. *J Neurol Neurosurg Psychiatry* 1980; 43:516–521.

69. Terry SI, Golden MHN, Hanchard B, et al: Adult Reye's syndrome after dengue. *Gut* 1980; 21:436–438.

70. Stillman A, Gitter H, Shillington D, et al: Reye's syndrome in the adult: case report and review of the literature. *Am J Gastroenterol* 1983; 78:365–368.

71. Peters LJ, Wiener GJ, Gilliam J, et al: Reye's syndrome in adults. *Arch Intern Med* 1986; 146:2401–2403.

72. Meythaler JM, Varma RR: Reye's syndrome in adults. *Arch Intern Med* 1987; 147:61–64.

73. Ede RJ, Williams R: Reye's syndrome in adults. *Br Med J* 1988; 296:517–518.

74. Harris HB, Vogler LB, Cassady G: Reye's syndrome in a neonate. *South Med J* 1976; 69:1511–1512.

75. Huttenlocher PR, Trauner DA: Reye's syndrome in infancy. *Pediatrics* 1978; 62:84–90.

76. Sullivan-Bolyai JZ, Nelson DB, Morens DM, et al: Reye syndrome in children less than 1 year old: Some epidemiologic observations. *Pediatrics* 1980; 65:627–629.

77. Morris JA, Shapiro DZ: Social class and age distribution in Reye's syndrome. *Br Med J* 1986; 292:379.

78. Glick TH, Ditchek NT, Salitsky S, et al: Acute encephalopathy and hepatic dysfunction. *Am J Dis Child* 1970; 119:68–71.

79. Kumari S: Reye's syndrome. *J La State Med Soc* 1974; 126:155–159.

80. Hilty MD, McClung HJ, Haynes RE, et al: Reye syndrome in siblings. *J Pediatr* 1979; 94:576–579.

81. Wilson R, Miller J, Greene H, et al: Reye's syndrome in three siblings. *Am J Dis Child* 1980; 134:1032–1034.

82. Van Callie M, Morin CL, Roy CC, et al: Reye's syndrome: Relapses and neurological sequelae. *Pediatrics* 1977; 59:244–249.

83. Wilson R, Miller J, Greene H, et al: Reye's syndrome in three siblings. Association with type A influenza infection. *Am J Dis Child* 1980; 134:1032–1034.

84. Thaler MM, Bruhn FW, Applebaum MN, et al: Reye's syndrome in twins. *J Pediatr* 1970; 77:638–646.

85. Glasgow JFT, Halliday HL: Recurrence of Reye's syndrome. *Lancet* 1976; 1:974.

86. Hurwitz ES, Goodman RA: A cluster of cases of Reye syndrome associated with chickenpox. *Pediatrics* 1982; 70:901–906.

87. Edwards KM, Bennett SR, Garner WL, et al: Reye's syndrome associated with adenovirus infections in infants. *Am J Dis Child* 1985; 139:343–346.

88. Schroder H, Siemes H, Spohr HL, et al: Reye's syndrome *Monatsschr Kinderheilkd* 1981; 129:171–174.

89. Kaul A, Cohen ME, Broffman G, et al: Reye-like syndrome associated with Coxsackie B$_2$ virus infection. *J Pediatr* 1979; 94:67–69.

90. Kho LK, Dsumarmo Wulur H, et al: Dengue hemorrhagic fever accompanied by encephalopathy in Jakarta. *Southeast Asian J Trop Med Public Health* 1981; 12:83–86.

91. Rahall JJ Jr, Henle G: Infectious mononucleosis and Reye's syndrome: A fatal case with studies for Epstein-Barr virus. *Pediatrics* 1970; 46:776–780.

92. Fleisher G, Schwartz J, Lennette E: Primary Epstein-Barr virus infection in association with Reye syndrome. *J Pediatr* 1980; 97:935–937.

93. Roe CR, Schonberger LB, Gelbach SH, et al: Enzymatic alterations in Reye's syndrome: Prognostic implications. *Pediatrics* 1975; 55:119–126.

94. Morens DM, Halsey NA, Schonberger LB, et al: Reye syndrome associated with vaccination with live virus vaccines. An exploration of possible etiologic relationships. *Clin Pediatr* 1979; 18:42–44.

95. Powell HC, Rosenberg RN, McKellar B: Reye's syndrome: Isolation of parainfluenza virus. *Arch Neurol* 1973; 29:135–139.

96. Brunberg JA, Bell WE: Reye syndrome. An association with type 1 vaccine-like poliovirus. *Arch Neurol* 1974; 30:304–306.

97. Griffin N, Keeling JW, Tomlinson AH: Reye's syndrome associated with respiratory synctyial virus infection. *Arch Dis Child* 1979; 54:74–76.

98. Salmi TT, Arstilla P, Koivikko A: Central nervous system involvement in patients with rotavirus gastroenteritis. *Scand J Infect Dis* 1978; 10:29–31.

99. Yamada T, Young S, Kimura J: Significance of positive spike bursts in Reye syndrome. *Arch Neurol* 1977; 34:376–380.

100. Stechenberg BW, Keating JP, Koslov S, et al: Epidemiologic investigation of Reye syndrome. *J Pediatr* 1975; 87:234–237.

101. Sundwall DA, Bergeson ME, Ortiz A: Reye syndrome associated with Haemophilus influenzae infection. *Clin Pediatr* 1980; 19:357–360.

102. Schuit K: Personal communication, Children's Hospital of Pittsburgh, March 1980.

103. DeVivo DC, Keating JP: Reye's syndrome. *Adv Pediatr* 1976; 22:175–229.

104. Schubert WK, Partin JC, Partin JS: Encephalopathy and fatty liver (Reye's syndrome), in Popper H, Schaffner F (eds): Progress in Liver Diseases. New York, Grune & Stratton, 1972, pp 489–509.

105. Heubi JE, Daugherty CC, Partin, et al: Grade I Reye's syndrome—outcome and predictors of progression to deeper coma grades. *N Engl J Med* 1984; 311:1529–1542.

106. Luscombe FA, Monto AS, Baublis JA: Mortality due to Reye's syndrome in Michigan: Distribution and longitudinal trends. *J Infect Dis* 1980; 142:363–371.

107. Crocker JF, Bagnell PC: Reye's syndrome: A clinical review. *Can Med Assoc J* 1981; 124:375–382.

108. Brown RE, Madge GE: Hepatic degeneration and dysfunction in Reye's syndrome. *Am J Dig Dis* 1971; 16:1116–1122.

109. Schwartz AD: The coagulation defect in Reye's syndrome. *J Pediatr* 1971; 78:326–328.

110. Pegelow C, Goldberg R, Turkel S, et al: Severe coagulation abnormalities in Reye's syndrome. *J Pediatr* 1977; 91:413–416.

111. DeVivo DC, Keating JP, Hammond MW: Reye syndrome: Results of intensive supportive care. *J Pediatr* 1975; 87:875–880.

112. Samaha FJ, Blau E, Berardinelli JL: Reye's syndrome: Clinical diagnosis and treatment with peritoneal dialysis. *Pediatrics* 1974; 53:336–340.

113. Alvira MM, Foreman DT: Biochemical abnormalities in Reye's syndrome. *Ann Clin Lab Sci* 1974; 4:477–483.

114. Mamunes P, DeVries GH, Miller CD, et al: Fatty acid quantitation in Reye's syndrome, in Pollack JD (ed): *Reye's Syndrome.* New York, Grune & Stratton, 1975, pp 245–254.

115. Pollack JD, Cramblett HG, Flynn D, et al: Serum and tissue lipids in Reye's syndrome, in Pollack JD (ed): *Reye's Syndrome.* New York, Grune & Stratton, 1975, pp 227–243.

116. Hilty MD, Romshe CA, Delamater PV: Reye's syndrome and hyperaminoacidemia. *J Pediatr* 1974; 84:362–365.

117. Trauner D, Sweetman L, Holm J, et al: Biochemical correlates of illness and recovery in Reye's syndrome. *Ann Neurol* 1977; 2:238–241.

118. Pickering RJ, Urizar PE, Hanson PA, et al: Abnormalities of the complement system in Reye syndrome. *J Pediatr* 1979; 94:218–222.

119. Marder HK, Strife CF, Forristal J, et al: Hypocomplementemia in Reye syndrome: Relationship to disease stage, circulating immune complexes, and C3b amplification loop, protein synthesis. *Pediatr Res* 1981; 15:362–365.

120. Tonsgard JH, Huttenlocker PR, Thisted RA: Lactic acidemia in Reye's syndrome. *Pediatrics* 1982; 69:64–69.

121. Faraj BA, Caplan DB, Newman SL, et al: Hypercatecholaminemia in Reye's syndrome. *Pediatrics* 1984; 73:481–488.

122. Arcinue LE, Mitchell RA, Sarniak AP, et al: The metabolic course of Reye's syndrome: distinction between survivors and nonsurvivors. *Neurology* 1986; 36:435–438.

123. Brown RE, Madge GE: The pathology of Reye's syndrome: An overview, in Pollack JD (ed): *Reye's Syndrome.* New York, Grune & Stratton, 1975, pp 77–92.

124. Bourgeois C, Olson L, Comer D, et al: Encephalopathy and fatty degeneration of the viscera: A clinicopathologic analysis of 40 cases. *Am J Clin Pathol* 1971; 56:558–571.

125. Bove KE, McAdams AM, Partin JC, et al: The hepatic lesion in Reye's syndrome. *Gastroenterology* 1975; 69:685–697.

126. Partin JC, Partin JS, Schubert WK, et al: Brain ultrastructure in Reye's syndrome. *J Neuropathol Exp Neurol* 1975; 34:425–444.

127. Partin JS, McAdams AJ, Partin JC, et al: Brain ultrastructure in Reye's disease. II. Acute injury and recovery processes in three children. *J Neuropathol Exp Neurol* 1978; 37:796–819.

128. Aoki-Y, Lombroso CT: Prognostic value of electroencephalography in Reye's syndrome. *Neurology* 1973; 23:333–343.

129. Gottschalk PG, Hansotia PL, Berendes J: EEG in Reye's syndrome: A report of 15 cases. *Am J EEG Technol* 1978; 18:141–150.

130. Russell EJ, Zimmerman RD, Leeds NE, et al: Reye syndrome: Computed tomographic documentation of disordered intracerebral structure. *J Comput Assist Tomogr* 1979; 3:217–220.

131. Garrel S, Reymond F, Detter M: Reye's syndrome: A clinical and electrophysiological study of four patients. *Rev Electroencephalogr Neurophysiol Clin* 1977; 7:479–485.

132. Coin CG, Pennink M, Gray R, et al: Cerebral computed tomography in Reye syndrome. *J Comput Assist Tomogr* 1979; 3:276–277.

133. Ruskin JA, Haughton VM: CT findings in adult Reye syndrome. *AJNR* 1985; 6:446–447.

134. Crocker JFS: Reye's syndrome. *Semin Liver Dis* 1982; 2:340–352.

135. Mowat AP: Reye's syndrome: 20 years on. *Br Med J* 1983; 286:1999–2000.

136. DeVivo DC, Keating JP, Haymond MW: Acute encephalopathy with fatty infiltration of the viscera. *Pediatr Clin North Am* 1976; 23:527–540.

137. Thaler MM: Metabolic mechanisms in Reye Syndrome. *Am J Dis Child* 1976; 130:241–243.

138. Authors Unknown: Metabolic abnormalities in Reye's syndrome. *Lancet* 1976; 2:183–184.

139. Smith AL: Ammonia disposal in Reye's syndrome. *N Engl J Med* 1976; 294:897–898.

140. DeVivo DC: Reye syndrome: A metabolic response to an acute mitochondrial insult? *Neurology* 1978; 28:105–108.

141. Haller JS: Recent developments in etiology and therapy of Reye syndrome. *Clin Neurosurg* 1978; 25:591–597.

142. Boutros AR, Esfandiari S, Orlowski JP, et al: Reye syndrome: A predictably curable disease. *Pediatr Clin North Am* 1980; 27:539–552.

143. Wehinger H: Reye syndrome. *Klin Padiatr* 1977; 189:206–210.

144. Boehles H: Reye's syndrome. *Dtsch Med Wochenschr* 1977; 102:446–451.

145. Moren DM, Noble GR: Reye syndrome and influenza. *Lancet* 1977; 1:807–808.

146. Brown JM: Reye's syndrome associated with adenovirus type 3 infection. *Med J Aust* 1974; 24:873–875.

147. Partin JC, Partin JS, Schubert WK, et al: Isolation of influenza virus from liver and muscle biopsy specimens from a surviving case of Reye's syndrome. *Lancet* 1976; 2:599–602.

148. Reynolds DW, Riley HD, LaFont DS, et al: An outbreak of Reye's syndrome associated with influenza B. *J Pediatr* 1972; 80:429–432.

149. Crocker JFS, Ozere RL: The incidence and etiology of Reye's syndrome in Eastern Canada, in Crocker JFS (ed): *Reye's Syndrome*. New York, Grune & Stratton, 1979, vol 2, pp 3–12.

150. Chaves-Carballo E, Ellefson RD, Gomez MR: An aflatoxin in the liver of a patient with Reye Johnson syndrome. *Mayo Clin Proc* 1976; 51:48–50.

151. Nelson DB, Kimbrough R, Landrigan PS, et al: Aflatoxin and Reye's syndrome: A case control study. *Pediatrics* 1980; 66:865–869.

152. Glasgow AM, Chase HP: Reye's syndrome, Jamaican vomiting sickness and 4-pentenoic acid, in Pollack JD (ed): *Reye's Syndrome*. New York, Grune & Stratton, 1975, pp 273–279.

153. Trauner DA, Nyhan WL, Sweetman L, et al: Jamaican vomiting sickness and Reye's syndrome. *N Engl J Med* 1976; 295:1481–1482.

154. Tanaka K, Kean EA, Johnson B: Jamaican vomiting sickness. Biochemical investigation of two cases. *N Engl J Med* 1976; 295:461–467.

155. Aprille JR: Reye's syndrome: Patient serum alters mitochondrial function and morphology in vitro. *Science* 1977; 197:908–910.

156. Asimakis GK, Aprille JR: Reye's syndrome, The effect of patient serum on mitochondrial respiration in vitro. *Biochem Biophys Res Commun* 1977; 79:1122–1129.

157. Cooperstock MS, Tucker RP, Baublis JV: Possible pathogenic role of endotoxin in Reye's syndrome. *Lancet* 1975; 1:1272–1274.

158. FDA Drug Bulletin: Reye's syndrome: Etiology uncertain but avoid antiemetics in children. *FDA Drug Bull* 1976; 6:40–41.

159. Centers for Disease Control: Reye syndrome—Ohio, Michigan. *MMWR* 1980; 29:532–539.

160. Rosenfeld RG, Liebhaber MI: Acute encephalopathy in siblings. Reye syndrome vs salicylate intoxication. *Am J Dis Child* 1976; 130:295–297.

161. Christoffersen P, Faarup P, Geertinger P, et al: Reye's syndrome in a child on long-term salicylate medication. *Forensic Sci Int* 1980; 15:129–133.

162. Hurwitz ES, Barrett MJ, Bregman D, et al: Public Health Service study on Reye's syndrome and medication: Report of the pilot phase. *N Engl J Med* 1985; 313:849–857.

163. Hurwitz ES, Barrett MJ, Bregman D, et al: Public Health Service Study of Reye's syndrome and medications: Report of the main study. *JAMA* 1987; 257:1905–1911.

164. Mortimer EA: Reye's syndrome, salicylates, epidemiology, and public health policy. *JAMA* 1987; 257:1941.

165. Reye's syndrome and aspirin: Epidemiological associations and inborn errors of metabolism, editorial. *Lancet* 1982; 2:429–431.

166. Glenn-Bott AM: Aspirin and Reye's syndrome: a reappraisal. *Med Toxicol* 1987; 2:161–165.

167. Taylor JP, Gustafson TL, Johnson CC, et al: Antipyretic use among children during the 1983 influenza season. *Am J Dis Child* 1985; 139:486–488.

168. Morris LA, Klimberg R: A survey of aspirin use and Reye's syndrome awareness among patients. *Am J Public Health* 1986; 76:1422–1424.

169. Arrowsmith JB, Kennedy DL, Kuritsky JN, et al: National patterns of aspirin use and Reye syndrome reporting, United States 1980 to 1985. *Pediatrics* 1987; 79:858–863.

170. Kauffman RE, Roberts RJ: Aspirin use and Reye syndrome. *Pediatrics* 1987; 79:1049–1050.

171. Remington PL, Rowley D, McGee H, et al: Decreasing trends in Reye syndrome and aspirin use in Michigan, 1979 to 1984. *Pediatrics* 1986; 77:93–98.

172. Sienko DG, Anda RF, McGee HB, et al: Reye's syndrome and salicylates (letter). *JAMA* 1987; 258:3119.

173. Rennebohm RM, Heubi JE, Daugherty CC, et al: Reye syndrome in children receiving salicylate therapy for connective tissue disease. *J Pediatr* 1985; 107:877–880.

174. Roman GC, Munden PM, Waagner D, et al: Reye's syndrome and juvenile rheumatoid arthritis: a case report in Texas. *Tex Med* 1987; 83:46–47.

175. Hansen JR, McCray PB, Bale JF, et al: Reye syndrome associated with aspirin therapy for systemic lupus erythematosus. *Pediatrics* 1985; 76:202–205.

176. Jaklitsch M, Leyland S: Aspirin anticoagulation for mechanical heart valves and Reye's syndrome. *J Thorac Cardiovasc Surg* 1988; 95:146–147.

177. Chu AB, Neururkar LS, Witzel N, et al: Reye's syndrome. *Am J Dis Child* 1986; 140:1009–1012.

178. Nelson DB, Sullivan-Bolyai JZ, Morens DM, et al: The epidemiology of Reye's syndrome: A review—with emphasis on recent observations. *Univ Mich Med Center J* 1980; 46:4–8.

179. Arcinue EL, Partin JC: Workshop B: Can lay and professional educational programs reduce deaths due to Reye's syndrome? *Univ Mich Med Center J* 1980; 46:16.

180. Huttenlocher PR, DeVivo DC: Workshop C: How can health planning provide appropriate access to emergency care for the patient with Reye's syndrome? *Univ Mich Med Center J* 1980; 46:17.

181. Pollack LD: A standardized approach to the management of patients with Reye's syndrome. *Univ Mich Med Center J* 1980; 46:20–26.

181a. Centers for Disease Control: Surgeon General's advisory of the use of salicylates and Reye syndrome. *MMWR* 1982; 31:289–290.

181b. Centers for Disease Control: Recommendations of the Immunization Practices Advisory Committee (ACIP): Prevention and control of influenza. I: Vaccines. *MMWR* 1989; 38:297–311.

182. DeLong GR, Glick TH, Shannon DG: Citrulline for Reye's syndrome. *N Engl J Med* 1974; 290:1488.

183. Oetgen WJ: The use of citrulline for the treatment of Reye's syndrome: Case reports. *Milit Med* 1977; 141:162–164.

184. Gelfman NA, Kranwinkel RN, Pezzimenti JF, et al: Reye's syndrome treated by hemodialysis. *Conn Med* 1975; 39:405–407.

185. Bobo RC, Schubert WK, Partin JC, et al: Reye syndrome: Treatment by exchange transfusion with special reference to the 1974 epidemic in Cincinnati, Ohio. *J Pediatr* 1975; 87:881–886.

186. Berman W, Pizzi F, Schut L, et al: The effects of exchange transfusion on intracranial pressure in patients with Reye's syndrome. *J Pediatr* 1975; 87:887–891.

187. Samaha FJ, Blau E: The role of peritoneal dialysis in Reye's syndrome, in Pollack JD (ed): *Reye's Syndrome*. New York, Grune & Stratton, 1975, pp 295–299.

188. Ausman JI, Rogers C, Sharp HL: Decompressive craniectomy for the encephalopathy of Reye's syndrome. *Surg Neurol* 1976; 6:97–99.

189. Trauner DA: Treatment of Reye's syndrome. *Ann Neurol* 1980; 7:2–4.

190. Haller JS: Clinical experience with Reye's syndrome, in Pollack JD (ed): Reye's Syndrome, New York, Grune & Stratton, 1975, pp 3–14.

191. Corey L, Rubin RJ, Hattwick MAW: Reye's syndrome: Clinical progression and evaluation of therapy. *Pediatrics* 1977; 69:708–714.

192. DeVivo DC, Keating JP, Haymond MW: Reye syndrome: Results of intensive supportive care. *J Pediatr* 1975; 87:875–880.

193. Partin JC: Management of Reye's syndrome: Need for early diagnosis and intravenous treatment in Stage I noncomatose patients. *Pediatr Ann* 1985; 14:511–515.

194. Shaywitz BA, Liste G, Duncan CC: What is the best treatment for Reye's syndrome? *Arch Neurol* 1986; 43:730–731.

195. Trauner DA: What is the best treatment for Reye's syndrome? *Arch Neurol* 1986; 43:729.

196. Gold F, Chantepie A, Weil D, et al: Monitoring of intracranial pressure in two cases of Reye's syndrome. *Arch Fr Pediatr* 1979; 36:1052–1056.

197. Shaywitz BA, Rothstein P, Venes JL: Monitoring and management of increased intracranial pressure in Reye syndrome: Results in 29 children. *Pediatrics* 1980; 66:198–204.

198. Pizzi FJ, Schut L, Berman W, et al: Intracranial pressure monitoring in Reye's syndrome. *Childs Brain* 1976; 2:59–66.

199. Shaywitz BA, Leventhal JM, Kramer MS, et al: Prolonged continuous monitoring of intracranial pressure in severe Reye's syndrome. *Pediatrics* 1977; 59:595–605.

200. Jenkins JG, Glasgow JFT, Black GW, et al: Reye's syndrome: assessment of intracranial monitoring. *Br Med J* 1987; 294:337–338.

201. Dezateux CA, Dinwiddie R, Helms P, et al: Recognition and early management of Reye's syndrome. *Arch Dis Child* 1986; 61:647–651.

202. Haller J: Intracranial pressure monitoring in Reye's syndrome. *Hosp Pract* 1980; 15(Feb):101–108.

203. Hurley RM: Development of Reye's syndrome protocol in the Hamilton health region. *Can Med Assoc J* 1980; 122:1351.

204. Davidson PW, Willoughby RH, O'Tuama LA, et al: Neurological and intellectual sequelae of Reye's syndrome. *Am J Ment Defic* 1978; 82:535–541.

205. Brunner RL, O'Grady DJ, Partin JC, et al: Neuropsychologic consequences of Reye's syndrome. *J Pediatr* 1979; 95:706–711.

205a. Thompson JW, Rosenthal P, Camilon FS: Vocal cord paralysis and superior laryngeal nerve dysfunction in Reye's syndrome. *Arch Otolaryngol Head Neck Surg* 1990; 116:46–48.

206. Heick HMC, Shipman RT, Norman MG, et al: Reye-like syndrome associated with use of insect repellent in a presumed heterozygote for ornithine carbamoyl transferase deficiency. *J Pediatr* 1980; 97:471–473.

207. Coeckelberghs M, Van Caillie-Bertrand M, Bultinck J, et al: Severe liver lesions due to sodium valproate or Depakine. *Ned Tijdschr Geneeskd* 1980; 124:1428–1431.

208. Shield LK, Coleman TL, Markesbery WR: Methyl bromide intoxication: Neurologic features, including simulation of Reye syndrome. *Neurology* 1977; 27:959–962.

209. Sinniah D, Baskaran G: Margosa oil poisoning as a cause of Reye's syndrome. *Lancet* 1981; 1:487–489.

210. Orlowski JP, Johannsson JH, Ellis NG: Encephalopathy and fatty metamorphosis of the liver associated with cold-agglutinin autoimmune hemolytic anemia. *J Pediatr* 1979; 94:569–575.

211. Washington RL, Barkin RM, Hillman JR: Septicemic plague that mimics Reye's syndrome. *Am J Dis Child* 1979; 133:434–435.

212. Chalmers RA, Lawson AM, Whitelaw A, et al: Organic acids in Reye's like syndrome: Similarities with Jamaican vomiting sickness. *Lancet* 1977; 1:1156–1157.

213. Bourgeois CH, Shank RC, Grossman RA, et al: Acute aflatoxin B_1 toxicity in the macaque and its similarities to Reye's syndrome. *Lab Invest* 1971; 24:206–216.

214. Ryan NJ, Hogan GR, Hayes AW, et al: Aflatoxin B_1: Its role in the etiology of Reye's syndrome. *Pediatrics* 1979; 64:71–75.

215. Thayler MM: Reye's syndrome: Cause-and-effect relationships, in Berenberg S (ed): *Liver Disease in Infancy and Childhood*. The Hague, M Nijhoff, 1976, pp 72–89.

216. Leonard JV, Seakins JWT, Griffin NK: β-Hydroxy-β-methyl-glutaricaciduria presenting as Reye's syndrome. *Lancet* 1979; 1:680.

217. Chapoy PR, Angelini C, Brown WJ, et al: Systemic carnitine deficiency—A treatable inherited lipid-storage disease presenting as Reye's syndrome. *N Engl J Med* 1980; 303:1389–1394.

218. Thaler MM, Hoogenraad NJ, Boswell M: Reye's syndrome due to a novel protein-tolerant variant of ornithine-transcarbamylase deficiency. *Lancet* 1974; 2:438–440.

219. Krieger I, Snodgrass PJ, Roskamp J: Atypical clinical course of ornithine transcarbamylase deficiency due to a new mutant (comparison with Reye's disease). *J Clin Endocrinol Metab* 1979; 48:388–392.

220. Pierson DL, Cox SL, Gilbert BE: Human ornithine transcarbamylase. Purification and characterization of the enzyme from normal liver and the liver of a Reye's syndrome patient. *J Biol Chem* 1977; 252:6464–6469.

220a. Hsia YE: Changing trends of inborn errors in Reye's syndrome: Rarity is relative. *Hepatology* 1990; 11:327–328.

221. Crocker JFS, Ozere RL, Rozee KR, et al: Insecticide and viral interaction as a cause of fatty visceral changes and encephalopathy in the mouse. *Lancet* 1974; 2:22–24.

222. Crocker J, Digout S, Bagnell P, et al: Viral interaction with pesticide emulsifiers in vivo. *Chemosphere* 1978; 7:597–606.

223. Crocker JFS, Ozere RL, Safe SH, et al: Lethal interaction of ubiquitous insecticide carriers with virus. *Science* 1976; 192:1351–1353.

224. Friend M, Trainer DO: Polychlorinated biphenyl: Interaction with duck hepatitis virus. *Science* 1970; 170:1314–1316.

225. Colon AR, Pardo MD, Sandberg DH: Experimental Reye's syndrome induced by viral potentiation of chemical toxin, in Pollack JD (ed): *Reye's Syndrome*. New York, Grune & Stratton, 1975, pp 199–214.

226. Colon AR, Ledesma BS, Pardo V, et al: Viral potentiation of chemical toxins in the experimental syndrome of hypoglycemia, encephalopathy, and visceral fatty degeneration. *Dig Dis Sci* 1974; 19:1091–1101.

227. Hug G, Bosken J, Bove K, et al: Reye's syndrome simulacra in liver of mice after treatment with chemical agents and encephalomyocarditis virus. *Lab Invest* 1981; 45:89–109.

228. Brooks SEH, Audretsch JJ: Studies on hypoglycin toxicity in rats. I. Changes in hepatic ultrastructure. *Am J Pathol* 1970; 59:161–168.

229. Tsai MY, Truong VM, Good TA: Reye's syndrome: An experimental model for the treatment of the disease, in Pollack JD (ed): *Reye's Syndrome* New York, Grune & Stratton, 1975, pp 337–339.

230. Glasgow AM, Chase HP: Reye's syndrome, Jamaican vomiting sickness and 4-pentenoic acid, in Pollack JD (ed): *Reye's Syndrome*. New York, Grune & Stratton, 1975, pp 273–279.

231. Pierson D, Knight V, Hansard P, et al: Hepatic carbamyl phosphate synthetase and ornithine transcarbamylase in mouse influenza A and influenza B infection. *Proc Soc Exp Biol Med* 1976; 152:67–70.

232. Ruben FL: Recent developments and contributions from experimental models of Reye's syndrome, in Crocker JFS (ed): *Reye's Syndrome*. New York, Grune & Stratton, 1979, vol 2, pp 385–393.

233. Menna JH, Moses EB, Barron AL: Influenza type A virus infection of sucking mice pre-exposed to insecticide carrier. *Toxicol Lett* 1980; 6:357–363.

234. Linnemann CC Jr, Ueda K, Hug G, et al: Salicylate intoxication and influenza in ferrets. *Pediatr Res* 1979; 13:44–47.

235. Trauner DA: Pathologic changes in a rabbit model of Reye's syndrome. *Pediatr Res* 1982; 16:950–993.

236. Davis LE, Kornfeld M: Mouse influenza B virus model of Reye's syndrome. *Am J Pathol* 1986; 122:190–193.

237. Crocker JF, Renton KW, Lee SH, et al: Biochemical and morphological characteristics of a mouse model of Reye's syndrome induced by the interaction of influenza B virus and a chemical emulsifier. *Lab Invest* 1986; 54:32–40.

238. Deskmukh DR, Thomas PE: Arginine deficiency, hyperammonemia and Reye's syndrome in ferrits. *Lab Anim Sci* 1985; 35:242–245.

239. Deskmukh DR: Animal models of Reye's syndrome. *Rev Infect Dis* 1985; 7:31–40.

240. Kilpatrick-Smith L, Hale DE, Douglas SC: Progress in Reye syndrome: Epidemiology, biochemical mechanisms and animal models. *Dig Dis* 1989; 7:135–146.

INDEX

history, 944
laboratory studies, 944
treatment, 944
vaccines, recombinant, 940
Vaccinia virus, 932
core enzymes of, 57
extracellular, diagram of, 56
Vagina bleeding in dengue, 655
Varicella, 844–845
immunoglobulin for prophylaxis, 223
Varicella-zoster
adenine arabinoside in, 180
immunoglobulin in varicella prophylaxis, 223
Varicella-zoster virus, 842–861
biology, 842–844
complications, 849–851
diagnosis, laboratory, 851
epidemiology, 844–845
in fetus, 848–849
immunity, 847
in immunocompromised hosts, 847–848
immunoglobulins and, 851–852
infection, 845–847
control, 851
isolation precautions, 222
lesions of all stages of evolution, 846
in newborn, 848–849
nosocomial, 222
pathogenesis, 845–851
prevention, 851–853
prophylaxis, 222
structure, 842–844
transfer factor, 851–852, 853
treatment, 853–855
antiviral, 853–855
nonspecific measures, 853
vaccine, 852–853
virion of, 843
Varicellovirus, 7
Vasculitis: cytomegalovirus, 910
Venezuelan Equine encephalitis (*see* Encephalitis, Venezuelan Equine)
Ventilator
Drinker, 429
''iron lung,'' 429
Verruca (*see* Wart)
Vesicular fluid specimens, 158
Vesiculovirus, 13
Vidarabine (*see* Adenine arabinoside)
Virion(s)
forms of, simple, schematic diagram, 2
of JC virus, 971
poliovirus, RNA molecules, 442
structure of enterovirus, 431

of varicella-zoster virus, 843
Viroids, 16
Virus(es)
adeno-associated, 793
adenovirus (*see* Adenovirus)
alphavirus (*see* Alphavirus)
animal, shapes and sizes of, 3
antigen-antibody interactions, 116–117
standardization of, 116–117
antiviral drugs, 167–215
arenavirus (*see* Arenavirus)
astrovirus, 816
Bhanja, 599–600
Birnavirus, 10
BK (*see* BK virus)
bunyavirus (*see* Bunyavirus)
calicivirus, 10, 816
diagnosis, 816
Changuinola, 716
Chikungunya (*see* Chikungunya virus)
classification, 1–23
problems in, emerging, 15–18
coronavirus (*see* Coronavirus)
cultivation, 156–161
cytomegalovirus (*see* Cytomegalovirus)
dependovirus (*see* Dependovirus)
detection, 161–162
serologic, 162–164
diagnosis, 156–166
with cell cultures, 160–161
DNA (*see under* DNA)
echovirus (*see* Echovirus)
encephalitis due to (*see under* Encephalitis)
enterovirus (*see* Enterovirus)
Epstein-Barr (*see* Epstein-Barr virus)
Eyach, 716
filovirus (*see* Filovirus)
flavivirus (*see* Flavivirus)
gastroenteritis (*see* Gastroenteritis viruses)
Germiston, 602
Hantaan (*see* Hantaan virus)
hantavirus (*see* Hantavirus)
hepadnavirus, characteristics, 721
hepatitis (*see under* Hepatitis)
herpes (*see under* Herpes)
hybrids, 16
infections
cellular response to, components of, 126–127
diagnosis, rapid, 140–141
immunization against, 141–142
immunoglobulins in, role of, 123–124

immunology of, 116–155
immunopathology of, 135–136
nosocomial (*see* Nosocomial viral infections)
infectivity neutralization, 117–118
influenza (*see* Influenza viruses)
JC (*see* JC virus)
in Kawasaki syndrome etiology, 1028
Kemerovo, 716
La Crosse (*see* La Crosse virus)
latency, and immunity, 142
lentiviruses (*see* Lentiviruses)
leukemia (*see* Leukemia viruses)
Marburg (*see* Marburg virus)
Mayaro (*see* Mayaro virus)
measles (*see* Measles virus)
mumps (*see* Mumps virus)
Nairovirus, 14, 594–599
Negishi, causing encephalitis, 644
Norwalk (*see* Norwalk virus)
Ockelbo, 672
O'nyong-nyong (*see* O'nyong-nyong virus)
orbivirus (*see* Orbivirus)
orthomyxovirus (*see* Orthomyxovirus)
papillomavirus (*see* Papillomavirus)
parainfluenza (*see* Parainfluenza viruses)
paramyxovirus, 98–99
glycoproteins, 98–99
parvovirus (*see* Parvovirus)
period of greatest activity, 219
phlebovirus (*see* Phlebovirus)
picornavirus (*see* Picornavirus)
poliovirus (*see* Poliovirus)
polyomavirus (*see* Polyomavirus)
Porogia, 621–622
hemorrhagic fever and renal syndrome due to, 625
poxvirus (*see* Poxvirus)
Prospect Hill, 622
proteins, biologically active, inhibition of, 119
Puumala, 619–620
rabies (*see* Rabies virus)
reovirus (*see* Reovirus)
respiratory (*see* Respiratory virus)
respiratory syncytial (*see* Respiratory syncytial virus)

retroviruses (*see* Retroviruses)
in Reye syndrome, 1035
rhabdovirus (*see* Rhabdovirus)
rhinovirus (*see* Rhinovirus)
Rio Bravo, causing encephalitis, 644
RNA (*see* RNA viruses)
RNA-containing (*see* RNA-containing viruses)
with RNA genome, 8–15
Rocio (*see* Encephalitis, Rocio virus causing)
Ross River (*see* Ross River virus)
rotavirus (*see* Rotavirus)
rubella (*see* Rubella virus)
sandfly fever (*see* Sandfly fever)
Seoul, 621
hemorrhagic fever and renal syndrome due to, 625
simian (*see* Simian virus)
Sindbis, 671
structure, 1–23
Tahyna, 585–586
Tataguine, 600
togavirus (*see* Togavirus)
Toscana, 590–591
Uukuvirus, 14, 594
vaccinia (*see* Vaccinia virus)
varicella-zoster (*see* Varicella-zoster virus)
vertebrate, families, members of, 20–23
visnamaedi, 262
electron micrograph of, 263
Visitor policies: in nosocomial infections, 236
Visnamaedi virus, 262
electron micrograph of, 263
Vulva: papillomavirus, bowenoid papulosis of, 958

W

Wart
of palate, hard, of oral cavity, 961
plantar, 961
electron micrograph of, 959
with papillomavirus, 960
Wesselsbron fever, 645
West Nile fever, 644–645
biology of agent, 644–645
diagnosis, laboratory, 645
epidemiology, 645
pathogenesis, 645
prevention, 645
structure of agent, 644–645
treatment, 645
Western blot patterns: for HIV, 164